ANNUAL REGISTER OF
GRANT SUPPORT™
A DIRECTORY OF FUNDING SOURCES

Annual Register of Grant Support™
48th Edition

Publisher
Thomas H. Hogan

Vice President, Content
Dick Kaser

Director, ITI Reference Group
Owen O'Donnell

Managing Editor
Beverley McDonough

Associate Editor
Daniel Bazikian

Operations Manager, Tampa Editorial
Debra James

ANNUAL REGISTER OF GRANT SUPPORT™

A DIRECTORY OF FUNDING SOURCES

48th EDITION | 2015

Published by

Information Today, Inc.
143 Old Marlton Pike
Medford, NJ 08055-8750
Phone: (609) 654-6266
Fax: (609) 654-4309
E-mail (Orders): **custserv@infotoday.com**
Web site: http://www.infotoday.com

ISSN 0066-4049
ISBN 978-1-57387-489-2
Library of Congress Catalog Card Number: 69-18307

Information Today, Inc.
143 Old Marlton Pike
Medford, NJ   08055-8750
Phone: 800-300-9868 (Customer Service)
         800-409-4929 (Editorial)
Fax: 609-654-4309
E-mail (orders):   custserv@infotoday.com
Web Site: www.infotoday.com

Printed and bound in the United States of America

US $309.00

Contents

PREFACE...vii
INTRODUCTION..ix
PROGRAM PLANNING AND PROPOSAL WRITING...xv
KEY TO ENTRY INFORMATION..xxvi
NEW LISTINGS IN 2015 EDITION..xxix

MULTIPLE SPECIAL PURPOSE..1

HUMANITIES...119
    Architecture..143
    Arts (multiple disciplines)..149
        Performing Arts 184
        Fine Arts...191
    History...202
    Languages..228
    Literature...234
    Museums and Libraries...249
    Music...262
    Religion and Theology..279

INTERNATIONAL AFFAIRS AND AREA STUDIES..293
    International Studies and Research Abroad...308
    Programs for Foreign Scholars..342
    Technical Assistance and Cooperative Research...347

SPECIAL POPULATIONS..351
    African-American..372
    Native American..377
    Spanish-speaking...386
    Women...388

URBAN AND REGIONAL AFFAIRS...403
    Children and Youth...405
    Community Development and Services...422
    Crime Prevention..497
    Public Health...500
    Social Welfare...519

EDUCATION...535
    Educational Projects and Research (general)...537
    Elementary and Secondary Education...562
    Higher Education Projects and Research...568
    Scholar Aid Programs (all disciplines)...580

Continued

SCIENCES (multiple disciplines)...637

SOCIAL SCIENCES..657
    Business and Economics...671
    Communications..682
    Labor...697
    Law..699
    Political Science..705
    Sociology and Anthropology...717

PHYSICAL SCIENCES..725
    Astronomy and Aerospace Science...730
    Chemistry..734
    Earth Sciences..737
    Mathematics...744
    Physics..747

LIFE SCIENCES...753
    Agriculture, Land Resources, Rural Development................................755
    Biology..764
    Environment...773
    Medicine (multiple disciplines)..792
    Allergy, Immunology, Infectious Diseases...832
    Dentistry...834
    Internal Medicine...838
        Cardiovascular and Pulmonary.......................................844
        Metabolism, Gastroenterology, Nephrology....................853
        Oncology..862
        Rheumatology..871
    Neurology...872
    Nursing...883
    Obstetrics and Gynecology...889
    Ophthalmology and Otolaryngology...890
    Osteopathy..896
    Pediatrics...897
    Pharmacology...900
    Physical Medicine and Rehabilitation..905
    Psychiatry, Psychology, Mental Health...910

TECHNOLOGY AND INDUSTRY...923
    Aeronautics and Astronautics...931
    Engineering..936
    Home Economics and Nutrition...949
    Mining and Metallurgy...953

INDEXES..957
    Entry Listing by Chapter..958
    Subject Index..959
    Organization and Program Index..977
    Geographical Index...1043
    Personnel Index..1059

Preface

Now in its 48th edition, the *Annual Register of Grant Support™: A Directory of Funding Sources* has achieved a deserved reputation as an authoritative standard reference source on financial support. Known and relied upon by academic scholars and researchers, *Grant Support* also responds to the needs of those in the fields of business, civic improvement, and social welfare. Recognized for its value to the individual, *Grant Support* assists hospitals, arts organizations, community service groups, medical research facilities, and other institutional applicants as well.

The 2015 edition includes details of 2,684 grant support programs of government agencies, public and private foundations, corporations, community trusts, unions, educational and professional associations, and special interest organizations. It covers a broad spectrum of interests from academic and scientific research, project development, travel and exchange programs, and publication support to equipment and construction grants, in-service training, and competitive awards and prizes in a variety of fields.

Each complete program description contains details of the type, purpose, and duration of the grant; amount of funding available for each award and for the entire program or all programs of the organization; eligibility requirements; geographic restrictions; number of applicants and recipients in the most recent year for which statistics are available; representative awards made under the program in the most recent year; application instructions and deadline; personnel of the funding organization as well as its address, founding date, and telephone and fax numbers; e-mail address and web site address if available; data concerning the organization's areas of interest, cooperative funding programs, and consulting or volunteer services; publications available; IRS tax identification number, if applicable; and other pertinent information and special stipulations.

Grant Support attempts to be as comprehensive as possible by including the following forms of financial aid: programs that offer non-repayable financial assistance directly to the grantee or indirectly through payment to the sponsoring institution; programs that accept applicants from the United States or Canada or directly benefit the United States or Canada; study grants and fellowships aimed principally though not exclusively at the graduate or postgraduate levels; grants for construction, facilities, or project costs for education, medical research, health care, civic improvement, etc.; and programs donating consulting services in lieu of a direct monetary grant.

Funding sources are given the opportunity annually to update entry data. Staff research continues to within weeks of *Grant Support*'s publication date to assure information is as current and complete as possible and to identify new funding sources for inclusion. Essential programs for which no updated information has been returned are included, either as they appeared in the last edition, revised where possible, or compiled entirely through secondary research.

Support programs are divided into eleven major areas, further subdivided into more specific subject fields. Each entry contained in *Grant Support* has been placed in the section that reflects its principal interest. If program interests equally emphasize diverse fields, such as communications and business and economics, one full entry and a cross-reference will appear in the respective sections. Similarly, a program for minority political scientists will appear in either "Special Populations" or "Political Science," with a cross-reference in the appropriate section. However, organizations with broad support purposes or interests in three or more well-defined areas are listed in the "Multiple Special Purpose" section.

Four indexes—Subject, Organization and Program, Geographic, and Personnel—facilitate the potential applicant's search for appropriate grant programs. References in each index are to program entry number. While consulting the Subject Index, should the reader wish to know in which chapter a particular entry appears, he or she may consult the Entry Listing by Chapter Index, which precedes the Subject Index.

In the Subject Index, each grant has been indexed in terms of the specific areas to which it may be applied (e.g., Cartography, Mathematics), the type of grant (e.g., Construction and Facilities Projects, Medical Research), and the individuals or organizations eligible for support, if limitations are specified (e.g., Religious Institutions, Women). The Organization and Program Index alphabetically lists grant programs in upper-lower case and funding organizations in upper case. In addition, programs are also listed following the organizations that sponsor them. The Geographic Index groups grantmaking organizations according to the state or country in which they are located. In the Personnel Index, officers of the organizations, Trustees, Directors, and Awards Committee members appear alphabetically.

The editorial staff of *Annual Register of Grant Support*™ strives continually to provide the professional community with the most comprehensive, up-to-date information on existing forms of financial aid from as wide a variety of sources as possible. The staff urges the users of this edition to inform us of any corrections or additions to existing entries and of funding sources not included, and invites suggestions for improvement of future editions.

Introduction

Grant support in America has increased dramatically, both in size and sophistication, since the days when John D. Rockefeller, Sr. walked the streets of New York passing out dimes to the needy.

Today, the support of human services through grants, awards, fellowships, and private gifts is a multibillion-dollar enterprise. Private foundations, corporations, individuals, charitable organizations, and agencies gave an estimated $335.17 billion to charity in 2013, an increase of 4.4 percent compared with the revised estimate of $320.97 billion given in 2012 according to the Giving USA Foundation.

Of the total $335.17 billion given in 2013, $240.6 billion came from individuals and accounts for 72 percent of all estimated giving. Grants from foundations, excluding those affiliated with business enterprises, totalled $48.96 billion, an increase of 5.7 percent. Gifts received through bequests increased an estimated 8.7 percent to $27.73 billion; corporations contributed $17.88 billion, a decrease of 1.9 percent.

When total charitable giving is analyzed by field, religion received the largest share of 2013 dollars—$105.53 billion—followed by education ($52.07 billion); human services ($41.51 billion); health ($31.86 billion); public-society benefit ($23.89 billion); arts, culture, and humanities ($16.7 billion); international affairs ($14.93 billion); and environment and animals ($9.72 billion).

The 2,684 entries listed in this edition of *Annual Register of Grant Support*™ represent billions of dollars in financial assistance to potential grant seekers.

Part of the success in using the *Annual Register of Grant Support*™ will depend on an understanding of the various types of grantmaking entities, how they differ in their objectives and grantmaking procedures, what they look for in the grant applicant, and how they are approached. It is hoped that the following descriptions of grant-supporting organizations will increase the usability of Grant Support to the potential grant seeker.

PRIVATE FOUNDATIONS

Probably no area of philanthropy is so misunderstood and misused as that of private foundations. According to studies, as many as 80 percent of all applications to private foundations are inappropriate or misdirected. While at least part of the blame for this error must be attributed to private foundations themselves, grant seekers often compound the error by tending to lump all private foundations together as if they shared a common purpose.

Not only do private foundations differ greatly from public funding sources, but there is a wide diversity among private foundations themselves. What may be an appropriate application to the Ford Foundation, for example, may be totally inappropriate to the San Francisco Foundation.

There are more than 37,500 grantmaking foundations in the United States. The reason that an approximate figure must be used is that the federal government defines private foundations more by exclusion than by anything else. If an organization cannot qualify as a charitable, religious, educational, scientific, or governmental organization, it may be classified as a private foundation even if it has never made a grant nor intends to make one. Potential grant seekers should be aware that the mere use of the word "foundation" in the title of an organization is not evidence that the organization will make grants.

Until the tax reform act of 1976, private foundations bore a 4 percent excise tax on net investment income (Section 4940 of the Tax Reform Act of 1969), and annual giving requirements were based on greater of "adjusted net income" or a *variable* percentage of the market value of investment assets—in effect discouraging the foundations from building their assets.

After 1976, the variable percentage was eliminated, and giving requirements were set at 5 percent of market value of assets or of net income. The Economic Recovery Tax Act of 1981 (ERTA) further amended the requirements to a flat 5 percent of market value of assets. In addition, the excise tax on net investment income was reduced to 2 percent in 1978, which further encouraged growth by private foundations.

Several provisions of the Tax Reform Act of 1969 still regulate the activities of foundations. For instance, foundations face restrictions on self-dealing and are limited in the ownership of businesses. One provision of particular interest to the potential grant seeker is a requirement that every private foundation with assets of $5,000 or more (virtually all of them) must submit an annual report that is available for public inspection. These annual reports, printed on special Internal Revenue Service form 990-PF, include the names and addresses of all principal officers of the foundation, the total assets and investments of the foundation and, most important, a complete listing of every grant made during the year of record. Readers of *Grant Support* may wish to review selected 990-PFs of those foundations included in this edition in order to supplement information on current grants.

These 990-PF forms may be obtained directly from the private foundations themselves, or they may be found in over 200 Foundation Center Network member libraries located throughout the country, and are available for public use. (A list of these libraries may be obtained by writing the Foundation Center, 79 Fifth Avenue, New York, NY 10003-3076, or via their web site at www.foundationcenter.org).

A substantial number of private foundations publish their own annual reports over and above the 990-PF requirement mentioned earlier. Copies of these annual reports may be obtained by writing the foundation directly.

TYPES OF FOUNDATIONS

There are certain aspects common to all private foundations in the United States. However, foundations can be broken down into five types, which will assist the grant seeker in understanding their current objectives and grant distribution patterns.

1. National Foundations

Most of the foundations listed in Grant Support are national foundations, meaning that they are not limited to any geographic area in their grant support. National foundations are usually quite large, with assets of $25 million or more. They include all the better-known foundations, such as The Ford Foundation, the Lilly Endowment, The Rockefeller Foundation, and the Carnegie Corporation of New York. Because national foundations may make grants anywhere in the country, it is important to remember that these foundations are usually more attracted to programs and proposals with national, or at least regional, implications. Most of the national foundations are staffed with professional grantmakers, publish their own annual reports, and often have well-defined philanthropic goals.

While national foundations are large enough to fund projects of almost any size—and have been known to make grants of a million dollars or more—it should be remembered that competition for these national foundation grants is extremely fierce. The Ford Foundation, for example, will receive as many as 30,000 proposals every year and will fund only about 2,000.

2. Special-Interest Foundations

Many foundations listed in this edition of Grant Support devote their entire grant efforts to programs within a single field of interest. These special-interest foundations, just as the national foundations, often make grants without any geographic limitations so long as the projects relate to the specific areas. Special-interest foundations range from the massive Robert Wood Johnson Foundation (health) to the Joseph P. Kennedy Foundation (mental retardation) to those supporting research on a single disease.

Some of the larger special-interest foundations employ staff whose purpose is not only to review grants but to stay abreast of information being gathered about that special field of interest. Potential grant seekers, then, should consider special-interest foundations as a potential source of information about a given subject as well as a potential source of funds.

3. Corporate Foundations

During the 1950s, many major corporations created private foundations to serve as the corporate philanthropic arm, although the Tax Reform Act of 1969 greatly slowed the increase in their number. The ExxonMobil Foundation,

Inc. and the Sears-Roebuck Foundation are examples. Readers should be alerted to the fact that while many foundations carry names of large corporations, they are not corporate foundations. The Ford Foundation, for example, is not a corporate foundation; it was created by the Ford family.

Most corporate foundations, while "independent," are very much creatures of the corporations that founded them and fund them. Corporate foundations will, therefore, often be more receptive to proposals that are in line with their corporate interest. Historically, corporate foundations more often have made grants in the fields of education, federated giving (United Way, etc.), minority enterprises, and local social services that demonstrate a benefit to the company employees as well as the community at large.

Most corporate foundations will have relatively small assets in comparison with the amount of grants. This is because once the money has moved from the corporation to the corporate foundation, it can never go back to the corporation. Usually corporations will keep only enough funds in the corporate foundation to sustain the foundation's grant efforts without harming the corporate financial position.

4. Family Foundations

By far, the largest number of private foundations are family foundations. They range in assets from hundreds of millions of dollars, such as those of the several Rockefeller Foundations, to a few thousand dollars.

The grant support pattern of family foundations is very often a personal matter. Often the family foundation will be controlled entirely by family members, and even when these family members have died, the family foundation will often continue to reflect their wishes. Unlike special-interest foundations, family foundations seldom have set fields of interest. Grants more probably will reflect areas of current family interest rather than any recognizable pattern of traditional philanthropy.

Most family foundations are small, and few will have staff or guidelines for submitting proposals. A vast majority of family foundations limit their grants to the city or locality in which the family resides and accumulated its wealth. Unlike national foundations, family foundations are best approached as if they were individual donors, not private foundations.

Because most family foundations are relatively small and have such a limited geographic giving pattern, few are included in Grant Support. These foundations should be explored, however, for modest gifts of a local nature. While the average gift of small family foundations is less than $5,000, the sheer volume of family foundations makes them an important factor in grant support.

5. Community Foundations

In a strictly legal sense, community foundations are not really foundations at all but, rather, public charities. Community foundations maintain this favored tax status by collecting money from the public and directing grants within the community for which they are named. Because community foundations are not private foundations, they have no minimum giving requirements and pay no excise taxes on their net investment income. This is partly responsible for their rapid growth during the past decade, for hundreds of foundations (including some with assets in the many millions of dollars) have given all their money to community foundations.

A number of the larger community foundations, such as the Cleveland Foundation and the New York Community Trust, are listed in *Grant Support*. It is easy to distinguish a community foundation, for it will always be named for the community it serves. The San Francisco Foundation serves San Francisco, the Chicago Community Trust serves Chicago, and so forth. Readers of *Grant Support* should bear in mind that community foundations cannot, by law, make grants outside the geographic regions they serve. The San Francisco Foundation, for example, is not likely to fund a project in Texas, regardless of the merit of the proposal.

For more information about the existence of a community foundation in a given city, readers may wish to consult the local trust bank in that city. (Information can also be obtained by writing the Council on Foundations, Inc., 2121 Crystal Drive, Suite 700, Arlington, VA 22202 or via their web site at www.cof.org.)

CORPORATE GIVING

Although the practice of corporations making grants and gifts to charity is now largely accepted, it was not until 1935 that the Internal Revenue Service allowed a charitable deduction for corporate gifts. In 1982, changes in the tax law enhanced the value of donations of company products, and increased the deduction of corporate contributions from 5 to 10 percent of net income.

Yet while this modest federal government incentive has spurred corporate philanthropy, approximately only one-third of all corporations in the United States make corporate gifts.

Corporations made the largest percentage of their donations to education over the last several years, with health and human services receiving the second largest amounts. Cultural and arts groups, civic and community activities, and various other recipients received the balance of corporate dollars.

Most corporations do not have professional grant reviewers but will often have grant guidelines, specific philanthropic objectives, or well-defined procedures for grant applicants.

An important consideration when approaching corporations is to introduce a benefit, either directly to the company or indirectly through its employees, that grant support can make. A proposal for support of an alcoholism program may be received more readily if the corporation feels alcoholism is a problem among its employees.

Many corporations are willing to provide volunteer service and specific expert assistance as well as money. Corporations also make in-kind contributions, such as free printing, equipment, etc., and will sometimes match gifts made by individual employees.

FEDERATED GIVING

Grant Support lists many grant opportunities from funding sources which, though neither foundations nor corporations, provide many millions of dollars of grant support every year. These funding sources can best be described as federated giving organizations, in that a number of small organizations combine their funding efforts for maximum effect.

The largest and best known federated agency is, of course, United Way. Most United Ways, however, do not make grants so much as they support existing agencies.

There are a number of other federated agencies that do make grants. The Catholic Campaign for Human Development, which is the federated arm of the Catholic Church in America, provides some $8 million in grant support annually. Other federated agencies include the United Negro College Fund, the United Jewish Appeal, the American Association of University Women, and the American Federation of Teachers.

PUBLIC MONEY

Government funding is as complex and confusing as it is big, and the special terms and language of government grants make the subject seem more confusing than it really is. An understanding of the various types of grants and some of the most often used terms may help readers break through the perplexing language of government grants.

Types of Grants

The federal government makes grants in many forms, some of which allow the independent grant seeker an opportunity to be funded, and some which do not. Below are some of the most common types of government grants.

Block Grants: Sometimes called "bloc" grants, these are made from the federal government directly to states or local units of government, such as counties and municipalities. The grant most often comes to the state in a "block," and the state may spend the money as it wishes as long as the funds are being used to fulfill the basic purposes for which they were authorized. Many of the more recent federal grants under what is called "new federalism" have been block grants such as the Housing and Community Development Act money, the Comprehensive Employment and Training Act money, and funds to support programs for older Americans. Under the rules of most block grants, the state must submit an annual "state plan" to the federal government explaining how and where the funds are to be used. This state plan is public information, and potential grant seekers may wish to review it for programs under which they wish to seek grant support. One important aspect of block grants is that while the money is federal, the authority to spend it is local, and the recipients of block grant funds are allowed great flexibility in how they use the money.

Capitation Grants: Stemming from a concept of providing funds per capita of service, capitation grants are awarded based on the actual number of people served, rather than on the task to be performed. For example, an organization may be providing housing for runaway youths. This organization's annual budget is $100,000, and last year it provided housing for 1,000 youths. A capitation grant would provide $100 for each youth housed during the coming year ($100,000 divided by 1,000 youths). Capitation grants are most often used for training grants where payment is based on enrollment, rather than training outcome.

Categorical Grants: Simply stated, funds under a certain "category" must be expended within a certain field of interest, such as mental health, services for the handicapped, or maternity and child care. Although the number of categorical grants provided by the federal government has decreased in the past few years because of an increase in block grants, there are still more than 850 federal grant programs active within the federal government.

Construction Grants: Unless specifically stated, most federal grants will not provide funds for capital purposes, requiring instead that the grantee rent or lease the appropriate facility. Special construction grants, especially in the fields of health and mental health, have been made in the past for construction, renovation, and expansion. Many more important construction grant programs have been severely cut in the past few years, however, and it appears that the federal government is less enamored with this type of grant than in the past.

Demonstration Grants: Among the most common types of grants made in the human services field, demonstration grants, as opposed to basic research grants, are made to agencies in order to illustrate the effectiveness of a certain procedure or methodology, while at the same time providing a direct benefit to a group of clients. Unlike research grants, there is usually a large amount of evidence that the methodology to be demonstrated should prove effective before the grant is awarded. Often, demonstration grants are the second step of research grants, attempting to show that the success of a research grant may have greater applicability or a wider target population than originally envisioned.

Formula Grants: Not so much a type of grant as a method of determining the amount of funds to be made available, formula grants are based most often on the population, income, taxation, and special need of a given area.

The formula for grants will be written into the legislation or regulation that established the fund. The capitation grant mentioned earlier is one type of formula.

Matching Grants: Often confused with formula grants in that there is usually a "formula" for establishing the matching grant requirement, a matching grant means that the agency or individual who is receiving the grant guarantees to provide a certain portion of the total grant funds from sources other than the government. This "match" may be as small as 1 percent to as much as 50 percent with organizations such as the National Endowment for the Arts and National Endowment for the Humanities. Often there is a "sliding match" requirement, which means that the agency receiving the grant will provide a greater share of the total costs in the second and subsequent years of the award. Matching requirements may be for a "hard" or "soft" match. A "hard" match means that actual dollar matches must be secured, whereas a "soft" match allowed for such donated services as volunteer time and goods or equipment to be counted in lieu of "hard" dollars.

Project Grants: The grants allow the granting agency, usually a department or agency of the federal government, to determine funding based solely on the merits of the project of an individual or organization, rather than by formula requirements mentioned earlier. This is one of the most flexible types of grants in that the granting agency may have complete control in selecting the project, the grant recipient, and the amount of the award.

Research Grants: As opposed to demonstration grants and project grants, research grants are provided to test theories and hypotheses, develop or interpret new information, or revise accepted theories without the requirement that some benefit be immediately passed on to the clients. In fact the term "client" is often replaced with the term "subject" in research grants. There are two types, basic and applied. Basic research, which enjoyed great favor in the 1960s, has found funding harder to obtain lately, while applied research funds have continued to grow, especially in environmental programs.

Staffing Grants: As the phrase implies, these grants are provided for support of salaries of professional and technical staff members, plus in-service training in many cases. Most staffing grants come with a sliding match requirement.

Training Grants: These are awarded to organizations, corporations, or individuals to support the costs of training existing staff, students, or potential staff in the techniques or procedures needed to develop skills in a particular field, such as nursing, paramedical training and legal aid.

Seeking Governmental Sources

In addition to the *Annual Register of Grant Support*™, there are several places potential grant seekers can look for information about federal grants.

Catalog of Federal Domestic Assistance

The most important index for identifying federal resources is the *Catalog of Federal Domestic Assistance* (CFDA). Available online at www.cfda.gov, the catalog gives you access to a database of all Federal programs available to State and local governments (including the

District of Columbia); federally-recognized Indian tribal governments; Territories (and possessions) of the United States; domestic public, quasi-public, and private profit and nonprofit organizations and institutions; specialized groups; and individuals.

Available from the web site as a PDF download, the first section contains the indexes. An Agency Index Summary describes the functions and activities of the respective agencies responsible for administering the programs. The Agency Program Index lists, in numerical order, all programs, titles, the agency responsible, and the kind of assistance being offered—financial, nonfinancial, or combined. The Functional Index Summary lists categories of support, while a Subject Index provides a listing of programs by various topics. The second section provides the Program Descriptions, including detailed information for each program. Also included in the CFDA is a deadlines index and several informational appendices. After you find the program you want, contact the office that administers the program and find out how to apply.

Federal Register

Another valuable source is the *Federal Register*, available at www.gpoaccess.gov. Published by the Office of the Federal Register, National Archives and Records Administration (NARA), the Federal Register is the official daily publication for rules, proposed rules, and notices of Federal agencies and organizations. It includes such items as presidential orders, advisory meetings, program announcements, requests for applications and deadline dates.

Grants.gov

Grants.gov is a central storehouse for information on over 1,000 grant programs and provides access to approximately $500 billion in annual awards. The Department of Health and Human Services is the Grants.gov program's managing partner, and allows access to 26 federal grant-making agencies through the grants.gov web site.

Clearinghouses

Begun in the 1960s on a limited basis, a coordinated grant support process known as clearinghouse review was once required on hundreds of government grants.

As part of this review process, an applicant submits a brief description of the project or activity for which federal support is sought. Some clearinghouses have developed special forms for this "notification of intent," while others ask for a simple program description, along with the name and location of the applicant agency. Clearinghouses then notify the government agencies and elected officials of local governments that might be interested in the project, in order for the departments and agencies to comment.

If the clearinghouse does not identify any problems or possible conflicts, the applicant may complete and submit the proposal to the funding agency unless the clearinghouse specifies that it wants to review the completed proposal.

If there are concerns or unresolved issues, the clearinghouse may arrange a meeting between the applicant and the various departments that have expressed the concern. After any issues have been addressed, the applicant may wish to rewrite the proposal, continue discussions with the departments that are expressing concern, or submit the proposal to the funding source with the comments of the clearinghouse attached.

Program planning and proposal writing

Introductory version

By Norton J. Kiritz and Jerry Mundel

Proposals written for private foundations and those written for government grants (Federal, State, County or City) usually differ in their final form. Foundations often require a brief letter as an initial approach. A full proposal may follow in many situations. Government funding sources almost always require completion of a number of forms along with a detailed proposal narrative. Therefore, proposals to private and government grantmakers look quite different.

The package to a foundation or corporation will usually contain these elements:

1. The cover letter
2. The proposal
3. Additional materials.

1. The cover letter is signed by the Chairperson of the Board of a nonprofit agency, or the top authority in a governmental agency. It briefly describes the program, and tells the grantmaker how important the grant would be to the community served by the applicant agency. It shows strong support of the Board of Directors, which is essential in gaining foundation grants.

2. The body of the proposal may be as modest as one page (in the case of a foundation that limits requests to a page) or voluminous. It may be in letter form or a more formal presentation. In either case, following the instructions in Program Planning & Proposal Writing (PP&PW) will help to assure that the necessary items are included and are presented in a logical manner. Remember one thing: PP&PW can help you structure your thinking and even plan your project or program. It can serve as your proposal format where the funding source has not provided one as often the case with foundation proposals. But it should not be substituted for any format required by a foundation. If they ask you to follow a set format, do it!

3. Additional materials should be limited to those required by the funding source supplemented by only the most important addenda. Reviewers don't grade proposals by the pound, so save your postage.

The proposal package to a government funding source usually contains these elements:

1. Letter of transmittal
2. The proposal
3. Additional materials.

1. The letter of transmittal is a brief statement (2-3 paragraphs) signed by the highest level person within your organization. It briefly describes the request, the amount asked for, and may indicate the significance and importance of the proposed project. It should reflect the Board's support and approval of the request as reflected in the signature of the Board Chairperson (possibly as a dual signature along with the Executive Director/Chief Executive Officer).

2. The proposal going to a government funding source will generally be more lengthy than one going to a private foundation. It will often be 10-20 pages long, and the funding source guidelines will contain the sequence to be followed in writing the narrative portion.

It is a good idea to read the information describing how your proposal will be evaluated. Quite often, government agency guidelines describe exactly how each section of your proposal will be weighed. This tells you what the reviewers look for and helps you to organize your thoughts. If you are told to limit your proposal to 10 single-spaced pages, don't include one or two more thinking that it won't be viewed in a negative light. Follow the guidelines meticulously, because the reviewers will. Proposals can be deemed inappropriate simply because you failed to follow specific instructions.

Proposals going to government funders may also contain unique forms such as fact sheet forms where the entire project, names of key staff, budget, numbers of people impacted by the project, etc. are indicated; assurance forms (addressing issues

Adapted from "Program Planning & Proposal Writing" by Norton J. Kiritz and Jerry Mundel. Copyright 1988 The Grantsmanship Center. All rights reserved. The Grantsmanship Center introduced the world's first training program for grantseekers in 1972. Since then, nonprofit organizations and government agencies throughout the U.S. as well as in Africa, the Caribbean, Europe, and Latin America have sent more than 120,000 staff to the Center's acclaimed training programs. For effective, interactive training on how to win grants and helpful publications, many of which are free, contact: The Grantsmanship Center, 350 S. Bixel St., Los Angeles, CA 90017; (800) 421-9512; www.tgci.com.

such as human subjects at risk); equal opportunity policy statements, facility access to the handicapped; and a number of other such forms. It is important to understand which items must be submitted along with your proposal and how they are to be completed, so read the instructions carefully.

3. Additional materials will generally include those items suggested by the funding source. This usually consists of job descriptions, resumes, letters of support or commitment, your IRS tax exemption designation, an annual report, financial statement, and related documents. This section (or Appendix) can be extensive when a funding source requests a great deal of information. There are instances in which the funding source will request copies of certain agency policies and procedures, copies of negotiated indirect cost rates, etc.

Generally, this will happen only once, and for refunding packages to the same public agency, you will probably not need to resubmit the same documents.

We suggest the following as a basic format for planning all of your proposals. Thinking through the various sections should enable you to create virtually all that either a private or government funding source will ask of you. It will also enable you to develop a logical approach to planning and proposal writing.

This is our proposed format:

PROPOSAL SUMMARY
I.   **INTRODUCTION**
II.   **PROBLEM STATEMENT**
III.   **PROGRAM GOALS AND OBJECTIVES**
IV.   **METHODS**
V.   **EVALUATION**
VI.   **FUTURE FUNDING**
VII. **BUDGET**
VIII. **APPENDIX**

PROPOSAL SUMMARY

The summary is a very important part of a proposal, not just something you jot down as an afterthought. There may be a box for a summary on the first page of a federal grant application form. It may also be called a proposal abstract. In writing to a foundation, the summary should be the first paragraph of a letter-type proposal, or the first section of a more formal proposal. The summary is probably the first thing that a funding source will read. It should be clear, concise and specific. It should describe who you are, the scope of your project, and the cost. The summary may be all that some in the review process will see, so make it good.

I. INTRODUCTION

In this part of the proposal you introduce your organization as an applicant for funds. More often than not proposals are funded on the reputation of the applicant organization or its key personnel, rather than on the basis of the program's content alone. The Introduction is the section in which you build your credibility, and make the case that your organization should be supported.

Credibility

What gives an organization credibility in the eyes of a funding source? First of all, it depends on the funding source. A traditional, conservative funding source might be more responsive to persons of prominence on your Board of Directors, how long you have been in existence and how many other funding sources have been supporting you. An avant garde funding source might be more interested in a Board of community persons rather than of prominent citizens and in organizations that are new rather than established.

Potential funding sources should be selected because of their possible interest in your type of organization as well as the kind of program you offer. You can use the Introduction to reinforce the connection you see between your interests and those of the funding source.

What are some of the things you can say about your organization in an introductory section?

- How you got started, your purpose and goals
- How long you have been around, how you've grown, and the breadth of your financial support
- Unique aspects of your agency (the fact that you were the first organization of its kind in the nation, etc.)
- Some of your most significant accomplishments as an organization or, if you are a new organization, some of the significant accomplishments of your Board or staff in their previous roles
- Your success with related projects
- The support you have received from other organizations and individuals (accompanied by a few letters of endorsement which can be attached in the Appendix)

We strongly suggest that you start a credibility file which you can use as a basis for the Introduction in your future proposals. In this file you can keep copies of newspaper articles about your organizations, letters of support you receive from other agencies and from your clients. Include statements made by key figures in your field or in the political arena that endorse your kind of program even if they do not mention your agency. For example, by including a presidential commission's statement that the type of program which you are proposing has the most potential of solving the problems with which you deal, you can borrow credibility from those who made the statement (if they have any).

Remember, in terms of getting funded, the credibility you establish in your Introduction may be more important than the rest of your proposal. Build it! But here, as in all of your proposal, be as brief and specific as you can. Avoid jargon and keep it simple.

II. PROBLEM STATEMENT OR ASSESSMENT OF NEED

In the Introduction you have told who you are. From the Introduction we should know your areas of interest—the field in which you are working. Now you will zero in on the specific problem or problems that you want to solve through your proposed program. If the Introduction is the most important part of your proposal in getting funded, the Problem Statement is most important in planning a good program.

The Problem Statement or Needs Assessment describes the situation that caused you to prepare this proposal. It should refer to situation(s) that are outside of your organization (i.e. situations in the life of your clients or community). It does not refer to need internal to your organization, unless you are asking someone to fund an activity to improve your own effectiveness. In particular, the Problem Statement does not describe your lack of money as the problem. Everyone understands that you are asking for money in your solicitation. That is a given. But what external situation will be dealt with if you are awarded the grant? That is what you should describe, and document, in the Problem Statement.

Problem Statements deal with such issues as the homeless, offenders returning to prison with regularity, children who are far behind in their reading skills, youths dropping out of school, and the myriad other problems in contemporary society. Needs Statements are often used when dealing with a less tangible subject. They are especially useful in programs that are artistic, spiritual, or otherwise value-oriented. These are certainly no less important as subjects, but they do not lend themselves as directly to the problem-solving model of PP&PW. You would ordinarily deal with them as Needs and Satisfaction of Needs instead of Problems and Objectives.

You should not assume that "everyone knows this problem is valid." That may be true, but it doesn't give a fund source assurance about your expertise if you fail to demonstrate your knowledge of the problem. Use some appropriate statistics. Augment them with quotes from authorities, especially those in your own community. And make sure that you make the case for the problem in your area of service, not just on a national level. Charts and graphs will probably turn off the reader. If you use excessive statistics, save them for an Appendix, but pull out the key figures for your Problem Statement. And know what the statistics say.

In the Problem Statement, you need to do the following:

- Make a logical connection between your organization's background and the problems and the needs with which you propose to work.
- Clearly define the problem(s) with which you intend to work. Make sure that what you want to do is workable—that it can be done within a reasonable time, by your agency and with a reasonable amount of money.
- Support the existence of the problem by evidence. Statistics, as mentioned above, are but one type of support. You may also use statements from groups in your community concerned about the problem, from prospective clients, and from other organizations working in your community and from professionals in the field.
- Be realistic—don't try and solve all the problems in the world in the next six months.

Note: Many grant applicants fail to understand the difference between problems or needs and methods of solving problems or satisfying needs. For example, an agency working with the elderly in an urban area said that what the community needed were vans to get the elderly to various agencies. They determined that this need existed because not enough seniors were able to get to the social security office, health services, and related human service programs. What they had done was to immediately jump to a method by which the seniors would now be able to readily receive services. The problem with that logic is that the transportation suggested is a method and there are other methods as well. For example, what about the possibility of working with the agencies to decentralize services? Alternatively, volunteer advocates could work with seniors, acting on their behalf with some of these service providers. Ultimately, buying vans might be the best method, but it is clearly a method and not a problem or client need. Be very cautious about this. If you find yourself using lack of statements in the problem section, you are probably saying lack of method. This starts you on a circular reasoning track that will ruin the planning process.

III. PROGRAM GOALS AND OBJECTIVES

A well-prepared proposal has continuity—a logical flow from one section to another. Your Introduction can establish the context for your Problem Statement. Similarly, the Problem Statement will prepare the funding source for your logical Goals and Objectives.

Goals are broad statements such as: Develop additional resources to provide AIDS information to bilingual populations; Reduce underemployment rates among adults; Increase the availability of resources to address the problem of adolescent pregnancies; Create an environment in which folk art is fully appreciated; or Enhance self-images of senior adults.

These types of statements cannot be measured as they are stated. They offer the reader an understanding of the general thrust of a program. They are not the same as objectives.

Objectives are specific, measurable outcomes of your program. Objectives are your promised improvements in the situation you described in the Problem Statement. When you think of Objectives this way, it should be clear in most proposals what your Objective should look like. For example, if the problem was that certain children in your school read at least three grade levels below the norm for their age, then an objective would be that a certain number of those children would read significantly better when you had classmates who had also been reading poorly, but who did not have the benefit of your intervention. These outcome Objectives should state who is to change, what behaviors are to change, in what direction the changes will occur, how much change will occur, and by what time the change will occur.

Another example of a measurable objective would be:

"Within 30 days of completion of the JTPA Classroom Training Program, 75% of the 80 participating welfare recipients will have secured unsubsidized employment at a minimum of $5.25 per hour, and will maintain those positions for a minimum of 90 days."

The Importance of Distinguishing Between Methods and Objectives

Many, if not most, proposals state that the purpose of the program is to establish a program or provide a service. This is consistent with most thinking in the nonprofit sector, which sees the nonprofit organization as a "service provider." This results in Objectives that read like this:

"The objective of this project is to provide counseling and guidance services to delinquent youth between the ages of 8 and 14 in the blank community."

The difficulty with this kind of objective is that it says nothing about outcome. It says nothing about the change in a situation that was described in the Problem. That is, unless the Problem Statement (perish the thought) said that the problem was a "lack of counseling." Presumably the Problem Statement said something about youth being arrested, going to jail, dropping out of school, or whatever.

Objectives should be specific, estimating the amount of benefit to be expected from a program. Some applicants, trying to be as specific as they can, pick a number out of the air. For example, an agency might say that their objective was to decrease unemployment among adults in the XYZ community by 10% within a certain time period. The question you need to ask is: where did that figure come from? Usually it is made up because it sounds good. It sounds like a real achievement. But it should be made of something more substantial than that. Perhaps no program has ever achieved that high a percentage. Perhaps similar programs have resulted in a range of achievement of from 2-6% decrease in unemployment. In that case, 5% would be very good and 6% would be as good as has ever

been done. Ten percent is just plain unrealistic. And it leads one to expect that you don't really know the field very well. Just remember that Objectives should be realistic and attainable. Decide whether the 10% figure is attainable. If not, then it is a poor objective because you cannot achieve it.

If you are having difficulty in defining your Objectives, try projecting your agency a year or two into the future. What differences would you hope to see between then and now? What changes would have occurred? These changed dimensions may be the Objectives of your program.

A Note About Process Objectives

You may be used to seeing Objectives that read like this:

"The objective of this training program is to offer classes in automotive repair three times each week, for a period of 36 weeks, to a group of 40 unemployed individuals,"

or

"The objective of this program is to provide twice-weekly counseling sessions, for a period of 18 weeks, to no less than 50 parents who have been reported to Child and Protective Services for child abuse."

These are Process Objectives, and belong in the Methods section of your proposal. They tell what you will do, and do not address the outcome or benefit of what you will do. It is critically important to distinguish between these process Objectives and true outcome Objectives. If you do not do so, you will end up knowing only what has occurred during your program, and will not have dealt with the changes attributed to your program. Remember, you have proposed your program in order to make some change in the world, not to add one more service to a world already overcrowded with services and service providers.

Process Objectives may be very useful, but they should only appear in the Methods section of your proposal, so they are not confused with the results of your proposed program.

IV. METHODS

You now have told the reviewer who you are, the problems you intend to work with, and your Objectives (which promise a solution to or reduction of the problems). Now you are going to describe the Methods you will use to accomplish your Objectives.

The Methods component of your proposal should describe, in some detail, the activities that will take place in order to achieve the desired results. It is the part of the proposal where the reader should be able to gain a picture in his/her mind of exactly how things work, what your facility looks like, how staff are deployed, how clients are dealt with, what the exhibits look like, how the community center recruits and assigns volunteers, or how the questionnaires will be administered and results interpreted.

There are two basic issues to be dealt with in the Methodology section. What combination of activities and strategy have you selected to employ to bring about the desired results? And why have you selected this particular approach, of all the possible approaches you could have employed?

Justifying your approach requires that you know a good deal about other programs of a similar nature. Who is working on the problem in your community or elsewhere? What Methods have been tried in the past and are being tried now and with what results? In other words, you need to substantiate your choice of Methods.

The consideration of alternatives is an important aspect of describing your methodology. Showing that you are familiar enough with your field to be aware of different program models and showing your reasons for selecting the model you have gives a funding source a feeling of security and adds greatly to your credibility. Obviously then, building credibility only starts in your Introduction, and can be enhanced as you demonstrate that you are knowledgeable throughout your proposal.

Your methodology section should describe who is doing what to whom, and why it is being done that way. Your approach should appear realistic to the reviewer, and not suggest that so much will be performed by so few that the program appears unworkable. A realistic and justified program will be impressive. An unrealistic program will not win you points for good intentions.

V. EVALUATION

Evaluation of your program can serve two purposes. Your program can be evaluated in order to determine how effective it is in reaching its stated Objectives. This concept of Evaluation is aimed at measuring results of your program (outcome Evaluation).

Evaluation can also be used as a tool to provide information necessary to make appropriate changes and adjustments in your program as it proceeds. This concept is focused on the way your program has been conducted (process Evaluation).

Measurable Objectives set the stage for effective outcome Evaluation. If you have difficulty in determining what criteria to use in evaluating your program, better take another look at your Objectives. They probably aren't very specific.

Subjective and Objective Evaluations

Many Evaluation plans are subjective in nature. Subjective Evaluations tell you how people feel about a program, but seldom deal with the concrete results of a program. For example, the Evaluation of an educational program that surveyed students, parents, teachers and administrators of the program would be eliciting attitudes about the program. It would not speak to the tangible improvement in performance attributed to the program.

Subjectivity also allows the introduction of our own biases into an Evaluation. This could easily happen if you

evaluate your own programs, especially if you feel that continued funding depends on producing what looks like good results.

One way of obtaining a more objective Evaluation, and sometimes a more professionally prepared Evaluation, is to look to an outside organization to conduct an Evaluation for you. Sometimes it is possible to get an outside organization to develop an Evaluation design that can be submitted to a funding source as part of your proposal. This not only can suggest a more objective Evaluation, but can also add to the credibility of your proposal, since you have added the credibility of the evaluating institution.

It is essential to build an Evaluation plan into your proposal and be prepared to implement your Evaluation at the same time that you start your program. If you want to determine change along some dimension, then you have got to show where your clients have come from. It is very difficult to start an Evaluation at or near the conclusion of the program, for at that time you may not know the characteristics of your clients at the time of their entry into the program.

VI. FUTURE AND OTHER NECESSARY FUNDING

No grantmaker wants to adopt you. Funding sources want to know how you will continue your program when their grant runs out. If you are requesting funds to start a new program, or to expand an existing program, then how will you maintain it after the grant funds have been spent?

A promise to continue looking for alternative sources of support is not sufficient. You should present a plan that will assure the funding source, to the greatest extent possible, that you will be able to maintain this new program after the grant has been completed. Indeed, if you are having difficulty keeping your current operations supported, you will probably have more difficulty in maintaining a level of operation which includes additional programs. The funding source may be doing you no favor by supporting a new project and putting you in the position of having to raise even more money next year than you do now.

At this point in your planning you may realize that there is little likelihood of any other sources of support one or two years hence. This ought to bring you to a decision-making point whether you should even try to implement a new program at this time in your agency's history.

What would constitute a satisfying response in this proposal component? Could you get a local institution or governmental agency to agree to continue to support your program, should it demonstrate the desired results? Can you get such a commitment in writing? Can you generate funds through the project itself—such as fees from services that will build up over a year or two, subscriptions to publications, etc.? Are there third parties available to provide reimbursement for services? Are you expanding your nongrant fundraising activities? The best plan for Future Funding is the plan that does not require continued grant support.

Other Necessary Funding

Other necessary funding refers to what are sometimes called "non-recurring grants." That is, one-time only requests. This could be a request for a vehicle to transport your clientele, or the purchase of a piece of medical equipment for your hospital. While these are not program grants, the funds you request are not all you will need either to utilize the vehicle, or to operate the medical device. For the vehicle to be used, you must cover the costs of a driver, insurance, gas and maintenance. Similarly, the medical equipment must be operated by trained personnel. The funding source will want to know if you are aware of what you need beyond the purchase requested in your grant, and have the funds needed to cover these costs. They surely will not want to fund a bus that will sit in your garage for a year.

VII. BUDGET

Funding source requirements for Budgets vary, with foundations requiring less extensive Budgets than government funding sources. The following Budget design should satisfy most funding sources that allow you to design your own Budget and, with minor changes that the sources will tell you about, can be adapted to fit most government agency requirements. This recommended Budget contains three sections: The first is Personnel, the second is Non-Personnel, and the third is Indirect Costs.

When planning your Budget, it is wise to look closely at your Goals and Objectives to determine the level of activity in the program, and at your Methods section to review the specific plan you have proposed. For example, a Volunteer Senior Peer Counseling program would, one hopes, be less costly to operate than a Senior Peer Counseling program involving paid staff. Budgets should be built from the ground up—that is, based on your Goals and Objectives and the methodology you have proposed. In the context of your program you can begin to itemize such things as the staffing called for, the facilities needed, the equipment required, the supplies necessary, travel costs to be paid, and the range of costs for which your agency must be reimbursed, i.e., time of the CEO, bonding of employees, fundraising, use of space, payroll services, in-service training offered, etc.

It is important to go through this exercise in developing a Budget. Without it, there is a risk of developing unrealistic or impractical requests, where program and Budget are unrelated.

This is how we suggest you structure your Budget:

I. PERSONNEL
A. Salaries & Wages

In this section you can list all full- and part-time staff in the proposed program. We suggest a format which includes the following information:

# of persons per title	Title	Full monthly salary	% of time employed in grant	# of months during grant period	Amount requested	Amount donated or volunteered	Total

How does this look on a completed line item of a Budget? If you are employing a Project Coordinator at a salary of $2,000 per month, working full time (100%) for the entire grant period (12 months) and are asking the funding source to provide the full amount of this salary, then it looks like this:

	Req.	Donated	Total
Proj Coord @ $2,000/ea. 100% x 12 months	$24,000	-0-	$24,000

You can list all of your staff in the same way. If any of your staff are being paid out of another source of funds (for example, a staff person assigned to your project by a County agency), then you total up their salary and put it in the donated column (also referred to as in-kind, local share, or applicant share). Like this:

	Req.	Donated	Total
Soc Workers @ $1500 ea. 50% x 12 months	-0-	$18,000	$18,000

This means that you will have two half-time Social Workers on your staff for the full year and their salaries are being paid by somebody other than the funding source. You take their full salary in the Budget ($1,500/mo.) and halve it ($750) as they are only working 50% time; multiply the $750 by 12 months they will be working (giving you $9,000) and multiply it by 2 (the number of people employed in this capacity). This gives you a total of $18,000 of donated Social Worker services in this project.

What does the $2,000 per month figure for the salary of the Project Coordinator represent? It may represent the actual salary paid the Project Coordinator, but not necessarily. If this is a new project, and if your organization has a typical five-step salary schedule for job classifications, the monthly salary range for the Project Coordinator may look like this:

Step A	Step B	Step C	Step D	Step E
$1,500	$1,750	$2,000	$2,250	$2,500

If you have developed a salary schedule like this for each position, then you should request the mid-point ($2,000) unless you know in advance who will fill that position. In that case, list the actual salary anticipated. If not, the mid-point of the salary schedule allows you to hire someone currently making $1,300/mo., who would welcome the increase even in Step A. You have the flexibility to hire at any point along the range with the assumption that all staff salaries will average out toward the middle of the salary range. (This works if there are a number of positions in your project, not just one or two.)

How do you determine what the salary range of a Project Coordinator ought to be? The federal government prefers that salaries be comparable to the prevailing practice in similar agencies in your community. To justify the salaries you build into your Budget you should obtain information from other local agencies regarding the salaries of persons with job descriptions, qualifications, and responsibilities similar to those of the jobs in your agency. You might go to the local city and/or county government, the school district, or United Way. By comparing the jobs at your agency with the jobs at other local agencies, you plan a salary for each position, and you keep the comparability data on hand, should you be asked by the funding source to justify your staff salaries.

Another final item to be included in your Budget for most public agency applications is the matching support being contributed by your organization, or the donated services. They can either be personnel contributed by you (the applicant organization), or by a third party (another participating agency, a corporation giving you a loaned executive, students, etc.). In many cases this will involve the use of volunteers. You should place a value on the service being performed by that volunteer, e.g. plumber, attorney, carpenter, receptionist, etc. That value is based upon the function being performed by the volunteer, not the professional background or education of the volunteer. A physician volunteering time at a community center where he/she helps out in painting the facility is shown at the hourly wage paid painters, not physicians.

Governmental grantmakers sometimes require financial participation on the part of an applicant, i.e., 10% or 25% match. You may be able to make this contribution in "cash" or in-kind. For example, if you are going to pay the salary of a staff member, that is cash. If you are using volunteers, or receive an executive on loan from a local corporation, that is "in-kind."

If you promise volunteers in your program, you are required to deliver the required volunteer services, just as if the funding source was actually paying their salary. You will be asked to document the work they perform and to keep records of their time. Records may be audited in the case of a government grant. Always be able to document 5-10% more than the required percentage match just in the event that you are audited and some of your volunteer time is disallowed.

Why is it important to develop a match (applicant share) and show the total costs of a project when some of the money or services are not being provided by the funding source? There are several reasons. First the government funding source wants to know that there is a commitment on the part of your agency—a commitment beyond just conducting a program. It helps for them to know there is some likelihood that you have resources with which to continue the program after the funding has ceased. It also provides some clarity as to the exact cost in delivering a service. If the program were

to be replicated elsewhere, and donated services are not available, it tells the funding source what the total cost would be. Finally, when you have local resources (volunteers, cash, staff, equipment, etc.), it reduces the amount of money required of the grantor, thereby allowing additional projects to be funded in other locations.

B. Fringe Benefits

In this section you list the fringe benefits your employees will be receiving, and the dollar cost of these benefits. Some fringe benefits are mandatory, but they vary from state to state, so you will have to determine what they are for your agency in your state. Mandatory fringe benefits may include State Disability Insurance, State Unemployment, FICA, etc. They are usually based on percentages of salaries. For example, if FICA is currently 7.51% of the first $45,000 of each person's salary, an entry for FICA on your Budget might look like this:

	Req.	Donated	Total
FICA @ 7.51% of $90,000	$6,759	-0-	$6,759

$90,000 would be the total of all your salaries, up to $45,000 for any one person.

Some fringe benefits are calculated on a flat amount per month per staff member, and not on a percentage, e.g., health insurance. For example:

	Req.	Donated	Total
Health insurance @ $100/mo. per staff member x 4 staff @ 12 months	$4,800	-0-	$4,800

As with your salary schedule, your fringe benefits should be comparable to the benefits offered in similar agencies in your community.

While you will need to calculate fringe benefits for your own information, in some grant applications you simply indicate the fringe benefit total as a percentage of salary.

C. Consultant and Contract Services

This is the third and final part of the Personnel section of your Budget. In this section you include paid and unpaid consultants (i.e., volunteers). You can differentiate between which items go here and which go in Salaries and Wages on the basis of the manner in which the individual or business normally operates. If a bookkeeping firm generally operates on a fee-for-service basis and is volunteering their service to your organization, that would fit best under Consultant and Contract Services. Essentially, be logical and if a Fed yells at you, change it. (Foundation persons never yell.) Entries might look like these:

	Req.	Donated	Total
Bookkeeping Services @ $200/mo. x 12 mos.	-0-	$2,400	$2,400

Contracted Fundraising Svc. @ $400/day x 10 days	$4,000	-0-	$4,000
Trainer @ $250/day x 8 days	$2,000	-0-	$2,000

II. NON-PERSONNEL

A. Space Costs

In this section, you list all of the facilities you will be using, both those on which you pay rent and those which are being donated for your use. Rent you pay, or the valuation of donated facilities, should be comparable to prevailing rents in the geographic area in which you are located. In addition to the actual rent, you should also include the cost of utilities, maintenance services and renovations, if they are absolutely essential to your program, insurance on the facility, telephones (number of instruments needed, installment costs, and monthly cost of instruments), and out-of-town facilities needed. Include these items in line item fashion like this:

	Req.	Donated	Total
Office Space of 900 sq. feet $1.25/foot/mo. x 12 mos.	$13,500	-0-	$13,500
Facility insurance	-0-	$600	$600

B. Rental, Lease or Purchase of Equipment

Here you list all the equipment, donated or to be purchased, that will be used in the proposed program. This includes office equipment, desks, duplicating machines, word processors, etc. Let discretion be your guide in this section. Try to obtain as much donated equipment as you can. It not only lowers the funding source cost, but it shows the funding source that other people are involved in trying to make the program happen. Be careful to read guidelines closely when working with government grant applications—especially as to their definition of equipment and restrictions which apply. For example, equipment is often defined as something costing more than $500 per unit and/or having a lifetime of greater than one year. Additionally, there may be prohibitions against purchasing equipment, and you may be encouraged to lease rather than purchase.

C. Supplies

This generally means "desk top" supplies such as paper clips, pens, paper, stationery, etc. A reasonable figure to use is $125 per year for each of your staff. If you have any unusual needs for supplies—perhaps you are running an art education program, a sheltered workshop, or some classroom activity requiring a good deal of educational materials—then have a separate line item for such supplies. This component can also include publications, subscriptions, and postage.

D. Travel

All transportation related expenses are included here. Don't put in any big lump sums which will require interpretation or raise a question by the funding source. Include all staff travel, per diem rates approved by your agency and/or the state or federal agency you are applying to, ground transportation, taxi, reimbursement to staff for use of their automobiles, consultant travel costs, use of agency vans or automobiles (if this has not been included under equipment), etc. Examples include the following:

	Req.	Donated	Total
Four round trip air fares LA-NY for workshop on Creative Accounting @ $550/each	$2,000	-0-	$2,000
Reimbursement for staff travel @ .20/mile x average of 400 miles/mo. x 12 mos.	$960	-0-	$960
Per Diem (NY) @ $150/day x 8 days for 4 staff at Creative Accounting Workshop	$1,200	-0-	$1,200

Be sure that you use per diem (hotel and meals) rates which are consistent for the location. Attending a workshop in Weed, California will be considerably less expensive than New York City.

E. Other Costs

This is generally a catch-all category which includes items not reasonable to include elsewhere. For example:

1. Bonding of employees
2. Tuition for classes
3. Professional Association dues
4. Printing (unless you placed this under Consultant and Contract Services)

III. INDIRECT COSTS

The third component of your Budget is called Indirect Costs. The federal government defines indirect costs as those costs of an institution which are not readily identifiable with a particular project or activity, but nevertheless are necessary to the general operation of the institution and the conduct of the activities it performs. The cost of operating and maintaining buildings and equipment, depreciation, administrative salaries, general telephone expenses, general travel and supplies expenses are types of expenses usually considered as indirect costs. While it is possible for all such costs to be charged directly—that is, to the line items listed above—this is often impractical, and you may group them into a common pool. The federal government indicates that "an Indirect Cost Rate is simply a device for determining fairly and expeditiously ... that proportion of an intitution's general expenses each of its projects or activities should bear." An organization or institution can negotiate an Indirect Cost Rate (generally a percentage of Salaries and Wages or Total Direct Costs) with any federal agency from whom it has received funds. This is an important issue since many larger institutions find that every new project undertaken

SAMPLE BUDGET

	Req.	Donated	Total
I. PERSONNEL			
A. Salaries and Wages			
Project Coordinator @$2,000/month @ 100% x 12 months	24,000	-0-	24,000
2 Social Workers @$1,500/month each @50% time x 12 months	-0-	18,000	18,000
20 Volunteer Recreational Aides @50 hours each/year x 7.00/hour	-0-	7,000	7,000
B. Fringe Benefits			
20% of $42,000	4,800	3,600	8,400
C. Consultant and Contract Services			
Bookeeping Services @$200/month x 12 months	-0-	2,400	2,400
Fundraising Services @$400/day x 10 days	4,000	-0-	4,000
Trainer @$250/day x 8 days	2,000	-0-	2,000
Annual Audit	2,000	2,000	4,000
II. NON-PERSONNEL			
A. Space			
900 square feet @$1.25/square foot/month x 12 months	13,500	-0-	13,500
Telephones @$200/month x 12 months	2,400	-0-	2,400
Utilities @$300/month x 12 months	-0-	3,600	3,600
Facility Insurance @$600/year	600	-0-	600
B. Rental, Lease, Purchase of Equipment			
Word Processor/printer	2,000	-0-	2,000
12-passenger van @$400/month x 10 months	4,000	-0-	4,000
3 desk/chair sets @$250/each	750	-0-	750
C. Supplies			
Desk top supplies @$125/year/staff x 3	375	-0-	375
Educational materials @$50/month x 12 months	600	-0-	600
D. Travel			
4 roundtrip airfares LA-NY @$500/each	2,200	-0-	2,200
Reimbursement for staff auto travel @$.20/mile x average of 400 miles/month x 12 months	960	-0-	960
8 days per diem (NY) @$1.50/day	1,200	-0-	1,200
E. Other Costs			
Conference Tuition (Creative Accounting) @$200/each x 4 staff	800	-0-	800
Board Liability Insurance	600	-0-	600
III. INDIRECT COSTS			
15.3% of TADC (Total Allowable Direct Costs) as per att. negot. rate with Dept. of Labor, 1998	10,860	-0-	10,860
TOTAL PROJECT COST:	77,645	36,600	114,245

costs the institution money unless it is reimbursed for the indirect cost associated with operating the institution.

For further clarification of Indirect Cost Rates, contact the Federal Office's Regional Comptroller or your Program Officer for Contract Officer to find out exactly how to go about negotiating Indirect Cost Rates. Once you have such a rate, there may still be instances in which the funding source refuses to pay indirect cost rates or places a cap (a maximum) on the percentage of total direct costs they will pay. Nevertheless, this is an area which should be explored and understood.

VIII. APPENDIX

Addenda to a foundation or corporate proposal should be limited. It is an imposition to suggest that a reviewer plod through many pages of additional material that you decided were important enough to include with your proposal. In the case of a government grant, however, the Appendix may be longer than the body of the proposal. It contains material which needs to be submitted to the funding source, but should not detract from the continuity and flow of the proposal by being included in the narrative. The rationale for any decision about what to include in the body of a proposal should be based on your answering the question, "Do I really want the funding source to read/scan the census runs, flow chart, or job descriptions while reading the proposal?" If the answer is "Yes" then definitely include the item at that juncture. If the answer is "No" then include the item in the Appendix and refer the reader to it.

Funding sources will usually stipulate the attachments they want you to include with your grant application. This will involve a variety of documents, many of which will be required routinely by other funding sources. It is a good idea for Development Officers, Program Planners, Grantwriters, or related personnel to maintain a file of materials which can be included in a proposal package. Such items ought to be accessible to you at all times.

Items which are routinely requested by many funding sources include the following:

1. An Audited Financial Statement

Funding sources generally require an audited financial statement. Many smaller organizations do not routinely have an audit conducted, or cannot afford an audit, and an "unaudited" financial statement is often developed by the agency's accountant or bookkeeper. it is important that the applicants know whether the funding source will accept an unaudited financial statement. A telephone call to the program officer, foundation staff member, or related contact person at the offices of the funding source will provide you with the answer.

2. I.R.S. Documentation Letter

This letter from the I.R.S. indicates that your organization is exempt from federal corporate income taxes. It contains important information regarding the basis for your exemption and the requirements associated with maintaining it. In some cases, individual states may also grant such exemptions, and copies of both letters may be appropriate for submission.

3. Indication of Nonprofit Corporation Status

A copy of the receipt of nonprofit corporation status by the state in which your organization was incorporated may be required by funding sources. In most instances, the favorable determination of tax exemption (above) will be sufficient in that it lists the name of the incorporated nonprofit organization.

4. Roster of Board of Directors

A document more and more requested by funding sources is a roster of board members by affiliation. Of concern is more than simply the names of your board members, but who they represent. By this is meant their job function: minister, doctor, banker, social worker, building contractor, etc. In the cases of retired individuals, indicate their former job or profession.

In situations where organizations have board members who are welfare recipients, housewives, unemployed persons, students, etc., select an area of interest or specialty for such individuals, and indicate that after their name. Don't just list a name without any affiliation.

5. Table of Organization

Another item which may be useful is a table of organization. This table should include the proposed staffing pattern for the project for which funds are being requested, and should also include the larger agency/department/section to whom the new project personnel report. With large organizations, it is not critical that each position be indicated, but units or departments should be shown. In many instances it is more important that the funding source understand how the major "functions" of the organization are carried out, and how boards, committees and staff interrelate. The only problem with these tables is that they often present such a confusing picture that one wonders how the organization could ever work.

6. Organizational Budget

Some funding sources will require submission of an organizational Budget for the current or forthcoming program year. This organizational Budget differs from the Budget for the project itself, previously discussed. This allows the reviewer to put the grant request in a larger context.

7. Summary Chart of Key Events

Most public grant applications will require that you submit some form of timeline for major milestones or activities. This can be done in a variety of formats—Gantt charts, PERT charts, flow charts, etc., and can be done by month, quarterly, or by time elapsed from the initiation of the project. Whatever format you use, it should be clear and easily understood by the funding source.

Other documents are often needed for inclusion as an attachment to a proposal:

8. Negotiated Indirect Cost Rate

A copy of your agency's negotiated indirect cost rate should be included in the Appendix when you are citing a "percentage" amount for indirect costs. This is required when submitting public agency applications where such costs are being charged.

Private foundations may also pay indirect cost rates, but be sure to review foundation guidelines closely in that some place a limit on the percentage they will pay. In some cases this percentage is only ten percent (10%) of total direct costs—considerably less than the negotiated percentage with the federal agency.

9. Letters of Support or Endorsement

Letters from elected officials, other organizations and individuals will need to be submitted as required by a funding source or on the basis of your organization's decision that such indicators of support would be a good idea.

In general, such letters should be addressed to your organization (Executive Director, Board Chairman, etc.) and sent to you for submission along with the proposal. Letters should not be sent under separate cover to the funding source because they may not get there in time or may not be filed appropriately with your proposal. More significantly, many funding sources simply will not accept documents submitted separately.

To aid in the process of securing letters of support, many grantwriters and development officers have developed a procedure designed to aid those individuals and organizations from whom you want such letters. Many elected officials and agency executives are continually asked for such letters of support, but it speeds up the process if they can see an example of the type of letter desired.

It is a good idea to draft letters of support and share them with potential signees. This will ensure that you do not receive a glowing endorsement for your program "to provide a shelter for homeless immigrant families" when you are actually seeking support for "establishing a source of food and shelter for migrating birds." Telephone discussions which summarize project ideas often do not get heard exactly as you think you've transmitted them.

If you plan to include "motherhood letters" along with your proposal, i.e., "As a mother in Centerville with six children, I have nothing but praise for the Headstart program and urge you to continue funding it," try to keep such endorsements to a minimum—no more than two such letters per proposal!

10. Resumes

Whenever possible, resumes/curriculum vitae of key staff should be updated periodically so that you are not submitting the exact resume which was placed in the agency's file ten years ago when the person was hired.

Also, it helps the ease of reading if different resumes are written in the same format, so when updating resumes you might consider developing a similar format for each. With the exclusion of academic and medical personnel, they need be no longer than 2-3 pages.

11. Job Descriptions

While in some instances it is important to create a capsule resume for inclusion in the body of the proposal, in most cases the description of positions ought to be an Appendix item.

Key to entry information

(1) **XYZ FOUNDATION** (2) **[101]**

(3) One Central Commerce Building
Main and Division Streets
Anytown, IL 60009

(4) (312) 555-5555
Fax: (312) 555-1234
E-Mail Address: abcd@xyzfdn.edu
Web Site Address: www.xyzfdn.edu

(5) FOUNDED: 1990

(6) AREAS OF INTEREST:
Education, medical research, the environment, youth groups, law and social welfare.

(7) CONSULTING OR VOLUNTEER SERVICES:
Technical assistance to community groups, particularly to those providing cultural activities.

(8) NAME OF PROGRAM
John Doe Project Grants Fund

(9) TYPE:
Project/Program grants. Support for a variety of activities in the areas of education, medical research, desert research, atmospheric, earth, and oceanographic sciences, youth organizations, libraries, conservation projects, water pollution studies, fish and game management, preservation, parks and recreation, environmental studies, law, judicial education, crime delinquency, law enforcement, relief and social agencies, museums and historical projects, health, hospitals, and community improvement organizations. Awards are not available for endowment, contingency or reserve purposes.

(10) YEAR PROGRAM STARTED: 1950

(11) PURPOSE:
To support endeavors for the benefit of mankind.

(12) LEGAL BASIS:
Private foundation; tax-exempt under statute 501(c)(3) of the Internal Revenue Code.

(13) ELIGIBILITY: U.S. tax-exempt nonprofit organizations with appropriate interests are eligible to apply. Grants are not made, however, to organizations which distribute them to beneficiaries of their own selection. Priority is given to projects which are not normally financed by public tax funds.

(14) GEOGRAPHIC RESTRICTIONS:
United States.

(15) FINANCIAL DATA:
Grants vary in amount depending upon the needs and nature of the request.

(16) *Amount of support per award:* $1,000 to $500,000.

(17) *Total amount of support:* $6,005,000 for the year ended May 31, 2014.

(18) *Matching fund requirements:* Grants exceeding $25,000 must be matched by an amount not less than one-third the total amount of the grant.

(19) COOPERATIVE FUNDING PROGRAMS:
The Foundation prefers joint funding whenever possible.

(20) NUMBER OF APPLICANTS MOST RECENT YEAR: 512

(21) NUMBER OF AWARDS: 92 for the year ended May 31, 2014.

(22) REPRESENTATIVE AWARDS:
$75,000 to Anytown Hospital, toward facilities and equipment for its new Community Health Center; $25,000 to State University, for development of an interdisciplinary studies program; $15,000 to City Youth Center, toward purchase of equipment for its model reading laboratory program for youths.

(23) APPLICATION INFORMATION:
No official application forms are issued. Interested applicants should submit an informal proposal which briefly includes:
(1) amount requested and an explanation of the necessity or purpose therefore;
(2) aid sought and amounts received from other foundations and sources (include names) during the preceding three years;
(3) aid presently being sought from other sources (or whether such solicitation is contemplated) and, if so, from whom;
(4) copy of tax-exempt letter from the U.S. Treasury and Section 509 classification determination;
(5) latest audited balance sheet and detailed income account and;
(6) signature and approval of the overall head of the applicant institution or organization. Seven copies of application proposals and covering letters should be submitted. Letters of support from appropriate authorities and/or organizations are also encouraged.

(24) *Duration:* Varies according to length of project. Grants may be renewed if continued support can be shown to be beneficial and vital to project success.

(25) *Deadline:* Formal proposals and supporting documents must be received two months prior to board meetings, held in June and December.

(26) PUBLICATIONS:
Annual report; application guidelines.

(27) IRS IDENTIFICATION NUMBER:
00-1234567

(28) BOARD OF TRUSTEES:
John Doe III, Chairman
Margaret Lee, Vice Chairman
Samuel Smith, Treasurer
Robert Johnson, Secretary
Arthur Boyle
Anthony Cates
Phillip Sevoy

(29) OFFICERS:
Phyllis Hartley, Executive Director
David Lisle, President
Susan Banks, Vice President
John Quincy Smith, Project Grants Coordinator

(30) ADDRESS INQUIRIES TO:
John Quincy Smith, Project Grants Coordinator
P.O. Box 777
Neartown, IL 60008

(31) * PLEASE NOTE:
If an applicant is unclear as to the Foundation's current fields of interest, an inquiry directed to it describing the applicant's project may save the trouble or expense of preparing and submitting a formal application.

(1)   Grantmaking organization.

(2)   Entry number, reference corresponding to numbers used in the indexes.

(3)   Address.

(4)   Telephone and fax numbers. E-mail, Web Site addresses, and TDD numbers when available.

(5)   Date organization was founded.

(6)   Major fields of organizational interest.

(7)   Fields in which the organization donates consulting, volunteer, or similar services, if applicable; nature of the service.

(8)   Name(s) of grant program(s).

(9)   Nature of support available under the program(s), e.g., fellowships, project grants, research grants, technical assistance, etc.

(10)   Date program was established.

(11)   Objective of the grant program and/or sponsoring institution.

(12)   Organization's legal status or type (e.g., IRS ruling, state statute, corporate giving program, etc.); legal authority for expenditure of government funds, etc.

(13)   Qualifications required of the applicant individual or project and/or sponsoring institution.

(14)   Restrictions or preferences as to geographic location of the applicant individual or project and/or sponsoring institution.

(15)   Fiscal nature of the grant, including expenses to which it may be applied, restrictions on its use and non-cash benefits.

(16)   Fixed sum, average amount, or range of funds offered for each award.

(17)   Total funding available for the program or, when indicated, for all programs of a grantmaking organization, and the year in question.

(18)   Cost-sharing stipulations.

(19)   Nature of participation with other donors for project support.

(20)   Total applicants, for the most recent year statistics are available.

(21)   Total recipients, and the year in question.

(22)   Representative awards made under the program for the most recent year, including the amount, recipient, and project title or purpose of the award.

(23)   Application requirements and procedures, or references for further information.

(24)   Period for which support is provided; renewal possibilities.

(25)   Closing date(s) for application submission; award announcement date(s).

(26)   Publications that are available from the organization, e.g., annual report, application guidelines, program announcements, etc.

(27)   Internal Revenue Service tax identification number, if applicable.

(28)   Names and titles of principal personnel, e.g., Trustees, Directors, Awards Committee members, etc.

(29)   Names and titles of organization and/or program officers.

(30)   Source of further information and/or recipient of applications.

(31)   Unusual specifications or conditions concerning the program.

An asterisk (*) following an organization name indicates no or incomplete data was received from the source to update or compile the entry. The program listing is then reprinted from the last edition of *Grant Support*, revised where possible, or compiled entirely through staff research.

New listings in 2015 edition

The following is a list of foundations that are offering new grant programs. Bulleted items (•) reflect new program names for the foundation listed.

MULTIPLE SPECIAL PURPOSE
Multiple Special Purpose
The Annenberg Foundation, Los Angeles, CA

Daniels Fund, Denver, CO
- (•) Daniels Fund Grants Program
- (•) Daniels Fund Scholarship Program

Hall Family Foundation, Kansas City, MO

HUMANITIES
History
Kentucky Historical Society, Frankfort, KY
- (•) Scholarly Research Fellowship Program

Literature
Carnegie Fund for Authors, New York, NY

Children's Literature Association, Oak Brook, IL
- (•) ChLA Diversity Research Grant

The Word Works, Inc., Washington, DC
- (•) Tenth Gate Prize

Religion and theology
American Catholic Historical Association, Bronx, NY
- (•) The Msgr. Harry C. Koenig Award for Catholic Biography

INTERNATIONAL AFFAIRS AND AREA STUDIES
International studies and research abroad
The American School of Classical Studies at Athens, Princeton, NJ
- (•) Kress Publication Fellowships
- (•) The George Papaioannou Fellowship
- (•) Henry S. Robinson Corinth Research Fellowship

Kobe College Corporation-Japan Education Exchange, Northfield, IL
- (•) KCC JEE High School Essay Contest

SPECIAL POPULATIONS
Native American
American Indian College Fund, Denver, CO
- (•) Full Circle Scholarship Program
- (•) TCU Scholarship Program

Spanish Speaking
Congressional Hispanic Caucus Institute, Washington, DC
- (•) CHCI Congressional Internship
- (•) CHCI Graduate Fellowship Program
- (•) CHCI Public Policy Fellowship
- (•) CHCI Scholarship Fund

SOCIAL SCIENCES
Political science
The Heritage Foundation/B. Kenneth Simon Center for American Studies, Washington, DC
- (•) Research Fellowship in American Studies

LIFE SCIENCES
Medicine (multiple disciplines)
Scleroderma Foundation, Danvers, MA
- (•) Scleroderma Foundation Multi-Center Collaborative Research Grant

Oncology
Cancer Research Society, Montreal, QC, Canada
- (•) Scholarship for the Next Generation of Scientists

Neurology
Alzheimer's Association, Inc., Chicago, IL
- (•) Mentored New Investigator Research Grant to Promote Diversity (MNIRGD)
- (•) New Investigator Research Grant to Promote Diversity (NIRGD)
- (•) U.S.-U.K. Young Investigator Exchange Fellowship

Psychiatry, psychology, mental health
American Psychiatric Foundation, Arlington, VA
- (•) APF-Merck & Co. Early Academic Career Research Award
- (•) Kempf Fund Award for Research Development in Psychobiological Psychiatry

TECHNOLOGY AND INDUSTRY
Aeronautics and astronautics
Smithsonian National Air and Space Museum, Washington, DC
- (•) Summer Internship Program

URBAN AND REGIONAL AFFAIRS
Community development and services
Capitol Federal Foundation, Topeka, KS

EDUCATION
Higher education projects and research
The American-Scandinavian Foundation, New York, NY
- (•) Visiting Lectureships

Lumina Foundation, Indianapolis, IN

Scholar aid programs (all disciplines)
The Carson Scholars Fund, Inc., Towson, MD
- (•) Casrson Scholarships

Jack Kent Cooke Foundation, Lansdowne, VA
- (•) College Scholarship Program
- (•) Dissertation Fellowship Award
- (•) Graduate Arts Award
- (•) Undergraduate Transfer Scholarship
- (•) Young Scholars Program

National Society of Black Engineers, Alexandria, VA

U.S. Department of Education, Washington, DC
- (•) Federal Supplemental Educational Opportunity Grant (FSEOG)
- (•) Iraq and Afghanistan Service Grant
- (•) Teacher Education Assistance for College and Higher Education (TEACH) Grant

University of Southern California, Los Angeles, CA
- (•) Rose Hills Foundation Summer Science and Engineering Fellowships

MULTIPLE SPECIAL PURPOSE

Multiple special purpose

ABBOTT FUND [1]

100 Abbott Park Road, D379/AP6D
Abbott Park, IL 60064-3500
(847) 937-7075
Fax: (847) 935-5051

WEB SITE ADDRESS:
www.abbottfund.org

FOUNDED: 1951

AREAS OF INTEREST:
Health and welfare, education, culture and
arts, civic and public policy.

NAME(S) OF PROGRAMS:
• **General Grant Program**

TYPE:
General operating grants; Project/program
grants. Primary interest in the fields of higher
education and human health and welfare. In
addition, support of appropriate programs in
culture, the arts and civic activities will
continue to be a portion of Abbott's program.

YEAR PROGRAM STARTED: 1951

PURPOSE:
To provide support through cash grants to
U.S.-based recipients whose areas of interest
are consistent with Abbott's basic
philanthropic policies and objectives.

LEGAL BASIS:
Corporate nonprofit giving program.

ELIGIBILITY:
Grants will be made only to associations and
organizations and not directly to individuals.
Grantees must be able to provide evidence of
nonprofit, tax-exempt status and must
complete the eligibility test to ensure that the
organization or program falls within the
funding criteria.

Preference is given to requests for one-time
contributions and for programmatic and
operating purposes. However, grants
extending over a defined period of years or
directed towards the support of specific
building or other capital projects will be
considered on an exception basis.

Priority will be given to organizations serving
communities in which Abbott has significant
operations or employee populations, to
organizations whose activities are directed
towards the support of professions which
provide, directly or indirectly, health care or
other services related to Abbott's primary
areas of operation.

Grants will not be made to individuals,
purely social organizations, political parties
or candidates, religious organizations,
advertising journals, booklets, symposiums or
conferences, social events, for ticket
purchases, memberships, business-related
purposes or for-profit entities.

FINANCIAL DATA:
Grants vary in amount, depending upon the
needs and nature of the request.

APPLICATION INFORMATION:
Online application only.
Duration: One year. Possible multiyear.
Deadline: Applications may be submitted at
any time. Most proposals are reviewed within
12 weeks after receipt.

ADDRESS INQUIRIES TO:
Grant Program
(See address above.)

THE ABELL FOUNDATION, INC. [2]

111 South Calvert Street
Suite 2300
Baltimore, MD 21202-6174
(410) 547-1300
Fax: (410) 539-6579

E-MAIL ADDRESS:
abell@abell.org

WEB SITE ADDRESS:
www.abell.org

FOUNDED: 1953

AREAS OF INTEREST:
Arts and culture, community development,
education, conservation and environment,
health and human services, workforce
development, criminal justice and addictions.

TYPE:
Capital grants; Challenge/matching grants;
Demonstration grants; Development grants;
General operating grants; Matching gifts;
Project/program grants; Seed money grants.

YEAR PROGRAM STARTED: 1953

PURPOSE:
To improve the quality of life in the area
around Baltimore, MD.

LEGAL BASIS:
Private foundation.

ELIGIBILITY:
Individuals are not eligible for grants.
Qualifying organizations must have IRS
509(a) and 501(c)(3) not-for-profit status.
Religious organizations are eligible.

GEOGRAPHIC RESTRICTIONS:
Maryland.

FINANCIAL DATA:
Amount of support per award: $500 to
$500,000; average: $65,354.
Total amount of support: Approximately
$13,999,622 for the year 2012.

NUMBER OF APPLICANTS MOST RECENT YEAR:
504.

NUMBER OF AWARDS: 293.

REPRESENTATIVE AWARDS:
$20,000 to Banner Neighborhoods
Community Corporation, Baltimore, MD, for
continued support of the Home Maintenance
Program providing minor but necessary
repair services for elderly low-income
homeowners in southeast Baltimore to enable
them to stay in their homes; $75,000 to
Druid Heights Community Development,
Baltimore, MD, toward the purchase of a
six-unit apartment building to provide
supportive housing and services to clients in
the Maryland Re-entry program; $120,000 to
The Urban Alliance Foundation, Inc.,
Baltimore, MD, to provide two-year funding
for staffing costs of the Urban Alliance
Baltimore Program, a pilot youth
employment program for students at
Northwestern High School.

APPLICATION INFORMATION:
Foundation application form must be
completed and submitted. Applicant
organizations must provide IRS 501(c)(3) and
509(a) documentation, the most recently
audited financial statement, operating budget,
projected budget for each year funding is
requested, a list of the board of directors as
well as pertinent information regarding the
program. Application needs to be preceded
by a two-page letter of inquiry.

Duration: Primarily one-year grants; few
multiyear awards.
Deadline: Grants will be awarded six times a
year; January 1, March 1, May 1, August 1,
September 1 and November 1.

PUBLICATIONS:
Annual Report; *Abell Report*, newsletter;
periodic research reports.

IRS IDENTIFICATION NUMBER: 52-6036106

OFFICER:
Robert C. Embry, Jr., President
Sita Culman, Vice President

ADDRESS INQUIRIES TO:
Sita Culman, Vice President
(See address above.)

THE ABNEY FOUNDATION [3]

100 Vine Street
Anderson, SC 29621
(864) 964-9201
Fax: (864) 964-9209

E-MAIL ADDRESS:
info@abneyfoundation.org

WEB SITE ADDRESS:
www.abneyfoundation.org

FOUNDED: 1957

AREAS OF INTEREST:
Religious, charitable, scientific, literary or
educational, including encouragement of art
and music.

TYPE:
Capital grants; Development grants;
Endowments; Project/program grants;
Research grants.

YEAR PROGRAM STARTED: 1957

PURPOSE:
To make grants for innovative and creative
projects and to programs which are
responsive to changing community needs in
the areas of education, health, social service
and cultural affairs.

LEGAL BASIS:
Tax-exempt, private foundation.

ELIGIBILITY:
Applicants must be tax-exempt organizations.
No grants to individuals.

GEOGRAPHIC RESTRICTIONS:
South Carolina.

FINANCIAL DATA:
Amount of support per award: $1,000 to
$250,000.
Total amount of support: $1,875,000 for the
year 2013.

NUMBER OF APPLICANTS MOST RECENT YEAR:
100.

NUMBER OF AWARDS: 46.

APPLICATION INFORMATION:
Applicants may submit a Letter of Intent
briefly describing the project before
submitting a proposal in order to find out if
their ideas are potentially fundable by the
Foundation.
Duration: No grants on a continuing basis.
Deadline: November 15.

PUBLICATIONS:
Application guidelines.

IRS IDENTIFICATION NUMBER: 57-6019445

STAFF:
David C. King, Executive Director

TRUSTEES AND OFFICERS:
John R. Fulp, Jr., Chairman
David C. King, Vice Chairman
Johnnye K. Palmer, Treasurer and Secretary
Lebrena Fulp Campbell
Carl T. Edwards
John R. Fulp, III
Edd Sheriff

ADDRESS INQUIRIES TO:
David C. King, Executive Director
(See address above.)

ACADIA UNIVERSITY   [4]
18 University Avenue
Wolfville NS B4P 2R6 Canada
(902) 585-1498
Fax: (902) 585-1096

E-MAIL ADDRESS:
theresa.starratt@acadiau.ca

WEB SITE ADDRESS:
www.acadiau.ca

AREAS OF INTEREST:
English, political science, sociology, biology, chemistry, computer science, geology, psychology, education, recreation management, mathematics, statistics and applied geomatics, and social and political thought.

NAME(S) OF PROGRAMS:
● **Acadia Graduate Awards**

TYPE:
Awards/prizes.

PURPOSE:
To financially support graduate students.

ELIGIBILITY:
Open to registered full-time graduate students at Acadia University. Candidates must possess a 3.0/4.0 grade point average in each of the last two years of undergraduate study in their major.

FINANCIAL DATA:
Amount of support per award: Up to $9,000 for first-year students and a maximum of $8,000 for second-year students.

APPLICATION INFORMATION:
Consult the University for guidelines.
Duration: One or two years.
Deadline: February.

ADDRESS INQUIRIES TO:
Theresa Starratt, Graduate Studies Officer
(See address above.)

*SPECIAL STIPULATIONS:
Recipients should expect to undertake certain duties during the academic year (up to maximum of 10 hours per week and to a maximum of 120 hours per semester) as a condition of tenure of the award. Specific duties will be established by agreement at the beginning of each academic year.

THE ACHELIS FOUNDATION [5]
767 Third Avenue, 4th Floor
New York, NY 10017-2023
(212) 644-0322
Fax: (212) 759-6510

E-MAIL ADDRESS:
main@achelis-bodman-fnds.org

WEB SITE ADDRESS:
www.achelis-bodman-fnds.org

FOUNDED: 1940

AREAS OF INTEREST:
Primarily arts and culture, education, employment, health, public policy and youth and families.

TYPE:
Challenge/matching grants; Conferences/seminars; Development grants; General operating grants; Internships; Matching gifts; Project/program grants; Research grants; Scholarships; Technical assistance; Training grants. Over 90% of the Foundation's grants fall into its six program categories.

PURPOSE:
To impact the greater New York City region and enhance the quality of life for its people, especially the disadvantaged; to advance human dignity, inspire personal achievement and foster self-reliance.

LEGAL BASIS:
Private foundation under Section 501(c)(3) of the Internal Revenue Code.

ELIGIBILITY:
Nonprofit organizations based in New York City and northern New Jersey that are tax-exempt under Section 501(c)(3) of the Internal Revenue Code and fall within the program areas of the Foundation are welcome to submit an inquiry or proposal letter.

The Foundation generally does not make grants to nonprofit organizations outside of New York, annual appeals, dinner functions and fund-raising events, endowments and capital campaigns, loans and deficit financing, direct grants to individuals (such as scholarships and financial aid), individual day-care and after-school programs, housing, international projects, films and travel, projects for the elderly, small art, dance, music and theater groups, independent or public K-12 schools (except charter schools), national health and mental health organizations, and government agencies and nonprofit programs and services significantly funded or substantially reimbursed by government.

GEOGRAPHIC RESTRICTIONS:
Northern New Jersey and New York, New York.

FINANCIAL DATA:
Amount of support per award: $5,000 to $125,000 for the year 2013.
Total amount of support: $1,235,000 for the year 2013.

APPLICATION INFORMATION:
It is recommended that an organization's initial contact with the Foundation include only the following items:
(1) an inquiry or proposal letter briefly summarizing the history of the project, need, research, objectives, time period, key staff, project budget, and evaluation plan emphasizing measurable outcomes and specific program results;
(2) latest annual report;
(3) current and complete audited financial statements and;
(4) copy of the organization's IRS 501(c)(3) tax-exemption letter.
Duration: One year.

OFFICERS:
John N. Irwin, III, Chairman
Russell P. Pennoyer, President
Peter Frelinghuysen, Vice President
Mary S. Phipps, Vice President

Horace I. Crary, Jr., Treasurer
John B. Krieger, Executive Director, Secretary and Assistant Treasurer

BOARD OF TRUSTEES:
Horace I. Crary, Jr.
Walter J.P. Curley, Jr.
Peter Frelinghuysen
John N. Irwin, III
Leslie Lenkowsky
Russell P. Pennoyer
Mary S. Phipps
Tatiana Pouschine

ADDRESS INQUIRIES TO:
John B. Krieger, Executive Director
(See address above.)

AETNA FOUNDATION, INC.   [6]
151 Farmington Avenue
Hartford, CT 06156-3180
(860) 273-6382
Fax: (860) 273-7764

E-MAIL ADDRESS:
aetnafoundation@aetna.com

WEB SITE ADDRESS:
www.aetna-foundation.org

FOUNDED: 1972

AREAS OF INTEREST:
Obesity, racial and ethnic health care equity, and integrated health care.

NAME(S) OF PROGRAMS:
● **National Grants**
● **Regional Grants**

TYPE:
Matching gifts; Project/program grants; Research grants.

YEAR PROGRAM STARTED: 1972

PURPOSE:
To promote wellness, health and access to high-quality health care for everyone, while supporting the communities Aetna serves.

LEGAL BASIS:
Corporate giving program.

ELIGIBILITY:
Nonprofit organizations with evidence of IRS 501(c)(3) designation of de facto tax-exempt status may apply for a grant. Complete details available on the Foundation web site.

APPLICATION INFORMATION:
Guidelines available on the Foundation web site.
Duration: Varies.
Deadline: Varies.

PUBLICATIONS:
Aetna Annual Giving Report.

IRS IDENTIFICATION NUMBER: 23-7241940

STAFF:
Garth N. Graham, M.D., M.P.H., President
Gillian R. Barclay, D.D.S., Dr.P.H., Vice President
Sharon C. Dalton, MBA, Vice President
Sharon R. Ions, Program Officer
Kristyn L. Neal, Program Officer
Alyse B. Sabina, M.P.H., Program Officer
Saima R. Siddiqi, Program Associate
Cheryl A. Tourigny, Program Associate
Melenie O. Magnotta, Grants Manager

BOARD OF DIRECTORS:
Mark T. Bertolini
Sheryl A. Burke
Molly J. Coye, M.D.
Jeffrey E. Garten
Steven B. Kelmar
Susan Kosman, R.N., B.S.N.
Andrew J. Lee

Margaret M. McCarthy
Kay D. Mooney
Joseph P. Newhouse

ADDRESS INQUIRIES TO:
See e-mail address above.

THE AHMANSON FOUNDATION [7]
9215 Wilshire Boulevard
Beverly Hills, CA 90210
(310) 278-0770

E-MAIL ADDRESS:
info@theahmansonfoundation.org

WEB SITE ADDRESS:
www.theahmansonfoundation.org

FOUNDED: 1952

AREAS OF INTEREST:
Arts and humanities, education, human services, medicine and health.

TYPE:
Capital grants; Endowments; Matching gifts; Project/program grants; Scholarships.

PURPOSE:
To support programs that improve the quality of life in southern California.

LEGAL BASIS:
Private family foundation.

ELIGIBILITY:
Grants are made to organizations that have tax-exempt status under Section 501(c)(3) of the Internal Revenue Code. No grants are made to individuals. Nonsectarian religious programs may apply.

GEOGRAPHIC RESTRICTIONS:
Los Angeles County, California.

FINANCIAL DATA:
Amount of support per award: Varies.

NUMBER OF AWARDS: 464.

APPLICATION INFORMATION:
Send letter of inquiry to the Grants Administrator.
Duration: Varies.

ADDRESS INQUIRIES TO:
Yvonne de Beixedon, Grants Administrator
(See address above.)

ALABAMA POWER FOUNDATION, INC. [8]
600 North 18th Street
Birmingham, AL 35291
(205) 257-2508
Fax: (205) 257-1860

WEB SITE ADDRESS:
www.alpowercharitablegiving.org

FOUNDED: 1989

AREAS OF INTEREST:
Education, arts and culture, civic and community, health and human services, and environment.

NAME(S) OF PROGRAMS:
- **Educational Grant Program**
- **Gateway Grant**
- **Good Roots Grant**

TYPE:
Capital grants; Challenge/matching grants; Endowments; General operating grants; Project/program grants; Scholarships; Seed money grants.

PURPOSE:
To improve the quality of life of Alabamians and to strengthen the communities in which they live.

LEGAL BASIS:
Corporate foundation.

ELIGIBILITY:
Applicant must be a 501(c)(3) tax-exempt, nonprofit Alabama organization. No grants to individuals, religious or political groups.

GEOGRAPHIC RESTRICTIONS:
Alabama.

FINANCIAL DATA:
Amount of support per award: $2,000 to $200,000; $7,000 average.
Total amount of support: Approximately $8,000,000 annually.

APPLICATION INFORMATION:
Contact the Foundation for guidelines.
Duration: One-time funding.
Deadline: March, June, September, and December.

PUBLICATIONS:
Annual report; information and guidelines.

ADDRESS INQUIRIES TO:
President
(See address above.)

ALCOA FOUNDATION [9]
201 Isabella Street
Pittsburgh, PA 15212-5858
(412) 553-4545
Fax: (412) 553-4532

WEB SITE ADDRESS:
www.alcoa.com

FOUNDED: 1952

AREAS OF INTEREST:
Environment and education.

TYPE:
Project/program grants. Grants support a variety of special-interest programs with emphasis on projects which enhance the environment of communities where Alcoa has a presence.

YEAR PROGRAM STARTED: 1964

PURPOSE:
To strengthen the communities where employees live and in which the company does business.

LEGAL BASIS:
Nonprofit foundation.

ELIGIBILITY:
Organizations classified as public charities and tax-exempt under Section 501(c)(3) of the Internal Revenue Code will be considered. Preference is given to institutions:
(1) located in communities where Alcoa plants or subsidiaries are located;
(2) conducting technical programs and;
(3) capable of exercising great influence in attacking and solving national educational problems.

Unsolicited requests rarely considered.

FINANCIAL DATA:
Amount of support per award: Varies.
Total amount of support: Varies.

APPLICATION INFORMATION:
Applications are accepted on an invitation-only basis.
Duration: Varies.

Deadline: Generally July 31.

GEORGE I. ALDEN TRUST [10]
c/o Fletcher, Tilton & Whipple, P.C.
370 Main Street
Worcester, MA 01608
(508) 459-8005
Fax: (508) 459-8305

E-MAIL ADDRESS:
trustees@aldentrust.org

WEB SITE ADDRESS:
www.aldentrust.org

FOUNDED: 1912

AREAS OF INTEREST:
Higher education.

TYPE:
Capital grants; Challenge/matching grants. Capital projects related to teaching and learning technology, in general, and to the sciences, in particular; some support for need-based scholarship endowment and faculty development.

YEAR PROGRAM STARTED: 1912

LEGAL BASIS:
Probate Trust.

ELIGIBILITY:
Principal focus is on independent colleges and universities with full-time, undergraduate enrollments of 1,000 to 5,000 students. Also, educationally related entities in the Worcester (MA) area and at YMCAs in Massachusetts.

GEOGRAPHIC RESTRICTIONS:
New Jersey, New York, Pennsylvania and the six New England states.

FINANCIAL DATA:
Total amount of support: Varies.
Matching fund requirements: Usually 1:2 or 1:3 (Alden Trust:matching dollars), with 18-month challenge period. The Trust only pays when the challenge is met in full. The Trust makes no interim or partial payments.

NUMBER OF APPLICANTS MOST RECENT YEAR: 80 for the year 2011.

NUMBER OF AWARDS: 80; 58 plus 22 unsolicited grants for the year 2011.

APPLICATION INFORMATION:
Guidelines for colleges and universities are available on the web site.

IRS IDENTIFICATION NUMBER: 04-6023784

TRUSTEES:
Warner S. Fletcher, Chairperson
James E. Collins
Douglas Q. Meystre
Gail T. Randall

ADDRESS INQUIRIES TO:
Warner S. Fletcher, Chairperson
(See address above.)

ALLEGHENY FOUNDATION [11]
One Oxford Centre
301 Grant Street, Suite 3900
Pittsburgh, PA 15219-6401
(412) 392-2900

WEB SITE ADDRESS:
www.scaife.com

AREAS OF INTEREST:
Education, civic development and historic preservation.

TYPE:
General operating grants.

ELIGIBILITY:
Applicant must be a 501(c)(3) nonprofit organization.

GEOGRAPHIC RESTRICTIONS:
Western Pennsylvania.

FINANCIAL DATA:
Amount of support per award: Varies.
Total amount of support: $2,568,000 for the year 2012.

APPLICATION INFORMATION:
Contact Foundation for guidelines.
Duration: Typically one year.
Deadline: The Foundation normally considers grants at an Annual Meeting held in November. However, grant requests may be submitted at any time.

ADDRESS INQUIRIES TO:
Matthew A. Groll, Executive Director
(See address above.)

THE PAUL G. ALLEN FAMILY FOUNDATION   [12]
505 Fifth Avenue South, Suite 900
Seattle, WA 98104
(206) 342-2030
Fax: (206) 342-3030

E-MAIL ADDRESS:
info@pgafamilyfoundation.org

WEB SITE ADDRESS:
www.pgafamilyfoundation.org

FOUNDED: 1988

NAME(S) OF PROGRAMS:
● **Arts and Culture**
● **Asset Building**
● **Basic Needs**
● **Education**
● **Libraries**
● **Science and Technology**

TYPE:
Awards/prizes; Capital grants; Challenge/matching grants; Conferences/seminars; Matching gifts; Project/program grants; Research grants.

PURPOSE:
To create meaningful change in communities by partnering with exceptional organizations and leaders who are bold enough to reinvent the world.

LEGAL BASIS:
Private family foundation.

ELIGIBILITY:
Applicants must be organizations organized and operated exclusively for charitable purposes in the Pacific Northwest area, tax-exempt under 501(c)(3) of the IRS code, and not be a private foundation as defined in Section 509(a).

GEOGRAPHIC RESTRICTIONS:
Alaska, Idaho, Montana, Oregon and Washington.

FINANCIAL DATA:
Amount of support per award: Varies.
Total amount of support: Varies.
Matching fund requirements: Varies by grant.

NUMBER OF APPLICANTS MOST RECENT YEAR:
125 for the year 2012.

NUMBER OF AWARDS: 120.

REPRESENTATIVE AWARDS:
$100,000 to Adelante Mujeres for the expansion of a microenterprise assistance program; $100,000 to Bellingham Food Bank

for the addition of fresh produce and essential items to its food distribution program in the northern Puget Sound region; $10,000 to Bunnell Street Gallery for its 2013 Visual Arts Exhibition program; $150,000 to Pierce County Library Foundation to build an interactive platform on its web site; $600,000 to Seattle Public Schools to improve graduation rates.

APPLICATION INFORMATION:
The Foundation encourages applicants to contact it via its web site if their projects are aligned with Foundation's programs.
Duration: One year. Some multiyear.
Deadline: Varies.

PUBLICATIONS:
Grants List, online.

IRS IDENTIFICATION NUMBER: 94-3082532

STAFF:
Susan Coliton, Vice President
Dave Ferrero, Senior Program Officer
Jim McDonald, Senior Program Officer
Kathy Richmond, Senior Program Officer
Lisa Arnold, Manager, Grants and Library Program
Val Bush, Grants Specialist

ADDRESS INQUIRIES TO:
Lisa Arnold, Grants Manager
(See address above.)

ALTRIA GROUP, INC.   [13]
6603 West Broad Street
Richmond, VA 23230
(804) 484-8651

WEB SITE ADDRESS:
www.altria.com

FOUNDED: 1956

AREAS OF INTEREST:
Arts and culture, education, environment and youth development.

TYPE:
Project/program grants.

YEAR PROGRAM STARTED: 1956

PURPOSE:
To make strategic and effective grants that strengthen people and communities.

LEGAL BASIS:
Corporate giving program.

ELIGIBILITY:
Grants are only made to organizations that are registered as 501(c)(3) tax-exempt by the Internal Revenue Code. Altria Group does not support individuals.

FINANCIAL DATA:
Amount of support per award: Varies depending on program/initiative.
Total amount of support: Varies.

NUMBER OF AWARDS: 4,000.

APPLICATION INFORMATION:
Each grant program has specific guidelines. Detailed instructions are available online.
Duration: One year.

ADDRESS INQUIRIES TO:
Charlie Agee, Director, Contributions
(See address above.)

AMERICAN PHILOSOPHICAL SOCIETY   [14]
104 South Fifth Street
Philadelphia, PA 19106-3387
(215) 440-3429

E-MAIL ADDRESS:
lmusumeci@amphilsoc.org

WEB SITE ADDRESS:
www.amphilsoc.org

FOUNDED: 1743

AREAS OF INTEREST:
Scholarly research.

NAME(S) OF PROGRAMS:
● **Franklin Research Grants**

TYPE:
Grants-in-aid; Research grants. Postdoctoral grants toward the cost of scholarly research in all areas of knowledge except those in which support by government or corporate enterprise is more appropriate. Scholarly research covers most kinds of scholarly inquiry by individuals. It does not include journalistic or other writing for general readership; the preparation of textbooks, casebooks, anthologies, or other materials for classroom use by students; or the work of creative and performing artists.

The Society does not have fellowships or scholarships for study, nor does it give grants for travel to conferences.

YEAR PROGRAM STARTED: 1933

PURPOSE:
To support scholarly research by individual scholars.

LEGAL BASIS:
Nonprofit learned society.

ELIGIBILITY:
Applications may be made by residents of the U.S., by American citizens resident abroad and by foreign nationals. American citizens and foreign nationals employed by an American institution may apply for support to carry out work anywhere in the world. Foreign nationals not employed by an American institution may apply for funding to work in the U.S. Applicants expecting to use materials or conduct interviews in a foreign language must possess the necessary competence in the language or languages involved. Grants are never made for predoctoral study or research.

It is the Society's long-standing practice to encourage research by younger and less well-established scholars.

FINANCIAL DATA:
Grants are made payable to the applicant.

The Society offers no funds for conference support, fellowships and scholarships, maintenance work already done, or costs of publication.

Amount of support per award: Funding is offered in multiples of $1,000, up to a maximum of $6,000 for one year.
Total amount of support: $438,500 for the year 2013.

COOPERATIVE FUNDING PROGRAMS: If an applicant receives an award for the same project from another granting insititution, the Society will consider limiting its award to costs that are not covered by the other grant.

NUMBER OF APPLICANTS MOST RECENT YEAR:
454 for the year 2011.

NUMBER OF AWARDS: 85 for the year 2013.

APPLICATION INFORMATION:
Applications are submitted through the Society's online application portal.
Duration: One year.

Deadline: October 1 and December 1.

ADDRESS INQUIRIES TO:
Linda Musumeci
Director of Grants and Fellowships
(See address above.)

AMERICAN PHILOSOPHICAL SOCIETY [15]

The Lewis and Clark Fund
104 South Fifth Street
Philadelphia, PA 19106-3387
(215) 440-3429

E-MAIL ADDRESS:
lmusumeci@amphilsoc.org

WEB SITE ADDRESS:
www.amphilsoc.org

FOUNDED: 1743

AREAS OF INTEREST:
Scholarly research.

NAME(S) OF PROGRAMS:
• **The Lewis and Clark Fund for Exploration and Field Research**

TYPE:
Research grants. The Lewis and Clark Fund for Exploration and Field Research (initially supported by the Stanford Ascherman/Baruch Blumberg Fund for Basic Science, established by a benefaction from the late Stanford Ascherman, M.D., of San Francisco) encourages exploratory field studies for the collection of specimens and data and to provide the imaginative stimulus that accompanies direct observation. Applications are invited from disciplines with a large dependence on field studies, such as archeology, anthropology, biology, ecology, geography, geology, linguistics, and paleontology, but grants will not be restricted to these fields.

YEAR PROGRAM STARTED: 2005

PURPOSE:
To support scholarly research by individual scholars.

LEGAL BASIS:
Nonprofit learned society.

ELIGIBILITY:
Grants will be available to doctoral students. Postdoctoral fellows, Master's degree candidates, and undergraduates are not eligible. Applicants who have received Lewis and Clark Fund grants may reapply after an interval of two years.

The competition is open to U.S. residents wishing to carry out research anywhere in the world. Foreign applicants must either be based at a U.S. institution or plan to carry out their work in the U.S.

FINANCIAL DATA:
Amount of support per award: Up to $5,000.
Total amount of support: $104,400 for the year 2013.

NUMBER OF APPLICANTS MOST RECENT YEAR:
444 for the year 2013.

NUMBER OF AWARDS: 25 for the year 2013.

APPLICATION INFORMATION:
The applicant should ask his or her academic advisor to write one of the two letters of recommendation, specifying the student's qualifications to carry out the proposed work and the educational content of the trip. Budgets should be limited to travel and related expenses, including personal field equipment.

When appropriate, the applicant should provide assurances that safety measures will be taken for potentially hazardous projects. When necessary, the applicant and his or her supervisor should discuss the field training that will be provided and the provisions for experienced supervision.

Duration: Preferably one year.

Deadline: February 1, with notification in May, for work in June and beyond.

ADDRESS INQUIRIES TO:
Linda Musumeci
Director of Grants and Fellowships
(See address above.)

AMERICAN SCHLAFHORST FOUNDATION [16]

P.O. Box 240828
Charlotte, NC 28224
(704) 554-0800
Fax: (704) 556-1643

AREAS OF INTEREST:
Arts, children, education, health care, sciences, senior citizens and social services.

TYPE:
Capital grants; Endowments; General operating grants; Research grants; Scholarships; Seed money grants.

PURPOSE:
To improve the quality of life in the community.

LEGAL BASIS:
Corporate foundation.

ELIGIBILITY:
Grants are made to organizations that have tax-exempt status under Section 501(c)(3) of the Internal Revenue Code. No grants are made to individuals.

GEOGRAPHIC RESTRICTIONS:
Greater Charlotte, North Carolina.

FINANCIAL DATA:
Amount of support per award: Varies.
Total amount of support: Varies.

APPLICATION INFORMATION:
Applicants should submit a Letter of Inquiry to the Foundation at the address above.

Duration: Varies.

Deadline: October 15.

ADDRESS INQUIRIES TO:
Dan Loftis, Grant Administrator
(See address above.)

AMGEN FOUNDATION, INC. [17]

One Amgen Center Drive, M.S. 28-1-B
Thousand Oaks, CA 91320
(805) 447-4056
Fax: (805) 376-1258

E-MAIL ADDRESS:
amgenfoundation@amgen.com

WEB SITE ADDRESS:
www.amgen.com/citizenship/foundation.html

FOUNDED: 1991

AREAS OF INTEREST:
Science education, health and human services and community life including arts and culture, social services and environment.

TYPE:
Challenge/matching grants; General operating grants; Grants-in-aid; Matching gifts; Project/program grants. The Foundation funds national-level science education and patient-focused programs.

YEAR PROGRAM STARTED: 1991

PURPOSE:
To advance science education, improve quality of care and access for patients, and support resources that create sound communities where Amgen staff members live and work.

LEGAL BASIS:
Company-sponsored foundation.

ELIGIBILITY:
The Foundation will consider grant requests from nonprofit organizations that are recognized by the IRS as tax-exempt public charities under Sections 501(c)(3) and 509(a)(1), (2) or (3) of the Internal Revenue Code, located in the U.S. and Puerto Rico. In addition, the Foundation will consider requests for funding from governmental organizations located in the U.S. where the purpose of the grant is to support a charitable, educational, scientific or literary purpose. Thus, eligible grantees may include public elementary and secondary schools, as well as public colleges and universities, public libraries and public hospitals. Successful requests will fall within both the current eligibility guidelines and funding priority areas established by the Foundation. The Foundation has established a grantmaking partnership with United Way Worldwide (UWW) to manage donations to organizations chartered in Europe.

GEOGRAPHIC RESTRICTIONS:
California, Colorado, Massachusetts, Puerto Rico, Rhode Island, Washington, and parts of Europe.

NUMBER OF AWARDS: 140 for the year 2012.

APPLICATION INFORMATION:
Letter of intent must first be submitted online.
Duration: Typically one year. Possible multiyear funding.

THE ANNENBERG FOUNDATION [18]

2000 Avenue of the Stars
Suite 1000 S
Los Angeles, CA 90067
(310) 209-4560
Fax: (310) 209-1631

E-MAIL ADDRESS:
requests@annenbergfoundation.org

WEB SITE ADDRESS:
www.annenbergfoundation.org

FOUNDED: 1989

AREAS OF INTEREST:
Arts, culture and humanities; animal welfare; civic and community; environment; education; human health and wellness; military veterans.

TYPE:
General operating grants; Grants-in-aid; Project/program grants; Technical assistance.

PURPOSE:
To provide funding and support to nonprofit organizations in the U.S. and globally; to advance the public well-being through improved communication; to encourage the development of effective ways to share ideas and knowledge.

ELIGIBILITY:
The Foundation seeks to fund organizations that have a deep level of community involvement, are led by effective leaders and tackle challenging and timely problems. The Foundation values the following organizational attributes: visionary leadership, impact, sustainability, innovation, organizational strength, network of partnerships, plus the population being served (hence the acronym VISION).

Only organizations that have 501(c)(3) not-for-profit status are eligible.

GEOGRAPHIC RESTRICTIONS:
Greater Los Angeles, California area (five-county region including Los Angeles, Orange, Riverside, San Bernardino and Ventura.

FINANCIAL DATA:
Total assets of $1,720,105,771 for year ended June 30, 2011.
Amount of support per award: Typically, $10,000 to $250,000. Average grant: $75,280.
Total amount of support: $114,887,527 for year ended June 30, 2011.

APPLICATION INFORMATION:
Application is online only.
Duration: One year; multiyear commitments are discouraged. Grants are renewable, but applicant must reapply.

APPLIED MATERIALS, INC. [19]
3050 Bowers Avenue
Mail Stop 0106
Santa Clara, CA 95052
(408) 727-5555
Fax: (408) 986-7115

E-MAIL ADDRESS:
community_affairs@amat.com

WEB SITE ADDRESS:
www.appliedmaterials.com

FOUNDED: 1967

AREAS OF INTEREST:
Arts and culture, community development, education and the environment.

NAME(S) OF PROGRAMS:
● **Applied Materials Corporate Philanthropy Program**

TYPE:
Project/program grants.

YEAR PROGRAM STARTED: 1990

PURPOSE:
To support the arts and culture, education, community development and the environment.

LEGAL BASIS:
Corporate giving program.

ELIGIBILITY:
Organizations classified as 501(c)(3) by the IRS can apply. Preference is given to areas of company operation. Individuals and religious organizations are ineligible.

FINANCIAL DATA:
Amount of support per award: Varies.
Total amount of support: Varies.

APPLICATION INFORMATION:
Application procedures are available online.
Duration: One year. May be renewed for up to two additional years based on results.

PUBLICATIONS:
Annual report; community report; guidelines.

ADDRESS INQUIRIES TO:
See e-mail address above.

*SPECIAL STIPULATIONS:
Progress is requested to be shared in writing with the Corporate Contribution Committee at least once a year.

APS CORPORATE GIVING PROGRAM [20]
Arizona Public Service Company
400 North 5th Street, 10th Floor
Phoenix, AZ 85004
(602) 250-2702
Fax: (602) 250-2113

E-MAIL ADDRESS:
corporategiving@aps.com

WEB SITE ADDRESS:
www.aps.com/corporategiving

FOUNDED: 1888

AREAS OF INTEREST:
Education, most specifically STEM engineering; community vitality; community and economic development in APS service territories.

TYPE:
Challenge/matching grants; Development grants; Project/program grants. Primary focus is on program support.

YEAR PROGRAM STARTED: 1981

PURPOSE:
To enhance the quality of life in Arizona.

LEGAL BASIS:
Corporate giving program.

ELIGIBILITY:
Applicants must be 501(c) nonprofit organizations. Preference is given to organizations within the APS service territory, although there are exceptions. No funds for individuals, individual scholarships, religious, political, fraternal, legislative or lobbying efforts, travel or hotel expenses.

GEOGRAPHIC RESTRICTIONS:
Arizona.

FINANCIAL DATA:
Amount of support per award: $2,500 to $250,000.
Total amount of support: Over $8,200,000 for the year 2013.

NUMBER OF AWARDS: Varies.

APPLICATION INFORMATION:
Applications must be submitted online and will require the following documentation:
(1) 501(c) IRS letter of determination;
(2) current list of board members;
(3) list of sponsorship levels (if applicable);
(4) line item budget;
(5) list of other funders and dollar amounts and;
(6) grant evaluation form (if applicable).
Duration: One year. Renewable by reapplication.
Deadline: APS Foundation: March 1 and September 1.

PUBLICATIONS:
Community Investment Report.

IRS IDENTIFICATION NUMBER: 95-3735903

THE ARCA FOUNDATION [21]
1308 19th Street, N.W.
Washington, DC 20036
(202) 822-9193
Fax: (202) 785-1446

E-MAIL ADDRESS:
proposals@arcafoundation.org

WEB SITE ADDRESS:
www.arcafoundation.org

FOUNDED: 1952

AREAS OF INTEREST:
Wall Street reform, financial regulation, corporate accountability, and advocating for a U.S. foreign policy approach that increases peace and security.

TYPE:
Challenge/matching grants; Conferences/seminars; General operating grants; Project/program grants; Travel grants.

YEAR PROGRAM STARTED: 1952

PURPOSE:
To provide funding for nonprofit organizations working on ways to engage citizens in social change, promote democracy, and reform unjust practices in public policy.

LEGAL BASIS:
Private foundation.

ELIGIBILITY:
Nonprofit organizations.

GEOGRAPHIC RESTRICTIONS:
United States.

FINANCIAL DATA:
Amount of support per award: $50,000.
Total amount of support: Approximately $2,000,000 annually.

NUMBER OF APPLICANTS MOST RECENT YEAR:
500.

NUMBER OF AWARDS: Approximately 60 to 70 annually.

APPLICATION INFORMATION:
Applications must be submitted online. Applications submitted by any other method will not be considered.

The Foundation highly recommends the applicant review the instructions on using the system and online application system FAQs before beginning the application process. The Proposal FAQs outlines the information to be included in the narrative of the proposal, as well as the list of documents that the organization should be prepared to submit/upload electronically. Documents include the organization's IRS 501(c)(3) letter and Arca's Lobbying Expenditure Form. As always, the Foundation only considers full proposals and does not accept letters of inquiry.
Duration: One year, or the program period.
Deadline: February 1 or August 1 or first business day following if the first falls on a weekend.

PUBLICATIONS:
Annual report with guidelines; past grantee profiles.

STAFF:
Anna Lefer Kuhn, Executive Director
Becca Freedman, Program Associate

BOARD OF DIRECTORS AND OFFICERS:
Nancy R. Bagley, President
Nicole Bagley, Vice President
Mary E. King, Secretary
Rev. Joseph Elderidge
Mike Lux
Janet Shenk
Margery Tabankin

ADDRESS INQUIRIES TO:
See e-mail address above.

ASSISI FOUNDATION OF MEMPHIS INC. [22]

515 Erin Drive
Memphis, TN 38117
(901) 684-1564
Fax: (901) 684-1997

WEB SITE ADDRESS:
www.assisifoundation.org

AREAS OF INTEREST:
Education, health and human services, social justice, ethics and literacy.

TYPE:
Challenge/matching grants; Endowments; General operating grants; Matching gifts; Project/program grants; Research grants; Technical assistance.

YEAR PROGRAM STARTED: 1994

PURPOSE:
To support health, lifelong learning, social justice, and community enrichment.

ELIGIBILITY:
Grants are made to organizations that already have tax-exempt status under Section 501(c)(3) of the Internal Revenue Code.

GEOGRAPHIC RESTRICTIONS:
Memphis area and Shelby County, Tennessee.

FINANCIAL DATA:
Amount of support per award: Varies.
Total amount of support: Varies.

APPLICATION INFORMATION:
Grant application process and required forms are available to download from the Foundation's web site.
Duration: Varies.
Deadline: Third Thursday after Board meetings held in January, April, July and October.

ADDRESS INQUIRIES TO:
Dr. Jan Young, Executive Director
(See address above.)

ATHWIN FOUNDATION [23]

5200 Wilson Road
Suite 307
Edina, MN 55424
(612) 379-3817
Fax: (952) 915-6148

E-MAIL ADDRESS:
jstormcod1@aol.com

WEB SITE ADDRESS:
www.catchcod.com

FOUNDED: 1956

AREAS OF INTEREST:
Arts and humanities, education, human services, environmental enhancement and organizational capacity building.

TYPE:
Capital grants; General operating grants; Project/program grants.

YEAR PROGRAM STARTED: 1956

PURPOSE:
To provide funds for charitable, scientific, literary or educational purposes.

LEGAL BASIS:
Tax-exempt private foundation.

ELIGIBILITY:
Only tax-exempt organizations may apply. No grants are awarded to individuals.

GEOGRAPHIC RESTRICTIONS:
Primarily Minnesota.

FINANCIAL DATA:
Amount of support per award: Varies.

NUMBER OF APPLICANTS MOST RECENT YEAR:
250.

NUMBER OF AWARDS: Varies.

REPRESENTATIVE AWARDS:
$1,000 to American Indian OIC for program support; $25,000 to the American Red Cross-Minneapolis Chapter for a capital campaign; $100,000 to Blake School for a two-year capital campaign.

APPLICATION INFORMATION:
Applicants must submit a letter of inquiry to the Foundation. Early submission is encouraged.
Duration: Varies.
Deadline: Letters of inquiry by March 1 and October 1. Decisions are made two to three months after cutoff.

PUBLICATIONS:
Annual report.

IRS IDENTIFICATION NUMBER: 41-6021773

TRUSTEES:
Bruce W. Bean
Glen Bean
Mary F. Bean
Eleanor Nolan

ADDRESS INQUIRIES TO:
Jim Storm, Administrator
(See address above.)

ATKINSON FOUNDATION [24]

1720 South Amphlett Boulevard
Suite 100
San Mateo, CA 94402-2710
(650) 357-1101
Fax: (650) 655-2102

E-MAIL ADDRESS:
atkinfdn@aol.com

WEB SITE ADDRESS:
www.atkinsonfdn.org

FOUNDED: 1939

AREAS OF INTEREST:
Social services and education in San Mateo County, CA, as well as American private volunteer organizations providing technical assistance and development in Mexico and Central America.

TYPE:
Development grants; General operating grants; Project/program grants; Scholarships; Seed money grants.

YEAR PROGRAM STARTED: 1939

PURPOSE:
To foster the efforts of individuals and families to become socially, economically and physically self-sufficient, and to increase their economic and social welfare.

LEGAL BASIS:
Private foundation.

ELIGIBILITY:
Applicants must be organizations with Internal Revenue Code 501(c)(3) status.

No loans or grants to individuals or for doctoral study or research. The Foundation does not sponsor nor contribute to one-time events or nationwide appeals from organizations and does not fund publications, films or conferences.

GEOGRAPHIC RESTRICTIONS:
San Mateo County, California, Mexico and Central America.

FINANCIAL DATA:
Amount of support per award: $1,000 to $30,000. Average $8,000.
Total amount of support: $602,720 for the year 2013.

NUMBER OF APPLICANTS MOST RECENT YEAR:
173 for the year 2013.

NUMBER OF AWARDS: 95 for the year 2013.

REPRESENTATIVE AWARDS:
$10,000 to Boys & Girls Club of the Coastside for general program support; $15,000 to Second Harvest Food Bank for mobile pantry program; $9,000 to San Mateo Union High School District for workability program; $10,000 to Adelante Foundation microcredit programs, Honduras.

APPLICATION INFORMATION:
Organizations should submit their request to the administrator using a cover sheet provided by the Foundation. It should include:
(1) a listing of personnel and officials of the agency;
(2) names and primary affiliations of the directors and officers;
(3) brief historical statement;
(4) description of the proposed program, showing the need, population to be served, specific objectives, activities to be carried out, necessary staff, their qualifications and anticipated outcomes;
(5) an organization budget, a project budget and a recent balance sheet;
(6) IRS tax-exempt letter and;
(7) any supplementary information that may strengthen application.

One hard copy of the proposal and five copies of any attached printed material must be submitted.
Duration: Usually one year.
Deadline: February 1, May 1, August 1 and November 1.

PUBLICATIONS:
Annual report; grant guidelines; application procedures.

IRS IDENTIFICATION NUMBER: 94-6075613

OFFICERS AND DIRECTORS:
Linda L. Lanier, President
Elizabeth H. Curtis, Vice President, Administration
James R. Avedisian, Vice President, Finance
William Crandall, Assistant Treasurer
Jean S. Atkinson, Secretary
Olivia O. Aranda, Director
Susan R. Atkinson, Director
Robert H. Griffin, Director
John E. Herrell, Director
Stephen A. Way, Director
Elizabeth Woodward, Director

ADDRESS INQUIRIES TO:
Elizabeth H. Curtis, Administrator
(See address above.)

ATRAN FOUNDATION, INC. [25]

155 North Dean Street, Suite 3-B
Englewood, NJ 07631
(201) 569-9677
Fax: (201) 569-2290

E-MAIL ADDRESS:
foundatran@gmail.com

FOUNDED: 1945

AREAS OF INTEREST:
Yiddish culture, labor, medical research in narrow areas of interest and social services.

TYPE:
General operating grants; Project/program grants.

PURPOSE:
To support programs relating to labor and labor relations, Yiddish language and culture, Yiddish literature, medical science and sociology.

LEGAL BASIS:
Tax-exempt under Section 501(c)(3) of the Internal Revenue Code.

ELIGIBILITY:
Grants are made only to 501(c)(3) tax-exempt organizations. No grants to individuals.

GEOGRAPHIC RESTRICTIONS:
United States.

FINANCIAL DATA:
Amount of support per award: Varies.
Total amount of support: Varies.

NUMBER OF AWARDS: Approximately 35 per year.

APPLICATION INFORMATION:
No formal application form is required. Application guidelines may be requested from the Foundation.
Duration: One year.
Deadline: September 30.

PUBLICATIONS:
Guideline for application procedure.

IRS IDENTIFICATION NUMBER: 13-5566548

OFFICERS:
Diane Fischer, President
Robert Kaplan, Vice President
Samuel Norich, Treasurer
Alison Fischer, Secretary

ADDRESS INQUIRIES TO:
Judah Fischer, Executive Director
(See address above.)

MARY REYNOLDS BABCOCK FOUNDATION   [26]
2920 Reynolda Road
Winston-Salem, NC 27106
(336) 748-9222
Fax: (336) 777-0095

E-MAIL ADDRESS:
info@mrbf.org

WEB SITE ADDRESS:
www.mrbf.org

FOUNDED: 1953

AREAS OF INTEREST:
Racism and poverty in the southeastern U.S.

NAME(S) OF PROGRAMS:
- **Moving People and Places Out of Poverty**

TYPE:
Challenge/matching grants; Development grants; General operating grants; Travel grants. Program-related investments.

YEAR PROGRAM STARTED: 2005

PURPOSE:
To help to move people and places out of poverty.

LEGAL BASIS:
Private foundation.

ELIGIBILITY:
Applicants must be nonprofit tax-exempt organizations with appropriate interests, located or working in the Southeast.

GEOGRAPHIC RESTRICTIONS:
Southeastern United States.

FINANCIAL DATA:
Amount of support per award: $5,000 to $100,000. Average $50,000.
Total amount of support: Varies.
Matching fund requirements: Varies.

NUMBER OF APPLICANTS MOST RECENT YEAR:
300.

NUMBER OF AWARDS: Varies.

APPLICATION INFORMATION:
Applications must be submitted electronically.
Duration: Three to five years depending on the grant.
Deadline: Applications are accepted on a rolling basis.

PUBLICATIONS:
Application form.

IRS IDENTIFICATION NUMBER: 56-0690140

BOARD OF DIRECTORS:
Dee Davis, President
Mary Mountcastle, Vice President
Ken Mountcastle, Treasurer
Ivan Kohar Parra, Secretary
Bruce Babcock
LaVeeda Battle
Chad Berry
David Dodson
Jerry Gonzalez
Derrick Johnson
Barbara Millhouse
James Mitchell
Katharine B. Mountcastle
Katherine R. Mountcastle
Laura Mountcastle
Kevin Trapani

ADDRESS INQUIRIES TO:
Program Officers
(See address above.)

HELEN BADER FOUNDATION, INC.   [27]
233 North Water Street, 4th Floor
Milwaukee, WI 53202
(414) 224-6464
Fax: (414) 224-1441

E-MAIL ADDRESS:
info@hbf.org

WEB SITE ADDRESS:
www.hbf.org

FOUNDED: 1991

AREAS OF INTEREST:
Alzheimer's disease and dementia, workforce development, children and youth, Jewish education, program-related investments, and youth development.

TYPE:
Capital grants; Challenge/matching grants; Conferences/seminars; General operating grants; Matching gifts; Project/program grants; Technical assistance; Training grants.

YEAR PROGRAM STARTED: 1991

PURPOSE:
To fund innovative projects and programs in four primary areas including Alzheimer's

disease and dementia, workforce development, children and youth, and Jewish education.

LEGAL BASIS:
Family foundation.

ELIGIBILITY:
U.S. organizations must be tax-exempt under Section 501(c)(3) of the IRS or governmental entities. Grants will only be approved for foreign entities which meet specific charitable status requirements.

GEOGRAPHIC RESTRICTIONS:
Milwaukee, Wisconsin.

FINANCIAL DATA:
Amount of support per award: $500 to $180,000. Median is $10,000.
Total amount of support: $8,171,727 for the year 2012-13.

NUMBER OF APPLICANTS MOST RECENT YEAR:
565 for the year 2012-13.

NUMBER OF AWARDS: 225 grants awarded for the year 2012-13.

REPRESENTATIVE AWARDS:
$6,000 to SHARP Literacy, Inc.; $15,000 to Grand Avenue Club; $150,000 to Milwaukee Public Schools.

APPLICATION INFORMATION:
Application information is available on the Foundation web site.
Duration: Varies. Renewal possible.
Deadline: Applications are accepted at any time.

IRS IDENTIFICATION NUMBER: 39-1710914

BOARD OF DIRECTORS:
Jere D. McGaffey, Chairman and Treasurer
Daniel J. Bader, President
David M. Bader, Vice President
Deirdre Britt, Secretary
Linda C. Bader
Frances Wolff

ADDRESS INQUIRIES TO:
Daniel J. Bader, President
(See address above.)

R.C. BAKER FOUNDATION   [28]
330 Encinitas Boulevard
Suite 101
Encinitas, CA 92024-8705
(760) 632-8322

FOUNDED: 1952

AREAS OF INTEREST:
Education, health, cultural, scientific research, social services for youth and elderly, and crime prevention.

TYPE:
Capital grants; Fellowships; General operating grants; Project/program grants; Scholarships; Technical assistance; Training grants; Work-study programs.

LEGAL BASIS:
Private foundation.

ELIGIBILITY:
Applicant organizations must have IRS tax-exempt status. No grants are made to individuals, endowments or loans. No grants to capital programs of tax-supported institutions.

GEOGRAPHIC RESTRICTIONS:
United States.

FINANCIAL DATA:
Amount of support per award: Varies.
Total amount of support: $1,564,600.

APPLICATION INFORMATION:
Applications should include a description of the proposed project and goals, a recently audited financial statement, amount requested, and a list of other sources of support. In addition, the applicant should include its IRS statement of tax-exempt status. The Foundation does not grant personal interviews.
Duration: Typically, one-time grants.
Deadline: May 1 and October 1.

IRS IDENTIFICATION NUMBER: 95-1742283

BOARD OF TRUSTEES:
Frank L. Scott, Chairman
James Benedict
Dennis Cronin
F. Lawrence Scott, Jr.

ADDRESS INQUIRIES TO:
F. Lawrence Scott, Jr., Board of Trustees
(See address above.)

BALL BROTHERS
FOUNDATION   [29]
222 South Mulberry
Muncie, IN 47305
(765) 741-5500
Fax: (765) 741-5518

E-MAIL ADDRESS:
donna.munchel@ballfdn.org

WEB SITE ADDRESS:
www.ballfdn.org

FOUNDED: 1926

AREAS OF INTEREST:
Education, arts, culture and humanities, human services, public/society benefit, health and environment.

TYPE:
Challenge/matching grants; General operating grants; Project/program grants; Seed money grants; Technical assistance; Training grants.

YEAR PROGRAM STARTED: 1926

PURPOSE:
To promote recreational, educational or charitable purposes within the state of Indiana.

LEGAL BASIS:
Private foundation.

ELIGIBILITY:
Indiana not-for-profit organizations or institutions are eligible to apply. No grants to individuals.

GEOGRAPHIC RESTRICTIONS:
Indiana.

FINANCIAL DATA:
Amount of support per award: $1,000 to $1,000,000.
Total amount of support: $6,840,000 for the year 2013.

NUMBER OF APPLICANTS MOST RECENT YEAR:
233 for the year 2013.

NUMBER OF AWARDS: 102 for the year 2013.

REPRESENTATIVE AWARDS:
$5,000 to A Better Way Services, Inc.; $585,100 to Ball State University; $100,000 to City of Muncie; $1,000 to Hoosiers Feeding the Hungry; $45,000 to Motivate Our Minds, Inc.

APPLICATION INFORMATION:
Application must include a description of the project, project staff and budget, IRS determination letter, objective of the proposal, plan of development, expected results and method of evaluation.
Duration: One year.
Deadline: February 15 and July 15.

PUBLICATIONS:
Guidelines; annual report.

OFFICERS:
Frank E. Ball, Chairman and Chief Executive Officer
James A. Fisher, Vice Chairman
Tammy Phillips, Treasurer
Terry L. Walker, Secretary

DIRECTORS:
Charles Ball
William Bracken
Stephanie Duckmann
Brannon Fisher
Jud Fisher
Douglas J. Foy
Nancy B. Keilty
Terri Matchett
Stacy McHenry
Judy Oetinger
Frank Petty
Scott E. Shockley

ADDRESS INQUIRIES TO:
Donna Munchel, Grant Process Manager
(See address above.)

GEORGE AND FRANCES BALL
FOUNDATION   [30]
222 South Mulberry
Muncie, IN 47305
(765) 741-5500
Fax: (765) 741-5518

E-MAIL ADDRESS:
kris@ballassociates.org

FOUNDED: 1937

AREAS OF INTEREST:
Education, arts and culture, civic community projects, health and human services, environment and conservation.

TYPE:
Challenge/matching grants; Endowments; General operating grants; Professorships; Project/program grants.

LEGAL BASIS:
Family foundation.

ELIGIBILITY:
Applicants must be 501(c)(3) organizations or institutes.

GEOGRAPHIC RESTRICTIONS:
East central Indiana, primarily Delaware County.

FINANCIAL DATA:
Amount of support per award: $25,000 median.
Total amount of support: $4,136,000 for the year ended December 31, 2013.
Matching fund requirements: Usually 1:1.

NUMBER OF APPLICANTS MOST RECENT YEAR:
60.

NUMBER OF AWARDS: 35 for the year 2013.

APPLICATION INFORMATION:
General grant request guidelines provided upon request.
Deadline: Applications accepted year-round.

OFFICERS AND DIRECTORS:
Stefan S. Anderson, Chairman
Jon H. Moll, Vice Chairman
Thomas C. Bracken, President
Tamara S. Phillips, Treasurer
Joan H. McKee, Secretary
Norman E. Beck
Frank A. Bracken
Ronald K. Fauquher
Mike Galliher
Robert M. Smitson
Joseph F. Wiese, III

ADDRESS INQUIRIES TO:
Kris Gross, Executive Assistant
(See address above.)

BALTIMORE COMMUNITY
FOUNDATION   [31]
2 East Read Street, 9th Floor
Baltimore, MD 21202
(410) 332-4171
Fax: (410) 837-4701

E-MAIL ADDRESS:
info@bcf.org

WEB SITE ADDRESS:
www.bcf.org

FOUNDED: 1972

AREAS OF INTEREST:
Education and neighborhoods.

TYPE:
Scholarships. Neighborhood grants. Education grants.

YEAR PROGRAM STARTED: 1972

PURPOSE:
To work for a healthy productive Baltimore region and to provide a flexible effective way for charitable individuals, corporations and foundations to invest in those efforts.

LEGAL BASIS:
Community foundation.

ELIGIBILITY:
The Foundation welcomes grant applications from organizations in the Greater Baltimore region that are tax-exempt under Section 501(c)(3) of the Internal Revenue Code.

The Foundation will be most likely to fund programs that:
(1) address underlying causes of specific problems and seek long-term systemic solutions;
(2) are preventive rather than remedial;
(3) reach a broad segment of the community;
(4) increase individual access and opportunity;
(5) attract financial or volunteer resources or involve collaboration;
(6) build the capacity of grantee organizations and;
(7) strengthen the private, nonprofit sector.

The Foundation does not make grants for annual fund campaigns, operating support except for start-up, religious or sectarian purposes, capital campaigns, or individuals (including scholarships and fellowships).

GEOGRAPHIC RESTRICTIONS:
Baltimore city and Baltimore County, Maryland.

FINANCIAL DATA:
Amount of support per award: Varies.
Total amount of support: Approximately $24,000,000 for the year 2012.

REPRESENTATIVE AWARDS:
$15,000 to create a support network for charter schools; $20,000 to increase

affordable housing opportunities; $10,000 for consulting services to a growing arts organization.

APPLICATION INFORMATION:
Contact the Foundation for guidelines and application form.
Duration: One year.
Deadline: Letters of inquiry are welcomed throughout the year.

PUBLICATIONS:
The BCF Edge, newsletter; annual report.

OFFICERS:
Ray Bank, Chairman
Thomas E. Wilcox, President
Laura Gamble, Treasurer
Juliet A. Eurich, Secretary

STAFF:
Thomas E. Wilcox, President and Chief Executive Officer
Amy Seto, Chief Financial Officer
Danista Hunte, Vice President, Community Investments
Ralph Serpe, Vice President, Development

ADDRESS INQUIRIES TO:
Danista Hunte
Vice President, Community Investments
(See address above.)

C.R. BARD FOUNDATION   [32]
730 Central Avenue
Murray Hill, NJ 07974
(908) 277-8182
Fax: (908) 277-8098

E-MAIL ADDRESS:
linda.hrevnack@crbard.com

WEB SITE ADDRESS:
www.crbard.com

FOUNDED: 1988

AREAS OF INTEREST:
Health care, community, employee activities and education.

TYPE:
Matching gifts; Project/program grants; Scholarships.

YEAR PROGRAM STARTED: 1988

PURPOSE:
To assist nonprofit organizations which improve the quality of life for local communities in areas where Bard has a facility or substantial employee population.

LEGAL BASIS:
Corporate foundation.

ELIGIBILITY:
The Foundation does not contribute to private foundations, individuals, political parties, fraternal groups, religious groups, veterans' organizations or sectarian groups. Organizations receiving major support from the United Way or similar programs are also not eligible. For matching gifts, the individual must be a member of the board of directors or an active U.S. employee of C.R. Bard, Inc., or any of its domestic operating divisions or subsidiaries at the time of the contribution. Nonprofit organizations eligible for matching gifts must be recognized as tax-exempt by the IRS under Section 501(c)(3) of the Internal Revenue Code and must be open to, or operated for the benefit of, the general public.

FINANCIAL DATA:
Amount of support per award: $1,000 to $25,000.

Total amount of support: Varies.
Matching fund requirements: Bard will match employee gifts of $25 to $15,000 per employee per calendar year and $25 to $5,000 per director per calendar year.

NUMBER OF AWARDS: Varies.

APPLICATION INFORMATION:
Requests for funding must be in writing and include the following:
(1) name, address, history, objectives and description of the organization;
(2) the purpose for which the grant is requested and the amount requested;
(3) a copy of the organization's IRS document indicating 501(c)(3) status;
(4) a copy of the organization's operating budget and its most recent audited financial statement and;
(5) a list of the organization's Board of Directors and/or trustees.
Duration: One to five years.

PUBLICATIONS:
Guidelines.

ADDRESS INQUIRIES TO:
Linda Hrevnack
Manager, Community Affairs and Contributions

BARRA FOUNDATION   [33]
200 West Lancaster Avenue
Suite 202
Wayne, PA 19087-4046
(610) 964-7601
Fax: (610) 964-0155

E-MAIL ADDRESS:
info@barrafoundation.org

WEB SITE ADDRESS:
www.barrafoundation.org

FOUNDED: 1963

AREAS OF INTEREST:
Arts and culture, human services, education and health.

TYPE:
Demonstration grants; Project/program grants; Seed money grants.

LEGAL BASIS:
Private foundation.

ELIGIBILITY:
501(c)(3) nonprofit organizations only.

GEOGRAPHIC RESTRICTIONS:
Philadelphia, Pennsylvania metropolitan area.

FINANCIAL DATA:
Amount of support per award: $2,000 to $100,000.

Total amount of support: Approximately $3,005,000.

APPLICATION INFORMATION:
Applications are accepted online only.
Duration: Varies.
Deadline: Applications accepted on a continuous basis.

PUBLICATIONS:
Policy statement.

STAFF:
Kristina L. Wahl, President

ADDRESS INQUIRIES TO:
Kristina L. Wahl, President
(See address above.)

*SPECIAL STIPULATIONS:
No grants for environmental programs, exhibitions, publications or religious organizations.

BATTLE CREEK COMMUNITY FOUNDATION   [34]
34 West Jackson Street
One Riverwalk Center
Battle Creek, MI 49017-3505
(269) 962-2181
Fax: (269) 962-2182

E-MAIL ADDRESS:
bccf@bccfoundation.org

WEB SITE ADDRESS:
www.bccfoundation.org

FOUNDED: 1974

AREAS OF INTEREST:
Education, health, and liveable communities.

TYPE:
Challenge/matching grants; Conferences/seminars; Demonstration grants; Development grants; Endowments; Exchange programs; Internships; Matching gifts; Project/program grants; Research grants; Scholarships; Technical assistance; Training grants; Travel grants. Emerging needs grants.

YEAR PROGRAM STARTED: 1974

PURPOSE:
To promote philanthropic giving and the use of endowment funds; to serve as a leader in coordinating local resources to meet the current and future needs of the Battle Creek community.

LEGAL BASIS:
Community foundation.

ELIGIBILITY:
Applicants must be nonprofit organizations whose programs will benefit residents or students of the greater Battle Creek community.

No grants for general operating support, endowments, annual fund-raising programs, or projects outside of the Battle Creek area which do not benefit the local community.

General operating support is only given for arts and culture initiatives.

GEOGRAPHIC RESTRICTIONS:
Battle Creek, Michigan area.

FINANCIAL DATA:
Amount of support per award: Average: $10,000 to $15,000.

Total amount of support: $8,500,000.

NUMBER OF APPLICANTS MOST RECENT YEAR: 1,824.

NUMBER OF AWARDS: 1,234.

APPLICATION INFORMATION:
Prospective grant applicants must attend a grantseeker orientation and should contact Foundation staff to gather information on upcoming orientations, dates/times, etc.
Duration: One year.
Deadline: Varies by program.

PUBLICATIONS:
Guidelines; annual report.

ADDRESS INQUIRIES TO:
Annette Chapman, Vice President of Grantmaking and Scholarships
(See address above.)

THE BAXTER INTERNATIONAL FOUNDATION [35]
One Baxter Parkway
Deerfield, IL 60015
(847) 948-4605
Fax: (847) 948-2887

E-MAIL ADDRESS:
fdninfo@baxter.com

WEB SITE ADDRESS:
www.baxter.com

FOUNDED: 1982

AREAS OF INTEREST:
Health care and its enhancement.

TYPE:
Matching gifts; Project/program grants. The Foundation supports health care awards programs, including the Foster G. McGaw Prize, a $100,000 grant awarded annually to a U.S. hospital that has distinguished itself in community service and the William Graham Health Services Research Award, a $50,000 award made annually to an individual who has made significant contributions to the improved delivery of medical care through innovative health-services research.

YEAR PROGRAM STARTED: 1982

PURPOSE:
To increase access to health care services for the disadvantaged; to improve the quality and cost-effectiveness of health care.

LEGAL BASIS:
Corporate foundation.

ELIGIBILITY:
Grants are made to nonprofit 501(c)(3) organizations with new or expanded programs or direct health care services proposals consistent with the Foundation's priorities. In evaluating a grant application, the Foundation looks for eligibility under Foundation guidelines, including geographies where Baxter employees work and live, evidence that the project is a response to a valid need and is superior to other competing projects, and evidence of the agency's capacity to accomplish its goals.

In general, the Foundation does not make grants to capital and endowment campaigns, hospitals, disease-specific organizations, educational institutions, individuals, organizations with a limited constituency such as fraternal, veterans' or religious organizations, organizations soliciting contributions for advertising space, tickets to dinners and fund-raising events and promotional materials.

FINANCIAL DATA:
Amount of support per award: Average grant $50,000.
Total amount of support: $1,500,000 annually.

REPRESENTATIVE AWARDS:
$50,000 to George Mark Children's Home; $36,704 to Associacao Pro-Hope Apoio a Crianca; $46,070 to Hogar Bambi Venezuela; $60,000 to Family Life Services.

APPLICATION INFORMATION:
All grants must utilize the Foundation's online application process. Proposals and requests must include the following information:
(1) a brief description of the organization, its purpose, history, programs and achievements;
(2) a statement describing the specific purpose of the grant requested, including how the project meets the Foundation priorities;
(3) a plan for measuring results and reporting periodic progress, as well as for a final evaluation;
(4) financial information, including the organization's current operating budget and the budget for the proposed project;
(5) an audited financial statement;
(6) a copy of the organization's certificate of tax-exemption from the IRS as a 501(c)(3) or equivalent organization;
(7) a list of officers and board members and their affiliations and;
(8) sources of income, including support from corporate donors (with amounts noted), the United Way, foundations and the government.
Duration: Typically one to two years.
Deadline: Submissions accepted January 1 to February 11, May 1 to June 11 and September 1 to October 11.

BOARD OF DIRECTORS:
Donna Namath, Executive Director
Katherine Azuara
Alice J. Campbell
Robert Hombach
Douglas Hunt
Wolf Kupatt
Timothy Lawrence

EXECUTIVE DIRECTOR:
Donna Namath

ADDRESS INQUIRIES TO:
See e-mail address above.

ADELAIDE BREED BAYRD FOUNDATION [36]
350 Main Street
Malden, MA 02148
(781) 324-0322
Fax: (781) 397-0531

E-MAIL ADDRESS:
kezer@kezer.com

FOUNDED: 1927

AREAS OF INTEREST:
Community services, education and cultural projects, health-related projects and youth-related projects.

TYPE:
Capital grants; Project/program grants; Seed money grants.

PURPOSE:
To support organizations whose activities are centered in the Malden, MA, area, and to support organizations elsewhere, whose activities give substantial benefit to the citizens of Malden.

LEGAL BASIS:
Private foundation.

ELIGIBILITY:
Grants are made to nonprofit, 501(c)(3) organizations in the Foundation's areas of interest. Requests from individuals, endowment funds, performing arts (excepting educational projects and programs) and research will generally be excluded.

In general, the Foundation favors grants toward project services over capital expenditures.

GEOGRAPHIC RESTRICTIONS:
Boston area, with emphasis on Malden and vicinity.

FINANCIAL DATA:
Amount of support per award: Varies.
Total amount of support: Average $700,000 annually.

REPRESENTATIVE AWARDS:
$33,000 to ABBF New Scholarships; $5,000 to Agassiz Village; $10,000 to American Red Cross; $3,000 to Boston Ballet.

APPLICATION INFORMATION:
No particular form of request is required. A letter stating the need, the purpose of the organization and other salient matters will suffice. Copies of summaries of current budget or recent financial statements may be helpful. Organizations should be prepared to furnish a copy of IRS tax form 501(c)(3) or another tax-exempt certificate.
Duration: Typically one year.
Deadline: Second Tuesday in February.

PUBLICATIONS:
Annual report.

IRS IDENTIFICATION NUMBER: 04-6051258

TRUSTEES:
C. Henry Kezer, President
Susan C. Mansur, Treasurer
Francis K. Brown, II
Richard R. Burns, Jr.
Rev. Paul C. McPheeters
H. Allen Stevens
Dorothy Whittier

ADDRESS INQUIRIES TO:
C. Henry Kezer, President
(See address above.)

THE BELO FOUNDATION [37]
901 Main Street
Suite 609
Dallas, TX 75202
(214) 977-8267
Fax: (214) 760-1254

E-MAIL ADDRESS:
ameadows@ahbelo.com

WEB SITE ADDRESS:
www.ahbelo.com/about/foundation

FOUNDED: 1952

AREAS OF INTEREST:
College-level journalism education; urban parks and green space.

TYPE:
Capital grants; Endowments; General operating grants; Professorships; Project/program grants; Scholarships.

YEAR PROGRAM STARTED: 1952

PURPOSE:
To provide funds for the development of urban parks and green space; to support college-level journalism education.

LEGAL BASIS:
Corporate foundation.

ELIGIBILITY:
Eligible organizations must have IRS 501(c)(3) status.

GEOGRAPHIC RESTRICTIONS:
Urban park grants are awarded in Dallas, Texas. College-level journalism grants are awarded in Austin and Dallas, Texas.

FINANCIAL DATA:
Amount of support per award: Varies greatly.
Total amount of support: $2,007,099 paid in grants plus an additional $40,789 in direct charitable support in 2013.

NUMBER OF AWARDS: 2 new grants for 2013 plus pledge payment to the University of Texas Belo Center for New Media.

APPLICATION INFORMATION:
Initial requests should be in the form of a letter with a minimum of background material to support the request. Include information on your organization's officers and directors and a copy of the 501(c)(3) tax-exemption letter from the IRS.

The Foundation also encourages telephone calls or letters of inquiry before submission of a complete proposal.

Duration: Varies.

Deadline: Applications are accepted throughout the year.

IRS IDENTIFICATION NUMBER: 75-2564365

TRUSTEES:
Robert W. Decherd, Chairman
Marian Spitzberg, President
Guy H. Kerr
Dunia A. Shive

STAFF:
Amy M. Meadows, Vice President and Executive Director

ADDRESS INQUIRIES TO:
Amy M. Meadows
Vice President and Executive Director
(See address above.)

BEMIS COMPANY FOUNDATION   [38]
One Neenah Center
P.O. Box 669
Neenah, WI 54957
Fax: (920) 527-7600

E-MAIL ADDRESS:
kwetzel@bemis.com

WEB SITE ADDRESS:
www.bemis.com

FOUNDED: 1959

AREAS OF INTEREST:
Education, social welfare and health, cultural and civic needs.

NAME(S) OF PROGRAMS:
● **Bemis Scholarship Program**
● **Educational Gift Matching**
● **FoodShare Program**
● **Nonprofit Gift Matching Program**
● **United Way Program**

TYPE:
Capital grants; Challenge/matching grants; General operating grants; Matching gifts; Project/program grants. Grants to tax-exempt organizations in the communities in which the Bemis Company operates. Scholarships, matching educational and matching nonprofit gifts are for employees only.

The Bemis Scholarship Program provides financial aid to sons and daughters of employees of the company and its subsidiaries. The Program is open to the sons and daughters under age 25 who wish to attend community colleges, four-year colleges, universities or vocational schools.

The Educational Gift Matching program gives employees an opportunity to have their personal contributions to eligible secondary schools, vocational/technical schools, colleges and universities double-matched by the Bemis Company.

Through the Bemis FoodShare Program, employees have the opportunity to have their contributions to local food banks and food shelves matched by the company.

In the United Way program, Bemis contributes to the United Way in communities where the company has facilities.

YEAR PROGRAM STARTED: 1959

PURPOSE:
To match available funds with those public needs where the interests of the company and its employees are inseparable.

LEGAL BASIS:
Corporate foundation.

ELIGIBILITY:
Grants are made to tax-exempt, U.S.-based organizations only. Priorities in grants will be given to those organizations and/or programs that will contribute the most to advancing the quality of life for all peoples in the communities in which the Bemis Company operates. Emphasis will be on those programs that encourage the development of our human resources, education programs and, in a lesser degree, civic and art institutions that encourage participation by the general public. Special consideration will be given to those programs in which the company's employees actively participate or are directly benefited.

The Foundation will not make grants to individuals or to organizations for religious purposes or for political purposes, either for lobbying efforts or campaigns. The Foundation prefers not to make grants for educational capital funds programs, endowment purposes or to support trips or tours. Grants will not exceed 5% of the total requirements of any organization or specific campaign goal.

GEOGRAPHIC RESTRICTIONS:
United States.

FINANCIAL DATA:
Amount of support per award: Varies.
Total amount of support: $3,250,000 per year.
Matching fund requirements: Educational Gift Matching: The Plan provides that the employee's contribution to an eligible educational institution will be double-matched.

APPLICATION INFORMATION:
Complete application information may be obtained online. Grant proposals need not follow a specific format, but all proposals should include:
(1) name of the organization and amount requested;
(2) brief description of the objectives for which the grant is sought;
(3) details as to how the objectives are to be attained;
(4) budget, including information about existing and other possible sources of income;
(5) officers and board members and;
(6) statement that the organization has tax-exempt status under Section 501(c)(3) of the Internal Revenue Code and that contributions to it are tax-deductible. It is preferred that all initial inquiries be by e-mail and not by telephone or personal visits.

Duration: Varies.

Deadline: March, June and December.

PUBLICATIONS:
Application guidelines.

IRS IDENTIFICATION NUMBER: 41-6038616

ADDRESS INQUIRIES TO:
See e-mail address above.

*SPECIAL STIPULATIONS:
All initial inquiries should be made by e-mail.

H.N. AND FRANCES C. BERGER FOUNDATION   [39]
P.O. Box 13390
Palm Desert, CA 92255
(760) 341-5293
Fax: (760) 341-3518

WEB SITE ADDRESS:
www.hnberger.org

FOUNDED: 1961

AREAS OF INTEREST:
Arts, culture, children, education, environment, health, human services and youth.

TYPE:
Project/program grants.

PURPOSE:
To provide people with the opportunity to improve their own situations.

LEGAL BASIS:
Private family foundation.

ELIGIBILITY:
Grants are made to organizations that have tax-exempt status under Section 501(c)(3) of the Internal Revenue Code. No grants are made to individuals. Nonsectarian religious programs may apply.

GEOGRAPHIC RESTRICTIONS:
United States, primarily southern California.

FINANCIAL DATA:
Amount of support per award: Grants vary in amount, depending upon the needs and nature of the request.
Total amount of support: Varies.

APPLICATION INFORMATION:
Submit a one- to two-page request for consideration. This should include a concise statement of intent as well as a brief history of the organization and its activities.

Duration: Typically one year.

ADDRESS INQUIRIES TO:
Christopher McGuire
Vice President of Programs
(See address above.)

THE GRACE AND FRANKLIN BERNSEN FOUNDATION   [40]
15 West 6th Street, Suite 1308
Tulsa, OK 74119-5407
(918) 584-4711
Fax: (918) 584-4713

E-MAIL ADDRESS:
gfbernsen@aol.com

WEB SITE ADDRESS:
www.bernsen.org

FOUNDED: 1968

AREAS OF INTEREST:
Arts, civic, education, medical, religious, United Way, and children.

TYPE:
Capital grants; Challenge/matching grants; Project/program grants.

YEAR PROGRAM STARTED: 1968

PURPOSE:
To provide grants in support of religious, charitable, scientific, literary or educational purposes, or for the prevention of cruelty to children.

LEGAL BASIS:
Private family foundation.

ELIGIBILITY:
The Foundation gives priority to applications from nonprofit organizations with clearly defined benefits, such as those for building and capital funding purposes, and other special program needs. Education programs, including those in the arts, higher education, human services and community programs, religious causes and youth programs are eligible for support.

Grants may require matching funds to be raised by the recipient.

No grants are made to elementary or secondary education institutions unless they involve programs for at-risk, handicapped or learning-disabled children. No grants are made to individuals, or for the benefit of specific individuals.

GEOGRAPHIC RESTRICTIONS:
Tulsa, Oklahoma area.

FINANCIAL DATA:
Amount of support per award: Average: $5,000.
Total amount of support: $1,300,000.
Matching fund requirements: Typically one half.

NUMBER OF APPLICANTS MOST RECENT YEAR: 135.

NUMBER OF AWARDS: 45.

APPLICATION INFORMATION:
Applications should be submitted in writing by the chief executive officer of the applicant organization. They must include a brief description of the organization, an explanation of its importance, a clear statement of its goals, financial need including the other sources of funds and copies of a tax-exemption letter from the IRS.

Additional information required with summary letter:
(1) list of current officers and Board of Trustees;
(2) most recent audited financial statement or last year's IRS Form 990;
(3) current year-to-date financial statements and budget and;
(4) project budget (if applicable) and plans to support the project after the grant period.

If additional information is required, the organization making application will be notified by the Foundation.

Deadline: Grant applications must be received before the 10th day of any given month in order to be considered for the next trustee meeting.

IRS IDENTIFICATION NUMBER: 23-7009414

TRUSTEES:
Donald F. Marlar
Donald E. Pray
John D. Strong, Jr.
W. Bland Williamson

ADDRESS INQUIRIES TO:
Margaret Skyles, Administrator
(See address above.)

BERRIEN COMMUNITY FOUNDATION [41]
2900 South State Street
Suite 2 East
St. Joseph, MI 49085
(269) 983-3486
Fax: (269) 983-4939

E-MAIL ADDRESS:
bcf@berriencommunity.org

WEB SITE ADDRESS:
www.berriencommunity.org

FOUNDED: 1952

AREAS OF INTEREST:
Building spirit of community/arts and culture, nurturing our children, encouraging youth leadership and development.

TYPE:
Development grants; General operating grants; Project/program grants; Scholarships; Seed money grants; Technical assistance.

PURPOSE:
To promote philanthropy, build a spirit of community and enhance the quality of life in Berrien County, MI.

ELIGIBILITY:
501(c)(3) or equivalent.

GEOGRAPHIC RESTRICTIONS:
Berrien County, Michigan.

FINANCIAL DATA:
Amount of support per award: Varies.
Total amount of support: More than $3,900,000 for the year 2013.

APPLICATION INFORMATION:
Contact the Foundation.
Duration: Typically one year.

ADDRESS INQUIRIES TO:
Lisa Cripps-Downey, President
(See address above.)

BERWIND CORPORATION [42]
3000 Centre Square West
1500 Market Street
Philadelphia, PA 19102
(215) 575-2306
Fax: (215) 606-1849

E-MAIL ADDRESS:
requests@berwind.com

WEB SITE ADDRESS:
www.berwind.com

FOUNDED: 1886

AREAS OF INTEREST:
Animal welfare, after-school education and urban revitalization.

TYPE:
General operating grants; Matching gifts; Project/program grants.

ELIGIBILITY:
Applicants must be 501(c)(3) organizations within Berwind operating areas.

GEOGRAPHIC RESTRICTIONS:
Primarily Philadelphia area, Pennsylvania.

FINANCIAL DATA:
Amount of support per award: Varies.
Matching fund requirements: Dollar-for-dollar up to $10,000 for employee grants only.

APPLICATION INFORMATION:
Contact the Corporation.
Duration: One year.
Deadline: Varies.

ADDRESS INQUIRIES TO:
Catherine Murphy, Managing Director
Berwind Family Office
(See address above.)

BING FUND [43]
9700 West Pico Boulevard
Los Angeles, CA 90035
(310) 277-5711
Fax: (310) 277-6368

FOUNDED: 1920

AREAS OF INTEREST:
Museums, higher education, performing arts, population control, and hospitals.

TYPE:
Project/program grants.

PURPOSE:
To fund a variety of worthwhile projects in the community.

LEGAL BASIS:
501(c)(3) tax-exempt organizations.

ELIGIBILITY:
Must be a tax-exempt organization under Section 501(c)(3) of the Internal Revenue Code. Funding is at the discretion of the Directors.

GEOGRAPHIC RESTRICTIONS:
Southern California.

FINANCIAL DATA:
Amount of support per award: Varies.
Total amount of support: Varies.

NUMBER OF APPLICANTS MOST RECENT YEAR: 100.

NUMBER OF AWARDS: Varies.

APPLICATION INFORMATION:
Contact the Fund for details.
Duration: Varies. Renewal possible.
Deadline: Varies.

ADDRESS INQUIRIES TO:
Sue Porto, Office Manager
(See address above.)

THE WILLIAM BINGHAM FOUNDATION [44]
1111 Superior Avenue, Suite 700
Cleveland, OH 44114-2540
(216) 344-5200

E-MAIL ADDRESS:
info@wbinghamfoundation.org

WEB SITE ADDRESS:
www.wbinghamfoundation.org

FOUNDED: 1955

AREAS OF INTEREST:
Education, science, health and human services, and the arts.

TYPE:
Capital grants; Challenge/matching grants; Endowments; General operating grants; Project/program grants.

YEAR PROGRAM STARTED: 1955

PURPOSE:
To provide funding to nonprofit organizations that sponsor programs in the areas of education, science, health and human services, and the arts.

LEGAL BASIS:
Private family foundation.

ELIGIBILITY:
Grants are made only to public charities. Grants are not made to individuals or to organizations located outside of the U.S.

GEOGRAPHIC RESTRICTIONS:
United States.

FINANCIAL DATA:
Amount of support per award: $10,000 to $20,000 average.

NUMBER OF APPLICANTS MOST RECENT YEAR:
600.

NUMBER OF AWARDS: 20.

REPRESENTATIVE AWARDS:
$25,000 to By the River, Sebastian, FL, for operating support of organization that operates senior housing facility; $24,550 to Holden Arboretum, Kirtland, OH, for Adventures in Plant Science program for school groups; $25,000 to Rhode Island Free Clinic Inc., Providence, RI, for support of Physician Network.

APPLICATION INFORMATION:
The majority of grantmaking is by invitation only.
Duration: Generally one year.

ADDRESS INQUIRIES TO:
Laura H. Gilbertson, Chief Administrator
(See address above.)

THE BLUESCOPE FOUNDATION NORTH AMERICA [45]

1540 Genessee
P.O. Box 419917
Kansas City, MO 64141-0917
(816) 968-3208
Fax: (816) 627-8993

E-MAIL ADDRESS:
jcharmon@butlermfg.com

WEB SITE ADDRESS:
www.butlermfg.com

FOUNDED: 1952

AREAS OF INTEREST:
United charities, scholarship program, aid to education, community needs, youth and civic cultural activities, hospitals and health, and minorities.

TYPE:
Capital grants; General operating grants; Matching gifts; Project/program grants; Scholarships. Scholarship program available to children of Company employees only. Matching gift program for employee contributions to eligible educational or cultural institutions.

In the area of community needs, support is given to organizations which serve broadly the communities in which the Company has employees and significant capital investment. Programs falling within this category include United Way organizations in Company plant cities, minority assistance limited to nonprofit agencies that help provide jobs or job training for the disadvantaged, foster the movement of minorities into the mainstream of economic life and enable minorities to improve their level of educational attainment, and neighborhood and nonresidential building programs utilizing the company's products.

In the area of education, grants are made to colleges and universities which supply significant numbers of employees to the Company and/or which provide opportunities for continuing education to employees, help disadvantaged students who demonstrate ability and desire to prepare for and remain in colleges and universities, have programs which have the objective of providing education to residents of Company plant locations and provide educational opportunities which advance minorities, women and individuals with disabilities.

In the area of culture, the Foundation considers programs which help broaden the cultural experience of the residents of local communities through the support of visual and performing arts organizations, demonstrate concern for excellence and innovation in the arts, and bring cultural opportunity to the economically disadvantaged.

In the area of public affairs, the Foundation helps promote strong relationships between the public and private sectors to assist in the solution to urban problems, reinforce the efforts of groups formed to gather and disseminate information that is in the general public interest, encourage community volunteerism, and promote economic education and the merits of the free enterprise system.

YEAR PROGRAM STARTED: 1952

PURPOSE:
To provide sustained financial assistance to worthy charitable, educational, health and welfare programs in the U.S.; to enhance the quality of life in those communities where employees of BlueScope Steel reside.

LEGAL BASIS:
A nonprofit, benevolent and charitable corporation under the laws of the State of Missouri. A 501(c)(3) private foundation under IRS code.

ELIGIBILITY:
Grants are made only to nonprofit organizations located in areas where the company has facilities. Organizations must have a clear statement of purpose in the public interest, a program consistent with the organization's stated purpose, evidence of interagency cooperation to avoid duplication of services, an active and responsive governing body of volunteers holding regular meetings, evidence of professional program management and reasonable fund-raising expenses, maintenance of ethical publicity and promotion of the program that excludes exaggerated or misleading claims, and fund solicitation policies which prohibit the payment of commission or other compensation based on total funds raised or undue pressures.

Grants are not normally made to individuals, political organizations, religious organizations for sectarian purposes, pre-school, primary and secondary educational institutions, fraternal or veteran's organizations, organizations receiving United Way support for operating expenses, national health organizations, including local or regional chapters, hospitals (except those providing unique services, burn centers or children's services), tours, conferences, seminars, workshops, testimonial dinners, tables, tickets, advertisements, walk-a-thons, endowment funds, and other foundations of any type providing grants to not-for-profits or programs beyond the Foundation's stated geographic areas of interest.

GEOGRAPHIC RESTRICTIONS:
Rainsville, Alabama; Pine Bluff, Arkansas; Turlock and Visalia, California; Kansas City and St. Joseph, Missouri; Greensboro and Laurinburg, North Carolina; Annville, Pennsylvania; Jackson and Memphis, Tennessee; San Marcos, Texas; and Evansville, Wisconsin.

FINANCIAL DATA:
Amount of support per award: $1,000 to $10,000.
Total amount of support: $300,000 annually.
Matching fund requirements: The minimum single gift the Foundation will match per eligible donor is $25. The maximum single gift or total of annual gifts to be matched per eligible donor for full-time employees is $2,000 per calendar year.

NUMBER OF APPLICANTS MOST RECENT YEAR:
100.

NUMBER OF AWARDS: 90 for fiscal year 2012, excluding matching gifts.

REPRESENTATIVE AWARDS:
$7,500 to Harvesters, Kansas City, MO; $1,500 to River City Dance Theatre, San Marcos, TX; $4,000 to Genesis School, Kansas City, MO.

APPLICATION INFORMATION:
Initial contact should be made by phone, e-mail or letter addressed to the Foundation Administrator or, in non-Kansas City locations, to the plant or division manager describing the need, purpose and general activities of the requesting charitable organization. The letter will be reviewed by the plant or division manager to assure compliance with the policies established by the Foundation Trustees with a recommendation and forwarded to the Foundation Administrator.

Applicants must provide evidence of compliance with eligibility requirements, plus an annual report describing program activities and supporting services including financial statements, detailed annual budget and copy of IRS not-for-profit determination.
Duration: One year.
Deadline: Announcements are made after quarterly Trustee meetings.

PUBLICATIONS:
Annual report; contributions policy; application guidelines.

IRS IDENTIFICATION NUMBER: 44-0663648

ADDRESS INQUIRIES TO:
Jill Harmon, Foundation Director
(See address above.)

THE BODMAN FOUNDATION [46]

767 Third Avenue, 4th Floor
New York, NY 10017-2023
(212) 644-0322
Fax: (212) 759-6510

E-MAIL ADDRESS:
main@achelis-bodman-fnds.org

WEB SITE ADDRESS:
www.achelis-bodman-fnds.org

FOUNDED: 1945

AREAS OF INTEREST:
Primarily arts and culture, education, employment, health, public policy and youth and families.

TYPE:
Challenge/matching grants; Conferences/seminars; Development grants; General operating grants; Internships;

Matching gifts; Project/program grants; Research grants; Scholarships; Technical assistance; Training grants. Over 90% of the Foundation's grants fall into its six program areas.

PURPOSE:
To impact the greater New York City region and enhance the quality of life for its people, especially the disadvantaged; to advance human dignity, inspire personal achievement and foster self-reliance.

LEGAL BASIS:
Private foundation under Section 501(c)(3) of the Internal Revenue Code.

ELIGIBILITY:
Nonprofit organizations based in New York City and northern New Jersey that are tax-exempt under Section 501(c)(3) of the Internal Revenue Code and fall within the program areas of the Foundation are welcome to submit an inquiry or proposal letter.

The Foundation generally does not make grants to nonprofit organizations outside of New York and New Jersey; annual appeals, dinner functions and fund-raising events; endowments and capital campaigns; loans and deficit financing; direct grants to individuals (such as scholarships and financial aid); individual day-care and after-school programs; housing; international projects; films and travel; projects for the elderly; small art, dance, music and theater groups; independent or public K-12 schools (except charter schools); national health and mental health organizations and; government agencies and nonprofit programs and services significantly funded or substantially reimbursed by government.

GEOGRAPHIC RESTRICTIONS:
Primarily New York City, but also northern New Jersey.

FINANCIAL DATA:
Amount of support per award: $2,500 to $200,000 for the year 2013.
Total amount of support: $2,800,000 for the year 2013.

APPLICATION INFORMATION:
It is recommended that an organization's initial contact with the Foundation include only the following items:
(1) an inquiry or proposal letter briefly summarizing the history of the project, need, research, objectives, time period, key staff, project budget, and evaluation plan emphasizing measurable outcomes and specific program results;
(2) latest annual report;
(3) current and complete audited financial statements and;
(4) copy of the organization's IRS 501(c)(3) tax-exemption letter.
Duration: One year. Renewal does not generally follow the year of a grant.

OFFICERS:
John N. Irwin, III, Chairman
Russell P. Pennoyer, President
Peter Frelinghuysen, Vice President
Mary S. Phipps, Vice President
Horace I. Crary, Jr., Treasurer
John B. Krieger, Executive Director, Secretary and Assistant Treasurer

BOARD OF TRUSTEES:
Horace I. Crary, Jr.
Walter J.P. Curley, Jr.
Peter Frelinghuysen
John N. Irwin, III

Leslie Lenkowsky
Russell P. Pennoyer
Mary S. Phipps
Tatiana Pouschine

ADDRESS INQUIRIES TO:
John B. Krieger, Executive Director
(See address above.)

THE BOOTH-BRICKER FUND [47]

826 Union Street
Suite 300
New Orleans, LA 70112
(504) 581-2430
Fax: (504) 566-4785

FOUNDED: 1966

AREAS OF INTEREST:
The Fund makes contributions for the purposes of promoting, developing and fostering religious, charitable, scientific, literary and educational nonprofit organizations.

TYPE:
Capital grants; Development grants; Project/program grants.

PURPOSE:
To promote, develop and foster religious, charitable, scientific, literary and educational nonprofit organizations. Starting in 2006, the Fund's program of charitable distributions has focused primarily on taking advantage of the historic opportunity to reform public education in New Orleans.

ELIGIBILITY:
The Fund generally does not provide sustaining (operations and maintenance) funding. Requests are welcomed for capital needs, special projects and other one-time requirements. No grants are made to individuals or supporting organizations–i.e., a Section 501(c)(3) organization with further designation under Section 509(a)(3).

GEOGRAPHIC RESTRICTIONS:
Louisiana, with priority given to the New Orleans area.

FINANCIAL DATA:
Market value of assets as of December 31, 2012: $36,828,217.
Amount of support per award: Varies.
Total amount of support: Charitable distributions of $1,644,509.36 for the year 2012. Since its inception, the Fund has made charitable contributions exceeding $32,000,000.

NUMBER OF AWARDS: 71 gifts made in 2012.

APPLICATION INFORMATION:
Applications, which should be made by letter, are considered by the board of trustees at its quarterly meetings. There are no forms or deadlines. Requests should include complete information about the applicant organization, including its history, purpose, finances, current operations, governing board and tax status. A detailed explanation of the proposed use of the funds must be provided. Videotapes or DVDs should not be submitted.
Duration: Varies.

BOARD OF TRUSTEES:
Henry N. Kuechler, III
Charles B. Mayer
Gray S. Parker
Mary Kay Parker

Nathaniel P. Phillips, Jr.
H. Hunter White, Jr.

OFFICERS:
Gray S. Parker, Chairman
Ingrid C. Laffont, Treasurer
Heather A. Riley, Secretary

ADDRESS INQUIRIES TO:
Gray S. Parker, Chairman
(See address above.)

JAMES GRAHAM BROWN FOUNDATION, INC. [48]

4350 Brownsboro Road
Suite 200
Louisville, KY 40207
(502) 896-2440
Fax: (502) 896-1774

E-MAIL ADDRESS:
grants@jgbf.org

WEB SITE ADDRESS:
www.jgbf.org

FOUNDED: 1943

AREAS OF INTEREST:
Education, economic development, cultural and human services.

TYPE:
Capital grants; Project/program grants.

YEAR PROGRAM STARTED: 1943

PURPOSE:
To foster the well-being, quality of life and image of Louisville and Kentucky.

LEGAL BASIS:
Private foundation.

ELIGIBILITY:
Only Kentucky organizations that have a tax-exempt designation under Section 501(c)(3) of the IRS Code can apply.

GEOGRAPHIC RESTRICTIONS:
Kentucky, with emphasis on Louisville.

FINANCIAL DATA:
Amount of support per award: $25,000 and up.

NUMBER OF AWARDS: 70.

REPRESENTATIVE AWARDS:
$500,000 to Asbury University for support of a Virtual Teaching School; $400,000 to Boys and Girls Clubs of Kentuckiana for support of three new clubs to serve at-risk youth; $1,000,000 to Filson Historical Society for capital campaign to expand the Old Louisville Campus; $750,000 to Habitat for Humanity of Metro Louisville for the Portland Initiative; $100,000 to Kentuckiana Works Foundation for SummerWorks 2012 Summer Jobs program.

APPLICATION INFORMATION:
Contact the Foundation for details.
Duration: One year.

PUBLICATIONS:
Annual report.

ADDRESS INQUIRIES TO:
Mason Rummel, President
(See address above.)

THE JOE W. AND DOROTHY DORSETT BROWN FOUNDATION [49]

320 Hammond Highway, Suite 500
Metairie, LA 70005
(504) 834-3433
Fax: (504) 834-3441

E-MAIL ADDRESS:
bethbuscher@thebrownfoundation.org

WEB SITE ADDRESS:
www.thebrownfoundation.org

FOUNDED: 1959

AREAS OF INTEREST:
Health and science, community benefit, human services, religion and education, conservation, environment and the arts.

TYPE:
General operating grants; Project/program grants; Research grants; Training grants.

PURPOSE:
To alleviate human suffering.

ELIGIBILITY:
Applicants must be nonprofit 501(c)(3). Religious organizations are eligible to apply. The Foundation favors requests for funds where funds are generally unavailable from most other sources. Within the five focus areas, the focus is primarily on relieving human suffering; secondary interest includes cultural, spiritual, educational or scientific initiatives. No grants are made to individuals.

GEOGRAPHIC RESTRICTIONS:
Louisiana and Mississippi. Preference is given to the greater New Orleans area and Mississippi gulf coast.

FINANCIAL DATA:
Amount of support per award: Varies.
Total amount of support: Varies.

APPLICATION INFORMATION:
Contact the Foundation.
Duration: One year. Must reapply.
Deadline: August 30.

ADDRESS INQUIRIES TO:
Beth Buscher
Secretary to Board President
(See address above.)

BROWN SHOE COMPANY, INC. CHARITABLE TRUST   [50]
8300 Maryland Avenue
St. Louis, MO 63105-3693
(314) 854-4000
Fax: (314) 854-4205

E-MAIL ADDRESS:
charitablegiving@brownshoe.com

WEB SITE ADDRESS:
wwwstage.brownshoe.com/company-community-charitabletrust.asp

FOUNDED: 1951

AREAS OF INTEREST:
Culture and education.

TYPE:
Capital grants; General operating grants; Matching gifts.

YEAR PROGRAM STARTED: 1951

PURPOSE:
To help fund worthwhile ongoing programs in the areas of education, health and human services.

LEGAL BASIS:
Corporate contributions program.

ELIGIBILITY:
Grants are restricted to major 501(c)(3) organizations participating in the health, cultural and educational areas. Educational institutions must be private and above the secondary school level. All organizations must be geographically located in areas of employee concentration and with expenditures restricted to the U.S.

No grants are made to individuals.

GEOGRAPHIC RESTRICTIONS:
Primarily St. Louis, Missouri.

FINANCIAL DATA:
Amount of support per award: Varies.
Total amount of support: Varies.
Matching fund requirements: Matches gifts from full-time salaried employees and directors to educational institutions and cultural organizations, $50 to $2,500 per employee per year, and are matched on a 2:1 basis, up to $5,000.

APPLICATION INFORMATION:
Guidelines and application forms are available on the Company web site.
Duration: One year.
Deadline: Varies.

THE MARGARET E. BURNHAM CHARITABLE TRUST   [51]
c/o H.M. Payson & Co.
P.O. Box 31
Portland, ME 04112-0031
(207) 772-3761
Fax: (207) 871-7508

E-MAIL ADDRESS:
jbe@hmpayson.com

WEB SITE ADDRESS:
www.megrants.org/burnham.html

AREAS OF INTEREST:
Community/social services, medical, educational, arts and culture, and environment.

TYPE:
Grants-in-aid; Project/program grants. Annual grant dedicated to responding to the needs of the Maine communities served.

PURPOSE:
To benefit nonprofit organizations located or operating in the state of Maine.

ELIGIBILITY:
Organizations must be 501(c)(3) and must operate in and serve the state of Maine. Individuals, private foundations under Section 509, and religious organizations are not eligible.

GEOGRAPHIC RESTRICTIONS:
Maine.

FINANCIAL DATA:
Amount of support per award: $1,000 to $20,000.
Total amount of support: Varies.

APPLICATION INFORMATION:
A completed application consists of the following:
(1) certification, application, project description, and budget pages;
(2) copy of the organization's most recent 501(c)(3) IRS ruling;
(3) copy of the organization's most recent financial statement or tax return and;
(4) list of the organization's officers and directors.
Duration: One year.
Deadline: October 1.

ADDRESS INQUIRIES TO:
Thomas M. Pierce, Trustee
(See address above.)

EDYTH BUSH CHARITABLE FOUNDATION, INC.   [52]
199 East Welbourne Avenue, Suite 100
Winter Park, FL 32789
(407) 647-4322
(888) 647-4322
Fax: (407) 647-7716

E-MAIL ADDRESS:
dhessler@edythbush.org

WEB SITE ADDRESS:
www.edythbush.org

FOUNDED: 1973

AREAS OF INTEREST:
Children, youth and families, education, health care, limited interest in the arts, improvement of nonprofit organizations, and human services.

TYPE:
Capital grants; Challenge/matching grants; Demonstration grants; Development grants; Matching gifts; Project/program grants; Technical assistance; Training grants.

PURPOSE:
To provide nonprofit programs and grantmaking designed to help people help themselves.

LEGAL BASIS:
Private foundation.

ELIGIBILITY:
The Foundation welcomes grant applications from nonprofit organizations that have secured their 501(c)(3) and 509(a) IRS rulings. The Foundation has elected to focus its resources within Lake, Orange, Osceola and Seminole counties, FL. The Foundation will not fund organizations that are chiefly tax-supported, nor does it fund individual scholarships, individual research (even if through an exempt or otherwise qualified educational organization), alcoholism or drug abuse programs or facilities, routine operating expenses, the pay-off of deficits or pre-existing debt, foreign organizations or foreign expenditures, travel projects or fellowships, chiefly church, sacramental, denominational or interdenominational purposes (except those outreach programs for elderly, indigents, needy, youth or homeless, regardless of belief, race, color, creed, or sex), endowment funds, advocacy organizations, cultural or arts organizations or organizations that have receipts or revenues from memberships and/or contributions of less than $25,000.

GEOGRAPHIC RESTRICTIONS:
Lake, Orange, Osceola and Seminole counties, Florida.

FINANCIAL DATA:
Amount of support per award: Typically $5,000 to $50,000. Maximum grant has been $1,000,000 spread over five years. Large grants are typically spread over two or three years.
Total amount of support: Varies.
Matching fund requirements: Must be new or increased cash contributions or pledges.

APPLICATION INFORMATION:
Detailed information is available on the web site.
Duration: One year.
Deadline: Applications are accepted year-round.

PUBLICATIONS:
Guidelines; brochure.

IRS IDENTIFICATION NUMBER: 23-7318041

OFFICERS:
David A. Odahowski, President and Chief Executive Officer
Mary Ellen Hutcheson, CPA, Vice President and Treasurer
Deborah J. Hessler, Program Officer and Corporate Secretary

BOARD OF DIRECTORS:
Gerald F. Hilbrich, Chairman
Matthew W. Certo
Elizabeth Dvorak
Deborah C. German, M.D.
Herbert F. Holm
Harvey Massey
David A. Odahowski
Richard J. Walsh

ADDRESS INQUIRIES TO:
Deborah J. Hessler, Program Officer and Corporate Secretary
(See address above.)

CABOT FAMILY CHARITABLE TRUST [53]

70 Federal Street
Boston, MA 02110
(617) 226-7505
Fax: (617) 451-1733

E-MAIL ADDRESS:
kmchugh@cabwel.com

WEB SITE ADDRESS:
www.cabwel.com

FOUNDED: 1942

AREAS OF INTEREST:
Arts and culture, education and youth development, environment and conservation, health and human services, and for the public benefit.

TYPE:
Capital grants; Challenge/matching grants; Endowments; General operating grants; Project/program grants. Capital campaigns.

YEAR PROGRAM STARTED: 1942

PURPOSE:
To provide funding for nonprofit organizations working in the arts, environment, youth development, education, health and human services.

LEGAL BASIS:
Charitable trust.

ELIGIBILITY:
The Trust supports only nonprofit organizations holding active 501(c)(3) status under the IRS code. The Trust does not make contributions to individuals, political organizations, religious institutions, advertising, sponsorship or fraternal organizations.

Applicants must meet the following criteria:
(1) reflect Cabot family interests and provide benefits to communities and organizations that have been supported by family philanthropy;
(2) extend important services to individuals and groups not served adequately through other programs and institutions;
(3) manage change by assessing community needs and developing programs to meet emerging needs;
(4) promote productive cooperation and full use of resources by nonprofit organizations and community groups and;

(5) test new approaches to problems or adapt solutions that have been successful elsewhere.

GEOGRAPHIC RESTRICTIONS:
Boston and other contiguous communities.

FINANCIAL DATA:
Assets of $44,000,000.
Amount of support per award: $5,000 to $50,000 per year.
Total amount of support: $1,600,000.

NUMBER OF APPLICANTS MOST RECENT YEAR:
380 for the year 2011.

NUMBER OF AWARDS: Approximately 40.

REPRESENTATIVE AWARDS:
$30,000 to Generations Inc. for intergenerational tutoring progam that matches 2,700 children in the Boston Public Schools to mentors who are local residents; $15,000 to Boston Area Rape Crisis Center for programs and services for victims of sexual assault in 27 communities; $25,000 to the Boston Ballet for new work and performances.

APPLICATION INFORMATION:
Applicants should submit a concept paper of three pages plus cover sheet and budget. Application form is available on the web site.
Duration: Usually, one year.
Deadline: February 1 and September 1.

PUBLICATIONS:
Annual report.

IRS IDENTIFICATION NUMBER: 04-6035446

TRUSTEES:
Frank Bradley
John G.L. Cabot
Laura C. Carrigan
Mary Schneider Enriquez
Greenfield Sluder
Hendrika Sluder

EXECUTIVE DIRECTOR:
Katherine S. McHugh

ADDRESS INQUIRIES TO:
Katherine S. McHugh, Executive Director
(See address above.)

THE MORRIS AND GWENDOLYN CAFRITZ FOUNDATION [54]

1825 K Street, N.W.
Suite 1400
Washington, DC 20006
(202) 223-3100
Fax: (202) 296-7567

E-MAIL ADDRESS:
info@cafritzfoundation.org

WEB SITE ADDRESS:
www.cafritzfoundation.org

FOUNDED: 1948

AREAS OF INTEREST:
Community services, arts and humanities, education, health and the environment.

TYPE:
Challenge/matching grants; General operating grants; Project/program grants; Scholarships; Technical assistance.

YEAR PROGRAM STARTED: 1948

PURPOSE:
To build a stronger community for residents of the Washington, DC area through support of programs in arts and humanities, community services, education, health and the environment.

LEGAL BASIS:
Private foundation.

ELIGIBILITY:
Grants are made only to charitable, educational and cultural institutions exempt from taxation under the Internal Revenue Code. IRS-registered, tax-exempt, 501(c)(3) organizations with a public charity status of 509(a)(1) or 509(a)(2) only. The general policy is to concentrate grants to organizations, operating within the greater Washington metropolitan area, with projects of direct assistance to the District of Columbia and its environs. Grants are not made for capital purposes, endowments or to individuals.

GEOGRAPHIC RESTRICTIONS:
Montgomery and Prince George's counties in Maryland; Arlington and Fairfax counties, and the cities of Alexandria and Falls Church in Virginia; and Washington, DC.

FINANCIAL DATA:
Amount of support per award: Varies.
Total amount of support: $18,226,076 for the fiscal year ended April 30, 2012.

NUMBER OF APPLICANTS MOST RECENT YEAR:
700.

NUMBER OF AWARDS: 399.

REPRESENTATIVE AWARDS:
$30,000 to Montgomery County Coalition for the Homeless, Rockville, MD, for general support; $15,000 to Public Allies - DC, Washington, DC, for general support for the leadership development and community service program; $30,000 to Smith Center for Healing and the Arts, Washington, DC, for general support; $25,000 to The Textile Museum, Washington, DC, for general support; $25,000 to University System of Maryland Foundation for the Universities at Shady Grove, Rockville, MD, for need-based scholarship assistance to full-time and part-time students transferring to USG from Montgomery and Prince George's Community Colleges.

APPLICATION INFORMATION:
To be considered for funding, an organization must submit a complete proposal, not a Letter of Inquiry (LOI). LOIs are not required. Organizations may submit a proposal for only one deadline within a 12-month period. The Foundation requires that all organizations use the Washington Grantmakers' Common Grant Application.
Duration: One year.
Deadline: November 1, March 1 and July 1.

PUBLICATIONS:
Annual report; application guidelines.

OFFICERS:
Calvin Cafritz, President and Chief Executive Officer
John E. Chapoton, Vice Chairman
Ed McGeogh, Vice President, Asset Management
F. Joseph Moravec, Treasurer

STAFF:
Rose Ann Cleveland, Executive Director

DIRECTORS:
Calvin Cafritz, Chairman of the Board
Michael F. Brewer
John E. Chapoton
LaSalle D. Leffall, Jr., M.D., F.A.C.S.

Patricia McGuire
F. Joseph Moravec
Robert Peck
Earl A. Powell, III
Alice M. Rivlin, Ph.D.
Norman O. Scribner

ADVISORY BOARD:
Anthony W. Cafritz
Elliot S. Cafritz
Jane Lipton Cafritz
Carolyn J. Deaver
The Hon. Constance A. Morella
Elizabeth M. Peltekian
Julia Sparkman Shepard

ADDRESS INQUIRIES TO:
Rose Ann Cleveland, Executive Director
(See address above.)

CAMPBELL SOUP FOUNDATION   [55]

One Campbell Place
Camden, NJ 08103-1799
(856) 342-6423
Fax: (856) 342-5217

E-MAIL ADDRESS:
wendy_milanese@campbellsoup.com

WEB SITE ADDRESS:
www.campbellsoupcompany.com

FOUNDED: 1954

AREAS OF INTEREST:
Quality of life in plant communities, home community of Camden, NJ.

NAME(S) OF PROGRAMS:
• **Campbell Summer Program**
• **Dollars for Doers Fund**

TYPE:
Challenge/matching grants; Project/program grants. The Dollars for Doers Fund is a program designed to fund nonprofit organizations where Campbell employees volunteer in communities.

Campbell Summer Program funds organizations that provide summer employment, recreation, academic and cultural programs in the city of Camden.

YEAR PROGRAM STARTED: 1954

PURPOSE:
To improve the quality of life in those communities where Campbell Soup Company has a presence.

LEGAL BASIS:
Tax-exempt private foundation.

ELIGIBILITY:
Grants are made to tax-exempt organizations providing service consistent with Fund objectives. The Fund does not make grants to individuals for any purpose, nor does it make grants to organizations outside the U.S. and its possessions.

GEOGRAPHIC RESTRICTIONS:
United States.

FINANCIAL DATA:
Amount of support per award: Varies.
Total amount of support: $1,600,000 for the year ended June 30, 2013.
Matching fund requirements: Active employee and directors; $100 to $3,000 per person per year to higher education facilities only.

APPLICATION INFORMATION:
Foundation guidelines are available online.
Duration: Usually one-time grants.

Deadline: Two funding cycles per year, one in the fall and one in the spring, typically four months in length. Fall cycle runs August through November and Spring cycle runs January through April.

OFFICERS:
David P. Stangis, President
Anthony DiSilvestro, Controller

TRUSTEES:
Helen Bray
Mark Cacciatore
Richard Landers
Karen Lewis
Maureen Linder
Joseph Spagnoletti
David P. Stangis

ADDRESS INQUIRIES TO:
Wendy Milanese, Grant Administrator
(See address above.)

THE CANNON FOUNDATION, INC.   [56]

52 Spring Street, N.W.
Concord, NC 28025
(704) 786-8216
Fax: (704) 782-2812

E-MAIL ADDRESS:
fdavis@cannonfoundation.org

WEB SITE ADDRESS:
www.cannonfoundation.org

FOUNDED: 1943

AREAS OF INTEREST:
Primarily health care, higher education and human services. Limited grants to arts, historical preservation and environment.

TYPE:
Capital grants.

YEAR PROGRAM STARTED: 1943

LEGAL BASIS:
Private foundation.

ELIGIBILITY:
Applicant must be 501(c)(3) nonprofit organization. No grants to individuals.

GEOGRAPHIC RESTRICTIONS:
North Carolina.

FINANCIAL DATA:
Amount of support per award: $5,000 to $200,000.
Total amount of support: Approximately $6,793,000 for fiscal year ended September 30, 2013.

NUMBER OF APPLICANTS MOST RECENT YEAR:
155 for the year 2013.

NUMBER OF AWARDS: 115 for the year 2013.

APPLICATION INFORMATION:
Applications are requested through the web site. Links to the online application are sent to the applying organization's chief executive officer/executive director, not to grant writers or consultants.
Duration: One year.
Deadline: January 5, April 5, July 5 and October 5. Notification within two months of deadlines.

STAFF:
Frank Davis, Executive Director

ADDRESS INQUIRIES TO:
Frank Davis, Executive Director
(See address above.)

CARNEGIE CORPORATION OF NEW YORK   [57]

437 Madison Avenue
New York, NY 10022
(212) 371-3200

WEB SITE ADDRESS:
www.carnegie.org

FOUNDED: 1911

AREAS OF INTEREST:
Higher education and libraries in Africa, higher education in Eurasia, urban and higher education in the U.S., international peace and security, and strengthening U.S. democracy/immigrant civic integration.

TYPE:
Conferences/seminars; Development grants; Project/program grants; Research grants; Seed money grants.

YEAR PROGRAM STARTED: 1911

PURPOSE:
To promote the advancement and diffusion of knowledge and understanding.

LEGAL BASIS:
Private foundation.

ELIGIBILITY:
Grants are made primarily to academic institutions and national or regional organizations.

FINANCIAL DATA:
Amount of support per award: Varies.
Total amount of support: Approximately $111,000,000 for the year 2012.

NUMBER OF AWARDS: Varies.

APPLICATION INFORMATION:
Only Letters of Inquiry submitted via the Corporation's online system will be considered.
Duration: Varies.

PUBLICATIONS:
Program guidelines; pamphlet; meeting and occasional papers; *Carnegie Reporter*, magazine; annual report.

IRS IDENTIFICATION NUMBER: 13-1628151

ADDRESS INQUIRIES TO:
E-mail: grantsinfo@carnegie.org

AMON G. CARTER FOUNDATION   [58]

201 Main Street, Suite 1945
Fort Worth, TX 76102
(817) 332-2783
Fax: (817) 332-2787

E-MAIL ADDRESS:
tlwoodfin@agcf.org

WEB SITE ADDRESS:
www.agcf.org

FOUNDED: 1945

AREAS OF INTEREST:
The arts, health and medical services, youth and elderly, and human and social services.

TYPE:
Capital grants; Challenge/matching grants; Development grants; Matching gifts; Project/program grants; Seed money grants.

PURPOSE:
To support arts, education, health and medical services, programs benefiting youth and elderly, and civic and community endeavors that enhance quality of life.

LEGAL BASIS:
Private foundation.

ELIGIBILITY:
Applicants must be 501(c)(3) organizations. Board focus on Fort Worth and Tarrant County, TX.

No loans. No grants to individuals.

GEOGRAPHIC RESTRICTIONS:
Texas.

FINANCIAL DATA:
Amount of support per award: $10,000 to $500,000.

Total amount of support: Varies.

NUMBER OF APPLICANTS MOST RECENT YEAR:
400 for the year 2013.

NUMBER OF AWARDS: 200 for the year 2013.

REPRESENTATIVE AWARDS:
$7,557,570 to Amon Carter Museum; $2,500,000 to Texas Christian University.

APPLICATION INFORMATION:
Send brief letter request supplemented with project budget and/or other pertinent information in support of request.
Duration: Three years maximum. Renewal rare.

PUBLICATIONS:
Grant policy and guideline statement.

OFFICERS:
Robert W. Brown, M.D., Vice President
W. Patrick Harris, Executive Vice President, Finances
John H. Robinson, Executive Vice President, Grant Administration
Kathy King, Controller

BOARD OF DIRECTORS:
Robert W. Brown, M.D.
Kate L. Johnson
Mark L. Johnson
Sheila B. Johnson

ADDRESS INQUIRIES TO:
John H. Robinson
Executive Vice President
Grant Administration
(See address above.)

HAROLD K.L. CASTLE
FOUNDATION   [59]
1197 Auloa Road
Kailua, HI 96734-4606
(808) 263-7073
Fax: (808) 261-6918

E-MAIL ADDRESS:
bmurph@castlefoundation.org

WEB SITE ADDRESS:
www.castlefoundation.org

FOUNDED: 1962

AREAS OF INTEREST:
Hawaii's public education redesign and enhancement, Hawaii's nearshore marine resource conservation, strengthening the communities of Windward Oahu, and other areas of focus when the Foundation sees a special opportunity to make a difference with limited resources.

TYPE:
Capital grants; Project/program grants; Seed money grants.

PURPOSE:
To benefit the people of Hawaii.

LEGAL BASIS:
Family foundation.

ELIGIBILITY:
Nonprofit organizations serving the state of Hawaii with Internal Revenue Code Sections 501(c)(3) and 509(a) public charity status and public schools in Hawaii.

GEOGRAPHIC RESTRICTIONS:
Hawaii.

FINANCIAL DATA:
Amount of support per award: $190 to $922,815.33 for fiscal year 2012.

Total amount of support: $5,948,273.06 for fiscal year 2012.

COOPERATIVE FUNDING PROGRAMS: Hawaii Community Stabilization Initiative.

NUMBER OF APPLICANTS MOST RECENT YEAR:
116.

NUMBER OF AWARDS: 48.

REPRESENTATIVE AWARDS:
$922,815.33 to University of Hawaii Foundation; $475,000 to Teach for America; $95,000 to Hawaii Conservation Alliance Foundation; $750,000 to Bishop Museum.

APPLICATION INFORMATION:
Prospective grant applicants must submit an Online Inquiry Form, which is the first step in requesting funds from the Foundation. The Foundation will contact applicants within one month to request more information, invite the submission of a full proposal, or to inform applicant that the Foundation will be unable to consider a full proposal due to limited resources and/or a mismatch with Foundation priorities.
Duration: Program grants: Up to five years.
Deadline: Applications accepted on a rolling basis. Capital support requests due each year by October 1.

PUBLICATIONS:
Application guidelines; annual report.

IRS IDENTIFICATION NUMBER: 99-6005445

STAFF:
Terrence R. George, President and Chief Executive Officer
Carlton K.C. Au, Vice President, Chief Financial Officer and Treasurer
Eric Co, Senior Program Officer for Marine Conservation
Alex Harris, Senior Program Officer for Education
Ann Matsukado, Controller

BOARD OF DIRECTORS:
H. Mitchell D'Olier, Chairman of the Board
Dr. Claire L. Asam
Dr. Kittredge A. Baldwin
Corbett A.K. Kalama
James C. McIntosh
Randolph G. Moore
Eric K. Yeaman

ADDRESS INQUIRIES TO:
Elizabeth Murph, Grants Manager
(See address above.)

CENTRAL MAINE POWER
COMPANY   [60]
83 Edison Drive
Augusta, ME 04336
(800) 565-0121 ext. 2967
(207) 629-1067
Fax: (207) 623-5908

WEB SITE ADDRESS:
www.cmpco.com

AREAS OF INTEREST:
Education, civic, science, technology education and economic development.

NAME(S) OF PROGRAMS:
- **Central Maine Power Company Corporate Contributions Program**

TYPE:
Capital grants; Challenge/matching grants; Demonstration grants; General operating grants; Project/program grants; Research grants.

LEGAL BASIS:
Corporation giving program.

ELIGIBILITY:
Applicants must be nonprofit organizations, limited to the area serviced by Central Maine Power.

GEOGRAPHIC RESTRICTIONS:
Maine.

FINANCIAL DATA:
Amount of support per award: $100 to $1,000.

NUMBER OF APPLICANTS MOST RECENT YEAR:
500.

NUMBER OF AWARDS: 100.

APPLICATION INFORMATION:
Applicants should send a proposal letter.
Duration: Typically one year. Some multiyear funding.
Deadline: Applications accepted throughout the year. Grants announced monthly.

STAFF:
John H. Carroll, Manager of Public Affairs

ADDRESS INQUIRIES TO:
Shelley Morris
Public Affairs Department
(See address above.)

*SPECIAL STIPULATIONS:
Only available to schools and nonprofits within company's service territory in Maine.

THE CHAMPLIN
FOUNDATIONS   [61]
2000 Chapel View Boulevard, Suite 350
Cranston, RI 02920
(401) 944-9200
Fax: (401) 944-9299

WEB SITE ADDRESS:
champlinfoundations.org

FOUNDED: 1932

AREAS OF INTEREST:
Conservation, environment, education, health, cultural programs, youth, social service, historic preservation and libraries.

TYPE:
Capital grants; Challenge/matching grants; Scholarships. Direct grants for capital needs including the purchase of equipment, real estate, renovations, construction and reduction of mortgage indebtedness.

Other grants are made only in certain circumstances.

Challenge grants are made at the Foundations' discretion.

Scholarships are only to Brown University for graduates of Rhode Island public high schools.

YEAR PROGRAM STARTED: 1932

PURPOSE:
To make grants to qualified charitable organizations to promote the general well-being of humanity, with preference to Rhode Island.

LEGAL BASIS:
Tax-exempt private foundation.

ELIGIBILITY:
Tax-exempt organizations, preferably in Rhode Island, may apply. No grants are awarded to individuals. Scholarships are limited to Rhode Island public high school graduates accepted at Brown University.

GEOGRAPHIC RESTRICTIONS:
Rhode Island.

FINANCIAL DATA:
Amount of support per award: Average: $25,000 to $65,000.
Total amount of support: $18,993,361 for the year 2012.

NUMBER OF APPLICANTS MOST RECENT YEAR:
404 for the year 2012.

NUMBER OF AWARDS: 201 for the year 2012.

REPRESENTATIVE AWARDS:
For 2012: Health Care: $850,000 to Bradley Hospital; Education: $700,000 to Brown University; Libraries: $914,400 to Ocean State Libraries; Youth/Fitness: $925,000 to Greater Providence YMCA; Open Space/Parks/Environment: $1,750,000 to The Nature Conservancy; Social Services: $128,615 to The Providence Center.

APPLICATION INFORMATION:
Applicants must submit a brief letter concisely describing the project and its intended purpose, status of any fund-raising effort and other sources of funds available. Copies of IRS 501(c)(3) tax-exemption and 509(a) letters must be furnished. Audited financial statements may be required on request.
Duration: No grants are awarded on a continuing basis. Applicants must apply for renewal.
Deadline: April 30. Grants awarded in November; checks issued in December.

PUBLICATIONS:
Annual report; guidelines; Report on Open Space and Recreation Grants.

IRS IDENTIFICATION NUMBER: 51-0165988

EXECUTIVE COMMITTEE:
John Gorham, Chairman
Keith H. Lang, Executive Director
Timothy N. Gorham, Associate Director

ADDRESS INQUIRIES TO:
Keith H. Lang, Executive Director
(See address above.)

*SPECIAL STIPULATIONS:
Preference is given to Rhode Island tax-exempt organizations.

All initial inquiries must be made by mail.

BEN B. CHENEY FOUNDATION   [62]
3110 Ruston Way, Suite A
Tacoma, WA 98402
(253) 572-2442

E-MAIL ADDRESS:
info@benbcheneyfoundation.org

WEB SITE ADDRESS:
www.benbcheneyfoundation.org

AREAS OF INTEREST:
Charity, civic affairs, culture, education, the elderly, health, social services and youth.

TYPE:
Capital grants; Project/program grants; Seed money grants.

PURPOSE:
To improve the quality of life in communities where the Cheney Lumber Company operated.

LEGAL BASIS:
Foundation.

ELIGIBILITY:
Applicants must be 501(c)(3) tax-exempt organizations.

GEOGRAPHIC RESTRICTIONS:
Tacoma and Pierce County, Washington; Medford and Jackson County, Oregon and the seven northernmost counties in California.

FINANCIAL DATA:
Amount of support per award: $1,000 to $15,000 for small grants; $16,000 to $50,000 for regular grants.
Total amount of support: Varies.

NUMBER OF APPLICANTS MOST RECENT YEAR:
300.

NUMBER OF AWARDS: 100.

APPLICATION INFORMATION:
Begin with a query letter; projects of interest will be contacted for a follow-up interview.
Duration: Typically one to two years. No renewals.

ADDRESS INQUIRIES TO:
Brad Cheney, Executive Director
(See address above.)

CHICAGO TRIBUNE FOUNDATION   [63]
Community Giving, 2nd Floor
435 North Michigan Avenue
Chicago, IL 60611-4041
(312) 222-3928
Fax: (312) 222-3882

E-MAIL ADDRESS:
jwoelffer@tribune.com

WEB SITE ADDRESS:
www.chicagotribune.com/communitygiving

FOUNDED: 1958

AREAS OF INTEREST:
Civic, culture, employee matching gifts and journalism.

TYPE:
General operating grants; Internships; Matching gifts; Project/program grants. Civic: Grants in this program area primarily support initiatives that focus on providing educational opportunities for low-income youth from the Chicago area. Grant requests in the civic program area will be considered by invitation only.

Culture: Grants support arts organizations within the Chicago metropolitan area that provide access to the arts through educational programs for low-income youth in grades K-12. Grant support priority is given to arts organizations with an operating budget of less than $2,000,000. (The definition of cultural organizations is organizations whose entire mission is the arts or arts education.)

Journalism: The Foundation strives for journalistic excellence by building a broad and diverse pool of journalists to serve readers in Chicago and encouraging youths to have a voice. It seeks to focus its resources on local programs that will help train journalists who might otherwise not enter the field, and help them thrive in newsrooms. The Foundation provides support in five categories: (1) internships; (2) training and education programs; (3) hands-on journalism production or media literacy programs offered by local nonprofit organizations that reach low-income youth and diverse students in metropolitan Chicago; (4) local reading services of media news and information and; (5) programs that provide opportunities for youth or diverse journalists to attend journalism conferences held in Chicago.

PURPOSE:
To improve the future of the Chicago metropolitan area by helping underserved youth succeed and be safe; to provide resources, partnerships and a voice to help strengthen at-risk youths and families in its diverse community; to support educational civic programs for at-risk families, access to the arts for low-income youths, and diversity and youth voices in journalism.

LEGAL BASIS:
Corporate private foundation.

ELIGIBILITY:
All grant requests must fall within the described geographic and program areas in order to be considered for either general support or program support. The Foundation does not fund individual, capital or international grants. The grant requests must be received by the required dates described in the program area.

GEOGRAPHIC RESTRICTIONS:
City of Chicago, Illinois and the Chicago metropolitan area.

FINANCIAL DATA:
Amount of support per award: $2,500 to $5,000.
Total amount of support: Approximately $268,000 for the year 2013.
Matching fund requirements: The Foundation matches Chicago Tribune employee donations to most U.S. nonprofit organizations on a 2:1 basis; the match is $1,000 per employee on the calendar year.

COOPERATIVE FUNDING PROGRAMS: Chicago Tribune Company bears the administrative costs of Chicago Tribune Foundation. Donations from Chicago Tribune's pretax profits or assets of the Foundation fund Chicago Tribune Foundation.

REPRESENTATIVE AWARDS:
Civic: $5,000 to Chicago Youth Centers, Chicago, IL, to develop college-to-career readiness programs; Culture: Maywood Fine Arts Association, Maywood, IL, to support Books Alive performances to encourage the joy of reading; Journalism: Community Renewal Society, Chicago, IL, to support journalism internships focusing on issues of race or poverty.

APPLICATION INFORMATION:
The Foundation advises the applying organization to initially send a one-page e-mail of inquiry that briefly includes organization's mission, geographic area and population served, program summary, organization budget and program budget. Include contact name, phone number and e-mail. To submit this letter of inquiry, please

contact Jan Ellen Woelffer, Chicago Tribune, at the above address, phone number, fax number or e-mail.

The Foundation accepts, but does not require, the Chicago Area Grant Application Form. Use the information requested on the Chicago Area Grant Application Form as a guide for the proposal. Provide the information requested on the Form in a two-page narrative. The following attachments must be included with the proposal:
(1) a one-sided, one-page list of one's board of directors and their business affiliation and title;
(2) a copy of the most recent IRS tax-exempt status form;
(3) audited financial statements or Form 990 from the most recent fiscal year;
(4) organization budget for year in which funding is sought;
(5) sources of support listing which funds have been committed and;
(6) annual report or other literature on the organization's programmatic, financial and strategic accomplishments.

PUBLICATIONS:
Corporate contributions guidelines; annual report.

IRS IDENTIFICATION NUMBER: 36-3689171

STAFF:
Jan Ellen Woelffer, Grant and Charitable Programs Specialist

BOARD OF DIRECTORS AND OFFICERS:
Tony Hunter, Chairman
Joseph Schiltz, President
Joetta Fields-Taylor, Secretary
Maggie Wartik
Joyce Winnecke

ADDRESS INQUIRIES TO:
Jan Ellen Woelffer, Grant and Charitable Programs Specialist
(See address above.)

*SPECIAL STIPULATIONS:
If an organization previously received a grant from the Foundation, an updated report on that year's grant must be received before another grant request can be submitted. The report can be a two-page summary of accomplishments and challenges including the financial summary about the program supported by the grant.

If an organization has received grant support from the Foundation for three consecutive years, the organization is not eligible for funding in the fourth year. The organization can re-apply after taking a year away from funding.

THE CHRISTENSEN FUND   [64]
260 Townsend Street
Suite 600
San Francisco, CA 94107
(415) 644-1630
Fax: (415) 644-1670

E-MAIL ADDRESS:
info@christensenfund.org

WEB SITE ADDRESS:
www.christensenfund.org

FOUNDED: 1957

AREAS OF INTEREST:
Supporting organizations working on biological and cultural diversity.

NAME(S) OF PROGRAMS:
● **African Rift Valley**
● **Central Asia**
● **Global**
● **Melanesia**
● **San Francisco-Bay Area**
● **Southwest U.S. and Northern Mexico**

TYPE:
General operating grants; Project/program grants; Research grants.

YEAR PROGRAM STARTED: 2003

PURPOSE:
To buttress the indigenous and traditional stewards of bio-cultural diversity in the landscapes which have provided their cultural and ecological heritages.

LEGAL BASIS:
Private, independent foundation.

ELIGIBILITY:
Must have nonprofit 501(c)(3) status or similar not-for-profit organization based outside U.S.

GEOGRAPHIC RESTRICTIONS:
Southwest United States, northwest Mexico, Central Asia, Melanesia, and the Africa Rift Valley (Southwest Ethiopia/Northern Kenya).

FINANCIAL DATA:
Amount of support per award: $50,000 to $100,000.
Total amount of support: $13,500,000 for 2013.

NUMBER OF APPLICANTS MOST RECENT YEAR: 360.

NUMBER OF AWARDS: 175 on average.

APPLICATION INFORMATION:
Information may be obtained from the Fund's web site.
Duration: Typically one to two years.
Deadline: Varies.

ADDRESS INQUIRIES TO:
See e-mail address above.

EDNA McCONNELL CLARK FOUNDATION   [65]
415 Madison Avenue, 10th Floor
New York, NY 10017
(212) 551-9100
Fax: (212) 421-9325

E-MAIL ADDRESS:
info@emcf.org

WEB SITE ADDRESS:
www.emcf.org

FOUNDED: 1970

AREAS OF INTEREST:
Youth development.

NAME(S) OF PROGRAMS:
● **Youth Development Fund**

TYPE:
General operating grants. Business planning grants. Focus areas for the Youth Development Fund are academic achievement, preparation for workforce, and avoidance of risky behavior.

PURPOSE:
To support efforts by high-performing nonprofit organizations to increase their capacity to serve more kids (ages 9 to 24) with proven programs during the nonschool hours.

LEGAL BASIS:
Private foundation.

GEOGRAPHIC RESTRICTIONS:
United States.

FINANCIAL DATA:
Amount of support per award: Varies.

COOPERATIVE FUNDING PROGRAMS: When Foundation interests are shared with other organizations.

APPLICATION INFORMATION:
Organizations need to complete survey online.
Duration: Varies.
Deadline: No official deadlines. Board meets four times a year, plus standing committee meetings.

PUBLICATIONS:
Annual report.

IRS IDENTIFICATION NUMBER: 23-7047034

OFFICERS:
Nancy Roob, President
Ralph Stefano, Vice President, Director of Finance and Administration
Woodrow McCutchen, Vice President, Senior Portfolio Manager

TRUSTEES:
Theodore E. Martin, Chairman
H. Lawrence Clark
James McConnell Clark, Jr.
Alice F. Emerson
Simon Hemus
Janice C. Kreamer
James E. Moltz
Nancy Roob
Joyce Shields

ADDRESS INQUIRIES TO:
Albert Chung
Director of Communications Operations
(See address above.)

*PLEASE NOTE:
The Foundation does not accept unsolicited proposals.

THE CLIFFS FOUNDATION   [66]
200 Public Square
Suite 3300
Cleveland, OH 44114-2589
(216) 694-5700
Fax: (216) 694-4880

WEB SITE ADDRESS:
www.cliffsnaturalresources.com

FOUNDED: 1962

AREAS OF INTEREST:
Education, health, welfare, civic affairs, cultural affairs and the arts.

TYPE:
General operating grants.

PURPOSE:
To enhance the quality of life of the Company's employees and communities in which the Company operates.

ELIGIBILITY:
Nonprofit organizations may apply.

GEOGRAPHIC RESTRICTIONS:
Adger, Alabama; Upper Peninsula of Michigan; northeastern Minnesota; Cleveland, Ohio; and Pineville, West Virginia.

FINANCIAL DATA:
Amount of support per award: $250 to $5,000.
Matching fund requirements: Education only. Employees, retired officers and active directors are eligible.

APPLICATION INFORMATION:
All requests for support must be in writing.
Duration: One year.
Deadline: Applications accepted throughout
the year.

PUBLICATIONS:
Guidelines.

STAFF:
Dana W. Byrne, Vice President and Assistant
Treasurer

ADDRESS INQUIRIES TO:
Dana W. Byrne
Vice President and Assistant Treasurer
(See address above.)

*SPECIAL STIPULATIONS:
No consideration will be given to any
solicitation made by telephone or e-mail.

COASTAL BEND COMMUNITY FOUNDATION [67]
600 Leopard Street, Suite 1716
Corpus Christi, TX 78401
(361) 882-9745
Fax: (361) 882-2865

E-MAIL ADDRESS:
kselim@cbcfoundation.org

WEB SITE ADDRESS:
www.cbcfoundation.org

FOUNDED: 1981

AREAS OF INTEREST:
Arts, children and youth, community
development, crime prevention, elderly,
environment, health, social welfare, education
and human services.

TYPE:
Capital grants; Challenge/matching grants;
Development grants; General operating
grants; Project/program grants; Scholarships;
Seed money grants; Training grants.

YEAR PROGRAM STARTED: 1981

PURPOSE:
To improve the quality of life in the Coastal
Bend area.

LEGAL BASIS:
Community foundation.

ELIGIBILITY:
Grants are made to organizations that have
tax-exempt status under Section 501(c)(3) of
the Internal Revenue Code. No grants are
made to individuals.

GEOGRAPHIC RESTRICTIONS:
Aransas, Bee, Jim Wells, Kleberg, Nueces,
Refugio and San Patricio counties, Texas.

FINANCIAL DATA:
Amount of support per award: Varies.
Total amount of support: $3,280,678 for the
year 2012.
Matching fund requirements: Determined on
individual basis.

COOPERATIVE FUNDING PROGRAMS: Coastal
Bend Day of Giving.

APPLICATION INFORMATION:
Organizations should submit application with
requested documentation by the application
deadline. Applications that do not conform to
the required format will not be considered.
Duration: Grants must be completed by the
following September 30.
Deadline: Deadlines are posted online.

PUBLICATIONS:
Annual report.

IRS IDENTIFICATION NUMBER: 74-2190039

ADDRESS INQUIRIES TO:
Karen W. Selim
President and Chief Executive Officer
(See address above.)

THE COCKRELL FOUNDATION [68]
1000 Main Street
Suite 3250
Houston, TX 77002
(713) 209-7500
Fax: (713) 209-7599

E-MAIL ADDRESS:
foundation@cockrell.com

WEB SITE ADDRESS:
www.cockrell.com

FOUNDED: 1957

AREAS OF INTEREST:
Education, arts, health care, youth activities
and medical research.

TYPE:
Capital grants; Fellowships; General
operating grants; Professorships;
Project/program grants; Scholarships.
Professorships and scholarships at University
of Texas, Cockrell School of Engineering.

YEAR PROGRAM STARTED: 1966

PURPOSE:
To provide financial support for charitable
organizations in the Houston area in support
of education, health, civic, religious and
social services.

LEGAL BASIS:
Private foundation.

ELIGIBILITY:
Fellowships, professorships and scholarships
to the University of Texas School of
Engineering only.

In general, the Foundation gives support for
annual and capital campaigns, building funds,
endowment funds, general purposes,
matching funds, and special projects. Grants
are made only to nonprofit, tax-exempt
organizations. To be eligible, an organization
must have a determination letter from the
IRS indicating that it is an organization
described in Section 501(c)(3) of the Internal
Revenue Code and is not a private foundation
within the meaning of Section 509(a) of the
Code.

GEOGRAPHIC RESTRICTIONS:
Primarily Houston, Texas.

FINANCIAL DATA:
Amount of support per award: Varies.
Total amount of support: $6,122,924 in
grants for the year 2011.

NUMBER OF APPLICANTS MOST RECENT YEAR:
200.

NUMBER OF AWARDS: 43 grants for the year
2011.

APPLICATION INFORMATION:
The Foundation supplies no application form.
Applicants should submit a written
description, no longer than five pages, of
how the grant money will be used, covering
the following items:
(1) description of the need or problem;
(2) a simple statement of what is hoped to be
accomplished;
(3) a budget for the project, giving the total
cost, the amount raised to date toward the

project or program, the sources from which it
has come, including private, religious
organizations and/or government sources,
and, in particular, the amount contributed by
the individuals on the Board of Directors;
(4) plans for raising any uncovered balance;
(5) an explanation of why it is necessary to
seek outside support;
(6) the current status of the project - where it
stands now and how long it will take to
complete;
(7) the specific sum being requested of the
Foundation;
(8) plans for putting continuing projects on a
self-sustaining basis and an estimate of when
this will occur;
(9) name and address of tax-exempt
organization which will be the recipient if a
donation is made and a copy of the
exemption letter from the U.S. Treasury
Department;
(10) copy of the organization's current annual
budget;
(11) copy of the organization's latest
IRS-990;
(12) copy of the organization's latest audited
financials;
(13) a list of the members of the Board of
Directors;
(14) a list of the officers of the organization
and;
(15) an Executive Summary Sheet.
Duration: One year. Occasionally multiple
years.

PUBLICATIONS:
The Cockrell Foundation Fact Sheet.

IRS IDENTIFICATION NUMBER: 74-6076993

OFFICERS AND DIRECTORS:
Ernest H. Cockrell, President and Director
M. Nancy Williams, Executive Vice President
Milton T. Graves, Vice President and
Director
David A. Cockrell, Director
Ernest D. Cockrell, Director
Janet S. Cockrell, Director
Carol Cockrell Curran, Director
Richard B. Curran, Director
J. Webb Jennings, III, Director
Laura Jennings Turner, Director

ADDRESS INQUIRIES TO:
M. Nancy Williams
Executive Vice President
(See address above.)

THE OGDEN CODMAN TRUST [69]
c/o Rackemann, Sawyer & Brewster
160 Federal Street, 15th Floor
Boston, MA 02110-1700
(617) 951-1108
Fax: (617) 542-7437

E-MAIL ADDRESS:
smonahan@rackemann.com

WEB SITE ADDRESS:
www.codmantrust.org

FOUNDED: 1968

AREAS OF INTEREST:
Environment, conservation, historic
preservation, cultural, health and social
services in the town of Lincoln, MA.

TYPE:
Project/program grants. Support for special
programs.

PURPOSE:
To improve the quality of life in Lincoln.

LEGAL BASIS:
Private independent foundation.

ELIGIBILITY:
The Foundation does not generally fund operating expenses.

GEOGRAPHIC RESTRICTIONS:
Lincoln, Massachusetts.

FINANCIAL DATA:
Amount of support per award: $2,000 to $50,000.
Total amount of support: $172,420 for the year 2012.
Matching fund requirements: Case-by-case basis.

NUMBER OF APPLICANTS MOST RECENT YEAR:
12 for the year 2012.

NUMBER OF AWARDS: 12 for the year 2012.

REPRESENTATIVE AWARDS:
Town of Lincoln; Codman Community Farm; Lincoln School Foundation.

APPLICATION INFORMATION:
Contact Grants Coordinator prior to submitting an application.
Duration: Varies.
Deadline: Quarterly.

PUBLICATIONS:
Application guidelines.

TRUSTEES:
Daniel W. Fawcett
William B. Tyler, Esq.
Walter G. Van Dorn

ADDRESS INQUIRIES TO:
Susan T. Monahan, Grants Coordinator
(See e-mail address above.)

THE GEORGE W. CODRINGTON CHARITABLE FOUNDATION [70]
3900 Key Center
127 Public Square
Cleveland, OH 44114-1291
(216) 566-5699
Fax: (216) 566-5800

E-MAIL ADDRESS:
craig.martahus@thompsonhine.com

FOUNDED: 1955

AREAS OF INTEREST:
Humanitarian projects.

TYPE:
Capital grants; Challenge/matching grants; Endowments; General operating grants; Matching gifts. Annual grants to public charitable or educational projects.

YEAR PROGRAM STARTED: 1955

PURPOSE:
To assist, encourage and promote the well-being of mankind, regardless of race, color or creed.

LEGAL BASIS:
Private foundation.

ELIGIBILITY:
The Foundation's supportive services are limited to public charitable or educational projects. No grants are made to individuals.

GEOGRAPHIC RESTRICTIONS:
Cuyahoga County, Ohio and immediately adjacent areas.

FINANCIAL DATA:
Amount of support per award: $500 to $200,000.
Total amount of support: Varies.

REPRESENTATIVE AWARDS:
$8,000 to the Cleveland Society for the Blind; $3,000 to the Lyric Opera Cleveland; $60,000 to the Free Medical Clinic of Greater Cleveland.

APPLICATION INFORMATION:
Applications should be directed to the Supervisory Board of the Foundation. The application should state fully but briefly the amount requested, the need for the grant, the area served by the applicant, a brief history of the applicant's organization, description of the applicant's contributions to the area and listing of the applicant's officers and trustees. Original plus two copies should be submitted.
Deadline: Pending applications are considered at meetings of the Supervisory Board held in April, June, September and December.

PUBLICATIONS:
Annual report.

IRS IDENTIFICATION NUMBER: 34-6507457

SUPERVISORY BOARD:
Craig R. Martahus, Esq., Chairman
William R. Seelbach, Vice Chairman
Raymond T. Sawyer, Esq., Secretary

ADDRESS INQUIRIES TO:
Craig R. Martahus, Esq.
Chairman, Supervisory Board
(See address above.)

THE COLEMAN FOUNDATION, INC. [71]
651 West Washington Boulevard
Suite 306
Chicago, IL 60661-2134
(312) 902-7120
Fax: (312) 902-7124

E-MAIL ADDRESS:
info@colemanfoundation.org

WEB SITE ADDRESS:
www.colemanfoundation.org

FOUNDED: 1951

AREAS OF INTEREST:
Entrepreneurship education, cancer care, and developmental disability services.

TYPE:
Capital grants; Challenge/matching grants; Conferences/seminars; Project/program grants. The major areas of grantmaking include:
(1) education, with a strong emphasis on entrepreneurship education (national in scope, with focus in Chicago);
(2) cancer care and treatment in the Chicago metropolitan area and;
(3) services for the disabled in the Chicago metropolitan area, with a strong emphasis on developmental disabilities.

ELIGIBILITY:
Grants are only made to IRS-certified tax-exempt nonprofit organizations, 501(c)(3) or 509(a)(1) and that are not supporting foundations. Funding is prohibited to individuals, for-profit businesses, advertising books and tickets. General solicitations and annual appeals will not be considered.

Only programs within the U.S. will be considered.

GEOGRAPHIC RESTRICTIONS:
Primarily metropolitan Chicago and other select parts of the Midwest.

FINANCIAL DATA:
Amount of support per award: Varies.
Total amount of support: Varies.

NUMBER OF AWARDS: Approximately 100.

APPLICATION INFORMATION:
A two-page letter of inquiry should be sent by the applicant which includes the following:
(1) brief description of the organization;
(2) synopsis of the program to be proposed;
(3) clear statement of program/grant objectives and how they will be evaluated;
(4) estimate of the size grant to be proposed or range of proposed funding;
(5) statement of how the program/project will be sustained following the grant period and;
(6) contact name and information, including e-mail address of the project manager, for further communication.

Brochures, video tapes, CDs and other attachments should not be sent with the letter of inquiry. Any such attachments will not be considered at this stage of review.
Duration: Typically one year.
Deadline: Letters of Inquiry are accepted on a continuing basis.

ADDRESS INQUIRIES TO:
Rosa Berardi, Program Officer
(See address above.)

THE COLLINS FOUNDATION [72]
1618 S.W. First Avenue
Suite 505
Portland, OR 97201
(503) 227-7171
Fax: (503) 295-3794

E-MAIL ADDRESS:
information@collinsfoundation.org

WEB SITE ADDRESS:
www.collinsfoundation.org

FOUNDED: 1947

AREAS OF INTEREST:
Quality of life issues. Projects that will have an immediate and long-term impact on life in the community.

TYPE:
Challenge/matching grants; Project/program grants. Grants made to agencies exclusively in the state of Oregon to improve, enrich and give greater expression to its religious, educational, cultural and scientific endeavors. Also, to assist in improving the quality of life in the state.

YEAR PROGRAM STARTED: 1947

PURPOSE:
To help fund programs or projects that will make life better in the community.

LEGAL BASIS:
Private, nonprofit foundation.

ELIGIBILITY:
The Foundation is organized in the state of Oregon for projects within the state. All applicant agencies must be tax-exempt, as established by the Treasury Department of the United States. No support is given to private foundations.

GEOGRAPHIC RESTRICTIONS:
Oregon.

FINANCIAL DATA:
Amount of support per award: Varies.

Total amount of support: $9,100,000 for the year 2013.

Matching fund requirements: The Foundation looks favorably on grants which must be matched.

NUMBER OF AWARDS: 268 for the year 2013.

APPLICATION INFORMATION:
Application information is available online.

Duration: Varies.

Deadline: Deadline is not specified. Awards are announced periodically throughout the year.

OFFICERS:
Truman W. Collins, Jr., President
Cynthia G. Addams, Executive Vice President
Timothy R. Bishop, Treasurer

BOARD OF TRUSTEES:
Ralph Bolliger
Maribeth W. Collins
Truman W. Collins, Jr.
Jerry E. Hudson
Cherida Collins Smith
Lee Diane Collins Vest

ADDRESS INQUIRIES TO:
Cynthia G. Addams, Executive Vice President
(See address above.)

COMMUNITIES FOUNDATION OF TEXAS, INC.   [73]
Grants Department
5500 Caruth Haven Lane
Dallas, TX 75225
(214) 750-4222
Fax: (214) 750-4210

E-MAIL ADDRESS:
grants@cftexas.org

WEB SITE ADDRESS:
www.cftexas.org

AREAS OF INTEREST:
Arts, community improvement, disaster relief, education, health, housing, religion, scientific research, social services and youth.

NAME(S) OF PROGRAMS:
● **Community Impact Grants**
● **Donor-Advised Grants**

TYPE:
Project/program grants.

YEAR PROGRAM STARTED: 1953

LEGAL BASIS:
Public charity.

ELIGIBILITY:
Organizations with IRS 501(c)(3) tax-exempt designation.

GEOGRAPHIC RESTRICTIONS:
Dallas, Denton, Colin, Rockwell and Tarrant counties in Texas.

FINANCIAL DATA:
Amount of support per award: Varies.
Total amount of support: Varies.

APPLICATION INFORMATION:
Requests must be submitted using the Foundation Letter of Inquiry checklist and form, which can be downloaded from their web site.

Duration: One year.

Deadline: Letter of Intent: May 1.

ADDRESS INQUIRIES TO:
Grants Processing
(See address above.)

THE COMMUNITY FOUNDATION   [74]
7501 Boulders View Drive, Suite 110
Richmond, VA 23225
(804) 330-7400
Fax: (804) 330-5992

E-MAIL ADDRESS:
info@tcfrichmond.org

WEB SITE ADDRESS:
www.tcfrichmond.org

FOUNDED: 1968

AREAS OF INTEREST:
Basic human needs for children and families, child and youth development, community and economic development, community enrichment and promoting philanthropy/strengthening nonprofit capacity.

NAME(S) OF PROGRAMS:
● **Strengthening Families - Strengthening Communities**

TYPE:
Awards/prizes; Capital grants; Challenge/matching grants; Conferences/seminars; Development grants; General operating grants; Project/program grants; Research grants; Scholarships; Seed money grants; Technical assistance; Training grants. Community grants programs.

YEAR PROGRAM STARTED: 1995

PURPOSE:
To give financial assistance to worthwhile charitable organizations serving people in the community.

LEGAL BASIS:
Community foundation.

ELIGIBILITY:
Proposals will be accepted from charitable organizations which serve the city of Richmond, outlying counties or the Tri-Cities.

GEOGRAPHIC RESTRICTIONS:
Richmond, Virginia metropolitan area and the Tri-Cities, Colonial Heights, Goochland, Hopewell and Petersburg.

FINANCIAL DATA:
Amount of support per award: Average $30,000.
Total amount of support: $3,800,000 for the year 2012.

NUMBER OF APPLICANTS MOST RECENT YEAR:
250 organizations for the year 2012.

NUMBER OF AWARDS: 109 for the year 2012.

APPLICATION INFORMATION:
Instructions for submitting preliminary proposals are available on the Foundation's web site.

Duration: Usually one year. Renewal possible.

Deadline: May 5 and November 5. Announcement in September and March.

PUBLICATIONS:
Annual report; policy and guidelines for grant requests.

IRS IDENTIFICATION NUMBER: 23-7009135

OFFICERS:
Farhad Aghdami, Chairperson

ADDRESS INQUIRIES TO:
Susan H. Hallett or
Elaine Summerfield
Program Officers
(See address above.)

COMMUNITY FOUNDATION FOR SOUTHEAST MICHIGAN   [75]
333 West Fort Street
Suite 2010
Detroit, MI 48226
(313) 961-6675
Fax: (313) 961-2886

E-MAIL ADDRESS:
cfsem@cfsem.org

WEB SITE ADDRESS:
www.cfsem.org

FOUNDED: 1984

AREAS OF INTEREST:
Environment, health, arts and culture, economic development, human services and civic affairs.

TYPE:
Development grants; Project/program grants; Seed money grants.

LEGAL BASIS:
Public Foundation.

ELIGIBILITY:
No grants for buildings, equipment, religious programs, fund-raising, individuals, conferences or annual meetings.

GEOGRAPHIC RESTRICTIONS:
The seven counties of Southeast Michigan: Livingston, Macomb, Monroe, Oakland, St. Clair, Washtenaw and Wayne.

FINANCIAL DATA:
Amount of support per award: Varies.

NUMBER OF AWARDS: 3,000 grants were awarded for the year 2013.

APPLICATION INFORMATION:
Telephone Foundation to discuss proposal before submitting application.

Duration: One year.

Deadline: Generally quarterly: March, June, September and December.

PUBLICATIONS:
Annual report; newsletters.

STAFF:
Mariam C. Noland, President
Karen L. Leppanen, Vice President, Finance and Administration
Robin D. Ferriby, Vice President, Philanthropic Services
Katie G. Brisson, Vice President, Programs
Theresa Fraley, Communications Director and Special Assistant to the President
Randall Ross, Manager, Philanthropic Services

OFFICERS OF THE TRUSTEES:
Allan D. Gilmour, Chairman
Joseph L. Hudson, Jr., Founding Chairperson
Alfred R. Glancy, III, Vice Chairman
Alan E. Schwartz, Vice Chairman
Barbara C. Van Dusen, Vice Chairman
Michael T. Monahan, Treasurer
W. Frank Fountain, Secretary
Vivian Day Stroh, Program and Distribution Committee Chair

ADDRESS INQUIRIES TO:
Mariam C. Noland, President
(See address above.)

COMMUNITY FOUNDATION OF EASTERN CONNECTICUT

147 State Street
New London, CT 06320
(860) 442-3572
Fax: (860) 442-0584

E-MAIL ADDRESS:
jennob@cfect.org

WEB SITE ADDRESS:
www.cfect.org

TYPE:
General operating grants; Project/program grants; Scholarships.

See entry 1225 for full listing.

COMMUNITY FOUNDATION OF GREATER MEMPHIS   [76]

1900 Union Avenue
Memphis, TN 38104
(901) 728-4600
(901) 722-0054
Fax: (901) 722-0010

E-MAIL ADDRESS:
shayes@cfgm.org

WEB SITE ADDRESS:
www.cfgm.org

FOUNDED: 1969

AREAS OF INTEREST:
Grants administered for charitable purposes in metropolitan Memphis.

NAME(S) OF PROGRAMS:
● **Nonprofit Capacity Building Grants**
● **Scholarship Funds**

TYPE:
Challenge/matching grants; Project/program grants; Scholarships; Technical assistance.

YEAR PROGRAM STARTED: 1974

PURPOSE:
To provide support for the benefit of the geographic area that the Foundation serves; to strengthen the community through philanthropy.

LEGAL BASIS:
Community foundation.

ELIGIBILITY:
Applicants must be charitable and nonprofit under IRS regulations, holding a 501(c)(3) tax-exempt status. Applicants must be located in the geographic area that the Foundation serves.

GEOGRAPHIC RESTRICTIONS:
Metropolitan Memphis, Tennessee.

FINANCIAL DATA:
Amount of support per award: $250 to $75,000.
Total amount of support: Varies.
Matching fund requirements: Stipulated with some grant awards.

NUMBER OF APPLICANTS MOST RECENT YEAR:
Varies.

APPLICATION INFORMATION:
Grant guidelines and application forms are available online.
Duration: One year. Some grants are awarded on a multiyear basis.
Deadline: Varies.

PUBLICATIONS:
Newsletters; annual report.

IRS IDENTIFICATION NUMBER: 58-1723645

ADDRESS INQUIRIES TO:
Sutton Mora Hayes
Vice President of Grants and Initiatives
(See address above.)

THE COMMUNITY FOUNDATION OF MOUNT VERNON & KNOX COUNTY   [77]

One South Main Street
Mount Vernon, OH 43050
(740) 392-3270
Fax: (740) 399-5296

E-MAIL ADDRESS:
sbarone@mvkcfoundation.org

WEB SITE ADDRESS:
www.mvkcfoundation.org

FOUNDED: 1944

AREAS OF INTEREST:
New projects in educational, charitable and civic fields.

TYPE:
Capital grants; Challenge/matching grants; Matching gifts; Project/program grants; Scholarships; Seed money grants.

YEAR PROGRAM STARTED: 1944

PURPOSE:
To improve the quality of life for the people of Mount Vernon and Knox County, OH.

LEGAL BASIS:
Nonprofit, community foundation.

ELIGIBILITY:
Grants from unrestricted funds generally limited to projects in Knox County, OH.

GEOGRAPHIC RESTRICTIONS:
Knox County, Ohio.

FINANCIAL DATA:
Amount of support per award: Varies.
Total amount of support: $1,700,000.

APPLICATION INFORMATION:
Application forms are available online. Personal presentations only at invitation of Distribution Committee.

PUBLICATIONS:
Annual report.

IRS IDENTIFICATION NUMBER: 23-7002871

BOARD OF DIRECTORS:
Bruce E. Hawkins, Chairman
Karen Buchwald Wright, Vice Chairman
Kurt E. Schister, Treasurer
Robert L. Rauzi, Secretary
R. Leroy Bumpus
Terry L. Divelbiss
Marc Hawk
Gene Jackson
Dr. Amy Murnen
Marsha Rinehart
Kim Rose
Gordon Yance

ADDRESS INQUIRIES TO:
Sam Barone, Executive Director
(See address above.)

COMMUNITY FOUNDATION OF THE EASTERN SHORE

1324 Belmont Avenue, Suite 401
Salisbury, MD 21804
(410) 742-9911
Fax: (410) 742-6638

E-MAIL ADDRESS:
cfes@cfes.org

WEB SITE ADDRESS:
www.cfes.org

TYPE:
Awards/prizes; Challenge/matching grants; Demonstration grants; Project/program grants; Scholarships; Seed money grants; Technical assistance; Training grants.

See entry 1239 for full listing.

THE COMMUNITY FOUNDATION OF THE HOLLAND/ZEELAND AREA   [78]

85 East Eighth Street
Suite 110
Holland, MI 49423
(616) 396-6590
Fax: (616) 396-3573

E-MAIL ADDRESS:
info@cfhz.org

WEB SITE ADDRESS:
www.cfhz.org

FOUNDED: 1951

AREAS OF INTEREST:
Education, the arts, recreation, community development, the needs of youth and the elderly, and health and human services.

TYPE:
Research grants; Scholarships; Technical assistance.

YEAR PROGRAM STARTED: 1951

PURPOSE:
To create lasting positive change; to work to build a permanent community endowment that supports high-impact charitable projects; to help donors achieve their charitable goals; to lead and partner in community-level initiatives.

LEGAL BASIS:
Corporation and public charity, 509(a)(1) and 170(b)(1)(A)(vi).

ELIGIBILITY:
Grants are made to organizations that have tax-exempt status under Section 501(c)(3) of the Internal Revenue Code or governmental agencies. No grants are made to individuals. Nonsectarian religious programs may apply.

GEOGRAPHIC RESTRICTIONS:
Holland and Zeeland, Michigan area only.

FINANCIAL DATA:
Amount of support per award: $500 to $75,000.
Total amount of support: Varies.

NUMBER OF APPLICANTS MOST RECENT YEAR:
770.

NUMBER OF AWARDS: 285.

APPLICATION INFORMATION:
Grant applicants must contact the Foundation to discuss a proposal prior to submitting an application.

Scholarship applications must be completed on the Foundation web site.
Duration: One year.
Deadline: Varies.

PUBLICATIONS:
Annual report; application guidelines.

IRS IDENTIFICATION NUMBER: 38-6095283

STAFF:
Elizabeth Kidd, Director of Grantmaking
Stacy Timmerman, Director of Scholarship and Education

ADDRESS INQUIRIES TO:
Director of Grantmaking
(See address above.)

THE COMMUNITY FOUNDATION OF WESTERN NORTH CAROLINA [79]

4 Vanderbilt Park Drive
Suite 300
Asheville, NC 28803
(828) 254-4960
Fax: (828) 251-2258

E-MAIL ADDRESS:
info@cfwnc.org

WEB SITE ADDRESS:
www.cfwnc.org

FOUNDED: 1978

AREAS OF INTEREST:
Food and farming, people in need, early childhood development, and preserving natural and cultural resources.

TYPE:
Project/program grants; Scholarships.

YEAR PROGRAM STARTED: 1978

PURPOSE:
To inspire philanthropy and mobilize resources to enrich lives and communities in western North Carolina.

ELIGIBILITY:
501(c)(3) required for grants. Eligibility varies by program.

GEOGRAPHIC RESTRICTIONS:
Western North Carolina.

FINANCIAL DATA:
Total amount of support: $11,040,754 in grants and scholarships for the year 2012.

NUMBER OF AWARDS: Varies.

APPLICATION INFORMATION:
Application information is available on the web site.
Duration: Varies.

PUBLICATIONS:
Good Works, quarterly newsletter; annual report.

IRS IDENTIFICATION NUMBER: 56-1223384

ADDRESS INQUIRIES TO:
Diane Crisp, Program Administrator
(See address above.)

COMPTON FOUNDATION, INC. [80]

101 Montgomery Street, Suite 850
San Francisco, CA 94104
(415) 391-9001

E-MAIL ADDRESS:
info@comptonfoundation.org

WEB SITE ADDRESS:
www.comptonfoundation.org

FOUNDED: 1946

AREAS OF INTEREST:
Peace, environment, reproductive health and rights, and money and politics.

TYPE:
Project/program grants.

PURPOSE:
To ignite change; to support transformative leadership and courageous storytelling, inspiring action toward a peaceful, just, sustainable future.

ELIGIBILITY:
Organizations classified as 501(c)(3) by the IRS. Individuals and religious organizations are ineligible.

FINANCIAL DATA:
Amount of support per award: Varies.
Total amount of support: $3,563,239 for the year 2012.

APPLICATION INFORMATION:
Application procedures are available online.
Duration: One year. Grants are renewable.
Deadline: Varies.

PUBLICATIONS:
Grant Highlights (available on web site).

STAFF:
Ellen Friedman, Executive Director
Deborah K. Daughtry, Director of Operations
Jennifer L. Sokolove, Program Director
Jennifer Turnage, Manager of Grants and Accounting
Nicole Lopez-Hagen, Foundation Assistant

BOARD OF DIRECTORS:
Rebecca DiDomenico, President
Vanessa Compton, Vice President
Marty Krasney, Treasurer
W. Danforth Compton, Secretary
Betty L. Farrell
Stephen Perry
Steven M. Riskin
Terry Tempest Williams

ADDRESS INQUIRIES TO:
Deborah K. Daughtry, Director of Operations
(See address above.)

THE CONNELLY FOUNDATION [81]

One Tower Bridge
100 Front Street, Suite 1450
West Conshohocken, PA 19428
(610) 834-3222
Fax: (610) 834-0866

E-MAIL ADDRESS:
eawilcox@connellyfdn.org

WEB SITE ADDRESS:
www.connellyfdn.org

FOUNDED: 1955

AREAS OF INTEREST:
Educational, civic and cultural institutions, health with emphasis on human services. A significant portion of funding is directed toward organizations affiliated with the Catholic Church.

TYPE:
Capital grants; General operating grants; Project/program grants.

PURPOSE:
To enhance the quality of life in the Delaware Valley.

LEGAL BASIS:
Private foundation.

ELIGIBILITY:
No grants to individuals, political or national organizations or other foundations, nor does the Foundation respond to annual appeals or general letters of solicitation. Foundation guidelines restrict funding any organization more than once during a 12-month period. Applicants who have received previous grants from the Foundation should submit final reports under separate cover.

GEOGRAPHIC RESTRICTIONS:
Camden, New Jersey; Bucks, Chester, Delaware and Montgomery counties and city of Philadelphia, Pennsylvania.

FINANCIAL DATA:
Amount of support per award: $5,000 to $50,000.
Total amount of support: $8,632,087 for the year 2013.

NUMBER OF AWARDS: 555 for the year 2013.

APPLICATION INFORMATION:
A single copy of the proposal must include:
(1) executive summary of the project, its goals, financial requirements and present status. A specific grant amount must be requested;
(2) brief history of the organization, an annual report, two most recent audited financial statements along with most recent IRS Form 990 (with all schedules);
(3) detailed proposal including projects objectives, budget, timetable for implementation and target population. For capital projects (construction, renovation, equipment), expenses must be documented as follows:
(a) for new construction or renovation to existing space - a complete breakdown of all costs including professional fees and expenses, a visual rendering of the project, square footage, copies of preliminary or final bids, and financing arrangements (if applicable);
(b) for acquisition of equipment - a copy of the most appropriate of three bids, costs of installation and financing arrangements (if applicable);
(4) anticipated outcomes and a plan for assessing them;
(5) committed and prospective financial support for this project (sources and amounts), also plans to fund the project on an ongoing basis;
(6) names and occupations of all directors or trustees, a listing of key staff and their qualifications, and resume of project officer and;
(7) copy of the Internal Revenue Service determination letter granting tax exemption status.

Duration: One year.

Deadline: Written proposals are accepted and reviewed by the Foundation throughout the year. With the exception of Foundation initiatives, there are no deadlines. Applicants receive a response within approximately three months.

PUBLICATIONS:
Application guidelines.

OFFICERS:
Josephine C. Mandeville, President
Emily C. Riley, Executive Vice President
Lewis W. Bluemle, Senior Vice President
Victoria K. Flaville, Senior Vice President and Chief Operating Officer
Thomas A. Riley, Vice President for Planning
Amy M. Snyder, Chief Financial Officer

ADDRESS INQUIRIES TO:
E. Ann Wilcox
Associate Vice President, Administration
(See address above.)

*PLEASE NOTE:
Visits to the Foundation office or contacts with its staff initiated by applicants during the proposal review process are discouraged.

CONSUMERS ENERGY FOUNDATION   [82]

One Energy Plaza, Room EP8-210
Jackson, MI 49201-2276
(517) 788-0432
(877) 501-4952
Fax: (517) 788-2281

E-MAIL ADDRESS:
foundation@consumersenergy.com

WEB SITE ADDRESS:
www.consumersenergy.com/foundation

FOUNDED: 1989

AREAS OF INTEREST:
Social welfare, education, culture and arts, community and civic affairs, Michigan growth and environmental enhancement.

CONSULTING OR VOLUNTEER SERVICES:
Employee volunteer program.

NAME(S) OF PROGRAMS:
● **Volunteer Investment Program**

TYPE:
Capital grants; General operating grants; Internships; Matching gifts; Project/program grants; Scholarships; Seed money grants; Technical assistance.

YEAR PROGRAM STARTED: 1992

PURPOSE:
To encourage employees to volunteer their time to nonprofit organizations.

LEGAL BASIS:
Corporate program.

ELIGIBILITY:
501(c)(3) tax-exempt status, nonprofit organizations are eligible for support. The Foundation will not fund individuals, political, religious, labor or veteran's organizations or agencies supported by United Way.

Requests will be considered from organizations elsewhere for programs or projects that significantly benefit the state of Michigan.

GEOGRAPHIC RESTRICTIONS:
Michigan.

FINANCIAL DATA:
Employees are encouraged to volunteer 45 hours per year to nonprofit organizations. The Foundation will fund up to $500 per organization.
Amount of support per award: $1,000 to $20,000.
Total amount of support: $2,400,000 for the year 2013.
Matching fund requirements: Foundation will match employee and retiree contributions to education, Michigan Food Banks and community foundations. Minimum $25 and maximum $1,000 per year per employee and retiree.

NUMBER OF APPLICANTS MOST RECENT YEAR: 1,200.

NUMBER OF AWARDS: 920 for the year 2013.

REPRESENTATIVE AWARDS:
$1,250,000 to 10 community projects as part of the company's 125th year birthday celebration; $100,000 to Gerald R. Ford Foundation; $25,000 to Traverse City Bayfront Project; $50,000 to Nature Conservancy-Michigan Chapter; $20,000 to Sandcastles Children's Museum.

APPLICATION INFORMATION:
Cover letter and completed grant application required by mail only.

Duration: Varies. Renewal unlikely.

PUBLICATIONS:
Guidelines brochure.

DIRECTORS:
J.G. Russell, Chairman
David G. Mengebier, President
Carolyn A. Bloodworth, Secretary and Treasurer
James E. Brunner
John M. Butler
William E. Garrity
Jackson L. Hanson
Daniel J. Malone
Ronn J. Rasmussen
T.J. Webb

ADDRESS INQUIRIES TO:
Carolyn A. Bloodworth
Secretary and Treasurer
(See address above.)

V.V. COOKE FOUNDATION   [83]

220 Mount Mercy Drive
Suite 2
Pewee Valley, KY 40056
(502) 241-0303

E-MAIL ADDRESS:
merhoff@bellsouth.net

FOUNDED: 1947

AREAS OF INTEREST:
Civic affairs, education, religion and humanitarianism.

TYPE:
Capital grants; Endowments; General operating grants; Scholarships; Seed money grants.

LEGAL BASIS:
Private foundation.

ELIGIBILITY:
Grants are made to organizations that have tax-exempt status under Section 501(c)(3) and are not described in Section 509(a)(3) of the Internal Revenue Code. Grants are made for religious, educational, humanitarian and civic purposes. No grants are made to individuals.

GEOGRAPHIC RESTRICTIONS:
Louisville, Kentucky.

FINANCIAL DATA:
Amount of support per award: $100 to $25,000.
Total amount of support: $171,000 for the year ended August 31, 2013.

NUMBER OF APPLICANTS MOST RECENT YEAR: 46.

NUMBER OF AWARDS: 72.

REPRESENTATIVE AWARDS:
$1,000 to Alice Lloyd College; $10,000 to Georgetown College.

APPLICATION INFORMATION:
Applications should be in letter form.
Applicants must:
(1) outline the organization's goals and purposes, and the intended use and amount of the grant requested;
(2) list other organizations that serve the needs addressed by this application and what distinguishes this organization and;
(3) identify the percentage of the organization's budget that is used for fund-raising and for administrative expenses.

Eight copies of the application are required.
Deadline: Applications are considered in mid-January, April, July and October.

PUBLICATIONS:
Application guidelines.

IRS IDENTIFICATION NUMBER: 61-6033714

STAFF:
Theodore L. Merhoff, Executive Director

ADDRESS INQUIRIES TO:
Theodore L. Merhoff, Executive Director
(See address above.)

COOPER FOUNDATION   [84]

1248 O Street, No. 870
Lincoln, NE 68508-1493
(402) 476-7571
Fax: (402) 476-2356

E-MAIL ADDRESS:
info@cooperfoundation.org

WEB SITE ADDRESS:
www.cooperfoundation.org

FOUNDED: 1934

AREAS OF INTEREST:
Education, human services, arts and humanities, and the environment.

TYPE:
Challenge/matching grants; Demonstration grants.

PURPOSE:
To support the operations and core programs of strong, well-managed and effective nonprofit organizations located in and working in Lancaster County, NE.

LEGAL BASIS:
Private foundation.

ELIGIBILITY:
Most grants are made to organizations located in and impacting residents of Lancaster County, NE.

The Foundation does not fund individuals, businesses, health organizations or issues, churches, religious organizations or issues, travel, memberships, endowments, non-501(c)(3) organizations, 509(a)(3) supporting organizations, fiscal agents, or private foundations.

GEOGRAPHIC RESTRICTIONS:
Nebraska.

FINANCIAL DATA:
Amount of support per award: $1,000 to $15,000; Average: $5,000.
Total amount of support: $556,362 for the year 2013.

NUMBER OF APPLICANTS MOST RECENT YEAR: 60.

NUMBER OF AWARDS: 60.

APPLICATION INFORMATION:
The Foundation accepts formal applications only from organizations that have already communicated with them and have been asked to complete an application form. The initial communication may be in person, by phone, by mail or by facsimile. The Foundation staff is available for consultation at any stage in the process.

Applications must include:
(1) amount of the request;
(2) project budget, including sources and amounts of income and detailed expenses;
(3) development plan explaining how, from whom and in what amounts funds will be raised and how the project will be sustained after the grant period;

(4) plan to evaluate the effectiveness of the project during the grant period and;
(5) clear, complete financial information that matches the supporting documentation. Accuracy and evidence of good financial management is important.

Reapplication cannot be made sooner than 12 months after grant approval or decline, or the final payment date, whichever is later. Organizations submitting a collaborative grant may apply on their own, but not during the same grant application cycle.

Duration: One year. Must reapply annually.

Deadline: January 15, April 1, August 1 and October 1.

ADDRESS INQUIRIES TO:
Victoria Kovar, Program Officer
(See address above.)

THE MARY S. AND DAVID C. CORBIN FOUNDATION   [85]

Akron Centre Plaza
50 South Main Street, Suite 730
Akron, OH 44308-1830
(330) 762-6427
Fax: (330) 762-6428

E-MAIL ADDRESS:
corbin@nls.net

WEB SITE ADDRESS:
www.foundationcenter.org/grantmaker/corbin

AREAS OF INTEREST:
Arts, culture, environment, health, housing, human services, education, youth and medical research.

TYPE:
Project grants.

PURPOSE:
To benefit charities in the Akron and Summit County, OH areas and national charities that have a presence in the Akron and Summit County areas of Ohio.

ELIGIBILITY:
Organizations classified as 501(c)(3) by the IRS and non-private foundations can apply. The Foundation gives primary consideration to the City of Akron and Summit County, OH charitable organizations and/or local chapters of national charities located in the Akron, Summit County area of Ohio.

The Foundation does not fund individuals, annual fund-raising campaigns, ongoing requests for general operating support, operating deficits, or organizations which in turn make grants to others. The Foundation generally does not fund religious organizations.

GEOGRAPHIC RESTRICTIONS:
City of Akron and Summit County, Ohio.

FINANCIAL DATA:
Amount of support per award: $150 to $2,000,000.

APPLICATION INFORMATION:
Contact the Foundation for application procedures. The Foundation application can also be downloaded from the web site. Organizations should send a brief letter on their letterhead and should submit one original and one copy of all application materials. Letter should include:
(1) a brief description of the organization and;
(2) a description of the proposed project,

proposed accomplishments, duration, the total cost of the project and the specific amount requested from the Foundation.

Duration: One year.

Deadline: March 1 and September 1, for consideration in May and November respectively.

ADDRESS INQUIRIES TO:
Erika J. May, Grants Administrator
(See address above.)

*SPECIAL STIPULATIONS:
Only written applications will be considered. Both telephone and personal interviews are discouraged unless requested by the Foundation.

MARION STEDMAN COVINGTON FOUNDATION   [86]

P.O. Box 29304
Greensboro, NC 27429-9304
(336) 282-0480

E-MAIL ADDRESS:
info@mscovingtonfoundation.org

WEB SITE ADDRESS:
www.mscovingtonfoundation.org

AREAS OF INTEREST:
Historic preservation; arts and culture, and education as related to historic preservation.

TYPE:
Capital grants; Challenge/matching grants; Conferences/seminars; General operating grants; Project/program grants; Research grants; Seed money grants.

YEAR PROGRAM STARTED: 1986

PURPOSE:
To provide grants to nonprofit organizations operating in the area of historic preservation.

ELIGIBILITY:
Grants are made to federally tax-exempt, nonprofit organizations.

GEOGRAPHIC RESTRICTIONS:
Primarily North Carolina.

FINANCIAL DATA:
Funds are also provided for construction/renovation projects, equipment and materials, operating support, program support and publications.

Amount of support per award: $10,000 average.

Total amount of support: $250,000.

NUMBER OF APPLICANTS MOST RECENT YEAR: 25.

NUMBER OF AWARDS: 13.

APPLICATION INFORMATION:
Contact the Foundation for application procedures.

Duration: Varies.

Deadline: September 1 and March 1. Announcement approximately six weeks after the deadline.

PUBLICATIONS:
Annual report; guidelines.

IRS IDENTIFICATION NUMBER: 56-6286555

ADDRESS INQUIRIES TO:
Alexa S. Aycock, Executive Director
(See address above.)

*PLEASE NOTE:
Challenge grants may be requested or the Foundation may designate a grant as such. In

either event, there will be a specified time period in which the matching funds are to be raised.

S.H. COWELL FOUNDATION   [87]

595 Market Street, Suite 950
San Francisco, CA 94105
(415) 397-0285
Fax: (415) 986-6786

E-MAIL ADDRESS:
info@shcowell.org

WEB SITE ADDRESS:
www.shcowell.org

FOUNDED: 1955

AREAS OF INTEREST:
Affordable housing, family resource centers, grades K-12 public education, youth development, and improving the quality of life of low-income children and families in neighborhoods that meet the Foundation's place-based criteria.

TYPE:
Capital grants; Challenge/matching grants; Project/program grants; Technical assistance; Training grants. Community building.

YEAR PROGRAM STARTED: 1955

PURPOSE:
To improve the quality of life of children living in poverty in northern California by making grants that support and strengthen their families and the neighborhoods where they live.

LEGAL BASIS:
Independent nonprofit foundation.

ELIGIBILITY:
Organization must be tax-exempt and must submit evidence that a grant would qualify under the Tax Reform Act of 1969. Grants are restricted to organizations, projects and programs in northern California, except by invitation of the Foundation.

As a matter of policy, the Foundation typically does not make grants to hospitals for construction or research, sectarian religious groups, individuals for scholarships or financial aid and rarely for operating expenses.

GEOGRAPHIC RESTRICTIONS:
Northern and central California.

FINANCIAL DATA:
Amount of support per award: $1,000 to over $500,000.

Total amount of support: $4,732,935 for the year ended December 31, 2012.

REPRESENTATIVE AWARDS:
$200,000 to Bay Area Partnership for Children and Youth, Oakland, CA, for coaching and technical support for after-school programs; $316,000 to Sanger Unified School District, Sanger, CA, to build on a literacy program in four elementary schools; $20,500 to California Family Resource Association for leadership development.

APPLICATION INFORMATION:
The application process is rigorous, and prospective grantees should expect to work with Cowell staff before, during, and after a formal proposal is submitted. There are five steps to the process:
(1) make sure that your project meets Foundation funding criteria;
(2) call the Foundation;

(3) if asked to do so, submit a letter of inquiry;
(4) if asked to do so, submit a full proposal. Please do not send a formal proposal unless a program officer requests one. If you are asked to submit a proposal, staff will give you a list of required information and;
(5) plan on at least one site visit.

Duration: Varies.

Deadline: The Directors meet regularly and review only those proposals recommended by staff.

PUBLICATIONS:
Annual report; application guidelines.

OFFICERS AND BOARD OF DIRECTORS:
Ann Alpers, President
Donald D. Roberts, Secretary and General Counsel
Lisa Backus
Charles E. Ellwein
Dr. Mikiko Huang
Scott Mosher
Lydia Tan
Kim Thompson

ADDRESS INQUIRIES TO:
Lise Maisano
Vice President of Grant Programs
(See address above.)

*SPECIAL STIPULATIONS:
No grants to individuals, for media projects, conferences, seminars, to sectarian organizations, hospitals or public/governmental agencies.

HENRY P. AND SUSAN C. CROWELL TRUST   [88]
102 North Cascade Avenue
Suite 300
Colorado Springs, CO 80903
(719) 645-8119
Fax: (719) 418-2695

E-MAIL ADDRESS:
info@crowelltrust.org

WEB SITE ADDRESS:
www.crowelltrust.org

FOUNDED: 1927

AREAS OF INTEREST:
Evangelical foreign missions.

TYPE:
General operating grants; Project/program grants.

YEAR PROGRAM STARTED: 1927

PURPOSE:
To aid evangelical Christianity by support to organizations having for their purposes its teaching, advancement and active extension at home and abroad.

LEGAL BASIS:
Private foundation.

ELIGIBILITY:
No grants to churches, individuals or for endowment funds or research. No loans.

GEOGRAPHIC RESTRICTIONS:
United States.

FINANCIAL DATA:
Amount of support per award: Average $35,000.
Total amount of support: $3,500,000.

NUMBER OF APPLICANTS MOST RECENT YEAR: 375.

NUMBER OF AWARDS: 100.

APPLICATION INFORMATION:
Applicants must ensure the project fits the guidelines of the Trust by completing the online Self-Screening Aid to determine eligibility and begin the application process. If the organization and project fit the minimum requirements, applicants should proceed to the online grant management system. No proposals will be accepted in hard copy or through e-mail.

Duration: One year only; may resubmit annually.

Deadline: Proposals should be submitted by February 28 and July 31 for spring and fall consideration, respectively. Proposals received after the deadline may be held over for the following grant cycle.

PUBLICATIONS:
Application guidelines.

IRS IDENTIFICATION NUMBER: 36-6038028

STAFF:
Candace Sparks, Chief Executive Officer

ADDRESS INQUIRIES TO:
Becky Andler
Assistant to the Executive Director
(See address above.)

THE CULLEN FOUNDATION [89]
601 Jefferson, 40th Floor
Houston, TX 77002
(713) 651-8837
Fax: (713) 651-2374

E-MAIL ADDRESS:
salexander@cullenfdn.org

WEB SITE ADDRESS:
www.cullenfdn.org

FOUNDED: 1947

AREAS OF INTEREST:
Arts, education, medicine, science, handicapped and public service.

TYPE:
Capital grants; Challenge/matching grants; Development grants; Endowments; Fellowships; General operating grants; Professorships; Project/program grants; Research grants; Scholarships.

PURPOSE:
To provide charitable, educational and medical grants for hospitals, medical research, higher education and music and the performing arts; to provide aid to the handicapped and community funds.

LEGAL BASIS:
Tax-exempt, private foundation.

ELIGIBILITY:
Grants are limited to the state of Texas by indenture. No grants are made to individuals or businesses.

GEOGRAPHIC RESTRICTIONS:
Texas, primarily Houston.

FINANCIAL DATA:
Amount of support per award: $10,000 to $5,000,000.
Total amount of support: $12,051,500 for the year 2013.

NUMBER OF APPLICANTS MOST RECENT YEAR:
135 proposals.

NUMBER OF AWARDS: 45 new grants.

REPRESENTATIVE AWARDS:
$1,000,000 to Menil Foundation; $2,000,000 to University of Houston System; $200,000

to Health Museum; $30,000 to Houston Center for Literacy; $100,000 to Prism Entrepreneurship Program.

APPLICATION INFORMATION:
A brief letter describing concisely the project and its purpose together with pertinent brochures, etc. No formal application forms, but a check list of suggested format is available on request and on the Foundation's web site.

Duration: No grants are awarded on a continuing basis.

PUBLICATIONS:
Application guidelines.

IRS IDENTIFICATION NUMBER: 76-0647361

DIRECTORS AND OFFICERS:
Isaac Arnold, Jr., President and Director
Alan M. Stewart, Treasurer and Executive Director
Wilhemina E. Robertson, Secretary and Director
Meredith T. Cullen, Assistant Secretary and Director
Bert L. Campbell, Director
William H. Drushel, Jr., Director

ADDRESS INQUIRIES TO:
Sue Alexander, Grant Manager
(See address above.)

*SPECIAL STIPULATIONS:
Grants are made to qualified charities in the state of Texas, primarily in the Houston area. No grants to individuals or businesses.

THE NATHAN CUMMINGS FOUNDATION, INC.   [90]
475 10th Ave, 14th Floor
New York, NY 10018
(212) 787-7300
Fax: (212) 787-7377

E-MAIL ADDRESS:
contact@nathancummings.org

WEB SITE ADDRESS:
www.nathancummings.org

FOUNDED: 1949

AREAS OF INTEREST:
The arts, the environment, health and Jewish life.

NAME(S) OF PROGRAMS:
- **Arts and Culture**
- **Collaborative Initiatives**
- **Contemplative Practice**
- **Ecological Innovation**
- **Health**
- **Jewish Life and Values**

TYPE:
General operating grants; Project/program grants.

YEAR PROGRAM STARTED: 1989

PURPOSE:
To promote democratic values and social justice, including fairness, diversity and community; to build a socially and economically just society that values and protects the ecological balance for future generations; to promote humane health care; to foster arts and culture that enrich communities.

LEGAL BASIS:
Private foundation.

GEOGRAPHIC RESTRICTIONS:
United States.

FINANCIAL DATA:
Amount of support per award: Varies.

APPLICATION INFORMATION:
The application process is very competitive; only those organizations whose projects fit most closely with the Foundation's programmatic goals will be invited to submit a Foundation Application Form.

Duration: Varies.

Deadline: Prior to Board of Trustees meetings held in April and November.

IRS IDENTIFICATION NUMBER: 23-7093201

STAFF:
Simon Greer, President and Chief Executive Officer
Armanda Famiglietti, Director of Grants Management
Ethan Richardson, Director of Information Technology
Laura Shaffer, Director of Shareholder Activities
Maurine Knighton, Program Director, Arts & Culture

ADDRESS INQUIRIES TO:
Simon Greer
President and Chief Executive Officer
(See address above.)

THE CUMMINS FOUNDATION [91]
500 Jackson Street, MC 60028
Columbus, IN 47201
(812) 377-3114
Fax: (812) 377-9694

WEB SITE ADDRESS:
www.cummins.com

FOUNDED: 1954

AREAS OF INTEREST:
Focus on environment, education and social justice.

TYPE:
Project/program grants.

YEAR PROGRAM STARTED: 1954

PURPOSE:
To improve the quality of life in communities where Cummins has manufacturing operations and subsidiaries; to promote the Foundation's philanthropic objectives through grants in priority areas as well as projects of special interest in Columbus and subsidiary communities.

LEGAL BASIS:
Corporate foundation.

ELIGIBILITY:
Grantees must be tax-exempt organizations or institutions located in areas where Cummins has a presence. No grants are made to individuals or for denominational religious organizations. No scholarships are granted.

FINANCIAL DATA:
Amount of support per award: Varies.
Total amount of support: Varies.

APPLICATION INFORMATION:
Contact the Foundation.

PUBLICATIONS:
Sustainability report.

DIRECTORS:
Tom Linebarger, Chairman
William I. Miller

DANIELS FUND [92]
101 Monroe Street
Denver, CO 80206-4467
(303) 393-7220
Fax: (720) 941-4110

E-MAIL ADDRESS:
info@danielsfund.org
grantsinfo@danielsfund.org
scholarrelations@danielsfund.org

WEB SITE ADDRESS:
www.danielsfund.org

FOUNDED: 2000

AREAS OF INTEREST:
Daniels Fund Grants Program: Aging, alcoholism and substance abuse, amateur sports, disabilities, early childhood education, K-12 education reform, ethics and integrity in education, homeless and disadvantaged, youth development.

NAME(S) OF PROGRAMS:
● **Daniels Fund Grants Program**
● **Daniels Fund Scholarship Program**

TYPE:
Capital grants; General operating grants; Project/program grants; Scholarships. Daniels Fund Grants Program supports nonprofit organizations in the four-state region as well as national programs.

Daniels Fund Scholarship Program consists of the Daniels Scholarship and the Daniels Boundless Opportunity Scholarship. The Daniels Scholarship is a four-year scholarship that applies toward the expenses of attaining a Bachelor's degree at any nonprofit, accredited college or university in the U.S. The Daniels Boundless Opportunity Scholarships are distributed to select two- and four-year colleges and universities in Colorado, New Mexico, Utah and Wyoming, which then provide scholarships to support nontraditional students.

PURPOSE:
To help excellent nonprofits achieve a high level of effectiveness and impact.

ELIGIBILITY:
Daniels Grants Program: Applying organizations must have 501(c)(3) not-for-profit status. No grants are made to religious organizations.

Daniels Scholarship: High school seniors seeking to obtain a Bachelor's degree. Applicants must meet the core values of character, leadership and service and the desire to give back to their communities.

Boundless Opportunity Scholarship: Applicants must demonstrate financial need and be:
(1) an adult entering or returning to college;
(2) a GED recipient;
(3) a foster care youth;
(4) a juvenile justice youth or;
(5) a returning military or an individual pursuing EMT/paramedic training.

GEOGRAPHIC RESTRICTIONS:
Colorado, New Mexico, Utah and Wyoming.

FINANCIAL DATA:
Total assets of $1,285,502,021 for the year ended December 31, 2012.

Amount of support per award: Daniels Grants Program: Varies. Daniels Scholarship: Varies. Daniels Boundless Opportunity Scholarship: $500 to $5,000.

Total amount of support: $46,209,270 for the year ended December 31, 2012.

NUMBER OF AWARDS: Daniels Grants Program: Varies. Daniels Boundless Opportunity Scholarship: 300 to 500. Daniels Scholarship: Approximately 250.

APPLICATION INFORMATION:
Organizations with a nationwide impact should call before applying.

Online application process. Daniels Scholarship application process opens September 1. Organizations applying must include the 501(c)(3) IRS Letter of Determination.

Duration: Grants: One to four years; must reapply. Daniels Scholarship: Four years. Daniels Boundless Opportunity Scholarship: Varies.

Deadline: Daniels Scholarship: October 31.

MARGARET A. DARRIN FOUNDATION, INC. [93]
120 Columbia Turnpike
Florham Park, NJ 07932
(973) 822-2905

FOUNDED: 1987

AREAS OF INTEREST:
Arts, humanities, civic affairs, education, health, social services and women's issues.

TYPE:
General operating grants.

YEAR PROGRAM STARTED: 1987

ELIGIBILITY:
No restrictions or limitations on funding. Grants made to nonprofit 501(c)(3) organizations only.

GEOGRAPHIC RESTRICTIONS:
Northeastern United States.

FINANCIAL DATA:
Total assets of $4,971,019 for year ended December 31, 2011.

Amount of support per award: Maximum approximately $500 to $15,000.

Total amount of support: $110,000 for year ended December 31, 2011.

REPRESENTATIVE AWARDS:
$41,000 to Hague Adirondacks Historical Museum; $10,000 to Williston Northampton School, Easthampton, MA; $1,000 to Hutchinson Island Fire Department.

APPLICATION INFORMATION:
Applications should take the form of a brief letter describing the charity, its background and the purpose of the contribution.

Applicant will be notified only if approved.

Duration: One year. Must reapply for additional funding.

Deadline: October 31.

IRS IDENTIFICATION NUMBER: 22-6426771

STAFF:
Michael Hanifin, President

ADDRESS INQUIRIES TO:
Charitable Contributions
(See address above.)

THE ARTHUR VINING DAVIS FOUNDATIONS [94]
225 Water Street
Suite 1510
Jacksonville, FL 32202
(904) 359-0670
Fax: (904) 359-0675

E-MAIL ADDRESS:
office@avdf.org

WEB SITE ADDRESS:
www.avdf.org

FOUNDED: 1952

AREAS OF INTEREST:
Private higher education, health care (caring attitudes), graduate theological education (seminaries fully accredited by the Association of Theological Schools), public television (major educational series for viewing nationally on PBS), secondary education (professional development programs that strengthen teachers and teaching in grades nine-12), and programs that promote and strengthen caring attitudes in health care.

TYPE:
Project/program grants.

LEGAL BASIS:
Privately endowed foundation established by the will of Arthur Vining Davis.

ELIGIBILITY:
Grants are limited to institutions in the U.S. and its territories. Activities and functions not supported include assistance to individuals (except as participants in an organized institutional scholarship program), voter registration drives and voter education, efforts to influence elections or legislation, expenditures for noncharitable purposes and projects incurring obligations extending over many years. Support is not granted to institutions primarily supported by government funds except medical institutions and secondary education programs.

GEOGRAPHIC RESTRICTIONS:
United States.

FINANCIAL DATA:
Amount of support per award: $150,000 to $400,000, depending on program area.
Total amount of support: Approximately $9,600,000 for the year 2012.

COOPERATIVE FUNDING PROGRAMS: As a policy, the Foundations' support increased cooperation among foundations and expanded communication with the public. The staff has taken an active part in national and regional efforts in this direction.

APPLICATION INFORMATION:
No application forms are used and elaborate presentations are unnecessary. Preliminary inquiry should take the form of a letter stating the proposal's purpose, methods and expected results, together with a brief budget. This request should come from the head of the institution. If the proposal seems to fall within the Foundation's areas of interest and capability, the staff may request further data, discussion and the opportunity to visit the institution, as necessary. Proposals are not accepted via fax or e-mail.
Duration: Re-grants in higher education and religion generally are not considered until at least four years after a previous grant.
Deadline: Proposals may be submitted at any time.

PUBLICATIONS:
Guideline brochure; annual report.

OFFICERS:
Dr. Nancy J. Cable, President
Doreen Flippin, Vice President for Administration
William C. Keator, Vice President for Programs
Jane M. Estes, Chief Financial Officer
Cheryl Tupper, Program Director
Dr. James L. Waits, Consultant

TRUSTEES:
J.H. Dow Davis, Chairman

Jonathan P. Davis
Maynard K. Davis
Tamara Davis
Serena Davis Hall
Dorothy Davis Kee
Dorothy Given Kee
Hilary Rosenthal

ADDRESS INQUIRIES TO:
Dr. Nancy J. Cable, President
(See address above.)

EDWIN W. AND CATHERINE M. DAVIS FOUNDATION [95]
30 East 7th Street, Suite 2000
St. Paul, MN 55101-1394
(651) 228-0935

FOUNDED: 1956

AREAS OF INTEREST:
The Foundation's program is directed to the amelioration of social problems and to increasing the opportunities available to disadvantaged peoples. Grants are given in the fields of education, social welfare, mental health, the arts, and environmental problems.

TYPE:
General operating grants; Project/program grants.

YEAR PROGRAM STARTED: 1956

PURPOSE:
To receive, manage and apply a fund or funds exclusively for charitable, religious, scientific or educational purposes.

LEGAL BASIS:
Founded as a nonprofit corporation under Chapter 317, Minnesota Statutes.

ELIGIBILITY:
Grants are made to nonprofit, 501(c)(3) organizations.

The Foundation does not usually make grants to individuals, capital campaigns for buildings or equipment or endowment campaigns.

The Foundation also does not make loans to organizations or individuals.

In general, the Foundation prefers not to make long-term commitments, in order to preserve flexibility in its program to meet changing conditions from year to year.

FINANCIAL DATA:
Amount of support per award: Varies.
Total amount of support: Varies.

APPLICATION INFORMATION:
Applications to the Foundation are to be in the form of a letter, no longer than three pages, which includes the background of the organization, the need for the services or specified project, the plan to address the need, the benefits provided by the services or project, the plans for evaluation of results and the program and/or organizational budget.

Applications must include a copy of the applicant's letters concerning federal income tax exemption issued by the IRS.
Duration: Typically one year.

PUBLICATIONS:
Annual report.

ADDRESS INQUIRIES TO:
Grants Administrator
(See address above.)

JOHN DEERE FOUNDATION [96]
One John Deere Place
Moline, IL 61265
(309) 748-7950
Fax: (309) 748-7953

WEB SITE ADDRESS:
www.deere.com

FOUNDED: 1948

AREAS OF INTEREST:
Higher education, community development, and solutions for world hunger.

TYPE:
Project/program grants.

PURPOSE:
To support programs and activities that responsibly seek to build a better future for everyone.

LEGAL BASIS:
Corporate foundation.

ELIGIBILITY:
The Foundation only considers grant requests from tax-exempt, nonprofit organizations located in the U.S. or its possessions. No grants to individuals.

GEOGRAPHIC RESTRICTIONS:
United States and its territories.

FINANCIAL DATA:
Amount of support per award: Varies.
Total amount of support: $12,250,000.

APPLICATION INFORMATION:
Application is available online.
Duration: One to two years, with review.

OFFICERS:
Mara Sovey, President
Nate Clark, Vice President

ADDRESS INQUIRIES TO:
Shirley Wadsager, Administrative Assistant
(See address above.)

DELAWARE COUNTY FOUNDATION
3954 North Hampton Drive
Powell, OH 43065
(614) 764-2332
Fax: (614) 764-2333

E-MAIL ADDRESS:
foundation@delawarecf.org

WEB SITE ADDRESS:
www.delawarecf.org

TYPE:
Scholarships.

See entry 1252 for full listing.

DELUXE CORPORATION FOUNDATION [97]
3680 Victoria Street North
Shoreview, MN 55126-2966
(651) 787-5124
(651) 483-7842
Fax: (651) 481-4371

E-MAIL ADDRESS:
pam.bridger@deluxe.com

WEB SITE ADDRESS:
www.deluxe.com

FOUNDED: 1952

AREAS OF INTEREST:
Human services, culture and the arts, K-12 economic education programs, tutoring programs, employment programs, and small business coaching.

TYPE:
Capital grants. Volunteer match on behalf of employee volunteerism at 501(c)(3) nonprofit.

LEGAL BASIS:
Corporate foundation.

ELIGIBILITY:
The Foundation will generally not make grants to organizations that are not exempt under Sections 501(c)(3) or 509(a)(1), (2) or (3), individuals, colleges and universities, religious organizations, organizations designed primarily for lobbying, seminars, conferences, workshops or fund-raisers, endowments, research projects, tours and travel expenses, health, start-up organizations, athletic events or sponsorships.

It is not a common practice of the Foundation to consider requests for multiyear commitments.

GEOGRAPHIC RESTRICTIONS:
United States.

FINANCIAL DATA:
Amount of support per award: $5,000 to $10,000 average.
Total amount of support: Varies.

COOPERATIVE FUNDING PROGRAMS: United Way.

NUMBER OF AWARDS: 145.

REPRESENTATIVE AWARDS:
Boys and Girls Club of the Antelope Valley, Antelope, CA; Junior Achievement of Chicago, Chicago, IL; DeLaSalle Education Center, Kansas City, MO; Boston Symphony Orchestra, Boston, MA; WomenVenture LLC, St. Paul, MN.

APPLICATION INFORMATION:
Grant applications should include the following information:
(1) evidence of tax-exempt status under Section 501(c)(3) or under Section 509(a)(1), (2) or (3) of the Internal Revenue Code;
(2) intended purpose of funds requested;
(3) number of persons and types of groups served;
(4) history, purpose and brief description of the organization;
(5) budget for the fiscal year and recent audited financial statement;
(6) sources and amounts of secured corporate support;
(7) list of others being solicited for support;
(8) copy of 990-PF (complete with schedules and statements) and;
(9) list of Board of Directors.
Duration: One year.
Deadline: The Foundation accepts grant requests outside of Minnesota March 1 to November 1, but applicants should not repeat requests during a calendar year. Within Minnesota, applications are accepted February 1 through November 1. Minnesota-based nonprofit arts organizations' applications are accepted March 1 through April 15. Minnesota-based nonprofit youth organizations' applications are accepted May 1 through June 30. All other organizations' applications are accepted July 1 through October 15.

BOARD OF DIRECTORS:
Lee J. Schram, President
Jennifer A. Anderson, Director of Foundations and Community Affairs
Julie Loosbrock
Terry Peterson
Anthony C. Scarfone

ADDRESS INQUIRIES TO:
Pamela G. Bridger, Foundations and Community Affairs Administrator
(See address above.)

DICKSON FOUNDATION   [98]
301 South Tryon Street
Suite 1800
Charlotte, NC 28202
(704) 372-5404

FOUNDED: 1944

AREAS OF INTEREST:
Education and health care.

TYPE:
Capital grants; Project/program grants.

YEAR PROGRAM STARTED: 1944

PURPOSE:
To support programs that meet the needs of and improve the quality of life in the Southeast.

LEGAL BASIS:
Private foundation.

ELIGIBILITY:
Grants are made to organizations that have tax-exempt status under Section 501(c)(3) of the Internal Revenue Code. No grants are made to individuals.

GEOGRAPHIC RESTRICTIONS:
Southeastern United States, mainly North Carolina.

FINANCIAL DATA:
Amount of support per award: Varies.
Total amount of support: Varies.

APPLICATION INFORMATION:
Send a letter of inquiry outlining the organization's goal and purposes, and the intended use and amount of the grant requested. Further information may be obtained from the Foundation.
Duration: Varies.

ADDRESS INQUIRIES TO:
Susan Patterson, Secretary and Treasurer
(See address above.)

GERALDINE R. DODGE
FOUNDATION   [99]
14 Maple Avenue, Suite 400
Morristown, NJ 07960
(973) 540-8442
Fax: (973) 540-1211

E-MAIL ADDRESS:
info@grdodge.org

WEB SITE ADDRESS:
www.grdodge.org

FOUNDED: 1974

AREAS OF INTEREST:
The arts, environment, education, and Morris County projects.

TYPE:
General operating grants; Project/program grants. Grants in four key areas:
(1) Art grants enhance the cultural richness of the community in which citizens reside and contribute to New Jersey's creative economy;
(2) Educational grants provide transformational experiential educational opportunities both inside and outside of the classroom for young people who have limited access to educational excellence;
(3) Environmental grants help to achieve ecosystem resilience and sustainable community solutions and;
(4) Media grants support traditional and innovative uses of media to educate and engage the public around issues of importance to New Jersey and its citizens, as well as efforts to uncover the abuses of power by the institutions in which citizens have placed their trust.

PURPOSE:
To support and encourage those educational, cultural, social and environmental values that contribute to making our society more humane and our world more livable.

LEGAL BASIS:
Private foundation.

ELIGIBILITY:
Applicants must be nonprofit, 501(c)(3) tax-exempt organizations located in or providing benefits to the residents of the state of New Jersey. No grants in areas of higher education, health and religion. No support for capital programs, endowments, equipment purchases, scholarships, indirect costs or deficit reduction. No direct awards to individuals nor grants to conduit organizations, nor is funding made for lobbying efforts.

GEOGRAPHIC RESTRICTIONS:
New Jersey.

APPLICATION INFORMATION:
Unsolicited requests for scholarships and grants are not accepted. New applicants should submit a one-page letter of inquiry to determine if a project falls within the Foundation's guidelines. Letters of inquiry may be submitted throughout the year, but must be received at least two weeks prior to the corresponding submission deadline. Letters of inquiry must be submitted online or e-mailed, without attachments. Following staff review of initial inquiries, applicants will be notified whether or not to submit a full proposal.

Applicants invited to apply are then required to submit an electronic copy of their proposal.
Duration: Typically 12 months.
Deadline: Letter of Inquiry: February 15 and August 1; Application: March 1 and September 1. Notification early July and mid-December, respectively.

PUBLICATIONS:
Application guidelines; biannual report.

IRS IDENTIFICATION NUMBER: 23-7406010

STAFF:
Christopher J. Daggett, President and Chief Executive Officer

ADDRESS INQUIRIES TO:
Rose Ann DeBois, Grants Manager
Tel: (973) 540-8442 ext. 109
E-mail: rdebois@grdodge.org

*SPECIAL STIPULATIONS:
The Foundation does not accept fax proposals or proposals sent via express mail carriers.

DOMINION FOUNDATION   [100]
701 East Cary Street
Richmond, VA 23219
(804) 771-3169
Fax: (804) 771-3910

E-MAIL ADDRESS:
dominion.foundation@dom.com

WEB SITE ADDRESS:
www.domfoundation.org

FOUNDED: 1985

AREAS OF INTEREST:
United Way, health and human services, culture and the arts, civic and community development, the environment, and education.

TYPE:
Capital grants; General operating grants; Matching gifts; Project/program grants.

PURPOSE:
To invest in communities in states where Dominion provides electricity and natural gas service, including North Carolina, Ohio, Virginia and West Virginia; to support selected charitable endeavors in locations where it has facilities and business interests, including Connecticut, Illinois, Indiana, Maryland, Massachusetts, New York, Pennsylvania, Rhode Island and Wisconsin.

ELIGIBILITY:
Applicants must be 501(c)(3) organizations. No grants to individuals, sectarian purposes, fraternal, political, advocacy or labor organizations, religious programs of churches, or operating funds of individual United Way agencies.

FINANCIAL DATA:
Amount of support per award: Generally $1,000 to $15,000.
Total amount of support: Over $15,000,000 annually.
Matching fund requirements: Must be employee or retiree of Dominion.

NUMBER OF AWARDS: Over 1,400.

APPLICATION INFORMATION:
Online application is available at the web site.

PUBLICATIONS:
Grant guidelines.

EXECUTIVE DIRECTOR:
Katharine Bond

*SPECIAL STIPULATIONS:
Organizations seeking support should direct their requests to the operating company in their area.

GAYLORD AND DOROTHY DONNELLEY FOUNDATION [101]
35 East Wacker Drive, Suite 2600
Chicago, IL 60601
(312) 977-2700
Fax: (312) 977-1686

E-MAIL ADDRESS:
info@gddf.org

WEB SITE ADDRESS:
www.gddf.org

FOUNDED: 1952

AREAS OF INTEREST:
Artistic vitality and land conservation in the Chicago region, the Lowcountry of South Carolina, and regionally significant collections.

TYPE:
Challenge/matching grants; Development grants; General operating grants; Matching gifts; Project/program grants; Technical assistance.

YEAR PROGRAM STARTED: 1952

PURPOSE:
To promote artistic vitality and land conservation.

LEGAL BASIS:
Tax-exempt, private foundation.

ELIGIBILITY:
Grants are made to tax-exempt, nonprofit 501(c)(3) organizations. Grants are not made to individuals, for community welfare, education, benefits, conferences, loans or pledges.

GEOGRAPHIC RESTRICTIONS:
Chicago region and South Carolina's Lowcountry.

FINANCIAL DATA:
Amount of support per award: Varies.
Total amount of support: Varies.

NUMBER OF APPLICANTS MOST RECENT YEAR: 270.

NUMBER OF AWARDS: 211.

APPLICATION INFORMATION:
Proposals should be submitted in response to guidelines, if projects are applicable.
Duration: Typically one year.
Deadline: Varies.

OFFICERS AND DIRECTORS:
Laura Donnelley, Chairman
David Farren, Executive Director
Julia Antonatos, Director
Timothy Brown, Director
Sir Peter Crane, Director
Ceara Donnelley, Director
Shawn M. Donnelley, Director
Vivian Donnelley, Director
Charles Lane, Director
Cheryl Mayberry McKissack, Director
Dr. John Rashford, Director
Alex Shuford, Director
Max Wheeler, Director
Mimi Wheeler, Director
Tom Trinley, Director of Finance and Administration

ADDRESS INQUIRIES TO:
Program Director
(See address above.)

R.R. DONNELLEY [102]
4101 Winfield Road
Warrenville, IL 60555-3521
(630) 322-6946
Fax: (630) 322-6994

E-MAIL ADDRESS:
communityrelations@rrd.com

WEB SITE ADDRESS:
www.rrdonnelley.com

FOUNDED: 1864

AREAS OF INTEREST:
Youth, education, inclusion and diversity.

NAME(S) OF PROGRAMS:
● **Corporate Contributions Program**

TYPE:
Capital grants; Internships; Scholarships. Scholarships are for children of employees only. Geographical focus on communities with manufacturing operations.

YEAR PROGRAM STARTED: 1964

PURPOSE:
To exercise corporate social responsibility, with special emphasis on enhancing the Company's manufacturing communities.

LEGAL BASIS:
Corporate contributions program.

ELIGIBILITY:
Grants are made only to nonprofit organizations. No grants are made to individuals.

FINANCIAL DATA:
Amount of support per award: Varies.
Total amount of support: Varies.

APPLICATION INFORMATION:
Grant requests should be made online. Requests should be in the form of a short proposal containing a description of the organization, its activities and its clients, a clear statement of what the organization wants from R.R. Donnelley and an explanation of what it plans to accomplish with such assistance. Attach a copy of the organization's IRS status letter, a list of board members and an audited financial statement. A limited amount of other supporting materials, such as an annual report, brochure or newsletter, is also welcome.
Duration: One year. Must reapply for additional funding.
Deadline: Proposals are accepted from January 1 to November 1 and referred to the next Contributions Committee meeting.

PUBLICATIONS:
Corporate Social Responsibility Report.

ADDRESS INQUIRIES TO:
Kamala L. Martinez
Community Relations Manager
(See address above.)

THE DOUTY FOUNDATION [103]
P.O. Box 1437
Philadelphia, PA 19105
(215) 620-1869

E-MAIL ADDRESS:
jennifer@doutyfoundation.org

WEB SITE ADDRESS:
www.doutyfoundation.org

FOUNDED: 1968

AREAS OF INTEREST:
Economic and educational opportunities to disadvantaged people, especially children.

TYPE:
General operating grants; Project/program grants. Projects with social impact, innovative projects and general operations.

YEAR PROGRAM STARTED: 1969

PURPOSE:
To support programs that provide either educational opportunities for the disadvantaged or local innovative social services.

LEGAL BASIS:
Tax-exempt private foundation.

ELIGIBILITY:
Qualifying tax-exempt organizations are eligible. Grants are not made for capital expenditures, agency promotions, annual reports, renovations or to organizations with annual budgets of more than $1,000,000. Grants are not made to individuals or for religious or political purposes.

GEOGRAPHIC RESTRICTIONS:
Greater Philadelphia, Pennsylvania area with preference to Montgomery and Philadelphia counties.

FINANCIAL DATA:
Amount of support per award: Up to $7,500.
Total amount of support: $269,300 for the year 2012.

NUMBER OF AWARDS: 81 for the year 2012.

APPLICATION INFORMATION:
Applications may be submitted online via the Foundation web site.
Duration: One year. Renewals are usually limited to six years.
Deadline: March 15 and September 15.

IRS IDENTIFICATION NUMBER: 23-6463709

TRUSTEES:
Judith L. Bardes
Carrolle Perry Devonish
Thomas B. Harvey, Esq.
Nancy J. Kirby
Elbert Sampson

STAFF:
Jennifer Leith, Executive Director

ADDRESS INQUIRIES TO:
Jennifer Leith, Executive Director
(See address above.)

*SPECIAL STIPULATIONS:
Organizations that have been funded for a six-year period may not reapply until at least two years have passed.

DOW JONES FOUNDATION   [104]
1211 Avenue of the Americas, 7th Floor
New York, NY 10036
(212) 416-3202

E-MAIL ADDRESS:
brad.rolston@dowjones.com

FOUNDED: 1954

AREAS OF INTEREST:
Journalism, free press, literacy and education, arts and culture, and community.

TYPE:
General operating grants; Scholarships. Program support.

PURPOSE:
To support causes engaged in the promotion and protection of journalism and free press, as well as causes devoted specifically to literacy and education, arts and culture, or local communities.

LEGAL BASIS:
Corporate foundation.

ELIGIBILITY:
The Foundation does not currently make grants in medical and scientific research.

FINANCIAL DATA:
Amount of support per award: Varies.

APPLICATION INFORMATION:
All requests for Foundation support must be submitted in writing. Each request must indicate IRS tax-exemption certificate number.
Deadline: Normally, requests received will be considered by the board of directors only at their annual meeting in June for distribution in the next fiscal year.

PUBLICATIONS:
Application guidelines.

IRS IDENTIFICATION NUMBER: 13-6070158

OFFICERS:
Bradley P. Rolston, Esq., Secretary and Director

ADDRESS INQUIRIES TO:
Bradley P. Rolston, Esq., Director
(See address above.)

JOSEPH DROWN FOUNDATION   [105]
1999 Avenue of the Stars, Suite 2330
Los Angeles, CA 90067
(310) 277-4488
Fax: (310) 277-4573

E-MAIL ADDRESS:
staff@jdrown.org

WEB SITE ADDRESS:
www.jdrown.org

FOUNDED: 1953

AREAS OF INTEREST:
Education.

TYPE:
General operating grants; Project/program grants.

YEAR PROGRAM STARTED: 1953

PURPOSE:
To assist individuals in becoming successful, self-sustaining and contributing members of society.

ELIGIBILITY:
No funds to individuals, endowments, capital campaigns or building funds. The Foundation will not underwrite annual meeting or conferences. No funding for religious programs and special events.

In the area of medical research, the Foundation does not accept unsolicited requests.

GEOGRAPHIC RESTRICTIONS:
Los Angeles, California.

FINANCIAL DATA:
Amount of support per award: $5,000 to $50,000.
Total amount of support: Approximately $4,000,000 for the fiscal year ended March 31, 2013.

NUMBER OF APPLICANTS MOST RECENT YEAR: 1,200.

NUMBER OF AWARDS: 150.

APPLICATION INFORMATION:
No special application form is required. Proposals should include a letter with information about both the organization as a whole and the project in particular, a 501(c)(3) tax determination letter from the IRS, a budget for both the organization as a whole and the project in particular, the most recent audited financial statements, a copy of the most recent Form 990 filed with the IRS and a list of the current board of directors. Any additional materials, such as an annual report, may be attached.
Duration: One year.
Deadline: January 15, April 15, July 15 and October 15 (postmark).

PUBLICATIONS:
Application guidelines.

OFFICERS AND STAFF:
Norman C. Obrow, Chairman
Wendy Wachtell, President
Ann T. Miller, Chief Financial Officer
Alyssa Ichelberger, Program Administrator

ADDRESS INQUIRIES TO:
Wendy Wachtell, President
(See address above.)

*SPECIAL STIPULATIONS:
In the area of medical research, the Foundation does not accept unsolicited requests.

THE DUCHOSSOIS FAMILY FOUNDATION   [106]
1515 West 22nd Street, Suite 650
Oak Brook, IL 60523
(630) 995-0905
Fax: (630) 993-6911

FOUNDED: 1984

AREAS OF INTEREST:
Cancer research.

TYPE:
General operating grants; Project/program grants; Research grants.

YEAR PROGRAM STARTED: 1984

PURPOSE:
To provide funding to nonprofit organizations to conduct research and program support in the treatment of cancer.

LEGAL BASIS:
Family foundation.

ELIGIBILITY:
Grants are made to nonprofit organizations that are IRS 501(c)(3) tax-exempt. Selection is based on the organization's value and performance. The Foundation does not provide support for individuals, including scholarships or fellowships, sectarian institutions or organizations or programs for which grants would be used primarily for the study and/or propagation of a particular field and/or organizations which are not recognized by the IRS as tax-exempt public charities.

GEOGRAPHIC RESTRICTIONS:
Chicago, Illinois metropolitan area.

FINANCIAL DATA:
Amount of support per award: Grants vary in amount, depending upon the needs and nature of the request.
Total amount of support: Varies.

APPLICATION INFORMATION:
Unsolicited applications are not accepted.
Duration: One year. Renewals possible.

OFFICER:
Kimberly Duchossois, President

*SPECIAL STIPULATIONS:
The Foundation does not accept unsolicited proposals.

DORIS DUKE CHARITABLE FOUNDATION   [107]
650 Fifth Avenue, 19th Floor
New York, NY 10019
(212) 974-7000
Fax: (212) 974-7590

WEB SITE ADDRESS:
www.ddcf.org

FOUNDED: 1996

AREAS OF INTEREST:
Environment, performing arts, child abuse prevention and clinical research.

NAME(S) OF PROGRAMS:
- **Arts Program**
- **Child Abuse Prevention Program**
- **Environment Program**
- **Medical Research Program**

TYPE:
Grants-in-aid. The Arts Program supports performing artists with the creation and public performance of their work. The Program focuses its support on contemporary dance, jazz and theatre, and the organizations that nurture, present and produce them.

The Child Abuse Prevention Program promotes children's healthy development and protects them from abuse and neglect. The Program favors a public health approach and is especially interested in place-based, whole-community approaches that seek to engage a range of participants from various disciplines to ensure that family well-being is supported by strong communities.

The Environment Program enables communities to protect and manage wildlife habitat and create efficient built environments. The Program's awareness of climate change as the greatest emerging threat to biodiversity - and the need to aggressively mitigate it without unnecessarily sacrificing wildlife habitat - shapes the Program's grantmaking priorities.

The Medical Research Program supports the prevention, treatment and cure of human disease. The goal of the Program is to strengthen and support clinical research to help advance the translation of basic biomedical discoveries into new treatments, preventions and cures for human diseases.

YEAR PROGRAM STARTED: 1997

PURPOSE:
To improve the quality of people's lives through grants supporting the performing arts, environmental conservation, medical research and the prevention of child abuse, and through the preservation of the cultural and environmental legacy of Doris Duke's properties.

LEGAL BASIS:
Nonprofit foundation.

ELIGIBILITY:
While all Foundation programs require that grantee organizations be publicly supported 501(c)(3) tax-exempt organizations based in the U.S., each program has a customized approach to its grantmaking strategy.

FINANCIAL DATA:
Total amount of support: Approximately $100,000 to $1,000,000.

APPLICATION INFORMATION:
The majority of the Foundation's grants are awarded through competitive (request-for-proposal) processes or by invitation. Open competitions and funding opportunities for grants are listed on the Foundation's web site. Foundation staff also welcome letters of inquiry from qualifying organizations.

To submit a letter of inquiry, the Foundation requests that organizations visit its web site and submit letters of inquiry through the online form. To do so, applicant will need a nonprofit tax ID as well as the title of the proposed project, a brief description of the specific project for which funding is sought, the requested funding amount, a description of how the objectives of the proposed project relate to those of the Foundation, the organization's mission and strategies, and a primary contact for the organization. Staff will respond to the letters of inquiry within two months and will notify the writer if additional information is desired.

Duration: Short-term or multiyear grants are awarded.

TRUSTEES:
John E. Zuccotti, Chairperson
Harry B. Demopoulos
Anthony S. Fauci
James F. Gill

Kathy Halbreich
Nannerl O. Keohane
Angela K. Mwanza
Peter A. Nadosy
William H. Schlesinger
Nicholas Scoppetta
Jide J. Zeitlan

STAFF:
Edward P. Henry, President

THE DUKE ENDOWMENT   [108]
800 East Morehead Street
Charlotte, NC 28202
(704) 376-0291
Fax: (704) 376-9336

E-MAIL ADDRESS:
gcochrane@tde.org

WEB SITE ADDRESS:
www.dukeendowment.org

FOUNDED: 1924

AREAS OF INTEREST:
Not-for-profit hospitals in North Carolina and South Carolina; children's welfare and adoption assistance institutions in North Carolina and South Carolina; rural United Methodist churches and retired ministers in North Carolina and four colleges: Duke, Furman and Johnson C. Smith universities and Davidson College.

TYPE:
Capital grants; Challenge/matching grants; Conferences/seminars; Endowments; General operating grants; Matching gifts; Project/program grants; Scholarships.

YEAR PROGRAM STARTED: 1924

PURPOSE:
To carry out the terms of the Trust Indenture, as written by James B. Duke, by supporting four institutions in higher education, not-for-profit hospitals and children's homes in North Carolina and South Carolina, retired pastors of the United Methodist Church and programs and projects of rural United Methodist Churches in North Carolina.

LEGAL BASIS:
Charitable trust.

ELIGIBILITY:
North and South Carolina organizations and institutions with appropriate interests and activities are eligible.

GEOGRAPHIC RESTRICTIONS:
North Carolina and South Carolina.

FINANCIAL DATA:
Amount of support per award: Varies.
Total amount of support: $109,653,541 for the year 2012.
Matching fund requirements: Varies with grant.

NUMBER OF APPLICANTS MOST RECENT YEAR:
Varies.

NUMBER OF AWARDS: Varies.

REPRESENTATIVE AWARDS:
$35,000,000 multiyear grant to Johnson C. Smith University to support science programs, scholarships and capital improvements on campus; $11,250,000 multiyear grant to Health Science South Carolina to advance leading-edge programs; $2,000,000 to Furman University to enrich the University's fine arts program.

APPLICATION INFORMATION:
Applicants must take the eligibility questionnaire before applying. Complete guidelines and application form is available on the web site.
Duration: Varies. All eligible beneficiaries may request continued and renewed support.
Deadline: Child Care and Health Care: June 15 and December 15. Higher Education: December 15. Rural Church: May 9 and November 7.

PUBLICATIONS:
Annual report; e-newsletter, occasional papers and reports on projects and programs.

IRS IDENTIFICATION NUMBER: 56-0529965

TRUSTEES AND OFFICERS:
Minor Mickel Shaw, Chairman
Dennis M. Campbell, Ph.D., Vice Chairman
Mary Duke Trent Jones, Vice Chairman
Eugene W. Cochrane, Jr., President
Rhett N. Mabry, Vice President
Mary L. Piepenbring, Vice President
Karen H. Rogers, Treasurer
Terri W. Honeycutt, Corporate Secretary
Arthur E. Morehead, IV, General Counsel
Todd Walker, Managing Director, Investments
William G. Anlyan, M.D.
William Barnet, III
Ravenel B. Curry, III
Harris E. DeLoach, Jr.
Constance F. Gray
Thomas S. Kenan, III
Charles C. Lucas, III
Wilhelmina Reuben-Cooke, J.D.
Russell M. Robinson, II
Jean G. Spaulding, M.D.
Kenneth D. Weeks, Jr., M.D.
Judy Woodruff

ADDRESS INQUIRIES TO:
Eugene W. Cochrane, Jr., President
(See address above.)

THE CALEB C. AND JULIA W. DULA EDUCATIONAL AND CHARITABLE FOUNDATION   [109]
7800 Forsyth Boulevard
Suite 600
Clayton, MO 63105
(314) 898-9442
Fax: (314) 898-9264

E-MAIL ADDRESS:
todd.s.snyder@ustrust.com

FOUNDED: 1939

AREAS OF INTEREST:
Higher and secondary education, libraries, hospitals, social service, church support, cultural programs and historic preservation.

TYPE:
General operating grants; Project/program grants. Grants for projects and, to a lesser degree, general support.

PURPOSE:
To provide funding to projects of interest to the Foundation.

LEGAL BASIS:
Missouri nonprofit corporation; educational and charitable foundation.

ELIGIBILITY:
501(c)(3) tax-exempt organizations in the Foundation's areas of interest are eligible to apply. No grants are made to individuals.

GEOGRAPHIC RESTRICTIONS:
United States.

FINANCIAL DATA:
Amount of support per award: $5,000 to
$100,000.

APPLICATION INFORMATION:
There are no set requirements. A
letter/proposal describing the organization
and the project along with the amount
requested should be sent to the Trustees in
care of Todd S. Snyder. Requests are
forwarded to the Trustees who meet in the
spring and the fall.

Duration: Varies.

Deadline: March 31 and September 30.

ADDRESS INQUIRIES TO:
Todd S. Snyder
(See address above.)

DUNSPAUGH DALTON FOUNDATION [110]

1500 San Remo Avenue, Suite 103
Coral Gables, FL 33146
(305) 668-4192
Fax: (305) 668-4247

E-MAIL ADDRESS:
dunspaughdalton@aol.com

WEB SITE ADDRESS:
dunspaughdalton.com

AREAS OF INTEREST:
Higher, secondary, and elementary education;
social services; youth; health associations and
hospitals; cultural programs; and civic affairs.

TYPE:
Capital grants; Endowments; General
operating grants; Professorships;
Project/program grants.

ELIGIBILITY:
Grants are made to organizations that have
tax-exempt status under Section 501(c)(3) of
the Internal Revenue Code. No grants are
made to individuals.

GEOGRAPHIC RESTRICTIONS:
Monterey Peninsula and northern California;
Miami-Dade County, Florida.

FINANCIAL DATA:
Amount of support per award: $10,000
average.

APPLICATION INFORMATION:
Applicant must submit:
(1) proposal summary (not to exceed one-half
page) explaining why the grant is requested,
what outcomes are hoped to be achieved and
how funds will be spent;
(2) narrative including background, funding
requirements and evaluation (not to exceed
five pages);
(3) completed Grant Application Form and;
(4) the most recent financial statements used
as the basis for filing IRS Form 990.

Submit all application documents to either
office listed on the Grant Application Form.

Duration: One year. Can reapply.

ADDRESS INQUIRIES TO:
Leslie W. Buchanan, Secretary/Treasurer or
Sarah L. Bonner, President or
Alexina Lane, Vice-President
(See address above.)

JESSIE BALL DUPONT FUND [111]

One Independent Drive
Suite 1400
Jacksonville, FL 32202-5011
(904) 353-0890
(800) 252-3452
Fax: (904) 353-3870

E-MAIL ADDRESS:
contactus@dupontfund.org

WEB SITE ADDRESS:
www.dupontfund.org

FOUNDED: 1976

AREAS OF INTEREST:
Education, religion, health and human
services, arts and culture, juvenile justice,
environment, housing, community and
economic development, historic preservation,
nonprofit capacity building and financial asset
building.

TYPE:
Challenge/matching grants; General operating
grants; Project/program grants; Technical
assistance. Organizational capacity building.

Geared to nonprofit, religious organizations
and educational institutions.

YEAR PROGRAM STARTED: 1976

PURPOSE:
To expand access and create opportunity
through investing in people, organizations
and communities that were important to
Jessie Ball duPont.

LEGAL BASIS:
Private foundation.

ELIGIBILITY:
The Fund makes grants only to a defined
universe of organizations. An organization is
eligible if it received a contribution from
Mrs. duPont between January 1, 1960 and
December 31, 1964. Proof of eligibility is
determined by examining Mrs. duPont's
personal or tax records or by the applicant
presenting written, verifiable evidence of
having received a contribution during the
eligibility period.

GEOGRAPHIC RESTRICTIONS:
Primarily the South, especially Delaware,
Florida, and Virginia.

FINANCIAL DATA:
Amount of support per award: $313 to
$500,000 for the year 2013. Average:
$10,000.

Total amount of support: $10,429,705
(unaudited) in grants paid for the year 2013.

NUMBER OF APPLICANTS MOST RECENT YEAR:
369 for the year 2012.

NUMBER OF AWARDS: 352 for the year 2012.

APPLICATION INFORMATION:
Duration: One to three years.

Deadline: Trustees meet quarterly in
February, May, August and November to
consider grant applications. Awards are
announced immediately after the meetings.

PUBLICATIONS:
Annual report; policy briefings; *Notes from
the Field.*

IRS IDENTIFICATION NUMBER: 59-6368632

TRUSTEES:
Rev. Eddie E. Jones, Jr., Chairperson and
Clerical Trustee
Leroy Davis, Vice Chairperson
David Llewellyn, Representing Corporate
Co-Trustee, Northern Trust

Mary Lynn Huntley
Thomas H. Jeavons
Martha T. Lanahan
Mary K. Phillips

STAFF:
Sherry P. Magill, Ph.D., President
Mark Constantine, Senior Vice President
Katie Ensign, Senior Program Officer
Barbara Roole, Senior Program Officer
Chris Crothers, Program Officer
Mark Walker, Knowledge Management and
Technology Officer

ADDRESS INQUIRIES TO:
Sherry P. Magill, Ph.D., President
(See address above.)

*PLEASE NOTE:
Guidelines must be followed carefully when
submitting proposal.

EASTERN BANK CHARITABLE FOUNDATION [112]

195 Market Street
Lynn, MA 01901
(781) 598-7595
Fax: (781) 596-4445

E-MAIL ADDRESS:
l.kurzrok@easternbank.com

WEB SITE ADDRESS:
www.easternbank.com

FOUNDED: 1994

AREAS OF INTEREST:
Human services, family and children,
affordable housing, community health, civil
liberties, sustainability, and workforce
development.

TYPE:
Capital grants; Endowments; Project/program
grants. Community grants; Partnership grants.

YEAR PROGRAM STARTED: 1994

PURPOSE:
To contribute, in a meaningful way, to the
health and vitality of the various
communities which are served by Eastern
Bank, by providing financial support to
selected nonprofit organizations operating
within those communities; to support
organizations providing services to the
underserved and neediest members of our
community; to ensure all our neighbors have
equal access to food, shelter, education,
employment, child care and other basic
human needs.

LEGAL BASIS:
Corporate foundation.

ELIGIBILITY:
Applicants must be nonprofit 501(c)(3)
organizations and be located in the market
area served by Eastern Bank. The Foundation
does not accept applications from
organizations with 509(a)(3) designation or
private foundations.

GEOGRAPHIC RESTRICTIONS:
Eastern Massachusetts area.

FINANCIAL DATA:
Amount of support per award: $50 to
$50,000.

Total amount of support: $3,385,360 for the
year 2013.

Matching fund requirements: Full-time
employees, trustees and directors: Minimum
$50, maximum $1,000 per year.

NUMBER OF APPLICANTS MOST RECENT YEAR:
2,500.

NUMBER OF AWARDS: 1,500.

APPLICATION INFORMATION:
Applications are only accepted through the online application site.

Deadline: Ongoing for requests up to $10,000. Requests for Eastern Bank grants ($10,000 to $50,000): March 1 and September 1.

PUBLICATIONS:
Annual report, available online.

IRS IDENTIFICATION NUMBER: 22-3317340

ADDRESS INQUIRIES TO:
Laura Kurzrok, Executive Director
(See address above.)

EATON CHARITABLE FUND   [113]
Eaton Center
1000 Eaton Boulevard
Cleveland, OH 44122
(440) 523-4944
Fax: (440) 523-3439

E-MAIL ADDRESS:
barrydoggett@eaton.com

WEB SITE ADDRESS:
www.eaton.com

FOUNDED: 1953

AREAS OF INTEREST:
Education, arts and culture, children at-risk, community improvement and neighborhood development.

TYPE:
Capital grants; Challenge/matching grants; Matching gifts; Product donations; Project/program grants. The Corporation places a priority on contributing to those organizations in which Eaton employees are personally involved and which serve their needs. Contributions are made to health, human service, civic, arts and cultural organizations and educational institutions.

Support of capital campaigns at educational institutions is generally limited to programs of direct interest to Eaton, which prefers to invest in engineering, scientific, technological and business-related projects.

YEAR PROGRAM STARTED: 1953

PURPOSE:
To contribute to the betterment of life in communities where Eaton employees live and work; to support employee involvement and investment; to promote self-sufficiency; to sustain arts and cultural institutions; to enhance education.

LEGAL BASIS:
Corporate foundation.

ELIGIBILITY:
501(c)(3) organizations within the Corporation's areas of interest are eligible for support. Grants are not made to religious, fraternal or labor organizations; to individuals or individual endeavors; debt retirement; medical research; endowment funds; fund-raising benefits, sponsorships or other events; or annual operating budgets of United Way agencies or hospitals.

Grants are only made in communities where Eaton has operations.

FINANCIAL DATA:
Cash grants are mainly from the Charitable Fund, but also from the company.

Amount of support per award: Typically, $1,000 to $100,000. Average: $5,000 to $15,000.

Total amount of support: Approximately $9,300,000 for the year 2013.

Matching fund requirements: The Corporation single-matches employee contributions to nationally accredited educational institutions and arts and cultural organizations approved by the Corporate Contributions Committee.

REPRESENTATIVE AWARDS:
$20,000 to Rhode Island Mentoring Partnership, Warwick, RI; $5,000 to Lakewood Ranch YMCA, Sarasota, FL; $13,600 to Manavya Home, Pune, India; $16,225 to Belmond Area United Way, Belmond, IA.

APPLICATION INFORMATION:
Send requests to the nearest company facility. All requests for contributions must be in writing. Each should include a one-page cover letter (on organization letterhead), a one- to three-page description of organization's program, and an attached description of the organization's history and purpose, identification of other organizations (including corporations) involved in funding the program and gift amounts committed, names of Eaton employees and a description of their involvement (if applicable), copies of the most recently audited financial statements and the current budget, a roster of officers and directors or trustees of the organization and their affiliations, and official government documentation of the organization's 501(c)(3) tax-exempt IRS status (or its non-U.S. equivalent).

Grants are generally limited to one grant per organization in a given year. Previous grants are not considered as precedent for additional support. Proposals should not be submitted in binders or with videotapes, CD-ROMs and/or in other costly manners.

Duration: Grants are typically given for one year. Multiyear commitments are usually capital grants.

Deadline: Grant requests are accepted and reviewed throughout the year.

PUBLICATIONS:
Annual report; guidelines.

STAFF:
Veronica M. Runcis, Manager, Public Affairs
Emily A. Stitt, Administrator, Gift Matching Program

CONTRIBUTIONS COMMITTEE:
W.B. Doggett, Chairman
Craig Arnold
Bill Blausey
Cynthia Brabander
Thomas Gross

ADDRESS INQUIRIES TO:
W.B. Doggett, Senior Vice President
Public and Community Affairs
(See address above.)

EDISON INTERNATIONAL   [114]
2244 Walnut Grove Avenue
Quad 4A G.O. No. 1
Rosemead, CA 91770
(626) 302-5538
Fax: (626) 302-7985

E-MAIL ADDRESS:
tammy.tumbling@sce.com

WEB SITE ADDRESS:
www.sce.com

FOUNDED: 1996

AREAS OF INTEREST:
Education (science, technology, engineering, arts and math), environment, public safety preparedness, and civic engagement.

CONSULTING OR VOLUNTEER SERVICES:
Volunteer Program, Energy in Action.

NAME(S) OF PROGRAMS:
- **Corporate Contributions Program**
- **Employee Matching Gifts Program**

TYPE:
Challenge/matching grants; General operating grants; Matching gifts; Project/program grants; Scholarships. Matching gifts and employees for education only: private and public schools (K-University).

YEAR PROGRAM STARTED: 1986

PURPOSE:
To promote the economic prosperity and overall quality of life in the areas where its employees live and work by supporting numerous community initiatives and historically supporting a variety of effective educational, civic and charitable activities.

ELIGIBILITY:
Primary focus on Southern California and other areas where Edison International operates.

No grants to individuals, political organizations or candidates, veterans organizations, fraternal orders, labor groups, commercial profit-making enterprises, religious or sectarian organizations or any group whose activities are not in the best interests of Edison International, its employees, shareholders, customers or the communities it serves.

FINANCIAL DATA:
Amount of support per award: Grants: Up to $5,000 for non-established grantees.

Matching fund requirements: Equal match to $2,000 for accredited public and private educational institutions.

NUMBER OF APPLICANTS MOST RECENT YEAR:
Varies.

NUMBER OF AWARDS: Varies.

REPRESENTATIVE AWARDS:
$1,500,000 to American Red Cross for public safety and awareness in southern California.

APPLICATION INFORMATION:
Applications for Edison grants and sponsorships must be submitted online during Edison's funding cycles. Application links are active only during funding cycles.

Deadline: Funding cycles are during the months of February, May and August.

PUBLICATIONS:
Annual report; contributions policy; application guidelines.

OFFICERS:
Theodore Craver, Chairman

ADDRESS INQUIRIES TO:
Tammy Tumbling
Director of Community Investment
(See address above.)

EL POMAR FOUNDATION   [115]
10 Lake Circle
Colorado Springs, CO 80906
(719) 633-7733
Fax: (719) 577-7010

E-MAIL ADDRESS:
fellowship@elpomar.org
grants@elpomar.org

WEB SITE ADDRESS:
www.elpomar.org

FOUNDED: 1937

AREAS OF INTEREST:
Health, education, welfare, arts and culture, humanities, civic and community, and leadership.

NAME(S) OF PROGRAMS:
● **Fellowship Program**
● **Grants Program**

TYPE:
Capital grants; Challenge/matching grants; Fellowships; General operating grants; Matching gifts; Project/program grants; Scholarships; Technical assistance. The Fellowship Program brings highly qualified college graduates with diverse backgrounds and interests to the Foundation. This program focuses on professional development and prepares Fellows for positions of leadership in Colorado and the nation.

Grants Program is to support construction, development and acquisition of buildings and equipment and other projects in education, health, humanities, resources, environment and welfare in the state of Colorado.

PURPOSE:
To support general-purpose grantmaking, civic collaboration, projects of major community importance and initiatives that provide various kinds of assistance to nonprofit organizations; to provide leadership development opportunities for a range of individuals, from those just out of college to those responsible for the state's most important nonprofits; to help those least able to help themselves.

LEGAL BASIS:
Private nonprofit charitable foundation.

ELIGIBILITY:
Colorado organizations with appropriate interests may apply. Fully tax-supported institutions are not eligible, but requests from municipalities will be considered if funds are required for a specific project. Scholarships and fellowships are not granted directly.

The Foundation does not make grants under the following conditions:
(1) to another foundation or organization which distributes money to recipients of its own selection;
(2) to organizations that practice discrimination of any kind;
(3) to cover deficits, debt elimination or for endowment;
(4) for the making of films or other media projects;
(5) for primary or secondary education (K-12), although the Foundation will consider, on a limited basis, capital requests from nonpublicly funded secondary schools;
(6) for research or studies;
(7) to organizations which do not have fiscal responsibility for the proposed project;
(8) to nonprofit organizations that do not have an active 501(c)(3) nonprofit determination letter from the IRS;
(9) to individuals;
(10) for travel, conferences, conventions, group meetings or seminars;
(11) for camps, camp programs or other seasonal activities;
(12) to religious organizations for support of religious programs and;

(13) for grants intended to influence legislation or support candidates for political office.

Because of the tremendous needs throughout the state of Colorado, grant requests of more than $100,000 will be considered only in exceptional circumstances.

GEOGRAPHIC RESTRICTIONS:
Colorado.

FINANCIAL DATA:
Amount of support per award: Fellowship Program: $32,000; Grants Program: $2,500 to $50,000.

Total amount of support: Approximately $24,000,000 for the year 2014.

NUMBER OF AWARDS: 708 for the year 2011.

APPLICATION INFORMATION:
All inquiries to the Foundation should be in writing and no interviews are granted until after an application is received.
Duration: Fellowship Program: Two years; Grant Program: Typically one year.

PUBLICATIONS:
Annual report; application guidelines.

IRS IDENTIFICATION NUMBER: 84-6002373

OFFICERS:
William J. Hybl, Chairman and Chief Executive Officer
R. Thayer Tutt, Jr., President and Chief Investment Officer
Robert J. Hilbert, Secretary, Treasurer and Chief Financial Officer
Kyle H. Hybl, Chief Operating Officer

TRUSTEES:
Andrea Aragon
Judy Bell
Robert J. Hilbert
Kyle H. Hybl
William J. Hybl
Dennis Maes
Christina McGrath
David J. Palenchar
Victor Eugene Renuart
R. Thayer Tutt, Jr.
William R. Ward

ADDRESS INQUIRIES TO:
William J. Hybl
Chairman and Chief Executive Officer
(See address above.)

RUTH H. AND WARREN A. ELLSWORTH FOUNDATION   [116]
c/o Fletcher Tilton
370 Main Street, 11th Floor
Worcester, MA 01608
(508) 459-8000
(508) 459-8042
Fax: (508) 459-8342

E-MAIL ADDRESS:
stilton@fletchertilton.com

AREAS OF INTEREST:
Culture, education, health and human services.

TYPE:
Project/program grants.

PURPOSE:
To support organizations that are providing solutions to or preventing problems within the immediate community.

ELIGIBILITY:
Grants are made to organizations that have tax-exempt status under Section 501(c)(3) of

the Internal Revenue Code. No grants are made to individuals. Nonsectarian religious programs may apply.

The Foundation does not usually fund grants for general operating expense.

GEOGRAPHIC RESTRICTIONS:
Worcester, Massachusetts and surrounding area.

FINANCIAL DATA:
Amount of support per award: $5,000 to $25,000.
Total amount of support: Varies.

APPLICATION INFORMATION:
Submit a proposal in a letter form and a grant application summary.
Duration: Varies.
Deadline: June 1.

ADDRESS INQUIRIES TO:
Sumner B. Tilton, Jr., Trustee
(See address above.)

EMERSON   [117]
8000 West Florissant Avenue
St. Louis, MO 63136
(314) 553-2000
(314) 553-3621

WEB SITE ADDRESS:
www.emerson.com

FOUNDED: 1944

AREAS OF INTEREST:
Education; youth, culture and the arts; health, welfare and civic needs.

TYPE:
Capital grants; Challenge/matching grants; Development grants; Endowments; General operating grants; Matching gifts; Project/program grants.

YEAR PROGRAM STARTED: 1950

PURPOSE:
To encourage sound, innovative programs that enrich human lives, promote volunteerism, provide services directly to those in need and increase the overall impact of contributed funds.

LEGAL BASIS:
Corporate contributions program.

ELIGIBILITY:
Grants are made to organizations having IRS 501(c)(3) tax-exempt status, located in areas where Emerson has facilities. The Trust does not contribute to organizations that practice discrimination by race, color, creed, sex, age or national origin, religious or politically partisan organizations, projects requiring funding directly to an organization located outside the U.S. or its territories, loans or investment funds, fraternal, veterans' or labor groups unless they furnish services benefiting the general public, aid to individuals, underwriting of deficits or post-event funding.

FINANCIAL DATA:
Amount of support per award: Varies.
Total amount of support: Approximately $32,000,000 for the year 2013.

APPLICATION INFORMATION:
Proposals should be submitted in writing and include the following information:
(1) brief description and history of the organization submitting the proposal;
(2) a clear statement of the purpose and objectives of the project or program

(including expected results), the program budget, the amount requested, a statement of how the funds will be used and a timetable of project completion;
(3) statement of the relationship of the project's goals to the priorities of the Emerson Charitable Trust;
(4) annual report or audited financial statement of the requesting organization showing income and expenses, operational budget and which may include a copy of the most recent IRS 990 report;
(5) supporting factual information that may be useful as a basis of evaluation, such as a list of sources providing support to the organization;
(6) copy of the organization's IRS 501(c)(3) tax-exemption statement;
(7) listing of the organization's Board of Directors and a statement regarding staff who will manage the project and;
(8) statement of general plans for sustaining activities and post-grant evaluation of the project.
Applicants should expect a 30- to 60-day turnaround on all written proposals.
Duration: One year. Must reapply, unless multiyear funding at outset.

PUBLICATIONS:
Annual report; guidelines.

ADDRESS INQUIRIES TO:
Patrick J. Sly, Executive Vice President
(See address above.)

ERION FOUNDATION   [118]
P.O. Box 732
Loveland, CO 80539
(970) 667-4549
Fax: (970) 663-6187

E-MAIL ADDRESS:
contact@erionfoundation.org

WEB SITE ADDRESS:
www.erionfoundation.org

FOUNDED: 1986

AREAS OF INTEREST:
Education, health, welfare, and culture.

TYPE:
Capital grants; Challenge/matching grants; Development grants.

YEAR PROGRAM STARTED: 1986

PURPOSE:
To support the Loveland, Colorado community.

LEGAL BASIS:
Private foundation.

ELIGIBILITY:
Eligible organizations must be IRS 501(c)(3) tax-exempt.

GEOGRAPHIC RESTRICTIONS:
Loveland, Colorado and the immediate surrounding area.

FINANCIAL DATA:
Amount of support per award: Varies.

APPLICATION INFORMATION:
Applicants must submit via mail:
(1) completed application form;
(2) a copy of the organization's 501(c)(3) designation letter and;
(3) page one of the organization's most recent IRS Form 990.
Duration: Varies.

ADDRESS INQUIRIES TO:
Doug Erion, Grants Administrator
(See address above.)

EXELON CORPORATION   [119]
Corporate Relations
10 South Dearborn
Chicago, IL 60603
(312) 394-4361

E-MAIL ADDRESS:
steve.solomon@exeloncorp.com

WEB SITE ADDRESS:
www.exeloncorp.com

FOUNDED: 1888

AREAS OF INTEREST:
Math and science, environmental education, arts and culture, neighborhood development, and environmental conservation.

NAME(S) OF PROGRAMS:
● **Corporate Giving Program**

TYPE:
General operating grants; Project/program grants. Sponsorship for events.

PURPOSE:
To strengthen customer and community relations by promoting the advancement of math, science and energy education, contributing to charitable organizations that promote efficiency and renewable energy, promoting economic and community development, and contributing to organizations that promote diversity in the workplace and community.

LEGAL BASIS:
Corporate contributions program.

ELIGIBILITY:
Grants are made to institutions, organizations and agencies located in Exelon's service area (northern Illinois, Maryland and southeastern Pennsylvania). Educational giving is limited to private colleges and universities. The company does not purchase ads in benefit programs. No contributions are made to religious organizations for religious purposes, political organizations, or to individuals.

GEOGRAPHIC RESTRICTIONS:
Northern Illinois, Maryland and southeastern Pennsylvania.

FINANCIAL DATA:
Amount of support per award: Average: $15,000.
Total amount of support: $32,200,000 for the year 2013.
Matching fund requirements: Education only.

NUMBER OF AWARDS: 3,000.

APPLICATION INFORMATION:
Application must be submitted online.
Duration: One year.
Deadline: Applications are reviewed on an ongoing basis.

PUBLICATIONS:
Guidelines.

STAFF:
Christopher Crane, Chairman and Chief Executive Officer of Exelon Corporation
Denis O'Brien, Executive Vice President of Exelon Utilities

ADDRESS INQUIRIES TO:
Steve Solomon
Vice President, Corporate Relations
(See address above.)

EXXON MOBIL CORPORATION   [120]
5959 Las Colinas Boulevard
Irving, TX 75039
(972) 444-1106
Fax: (972) 444-1405

E-MAIL ADDRESS:
citizenship@exxonmobil.com

WEB SITE ADDRESS:
www.exxonmobil.com/community

FOUNDED: 1998

AREAS OF INTEREST:
Environment, public information and policy research, higher education and pre-college education, health, minority and women-oriented service organizations.

CONSULTING OR VOLUNTEER SERVICES:
The corporation encourages its employees and annuitants to volunteer at nonprofit agencies which serve their local communities with Volunteer Involvement Fund (VIF) grants of up to $500 each.

TYPE:
Capital grants; General operating grants; Matching gifts; Project/program grants.

YEAR PROGRAM STARTED: 1998

PURPOSE:
To provide funding to worthwhile organizations with interests that mirror those of the company.

LEGAL BASIS:
Corporate contributions program.

ELIGIBILITY:
Exxon Mobil makes grants to organizations which have tax-deductible status under Section 501(c)(3) of the Internal Revenue Code. In general, Exxon Mobil contributes to organizations and activities which are national or international in scope or significance and to local agencies only in geographic areas where there is a significant concentration of Exxon Mobil employees or facilities.

Exxon Mobil does not provide funds to be used for religious or political purposes or to individuals. Generally excluded from the grants program are contributions to endowments, organizations formed to combat a single disease and operating support to agencies funded by United Way. Exxon Mobil does not seek, and rarely funds, unsolicited applications and project proposals.

GEOGRAPHIC RESTRICTIONS:
Baldwin and Mobile counties, Alabama; Anchorage, Fairbanks, Juneau and North Slope, Alaska; Santa Barbara County and Torrance, California; District of Columbia; Joliet and vicinity, Illinois; Kingman and Stevens County, Kansas; Baton Rouge, Chalmette, Louisiana; Billings, Montana; Clinton and Paulsboro, New Jersey; Lea County, New Mexico; Akron, Ohio; Texas County, Oklahoma; Baytown, Beaumont, Dallas/Fort Worth, Houston and vicinity, Midland/Odessa and Tyler/Longview, Texas; San Juan County, Utah; Fairfax County and northern Virginia; Lincoln, Sublette and Sweetwater counties, Wyoming.

FINANCIAL DATA:
Amount of support per award: Varies.

APPLICATION INFORMATION:
Exxon Mobil does not seek, and rarely funds, unsolicited applications and project proposals.

PUBLICATIONS:
Annual report.

ADDRESS INQUIRIES TO:
Patrick McCarthy, Manager
Corporate Citizenship COE
(See address above.)

FARGO-MOORHEAD AREA FOUNDATION   [121]
502 First Avenue North, Suite 202
Fargo, ND 58102
(701) 234-0756
Fax: (701) 234-9724

E-MAIL ADDRESS:
office@areafoundation.org

WEB SITE ADDRESS:
www.areafoundation.org

FOUNDED: 1960

AREAS OF INTEREST:
Arts; education; human, youth, civic and
health services.

TYPE:
Project/program grants; Scholarships.

PURPOSE:
To encourage philanthropy; to develop a
permanent endowment to assess and respond
to emerging and changing community needs;
to provide a permanent charitable trust to
donors with varied interests and giving
capacities.

ELIGIBILITY:
Must be 501(c)(3) nonprofit organization.

GEOGRAPHIC RESTRICTIONS:
Cass and Clay counties, Minnesota and North
Dakota.

FINANCIAL DATA:
Amount of support per award: Varies per
award.
Total amount of support: Approximately
$2,300,000 annually.

NUMBER OF AWARDS: Varies.

APPLICATION INFORMATION:
Organizations applying for funds are required
to use the Foundation Grant Proposal Forms
available online, by regular mail, phone or
e-mail (cher@areafoundation.org).
Duration: One year.
Deadline: Grant Proposals will be accepted
anytime before 4:30 P.M., on April 20.
Applicants will be notified on or before May
31.

ADDRESS INQUIRIES TO:
Cher Hersrud, Advancement Officer
(See address above.)

FIELD FOUNDATION OF ILLINOIS   [122]
200 South Wacker Drive, Suite 3860
Chicago, IL 60606
(312) 831-0910
Fax: (312) 831-0961

E-MAIL ADDRESS:
apennick@fieldfoundation.org

WEB SITE ADDRESS:
www.fieldfoundation.org

FOUNDED: 1960

AREAS OF INTEREST:
Health, community welfare, primary and
secondary education, cultural activities,
conservation, and urban and community
affairs.

TYPE:
Capital grants; Challenge/matching grants;
General operating grants; Matching gifts;
Project/program grants; Research grants;
Technical assistance; Training grants. Support
is available for general and capital support
and special programs.

Requests from major cultural institutions for
capital gifts is restricted to
repairs/maintenance or replacement.

Urban affairs grants are made for programs
that strengthen, unify and build urban
communities' metropolitan areas or
neighborhoods.

Through its grants program in primary and
secondary education, the Foundation is
interested in supporting individual public
schools or clusters of schools in three areas:
(1) curriculum development;
(2) teaching quality and;
(3) parental involvement.

YEAR PROGRAM STARTED: 1960

PURPOSE:
To provide support for community, civic and
cultural organizations in the Chicago area,
enabling both new and established programs
to test innovations, to expand proven
strengths or to address specific, time-limited
operational needs.

LEGAL BASIS:
Private foundation.

ELIGIBILITY:
Support is limited to programs primarily
serving Chicago residents. Grants are made
to nonprofit institutions. Grants are not made
directly to individuals.

GEOGRAPHIC RESTRICTIONS:
Chicago, Illinois.

FINANCIAL DATA:
Amount of support per award:
Programs/projects: $10,000 to $25,000.
Grants to individual schools do not exceed
$20,000 a year.
Total amount of support: Approximately
$3,000,000 annually.
Matching fund requirements: Only Board of
Directors and staff can submit matching gift
applications.

NUMBER OF APPLICANTS MOST RECENT YEAR:
335.

NUMBER OF AWARDS: 135.

APPLICATION INFORMATION:
Letter of application should include a brief
description of the project, the proposed
budget, history and background of the
applying organization and certification of the
organization's IRS status.

In order to facilitate staff review, prospective
grantees are encouraged to include the
Self-Certification Checklist.
Duration: One year. Project/program and
capital funding: Possible renewals up to three
years.
Deadline: May 15, September 15 and
January 15.

PUBLICATIONS:
Biennial reports; information brochure
(including application guidelines).

IRS IDENTIFICATION NUMBER: 36-6059408

OFFICERS:
Lyle Logan, Chairman
Aurie Pennick, Executive Director and
Treasurer
Sarah Linsley, Secretary and General Counsel

BOARD OF DIRECTORS:
Judith S. Block
Gloria Castillo
Marshall Field, V
Rita A. Fry
Philip Wayne Hummer
F. Oliver Nicklin
George A. Ranney, Jr.

ADDRESS INQUIRIES TO:
Grants Manager
(See address above.)

FIFTH & PACIFIC FOUNDATION   [123]
2 Park Avenue, 12th Floor
New York, NY 10016
(212) 626-5704

E-MAIL ADDRESS:
foundation@katespade.com

WEB SITE ADDRESS:
www.katespadeandcompany.com

FOUNDED: 1981

AREAS OF INTEREST:
Women's programs only, specifically
economic independence.

TYPE:
Challenge/matching grants; General operating
grants; Matching gifts; Project/program
grants; Seed money grants; Technical
assistance.

YEAR PROGRAM STARTED: 1981

LEGAL BASIS:
Corporate foundation.

ELIGIBILITY:
Organizations classified as 501(c)(3) by the
IRS can apply. Individuals and religious,
political and fraternal organizations are
ineligible.

GEOGRAPHIC RESTRICTIONS:
Hudson County, New Jersey and New York,
New York.

FINANCIAL DATA:
Amount of support per award: $15,000 to
$75,000.
Total amount of support: $1,500,000
annually.
Matching fund requirements: 1:1; $25
minimum and $10,000 annual total per
employee; includes arts, education, health,
human services and the environment.

REPRESENTATIVE AWARDS:
$50,000 to WomenRising, Jersey City, NJ;
$25,000 to Women in Non Traditional
Employment Roles, Los Angeles, CA.

APPLICATION INFORMATION:
Guidelines and application form are available
online.
Duration: One year. Grants are renewable.
Deadline: Applications are accepted
throughout the year.

PUBLICATIONS:
Application guidelines.

IRS IDENTIFICATION NUMBER: 13-3060673

ADDRESS INQUIRIES TO:
Sheila M. Renovitch, Director
(See address above.)

FIRMAN FUND [124]

1422 Euclid Avenue
Hanna Building, Suite 1030
Cleveland, OH 44115-2004
(216) 363-1030
Fax: (216) 363-1038

AREAS OF INTEREST:
Medicine, education, culture, youth, welfare, conservation and community funds.

TYPE:
Capital grants; Endowments; General operating grants; Project/program grants; Research grants.

LEGAL BASIS:
Tax-exempt, private foundation.

ELIGIBILITY:
No grants are awarded to individuals. No unsolicited requests accepted.

GEOGRAPHIC RESTRICTIONS:
Denver, Colorado; Thomasville, Georgia and Cleveland, Ohio.

FINANCIAL DATA:
Amount of support per award: $1,000 to $250,000.
Total amount of support: Approximately $500,000 for the year 2013.

NUMBER OF AWARDS: Approximately 25.

APPLICATION INFORMATION:
First Contact: Letter or Proposal.
Duration: Grants awarded are not to be considered on a continuing basis. Yearly renewal on request.
Deadline: Six weeks prior to the board meetings (April and November).

TRUSTEES:
Royal Firman, III, President
Stephanie Firman
Cynthia F. Webster

*PLEASE NOTE:
The Fund does not accept unsolicited requests for funds.

FIRST COMMUNITY FOUNDATION PARTNERSHIP OF PENNSYLVANIA [125]

330 Pine Street, Suite 400
Williamsport, PA 17701
(570) 321-1500
Fax: (570) 321-6434

E-MAIL ADDRESS:
bettyg@fcfpartnership.org

WEB SITE ADDRESS:
www.fcfpartnership.org

FOUNDED: 1916

AREAS OF INTEREST:
Arts and culture, education, recreation and environment, health, human services, economic and community development.

CONSULTING OR VOLUNTEER SERVICES:
Estate planning seminars, grant applicant training.

NAME(S) OF PROGRAMS:
- **The Ralph and Josephine Smith Fund for Northumberland County**
- **The Margaret Waldron Memorial Fund**
- **The Williamsport-Lycoming Community Fund**

TYPE:
Project/program grants.

YEAR PROGRAM STARTED: 1998

PURPOSE:
To improve the quality of life in Williamsport and Lycoming County, PA.

LEGAL BASIS:
Community foundation.

ELIGIBILITY:
Central and northcentral Pennsylvania qualified 501(c)(3) organizations only.

GEOGRAPHIC RESTRICTIONS:
Bradford, Clinton, Lycoming, Montour, Northumberland, Sullivan and Union counties, Pennsylvania.

FINANCIAL DATA:
Amount of support per award: Varies.
Total amount of support: Varies.

COOPERATIVE FUNDING PROGRAMS:
Scholarships in combination with donor-advised funds.

APPLICATION INFORMATION:
Application must include a copy of the IRS tax determination letter.
Duration: Typically one year.
Deadline: Varies.

PUBLICATIONS:
Annual report; grants and loans policy; *Insights in Estate and Financial Planning*; other tax and estate planning brochures.

IRS IDENTIFICATION NUMBER: 24-6013117

ADDRESS INQUIRIES TO:
Betty Gilmour
Director of Grantmaking
(See address above.)

FIRSTENERGY FOUNDATION [126]

76 South Main Street
Akron, OH 44308
(330) 384-5022

WEB SITE ADDRESS:
www.firstenergycorp.com

FOUNDED: 1961

AREAS OF INTEREST:
Principally education, the arts, community improvements, and overall health of the community.

TYPE:
Capital grants; General operating grants; Matching gifts; Project/program grants.

PURPOSE:
To improve the vitality of our communities and support key safety initiatives; to promote local and regional economic development and revitalization efforts; to support FirstEnergy employees' community leadership and volunteer interests.

LEGAL BASIS:
Corporate foundation.

ELIGIBILITY:
The Foundation supports nonprofit, tax-exempt organizations within the FirstEnergy operating companies' service area including Ohio Edison, The Illuminating Company and Toledo Edison in Ohio; Met-Ed, Penelec, Penn Power and West Penn Power in Pennsylvania; Jersey Central Power and Light in New Jersey; Mon Power and Potomac Edison in West Virginia and Maryland; and where FirstEnergy Solutions Corp., FirstEnergy Generation and FirstEnergy Nuclear Operations conduct business.

Generally, no grants are made to individuals or for political organizations, endowment funds, deficit financing, research, scholarships or fellowships. No loans.

FINANCIAL DATA:
Amount of support per award: Grants vary in amount, depending upon the needs and nature of the request.
Matching fund requirements: Employees only.

NUMBER OF AWARDS: 446.

APPLICATION INFORMATION:
Guidelines available at the Foundation web site.
Deadline: Proposals are accepted throughout the year. Decisions may take up to 12 weeks.

ADDRESS INQUIRIES TO:
Dee Lowery, President
(See address above.)

*SPECIAL STIPULATIONS:
Currently, unsolicited grant applications are not accepted.

A.J. FLETCHER FOUNDATION [127]

909 Glenwood Avenue
Raleigh, NC 27605
(919) 322-2580
Fax: (919) 322-2581

E-MAIL ADDRESS:
natalie@ajf.org

WEB SITE ADDRESS:
www.ajf.org

AREAS OF INTEREST:
Arts, technology, adolescent services, public education, human services, and statewide service needs.

TYPE:
General operating grants.

PURPOSE:
To support nonprofit organizations in their endeavors to improve the quality of life in North Carolina.

ELIGIBILITY:
Eligible organizations must be IRS 501(c)(3) tax-exempt.

GEOGRAPHIC RESTRICTIONS:
North Carolina.

FINANCIAL DATA:
Amount of support per award: Varies.
Total amount of support: Varies.

APPLICATION INFORMATION:
Applicant organizations must include a copy of the IRS tax-exempt determination letter.
Duration: One-time to multiyear funding.

ADDRESS INQUIRIES TO:
Natalie Fogg
Executive Assistant
(See address above.)

THE FLINN FOUNDATION [128]

1802 North Central Avenue
Phoenix, AZ 85004
(602) 744-6800
Fax: (602) 744-6815

E-MAIL ADDRESS:
info@flinn.org

WEB SITE ADDRESS:
www.flinn.org

FOUNDED: 1965

AREAS OF INTEREST:
Biosciences, education, arts and culture, and civic leadership in Arizona.

NAME(S) OF PROGRAMS:
- **Arizona Center for Civic Leadership**
- **Flinn Scholars Program**

TYPE:
Demonstration grants; Fellowships; Project/program grants; Scholarships; Seed money grants. The arts and culture grants program assists Arizona's large arts and culture organizations in generating capital through creative programming and fiscal planning.

The Foundation's biosciences grant projects aim to strengthen Arizona's biosciences infrastructure and thereby improve the state's capacity to compete nationally and internationally in the biosciences economy.

The Arizona Center for Civic Leadership seeks to strengthen civic leadership in Arizona.

The Flinn Scholars Program annually awards top Arizona high school graduates full scholarship support.

YEAR PROGRAM STARTED: 1981

PURPOSE:
To improve the quality of life in Arizona to benefit future generations through support of the biosciences, arts and culture, the Flinn Scholars and civic leadership.

LEGAL BASIS:
Tax-exempt private foundation.

ELIGIBILITY:
Grant applicants must be tax-exempt, nonprofit organizations which have qualified for exemption under Section 501(c)(3) of the IRS code and, generally, are not those classified as private foundations.

Grants are made only for charitable purposes that support organizations and activities in Arizona. The Foundation generally does not make grants to support individuals, building and equipment projects, endowment or annual fund-raising campaigns or to meet ongoing operating costs or deficits.

GEOGRAPHIC RESTRICTIONS:
Arizona.

FINANCIAL DATA:
Foundation assets of $194,800,000 for the year ended 2012.

Amount of support per award: Varies.

Total amount of support: The Foundation awarded $6,200,000 in new grants in 2012 and made cash payments of $5,300,000 toward current and prior-year grant awards.

COOPERATIVE FUNDING PROGRAMS: The Flinn-Brown Civic Leadership Academy, a component of the Arizona Center for Civic Leadership, is co-funded by the Thomas R. Brown Foundations.

NUMBER OF AWARDS: Payments were made on 61 grants in 2012, including 15 grants awarded in prior years and 46 new grants authorized in 2012.

REPRESENTATIVE AWARDS:
$200,000 to Northern Arizona University to partner with Flagstaff Medical Center on collaboration between basic scientists and clinical researchers; $1,840,000 to Arizona State University for Flinn Scholarship awards; $75,000 to Tucson Symphony Orchestra to attract younger audiences through contemporary programming.

APPLICATION INFORMATION:
No unsolicited applications accepted. There is no standard application form, except for those proposals submitted in response to a Foundation-initiated program.

Duration: Varies.

PUBLICATIONS:
Annual report; special reports; electronic newsletters.

ADMINISTRATIVE STAFF:
Jack B. Jewett, President and Chief Executive Officer
Catherine McGonigle, Executive Vice President
William A. Read, Ph.D., Senior Vice President, Research and Special Programs
Don P. Snider, C.P.A., Vice President and Chief Financial Officer
Bradley W. Halvorsen, Vice President, Communications
Nancy Welch, Vice President, Arizona Center for Civic Leadership

*SPECIAL STIPULATIONS:
No unsolicited applications accepted.

THE FORD FOUNDATION   [129]

320 East 43rd Street
New York, NY 10017
(212) 573-5000
Fax: (212) 351-3677

E-MAIL ADDRESS:
office-secretary@fordfoundation.org

WEB SITE ADDRESS:
www.fordfoundation.org

FOUNDED: 1936

NAME(S) OF PROGRAMS:
- **Democracy, Rights and Justice Program**
- **Economic Opportunity and Assets Program**
- **Education, Creativity and Free Expression Program**

TYPE:
Conferences/seminars; Endowments; Fellowships; General operating grants; Matching gifts; Project/program grants; Research grants; Seed money grants; Technical assistance. General purposes, publications, program-related investments, special projects, individual grants.

Democracy, Rights and Justice Program deals with the issues of democratic and accountable government, human rights, and social justice philanthropy.

Economic Opportunity and Assets Program deals with the issues of economic fairness, metropolitan opportunity, and sustainable development.

Education, Creativity and Free Expression Program deals with the issues of educational opportunity and scholarship, freedom of expression, and sexuality and reproductive health and rights.

PURPOSE:
To reduce poverty and injustice and to promote democratic values, international cooperation and human achievement.

LEGAL BASIS:
Private foundation.

ELIGIBILITY:
Qualified institutions, individuals and communities with appropriate interests are eligible to apply. Most of the Foundation's grant funds are given to organizations. Although the Foundation also makes grants to individuals, such grants are few in number relative to demand. These are limited to research, training and other activities related to the Foundation's program interests and subject to certain limitations and procedural requirements under the U.S. Internal Revenue Code.

The Foundation does not award undergraduate scholarships or make grants for purely personal or local needs. Support for graduate fellowships is generally funneled through grants to universities and other organizations, which are responsible for the selection of recipients. Support is not normally given for routine operating costs of institutions or for religious activities. Except in rare cases, funding is not available for the construction or maintenance of buildings.

FINANCIAL DATA:
Amount of support per award: Grants vary in amount, depending upon the needs and nature of the request. Average grant to organizations: $230,000.

Total amount of support: Approximately $423,000,000 total grants, program-related investments and Foundation-administered projects for fiscal year ended December 31, 2013.

APPLICATION INFORMATION:
Prospective applicants should, as a first step, submit a brief letter of inquiry in order to determine whether the Foundation's present interests and funds permit consideration as a proposal.

There is no application form. Proposals should set forth objectives, the proposed program for pursuing objectives, qualifications of persons engaged in the work, a detailed budget, present means of support and status of applications to other funding sources and legal and tax status.

Duration: Varies.

Deadline: Applications are considered throughout the year.

PUBLICATIONS:
Annual report; program policy statement including application guidelines; *Ford Foundation Report,* issued quarterly.

IRS IDENTIFICATION NUMBER: 13-1684331

OFFICERS:
Darren Walker, President
Nicholas M. Gabriel, Vice President, Treasurer and Chief Financial Officer
Ricardo Castro, Vice President, Secretary and General Counsel
Eric Doppstadt, Vice President and Chief Investment Officer
Martin Abregu, Vice President, Democracy, Rights and Justice
Xavier de Souza Briggs, Vice President, Economic Opportunity and Assets
Hilary Pennington, Vice President, Education, Creativity and Free Expression
Marta Lourdes Tellado, Vice President for Communications

BOARD OF TRUSTEES:
Irene Hirano Inouye, Chairperson of the Board
Kofi Appenteng
Tim Berners-Lee
Martin Eakes
Amy C. Falls
Juliet V. Garcia
J. Clifford Hudson
Robert S. Kaplan

Lourdes Lopez
Thurgood Marshall, Jr.
N.R. Narayana Murthy
Peter A. Nadosy
Cecile Richards
Darren Walker

ADDRESS INQUIRIES TO:
Office of the Secretary
(See address above.)

FORD MOTOR COMPANY FUND & COMMUNITY SERVICES [130]

One American Road, 11th Floor
Dearborn, MI 48126-2798
(313) 248-7210
Fax: (313) 337-1713

E-MAIL ADDRESS:
fordfund@ford.com

WEB SITE ADDRESS:
www.community.ford.com

FOUNDED: 1949

AREAS OF INTEREST:
Innovation and education, community
development and American legacy, and
auto-related safety education.

NAME(S) OF PROGRAMS:
● **Community Grants Program**

TYPE:
Project/program grants. Support largely for
education, including basic research grants,
community funds and urban affairs, and civic
and cultural programs.

PURPOSE:
To support initiatives and institutions that
enhance and/or improve opportunities for
those who live in communities where Ford
Motor Company operates.

LEGAL BASIS:
Corporate foundation.

ELIGIBILITY:
No grants are made directly to individuals.
Not-for-profit organizations with 501(c)(3)
tax-exempt status may apply.

GEOGRAPHIC RESTRICTIONS:
United States.

FINANCIAL DATA:
Amount of support per award: Varies.
Total amount of support: Varies.

APPLICATION INFORMATION:
Application form available online. Paper
proposals not accepted.
Duration: Varies.

ADDRESS INQUIRIES TO:
Jim Vella, President
(See address above.)

FREEMAN FOUNDATION [131]

c/o The Rockefeller Trust Company
10 Rockefeller Plaza
New York, NY 10020
(212) 549-5270
Fax: (212) 549-5519

FOUNDED: 1978

AREAS OF INTEREST:
Asian studies, environmental conservation
and preservation, and Vermont programs.

TYPE:
Challenge/matching grants; Exchange
programs; Fellowships; General operating
grants; Professorships; Project/program
grants; Research grants; Scholarships; Seed
money grants; Technical assistance; Training
grants; Travel grants; Visiting scholars.

PURPOSE:
To support a range of charitable
organizations.

ELIGIBILITY:
Eligible organizations must be IRS 501(c)(3)
tax-exempt.

GEOGRAPHIC RESTRICTIONS:
Hawaii, Vermont and Asia.

FINANCIAL DATA:
Amount of support per award: $5,000 to
$750,000.
Total amount of support: $13,809,079 for
2012.

NUMBER OF APPLICANTS MOST RECENT YEAR:
50.

NUMBER OF AWARDS: 200.

APPLICATION INFORMATION:
Applicants should submit a letter describing
the program and financial needs.
Duration: Varies by the program. Renewal
possible.
Deadline: Applications must be received at
least one month prior to quarterly Trustee's
meetings.

PUBLICATIONS:
Annual report.

IRS IDENTIFICATION NUMBER: 13-2965090

TRUSTEES AND OFFICERS:
Graeme Freeman, President
George Snell
George Tsandikos

ADDRESS INQUIRIES TO:
The Rockefeller Trust Company
George S. Tsandikos, Managing Director
(See address above.)

FREEPORT-MCMORAN COPPER & GOLD FOUNDATION [132]

333 North Central Avenue
Phoenix, AZ 85004
(602) 366-8018
(602) 366-8100
Fax: (602) 366-7368

E-MAIL ADDRESS:
foundation@fmi.com

WEB SITE ADDRESS:
www.fcx.com

FOUNDED: 1953

AREAS OF INTEREST:
Community safety, health and wellness,
environment, cultural preservation and the
arts, economic development, and education
and training.

NAME(S) OF PROGRAMS:
● **Matching Gifts Program**
● **Social Investment Program**

TYPE:
Matching gifts; Project/program grants.

YEAR PROGRAM STARTED: 1932

PURPOSE:
To serve as a catalyst of positive change in
the communities where the company has
major facilities and update the quality of life.

LEGAL BASIS:
Corporate foundation.

ELIGIBILITY:
Nonprofit programs and organizations aligned
with the core values of the company. Must be
located in communities where the company
has a presence.

GEOGRAPHIC RESTRICTIONS:
United States.

FINANCIAL DATA:
Amount of support per award: Varies.
Matching fund requirements: Minimum $25.
First $500 is matched 2:1; above $500 is
matched dollar-for-dollar.

APPLICATION INFORMATION:
Guidelines and application are available on
the Foundation web site.
Duration: One year. Renewable.
Deadline: Proposals are accepted throughout
the year. Social Investment Program: August
30 for grant award the following year.

OFFICERS:
Tracy Bame, Director of Social
Responsibility and Community Development

ADDRESS INQUIRIES TO:
Contributions Administrator
(See address above.)

FRESNO REGIONAL FOUNDATION [133]

5250 North Palm Avenue
Suite 424
Fresno, CA 93704
(559) 226-5600
Fax: (559) 230-2078

E-MAIL ADDRESS:
info@fresnoregfoundation.org

WEB SITE ADDRESS:
fresnoregfoundation.org

FOUNDED: 1966

AREAS OF INTEREST:
Primarily arts and culture, health and human
services, and youth services, environment,
high impact with a lesser emphasis on parks
and music.

NAME(S) OF PROGRAMS:
● **Arts and Culture**
● **Environment**
● **High Impact**
● **Human Services**
● **Teen Pregnancy Prevention Initiative**
● **Youth Grants**

TYPE:
General operating grants; Project/program
grants.

LEGAL BASIS:
Community foundation.

ELIGIBILITY:
Generally, applicants must be exempt under
Internal Revenue Code Section 501(c)(3).
However, if it is found that a grant to an
agency or organization presents an
opportunity to be of substantial service to the
community, and there are no others that
provide the program or activity within the
applicant's service area, such proposals will
be considered. Public schools, municipalities
and public agencies may also be eligible
applicants.

GEOGRAPHIC RESTRICTIONS:
Central San Joaquin Valley, California;
primarily the counties of Fresno, Kings,
Madera, Mariposa, Merced, and Tulare.

FINANCIAL DATA:
Amount of support per award: Varies.

Total amount of support: $5,500,000 for the year 2012.

APPLICATION INFORMATION:
There is an online application process; the beginning step is to complete the organization profile form.
Duration: One year. Renewal possible. High Impact grants: Multiyear. Teen Pregnancy Prevention Initiative: Two-year grants.
Deadline: Varies.

STAFF:
Daniel DeSantis, Chief Executive Officer
Sandra Flores, Senior Program Officer

ADDRESS INQUIRIES TO:
Sandra Flores, Senior Program Officer
(See address above.)

FREY FOUNDATION   [134]
40 Pearl Street, N.W.
Suite 1100
Grand Rapids, MI 49503-3028
(616) 451-0303
Fax: (616) 451-8481

E-MAIL ADDRESS:
contact@freyfdn.org

WEB SITE ADDRESS:
www.freyfdn.org

FOUNDED: 1974

AREAS OF INTEREST:
Children and their families, environment, community arts, civic progress, and philanthropy.

NAME(S) OF PROGRAMS:
• **Community Capital Projects**
• **Encouraging Civic Progress**
• **Enhancing the Lives of Children and Their Families**
• **Nurturing Community Arts**
• **Protecting the Environment**
• **Strengthening Philanthropy**

TYPE:
Capital grants; Demonstration grants; Project/program grants; Seed money grants; Technical assistance. Grants are available for special one-time only or time-limited purposes, such as "start-up" or program expansion, demonstration projects, planning or other forms of technical assistance, evaluation, advocacy, and applied research. Capital is available in some program areas.

YEAR PROGRAM STARTED: 1974

PURPOSE:
To promote healthy development of children and their families, particularly infants and children under the age of six and their parents, with special attention to traditionally disadvantaged populations; to protect, preserve and improve the ecological health of natural resources; to stimulate vitality, effectiveness and growth of community-based arts; to encourage civic action to improve the livability of cities and communities; to improve the effectiveness of organized philanthropy and stimulate its growth.

LEGAL BASIS:
Private family foundation.

ELIGIBILITY:
Applicants must be public institutions and 501(c)(3) nonprofit organizations. No grants to individuals, endowment funds, debt retirement, general operating expenses, scholarships, travel, to cover routine, current or emergency expenses and/or sectarian charitable activities.

GEOGRAPHIC RESTRICTIONS:
Grand Rapids area, Emmet or Charlevoix counties, Michigan.

FINANCIAL DATA:
Amount of support per award: Varies upon nature of request.
Total amount of support: $7,400,000.

NUMBER OF AWARDS: Average 75 per year.

APPLICATION INFORMATION:
Eligible applicants are encouraged to contact the Foundation to discuss prospective proposals and to receive a set of guidelines and application materials.
Duration: One year.
Deadline: February 15, May 15, August 15 and November 15.

PUBLICATIONS:
Annual report; *Taking Care of Civic Business*; *Charting the Course*; *Today's Winners, Tomorrow's Losers.*

STAFF:
Steve Wilson, President
Joyce Bobolts, Director of Finance and Administration
Lynne J. Ferrell, Program Officer
Kristine L. Huizen, Program Officer
Teresa J. Crawford, Grants Manager

BOARD OF TRUSTEES:
David G. Frey, Chairman
John M. Frey, Vice Chairman
Edward J. Frey, Jr., Secretary, Treasurer and Trustee

ADDRESS INQUIRIES TO:
Steve Wilson, President
(See address above.)

THE FROST FOUNDATION, LTD.   [135]
511 Armijo Street, Suite A
Santa Fe, NM 87501
(505) 986-0208
Fax: (505) 986-0430

E-MAIL ADDRESS:
frost0729@aol.com
info@frostfound.org

WEB SITE ADDRESS:
www.frostfound.org

FOUNDED: 1959

AREAS OF INTEREST:
Social service and humanitarian needs, the environment and education.

CONSULTING OR VOLUNTEER SERVICES:
Professional services of staff are offered for special projects.

TYPE:
Challenge/matching grants; Project/program grants; Research grants; Seed money grants.

YEAR PROGRAM STARTED: 1959

PURPOSE:
To seek and assist innovative projects that will have positive impact beyond the boundaries of a single state.

LEGAL BASIS:
Tax-exempt private foundation.

ELIGIBILITY:
The Foundation encourages self-reliance, creativity and ingenuity on the part of prospective recipients.

Its efforts are directed primarily to support exemplary organizations and programs which can generate positive change beyond

traditional boundaries, to encourage creativity which recognizes emerging needs, and to assist innovation which addresses current urgent problems.

Within these parameters, it provides initial impetus to exemplary organizations and programs, to operating funds, to pioneering organizations and programs which other institutions might similarly use, and to programs which have potential for wider service or educational exposure than an individual community.

The Foundation encourages collaborations, mergers and the formation of alliances among agencies within the community to reduce duplication of effort and to promote a maximum effective use of funds. The Foundation also considers requests for operating. It is prepared to review applications of human service needs, environmental and education programs in New Mexico and Louisiana from organizations which have an IRS 501(c)(3) determination.

GEOGRAPHIC RESTRICTIONS:
Louisiana and New Mexico.

FINANCIAL DATA:
Amount of support per award: $15,000 average.
Total amount of support: Approximately $2,000,000 annually.

NUMBER OF APPLICANTS MOST RECENT YEAR:
Approximately 500.

NUMBER OF AWARDS: Approximately 65.

APPLICATION INFORMATION:
A brief description of the institution/organization, including its mission, must be submitted along with evidence of tax-exempt status, the amount requested, a statement of the specific need(s) to be met by the project, a budget projection with the time frame expected and the qualifications of the staff members selected to serve the project. Faxed summaries are not accepted.
Duration: Typically one year. On rare occasions, because of special circumstances, grants will be renewed.
Deadline: December 1 for March Board meeting and June 1 for September Board meeting.

PUBLICATIONS:
Annual report; application guidelines.

OFFICERS:
Mary Amelia Whited-Howell, President
Philip B. Howell, Executive Vice President and Treasurer
Taylor F. Moore, Secretary

BOARD OF DIRECTORS:
Ann Rogers Gerber
Philip B. Howell
Taylor F. Moore
Mary Amelia Whited-Howell

EXECUTIVE COMMITTEE:
Philip B. Howell
Mary Amelia Whited-Howell

ADDRESS INQUIRIES TO:
Mary Amelia Whited-Howell, President
(See address above.)

LLOYD A. FRY FOUNDATION [136]
120 South LaSalle Street
Suite 1950
Chicago, IL 60603
(312) 580-0310
Fax: (312) 580-0980

E-MAIL ADDRESS:
usong@fryfoundation.org

WEB SITE ADDRESS:
www.fryfoundation.org

FOUNDED: 1983

AREAS OF INTEREST:
Education, arts and culture education, access to health care, and employment, with special emphasis on support of inner-city projects.

TYPE:
Project/program grants.

LEGAL BASIS:
Private foundation.

ELIGIBILITY:
501(c)(3).

GEOGRAPHIC RESTRICTIONS:
Inner-city Chicago, Illinois.

FINANCIAL DATA:
Amount of support per award: $15,000 to $50,000 average.
Total amount of support: Varies.

NUMBER OF AWARDS: 350.

APPLICATION INFORMATION:
Application and guidelines are available at the Foundation web site.
Duration: One year.
Deadline: December 1, March 1, June 1 and September 1.

PUBLICATIONS:
Annual report.

IRS IDENTIFICATION NUMBER: 36-6108775

STAFF:
Unmi Song, President
Diane Sotiros, C.P.A., Controller
Soo Na, Program Officer
Jessica Leggin, Program Assistant
Jennifer Moss, Program Assistant
Lisa Torres, Program Assistant

ADDRESS INQUIRIES TO:
Unmi Song, President
(See address above.)

GANNETT FOUNDATION [137]
7950 Jones Branch Drive
McLean, VA 22107-0150
(703) 854-6047
(703) 854-6000
Fax: (703) 854-2167

E-MAIL ADDRESS:
foundation@gannett.com

WEB SITE ADDRESS:
www.gannettfoundation.org

FOUNDED: 1991

AREAS OF INTEREST:
Education and neighborhood improvement, economic development, youth development, community problem-solving, assistance to disadvantaged people, environmental conservation and cultural enrichment.

TYPE:
General operating grants; Matching gifts; Project/program grants.

PURPOSE:
To improve the education, health and advancement of the people who live in Gannett communities.

LEGAL BASIS:
Corporate foundation.

ELIGIBILITY:
Local organizations determined by the IRS to be tax-exempt under 501(c)(3) in communities where the Gannett Company, Inc. owns a daily newspaper or broadcast station.

FINANCIAL DATA:
Amount of support per award: $4,000 to $6,000.
Matching fund requirements: Gifts for programs or initiatives where the primary purpose is the promotion of religious doctrine or tenets are excluded.

NUMBER OF AWARDS: 1,200.

APPLICATION INFORMATION:
Application form and guidelines are available online.
Duration: One year. Renewal possible.

ADDRESS INQUIRIES TO:
Pat Lyle, Program Administrator
(See address above.)

GATX CORPORATION [138]
222 West Adams Street
Chicago, IL 60606
(312) 621-6200
Fax: (312) 621-6648

E-MAIL ADDRESS:
community@gatx.com
contactgatx@gatx.com

WEB SITE ADDRESS:
www.gatx.com

FOUNDED: 1898

AREAS OF INTEREST:
Education, family and environment, cultural, health care, and social service issues.

NAME(S) OF PROGRAMS:
- **Dollars-for-Doers**
- **Employee Matching Gifts**

TYPE:
Challenge/matching grants; Development grants; General operating grants; Grants-in-aid; Internships; Matching gifts; Project/program grants; Seed money grants; Technical assistance. United Way support, employee matching gift program for 501(c)(3) organizations, education, family issues, and environment.

YEAR PROGRAM STARTED: 1953

PURPOSE:
To improve communities by proactively supporting significant issues relevant to the economic viability of the Corporation's local communities through initiatives that are consistent with the Corporation's business interests.

LEGAL BASIS:
Corporate contributions program.

ELIGIBILITY:
Applicants must be nonprofit tax-exempt organizations with a 501(c)(3) tax-exempt status. The Corporation will not fund individuals, political or religious organizations, foundations, capital campaigns or endowment funds.

GEOGRAPHIC RESTRICTIONS:
Chicago neighborhoods of Englewood, Grand Boulevard and Humboldt Park.

FINANCIAL DATA:
Amount of support per award: $5,000 to $50,000.
Matching fund requirements: $50 minimum and $2,000 maximum per employee and calendar year.

NUMBER OF APPLICANTS MOST RECENT YEAR: 295.

NUMBER OF AWARDS: 75.

REPRESENTATIVE AWARDS:
Education: $20,000 to Chicago Communities in Schools; $53,000 to Waterford Institute; Families: $14,600 to the Robert Crown Center for Health Education; Environment: $25,000 to Wildlife Habitat Council.

APPLICATION INFORMATION:
All applicants must use the Chicago Area Grant Application. A complete application includes the following materials:
(1) Chicago Area Grant Application (CAGA);
(2) application narrative as described in the CAGA;
(3) itemized budget for the project;
(4) itemized organizational budget for the current fiscal year;
(5) audited financial statement for the most recently completed fiscal year;
(6) brief biographies of key organizational staff, including job description and professional qualifications;
(7) list of institutional funding for the current fiscal year, including amounts;
(8) a list of members of the board of directors, including affiliations;
(9) annual report for the most recently completed fiscal year, if available, and;
(10) IRS tax determination letter indicating the applicant's status as a 501(c)(3) nonprofit organization or equivalent.
Duration: One year. Renewals are possible after formal request has been received.
Deadline: January 15, April 15, July 15 and October 15. Announcement approximately three weeks after committee meeting.

PUBLICATIONS:
Application guidelines; grant application form.

THE CARL GELLERT AND CELIA BERTA GELLERT FOUNDATION [139]
2171 Junipero Serra Boulevard, Suite 310
Daly City, CA 94014
(650) 985-2080
Fax: (650) 985-2084

E-MAIL ADDRESS:
info@gellertfoundation.org

WEB SITE ADDRESS:
www.gellertfoundation.org

FOUNDED: 1958

AREAS OF INTEREST:
Religious, charitable, scientific, literary or educational purposes.

TYPE:
Capital grants; Development grants; Endowments; General operating grants; Project/program grants; Scholarships; Technical assistance.

YEAR PROGRAM STARTED: 1958

LEGAL BASIS:
Private foundation.

ELIGIBILITY:
Grants are available for nonprofit tax-exempt organizations which are not private foundations, that have and can prove 501(c)(3) and 509(a)170(b) status. No grants to individuals.

GEOGRAPHIC RESTRICTIONS:
Alameda, Contra Costa, Marin, Napa, San Francisco, San Mateo, Santa Clara, Solano and Sonoma, the nine counties of the Greater San Francisco Bay area, California.

FINANCIAL DATA:
Amount of support per award: Varies.

APPLICATION INFORMATION:
One copy of the following items are to be submitted to the Foundation:
(1) Grant Request Application with an original signature and all line items on the form completed;
(2) documentation of 501(c)(3) tax-exempt classification;
(3) documentation of 509(a)(1) and 170(b)(1)(A) status;
(4) an unbound copy of the most recently filed Form 990;
(5) one unbound proposal, five pages or less, to include a brief history and statement of the current goals and activities of the organization and a brief outline of the project and phase of project for which the organization seeks funding, showing demonstration of need, population served, specific objectives and outcomes, time line of the project, amount of funding required for the project, and the specific amount of funding (no ranges) requested from the Foundation and;
(6) project budget.

Name of the organization applying for a grant must be consistent on all required documentation (application, letterhead, IRS letters, Form 990). Tax ID number/EIN must also be the same. All documentation must show the address of the organization to be within one of the nine counties of the San Francisco Bay area.

Electronic submissions will not be accepted.

Deadline: August 15, annually or following Monday if 15th falls on a weekend.

IRS IDENTIFICATION NUMBER: 94-6062858

DIRECTORS:
Marie C. Bentley
Andrew A. Cresci
Lorraine D'Elia
Jack Fitzpatrick
Robert J. Grassilli, Jr.
Michael J. King
J. Malcolm Visbal

ADDRESS INQUIRIES TO:
Jack Fitzpatrick, Executive Director
(See address above.)

THE FRED GELLERT FAMILY FOUNDATION   [140]
1038 Redwood Highway
Building B, Suite 2
Mill Valley, CA 94941
(415) 381-7575
Fax: (415) 381-8526

E-MAIL ADDRESS:
sgfamilyfoundation@gmail.com

WEB SITE ADDRESS:
www.sgfamilyfoundation.com

FOUNDED: 1958

AREAS OF INTEREST:
Long-term sustainability planning: Environmental, advanced and specialized education, local community support through social service organizations, and reproductive health.

TYPE:
Challenge/matching grants; General operating grants; Matching gifts; Project/program grants; Seed money grants.

YEAR PROGRAM STARTED: 1958

PURPOSE:
To advance positive forces for social change to ensure quality of life for future generations.

LEGAL BASIS:
Private family foundation.

ELIGIBILITY:
Applicants must be 501(c)(3) organizations. No grants to individuals or for purchasing development rights or land. No unsolicited grant proposals are accepted.

GEOGRAPHIC RESTRICTIONS:
California Bay area.

FINANCIAL DATA:
Amount of support per award: $1,000 to $40,000; Average: $5,000.

Total amount of support: $345,000 for the year 2013.

Matching fund requirements: Provide information on challenge grant.

NUMBER OF APPLICANTS MOST RECENT YEAR:
Approximately 120 for the year 2012.

REPRESENTATIVE AWARDS:
$3,000 to Richardson Bay Audubon; $4,000 to Campaign to Safeguard America's Waters; $20,000 to Resource Renewal Institute.

APPLICATION INFORMATION:
The Foundation does not accept unsolicited inquiries.

Duration: Typically one year.

Deadline: Grantee annual reports due December 31. Grant monies released in April.

ADDRESS INQUIRIES TO:
See e-mail address above.

GENERAL SERVICE FOUNDATION   [141]
557 North Mill Street
Suite 201
Aspen, CO 81611
(970) 920-6834
Fax: (970) 920-4578

WEB SITE ADDRESS:
www.generalservice.org

FOUNDED: 1946

AREAS OF INTEREST:
Human rights and economic justice, reproductive justice, and Colorado.

NAME(S) OF PROGRAMS:
● **Colorado Program**
● **Human Rights and Economic Justice**
● **Reproductive Justice**

TYPE:
Challenge/matching grants; Demonstration grants; Development grants; General operating grants; Project/program grants; Seed money grants; Technical assistance; Travel grants. The goal of the Human Rights

and Economic Justice program is to advance and strengthen human rights, democratic reform, and economic justice in Mexico.

The goal of the Reproductive Justice program is to ensure that women and girls in the U.S. have the power and resources to make healthy decisions about their bodies, sexuality and reproduction.

The goal of the Foundation's grantmaking program in Colorado is to (a) build the capacity of key base-building organizations committed to justice and equity in the state, and (b) to facilitate collaboration among its grantees and also between its grantees and other sectors (including media, research, leadership, policy and issue-advocacy groups) to create a powerful, permanent infrastructure capable of affecting statewide policy change over the long term.

YEAR PROGRAM STARTED: 1946

PURPOSE:
To address some of the world's basic long-term problems; to bring about a more just and sustainable world; to nurture and learn from strategic partnerships, embracing risk and possibility; to align every aspect of Foundation's organization with its deeply held values which include a commitment to leadership, integrity, diversity, experimentation, accountability, justice and excellence.

LEGAL BASIS:
Private foundation, tax-exempt under IRS statute 501(c)(3).

ELIGIBILITY:
Organizations must be tax-exempt under U.S. law.

In general, the Foundation does not contribute to annual campaigns, nor to capital campaigns, to individuals or for relief.

Because the Foundation's areas of concern are broad, the Board has determined guidelines within each area. All applicants are urged only to submit applications falling within the Foundation's Contribution Policy and Guidelines.

GEOGRAPHIC RESTRICTIONS:
Mexico and the United States.

FINANCIAL DATA:
Amount of support per award: $2,000 to $50,000.

NUMBER OF APPLICANTS MOST RECENT YEAR:
Approximately 165.

NUMBER OF AWARDS: 66.

APPLICATION INFORMATION:
The Foundation requests that applications for contributions be in line with the approved guidelines and be submitted online.

Duration: One to two years.

Deadline: February 1 and September 1 for letters of inquiry.

IRS IDENTIFICATION NUMBER: 36-6018535

OFFICERS:
Robin Snidow, Board Chairperson
Zoe Estrin, Vice Chairperson
Will Halby, Treasurer
Marcie J. Musser, Secretary
Sara Samuels, Assistant Secretary

DIRECTORS:
Eliot Estrin
Mary Lloyd Estrin
Robert L. Estrin
Griff Foxley

THE GEORGE FOUNDATION [142]

215 Morton Street
Richmond, TX 77469
(281) 342-6109
Fax: (281) 341-7635

E-MAIL ADDRESS:
dkoch@thegeorgefoundation.org

WEB SITE ADDRESS:
www.thegeorgefoundation.org

FOUNDED: 1945

AREAS OF INTEREST:
Basic human needs and education.

TYPE:
Capital grants; General operating grants;
Project/program grants; Scholarships.
Preventative programs for children and
families.

YEAR PROGRAM STARTED: 1947

PURPOSE:
To support organizations and programs that
assist in developing strong, stable families
with emphasis on the economically
disadvantaged.

ELIGIBILITY:
Applicants must be 501(c)(3) nonprofit
organizations. No grants to individuals.

GEOGRAPHIC RESTRICTIONS:
Fort Bend County area, Texas.

FINANCIAL DATA:
Amount of support per award: Varies.
Total amount of support: $12,000,000.

APPLICATION INFORMATION:
Guidelines and application are available at
the web site.
Duration: One year. Reapplication must be
made for additional funding.
Deadline: January 15, April 15, July 15 and
October 15.

TRUSTEES:
William Jameson
Pat McDonald
Thomas McNutt
John Null
Don Wenzel

ADDRESS INQUIRIES TO:
Dee Koch, Grants Officer
(See address and e-mail above.)

GEORGIA-PACIFIC FOUNDATION [143]

133 Peachtree Street, N.E.
32nd Floor
Atlanta, GA 30303
(404) 652-4182
Fax: (404) 749-2754

WEB SITE ADDRESS:
www.gp.com/gpfoundation

FOUNDED: 1927

AREAS OF INTEREST:
Education, environment, entrepreneurship,
community enrichment and employee
involvement.

TYPE:
Project/program grants; Scholarships.

PURPOSE:
To make investments that improve the quality
of life in communities where Georgia-Pacific
employees live and work.

LEGAL BASIS:
Corporate foundation.

ELIGIBILITY:
Organizations must have 501(c)(3)
tax-exemption status from the IRS.

The Foundation does not support
organizations that discriminate on the basis
of race, color, creed, national origin or
gender; private organizations; "bail-out"
funds given to provide emergency assistance
to organizations for general operating
purposes; individuals, other than through
scholarship and community service programs;
political causes, candidates and legislative
lobbying or advocacy efforts of any type;
churches or religious denominations,
religious or theological schools; general
operating support for United Way member
agencies; operating support for colleges and
universities; fund-raising events such as
raffles, telethons, walk-a-thons and auctions;
and for trips and tours.

FINANCIAL DATA:
Amount of support per award: Minimum
$1,000.

APPLICATION INFORMATION:
Send a written proposal including the project
goals, budget and anticipated results.
Deadline: January 1 through October 31.
Within 45 days of receipt of the request with
the appropriate documentation, the
Foundation will respond with written
notification as to whether the grant is
accepted.

GHEENS FOUNDATION [144]

401 West Main Street
Suite 705
Louisville, KY 40202
(502) 584-4650
Fax: (502) 584-4652

E-MAIL ADDRESS:
carl@gheensfoundation.org

WEB SITE ADDRESS:
gheensfoundation.org

FOUNDED: 1957

AREAS OF INTEREST:
Culture, education and health.

TYPE:
Capital grants; Challenge/matching grants;
Development grants; General operating
grants; Project/program grants; Research
grants; Scholarships; Technical assistance.

YEAR PROGRAM STARTED: 1957

PURPOSE:
To support programs that meet the needs of
society and improve the quality of life in the
community.

LEGAL BASIS:
501(c)(3), private foundation.

ELIGIBILITY:
Grants are made to organizations that have
tax-exempt status under Section 501(c)(3) of
the Internal Revenue Code. No grants are
made to individuals.

GEOGRAPHIC RESTRICTIONS:
Louisville, Kentucky, Terrebone and
Lafourche parishes in Louisiana.

FINANCIAL DATA:
Amount of support per award: Varies
depending on the nature of the request.
Total amount of support: Varies.

NUMBER OF APPLICANTS MOST RECENT YEAR:
219.

NUMBER OF AWARDS: 100.

APPLICATION INFORMATION:
All applications must have written approval
from the President, Chief Executive Officer,
or Head of the nonprofit applicant.

The following items must be included in the
application package:
(1) seven copies of the application form
(pages 1 and 2, program and financial
summaries, questions 1 to 7);
(2) one copy of the IRS tax determination
letter and certificate;
(3) one copy of the Annual Federal Return
(Form 990) and;
(4) seven copies of any supporting materials,
such as a larger proposal, brochures, needs
assessment, or letters of support.
Duration: One year. May reapply.
Deadline: Prior to meetings in March, June,
September and December.

ADDRESS INQUIRIES TO:
Carl M. Thomas, Executive Director
(See address above.)

HERMAN GOLDMAN FOUNDATION [145]

44 Wall Street
Suite 1212
New York, NY 10005
(212) 461-2132
Fax: (212) 461-2223

E-MAIL ADDRESS:
rbaron@hermangoldman.com

FOUNDED: 1942

AREAS OF INTEREST:
Arts, health, social justice and education.

TYPE:
General operating grants; Grants-in-aid;
Project/program grants.

YEAR PROGRAM STARTED: 1943

PURPOSE:
To benefit those in need.

LEGAL BASIS:
Private foundation.

ELIGIBILITY:
Grants for individuals are not considered. It
is not possible to respond to emergency
requests, nor to financial needs of crash
programs because of the time the Foundation
requires to study grant proposals. Applicants
must be tax-exempt organizations.

GEOGRAPHIC RESTRICTIONS:
Primarily, New York City metropolitan area.

FINANCIAL DATA:
Amount of support per award: $1,000 to
$50,000.
Total amount of support: Varies.

APPLICATION INFORMATION:
Applicants should submit one copy only of a written proposal and/or can use the New York-New Jersey area Common Grant Application Form. No letter of inquiry required. Applicants must provide IRS tax-exempt documentation.

Duration: One year.

Deadline: Applications accepted throughout the year.

PUBLICATIONS:
Annual report.

ADDRESS INQUIRIES TO:
Richard K. Baron, Executive Director
(See address above.)

THE GOODYEAR TIRE & RUBBER COMPANY   [146]
200 Innovation Way
Akron, OH 44316-0001
(330) 796-2244

E-MAIL ADDRESS:
ljfleisher@goodyear.com

WEB SITE ADDRESS:
www.goodyear.com
www.goodyear.com/corporate/about/about_community.html

FOUNDED: 1898

AREAS OF INTEREST:
Safety, health and human services, culture and the arts, education, civic and community improvement.

TYPE:
Project/program grants.

PURPOSE:
To promote healthy, high-functioning communities in locations where Company major plants and offices reside; to be a socially aware and responsive global citizen wherever the Company operates or does business.

LEGAL BASIS:
Corporate contributions program.

ELIGIBILITY:
Grants are made to nonprofit, tax-exempt organizations in communities where Goodyear plants and headquarters offices are located. No grants are made to individuals.

Requests are required to meet guidelines of strategic giving based on safety by focusing on safety programs plus at least one additional category noted below and/or provide volunteer opportunities for Company associates which are appropriately aligned with Company strategy:
(1) Civic and Community and Other: Grant awards will depend on local needs and customs in the communities in which the Company operates;
(2) Culture and the Arts: Requests from organizations and institutions serving plant communities and selected national arts organizations will be considered provided they comply with the connection to safety;
(3) Education: Requests for support from colleges, universities, and other educational institutions serving the areas in which Company plants and principal offices are located must demonstrate a connection with safety and/or must be a source of subsidized educational opportunities for Company associates and their families; a limited number of private and public universities of national or regional significance whose

programs are of special interest or those that provide a continuing source of associates to the Company may also receive priority and;
(4) Health and Human Services: Highest priority is given to United Way campaigns in communities where Company plants and principal offices are located; organizations receiving United Way support may not be eligible for additional funding.

A limited number of traditional grants will be honored at the Company's discretion.

FINANCIAL DATA:
Amount of support per award: Varies.
Total amount of support: Varies.

APPLICATION INFORMATION:
Applicants should visit the web site for complete application information. Application may be made online. The following documents and information are required:
(1) the purpose, amount and community need that will be met by the request;
(2) the program's potential connection to safety for priority consideration;
(3) the geographical area and audience served by the applicant's organization and the request;
(4) a board of trustees list;
(5) a copy of the organization's 501(c)(3) IRS Letter of Determination proving tax-exempt status or equivalent;
(6) the most recent organizational financial statement and income-and-expense budget;
(7) a list of other current and projected sources of funding for the program;
(8) a breakdown, by percentage, of how grant funds are utilized by the organization (i.e., administration, services, research, etc.) and;
(9) the nature of Goodyear goods and services utilized by the organization.

Organizations in the greater Akron, OH area should send requests to the address listed above. Those located in U.S. communities where Goodyear has plants and major facilities should contact the local plant manager's office for mailing instructions.

PUBLICATIONS:
Overview.

ADDRESS INQUIRIES TO:
Community Affairs
(See address above.)

*PLEASE NOTE:
The Company does not accept grant requests by telephone. E-mail requests accepted per guidelines on web site.

W. R. GRACE FOUNDATION, INC.   [147]
7500 Grace Drive
Columbia, MD 21044
(410) 531-4000
Fax: (410) 531-4233

E-MAIL ADDRESS:
janet.davis@grace.com

WEB SITE ADDRESS:
www.grace.com

FOUNDED: 1961

AREAS OF INTEREST:
Higher education, civic, youth development, cultural programs, community funds, health and human services, and science, technology, engineering and mathematics education (STEM).

TYPE:
Challenge/matching grants; Matching gifts; Project/program grants.

YEAR PROGRAM STARTED: 1961

PURPOSE:
To provide primary support for education, particularly programs emphasizing math, sciences and chemistry.

LEGAL BASIS:
Company-sponsored foundation.

ELIGIBILITY:
Nonprofit, tax-exempt organizations with a 501(c)(3) tax-exempt status are eligible for support. The Foundation will not support individuals, political or religious organizations.

Grants to organizations in communities where W. R. Grace & Co. has significant employee population.

GEOGRAPHIC RESTRICTIONS:
United States and Canada.

FINANCIAL DATA:
Amount of support per award: Grants vary in amount based on the needs and nature of the request; Average: $1,000.
Total amount of support: Approximately $761,000 for the year 2013.

NUMBER OF AWARDS: Approximately 200 each year.

APPLICATION INFORMATION:
Applications accepted online only. Complete details available at the web site.

Duration: Usually one year. Multiyear commitments possible.

Deadline: November 30.

DIRECTORS:
Pamela K. Wagoner, Chairman

ADDRESS INQUIRIES TO:
Janet Davis, Deputy Executive Director
(See address above.)

GRAHAM HOLDINGS COMPANY   [148]
1150 15th Street, N.W.
Washington, DC 20071
(202) 334-6617
Fax: (202) 334-4605

E-MAIL ADDRESS:
rima.calderon@ghco.com

WEB SITE ADDRESS:
www.ghco.com

FOUNDED: 1947

AREAS OF INTEREST:
Civic and community, education and cultural programs.

TYPE:
General operating grants. Employee Matching Gifts Program.

PURPOSE:
To support communities where Graham Holdings Company operates.

ELIGIBILITY:
Applicants must be nonprofit 501(c)(3) organizations.

GEOGRAPHIC RESTRICTIONS:
Metropolitan Washington, DC area.

FINANCIAL DATA:
Amount of support per award: Average $500 to $2,500.
Total amount of support: Varies.

Matching fund requirements: $25 minimum, $2,000 per year/per employee maximum. 1:1 or 1:2 for schools or where employee is an active volunteer.

REPRESENTATIVE AWARDS:
The Phillips Collection; Martha's Table; Capital Area Food Bank; Inner City-Inner Child; Northern Virginia Family Services.

APPLICATION INFORMATION:
Send a short letter describing proposed program and budget.
Duration: One year. Renewal possible.
Deadline: Proposals are accepted on an ongoing basis.

ADDRESS INQUIRIES TO:
Rima Calderon, Vice President-Communications and External Relations
(See address above.)

PHILIP L. GRAHAM FUND [149]
c/o Graham Holdings Company
1150 15th Street, N.W.
Washington, DC 20071
(202) 334-6640
Fax: (202) 334-4498

E-MAIL ADDRESS:
plgfund@ghco.com

WEB SITE ADDRESS:
www.plgrahamfund.org

FOUNDED: 1963

AREAS OF INTEREST:
Primarily health and human services, education, arts and humanities, and community endeavors in the Washington, DC metropolitan area. Secondly, journalism and communications.

TYPE:
Capital grants; Development grants; Project/program grants. Technology enhancement. Other infrastructure investments.

YEAR PROGRAM STARTED: 1963

PURPOSE:
To use resources for the betterment of the Washington, DC metropolitan area; to provide assistance to activities in the field of journalism and communication.

LEGAL BASIS:
General interest foundation.

ELIGIBILITY:
Applicants must be 501(c)(3) organizations located in the Washington, DC metropolitan area. Journalism and communication organizations outside the Washington, DC area may be eligible.

No grants to individuals, for religious or political purposes, research, conferences, travel, fund-raising, event sponsorships, hospitals or publications.

GEOGRAPHIC RESTRICTIONS:
Primarily Washington, DC metropolitan area.

FINANCIAL DATA:
Amount of support per award: $2,500 to $300,000. Average grant approximately $25,000.

NUMBER OF AWARDS: Approximately 100 for the year 2013.

REPRESENTATIVE AWARDS:
$120,000 to Washington National Dreams Foundation; $150,000 to Community of Hope; $100,000 to Washington Latin Public Charter School.

APPLICATION INFORMATION:
Organizations interested in applying for funding must first submit a letter of inquiry (LOI) through their online application system prior to one of the three deadlines each year.
Duration: Varies.
Deadline: Early March, July and December.

IRS IDENTIFICATION NUMBER: 52-6051781

TRUSTEES:
Martin Cohen
Donald E. Graham
Theodore C. Lutz
Pinkie Mayfield
Carol Melamed

ADDRESS INQUIRIES TO:
Eileen Daly, President
(See address above.)

*PLEASE NOTE:
Proposals accepted only through the Fund web site.

GRAND RAPIDS COMMUNITY FOUNDATION [150]
185 Oakes Street, S.W.
Grand Rapids, MI 49503
(616) 454-1751
Fax: (616) 454-6455

E-MAIL ADDRESS:
grfound@grfoundation.org

WEB SITE ADDRESS:
www.grfoundation.org

FOUNDED: 1922

AREAS OF INTEREST:
Education, environment, engagement, health, neighborhoods and prosperity.

NAME(S) OF PROGRAMS:
• **Access Camps**

TYPE:
Capital grants; Challenge/matching grants; Demonstration grants; Development grants; Project/program grants; Scholarships; Technical assistance.

PURPOSE:
To build and manage our community's permanent endowment and lead the community to strengthen the lives of its people.

LEGAL BASIS:
Nonprofit organization established by resolution and declaration of trust. Incorporated in 1989.

ELIGIBILITY:
Applicant must have a current 501(c)(3) nonprofit designation from the IRS or be a governmental organization located in Kent County and serve local residents. No grants to individuals except through the scholarship program.

GEOGRAPHIC RESTRICTIONS:
Grand Rapids, Michigan and surrounding communities.

FINANCIAL DATA:
Amount of support per award: General grants: Varies; Access Camps: $5,000 to $10,000.
Total amount of support: $9,683,533 in grants for fiscal year ended June 30, 2013.

NUMBER OF APPLICANTS MOST RECENT YEAR: 2,531 for fiscal year ended June 30, 2013.

NUMBER OF AWARDS: 1,483 for fiscal year ended June 30, 2013.

REPRESENTATIVE AWARDS:
Kent Intermediate School District to continue the work of a school-based program that will coordinate and deliver health and human services to students and their families.

APPLICATION INFORMATION:
For the general fund, applicants fill out an online pre-application on the Foundation's web site. After committee review, applicants may be asked to submit a Full Proposal, with final grant disposition determined by the Board of Trustees.
Duration: Generally, one-time grants. Foundation will, under certain circumstances, award multiyear grants.
Deadline: Varies by Fund. No deadline for the General Fund; pre-applications are reviewed every two weeks.

PUBLICATIONS:
Annual report; quarterly newsletter.

IRS IDENTIFICATION NUMBER: 38-2877959

OFFICERS:
Wayman P. Britt, Chairperson
Diana R. Sieger, President
Marilyn Zack, Vice President of Development
Lynne Black, Vice President of Finance and Administration
Marcia L. Rapp, Vice President of Programs
Roberta F. King, Vice President of Public Relations and Marketing

ADDRESS INQUIRIES TO:
Shavon Doyle, Assistant Grants Manager
(See address above.)

JOHN SIMON GUGGENHEIM MEMORIAL FOUNDATION [151]
90 Park Avenue
New York, NY 10016
(212) 687-4470
Fax: (212) 697-3248

E-MAIL ADDRESS:
fellowships@gf.org

WEB SITE ADDRESS:
www.gf.org

FOUNDED: 1925

AREAS OF INTEREST:
Sciences, social sciences, humanities and the creative arts.

NAME(S) OF PROGRAMS:
• **Guggenheim Fellowships**

TYPE:
Fellowships.

YEAR PROGRAM STARTED: 1925

PURPOSE:
To further the development of scholars and artists by assisting them to engage in research in any field of knowledge and creation in any of the arts.

LEGAL BASIS:
Private foundation.

ELIGIBILITY:
The Fellowships are awarded to men and women who have already demonstrated exceptional capacity for productive scholarship or exceptional creative ability in the arts.

Fellowships are awarded through two annual competitions: one open to citizens and permanent residents of the U.S. and Canada, and the other open to citizens and permanent residents of Latin America and the Caribbean. The Fellowships will be awarded by the Trustees upon nominations made by a Committee of Selection.

FINANCIAL DATA:
The amounts of the grants will be adjusted to the needs of the Fellows, considering their other resources and the purpose and scope of their plans, in accord with the Foundation's annual fellowship budget.
Amount of support per award: Varies.
Total amount of support: Approximately $8,100,000 annually.

NUMBER OF AWARDS: Approximately 187 annually.

APPLICATION INFORMATION:
Online application is available at the Foundation web site.
Duration: Appointments must be from six to 12 months. Fellows of the Foundation, until further notice from the Board of Trustees, may no longer seek renewed assistance.
Deadline: Applications must be submitted on or before September 19 for U.S. and Canadian competition. Fellowships to be announced the following April for U.S. competition. Latin American competition: December 1, with fellowship awards to be announced the following June.

PUBLICATIONS:
Annual report; announcement of Fellowship competition and recipients; application guidelines.

IRS IDENTIFICATION NUMBER: 13-5673173

OFFICERS:
Edward Hirsch, President
Coleen P. Higgins-Jacob, Vice President, Chief Financial Officer and Treasurer
Andre Bernard, Vice President and Secretary
Richard V. Hatter, Director, Development and Public Relations

TRUSTEES:
Robert A. Caro
Joel Conarroe
Dorothy Tapper Goldman
Michael Hegarty
Edward Hirsch
William P. Kelly
Dwight E. Lee
Joyce Carol Oates
A. Alex Porter
Joseph A. Rice
Richard A. Rifkind
Stacy Schiff
Charles P. Stevenson, Jr.
Waddell W. Stillman
Patrick J. Waide, Jr.
Ellen Taaffe Zwilich

ADDRESS INQUIRIES TO:
Keith Lewis, Program Officer
Fellowships Program
(See address above.)

THE GEORGE GUND FOUNDATION   [152]
1845 Guildhall Building
45 Prospect Avenue West
Cleveland, OH 44115
(216) 241-3114
Fax: (216) 241-6560

E-MAIL ADDRESS:
info@gundfdn.org

WEB SITE ADDRESS:
www.gundfoundation.org

FOUNDED: 1952

AREAS OF INTEREST:
Education, economic development and community revitalization, human services, arts and environment.

TYPE:
General operating grants; Project/program grants.

YEAR PROGRAM STARTED: 1952

PURPOSE:
To enhance the quality of life, particularly for those living in the greater Cleveland area; to solve community problems; to improve living conditions, particularly for the poor and underprivileged; to provide opportunities for all people to live constructive lives in a peaceful world.

LEGAL BASIS:
Private foundation.

ELIGIBILITY:
Grants are made only to nonprofit, tax-exempt educational and philanthropic organizations. No awards are made to individuals. Grants for operating budget support will be considered only if the need is for limited duration and will accomplish some important purpose which will strengthen the future position of the institution. Preference will be given to pilot projects, innovative programs and research which hold promise of significant benefits of broad applicability.

GEOGRAPHIC RESTRICTIONS:
Primarily greater Cleveland and Cuyahoga County, Ohio.

FINANCIAL DATA:
Amount of support per award: Varies.
Total amount of support: $24,766,145 for the year 2013.

NUMBER OF APPLICANTS MOST RECENT YEAR:
343 proposals submitted in 2013.

NUMBER OF AWARDS: 233 grants for the year 2013.

APPLICATION INFORMATION:
Foundation requires that all applications for grants be submitted online at the Foundation's web site. Application materials to be uploaded with application include:
(1) organizational background;
(2) project description;
(3) project budget;
(4) organizational budget;
(5) list of current trustees;
(6) most recent audited financial statements and;
(7) climate change statement.
Duration: One year to multiyear.
Deadline: March 15, July 15 and November 15, for board meetings to be held in July, November and February, respectively.

PUBLICATIONS:
Annual report; Guidelines for Grant Applicants (on Foundation web site).

TRUSTEES:
Geoffrey Gund, President
Ann L. Gund, Vice President
Catherine Gund, Secretary
George Gund, IV
Zachary Gund
Randell McShepard
Robyn Minter Smyers
Anna Traggio

ADMINISTRATIVE STAFF:
David T. Abbott, Executive Director

Robert B. Jaquay, Associate Director and Senior Program Officer for Economic Development and Community Revitalization
Deena M. Epstein, Senior Program Officer, Arts
Ann K. Mullin, Senior Program Officer, Education
John Mitterholzer, Senior Program Officer, Environment
Marcia Egbert, Senior Program Officer, Human Services

ADDRESS INQUIRIES TO:
David T. Abbott, Executive Director or Cynthia Gasparro
Grants and Office Administrator
(See address above.)

HALL FAMILY FOUNDATION   [153]
P.O. Box 419580
Maildrop 323
Kansas City, MO 64141-6580
(816) 274-8516
Fax: (816) 274-8547

WEB SITE ADDRESS:
www.hallfamilyfoundation.org

FOUNDED: 1943

AREAS OF INTEREST:
Early and K-12th-grade education; higher education; children, youth and families; community development; the arts; and support of communitywide efforts that seek to provide long-term solutions to high-priority local issues.

TYPE:
Capital grants; Project/program grants; Technical assistance; Training grants.

PURPOSE:
To promote the health, welfare and happiness of school-age children; the advancement and diffusion of knowledge; activities for the improvement of public health; and advancement of social welfare.

ELIGIBILITY:
Applying nonprofit organizations must be 501(c)(3) and must have been in operation for at least five years. No grants are made to individuals. Grants are made to a religious organization only if its program is of a nonsectarian nature.

GEOGRAPHIC RESTRICTIONS:
Organizations in the greater Kansas City, Missouri area.

FINANCIAL DATA:
Total assets of approximately $819,400,000 for the year 2012.
Amount of support per award: Varies.
Total amount of support: Approximately $35,400,000 for the year 2012.

APPLICATION INFORMATION:
Prospective grant recipients should first submit a brief letter of inquiry. Those applicants whose request appears to fall within the Foundation's areas of interest and to meet its guidelines will be asked to submit a full proposal. See web site for requirements.
Duration: One year; nonrenewable.

HANCOCK COUNTY COMMUNITY FOUNDATION
312 East Main Street
Greenfield, IN 46140
(317) 462-8870
Fax: (317) 467-3330

E-MAIL ADDRESS:
mgibble@hccf.cc

WEB SITE ADDRESS:
www.hccf.cc

TYPE:
Project/program grants; Scholarships.

See entry 1297 for full listing.

HARDEN FOUNDATION [154]
1636 Ercia Street
Salinas, CA 93906
(831) 442-3005
Fax: (831) 443-1429

E-MAIL ADDRESS:
jgrainger@hardenfoundation.org

WEB SITE ADDRESS:
www.hardenfoundation.org

FOUNDED: 1963

AREAS OF INTEREST:
Children, youth and family, senior citizens, animal welfare and the environment, agriculture, education, arts and culture, and health.

TYPE:
Capital grants; General operating grants; Project/program grants.

YEAR PROGRAM STARTED: 1963

PURPOSE:
To fund groups working in the Foundation's areas of interest.

LEGAL BASIS:
Private foundation.

ELIGIBILITY:
The Foundation does not fund schools, churches or religious activities, or individuals for endowments or fund-raising. Eligible organizations must be of a 501(c)(3), not-for-profit character.

GEOGRAPHIC RESTRICTIONS:
Monterey County, California.

FINANCIAL DATA:
Amount of support per award: $5,000 to $100,000.
Total amount of support: Varies.

APPLICATION INFORMATION:
Guidelines and application forms are available online.
Duration: Grants are biannual.
Deadline: March 1 and September 1.

ADDRESS INQUIRIES TO:
Joseph Grainger, Executive Director
(See address above.)

THE JOHN A. HARTFORD FOUNDATION, INC. [155]
55 East 59th Street
New York, NY 10022
(212) 832-7788
Fax: (212) 593-4913

E-MAIL ADDRESS:
mail@jhartfound.org

WEB SITE ADDRESS:
www.jhartfound.org

FOUNDED: 1929

AREAS OF INTEREST:
Aging and health.

NAME(S) OF PROGRAMS:
● **Aging and Health Program**

TYPE:
Demonstration grants; Fellowships; Matching gifts; Project/program grants; Research grants; Technical assistance.

YEAR PROGRAM STARTED: 1983

PURPOSE:
To enhance the capacity of the health care system to accommodate the nation's growing elderly population.

LEGAL BASIS:
Private foundation.

ELIGIBILITY:
Grantee organizations must be located in the U.S. and must have 501(c)(3) IRS tax-exempt designation.

The Foundation's prior grantmaking related to enhancing geriatric research and training, and integrating and improving health-related services to the elderly. Currently, the Foundation makes grants that will put geriatrics expertise to work in all health care settings by:
(1) advancing practice change and innovation;
(2) supporting team-based care through interdisciplinary education of all health care providers;
(3) supporting policies and regulations that promote better care and;
(4) developing and disseminating new, evidence-based models that deliver better, more cost-effective health care.

The Foundation awards both single and multiple-year grants. No support for general purposes, endowment funds or capital budgets.

GEOGRAPHIC RESTRICTIONS:
United States.

FINANCIAL DATA:
Amount of support per award: $1,000 to more than $3,000,000.
Total amount of support: $18,823,189 for the year 2013.

NUMBER OF APPLICANTS MOST RECENT YEAR: 398 for the year 2013.

NUMBER OF AWARDS: 30 for the year 2013.

APPLICATION INFORMATION:
All proposals are by invitation only from one of the Foundation's program officers, program director, or the executive director.
Duration: One to three years.

PUBLICATIONS:
Annual report.

TRUSTEES:
Norman H. Volk, Chairman
Kathryn D. Wriston, President
Barbara Paul Robinson, Secretary
John H. Allen
John J. Curley
Charles A. Dana
Lile R. Gibbons
John R. Mach, Jr., M.D.
Audrey A. McNiff
Elizabeth A. Palmer
Christopher T.H. Pell
Earl A. Samson, III
Margaret L. Wolff

STAFF:
Corinne H. Reider, Executive Director and Treasurer
Eva Cheng, Finance Director and Controller
Marcia E. Brown, Executive Secretary
Christopher A. Langston, Program Director
Amy J. Berman, Senior Program Officer

Nora OBrien-Suric, Senior Program Officer
Rachael A. Watman, Senior Program Officer
Marcus R. Escobedo, Program Officer
Wally B. Patawaran, Program Officer
Francisco J. Doll, Grants Manager
Benita B. Cox, Administrative Officer
Rutuma M. Gandhi, Accountant
Julianne N. McLean, Program Secretary
Ann E. Raffel, Information Technology Officer
Jessica L. White, Grants/Evaluations Coordinator

ADDRESS INQUIRIES TO:
Francisco J. Doll, Grants Manager
(See address above.)

H.J. HEINZ COMPANY FOUNDATION [156]
One PPG Place, Suite 3100
Pittsburgh, PA 15222
(412) 456-5700

WEB SITE ADDRESS:
www.heinz.com/sustainability/communities/heinz-foundation.aspx

FOUNDED: 1951

AREAS OF INTEREST:
Nutrition, diversity and fostering healthy communities.

CONSULTING OR VOLUNTEER SERVICES:
Employee volunteer program.

TYPE:
Matching gifts; Project/program grants.

YEAR PROGRAM STARTED: 1951

PURPOSE:
To fulfill corporate responsibility through philanthropic giving in communities with Heinz operating companies and in cities where Heinz holds a major corporate presence.

LEGAL BASIS:
Corporate foundation.

ELIGIBILITY:
All organizations seeking funding must be tax-exempt under 501(c)(3) of the Internal Revenue Code.

The Foundation does not make grants for loans or assistance to individuals, general scholarships, fellowships, travel grants, political campaigns either local or national and/or sectarian religious purposes.

FINANCIAL DATA:
Amount of support per award: Varies.
Total amount of support: Varies.
Matching fund requirements: The Foundation will match gifts in amounts of no less than $25 and no more than $5,000 for employees. A personal gift must be made to an eligible organization in the form of cash or securities and must be paid, not merely pledged. The market value of the securities will be the closing price on the day the gift was made or if there was no sale on that day, the most recently published closing price preceding the date of the gift.

The Foundation will not match payments made for services, tuition, membership dues, subscriptions, preferential seating or any type of payment not made as a direct contribution. In addition, the Foundation will not match any payment to the extent that the match would satisfy a pledge which the individual has made.

REPRESENTATIVE AWARDS:
Extra Mile Education Foundation;
Make-A-Wish Foundation of Western
Pennsylvania.

APPLICATION INFORMATION:
A written project summary may be sent
including the goals of the applying
organization, the specific purpose for which
funds are requested, how the objective will
be accomplished, to whom and where the
program will be offered and whether the
project is a single project or one that requires
additional phases. A letter of intent is
recommended to approach the H.J. Heinz
Company Foundation.
Duration: Mostly one year. Renewal requests
are considered.

TRUSTEES:
Tammy B. Aupperle, Chairperson
Ted Bobby
Kristen Clark
Beth Eckenrode
Michael Mullen
Michael Okoroafer

ADDRESS INQUIRIES TO:
Tammy B. Aupperle, Chairperson
(See address above.)

HENDERSON FOUNDATION [157]
P.O. Box 420
Sudbury, MA 01776-0420
(978) 443-4646
Fax: (978) 443-9510

FOUNDED: 1947

AREAS OF INTEREST:
Charitable, educational, religious, health,
political, environmental, and community
outreach.

TYPE:
General operating grants.

PURPOSE:
To continue support to general operations of
those organizations now supported.

LEGAL BASIS:
Nonprofit foundation.

ELIGIBILITY:
Funding limited to public charities with a
nonprofit 501(c)(3) tax-exempt status. The
Foundation does not support activities for
which the IRS requires grantor's
responsibility and reports.

FINANCIAL DATA:
Amount of support per award: Minimum
$500.
Total amount of support: Varies.

APPLICATION INFORMATION:
Send letter of inquiry with documentation of
nonprofit 501(c)(3) tax-exempt status.
Duration: Varies.

TRUSTEES:
Barclay G. Henderson
Roberta Henderson
Mrs. Joseph C. Petrone

ADDRESS INQUIRIES TO:
Roberta Henderson, Trustee
(See address above.)

B. KEITH & NORMA F. HEUERMANN FOUNDATION [158]
Whitney, Newman, Mersch and Otto
1228 L Street
Aurora, NE 68818
(402) 694-3161

FOUNDED: 1994

AREAS OF INTEREST:
Children, the aged, the developmentally
challenged, disabled, physically impaired,
youth education and agriculturally related
activities.

TYPE:
Capital grants; Matching gifts;
Project/program grants; Research grants;
Technical assistance.

YEAR PROGRAM STARTED: 1994

PURPOSE:
To support programs that meet the needs of
society and improve the quality of life
preferably in communities in rural Nebraska.

LEGAL BASIS:
Private foundation.

ELIGIBILITY:
Grants are made to organizations that have
tax-exempt status under Section 501(c)(3) of
the Internal Revenue Code. No grants are
made to individuals. The Foundation does not
loan funds to grant applicants.

GEOGRAPHIC RESTRICTIONS:
Rural areas in Nebraska.

FINANCIAL DATA:
Amount of support per award: $1,000 to
$25,000.
Total amount of support: Varies.

APPLICATION INFORMATION:
The Foundation does not have an application
form. The Grant Proposal should identify a
special need or project to which funds will
be applied including the objectives to be
attained, people or groups who will benefit,
work plans or timetables for achieving the
stated objectives, and any other means of
support. A copy of the 501(c)(3) letter from
the IRS should accompany the application.
Provide the grant applicant's federal ID
number.
Grant Proposal should be limited to two
pages. Supporting documents such as project
budget, other resources, names of supporters,
and background information about the
organization may be attached to the proposal.
Stapled proposals are favored over bound
ones. Brevity is appreciated.

Applicants must submit five original copies
of the proposal.
Duration: Proposal may be for a project
which extends over several years; however,
the Foundation may review and make grants
only on an annual basis.
Deadline: Proposals may be submitted at any
time. The Directors convene at least three
times per year at meetings to be scheduled in
its discretion to review requests for grants.

PUBLICATIONS:
Guidelines.

IRS IDENTIFICATION NUMBER: 47-0748466

ADDRESS INQUIRIES TO:
Timothy J. Otto
(See address above.)

THE WILLIAM AND FLORA HEWLETT FOUNDATION [159]
2121 Sand Hill Road
Menlo Park, CA 94025
(650) 234-4500
Fax: (650) 234-4501

WEB SITE ADDRESS:
www.hewlett.org

FOUNDED: 1966

AREAS OF INTEREST:
Education, the environment, performing arts,
and global development and population.

NAME(S) OF PROGRAMS:
- **Education**
- **Environment**
- **Global Development and Population**
- **Performing Arts**
- **Philanthropy**

TYPE:
Challenge/matching grants; General operating
grants; Matching gifts; Project/program
grants.

YEAR PROGRAM STARTED: 1966

PURPOSE:
To provide grants to solve social and
environmental problems at home and around
the world.

LEGAL BASIS:
Private foundation.

ELIGIBILITY:
The Foundation does not fund individuals
and generally does not fund:
(1) scholarships;
(2) endowments;
(3) capital campaigns;
(4) building construction;
(5) for-profit organizations or;
(6) unincorporated associations or groups.

Requirements vary by area of interest and are
available on the Foundation web site.

FINANCIAL DATA:
Total assets of $7.74 billion as of December
31, 2012.
Amount of support per award: $336,532
average for the year 2012.
Total amount of support: $304,089,000 in
grants awarded for the year ended December
31, 2012.
Matching fund requirements: Foundation
matches eligible employees' contributions to
qualifying organizations.

NUMBER OF AWARDS: 609 for the year 2012.

APPLICATION INFORMATION:
Information may be obtained at the
Foundation web site.
Duration: Generally, one to three years.
Deadline: Varies according to program.

PUBLICATIONS:
Annual report; application guidelines;
newsletter.

BOARD OF DIRECTORS:
Harvey Fineberg, Chairman
Eric Gimon
Walter B. Hewlett
Patricia A. House
Koh Boon Hwee
Mary H. Jaffe
Larry Kramer
Richard Levin
Stephen C. Neal
Rakesh Rajani
Jean G. Stromberg

CORINA HIGGINSON TRUST [160]
3400 Bryan Point Road
Accokeek, MD 20607
(301) 283-2113

E-MAIL ADDRESS:
info@corinahigginsontrust.org

WEB SITE ADDRESS:
www.corinahigginsontrust.org

AREAS OF INTEREST:
Education and human services.

TYPE:
General operating grants.

PURPOSE:
To improve the quality of life in the mid-Atlantic region.

ELIGIBILITY:
Eligible organizations must be IRS 501(c)(3) tax-exempt. An organization cannot be awarded more than one grant per year.

GEOGRAPHIC RESTRICTIONS:
Maryland, Virginia and Washington, DC.

FINANCIAL DATA:
Amount of support per award: Typically $5,000.

APPLICATION INFORMATION:
Applicants must include a copy of the tax-exempt determination letter with the application.
Duration: One year.
Deadline: Spring and fall for Letters of Inquiry. Full proposals by invitation only.

ADDRESS INQUIRIES TO:
Wilton Corkern, Jr., President
(See address above.)

HILLSDALE FUND, INC. [161]
701 Green Valley Road, Suite 300
Greensboro, NC 27408
(336) 574-8696

FOUNDED: 1963

TYPE:
Project/program grants.

LEGAL BASIS:
Family foundation.

ELIGIBILITY:
Must have 501(c)(3) status of Internal Revenue Code to be eligible. Grants will not be made available for indirect costs or overhead as opposed to direct funding, routine, recurring operating expenses, conferences and seminars, travel and study, or individuals for any purpose.

FINANCIAL DATA:
Amount of support per award: Varies.
Total amount of support: $1,315,354 for the year 2012.

APPLICATION INFORMATION:
Applicants should contact the Foundation for guidelines and application form.
Duration: Varies.
Deadline: Spring and fall. Contact Fund for specific deadlines.

ADDRESS INQUIRIES TO:
Mary Scott, Executive Director
P.O. Box 20124
Greensboro, NC 27420

THE HITACHI FOUNDATION [162]
1215 17th Street, N.W.
Washington, DC 20036
(202) 457-0588
Fax: (202) 296-1098

E-MAIL ADDRESS:
info@hitachifoundation.org

WEB SITE ADDRESS:
www.hitachifoundation.org

FOUNDED: 1985

AREAS OF INTEREST:
Entrepreneurship and workforce development.

NAME(S) OF PROGRAMS:
- **Entrepreneurship @ Work: SOURCE**
- **Good Companies @ Work Program**

TYPE:
Project/program grants. Entrepreneurship @ Work: SOURCE links entrepreneurs and investors focused on social challenges that affect low-wealth Americans.

Good Companies @ Work program is designed to achieve integration between business actions and societal well-being.

YEAR PROGRAM STARTED: 1985

PURPOSE:
To improve the ability of individuals, institutions and communities to participate in a global society, one which manifests itself in every aspect of our lives, including environmental, economic, cultural and social.

LEGAL BASIS:
Private foundation.

ELIGIBILITY:
Grant applicants must be nonprofit 501(c)(3) organizations.

GEOGRAPHIC RESTRICTIONS:
United States.

FINANCIAL DATA:
Amount of support per award: Varies.
Total amount of support: Varies.

APPLICATION INFORMATION:
Guidelines and application are available on the Foundation web site.
Duration: Varies.
Deadline: Varies.

STAFF:
Mark G. Popovich, Senior Program Officer
Katrinka Hall, Manager of Executive Operations

OFFICERS AND BOARD OF DIRECTORS:
Patrick Gross, Chairman
Barbara Dyer, President and Chief Executive Officer
Jason Baron
Sherry Salway Black
Albert Fuller
David Langstaff
Jennifer Pryce
Kelly Ryan

ADDRESS INQUIRIES TO:
See e-mail address above.

HOBLITZELLE FOUNDATION [163]
5556 Caruth Haven Lane, Suite 200
Dallas, TX 75225
(214) 373-0462
Fax: (214) 750-7412

E-MAIL ADDRESS:
pharris@hoblitzelle.org

WEB SITE ADDRESS:
www.hoblitzelle.org

FOUNDED: 1942

AREAS OF INTEREST:
Education, cultural affairs, social welfare and health.

TYPE:
Capital grants; Challenge/matching grants; Matching gifts; Project/program grants.

YEAR PROGRAM STARTED: 1942

LEGAL BASIS:
Private foundation.

ELIGIBILITY:
Educational institutions, hospitals, community agencies, youth and other welfare programs and organizations with appropriate interests are eligible.

GEOGRAPHIC RESTRICTIONS:
Texas, primarily Dallas.

FINANCIAL DATA:
Amount of support per award: $25,000 to $500,000.
Total amount of support: Approximately $5,500,000 annually.

NUMBER OF APPLICANTS MOST RECENT YEAR:
600.

NUMBER OF AWARDS: 65.

REPRESENTATIVE AWARDS:
University of Texas Southwestern Medical Center; Carter Bloodcare World Affairs Council of Greater Dallas.

APPLICATION INFORMATION:
Applications for grants should be made in writing to the Foundation. Oral presentations will not be entertained.
Duration: One year and multiyear.
Deadline: April 15 for May meeting, August 15 for September meeting and December 15 for January meeting. If holiday or weekend, next business day.

PUBLICATIONS:
Annual report; application guidelines.

IRS IDENTIFICATION NUMBER: 75-6003984

OFFICERS:
William T. Solomon, Chairman
Caren H. Prothro, Vice Chairman
Paul W. Harris, President
J. McDonald Williams, Treasurer
Kathy Stone, Corporation Secretary

DIRECTORS:
Raphael M. Anchia
John Dayton
Deedie Rose
Karen L. Shuford
Jere W. Thompson, Jr.
Kern Wildenthal, M.D., Ph.D.

ADDRESS INQUIRIES TO:
Paul W. Harris, President and Chief Executive Officer
(See address above.)

HOUSTON ENDOWMENT INC. [164]
600 Travis, Suite 6400
Houston, TX 77002-3000
(713) 238-8100
Fax: (713) 238-8102

E-MAIL ADDRESS:
info@houstonendowment.org

WEB SITE ADDRESS:
www.houstonendowment.org

FOUNDED: 1937

AREAS OF INTEREST:
Arts, education, environment, health, human services, neighborhood development and community enhancement.

TYPE:
Capital grants; Challenge/matching grants;
Conferences/seminars; Development grants;
Fellowships; General operating grants;
Internships; Matching gifts; Project/program
grants; Scholarships; Technical assistance.
Program support.

LEGAL BASIS:
Private foundation.

ELIGIBILITY:
Organizations exempt under Section
501(c)(3). No grants are made directly to
individuals. All scholarship funds are
disbursed through recipient institutions. No
grants made outside the U.S.

GEOGRAPHIC RESTRICTIONS:
Harris County and contiguous counties
(Brazoria, Chambers, Fort Bend, Galveston,
Liberty, Montgomery and Waller).

FINANCIAL DATA:
Amount of support per award: Varies.
Total amount of support: Approximately
$91,964,626 for the year 2012.

APPLICATION INFORMATION:
Application must be made online. Written
applications will not be considered.
Scholarships are never awarded directly on
the basis of personal inquiry but are
administered by colleges and universities.
Duration: One year to multiyear.

PUBLICATIONS:
Annual report.

ADDRESS INQUIRIES TO:
Grant Department
(See address above.)

MABEL Y. HUGHES
CHARITABLE TRUST   [165]
Wells Fargo Bank
MAC No. C7300-493
1740 Broadway
Denver, CO 80274
(720) 947-6766
Fax: (720) 947-6804

E-MAIL ADDRESS:
kathy.cordova@wellsfargo.com

WEB SITE ADDRESS:
www.wellsfargo.
com/privatefoundationgrants/hughes

FOUNDED: 1969

AREAS OF INTEREST:
Youth, health, education, culture and human
services in the state of Colorado, with
emphasis on Denver metropolitan area.

TYPE:
General operating grants; Project/program
grants.

PURPOSE:
To provide funding to nonprofit and
educational institutions that address vital
community needs especially, but not limited
to, human services.

LEGAL BASIS:
Private tax-exempt foundation.

ELIGIBILITY:
501(c)(3) tax-exempt organizations in
Colorado only may apply. No grants are
awarded to individuals.

GEOGRAPHIC RESTRICTIONS:
Colorado.

FINANCIAL DATA:
Amount of support per award: $5,000 to
$10,000.
Total amount of support: Approximately
$500,000 per year.

NUMBER OF APPLICANTS MOST RECENT YEAR:
Approximately 300.

APPLICATION INFORMATION:
Submit a brief letter describing project, why
needed, population to be served, brief
line-item budget, information about
organization seeking funds and its
accomplishments to date, starting and ending
dates, plans for postgrant funding and project
evaluation, and a copy of latest 501(c)(3)
exemption.
Duration: No grants awarded on a continuing
basis.
Deadline: March 1, July 1 and November 1.

TRUSTEES:
W.R. Alexander

ADDRESS INQUIRIES TO:
Kathy Cordova
(See e-mail address above.)

THE HUMANA
FOUNDATION   [166]
500 West Main Street, Suite 208
Louisville, KY 40202
(502) 580-4140
Fax: (502) 580-1256

E-MAIL ADDRESS:
humanafoundation@humana.com

WEB SITE ADDRESS:
www.humanafoundation.org

FOUNDED: 1981

AREAS OF INTEREST:
Childhood health, intergenerational health
and active lifestyles in communities that the
corporation serves.

TYPE:
Capital grants; Challenge/matching grants;
Fellowships; General operating grants;
Internships; Matching gifts; Professorships;
Project/program grants; Scholarships. General
program grants, capital campaigns and
scholarships for children of employees.
Executive matching gift and all-associate
matching gift programs.

The Humana Foundation supports and
nurtures charitable activities that promote
healthy lives and healthy communities.

YEAR PROGRAM STARTED: 1981

PURPOSE:
To act as the philanthropic arm of Humana
Inc.

LEGAL BASIS:
Corporate foundation.

FINANCIAL DATA:
Amount of support per award: Varies.
Total amount of support: $9,600,000.

REPRESENTATIVE AWARDS:
$325,000 to Fund for the Arts; $775,000 to
Humana Foundation Scholarship Program;
$600,000 to Metro United Way.

APPLICATION INFORMATION:
Guidelines are available on the Foundation
web site. Scholarship applications become
available online November 16.
Duration: One year.
Deadline: Scholarships: January 15.

IRS IDENTIFICATION NUMBER: 61-1004763

ADDRESS INQUIRIES TO:
Virginia K. Judd, Executive Director
(See address above.)

THE HYDE AND WATSON
FOUNDATION   [167]
31-F Mountain Boulevard
Warren, NJ 07059
(908) 753-3700
Fax: (908) 753-0004

E-MAIL ADDRESS:
info@hydeandwatson.org

WEB SITE ADDRESS:
www.hydeandwatson.org

FOUNDED: 1983

AREAS OF INTEREST:
Broad fields include education, social
services, arts, health, religion and humanities.

TYPE:
Capital grants; Challenge/matching grants.
The Foundation supports capital projects such
as hard costs related to purchase and
relocation of facilities and/or building
improvements, purchase of capital equipment,
and other one-time capital needs.

LEGAL BASIS:
Private.

ELIGIBILITY:
Grants are made to nonprofit organizations
that have received 501(c)(3) and 509(a)(1) or
509(a)(2) status from the IRS. In general, the
Foundation does not accept applications for
endowment, operating support, benefit
fund-raisers, annual fund appeals, or from
fiscal agents.

GEOGRAPHIC RESTRICTIONS:
Primarily the five boroughs of New York
City, and Essex, Morris and Union counties
in New Jersey.

FINANCIAL DATA:
Amount of support per award: Typical grant
$5,000 to $20,000.
Total amount of support: $4,580,000 for the
year ended December 31, 2012.

NUMBER OF APPLICANTS MOST RECENT YEAR:
741 for the year 2012.

NUMBER OF AWARDS: 412 for the year 2012.

APPLICATION INFORMATION:
Applicants must submit the following:
(1) a completed Grant Application Form;
(2) a brief narrative (no longer than three
pages), signed by an authorized official,
summarizing the background of the
organization and constituency served, the
purpose of the appeal, project total and
amount requested, and anticipated time frame
for the project;
(3) a project budget with line items,
including amount raised and balance needed;
(4) an operating budget for the current fiscal
year;
(5) a list of supporters for the most recent
fiscal year;
(6) a list of the board of directors/trustees
and their business affiliations;
(7) a copy of the most recent audited
financial report or Form 990 (if not available,
call the Foundation to discuss);
(8) a copy of the organization's annual report
(if available) and;
(9) a copy of the organization's most recent
501(c)(3) and 509(a)(1) or 509(a)(2) IRS
ruling letter(s).

If your organization is a former grantee, in accordance with current guidelines, the Foundation will not consider any future proposals from your organization until a report is provided for any previous grants received from the Foundation. You may use the "Grant Report Form" available on the web site.

Appeals or inquiries submitted by e-mail will not be considered.

Duration: Typically one year.

Deadline: Applications should be received no later than February 15 for the Spring meeting and no later than September 15 for the Fall meeting.

PUBLICATIONS:
Program policy statement and grant application guidelines.

IRS IDENTIFICATION NUMBER: 22-2425725

OFFICERS:
Hunter W. Corbin, Chairman
William V. Engel, President
Brunilda Moriarty, Executive Vice President
Thomas W. Berry, Treasurer
Robert W. Parsons, Jr., Secretary
John W. Holman, III, Assistant Treasurer
Maureen T. McCutcheon, Assistant Treasurer
Sarah A. Kalra, Assistant Secretary
Allison J. Pena, Assistant Secretary

DIRECTORS:
Thomas W. Berry
Hunter W. Corbin
Elizabeth R. Curry
Hans Dekker
William V. Engel
John W. Holman, Jr.
John W. Holman, III
Thomas H. MacCowatt
Robert W. Parsons, Jr.
Anita V. Spivey
Kate B. Wood

ADDRESS INQUIRIES TO:
William V. Engel, President
(See address above.)

*PLEASE NOTE:
Appeals or inquiries submitted by e-mail will not be considered.

IDAHO COMMUNITY FOUNDATION [168]
210 West State Street
Boise, ID 83702
(208) 342-3535
Fax: (208) 342-3577

E-MAIL ADDRESS:
info@idcomfdn.org

WEB SITE ADDRESS:
www.idcomfdn.org

FOUNDED: 1988

AREAS OF INTEREST:
Arts, civic affairs, community, conservation, culture, education, environment, health and human services.

NAME(S) OF PROGRAMS:
- **Deer Creek Fund Grants**
- **Geography Grants**
- **IFFT Fund Grants**
- **Northern, Eastern and Southwestern Region Competitive Grants**
- **Perc H. Shelton and Gladys A. Pospisil Shelton Foundation Advised Fund Grants**

TYPE:
Capital grants; General operating grants; Scholarships.

YEAR PROGRAM STARTED: 1988

PURPOSE:
To enrich the quality of life throughout Idaho.

LEGAL BASIS:
Community foundation; 501(c)(3) public charity.

ELIGIBILITY:
Grants are made to organizations that are nonprofit. Nonsectarian religious programs and government entities may apply. No grants are made to individuals.

GEOGRAPHIC RESTRICTIONS:
Idaho.

FINANCIAL DATA:
Amount of support per award: Competitive grants to $5,000. Others unlimited.
Total amount of support: $7,100,000 in grants for the year 2012.

NUMBER OF APPLICANTS MOST RECENT YEAR:
439 through competitive programs for the year 2011.

NUMBER OF AWARDS: 208 in competitive programs for the year 2011.

APPLICATION INFORMATION:
Form can be downloaded from the Foundation web site.
Duration: Varies.
Deadline: Northern Region: January 15; Eastern Region: April 1; Southwestern Region: July 1.

PUBLICATIONS:
Annual report; monthly e-newsletters; *Gift Law*, e-newsletter.

IRS IDENTIFICATION NUMBER: 82-0425063

ADMINISTRATION:
Robert A. Hoover, President and Chief Executive Officer
Holly Motes, Controller
Lauren Tassos, Donor Development Officer

ADDRESS INQUIRIES TO:
Holly Motes, Controller
(See address above.)

IDDINGS BENEVOLENT TRUST [169]
Kettering Tower, 40 North Main Street
Suite 1620
Dayton, OH 45423-2490
(937) 224-1773

E-MAIL ADDRESS:
bcoughlin@iddingsfoundation.org

WEB SITE ADDRESS:
www.iddingsfoundation.org

FOUNDED: 1973

AREAS OF INTEREST:
The needs of youth and human services within the greater Dayton area only with limited consideration for all other interest areas.

TYPE:
Capital grants; Challenge/matching grants; Demonstration grants; Project/program grants; Seed money grants. Funds for development of new projects, emerging social needs of youth, human services and capital improvements. Grants are made only in Ohio, with a special focus on the greater Dayton area. No consideration for endowment funds or grants to individuals.

YEAR PROGRAM STARTED: 1973

PURPOSE:
To improve community environment and lives of citizens.

LEGAL BASIS:
Private, tax-exempt trust.

ELIGIBILITY:
Applicants must be nonprofit organizations. Proof of tax exemption required. Primary area of interest is greater Dayton area, but is legally limited to Ohio-based organizations. No consideration for endowment funds, grants to individuals, or sponsorship of fund-raiser events.

GEOGRAPHIC RESTRICTIONS:
Ohio, with emphasis on Montgomery County (Dayton) and adjacent counties.

FINANCIAL DATA:
Amount of support per award: Usually $1,000 to $50,000.
Total amount of support: $500,000 in grants for the year 2012.
Matching fund requirements: Stipulated in specific grants.

COOPERATIVE FUNDING PROGRAMS: On special projects.

REPRESENTATIVE AWARDS:
$5,000 to YWCA to help with new phone system; $300,000 to Dayton Public Schools for the first year of a three-year commitment for the Positive Behavior Project; $15,000 to AIDS Resource Center for "Protecting our Youth" project.

APPLICATION INFORMATION:
Contact the Foundation office prior to submitting a proposal.

Applicants must submit:
(1) proof of tax-exempt 501(c)(3) status (single copy);
(2) seven copies of Foundation's official application form which includes a synopsis page, a budget page for the specific project, and three pages describing the purpose and benefits of grant and;
(3) single copies of the organization's annual budget, income sources, Board of Trustees and supportive information as requested.
Duration: Usually one year. Projects may be considered for a one-year renewal after proper evaluation. Three-year maximum for capital campaigns.
Deadline: March 1, June 1, September 1 and November 1. Award announcements are made within 10 days following board meeting in month after deadline.

PUBLICATIONS:
Information brochure; application guidelines and form.

OFFICERS:
Kenneth Kent, Vice President, Trust Department
Becky Coughlin, Administrator

ADDRESS INQUIRIES TO:
Becky Coughlin, Administrator
(See address above.)

*PLEASE NOTE:
Applications through bank are not acceptable.

*SPECIAL STIPULATIONS:
Recipients of grants must submit quarterly evaluations as long as the project is funded by the Foundation. A final report must be

submitted on completion of the project. The Trust is not able to consider proposals outside Ohio.

INDEPENDENCE FOUNDATION
Offices at the Bellevue
200 South Broad Street, Suite 1101
Philadelphia, PA 19102
(215) 985-4009
Fax: (215) 985-3989

E-MAIL ADDRESS:
ssherman@independencefoundation.org

WEB SITE ADDRESS:
www.independencefoundation.org

TYPE:
Challenge/matching grants; Fellowships; General operating grants; Project/program grants.

See entry 2491 for full listing.

INTEL FOUNDATION [170]
RS5-110
5200 Northeast Elam Young Parkway
Hillsboro, OR 97124-6497
(503) 613-3409

E-MAIL ADDRESS:
intel.foundation@intel.com

WEB SITE ADDRESS:
www.intel.com/foundation

FOUNDED: 1989

AREAS OF INTEREST:
K-12 education; math, science and engineering education; women and underrepresented minorities in science and engineering; and public understanding of technology and its impact on contemporary life. Additional areas of interest in communities where Intel is located.

CONSULTING OR VOLUNTEER SERVICES:
Volunteer programs at sites where Intel has facilities.

TYPE:
Matching gifts; Project/program grants.

YEAR PROGRAM STARTED: 1988

PURPOSE:
To foster educational opportunities and quality-of-life improvements for communities worldwide. By developing programs, exercising leadership and providing funding for grants, the Foundation works:
(1) to fuel innovation in science, technology, engineering and math (STEM);
(2) to empower girls and women;
(3) to inspire underserved youth and;
(4) to engage with its communities.

Through these efforts, the Foundation works to increase opportunities for all - especially girls and underrepresented populations - in STEM education and related careers.

ELIGIBILITY:
The Foundation does not accept unsolicited requests, regardless of location. Unsolicited grants will not be considered.

The Foundation awards cash grants to nonprofit, tax-exempt organizations for specific projects. The Foundation does not fund individuals, events such as dinners and auctions, advertising, annual fund drives, endowment or capital improvement campaigns, lobbying activities, private

foundations, organizations which promote discrimination or religious, fraternal or political organizations.

FINANCIAL DATA:
Amount of support per award: Varies.

APPLICATION INFORMATION:
The Intel Foundation does not accept unsolicited requests.
Duration: Varies.
Deadline: Applications are reviewed throughout the year.

ANN JACKSON FAMILY FOUNDATION [171]
P.O. Box 5580
Santa Barbara, CA 93150-5580
(805) 969-2258
Fax: (805) 969-0315

WEB SITE ADDRESS:
www.annjacksonfamilyfoundation.org

AREAS OF INTEREST:
Community infrastructure, art, human services and health.

TYPE:
Capital grants; General operating grants.

PURPOSE:
To enhance the community.

LEGAL BASIS:
Private foundation.

ELIGIBILITY:
Grants are made to organizations that have tax-exempt status under Section 501(c)(3) of the Internal Revenue Code. No grants are made to individuals.

GEOGRAPHIC RESTRICTIONS:
Primarily Santa Barbara County, California.

FINANCIAL DATA:
Amount of support per award: Typically $1,000 to $10,000 for general operating grants.

APPLICATION INFORMATION:
The Foundation encourages applicants to use the Common Grant Application form, a link to which is available on the web site.
Duration: One year, with occasional multiyear. Renewal by reapplication.

ADDRESS INQUIRIES TO:
Palmer G. Jackson, Sr., President
(See address above.)

THE JACKSON FOUNDATION [172]
c/o U.S. Bank, NA
P.O. Box 3168
Portland, OR 97208
(503) 275-4414
Fax: (503) 275-4177

E-MAIL ADDRESS:
march.voyles@usbank.com

WEB SITE ADDRESS:
www.thejacksonfoundation.com

FOUNDED: 1960

AREAS OF INTEREST:
Arts/performing arts, economic development, substance abuse, human services, minorities, housing, disabilities, humanities, education, environment, health, children/youth, aged and women.

TYPE:
Capital grants; Challenge/matching grants; Development grants; General operating grants; Matching gifts; Project/program grants; Research grants.

YEAR PROGRAM STARTED: 1963

PURPOSE:
To support new programs that will enhance and expand the well-being of individuals, with a focus on children in the Portland metropolitan area, by granting funds for the purpose of health and education.

LEGAL BASIS:
Private foundation.

ELIGIBILITY:
Grants are made to 501(c)(3) organizations. Priority is given to one-time special projects and development projects.

GEOGRAPHIC RESTRICTIONS:
Oregon.

FINANCIAL DATA:
Amount of support per award: $1,000 to $50,000; average $3,370.

NUMBER OF APPLICANTS MOST RECENT YEAR:
250.

NUMBER OF AWARDS: 125.

APPLICATION INFORMATION:
Guidelines and application forms are available online.
Duration: One year.
Deadline: March 31, June 30, September 30 and December 31.

ADDRESS INQUIRIES TO:
Libby Voyles, Trust Relationship Associate
(See e-mail address above.)

HENRY M. JACKSON FOUNDATION [173]
1501 Fourth Avenue
Suite 1580
Seattle, WA 98101
(206) 682-8565
Fax: (206) 682-8961

E-MAIL ADDRESS:
foundation@hmjackson.org

WEB SITE ADDRESS:
www.hmjackson.org

FOUNDED: 1983

AREAS OF INTEREST:
International affairs, public service, environment/natural resources and human rights.

NAME(S) OF PROGRAMS:
- **Environmental and Natural Resources Management Program**
- **Human Rights Program**
- **International Affairs Education Program**
- **Public Service Program**

TYPE:
Challenge/matching grants; Conferences/seminars; Internships; Professorships; Project/program grants; Seed money grants.

YEAR PROGRAM STARTED: 1983

PURPOSE:
To advance education and public understanding of critical public policy issues in the four priority areas above.

LEGAL BASIS:
Publicly supported foundation.

ELIGIBILITY:
Grants are made to private, nonprofit, tax-exempt organizations under 501(c)(3) and public, tax-exempt entities under 170(c). No grants are made to individuals.

No grants for capital or general operating expenses.

FINANCIAL DATA:
Amount of support per award: $1,000 to $50,000.
Total amount of support: Average: $250,000.

REPRESENTATIVE AWARDS:
$71,000 to support guest faculty on topics of current foreign policy concerns for senior-level courses at the University of Washington's Jackson School of International Studies; $15,000 to support the publication and dissemination of a report on urban sprawl's toll on open space and farmland; $10,000 to create two new exhibits representing gulag life during different epochs of Soviet history on the site of a former prison labor camp; $34,536 for a program that places young adults on city boards and commissions.

APPLICATION INFORMATION:
Proposals should include:
(1) a cover letter summarizing the project and amount requested;
(2) a detailed budget, implementation strategy, identification of board and/or those responsible for the project and plans for evaluation;
(3) IRS tax-exempt status determination letter and;
(4) most recent financial statements (preferred audited).
Duration: Varies.
Deadline: December 1, March 1, June 1 and September 1, for awards announced in March, June, September and December, respectively.

PUBLICATIONS:
Application guidelines; annual report; newsletter.

IRS IDENTIFICATION NUMBER: 52-1313011

OFFICERS:
Helen H. Jackson, Chairman
John Hempelmann, President
Craig Gannett, Vice President
Linda Mason Wilgis, Vice President
David Rostov, Treasurer
Anna Marie Laurence, Secretary
Joel C. Merkel, General Counsel

ADDRESS INQUIRIES TO:
Lara Iglitzin, Executive Director
(See address above.)

JACKSONVILLE JAGUARS FOUNDATION [174]

One EverBank Field Drive
Jacksonville, FL 32202
(904) 633-5437
Fax: (904) 633-5683

WEB SITE ADDRESS:
www.jaguars.com

FOUNDED: 1993

AREAS OF INTEREST:
Social welfare for disadvantaged youths.

TYPE:
General operating grants; Project/program grants. Limited capital grants that target economically and socially "at-risk" youths in northeast Florida.

YEAR PROGRAM STARTED: 1994

PURPOSE:
To help meet the needs of disadvantaged youths (prenatal through teens), striving to address the causes of those needs through enhanced participation of parents, legal guardians and local mentors in northeast Florida.

LEGAL BASIS:
Corporation foundation.

ELIGIBILITY:
Organizations in northeast Florida that work for disadvantaged youths on a nonsectarian nature. Must have 501(c)(3) IRS documentation.

No grants to individuals, schools or single-disease organizations.

GEOGRAPHIC RESTRICTIONS:
Baker, Clay, Duval, Nassau, and Saint Johns counties, Florida.

FINANCIAL DATA:
Amount of support per award: Varies.
Total amount of support: $1,000,000 annually.

COOPERATIVE FUNDING PROGRAMS: Youth Anti-Obesity Grants with Baptist Health; Teen Pregnancy Prevention Grants with Blue Cross Blue Shield of Florida.

NUMBER OF APPLICANTS MOST RECENT YEAR: 42.

NUMBER OF AWARDS: 37.

APPLICATION INFORMATION:
Submit a one-page summary that includes the specific goals, objectives, proposed activities and results expected to the Foundation.
Duration: One year. Renewal by reapplication.
Deadline: July and February.

ADDRESS INQUIRIES TO:
Peter Racine, President
(See address above.)

JOHNSON & JOHNSON FAMILY OF COMPANIES [175]

One Johnson & Johnson Plaza
New Brunswick, NJ 08933
(732) 524-0400
Fax: (732) 524-3300

WEB SITE ADDRESS:
www.jnj.com

FOUNDED: 1953

AREAS OF INTEREST:
Health care.

TYPE:
Matching gifts; Project/program grants; Research grants. International programs, product donation, cash grants. Emphasis on health care, with a special interest in maternal and child health care issues. The Company administers major programs in partnership with selected nonprofit organizations. Grants largely extended through these programs on a Request for Proposal basis.

The Corporation conducts extensive product giving program but only through established partnerships with selected nonprofit organizations. No unsolicited requests accepted.

The Corporation also conducts large matching gifts program in areas of higher education, hospitals, disease-specific organizations, cultural organizations and prevention and treatment of substance abuse.

PURPOSE:
To make life-changing, long-term differences in human health by targeting the world's major health-related issues through community-based partnerships.

ELIGIBILITY:
Grants are made to organizations with 501(c)(3) status. Grants are not made for endowments, appeals for unrestricted funds, tours, fund-raising galas and sporting events, political, fraternal or athletic groups, sectarian or religious organizations, capital expenditures, individuals or loans. Priority is given to activities and needs in locations where the company has a presence in the U.S. and Puerto Rico.

FINANCIAL DATA:
Amount of support per award: Varies.
Total amount of support: Varies.

NUMBER OF AWARDS: More than 600.

APPLICATION INFORMATION:
No unsolicited requests are accepted.

PUBLICATIONS:
Corporate Contributions report; application guidelines, policy statement.

STAFF:
Michael J. Bzdak, Director, Corporate Contributions
William Lin, Ph.D., Director, Corporate Contributions
Joy Marini, Director, Corporate Contributions
Rick Martinez, M.D., Director, Corporate Contributions
Conrad Person, Director, Corporate Contributions
Bonnie J. Petrauskas, Director, Corporate Contributions

ADDRESS INQUIRIES TO:
William Lin, Ph.D., Director
Corporate Contributions
(See address above.)

JOHNSON CONTROLS FOUNDATION [176]

5757 North Green Bay Avenue
Milwaukee, WI 53209
(414) 524-2296
Fax: (414) 524-2077

WEB SITE ADDRESS:
www.johnsoncontrols.com

FOUNDED: 1952

AREAS OF INTEREST:
Higher education, health and social services, civic activities, culture and arts.

TYPE:
Matching gifts; Project/program grants. The Foundation matches the personal gifts of employees, retirees and directors to accredited colleges and universities, community arts and cultural organizations and to United Way in the aggregate from its U.S. company units.

PURPOSE:
To be operated for charitable purposes which include the distribution and application of financial support to soundly managed and operated organizations or causes which are fundamentally philanthropic.

LEGAL BASIS:
Corporate foundation.

ELIGIBILITY:
Contributions are limited to organizations which are exempt from taxation under the Internal Revenue Code. No gifts will be made to any municipal, state, federal agency or department or to any organization established to influence legislation. No distribution will be made to a private individual. No gifts will be made to sectarian institutions or programs whose services are limited to members of any one religious group or whose funds are used primarily for the propagation of religion. Grants are not usually given to public or private pre-schools, elementary or secondary institutions, but are limited to colleges and universities.

GEOGRAPHIC RESTRICTIONS:
United States.

FINANCIAL DATA:
Amount of support per award: $50 to $100,000.
Total amount of support: $15,400,000 including matching gifts for the year 2011.

NUMBER OF AWARDS: Up to 40.

REPRESENTATIVE AWARDS:
$50,000 to Discovery World Museum; $75,000 to Milwaukee Symphony Orchestra; $50,000 to Milwaukee Performing Arts; $125,000 to the University of Wisconsin, Milwaukee.

APPLICATION INFORMATION:
Proposals, preferably in concise letter form, should include statement regarding tax-exempt status, description of the structure, governing board, purpose, history and programs of the organization, summary of the need for support and how it will be used, geographic areas served by the organization, budget information about the organization and statement regarding other sources of income from corporations and foundations, community support and involvement. Must include 501(c)(3) letter.

ADDRESS INQUIRIES TO:
Johnson Controls Foundation
P.O. Box 591
Milwaukee, WI 53201-0591

MAGIC JOHNSON FOUNDATION, INC. [177]
9100 Wilshire Boulevard
Suite 700, East Tower
Beverly Hills, CA 90212
(310) 246-4400
Fax: (310) 246-1106

WEB SITE ADDRESS:
www.magicjohnson.org

FOUNDED: 1991

AREAS OF INTEREST:
Youth; HIV/AIDS education, prevention and care.

NAME(S) OF PROGRAMS:
- **Magic Johnson Foundation HIV/AIDS Grant**
- **Taylor Michaels Scholarship**

TYPE:
Project/program grants; Scholarships; Technical assistance.

PURPOSE:
To support organizations and programs specializing in HIV/AIDS education, prevention and care, and in the areas of education, social needs and health issues of young people.

LEGAL BASIS:
National public charity.

ELIGIBILITY:
Organizations classified as 501(c)(3) by the IRS can apply. Funding will not be considered for projects by individuals and families. Advertising or sponsorship for other funding events are not eligible to receive funds. Research grants, conferences, travel, videos and capital acquisitions are also excluded.

GEOGRAPHIC RESTRICTIONS:
Northern and southern California; Washington, DC; Atlanta, Georgia; Chicago, Illinois; Baltimore, Maryland; New York, New York; Cleveland, Ohio; Houston, Texas.

FINANCIAL DATA:
Amount of support per award: Grants: $5,000 to $25,000; Scholarships: Varies by need.
Total amount of support: Varies.

APPLICATION INFORMATION:
By invitation only, but do accept letters of intent on an ongoing basis. Applicants should request in writing (maximum two pages) to be placed on the Magic Johnson Foundation's database. Requests must contain the name of the organization, address, telephone and fax numbers, e-mail address, contact person, a brief explanation of specific funding needs and a history of services provided.
Deadline: Letters of Intent accepted on an ongoing basis.

PUBLICATIONS:
Annual report; grant guidelines.

ADDRESS INQUIRIES TO:
Shane Jenkins, Director of HIV and Social Programs
(See address above.)

DAISY MARQUIS JONES FOUNDATION [178]
1600 South Avenue
Suite 250
Rochester, NY 14620-3921
(585) 461-4950
Fax: (585) 461-9752

E-MAIL ADDRESS:
mail@dmjf.org

WEB SITE ADDRESS:
www.dmjf.org

FOUNDED: 1968

AREAS OF INTEREST:
Disadvantaged children and families, access to health care, assistance to senior citizens and economic security for families.

TYPE:
Capital grants; Challenge/matching grants; Demonstration grants; Development grants; General operating grants; Matching gifts; Project/program grants; Seed money grants.

YEAR PROGRAM STARTED: 1968

PURPOSE:
To improve the well-being of residents of Monroe and Yates counties, NY, particularly within the city of Rochester; to meet the needs of the disadvantaged, focusing on prevention; to develop children and families to their maximum potential.

LEGAL BASIS:
Not-for-profit, private foundation.

ELIGIBILITY:
Applicants must be nonprofit, tax-exempt organizations in Monroe and Yates counties,

NY. The Foundation does not consider requests for aid for basic research, private schools, the arts, or religious purposes. The Foundation does not make grants to individuals.

GEOGRAPHIC RESTRICTIONS:
Monroe and Yates counties, New York.

FINANCIAL DATA:
Amount of support per award: Varies.
Total amount of support: $1,815,120 for the year 2013.
Matching fund requirements: Stipulated with specific programs.

NUMBER OF AWARDS: 87.

REPRESENTATIVE AWARDS:
$50,000 to Children's Institute to help enhance the Parents as Teachers program offered by Family Resource Centers; $20,000 to Flower City Habitat for Humanity, Inc. to support the revitalization project with repairs to low-income, owner-occupied homes; $15,000 to Sisters of St. Joseph of Rochester to help support Americorps/Notre Dame Volunteer positions at the Neighborhood Center; $25,000 to Seneca Park Zoo Society in support of the Butterfly Beltway Program; $50,000 to Sojourner House in support of a transitional housing program for women and their families.

APPLICATION INFORMATION:
A short letter of inquiry is the preferred form of initial contact. The letter should include a brief description of the proposal, the amount requested and the intended starting date. If the proposed project is consistent with the Foundation's objectives and areas of interest, the applicant will be sent an application form to be completed and returned to the Foundation.
Duration: Typically one year.

PUBLICATIONS:
Annual report.

TRUSTEES AND OFFICERS:
Donald W. Whitney, President
Roger L. Gardner

ADDRESS INQUIRIES TO:
Donald W. Whitney, President
(See address above.)

THE JOYCE FOUNDATION [179]
321 North Clark Street
Suite 1500
Chicago, IL 60654
(312) 782-2464
Fax: (312) 782-4160

E-MAIL ADDRESS:
info@joycefdn.org

WEB SITE ADDRESS:
www.joycefdn.org

FOUNDED: 1948

AREAS OF INTEREST:
Education, employment, environment, gun violence prevention, democracy, and culture.

TYPE:
Awards/prizes; Challenge/matching grants; Demonstration grants; Development grants; General operating grants.

YEAR PROGRAM STARTED: 1948

PURPOSE:
To support efforts to protect the natural environment of the Great Lakes; to reduce poverty and violence in the region; to ensure

that its people have access to good schools, decent jobs, and a diverse and thriving culture; to reform the system of financing elections campaigns to ensure that public policies truly reflect public rather than private interests.

LEGAL BASIS:
Private foundation.

ELIGIBILITY:
Applicants must be tax-exempt, charitable organizations that are based or have a program in the Midwest, which the Foundation defines as including Illinois, Indiana, Michigan, Minnesota, Ohio and Wisconsin. A limited number of environment grants are made to organizations in Canada. The Foundation generally does not support capital proposals, endowment campaigns, religious activities, commercial ventures, direct service programs or scholarships.

GEOGRAPHIC RESTRICTIONS:
Midwest, including Illinois, Indiana, Michigan, Minnesota, Ohio and Wisconsin.

FINANCIAL DATA:
Amount of support per award: Up to $1,900,000 over three years; average grant: $140,000.
Total amount of support: $40,000,000 for the year 2013.

NUMBER OF APPLICANTS MOST RECENT YEAR:
713.

NUMBER OF AWARDS: 280.

REPRESENTATIVE AWARDS:
$1,000,000 to the Illinois Community College Board, Springfield, IL, to test new programs and policies aimed at increasing the number of adult basic and developmental education students who transition to postsecondary occupational education and ultimately to better jobs in Illinois; $350,000 to William J. Brennan, Jr. Center for Justice, New York, NY, to support its campaign finance and judicial reform initiatives, particularly in the Midwest; $50,000 to the Cuyahoga Community College Foundation, Cleveland, OH, to support a multiyear collaborative that includes a long-term residency and commissioning of a new work by African-American jazz artist and composer, Cecilia Smith.

APPLICATION INFORMATION:
Guidelines on how to apply and other details are available on the web site.
Duration: The majority of awards are for one year, although multiyear grants are also considered. Renewal of funding is primarily based on grantee's fulfillment of terms and goals of the previous grant and the program's continued advancement of Foundation priorities.
Deadline: Early April for July; August 15 for December; December 1 for the following April.

PUBLICATIONS:
Program and Grant Proposal Guidelines (online); newsletters; annual report.

IRS IDENTIFICATION NUMBER: 36-6079185

STAFF:
Ellen S. Alberding, President
Deborah Gillespie, Vice President of Finance and Administration
Gretchen Crosby Sims, Vice President of Programs
Katie McCormick Lelyveld, Director of Communications
Jane R. Patterson, Chief Investment Officer

Whitney Smith, Program Director, Employment
Edmund Miller, Program Director, Environment
Nina Vinik, Program Director, Gun Violence
Angelique Power, Senior Program Officer, Culture
Jason Quiara, Program Officer, Education
Mattthew Muench, Program Officer, Employment
Molly Flanagan, Program Officer, Environment
Ginny Simmons, Program Officer, Gun Violence
Mary Gerlach, Communications and Technology Specialist
Kerry M. Goese, Senior Accountant
Veronica Salter, Manager of Grants
Gil M. Sarmiento, Controller

BOARD OF DIRECTORS:
Roger R. Fross, Chairman
Charles U. Daly, Vice Chairman
Ellen S. Alberding
Jose B. Alvarez
John T. Anderson
Michael Brewer
Anthony S. Earl
Carlton L. Guthrie
Daniel P. Kearney
Tracey L. Meares
Margot M. Rogers
Paula Wolff

ADDRESS INQUIRIES TO:
E-mail: applications@joycefdn.org

THE JPMORGAN CHASE FOUNDATION   [180]
270 Park Avenue, 37th Floor
New York, NY 10017-2014
(212) 270-6000

E-MAIL ADDRESS:
gayle.jennings@jpmorgan.com

WEB SITE ADDRESS:
www.jpmorganchase.com/grants

FOUNDED: 1969

AREAS OF INTEREST:
Community development, education, arts and culture.

TYPE:
Challenge/matching grants; Matching gifts; Project/program grants; Technical assistance.

YEAR PROGRAM STARTED: 1969

LEGAL BASIS:
Corporate foundation.

ELIGIBILITY:
Charitable, not-for-profit organizations as defined by Section 501(c)(3) of the IRS tax code.

GEOGRAPHIC RESTRICTIONS:
United States.

FINANCIAL DATA:
Amount of support per award: Varies.

APPLICATION INFORMATION:
Potential grantee must first submit an online Letter of Inquiry. Complete details and instructions are available on the Foundation web site.
Duration: Varies.
Deadline: Grant applications may be submitted throughout the year.

PUBLICATIONS:
Annual report; *Community Partnership Report.*

IRS IDENTIFICATION NUMBER: 23-7049738

ALICE AND JULIUS KANTOR CHARITABLE TRUST   [181]
809 North Bedford Drive
Beverly Hills, CA 90210
(310) 360-7541
Fax: (310) 360-7580

FOUNDED: 1977

AREAS OF INTEREST:
Medical research, arts and cultural programs, education and human services.

TYPE:
Development grants; Project/program grants; Research grants.

YEAR PROGRAM STARTED: 1977

PURPOSE:
To find cures for diseases and aid mankind.

LEGAL BASIS:
Trust.

ELIGIBILITY:
Grants are made to organizations that have tax-exempt status under Section 501(c)(3) of the Internal Revenue Code. No grants are made to individuals, religious organizations or political organizations.

FINANCIAL DATA:
Amount of support per award: Varies.
Total amount of support: Varies.

APPLICATION INFORMATION:
Applicants must submit a brief letter outlining the purpose of the grant, as well as a letter certifying the organization's 501(c)(3) status under the Internal Revenue Code.
Duration: Varies.

ADDRESS INQUIRIES TO:
Arnold Seidel, Trustee
(See address above.)

THE J.M. KAPLAN FUND, INC.   [182]
261 Madison Avenue
19th Floor
New York, NY 10016
(212) 767-0630
Fax: (212) 767-0639

E-MAIL ADDRESS:
jdorak@jmkfund.org

WEB SITE ADDRESS:
www.jmkfund.org

FOUNDED: 1945

AREAS OF INTEREST:
Marine conservation, historic preservation and migrations, public spaces and public services.

NAME(S) OF PROGRAMS:
- **City Life Grant**
- **Discretionary Grants**
- **Environment Program Grant**
- **Furthermore Grant**
- **Historic Preservation Grant**
- **Migrations Grant**

TYPE:
General operating grants; Project/program grants.

YEAR PROGRAM STARTED: 1945

PURPOSE:
To support programs that meet the needs of society and improve the quality of life.

LEGAL BASIS:
Tax-exempt private foundation under provisions of Section 501(c)(3) of the Internal Revenue Code.

ELIGIBILITY:
Grants are made to organizations that have tax-exempt status under Section 501(c)(3) of the Internal Revenue Code. No grants are made to individuals. Nonsectarian religious programs may apply. Unsolicited requests are not accepted.

FINANCIAL DATA:
Amount of support per award: $30,000 to $200,000 for program grants; $2,500 to $100,000 for discretionary grants.
Total amount of support: $8,000,000 for the year 2011.

NUMBER OF APPLICANTS MOST RECENT YEAR:
Over 750.

APPLICATION INFORMATION:
Organizations should submit a brief letter, no more than two pages, describing their work and its relevance to the specific program interests of the Fund. Application is by invitation only.
Duration: 12 to 18 months.

TRUSTEES:
Peter Davidson, Chairman
Betsy Davidson
Bradford Davidson
Matthew Davidson
Caio Fonseca
Elizabeth K. Fonseca
Isabel Fonseca
Quina Fonseca
Mary E. Kaplan
Richard D. Kaplan

STAFF:
Amy Freitag, Executive Director
William Falahee, Controller
Angela Carabine, Grants Manager
Ken Lustbader, Program Director, Historic Preservation
Suzette Brooks Masters, Program Director, Migrations
Ann Birckmayer, Program Associate, Furthermore Grants

ADDRESS INQUIRIES TO:
Angela Carabine, Grants Manager
(See address above.)

MAY GORDON LATHAM KELLENBERGER HISTORICAL FOUNDATION [183]
529 South Front Street
New Bern, NC 28562
(252) 639-3500
Fax: (252) 514-4876

FOUNDED: 1978

AREAS OF INTEREST:
Historic preservation in the city of New Bern and Craven County, NC.

TYPE:
Project/program grants.

YEAR PROGRAM STARTED: 1978

PURPOSE:
To aid in the preservation of significant structures in New Bern as well as to assist in historical research and study pertaining to the city of New Bern and Craven County, NC.

LEGAL BASIS:
Special-interest foundation.

ELIGIBILITY:
Applicants must be organizations, agencies and institutions which are tax-exempt under the provisions of the U.S. Internal Revenue Code.

GEOGRAPHIC RESTRICTIONS:
Craven County and New Bern, North Carolina.

APPLICATION INFORMATION:
Contact Foundation for application form and guidelines.
Duration: One year. Can be renewed for one additional year.
Deadline: June 10 and December 10. Announcement on August 1 and February 1.

PUBLICATIONS:
Application guidelines.

OFFICERS:
Millie Barbee, Chairperson
William C. Cannon, Secretary and Treasurer
Nelson McDaniel, Project Review Committee Chairperson

ADDRESS INQUIRIES TO:
Laurie Bowles, Administrative Support
(See address above.)

W.K. KELLOGG FOUNDATION [184]
One Michigan Avenue East
Battle Creek, MI 49017-4012
(269) 968-1611
Fax: (269) 968-0413

E-MAIL ADDRESS:
proposalsprocessing@wkkf.org

WEB SITE ADDRESS:
www.wkkf.org

FOUNDED: 1930

AREAS OF INTEREST:
Family economic security; education and learning; food, health and well-being; civic engagement; and racial equity.

TYPE:
Challenge/matching grants; Project/program grants; Seed money grants. Grants for pilot projects to improve human well-being are made in the U.S., Mexico, Haiti, northeastern Brazil and Southern Africa.

The Foundation encourages grant seekers to review the latest information on its web site regarding its focus areas of educated kids, healthy kids, secure families, racial equity, and civic engagement before beginning the application process. This will assist in determining if/how grant seeker's idea might be a fit with the Foundation's current programming framework.

YEAR PROGRAM STARTED: 1930

PURPOSE:
To support children, families and communities as they strengthen and create conditions that propel vulnerable children to achieve success as individuals and as contributors to the larger community and society.

LEGAL BASIS:
Independent private foundation.

ELIGIBILITY:
To be eligible for support, applying organization or institution, as well as the purpose of the proposed project, must qualify under the regulations of the U.S. IRS. Grantees must have the financial potential to sustain the project on a continuing basis after Foundation funding is ended. The Foundation is not able to provide funding directly to individuals.

GEOGRAPHIC RESTRICTIONS:
Haiti, Mexico and United States, with priority in Michigan, Mississippi, New Mexico and New Orleans, Louisiana.

FINANCIAL DATA:
Amount of support per award: Varies.
Total amount of support: Varies.

APPLICATION INFORMATION:
The preferred method for grant submissions is the Foundation's online application. Grant applicants who are not able to apply electronically may submit their grant request via regular mail. The Foundation will give prompt consideration to all preproposal submissions. The initial review may take up to three months to complete. If the proposed project falls within the Foundation's priorities and available resources, applicants may be asked to develop a more detailed proposal.

Letters not submitted online should be directed to Central Proposal Processing, at the address above.
Duration: Varies.
Deadline: The Foundation accepts proposals on an ongoing basis, and staff members review them as they are received.

PUBLICATIONS:
Annual report.

ADDRESS INQUIRIES TO:
See e-mail address above.

HARRIS AND ELIZA KEMPNER FUND [185]
2201 Market Street, Suite 1250
Galveston, TX 77550-1529
(409) 762-1603 ext. 123
Fax: (409) 762-5435

E-MAIL ADDRESS:
information@kempnerfund.org

WEB SITE ADDRESS:
www.kempnerfund.org

FOUNDED: 1946

AREAS OF INTEREST:
Arts, historic preservation, community development, education, and health and human services.

NAME(S) OF PROGRAMS:
● **Matching Gifts Program**
● **Primary Grant Program**
● **Program Related Investments**

TYPE:
Capital grants; Challenge/matching grants; Conferences/seminars; Demonstration grants; Endowments; Fellowships; General operating grants; Matching gifts; Professorships; Project/program grants; Scholarships; Seed money grants. Primary Grant Program provides grants to qualifying organizations in the greater Galveston, TX area in the arts and historic preservation, community development, education, and health and human services.

Program Related Investments are recommended by Fund trustees for Galveston projects.

YEAR PROGRAM STARTED: 1946

PURPOSE:
To support a wide range of innovative as well as traditional programs for the enhancement of the local community.

LEGAL BASIS:
Independent private foundation.

ELIGIBILITY:
Primary Grant Program: Preferred applicants are programs/projects that benefit the greater Galveston, TX community. Seed money, operating funds, small capital needs and special projects, and partnering with other funding sources are supported. Proposals will not be considered for fund-raising benefits, direct-mail solicitations, grants to individuals, or grants to non-U.S.-based organizations.

Matching Gifts Program: Restricted to Kempner family members and trustees of the Kempner Fund.

GEOGRAPHIC RESTRICTIONS:
Galveston, Texas.

FINANCIAL DATA:
Amount of support per award: Grants: $1,000 to $75,000 for the year ended December 31, 2013.
Total amount of support: $1,617,141 in grants and $303,000 in matching gifts for the year ended December 31, 2012.
Matching fund requirements: Restricted to descendants of Harris and Eliza Kempner.

NUMBER OF APPLICANTS MOST RECENT YEAR:
80 for the year 2013.

NUMBER OF AWARDS: 60 for the year 2013.

REPRESENTATIVE AWARDS:
$50,000 to the Grand 1894 Opera House; $12,000 to the City of Galveston Police Department; $40,000 to the Galveston ISD Educational Foundation; $48,000 to Teen Health Center; $9,375 to D'Feet Breast Cancer.

APPLICATION INFORMATION:
Applicants should submit a brief cover letter, signed by the Executive Director and Board Chairman, stating the need and amount being requested. Complete guidelines and forms are available at the web site.

The following project/program information also needs to be submitted:
(1) name and telephone number of contact person;
(2) description;
(3) timeline;
(4) budget (income and expenses);
(5) list of sources and amounts being solicited and/or received or pledged;
(6) future funding plans (for new and continuing programs) and;
(7) plans for evaluating program's progress and/or results.

The following organization information should be attached:
(1) statement of purpose and brief history;
(2) names of present officers and board members;
(3) operating budget (revenue and expenses) for year for which funds are sought;
(4) financial statements (year-to-date), audit, and/or Tax Form 990 for most recent fiscal year;
(5) copy of post-1969 IRS determination letter to document tax-exempt status and;
(6) statement on organization letterhead that there has been no change in IRS status since issuance of ruling letter.
Duration: Varies.
Deadline: Health or Human Services: March 15. Arts, Community Development or Education: October 15.

IRS IDENTIFICATION NUMBER: 74-6042458

STAFF:
Anne Brasier, Executive Director

DIRECTORS:
Arthur Alpert, Honorary Director
Barbara W. Sasser, Honorary Director
Lyda Ann Thomas, Honorary Director
Lisa Allen, Director
Carroll Goldstone, Director
Hetta T. Kempner, Director
Victoria Marchand, Director
Andrew Mytelka, Director
Carol Roberts, Director
Brooke Thompson, Director

OFFICERS AND TRUSTEES:
Robert K. Lynch, President
Daniel Thorne, Vice President
Randall Kempner, Treasurer
Armin Cantini, Secretary

JOHN F. KENNEDY PRESIDENTIAL LIBRARY [186]
Columbia Point
Boston, MA 02125-3313
(617) 514-1653
Fax: (617) 514-1625

E-MAIL ADDRESS:
kennedy.library@nara.gov

WEB SITE ADDRESS:
www.jfklibrary.org

FOUNDED: 1964

AREAS OF INTEREST:
History, government, archival administration and library science, journalism, communications and other related disciplines.

NAME(S) OF PROGRAMS:
● **Kennedy Library Archival Internships**

TYPE:
Internships. Awarded to undergraduate and graduate students majoring in history, government, archival administration, library science, journalism, communications and related disciplines for on-site work with the archives staff at the Kennedy Library.

YEAR PROGRAM STARTED: 1970

LEGAL BASIS:
Private foundation in cooperation with a U.S. government agency.

FINANCIAL DATA:
Amount of support per award: Monthly stipend of $560 for part-time interns (16 hours per week); $1,120 for full-time interns (32 hours per week); $1,400 for full-time summer interns (40 hours per week).

APPLICATION INFORMATION:
Candidate must complete application form, submit a copy of current college transcript, and a letter of reference.
Duration: Varies.

THE KERR FOUNDATION, INC. [187]
12501 North May Avenue
Oklahoma City, OK 73120
(405) 749-7991
Fax: (405) 749-2877

WEB SITE ADDRESS:
www.thekerrfoundation.org

FOUNDED: 1963

AREAS OF INTEREST:
Education, cultural activities and health.

TYPE:
Challenge/matching grants; Development grants; Endowments; General operating grants; Project/program grants.

YEAR PROGRAM STARTED: 1986

PURPOSE:
To support programs of interest to the Foundation in the areas of health, education, youth services and cultural activities.

LEGAL BASIS:
Private, charitable foundation.

ELIGIBILITY:
Application is limited to nonprofit, 501(c)(3) tax-exempt organizations. No grants to individuals.

GEOGRAPHIC RESTRICTIONS:
Arkansas, Colorado, Kansas, Missouri, New Mexico, Oklahoma, Texas, and Washington, D.C.

FINANCIAL DATA:
Grant-seeking organizations must first raise a specified amount in actual new dollars donations or up-to-three-year pledges. The grant will be paid upon successful raising of the funds or pledges, which must occur within one year or a mutually agreed-upon time limit.
Amount of support per award: $5,000 to $50,000.

COOPERATIVE FUNDING PROGRAMS: All Oklahoma foundations.

NUMBER OF APPLICANTS MOST RECENT YEAR: 150.

NUMBER OF AWARDS: 50.

APPLICATION INFORMATION:
Forms and guidelines are available online.
Duration: Most grants awarded on a one-time basis.

OFFICERS AND TRUSTEES:
Mrs. Robert S. Kerr, Jr., President and Chairperson
Steven Kerr, Treasurer
Laura Kerr Ogle, Secretary
Cody T. Kerr

ADDRESS INQUIRIES TO:
Mrs. Robert S. Kerr, Jr.
President and Chairman of the Board
(See address above.)

GRAYCE B. KERR FUND, INC. [188]
117 Bay Street
Easton, MD 21601
(410) 822-6652
Fax: (410) 822-4546

E-MAIL ADDRESS:
office@gbkf.org

WEB SITE ADDRESS:
www.gbkf.org

FOUNDED: 1986

AREAS OF INTEREST:
Education, cultural programs, and public policy research, with major emphasis on education.

TYPE:
Project/program grants. Grants to nonprofit organizations. Grants are not limited to any one specific area of interest or geographical location. Currently, the Fund's principal areas of interest include nurturing educational achievement and excellence, fostering life skills critical to self-sufficiency, and encouraging cultural growth. The Fund

supports research and other activities directed toward improving the information base available to the public.

YEAR PROGRAM STARTED: 1986

PURPOSE:
To provide financial support to worthy nonprofit organizations that enhance the quality of life, significantly impact and sustain long-term change and growth in organizations and institutions.

LEGAL BASIS:
Private, charitable foundation.

ELIGIBILITY:
Applicants must be nonprofit, 501(c)(3) tax-exempt organizations. No grants to individuals.

GEOGRAPHIC RESTRICTIONS:
United States.

FINANCIAL DATA:
Grant minimums and maximums are not designated. Preference may be given, in some years, to large grants where a genuine impact may be accomplished.
Amount of support per award: Varies.
Total amount of support: Varies.

APPLICATION INFORMATION:
Applications are by invitation only.
Duration: Usually one year.

PUBLICATIONS:
Annual report; application.

IRS IDENTIFICATION NUMBER: 73-1256124

BOARD OF TRUSTEES:
Sheryl V. Kerr, Chairperson
Marcy Kerr Yuknat, Vice Chairperson
John R. Valliant, President and Trustee
David A. Yuknat, Secretary and Treasurer
James S. Maffitt

ADDRESS INQUIRIES TO:
John R. Valliant, President
(See address above.)

KIMBERLY-CLARK FOUNDATION, INC. [189]
P.O. Box 619100
Dallas, TX 75261-9100
(972) 281-1477

E-MAIL ADDRESS:
kcfoundation@kcc.com

WEB SITE ADDRESS:
www.kimberly-clark.com

FOUNDED: 1952

AREAS OF INTEREST:
Social welfare, medicine and health.

TYPE:
Project/program grants.

YEAR PROGRAM STARTED: 1952

PURPOSE:
To support organizations that strengthen today's families.

LEGAL BASIS:
Corporate foundation.

ELIGIBILITY:
Grants are made to tax-exempt, charitable, 501(c)(3) nonprofit organizations in communities where Kimberly-Clark has operations. There are a limited number of contributions to national organizations.

FINANCIAL DATA:
Amount of support per award: Varies.

Total amount of support: $12,000,000 for the year 2013.

REPRESENTATIVE AWARDS:
$1,300,000 to Boys and Girls Clubs of America; $20,000 to Susan G. Komen Foundation; $50,000 to Catalyst for Women; $200,000 to American Red Cross.

APPLICATION INFORMATION:
Written requests must be sent to the Foundation. Please call before sending requests.
Duration: One to five years.

PUBLICATIONS:
Annual report.

OFFICERS:
Tony Palmer, President
Mark A. Buthman, Vice President
Jenny Lewis, Vice President
Nancy Loewe, Treasurer
John Wesley, Secretary

DIRECTORS:
Mark A. Buthman
Thomas J. Falk
Tony Palmer

ADDRESS INQUIRIES TO:
Jenny Lewis, Vice President
(See address above.)

STEPHEN AND TABITHA KING FOUNDATION [190]
P.O. Box 855
Bangor, ME 04402
(207) 990-2910
Fax: (207) 990-2975

E-MAIL ADDRESS:
info@stkfoundation.org

WEB SITE ADDRESS:
www.stkfoundation.org

FOUNDED: 1985

AREAS OF INTEREST:
Arts, children/youth, health, education, libraries, recovery, women's issues, human rights and literacy.

TYPE:
Awards/prizes; Capital grants; Challenge/matching grants; Demonstration grants; Development grants; Endowments; General operating grants; Matching gifts; Project/program grants; Seed money grants; Training grants.

YEAR PROGRAM STARTED: 1985

PURPOSE:
To improve the quality of life in Maine.

LEGAL BASIS:
Private family foundation.

ELIGIBILITY:
Organizations classified as 501(c)(3) by the IRS and located in Maine can apply. Grants are only awarded to nonprofit organizations operating in the state of Maine. Individuals and religious organizations are ineligible.

GEOGRAPHIC RESTRICTIONS:
Maine.

FINANCIAL DATA:
Amount of support per award: $50,000 maximum request.
Total amount of support: Varies, dependent on investment revenue.
Matching fund requirements: Must be met through grassroots local community funding.

NUMBER OF APPLICANTS MOST RECENT YEAR: 1,000.

NUMBER OF AWARDS: Approximately 250.

APPLICATION INFORMATION:
Contact the Foundation for application procedures.
Duration: Foundation prefers one-time grants. Multiyear commitments occasionally.
Deadline: June 30 and December 31.

IRS IDENTIFICATION NUMBER: 13-3364647

STAFF:
Stephanie Leonard, Administrator

ADDRESS INQUIRIES TO:
Stephanie Leonard, Administrator
(See address above.)

F.M. KIRBY FOUNDATION, INC. [191]
17 DeHart Street
Morristown, NJ 07963-0151
(973) 538-4800
Fax: (973) 538-4801

WEB SITE ADDRESS:
www.fmkirbyfoundation.org

FOUNDED: 1931

AREAS OF INTEREST:
General charitable support.

TYPE:
Capital grants; Challenge/matching grants; Endowments; Fellowships; General operating grants; Professorships; Project/program grants; Research grants; Scholarships. Grants usually are reflective of personal interest by one or more members of the Kirby family who are, or have been, active in the affairs of the Foundation.

YEAR PROGRAM STARTED: 1931

LEGAL BASIS:
Private foundation.

ELIGIBILITY:
Organizations must be tax-exempt under applicable provisions of the IRS code and not private foundations. No grants are made to individuals. No grants are made to public foundations which would, as a result thereof, become private foundations. No grants for fund-raising activities such as benefits, charitable dinners, sports or theater events, etc. No loans are made.

GEOGRAPHIC RESTRICTIONS:
Morris County, New Jersey; Hillsborough, North Carolina area; and Wilkes-Barre, Pennsylvania area.

FINANCIAL DATA:
Amount of support per award: Varies.
Total amount of support: $20,404,834 for the year 2013.
Matching fund requirements: Determined on a case-by-case basis.

NUMBER OF APPLICANTS MOST RECENT YEAR: Approximately 500 for the year 2013.

NUMBER OF AWARDS: 262 for the year 2013.

APPLICATION INFORMATION:
The preferred method of initial contact is a full proposal with a cover letter. The Foundation provides no formal application forms and sets down no specific guidelines. Proposals should include:
(1) a report on the use of previous grants if applicable;
(2) a description of the organization, its purpose and the project, if any;
(3) an indication of the budget for which

financial support is requested;
(4) roster of directors and principal officers;
(5) copy of the current audited financial statement;
(6) copy of the valid IRS tax determination letter and;
(7) copy of current annual budget.

Duration: One year. Renewal possible.

Deadline: October 31. Solicitations received after deadline will be held over to following year.

PUBLICATIONS:
Application guidelines.

IRS IDENTIFICATION NUMBER: 51-6017929

STAFF:
JoAnn F. Tiefau, Program Officer
Thomas J. Bianchini, Financial Advisor

DIRECTORS AND OFFICERS:
S. Dillard Kirby, President and Director
Jefferson W. Kirby, Vice President and Director
William H. Byrnes, Vice President-Grants
Frank N. Barra, Treasurer and Secretary
Alice K. Horton, Director
F.M. Kirby, Director
Walker D. Kirby, Director
Laura H. Virkler, Director

ADDRESS INQUIRIES TO:
William H. Byrnes, Vice President-Grants
(See address above.)

KITSAP COMMUNITY FOUNDATION

9657 Levin Road, N.W.
Suite L0-8
Silverdale, WA 98383
(360) 698-3622
Fax: (360) 698-6043

E-MAIL ADDRESS:
kcf@kitsapfoundation.org

WEB SITE ADDRESS:
www.kitsapfoundation.org

TYPE:
General operating grants; Project/program grants; Scholarships.

See entry 1313 for full listing.

JOSIAH W. AND BESSIE H. KLINE FOUNDATION, INC. [192]

515 South 29th Street
Harrisburg, PA 17104
(717) 561-4373
Fax: (717) 561-0826

E-MAIL ADDRESS:
info@kline-foundation.org

WEB SITE ADDRESS:
www.kline-foundation.org

FOUNDED: 1952

AREAS OF INTEREST:
Medical, academic, benevolent, community and cultural.

NAME(S) OF PROGRAMS:
● **Kline Foundation Grants**

TYPE:
Project/program grants; Research grants.

YEAR PROGRAM STARTED: 1952

PURPOSE:
To aid blind or incapacitated persons or crippled children in need of financial assistance; to make grants to Pennsylvania

colleges and universities, to hospitals and institutions for crippled children or to any other benevolent or charitable institution; to make grants for scientific or medical research to be performed by scientific persons or by colleges, universities or research institutions.

LEGAL BASIS:
Community foundation.

ELIGIBILITY:
The Foundation does not make loans and does not make grants to individuals and generally does not make grants for normal operational phases of established programs or to national organizations or religious programs.

Normally grants are not made to state-affiliated schools, colleges, or universities.

GEOGRAPHIC RESTRICTIONS:
South central Pennsylvania, with emphasis on Cumberland and Dauphin counties.

FINANCIAL DATA:
Amount of support per award: $500 to $250,000.

Total amount of support: Varies.

NUMBER OF AWARDS: 49 for the year 2012.

APPLICATION INFORMATION:
Application information is available on the web site. To be considered for Foundation aid, a copy of the Foundation's completed application form must be submitted and the following information must be fully stated:
(1) a description of the need and purpose, the qualifications of the requesting organization and the location as to where and how the support will be used;
(2) a budget for the project and any support that will be received from other sources;
(3) the amount of the request from the Foundation and the dates the funds are needed and;
(4) a copy of a letter from the IRS showing that the organization is exempt from federal income tax under Section 501(c)(3) of the Internal Revenue Code and that the organization is not a private foundation under Section 509(a).

Application may be submitted online.

Deadline: April and October. Some grants are awarded in June, while others are generally awarded after December 1 of each year.

PUBLICATIONS:
Annual report; application guidelines; application.

ADDRESS INQUIRIES TO:
John A. Obrock, C.P.A.
(See address above.)

*SPECIAL STIPULATIONS:
One grant per year per organization.

JOHN S. AND JAMES L. KNIGHT FOUNDATION [193]

200 South Biscayne Boulevard
Suite 3300
Miami, FL 33131-2349
(305) 908-2600
Fax: (305) 908-2698

E-MAIL ADDRESS:
grants@knightfoundation.org

WEB SITE ADDRESS:
www.knightfoundation.org

FOUNDED: 1950

AREAS OF INTEREST:
Journalism and engaged and informed communities.

NAME(S) OF PROGRAMS:
● **Arts Program**
● **Communities Program**
● **Journalism Program**
● **National Program**

TYPE:
Capital grants; Challenge/matching grants; Development grants; Endowments; Matching gifts; Project/program grants; Seed money grants; Technical assistance. The Foundation promotes excellence in journalism worldwide and invests in the vitality of 26 U.S. communities.

The Foundation focuses on three areas:
(1) Innovating Media and Journalism: The Foundation aims to help sustain democracy by leading journalism to its best possible future in the 21st century;
(2) Engaging Communities: To sustain healthy communities in a democracy, the Foundation's community engagement initiatives aim to give all residents a strong sense of belonging and caring, timely access to relevant information, the ability to understand that information, and the motivation to take sustainable action on the issues that matter most to them and;
(3) Fostering the Arts: Through its national arts program, the Foundation seeks to weave the arts into the fabric of the Knight resident communities to engage and inspire their residents; the Foundation believes that the arts are a catalyst for public dialogue, and that shared cultural experiences contribute to a sense of place and communal identity.

YEAR PROGRAM STARTED: 1950

PURPOSE:
To sustain democracy in the digital age by fostering informed and engaged communities; to back transformational ideas at the intersection of media, journalism, community engagement and the arts; to advance media innovation with a wide range of initiatives; to support projects, including in the arts, that increase community engagement through the use of technology and other innovative approaches.

LEGAL BASIS:
Private non-operating foundation.

ELIGIBILITY:
A segment of the Foundation's activities focuses on 26 communities where the Knight brothers owned newspapers, with donor-advised programs in 18 and program director-led programs in the eight "resident Knight communities."

An applicant organization must have received a letter of determination from the Internal Revenue Service granting it 501(c)(3) tax-exempt status and stating that it is not a private foundation according to the definition in Section 509(a) of the Internal Revenue Code.

The Knight News Challenge permits for-profit entities and individuals to apply from anywhere in the world.

The Knight Community Information Challenge accepts applications from community and place-based foundations in the U.S. and its territories, as well as Mexico and Canada.

The Knight Arts Challenge accepts applications from South Florida, Detroit (MI), and Greater Philadelphia individuals, for-profit and nonprofit organizations.

FINANCIAL DATA:
  Amount of support per award: Varies.
  Total amount of support: $108,000,000 for the year 2012.

NUMBER OF APPLICANTS MOST RECENT YEAR:
  5,349 for the year 2012.

NUMBER OF AWARDS: 410 grants for the year 2012.

APPLICATION INFORMATION:
  Applicants must submit an online letter of inquiry. If the inquiry is determined to fall into Knight Foundation funding priorities, applicants are asked to submit a full proposal.
  Duration: Varies per project; usually from one to five years.

PUBLICATIONS:
  Evaluation and Assessment publications; Reporter Analysis evaluation articles; KnightBlog posts.

IRS IDENTIFICATION NUMBER: 65-0464177

STAFF:
  Terese Coudreaut, Vice President and Chief Administrative Officer
  Juan Martinez, Vice President and Chief Financial Officer
  Dennis Scholl, Vice President/Arts
  Andrew Sherry, Vice President of Communications
  Jorge Martinez, Vice President of Information Technology
  Michael Maness, Vice President/Journalism Program
  Mayur Patel, Vice President/Strategy and Assessment
  Eric Newton, Senior Adviser to the President

TRUSTEES AND OFFICERS:
  Robert W. Briggs, Chairman
  Alberto Ibarguen, President and Chief Executive Officer
  Stephanie Bell-Rose
  Francisco L. Borges
  William H. Considine
  Marjorie Knight Crane
  James N. Crutchfield
  Chris Hughes
  Joichi Ito
  Susan D. Kronick
  Rolfe Neill
  Anna Spangler Nelson
  Mariam C. Noland
  Beverly Knight Olson
  John Palfrey
  Earl W. Powell
  Ray Rodriguez
  E. Roe Stamps, IV
  Paul E. Steiger

ADDRESS INQUIRIES TO:
  Grants Administrator
  (See address above.)

MARION I. AND HENRY J. KNOTT FOUNDATION, INC. [194]
3904 Hickory Avenue
Baltimore, MD 21211
(410) 235-7068
Fax: (410) 889-2577

E-MAIL ADDRESS:
  choffman@knottfoundation.org

WEB SITE ADDRESS:
  www.knottfoundation.org

FOUNDED: 1977

AREAS OF INTEREST:
  Education (private and Catholic schools only), health care, human and social services, arts and humanities.

TYPE:
  Capital grants; Challenge/matching grants; Development grants; General operating grants; Project/program grants; Technical assistance; Training grants.

YEAR PROGRAM STARTED: 1977

PURPOSE:
  To further Roman Catholic activities and other charitable, cultural, educational, health care and human service activities within the meaning of Section 501(c)(3) of the Internal Revenue Code.

LEGAL BASIS:
  Private family foundation.

ELIGIBILITY:
  Applicants must be nonprofit, charitable organizations with evidence of tax-exemption ruling under Section 501(c)(3) of the Internal Revenue Code. No grants pertaining to scholarships, individuals, annual giving, pro-choice causes, public education or institutions, or politically oriented activities.

  The Foundation does not favor multiyear requests.

GEOGRAPHIC RESTRICTIONS:
  All counties in the state of Maryland excluding the entire Eastern Shore, Calvert, Cecil, Charles, Montgomery, Prince George's, and St. Mary's counties.

FINANCIAL DATA:
  Amount of support per award: $10,000 to $100,000. Average $40,000.
  Total amount of support: $1,963,399 for the year 2012.
  Matching fund requirements: Specific to grantee. Usually matched within a six-month period.

NUMBER OF APPLICANTS MOST RECENT YEAR:
  210.

NUMBER OF AWARDS: 52.

REPRESENTATIVE AWARDS:
  $35,000 to Baltimore Reads; $74,231 to Adoptions Together; $50,000 to Red Devils; $120,000 to Sacred Heart of Mary Parish; $49,500 to St. Louis School.

APPLICATION INFORMATION:
  Required documentation includes proof of 501(c)(3) status, brief narrative of objective of proposal, history of requesting agency, list of trustees and officers, administrating personnel with resume, budget for project, most recent audited report and list of foundations and corporations that have supported previous requests and are being solicited for this request. Must call Executive Director before submitting a proposal.
  Duration: Usually one year.
  Deadline: Letters of Inquiry and Financials: February, June and October. Full Proposal: March 24, July 21 and November 24, respectively.

IRS IDENTIFICATION NUMBER: 52-1517876

TRUSTEES AND OFFICERS:
  Owen M. Knott, President
  Daniel Gallagher
  Lindsay R. Gallagher
  Marty Voelkel Hanssen
  E.B. Harris
  Kelly L. Harris
  Thomas Harris
  Erin Knott
  Marion I. Knott
  Martin G. Knott, Jr.
  Martin G. Knott, Sr.
  Teresa A. Knott
  Brian McDonald
  Meghan McDonald
  Peter McGill
  David L. Porter
  Joanna O. Porter
  Laurel Porter
  Margie Riehl
  Michael Riehl
  Brooke Rodgers
  Michael Rodgers
  Patrick Rodgers
  Geralynn D. Smyth
  John Smyth
  Patrick Smyth
  Peggy Smyth
  Jan Steendam
  Alice Voelkel
  Emmett Voelkel

ADDRESS INQUIRIES TO:
  Kelly Medinger, Executive Director
  (See address above.)

KORET FOUNDATION [195]
33 New Montgomery Street
Suite 1090
San Francisco, CA 94105-4526
(415) 882-7740
Fax: (415) 882-7775

E-MAIL ADDRESS:
  koret@koretfoundation.org

WEB SITE ADDRESS:
  www.koretfoundation.org

FOUNDED: 1979

AREAS OF INTEREST:
  Arts, community service and volunteerism, Jewish community services, education and employment for youth, elderly, hunger and homelessness.

TYPE:
  Capital grants; General operating grants; Project/program grants; Seed money grants.

YEAR PROGRAM STARTED: 1979

PURPOSE:
  To address societal challenges and strengthen Bay Area life; to invest in strategic, local solutions that help to inspire a multiplier effect, encouraging collaborative funding and developing model initiatives.

LEGAL BASIS:
  Private foundation.

ELIGIBILITY:
  Grant applicants must be 501(c)(3) organizations. Private foundations are not eligible to apply.

  Although the majority of funding is granted to six of nine bay area counties, the Foundation will consider national and Israeli projects.

GEOGRAPHIC RESTRICTIONS:
  Alameda, Contra Costa, Marin, San Francisco, San Mateo and Santa Clara counties, California.

FINANCIAL DATA:
  Amount of support per award: Grants vary in amount, depending upon the needs and nature of the request.

Total amount of support: $24,312,015 for the year 2012.

APPLICATION INFORMATION:
Contact the Foundation for application guidelines.
Duration: Varies.

PUBLICATIONS:
Annual report; application guidelines.

IRS IDENTIFICATION NUMBER: 94-1624987

OFFICERS:
Jeff Farber, Chief Executive Officer

ADDRESS INQUIRIES TO:
Marina Lum
Grants Manager
(See address above.)

THE KRESGE FOUNDATION [196]
3215 West Big Beaver Road
Troy, MI 48084
(248) 643-9630
Fax: (248) 643-0588

E-MAIL ADDRESS:
info@kresge.org

WEB SITE ADDRESS:
www.kresge.org

FOUNDED: 1924

AREAS OF INTEREST:
Arts and culture, Detroit/community development, education, environment, and health and human services.

TYPE:
General operating grants; Project/program grants. Program-related investments.

YEAR PROGRAM STARTED: 1924

PURPOSE:
To promote the well-being of mankind.

LEGAL BASIS:
Independent private foundation.

ELIGIBILITY:
Tax-exempt charitable organizations operating in the fields of higher education (including community colleges), health care and long-term care, human services, science and the environment, arts and humanities and public affairs. Governmental agencies are also eligible to apply. Full accreditation is required for higher education and hospital applicants and preferred in all other fields that offer it. Evidence of initial funding for the requested project is considered essential.

The following projects are eligible:
(1) construction of facilities;
(2) renovation of facilities;
(3) purchase of major equipment or an integrated system at a cost of at least $300,000; equipment costs may include computer software expenses, if applicable and;
(4) purchase of real estate.

Religious organizations, elementary and secondary schools, private foundations and individuals are not eligible to apply. However, accredited seminaries are eligible to apply. Also, agencies operated by religious organizations that serve secular needs may be eligible if the programs have financial and governing autonomy separate from the parent organization. They must also have space formally dedicated to their programs.

Some elementary and secondary schools may be eligible in the Foundation's Human Services category, if they predominantly serve individuals with physical and/or developmental disabilities.

FINANCIAL DATA:
Amount of support per award: Varies.

APPLICATION INFORMATION:
Only electronic application is accepted. Detailed guidelines and form are available on the Foundation web site.
Duration: Varies.

PUBLICATIONS:
Annual report.

ADDRESS INQUIRIES TO:
Grants Inquiry Coordinator
(See address above.)

ALBERT AND BESSIE MAE KRONKOSKY CHARITABLE FOUNDATION [197]
112 East Pecan, Suite 830
San Antonio, TX 78205
(210) 475-9000
Fax: (210) 354-2204

E-MAIL ADDRESS:
kronfndn@kronkosky.org

WEB SITE ADDRESS:
www.kronkosky.org

FOUNDED: 1991

AREAS OF INTEREST:
Elderly, youth, child abuse and neglect, persons with disabilities, culture and the arts, museums, libraries, prevention of cruelty to animals, health, parks, zoos and wildlife sanctuaries.

NAME(S) OF PROGRAMS:
● **Precious Minds, New Connections**

TYPE:
Capital grants; Challenge/matching grants; Endowments; General operating grants; Matching gifts; Project/program grants; Research grants; Seed money grants; Technical assistance; Training grants; Research contracts.

YEAR PROGRAM STARTED: 1999

PURPOSE:
To produce profound good that is tangible and measurable in Bandera, Bexar, Comal, and Kendall counties in Texas by implementing the Kronkoskys' charitable purposes.

LEGAL BASIS:
Private foundation.

ELIGIBILITY:
Corporate organizations that are exempt under Section 501(c)(3) of the Internal Revenue Code. The Foundation will not make grants to individuals or for-profit organizations. In addition, the Foundation has a geographic limitation that requires that grant funds be used in the specific counties listed below.

GEOGRAPHIC RESTRICTIONS:
Bandera, Bexar, Comal and Kendall counties, Texas.

FINANCIAL DATA:
Amount of support per award: $1,700 to $750,000 for the year 2013. Average grant: $50,000.
Total amount of support: $15,413,185 for the year 2013.

NUMBER OF APPLICANTS MOST RECENT YEAR: 166 for the year 2013.

NUMBER OF AWARDS: 143 for the year 2013.

APPLICATION INFORMATION:
Send a Letter of Inquiry to the address above. If the Letter of Inquiry meets requirements, it will be reviewed by Foundation's staff within 10 days of receipt. If the proposal is accepted, an application package as well as a timeline for submission of the grant proposal will be forwarded. If proposal is not accepted, notification in writing will be sent. Please note geographic requirement.
Duration: Usually one year.
Deadline: Letters of Inquiry will be accepted throughout the year and reviewed on a rolling basis.

PUBLICATIONS:
Program guidelines; annual report (online only).

IRS IDENTIFICATION NUMBER: 74-6385152

ADDRESS INQUIRIES TO:
Palmer Moe, Managing Director
(See address above.)

THE JEAN AND E. FLOYD KVAMME FOUNDATION
P.O. Box 2494
Saratoga, CA 95070
(408) 395-2829
Fax: (408) 354-0804

TYPE:
Capital grants; Development grants; General operating grants; Project/program grants.

See entry 1563 for full listing.

LAIDLAW FOUNDATION [198]
365 Bloor Street East
Suite 2000
Toronto ON M4W 3L4 Canada
(416) 964-3614 ext. 307
Fax: (416) 975-1428

E-MAIL ADDRESS:
askinner@laidlawfdn.org

WEB SITE ADDRESS:
www.laidlawfdn.org

FOUNDED: 1949

AREAS OF INTEREST:
Youth engagement, youth social infrastructure and policy development.

NAME(S) OF PROGRAMS:
● **Youth-led Community Change (YLCC)**

TYPE:
Project/program grants.

YEAR PROGRAM STARTED: 1949

PURPOSE:
To invest in innovative ideas, convene interested parties, share learning and advocate for change in support of young people becoming healthy, creative and fully engaged citizens.

LEGAL BASIS:
Private family foundation.

ELIGIBILITY:
The Foundation will fund youth-led initiatives. Applicants must be young people 14 to 25 years of age.

GEOGRAPHIC RESTRICTIONS:
Greater Golden Horseshoe area of Canada.

FINANCIAL DATA:
Amount of support per award: Project
Grants: Up to $25,000.

Total amount of support: Approximately
$650,000.

APPLICATION INFORMATION:
Applicants must submit:
(1) Grant Application Cover Sheet;
(2) three- to five-page proposal;
(3) work plan;
(4) budget;
(5) contact information for other community
groups, agencies or individuals that will play
a role in the proposal, if applicable;
(6) partnership agreement between main
applicant and administrative partner and/or
letter from administrative partner, if
applicable;
(7) list of board of directors or governing
committee members, if applicable;
(8) current operating budget for the
group/organization, if applicable;
(9) most recent audited financial statements,
if applicable and;
(10) most recent final report if applicant has
been previously funded from Laidlaw.

Submit 12 hard copies and one electronic
copy (by e-mail). Confirmation will be sent
by e-mail when proposal is received.

Duration: Typically one year.

Deadline: Varies.

ADDRESS INQUIRIES TO:
Ana Skinner
Program Manager, Youth Organizing
(See address and e-mail above.)

LAMB FOUNDATION   [199]
P.O. Box 1705
Lake Oswego, OR 97035
(503) 635-8010
Fax: (503) 635-6544

E-MAIL ADDRESS:
lambfnd@lambfoundation.org

WEB SITE ADDRESS:
www.lambfoundation.org

FOUNDED: 1971

AREAS OF INTEREST:
Social services for youth and children, arts,
and environment.

TYPE:
Challenge/matching grants; General operating
grants; Project/program grants.

LEGAL BASIS:
Private foundation.

ELIGIBILITY:
Applicants must be nonprofit 501(c)(3) public
charity organizations.

GEOGRAPHIC RESTRICTIONS:
Pacific Northwest.

FINANCIAL DATA:
Amount of support per award: Typical grants:
$5,000 to $15,000.

Total amount of support: Approximately
$200,000.

NUMBER OF APPLICANTS MOST RECENT YEAR:
20.

NUMBER OF AWARDS: 59.

REPRESENTATIVE AWARDS:
$10,000 to Janus Youth Programs; $10,000 to
Oregon Symphony; $12,000 to Willamette
Riverkeeper.

APPLICATION INFORMATION:
The Foundation is not currently accepting
unsolicited applications. Upon invitation,
application information will be sent to the
prospective applicant.

Duration: One year.

Deadline: Included in application materials
sent to invited applicants.

PUBLICATIONS:
Brochure.

IRS IDENTIFICATION NUMBER: 23-7120564

STAFF:
Debra Iguchi, Administrator

ADDRESS INQUIRIES TO:
Debra Iguchi, Administrator
(See address above.)

*PLEASE NOTE:
Prospective applicants are encouraged to
contact the office or web site periodically for
changes.

LAND O'LAKES
FOUNDATION   [200]
4001 Lexington Avenue North
Arden Hills, MN 55126
(651) 375-2470
Fax: (651) 375-2000

E-MAIL ADDRESS:
landolakesfoundation@landolakes.com

WEB SITE ADDRESS:
www.foundation.landolakes.com

FOUNDED: 1997

AREAS OF INTEREST:
Hunger, education and community.

CONSULTING OR VOLUNTEER SERVICES:
Group projects.

NAME(S) OF PROGRAMS:
- **California Regions Grant Program**
- **Community Grants Program**
- **Dollars for Doers Program**
- **Matching Gifts to Education Program**
- **Member Co-op Match Program**
- **Mid-Atlantic Grant Program**

TYPE:
Capital grants; Challenge/matching grants;
Endowments; General operating grants;
Matching gifts; Project/program grants; Seed
money grants; Technical assistance. Major
support is in the form of cash contributions,
supplemented with food and product
donations to Feeding America National Food
Bank Network only.

California Regions Grant Program funds
community projects in three areas of
California: Orland, Tulare/Kings/Bakersfield
and Ontario, initiated by Land O'Lakes dairy
member-leaders.

Community Grants Program provides support
through cash grants to nonprofit organizations
that are working to improve communities
where Land O'Lakes has a significant
concentration of members or employees.
Foundation's primary focus area is hunger
and hunger-related issues.

Dollars for Doers Program recognizes
employee and retiree volunteerism with
financial contributions to 501(c)(3) nonprofit
organizations based on volunteer hours.

Matching Gifts to Education Program
matches gifts by full- and part-time
employees, Board of Directors members and

Leadership Council members to grades K-12,
postsecondary education, and public radio
and public television stations.

Member Co-op Match Program matches
dollar-for-dollar the cash donations of
member cooperatives, thus doubling the
funds available for hometown projects.

Mid-Atlantic Grant Program funds
community projects in Maryland, New York,
Pennsylvania and Virginia, initiated by Land
O'Lakes dairy member-leaders.

YEAR PROGRAM STARTED: 1981

PURPOSE:
To demonstrate a commitment to improving
and enhancing the quality of life in
communities where Land O'Lakes has
facilities, plants, members and employees; to
invest and participate in community programs
that strengthen and preserve the quality of
rural life; to encourage and support employee
volunteerism.

LEGAL BASIS:
Corporate foundation.

ELIGIBILITY:
Contributions are generally restricted to
organizations which have been granted
501(c)(3) tax-exempt status and are working
to improve communities where Land
O'Lakes has a significant concentration of
members or employees. Contributions are
focused in the western, north central and
eastern states. Of our donations, 85% will be
made in rural areas and 15% in urban areas
within those states.

Funds generally will not be used for
lobbying, political and religious
organizations, veteran, fraternal and labor
organizations, fund-raising events, benefits or
advertising, national groups, individuals,
scholarships, private colleges and universities,
disease/medical research or treatment or
racing/sports sponsorships.

Matching Gift recipient organizations must
be located in the U.S. and be tax-exempt
under Section 501(c)(3) of the Internal
Revenue Code. Eligible institutions include
the following:
(1) elementary and secondary schools that are
fully accredited by the Department of
Education;
(2) public or private colleges, universities,
junior colleges, technical/vocational institutes,
community colleges and graduate
professional schools with appropriate regional
or professional accreditation, or tax-exempt
alumni funds, foundations or associations that
collect funds exclusively for the direct benefit
of an eligible institution and;
(3) public radio and television stations that
meet the criteria established by the
Corporation for Public Broadcasting.

Organizations are eligible for only one grant
per calendar year.

FINANCIAL DATA:
Amount of support per award: Varies.

Total amount of support: Approximately
$4,200,000 for the year 2013.

Matching fund requirements: Cash only.

COOPERATIVE FUNDING PROGRAMS: Through
the Member Co-op Match Program, Land
O'Lakes member cooperatives may request
that the Foundation match their donations to
local nonprofits, within the parameters of the
program.

NUMBER OF APPLICANTS MOST RECENT YEAR:
More than 6,000.

NUMBER OF AWARDS: 1,126 for the year 2011.

REPRESENTATIVE AWARDS:
Feeding America National Food Bank
Network.

APPLICATION INFORMATION:
See web site for complete application
information.

Duration: Varies.

PUBLICATIONS:
Contributions program guidelines.

IRS IDENTIFICATION NUMBER: 41-1864977

ADDRESS INQUIRIES TO:
Executive Director
Land O'Lakes Foundation
P.O. Box 64150
St. Paul, MN 55164-0150

LAND O'LAKES FOUNDATION [201]
4001 Lexington Avenue North
Arden Hills, MN 55126
(651) 481-2123
Fax: (651) 481-2000

E-MAIL ADDRESS:
lrbotham@landolakes.com

WEB SITE ADDRESS:
www.foundation.landolakes.com

AREAS OF INTEREST:
Dairy science or dairy
manufacturing/marketing.

NAME(S) OF PROGRAMS:
● **John Brandt Memorial Scholarship Fund**

TYPE:
Scholarships. John Brandt Memorial
Scholarship Program is a $25,000 scholarship
available to graduate students pursuing
dairy-related degrees. One or two
scholarships are awarded annually to
deserving candidates who have demonstrated
exceptional commitment and aptitude toward
their field of study.

PURPOSE:
To encourage graduate study in dairy science
or dairy marketing/manufacturing.

LEGAL BASIS:
Corporate foundation.

ELIGIBILITY:
Applicants must be pursuing a program of
study leading to a Master's or Doctorate
degree in dairy cattle nutrition, genetics,
physiology or management, or the
manufacturing, processing or marketing of
milk and dairy products at one of the four
following institutions: University of
Minnesota, University of Wisconsin, Iowa
State University and South Dakota State
University. Such factors as personal
recommendations, scholastic record, planned
program of study and research and future
plans for working in the dairy industry or
closely related fields shall be considered in
making the award.

FINANCIAL DATA:
Amount of support per award: $25,000.
Total amount of support: Up to $50,000,
depending on need and endowment market
performance.

NUMBER OF APPLICANTS MOST RECENT YEAR:
Over 450.

NUMBER OF AWARDS: 1 to 2 annually.

APPLICATION INFORMATION:
The Foundation sends out Requests for
Proposals (RFPs) to the qualifying schools to
begin the application process. Those with
recommendations should send an application
form including personal history, transcripts of
scholastic record, and a plan of study and
research to be followed in pursuit of an
advanced degree. Applications should be sent
to the Executive Director, Land O'Lakes
Foundation, P.O. Box 64150, St. Paul, MN
55164-0150.

Duration: One academic year. No renewals.
Deadline: Applications must be postmarked
by April 30. Notification by early June.

ADDRESS INQUIRIES TO:
Executive Director
Land O'Lakes Foundation
P.O. Box 64150
St. Paul, MN 55164-0150

*SPECIAL STIPULATIONS:
Scholarships for graduate-level studies.

HERBERT AND GERTRUDE LATKIN CHARITABLE FOUNDATION [202]
1021 Anacapa Street
Santa Barbara, CA 93101
(805) 899-8471
Fax: (805) 884-1404

FOUNDED: 1991

AREAS OF INTEREST:
Animal cruelty, child abuse, emergency
medical services, health and welfare to
elderly and needy people, scholarships to
deserving college students.

TYPE:
Project/program grants; Scholarships.

YEAR PROGRAM STARTED: 1991

PURPOSE:
To promote the health and welfare of the
elderly; to prevent cruelty to animals; to
provide emergency medical service for
persons suffering as a result of calamity or
disaster; to prevent child abuse; to provide
assistance to the needy; to provide
scholarships to college students.

LEGAL BASIS:
Private family foundation.

ELIGIBILITY:
Grants are made to organizations that have
tax-exempt status under Section 501(c)(3) of
the Internal Revenue Code. No grants are
made to individuals or religious
organizations.

GEOGRAPHIC RESTRICTIONS:
Santa Barbara County, California.

FINANCIAL DATA:
Amount of support per award: Varies.
Total amount of support: $213,880 for the
year 2013.

NUMBER OF APPLICANTS MOST RECENT YEAR:
66.

NUMBER OF AWARDS: 55.

APPLICATION INFORMATION:
Send a letter of inquiry outlining the
organization's goal and purposes, and the
intended use and amount of the grant
requested.

Duration: One year. Renewal possible.
Deadline: April 1 and October 1.

IRS IDENTIFICATION NUMBER: 77-6070540

ADDRESS INQUIRIES TO:
Janice Gibbons, Trust Officer
(See address above.)

THE BLANCHE AND IRVING LAURIE FOUNDATION [203]
P.O. Box 53
Roseland, NJ 07068-5788
(973) 993-1743
Fax: (973) 993-3146

AREAS OF INTEREST:
Arts, children, needs of the elderly,
education, medical care and needs of the
Jewish community.

TYPE:
Capital grants; Project/program grants.

LEGAL BASIS:
Private foundation.

ELIGIBILITY:
Funds given for specific projects only. No
funds for general organization endowments,
nor to meet general operating expenses or
budget deficits.

GEOGRAPHIC RESTRICTIONS:
Middlesex County, New Jersey.

FINANCIAL DATA:
Amount of support per award: $25,000 to
$50,000.

APPLICATION INFORMATION:
Submit seven copies of proposal including
statement of program objectives, project
budget, plans for publicizing the project,
background information about the
organization and copy of IRS tax-exemption
letter.

Duration: Varies.
Deadline: Proposals accepted year-round.

PUBLICATIONS:
Informational brochure.

BOARD OF TRUSTEES:
Laura Barron
Gene R. Korf, Esq.
Scott Korf
Richard A. Patt
Harvey Rich
Robert M. Zagoren

ADDRESS INQUIRIES TO:
Gene R. Korf, Esq., Executive Director
(See address above.)

JACOB AND CHARLOTTE LEHRMAN FOUNDATION, INC. [204]
1836 Columbia Road, N.W.
Washington, DC 20009
(202) 328-8400
Fax: (202) 328-8405

E-MAIL ADDRESS:
info@lehrmanfoundation.org

WEB SITE ADDRESS:
lehrmanfoundation.org

FOUNDED: 1971

AREAS OF INTEREST:
Jewish life in Washington, DC; Israel; arts;
education; underserved children; health and
environment.

NAME(S) OF PROGRAMS:
● **Impact Award**

TYPE:
Awards/prizes; Project/program grants.
Recognizes a Washington, DC, emerging

nonprofit organization that supports education and underserved children by making an extraordinary difference in their lives.

YEAR PROGRAM STARTED: 2001

ELIGIBILITY:
The Foundation does not accept unsolicited grants.

GEOGRAPHIC RESTRICTIONS:
Primarily greater Washington, DC area.

FINANCIAL DATA:
Total amount of support: $25,000.

ADDRESS INQUIRIES TO:
Robert Lehrman, President
(See address above.)

LIBRA FOUNDATION   [205]

3 Canal Plaza
Portland, ME 04101
(207) 879-6280
Fax: (207) 879-6281

E-MAIL ADDRESS:
jennifer@librafoundation.org

WEB SITE ADDRESS:
www.librafoundation.org

FOUNDED: 1989

AREAS OF INTEREST:
Arts, culture and humanities, education, environment, health, human services, public/society benefit and religion.

TYPE:
Grants-in-aid; Project/program grants.

PURPOSE:
To strive for innovative ways to enrich Maine, empower communities, and enhance the quality of life of all Maine citizens.

ELIGIBILITY:
Charitable nonprofit organizations whose activities, operations, or purposes take place only within the state of Maine. Religious organizations are eligible. Organizations must supply a copy of tax-exempt 501(c)(3) letter. Grants are not made to individuals.

GEOGRAPHIC RESTRICTIONS:
Maine.

FINANCIAL DATA:
Amount of support per award: Up to $25,000.
Total amount of support: Approximately $5,228,000 for the year 2013.

NUMBER OF APPLICANTS MOST RECENT YEAR: 312.

NUMBER OF AWARDS: 57.

APPLICATION INFORMATION:
Applicants are asked to complete a two-paged application in accordance with the Foundation's guidelines, both of which may be obtained from the Foundation web site.
Duration: One-time grant. Must reapply after expiration of one year.
Deadline: February 15, May 15, August 15 and November 15.

ADDRESS INQUIRIES TO:
Jennifer Cook, Administrative Assistant
(See address above.)

LILLY ENDOWMENT INC.   [206]

2801 North Meridian Street
Indianapolis, IN 46208
(317) 924-5471
Fax: (317) 926-4431

E-MAIL ADDRESS:
klothr@lei.org

WEB SITE ADDRESS:
www.lillyendowment.org

FOUNDED: 1937

AREAS OF INTEREST:
Religion, education and community development.

TYPE:
Awards/prizes; Capital grants; Challenge/matching grants; Conferences/seminars; Development grants; Fellowships; General operating grants; Internships; Matching gifts; Project/program grants; Research grants; Scholarships; Training grants. In the area of religion, support for programs that enrich the religious lives of American Christians, mainly by supporting efforts to call, support and educate a new generation of talented pastors and to strengthen current pastors in their capacities for excellence in ministry; support for programs that seek to help congregations be healthy communities of faith; support for theological seminaries and other educational and religious institutions that share these aims; support for projects which strengthen the contributions that religious ideas, practices, values and institutions make to the common good.

In the area of education, support for initiatives and programs that improve education in Indiana, with special emphasis on higher education and on programs designed to increase the number of Indiana residents with Bachelor's degrees; support for a number of invitational grant programs, many of which are aimed at Indiana's colleges' and universities' abilities to increase the state's educational attainment level; support on an invitational basis for minority higher education.

In the area of youth, support for direct-service organizations in central Indiana; support for building capacity of intermediary organizations throughout the state; support for professional development for the staffs and volunteer leadership of these organizations.

In the area of leadership education, support for projects that nurture good stewardship among the trustees and executives of charitable organizations; support for scholarship on the characteristics of able trusteeship and good governance of nonprofit organizations.

In the area of fund-raising and philanthropy, support for programs (nationally and in Indiana) to increase the charitable giving among Americans; support for efforts to create a body of reliable knowledge about giving and fund-raising; support for scholarly pursuit of the subject.

In the areas of community development, support is available for programs that involve Indianapolis initiatives in the arts, culture and preservation, human services and community development and revitalization. Indiana initiatives include Indiana United Ways and community foundations. Economic public-policy general support grants are offered on an invitational basis limited to a limited number of organizations that promote free market and democratic principles.

YEAR PROGRAM STARTED: 1937

PURPOSE:
To support the causes of religion, education and community development.

LEGAL BASIS:
Private foundation.

ELIGIBILITY:
Applicants must be 501(c)(3) tax-exempt public organizations and institutions with appropriate interests in targeted areas. Grantmaking prohibitions generally include loans or cash to individuals, health care projects, mass media projects, endowments, libraries outside Indianapolis, student scholarships (except in Indiana), general operating support/capital campaigns for organizations outside of Indiana.

GEOGRAPHIC RESTRICTIONS:
Community development and education in Indiana.

FINANCIAL DATA:
Grants vary in amount depending on the needs and nature of the request.
Amount of support per award: Varies.
Total amount of support: $230,022,852 paid for the year 2012.
Matching fund requirements: Varies.

NUMBER OF APPLICANTS MOST RECENT YEAR:
1,773 for the year 2012.

NUMBER OF AWARDS: 801 approved grants for the year 2012.

APPLICATION INFORMATION:
Except for specialized programs, no official application forms are required. Guidelines for applicants are found on the web site. The usual first step is a two-page letter outlining the project and budget and a description of the applicant organization, including a statement of federal tax-exempt status.
Duration: One to three years; typically, one year.
Deadline: Applications accepted on an ongoing basis.

PUBLICATIONS:
Application guidelines; annual report.

IRS IDENTIFICATION NUMBER: 35-0868122

OFFICERS:
Thomas M. Lofton, Chairman
N. Clay Robbins, President and Chief Executive Officer
Wallace R. (Ace) Yakey, Jr., Vice President, Community Development
Sara B. Cobb, Vice President, Education
E.G. White, Vice President, Finance
Christopher L. Coble, Vice President, Religion
Diane M. Stenson, Treasurer and Vice President
David D. Biber, Secretary

DIRECTORS:
Daniel P. Carmichael
Craig R. Dykstra
William G. Enright
Charles E. Golden
Eli Lilly, II
Mary K. Lisher
Thomas M. Lofton
N. Clay Robbins
David N. Shane

ADDRESS INQUIRIES TO:
Program Office
(See address above.)

*SPECIAL STIPULATIONS:
Awards are made to 501(c)(3) groups only.

LINCOLN FINANCIAL FOUNDATION [207]
1300 South Clinton Street
Fort Wayne, IN 46802
(260) 455-3636
Fax: (260) 455-4004

E-MAIL ADDRESS:
patti.grimm@lfg.com

WEB SITE ADDRESS:
www.lincolnfinancial.com

FOUNDED: 1962

AREAS OF INTEREST:
Arts, youth education, human services and workforce/economic development.

CONSULTING OR VOLUNTEER SERVICES:
Volunteer Involvement Program for employees of Lincoln Financial Group.

TYPE:
Matching gifts; Project/program grants; Technical assistance.

YEAR PROGRAM STARTED: 1962

PURPOSE:
To enhance the quality of life and help individuals face their futures with confidence in communities where employees work.

LEGAL BASIS:
Corporate Foundation.

ELIGIBILITY:
Applicants must be 501(c)(3) organizations.

No grants to individuals, for endowments, for sponsorship of sporting events or for the purchase of tickets.

GEOGRAPHIC RESTRICTIONS:
Hartford, Connecticut; Fort Wayne, Indiana; Omaha, Nebraska; Concord, New Hampshire; Greensboro, North Carolina; Philadelphia, Pennsylvania.

FINANCIAL DATA:
Amount of support per award: Varies.
Total amount of support: Up to 2% of the corporation's pre-tax earnings annually.
Matching fund requirements: Qualified 501(c)(3).

NUMBER OF APPLICANTS MOST RECENT YEAR: 420.

NUMBER OF AWARDS: 340.

APPLICATION INFORMATION:
Online application form required. Some attachments requested.
Duration: Quarterly.
Deadline: Varies.

PUBLICATIONS:
Guidelines.

IRS IDENTIFICATION NUMBER: 35-6042099

ADDRESS INQUIRIES TO:
Program Officer
(See address above.)

THE LOATS FOUNDATION, INC. [208]
35 East Church Street
Frederick, MD 21701
(301) 663-6361
Fax: (301) 663-7747

FOUNDED: 1979

AREAS OF INTEREST:
Scholarship for Frederick County residents only and charitable organizations of Frederick County, MD.

TYPE:
Scholarships.

YEAR PROGRAM STARTED: 1979

PURPOSE:
To help residents of Frederick County, MD go on to higher education by providing financial aid.

LEGAL BASIS:
Nonprofit foundation.

ELIGIBILITY:
Applicant must be a resident of Frederick County, MD. Scholarships are distributed by colleges on a need basis.

GEOGRAPHIC RESTRICTIONS:
Frederick County, Maryland.

FINANCIAL DATA:
Amount of support per award: $3,000 cap.
Total amount of support: Varies.

APPLICATION INFORMATION:
Applications for scholarships are available at all Maryland colleges and universities.
Duration: One year. Renewable on need basis.

ADDRESS INQUIRIES TO:
Helen Hahn, Secretary
(See address above.)

THE LUBRIZOL FOUNDATION [209]
29400 Lakeland Boulevard, Suite 054B
Wickliffe, OH 44092-2298
(440) 347-1797
Fax: (440) 347-1858

E-MAIL ADDRESS:
kal@lubrizol.com

WEB SITE ADDRESS:
www.lubrizol.com

FOUNDED: 1952

AREAS OF INTEREST:
Education, health and human services, civic, cultural, environmental and youth activities.

NAME(S) OF PROGRAMS:
- **Community Connection Employee Volunteer Gift Program**
- **Matching Gift Program**

TYPE:
Capital grants; Fellowships; General operating grants; Matching gifts; Project/program grants; Scholarships. The Foundation has scholarship programs at 38 selected colleges and universities. It also matches gifts of Lubrizol employees to most charitable organizations on a dollar-for-dollar basis.

In the area of education, support is given for scholarships, fellowships and awards in selected fields of study through selected colleges and universities, with major emphasis on the study of chemistry and chemical and mechanical engineering, capital and operating grants to colleges, universities, schools, educational programs and combined educational funds.

In the area of health and human services, support is provided for combined funds, direct grants to health and human service activities.

In the area of civic and cultural, support is provided for public television stations, performing arts organizations, schools of fine arts and museums.

In the area of youth activities, support is given to programs that contribute to character-building, such as those which promote good citizenship, self-reliance, an understanding of free enterprise and an appreciation of nature and the environment.

In the environmental area, support is given to parks, nature centers, conservancies and local environmental education efforts.

YEAR PROGRAM STARTED: 1952

PURPOSE:
To support educational, youth, health, human services, civic and cultural and environmental activities of a tax-exempt, charitable nature.

LEGAL BASIS:
Private, tax-exempt foundation.

ELIGIBILITY:
Grants are made to U.S. nonprofit, educational or other charitable tax-exempt organizations. Grants are not generally made to endowments, religious or political purposes or individuals.

GEOGRAPHIC RESTRICTIONS:
Primarily Greater Cleveland, Ohio and Houston, Texas.

FINANCIAL DATA:
Amount of support per award: Grants vary in amount, depending upon the needs and nature of the request.
Total amount of support: $4,841,262, including matching gifts, for the year 2013.
Matching fund requirements: 1:1 match; $100 minimum; $5,000 maximum, and five gifts maximum.

NUMBER OF APPLICANTS MOST RECENT YEAR: 320.

NUMBER OF AWARDS: 38 discretionary grants; 235 total awards including operating, capital and discretionary.

REPRESENTATIVE AWARDS:
$110,200 to the United Way of Lake County, Inc. for general operating support; $84,800 to the United Way of the Texas Gulf Coast for general operating support; $183,300 to the United Way Services of Cleveland for general operating support.

APPLICATION INFORMATION:
Grant proposals should include the following: (1) a cover letter that summarizes the purpose of the request signed by the executive officer of the organization; (2) a narrative of specific information related to the subject of the request; (3) current audited financial statements and a specific project budget, if applicable and; (4) documentation of the organization's Federal tax-exempt status.

Additional descriptive literature (annual report, brochures, etc.) that accurately characterizes the overall activities of the organization is appreciated. Upon review, further information may be requested including an interview or site visit.

Applicants will receive written notification of the decision on their proposal. An organization whose request has been declined should not submit another proposal for at least 12 months after such notification.
Duration: One year, with possible renewal. Some grants are ongoing.

PUBLICATIONS:
Annual report.

IRS IDENTIFICATION NUMBER: 34-6500595

OFFICERS:
  J.L. Hambrick, Chairman
  D.J. Enzerra, President
  B.A. Valentine, Treasurer
  K.A. Lerchbacher, Secretary

TRUSTEES:
  D.J. Enzerra
  R.T. Graf
  J.L. Hambrick
  K.L. Jethrow
  K.A. Lerchbacher
  B.A. Valentine

ADDRESS INQUIRIES TO:
  Karen A. Lerchbacher
  Foundation Administrator
  (See address above.)

THE HENRY LUCE FOUNDATION, INC.   [210]

51 Madison Avenue, 30th Floor
New York, NY 10010
(212) 489-7700
Fax: (212) 581-9541

E-MAIL ADDRESS:
  hlf1@hluce.org

WEB SITE ADDRESS:
  www.hluce.org

FOUNDED: 1936

AREAS OF INTEREST:
  Interdisciplinary exploration of higher
  education, increased understanding between
  Asia and the U.S., the study of religion and
  theology, scholarship in American art,
  opportunities for women in science and
  engineering, and environmental and public
  policy programs.

NAME(S) OF PROGRAMS:
  • **American Art Program**
  • **Clare Boothe Luce Program**
  • **Luce Foundation Theology Program**
  • **Henry Luce III Fellows in Theology
    Program**
  • **Luce Scholars Program**

TYPE:
  Fellowships; Internships; Project/program
  grants; Scholarships. American Art Program
  focuses on the American fine and decorative
  arts and is committed to scholarship and the
  overall enhancement of this field. The
  program is national in scope and provides
  support for all periods and genres of
  American art history.

  The Clare Boothe Luce Program promotes
  the advancement of American women
  through higher education in the sciences,
  engineering and mathematics.

  The Luce Foundation's Theology program
  encourages the development of leadership for
  religious communities through theological
  education, and fosters scholarship that links
  the academy to churches and the wider
  public. The program provides funding for
  seminary education, leadership, ecumenical
  and interreligious programs, and religion and
  the arts.

  The Henry Luce III Fellows in Theology
  program, administered by the Association of
  Theological Schools, supports innovative
  research and publication by full-time
  seminary faculty.

  The Luce Scholars Program provides stipends
  and internships for young Americans to live
  and work in Asia each year.

PURPOSE:
  To promote interdisciplinary exploration of
  higher education, increased understanding
  between Asia and the U.S., the study of
  religion and theology, scholarship in
  American art, opportunities for women in
  science and engineering, and environmental
  and public policy programs.

ELIGIBILITY:
  The Foundation does not support health care
  or medical projects and does not fund
  development assistance work overseas. It
  does not normally assist journalism, media
  and film projects or the performing arts. The
  Foundation does not offer funding for
  individuals.

APPLICATION INFORMATION:
  No special forms are required, although
  separate guidelines and deadlines exist for
  specific programs. In most cases, an initial
  letter of inquiry, to determine whether a
  project falls within the Foundation's
  guidelines, can be addressed to the
  appropriate program director or officer.

LYNDHURST FOUNDATION [211]

517 East Fifth Street
Chattanooga, TN 37403-1826
(423) 756-0767
Fax: (423) 756-0770

E-MAIL ADDRESS:
  bclark@lyndhurstfoundation.org

WEB SITE ADDRESS:
  www.lyndhurstfoundation.org

FOUNDED: 1938

AREAS OF INTEREST:
  Enhancing the quality of Chattanooga's
  public gathering places in downtown and
  along the riverfront, plus its public schools,
  its diverse arts and cultural organizations and
  its natural environment. Beyond the city's
  boundaries, the Foundation wants to be
  involved in projects that protect and enhance
  the natural environment of the southern
  Appalachian region.

TYPE:
  Challenge/matching grants;
  Conferences/seminars; Demonstration grants;
  Development grants; Endowments; General
  operating grants; Matching gifts;
  Project/program grants; Seed money grants;
  Technical assistance. The Foundation intends
  to focus upon continued development of the
  Tennessee Riverpark, redevelopment of the
  Southside as a live-and-work urban
  neighborhood, facilitation of historic
  preservation, stimulation of downtown
  housing development, strengthening of the
  city's arts and cultural life, protection and
  enhancement of the community's natural
  environment, the reform of the community's
  public schools, the continued development of
  improved housing opportunities for people of
  modest means and innovations in social
  service programs that provide genuine
  progress against social problems and genuine
  enhancement of community strengths in
  Chattanooga.

YEAR PROGRAM STARTED: 1978

PURPOSE:
  To support a variety of nonprofit programs to
  make life better within the city of
  Chattanooga.

LEGAL BASIS:
  Private foundation.

ELIGIBILITY:
  Applicants must be 501(c)(3) organizations in
  the southeastern U.S.

  Most of the Foundation's grants are
  distributed solely at the Foundation's
  initiative. This means that, in most
  categories, the Foundation does not seek or
  fund unsolicited requests.

GEOGRAPHIC RESTRICTIONS:
  Southeast, with special consideration given to
  certain developments in Chattanooga,
  Tennessee.

FINANCIAL DATA:
  Amount of support per award:
  Approximately $30,000 average grant.
  Total amount of support: Over $10,000,000.

NUMBER OF AWARDS: Varies.

REPRESENTATIVE AWARDS:
  $10,000 to Cumberland Trail Conference for
  the construction of a foot bridge; $100,000 to
  Public Education Foundation in support of an
  education data analyst for the Hamilton
  County Department of Education; $55,000 to
  Chattanooga Neighborhood Enterprise for
  technical assistance and neighborhood
  revitalization activities.

APPLICATION INFORMATION:
  A grant request should be initiated by a brief
  letter of two or three pages describing the
  organization and the specific project for
  which support is being sought. Included
  should be an estimated project budget, a copy
  of the organization's tax-exempt ruling from
  the IRS and a list of directors and staff
  members. Further information and an
  interview or visit may be requested.
  Duration: One year. Renewal possible for up
  to three years.
  Deadline: July 5 for August meeting,
  September 30 for November meeting.

PUBLICATIONS:
  Annual report.

OFFICERS:
  Robert C. Taylor, Chairman of the Board
  Benic M. Clark, III, President/Treasurer
  Katherine Currin, Secretary

TRUSTEES:
  Stephen A. Culp
  Katherine Currin
  Kathleen S. Hunt, M.D.
  James O. Kennedy
  Alison G. Lebovitz
  James J. McGinness
  Robert K. Mills
  Robert C. Taylor, Jr.
  Margaret W. Townsend

STAFF:
  Benic M. Clark, III, President/Treasurer
  Margaret Stakely, Controller
  Karen Rudolph, Program Officer

ADDRESS INQUIRIES TO:
  Benic M. Clark, III, President/Treasurer
  (See address above.)

M & M AREA COMMUNITY FOUNDATION

1101 11th Avenue, Suite One
Menominee, MI 49858-3018
(906) 864-3599
Fax: (906) 864-3657

E-MAIL ADDRESS:
  info@mmcommunityfoundation.org

WEB SITE ADDRESS:
  www.mmcommunityfoundation.org

TYPE:
Project/program grants; Scholarships;
Training grants.

See entry 1322 for full listing.

THE J.E. AND L.E. MABEE FOUNDATION, INC.   [212]
401 South Boston Avenue
Suite 3001
Tulsa, OK 74103-4017
(918) 584-4286
Fax: (918) 585-5540

WEB SITE ADDRESS:
www.mabeefoundation.com

FOUNDED: 1948

AREAS OF INTEREST:
Education, scientific and medical research,
religion and charities.

TYPE:
Capital grants.

PURPOSE:
To assist religious, charitable and educational
organizations.

LEGAL BASIS:
Nonprofit foundation.

ELIGIBILITY:
Grants are awarded to nonprofit, tax-exempt,
non-tax-supported, established institutions
which combine sound character and stability
with progressiveness and purpose. The
Foundation does not generally favor deficit
financing and debt retirement, operating or
program funds, annual fund-raising
campaigns, endowments, government-owned
or operated institutions, educational
institutions below the college level,
furnishings or equipment (except major
medical equipment) or grants to churches.

Grants are made toward building and facility
construction, renovation projects and the
purchase of major capital grants.

GEOGRAPHIC RESTRICTIONS:
Arkansas, Kansas, Missouri, New Mexico,
Oklahoma and Texas.

FINANCIAL DATA:
Amount of support per award: $25,000 to
$1,000,000.
Total amount of support: $25,000 to
$30,000,000.

NUMBER OF AWARDS: 100.

APPLICATION INFORMATION:
There is no application form. Proposals must
contain the following items:
(1) the legal name and address of the
organization;
(2) name, title, address and telephone number
of the primary contact person;
(3) brief description of the organization;
(4) description of the project, with goals and
objectives;
(5) description of the population expected to
benefit from the project;
(6) detailed budget for the project;
(7) a list of funding sources including those
received and any pending or pledged;
(8) the cut-off date for a challenge grant;
(9) a time schedule for start of construction;
(10) indicate how the project will be
sustained after the grant expires;
(11) verification of IRS tax-exempt status
under Section 501(c)(3) and not a private
foundation under Section 509(a);
(12) the organization's most recent audited
financial statement and interim financial
statement for the current fiscal period and;
(13) a list of officers with titles and names of
the governing body with primary professional
affiliations.
Duration: Varies.
Deadline: March 1, June 1, September 1 and
December 1.

PUBLICATIONS:
Program announcement; proposal guidelines.

ADDRESS INQUIRIES TO:
Ray Tullius, Vice Chairman
(See address above.)

JOHN D. AND CATHERINE T. MACARTHUR FOUNDATION   [213]
140 South Dearborn Street
Chicago, IL 60603-5285
(312) 726-8000
Fax: (312) 920-6258

E-MAIL ADDRESS:
4answers@macfound.org

WEB SITE ADDRESS:
www.macfound.org

FOUNDED: 1978

NAME(S) OF PROGRAMS:
● **MacArthur Fellows Program**

TYPE:
General operating grants; Project/program
grants; Research grants. The MacArthur
Fellows Program awards fellowships to
exceptionally creative individuals, regardless
of field.

YEAR PROGRAM STARTED: 1979

PURPOSE:
To support creative people.

LEGAL BASIS:
Private, independent foundation.

ELIGIBILITY:
Applicants are nominated by the Foundation
and must be either residents or citizens of the
United States.

GEOGRAPHIC RESTRICTIONS:
United States.

FINANCIAL DATA:
Stipend of $500,000 paid in quarterly
installments over five years.

APPLICATION INFORMATION:
Complete details are available on the
Foundation web site.
Duration: One to five years. Renewals by
reapplication.

PUBLICATIONS:
Annual report.

ADDRESS INQUIRIES TO:
Richard J. Kaplan
Associate Vice President for
Institutional Research and Grants
Management
(See address above.)

THE MACLELLAN FOUNDATION, INC.   [214]
820 Broad Street, Suite 300
Chattanooga, TN 37402
(423) 755-1366
Fax: (423) 755-1640

E-MAIL ADDRESS:
support@maclellan.net
info@maclellan.net

WEB SITE ADDRESS:
www.maclellan.net/family-
foundations/maclellan

FOUNDED: 1945

AREAS OF INTEREST:
Christian agencies and churches, Protestant
religious associations, adults, children,
Indigenous peoples, youth, sports ministry,
discipleship, church planting, training, and
project support.

TYPE:
Challenge/matching grants; Matching gifts;
Project/program grants; Training grants.

YEAR PROGRAM STARTED: 1945

PURPOSE:
To serve national and international
organizations committed to furthering the
Kingdom of Christ and select local
organizations, which foster the spiritual
welfare of the community, by providing
financial and leadership resources to extend
the Kingdom of God to every tribe, nation,
people and tongue.

LEGAL BASIS:
Tax-exempt private foundation.

ELIGIBILITY:
The Foundation only provides grants to
nonprofit Christian organizations.

NUMBER OF APPLICANTS MOST RECENT YEAR:
760.

NUMBER OF AWARDS: 445.

APPLICATION INFORMATION:
Application forms and guidelines are
available online.
Duration: Varies.
Deadline: Proposals are accepted throughout
the year.

IRS IDENTIFICATION NUMBER: 62-6041468

OFFICER:
Hugh O. Maclellan, Jr., Executive Chairman
of the Board

MARBROOK FOUNDATION [215]
730 Second Avenue South
Suite 1300
Minneapolis, MN 55402
(612) 752-1783
Fax: (612) 752-1780

E-MAIL ADDRESS:
jhara@marbrookfoundation.org

WEB SITE ADDRESS:
www.marbrookfoundation.org

FOUNDED: 1948

AREAS OF INTEREST:
The Foundation's primary interest is in
initiatives or organizations that create equal
opportunity for immigrants and refugees in
the Twin Cities metro area.

TYPE:
Capital grants; Endowments; General
operating grants; Project/program grants;
Scholarships; Technical assistance. As the
immigrant and refugee populations grow and
become increasingly diverse, so does the
potential for enrichment and transformation
in our communities. The Foundation believes
that addressing the opportunities and
challenges that come with blending cultures,
languages and beliefs will help to revitalize
our communities and contribute to our
well-being.

YEAR PROGRAM STARTED: 1948

PURPOSE:
To promote the values of the Brooks Family by making grants and focusing involvement in designated charitable areas and causes that reflect those values.

LEGAL BASIS:
Tax-exempt, private foundation.

ELIGIBILITY:
The Foundation will give priority to projects or organizations that address at least one of the following areas:
(1) initiatives working to create equal opportunity or to empower immigrants and refugees (e.g., affordable housing, job training, life skills);
(2) environmental justice and advocacy for neighborhoods with a high concentration of immigrants and refugees;
(3) expanding access to healthy food for neighborhoods with a high concentration of immigrants and refugees;
(4) academic success for children of immigrants and refugees;
(5) English language instruction for immigrants and refugees;
(6) cultural preservation for new Americans;
(7) integrating a comprehensive approach (of body, mind and spirit) to the well-being of immigrants and refugees, with a special interest in programs honoring the inherent spiritual and cultural richness of immigrant communities and;
(8) arts organizations/projects that highlight cultural awareness or address social issues of immigrants and refugees.

The Foundation does not fund start-up organizations, programs for the elderly, domestic abuse programs, disease-related organizations, homeless shelters, food shelves, conferences and events, programs serving the physically or mentally disabled, or individuals or organizations which attempt to influence legislation or to intervene in any political campaign.

GEOGRAPHIC RESTRICTIONS:
Minnesota, with emphasis on Minneapolis and St. Paul.

FINANCIAL DATA:
Amount of support per award: Grants vary in amount, depending upon the needs and nature of the request.
Total amount of support: $728,700 for the year 2013.

NUMBER OF AWARDS: 101 for the year 2013.

REPRESENTATIVE AWARDS:
$10,000 to the CSJ Ministry Collaborative for Learning in Style; $10,000 to the Sierra Club for the MN Environmental Justice Project; $15,000 to the Trust for Public Land for the Frogtown Park and Farm; $15,000 to the African Development Center for general operating support.

APPLICATION INFORMATION:
Applications must be submitted online. See Foundation web site to begin an online application.
Deadline: March 15 and September 15.

TRUSTEES:
Conley Brooks, Jr.
Markell Brooks
Minna Brooks
Sarah Brooks
Stephen B. Brooks
Markell Kiefer
Katherine M. Leighton

EXECUTIVE DIRECTOR:
Julia S. Hara

MARDAG FOUNDATION [216]
55 Fifth Street East, Suite 600
St. Paul, MN 55101-1797
(651) 224-5463
Fax: (651) 224-8123

E-MAIL ADDRESS:
inbox@mardag.org

WEB SITE ADDRESS:
www.mardag.org

FOUNDED: 1969

AREAS OF INTEREST:
Children, seniors and other at-risk populations, education and the arts.

TYPE:
Capital grants; Challenge/matching grants; Project/program grants; Seed money grants.

YEAR PROGRAM STARTED: 1969

PURPOSE:
To make grants to qualified nonprofit organizations within the state of Minnesota that help to enhance and improve the quality of life.

LEGAL BASIS:
Private foundation.

ELIGIBILITY:
Applicants must be 501(c)(3) nonprofit corporations or public entities. The Foundation does not make grants through fiscal agents or for ongoing annual operating purposes.

The Foundation will consider grants applications for:
(1) capital projects, program expansion, or special projects of a time-limited nature;
(2) start-up costs for promising new programs that demonstrate sound management and clear goals relevant to community needs;
(3) support for established agencies that have temporary or transition needs and;
(4) funds to match contributions received from other sources or to provide a challenge to help raise new contributions.

The Foundation will not consider grant applications for:
(1) programs serving Minneapolis and the surrounding West Metro area;
(2) scholarships and grants to individuals;
(3) annual operating expenses;
(4) sectarian religious programs;
(5) medical research;
(6) federated campaigns;
(7) conservation or environmental programs;
(8) events and conferences;
(9) programs serving the physically, developmentally and mentally disabled;
(10) capital campaigns of private secondary schools or;
(11) capital and endowment campaigns of private colleges and universities.

GEOGRAPHIC RESTRICTIONS:
East Metro area of Dakota, Ramsey and Washington counties, as well as greater Minnesota.

FINANCIAL DATA:
Amount of support per award: Varies.

APPLICATION INFORMATION:
Applicants are encouraged to request the Foundation's application form, narrative guidelines and evaluation plan summary form prior to submission. The applicant may wish

to submit a two- or three-page letter of inquiry describing the proposal prior to preparation of a full proposal to see if the project fits the interests and guidelines of the Foundation. Both letters of inquiry and full proposals (one copy) must be in writing. Proposals will not be returned to the applicant. Do not send applications in binders or folders, or include videotapes or audio tapes. Acceptance of either a letter of inquiry or a proposal for review does not assure that a grant will be awarded.
Duration: Typically one year.
Deadline: Applications must be postmarked by December 31 for April board meeting, May 1 for August board meeting, or August 1 for November board meeting.

PUBLICATIONS:
Application; narrative guidelines; annual report.

IRS IDENTIFICATION NUMBER: 41-1698990

OFFICERS:
Timothy M. Ober, President
Gretchen D. Davidson, Vice President
Richard B. Ober, Treasurer
Phyllis Rawls Goff, Secretary

TRUSTEES:
Janice K. Angell
Gretchen D. Davidson
Cornelia M. Eberhart
Phyllis Rawls Goff
Patrick Medure
Gayle M. Ober
Hon. Wilhelmina M. Wright

ADDRESS INQUIRIES TO:
Lisa Hansen, Grants Administration Manager
(See address above.)

MARIN COMMUNITY FOUNDATION [217]
5 Hamilton Landing, Suite 200
Novato, CA 94949
(415) 464-2500
Fax: (415) 464-2555

E-MAIL ADDRESS:
info@marincf.org

WEB SITE ADDRESS:
www.marincf.org

FOUNDED: 1986

AREAS OF INTEREST:
Human needs, education, community development, religion, environment and the arts.

TYPE:
Awards/prizes; Capital grants; Challenge/matching grants; Conferences/seminars; General operating grants; Project/program grants; Scholarships; Technical assistance.

YEAR PROGRAM STARTED: 1987

PURPOSE:
To encourage and apply philanthropic contributions to help improve the human condition, embrace diversity, promote a humane and democratic society, and enhance the community's quality of life, now and for future generations.

LEGAL BASIS:
Community foundation.

ELIGIBILITY:
Proposals must be consistent with the Foundation's program goals and must meet two additional requirements. First, the

applicant must be a public or nonprofit organization and, second, the proposed project must be conducted in and/or benefit the residents of Marin County, CA. Projects with a regional or multi-county benefit may be funded only in proportion to the extent that they benefit the Marin County community.

Ineligible activities include for-profit purposes, basic research, the start-up of new nonprofit organizations that will unnecessarily duplicate existing programs or services or undertake services that can be more effectively provided by other organizations and grants to individuals. Other limitations specific to each program area are outlined in the funding guidelines. No grants are made to individuals.

Buck Trust grants are limited to Marin County.

GEOGRAPHIC RESTRICTIONS:
Marin County, California.

FINANCIAL DATA:
Amount of support per award: $50,000 to $150,000.
Total amount of support: $58,900,000 for the year 2012.

NUMBER OF AWARDS: 345.

APPLICATION INFORMATION:
Applicants are encouraged to contact a program director to determine if a proposed project or program is consistent with Foundation goals. Following a discussion with the program officer, applicants may submit a letter of intent through its online Grant Application Center.
Duration: Varies. Renewal possible.
Deadline: Applications are accepted according to a schedule posted on the Foundation's web site.

PUBLICATIONS:
General information brochure.

IRS IDENTIFICATION NUMBER: 94-3007979

OFFICERS:
Thomas Peters, President and Chief Executive Officer
Sid Hartman, Chief Financial and Operating Officer

BOARD OF TRUSTEES:
Robert Reynolds, Chairperson
George Bull, Vice Chairperson
Cleveland Justis
Ann Mathieson
Jay L. Paxton
Maria Ramos-Chertok
Curtis Robinson
Fu Schroeder
Barbara Clifton Zarate

MARRIOTT INTERNATIONAL, INC. [218]
10400 Fernwood Road
Bethesda, MD 20817

WEB SITE ADDRESS:
marriott.versaic.com

FOUNDED: 1927

AREAS OF INTEREST:
Shelter and food, environment, readiness for hotel careers, vitality of children, and embracing diversity and people with disabilities.

TYPE:
Project/program grants. Support to national and global nonprofits that address help, support readiness for jobs, diversity and inclusion, poverty alleviation, and the environment.

LEGAL BASIS:
Corporate contributions program.

ELIGIBILITY:
Grants are made to tax-exempt 501(c)(3) organizations which fulfill important community needs.

FINANCIAL DATA:
Amount of support per award: Varies.
Total amount of support: Varies.

APPLICATION INFORMATION:
The Corporation only accepts requests online via its web site.
Duration: Varies.
Deadline: Before end of October.

PUBLICATIONS:
Application guidelines.

MCCORMICK FOUNDATION [219]
205 North Michigan Avenue
Suite 4300
Chicago, IL 60601-5927
(312) 445-5000
Fax: (312) 445-5001

E-MAIL ADDRESS:
info@mccormickfoundation.org

WEB SITE ADDRESS:
www.mccormickfoundation.org

FOUNDED: 1955

AREAS OF INTEREST:
Community strengthening, civic education, civic engagement, news literacy, youth media, early childhood education, and veterans affairs.

NAME(S) OF PROGRAMS:
● **Civic Program**
● **Communities Program**
● **Education Program**
● **Journalism Program**
● **Veterans Program**

TYPE:
General operating grants; Project/program grants.

YEAR PROGRAM STARTED: 1955

PURPOSE:
To foster communities of educated, informed and engaged citizens.

PUBLICATIONS:
Annual report; program brochures; conference reports.

J.M. MCDONALD FOUNDATION, INC. [220]
P.O. Box 3219
Evergreen, CO 80437-3219
(303) 674-9300
Fax: (303) 674-9216

E-MAIL ADDRESS:
info@jmmcdonaldfoundation.org

WEB SITE ADDRESS:
jmmcdonaldfoundation.org

FOUNDED: 1952

AREAS OF INTEREST:
Education, humanities, health, and a variety of social and human services.

TYPE:
Capital grants; Development grants; Project/program grants.

YEAR PROGRAM STARTED: 1952

LEGAL BASIS:
Private foundation.

ELIGIBILITY:
Nonprofit organizations with appropriate interests are eligible for support. Applicants must be located in the U.S. and have IRS-509A and 501(c)(3) letter. No grants are made to individuals.

GEOGRAPHIC RESTRICTIONS:
Primarily upstate New York.

FINANCIAL DATA:
Amount of support per award: Grants vary in amount, depending upon the needs and nature of the request.

APPLICATION INFORMATION:
Application for funding through online granting process is available at the Foundation web site.
Duration: One year.
Deadline: April 15 and September 15.

PUBLICATIONS:
Application guidelines.

OFFICERS AND TRUSTEES:
Donald R. McJunkin, President
Nancy J. Palmer, Vice President
Donald C. Berry, Jr., Treasurer
Janet E. Stanton, Secretary
Dana Amundson
Pamela Criswell
Scott Palmer

JAMES S. MCDONNELL FOUNDATION [221]
1034 South Brentwood Boulevard
Suite 1850
St. Louis, MO 63117
(314) 721-1532
Fax: (314) 721-7421

E-MAIL ADDRESS:
info@jsmf.org

WEB SITE ADDRESS:
www.jsmf.org

FOUNDED: 1950

AREAS OF INTEREST:
Brain cancer research, studying complex systems and understanding human cognition.

NAME(S) OF PROGRAMS:
● **Collaborative Activity Awards**
● **Postdoctoral Fellowship Awards in Studying Complex Systems**
● **Scholar Awards**
● **21st Century Research Awards**

TYPE:
Fellowships; Research grants. The Foundation provides funding for grants in the following four program areas:

Collaborative Activity Awards are to initiate interdisciplinary discussions on problems or issues, to help launch interdisciplinary research networks, or to fund communities of researchers dedicated to developing new methods, tools and applications of basic research.

Postdoctoral Fellowship Awards are intended to provide students in the final stages of completing a Ph.D. degree more leeway in identifying and securing postdoctoral training opportunities in complex systems research.

Scholar Awards provide funding in the area of Understanding Human Cognition.

21st Century Research Awards are designed to support research projects with a high probability of generating new knowledge and insights.

YEAR PROGRAM STARTED: 2000

PURPOSE:
To encourage investigators to engage difficult problems; to support ideas and approaches departing from conventional wisdom; to fund novel or interdisciplinary proposals.

LEGAL BASIS:
Private foundation.

FINANCIAL DATA:
Amount of support per award: Collaborative Activity Awards: Varies; Postdoctoral Fellowship: $200,000; Scholar Awards: Up to $600,000; 21st Century Research Awards: Up to $450,000.

NUMBER OF APPLICANTS MOST RECENT YEAR:
Over 200 for the year 2013.

NUMBER OF AWARDS: 51.

APPLICATION INFORMATION:
Guidelines and all program applications are available on the Foundation's web site.
Deadline: Postdoctoral Fellowship: July; Scholars Awards: February; 21st Century Research Awards: March. There are no deadlines for Collaborative Activity Awards.

Letters of inquiry are accepted year-round for collaborative fund seekers.

IRS IDENTIFICATION NUMBER: 54-2074788

OFFICERS:
Dr. John T. Bruer, President
Dr. Susan Fitzpatrick, Vice President

BOARD OF DIRECTORS:
Jeanne M. Champer
Holly M. James
Alicia S. McDonnell
James S. McDonnell, III
Jeffrey M. McDonnell
John F. McDonnell
Marcella M. Stevens

MCGREGOR FUND   [222]
333 West Fort Street, Suite 2090
Detroit, MI 48226-3134
(313) 963-3495
Fax: (313) 963-3512

E-MAIL ADDRESS:
info@mcgregorfund.org

WEB SITE ADDRESS:
www.mcgregorfund.org

FOUNDED: 1925

AREAS OF INTEREST:
Human services, education, health, the arts and public benefit in metropolitan Detroit.

TYPE:
General operating grants; Project/program grants. Limited capital grants; program and operational support. The Fund also supports aid to private liberal arts colleges and universities in Michigan.

YEAR PROGRAM STARTED: 1925

PURPOSE:
To relieve misfortunes and promote the well-being of mankind.

LEGAL BASIS:
Tax-exempt private foundation.

ELIGIBILITY:
Tax-exempt, Internal Revenue Code 501(c)(3) organizations in the Detroit metropolitan area.

The Fund does not provide loan funds, make direct grants to students for scholarships, make grants for travel, conferences, seminars or workshops, or make grants to individuals.

GEOGRAPHIC RESTRICTIONS:
Metropolitan Detroit, Michigan and Ohio.

FINANCIAL DATA:
Amount of support per award: $25,000 to $50,000.
Total amount of support: Varies.

NUMBER OF APPLICANTS MOST RECENT YEAR:
Approximately 200.

NUMBER OF AWARDS: 150.

REPRESENTATIVE AWARDS:
$250,000 to Coalition on Temporary Shelter to support homeless shelters; $200,000 to Forgotten Harvest to support the campaign to acquire and retrofit a new facility for food rescue operations.

APPLICATION INFORMATION:
Guidelines available on the Fund web site.
Duration: No grants are made on a continuing basis.
Deadline: Submit applications three months prior to Board meeting dates in March, June, September and December.

PUBLICATIONS:
Annual report; guidelines; application procedures.

IRS IDENTIFICATION NUMBER: 38-0808800

OFFICERS:
James B. Nicholson, Chairman
Ruth R. Glancy, Vice Chairman

BOARD OF TRUSTEES:
C. David Campbell, President
Gerard Anderson
Cynthia N. Ford
Ruth R. Glancy
Denise J. Lewis
Reuben Munday
James B. Nicholson
Susan Schooley, M.D.
William W. Shelden, Jr.

ADDRESS INQUIRIES TO:
C. David Campbell, President
(See address above.)

THE MCLEAN CONTRIBUTIONSHIP   [223]
Sugartown Square Offices, Suite 30
230 Sugartown Road
Wayne, PA 19087
(610) 989-8090
Fax: (610) 527-9733

WEB SITE ADDRESS:
fdnweb.org/mclean

FOUNDED: 1951

AREAS OF INTEREST:
Education, environment, health and hospitals, care of the elderly and youth development.

TYPE:
Capital grants; Endowments. The Contributionship makes a relatively limited

number of grants for projects of long-term benefit. Its trustees focus on capital projects: bricks and mortar and endowment; they may make grants in ways to encourage the successful funding of projects.

PURPOSE:
To support understanding and preserving the environment; to encourage compassionate and cost-effective healthcare; to improve the quality of life through education and through support of the communities' cultural assets usually in the form of capital projects.

LEGAL BASIS:
Private foundation.

ELIGIBILITY:
Organizations, including some religious, classified as 501(c)(3) by the IRS can apply. Individuals are ineligible.

The Contributionship favors projects that:
(1) stimulate a better understanding of the natural environment, and encourage the preservation of its important features;
(2) encourage more compassionate and cost-effective care for the ill and aging, in an atmosphere of dignity and self-respect and;
(3) promote education, or medical, scientific or (on occasion) cultural developments enhancing the quality of life.

In addition, the trustees from time to time support projects which:
(1) motivate promising young people to assess and develop their talents despite social and economic obstacles and;
(2) encourage those in newspaper and related fields to become more effective and responsible in helping people understand better how events in their communities and around the world affect them.

GEOGRAPHIC RESTRICTIONS:
Mainly in the Greater Philadelphia area.

FINANCIAL DATA:
Amount of support per award: $1,000 to $100,000.
Total amount of support: Approximately $2,089,933 for the year 2013.

NUMBER OF APPLICANTS MOST RECENT YEAR:
194 for the year 2013.

NUMBER OF AWARDS: 117 for the year 2013.

REPRESENTATIVE AWARDS:
$100,000 to Academy of Natural Sciences, Philadelphia, PA, for an endowment in the memory of William L. McLean, III, to help fund post-undergraduate, postdoctoral research projects in the areas of ornithology and environmental sciences; $50,000 to Pennsylvania NewsMedia Association Foundation, Harrisburg, PA, for constructing and equipping a new multi-media training and video facility; $50,000 to Pennsylvania Horticultural Society, Philadelphia, PA, for the Mantua Green Resource Center.

APPLICATION INFORMATION:
The Contributionship accepts the common grant application form of the Philanthropy Network Greater Philadelphia. Application should include:
(1) a letter, which describes and justifies the project;
(2) a budget and timetable, strategy for securing funding and latest financial statement;
(3) interim operating statements or budgets for future periods if appropriate;
(4) evidence of tax-exempt status and;
(5) a list of officers and directors.

Application can be submitted online or mailed to Sandra L. McLean, Executive Director, at the address above.

Duration: One to three years.

Deadline: Applications must be received six weeks prior to meeting date.

PUBLICATIONS:
Application guidelines.

IRS IDENTIFICATION NUMBER: 23-6396940

TRUSTEES:
Will McLean, Chairman
Sandra L. McLean, Executive Director and Trustee
John F. Bales
Diana L. McLean
Carolyn M. Raymond
Susannah McLean, Advisory Trustee

ADDRESS INQUIRIES TO:
Sandra L. McLean
Executive Director and Trustee
(See address above.)

*PLEASE NOTE:
No grants to individuals.

THE JOSEPH R. MCMICKING FOUNDATION   [224]

1004B O'Reilly Avenue
San Francisco, CA 94129
(415) 474-1784
Fax: (415) 474-1754

E-MAIL ADDRESS:
miriam@mcmickingfoundation.org

WEB SITE ADDRESS:
mcmickingfoundation.org

AREAS OF INTEREST:
Arts, computer science, education and science.

TYPE:
Project/program grants.

PURPOSE:
To improve the quality of life for San Francisco Bay Area residents through grants and scholarships for the education and welfare of children and their families.

ELIGIBILITY:
The Foundation makes grants only to organizations that are exempt from federal tax under Section 501(c)(3) of the Internal Revenue Code and are not classified as private foundations under Section 509(a) of the Code.

The Foundation does not provide support for grants to individuals or loans.

GEOGRAPHIC RESTRICTIONS:
San Francisco Bay Area, California.

APPLICATION INFORMATION:
Organizations seeking information should mail a letter and application to the Executive Director. The Foundation will not accept proposals sent by facsimile.

Complete guidelines and application form is available on the web site.

Duration: Applicants can reapply on a yearly basis, unless original proposal was for extended time.

Deadline: Proposals are accepted throughout the year.

ADDRESS INQUIRIES TO:
Miriam White, Executive Director
(See address above.)

THE MARGARET MCNAMARA MEMORIAL FUND (MMMF) [225]

The World Bank Family Network
1818 H Street, N.W.
MSN J2-202
Washington, DC 20433
(202) 473-8751
Fax: (202) 522-3142

E-MAIL ADDRESS:
mmmf@worldbank.org

WEB SITE ADDRESS:
mmmf-grants.org

FOUNDED: 1981

AREAS OF INTEREST:
Agriculture, architecture and urban planning, civil engineering, education, foresty, journalism, nursing, nutrition, pediatrics, public administration, public health, social sciences, social work and others.

TYPE:
Scholarships.

YEAR PROGRAM STARTED: 1981

PURPOSE:
To support the education of women from developing countries who are committed to improving the lives of women and children in their home countries.

LEGAL BASIS:
501(c)(3) public charity.

ELIGIBILITY:
Applicants must be nationals of developing countries, enrolled in U.S., Canadian or South African universities, that are current clients of the World Bank. The U.S./Canada program is open to women enrolled in an accredited educational institution in the U.S. or Canada where the grant will be used. The South Africa program is for students enrolled at the Universities of Pretoria or Cape Town. Women must be at least 25 years old and planning to return to their home country or another developing country within two years of program completion.

FINANCIAL DATA:
Amount of support per award: $12,000 in U.S./Canada; $4,000 in South Africa.

NUMBER OF AWARDS: 19 for the year 2011.

APPLICATION INFORMATION:
The application can only be completed and submitted online. Two recommendations from professors/supervisors must also be submitted electronically. At least one recommendation must be from a professor/advisor at the applicant's current institution and one must have known the applicant for at least one year.

The following documents are required for the U.S./Canada program and must be mailed:
(1) copy of Fall registration;
(2) official copy of transcript for Fall in a sealed envelope from the Registrar;
(3) official estimate of annual expenses for students published by applicant's institution;
(4) one passport-size photograph;
(5) copy of U.S./Canadian Visa;
(6) for applicants at U.S. universities, copy of I-20/DC-2019 (formally IAP-66) and;
(7) for applicants at Canadian universities, copy of study permit.

Additional information and requirements for the South Africa program can be found online.

Duration: One year.

ADDRESS INQUIRIES TO:
MMMF Coordinator
(See address above.)

MEADOWS FOUNDATION, INC.   [226]

Wilson Historic District
3003 Swiss Avenue
Dallas, TX 75204-6049
(214) 826-9431
(800) 826-9431
Fax: (214) 827-7042

E-MAIL ADDRESS:
grants@mfi.org

WEB SITE ADDRESS:
www.mfi.org

FOUNDED: 1948

AREAS OF INTEREST:
Arts and culture, civic and public affairs (including the natural environment), education, health (including mental health), and human services.

TYPE:
Awards/prizes; Capital grants; Challenge/matching grants; Demonstration grants; Development grants; Endowments; General operating grants; Matching gifts; Project/program grants; Research grants; Seed money grants; Technical assistance; Training grants; Loan forgiveness programs. Program-related investments. Support for organizations, agencies, programs and projects within the areas of the Foundation's interest. Areas of high interest: environment, mental health and public education.

YEAR PROGRAM STARTED: 1948

PURPOSE:
To assist people and institutions of Texas improve the quality and circumstances of life for themselves and future generations.

LEGAL BASIS:
Tax-exempt, private foundation.

ELIGIBILITY:
Applicants must be tax-exempt organizations, benefitting Texas. No grants are awarded to individuals. Generally, no contributions for church or seminary construction, annual fund-raising drives, out of state travel, or professional conferences/symposia.

GEOGRAPHIC RESTRICTIONS:
Texas.

FINANCIAL DATA:
Amount of support per award: $25,000 to $500,000.

Matching fund requirements: Stipulated with specific grants.

APPLICATION INFORMATION:
Application/proposal should include:
(1) a brief history of the organization, its current focus and recent accomplishments;
(2) a copy of the latest verification of tax-exempt status from the IRS;
(3) certified audits for the last three years, current operating budget and year-to-date financial statements;
(4) statement of need for the proposed project, to include population served, and how project will address need;
(5) a list of trustees or directors, corporate officers and key staff;
(6) the specific dollar amount requested and the date payment is needed;
(7) a list of all entities asked to give financial support and their responses;
(8) project line-item budget (include income

and expenses);
(9) plans to evaluate the project (include measurable, time-specific goals) and;
(10) support for the project after the grant period.

Duration: No grants are awarded on a continuing basis. Multiyear grants are utilized on occasion.

Deadline: Proposals are accepted throughout the year.

PUBLICATIONS:
Annual report; guidelines.

IRS IDENTIFICATION NUMBER: 75-6015322

STAFF:
Cynthia A. Cass, Grants Administrator
Adrianna Cuellar Rojas, Senior Program Officer
Michael K. McCoy, Senior Program Officer
Cindy Patrick, Senior Program Officer
Kathy Smith, Senior Program Officer
Brittani Trusty, Research Analyst

OFFICERS AND DIRECTORS:
Robert A. Meadows, Chairman, Board of Trustees, Director and Vice President
Linda P. Evans, President and Chief Executive Officer, Trustee and Director
Paula Herring, Vice President and Treasurer
Gregory C. Dowell, Vice President and Chief Investment Officer
Robert E. Weiss, Vice President for Administration
Bruce H. Esterline, Vice President for Grants
Olin Lancaster, III, Director
Dudley L. Rouse, Jr., Director
Daniel H. Chapman, Trustee and Director
John A. Hammack, Trustee and Director
Margaret Macdonald, Trustee and Director
P. Mike McCullough, Trustee and Director
Karen L. Meadows, Trustee and Director
William Nesbitt, Trustee and Director
Elizabeth Meadows Rouse, Trustee and Director

ADDRESS INQUIRIES TO:
Bruce H. Esterline
Vice President for Grants
(See address above.)

MEDICAL LIBRARY ASSOCIATION   [227]
65 East Wacker Place
Suite 1900
Chicago, IL 60601-7298
(312) 419-9094
Fax: (312) 419-8950

E-MAIL ADDRESS:
mlapd2@mlahq.org

WEB SITE ADDRESS:
www.mlanet.org/awards

FOUNDED: 1898

AREAS OF INTEREST:
Health sciences librarianship.

NAME(S) OF PROGRAMS:
• **MLA Continuing Education Grants**

TYPE:
Grants-in-aid. The Continuing Education Grants are designed to aid in the study of the theoretical, administrative and technical aspects of library and information science.

PURPOSE:
To provide professional health science librarians with the opportunity to continue their education.

ELIGIBILITY:
Candidates must be U.S. or Canadian citizens, or permanent residents who are mid-level librarians with a graduate degree in library science and at least two years of work experience at the professional level.

FINANCIAL DATA:
Amount of support per award: $100 to $500.

NUMBER OF AWARDS: 1.

APPLICATION INFORMATION:
Applicants must complete and submit an application form which is available online. Candidates should also identify a continuing education program.

Duration: One year.

Deadline: December 1.

ADDRESS INQUIRIES TO:
Grants and Scholarship Coordinator
(See address above.)

*PLEASE NOTE:
The award is not to support work towards a degree or certificate.

MEDTRONIC FOUNDATION [228]
710 Medtronic Parkway, MSLC110
Minneapolis, MN 55432-5604
(763) 505-2639
(800) 328-2518
Fax: (763) 505-2648

WEB SITE ADDRESS:
www.medtronic.com/philanthropy

FOUNDED: 1979

AREAS OF INTEREST:
Health, education, arts, civic affairs, culture and human services.

NAME(S) OF PROGRAMS:
• **Community Education**
• **Community Health Grants**
• **HeartRescue**
• **Patient Link**
• **Strengthening Health Systems**

TYPE:
Challenge/matching grants; Fellowships; Matching gifts; Scholarships. Matching Gifts to Education involves employees.

YEAR PROGRAM STARTED: 1979

PURPOSE:
To benefit the socioeconomically disadvantaged of Medtronic communities in the areas of education, health, human services, and arts, civic affairs and culture.

LEGAL BASIS:
Corporate foundation.

ELIGIBILITY:
Grants are made to 501(c)(3) tax-exempt organizations, schools or government agencies for specific projects or programs. The Foundation does not support individuals, continuing medical education, religious groups for religious purposes, fund-raising and social events, general operating support, political or fraternal activities, reimbursable health treatment, or scientific research.

GEOGRAPHIC RESTRICTIONS:
Primarily Tempe/Greater Phoenix, Arizona; Goleta, Santa Ana, Santa Rosa and Sunnyvale, California; Louisville and Metro Denver, Colorado; Jacksonville, Florida; Warsaw, Indiana; Beverly and Danvers, Massachusetts; Twin Cities and seven-county metropolitan area, Minnesota; Memphis,

Tennessee; Fort Worth and San Antonio, Texas; Redmond, Washington; and Humacao and Villalba, Puerto Rico.

FINANCIAL DATA:
Amount of support per award: Varies depending on need and nature of request.

APPLICATION INFORMATION:
Applicants should review the General Foundation Guidelines to ensure eligibility. Each grant program has its own set of guidelines and deadlines. U.S organizations must apply via the online application process. In addition to the completion of the online application, the following documents are required:
(1) budget form;
(2) interim/final report on the organization's most recent Medtronic Foundation Grant (if funding has previously been received);
(3) list of officers and directors and their affiliations;
(4) IRS tax exemption letter;
(5) latest annual report (only required if available electronically) and;
(6) financial statement from most recently completed fiscal year (whether audited or not).

Organizations based outside the U.S. must first complete a Letter of Inquiry. Upon receiving the letter, a Foundation representative may recommend the organization submit a full application.

Duration: Varies.

Deadline: Grants are generally reviewed within 90 days.

IRS IDENTIFICATION NUMBER: 41-1306950

THE ANDREW W. MELLON FOUNDATION   [229]
140 East 62nd Street
New York, NY 10065
(212) 838-8400
Fax: (212) 500-2302

E-MAIL ADDRESS:
inquiries@mellon.org

WEB SITE ADDRESS:
www.mellon.org

FOUNDED: 1969

AREAS OF INTEREST:
Higher education and scholarship, scholarly communications, museums and art conservation, and performing arts.

TYPE:
Challenge/matching grants; Endowments; General operating grants; Project/program grants; Research grants. Grants on a selective basis to institutions in the Foundation's areas of interest.

PURPOSE:
To build, strengthen and sustain institutions and their core capacities, rather than be a source for narrowly defined projects.

LEGAL BASIS:
Not-for-profit corporation.

ELIGIBILITY:
Organizations and institutions with appropriate interests are eligible. The Foundation does not award fellowships or grants to individuals or make grants to primarily local organizations.

FINANCIAL DATA:
Amount of support per award: Varies.

APPLICATION INFORMATION:
Applications are considered throughout the year and no special forms are required. Ordinarily a simple letter setting forth the need, the nature and the amount of the request and the justification for it, together with evidence of suitable classification by the IRS and any supplementary exhibits an applicant may wish to submit, will suffice to assure consideration. Unsolicited applications are rarely funded.
Duration: Varies.

PUBLICATIONS:
Annual report.

OFFICERS:
Earl Lewis, President
Philip E. Lewis, Vice President
Mariet Westermann, Vice President
Michele S. Warman, Vice President, General Counsel and Secretary
John E. Hull, Financial Vice President and Chief Investment Officer

TRUSTEES:
Lewis Bernard, Chairman
Danielle S. Allen
Richard H. Brodhead
Katherine Farley
Paul LeClerc
Earl Lewis
Glenn D. Lowry
Eric Mindich
Don Michael Randel
W. Taylor Reveley, III
Sarah E. Thomas

ADDRESS INQUIRIES TO:
Michele S. Warman
Vice President, General Counsel and Secretary
(See address above.)

*PLEASE NOTE:
The Foundation rarely funds unsolicited proposals.

MERCK FAMILY FUND   [230]
P.O. Box 870245
Milton Village, MA 02187
(617) 696-3580
Fax: (617) 696-7262

E-MAIL ADDRESS:
merck@merckff.org

WEB SITE ADDRESS:
www.merckff.org

FOUNDED: 1954

AREAS OF INTEREST:
Protecting the natural environment, meeting human needs and addressing the root causes of problems faced by social and economically disadvantaged people.

TYPE:
General operating grants; Project/program grants; Seed money grants.

YEAR PROGRAM STARTED: 1993

PURPOSE:
To protect and restore vital eastern ecosystems and promote economic practices for a sustainable environment.

LEGAL BASIS:
Tax-exempt corporation.

GEOGRAPHIC RESTRICTIONS:
United States.

FINANCIAL DATA:
Amount of support per award: $10,000 to $50,000.

Total amount of support: $2,500,000 for the year 2013.

APPLICATION INFORMATION:
New requests for support should be made through the online application system rather than with a full proposal or a request for a personal meeting. Applicants will be contacted if a full proposal is warranted. Unsolicited proposals will not be acknowledged.
Duration: Grants may be from one to three years. Progress reports must be received before continuation or renewal support will be considered.
Deadline: January 31 for spring; August 1 for fall.

PUBLICATIONS:
Annual report; grants list; guidelines.

IRS IDENTIFICATION NUMBER: 22-6063382

STAFF:
Jenny D. Russell, Executive Director
James Maguire, Director of Grants Management and Investment Accounting
Ruth Goldman, Consulting Program Officer

OFFICERS AND TRUSTEES:
Nathaniel Chamberlin, President
Eliza Hatch, Vice President
Wilhelm Merck, Treasurer
Max Abeles
Katie Chamberlin
Ian Hatch
Whitney Hatch
Elliott Merck
Serena Whitridge

ADDRESS INQUIRIES TO:
Jenny D. Russell, Executive Director
(See address above.)

METLIFE FOUNDATION   [231]
1095 Avenue of the Americas
New York, NY 10036
(212) 578-6272
Fax: (212) 578-0617

E-MAIL ADDRESS:
metlifefoundation@metlife.com

WEB SITE ADDRESS:
www.metlife.org

FOUNDED: 1976

AREAS OF INTEREST:
Financial empowerment and program-related investments.

CONSULTING OR VOLUNTEER SERVICES:
Employee volunteer programs.

TYPE:
Matching gifts; Project/program grants; Scholarships. Program-related investments. Grants are made in the areas of financial empowerment.

MetLife Foundation has a new global focus - financial inclusion - and it has committed $200,000,000 over a five-year period to this initiative. These grants are focused in the following three categories:
(1) Access and Knowledge: Grants to partners with the ability to reach large numbers of underserved households around the world and work with them to develop financial strategies and capabilities to improve lives;
(2) Access to Services: Partnering with experts in financial inclusion to deliver high-quality services like savings, microinsurance and credit to individuals in need and ensure they are prepared,

incentivized and motivated to improve the lives of their families and communities and; (3) Access to Insights: Sharing what the Foundation learns by gathering knowledge from its partners and the communities with which it works; the Foundation offers its insights to the financial inclusion community to help enhance the approach and advance the goals they share in common.

MetLife and the Foundation make below-market-rate investments with groups and projects working to improve communities across the country. Either directly or through relending with nonprofit intermediaries, social investments reach every major city in the nation and over 30 states. Loans support affordable housing developments with social services, organizations serving the homeless and mentally ill, health care services and community-based economic development.

YEAR PROGRAM STARTED: 1976

PURPOSE:
To advance financial inclusion, helping to build a secure future for individuals and communities around the world.

LEGAL BASIS:
The Foundation is a tax-exempt organization under Section 501(c)(3) and is classified as a private foundation as defined by Section 509(a) of the Internal Revenue Code.

ELIGIBILITY:
Applicants must be 501(c)(3) tax-exempt organizations in the Foundation's areas of interest.

No grants are made to private foundations or religious, fraternal, political, athletic, or social organizations, organizations receiving support from United Way, hospitals, capital fund campaigns, local chapters of national organizations, disease-specific organizations, labor groups, organizations primarily engaged in patient care or direct treatment, drug treatment centers and community health clinics, elementary and secondary schools, courtesy advertising or festival participation or individuals. Generally, no support is given for endowment funds.

FINANCIAL DATA:
Total amount of support: $42,488,850 for the year 2013.

Matching fund requirements: Employee contributions to colleges and universities.

NUMBER OF AWARDS: Varies.

APPLICATION INFORMATION:
The Foundation only accepts online grant proposals. Details available on the web site.
Duration: Generally one year. Two or three years occasionally.
Deadline: Requests and applications are reviewed throughout the year.

PUBLICATIONS:
Annual report of contributions; guidelines (available online).

BOARD OF DIRECTORS:
Michael Zarcone, Chairman
A. Dennis White, President and Chief Executive Officer
Jonathan Rosenthal, Treasurer
Frans Hijkoop
Michel Khalaf
Maria Morris
Oscar Schmidt
Christopher Townsend

ADDRESS INQUIRIES TO:
A. Dennis White
President and Chief Executive Officer
(See address above.)

MEYER MEMORIAL TRUST [232]

425 N.W. 10th Avenue, Suite 400
Portland, OR 97209
(503) 228-5512

E-MAIL ADDRESS:
mmt@mmt.org

WEB SITE ADDRESS:
www.mmt.org

FOUNDED: 1978

AREAS OF INTEREST:
Arts and humanities, education, health and
human services, conservation and
environment, public affairs/social benefit.

NAME(S) OF PROGRAMS:
● **Grassroots Grants**
● **Responsive Grants**

TYPE:
Capital grants; Challenge/matching grants;
Development grants; General operating
grants; Matching gifts; Project/program
grants; Seed money grants; Technical
assistance. Capacity Building Grants. Under
the Grassroots Grants program, the Trust
funds a wide variety of small projects.

Responsive Grants are awarded in the areas
of social services, health, affordable housing,
community development, conservation and
environment, public affairs and social benefit,
arts and culture, and education. They are
given for a wide variety of projects,
expansions, capacity building, capital
projects, and start-ups.

YEAR PROGRAM STARTED: 1982

PURPOSE:
To work with and invest in organizations,
communities, ideas and efforts that contribute
to a flourishing and equitable Oregon.

LEGAL BASIS:
Private, independent foundation.

ELIGIBILITY:
Applicants must:
(1) be an IRS-sanctioned tax-exempt
organization;
(2) be requesting support for a program that
operates in Oregon and/or Clark County, WA
(considered part of the Portland metropolitan
area);
(3) provide equal opportunity in leadership,
staffing and service regardless of age, gender,
race, ethnicity, sexual orientation, disability,
national origin, political affiliation or
religious belief and;
(4) be current on all reports owed to the
Trust on previous grants.

Generally, the Trust does not fund:
(1) direct grants, scholarships, or loans to
individuals;
(2) endowments;
(3) general fund drives, annual appeals,
special events or sponsorships;
(4) elimination of operating deficits;
(5) projects of sectarian or religious
organizations that principally benefit their
own members or adherents;
(6) direct replacement funding for activities
previously supported by federal, state or local
public sources;
(7) acquisition of land for conservation

purposes (except through Program Related
Investments);
(8) hospital capital construction projects
(except through Program Related
Investments);
(9) animal welfare organizations (both
domestic and wild animals);
(10) animal-assisted therapy programs;
(11) projects that primarily benefit students
of a single K-12 school, unless the school is
an independent alternative school primarily
serving low-income and/or special needs
populations and;
(12) projects for purposes of influencing
legislation, and the grantee cannot expend
any part of the grant in a way that violates
its tax-exempt status.

GEOGRAPHIC RESTRICTIONS:
Oregon and Clark County, Washington.

FINANCIAL DATA:
Amount of support per award: Varies.
Total amount of support: $29,088,607 in
grants and Program Related Investments for
fiscal year 2013.

NUMBER OF APPLICANTS MOST RECENT YEAR:
729.

NUMBER OF AWARDS: 336.

APPLICATION INFORMATION:
Organizations must register on the Trust's
online system to complete and submit the
application.
Duration: One or multiple years. Usually
nonrenewable.
Deadline: There are no deadlines for
Responsive Grants. The Trust accepts
proposals throughout the year. Grassroots
Grants: March 15, July 15 and October 15.

TRUSTEES:
George Puentes, Chairperson
Debbie F. Craig
John Emrick
Orcillia Z. Forbes
Charles Wilhoite

STAFF:
Doug Stamm, Chief Executive Officer
Wayne Pierson, Chief Financial Officer and
Investment Officer
Candy Solovjovs, Director of Programs
Paul Reich, Director, Program-Related
Investing
Theresa Deibele, Program Officer
Jill Fuglister, Program Officer
Kim Thomas, Program Officer
Elizabeth Woody, Program Officer
Sally Yee, Program Officer

ADDRESS INQUIRIES TO:
Phoebe O'Leary
Director of Grant Operations
(See address above.)

*SPECIAL STIPULATIONS:
No grants given to individuals or for
businesses.

ROBERT R. MEYER FOUNDATION [233]

1900 5th Avenue North, Suite 2500
Birmingham, AL 35203
(205) 326-5382
Fax: (205) 264-7052

E-MAIL ADDRESS:
carla.gale@regions.com

FOUNDED: 1942

AREAS OF INTEREST:
Arts, education, humanities, civic affairs,
health and human services, and charitable
work.

TYPE:
Assistantships; Challenge/matching grants;
Conferences/seminars; Development grants;
General operating grants; Matching gifts;
Project/program grants; Research grants;
Technical assistance; Training grants;
Work-study programs.

YEAR PROGRAM STARTED: 1942

PURPOSE:
To help in community affairs.

LEGAL BASIS:
Private foundation.

ELIGIBILITY:
Grants restricted to organizations that benefit
the Birmingham, AL area, or to Birmingham,
AL nonprofit organizations. No grants to
individuals or corporations.

GEOGRAPHIC RESTRICTIONS:
Birmingham, Alabama area.

FINANCIAL DATA:
Amount of support per award: $2,500 to
$200,000; Average: $30,000.
Total amount of support: Approximately
$2,000,000 for the year 2013.

NUMBER OF APPLICANTS MOST RECENT YEAR:
Approximately 140 for the year 2013.

NUMBER OF AWARDS: Approximately 70.

APPLICATION INFORMATION:
Call for grant guidelines and application.
Duration: One year.
Deadline: March 1 and September 1.

PUBLICATIONS:
Application form.

ADVISORY COMMITTEE:
Beverly Baker
Sharon L. Blackburn
Raymond Harbert
Elmer B. Harris

ADDRESS INQUIRIES TO:
Carla B. Gale, Senior Vice President
(See address above.)

THE MIAMI FOUNDATION [234]

200 South Biscayne Boulevard, Suite 505
Miami, FL 33131-2343
(305) 371-2711
Fax: (305) 371-5342

E-MAIL ADDRESS:
programs@miamifoundation.org

WEB SITE ADDRESS:
www.miamifoundation.org

FOUNDED: 1967

AREAS OF INTEREST:
Education, health and human services, arts
and culture, the environment, economic
development and community.

NAME(S) OF PROGRAMS:
● **Community Grants Program**
● **GLBT Community Projects Fund**
● **Safe Passage: Youth Transitioning from
   Foster Care**

TYPE:
Project/program grants. Special initiative
grants.

YEAR PROGRAM STARTED: 1967

PURPOSE:
To enhance the quality of life for all the
residents of Greater Miami.

LEGAL BASIS:
Community foundation.

ELIGIBILITY:
Applicants must be 501(c)(3) organizations as well as some grassroots organizations.

No grants to individuals. No grants for memberships, fund-raising events or memorials.

GEOGRAPHIC RESTRICTIONS:
Miami-Dade County, Florida.

FINANCIAL DATA:
Amount of support per award: Varies.
Total amount of support: Varies.

NUMBER OF APPLICANTS MOST RECENT YEAR:
600.

NUMBER OF AWARDS: 130.

APPLICATION INFORMATION:
Responsive grant applications must be made online. Application includes cover letter with the purpose of the grant and the amount requested as well as a narrative about the applicant organization and budget. Attachments should include IRS determination letter, board list, and current fiscal year operating budget. Slight variations per grant program may apply.
Duration: Typically one year.
Deadline: Varies.

PUBLICATIONS:
Annual report; quarterly newsletter; grant guidelines; professional advisors guides.

STAFF:
Javier Alberto Soto, President and Chief Executive Officer
Charisse Grant, Senior Vice President for Programs
Stuart Kennedy, Senior Programs Officer
Joy Lampkin, Programs Assistant

MICROSOFT
CORPORATION   [235]
One Microsoft Way
Redmond, WA 98052-6399
(425) 882-8080
(425) 706-8185
Fax: (425) 706-7329

WEB SITE ADDRESS:
www.microsoft.com/giving

FOUNDED: 1983

AREAS OF INTEREST:
U.S. Program Areas: Expanding opportunities through technology access, strengthening nonprofits through technology, developing a diverse technology workforce and building community through corporate funding and through matching employees' individual giving.

International Program Areas: Improving the quality of life for people in countries and communities where Corporation employees live and do business.

NAME(S) OF PROGRAMS:
- **Disaster Response and Humanitarian Relief**
- **Employee Giving and Volunteer Programs**
- **Microsoft Grants and Programs in Puget Sound**
- **Microsoft Unlimited Potential-Community Technology Skills Program**
- **Nongovernmental Organization Capacity Building**
- **Software Donations**

TYPE:
Grants-in-aid; Matching gifts; Product donations; Scholarships; Technical assistance.

YEAR PROGRAM STARTED: 1983

PURPOSE:
To bring the benefits of information technology to underserved people and communities who do not have access to this technology; to support organizations in the communities in which Microsoft employees live and work; to support Microsoft employees taking an active role in their community through volunteer and matching gift programs.

LEGAL BASIS:
Corporate giving program.

ELIGIBILITY:
Grants are restricted to nonprofit organizations with tax-exempt 501(c)(3) status.

Microsoft does not make charitable grants to individuals; private foundations; political, labor, religious or fraternal organizations; amateur or professional sports groups, teams or events; conferences or symposia; hospitals or medical clinics; sponsorship of events, tables, exhibitions or performances; fund-raising events such as luncheons, dinners, walks, runs or sports tournaments; or programs serving people and communities outside the U.S. (exceptions may be made for pilot programs initiated by a Microsoft subsidiary in another country).

FINANCIAL DATA:
Matching fund requirements: Employee donations to eligible organizations are matched up to $12,000 per employee per year.

APPLICATION INFORMATION:
All proposals should include:
(1) a copy of the organization's tax-exempt notification letter from the IRS;
(2) a description of the organization (including its mission, accomplishments, governance, area and population served);
(3) the operating budget for the current fiscal year including funding sources and;
(4) lists of current board members and key organizational staff.

Additional information may be requested by Microsoft. Proposal materials, including photographs, videos and special binders, cannot be returned.

Funding proposals are accepted through Microsoft subsidiary offices throughout the world. Locations can be found online.
Deadline: Proposals are reviewed February 15, May 15, and October 30. Award announcement approximately six weeks following deadline.

PUBLICATIONS:
Program brochure; annual report of giving.

ADDRESS INQUIRIES TO:
Community Affairs
(See address above.)

*SPECIAL STIPULATIONS:
Proposals submitted by e-mail, fax or phone will not be accepted.

MID-NEBRASKA COMMUNITY
FOUNDATION, INC.   [236]
120 North Dewey
North Platte, NE 69101
(308) 534-3315
Fax: (308) 534-6117

E-MAIL ADDRESS:
mncf@hamilton.net

WEB SITE ADDRESS:
www.midnebraskafoundation.org

FOUNDED: 1978

AREAS OF INTEREST:
Arts, education, civic development, environment, health and welfare.

TYPE:
Capital grants; Demonstration grants; Development grants; Endowments; Project/program grants; Scholarships.

PURPOSE:
To serve charitable people and nonprofit causes in North Platte and the surrounding area.

GEOGRAPHIC RESTRICTIONS:
Custer, Dawson, Frontier, Hayes, Keith, Lincoln, Logan, McPherson, and Perkins counties, Nebraska.

APPLICATION INFORMATION:
Application form required. Initial approach by letter or telephone.
Deadline: April 15, July 15, October 15 and January 15.

IRS IDENTIFICATION NUMBER: 47-0604965

ADDRESS INQUIRIES TO:
Eric Seacrest, Executive Director
(See address above.)

ADAH K. MILLARD
CHARITABLE TRUST   [237]
Northern Trust Company
50 South La Salle Street, Third Floor
Chicago, IL 60603
(312) 444-3761
Fax: (312) 557-7398

E-MAIL ADDRESS:
trm@ntrs.com

FOUNDED: 1976

AREAS OF INTEREST:
Youth agencies, arts, cultural programs and hospitals.

TYPE:
Capital grants; Project/program grants. Project grants in areas of the Foundation's interest.

YEAR PROGRAM STARTED: 1976

PURPOSE:
To make grants to charitable agencies in Omaha and Douglas County, NE.

LEGAL BASIS:
Tax-exempt.

ELIGIBILITY:
Tax-exempt organizations in Omaha and Douglas County, Nebraska. No grants are awarded to individuals.

GEOGRAPHIC RESTRICTIONS:
Douglas County and Omaha, Nebraska.

FINANCIAL DATA:
Total assets of $6,299,925 as of December 31, 2011.
Amount of support per award: Average $15,000 to $20,000.

Total amount of support: Total giving of $305,500 for year ended December 31, 2011.

Matching fund requirements: Stipulated with specific programs.

NUMBER OF AWARDS: 35.

REPRESENTATIVE AWARDS:
Salvation Army; United Way; Nebraska Food Bank.

APPLICATION INFORMATION:
A request should be made for guidelines to submit grant applications. Six copies of the application are required.

Duration: No grants are awarded on a continuing basis.

Deadline: March 20 and October 1. Announcements in May and November.

PUBLICATIONS:
Application guidelines.

IRS IDENTIFICATION NUMBER: 36-6629069

ADDRESS INQUIRIES TO:
Thomas R. Mitchell, Senior Vice President
(See address above.)

MILLIPORE CORPORATE GIVING PROGRAM   [238]
290 Concord Road
Billerica, MA 01821-7037
(978) 715-1796
Fax: (978) 715-1385

E-MAIL ADDRESS:
johanna.jobin@emdmillipore.com

WEB SITE ADDRESS:
www.emdmillipore.com/ourgivingprogram

FOUNDED: 1985

AREAS OF INTEREST:
Science, education (K-12), sustainability, and health care.

TYPE:
Capital grants; Challenge/matching grants; Matching gifts; Project/program grants; Research grants; Scholarships.

YEAR PROGRAM STARTED: 1985

PURPOSE:
To serve the public interest in ways that are meaningful to the company and its employees.

ELIGIBILITY:
Organizations, excluding religious and political, classified as 501(c)(3) by the IRS can apply.

FINANCIAL DATA:
Since inception, over $20,000,000 has been distributed to deserving nonprofit programs on a local and national level.

Amount of support per award: $5,000 to $10,000.

Matching fund requirements: $25 minimum gift.

APPLICATION INFORMATION:
Eligible programs may submit a copy of the 501(c)(3) certificate, tax identification number, and a letter of inquiry no more than two pages in length briefly describing the organization, the program for which funding is sought, and the amount of funding requested. Those organizations whose programs are of interest to Millipore will be invited to submit full proposals.

Millipore also accepts the Associated Grant Makers Common Proposal Form.

Duration: One year. Grants are renewable.

Deadline: Proposals are considered quarterly at Review Committee meetings.

ADDRESS INQUIRIES TO:
Johanna Jobin, Director of Corporate Responsibility
(See address above.)

THE MOODY FOUNDATION [239]
2302 Post Office Street, Suite 704
Galveston, TX 77550
(409) 797-1525
Fax: (409) 763-5564

E-MAIL ADDRESS:
amatthews@moodyf.org

WEB SITE ADDRESS:
www.moodyf.org

FOUNDED: 1942

AREAS OF INTEREST:
Arts, education, medical research, community and economic development, environment and youth programs.

TYPE:
Capital grants; Challenge/matching grants; Endowments; Grants-in-aid; Project/program grants; Research grants; Scholarships. Capital campaigns; Equipment; Matching funds; Building/renovation; Program development and research.

YEAR PROGRAM STARTED: 1942

PURPOSE:
To assist in supporting activities that are directed toward improving the general well-being of the citizens of the state of Texas, especially Galveston.

LEGAL BASIS:
Private family foundation.

ELIGIBILITY:
Tax-exempt organizations in the state of Texas only are eligible to apply. The Foundation generally does not make grant awards for deficit financing, operational expenses of established organizations, or grants for any activities considered a taxable expenditure under the 1969 Tax Reform Act. No grants to individuals (except for one scholarship program). No loans.

GEOGRAPHIC RESTRICTIONS:
Texas.

FINANCIAL DATA:
Amount of support per award: Average $10,000.

Total amount of support: Varies.

NUMBER OF AWARDS: 20 to 30.

REPRESENTATIVE AWARDS:
$30,000 to American Cancer Society Inc./Cattle Baron's Ball, Dallas, TX; $15,000 to Community Schools in Dallas; $5,000 to Garland Family Outreach, Inc., Garland, TX.

APPLICATION INFORMATION:
Prospective candidates should write or call the Foundation to ascertain if appropriate to request guidelines for making application.

Duration: Generally, grants are awarded for one year at a time.

PUBLICATIONS:
Annual report; application guidelines.

IRS IDENTIFICATION NUMBER: 74-1403105

STAFF:
Frances Anne Moody-Dahlberg, Executive Director
Garrik Addison, Chief Financial Officer

Allan Matthews, Grants Director
Gerald Smith, Program Officer
Bernice C. Torregrossa, Grants Analyst

BOARD OF TRUSTEES:
Robert L. Moody, Sr., Chairman
Ross R. Moody, Treasurer
Frances Anne Moody-Dahlberg

FOUNDERS:
Libbie Shearn Moody
W.L. Moody, Jr.

ADDRESS INQUIRIES TO:
Allan Matthews, Grants Director
(See address above.)

THE CLARENCE E. MULFORD TRUST   [240]
P.O. Box 290
Fryeburg, ME 04037
(207) 935-2061
Fax: (207) 935-3939

AREAS OF INTEREST:
Animals, education, literature, religion, science and youth.

TYPE:
Project/program grants.

PURPOSE:
To support charitable organizations that are working to improve the quality of life for Maine residents.

LEGAL BASIS:
Trust fund.

ELIGIBILITY:
Grants are made to organizations that have tax-exempt status under Section 501(c)(3) of the Internal Revenue Code. No grants are made to individuals. Religious organizations may apply.

GEOGRAPHIC RESTRICTIONS:
Fryeburg, Maine and adjoining towns.

FINANCIAL DATA:
Amount of support per award: $500 to $10,000.

Total amount of support: $540,000 for the year 2012.

APPLICATION INFORMATION:
Organizations should submit IRS tax exemption letter under 501(c)(3) of the Internal Revenue Code.

Duration: One year. Renewal by reapplication.

Deadline: January 10 and July 10.

TRUSTEES:
David R. Hastings, III
Peter Hastings

ADDRESS INQUIRIES TO:
Peter Hastings, Trustee
(See address above.)

M.J. MURDOCK CHARITABLE TRUST   [241]
703 Broadway, Suite 710
Vancouver, WA 98660
(360) 694-8415
Fax: (360) 694-1819

E-MAIL ADDRESS:
stevem@murdock-trust.org

WEB SITE ADDRESS:
www.murdock-trust.org

FOUNDED: 1975

AREAS OF INTEREST:
Education, science, health and human services, arts and culture.

TYPE:
Capital grants; Challenge/matching grants; Development grants; Project/program grants; Research grants. In addition to a special interest in education and scientific research, the Trust partners with a wide variety of organizations that serve the arts, public affairs, health and medicine, human services, leadership development and persons with disabilities.

PURPOSE:
To enrich the quality of life in the Pacific Northwest by providing grants and enrichment programs to organizations seeking to strengthen the region's educational, spiritual and cultural base in creative and sustainable ways.

LEGAL BASIS:
Private foundation.

ELIGIBILITY:
Applications for grants are considered only from organizations which have been ruled to be tax-exempt under Section 501(c)(3) of the Internal Revenue Code and are not private foundations. Primary attention is given to applications for the support of projects and programs conducted by qualified institutions within five states of the Pacific Northwest, including Alaska, Idaho, Montana, Oregon and Washington. Priority is given to organizations and projects which are not primarily or normally financed by public tax funds.

Applications are not considered for loans, endowment, debt retirement, operational deficits, contributions to general fund drives or annual charitable appeals, continuation of programs previously financed from external sources or emergency funding.

GEOGRAPHIC RESTRICTIONS:
Pacific Northwest.

FINANCIAL DATA:
Amount of support per award: Average $180,000.

NUMBER OF APPLICANTS MOST RECENT YEAR:
303.

NUMBER OF AWARDS: 265 grants approved for the year 2013.

APPLICATION INFORMATION:
Submit a letter of inquiry and request for guidelines to loi@murdock-trust.org or:
P.O. Box 1618
Vancouver, WA 98668-1618.

PUBLICATIONS:
Annual report; *Grants Proposal Guidelines*; proposal form.

TRUSTEES:
John W. Castles
Jeffrey T. Grubb
Lynwood W. Swanson

OFFICERS AND STAFF:
Steven G.W. Moore, Executive Director
Terry Stokesbary, Senior Program Director for Enrichment Programs
Dana L. Miller, Senior Program Director for Grant Programs
John Van Zytveld, Senior Fellow
John Franklin, Program Director
Christopher Gillem, Program Director
Barton A. Hadder, Program Director
Jan Kennedy, Program Director
Moses Lee, Program Director
Jill Tatum, Program Director

ADDRESS INQUIRIES TO:
Dana L. Miller, Senior Program Director for Grant Programs
(See address above.)

NATIONWIDE INSURANCE FOUNDATION [242]
One Nationwide Plaza
Mail Drop 1.2.16
Columbus, OH 43215-2220
(614) 249-4310
Fax: (866) 212-7960

E-MAIL ADDRESS:
blicklk@nationwide.com

WEB SITE ADDRESS:
www.nationwide.com/foundation

FOUNDED: 1959

AREAS OF INTEREST:
Health and welfare, education, culture and the arts and civic and community affairs.

TYPE:
Capital grants; Challenge/matching grants; General operating grants; Matching gifts; Project/program grants.

YEAR PROGRAM STARTED: 1959

PURPOSE:
To provide financial support for qualified tax-exempt organizations whose programs address basic human needs.

LEGAL BASIS:
Corporate foundation.

ELIGIBILITY:
Qualified, tax-exempt organizations in Columbus, OH and locations with a large number of Nationwide associates are eligible.

FINANCIAL DATA:
Amount of support per award: $5,000 to $7,000 average.
Total amount of support: $25,557,815 for the year 2012.
Matching fund requirements: Matching gifts to accredited colleges and universities.

APPLICATION INFORMATION:
Guidelines and application form are available at the Foundation web site.
Duration: One year. Renewal possible.
Deadline: September 1. Announcement in mid-March.

PUBLICATIONS:
Contributions guidelines.

ADDRESS INQUIRIES TO:
Karen H. Blickley, Senior Director
(See address above.)

*SPECIAL STIPULATIONS:
Preference is given to organizations in Columbus, OH or those recommended by a Nationwide regional office.

NEW ENGLAND BIOLABS FOUNDATION [243]
240 County Road
Ipswich, MA 01938
(978) 998-7990
Fax: (978) 356-3250

E-MAIL ADDRESS:
info@nebf.org

WEB SITE ADDRESS:
www.nebf.org

FOUNDED: 1982

AREAS OF INTEREST:
Environmental issues: landscapes and seascapes, and the associated biocultural diversity, ecosystem services and foodways.

TYPE:
Grants-in-aid; Project/program grants; Seed money grants. The Foundation prefers to help organizations start their projects with the understanding that once they are established, funding from other sources will be sought.

YEAR PROGRAM STARTED: 1982

PURPOSE:
To support grassroots organizations working with the environment.

ELIGIBILITY:
The Foundation prefers to fund grassroots organizations and/or projects (i.e., those conceived, developed and managed by the community). Grassroots organizations, emerging support groups and charitable organizations may apply. Grants are not made to religious organizations.

FINANCIAL DATA:
Amount of support per award: Average $7,000 per year, maximum of $10,000.
Total amount of support: Approximately $375,000 annually.

NUMBER OF APPLICANTS MOST RECENT YEAR:
100.

NUMBER OF AWARDS: 30.

APPLICATION INFORMATION:
Letters of Inquiry and Proposals should be submitted electronically to the e-mail address listed above.
Duration: Typically one year.
Deadline: Letters of Inquiry: March 1 and July 15. Proposals must be submitted by April 1 or September 1 to be accepted.

ADDRESS INQUIRIES TO:
Assistant Director
(See address above.)

THE NEW YORK COMMUNITY TRUST [244]
909 Third Avenue, 22nd Floor
New York, NY 10022
(212) 686-0010
Fax: (212) 532-8528

WEB SITE ADDRESS:
www.nycommunitytrust.org

FOUNDED: 1924

AREAS OF INTEREST:
Children, youth and families, community development and the environment, education, arts, human justice, health, people with special needs and special projects.

TYPE:
Project/program grants; Technical assistance. Since 1924, The New York Community Trust has built a permanent endowment to support the nonprofits that make New York City a vital and secure place in which to live and work. With thousands of charitable funds set up by individuals, families, and businesses, the Trust helps donors with their giving today and enables their generosity to continue after their lifetimes, supporting the causes they cared about and solving problems of the future.

Additionally, the Trust has an environmental program that makes grants to organizations working nationally and internationally.

Grants to improve the social work profession are made to groups nationwide.

YEAR PROGRAM STARTED: 1924

PURPOSE:
To support the nonprofits that make New York City a vital and secure place to live and work.

LEGAL BASIS:
Public nonprofit foundation.

ELIGIBILITY:
Priority is given to grant proposals from nonprofit organizations which deal with the problems of the New York metropolitan region. Preference is given to proposals that support specific programs or projects.

Grants are not made to support endowments or building fund campaigns, deficit financing or annual giving, religious purposes or financial assistance or to individual applicants.

GEOGRAPHIC RESTRICTIONS:
Primarily New York, New York.

FINANCIAL DATA:
Amount of support per award: $10,000 to $200,000.

Total amount of support: Competitive grants: Approximately $35,000,000 annually.

APPLICATION INFORMATION:
Applicants should begin by going to the Grantee Application Hub on the Trust's web site; click on "How to Apply," where one can read the Trust's guidelines for grant applicants and start the application process by completing the Proposal Cover Sheet.

Duration: Usually one year.

Deadline: Grant applications are accepted throughout the year. Trust's Board reviews grants five times per year.

PUBLICATIONS:
Annual report; application and individual program guidelines; proposal cover sheet; newsletter.

OFFICERS:
Lorie A. Slutsky, President
Patricia Jenny, Vice President, Grants
Mercedes Leon, Vice President, Administration
Alan Holzer, Chief Financial Officer

DISTRIBUTION COMMITTEE:
Charlynn Goins, Chairman
Jamie Drake
Roger J. Maldonado
Anne Moore, M.D.
Raffiq Nathoo
Valerie Peltier
Judith O. Rubin
Lorie A. Slutsky
Barron Tenny
Ann Unterberg
Mary Kay Vyskocil
Jason H. Wright

THE NORCLIFFE FOUNDATION [245]
Wells Fargo Center
999 Third Avenue, Suite 1006
Seattle, WA 98104
(206) 682-4820
Fax: (206) 682-4821

E-MAIL ADDRESS:
arline@thenorcliffefoundation.com

WEB SITE ADDRESS:
www.thenorcliffefoundation.com

FOUNDED: 1952

AREAS OF INTEREST:
Health, education, social services, civic improvement, religion, historic preservation, culture and the arts, youth programs, and environment.

TYPE:
Capital grants; Endowments; General operating grants; Project/program grants; Research grants; Seed money grants. Social service grants.

YEAR PROGRAM STARTED: 1952

PURPOSE:
To improve the lives of people.

LEGAL BASIS:
Private foundation.

ELIGIBILITY:
Eligible organizations must be of IRS 501(c)(3), not-for-profit status. Grants are not given to individuals.

GEOGRAPHIC RESTRICTIONS:
Puget Sound area of Washington state.

FINANCIAL DATA:
Amount of support per award: Varies.

Total amount of support: $12,161,460 for the year 2013.

NUMBER OF AWARDS: Over 300 for the year 2013.

APPLICATION INFORMATION:
An application form or letter of proposal is requested. Applying organizations must provide IRS 501(c)(3) documentation, a list of the board of directors, a financial statement and budget information, and background information on the agency applying. Applicants should also include a list of funders approached, dollar amounts, those denied and those pending.

Duration: Varies by project. Grants are generally not renewable.

Deadline: Applications are accepted throughout the year.

ADDRESS INQUIRIES TO:
Arline Hefferline, Foundation Manager (See address above.)

THE NORDSON CORPORATION FOUNDATION [246]
28601 Clemens Road
Westlake, OH 44145-1148
(440) 892-1580
Fax: (440) 414-5751

E-MAIL ADDRESS:
crender@nordson.com

WEB SITE ADDRESS:
www.nordson.com

FOUNDED: 1952

AREAS OF INTEREST:
Education, human welfare, civic, arts and culture.

CONSULTING OR VOLUNTEER SERVICES:
Corporate volunteer program.

NAME(S) OF PROGRAMS:
• **Time and Talent**

TYPE:
Capital grants; Challenge/matching grants; General operating grants; Matching gifts; Project/program grants; Technical assistance.

YEAR PROGRAM STARTED: 1988

PURPOSE:
To improve the quality of life in our communities by improving educational outcomes that enable individuals to become self-sufficient, active participants in the community.

LEGAL BASIS:
Corporate foundation.

ELIGIBILITY:
Grants are made to tax-exempt organizations, as defined in Section 501(c)(3) of the Internal Revenue Code. No grants to religious organizations.

GEOGRAPHIC RESTRICTIONS:
Mainly "North" San Diego County, California; northern Colorado; Emanuel and Gwinnett counties, Georgia; Mercer County, New Jersey; Youngstown and Lorain County, Ohio; New Castle, Pennsylvania; Providence, Rhode Island; Pulaski, Virginia; and Chippewa Falls, Wisconsin.

FINANCIAL DATA:
Amount of support per award: Varies.

Total amount of support: $6,000,000 for the year 2013.

Matching fund requirements: Foundation will match minimum contributions of $25 to a maximum of $10,000 for any calendar year.

NUMBER OF APPLICANTS MOST RECENT YEAR: 420 for the year 2012.

NUMBER OF AWARDS: 310 for the year 2012.

APPLICATION INFORMATION:
Application forms are available online.

Duration: Typically one year.

Deadline: February 15, May 15, August 15 and November 15 for meetings held in January, April, July and October, respectively.

TRUSTEES:
Doug Bloomfield
Beverly Coen
Michael Hilton
John Keane
Peter Lambert
Shelly Peet
Greg Thaxton

STAFF:
Kathy Ladiner, Grants Manager and Matching Gifts Coordinator
Jennifer Kuhn, Community Relations Liaison/New Jersey
Stephanie Shaw, Community Relations Liaison/Rhode Island
Ray McHenry, Community Relations Liaison/San Diego County
Joan Szczepanik, Program Assistant

ADDRESS INQUIRIES TO:
Cecilia H. Render, Tel: (440) 892-1580
Kathy Ladiner, Tel: (440) 892-1580 (Matching Gifts)
Ray McHenry, Tel: (760) 930-7258 (San Diego)
Stephanie Shaw, Tel: (401) 431-7127 (Providence, RI)
Jennifer Kuhn, Tel: (609) 259-9222 (NJ)
Johanna Friedrich, Tel: (330) 726-4000 ext. 6321 (Youngstown, OH)
Marcus Kinkaid, Tel: (970) 226-8254 (Fort Collins, CO)
Cindy Baumgardner, Tel: (770) 497-3672 (GA)
Wendy Crotteau, Tel: (715) 726-1201 ext. 184 (WI)

KENNETH T. AND EILEEN L. NORRIS FOUNDATION [247]
11 Golden Shore, Suite 450
Long Beach, CA 90802
(562) 435-8444
Fax: (562) 436-0584

E-MAIL ADDRESS:
grants@norrisfoundation.org

WEB SITE ADDRESS:
www.norrisfoundation.org

FOUNDED: 1963

AREAS OF INTEREST:
Funding categories include medicine, education and science, youth, community and culture.

TYPE:
Capital grants; Challenge/matching grants; Endowments; General operating grants; Project/program grants; Research grants.

YEAR PROGRAM STARTED: 1963

PURPOSE:
To support programs that advance better health and intellectual enlightenment through education, cultivation of the arts, individual responsibility, freedom and dignity.

LEGAL BASIS:
Family foundation.

ELIGIBILITY:
Applicants must be nonprofit, tax-exempt organizations. The Foundation does not support individuals and/or political or religious organizations.

GEOGRAPHIC RESTRICTIONS:
Southern California.

FINANCIAL DATA:
Amount of support per award: Grants vary in amount, depending upon the needs and nature of the request.
Total amount of support: Varies.

APPLICATION INFORMATION:
Potential applicants should contact the Foundation for guidelines and application form.
Duration: Most grants are for one year.
Deadline: Education/Science and Medical: May 1 to June 30. Decision in October; Youth: February 15 to March 31. Decision in August; Community and Cultural: December 1 to January 31. Decision in May.

PUBLICATIONS:
Biannual report.

IRS IDENTIFICATION NUMBER: 95-6080374

TRUSTEES AND OFFICERS:
Lisa D. Hansen, Chairman
Ronald R. Barnes
James R. Martin
Bradley K. Norris
Harlyne J. Norris
Kimberley Presley
Walter J. Zanino

ADDRESS INQUIRIES TO:
Walter J. Zanino, Executive Director
(See address above.)

NORTH CAROLINA COMMUNITY FOUNDATION [248]
4601 Six Forks Road, Suite 524
Raleigh, NC 27609-5286
(919) 828-4387
(800) 201-9533
Fax: (919) 828-5495

E-MAIL ADDRESS:
info@nccommunityfoundation.org

WEB SITE ADDRESS:
www.nccommunityfoundation.org

FOUNDED: 1988

AREAS OF INTEREST:
Arts and conservation, education, health, historical and culture resources, preservation of environmental and social services.

TYPE:
General operating grants; Project/program grants; Scholarships.

YEAR PROGRAM STARTED: 1988

PURPOSE:
To inspire North Carolinians to make lasting and meaningful contributions to their communities.

LEGAL BASIS:
501(c)(3).

ELIGIBILITY:
Nonprofit, tax-exempt organizations. No grants are made to individuals.

GEOGRAPHIC RESTRICTIONS:
North Carolina.

FINANCIAL DATA:
Amount of support per award: Varies.
Total amount of support: Approximately $6,000,000 for fiscal year ended March 31, 2013.

APPLICATION INFORMATION:
Complete details on how to apply is available on the Foundation web site.

ADDRESS INQUIRIES TO:
Grants and Scholarships
North Carolina Community Foundation
(See address above.)

THE NORTHWEST MINNESOTA FOUNDATION
201 Third Street, N.W.
Bemidji, MN 56601
(218) 759-2057
Fax: (218) 759-2328

E-MAIL ADDRESS:
nwmf@nwmf.org

WEB SITE ADDRESS:
www.nwmf.org

TYPE:
Development grants; Endowments; Project/program grants; Training grants.

See entry 1339 for full listing.

NSTAR FOUNDATION [249]
One NSTAR Way
Westwood, MA 02090
(781) 441-3587

E-MAIL ADDRESS:
nstarfoundation@nstar.com

WEB SITE ADDRESS:
www.nstar.com

FOUNDED: 1981

AREAS OF INTEREST:
Youth programs, quality of life services, and the economically disenfranchised.

TYPE:
Challenge/matching grants; Development grants; Matching gifts; Project/program grants; Research grants; Scholarships; Technical assistance. Financial support to qualified organizations serving communities within the Foundation's service territory.

YEAR PROGRAM STARTED: 1981

PURPOSE:
To be involved in and aware of the concern and needs facing the communities of which the Company is a part.

LEGAL BASIS:
Corporate foundation.

ELIGIBILITY:
Applicants must be institutions and organizations with a 501(c)(3) tax-exempt designation.

The Foundation does not support capital campaigns (building as well as renovation). Foundations and religiously focused groups do not qualify for funding.

FINANCIAL DATA:
Amount of support per award: $1,000 to $100,000. $2,500 average.
Total amount of support: $1,000,000 to $1,500,000.
Matching fund requirements: The Foundation matches dollar-for-dollar employee gifts to approved educational or cultural organizations and homeless shelters. Minimum of $100 and maximum of $2,500 in any calendar year.

REPRESENTATIVE AWARDS:
$5,000 to North End Against Drugs; $5,000 to Plymouth Philharmonic Orchestra.

APPLICATION INFORMATION:
Submit an electronic proposal letter to the Foundation describing your organization mission and the special program for which you are seeking funding. More information is available on the Foundation web site.
Duration: Usually one year.

PUBLICATIONS:
Guidelines; matching grants program brochure.

WILLIAM J. AND DOROTHY K. O'NEILL FOUNDATION [250]
30195 Chagrin Boulevard
Suite 106
Cleveland, OH 44124
(216) 831-4134
Fax: (216) 378-0594

E-MAIL ADDRESS:
info@oneill-foundation.org

WEB SITE ADDRESS:
www.oneill-foundation.org

FOUNDED: 1987

AREAS OF INTEREST:
Capacity building - all program areas.

TYPE:
Matching gifts. Capacity building; Proactive grants; Gifts in recognition of service; Youth Philanthropy grants; Responsive grants; Special initiative grants; Rapid responsive grants. In the area of capacity building, the Foundation funds projects that create and implement strategic plans, governance and board development, leadership succession planning, planning and implementing technology systems, fund development, and communications and marketing strategies.

Matching gifts and gifts in recognition of service are directed by O'Neill Family members.

Youth Philanthropy grants are made by O'Neill Family youth.

YEAR PROGRAM STARTED: 1987

PURPOSE:
To fund programs that address root causes of family strength and family disintegration, capacity building for nonprofits and areas of interest to individual family members.

LEGAL BASIS:
Family foundation.

ELIGIBILITY:
Nonprofit organizations with IRS 501(c)(3) tax-exempt status are eligible for support. No grants to individuals or to organizations which operate wholly outside the U.S. No grants in response to annual appeal form letters.

In order to be eligible, you must have either received a grant from the Foundation already and/or be notified that you are eligible.

GEOGRAPHIC RESTRICTIONS:
Washington, DC; Bonita Springs and Naples, Florida; Big Island, Hawaii; Annapolis and Baltimore, Maryland; New York, New York; Cleveland, Columbus and Licking counties, Ohio; Houston, Texas; and Richmond, Virginia.

FINANCIAL DATA:
Amount of support per award: Average: $35,000.

Total amount of support: $2,963,810 for the year 2010.

REPRESENTATIVE AWARDS:
$17,000 to Houston SPCA, Houston, TX; $10,000 to Shaker Historical Society, Shaker Heights, OH; $40,000 to Cleveland Botanical Garden, Cleveland, OH; $25,000 to National Marfan Foundation, Port Washington, NY; $15,000 to New York Youth at Risk, New York, NY.

APPLICATION INFORMATION:
The application process includes:
(1) Letter of inquiry;
(2) Site visit and;
(3) Invited proposal.

Complete details can be found on the Foundation web site.

Duration: One year.

Deadline: Letters of Inquiry: December 1, April 1 and September 1.

PUBLICATIONS:
Annual report; application guidelines.

IRS IDENTIFICATION NUMBER: 34-1560893

OFFICERS:
Leah S. Gary, President and Chief Executive Officer
Robert W. Donahey, Treasurer
Kelly Sweeney McShane, Secretary

TRUSTEES:
Timothy M. O'Neill, Chairperson
Leah S. Gary, President and Chief Executive Officer
Linda M. Clifford
Robert W. Donahey
Kelly Sweeney McShane
John H. O'Neill
Sara O'Neill Sullivan

ADDRESS INQUIRIES TO:
Symone McClain, Director
Grants Management and Foundation Operations
(See address above.)

THE JOHN R. OISHEI FOUNDATION   [251]
One HSBC Center
Suite 3650
Buffalo, NY 14203-2805
(716) 856-9490
Fax: (716) 856-9493

E-MAIL ADDRESS:
info@oishei.org

WEB SITE ADDRESS:
www.oishei.org

FOUNDED: 1940

AREAS OF INTEREST:
Strengthening neighborhoods and building communities, self-sufficiency, education and employment, community health and medical research, expanding the impact of regional assets, and building organizational strength through operational improvements.

TYPE:
Capital grants; Challenge/matching grants; General operating grants; Project/program grants; Seed money grants. Education grants.

PURPOSE:
To be a catalyst for change; to enhance the economic vitality and the quality of life for the Buffalo Niagara region.

LEGAL BASIS:
Private foundation.

ELIGIBILITY:
An organization seeking support must be determined by the Internal Revenue Code to be tax-exempt under Section 501(c)(3). Private Foundations, as defined in Section 509(a) of the Internal Revenue Code, will not be eligible for Foundation support. To receive Foundation support, an organization must be well managed, including an active board drawn from a cross section of the community. It must have a consistent record of sound fiscal management and a demonstrated track record of efficient operations and effective programming. The Foundation does not make grants to governmental institutions, agencies or projects. Organizations that rely heavily on government funding are eligible to apply, but must be able to demonstrate that a grant from the Foundation would supplement rather than supplant public funding.

GEOGRAPHIC RESTRICTIONS:
Buffalo Niagara region, New York.

FINANCIAL DATA:
Amount of support per award: $10,000 to $3,500,000.

Total amount of support: $17,800,000 for the year 2011.

NUMBER OF AWARDS: 150 for the year 2011.

REPRESENTATIVE AWARDS:
$2,000,000 to Canisius College Science Center; $525,000 to Community Health Center of Buffalo; $360,000 to Erie Community College Foundation; $300,000 to Riviera Theatre & Organ Preservation Society.

APPLICATION INFORMATION:
Letters of Inquiry (LOIs) and applications for general funding requests must be submitted online.

Deadline: The Foundation accepts and processes applications throughout the year. Notification within three months.

PUBLICATIONS:
Catalyst for Change, annual report and guidelines.

OFFICERS:
James M. Wadsworth, Chairman
Mary S. Martino, Vice Chairman
Robert D. Gioia, President
Edward F. Walsh, Jr., Treasurer
Gayle L. Houck, Secretary

DIRECTORS:
Robert M. Bennett
Ruth D. Bryant
Florence M. Conti
Christopher T. Dunstan
William G. Giesel, Jr.
Mary S. Martino
Ann M. McCarthy
James M. Wadsworth
Edward F. Walsh, Jr.

ADDRESS INQUIRIES TO:
Robert D. Gioia, President
(See address above.)

OMAHA COMMUNITY FOUNDATION   [252]
302 South 36th Street
Suite 100
Omaha, NE 68131
(402) 342-3458
Fax: (402) 342-3582

E-MAIL ADDRESS:
betty@omahafoundation.org

WEB SITE ADDRESS:
www.omahafoundation.org

FOUNDED: 1982

AREAS OF INTEREST:
General philanthropy.

CONSULTING OR VOLUNTEER SERVICES:
Nonprofit Capacity Building Initiative.

NAME(S) OF PROGRAMS:
● **African American Unity Fund**
● **Endowment Funds of Southwest Iowa**
● **Fund for Omaha**
● **Futuro Latino Fund**
● **Youth in Philanthropy**

TYPE:
Capital grants; Project/program grants; Scholarships. Donors can contribute through the Omaha Community Foundation to any nonprofit agency. The OCF also has five discretionary grant programs.

PURPOSE:
To facilitate charitable giving and serve as a vehicle for community improvement; to improve the quality of life in Greater Omaha by supporting needs not being met in the areas of civic, cultural, health, education and social service.

LEGAL BASIS:
Public foundation.

ELIGIBILITY:
Organizations applying for grants must be tax-exempt as defined by IRS 501(c)(3) status. Except under unusual circumstances, no grants for endowments, capital campaigns, deficit financing, annual fund drives or fund-raising activities. The grant request must have the approval of the governing board of the requesting organization.

GEOGRAPHIC RESTRICTIONS:
Greater Omaha area.

FINANCIAL DATA:
Amount of support per award: $5,000 to $15,000.

Total amount of support: Varies.

NUMBER OF AWARDS: Approximately 425.

APPLICATION INFORMATION:
Contact the Foundation for details.
Duration: Varies.
Deadline: African American Unity Fund and Futuro Latino Fund: August 1; Endowment Funds: February 1; Fund for Omaha: March 1 and September 1; Scholarships: March 31.

PUBLICATIONS:
Newsletter.

IRS IDENTIFICATION NUMBER: 47-0645958

STAFF:
Ayanna Boykins, Director of Community Investments

ADDRESS INQUIRIES TO:
Betty Carrico
Philanthropic Services Assistant
(See address above.)

ORANGE COUNTY COMMUNITY FOUNDATION   [253]
4041 MacArthur Boulevard
Suite 510
Newport Beach, CA 92660-2503
(949) 553-4202
Fax: (949) 553-4211

E-MAIL ADDRESS:
mconner@oc-cf.org

WEB SITE ADDRESS:
www.oc-cf.org

FOUNDED: 1989

AREAS OF INTEREST:
Children and youth, family relationships, diverse communities, music education and performance, classical music and education, health, environment and education.

TYPE:
Endowments; General operating grants; Project/program grants; Scholarships. The Foundation offers several grant programs throughout the year in human services, education, health, arts and culture, and the environment. Other special grant competitions also occur throughout the year.

YEAR PROGRAM STARTED: 1990

PURPOSE:
To encourage, support and facilitate philanthropy in Orange County.

LEGAL BASIS:
Community foundation.

ELIGIBILITY:
Applicant agencies must be tax-exempt, serve its residents, and operate without discrimination on the basis of race, religion, gender, sexual orientation, age, national origin or disability.

GEOGRAPHIC RESTRICTIONS:
Orange County, California.

FINANCIAL DATA:
Amount of support per award: Average grant: $5,000 to $25,000.
Total amount of support: $29,000,000 for fiscal year 2011-12.

COOPERATIVE FUNDING PROGRAMS: ReachOut OC; OC Founders Roundtable.

APPLICATION INFORMATION:
All applications and transcripts must be submitted through the online application system. Guidelines are available on the web site.

Duration: Generally one year for unrestricted grants. Renewal occasionally possible for scholarships.
Deadline: Varies.

PUBLICATIONS:
Annual report; newsletters; guidelines.

IRS IDENTIFICATION NUMBER: 33-0378778

ADDRESS INQUIRIES TO:
Marisa Conner
Donor and Community Engagement Associate
(See e-mail address above.)

THE BERNARD OSHER FOUNDATION   [254]
One Ferry Building, Suite 255
San Francisco, CA 94111
(415) 861-5587
Fax: (415) 677-5868

E-MAIL ADDRESS:
info@osherfoundation.org

WEB SITE ADDRESS:
www.osherfoundation.org

FOUNDED: 1977

AREAS OF INTEREST:
Scholarship funding to selected colleges and universities, integrative medicine, lifelong learning for seasoned adults, arts and humanities.

TYPE:
Project/program grants; Scholarships. The Foundation provides scholarship funding nationally to selected colleges and universities and funds integrative medicine centers at Harvard University, the University of California at San Francisco, and the Karolinska Institute in Stockholm. It also supports a growing network of lifelong learning institutes for seasoned adults located at nearly 120 colleges and universities from Maine to Hawaii. Arts and humanities grants are made to nonprofit organizations principally in the Greater San Francisco Bay Area, specifically Alameda and San Francisco counties, as well as the state of Maine.

YEAR PROGRAM STARTED: 1977

PURPOSE:
To provide scholarship funding nationally to selected colleges and universities and to fund integrative medicine centers; to support a network of lifelong learning institutes for seasoned adults; to support the arts and humanities.

ELIGIBILITY:
Requests will be accepted only from organizations which are classified by the IRS as nonprofit and designated as IRS 501(c)(3). Organizations seeking funds should have experience which is relevant to the proposed project.

The Foundation is precluded by its policies from making direct grants to individuals.

FINANCIAL DATA:
Amount of support per award: Varies.
Total amount of support: Varies.

APPLICATION INFORMATION:
A letter of inquiry is invited as the first step in communicating with the Foundation. If proposal is invited, it should include the following:
(1) a brief background of the applicant, including qualifications of people involved;

(2) description of the nature and scope of the proposed program and the anticipated results;
(3) preliminary timetable;
(4) preliminary budget outline;
(5) financial statement covering the most recent year of operation;
(6) evidence of tax-exempt status;
(7) names of appropriate governing authority and evidence of request approval and;
(8) a list of other foundations contributing support as well as the amount of support.
Duration: One year.

STAFF:
Mary G.F. Bitterman, President
Thomas Moffett, Chief Financial Officer/Chief Investment Officer
David Blazevich, Senior Program Officer
Andrew Lynch, Program Officer
Jeanie Hirokane, Executive Administrator/Corporate Secretary

BOARD OF DIRECTORS:
Barbro Osher, Chairman
Bernard Osher, Founder and Treasurer
Mary G.F. Bitterman, President
David Agger
Phyllis Cook
Robert Friend
John Gallo
Laura Lauder
John Pritzker

ADDRESS INQUIRIES TO:
Mary G.F. Bitterman, President
(See address above.)

PACCAR FOUNDATION   [255]
777 106th Avenue, N.E.
Bellevue, WA 98004
(425) 468-7400
Fax: (425) 468-8216

E-MAIL ADDRESS:
ken.hastings@paccar.com

WEB SITE ADDRESS:
www.paccar.com/foundation.asp

FOUNDED: 1951

AREAS OF INTEREST:
Education, science, arts and humanities.

TYPE:
Capital grants.

LEGAL BASIS:
Private foundation.

ELIGIBILITY:
No grants to individuals, political or lobbying groups, fraternal organizations or religious organizations for sectarian purposes.

GEOGRAPHIC RESTRICTIONS:
Columbus, Mississippi; Chillicothe, Ohio; Broken Arrow, Oklahoma; Denton, Texas; Bellevue, Kirkland, Renton, Seattle and Skagit, Washington.

FINANCIAL DATA:
Amount of support per award: $10,000 to $250,000.
Total amount of support: $5,000,000.

APPLICATION INFORMATION:
Guidelines and application procedures are available on the Foundation web site.
Duration: One year. Must reapply for continued funding.
Deadline: Applications accepted throughout the year. Decisions made semiannually.

STAFF:
Ken Hastings, Vice President and General Manager

ADDRESS INQUIRIES TO:
Ken Hastings
Vice President and General Manager
(See address above.)

PACIFIC GAS AND ELECTRIC COMPANY [256]

77 Beale Street
San Francisco, CA 94105
(415) 973-1081
Fax: (415) 973-5411

E-MAIL ADDRESS:
svy1@pge.com

WEB SITE ADDRESS:
www.pge.com/giving

AREAS OF INTEREST:
Education, economic and community vitality, and environment.

CONSULTING OR VOLUNTEER SERVICES:
Volunteer program.

TYPE:
Project/program grants; Scholarships. Signature programs.

YEAR PROGRAM STARTED: 2001

LEGAL BASIS:
Corporate contributions program.

ELIGIBILITY:
Applicants must have tax-deductible status from the IRS under Section 501(c)(3) or be a unit of government (including a public school). Contributions are not made to individuals, for tickets for contests, raffles or other prize-oriented activities, to religious organizations (unless for a program offered to the public on a nondiscriminatory basis and without regard to the recipient's religious affiliation), endowments, debt-reduction campaigns, films, or to political or partisan organizations or events.

The most successful grant applications are those that:
(1) address a demonstrated community need;
(2) link a nonprofit or government program to the Company's business goals and employee presence in the community and;
(3) can provide the grantee and the Company with recognition in the community.

GEOGRAPHIC RESTRICTIONS:
Northern and central California.

FINANCIAL DATA:
Amount of support per award: $1,000 to $25,000. Most grants are under $5,000.
Total amount of support: $23,160,000 for the year 2013.
Matching fund requirements: 1:1 basis: $25 to $2,500 per calendar year, per employee.

NUMBER OF APPLICANTS MOST RECENT YEAR:
Over 2,500.

NUMBER OF AWARDS: 1,500 for the year 2013.

REPRESENTATIVE AWARDS:
$7,000 to Burris Park Foundation, Hanford, CA, for projects that assist in green building efforts, energy efficiency programs, brownfields, and/or urban park projects; $10,000 to the Western Regional Office, Ducks Unlimited, Rancho Cordova, CA, for protection, conservation and restoration of natural resources, habitats, non-urban parks, tree planting/replanting, fire protection and restoration; $17,500 to Paramount Theatre of the Arts, Inc., Oakland, CA; $45,000 to The Alliance to Save Energy, Washington, DC, to

support organizations and projects in the realms of public policy and environmental justice organizations, and all other projects.

APPLICATION INFORMATION:
Prior to applying for a grant, applicants should contact the local PG&E representative in their project area to discuss the grant proposal. All applicants must use the online grant application. PG&E will neither accept nor process grant proposals in any other format. Please submit only a fully completed application. Incomplete applications will not be considered.
Duration: Generally one year.
Deadline: Applications are preferred before September 30 of each year.

ADDRESS INQUIRIES TO:
Stacey Young Chan, Director Assistant
(See address above.)

PACIFIC LIFE FOUNDATION [257]

700 Newport Center Drive
Newport Beach, CA 92660-6397
(949) 219-3787

E-MAIL ADDRESS:
plfoundation@pacificlife.com

WEB SITE ADDRESS:
www.pacificlifefoundation.com

FOUNDED: 1984

NAME(S) OF PROGRAMS:
- **Arts and Culture**
- **Civic, Community, and Environment**
- **Education**
- **Health and Human Services**

TYPE:
Capital grants; General operating grants; Matching gifts; Product donations; Project/program grants. Arts and Culture: Funds nonprofit agencies that provide the public with a broad spectrum of arts and cultural initiatives (e.g., workshops, performances) to help build the public's appreciation of and participation in dance, music, and theater.

Civic, Community, and Environment: Funding is directed to a wide range of programs that enhance communities through leadership development and environmental protection, as well as fund research to learn more about marine mammals.

Education: Funds nonprofit agencies committed to providing quality educational programs for youth and adults (e.g., mentoring, tutoring, literacy) to help them excel academically and in life.

Health and Human Services: Contributions are allocated to agencies that seek to improve the quality of life of those in need, including the working poor, the homeless, and individuals with physical or developmental disabilities.

PURPOSE:
To recognize and support employees' varied interests and community involvement and, through focus programs, to identify and respond to particular community needs so that, whenever possible, funds may be channeled to those areas in which the most good can be accomplished with the funds available.

LEGAL BASIS:
Corporate foundation and corporate contributions program.

ELIGIBILITY:
Grants are made to nonprofit, tax-exempt, 501(c)(3) organizations. The Foundation does not provide support for individuals, for political parties, candidates or partisan political organizations, for labor organizations, fraternal organizations, athletic clubs or social clubs, for K-12 schools, school districts, or school foundations (contact Foundation for exceptions), for sectarian or denominational religious organizations, except for programs which are broadly promoted, available to anyone, and free from religious orientation, for fund-raising events (e.g., membership drives, luncheons/dinners, tournaments and benefits), or for advertising sponsorships.

GEOGRAPHIC RESTRICTIONS:
The Greater Orange County, California area and other areas, such as Omaha, Nebraska.

FINANCIAL DATA:
Amount of support per award: General grants: $5,000 to $10,000 for a one-year period of funding; Capital grants: $10,000 to $100,000, paid out over multiple years; Matching Gift Program for Higher Education: Up to $2,000; Matching Gift Program to Nonprofits: Up to $500.
Total amount of support: Matching Gift Program: $242,690 for the year 2013. Pacific Life Charitable Contributions and Pacific Life Foundation Charitable Grants: $5,600,000 for the year 2013.

NUMBER OF AWARDS: Matching Gift Program for Higher Education: 63 colleges and universities for the year 2012.

APPLICATION INFORMATION:
Grant guidelines and application form are available online.
Duration: Agencies may reapply annually for funding; however, grants are made to any one agency for no more than three consecutive years. Support may again be requested after a two-year interim period.
Deadline: Submissions accepted July 15 to August 15.

PUBLICATIONS:
Annual report.

OFFICERS:
James T. Morris, Chairman and Chief Executive Officer
Carol R. Sudbeck, Vice Chairman
Tennyson S. Oyler, President
Michele A. Townsend, Vice President
Edward R. Byrd, Chief Financial Officer
Joseph J. Tortorelli, General Counsel
Jane M. Guon, Secretary
Marryn D. Santucci, Assistant Secretary

BOARD OF DIRECTORS:
Thomas D. Billiard
David R. Finear
Luther N. Martin
James T. Morris
Tennyson S. Oyler
Carol R. Sudbeck
Michele A. Townsend
Dawn M. Trautman
Chris van Mierlo
Madhu Vijay
Rebecca Warwar

ADDRESS INQUIRIES TO:
Tennyson S. Oyler, President
(See address above.)

THE DAVID AND LUCILE PACKARD FOUNDATION [258]

343 Second Street
Los Altos, CA 94022
(650) 948-7658
Fax: (650) 948-5793

E-MAIL ADDRESS:
inquiries@packard.org

WEB SITE ADDRESS:
www.packard.org

FOUNDED: 1964

AREAS OF INTEREST:
Arts; children, families and communities; conservation and sciences; organizational effectiveness; philanthropy; and Pueblo, CO.

NAME(S) OF PROGRAMS:
- **Children, Families and Communities**
- **Conservation and Science**
- **Population and Reproductive Health**

TYPE:
Capital grants; Challenge/matching grants; Conferences/seminars; Demonstration grants; Development grants; Fellowships; General operating grants; Matching gifts; Project/program grants; Research grants; Scholarships; Seed money grants; Technical assistance. Grants are made to provide support in the local five-county area for organizational development, arts education and traditional performing arts, as well as for areas of wetlands preservation and restoration, marine fisheries protection and restoration.

Funds are also provided to support fellowships for 20 young professors in science and engineering.

In addition, the Foundation supports children's health programs through children, families, and communities programs, population and family planning services.

Support is given for research of the deep ocean in the Monterey, CA area and community grants in Pueblo County, CO.

YEAR PROGRAM STARTED: 1964

PURPOSE:
To support private, voluntary charities.

LEGAL BASIS:
Private foundation incorporated under California law.

ELIGIBILITY:
Applicants must be qualified tax-exempt charitable organizations. Most community-oriented grants are made to organizations that serve the people of Santa Cruz, Santa Clara, San Mateo and Monterey counties. Requests for support of community and local activities outside of these geographical areas will rarely be considered. Grants are also made in Pueblo (CO) and for national and international programs in conservation, population, public policy and children's health. No proposals may be accepted that benefit individuals or that are for religious purposes.

FINANCIAL DATA:
Amount of support per award: $500 to $30,000,000.
Total amount of support: Approximately $265,000,000 for the year 2011.

APPLICATION INFORMATION:
Contact the Foundation for guidelines.
Duration: Grants are made for one year, with occasional multiyear grants.

PUBLICATIONS:
Annual report; guideline brochures.

OFFICERS:
Susan Packard Orr, Chairperson
Nancy Packard Burnett, Vice Chairperson
Julie E. Packard, Vice Chairperson
Carol S. Larson, President and Chief Executive Officer
Craig Neyman, Vice President and Chief Financial Officer
Mary Anne Rodgers, Secretary and General Counsel

BOARD OF TRUSTEES:
Ned Barnholt
Jason Burnett
Nancy Packard Burnett
Linda Griego
Carol S. Larson
Jane Lubchenco
Linda Mason
David Orr
Susan Packard Orr
Julie E. Packard
William K. Reilly
Colburn S. Wilbur
Ward Woods

PARK BANK FOUNDATION, INC. [259]

330 East Kilbourn Avenue
Milwaukee, WI 53202
(414) 270-3209
Fax: (414) 223-3022

E-MAIL ADDRESS:
susanb@parkbankonline.com

FOUNDED: 1980

AREAS OF INTEREST:
Arts and culture, community development, conservation, education, health, historic preservation and social services.

TYPE:
Capital grants; Development grants; General operating grants.

YEAR PROGRAM STARTED: 1980

PURPOSE:
To fund qualifying organizations in the Milwaukee Metropolitan area as well as surrounding communities.

ELIGIBILITY:
Must have 501(c)(3) status and be located in the Milwaukee area and surrounding communities. No grants are made to individuals. Nonsectarian religious programs may apply.

GEOGRAPHIC RESTRICTIONS:
Milwaukee, Wisconsin metropolitan area.

FINANCIAL DATA:
Amount of support per award: $50 to $6,000.

APPLICATION INFORMATION:
Send a request on the organization's letterhead, a copy of the 501(c)(3) status, a current financial statement of the organization, and a current listing of the Board of Directors.
Duration: One year.
Deadline: Request needs to be received six weeks prior to the meeting dates to be held mid-April, mid-August and mid-December.

THE PARKER FOUNDATION [260]

2604-B El Camino Real
Suite 244
Carlsbad, CA 92008
(760) 720-0630
Fax: (760) 720-1239

WEB SITE ADDRESS:
www.theparkerfoundation.org

FOUNDED: 1971

AREAS OF INTEREST:
Adult and youth services, visual and performing arts, museums and zoos, education, medical purposes, environment and community activities.

TYPE:
Capital grants; Challenge/matching grants; Matching gifts; Project/program grants. Programs and capital funding.

YEAR PROGRAM STARTED: 1971

PURPOSE:
To improve all aspects of life of the people of San Diego County, CA.

LEGAL BASIS:
Tax-exempt, independent private foundation.

ELIGIBILITY:
Applicants must be organizations operating in San Diego County, CA, qualified under IRS 501(c)(3). No grants to individuals or for support of conferences or symposia. No support provided for any project to the extent that it becomes dependent on the Foundation for continued existence.

GEOGRAPHIC RESTRICTIONS:
San Diego County, California.

FINANCIAL DATA:
Amount of support per award: Varies.
Total amount of support: $1,937,824 in grants paid in fiscal year 2013.

NUMBER OF APPLICANTS MOST RECENT YEAR:
236.

NUMBER OF AWARDS: 64.

PUBLICATIONS:
Annual report (available on Foundation web site).

ADDRESS INQUIRIES TO:
Robbin C. Powell
Chief Administrative Officer
(See address above.)

*SPECIAL STIPULATIONS:
Limited by governing documents to San Diego County, CA.

PARKER HANNIFIN CORPORATION FOUNDATION [261]

6035 Parkland Boulevard
Cleveland, OH 44124
(216) 896-3916
Fax: (216) 896-4057

E-MAIL ADDRESS:
csemik@parker.com

WEB SITE ADDRESS:
www.parker.com

AREAS OF INTEREST:
Educational, health, welfare, youth and other charitable organizations.

TYPE:
Capital grants; Matching gifts; Project/program grants. Through the National

Merit Scholarship for Parker employee children only. Matching gifts are for education.

LEGAL BASIS:
Corporate foundation.

ELIGIBILITY:
Grants are made to nonprofit organizations. Emphasis will be placed on organizations that benefit Parker employees and shareholders by improving services in communities with Parker operations and educational opportunities for current and potential employees.

Contributions will not be made to fraternal or labor organizations. Donations to religious organizations are limited to organizations serving the general public on a nondenominational basis, such as the Y's, Salvation Army, educational institutions, hospitals, etc.

GEOGRAPHIC RESTRICTIONS:
United States.

FINANCIAL DATA:
Amount of support per award: $20 to $600,000.
Total amount of support: $4,000,000.

APPLICATION INFORMATION:
Applicants should submit a proposal stating needs and what the grant will be used for, to the Parker division in their locality.
Duration: One-time award.
Deadline: June 30.

THE RALPH M. PARSONS FOUNDATION   [262]
888 West 6th Street, 7th Floor
Los Angeles, CA 90017
(213) 362-7600
Fax: (213) 362-7601

WEB SITE ADDRESS:
www.rmpf.org

FOUNDED: 1961

AREAS OF INTEREST:
Social impact, health, civic and cultural affairs, and higher education in Los Angeles County.

TYPE:
General operating grants; Project/program grants.

YEAR PROGRAM STARTED: 1978

LEGAL BASIS:
Not-for-profit corporation.

ELIGIBILITY:
Applicants must be 501(c)(3) organizations not classified under 509(a). Grants limited to organizations providing services in Los Angeles County.

No funding for mass mailings, fund-raisers, individuals, conferences, religious or political activities and/or dinners or endowments.

GEOGRAPHIC RESTRICTIONS:
Los Angeles County, California.

FINANCIAL DATA:
Amount of support per award: Varies.
Total amount of support: $19,000,000 for the year 2012.

NUMBER OF AWARDS: 220.

REPRESENTATIVE AWARDS:
$25,000 to Bet Tzedek, Los Angeles, CA, to train, recruit and evaluate the work of pro bono attorneys.

APPLICATION INFORMATION:
Submit preliminary letter outlining project and amount requested. Program staff will determine whether applicant is qualified and may request additional information.
Duration: One year.

PUBLICATIONS:
Annual report.

STAFF:
Wendy Garen, President and Chief Executive Officer
Astra Galang, Chief Financial Officer
Thomas Brewer, Program Officer
Mary Christian, Program Officer
Jennifer Price-Letscher, Program Officer
Ricardo Lima, Grants Administrator

BOARD OF DIRECTORS:
William R. Bamattre
Elizabeth Lowe
Walter B. Rose
Karen Hill Scott
James A. Thomas
Robert Tranquada, M.D.
Franklin Ulf
Gayle Wilson

ADDRESS INQUIRIES TO:
Wendy Garen
President and Chief Executive Officer
(See address above.)

AMELIA PEABODY CHARITABLE FUND   [263]
185 Devonshire Street
Suite 600
Boston, MA 02110
(617) 451-6178

WEB SITE ADDRESS:
apcfund.org

FOUNDED: 1984

AREAS OF INTEREST:
Social service and youth services in Massachusetts; environment, health and historic preservation.

TYPE:
Capital grants; Challenge/matching grants.

PURPOSE:
To support organizations that work to improve the quality of life in New England.

LEGAL BASIS:
Private foundation.

ELIGIBILITY:
Eligible organizations must be IRS 501(c)(3) tax-exempt and classified as a public charity under Section 509(a)(1) or 509(a)(2) of the Internal Revenue Code. No grants to individuals or religious organizations. No funding is provided for operating costs, start-ups or salaries, or education.

GEOGRAPHIC RESTRICTIONS:
New England states, primarily Massachusetts.

FINANCIAL DATA:
Amount of support per award: Varies per program.
Total amount of support: Approximately $8,000,000.

NUMBER OF APPLICANTS MOST RECENT YEAR:
Approximately 300.

NUMBER OF AWARDS: 100.

APPLICATION INFORMATION:
A complete proposal should have the following:
(1) Grant Request Summary Form;

(2) proposal checklist;
(3) proposal narrative which provides a clear description of the need, what the applicant is proposing to do about the need, what the organization is requesting, and what results are expected, including a detailed budget of how funds will be spent;
(4) a copy of the determination letter from the IRS classifying the organization as a nonprofit organization under Section 501(c)(3) and as a public charity under Section 509(a)(1) or 509(a)(2) of the Internal Revenue Code;
(5) a letter, dated and signed by the director on the organization's letterhead, affirming that the organization's determination letter from the IRS continues in full force and effect and that a grant from the Fund as applied for would not adversely affect the public charity status;
(6) a copy of the most recent IRS Form 990 and Schedule A;
(7) financial statement, clearly showing all income sources and expenses for the organization for the most recent tax year and;
(8) a list of the Board of Directors/Trustees.

Additionally, include four separate copies of the proposal narrative with the Grant Request Summary Form stapled to the front of each set.
Duration: Renewal possible after three years; four years for major grants.
Deadline: February 1 and July 1.

PUBLICATIONS:
Guidelines.

IRS IDENTIFICATION NUMBER: 23-7364949

STAFF:
Evan C. Page, Executive Director
Cheryl Gideon, Business and Grants Coordinator

ADDRESS INQUIRIES TO:
Cheryl Gideon
Business and Grants Coordinator
(See address above.)

PEACOCK FOUNDATION, INC.   [264]
100 S.E. Second Street, Suite 2370
Miami, FL 33131-2145
(305) 373-1386
Fax: (305) 375-0660

WEB SITE ADDRESS:
peacockfoundationinc.org

AREAS OF INTEREST:
Elderly, children, youth, art for educational purposes, environmental education, disabilities, health and hospitals, medical research and human services.

TYPE:
General operating grants; Project/program grants. Support is provided for projects/programs and limited operating funds.

ELIGIBILITY:
Organizations classified as 501(c)(3) by the IRS can apply. Individuals are ineligible.

GEOGRAPHIC RESTRICTIONS:
Broward, Miami-Dade and Monroe counties, Florida.

FINANCIAL DATA:
Amount of support per award: Average $25,000.

NUMBER OF AWARDS: 65.

APPLICATION INFORMATION:
Applicants must initially submit letter of inquiry.
Duration: One year.

ADDRESS INQUIRIES TO:
Joelle Allen, Executive Director
(See address above.)

THE WILLIAM PENN FOUNDATION [265]
Two Logan Square, 11th Floor
100 North 18th Street
Philadelphia, PA 19103-2757
(215) 988-1830
Fax: (215) 988-1823

E-MAIL ADDRESS:
grants@williampennfoundation.org

WEB SITE ADDRESS:
www.williampennfoundation.org

FOUNDED: 1945

AREAS OF INTEREST:
Art, communities, culture, environment, children, youth and families.

NAME(S) OF PROGRAMS:
- **Closing the Achievement Gap**
- **Creative Communities**
- **Watershed Protection**

TYPE:
Capital grants; Challenge/matching grants; Demonstration grants; Development grants; General operating grants; Project/program grants; Research grants; Seed money grants; Technical assistance. In the areas of children, youth and families, grants are made to promote a better early care and education system, more effective and equitable education policies, networks of developmental opportunities for older youth, and improvements to the systems supporting families. The program focuses on critical transitions in the lives of children as they progress from birth, through early childhood, and into young adulthood.

In the area of environment and communities, grants are made to foster greater cross-sector collaborations that build on the assets of our region through revitalization of its urban core and protection and restoration of watersheds, with a focus on key waterways. Investments are intended to catalyze innovation and leadership in the region.

In the area of arts and culture, the Foundation provides various types of core operating support for arts groups and cultural institutions, enabling them to pursue their creative missions. Work is also funded that broadly advances the region's cultural sector.

YEAR PROGRAM STARTED: 1945

PURPOSE:
To improve the quality of life in the Greater Philadelphia area, particularly for its economically disadvantaged residents; to serve nonprofit organizations that help people improve their lives within a more just and caring society.

LEGAL BASIS:
Private foundation.

ELIGIBILITY:
Applicants must be organizations which are defined as tax-exempt under Section 501(c)(3) of the Internal Revenue Code and which are not private foundations. Grants may be made to religious institutions for nonsectarian purposes, to governments and national organizations in support of policy and advocacy projects.

The Foundation does not fund scholarships, fellowships, or grants to individuals; loans or investment programs; debt reduction; sectarian religious activities; housing capital projects; exempt organizations that pass funds to nonexempt groups; profit-making enterprises; nonpublic schools; programs for rehabilitation or research; programs to replace discontinued government support or national or international grants.

GEOGRAPHIC RESTRICTIONS:
Philadelphia area (Bucks, Chester, Delaware and Montgomery counties), Pennsylvania and Camden, New Jersey.

FINANCIAL DATA:
Amount of support per award: Varies.

COOPERATIVE FUNDING PROGRAMS: The Foundation regularly joins with other foundations and institutions to fund projects.

APPLICATION INFORMATION:
All applicants must first submit a letter of inquiry. Guidelines are available on the Foundation web site.

PUBLICATIONS:
Annual report.

IRS IDENTIFICATION NUMBER: 23-1503488

BOARD OF DIRECTORS:
David Haas, Chairperson
Janet Haas, M.D., Vice Chairperson
Frederick Haas, Secretary
Judith Freyer
Andrew Haas
Christina Haas
Leonard C. Haas
Thomas W. Haas
Katherine Hanrahan
Don Kimelman
Howard Meyers

OFFICERS AND STAFF:
Peter Degnan, Managing Director
Olive Mosier, Director, Arts and Funding
Barbara Scace, Director, Grants Management

ADDRESS INQUIRIES TO:
Proposal Intake Department
(See address above.)

PEPSICO FOUNDATION [266]
700 Anderson Hill Road
Purchase, NY 10577
(914) 253-2000
Fax: (914) 253-2070

WEB SITE ADDRESS:
www.pepsico.com

FOUNDED: 1962

AREAS OF INTEREST:
Education, environment and health.

TYPE:
Capital grants.

LEGAL BASIS:
Nonprofit under 501(c)(3).

ELIGIBILITY:
Organizations seeking a grant must be registered and have an official tax-exemption under Section 501(c)(3) of the Internal Revenue Code, or the equivalent. The Foundation does not make grants to individuals, religious organizations or political causes.

FINANCIAL DATA:
Amount of support per award: Varies.

APPLICATION INFORMATION:
Submit a brief Letter of Interest. Complete details are available on the Foundation web site.

ADDRESS INQUIRIES TO:
Grants Manager
(See address above.)

THE CARL AND LILY PFORZHEIMER FOUNDATION, INC. [267]
950 Third Avenue, 30th Floor
New York, NY 10022
(212) 223-6500
Fax: (212) 223-2222

FOUNDED: 1942

AREAS OF INTEREST:
Education, primarily early 19th century English literature.

TYPE:
Grants-in-aid; Project/program grants.

PURPOSE:
To provide resources for the in-depth study of 19th century English literature.

LEGAL BASIS:
Private foundation.

ELIGIBILITY:
Grants are awarded only to IRS 501(c)(3) tax-exempt organizations. No grants are made directly to individuals.

GEOGRAPHIC RESTRICTIONS:
Primarily United States.

FINANCIAL DATA:
Amount of support per award: Average: $25,000 to $50,000.

APPLICATION INFORMATION:
Organizations may submit a proposal.
Duration: Varies.

ADDRESS INQUIRIES TO:
Carl H. Pforzheimer III, President
(See address above.)

THE ALBERT PICK, JR. FUND [268]
333 North Michigan Avenue
Suite 510
Chicago, IL 60601
(312) 236-1192
Fax: (312) 236-1209

E-MAIL ADDRESS:
iris@albertpickjrfund.org

WEB SITE ADDRESS:
www.albertpickjrfund.org

FOUNDED: 1947

AREAS OF INTEREST:
Civic and community, culture, education, health and human services.

TYPE:
Challenge/matching grants; Demonstration grants; Development grants; General operating grants; Project/program grants; Technical assistance.

YEAR PROGRAM STARTED: 1947

PURPOSE:
To offer a hand when help is needed.

LEGAL BASIS:
Private family foundation.

ELIGIBILITY:
Nonprofits with offices and budgeted programs operating within the city of Chicago.

GEOGRAPHIC RESTRICTIONS:
Chicago, Illinois.

FINANCIAL DATA:
Amount of support per award: Minimum $10,000.

NUMBER OF APPLICANTS MOST RECENT YEAR:
196.

NUMBER OF AWARDS: 53.

APPLICATION INFORMATION:
Eligible nonprofits are requested to complete an application form, available from the Fund. Only those proposals which completely meet the requirements outlined in the guidelines will be reviewed. Complete details are available on the Fund's web site.
Duration: Generally, one year.
Deadline: January 21 for the Spring quarter, April 1 for the Summer quarter, July 1 for Fall quarter and October 1 for Winter quarter.

PUBLICATIONS:
Guidelines; grant application form.

IRS IDENTIFICATION NUMBER: 36-6071402

OFFICERS AND BOARD OF DIRECTORS:
Robert B. Lifton, President
Shelly A. Davis, Vice President
Howard A. Sulkin, Treasurer
Gwendolyn M. Rice, Secretary
James W. Mabie

ADDRESS INQUIRIES TO:
Iris Krieg, Executive Director
(See address above.)

THE HAROLD WHITWORTH PIERCE CHARITABLE TRUST   [269]

c/o Nichols and Pratt
50 Congress Street
Boston, MA 02109
(617) 523-8368
Fax: (617) 523-8949

E-MAIL ADDRESS:
piercetrust@nichols-pratt.com

WEB SITE ADDRESS:
www.piercetrust.org

AREAS OF INTEREST:
Education, green and public spaces, capital projects and arts education.

TYPE:
Capital grants; Project/program grants.

PURPOSE:
To support projects that will bring long-range benefits to Boston's citizens.

ELIGIBILITY:
Eligible organizations must be IRS 501(c)(3) tax-exempt.

No grants are made for scholarships to individuals. In addition, no grants are made for fund-raising events, films, videos, travel, fund-raising training or advocacy.

GEOGRAPHIC RESTRICTIONS:
Boston, Massachusetts area.

FINANCIAL DATA:
Amount of support per award: $10,000 to $60,000.
Total amount of support: Average: $1,000,000.

NUMBER OF AWARDS: Varies.

REPRESENTATIVE AWARDS:
Education: $20,000 to Associated Day Care Services, Boston, MA, to train and mentor teachers of infants and toddlers in an intensive Literacy Curriculum specifically designed for infants and toddlers; Capital Projects: $50,000 to Ballet Theatre of Boston, Cambridge, MA, for a capital grant to help make possible the construction of a new home for the Ballet Theater within a church in Cambridge; Green and Public Spaces: $10,000 to Boston GreenSpace Alliance for a second installment of a two-year grant for operating support for the Alliance.

APPLICATION INFORMATION:
The application process consists of three steps:
(1) a telephone call to the Trust's grant administrator to determine eligibility;
(2) a concept letter describing the applicant organization and its mission, etc., and;
(3) after review of concept letters by the trustees, full proposals will be invited from a limited number of applicants. The Trust will then decide which proposals to fund.
Duration: Typically one year.
Deadline: Concept letter due (postmarked) March 1 and September 30; Invited proposals: mid-April and early November.

PUBLICATIONS:
Application guidelines.

ADDRESS INQUIRIES TO:
Elizabeth D. Nichols, Program Director
(See address above.)

IRWIN ANDREW PORTER FOUNDATION   [270]

P.O. Box 580057
Minneapolis, MN 55458-0057

E-MAIL ADDRESS:
iapfound@gmail.com

WEB SITE ADDRESS:
www.iapfoundation.org

FOUNDED: 1996

AREAS OF INTEREST:
Arts, education, environment and social programs.

TYPE:
Challenge/matching grants; Grants-in-aid; Project/program grants.

PURPOSE:
To fund innovative projects that foster connections between individuals, communities, the environment and the world at large.

ELIGIBILITY:
The Foundation provides funding for a variety of interest areas. The quality, innovation, thoughtfulness and effectiveness of a project are of more importance than the specific interest area. However, its areas of interest are the arts, education, environment and social programs.

International projects should be applicable to, and repeatable in, other regions. The Foundation gives funding to nonprofit organizations with U.S. IRS tax-exempt status only. International organizations must have a fiscal agent incorporated in the U.S. with an appropriate U.S. IRS tax-exempt designation.

The Foundation does not provide financial support for:
(1) general operating expenses;
(2) capital projects;
(3) endowments;
(4) scholarships;
(5) fund-raising events or activities, social events, goodwill advertising or marketing;
(6) lobbying, political, fraternal, athletic, social or veterans organizations;
(7) religious programs;
(8) travel for individuals or groups;
(9) individuals or;
(10) ordinary school funding.

GEOGRAPHIC RESTRICTIONS:
Illinois, Iowa, Michigan, Minnesota, North Dakota, South Dakota and Wisconsin.

FINANCIAL DATA:
Amount of support per award: Grants: $500 to $30,000 annually.
Total amount of support: Approximately $135,000 annually.

APPLICATION INFORMATION:
Two-phase application. Phase I is a short online application. Phase II is a full written proposal, due within 30 days of notification that the project was selected for further consideration.
Duration: Generally, one year.
Deadline: Phase I: March 31; Phase II: Within 30 days of notification.

ADDRESS INQUIRIES TO:
Amy L. Hubbard, Chairman
(See address above.)

PPG INDUSTRIES FOUNDATION   [271]

One PPG Place
Pittsburgh, PA 15272
(412) 434-2453 (voice mail)

E-MAIL ADDRESS:
foundation@ppg.com

WEB SITE ADDRESS:
www.ppgfoundation.com

FOUNDED: 1951

AREAS OF INTEREST:
Education, human services, culture and the arts, civic and community affairs.

NAME(S) OF PROGRAMS:
• **Grant Incentives for Volunteerism by PPG Employees and Retirees (GIVE)**
• **Matching Gifts Program**
• **National Merit Scholarships**
• **PPG CARE Fund**
• **Public Education Leadership Community Grants (PELC)**

TYPE:
Capital grants; General operating grants; Project/program grants; Scholarships. Grant Incentives for Volunteerism by PPG Employees and Retirees (GIVE) is a program to encourage PPG employee involvement in volunteerism. The GIVE Program recognizes personal involvement by active PPG employees and retirees who volunteer on their own time by providing grants to eligible institutions in the U.S.

Matching Gifts Program matches gifts of PPG employees and directors to qualified institutions.

National Merit Scholarships are awarded in three categories. The Employee-Child Scholarship Program is for sons and daughters of PPG Industries, Inc. employees. The Plant Community Scholarship Program offers a community scholarship program to major PPG facilities. The National Achievement Scholarship Program awards two scholarships per year to outstanding African-American students in this program.

Public Education Leadership Community Grants (PELC) provide financial resources to public schools where employees are involved.

YEAR PROGRAM STARTED: 1951

PURPOSE:
To enhance the quality of life in those communities within the U.S. where PPG Industries has a major presence; to develop human potential.

LEGAL BASIS:
Corporate, nonprofit foundation.

ELIGIBILITY:
Grants are made to tax-exempt organizations in the Foundation's areas of interest. Priority is given to applications from organizations dedicated to enhancing the welfare of communities in which PPG Industries is a resident. It gives consideration to those organizations whose activities either enhance individual opportunities or help to strengthen the nation's human services, educational, or economic systems on a regional or nationwide basis.

In general, the Foundation will not award grants to advertisement sponsorship for benefit purposes, endowments, individuals, organizations established to influence legislation or support political activities, organizations outside of the U.S. or its territories, projects which would directly benefit PPG Industries, Inc., religious groups solely for religious purposes, special events and telephone solicitations or United Way agencies for operating support.

GEOGRAPHIC RESTRICTIONS:
United States.

FINANCIAL DATA:
Amount of support per award: Varies.
Total amount of support: $4,647,000 in grants paid for the year 2013.
Matching fund requirements: Contributions by PPG employees and members of the board of directors of the company are matched on a 1:1 basis by the Foundation; $25 minimum, $10,000 maximum per year per donor.

APPLICATION INFORMATION:
Grant policies, guidelines and online application are available on the Foundation web site.
Duration: Varies.
Deadline: Requests for funding are accepted year-round.

STAFF:
Sue Sloan, Executive Director, PPG Industries Foundation

BOARD OF DIRECTORS:
Charles E. Bunch, Chairman and Chief Executive Officer
Frank Sklarsky, Executive Vice President and Chief Financial Officer
Glenn Bost, II, Senior Vice President and General Counsel
David Navikas, Senior Vice President, Strategic Planning and Corporate Development
J. Craig Jordan, Vice President, Human Resources

PRINCIPAL FINANCIAL GROUP FOUNDATION INC. [272]
711 High Street
Des Moines, IA 50392-0150
(515) 247-7227
Fax: (515) 246-5475

E-MAIL ADDRESS:
allen.andrew@principal.com

WEB SITE ADDRESS:
www.principal.com/about/giving

FOUNDED: 1987

AREAS OF INTEREST:
Health and human services, education, arts and culture, civic and community, and environment.

CONSULTING OR VOLUNTEER SERVICES:
The mission of the Principal Volunteer Network is to be the primary volunteer network for community service to educate and recruit employees, agents and retirees of the Principal Financial Group; thus enhancing the company's social responsibility goals and business objectives.

NAME(S) OF PROGRAMS:
● **The Charitable Giving Program**

TYPE:
Capital grants; General operating grants; Project/program grants.

YEAR PROGRAM STARTED: 1987

PURPOSE:
To support various educational, health and welfare, and civic and cultural organizations.

LEGAL BASIS:
Corporate foundation.

ELIGIBILITY:
Applicants must be nonprofit IRS 501(c)(3) organizations located in communities with significant employee presence.

Grants are generally not made to athletes or athletic organizations, conference or seminar attendance, goodwill advertising, endowments or memorials, festival participation, fraternal organizations, hospital or health care facility capital fund drives, individuals, K-12 schools, libraries, partisan political organizations, private foundations, sectarian, religious or denominational organizations, social organizations, tax-supported organizations, or United Way organizations seeking funds for United Way-funded programs.

GEOGRAPHIC RESTRICTIONS:
Wilmington, Delaware; Cedar Falls, Greater Des Moines, Mason City and Waterloo, Iowa; Grand Island, Nebraska; Spokane, Washington; Appleton, Wisconsin.

FINANCIAL DATA:
Amount of support per award: Varies.
Total amount of support: Varies.

NUMBER OF APPLICANTS MOST RECENT YEAR: 907.

APPLICATION INFORMATION:
Proposals should include:
(1) a grant request form;
(2) cover letter with amount requested, background and mission of organization, purpose of funding, desired outcome and how measured;
(3) evaluation of previous funding;
(4) budget;
(5) board list;
(6) IRS exemption letter of 501(c)(3) status;
(7) one audit 990 form and;
(8) annual report.

10 copies of proposal should be sent if request is more than $10,000.
Deadline: March 1 for health and human services grants, June 1 for education grants, September 1 for arts and culture grants, and December 1 for civic and community grants and environment grants.

PUBLICATIONS:
Guidelines.

ADDRESS INQUIRIES TO:
Andrew Allen
Director, Community Relations
(See address above.)

PUBLIC WELFARE FOUNDATION, INC. [273]
1200 U Street, N.W.
Washington, DC 20009-4443
(202) 965-1800
Fax: (202) 265-8851

E-MAIL ADDRESS:
info@publicwelfare.org

WEB SITE ADDRESS:
www.publicwelfare.org

FOUNDED: 1947

AREAS OF INTEREST:
Workers' rights, criminal justice and juvenile justice.

NAME(S) OF PROGRAMS:
● **Criminal Justice**
● **Juvenile Justice**
● **Workers' Rights**

TYPE:
General operating grants; Project/program grants.

YEAR PROGRAM STARTED: 1947

PURPOSE:
To support efforts to ensure fundamental rights and opportunities for people in need; to look for carefully defined points where the Foundation's funds can make a difference in bringing about systemic changes that can improve the lives of countless people.

LEGAL BASIS:
Private foundation.

ELIGIBILITY:
Applicants' requests must adhere to the Foundation's funding guidelines.

GEOGRAPHIC RESTRICTIONS:
United States.

FINANCIAL DATA:
Amount of support per award: Varies.
Total amount of support: $20,470,000 allocated for fiscal year 2014.

NUMBER OF APPLICANTS MOST RECENT YEAR: 339 for fiscal year 2013.

NUMBER OF AWARDS: 118 approved grants for fiscal year 2013.

APPLICATION INFORMATION:
Applicants should submit letters of inquiry using the online application system. This letter should contain facts and figures about the organization, describe its mission and explain the purpose of the request, including the Program under which a grant is being requested. Applicants will be invited by e-mail to submit full proposals. The Foundation cannot consider full proposals which have not been invited.
Duration: Usually one to two years. Renewal possible.

IRS IDENTIFICATION NUMBER: 54-0597601

ADDRESS INQUIRIES TO:
  Grants Management
  (See address above.)

THE QUAKER CHEMICAL FOUNDATION [274]

901 East Hector Street
Conshohocken, PA 19428-2380
(610) 832-4301
Fax: (610) 832-4496

E-MAIL ADDRESS:
  quakerfoundation@quakerchem.com

WEB SITE ADDRESS:
  www.quakerchem.com

FOUNDED: 1959

AREAS OF INTEREST:
  Civic and community; cultural, health and
  welfare; and education.

NAME(S) OF PROGRAMS:
  ● **Grant Program**
  ● **Matching Gift Program**
  ● **Scholarship Program**

TYPE:
  Matching gifts; Project/program grants;
  Scholarships. The Foundation matches
  employee gifts to qualified educational
  institutions, health and welfare organizations,
  civic and community, and arts or cultural
  institutions which are operated for the benefit
  of the general public.

YEAR PROGRAM STARTED: 1959

PURPOSE:
  To help community projects where the
  company has domestic operations.

LEGAL BASIS:
  Corporate foundation.

ELIGIBILITY:
  Applicants must be IRS 501(c)(3) tax-exempt
  organizations. As a general rule, the
  Foundation does not support national
  organizations, limiting its interest to those
  organizations that are active in the areas in
  which the Quaker Chemical Corporation has
  operations, generally located within a
  five-mile radius of company facilities and
  locations.

FINANCIAL DATA:
  Amount of support per award: $1,000 to
  $5,000; Average: $1,500.
  Matching fund requirements: Minimum $25
  and maximum $1,000 per employee, retiree,
  director or spouse thereof per fiscal year.

REPRESENTATIVE AWARDS:
  Conshohocken Fellowship House; Delaware
  Valley Science Fairs.

APPLICATION INFORMATION:
  Application must include the following
  information:
  (1) project description;
  (2) budget;

(3) list of board of directors and officers and;
(4) organization's tax-exempt ruling under
  Section 501(c)(3) of the Internal Revenue
  Code.
  Duration: One year.
  Deadline: April 30.

PUBLICATIONS:
  Grant application guidelines.

IRS IDENTIFICATION NUMBER: 23-6245803

TRUSTEES:
  Palitha Abeywardena
  Cindy Cemar
  Jennifer Hill
  Irene M. Kisleiko
  Christian Scholund
  Jane L. Williams

ADDRESS INQUIRIES TO:
  Quaker Chemical Foundation Secretary
  (See address above.)

THE NELL J. REDFIELD FOUNDATION [275]

P.O. Box 61
Reno, NV 89504
(775) 323-1373
Fax: (775) 323-4476

E-MAIL ADDRESS:
  redfieldfoundation@yahoo.com

FOUNDED: 1974

AREAS OF INTEREST:
  Aged, disadvantaged children, education,
  religion, health care and the homeless poor.

TYPE:
  Capital grants; Challenge/matching grants;
  Development grants; Matching gifts;
  Project/program grants. Grants for higher
  education. Medical and social welfare for
  disadvantaged children and seniors.

PURPOSE:
  To promote education, health care and care
  for the homeless poor.

LEGAL BASIS:
  Nonprofit foundation.

ELIGIBILITY:
  Grants are made to organizations that have
  tax-exempt status under Section 501(c)(3) of
  the Internal Revenue Code. Nonsectarian
  religious programs may apply. No grants are
  made to individuals or private foundations.

  Grants are restricted to organizations in
  northern Nevada.

GEOGRAPHIC RESTRICTIONS:
  Northern Nevada.

FINANCIAL DATA:
  Amount of support per award: Varies.
  Total amount of support: Varies.

NUMBER OF APPLICANTS MOST RECENT YEAR:
  125.

NUMBER OF AWARDS: 75.

APPLICATION INFORMATION:
  Initially, contact the fund with a two-page
  summary that includes the specific goals,
  objectives, proposed activities and results
  expected.
  Duration: One year. Renewal possible.
  Deadline: Quarterly during each calendar
  year.

ADDRESS INQUIRIES TO:
  Gerald C. Smith, Director
  (See address above.)

THE REEBOK FOUNDATION [276]

1895 J.W. Foster Boulevard
Canton, MA 02021
(781) 401-5000
Fax: (781) 401-4744

WEB SITE ADDRESS:
  www.reebok.com

FOUNDED: 1986

AREAS OF INTEREST:
  Programs for underserved youth in the
  greater Boston, MA area.

TYPE:
  General operating grants; Matching gifts.

YEAR PROGRAM STARTED: 1986

PURPOSE:
  To help children fulfill their potential.

LEGAL BASIS:
  Corporate foundation.

ELIGIBILITY:
  Grant applicants must be nonprofit
  organizations that provide equal access to
  funding and equal opportunity, and do not
  discriminate based on race, religion or sex.
  Grants are not made to individuals, political
  or fraternal organizations, or for advertising
  in program books or medical research.

GEOGRAPHIC RESTRICTIONS:
  Greater Boston, Massachusetts area.

FINANCIAL DATA:
  Amount of support per award: $500 to
  $10,000.
  Matching fund requirements: Employees of
  Reebok International Ltd, its subsidiaries and
  divisions. Organizations must be IRS
  501(c)(3). Employee contributions to
  qualified organizations are matched
  dollar-for-dollar, up to $1,500 maximum.

APPLICATION INFORMATION:
  An initial letter is requested to determine the
  interest and appropriateness of a full
  proposal.
  Deadline: Applications accepted throughout
  the year.

PUBLICATIONS:
  Guidelines.

IRS IDENTIFICATION NUMBER: 04-3073548

STAFF:
  Jessica Russo, Manager

BOARD OF TRUSTEES:
  Joe Keane, Chief Financial Officer and Chief
  Operating Officer

ADDRESS INQUIRIES TO:
  Jessica Russo, Manager
  (See address above.)

THE REGENSTEIN FOUNDATION [277]

225 West Wacker Drive
Suite 1500
Chicago, IL 60606
(312) 917-1833
Fax: (312) 917-1822

E-MAIL ADDRESS:
  regfound@aol.com

FOUNDED: 1950

TYPE:
  Capital grants; Endowments. Support for
  numerous fields including education,
  community services, medicine and health,

urban affairs, arts and music. In general, most grants are made to organizations located in and directly serving the residents of Illinois, basically in the metropolitan Chicago area.

YEAR PROGRAM STARTED: 1950

PURPOSE:
To help improve life and the community in and around Chicago.

LEGAL BASIS:
Private foundation.

ELIGIBILITY:
Any charitable organization other than private foundations for exempt purposes. No grants are made to individuals or for the benefit of designated individuals.

GEOGRAPHIC RESTRICTIONS:
Chicago, Illinois.

FINANCIAL DATA:
Only a small number of applicants will receive funds due to the relatively limited amount available and the number of organizations funded on trustee initiative.
Amount of support per award: Varies.
Total amount of support: Varies.

NUMBER OF APPLICANTS MOST RECENT YEAR:
45 for the year 2013.

NUMBER OF AWARDS: 35.

APPLICATION INFORMATION:
Contact the Foundation in writing for an application.
Duration: One year. Renewable.
Deadline: March 31 and September 30.

OFFICERS:
Susan Regenstein, Chairperson

EXECUTIVE DIRECTOR:
Patricia Wallies

ADDRESS INQUIRIES TO:
Susan Regenstein, Chairperson
(See address above.)

THE CHARLES H. REVSON FOUNDATION [278]
55 East 59th Street
23rd Floor
New York, NY 10022
(212) 935-3340
Fax: (212) 688-0633

E-MAIL ADDRESS:
info@revsonfoundation.org

WEB SITE ADDRESS:
www.revsonfoundation.org

FOUNDED: 1956

AREAS OF INTEREST:
Urban affairs, with emphasis on New York City, education, biomedical research policy and Jewish philanthropy and education.

TYPE:
Fellowships; Project/program grants; Research grants. The Foundation supports a number of ongoing fellowship programs in public policy, biomedical research and Jewish education.

YEAR PROGRAM STARTED: 1978

PURPOSE:
To make a commitment to spread knowledge and to improve human life.

LEGAL BASIS:
Private foundation.

ELIGIBILITY:
Grants are made to nonprofit, tax-exempt organizations. The Foundation does not make grants to individuals or for endowments, local health appeals, direct-service programs, building or construction funds, or routine budgetary support.

GEOGRAPHIC RESTRICTIONS:
New York, New York and Israel.

FINANCIAL DATA:
Amount of support per award: Varies.

APPLICATION INFORMATION:
The Foundation welcomes letters of inquiry from prospective grantees. Letters should be no longer than two pages and include:
(1) Revson program area of proposed project;
(2) brief description of project and of sponsoring organization and;
(3) amount requested.

In response to a letter of inquiry, the Foundation may invite the submission of a complete proposal.

Proposals can be sent to loi@revsonfoundation.org. No proposals accepted by fax.
Duration: Varies.

IRS IDENTIFICATION NUMBER: 13-6126105

STAFF:
Julie Sandorf, President
Azade Ardali, Administrative Officer
Nessa Rapoport, Senior Program Officer
Maria Marcantonio, Program Officer
Sylvia Abdullah, Grants Administrator
Karen Yu, Controller

BOARD OF DIRECTORS:
Reynold Levy, Chairman
Cheryl Cohen Effron, Secretary
Gerald Rosenfeld, Treasurer
Stacy Dick
Suzanne Gluck
Jeffrey Goldberg
Sharon Greenberger
Steven Hyman
Charles H. Revson, Jr.
Clifford Tabin

ADDRESS INQUIRIES TO:
See e-mail address above.

Z. SMITH REYNOLDS FOUNDATION, INC. [279]
102 West Third Street
Suite 1110
Winston-Salem, NC 27101-3940
(336) 725-7541 ext. 116
(800) 443-8319
Fax: (336) 725-6069

E-MAIL ADDRESS:
patw@zsr.org

WEB SITE ADDRESS:
www.zsr.org

FOUNDED: 1936

AREAS OF INTEREST:
Community economic development, environment, pre-collegiate education, social justice and equity, and strengthening democracy.

TYPE:
Challenge/matching grants; General operating grants; Project/program grants; Seed money grants. Sabbatical Program.

YEAR PROGRAM STARTED: 1936

PURPOSE:
To support charitable causes within the state of North Carolina.

LEGAL BASIS:
Private foundation.

ELIGIBILITY:
North Carolina public and nonprofit private institutions and organizations are eligible. No grants are made to individuals for any purpose.

GEOGRAPHIC RESTRICTIONS:
North Carolina.

FINANCIAL DATA:
Amount of support per award: $500 to $1,200,000.
Total amount of support: Approximately $19,982,000 for the year ended December 2013.

NUMBER OF APPLICANTS MOST RECENT YEAR:
Approximately 329 for the year 2013.

NUMBER OF AWARDS: Approximately 167 for the year 2013.

APPLICATION INFORMATION:
Application information can be downloaded from the web site.
Deadline: February 1 for the spring meeting and August 1 for the fall meeting.

PUBLICATIONS:
Annual report (online).

IRS IDENTIFICATION NUMBER: 58-6038145

OFFICERS:
David L. Neal, President
Nancy R. Bagley, Vice President
John O. McNairy, Treasurer
Terry Lockamy, Assistant Treasurer
Leslie J. Winner, Secretary
Patricia B. Williamson, Assistant Secretary

TRUSTEES:
Nancy R. Bagley
Piper Neal Beveridge
Anita Brown-Graham
Daniel G. Clodfelter
Ilana Dubester
John O. McNairy
Katharine B. Mountcastle, Life Trustee
Mary Mountcastle
David L. Neal
Stephen L. Neal
Jane S. Patterson
W. Noah Reynolds
Virgil Smith
Lloyd P. Tate, Jr.

ADDRESS INQUIRIES TO:
Leslie J. Winner, Secretary
(See address above.)

THE RHODE ISLAND FOUNDATION/RHODE ISLAND COMMUNITY FOUNDATION [280]
One Union Station
Providence, RI 02903-1746
(401) 274-4564
Fax: (401) 331-8085

WEB SITE ADDRESS:
www.rifoundation.org

FOUNDED: 1916

TYPE:
Challenge/matching grants; Conferences/seminars; Demonstration grants; Development grants; Fellowships; General operating grants; Project/program grants; Research grants; Scholarships; Technical

assistance; Travel grants; Loan forgiveness programs. Strategy grants; Small grants; Basic human needs grants; Regional grants.

YEAR PROGRAM STARTED: 1916

PURPOSE:
To improve the living conditions and well-being of the inhabitants of Rhode Island.

LEGAL BASIS:
Community foundation.

ELIGIBILITY:
Grants are not generally made directly to individuals. Programs must primarily benefit Rhode Island.

GEOGRAPHIC RESTRICTIONS:
Rhode Island.

FINANCIAL DATA:
Amount of support per award: Varies.

APPLICATION INFORMATION:
Guidelines available at the Foundation web site.

PUBLICATIONS:
Annual report; newsletter; guidelines; reports.

BOARD OF DIRECTORS:
Frederick K. Butler, Chairman
Lorne Adrain
Mary W.C. Daly
Jorge O. Elorza
Patricia J. Flanagan, M.D.
Ned Handy
Kathleen C. Hittner, M.D.
Marie Langlois
Mary F. Lovejoy
Hon. Ronald K. Machtley
Cynthia Reed
Anne Szostak
Hon. Ernst C. Torres

ADDRESS INQUIRIES TO:
Daniel Kertzner, Vice President of Grant Programs
(See address above.)

SID W. RICHARDSON FOUNDATION   [281]
309 Main Street
Fort Worth, TX 76102
(817) 336-0494
Fax: (817) 332-2176

E-MAIL ADDRESS:
cjohns@sidrichardson.org

WEB SITE ADDRESS:
www.sidrichardson.org

FOUNDED: 1947

AREAS OF INTEREST:
Education, health, human service, and the arts and humanities.

TYPE:
Capital grants; Challenge/matching grants; Development grants; General operating grants; Matching gifts; Professorships; Project/program grants; Research grants.

PURPOSE:
To support organizations that serve the people of Texas.

LEGAL BASIS:
Private foundation.

ELIGIBILITY:
All funds must be limited to the state of Texas for IRS 501(c)(3) tax-exempt institutions and organizations or 509(a) organizations (other than a private foundation under the latter code). An organization also

may qualify if it falls within the terms of Section 170(c)(1) and the contribution requested is to be used exclusively for public purposes. No grants are made to individuals.

GEOGRAPHIC RESTRICTIONS:
Texas.

FINANCIAL DATA:
Amount of support per award: $5,000 to $750,000.

NUMBER OF APPLICANTS MOST RECENT YEAR:
Approximately 500 to 600.

REPRESENTATIVE AWARDS:
Education: $200,000 to the University of Texas at Dallas for the UTeach Dallas Program; Health: $100,000 to Fort Worth Northside Community Health Center, Inc. for general support; Human Services: $135,000 to Safe Haven of Tarrant County for general support; Cultural: $50,000 to Performing Arts Fort Worth for the Children's Education Program.

APPLICATION INFORMATION:
Initial contact should be by letter briefly explaining project or program. If the project is within areas of current activity, an application will be provided.
Duration: Typically one year. Some multiyear grants.
Deadline: January 15.

PUBLICATIONS:
Annual report.

IRS IDENTIFICATION NUMBER: 75-6015828

BOARD OF DIRECTORS:
Edward P. Bass, Chairman
Lee M. Bass, Vice President
Sid R. Bass, Vice President

ADDRESS INQUIRIES TO:
Pete Geren, President
(See address above.)

ROCKEFELLER FAMILY FUND   [282]
475 Riverside Drive
Suite 900
New York, NY 10115-0066
(212) 812-4252
Fax: (212) 812-4299

E-MAIL ADDRESS:
ccaddle-steele@rffund.org

WEB SITE ADDRESS:
www.rffund.org

FOUNDED: 1967

NAME(S) OF PROGRAMS:
● **Economic Justice for Women**
● **Environment**
● **Institutional Accountability and Individual Liberty**

TYPE:
Challenge/matching grants; General operating grants. Economic Justice for Women program seeks to improve the quality of life for working women and their families by advocating for equitable employment opportunities and updated employment standards.

Initiatives under the Environment program are designed to enact aggressive policies at the state and national levels to reduce carbon emissions, highlight the risks of coal-burning power plants and mountaintop removal coal-mining, and sound climate science, while exposing those who distort it.

The Institutional Accountability and Individual Liberty program encourages the active participation of citizens in government, seeks to make government and private institutions more accountable and responsive, and supports efforts to ensure that individuals' rights and liberties under the Constitution are protected.

YEAR PROGRAM STARTED: 1967

PURPOSE:
To make grants to nonprofit organizations in the areas of economic justice for women, the environment, and institutional accountability and individual liberty.

LEGAL BASIS:
A not-for-profit charitable corporation existing under the New York state not-for-profit corporation law.

ELIGIBILITY:
Tax-exempt organizations engaged in educational and charitable activities of national significance are eligible for support.

The Fund does not ordinarily consider projects that pertain to a single community, except in the rare instance where a project is unique, strategically placed to advance a national issue, or is likely to serve as a national model. Grants are rarely made to organizations which traditionally enjoy popular support, such as universities, museums, hospitals or endowed institutions.

The Family Fund does not make grants for academic or scholarly research or social or human service programs. Grants are also not made to support individuals, scholarships, international programs, domestic programs dealing with international issues, profit-making businesses, construction or restoration projects, or to reduce an organization's debt. Instead, support is offered for advocacy efforts that are action-oriented and likely to yield tangible public policy results.

GEOGRAPHIC RESTRICTIONS:
United States.

FINANCIAL DATA:
Total net assets of $94,751,000 as of December 31, 2013.
Amount of support per award: $25,000 to $75,000.
Total amount of support: Approximately $2,500,000 annually.
Matching fund requirements: Fund will match employee contributions.

NUMBER OF AWARDS: 44 core grants funded for the year ended December 31, 2011.

REPRESENTATIVE AWARDS:
Citizen Participation and Government Accountability: $50,000 to the William J. Brennan Jr. Center for Justice, Inc., New York, NY, to support the Center's work to restore voting rights to citizens with criminal convictions; Economic Justice for Women: $50,000 to the National Partnership for Women & Families, Washington, DC, to support the Partnership's state and local paid sick days campaigns; Environment: $50,000 to CommunityWise Bellingham, Bellingham, WA, to support work on anti-coal issues; Institutional Responsiveness: $55,000 to MAPLight.org, Berkeley, CA, to continue publishing data on the connections between political contributions and votes.

APPLICATION INFORMATION:
Applications are submitted online.

Duration: Grants are normally given for no more than two years at a time and are normally not given for more than three or four consecutive years.

Deadline: Letters of inquiry are accepted throughout the year.

PUBLICATIONS:
Annual report.

OFFICERS:
Peter Gill Case, President
David Kaiser, Vice President
Rebecca Lambert, Vice President
Clare M. Pierson, Vice President
Wendy Gordon Rockefeller, Vice President
Leah D'Angelo, Treasurer
Lee Wasserman, Director and Secretary

BOARD OF TRUSTEES:
Peter Gill Case
Alexandra Chasin
Julia D'Amico
Eric Dayton
Adam Growald
David Kaiser
Rebecca Lambert
G. Todd Mydland
Clare M. Pierson
Nancy King Rockefeller
Wendy Gordon Rockefeller
Theo Spencer
Rachel Weber

ADDRESS INQUIRIES TO:
Carolyn Caddle-Steele, Grants Manager
(See address above.)

ROCKWELL FUND, INC.   [283]
770 South Post Oak Lane
Suite 525
Houston, TX 77056
(713) 629-9022
Fax: (713) 629-7702

E-MAIL ADDRESS:
grantsinfo@rockfund.org

WEB SITE ADDRESS:
www.rockfund.org

FOUNDED: 1931

AREAS OF INTEREST:
Education, health, housing and workforce development.

NAME(S) OF PROGRAMS:
● **Operating Funds**
● **Program/Project Support**

TYPE:
Challenge/matching grants; Development grants; General operating grants; Matching gifts; Project/program grants; Seed money grants; Technical assistance. Capacity building grants.

YEAR PROGRAM STARTED: 1949

PURPOSE:
To improve the quality of life in the greater Houston area; to pursue change through cooperative philanthropy.

LEGAL BASIS:
Nonprofit organization.

ELIGIBILITY:
Eligible organizations must have IRS 501(c)(3) not-for-profit status. Grants are not made to individuals.

GEOGRAPHIC RESTRICTIONS:
Greater Houston, Texas area.

FINANCIAL DATA:
Amount of support per award: Varies.

Total amount of support: Varies.

NUMBER OF APPLICANTS MOST RECENT YEAR: 55.

NUMBER OF AWARDS: 48.

APPLICATION INFORMATION:
Applying organizations must have IRS Form 990 and Internal Revenue Code 501(c)(3) documentation.

Duration: One year. Renewable by reapplication.

IRS IDENTIFICATION NUMBER: 74-6040258

STAFF:
R. Terry Bell, President and Chief Investment Officer
Margaret E. McConn, C.P.A., Vice President and Chief Financial Officer
Judy Ahlgrim, Grants Administrator
Quynh-Anh McMahan, Research and Planning Officer
Jana Mullins, Program Officer
Kerri Washburn, Accounting

ADDRESS INQUIRIES TO:
Judy Ahlgrim, Grants Administrator
(See address above.)

ROLEX SA   [284]
665 Fifth Avenue
New York, NY 10022-5385
(212) 758-7700
Fax: (212) 371-0371

WEB SITE ADDRESS:
www.rolexawards.com

FOUNDED: 1976

AREAS OF INTEREST:
Science and medicine, technology, exploration, environment and cultural heritage.

NAME(S) OF PROGRAMS:
● **Rolex Awards for Enterprise Program**

TYPE:
Awards/prizes; Project/program grants; Seed money grants. Awards are given biennially.

YEAR PROGRAM STARTED: 1976

PURPOSE:
To encourage groundbreaking personal enterprise and initiative; to improve the quality of life and expand the knowledge of the world.

ELIGIBILITY:
Awards given for original and innovative projects in the areas of science and medicine, technology and innovation, exploration and discovery, the environment and cultural heritage. Given to an individual based on originality, feasibility and potential impact and exceptional spirit of enterprise.

FINANCIAL DATA:
Amount of support per award: Varies.
Total amount of support: Varies.

NUMBER OF APPLICANTS MOST RECENT YEAR: 1,500 to 2,500.

NUMBER OF AWARDS: 5.

APPLICATION INFORMATION:
Complete application information is available on the web site.

Duration: One time per project.
Deadline: Varies.

PUBLICATIONS:
Applications; winners publication; journal.

ADDRESS INQUIRIES TO:
The Secretariat
(See address above.)

ST. CROIX VALLEY FOUNDATION
516 Second Street, Suite 214
Hudson, WI 54016
(715) 386-9490
Fax: (715) 386-1250

E-MAIL ADDRESS:
info@scvfoundation.org

WEB SITE ADDRESS:
www.scvfoundation.org

TYPE:
Project/program grants; Scholarships.

See entry 1365 for full listing.

SALISBURY COMMUNITY FOUNDATION   [285]
220 North Tryon
Charlotte, NC 28202
(704) 973-4559
Fax: (704) 973-4959

E-MAIL ADDRESS:
kcoppadge@fftc.org

WEB SITE ADDRESS:
www.salisbury-cf.org

FOUNDED: 1944

TYPE:
Project/program grants.

YEAR PROGRAM STARTED: 1944

PURPOSE:
To support charitable organizations in the Salisbury and Rowan County areas.

LEGAL BASIS:
Community foundation.

ELIGIBILITY:
Applicants must be 501(c)(3) organizations.

GEOGRAPHIC RESTRICTIONS:
Rowan County, North Carolina.

FINANCIAL DATA:
Amount of support per award: Varies.

APPLICATION INFORMATION:
Application information is available on the web site.

Duration: One year.
Deadline: September 2015.

PUBLICATIONS:
Annual report.

IRS IDENTIFICATION NUMBER: 56-0772117

BOARD OF TRUSTEES:
J. Steven Fisher, Chairperson
Edward Norvell, Vice Chairperson
Gregory M. Alcorn
Dr. Albert J.D. Aymer
Gwin Barr
Dr. Kathleen S. Boyd
Sarah Busby
Sara D. Cook
Diane L. Fisher
Dr. Michael Goodman
Carol M. Herndon
Richard L. Huffman
Dr. Catrelia Steele Hunter
Dwight F. Messinger
C. Cliff Ritchie
Charles D. Taylor, Jr.
Leo Wallace, III
Paul B. Woodson, Jr.

ADDRESS INQUIRIES TO:
  Karen Coppadge, Grants Specialist
  (See address above.)

THE FAN FOX AND LESLIE R. SAMUELS FOUNDATION, INC. [286]

350 Fifth Avenue
Suite 4301
New York, NY 10118
(212) 239-3030
Fax: (212) 239-3039

E-MAIL ADDRESS:
  info@samuels.org

WEB SITE ADDRESS:
  www.samuels.org

FOUNDED: 1959

AREAS OF INTEREST:
  The arts, health care, and quality of life for
  the elderly.

NAME(S) OF PROGRAMS:
  • **Performing Arts**

TYPE:
  Development grants; Project/program grants.
  General operating grants for performing
  artists only.

  The majority of the Foundation's funding in
  the arts is for the performing arts. In the area
  of health care, the Foundation will consider
  funding direct health care and social service
  programs to improve quality of life for New
  York City elderly.

  The Foundation realizes that it cannot
  support an organization indefinitely and
  expects the programs it funds to become
  self-supporting within a few years.

YEAR PROGRAM STARTED: 1959

PURPOSE:
  To provide funding in the arts, mainly for the
  performing arts; to improve the health care
  and quality of life of the elderly in New
  York, NY.

LEGAL BASIS:
  Private foundation.

ELIGIBILITY:
  Grants are made to organizations that are
  tax-exempt under Section 501(c)(3) of the
  Internal Revenue Code. The Foundation does
  not give grants to individuals or for
  scholarships. General operating support is for
  performing arts only.

GEOGRAPHIC RESTRICTIONS:
  New York City.

FINANCIAL DATA:
  Amount of support per award: $2,000 to
  $300,000.
  Total amount of support: Varies.

APPLICATION INFORMATION:
  A letter should briefly summarize the
  proposal and state the amount of the grant
  being requested. A copy of the organization's
  tax exemption letter issued by the IRS, most
  recent audited financial report, organization
  brochure (if available), Board of Directors
  list, project budget and current contributors
  list should be included.
  Duration: Health Care: One to two years;
  Performing Arts: One year.
  Deadline: December 1, March 1, June 1 and
  September 1.

IRS IDENTIFICATION NUMBER: 13-3124818

STAFF:
  Alexandra Francis, Program Associate

OFFICERS AND DIRECTORS:
  Joseph Mitchell, Chairman
  Robert Marx, President
  Julio Urbina, Vice President

ADDRESS INQUIRIES TO:
  Alexandra Francis, Program Associate
  (See address above.)

THE SAN FRANCISCO FOUNDATION [287]

225 Bush Street
Suite 500
San Francisco, CA 94104
(415) 733-8500
Fax: (415) 477-2783

E-MAIL ADDRESS:
  info@sff.org

WEB SITE ADDRESS:
  www.sff.org

FOUNDED: 1948

AREAS OF INTEREST:
  Community health, education, arts and
  culture, community development, and the
  environment.

NAME(S) OF PROGRAMS:
  • **Bay Area Grants Program**

TYPE:
  Project/program grants. The Foundation has a
  variety of special projects, mini-grant
  programs and initiatives. These grantmaking
  efforts are narrowly tailored to promote
  change around a particular issue or
  geographic area.

PURPOSE:
  To promote change in the areas of
  community health, education, arts and
  culture, community development, and the
  environment.

LEGAL BASIS:
  Community foundation.

ELIGIBILITY:
  Organizations must be 501(c)(3).

GEOGRAPHIC RESTRICTIONS:
  Alameda, Contra Costa, Marin, San
  Francisco and San Mateo counties,
  California.

FINANCIAL DATA:
  Amount of support per award: Varies.

APPLICATION INFORMATION:
  Requests for Proposals are released and
  publicized periodically through the
  Foundation's web site and through targeted
  communications. Only online applications
  will be accepted.
  Duration: Typically one year.

ADDRESS INQUIRIES TO:
  Bay Area Grants Program
  (See address above.)

SARKEYS FOUNDATION [288]

530 East Main Street
Norman, OK 73071
(405) 364-3703
Fax: (405) 364-8191

E-MAIL ADDRESS:
  sarkeys@sarkeys.org

WEB SITE ADDRESS:
  www.sarkeys.org

FOUNDED: 1962

AREAS OF INTEREST:
  Education, health care and medical research,
  cultural and humanitarian programs of
  regional interest.

TYPE:
  Capital grants; Challenge/matching grants;
  Development grants; Endowments; Matching
  gifts; Professorships; Project/program grants;
  Research grants; Technical assistance;
  Training grants.

YEAR PROGRAM STARTED: 1962

PURPOSE:
  To improve the quality of life in Oklahoma.

LEGAL BASIS:
  Private charitable foundation.

ELIGIBILITY:
  Applicants must be 501(c)(3) organizations
  which are not private foundations under
  509(a) of the Internal Revenue Code.
  Organization must be headquartered and
  operating within the state of Oklahoma.

GEOGRAPHIC RESTRICTIONS:
  Oklahoma.

FINANCIAL DATA:
  Amount of support per award: Varies.
  Total amount of support: $3,169,704 for the
  fiscal year 2012-13.

NUMBER OF APPLICANTS MOST RECENT YEAR:
  129.

NUMBER OF AWARDS: 62.

APPLICATION INFORMATION:
  The application form should be typed and all
  space limitations observed. The attachments
  should also be typed, unbound and printed on
  one side only. The Foundation does not
  accept faxed or e-mail proposals. A new
  application form should be requested each
  year.
  Duration: Varies.
  Deadline: Letters of inquiry: December 1 and
  June 1.

PUBLICATIONS:
  Application guidelines; annual report.

BOARD MEMBERS:
  Teresa B. Adwan
  Elizabeth Base
  Dr. John Bell
  Clay Christensen
  Dan Little
  Jim Loftis
  Joseph W. Morris
  Terry W. West

ADDRESS INQUIRIES TO:
  Kim Henry, Executive Director
  Susan Frantz, Senior Program Officer
  Linda English Weeks, Senior Program Officer

*SPECIAL STIPULATIONS:
  The recipient must sign an agreement
  outlining the terms of the award and provide
  reports as requested. Outside independent
  audit required for organizations whose
  operating budget exceeds $500,000 per year.

DR. SCHOLL FOUNDATION [289]

1033 Skokie Boulevard
Suite 230
Northbrook, IL 60062-4109
(847) 559-7430

WEB SITE ADDRESS:
  www.drschollfoundation.com

FOUNDED: 1947

AREAS OF INTEREST:
Private education at all levels, including elementary and secondary schools, colleges and universities, and medical and nursing institutions; general charitable programs, including grants to hospitals and programs for children, developmentally disabled and senior citizens, civic, cultural, social services, health care, economic and religious activities.

TYPE:
Project/program grants.

YEAR PROGRAM STARTED: 1947

PURPOSE:
To help support worthwhile projects and activities.

LEGAL BASIS:
Private foundation.

ELIGIBILITY:
Organization must submit copy of tax-exemption letter from the IRS identifying that the applicant is a tax-exempt organization under Internal Revenue Code 501(c)(3), but is not a private foundation under 509(a) of the Internal Revenue Code. All grant requests should be in the form of a special project or program.

GEOGRAPHIC RESTRICTIONS:
United States.

FINANCIAL DATA:
Amount of support per award: Average $1,000 to $25,000.
Total amount of support: Varies.

NUMBER OF APPLICANTS MOST RECENT YEAR:
1,100.

NUMBER OF AWARDS: 330.

APPLICATION INFORMATION:
A formal application form is required together with the tax-exemption letter, budget, financial statements and details about the organization, its officers, directors and specialized personnel.
Duration: Usually one year.
Deadline: March 1. Notification in November and distribution in December.

OFFICER:
Pamela Scholl, President

ADDRESS INQUIRIES TO:
Pamela Scholl, President
(See address above.)

CHARLES AND HELEN SCHWAB FOUNDATION [290]
201 Mission Street, Suite 1950
San Francisco, CA 94105
(415) 795-4920
Fax: (415) 795-4921

E-MAIL ADDRESS:
info@schwabfoundation.org

WEB SITE ADDRESS:
www.schwabfoundation.org
www.chsf.org

FOUNDED: 1987

AREAS OF INTEREST:
K-12 education reform, human services, and trustee grants.

NAME(S) OF PROGRAMS:
• **Foundation Initiative Grants**

TYPE:
General operating grants; Project/program grants; Technical assistance. Capacity building and human services programs.

YEAR PROGRAM STARTED: 2001

PURPOSE:
To improve education and student learning for children in the San Francisco Bay area, the state of California, and the nation more broadly.

LEGAL BASIS:
Private foundation.

GEOGRAPHIC RESTRICTIONS:
San Francisco Bay area, California; national.

FINANCIAL DATA:
Amount of support per award: Varies.
Total amount of support: $9,400,000 in grants for the year ended December 31, 2013.

NUMBER OF AWARDS: 120.

APPLICATION INFORMATION:
The Foundation does not accept unsolicited grant applications, grant proposals or letters of inquiry.
Duration: Varies.

PUBLICATIONS:
Foundation brochure; program reports.

IRS IDENTIFICATION NUMBER: 94-3188972

STAFF:
Kristi Kimball, Executive Director
Erin Gilbert, Administrative Director and Program Officer

BOARD OF DIRECTORS AND OFFICERS:
Charles R. Schwab, Chairman
Helen O. Schwab, President
Nancy Bechtle, Secretary
Katie Schwab Paige, Director

ADDRESS INQUIRIES TO:
Human Services Program
(See address above.)

THE ELLEN BROWNING SCRIPPS FOUNDATION [291]
6121 Terryhill Drive
La Jolla, CA 92037
(858) 212-3311
Fax: (858) 459-4809

E-MAIL ADDRESS:
dougdawson46@yahoo.com

FOUNDED: 1935

AREAS OF INTEREST:
Health care, medical research, education, conservation, recreation, family, youth and child welfare agencies, wildlife and animals, libraries and literacy.

TYPE:
Project/program grants; Research grants; Scholarships; Technical assistance.

YEAR PROGRAM STARTED: 1935

PURPOSE:
To provide funding for a number of social causes including medical research, health care, the arts, conservation and programs to help children.

LEGAL BASIS:
Private foundation.

ELIGIBILITY:
Applicant must be a tax-exempt, 501(c)(3) organization within San Diego County, CA.

GEOGRAPHIC RESTRICTIONS:
San Diego County, California.

FINANCIAL DATA:
Amount of support per award: $5,000 to $125,000.

Total amount of support: $1,125,000.

NUMBER OF AWARDS: 54.

APPLICATION INFORMATION:
Information is available from the Foundation.
Deadline: May 1.

ADDRESS INQUIRIES TO:
E. Douglas Dawson, Executive Director
(See address above.)

THE SEATTLE FOUNDATION [292]
1200 Fifth Avenue, Suite 1300
Seattle, WA 98101-3151
(206) 515-2131
Fax: (206) 622-7673

E-MAIL ADDRESS:
c.erickson@seattlefoundation.org

WEB SITE ADDRESS:
www.seattlefoundation.org

FOUNDED: 1946

AREAS OF INTEREST:
Arts and culture, education, basic needs, environment, economy, health and wellness, neighborhoods and communities.

NAME(S) OF PROGRAMS:
• **Community Grantmaking Program**

TYPE:
Capital grants; Development grants; General operating grants; Technical assistance. Equipment purchases; Facility renovation grants.

YEAR PROGRAM STARTED: 1946

PURPOSE:
To improve the quality of life in the Puget Sound area.

LEGAL BASIS:
Community foundation.

ELIGIBILITY:
Organizations must be IRS 501(c)(3) tax-exempt. No grants to individuals.

GEOGRAPHIC RESTRICTIONS:
King County, Washington.

FINANCIAL DATA:
Amount of support per award: Average $25,000.

APPLICATION INFORMATION:
Application form and guidelines are available on the web site.
Duration: One-time grants.

PUBLICATIONS:
Annual report; *Healthy Communities Report.*

STAFF:
Ceil Erickson, Program Director

ADDRESS INQUIRIES TO:
Ceil Erickson, Program Director
(See address above.)

THE SEAVER INSTITUTE [293]
12400 Wilshire Boulevard
Suite 1240
Los Angeles, CA 90025
(310) 979-0298
Fax: (310) 979-0297

E-MAIL ADDRESS:
vsd@theseaverinstitute.org

FOUNDED: 1955

AREAS OF INTEREST:
Arts and the sciences.

TYPE:
Project/program grants; Research grants; Seed money grants.

YEAR PROGRAM STARTED: 1955

PURPOSE:
To provide seed money to highly regarded organizations for particular projects which offer the potential for significant advancement in their fields.

LEGAL BASIS:
Tax-exempt private foundation.

ELIGIBILITY:
Applicant must be a legally tax-exempt organization. The Institute does not support endowments, scholarships, construction, ongoing projects or deficit grants.

GEOGRAPHIC RESTRICTIONS:
United States.

FINANCIAL DATA:
Amount of support per award: $75,000 to $400,000.

NUMBER OF APPLICANTS MOST RECENT YEAR: 30.

NUMBER OF AWARDS: 20.

REPRESENTATIVE AWARDS:
University of Hawaii for foundation reefs; National Geographic for Timur's Garrison at Lake Issyk Kul; Massachusetts Institute of Technology for music21: a toolkit for computer-aided musicology; Sustainable Conservation for ecosystem services.

APPLICATION INFORMATION:
A written request is required. No formal guidelines.
Duration: One year. Renewal is possible.
Deadline: Early April and early October.

PUBLICATIONS:
Official guidelines letter; annual report.

BOARD OF TRUSTEES:
Nancy Bekavac
Victoria Seaver Dean
Robert Flick
Margaret Keene
Marie Knowles
Thomas Pfister
Carlton Seaver
Christopher Seaver
Martha Seaver
Patrick Seaver
Roxanne Wilson

ADDRESS INQUIRIES TO:
Victoria Seaver Dean, President
(See address above.)

SIMMONS FAMILY FOUNDATION   [294]
722 West Shepard Lane
Suite 103
Farmington, UT 84025
(801) 550-5026
Fax: (801) 323-9314

E-MAIL ADDRESS:
elizabeth@simmonsfoundation.org

WEB SITE ADDRESS:
www.simmonsfoundation.org

FOUNDED: 1986

AREAS OF INTEREST:
Religion, community enhancement, education, art and medicine.

TYPE:
Challenge/matching grants; Development grants; General operating grants; Matching gifts; Project/program grants; Research grants; Scholarships; Seed money grants.

PURPOSE:
To foster virtues of good citizenship through religious, medical, community, art and educational purposes.

LEGAL BASIS:
Private family foundation.

ELIGIBILITY:
Grants to nonprofit organizations that are tax-exempt under Section 501(c)(3) or Section 170(c) of the Internal Revenue Code. No grants to individuals.

GEOGRAPHIC RESTRICTIONS:
Utah.

FINANCIAL DATA:
Amount of support per award: Varies.

APPLICATION INFORMATION:
E-mail a one-page letter of intent summarizing the organization and project to the address posted. Organizations will then be invited to submit a formal application. Additional information is available on the Foundation web site.
Deadline: August 15.

PUBLICATIONS:
Application guidelines.

IRS IDENTIFICATION NUMBER: 13-3420599

ADDRESS INQUIRIES TO:
Elizabeth W. Gerner
Executive Director
(See address above.)

J. MARION SIMS FOUNDATION   [295]
800 North White Street
Lancaster, SC 29720
(803) 286-8772
Fax: (803) 286-8774

E-MAIL ADDRESS:
jmorton@jmsims.org

WEB SITE ADDRESS:
www.jmsims.org

FOUNDED: 1995

AREAS OF INTEREST:
Education, community health and wellness, and adult literacy.

NAME(S) OF PROGRAMS:
● **Adult Literacy Transition Grants**
● **Responsive Grants**
● **Teachers' Pet Grants**

TYPE:
Challenge/matching grants; General operating grants; Project/program grants; Seed money grants; Technical assistance.

YEAR PROGRAM STARTED: 1995

PURPOSE:
To provide community support.

LEGAL BASIS:
Private foundation.

ELIGIBILITY:
Organizations and agencies classified as 501(c)(3) by the IRS can apply. Individuals are ineligible.

GEOGRAPHIC RESTRICTIONS:
Fort Lawn, Great Falls and Lancaster County, South Carolina.

FINANCIAL DATA:
Amount of support per award: $83,485.
Total amount of support: $2,470,333 for fiscal year ended September 30, 2012.

NUMBER OF APPLICANTS MOST RECENT YEAR: 30 for fiscal year ended September 30, 2012.

NUMBER OF AWARDS: 20 for fiscal year ended September 30, 2012.

APPLICATION INFORMATION:
Contact the Foundation for application guidelines.
Duration: Typically one year. Grants are renewable.
Deadline: April 15 and October 15.

PUBLICATIONS:
Annual report.

IRS IDENTIFICATION NUMBER: 57-0355295

STAFF:
James T. Morton, President
Holly C. Furr, Program Officer
Mary D. Henderson, Program Officer

ADDRESS INQUIRIES TO:
James T. Morton, President
(See address above.)

THE SIRAGUSA FOUNDATION   [296]
One East Wacker Drive
Suite 2910
Chicago, IL 60601
(312) 755-0064
Fax: (312) 755-0069

E-MAIL ADDRESS:
info@siragusa.org

WEB SITE ADDRESS:
www.siragusa.org

FOUNDED: 1950

AREAS OF INTEREST:
Arts and culture, education, environment, health and human services.

TYPE:
General operating grants; Project/program grants; Scholarships. Project grants or unrestricted support.

YEAR PROGRAM STARTED: 1950

PURPOSE:
To help people help themselves with the ultimate goal of improving their quality of life.

LEGAL BASIS:
Tax-exempt private foundation, incorporated in Illinois.

ELIGIBILITY:
Tax-exempt organizations are eligible. No grants are made to individuals.

GEOGRAPHIC RESTRICTIONS:
Greater Chicago, Illinois area.

FINANCIAL DATA:
Amount of support per award: Varies.

NUMBER OF AWARDS: 137 grants for the year 2013.

APPLICATION INFORMATION:
Unsolicited letters of inquiry and proposals are not currently accepted.
Duration: Varies.

PUBLICATIONS:
Annual report; guidelines.

STAFF:
Irene S. Phelps, President and Chief Executive Officer

ADDRESS INQUIRIES TO:
Irene S. Phelps
President and Chief Executive Officer
(See address above.)

THE SKILLMAN FOUNDATION   [297]

100 Talon Centre Drive
Suite 100
Detroit, MI 48207
(313) 393-1185
Fax: (313) 393-1187

E-MAIL ADDRESS:
info@skillman.org

WEB SITE ADDRESS:
www.skillman.org

FOUNDED: 1960

AREAS OF INTEREST:
Citywide education reform, education intermediaries, high-quality early education, high-quality schools, active and informed parents, college access, high-quality youth development, neighborhood hubs, youth employment, college and career exposure, youth violence prevention, services to meet the basic health and economic security needs of families with children in each neighborhood, equity and opportunity for boys and young men of color.

NAME(S) OF PROGRAMS:
- **Good Neighborhood**
- **Good Opportunities**
- **Good Schools**

TYPE:
Matching gifts; Project/program grants. Good Neighborhood Program strives to guide young people to be safe, healthy, well-educated and prepared for adulthood when they are embedded in a strong system of supports and opportunities, when they attend high-quality schools, when their neighborhoods have the capacities and resources to support youth and families, and when broader systems and policies create conditions under which youth can thrive. The program is targeted in six Detroit neighborhoods - Brightmoor, Chadsey/Condon, Cody/Rouge, Northend, Osborn, Southwest Detroit.

Good Opportunities Program is designed to support the Foundation's primary work and to invest in special opportunities that can accomplish significant results for children.

Good Schools Program aims to have children attend high-quality schools, to graduate from high school and to attend college so they can lead self-sufficient and prosperous lives. To accomplish this goal the Foundation focuses on four areas: creating a citywide schools infrastructure, ensuring high-quality early care and education opportunities, improving schools in target neighborhoods, and generating parent and public will for high-quality education.

YEAR PROGRAM STARTED: 1960

PURPOSE:
To improve the lives of children in metropolitan Detroit by improving their homes, schools and neighborhoods.

LEGAL BASIS:
Private foundation.

ELIGIBILITY:
The Foundation considers proposals only from organizations which have been ruled to be tax-exempt under Section 501(c)(3) of the Internal Revenue Code and which are not private foundations as defined in Section 509(a) of the Code. Applications from government and public-sector entities will be considered, both for projects within the program areas and for planning, training, technical assistance and evaluation to improve the way government entities deliver services.

GEOGRAPHIC RESTRICTIONS:
Detroit, Michigan.

FINANCIAL DATA:
Amount of support per award: $20,000 to $200,000.

Total amount of support: $17,000,000 for 2013.

REPRESENTATIVE AWARDS:
$85,000 to Arab Community Center for Economic and Social Services to support a project that mobilizes Arab-American and non-Arab organizers to engage residents and plan projects that create positive change in Chadsey Condon and Cody Rouge neighborhoods; $300,000 to Black Family Development, Inc., to support for community engagement in Osborn and Cody Rouge and to promote block club development and leadership training (the MAN Network collaboration will continue as a joint venture for community policing); $85,000 to Detroit Hispanic Development Corporation to support an afterschool program that promotes life skills and academic achievement through structured activities in the graphic arts for southwest Detroit youth, ages 11 to 18; $100,000 to First Children's Finance to continue the efforts to stabilize, improve and expand high-quality childcare businesses serving low- and moderate-income families in Detroit with a specific focus on the six Skillman neighborhoods; $90,000 to Michigan College Access Network to support the expansion of the National College Advising Corps in the Good Neighborhood Schools, a nationally recognized program that returns recent college graduates to their home communities as college advisors at neighborhood high schools.

APPLICATION INFORMATION:
Send a grant inquiry, and upon invitation, a full application.

Duration: Generally one year.

Deadline: New grant inquiries should be submitted approximately two months in advance of Trustee meetings in March, June, September and December.

PUBLICATIONS:
Annual report; application guidelines.

IRS IDENTIFICATION NUMBER: 38-1675780

ADDRESS INQUIRIES TO:
Suzanne Moran, Grants Manager
(See address above.)

ALFRED P. SLOAN FOUNDATION   [298]

630 Fifth Avenue, Suite 2550
New York, NY 10111-0242
(212) 649-1649
Fax: (212) 757-5117

E-MAIL ADDRESS:
lin@sloan.org

WEB SITE ADDRESS:
www.sloan.org

FOUNDED: 1934

AREAS OF INTEREST:
Research and related programs in science and technology, education in science, technology, management, economic growth, industrial competitiveness and selected national issues.

TYPE:
Fellowships; Project/program grants; Research grants. Grants for imaginative and constructive projects in the Foundation's areas of interest.

YEAR PROGRAM STARTED: 1934

PURPOSE:
To support imaginative and constructive approaches to problems of domestic needs and uses.

LEGAL BASIS:
Private foundation.

ELIGIBILITY:
Recognized tax-exempt educational and research institutions with appropriate interests are eligible to apply. The Foundation's activities do not extend to primary or secondary education, religion, the creative or performing arts, medical research, health care or to the humanities. Grants are not made for endowments, buildings or equipment and are very rarely made for general support or for activities outside the U.S.

GEOGRAPHIC RESTRICTIONS:
United States.

FINANCIAL DATA:
Amount of support per award: Varies.

Total amount of support: $78,000,000 in grants annually.

APPLICATION INFORMATION:
A brief letter of inquiry, rather than a fully developed proposal, is an advisable first step for an applicant, conserving his or her time

and allowing the Foundation to make a preliminary response as to the possibility of support.

Duration: One to three years. Extensions or renewals are possible.

PUBLICATIONS:
Annual report.

A.O. SMITH FOUNDATION   [299]
11270 West Park Place
Milwaukee, WI 53224-3690
(414) 359-4107
Fax: (414) 359-4180

WEB SITE ADDRESS:
www.aosmith.com

FOUNDED: 1955

AREAS OF INTEREST:
Education, civic and cultural affairs, human services, health and hospital, and United Way.

TYPE:
Project/program grants. Employee Education Matching Gift to secondary, four-year colleges and universities, junior colleges, community colleges, graduate and professional schools, technical and specialized schools.

YEAR PROGRAM STARTED: 1955

PURPOSE:
To strengthen higher education throughout the country; to promote the civic, cultural and social welfare of communities; to advance medical research and improve local health services where A.O. Smith plants are located.

LEGAL BASIS:
Corporate foundation.

ELIGIBILITY:
Organization must be located where A.O. Smith has operating facilities. The Foundation does not make contributions to politically active organizations or any other organization whose chief purpose is to influence legislation.

FINANCIAL DATA:
Amount of support per award: $500 minimum.
Total amount of support: $1,300,000.

NUMBER OF AWARDS: Over 200 annually.

APPLICATION INFORMATION:
No specific application form is required. Inquiries should be made on your organization's letterhead and include the following information:
(1) the exact name and location of the organization;
(2) a description of the organization, including its objectives and purpose;
(3) verification of IRS 501(c)(3) tax-exempt status;
(4) the geographic area served by the organization;
(5) an explanation of the activity for which support is being requested;
(6) the amount of support being requested;
(7) a description of the benefits to be achieved and who will receive them;
(8) budget information about the organization, including other sources of income and;
(9) plans for reporting results.
Duration: Varies.
Deadline: October 31.

PUBLICATIONS:
Annual report.

ADDRESS INQUIRIES TO:
Roger S. Smith
Director of Community Affairs
(See address above.)

THE ETHEL SERGEANT CLARK SMITH MEMORIAL FUND   [300]
Wells Fargo Bank, N.A.
123 South Broad Street
Philadelphia, PA 19109
(215) 670-4225
Fax: (215) 670-4190

E-MAIL ADDRESS:
paralee.knight@wellsfargo.com

WEB SITE ADDRESS:
www.wellsfargo.com/privatefoundationgrants/smith

FOUNDED: 1977

AREAS OF INTEREST:
Arts and culture, hospitals, education, libraries, social services, women's programs and people with disabilities in Delaware County, PA.

TYPE:
Capital grants; Challenge/matching grants; Development grants; Project/program grants. Grants and challenge grants to community interest organizations in southeastern Pennsylvania. Grants to hospitals, colleges and schools for program and capital projects. Grants for social services, arts/cultural events and centers.

YEAR PROGRAM STARTED: 1977

PURPOSE:
To promote the public welfare in Delaware County, PA.

LEGAL BASIS:
Private foundation.

ELIGIBILITY:
Candidates must be tax-exempt organizations not classified as private foundations or private operating foundations within the terms of the Tax Reform Act of 1969. Primary emphasis is on those serving community needs in Delaware County, the former home of Ethel Sergeant Clark Smith. Grants will be made for capital projects, operating expenses and special programs that are meaningful to the success of the individual endeavors of the organizations. As a general rule, requests for funds on a long-term basis or for deficit financing will not be considered.

GEOGRAPHIC RESTRICTIONS:
Southeastern Pennsylvania.

FINANCIAL DATA:
Amount of support per award: $5,000 to $25,000.
Total amount of support: Approximately $540,000 annually.
Matching fund requirements: Varies.

NUMBER OF APPLICANTS MOST RECENT YEAR:
Approximately 200.

NUMBER OF AWARDS: Approximately 60 annually.

APPLICATION INFORMATION:
Application process is online only.
Duration: Three consecutive years maximum.
Deadline: March 1 and September 1.

PUBLICATIONS:
Biennial report.

IRS IDENTIFICATION NUMBER: 23-6648857

ADVISORY COMMITTEE:
Diane R. Bricker
Jack Holefelder
Dr. Joseph E. Pappano, Jr.
Sen. Dominic Pileggi
Alice Strine, Esq.

ADDRESS INQUIRIES TO:
Paralee Knight, Grant Administrator
(See address above.)

THE W.W. SMITH CHARITABLE TRUST   [301]
200 Four Falls Corporate Center
Suite 300
West Conshohocken, PA 19428
(610) 397-1844
Fax: (610) 397-1680

E-MAIL ADDRESS:
mmontgomery@wwsmithcharitabletrust.org

WEB SITE ADDRESS:
www.wwsmithcharitabletrust.org

FOUNDED: 1976

AREAS OF INTEREST:
Basic medical research protocols dealing with cancer, AIDS and heart disease, financial aid programs for qualified needy undergraduate students at accredited four-year universities and colleges, and programs providing shelter, food and clothing for children and needy families with children and the elderly.

NAME(S) OF PROGRAMS:
- **College Scholarships**
- **Food, Clothing and Shelter**
- **Maritime Education**
- **Medical Research**

TYPE:
Project/program grants; Research grants; Scholarships. By invitation only, these grants are offered to provide financial aid programs for qualified needy undergraduate students at accredited four-year universities and colleges and also provide shelter, food and clothing for children and needy families with children and the elderly.

YEAR PROGRAM STARTED: 1978

PURPOSE:
To enhance medical excellence; to enable children, families and the elderly to improve their lives; to assure students of a college education.

LEGAL BASIS:
Private foundation.

ELIGIBILITY:
Grants are limited to nonprofit organizations within the Delaware Valley area: Bucks, Chester, Delaware, Montgomery and Philadelphia (PA), as well as the city of Camden (NJ). Grants are made only to tax-exempt, 501(c)(3) organizations, not classified as private foundations or private operating foundations within the terms of the Tax Reform Act of 1969.

Grants will be made for programs or organizations with proven or prudently predictable records of performance; never directly to individuals. Renovation projects, special programs that deal with food, clothing and shelter for children and the elderly may be funded, but requests for general operating expenses, deficit financing and capital campaigns are not considered.

As a rule, under the Basic Needs Grants, the further away any request is from direct provision of literal food, clothing or shelter, the less likely funding may be granted.

The Trust budgets no funds to purchase charity tables, program advertisements, golf tournament sponsorships, organizational memberships or analogous fund-raising events.

GEOGRAPHIC RESTRICTIONS:
Bucks, Chester, Delaware, Montgomery and Philadelphia counties, Pennsylvania and Camden, New Jersey.

FINANCIAL DATA:
Amount of support per award: $5,000 to $200,000 for fiscal year 2012-13.
Total amount of support: $6,000,475 for fiscal year 2012-13.

NUMBER OF APPLICANTS MOST RECENT YEAR:
132 for fiscal year 2010-11.

NUMBER OF AWARDS: 97 for fiscal year 2010-11.

APPLICATION INFORMATION:
Complete application information is available online. Proposals will be considered only for the following purposes:
(1) specific, basic medical research projects dealing with cancer, heart disease or AIDS;
(2) by invitation of the Trust only, accredited, four-year university and college financial aid programs for needy, worthy, full-time undergraduate students (no requests ever accepted directly from individual students) and;
(3) providing shelter, food or clothing for children age 18 or under (including needy families with dependent children) or the elderly age 60 and above.

The trustees endeavor to keep abreast of the needs and conditions in the area served by the Trust and variations from these policies may be made at their discretion.
Duration: Scholarship and Food, Clothing and Shelter grants: One year; Medical Research grant: Typically one year.
Deadline: Cancer and AIDS Research: June 15; Food, Clothing, and Shelter: December 15 and June 15; Heart Research: September 15; Scholarships: May 1.

PUBLICATIONS:
Biennial report (includes application guidelines).

IRS IDENTIFICATION NUMBER: 23-6648841

TRUSTEES:
Mary L. Smith

ADMINISTRATORS:
Michelle Montgomery, Grant Administrator, Food, Clothing and Shelter/Scholarships
Louise A. Havens, Grant Administrator, Medical Research
Deborah J. McKenna, Advisor

ADDRESS INQUIRIES TO:
Michelle Montgomery, Grant Administrator
(See address above.)

THE JOHN BEN SNOW FOUNDATION, INC. [302]
50 Presidential Plaza
Suite 106
Syracuse, NY 13202
(315) 471-5256
Fax: (315) 471-5256

E-MAIL ADDRESS:
johnbensnow@verizon.net

WEB SITE ADDRESS:
www.johnbensnow.com

FOUNDED: 1948

AREAS OF INTEREST:
Arts and culture, community initiatives, education, environment, journalism, special grants, youth programs and historic preservation.

TYPE:
Capital grants; Challenge/matching grants; Development grants; Fellowships; Project/program grants; Scholarships; Seed money grants; Technical assistance.

YEAR PROGRAM STARTED: 1948

PURPOSE:
To grant funds for educational, cultural and humanitarian purposes.

LEGAL BASIS:
Corporation.

ELIGIBILITY:
Applicants must be IRS 501(c)(3) organizations primarily in central and northern New York state. Grants are made to qualified organizations for educational and humanitarian purposes.

The general policy of the Board of Directors gives preference to proposals seeking one-year funding of program-related grants, matching grants, startup grants and capital grants and to reject proposals from individuals, religious organizations, government agencies, or for endowments, contingency funding, or general operating support.

GEOGRAPHIC RESTRICTIONS:
Central and northern New York state.

FINANCIAL DATA:
Amount of support per award: Typically $5,000 to $15,000.
Total amount of support: $307,565 in total grants for the year ended December 31, 2011.

NUMBER OF APPLICANTS MOST RECENT YEAR:
More than 60.

NUMBER OF AWARDS: 27.

REPRESENTATIVE AWARDS:
Arts and Culture: $2,500 to Syracuse Shakespeare Festival, Syracuse, NY, for Kids Doing Shakespeare Theatre Camp; Community Initiatives: $25,000 to Northern Oswego County Ambulance, Pulaski, NY, for facility expansion; Education: $20,000 to Clarkson University, Potsdam, NY, for

endowed scholarship fund; Historic Preservation: $5,000 to Half-Shire Historical Society, Richland, NY, for facility renovation; Literacy: $20,000 to ProLiteracy, Syracuse, NY, for LifeLinks on North Side.

APPLICATION INFORMATION:
The Foundation is pro-active in seeking grant proposals from qualifying 501(c)(3) organizations. Additionally, the Foundation accepts unsolicited proposals from qualifying organizations.

Applicants should inquire about funding first. Foundation will then supply guidelines and a formal application to be filled out. The inquiry should include:
(1) the name and complete address of the organization;
(2) a brief summary of the project to be funded;
(3) the name and address of the person responsible for the use of funds and;
(4) a photocopy of the organization's IRS tax-exemption letter.

If the proposal meets the stated guidelines and priorities of the Foundation, a grant application will be forwarded. All grant applications must be submitted using the Foundation grant application form and must be received by April 1 of the year in which a grant is requested.
Duration: One year. Renewals depend on the project.
Deadline: Letter of inquiry: No later than January 1 of the year in which the grant is requested. Grant application: April 1. Final or progress report: March 1 of the year following grant.

PUBLICATIONS:
Guidelines; annual report.

STAFF:
Ann M. Scanlon, Program Officer

BOARD MEMBERS:
Jonathan L. Snow, President
David H. Snow, Vice President and Treasurer
Valerie A. MacFie, Secretary
Angus M. Burton
Marion Hancock Fish
Emelie M. Williams

ADDRESS INQUIRIES TO:
Jonathan L. Snow, President
(See address above.)

SOUTHWEST FLORIDA COMMUNITY FOUNDATION
8771 College Parkway
Building 2, Suite 201
Fort Myers, FL 33919
(239) 274-5900
Fax: (239) 274-5930

E-MAIL ADDRESS:
info@floridacommunity.com

WEB SITE ADDRESS:
www.floridacommunity.com

TYPE:
Capital grants; Challenge/matching grants; Demonstration grants; Project/program grants; Scholarships; Seed money grants; Technical assistance; Training grants.

See entry 1378 for full listing.

SOWERS CLUB OF NEBRASKA FOUNDATION [303]

1701 South 17th Street
Suite 1H
Lincoln, NE 68502
(402) 438-2244
Fax: (402) 438-2426

E-MAIL ADDRESS:
sowersclub@windstream.net

WEB SITE ADDRESS:
www.thesowersclub.com

FOUNDED: 1986

AREAS OF INTEREST:
Charity and education.

TYPE:
Project/program grants; Scholarships.

PURPOSE:
To offer assistance to organizations that serve and educate the community.

ELIGIBILITY:
Agency must have been in existence for a minimum of five years and must qualify as exempt under Section 501(c)(3) of the Internal Revenue Code. Grant requests will not be considered for individuals, promoting religious purposes or for political purposes.

GEOGRAPHIC RESTRICTIONS:
Lincoln, Nebraska and surrounding communities.

FINANCIAL DATA:
Total amount of support: $75,000 per year.

APPLICATION INFORMATION:
Grant request must include eight copies of the following:
(1) Letter of Determination from the IRS regarding 501(c)(3) status and;
(2) annual report or current balance sheet outlining the organization's administrative costs. All information will be treated with strict confidentiality.

All blanks on the grant request form must be completed. Do not answer a question on the request form by reference to another question, document or party.
Deadline: February 15, June 15 and September 15.

BOARD OF DIRECTORS AND OFFICERS:
Ed Packard, President
Dick Stephenson, Vice President
Roger Zajicek, Treasurer
Michael Fiene, Secretary
Stan Dinges
Robby Robinson
Michael Rooney

ADDRESS INQUIRIES TO:
Michael Fiene, Secretary
(See address above.)

SETH SPRAGUE EDUCATIONAL AND CHARITABLE FOUNDATION [304]

c/o US Trust
114 West 47th Street, 10th Floor
New York, NY 10036
(646) 855-1011
Fax: (646) 855-5463

AREAS OF INTEREST:
Hospitals, educational institutions and social agencies.

TYPE:
Project/program grants.

ELIGIBILITY:
The Foundation makes grants to hospitals, educational institutions, social agencies and other charitable organizations. No grants to individuals.

GEOGRAPHIC RESTRICTIONS:
San Diego, California; Maine; Boston area, Massachusetts; and New York City, New York.

FINANCIAL DATA:
Amount of support per award: $10,000 to $20,000.
Total amount of support: $1,000,000 for the year 2013.

NUMBER OF APPLICANTS MOST RECENT YEAR:
450.

NUMBER OF AWARDS: 100.

APPLICATION INFORMATION:
Contact the Foundation for application information.
Duration: One year.
Deadline: April 1 and September 1. Award announcement in June and December.

ADDRESS INQUIRIES TO:
Christine O'Donnell, Senior Vice President
(See address above.)

THE STATE STREET FOUNDATION [305]

State Street Financial Center
One Lincoln Street
Boston, MA 02111-2900
(617) 664-8720
Fax: (617) 664-9577

WEB SITE ADDRESS:
www.statestreet.com

FOUNDED: 1804

AREAS OF INTEREST:
Providing economically disadvantaged citizens with the skills they need to be successful, with a focus on initiatives that seek to achieve systemic change and address core problems affecting local communities.

NAME(S) OF PROGRAMS:
● **Global Philanthropy Program**

TYPE:
General operating grants; Project/program grants. Particular emphasis is on programs that help the disadvantaged in the Greater Boston inner-city neighborhoods and communities where State Street has a presence. The Foundation supports public/private partnerships that serve this need, build community capabilities and promote collaborations between community institutions to increase effectiveness.

YEAR PROGRAM STARTED: 1977

PURPOSE:
To channel funds back into the communities where State Street employees work and live.

LEGAL BASIS:
Corporate foundation.

ELIGIBILITY:
Grant applicants must be tax-exempt, 501(c)(3) organizations located in communities where State Street has a presence.

The Foundation does not make individual scholarship grants, nor does it fund research, having a preference for programs emphasizing direct delivery of services. It

does not support organizations by purchasing advertisements, tables or tickets at dinners or other functions.

FINANCIAL DATA:
Each year the Corporation allocates a minimum of one percent for a three-year rolling average of the company's pre-tax income.
Amount of support per award: $3,000 to $50,000.
Total amount of support: Approximately $17,800,000.

APPLICATION INFORMATION:
Grant Proposal Summary Form and instructions are available at the Foundation web site.
Duration: One year.
Deadline: April 1, August 1 and December 1. Notification of decision mid-July, mid-November and mid-March, respectively.

PUBLICATIONS:
Contributions guidelines.

JOHN STAUFFER CHARITABLE TRUST [306]

301 North Lake Avenue, 10th Floor
Pasadena, CA 91101
(626) 793-9400
Fax: (626) 793-5900

E-MAIL ADDRESS:
lsjaynes@lagerlof.com

FOUNDED: 1974

AREAS OF INTEREST:
Colleges, universities and hospitals within California.

TYPE:
Capital grants; Challenge/matching grants; Endowments; Fellowships; Matching gifts; Professorships; Project/program grants; Scholarships.

YEAR PROGRAM STARTED: 1974

PURPOSE:
To support U.S. universities, colleges and hospitals in acquiring land, erecting buildings and other facilities, obtaining equipment, instruments, books, furnishings and providing scholarships, fellowships and professorships.

LEGAL BASIS:
Tax-exempt private foundation founded in 1974 as a Testamentary Trust under will of John Stauffer by Order of the Superior Court of the State of California in and for the County of Los Angeles.

ELIGIBILITY:
Tax-exempt hospitals, colleges and universities with a preference given to those which maintain balanced operating budgets.

GEOGRAPHIC RESTRICTIONS:
California.

FINANCIAL DATA:
Amount of support per award: $100,000 to $3,000,000.
Total amount of support: Varies.

NUMBER OF APPLICANTS MOST RECENT YEAR:
Approximately 200.

REPRESENTATIVE AWARDS:
$3,000,000 to Huntington Hospital; $300,000 to Claremont McKenna College; $500,000 to Stanford University; $2,500,000 to California Institute of Technology.

APPLICATION INFORMATION:
Applicants must submit three copies of a letter to the Office of the Trust setting forth the amount requested, the need for the subject of the grant, objective to be achieved and manner in which John Stauffer's name may be memorialized. If deemed appropriate, the Trustees will request supplemental information. Papers establishing tax-exempt status will be required. Requests for personal interviews are discouraged.

PUBLICATIONS:
Application guidelines.

IRS IDENTIFICATION NUMBER: 23-7434707

TRUSTEES:
John F. Bradley, Sr.
Tim Gosney
Michael S. Whalen, Esq.

ADDRESS INQUIRIES TO:
Lisa Jaynes, Assistant
(See address above.)

STEELCASE FOUNDATION [307]
P.O. Box 1967 GH-4E
Grand Rapids, MI 49501-1967
(616) 246-4695
Fax: (616) 475-2200

WEB SITE ADDRESS:
www.steelcasefoundation.org

FOUNDED: 1951

AREAS OF INTEREST:
Human service, health, education, social welfare, the arts and culture, and the environment in the areas of Steelcase, Inc. manufacturing plants. Particular concern is given to people who are disadvantaged, disabled, and young or elderly in an attempt to improve the quality of their lives.

TYPE:
Capital grants; Challenge/matching grants; Demonstration grants; Development grants; Matching gifts; Project/program grants; Seed money grants. Special projects, startup, capital and capacity building.

The Steelcase Foundation believes quality, accessible public education is paramount to achieving its vision. The Foundation assists its philanthropic partners in generating education initiatives, in addition to work and cultural opportunities.

YEAR PROGRAM STARTED: 1951

PURPOSE:
To improve the quality of life in the communities where Steelcase employees live; to empower people to reach their full potential.

LEGAL BASIS:
Corporate foundation.

ELIGIBILITY:
The Foundation makes grants to IRS-certified nonprofit organizations in areas where Steelcase manufacturing plants are located.

GEOGRAPHIC RESTRICTIONS:
Athens, Alabama and primarily western Michigan.

FINANCIAL DATA:
Amount of support per award: $1,000 to $1,000,000.
Total amount of support: $5,340,000 for the year 2013.

NUMBER OF APPLICANTS MOST RECENT YEAR: 300.

NUMBER OF AWARDS: 60.

APPLICATION INFORMATION:
To obtain a grant application, send a letter on organization's letterhead and signed by the Chief Executive Officer. Include the following items with the letter:
(1) description of organization or project;
(2) expected results of the project;
(3) amount of grant funds requested and;
(4) copy of IRS 501(c)(3) nonprofit certification.

If the proposal meets the Foundation criteria, a detailed application form will be sent to the organization.
Duration: Varies.
Deadline: Grant requests are reviewed quarterly.

PUBLICATIONS:
Annual report; application; guidelines.

IRS IDENTIFICATION NUMBER: 38-6050470

TRUSTEES:
Kate Pew Wolters, Chairperson
Mary Anne Hunting
James Keane
Elizabeth Welch Lykins
Mary Goodwillie Nelson
Craig Niemann
Robert C. Pew, III

STAFF:
Phyllis A. Gebben, Coordinator of Donations

ADDRESS INQUIRIES TO:
Phyllis A. Gebben, Coordinator of Donations
(See address above.)

THE WILLIAM B. STOKELY, JR. FOUNDATION [308]
620 Campbell Station Road, Station West
Suite 27
Knoxville, TN 37934
(865) 966-4878
Fax: (865) 675-5095

FOUNDED: 1951

AREAS OF INTEREST:
College and university scholarship programs and cultural, educational, religious and health service organizations.

TYPE:
General operating grants; Matching gifts; Scholarships.

YEAR PROGRAM STARTED: 1951

PURPOSE:
To provide funds for colleges and universities for scholarships.

LEGAL BASIS:
Tax-exempt private foundation.

ELIGIBILITY:
The Foundation does not extend funds to individuals but rather to colleges and universities in the form of scholarships to disburse under the guidelines of their particular program. Also considered are the needs of cultural, educational, religious (Christian) and health service organizations in areas where the Stokely family has ties. Regional priority is given to the southeastern U.S. and eastern Tennessee.

Organizations requesting funds must be approved, listed nonprofit organizations with 501(c)(3) status. All proposals must be submitted in writing for review by the Board of Directors.

GEOGRAPHIC RESTRICTIONS:
Southeastern United States and Eastern Tennessee.

FINANCIAL DATA:
Amount of support per award: $25 to $100,000.

APPLICATION INFORMATION:
All proposals must be submitted in writing for review by the Board of Directors.
Duration: Varies.
Deadline: Proposals are reviewed on an ongoing basis.

IRS IDENTIFICATION NUMBER: 35-6016402

BOARD OF DIRECTORS:
William B. Stokely, III, President
Kay H. Stokely, Executive Vice President
Andrea White, Vice President, Treasurer and Secretary
Stacy S. Byerly
Shelley S. Przewrocki
Clayton F. Stokely
William B. Stokely, IV

ADDRESS INQUIRIES TO:
William B. Stokely, III, President
(See address above.)

ROY AND CHRISTINE STURGIS CHARITABLE AND EDUCATIONAL TRUST [309]
c/o Bank of America, N.A.
901 Main Street, 19th Floor
Dallas, TX 75202-3714

E-MAIL ADDRESS:
tx.philanthropic@ustrust.com

WEB SITE ADDRESS:
www.bankofamerica.com/philanthropic/foundation

FOUNDED: 1981

AREAS OF INTEREST:
Education, arts and culture, youth and social services, science and health.

TYPE:
Capital grants; Challenge/matching grants; Matching gifts; Project/program grants.

LEGAL BASIS:
Private foundation (charitable trust).

ELIGIBILITY:
Applicants must have a 501(c)(3) exempt status from federal income tax as determined by the IRS before applying for a grant.

Charitable organizations which receive a one-payment grant must skip a year before applying again. Charitable organizations which receive multiyear payments cannot apply again while receiving payments and must skip a year after the last payment is received.

Trustee will consider grant requests for supplements for capital improvements, special projects, medical research and equipment, grants to meet challenges, endowments, start-up funds (extraordinary review), limited general operating expenses and construction or renovation of facilities.

The Trustee may favorably consider proposals which are unique, necessary and of high priority for the charitable organizations and which do not duplicate other services which are available, proposals for which funding may not be readily available from other sources and essential projects which are sufficiently described as worthwhile, important and of a substantive nature.

The Trustee will not consider providing support for political organizations, loans, scholarships for individuals, tuition for individuals or for seminars. No grants to individuals or for mass appeals for funding.

GEOGRAPHIC RESTRICTIONS:
Arkansas and Dallas area in Texas.

FINANCIAL DATA:
Amount of support per award: $5,000 to $200,000 for multiyear payments. Average: $23,500.

APPLICATION INFORMATION:
Guidelines and application forms are available on the Trust web site.
Duration: One year; occasional multiyear.
Deadline: March 1. Notification on or before June 30.

PUBLICATIONS:
Guidelines.

IRS IDENTIFICATION NUMBER: 75-6331832

SUNTRUST FOUNDATION   [310]
919 East Main Street
Richmond, VA 23219
(804) 782-7907
Fax: (804) 782-5191

E-MAIL ADDRESS:
jane.markins@suntrust.com

AREAS OF INTEREST:
Education, health and human services, culture and art, civic and community.

TYPE:
General operating grants; Matching gifts; Project/program grants. Employee matching gifts program is designed to encourage SunTrust employees to support educational institutions and cultural organizations.

PURPOSE:
To improve the quality of life in the communities in which SunTrust operates.

LEGAL BASIS:
Corporate giving program.

ELIGIBILITY:
Applicants must be 501(c)(3) organizations.

When considering a specific contribution request, the following are among the criteria that SunTrust applies:
(1) does the cause fall under one or more of the areas of interest of the Foundation?;
(2) does SunTrust have a business presence in the geographic area in which the contribution will have impact?;
(3) will the contribution support programs and activities for improvement of the quality of life in the community served? and;
(4) will the organization requesting financial support have good management and active involvement of community leaders?

No grants to individuals.

GEOGRAPHIC RESTRICTIONS:
Florida, Georgia, Maryland, North Carolina, South Carolina, Tennessee, Virginia and Washington, DC.

FINANCIAL DATA:
Amount of support per award: Varies.
Total amount of support: $12,000,000.
Matching fund requirements: SunTrust will match any employee contribution to educational institutions and for arts and culture.

APPLICATION INFORMATION:
Well-organized, fully documented requests for aid will facilitate the review process. The proposal must be in writing with appropriate documentation. The documentation should include project and/or operating budgets and a full description of the area of need and the reasons for the request. The applicant should give special attention to the guidelines applied by the Foundation when considering a proposal.

Applications are reviewed and approved on a local basis.
Duration: Varies. Renewal possible.
Deadline: September 1 for the next year's budget.

PUBLICATIONS:
Guidelines.

ADDRESS INQUIRIES TO:
Regional Headquarters or
SunTrust Foundation
(See address above.)

SURDNA FOUNDATION INC.   [311]
330 Madison Avenue, 30th Floor
New York, NY 10017-5001
(212) 557-0010 ext. 237
Fax: (212) 557-0003

E-MAIL ADDRESS:
info@surdna.org

WEB SITE ADDRESS:
www.surdna.org

FOUNDED: 1917

AREAS OF INTEREST:
Sustainable environments, strong local economies, and thriving cultures.

NAME(S) OF PROGRAMS:
● **Strong Local Economy**
● **Sustainable Environment**
● **Thriving Cultures**

TYPE:
General operating grants; Project/program grants.

YEAR PROGRAM STARTED: 1917

PURPOSE:
To foster catalytic, entrepreneurial programs which offer viable solutions to difficult systemic problems.

ELIGIBILITY:
Grants are not generally given to individuals or to fund capital campaigns or building construction, or for internationally based or focused projects.

GEOGRAPHIC RESTRICTIONS:
United States.

FINANCIAL DATA:
Amount of support per award: Varies.
Total amount of support: Approximately $40,000,000 allocated for fiscal year 2015.

NUMBER OF AWARDS: 220 for the year 2011.

APPLICATION INFORMATION:
Letters of Inquiry should be submitted on the Foundation web site. Application guidelines are available online.
Duration: One to three years. Grants are renewable.

PUBLICATIONS:
Annual report.

TAHOE TRUCKEE COMMUNITY FOUNDATION   [312]
11071 Donner Pass Road
Truckee, CA 96161
(530) 587-1776 ext. 106
Fax: (530) 550-7985

E-MAIL ADDRESS:
phebe@ttcf.net

WEB SITE ADDRESS:
www.ttcf.net

FOUNDED: 1998

AREAS OF INTEREST:
Education, environment, arts and culture, civic benefits, health, human services, youth development, recreation and animal welfare.

TYPE:
Block grants; Challenge/matching grants; Demonstration grants; General operating grants; Scholarships.

YEAR PROGRAM STARTED: 1998

PURPOSE:
To enhance the quality of life in the Truckee Tahoe community.

ELIGIBILITY:
Grants are made to organizations that have tax-exempt status under Section 501(c)(3) of the Internal Revenue Code. No grants are made to individuals.

GEOGRAPHIC RESTRICTIONS:
Truckee and Tahoe region, California.

FINANCIAL DATA:
Amount of support per award: $5,000 to $10,000.
Total amount of support: $1,100,000 to $1,500,000.

NUMBER OF APPLICANTS MOST RECENT YEAR: 102.

NUMBER OF AWARDS: 57.

APPLICATION INFORMATION:
Contact the Foundation for application procedures.
Duration: One year.
Deadline: Varies.

IRS IDENTIFICATION NUMBER: 68-0416404

ADMINISTRATIVE STAFF:
Jennifer Genstler, Administration Director
Phebe Bell, Program Officer

EXECUTIVE OFFICERS:
Stacy Caldwell, Chief Executive Officer

ADDRESS INQUIRIES TO:
Phebe Bell, Program Officer
(See address above.)

S. MARK TAPER FOUNDATION   [313]
12011 San Vicente Boulevard, Suite 400
Los Angeles, CA 90049
(310) 476-5413
Fax: (310) 471-4993

E-MAIL ADDRESS:
questions@smtfoundation.org

WEB SITE ADDRESS:
www.smtfoundation.org

FOUNDED: 1989

AREAS OF INTEREST:
Including, but not limited to, environment, independent living for the disabled, children, hunger, AIDS, teenage pregnancy prevention, economic revitalization, the arts, public education and civic affairs.

TYPE:
Capital grants; Challenge/matching grants; Demonstration grants; Development grants; Endowments; General operating grants; Matching gifts; Project/program grants; Scholarships; Seed money grants; Technical assistance; Training grants. Specific project grants.

YEAR PROGRAM STARTED: 1989

PURPOSE:
To enhance the quality of people's lives.

LEGAL BASIS:
Independent foundation.

ELIGIBILITY:
No grants to individuals. Applicants must be certified tax-exempt under Section 501(c)(3) of the Internal Revenue Code.

Previously funded nonprofit organizations are not eligible for another grant until after three full cycles have elapsed following the grant cycle during which previous grant was made.

GEOGRAPHIC RESTRICTIONS:
Southern California, primarily Los Angeles County.

FINANCIAL DATA:
Amount of support per award: Small grants: up to $50,000; medium grants: $50,001 to $250,000; large grants: over $250,000.
Total amount of support: Varies.

NUMBER OF APPLICANTS MOST RECENT YEAR: 400.

NUMBER OF AWARDS: 80.

APPLICATION INFORMATION:
Application form required. Make initial contact by way of Letter of Inquiry. Letter must include organization background information, purpose of project, amount requested and anticipated results. Documentation of 501(c)(3) status required. Letters of Inquiry submitted by e-mail or fax will not be accepted.
Duration: One year unless paid in installments.
Deadline: Letters of Inquiry are accepted December through February. Applications are mailed in April through June. Notification in September.

PUBLICATIONS:
Letter of Inquiry Guidelines.

OFFICERS:
Janice Taper Lazarof, President

ADDRESS INQUIRIES TO:
Adrienne Wittenberg, Grants Director (See address above.)

JOHN TEMPLETON FOUNDATION   [314]
300 Conshohocken State Road
Suite 500
West Conshohocken, PA 19428
(610) 941-2828
Fax: (610) 825-1730

WEB SITE ADDRESS:
www.templeton.org

FOUNDED: 1987

AREAS OF INTEREST:
Higher education, science and religion, theology, medicine, philosophy, spirituality and health, character development and free enterprise education.

TYPE:
Awards/prizes; Challenge/matching grants; Project/program grants; Research grants. Awards are financial in nature.

PURPOSE:
To promote and support relationships and progress between science and religion.

LEGAL BASIS:
Private foundation.

ELIGIBILITY:
Organizations classified as 501(c)(3) by the IRS can apply.

FINANCIAL DATA:
Amount of support per award: Varies.
Total amount of support: Varies.
Matching fund requirements: Defined on an individual grant basis.

APPLICATION INFORMATION:
Funding guidelines can be found at web site.
Duration: Varies.

PUBLICATIONS:
Brochures; newsletter; articles.

IRS IDENTIFICATION NUMBER: 62-1322826

TEXAS INSTRUMENTS FOUNDATION   [315]
12500 TI Boulevard
Dallas, TX 75243
(972) 995-2011

WEB SITE ADDRESS:
www.ti.com/giving

FOUNDED: 1964

AREAS OF INTEREST:
Education, arts and culture, and community investment.

TYPE:
Matching gifts; Project/program grants. Education grants.

YEAR PROGRAM STARTED: 1965

PURPOSE:
To better the communities in which Texas Instruments operates.

LEGAL BASIS:
Nonprofit foundation.

ELIGIBILITY:
Organization must be 501(c)(3) and tax-exempt. No grants to individuals, student scholarships, good will advertising or for contributions of Texas Instruments products.

GEOGRAPHIC RESTRICTIONS:
Texas.

FINANCIAL DATA:
Total amount of support: $11,600,000 for the year 2013.
Matching fund requirements: Up to $10,000 per person per category each year for education and arts and culture.

APPLICATION INFORMATION:
All requests for funding should be submitted online.
Duration: Varies. Renewals possible.

PUBLICATIONS:
Guidelines.

IRS IDENTIFICATION NUMBER: 75-6038519

STAFF:
Andy Smith, Executive Director

TEXTRON CHARITABLE TRUST   [316]
40 Westminster Street
Providence, RI 02903
(401) 421-2800
Fax: (401) 457-3598

WEB SITE ADDRESS:
www.textron.com

FOUNDED: 1969

AREAS OF INTEREST:
Culture and the arts, education, job training, health care, minorities and women, United Way, environment/conservation and youth groups.

TYPE:
Project/program grants. Employee matching gift programs.

YEAR PROGRAM STARTED: 1969

PURPOSE:
To support organizations, institutions and programs that contribute significantly to the quality of life in the communities where Textron employees live and work.

LEGAL BASIS:
Corporate contributions program.

ELIGIBILITY:
Grants are made to nonprofit, tax-exempt organizations. The Trust cannot contribute to organizations which are not determined to be a tax-exempt public charity as defined by the Internal Revenue Code 501(c)(3), separate appeals for operating funds by local United Way agencies, however, capital fund campaigns approved by local United Ways can be considered for support, fund-raising appeals from, or matching program contributions to churches, seminaries or other directly related religious organizations, individuals, including political candidates, endowment funds, or requests that intend to reduce operating deficits.

GEOGRAPHIC RESTRICTIONS:
Rhode Island.

FINANCIAL DATA:
Amount of support per award: Employee Matching Gifts: $25 to $7,500 per employee annually.
Total amount of support: Varies.

NUMBER OF AWARDS: Varies.

APPLICATION INFORMATION:
Applications will be accepted online only. See web site for complete application information.
Duration: Generally one year. Multiyear commitments are kept to a minimum.
Deadline: March 1 and September 1.

PUBLICATIONS:
Policy statement; guidelines.

ADDRESS INQUIRIES TO:
Karen Warfield
Community Affairs Manager
(See address above.)

3M FOUNDATION, INC.   [317]
Community Affairs
3M Center Building 225-01-S-23
St. Paul, MN 55144-1000
(651) 733-1721
(651) 733-0144
Fax: (651) 737-3061

E-MAIL ADDRESS:
cfkleven@mmm.com

WEB SITE ADDRESS:
www.3Mgives.com

FOUNDED: 1953

AREAS OF INTEREST:
Education, arts and culture, human services
and environment.

TYPE:
Capital grants; General operating grants;
Matching gifts; Product donations;
Project/program grants. 3Mgives consists of
gifts by the 3M Foundation, cash and product
donations by 3M and employee/retiree
volunteerism.

YEAR PROGRAM STARTED: 1953

PURPOSE:
To improve every life.

LEGAL BASIS:
Corporate contributions program.

ELIGIBILITY:
Grants are made in the program areas of
interest to established, well-managed
organizations which have an IRS 501(c)(3)
nonprofit status, and which are located in and
serving 3M communities. Essential qualities
are programs with broad-based community
support, a reputation for leadership and
high-quality service delivery and measurable
results.

The 3M Foundation will not fund
organizations in non-3M communities,
individuals, for-profit organizations,
disease-related organizations, hospitals, (in
general) individual K-12 schools,
organizations with a limited constituency,
such as religious, fraternal, social, veterans or
military organizations, and scholarship funds
or organizations.

Grants are not awarded for advocacy and
lobbying efforts to influence legislation;
conferences, seminars, workshops or
publications of their proceedings;
endowments; film/video production;
fund-raising, testimonial, athletic and special
events; purchase of equipment that has not
been manufactured by 3M; and travel for
individuals or groups.

3Mgives generally will not consider
organizations or causes that do not impact
3M communities, lease, conferences,
seminars, workshops, symposia, publication
of proceedings and all aspects relating to
conferences, fund-raising and testimonial
events/dinners, grants to individual K-12
schools, including tickets, silent auctions,
raffles, telethons, etc., not more than 10% of
the organization's campaign goal or annual
budget, whichever is smaller, programs or
projects beyond three years.

FINANCIAL DATA:
Amount of support per award: Varies.
Total amount of support: $58,200,000 for the
year 2013.
Matching fund requirements: Limited to 3M
employees and retirees.

NUMBER OF APPLICANTS MOST RECENT YEAR:
10,000.

NUMBER OF AWARDS: Approximately 3,000.

APPLICATION INFORMATION:
Applications are by invitation only.
Duration: Generally one year, and not more
than three years.
Deadline: April and October.

PUBLICATIONS:
Annual report; contributions guidelines.

IRS IDENTIFICATION NUMBER: 41-6038262

BOARD:
I.F. Hardgrove, President
K.F. Price, Vice President
S.D. Krohn, Treasurer
C.F. Kleven, Secretary
D.M. Amsden, Assistant Secretary
I.K. Fong
J. Garcia Galiana
H.M. Gindre
A.M. Hanrahan
A.K. Khandpur
J.R. Lavers
R. Rao
J.B. Sweeney
I.G. Thulin
S.K. Tokach

JOHN H. AND H. NAOMI TOMFOHRDE FOUNDATION [318]

c/o Rackemann, Sawyer & Brewster
160 Federal Street, 15th Floor
Boston, MA 02110-1700
(617) 951-1108
Fax: (617) 542-7437

E-MAIL ADDRESS:
smonahan@rackemann.com

WEB SITE ADDRESS:
www.cybergrants.com/tomfohrde

FOUNDED: 1996

AREAS OF INTEREST:
Cultural, social and civic betterment,
community health, higher education,
scientific research within the New England
area with a special focus on Greater Boston.

TYPE:
Capital grants; Conferences/seminars;
Matching gifts; Product donations;
Project/program grants; Seed money grants;
Technical assistance. The Foundation's
particular focus is on supporting the work of
charitable institutions, organizations and
agencies in the New England area and
particularly in Greater Boston, which are
dedicated to the cultural, social and civic
betterment of the community and particularly
which foster the advancement of higher
education, the classic arts, scientific research
in biomedicine and the improvement of
community health.

PURPOSE:
To bring about the cultural, social and civic
betterment of the community and particularly
to foster the advancement of higher
education, the classic arts, scientific research
in biomedicine and the improvement of
community health.

LEGAL BASIS:
Private, independent foundation.

ELIGIBILITY:
The Foundation supports nonprofit 501(c)(3)
organizations only.

GEOGRAPHIC RESTRICTIONS:
New England, with a preference for Greater
Boston.

FINANCIAL DATA:
Amount of support per award: $5,000 to
$10,000.
Total amount of support: $188,200 for the
year 2012.
Matching fund requirements: Determined on
a case-by-case basis.

NUMBER OF APPLICANTS MOST RECENT YEAR:
100 for the year 2011.

NUMBER OF AWARDS: 23 for the year 2011.

REPRESENTATIVE AWARDS:
Boston Health Care for the Homeless; Boston
History Center and Museum.

APPLICATION INFORMATION:
Applicants are required to submit a
Preliminary Application-Concept Cover
Letter. Only applicants whose preliminary
application has been approved will be invited
to submit a full proposal.
Deadline: January, April and August for
trustees meetings in February, June and
October, respectively.

IRS IDENTIFICATION NUMBER: 04-3338742

TRUSTEES:
Albert M. Fortier, Jr., Esq.
William B. Tyler, Esq.

STAFF:
Susan T. Monahan, Grants Coordinator

ADDRESS INQUIRIES TO:
Susan T. Monahan, Grants Coordinator
(See e-mail address above.)

TOPFER FAMILY FOUNDATION [319]

3600 North Capital of Texas Highway
Building B, Suite 310
Austin, TX 78746
(512) 329-0009
(866) 897-0298
Fax: (512) 329-6462

E-MAIL ADDRESS:
info@topferfoundation.org

WEB SITE ADDRESS:
www.topferfoundation.org

FOUNDED: 2000

AREAS OF INTEREST:
Child abuse prevention and treatment, youth
enrichment, job training and support services,
children's health, and aging in place.

TYPE:
Project/program grants.

PURPOSE:
To help people connect to the tools and
resources needed to build self-sufficient and
fulfilling lives; to address the needs of the
communities in which the Topfer family
resides.

ELIGIBILITY:
Organizations must be nonprofit, classified
501(c)(3). No grants to individuals.

GEOGRAPHIC RESTRICTIONS:
Greater Chicago, Illinois and greater Austin,
Texas metropolitan areas. In Illinois,
preference is given to Cook, DuPage and
Lake counties.

FINANCIAL DATA:
Amount of support per award: $5,000 to
$100,000.
Total amount of support: $2,800,000.

APPLICATION INFORMATION:
Application should be submitted online.
Duration: One year. Must reapply.
Deadline: Varies.

ADDRESS INQUIRIES TO:
Erica Gustafson, Program Officer
(See address above.)

TOTAL PETROCHEMICALS & REFINING USA FOUNDATION [320]

1201 Lousiana, Suite 1800
Houston, TX 77002
(713) 483-5000
Fax: (713) 483-5429

WEB SITE ADDRESS:
www.totalpetrochemicalsrefiningusa.com
www.usa.total.com

FOUNDED: 1974

AREAS OF INTEREST:
Education.

TYPE:
Development grants; Matching gifts;
Project/program grants.

LEGAL BASIS:
Corporate foundation.

ELIGIBILITY:
Grants are made to organizations which are
tax-exempt under Section 501(c)(3) of the
Internal Revenue Code. Grants may not be
made to individuals nor are grants made to
private foundations as defined in Section
509(a) of the Internal Revenue Code.

GEOGRAPHIC RESTRICTIONS:
Louisiana and Texas.

FINANCIAL DATA:
Amount of support per award: Varies.
Total amount of support: Varies.
Matching fund requirements: All gifts from
Total Petrochemicals & Refining USA, Inc.
full-time employees are matched to four-year
educational institutions from which the donor
received a degree. The minimum gift that
will be matched is $25 and the maximum gift
per person per calendar year is $5,000. The
contribution must be a personal gift of the
eligible donor and cannot include resources
from other people or institutions.

NUMBER OF APPLICANTS MOST RECENT YEAR:
Approximately 500.

NUMBER OF AWARDS: Varies.

APPLICATION INFORMATION:
No form is prescribed for submitting grant
applications; however, budgets and statements
of financial condition will assist the
Foundation in acting upon any request for
funds. A categorized statement regarding the
expected sources of funds, excluding
individual contributors and specifically
whether the organization is supported by the
United Way, are also of interest. Prior to
issuance of a grant, an organization will be
requested to furnish documentation of its
status under the Code and a statement
regarding its present operation and sources of
support.
Duration: Varies.

OFFICERS:
Philippe Doligez, Chief Executive Officer
Tricia Fuller, Secretary

ADDRESS INQUIRIES TO:
Tricia Fuller, Manager, Public Affairs
(See address above.)

THE HARRY A. AND MARGARET D. TOWSLEY FOUNDATION [321]

P.O. Box 349
Midland, MI 48640-0349
(989) 837-1100
Fax: (989) 837-3240

E-MAIL ADDRESS:
chatland@towsleyfoundation.org

FOUNDED: 1959

AREAS OF INTEREST:
Education, cultural arts, health and
community service.

TYPE:
Project/program grants.

YEAR PROGRAM STARTED: 1959

PURPOSE:
To assist religious, educational, charitable
and scientific organizations with their
programs; to prevent cruelty to children.

LEGAL BASIS:
Private foundation.

ELIGIBILITY:
The Foundation does not make direct grants
to individuals, provide loan funds, fund travel
or conferences, or make grants to students
for scholarships, books or other media.
Grants are not made to institutions which in
policy or practice unfairly discriminate
against age, race, color, creed or sex.

GEOGRAPHIC RESTRICTIONS:
Primarily Michigan.

FINANCIAL DATA:
Amount of support per award: $5,000 to
$1,000,000.
Total amount of support: Varies.

APPLICATION INFORMATION:
Organizations seeking aid should submit
verification of tax-exempt and nonprofit
status, amount of requested funds,
explanation of need, and most recent
financial statement along with operating
budget and other funding sources.
Duration: Varies. Renewal possible.
Deadline: Application should be made within
the first three months of the year.
Announcement will be made during the third
quarter of the year.

PUBLICATIONS:
Brochure; annual report.

IRS IDENTIFICATION NUMBER: 38-6091798

OFFICERS:
Lynn T. White, President
Judith D. Rumelhart, Vice President
Mary Ivers, Treasurer
Margaret E. Thompson, M.D., Secretary

TRUST FUNDS INCORPORATED [322]

100 Broadway, Third Floor
San Francisco, CA 94111
(415) 434-3323
Fax: (415) 434-2936

FOUNDED: 1934

AREAS OF INTEREST:
Elementary, secondary and graduate Catholic
education, Catholic religious and social
service organizations and programs, and
religious arts.

TYPE:
Project/program grants.

YEAR PROGRAM STARTED: 1934

PURPOSE:
To support worthwhile projects and programs
that share the interests of the Foundation.

LEGAL BASIS:
Private foundation.

ELIGIBILITY:
Grants are usually limited to the San
Francisco Bay area. No grants to individuals.
No grants for buildings or endowments,
annual campaigns, or to organizations which
draw substantial public support.

GEOGRAPHIC RESTRICTIONS:
San Francisco, California and surrounding
area.

FINANCIAL DATA:
Amount of support per award: $1,000 to
$15,000.

APPLICATION INFORMATION:
Application forms provided for all grant
proposals complying with guidelines. Write
or call first.

PUBLICATIONS:
Applications and guidelines.

IRS IDENTIFICATION NUMBER: 94-6062952

DIRECTORS:
James T. Healy, President
Thomas F. Kubasak, Chief Financial Officer
John Strain, Secretary
Thomas Kelley, Director
Joan C. O'Rourke, Director

ADDRESS INQUIRIES TO:
James T. Healy, President
(See address above.)

TULL CHARITABLE FOUNDATION, INC. [323]

50 Hurt Plaza
Suite 1245
Atlanta, GA 30303
(404) 659-7079
Fax: (404) 659-1223

E-MAIL ADDRESS:
carol@tullfoundation.org

WEB SITE ADDRESS:
www.tullfoundation.org

FOUNDED: 1952

AREAS OF INTEREST:
Education, health and human services, youth
development and the arts.

TYPE:
Capital grants.

YEAR PROGRAM STARTED: 1952

PURPOSE:
To respond to charitable and community
needs in the Atlanta metropolitan area and in
Georgia.

LEGAL BASIS:
Converted from Trust to Nonprofit
Corporation of Georgia.

ELIGIBILITY:
Nonprofit 501(c)(3) organizations located
within Georgia are eligible for support.

The Foundation does not make grants to
individuals or churches and does not
participate in the operation of a project other
than that of providing start-up funds.

The Foundation's trustees prefer to make
grants that will have a significant and lasting
impact on an organization, as well as the
community. Priority is given to grant requests
that:
(1) are strategically important to an
organization's growth and capacity;
(2) enable the organization to more
effectively address important community
needs and;
(3) are cost-effective.

Proposals that address education, health and human services, youth development, and the arts are given priority by Foundation trustees.

GEOGRAPHIC RESTRICTIONS:
Georgia.

FINANCIAL DATA:
Amount of support per award: Average $50,000.
Total amount of support: $2,100,000 for the year 2013.

APPLICATION INFORMATION:
Prior to receiving a full proposal, the Foundation prefers a concise letter-of-intent providing a brief description of the applicant organization, the project for which funding is being requested, the total cost of the project and the amount being requested and a copy of the organization's 501(c)(3) certification. If the Foundation determines that further consideration is to be given to the proposed project, additional information will be requested.
Duration: Typically one year.
Deadline: December 1, March 1, June 1 and September 1.

PUBLICATIONS:
Guidelines; policies.

TRUSTEES AND OFFICERS:
Larry Prince, Chairman
Claire Arnold
Sylvia Looney Dick
Lillian Giornelli
Jack Guynn
B. Harvey Hill, Jr.
Warren Jobe
Clay Rolader
Napoleon Rutledge

ADDRESS INQUIRIES TO:
Barbara T. Cleveland, Executive Director
Carol Aiken, Assistant
(See address above.)

THE TUSCHMAN FOUNDATION   [324]
4544 Post Oak Place
Suite 392
Houston, TX 77027
(713) 706-4000
Fax: (713) 963-9954

E-MAIL ADDRESS:
j.tusch@att.net

FOUNDED: 1983

AREAS OF INTEREST:
Sports philanthropy.

TYPE:
Capital grants; Challenge/matching grants; Development grants; Exchange programs; Internships; Matching gifts; Seed money grants.

YEAR PROGRAM STARTED: 1983

PURPOSE:
To provide funds on a matching basis to charitable institutions or as seed monies for fund-raising; to provide reoccurring benefits to recipients attending to the needs of others.

LEGAL BASIS:
Private foundation.

ELIGIBILITY:
Recipients must be 501(c)(3) qualified institutions and have BBB satisfactory ratings. No funds are provided for operational purposes.

FINANCIAL DATA:
Amount of support per award: Grants: $1,500 to $5,000.
Total amount of support: $7,500.
Matching fund requirements: Funds are provided on a matching basis, 1:1 to 1:3, except for seed monies for fund-raising campaigns.

NUMBER OF AWARDS: 3.

APPLICATION INFORMATION:
Grant requests should include the following:
(1) name, address and phone number of organization and the contact person;
(2) most recent annual report and information materials;
(3) explanation of need for the funds, including purposes, budgets, benefits to the organization and community, timing, and alternative funding;
(4) financial information including current-year budget and year-to-date figures;
(5) copy of IRS determination letter on 501(c)(3) status;
(6) potential sources of matching funds and;
(7) satisfactory rating from the Charity Watch section of the local Better Business Bureau.

PUBLICATIONS:
Annual report.

OFFICER:
John S. Tuschman, President

*PLEASE NOTE:
The Foundation is not accepting new grant applications until Fall 2015.

UNION PACIFIC FOUNDATION   [325]
1400 Douglas, Stop 1560
Omaha, NE 68179
(402) 544-5600
Fax: (402) 501-0011

E-MAIL ADDRESS:
upf@up.com

WEB SITE ADDRESS:
www.up.com/found

FOUNDED: 1955

AREAS OF INTEREST:
Health and human services, community and civic, and fine arts in communities served by Union Pacific.

TYPE:
Capital grants; General operating grants; Project/program grants. Support generally for capital campaigns, building funds, equipment and materials, renovation and operating support.

YEAR PROGRAM STARTED: 1959

PURPOSE:
To improve the quality of life in the communities served by Union Pacific and where its employees live and work.

LEGAL BASIS:
Incorporated in Utah, May 13, 1955.

ELIGIBILITY:
Organization must be a public charity, 501(c)(3) tax-exempt and located in a community served by Union Pacific.

GEOGRAPHIC RESTRICTIONS:
Arizona, Arkansas, California, Colorado, Idaho, Illinois, Iowa, Kansas, Louisiana, Minnesota, Missouri, Montana, Nebraska, Nevada, New Mexico, Oklahoma, Oregon, Texas, Utah, Washington, Wisconsin and Wyoming.

FINANCIAL DATA:
Amount of support per award: Varies.
Total amount of support: $6,900,000 for the year 2013.

NUMBER OF APPLICANTS MOST RECENT YEAR:
2,300.

NUMBER OF AWARDS: 984 for the year 2013.

APPLICATION INFORMATION:
Details may be obtained from the Foundation web site.
Duration: Most grants are awarded annually.
Deadline: August 15 for consideration for the following year's budget.

TRUSTEES:
Lance Fritz
R.M. Knight, Jr.
J.J. Koraleski
Gayla Thal
R.W. Turner

THE UPS FOUNDATION   [326]
55 Glenlake Parkway, N.E.
Atlanta, GA 30328
(404) 828-6374
Fax: (404) 828-7435

E-MAIL ADDRESS:
community@ups.com

WEB SITE ADDRESS:
www.community.ups.com

FOUNDED: 1951

AREAS OF INTEREST:
Economic and global literacy, environmental sustainability, nonprofit effectiveness, encouraging diversity and community safety, and volunteerism.

NAME(S) OF PROGRAMS:
• **James E. Casey Scholarship Program**
• **Neighbor to Neighbor**
• **George D. Smith Scholarship Program**

TYPE:
Project/program grants; Scholarships. James E. Casey Scholarship Program provides the opportunity for children of UPS employees to earn four-year scholarships at colleges and universities.

Neighbor to Neighbor program mobilizes UPS employees and their families to serve as volunteers in their communities.

George D. Smith Scholarship Program provides scholarships for children of full- and part-time UPS employees enrolled in a full-time study program of up to two years.

YEAR PROGRAM STARTED: 1951

PURPOSE:
To improve lives and strengthen the capacity of nonprofits through volunteerism, community grants and creative programs.

LEGAL BASIS:
Corporate foundation.

ELIGIBILITY:
Applicants must be any worthy philanthropic, nonprofit project or organization that is tax-exempt under 501(c)(3). The Foundation does not fund annual campaigns, building or endowment funds, deficit financing, emergency funds, individuals, land acquisition, loans, operating costs or capital expenses, publications, or religious organizations or theological functions.

FINANCIAL DATA:
Amount of support per award: Varies.
Total amount of support: Varies.

APPLICATION INFORMATION:
The Foundation does not accept unsolicited proposals, but does invite leading organizations in focus areas to submit proposals.

Duration: James E. Casey: Up to four years; Neighbor to Neighbor: Varies; George D. Smith: Up to two years.

Deadline: Varies.

ADDRESS INQUIRIES TO:
Eduardo Martinez, President
(See address above.)

USG FOUNDATION, INC.   [327]
550 West Adams Street
Chicago, IL 60661
(312) 436-4021
(312) 436-4000
Fax: (312) 672-4021

E-MAIL ADDRESS:
maclark@usg.com

WEB SITE ADDRESS:
www.usg.com

FOUNDED: 1978

AREAS OF INTEREST:
Homelessness and shelter, health and welfare, education, and arts and culture.

TYPE:
Project/program grants.

YEAR PROGRAM STARTED: 1978

PURPOSE:
To provide assistance to nonprofit organizations seeking solutions to educational, social or health problems or whose work contributes to cultural enrichment.

LEGAL BASIS:
Tax-exempt, corporate foundation.

ELIGIBILITY:
Applicants must be tax-exempt 501(c)(3) organizations. The Foundation supports the creation of economic opportunity through grants to organizations that provide affordable housing/shelter, encourage self-sufficiency and assist economic development.

The Foundation does not contribute to organizations without IRS tax-exempt 501(c)(3) status, sectarian organizations having an exclusively religious nature, individuals, political parties, offices or candidates, fraternal or veterans' organizations, primary or secondary schools, organizations that cannot provide adequate accounting records, procedures or courtesy advertising.

GEOGRAPHIC RESTRICTIONS:
Primarily Chicago, Illinois.

FINANCIAL DATA:
Amount of support per award: Varies.
Total amount of support: Varies.

APPLICATION INFORMATION:
Grant proposals should be submitted in writing to receive consideration. The Foundation does not use a printed application form; however, the proposal should include the following:
(1) cover letter briefly outlining a statement of the need or problem and a background summary of the need or problem with specific reasoning why the USG Foundation would be interested in the proposal;
(2) the amount requested and how it will be used;
(3) copy of the organization's 501(c)(3) tax-exemption letter from the IRS;
(4) copy of the organization's most recent financial statements;
(5) list of the members of the organization's governing board;
(6) statement of the program's purpose describing why the organization is involved in the project and a notation indicating any special qualifications the organization may possess for obtaining its stated objectives;
(7) detailed description of any proposed special project;
(8) program's measurable goals;
(9) itemized plan outlining how the organization intends to achieve those goals and;
(10) any additional literature that further defines the organization's goals and achievements such as an annual report, fund-raising literature, auditor's report, etc.

Duration: One year. Renewal possible upon reapplication.

PUBLICATIONS:
Guidelines.

ADDRESS INQUIRIES TO:
Margaret Clark, Assistant Secretary
(See address above.)

VERIZON FOUNDATION   [328]
One Verizon Way
Basking Ridge, NJ 07920
(866) 247-2687 (volunteers program)
Fax: (908) 630-2660

E-MAIL ADDRESS:
verizon.foundation@verizon.com

WEB SITE ADDRESS:
foundation.verizon.com

FOUNDED: 2001

AREAS OF INTEREST:
Domestic violence prevention and family safety, education, health care, and sustainability.

TYPE:
Matching gifts; Project/program grants.

PURPOSE:
To address critical disparities among targeted segments in education, family, safety, health care and sustainability.

LEGAL BASIS:
Private, nonprofit organization.

ELIGIBILITY:
To be considered for an invitation, an organization must be classified as tax-exempt under Section 501(c)(3) of the Internal Revenue Code and further classified as a public charity under Section 509(a)(1)-(3).

Proposals will also be considered from elementary and secondary schools (public and private) that are registered with the National Center for Education Statistics (NCES), providing that the grant is not for the sponsorship of a field trip.

GEOGRAPHIC RESTRICTIONS:
United States.

FINANCIAL DATA:
Amount of support per award: Average $5,000 to $10,000.
Total amount of support: Approximately $67,000,000 in grants for the year 2012.

APPLICATION INFORMATION:
Applications are considered on an invitation-only basis.

IRS IDENTIFICATION NUMBER: 13-3319048

ADDRESS INQUIRIES TO:
See e-mail address above.

THE WALLACE FOUNDATION   [329]
5 Penn Plaza, 7th Floor
New York, NY 10001
(212) 251-9700
Fax: (212) 679-6990

E-MAIL ADDRESS:
grantrequest@wallacefoundation.org

WEB SITE ADDRESS:
www.wallacefoundation.org

FOUNDED: 1965

AREAS OF INTEREST:
Education leadership, arts participation, arts education, and afterschool learning.

NAME(S) OF PROGRAMS:
- **Arts for Young People**
- **Principal Pipeline Initiative**
- **Principal Supervisor Initiative**
- **Summer Learning District Demonstration Project**

TYPE:
Conferences/seminars; Project/program grants; Research grants; Technical assistance; Research contracts.

YEAR PROGRAM STARTED: 2003

PURPOSE:
To enable institutions to expand learning and enrichment opportunities for all people by supporting and sharing effective ideas and practices.

LEGAL BASIS:
Private foundation.

ELIGIBILITY:
Grant applicants must be 501(c)(3) tax-exempt organizations. No grants are made to individuals.

GEOGRAPHIC RESTRICTIONS:
United States.

FINANCIAL DATA:
Estimated assets of $1.479 billion as of December 31, 2013.
Amount of support per award: Varies depending on needs and nature of request.
Total amount of support: Approximately $54,100,000 in grants paid for calendar year 2013.

NUMBER OF APPLICANTS MOST RECENT YEAR: 192.

NUMBER OF AWARDS: 93.

APPLICATION INFORMATION:
In most cases, the Foundation evaluates prospective grantees through the issuance of Requests for Proposals or other careful screening processes. Nevertheless, an organization may submit an inquiry by e-mail briefly describing the project, the organization, the estimated total for the project, and the portion requiring funding.
Duration: Varies.
Deadline: Varies.

PUBLICATIONS:
Annual report.

IRS IDENTIFICATION NUMBER: 13-6183757

OFFICERS AND BOARD OF DIRECTORS:
Kevin W. Kennedy, Chairman
Will Miller, President

Rob D. Nagel, Chief Investment Officer and Treasurer
Mary E. Geras, Chief Financial Officer and Assistant Treasurer
Kenneth W. Austin, Corporate Secretary
Lawrence T. Babbio, Jr., Director
Candace K. Beinecke, Director
Linda Darling-Hammond, Director
Augusta Souza Kappner, Director
Susan J. Kropf, Director
Ann S. Moore, Director
Joseph W. Polisi, Director
Amor H. Towles, Director
Mary Beth West, Director

ADDRESS INQUIRIES TO:
General Management
(See address above.)

*PLEASE NOTE:
Grants are rarely made to unsolicited projects, especially from local organizations.

THE WASIE FOUNDATION   [330]
230 Manitoba Avenue South
Suite 110
Wayzata, MN 55391-1612
(952) 955-8500
Fax: (952) 955-8509

WEB SITE ADDRESS:
www.wasie.org

FOUNDED: 1966

AREAS OF INTEREST:
Postsecondary educational scholarship programs for people of Polish ancestry in Minnesota; care, treatment and research regarding schizophrenia and arthritis; children's health; and organizations providing services and programs to people living with cancer.

NAME(S) OF PROGRAMS:
● **Arthritis Grants**
● **Cancer Grants**
● **Children's Medical Health Grants**
● **Schizophrenia Grants**
● **Scholarship Program**

TYPE:
Capital grants; Challenge/matching grants; Conferences/seminars; Development grants; General operating grants; Matching gifts; Project/program grants; Research grants. The grant program provides funding in four health areas: specifically, schizophrenia, arthritis, cancer, and children with medical problems.

YEAR PROGRAM STARTED: 1966

LEGAL BASIS:
Private foundation.

ELIGIBILITY:
Grants are made to 501(c)(3) nonprofit organizations.

GEOGRAPHIC RESTRICTIONS:
Minnesota and South Florida (Broward, Miami-Dade, and Palm Beach counties).

FINANCIAL DATA:
Amount of support per award: Varies.
Total amount of support: $847,233 for the year 2012.

NUMBER OF AWARDS: 29 grants paid for the year 2012.

REPRESENTATIVE AWARDS:
$150,000 to Joe DiMaggio Children's Hospital Foundation; $5,000 to Franciscan End of Life Care; $5,000 to Arthritis

Foundation Upper Midwest Region; $16,500 to Jessica June Children's Cancer Foundation.

APPLICATION INFORMATION:
The Foundation encourages organizations which believe they fall within their funding guidelines to initiate contact through a telephone call to one of the program staff who will gather information and assist with the proposal process.

Proposal submission is by invitation only.
Duration: One to three years. Renewal possible.
Deadline: Submissions are invited throughout the year.

STAFF:
Gregg D. Sjoquist, President and Chief Executive Officer
Dani Mathison, Chief Operating Officer
Jan Preble, Vice President of Programs
Jen Klaassens, Vice President of Programs, Florida
Gineen Bresso, Vice President of Special Projects and General Counsel

ADDRESS INQUIRIES TO:
Jan Preble
Vice President of Programs
(See address above.)

EDWIN S. WEBSTER FOUNDATION   [331]
c/o GMA
77 Summer Street, Suite 800
Boston, MA 02110-1006
(617) 391-3087
Fax: (617) 426-7087

E-MAIL ADDRESS:
mjenney@gmafoundations.com

WEB SITE ADDRESS:
www.gmafoundations.com

FOUNDED: 1948

AREAS OF INTEREST:
Charitable purposes, with emphasis on hospitals, medical research and education, youth agencies, cultural activities and programs addressing the needs of minorities.

TYPE:
Capital grants; Challenge/matching grants; Endowments; General operating grants.

YEAR PROGRAM STARTED: 1982

PURPOSE:
To work towards a better society by giving grants to organizations trying to help people with serious needs not otherwise being addressed.

LEGAL BASIS:
Nonprofit foundation.

ELIGIBILITY:
No grants are given to individuals or organizations outside the U.S. The majority of contributions are made to organizations in the New England area. It is the policy of the Foundation to support charitable organizations that are well known to the Trustees, with emphasis on hospitals, medical research, education, youth agencies, cultural activities and programs addressing the needs of minorities. Grantees must have tax-exempt status.

GEOGRAPHIC RESTRICTIONS:
Primarily New England.

FINANCIAL DATA:
Amount of support per award: $5,000 to $50,000.
Total amount of support: Approximately $1,800,000.

APPLICATION INFORMATION:
Proposals are submitted by using the online application form.
Duration: One year.
Deadline: For consideration at spring meeting, proposals should arrive by May 1. For consideration at the fall meeting, proposals should arrive by November 1.

PUBLICATIONS:
Guidelines.

TRUSTEES:
Henry U. Harris, III
Alexander Hiam
Suzanne Harte Sears

ADDRESS INQUIRIES TO:
Michelle Jenney, Administrator
(See address above.)

WEINGART FOUNDATION   [332]
1055 West 7th Street
Suite 3200
Los Angeles, CA 90017-2305
(213) 688-7799
Fax: (213) 688-1515

E-MAIL ADDRESS:
info@weingartfnd.org

WEB SITE ADDRESS:
www.weingartfnd.org

FOUNDED: 1951

AREAS OF INTEREST:
Human services, health and education, with an emphasis on projects that benefit children and youth.

NAME(S) OF PROGRAMS:
● **Capacity Building**
● **Capital Support**
● **Core Support**
● **Program Support**
● **Small Grant Program**

TYPE:
Capital grants; General operating grants; Project/program grants. The Foundation makes grants to assist organizations that work in the areas of health, human services and education. The Foundation gives highest priority to activities that provide greater access to people who are economically disadvantaged and underserved. The Foundation has particular interest in applications that specifically address the needs of low-income children and youth, older adults and people affected by disabilities and homelessness. The Foundation also funds activities that benefit the general community and improve the quality of life for all individuals in southern California.

Core Support: Unrestricted funding that enables an organization to carry out its mission. It can be used to underwrite administrative infrastructure and/or to maintain core programs and essential staff.

Capacity Building: For new or enhanced activities aimed at strengthening an organization's programmatic and/or administrative capacity. Projects must evidence a credible plan for sustaining costs.

Capital Support: For specific projects with capital expenditures. Funding is available to support land, facility, equipment purchases, renovations or new construction.

Program Support: For new, expansion or enhancement program requests. Projects must evidence a viable fund-raising and sustainability plan.

Small Grant Program: For increasing access to funding and strengthening the capacity of small, community-based, and developing organizations, with priority given to organizations with operating budgets under $1,000,000. The Program also supports small capital projects for organizations of any size.

PURPOSE:
To assist credible agencies and institutions serving children and youth, the aged, the disabled, the homeless, the sick, the poor or otherwise disadvantaged and projects benefiting the general community.

ELIGIBILITY:
An organization that is certified as tax-exempt under Section 501(c)(3) of the U.S. Internal Revenue Code and is not a private foundation as defined in Section 509(a) of that Code is eligible for consideration. The Foundation does not fund Section 509(a)(3) Type III nonfunctionally integrated supporting organizations.

Grants are not made:
(1) to organizations that discriminate against certain groups or individuals in the delivery of programs and services on the basis of race, religion, national origin, gender, age, sexual orientation or disability;
(2) for propagandizing, influencing legislation and/or elections, promoting voter registration; for political candidates, political campaigns; for litigation;
(3) for social or political issues outside the U.S.;
(4) to individuals;
(5) to federated appeals or for the collection of funds for redistribution to other nonprofit groups;
(6) for conferences, workshops, temporary exhibits, travel, surveys, films or publishing activities;
(7) for endowment funds;
(8) for contingencies, deficits or debt reduction;
(9) for fund-raising dinners or events or;
(10) for research.

Grants generally are not approved for:
(1) national organizations that do not have local chapters operating in the geographic area of grant focus;
(2) projects or programs normally financed by government sources;
(3) refugee or religious programs, consumer interest or environmental advocacy or;
(4) feasibility studies.

GEOGRAPHIC RESTRICTIONS:
Southern California, with priority given to Los Angeles, Orange, Riverside, San Bernardino, Santa Barbara, and Ventura counties.

FINANCIAL DATA:
Assets of $717,208,865 for the year ended June 30, 2013.
Amount of support per award: $5,000 to $750,000.
Total amount of support: $32,084,313 paid out for the fiscal year ended June 30, 2013.
Matching fund requirements: Organization matches 1:1.

COOPERATIVE FUNDING PROGRAMS: Nonprofit Sustainability Initiative, Home for Good.

NUMBER OF APPLICANTS MOST RECENT YEAR: 1,281.

NUMBER OF AWARDS: 626 approved grants for the fiscal year ended June 30, 2013.

APPLICATION INFORMATION:
It is recommended that all applicants apply to the Regular Grant Program using the online LOI process. If submitting the request online is not an option, applicants may also submit a letter via regular mail. The letter, which should be limited to two pages, should include a brief description of the organization's mission and activities, a brief explanation of how the funds would be used, and the total amount of funding requested from the Foundation. If the request is for a specific project or activity (capital, capacity building, or program), the applicant should also include the total cost of the project for which funding is sought and the amount raised to date.

If it is determined from the Letter of Inquiry that the request meets the Foundation's priorities and interests, the applicant will be provided with the instructions and forms required to prepare and submit a formal application.

There is no Letter of Inquiry required for the Small Grant Program.
Duration: Mostly, one to two years. Core Support grants are generally made for a two-year period.
Deadline: The Foundation accepts applications throughout the year.

PUBLICATIONS:
Annual report, only available on web site.

IRS IDENTIFICATION NUMBER: 95-6054814

OFFICERS:
Fred J. Ali, President and Chief Executive Officer
Deborah M. Ives, Vice President and Treasurer
Belen Vargas, Vice President, Programs

BOARD OF DIRECTORS:
Steven D. Broidy, Chairman
Aileen Adams
William C. Allen
Andrew E. Bogen
Monica L. Lozano
John W. Mack
Miriam Muscarolas
Steve L. Soboroff

ADDRESS INQUIRIES TO:
President and Chief Executive Officer
Weingart Foundation
(See address above.)

HERMAN O. WEST FOUNDATION [333]
530 Herman O. West Drive
Exton, PA 19341
(610) 594-2900

WEB SITE ADDRESS:
www.westpharma.com

FOUNDED: 1972

AREAS OF INTEREST:
Funding of nonprofit organizations serving cultural, health and public service needs of the areas/communities where West Pharmaceutical Services maintains operations.

TYPE:
Capital grants; Challenge/matching grants; General operating grants; Matching gifts; Project/program grants; Scholarships.

YEAR PROGRAM STARTED: 1972

PURPOSE:
To fund nonprofit organizations, provide employee scholarship programs and employee matching gifts program.

LEGAL BASIS:
Corporate contributions program; private foundation.

ELIGIBILITY:
Grant applicants must be organizations with tax-exempt status, located in areas where the company maintains operations in the U.S.

Employees of West Pharmaceutical Services may participate in the Employee Matching Gifts Program and Matching Gifts to Non-Profit Organizations Program.

Scholarships are available to children of West Pharmaceutical Services employees.

GEOGRAPHIC RESTRICTIONS:
United States.

FINANCIAL DATA:
Amount of support per award: $500 to $150,000.
Total amount of support: Approximately $790,663 for the year 2012.

APPLICATION INFORMATION:
Application includes description of service provided, financial statement, including sources of funding and how dispersed, list of future needs and services of program and documentation of tax-exempt status.
Duration: Varies. Renewal possible.

PUBLICATIONS:
Application guidelines.

OFFICERS AND TRUSTEES:
George R. Bennyhoff, Chairman
Paula Johnson, M.D., Trustee
Richard D. Luzzi, Trustee

ADDRESS INQUIRIES TO:
Maureen B. Goebel, Administrator
(See address above.)
Tel: (610) 594-2945

WESTERN INTERSTATE COMMISSION FOR HIGHER EDUCATION [334]
3035 Center Green Drive
Boulder, CO 80301
(303) 541-0270
Fax: (303) 541-0226

E-MAIL ADDRESS:
info-sep@wiche.edu

WEB SITE ADDRESS:
www.wiche.edu/psep

FOUNDED: 1953

AREAS OF INTEREST:
Allopathic medicine, dentistry, physical and occupational therapy, optometry, podiatry, osteopathic medicine, veterinary medicine, physician assistant and pharmacy.

NAME(S) OF PROGRAMS:
● **Professional Student Exchange Program (PSEP)**

TYPE:
Scholarships. Tuition assistance/loan for service.

YEAR PROGRAM STARTED: 1953

PURPOSE:
To provide affordable access to professional health care education.

ELIGIBILITY:
Must be a resident of a state listed below. Rules vary by state.

GEOGRAPHIC RESTRICTIONS:
Alaska, Arizona, Colorado, Hawaii, Montana, Nevada, New Mexico, North Dakota, Utah and Wyoming.

FINANCIAL DATA:
Amount of support per award: Varies.
Total amount of support: Varies.

NUMBER OF AWARDS: 690 for the year 2012-13.

APPLICATION INFORMATION:
Applicants should contact their state certifying officers, listed on the web site above, for more information.
Duration: One year. Grants are renewable for course of study; subject to available funding.
Deadline: October 15 of the year prior to admission.

PUBLICATIONS:
Brochure.

ADDRESS INQUIRIES TO:
Director of Student Exchange
(See address above.)

*PLEASE NOTE:
Grant is for residents of one western state making applications to participating schools in another western state.

E. L. WIEGAND FOUNDATION   [335]

Wiegand Center
165 West Liberty Street, Suite 200
Reno, NV 89501
(775) 333-0310
Fax: (775) 333-0314

FOUNDED: 1982

AREAS OF INTEREST:
Education, medical research, civic and community affairs, arts and cultural affairs, and public affairs.

TYPE:
Capital grants; Project/program grants.

YEAR PROGRAM STARTED: 1982

PURPOSE:
To support charitable organizations and Roman Catholic charitable institutions.

LEGAL BASIS:
Private charitable trust.

ELIGIBILITY:
The Foundation will consider applications from institutions that are tax-exempt under Section 501(c)(3) of the IRS, and which are not private foundations as defined in Section 509.

The review process by the Foundation will consider institutions that:
(1) are exemplary in their field;
(2) have a history of high achievement and sound management;
(3) demonstrate a stable financial condition;
(4) have the potential to be self-supporting after the stage of initial funding by the Foundation;
(5) focus on strengthening traditional values essential to the preservation of a democratic society nurtured by free market principles (in the area of public affairs) and;

(6) are developing programs and projects that have a significant impact in the area for which the grant is requested.

GEOGRAPHIC RESTRICTIONS:
Arizona, Hawaii, Idaho, Montana, Nevada, Oregon, Utah, Washington, and New York City/Washington, DC (public policy).

FINANCIAL DATA:
Amount of support per award: $1,000 to $470,507.
Total amount of support: $2,638,589 for the year 2013.

NUMBER OF AWARDS: 40 for the year 2013.

APPLICATION INFORMATION:
A prospective applicant should describe the highlights of the proposal (including data regarding the organization, sources of funding, a brief description of the project or program, estimated budget and timeline) in a letter addressed to the Foundation. If, after staff consideration, it is determined that the program or project complies with the preliminary review, a prospective applicant shall receive an application for grant form which shall be assigned numerically to such applicant. The Foundation is only able to support a small percentage of the proposals it receives.
Deadline: Letters of Inquiry accepted throughout the year.

IRS IDENTIFICATION NUMBER: 94-2839372

ADDRESS INQUIRIES TO:
Kristen A. Avansino
President and Executive Director
Grants Program
(See address above.)

*PLEASE NOTE:
Written communications to the Foundation are preferred.

MATILDA R. WILSON FUND   [336]

6th Floor at Ford Field
1901 St. Antoine Street
Detroit, MI 48226
(313) 259-7777
Fax: (313) 393-7579

E-MAIL ADDRESS:
roosterveen@bodmanlaw.com

FOUNDED: 1944

AREAS OF INTEREST:
Arts, education, health and human services.

TYPE:
Capital grants; Project/program grants.

PURPOSE:
To primarily fund pre-selected organizations supported by Matilda R. Wilson during her lifetime.

ELIGIBILITY:
Applicants must be 501(c)(3) organizations. No grants to individuals.

GEOGRAPHIC RESTRICTIONS:
Primarily southeast Michigan.

FINANCIAL DATA:
Amount of support per award: $500 to $50,000.
Total amount of support: Varies.

NUMBER OF APPLICANTS MOST RECENT YEAR: 40.

NUMBER OF AWARDS: 32.

REPRESENTATIVE AWARDS:
$7,000,000 to Oakland University, Rochester, MI, for exterior restoration projects at Meadow Brook Hall.

APPLICATION INFORMATION:
No application form. Applicants must submit tax-exempt documentation.
Duration: One year; some multiyear.
Deadline: January, April and August.

IRS IDENTIFICATION NUMBER: 38-6087665

STAFF:
Robin L. Oosterveen, Program Director

ADDRESS INQUIRIES TO:
Robin L. Oosterveen, Program Director
(See address above.)

*PLEASE NOTE:
Priority given to organizations that Mrs. Wilson supported during her lifetime, or with which the Fund has a long-standing commitment.

WOLFE ASSOCIATES, INC.   [337]

34 South Third Street
Columbus, OH 43215
(614) 460-3782
Fax: (614) 469-6173

E-MAIL ADDRESS:
rwolfe@10tv.com

FOUNDED: 1973

AREAS OF INTEREST:
Health and medicine, education, culture, community service and environment.

TYPE:
Project/program grants.

YEAR PROGRAM STARTED: 1973

LEGAL BASIS:
Private foundation.

ELIGIBILITY:
Grants are made to tax-exempt public foundations and charities.

GEOGRAPHIC RESTRICTIONS:
Primarily the central Ohio area.

FINANCIAL DATA:
Amount of support per award: Varies.
Total amount of support: Varies.

APPLICATION INFORMATION:
Applicants should submit a cover letter with a brief summary of the proposal and amount requested.
Deadline: The Foundation accepts and reviews applications throughout the year.

ADDRESS INQUIRIES TO:
Rita J. Wolfe, Vice President
(See address above.)

THE ROBERT W. WOODRUFF FOUNDATION   [338]

191 Peachtree Street, N.E.
Suite 3540
Atlanta, GA 30303
(404) 522-6755
Fax: (404) 522-7026

E-MAIL ADDRESS:
fdns@woodruff.org

WEB SITE ADDRESS:
www.woodruff.org

FOUNDED: 1937

AREAS OF INTEREST:
Elementary, secondary and higher education; health care and education; human services, particularly for children and youth; economic

development and civic affairs; art and cultural activities; conservation and environmental education.

TYPE:
Capital grants; Project/program grants.

YEAR PROGRAM STARTED: 1937

PURPOSE:
To support charitable, scientific and educational activities to achieve systemic improvement in public education, health care access, and family, children and youth services at the state and local levels.

LEGAL BASIS:
Independent, private foundation with a broad charter to support charitable, scientific and educational activities.

ELIGIBILITY:
Grants generally are limited to tax-exempt public charities located and operating in Georgia. Preference is given to one-time capital projects.

Grants to organizations for basic operating support are avoided. No grants made to individuals. The Foundation does not give out loans.

GEOGRAPHIC RESTRICTIONS:
Georgia.

FINANCIAL DATA:
Amount of support per award: Generally $50,000 to $1,000,000.

Total amount of support: Varies.

APPLICATION INFORMATION:
Application form not required. Proposal (one copy) should be made in letter form and should include the following information:
(1) a description of the organization, its purposes, programs, staffing and governing board;
(2) the organization's latest financial statements, including the most recent audit report;
(3) a description of the proposed project and full justification for its funding;
(4) an itemized project budget, including other sources of support in hand or anticipated and;
(5) evidence from the IRS of the organization's tax-exempt status and that the applying organization itself is not a private foundation.
Deadline: September 1 and February 1.

PUBLICATIONS:
Application guidelines.

OFFICERS:
P. Russell Hardin, President
J. Lee Tribble, Treasurer
Erik S. Johnson, Secretary and General Counsel

TRUSTEES:
James B. Williams, Chairman
James M. Sibley, Vice Chairman
Wilton D. Looney
Charles H. McTier
E. Jenner Wood, III

ADDRESS INQUIRIES TO:
P. Russell Hardin, President
(See address above.)

WYMAN-GORDON FOUNDATION [339]

c/o Fletcher, Tilton & Whipple, P.C.
370 Main Street, 11th Floor
Worcester, MA 01608
(508) 798-8621
(508) 459-8000
Fax: (508) 791-1201

FOUNDED: 1966

AREAS OF INTEREST:
Health and human services, education, civic and community affairs, culture and arts.

TYPE:
Grants-in-aid. The Foundation focuses its grantmaking in non-operating areas (i.e., capital campaigns, equipment).

YEAR PROGRAM STARTED: 1966

PURPOSE:
To operate exclusively for charitable, scientific and/or educational purposes.

ELIGIBILITY:
Applicants must be nonprofit organizations with a 501(c)(3) tax-exempt status.

GEOGRAPHIC RESTRICTIONS:
Primarily Worcester area, Massachusetts.

FINANCIAL DATA:
Amount of support per award: $100 to $150,000.

NUMBER OF APPLICANTS MOST RECENT YEAR:
200.

NUMBER OF AWARDS: 50.

REPRESENTATIVE AWARDS:
$150,000 to United Way of Central Massachusetts; $10,000 to Worcester Public Library; $3,000 to Mechanics Hall; $3,500 to Worcester Municipal Research Bureau.

APPLICATION INFORMATION:
Application includes 501(c)(3) tax-exempt letter, statement of purpose and specifics regarding project or program to be funded.
Deadline: April 1, August 1 and December 1.

IRS IDENTIFICATION NUMBER: 04-6142600

OFFICERS AND TRUSTEES:
David P. Gruber, President
Wallace F. Whitney, Jr., Secretary and Treasurer
Warner S. Fletcher, Trustee

ADDRESS INQUIRIES TO:
Warner S. Fletcher, Trustee
(See address above.)

THE WYOMISSING FOUNDATION [340]

960 Old Mill Road
Wyomissing, PA 19610-2522
(610) 376-7494
Fax: (610) 372-7276

E-MAIL ADDRESS:
pswavely@wyofound.org

WEB SITE ADDRESS:
www.wyofound.org

FOUNDED: 1929

AREAS OF INTEREST:
Charitable purposes, primarily local giving, with emphasis on hospitals, higher education, youth agencies and community funds, conservation, music and economic development.

TYPE:
Capital grants; Challenge/matching grants; Development grants; Grants-in-aid; Project/program grants; Research grants; Seed money grants.

YEAR PROGRAM STARTED: 1929

LEGAL BASIS:
Private donor foundation.

ELIGIBILITY:
No grants to individuals. Applicants must be 501(c)(3) organizations.

GEOGRAPHIC RESTRICTIONS:
Primarily Berks County, Pennsylvania.

FINANCIAL DATA:
No fiscal restrictions.
Amount of support per award: $5,000 to $250,000.

Total amount of support: Varies.

APPLICATION INFORMATION:
Guidelines available at the web site.
Duration: Primarily one year.
Deadline: Quarterly.

IRS IDENTIFICATION NUMBER: 23-1980570

OFFICERS AND BOARD OF DIRECTORS:
Glenn Moyer, Chairman
Alex Frazee, Vice Chairman
Karen A. Rightmire, President
Chris Pruitt, Treasurer

ADDRESS INQUIRIES TO:
Karen A. Rightmire, President
(See address above.)

XCEL ENERGY FOUNDATION [341]

414 Nicollet Mall
Minneapolis, MN 55401-1993
(800) 328-8226
Fax: (612) 215-4522

WEB SITE ADDRESS:
www.xcelenergy.com

FOUNDED: 2001

AREAS OF INTEREST:
Environment, math and science education, job training and placement, and access to the arts.

TYPE:
Project/program grants. Employee/retiree matching gifts program.

YEAR PROGRAM STARTED: 2001

PURPOSE:
To help promote a desirable, healthy environment in those areas served by Xcel Energy.

ELIGIBILITY:
Applicants must be 501(c)(3) nonprofit organizations in the service area. Grants will not be made to individuals, political parties, national organizations, research programs or government agencies. Grants are made to religious organizations only if program sponsored has a direct benefit to the community and not the religious organization.

GEOGRAPHIC RESTRICTIONS:
Cities within Xcel Energy service areas.

FINANCIAL DATA:
Amount of support per award: $1,000 to $25,000.

Total amount of support: Varies.

Matching fund requirements: 501(c)(3) nonprofits. Employee and retiree matching gifts program: Minimum donation $50, maximum $500.

APPLICATION INFORMATION:
The Foundation utilizes an online grant application system. Applications are accepted by invitation only.
Duration: Varies.
Deadline: Environment and Education: February. Job Training and Placement and Arts: May.

STAFF:
Jeanne Fox, Representative, Michigan and Wisconsin
Jim Garness, Representative, Minnesota, North Dakota and South Dakota
Terry Price, Representative, New Mexico and Texas
Shanda Vangas, Representative, Colorado

ADDRESS INQUIRIES TO:
Monique Lovato, Director
(See address above.)

XERIC FOUNDATION   [342]
351 Pleasant Street
Suite B, PMB No. 214
Northampton, MA 01060
(413) 585-0671

E-MAIL ADDRESS:
xericgrant@aol.com

WEB SITE ADDRESS:
www.xericfoundation.org

FOUNDED: 1991

AREAS OF INTEREST:
Assistance to charitable organizations in western Massachusetts.

NAME(S) OF PROGRAMS:
● **Grants for Nonprofit Organizations**

TYPE:
Project/program grants; Scholarships; Seed money grants.

YEAR PROGRAM STARTED: 1991

PURPOSE:
To provide funds to charitable and nonprofit organizations for unique projects or services.

LEGAL BASIS:
Private, nonprofit corporation.

ELIGIBILITY:
Organizations applying for grants must be charitable and nonprofit organizations with their own IRS letter of 501(c)(3) tax-exempt status. No funds for operating budgets or capital costs.

GEOGRAPHIC RESTRICTIONS:
Western Massachusetts.

FINANCIAL DATA:
Amount of support per award: Generally not over $5,000.

Total amount of support: $85,359 in charitable and nonprofit grants for the year 2013.

NUMBER OF APPLICANTS MOST RECENT YEAR:
Varies.

NUMBER OF AWARDS: Varies.

APPLICATION INFORMATION:
Grant proposals must be submitted in the form of a written request. Nonprofit organizations must include with their grant request a cover letter, history of the organization, description of the project, personnel list, projected calendar, budget and financial statements in addition to a copy of the organization's tax-exemption letter from the IRS. Six copies are required.
Duration: One year.
Deadline: January 31.

PUBLICATIONS:
Grant guidelines.

IRS IDENTIFICATION NUMBER: 22-3149258

ADDRESS INQUIRIES TO:
See e-mail address above.

THE XEROX FOUNDATION [343]
45 Glover Avenue
Norwalk, CT 06856
(203) 849-2453
Fax: (203) 849-2479

E-MAIL ADDRESS:
mark.conlin@xerox.com

FOUNDED: 1972

AREAS OF INTEREST:
Education and workforce preparedness, science and technology, employee and community affairs, cultural affairs, and national affairs.

TYPE:
Assistantships; Challenge/matching grants; Development grants; Fellowships; General operating grants; Grants-in-aid; Internships; Matching gifts; Professorships; Project/program grants; Research grants; Scholarships; Seed money grants; Technical assistance; Training grants.

YEAR PROGRAM STARTED: 1972

PURPOSE:
To assist a variety of social, civic, and cultural organizations that provide broad-based community programs and services in the cities where Xerox employees live and work; to support higher education to prepare qualified men and women for careers in business, government and education; to advance knowledge in science and technology; to enhance learning opportunities for minorities and disadvantaged; to foster debate on major national public policy issues; to support national leadership efforts around major social problems, education, employability and cultural affairs.

LEGAL BASIS:
Corporate foundation.

ELIGIBILITY:
Grants are made only to organizations that have been granted exemption from Federal Income Tax under Section 501(c)(3) and ruled to be publicly supported under Section 509(a) of the Internal Revenue Code. No grants for individuals; capital grants (except for special circumstances and approved by Board of Trustees); endowments or endowed chairs; political organizations or candidates; religious or sectarian groups; municipal, county, state, federal or quasi-government agencies.

GEOGRAPHIC RESTRICTIONS:
United States.

FINANCIAL DATA:
Amount of support per award: Grants vary in amount, depending upon the needs and nature of the request.
Total amount of support: $13,500,000 for the year 2012.
Matching fund requirements: Will match colleges/universities up to $1,000 per institution.

NUMBER OF APPLICANTS MOST RECENT YEAR:
Approximately 600 for the year 2013.

APPLICATION INFORMATION:
No specific application form is used. Applications must be submitted in letter form. The letter should contain:
(1) the legal name of the organization;
(2) the official contact person;
(3) its tax-exempt status;
(4) a brief description of its activities and programs;
(5) the purpose for which the grant is being requested;
(6) the benefits expected;
(7) the plans for evaluation;
(8) the projected budget and;
(9) the expected sources and amount of funds needed.

Any additional factual material related to the organization or request that may be deemed useful for evaluation, plus a copy of the latest annual financial statement if available, should also be included.
Duration: The Foundation usually does not make grants for continuing support without a follow-up request. Large grants may be approved for one year or on a multiyear basis.
Deadline: Grant reviews take place monthly.

OFFICERS:
Mark J. Conlin, President

ADDRESS INQUIRIES TO:
Mark J. Conlin, President
(See address above.)

HUMANITIES

Humanities (general)

AMERICAN ACADEMY IN ROME [344]

7 East 60th Street
New York, NY 10022-1001
(212) 751-7200
Fax: (212) 751-7220

E-MAIL ADDRESS:
info@aarome.org

WEB SITE ADDRESS:
www.aarome.org

FOUNDED: 1894

AREAS OF INTEREST:
Arts and humanities.

NAME(S) OF PROGRAMS:
● **Rome Prize Fellowships**

TYPE:
Awards/prizes; Fellowships; Residencies.
Fellowships for independent work in
architecture, landscape architecture, design,
musical composition, visual arts, historic
preservation/conservation, ancient studies,
medieval studies, renaissance and early
modern studies, and modern Italian studies.
Supported projects must be conducted at
American Academy in Rome facilities.

YEAR PROGRAM STARTED: 1894

PURPOSE:
To support emerging artists and scholars in
the early or middle stages of their careers; to
refine and expand their professional, artistic
or scholarly aptitudes, drawing on their
colleagues' erudition and experience, as well
as on the inestimable resources of the Italian
capital of Rome, Europe and the
Mediterranean.

LEGAL BASIS:
Private, not-for-profit.

ELIGIBILITY:
Must be U.S. citizen at the time of
application. Graduate students in the
humanities may apply only for Predoctoral
Fellowships. Previous winners of the Rome
Prize are not eligible to reapply.
Undergraduate students are not eligible for
Rome Prize Fellowships.

U.S. citizens and foreign nationals who have
lived in the U.S. for three years immediately
preceding the application deadline may apply
for the NEH Postdoctoral Fellowships.

FINANCIAL DATA:
Rome Prize includes stipend, meals, a
bedroom with private bath, and a study or
studio. Winners of six-month and 11-month
fellowships receive stipends.
Amount of support per award: Fellowships
provide stipends of $16,000 (six-month) and
$28,000 (11-month).
Total amount of support: $2,700,000.

COOPERATIVE FUNDING PROGRAMS: National
Endowment for the Arts, National
Endowment for the Humanities, Andrew W.
Mellon Foundation, Samuel Kress Foundation
and American Academy of Arts and Letters.

NUMBER OF APPLICANTS MOST RECENT YEAR:
901.

NUMBER OF AWARDS: 30.

APPLICATION INFORMATION:
Application forms are available online.

Duration: Six-month and 11-month
fellowships depending on field of application.
Predoctoral awards in the humanities include
11-month and two-year fellowships.
Deadline: November 1.

STAFF:
Shawn Miller, Program Director

ADDRESS INQUIRIES TO:
Programs Department
(See address above.)

AMERICAN ANTIQUARIAN SOCIETY (AAS) [345]

185 Salisbury Street
Worcester, MA 01609-1634
(508) 755-5221
Fax: (508) 754-9069

E-MAIL ADDRESS:
perickson@mwa.org

WEB SITE ADDRESS:
www.americanantiquarian.org

FOUNDED: 1812

AREAS OF INTEREST:
American history and culture through 1876.

NAME(S) OF PROGRAMS:
● **AAS American Society for Eighteenth
Century Studies Fellowship**
● **AAS National Endowment for the
Humanities Fellowships**
● **AAS-Northeast Modern Language
Association Fellowship**
● **American Historical Print Collectors
Fellowship**
● **Stephen Botein Fellowships**
● **The "Drawn to Art" Fellowship**
● **Linda F. and Julian L. Lapides
Fellowship**
● **Jay and Deborah Last Fellowship**
● **The Legacy Fellowship**
● **Barbara Packer Fellowship**
● **Kate B. and Hall J. Peterson
Fellowships**
● **The Reese Fellowship**
● **Justin G. Schiller Fellowship**
● **Joyce A. Tracy Fellowship**

TYPE:
Conferences/seminars; Fellowships.
Fellowships provide support for residence at
the Society's library for research on any topic
supported by the collections. All awards are
for research and writing using the library's
resources.

YEAR PROGRAM STARTED: 1972

PURPOSE:
To enable scholars to come to Worcester for
an extended period to do research in the
Society's collections.

LEGAL BASIS:
AAS was incorporated by the legislature of
Massachusetts, October 24, 1812.

ELIGIBILITY:
Fellows are selected on the basis of the
applicant's scholarly qualifications, the
scholarly significance of the project, and the
appropriateness of the proposed study to the
Society's collections.

The National Endowment for the Humanities
Fellowships are intended for scholars beyond
the Doctorate, for which senior and
midcareer scholars are encouraged to apply.
Applicant must be a U.S. citizen.

Short-term fellowships are available for
scholars holding Ph.D. and for doctoral
candidates engaged in dissertation research.

FINANCIAL DATA:
Amount of support per award: Long-term
fellowships carry stipends up to $4,200 per
month. Short-term fellowships are $1,850 per
month.
Total amount of support: Varies.

NUMBER OF APPLICANTS MOST RECENT YEAR:
170.

NUMBER OF AWARDS: Up to 40.

APPLICATION INFORMATION:
Application information is available online.
Duration: One month for short-term
fellowships. Four to 12 months for long-term
fellowships.
Deadline: January 15. Announcement by
March 15.

ADDRESS INQUIRIES TO:
Paul Erickson
Director of Academic Programs
(See address above.)

*SPECIAL STIPULATIONS:
Recipient must maintain regular and
continuous residence at the Society during
his or her period of tenure.

AMERICAN ANTIQUARIAN SOCIETY (AAS) [346]

185 Salisbury Street
Worcester, MA 01609-1634
(508) 755-5221
Fax: (508) 753-3311

E-MAIL ADDRESS:
cmcrell@mwa.org

WEB SITE ADDRESS:
www.americanantiquarian.org

AREAS OF INTEREST:
American history, literature and culture
through 1876.

NAME(S) OF PROGRAMS:
● **AAS Fellowship for Creative and
Performing Artists and Writers**

TYPE:
Fellowships. Visiting fellowship for historical
research by creative and performing artists,
writers, filmmakers and journalists.

YEAR PROGRAM STARTED: 1995

PURPOSE:
To multiply and improve ways in which an
understanding of history is communicated to
the American people.

ELIGIBILITY:
Creative and performing artists, writers,
filmmakers, journalists, and others whose
goals are to produce imaginative,
non-formulaic works dealing with pre-20th
century American history. Works are for the
general public, rather than for academic or
educational audiences.

FINANCIAL DATA:
Amount of support per award: Stipend of
$1,350 for Fellows living on campus; $1,850
for Fellows residing off-campus.
Total amount of support: Varies.

NUMBER OF APPLICANTS MOST RECENT YEAR:
40.

NUMBER OF AWARDS: 4.

APPLICATION INFORMATION:
A complete fellowship application consists of
the following materials:
(1) cover sheet;
(2) current resume, including a list of any
awards, scholarships or grants received;
(3) a statement of not more than five typed,

double-spaced pages briefly summarizing the applicant's educational and professional background and goals, describing the research for the project including readings in primary and secondary sources, and indicating the nature of the research program proposed for the AAS fellowship;
(4) 10 copies of representative samples of previous works must be included for distribution to the selection committee. Written works (play and video scripts; prose and poetry; works of nonfiction, etc.) cannot exceed 25 pages in length. Applicants are welcome to send two or three copies of full, completed works in addition to the 25-page sample. If submitting samples of films, videos, audio and music recordings, or reproductions (digital versions and/or photographs) of paintings, sculptures, prints and other art works, please send only three copies or sets with the completed application. Applicants are encouraged to include any relevant reviews of their work by professional critics. If the applicant wishes to have any of these samples returned, please enclose a self-addressed, stamped envelope and;
(5) two letters of reference should be sent directly to AAS by individuals familiar with the applicant's career accomplishments and goals.

Duration: Four-week residency.

Deadline: October 5, with notification on or about December 5.

ADDRESS INQUIRIES TO:
James David Moran
Director of Outreach
(See address above.)

AMERICAN COUNCIL OF LEARNED SOCIETIES   [347]
633 Third Avenue, 8th Floor
New York, NY 10017-6795
(212) 697-1505 ext. 136 or 138

E-MAIL ADDRESS:
fellowships@acls.org

WEB SITE ADDRESS:
www.acls.org

FOUNDED: 1919

AREAS OF INTEREST:
The humanities and related social sciences.

NAME(S) OF PROGRAMS:
● **ACLS Fellowship**

TYPE:
Fellowships. Postdoctoral fellowships to support research in the humanities or research projects with a predominantly humanities-related emphasis in the social sciences.

PURPOSE:
To provide opportunities for scholars to engage in humanities research.

LEGAL BASIS:
Nonprofit.

ELIGIBILITY:
U.S. citizens or permanent residents holding a Ph.D. degree conferred two years before application deadline or its equivalent (taken to mean scholarly maturity as demonstrated by professional experience and publications) may apply.

FINANCIAL DATA:
Amount of support per award: Fellowships are up to $65,000 for full professor (and career equivalent), up to $45,000 for

associate professor (and career equivalent), and up to $35,000 for assistant professor (and career equivalent).

Total amount of support: Varies.

NUMBER OF APPLICANTS MOST RECENT YEAR: 1,119.

NUMBER OF AWARDS: 65.

APPLICATION INFORMATION:
Applications must be submitted through the ACLS Online Fellowship Application system.
Duration: Fellows must devote six to 12 continuous months to full-time work on supported projects.
Deadline: September 24.

THE AMERICAN NUMISMATIC SOCIETY   [348]
75 Varick Street, 11th Floor
New York, NY 10013
(212) 571-4470 ext. 153
Fax: (212) 571-4479

E-MAIL ADDRESS:
vanalfen@numismatics.org

WEB SITE ADDRESS:
www.numismatics.org

FOUNDED: 1858

AREAS OF INTEREST:
Numismatics (coins and medals), history and archeology.

NAME(S) OF PROGRAMS:
● **The Eric P. Newman Graduate Summer Seminar**

TYPE:
Grants-in-aid. Grants for graduate students and junior faculty to attend the Society's summer seminar held at its museum in New York. The Graduate Seminar in Numismatics is an intensive program of study including lectures and conferences conducted by specialists in various fields, preparation and oral delivery of a research paper and actual contact with the coinage in the Society's collection. Curatorial staff and other experts from the U.S. and abroad will participate in the seminar.

YEAR PROGRAM STARTED: 1952

PURPOSE:
To familiarize students with numismatic methodology and scholarship; to provide a deeper understanding of the contributions made by numismatics to other fields of study.

ELIGIBILITY:
Applications are accepted from students of demonstrated competence who will have completed at least one year of graduate work in history, art history, classical studies, economics, economic history or other related fields. Applications are encouraged from junior faculty members with an advanced degree in one of these fields.

Applications are also accepted from outstanding students from foreign institutions who have completed at least one year of graduate work and are able to demonstrate fluency in English; however, no financial aid for them is offered.

FINANCIAL DATA:
Stipends are available to qualified applicants who are citizens or permanent residents of the U.S.
Amount of support per award: Stipends of $4,000.

Total amount of support: Varies.

COOPERATIVE FUNDING PROGRAMS: Support of attendance at the Seminar is made possible by a generous donation from Mr. and Mrs. Eric P. Newman.

NUMBER OF APPLICANTS MOST RECENT YEAR: 50.

NUMBER OF AWARDS: Up to 6.

APPLICATION INFORMATION:
See web site for complete information. Applications must be supported by three letters of recommendation. Additional information and application forms will be provided upon request.
Duration: Seven to eight weeks, June through July.
Deadline: February 14.

OFFICERS:
Dr. Peter Van Alfen, Director

ADDRESS INQUIRIES TO:
Dr. Peter Van Alfen, Director
(See address above.)

AMERICAN PHILOSOPHICAL SOCIETY   [349]
c/o American Philosophical Society Library
105 South Fifth Street
Philadelphia, PA 19106-3386
(215) 440-3443
Fax: (215) 440-3423

E-MAIL ADDRESS:
libfellows@amphilsoc.org

WEB SITE ADDRESS:
www.amphilsoc.org/grants/resident

FOUNDED: 1743

AREAS OF INTEREST:
Scholarly research.

NAME(S) OF PROGRAMS:
● **The Library Resident Research Fellowships**

TYPE:
Fellowships; Grants-in-aid; Research grants. Short-term residential fellowships for conducting research in the Library's collections.

YEAR PROGRAM STARTED: 1991

PURPOSE:
To encourage research by scholars in the Library's collections.

LEGAL BASIS:
Nonprofit learned society.

ELIGIBILITY:
Open to both U.S. citizens and foreign nationals who are holders of a Ph.D. or the equivalent, Ph.D. candidates who have passed their preliminary exams and degreed independent scholars. Applicants in any relevant field of scholarship may apply.

FINANCIAL DATA:
Amount of support per award: $2,500 per month.

NUMBER OF APPLICANTS MOST RECENT YEAR: 69.

NUMBER OF AWARDS: 27.

APPLICATION INFORMATION:
Applications must be submitted online. Applicants will provide name, project title, affiliation, address, e-mail and telephone number. Project description must state the specific relevance of the American Philosophical Society's collections to the project and indicate expected results of the

research (such as publications), a curriculum vitae or resume and two letters of reference (doctoral candidates must use their dissertation advisor). Referees will also provide letters online. Instructions are in application information.

Duration: One to three months, taken between June 1 and May 31.

Deadline: March 1. Notification by May 1.

PUBLICATIONS:
Program announcement; list of guides to the Society's collections.

ADDRESS INQUIRIES TO:
Earle Spamer
The Library Resident Research Fellowships
(See address above.)

*SPECIAL STIPULATIONS:
Fellows are expected to be in residence during the period of their award.

THE AMERICAN SCHOOL OF CLASSICAL STUDIES AT ATHENS

6-8 Charlton Street
Princeton, NJ 08540-5232
(609) 683-0800
Fax: (609) 924-0578

E-MAIL ADDRESS:
ascsa@ascsa.org (for information)
application@ascsa.org (to apply)

WEB SITE ADDRESS:
www.ascsa.edu.gr

TYPE:
Fellowships. Fellowships for postdoctoral scholars and professionals in the humanities.

See entry 885 for full listing.

THE AMERICAN SCHOOL OF CLASSICAL STUDIES AT ATHENS

6-8 Charlton Street
Princeton, NJ 08540-5232
(609) 683-0800
Fax: (609) 924-0578

E-MAIL ADDRESS:
ascsa@ascsa.org (for information)
application@ascsa.org (to apply)

WEB SITE ADDRESS:
www.ascsa.edu.gr

TYPE:
Fellowships. The M. Alison Frantz Fellowship and The Jacob Hirsch Fellowship are part of the Student Associate Program, which is open to advanced graduate students in the same fields as the Regular Academic Program (classical studies and ancient Mediterranean studies and related fields such as history of art, anthropology, prehistory, studies in postclassical Greece, etc.), who plan to pursue independent research projects and who do not wish to commit to the full Regular Academic Program.

The Jacob Hirsch Fellowship is also open to students from Israel.

See entry 886 for full listing.

THE AMERICAN SCHOOL OF CLASSICAL STUDIES AT ATHENS

6-8 Charlton Street
Princeton, NJ 08540-5232
(609) 683-0800
Fax: (609) 924-0578

E-MAIL ADDRESS:
ascsa@ascsa.org (for information)
application@ascsa.org (to apply)

WEB SITE ADDRESS:
www.ascsa.edu.gr

TYPE:
Fellowships. Several Fellowships awarded by the School for the full academic year: the Samuel H. Kress Fellowship in art and architecture of antiquity; the Gorham Phillips Stevens Fellowship in the history of architecture; the Ione Mylonas Shear Fellowship in Mycenaean archaeology or Athenian architecture and/or archaeology; the Homer A. and Dorothy B. Thompson Fellowship in the study of pottery. Additionally, three Fellowships are unrestricted as to field: the Edward Capps, the Doreen Canaday Spitzer, and the Eugene Vanderpool Fellowships.

See entry 890 for full listing.

THE AMERICAN SCHOOL OF CLASSICAL STUDIES AT ATHENS

6-8 Charlton Street
Princeton, NJ 08540-5232
(609) 683-0800
Fax: (609) 924-0578

E-MAIL ADDRESS:
ascsa@ascsa.org (for information)
application@ascsa.org (to apply)

WEB SITE ADDRESS:
www.ascsa.edu.gr

TYPE:
Scholarships. Four-week program in intermediate-level Medieval Greek language and philology at the Gennadius Library, with site and museum trips. Seminar given every other year. Next seminar to be held in 2015.

See entry 893 for full listing.

ARCHAEOLOGICAL INSTITUTE OF AMERICA   [350]

656 Beacon Street, 6th Floor
Boston, MA 02215
(617) 358-4184
Fax: (617) 353-6550

E-MAIL ADDRESS:
fellowships@aia.bu.edu

WEB SITE ADDRESS:
www.archaeological.org

FOUNDED: 1879

AREAS OF INTEREST:
Archaeological research and publication.

NAME(S) OF PROGRAMS:
● **Jane C. Waldbaum Archaeological Field School Scholarship**

TYPE:
Scholarships. Award to support participation in an archaeological excavation or survey project.

YEAR PROGRAM STARTED: 2006

ELIGIBILITY:
Open to junior and senior undergraduates or first-year graduate students. Applicants cannot previously have participated in archaeological excavation and must be at least a junior at the time of application. Applicants must be enrolled in a college or university in the U.S. or Canada, but do not have to be U.S. citizens or residents.

FINANCIAL DATA:
Amount of support per award: $1,000.
Total amount of support: Varies.

NUMBER OF APPLICANTS MOST RECENT YEAR:
150.

NUMBER OF AWARDS: 10.

APPLICATION INFORMATION:
All applications must be submitted electronically through the AIA web site. Required materials include the application form, two letters of reference, official transcript(s) and a letter of acceptance from the field school. All application materials must be received by the deadline.

Duration: Minimum one-month stay at the field school. Nonrenewable.

Deadline: March 1.

ADDRESS INQUIRIES TO:
Laurel Nilsen Sparks
Lecture and Fellowship Coordinator
(See address above.)

ARCHAEOLOGICAL INSTITUTE OF AMERICA   [351]

656 Beacon Street, 6th Floor
Boston, MA 02215
(617) 358-4184
Fax: (617) 353-6550

E-MAIL ADDRESS:
lsparks@aia.bu.edu

WEB SITE ADDRESS:
www.archaeological.org

FOUNDED: 1879

AREAS OF INTEREST:
Archaeological research and publication.

NAME(S) OF PROGRAMS:
● **Olivia James Traveling Fellowship**

TYPE:
Fellowships. Awarded, preferably, to individuals engaged in dissertation research or to recent recipients of the Ph.D. (within five years of the application deadline) for travel and study in Greece, the Aegean Islands, Cyprus, Sicily, Southern Italy, Asia Minor or Mesopotamia to conduct a project in (most suitably) classics, sculpture, architecture, archaeology or history.

YEAR PROGRAM STARTED: 1961

PURPOSE:
To encourage the continued study of archaeological sites; to provide fellowships for travel and study in Greece, the Aegean Islands, Cyprus, Sicily, Southern Italy, Asia Minor or Mesopotamia.

LEGAL BASIS:
Nonprofit, scientific and educational organization.

ELIGIBILITY:
Applicants must be U.S. citizens. Preference is given to individuals engaged in dissertation research or to recent Ph.D. recipients (within five years of application deadline). Preference is also given to projects of at least a half-year's duration. The award is for travel and study in Greece, the Aegean Islands, Cyprus, Sicily, Southern Italy, Asia Minor or Mesopotamia and is not intended to support field excavation projects. Recipients may not hold other major fellowships during the requested tenure.

FINANCIAL DATA:
  Amount of support per award: $25,000.
  Total amount of support: $25,000.

NUMBER OF APPLICANTS MOST RECENT YEAR:
  11.

NUMBER OF AWARDS: 1.

APPLICATION INFORMATION:
  Official application materials are available
  August of each year on the Institute's web
  site. Graduate transcript(s), three letters of
  reference, and a summary statement of
  proposed project are required. Applications
  for the fellowship can be submitted
  electronically.
  Duration: Single fellowship for work to be
  conducted between July 1 and the following
  June 30.
  Deadline: November 1. Announcement by
  February 1.

ADDRESS INQUIRIES TO:
  Laurel Nilsen Sparks
  Lecture and Fellowship Coordinator
  (See address above.)

ARCHAEOLOGICAL INSTITUTE OF AMERICA   [352]
656 Beacon Street, 6th Floor
Boston, MA 02215
(617) 358-4184
Fax: (617) 353-6550

E-MAIL ADDRESS:
  lsparks@aia.bu.edu

WEB SITE ADDRESS:
  www.archaeological.org

FOUNDED: 1879

AREAS OF INTEREST:
  Archaeological research and publication.

NAME(S) OF PROGRAMS:
  ● **Harriet and Leon Pomerance Fellowship**

TYPE:
  Fellowships. Awarded to support a person on
  an individual project of a scholarly nature
  relating to Aegean Bronze Age Archaeology.
  Preference will be given to candidates whose
  project requires travel to the Mediterranean
  for the purpose stated above.

YEAR PROGRAM STARTED: 1972

PURPOSE:
  To promote serious scholarly study of
  Aegean Bronze Age Archaeology.

LEGAL BASIS:
  Nonprofit, scientific and educational
  organization.

ELIGIBILITY:
  Applicants must be citizens or permanent
  residents of the U.S. or Canada, or be
  actively pursuing an advanced degree at a
  North American college or university.
  Previous Harriet Pomerance Fellows are not
  eligible. At the conclusion of the fellowship
  tenure, the recipient must submit a report on
  the use of the stipend to the president of the
  Institute.

FINANCIAL DATA:
  Amount of support per award: $5,000.
  Total amount of support: $5,000.

NUMBER OF APPLICANTS MOST RECENT YEAR:
  7.

NUMBER OF AWARDS: 1.

APPLICATION INFORMATION:
  Official application materials are available
  online in August of each year. Graduate
  transcript(s), three letters of reference, and a
  summary statement of proposed project are
  required. Applications for the fellowship can
  be submitted electronically.
  Duration: One academic year or less.
  Deadline: November 1. Announcement by
  February 1.

ADDRESS INQUIRIES TO:
  Laurel Nilsen Sparks
  Lecture and Fellowship Coordinator
  (See address above.)

ARCHAEOLOGICAL INSTITUTE OF AMERICA   [353]
656 Beacon Street, 6th Floor
Boston, MA 02215
(617) 358-4184
Fax: (617) 353-6550

E-MAIL ADDRESS:
  fellowships@aia.bu.edu

WEB SITE ADDRESS:
  www.archaeological.org

FOUNDED: 1879

AREAS OF INTEREST:
  Archaeological research and publication.

NAME(S) OF PROGRAMS:
  ● **Anna C. and Oliver C. Colburn Fellowship**

TYPE:
  Fellowships. Awarded to an applicant every
  other year contingent upon his or her
  acceptance as an incoming Associate
  Member or Student Associate Member of the
  American School of Classical Studies at
  Athens, Greece.

YEAR PROGRAM STARTED: 1991

PURPOSE:
  To support studies at the American School of
  Classical Studies at Athens, Greece.

LEGAL BASIS:
  Nonprofit, scientific and educational
  organization.

ELIGIBILITY:
  Applicants must be U.S. or Canadian citizens
  or permanent residents, or those who are
  actively pursuing an advanced degree at a
  North American college or university, who
  are at the predoctoral stage or who have
  recently received the Ph.D. degree (within
  five years of the date of application). They
  must apply concurrently to the American
  School for Senior Associate Membership or
  Student Associate Membership. Applicants
  may not be Members of the American School
  during the year of application.

  Other major fellowships may not be held
  during the requested tenure of the fellowship
  award.

  The fellowship recipient is required to submit
  a report on the use of the stipend both to the
  President of the Archaeological Institute of
  America and to the Director of the American
  School of Classical Studies at Athens at the
  conclusion of the tenure of the fellowship.

FINANCIAL DATA:
  Amount of support per award: $11,000.
  Total amount of support: $11,000.

NUMBER OF APPLICANTS MOST RECENT YEAR:
  6.

NUMBER OF AWARDS: 1.

APPLICATION INFORMATION:
  Official application materials are available on
  the web site. Graduate transcript(s), three
  letters of reference, and a summary statement
  of the proposed project are required.
  Candidates must apply concurrently to the
  American School for Senior Associate
  Membership or Student Associate
  Membership.
  Duration: One academic year.
  Deadline: January 15, 2016 and every other
  year thereafter.

ADDRESS INQUIRIES TO:
  Laurel Nilsen Sparks
  Lecture and Fellowship Coordinator
  (See address above.)

*SPECIAL STIPULATIONS:
  After the tenure of their fellowship, all
  fellows are expected to submit an abstract to
  the Program Committee within two years, in
  accordance with that committee's guidelines,
  in order to present a paper on their research
  at the Institute annual meeting.

  Other major fellowships may not be held
  during the requested tenure of the Colburn
  award.

THE AUSTRALIAN NATIONAL UNIVERSITY   [354]
Humanities Research Centre, RSHA
Sir Roland Wilson Building, No. 120
McCoy Circuit
Canberra, ACT 0200 Australia
61 2 612 54357
Fax: 61 2 612 51380

E-MAIL ADDRESS:
  leena.messina@anu.edu.au

WEB SITE ADDRESS:
  hrc.anu.edu.au

FOUNDED: 1973

AREAS OF INTEREST:
  European thought and culture, their influence
  overseas, any area of research in the
  humanities (broadly interpreted), and human
  rights.

NAME(S) OF PROGRAMS:
  ● **Visiting Fellowships**

TYPE:
  Conferences/seminars; Fellowships. Visiting
  Fellowships are offered with a grant, without
  a grant or with a partial grant.

YEAR PROGRAM STARTED: 1973

PURPOSE:
  To stimulate research in the humanities
  throughout Australia.

LEGAL BASIS:
  Integral part of the Australian National
  University, Research School of Humanities.

ELIGIBILITY:
  Applicants are usually established academics
  and must have a higher degree. Relevance of
  project proposed to research platforms,
  publications.

FINANCIAL DATA:
  Amount of support per award: Visiting
  Fellowships provide accommodation for 60
  days plus airfares up to $3,000.
  Total amount of support: Approximately
  $150,000 (AUD) annually.

NUMBER OF APPLICANTS MOST RECENT YEAR:
  Approximately 60.

NUMBER OF AWARDS: Approximately 8 to 12.

APPLICATION INFORMATION:
Application form, curriculum vitae, and three reports from referees are required.
Duration: One year. Not usually renewable.
Deadline: Late February. Award announcement around June.

PUBLICATIONS:
Annual report; descriptive brochure; journal; application guidelines; forms and HRC bulletin.

ADDRESS INQUIRIES TO:
Leena Messina, Programs Manager
(See address above.)

JOHN CARTER BROWN LIBRARY
Brown University
Box 1894
Providence, RI 02912
(401) 863-2725
Fax: (401) 863-3477

E-MAIL ADDRESS:
jcbl_fellowships@brown.edu

WEB SITE ADDRESS:
www.jcbl.org

TYPE:
Fellowships; Research grants. The John Carter Brown Library (JCB), an independently funded institution for advanced research at Brown University, contains one of the world's premier collections of primary materials related to the discovery, exploration, and settlement of the New World to 1825, including books, maps, newspapers and other printed objects.

The Library offers both Short-term and Long-term Fellowships.

See entry 584 for full listing.

CANADIAN FEDERATION FOR THE HUMANITIES AND SOCIAL SCIENCES
275 Bank Street, Suite 300
Ottawa ON K2P 2L6 Canada
(613) 238-6112 ext. 352
Fax: (613) 238-6114

E-MAIL ADDRESS:
aspp-paes@ideas-idees.ca

WEB SITE ADDRESS:
www.ideas-idees.ca

TYPE:
Grants-in-aid. Grants to support the publication of scholarly books in the social sciences and humanities.

See entry 1848 for full listing.

CANADIAN INSTITUTE IN GREECE/L'INSTITUT CANADIEN EN GRECE   [355]
330 Albert Street
Waterloo ON N2L 3T8 Canada
(519) 886-4428

E-MAIL ADDRESS:
gschaus@wlu.ca

WEB SITE ADDRESS:
www.cig-icg.gr

FOUNDED: 1974

AREAS OF INTEREST:
Modern Greek, classical languages and literatures, history, archaeology, history of art and music.

NAME(S) OF PROGRAMS:
- Elizabeth Alfoldi-Rosenbaum Fellowship
- Franz and Neda Leipen Fellowship
- Homer and Dorothy Thompson Fellowship

TYPE:
Conferences/seminars; Endowments; Fellowships; Internships. Intended to support the graduate work of a person who needs to study in Greece.

YEAR PROGRAM STARTED: 1974

PURPOSE:
To promote the study of classical languages and literatures, history, archaeology, history of art and music in Greece.

LEGAL BASIS:
Incorporated in Canada and Greece.

ELIGIBILITY:
Open to Canadian citizens or landed immigrants.

FINANCIAL DATA:
Amount of support per award: $8,000 (CAN) plus housing at the Institute.
Total amount of support: Varies each year.

NUMBER OF APPLICANTS MOST RECENT YEAR: 4 to 6.

NUMBER OF AWARDS: 1.

APPLICATION INFORMATION:
Applicants must write, enclosing a curriculum vitae and an outline of the proposed research. Applicants must also arrange for three referees to send letters to the Canadian address.
Duration: Nine months.
Deadline: March 1. All fellowships are not offered every year.

PUBLICATIONS:
CIG Bulletin, semi-annually.

ADDRESS INQUIRIES TO:
E-mail: cig-icg@cig-icg.gr

CENTER FOR HELLENIC STUDIES   [356]
3100 Whitehaven Street, N.W.
Washington, DC 20008
(202) 745-4400
Fax: (202) 797-1540

E-MAIL ADDRESS:
chs@chs.harvard.edu
fellowships@chs.harvard.edu

WEB SITE ADDRESS:
www.chs.harvard.edu

FOUNDED: 1961

AREAS OF INTEREST:
Postgraduate ancient Greek studies.

TYPE:
Fellowships; Residencies; Visiting scholars. The Center offers Residential Fellowships to scholars working on various aspects of ancient Greek civilization. Eligible fields of research include archaeology, art history, epigraphy, history, literary criticism, philology, philosophy, pedagogical applications and interdisciplinary research.

YEAR PROGRAM STARTED: 1961

PURPOSE:
To encourage research in Hellenic studies.

LEGAL BASIS:
A unit of Harvard University.

ELIGIBILITY:
Investigators holding a Ph.D. degree or equivalent are eligible to apply. Professional competence in ancient Greek, as evidenced by publication, is essential.

FINANCIAL DATA:
Residential fellowships provide a stipend (maximum $17,000) plus lodging. Travel and research assistance available ($1,000).

COOPERATIVE FUNDING PROGRAMS: Joint Fellowships with German Archaeological Institute.

NUMBER OF APPLICANTS MOST RECENT YEAR: 85.

NUMBER OF AWARDS: CHS/DAI Joint Fellowships: 2; Residential Fellowships: 15 semester.

APPLICATION INFORMATION:
Official application materials are available at the web site.
Duration: Support is available for a nine-month period beginning September 1 and ending May 31. Fellowships are available for an 18-week period in the spring or the fall.
Deadline: October.

PUBLICATIONS:
Application form and guidelines.

DIRECTORS:
Gregory Nagy

ADDRESS INQUIRIES TO:
Fellowships and Curricular Development
(See address above.)

CENTER FOR MEDIEVAL AND RENAISSANCE STUDIES   [357]
University of California, Los Angeles
302 Royce Hall
Box 951485
Los Angeles, CA 90095-1485
(310) 825-1880
Fax: (310) 825-0655

E-MAIL ADDRESS:
cmrs@humnet.ucla.edu

WEB SITE ADDRESS:
www.cmrs.ucla.edu

FOUNDED: 1963

AREAS OF INTEREST:
All aspects related to the Medieval and Renaissance periods.

NAME(S) OF PROGRAMS:
- Ahmanson Research Fellowships for the Study of Medieval and Renaissance Books and Manuscripts
- CMRS Travel Grants
- Research Assistantships in Medieval and Renaissance Studies
- The George T. and Margaret W. Romani Fellowship
- Summer Fellowships in Medieval and Renaissance Studies
- Lynn and Maude White Fellowship

TYPE:
Assistantships; Awards/prizes; Conferences/seminars; Fellowships; Project/program grants; Research grants; Travel grants; Visiting scholars.

PURPOSE:
To promote interdisciplinary and cross-cultural studies of modern civilization in its formative period between the fourth and mid-17th centuries and to provide added research opportunities, facilities and assistance.

LEGAL BASIS:
Nonprofit university research organization.

ELIGIBILITY:
For the Ahmanson Research Fellowships, graduate students or scholars holding a Ph.D. (or the foreign equivalent) who are engaged in graduate-level, postdoctoral or independent research are invited to apply.

For the CMRS Travel Grants, applicant must be a UCLA graduate student attending conferences, symposia, meetings of professional organizations to present research papers on any topic in the field of Medieval and Renaissance Studies.

For Research Assistantships, the applicant must expect to be a registered graduate student at UCLA and must have the goal of obtaining a Ph.D. in the field of Medieval and Renaissance Studies.

For Romani Fellowship, students must be nominated by their academic departments, pursuing studies in an aspect of the Middle Ages or Renaissance under mentorship of an active CMRS faculty member.

For Summer Fellowships, the applicant must hold a Ph.D.

For the Lynn and Maude White Fellowship, the applicant must be a graduate student advanced to candidacy for the Ph.D. at UCLA in a department associated with the Center for Medieval and Renaissance Studies.

FINANCIAL DATA:
Amount of support per award: Ahmanson Research Fellowships: A stipend of $2,500 per month for fellowships lasting up to three months; CMRS Travel Grants: Varies; Romani Fellowship: $20,000 per year; Summer Fellowships: $500 stipend; Lynn and Maude White Fellowship: $15,000.

COOPERATIVE FUNDING PROGRAMS: Ahmanson Research Fellowships are offered through the generosity of the Ahmanson Foundation, the UCLA Center for Medieval and Renaissance Studies (CMRS) and the UCLA Library Special Collections (LSC).

NUMBER OF AWARDS: CMRS Travel Grants: Varies; Research Assistantships: 3; Romani Fellowship and Lynn and Maude White Fellowship: 1 every other year; Summer Fellowships: 2 to 3.

APPLICATION INFORMATION:
For the Ahmanson Research Fellowships, the application should include a cover letter, a curriculum vitae, an outline of research and special collections to be used (two pages maximum), dates to be spent in residence, and two letters of recommendation from faculty or other scholars familiar with the research project. Application materials may be submitted by e-mail (PDF format preferred) to the e-mail address above or to the postal address above, Attention: Ahmanson Fellowships.

For CMRS Travel Grants, submit letter of request with conference or meeting name, date and place; title of paper or research project being presented; travel expense budget; conference program.

For Research Assistantships, applicant must submit a curriculum vitae, transcripts, statement of purpose and three letters of recommendation.

For the Romani Fellowship, applicant must be nominated by department, pursuing study in Middle Ages or Renaissance topic, under CMRS faculty member mentorship in three categories: (1) graduate students newly admitted to UCLA; (2) continuing UCLA graduate students and; (3) graduate or postdoctoral students from other universities who have been invited to study at UCLA for a full academic year.

For Summer Fellowships, applicant must submit a curriculum vitae and a letter stating research project and a letter of recommendation.

For the Lynn and Maude White Fellowship, applicant must submit a curriculum vitae, a research proposal, three current letters of recommendation and a letter from the student's dissertation director.

Duration: Ahmanson Research Fellowships: Up to three months. Research Assistantships: Nine months, October through June annually. Summer Fellowship: Mid-June to end of September. Lynn and Maude White Fellowship: One year.

Deadline: Ahmanson Research Fellowships: Applications are due March 1 for fellowships to be taken within the 12-month period beginning July 1. Research Assistantships and Lynn and Maude White Fellowship: Early April with announcement in May. Summer Fellowship: Early February with announcement in March.

PUBLICATIONS:
Viator, annual journal; *Comitatus*, graduate journal; *Cursor Mundi*, book series.

STAFF:
Massimo Ciavolella, Director
Karen E. Burgess, Assistant Director
Benay Furtivo, Administrative Analyst
Brett Landenberger, Programmer Analyst
Blair Sullivan, Publications Director

ADDRESS INQUIRIES TO:
Karen E. Burgess, Assistant Director
(See address above.)

CENTER FOR 17TH AND 18TH CENTURY STUDIES [358]

University of California, Los Angeles
10745 Dickson Plaza, 310 Royce Hall
Los Angeles, CA 90095-1404
(310) 206-8552
Fax: (310) 206-8577

E-MAIL ADDRESS:
c1718cs@humnet.ucla.edu

WEB SITE ADDRESS:
www.c1718cs.ucla.edu/fellowships.htm

FOUNDED: 1985

AREAS OF INTEREST:
England between 1640 and 1830 (history, language and literature, religion and theology), Oscar Wilde and the 1890s, and modern fine printing.

NAME(S) OF PROGRAMS:
● **Clark Predoctoral Fellowships**

TYPE:
Fellowships. Offered for three consecutive months during the period July 1 through June 30 to registered University of California

doctoral candidates whose dissertation project is on a specific subject relevant to the collections and interests of the Clark Library.

YEAR PROGRAM STARTED: 1990

PURPOSE:
To provide support for research in the humanities.

LEGAL BASIS:
University.

ELIGIBILITY:
Advanced, registered University of California doctoral candidates are eligible.

GEOGRAPHIC RESTRICTIONS:
California.

FINANCIAL DATA:
Amount of support per award: Stipends are $7,500 for three months.
Total amount of support: $7,500 to $22,500 per academic year.

APPLICATION INFORMATION:
Applicants must submit:
(1) a curriculum vitae (maximum of two pages);
(2) a bibliography of scholarly works (published and unpublished) and;
(3) a statement of research plans (maximum 1,000 words, double-spaced).

In addition to the information provided on the application form, applicants must submit three scholarly references with required reference cover sheets.
Duration: Three months. Nonrenewable.
Deadline: February 1 of each year.

PUBLICATIONS:
Application guidelines; brochure on the Center and Library and its holdings; biennial newsletters; proceedings of conferences.

OFFICERS:
Barbara Fuchs, Director of the Center and Clark Library
Candis Snoddy, Assistant Director

ADDRESS INQUIRIES TO:
Myrna Ortiz, Fellowship Coordinator
(See address above.)

CENTER FOR 17TH AND 18TH CENTURY STUDIES [359]

University of California, Los Angeles
10745 Dickson Plaza, 310 Royce Hall
Los Angeles, CA 90095-1404
(310) 206-8552
Fax: (310) 206-8577

E-MAIL ADDRESS:
c1718cs@humnet.ucla.edu

WEB SITE ADDRESS:
www.c1718cs.ucla.edu/fellowships.htm

FOUNDED: 1985

AREAS OF INTEREST:
England between 1640 and 1750 (history, language and literature, religion and theology), Oscar Wilde and the 1890s, and modern fine printing.

NAME(S) OF PROGRAMS:
● **ASECS/Clark Library Fellowships**

TYPE:
Fellowships. Postdoctoral fellowships for research in residence for a period of one month any time from July 1 through June 30 at the William Andrews Clark Memorial Library on a project in The Restoration or eighteenth century.

YEAR PROGRAM STARTED: 1985

PURPOSE:
To provide support for research in the humanities.

LEGAL BASIS:
University.

ELIGIBILITY:
Candidates must:
(1) have received the Doctorate prior to appointment;
(2) be members in good standing of the American Society for Eighteenth-Century Studies and;
(3) be working on a project in The Restoration or the eighteenth century.

FINANCIAL DATA:
Amount of support per award: $2,500 for one month.

APPLICATION INFORMATION:
Application information may be obtained from the Center.
Duration: One month. Nonrenewable.
Deadline: February 1 of each year.

PUBLICATIONS:
Application guidelines; brochure on the Center and Library and its holdings; biennial newsletters; proceedings of conferences.

OFFICERS:
Barbara Fuchs, Director of the Center and Clark Library
Candis Snoddy, Assistant Director

ADDRESS INQUIRIES TO:
Myrna Ortiz, Fellowship Coordinator
(See address above.)

CENTER FOR 17TH AND 18TH CENTURY STUDIES   [360]

University of California, Los Angeles
10745 Dickson Plaza, 310 Royce Hall
Los Angeles, CA 90095-1404
(310) 206-8552
Fax: (310) 206-8577

E-MAIL ADDRESS:
c1718cs@humnet.ucla.edu

WEB SITE ADDRESS:
www.c1718cs.ucla.edu/fellowships.htm

FOUNDED: 1985

AREAS OF INTEREST:
England between 1640 and 1830 (history, language and literature, religion and theology), Oscar Wilde and the 1890s, and modern fine printing.

NAME(S) OF PROGRAMS:
- **Ahmanson and Getty Postdoctoral Fellowships**

TYPE:
Fellowships. With the support of the Ahmanson Foundation of Los Angeles and the J. Paul Getty Trust, the UCLA Center for 17th- and 18th-Century Studies and the William Andrews Clark Memorial Library have a theme-based fellowship program to encourage the participation of junior scholars in the Center's cross-disciplinary, comparative research projects. The major theme for a given year is announced the preceding fall.

Participating fellows will be expected to make a substantive contribution to program seminars.

YEAR PROGRAM STARTED: 1992

PURPOSE:
To provide support for research in the humanities.

LEGAL BASIS:
University.

ELIGIBILITY:
Candidates must have received their Ph.D. in the last six years prior to application and be engaged in research pertaining to the theme.

FINANCIAL DATA:
Amount of support per award: Stipends are $39,264 for the academic year.

APPLICATION INFORMATION:
Applicants must submit:
(1) a curriculum vitae (maximum of two pages);
(2) a bibliography of scholarly works (published and unpublished) and;
(3) a statement of research plans (maximum 1,000 words, double-spaced).

In addition to the information provided on the application form, applicants must submit three scholarly references with required reference cover sheets.
Duration: Three academic quarters. Nonrenewable.
Deadline: February 1 of each year preceding the award.

PUBLICATIONS:
Application guidelines; brochure on the Center and Library and its holdings; fellowships brochure; biennial newsletters; proceedings of conferences.

OFFICERS:
Barbara Fuchs, Director of the Clark Library and Director, Center for 17th- and 18th-Century Studies
Candis Snoddy, Assistant Director

ADDRESS INQUIRIES TO:
Myrna Ortiz, Fellowship Coordinator
(See address above.)

CENTER FOR 17TH AND 18TH CENTURY STUDIES   [361]

University of California, Los Angeles
405 Hilgard Avenue, 310 Royce Hall
Los Angeles, CA 90095-1404
(310) 206-8552
Fax: (310) 206-8577

E-MAIL ADDRESS:
c1718cs@humnet.ucla.edu

WEB SITE ADDRESS:
www.c1718cs.ucla.edu/fellowships.htm

FOUNDED: 1985

AREAS OF INTEREST:
England between 1640 and 1830 (history, language and literature, religion and theology), Oscar Wilde and the 1890s, and modern fine printing.

NAME(S) OF PROGRAMS:
- **Short-Term Research Fellowships**

TYPE:
Fellowships. Short-term (one to three months) postdoctoral fellowships for research in residence for any period of the year (July 1 through June 30) at the William Andrews Clark Memorial Library on specific subjects relevant to the collections and interests of the Library.

YEAR PROGRAM STARTED: 1985

PURPOSE:
To provide support for research in the humanities.

LEGAL BASIS:
University.

ELIGIBILITY:
Candidates must have received the Doctorate prior to appointment. Preference will be given to applicants outside the southern California area.

FINANCIAL DATA:
Amount of support per award: $2,500 per month.
Total amount of support: Varies.

NUMBER OF AWARDS: Varies.

APPLICATION INFORMATION:
Application information may be obtained from the Center.
Duration: One to three months. Nonrenewable.
Deadline: February 1 of each year.

PUBLICATIONS:
Application guidelines; brochure on the Center and Library and its holdings; biennial newsletters; proceedings of conferences.

OFFICERS:
Barbara Fuchs, Director of the Center and Clark Library
Candis Snoddy, Assistant Director

ADDRESS INQUIRIES TO:
Myrna Ortiz, Fellowship Coordinator
(See address above.)

CENTER FOR THE HUMANITIES   [362]

Mellon Postdoctoral Fellowship Program
Wesleyan University
95 Pearl Street
Middletown, CT 06459-0069
(860) 685-3044
Fax: (860) 685-2171

E-MAIL ADDRESS:
esavage@wesleyan.edu

WEB SITE ADDRESS:
www.wesleyan.edu/humanities

FOUNDED: 1959

AREAS OF INTEREST:
The Center aims to explore fresh and vital aspects of the humanities, to realize an interdisciplinary response to human problems and to generate new possibilities for curricular reform. In fulfilling these aims, the Center must also examine the assumptions that underlie academic disciplines and humanistic theories. It must encourage research as well as the fundamental discourse of teachers and students.

NAME(S) OF PROGRAMS:
- **Andrew W. Mellon Postdoctoral Fellowship**

TYPE:
Fellowships. The aims of the Center are reflected in its constituency which includes scholars, artists, public figures and students. Fellows range in age and achievement from undergraduates to the most eminent humanists. Departments at Wesleyan University participating in the Center include Classics, Modern Languages and Literatures, English, the College of Letters, Philosophy, History, Religion, Anthropology, Psychology and the Fine Arts.

PURPOSE:
To promote advanced study and research in the humanities, arts and qualitative social sciences; to provide scholars who have lately completed their Ph.Ds. with free time to

further their own work in a cross-disciplinary setting, and to associate them with a distinguished faculty.

LEGAL BASIS:
Grant from Andrew W. Mellon Foundation to Wesleyan University.

ELIGIBILITY:
Scholars who have received their Ph.D. degree after June 2011 in any field of inquiry in the humanities or humanistic social sciences - broadly conceived - are invited to apply.

Fellows will be expected to participate in the lectures, colloquia and discussion groups that are organized each semester around a specific theme chosen for its theoretical interest and its pertinence to crucial problems in related disciplines of the humanities, the qualitative social sciences or the arts. Additional duties of the fellows will be to teach one course and to give one public lecture.

Fellow must reside in Middletown, CT for tenure of fellowship.

FINANCIAL DATA:
Amount of support per award: $40,000.

COOPERATIVE FUNDING PROGRAMS: Andrew W. Mellon Foundation.

NUMBER OF APPLICANTS MOST RECENT YEAR: 250.

NUMBER OF AWARDS: 1 to 2 each year.

APPLICATION INFORMATION:
There is no official application form. Applications should include:
(1) a letter from the applicant, including a statement of current research interests and a brief proposal for a one-semester undergraduate course related to the Center for the Humanities theme;
(2) a full curriculum vitae;
(3) three letters of recommendation and;
(4) copies of published work, extracts from the dissertation, or drafts of work in progress (not to exceed 25 pages).
Duration: One year.

PUBLICATIONS:
Brochure.

ADDRESS INQUIRIES TO:
Ethan Kleinberg, Director
(See address above.)

CONNECTICUT HUMANITIES   [363]
37 Broad Street
Middletown, CT 06457
(860) 685-2260
Fax: (860) 685-7597

E-MAIL ADDRESS:
info@cthumanities.org

WEB SITE ADDRESS:
www.cthumanities.org

FOUNDED: 1973

AREAS OF INTEREST:
Humanities in Connecticut, heritage and reading.

NAME(S) OF PROGRAMS:
• **Connecticut Center for the Book**
• **Connecticut Humanities Fund**
• **Humanities Resource Center**

TYPE:
Awards/prizes; Challenge/matching grants; Conferences/seminars; Development grants; Project/program grants; Technical assistance. Workshops.

YEAR PROGRAM STARTED: 1973

PURPOSE:
To create opportunities to think, learn and understand more about ourselves, our communities and our state.

ELIGIBILITY:
Applicants must be incorporated as private, nonprofit organizations or municipalities in Connecticut, and must regularly provide service to the public.

GEOGRAPHIC RESTRICTIONS:
Connecticut.

FINANCIAL DATA:
Amount of support per award: $1,000 to $50,000.
Total amount of support: Varies.
Matching fund requirements: All Connecticut Humanities Fund grants must be matched dollar for dollar through a combination of in-kind contributions and/or cash offered by applicants, partners, and/or third parties, i.e., grants or bequests. Funds from the State of Connecticut may not be used for matching purposes.

COOPERATIVE FUNDING PROGRAMS: Hartford Foundation for Public Giving.

NUMBER OF APPLICANTS MOST RECENT YEAR: 119.

NUMBER OF AWARDS: 85.

REPRESENTATIVE AWARDS:
$20,000 to Lockwood Mathews Mansion Museum for implementing an exhibition entitled "What Is It? Technologies and Discoveries of the Victorian Era;" $13,700 to Noah Webster House to develop an electronic tablet-guided tour that combines storytelling, interpretive illustrations and new technologies to tell the story of Noah Webster's life and times.

APPLICATION INFORMATION:
Preapplication discussion with CTH staff is strongly urged two months before submission of formal application. Specify the grant line and program category when submitting proposal.
Duration: Four months to two years.
Deadline: For grants up to $9,999: January 1, April 1, July 1 and October 1; For grants $10,000 or more: February 1, May 1, August 1 and November 1; For monthly grants $1,500 or less: First business day of the month.

STAFF:
Stuart Parnes, Executive Director
Brett Thompson, Deputy Director
Carolyn Buchholz, Director of Finance and Human Resources
Lauren Miller, Program Officer Grants
Scott Wands, Program Officer Human Resources
Susan Muro, Program Officer Public Humanities

ADDRESS INQUIRIES TO:
Lauren Miller, Program Officer Grants
(See address above.)

CORNELL UNIVERSITY   [364]
Society for the Humanities
A.D. White House
27 East Avenue
Ithaca, NY 14853-1101
(607) 255-9274
(607) 255-4086
Fax: (607) 255-1422

E-MAIL ADDRESS:
humctr@cornell.edu

WEB SITE ADDRESS:
www.arts.cornell.edu/sochum

FOUNDED: 1966

AREAS OF INTEREST:
Postdoctoral fellowships in the humanities.

NAME(S) OF PROGRAMS:
• **Mellon Postdoctoral Fellowships**

TYPE:
Fellowships. Postdoctoral teaching-research fellowships in the humanities, each awarded for a two-year period. While in residence at Cornell, postdoctoral fellows hold department affiliation and have limited teaching duties and the opportunity for scholarly work.

PURPOSE:
To encourage the academic growth of promising humanists with recent Ph.D. degrees.

LEGAL BASIS:
University.

ELIGIBILITY:
Applicants who will receive the Ph.D. degree by June 30 of the beginning program year are eligible to apply. Such applicants must include a letter of confirmation.

FINANCIAL DATA:
Fellows receive stipend while in residence.
Amount of support per award: $45,000 per year.
Total amount of support: Varies.

COOPERATIVE FUNDING PROGRAMS: Funded by a grant from the Andrew W. Mellon Foundation.

NUMBER OF AWARDS: 2 for the year 2013.

APPLICATION INFORMATION:
Application procedures are found on the web site.

If the applicant does not have a Ph.D. in hand at the time of application, a letter of confirmation must be received from applicant's committee chair or department stating that applicant will have the Ph.D. degree before the term of the fellowship begins on July 1 of the beginning program year. Faxed applications will not be accepted.
Duration: Two years.

ADDRESS INQUIRIES TO:
Program Administrator
Mellon Postdoctoral Fellowships
(See address above.)

CORNELL UNIVERSITY   [365]
Society for the Humanities
A.D. White House
27 East Avenue
Ithaca, NY 14853-1101
(607) 255-9274
(607) 255-4086
Fax: (607) 255-1422

E-MAIL ADDRESS:
humctr@cornell.edu

WEB SITE ADDRESS:
www.arts.cornell.edu/sochum

FOUNDED: 1966

AREAS OF INTEREST:
Humanities studies.

NAME(S) OF PROGRAMS:
- **Society for the Humanities Fellowships**

TYPE:
Fellowships. Yearly fellowships with a new focal theme each year. Fellows include scholars from other universities and members of the Cornell faculty released from regular duties.

The Focal Theme for 2015-16: Time.

PURPOSE:
To support research and encourage imaginative teaching in the humanities.

LEGAL BASIS:
University.

ELIGIBILITY:
Applicants must have received the Ph.D. degree before January 1 of the year of their application. They must have one or more years of teaching experience which may include teaching as a graduate student. Fellows should be working on topics related to the year's theme. Their approach to humanities should be broad enough to appeal to students and scholars in several humanistic disciplines.

FINANCIAL DATA:
Fellows receive a stipend and spend most of their time in research and writing but are encouraged to offer an informal seminar related to their research. Applicants living outside North America are eligible for an additional $2,000 to assist with travel costs.
Amount of support per award: $45,000.
Total amount of support: Varies.

NUMBER OF APPLICANTS MOST RECENT YEAR:
150.

NUMBER OF AWARDS: 6 to 8 each year.

APPLICATION INFORMATION:
Application procedures are found on the web site.

Candidates should inform the Society of their intention to apply. The following materials must be submitted:
(1) a curriculum vitae;
(2) a copy of one scholarly paper (no more than 35 pages in length);
(3) a one-page abstract and a detailed statement of the research project the applicant would like to pursue during the term of the fellowship (1,000 to 3,000 words);
(4) a two-page proposal for a seminar related to the applicant's research and;
(5) two letters of recommendation from senior colleagues to whom candidates should send their research proposal and teaching proposal.

Referees should send their letters of recommendation directly to the Society before the closing date. Faxed applications will not be accepted.
Duration: One academic year.
Deadline: Application materials, including letters of recommendation, must be postmarked on or before October 1 of the year prior to the beginning of the fellowship. Awards are announced by the end of December of that year of application.

PUBLICATIONS:
Brochure.

ADDRESS INQUIRIES TO:
Paula L. Epps-Cepero, Program Administrator
Society for the Humanities
(See address above.)

*SPECIAL STIPULATIONS:
Fellows spend their time in research and writing, participate in the weekly Fellows Seminar, and offer one seminar related to their research.

CULTURAL SERVICES OF THE FRENCH EMBASSY
972 Fifth Avenue
New York, NY 10075
(212) 439-1463
Fax: (212) 439-1455

E-MAIL ADDRESS:
puf.scac@ambafrance-us.org

WEB SITE ADDRESS:
www.facecouncil.org/puf

TYPE:
Project/program grants; Research grants. Grants provided by this Fund support research and graduate education partnerships between French and American universities with emphasis placed on novel, innovative and interdisciplinary projects when relevant.

See entry 909 for full listing.

GLADYS KRIEBLE DELMAS FOUNDATION [366]
275 Madison Avenue, 33rd Floor
New York, NY 10016-1101
(212) 687-0011
Fax: (212) 687-8877

E-MAIL ADDRESS:
info@delmas.org

WEB SITE ADDRESS:
www.delmas.org

FOUNDED: 1976

AREAS OF INTEREST:
Humanities, research libraries, performing arts and research in the history and culture of Venice and the Veneto.

NAME(S) OF PROGRAMS:
- **Humanities Program**
- **Performing Arts Program**
- **Research Library Program**
- **Venetian Research Program**

TYPE:
Conferences/seminars; Fellowships; General operating grants; Project/program grants; Research grants.

YEAR PROGRAM STARTED: 1977

PURPOSE:
To provide grants for research projects in Venice and the Veneto; to support performing arts organizations in New York and research libraries and humanities projects.

LEGAL BASIS:
Private foundation.

ELIGIBILITY:
For Venetian Research Program, applicants must be U.S. citizens or permanent residents at the predoctoral and postdoctoral levels. If graduate students, applicants must have fulfilled all doctoral requirements except for completion of the dissertation at the time of application.

GEOGRAPHIC RESTRICTIONS:
Performing Arts Grants to New York City only.

FINANCIAL DATA:
Amount of support per award: Varies.

NUMBER OF APPLICANTS MOST RECENT YEAR:
350.

NUMBER OF AWARDS: 150.

REPRESENTATIVE AWARDS:
$210,000 over three years to the New York Public Library for the Performing Arts; $25,000 to the American Philological Association for the Classical Atlas Project; $4,200 for "Theatrical Dance in 17th Century Venetian Opera;" $7,000 for "Pseudo-Dionysius and the Mathematical Culture of 16th Century Venice."

APPLICATION INFORMATION:
Contact the Foundation.
Duration: Varies.
Deadline: Venetian Research Program: December 15.

TRUSTEES:
George Labalme, Jr.
Joseph C. Mitchell
Deirdre C. Stam

DISTRICT OF COLUMBIA COMMISSION ON THE ARTS AND HUMANITIES
200 I Street, S.E.
Suite 1400
Washington, DC 20003
(202) 724-5613
Fax: (202) 727-4135
TDD: (202) 727-3148

E-MAIL ADDRESS:
moshe.adams@dc.gov

WEB SITE ADDRESS:
www.dcarts.dc.gov

TYPE:
Awards/prizes; Capital grants; Challenge/matching grants; Conferences/seminars; Exchange programs; Fellowships; General operating grants; Grants-in-aid; Project/program grants; Research grants; Residencies. Services provided to arts institutions and individual artists including inquiry services, technical assistance and funding.

See entry 447 for full listing.

DUMBARTON OAKS [367]
1703 32nd Street, N.W.
Washington, DC 20007
(202) 339-6410
(202) 339-6414
Fax: (202) 339-6419

E-MAIL ADDRESS:
FellowshipPrograms@doaks.org

WEB SITE ADDRESS:
www.doaks.org

FOUNDED: 1940

AREAS OF INTEREST:
Archaeology, gardens, history, history of art, philosophy, landscape, language, literature, religion and theology.

NAME(S) OF PROGRAMS:
- **Fellowships and Project Grants in Byzantine Studies, Pre-Columbian Studies and Garden and Landscape Studies**

TYPE:
Awards/prizes; Fellowships; Internships; Project/program grants; Residencies. Residential fellowships and project support in the area of Byzantine studies (including

related aspects of late Roman, early Christian, western medieval, Slavic and Near Eastern studies), Pre-Columbian studies (of Mexico, Central America and Andean South America), and Garden and Landscape studies (including garden history, landscape architecture and related disciplines).

YEAR PROGRAM STARTED: 1941

PURPOSE:
To promote research in Byzantine studies, Pre-Columbian studies, and Garden and Landscape studies.

LEGAL BASIS:
Research institute affiliated with Harvard University.

ELIGIBILITY:
Fellowships are awarded on the basis of demonstrated scholarly ability and preparation of the candidate, including knowledge of the requisite languages, interest and value of the study or project and the project's relevance to the resources of Dumbarton Oaks.

Junior Fellowships are awarded to degree candidates who at the time of application have fulfilled all preliminary requirements for a Ph.D. or appropriate final degree and plan to work on a dissertation or final project at Dumbarton Oaks under the direction of a faculty member from their own university.

Fellowships are awarded to scholars who hold a Ph.D. or appropriate final degree or have established themselves in their field and wish to pursue their own research. Graduate students who expect to have a Ph.D. prior to taking up residence at Dumbarton Oaks may also apply.

Summer Fellowships are awarded to Byzantine, Pre-Columbian, or Garden and Landscape scholars on any level beyond the first year of graduate (postbaccalaureate) study.

FINANCIAL DATA:
Fellowships and Junior Fellowships: Award includes stipend, housing (with the exception of residents from the greater Washington, DC metropolitan area), a dependent allowance, a research expense allowance, lunch on weekdays, and a health insurance contribution from Dumbarton Oaks. Travel expense reimbursement may be provided for Fellows and Junior Fellows if support cannot be obtained from other sources.

Summer Fellowships: Besides maintenance allowance, support includes housing in a Dumbarton Oaks apartment, lunch on weekdays, Dumbarton Oaks's health insurance contribution, and travel expense reimbursement if other travel support cannot be obtained. No housing allowances or dependents' allowances for families are available in the summer.

Amount of support per award: Fellowship awards are approximately $27,000 for an unmarried Junior Fellow to a maximum of $47,000 for a Fellow from outside the U.S. accompanied by family members. This includes a stipend of approximately $15,500 for a Junior Fellow; $28,000 stipend for a Fellow for the full academic year.

A maintenance allowance of $250 per week for Summer Fellowships.

NUMBER OF APPLICANTS MOST RECENT YEAR: 216.

NUMBER OF AWARDS: 10 Junior Fellowships; 12 Fellowships; 12 Summer Fellowships.

APPLICATION INFORMATION:
Applications must be submitted electronically. A brochure is available upon request to the Director's office.
Duration: Fellowships are usually awarded for a full academic year (mid-September to mid-May); however, requests for a single term of support (mid-September to early January or mid-January to mid-May) are also considered. Summer Fellowships are awarded for periods of six to nine weeks, beginning early June and ending early August.
Deadline: Applications must be received on or before November 1 preceding the academic year for which support is sought. Applicants are informed in mid-February.

PUBLICATIONS:
Fellowship and Project award brochure; application guidelines.

OFFICERS:
Jan Ziolkowski, Director

ADDRESS INQUIRIES TO:
E-mail specific program:
Byzantine@doaks.org
Pre-Columbian@doaks.org or
Landscape@doaks.org

*SPECIAL STIPULATIONS:
Fellowships are tenable only for full-time resident work.

DUQUESNE UNIVERSITY, DEPARTMENT OF PHILOSOPHY   [368]
600 Forbes Avenue
Pittsburgh, PA 15282
(412) 396-6500
Fax: (412) 396-5353

E-MAIL ADDRESS:
thompson@duq.edu

WEB SITE ADDRESS:
www.duq.edu/academics/schools/liberal-arts/graduate-school/programs/philosophy

FOUNDED: 1878

AREAS OF INTEREST:
The Ph.D. program in the Department of Philosophy at Duquesne University emphasizes continental philosophy, i.e., phenomenology and 20th Century French and German philosophy, as well as the history of philosophy.

NAME(S) OF PROGRAMS:
● **Duquesne University Graduate Assistantship**

TYPE:
Assistantships; Conferences/seminars; Exchange programs. Philosophy assistantship.

PURPOSE:
To provide a stipend to enable students to obtain a Ph.D. in philosophy.

ELIGIBILITY:
Open to holders of a Bachelor's degree in philosophy, or its equivalent, who have a grade point average of at least 3.7 and an excellent graduate record examination score. Candidates should have knowledge of a second language.

FINANCIAL DATA:
Amount of support per award: Stipend of $17,000 plus all tuition for coursework.

NUMBER OF APPLICANTS MOST RECENT YEAR: 170.

NUMBER OF AWARDS: 17.

APPLICATION INFORMATION:
Applicants must complete an application including a statement of intent and three letters of recommendation, Graduate Record Examination scores and application form and fee, plus test of English as a Foreign Language scores.
Duration: Four years.
Deadline: Ph.D. January 15; M.A. March 1.

ADDRESS INQUIRIES TO:
Ronald Polansky, Chairperson
(See address above.)

EARTHWATCH INSTITUTE
114 Western Avenue
Boston, MA 02134
(800) 776-0188
Fax: (978) 461-2332

E-MAIL ADDRESS:
research@earthwatch.org

WEB SITE ADDRESS:
www.earthwatch.org/research

TYPE:
Research grants. Both personnel and financial support to field research projects. Volunteers pay to support the project and also work as research assistants to the scholars, usually for two- to three-week periods. Teams range in size from four to 20, with the average expedition using three to five teams. Since numbers of dollars vary directly with numbers of volunteers, applicants are urged to pay close attention to that relationship in their research design.

See entry 1817 for full listing.

THE FIELDSTONE FOUNDATION   [369]
14 Corporate Plaza, Suite 100
Newport Beach, CA 92660
(949) 873-2717
Fax: (949) 515-8520

E-MAIL ADDRESS:
janinem@fieldstonefoundation.org

WEB SITE ADDRESS:
www.fieldstonefoundation.org

FOUNDED: 1983

AREAS OF INTEREST:
Educational, humanitarian, and Christian ministries and cultural arts.

CONSULTING OR VOLUNTEER SERVICES:
Nonprofit executive leadership training and peer coaching.

TYPE:
Challenge/matching grants; General operating grants; Project/program grants.

YEAR PROGRAM STARTED: 1983

PURPOSE:
To improve the quality of life for children and families.

ELIGIBILITY:
Eligible organizations must be IRS 501(c)(3) tax-exempt. The Foundation does not fund grants to individuals or churches.

GEOGRAPHIC RESTRICTIONS:
Orange and San Diego counties, California.

FINANCIAL DATA:
Amount of support per award: Varies.
Total amount of support: Varies.

NUMBER OF AWARDS: 44.

APPLICATION INFORMATION:
The application must include a copy of the IRS tax determination letter. Proposals by invitation only. Foundation staff will initiate all grant considerations.

Duration: One year.

STAFF:
Marcos Ramirez
Robin Stropko

ADDRESS INQUIRIES TO:
Janine Mason
(See address above.)

THE FOLGER INSTITUTE [370]
Folger Shakespeare Library
201 East Capitol Street, S.E.
Washington, DC 20003-1094
(202) 675-0333
Fax: (202) 544-4623

E-MAIL ADDRESS:
institute@folger.edu

WEB SITE ADDRESS:
www.folger.edu/institute

FOUNDED: 1970

AREAS OF INTEREST:
Early modern history, literature, political science, art and cultural studies.

NAME(S) OF PROGRAMS:
• **Early Modern Studies**

TYPE:
Conferences/seminars; Grants-in-aid; Internships; Travel grants. Fall and Spring seminars and workshops. Yearlong colloquia. Stipends for institutes. Grants for travel and lodging expenses, according to need, for workshops and seminars.

YEAR PROGRAM STARTED: 1986

PURPOSE:
To advance the teachings and study of the early modern period.

LEGAL BASIS:
Research center at an independent research library.

ELIGIBILITY:
Grants in support of program participation are available to affiliates of the member universities. The Folger Institute does not offer grants-in-aid support of scholars from outside of the consortium.

APPLICATION INFORMATION:
Application information and forms are available on the web site. Letters of recommendation should be sent to the e-mail address listed above.

Duration: Six to nine months.

Deadline: Long-term research fellowships: November 1. Short-term fellowships: March 1.

OFFICERS:
Kathleen Lynch, Executive Director
Owen Williams, Assistant Director, Scholarly Programs
Carol Brobeck, Fellowships Administrator

ADDRESS INQUIRIES TO:
Elyse Martin, Program Assistant
(See address above.)

*PLEASE NOTE:
Scholars wishing to apply for long- or short-term fellowships should contact Carol Brobeck, Fellowships Administrator at the address above or call (202) 675-0348; e-mail: brobeck@folger.edu.

THE GWATHMEY MEMORIAL TRUST [371]
Bank of America Center
VA2-300-12-92
1111 East Main Street
Richmond, VA 23219-3500
(804) 887-8773
Fax: (980) 233-7158

E-MAIL ADDRESS:
sarah.kay@ustrust.com

WEB SITE ADDRESS:
www.bankofamerica.com/philanthropic

FOUNDED: 1982

AREAS OF INTEREST:
History, literature, art and architecture, and direct services.

TYPE:
Development grants; Project/program grants.

YEAR PROGRAM STARTED: 1982

ELIGIBILITY:
Grants are made to Virginia institutions and organizations which are tax-exempt 501(c)(3) organizations and operate for charitable, scientific, literary, or educational purposes. Preference is given to specific, well-defined projects and programs whose results can be evaluated.

Grants are not made to private foundations, national or community organizations, or to individuals.

GEOGRAPHIC RESTRICTIONS:
Virginia.

FINANCIAL DATA:
Amount of support per award: $5,000 to $50,000; Average: $15,000 to $20,000.
Total amount of support: Average $650,000 annually.

NUMBER OF AWARDS: 30 to 40.

APPLICATION INFORMATION:
All applicants must submit a description of the organization, evidence of the organization's tax-exempt and private foundation status, financial statements, and names and affiliations of the organization's trustees, directors, advisors and principal staff. In addition, a concise description of the project including the needs and anticipated benefits to be met, detailed financial plan, brief biographical background of the person who will conduct or supervise the proposed program, plans for evaluation of the project's results, and covering letter from an official of the organization stating that the organization has formally approved the proposed program are required.

Duration: One year.

Deadline: March 1 and September 1.

PUBLICATIONS:
Guidelines for applicants.

ADDRESS INQUIRIES TO:
Sarah Kay, Vice President, Senior Philanthropic Relationship Manager
(See address above.)

THE HASTINGS CENTER
21 Malcolm Gordon Road
Garrison, NY 10524
(845) 424-4040
Fax: (845) 424-4545

E-MAIL ADDRESS:
visitors@thehastingscenter.org

WEB SITE ADDRESS:
www.thehastingscenter.org

TYPE:
Residencies; Visiting scholars. Independent study. Some financial aid is available.

See entry 2107 for full listing.

HAWAII STATE FOUNDATION ON CULTURE AND THE ARTS
250 South Hotel Street
Second Floor
Honolulu, HI 96813
(808) 586-0305
Fax: (808) 586-0308
TTY: (808) 586-0740

E-MAIL ADDRESS:
jonathan.johnson@hawaii.gov

WEB SITE ADDRESS:
hawaii.gov/sfca

TYPE:
Project/program grants.

See entry 456 for full listing.

THE GEORGE A. AND ELIZA GARDNER HOWARD FOUNDATION
80 Brown Street
Providence, RI 02912
(401) 863-2640
Fax: (401) 863-6280

E-MAIL ADDRESS:
howard_foundation@brown.edu

WEB SITE ADDRESS:
www.brown.edu/Howard_Foundation

TYPE:
Fellowships. The Foundation awards a limited number of fellowships each year for independent projects in fields selected on a rotational basis.

See entry 1632 for full listing.

THE HUNTINGTON FOUNDATION, INC. [372]
401 11th Street, Suite 306
Huntington, WV 25701-2239
(304) 522-0611

FOUNDED: 1986

AREAS OF INTEREST:
Charitable, religious, educational and scientific pursuits.

TYPE:
Challenge/matching grants.

YEAR PROGRAM STARTED: 1986

PURPOSE:
To encourage institutional change or to help grant recipients make more effective use of resources they generate from other sources (challenge grants); to promote strong public/private collaborative efforts to meet community needs and to foster volunteer efforts wherever possible.

ELIGIBILITY:
The Foundation does not make grants for salaries and normal operating expenses. Grants are made only to organizations qualifying for tax exemption under Section 501(c)(3) of the Internal Revenue Code.

Current priorities for grants include:
(1) health care programs;
(2) medical education and research;
(3) youth programs for educational, religious and physical development and;
(4) cultural, educational and recreational programs that enhance the quality of life in the community.

Construction grants are not accepted.

GEOGRAPHIC RESTRICTIONS:
Areas of Cabell and Wayne counties, West Virginia.

FINANCIAL DATA:
Amount of support per award: Varies.
Total amount of support: Varies.

APPLICATION INFORMATION:
A standard application form is required, which will be sent upon request. Five copies of the application should be sent to the president of the Foundation at the address above.
Duration: One to three years.
Deadline: January, April, July and October.

PUBLICATIONS:
Guidelines.

ADDRESS INQUIRIES TO:
Glenna J. Smoot, Executive Secretary
(See address above.)

HENRY E. HUNTINGTON LIBRARY AND ART GALLERY   [373]
1151 Oxford Road
San Marino, CA 91108
(626) 405-2194
Fax: (626) 449-5703

E-MAIL ADDRESS:
cpowell@huntington.org

WEB SITE ADDRESS:
www.huntington.org

FOUNDED: 1919

AREAS OF INTEREST:
British and American art history, history, literature and history of science.

NAME(S) OF PROGRAMS:
● **Research Awards at the Huntington Library and Art Gallery**

TYPE:
Fellowships; Research grants; Visiting scholars. Grants for studies in American or British literature, history, art history and history of science.

YEAR PROGRAM STARTED: 1927

PURPOSE:
To encourage significant scholarship in the areas of the Huntington collections.

LEGAL BASIS:
Private, nonprofit.

ELIGIBILITY:
Persons who have demonstrated unusual abilities as scholars are encouraged to apply. Consideration is given to the value of the candidate's project and the degree to which the Huntington Library will be used. Projects to be used for doctoral dissertations will be considered.

FINANCIAL DATA:
Amount of support per award: Short-term: $3,000 per month; Long-term: $50,000 for the academic year.
Total amount of support: Varies.

NUMBER OF APPLICANTS MOST RECENT YEAR:
Short-term: 416; Long-term: 144.

NUMBER OF AWARDS: Short-term: 136;
Long-term: 10.

APPLICATION INFORMATION:
Contact the Library.
Duration: Short-term grants: One to five months. Long-term awards: Minimum of nine months.
Deadline: November 15 for commencement on July 1.

IRS IDENTIFICATION NUMBER: 95-1644589

OFFICERS:
Steven Koblik, President
Laurie Sowd, Vice President, Operations
Alison Sowden, Vice President, Financial Affairs
Randy Shulman, Vice President, Advancement
Susan Turner-Lowe, Vice President, Communications
Catherine Allgor, Director, Education
James Folsom, Director, Botanical Gardens
Steve Hindle, Director, Research
Kevin Salatino, Director, Art Collections
David Zeidberg, Director, Library

TRUSTEES:
Stewart R. Smith, Chairman
Paul G. Haaga, Jr.
Anne F. Rothenberg
Loren R. Rothschild
Geneva H. Thornton

ADDRESS INQUIRIES TO:
Steve Hindle, Director of Research
(See address above.)

*SPECIAL STIPULATIONS:
Recipients of all fellowships are expected to be in continuous residence at the Huntington.

THE INSTITUTE FOR ADVANCED STUDIES IN THE HUMANITIES   [374]
The University of Edinburgh
Hope Park Square
Edinburgh EH8 9NW Scotland
44 (0)131 650 4671
Fax: 44 (0)131 651 1176

E-MAIL ADDRESS:
iash@ed.ac.uk

WEB SITE ADDRESS:
www.iash.ed.ac.uk/

FOUNDED: 1969

AREAS OF INTEREST:
Humanities and social science.

CONSULTING OR VOLUNTEER SERVICES:
Institute has connections with and is within easy reach of the National Library of Scotland, the National Archives of Scotland, the Royal Museum of Scotland and the Edinburgh University Library.

NAME(S) OF PROGRAMS:
● **Visiting Research Fellowships**

TYPE:
Fellowships. Visiting Research Fellowships with the use of a private office in the Institute with all the usual research facilities. Recipients of the Fellowships are expected to play a full part in the activities of the Institute.

YEAR PROGRAM STARTED: 1970

PURPOSE:
To further advanced studies in the humanities, broadly conceived.

LEGAL BASIS:
Institution of University of Edinburgh.

ELIGIBILITY:
Applicants should be scholars of established reputation or younger scholars holding a Doctorate or offering equivalent evidence of aptitude for advanced study.

The Election Committee will consider the academic record and the publications of all applicants, their capacity to disseminate their views effectively in public and the likelihood of completing the proposed research by task by the end of the fellowship or shortly afterwards. Students who have not completed their studies for a particular degree are not eligible.

No teaching is required of Fellows in the project, but each Fellow will be expected to make at least one public presentation of his or her research activities.

NUMBER OF APPLICANTS MOST RECENT YEAR:
21.

NUMBER OF AWARDS: 14.

APPLICATION INFORMATION:
Apply online through the Institute web site. The Election Committee will only consider applications accompanied by full documentation and supported by a minimum of two and a maximum of three references. It is the responsibility of each applicant to ensure that their referees submit their reports directly to Edinburgh. Candidates may like to submit a copy of an article or publication relevant to their application. The Institute will not return any documents to applicants.
Duration: Fellowships are tenable for two to six months. Nonrenewable.
Deadline: February. Notification by e-mail by end of March.

PUBLICATIONS:
Application guidelines.

OFFICERS:
Prof. Jo Shaw, Director

ADDRESS INQUIRIES TO:
Prof. Jo Shaw, Director
(See address above.)

*SPECIAL STIPULATIONS:
Fellows, as well as carrying out research, are required to live in or near Edinburgh and may be asked to give one seminar.

INSTITUTE FOR ADVANCED STUDY
Einstein Drive
Princeton, NJ 08540
(609) 734-8250
Fax: (609) 951-4457

E-MAIL ADDRESS:
donne@ias.edu

WEB SITE ADDRESS:
www.sss.ias.edu

TYPE:
Fellowships; Residencies. Postdoctoral research fellowships at the School of Social Science. In 2014-15, the thematic focus will be "Egalitarianisms."

See entry 1856 for full listing.

INSTITUTE FOR HUMANE STUDIES (IHS)
3351 Fairfax Drive, MSN 1C5
Arlington, VA 22201-4432
(703) 993-4880
Fax: (703) 993-4890

E-MAIL ADDRESS:
ihs@ihs.gmu.edu

WEB SITE ADDRESS:
www.theihs.org

TYPE:
Awards/prizes; Fellowships. Humane Studies Fellowships cover the fields of arts and humanities, fine and applied art, law, mass communication and information, religion and theology, or social and behavioral science.

Charles G. Koch Summer Fellowship deals with current public policy issues, career development workshops, writing projects with a professional editor, and the experience of spending a summer in a Washington, DC, or state-based policy community.

See entry 2003 for full listing.

MASS HUMANITIES [375]
66 Bridge Street
Northampton, MA 01060-2406
(413) 584-8440
Fax: (413) 584-8454

E-MAIL ADDRESS:
info@masshumanities.org

WEB SITE ADDRESS:
www.masshumanities.org

FOUNDED: 1974

AREAS OF INTEREST:
Humanities and areas of special concern in Massachusetts, historic societies and libraries.

NAME(S) OF PROGRAMS:
- **Project Grants**
- **Reading and Discussion Grants**
- **Research Inventory Grants**
- **Scholar in Residence Grants**

TYPE:
Project/program grants.

PURPOSE:
To identify and develop major initiatives in areas of special interest or concern.

LEGAL BASIS:
Private, nonprofit corporation.

ELIGIBILITY:
Applicants must be nonprofit organizations. The Foundation does not fund refreshments, travel expenses, or indirect costs.

GEOGRAPHIC RESTRICTIONS:
Massachusetts.

FINANCIAL DATA:
Amount of support per award: Up to $10,000.

Total amount of support: $300,000.

Matching fund requirements: Outright Funds must be matched equally by your organization through cost-sharing.

REPRESENTATIVE AWARDS:
"Shifting Gears: The Changing Meaning of Work in Massachusetts," for study of economic change; "Understanding the AIDS Challenge;" "Knowing Our Place: Humanistic Aspects of Environmental Issues;" "Seeing Through the Media: The Crisis of our Cultural Environment," for studying the impact of the media on American society.

APPLICATION INFORMATION:
Applicants should submit the Foundation's web-based Letter of Inquiry form six weeks before final proposal deadline. Application is an online process.

Duration: Typically one year.

Deadline: Proposal deadlines are on or before the first business day of November, February and May.

PUBLICATIONS:
Newsletter; application guidelines; brochure.

OFFICERS:
Benjamin Birnbaum, President

STAFF:
David Tebaldi, Executive Director
Pleun Bouricius, Director of Grants and Programs
John Sieracki, Director of Development and Communications
Anne Rogers, Systems Manager
Hayley Wood, Senior Program Officer
Rose Sackey-Milligan, Program Officer
Melissa Wheaton, Grants Administrator

ADDRESS INQUIRIES TO:
Pleun Bouricius
Director of Grants and Programs
(See address above.)

ALLETTA MORRIS MCBEAN CHARITABLE TRUST [376]
1200 Central Boulevard
Suite B
Brentwood, CA 94513
(925) 516-6212
Fax: (925) 516-4496

E-MAIL ADDRESS:
mcbeanproperties@att.net

FOUNDED: 1986

AREAS OF INTEREST:
Historic and land preservation in and around Newport, RI.

TYPE:
Capital grants; Challenge/matching grants; Endowments; Project/program grants.

YEAR PROGRAM STARTED: 1986

PURPOSE:
To enhance the quality of life in and around Newport and Aquidneck Island, RI.

LEGAL BASIS:
Private charitable trust.

ELIGIBILITY:
Applicants must be tax-exempt organizations.

GEOGRAPHIC RESTRICTIONS:
Aquidneck Island, Rhode Island.

FINANCIAL DATA:
Amount of support per award: $25,000 to $100,000.

Total amount of support: $2,800,000 per year.

Matching fund requirements: Varies.

NUMBER OF APPLICANTS MOST RECENT YEAR: 20 to 25.

REPRESENTATIVE AWARDS:
$50,000 to Edward King House Senior Citizens Center for building renovations; $6,000 to Lucy's Hearth for kitchen renovation; $250,000 to Newport Performing Arts Center Task Group for acquisition and facade restoration of the opera house.

APPLICATION INFORMATION:
Six formal proposals with budgets are preferred, as well as other sources of funding for project, tax-exempt status and other background material.

Deadline: February 28 and July 31.

IRS IDENTIFICATION NUMBER: 94-3019660

OFFICERS:
Donald C. Christ, Chairman
John J. Slocum, Jr., Secretary
Charlene C. Kleiner, Assistant Secretary
Dorienne Farzan
Gladys V. Szapary

ADDRESS INQUIRIES TO:
Donald C. Christ, Chairman
Charlene C. Kleiner, Assistant Secretary
(See address above.)

MICHIGAN SOCIETY OF FELLOWS [377]
University of Michigan
0540 Rackham Building
915 East Washington Street
Ann Arbor, MI 48109-1070
(734) 763-1259

E-MAIL ADDRESS:
society.of.fellows@umich.edu

WEB SITE ADDRESS:
www.societyoffellows.umich.edu

FOUNDED: 1970

AREAS OF INTEREST:
All schools and colleges at the University of Michigan.

NAME(S) OF PROGRAMS:
- **Postdoctoral Fellowships in the Humanities and the Arts, Sciences and Professions**

TYPE:
Fellowships. Fellows are appointed as Assistant Professors or Research Scientists in appropriate departments and as Postdoctoral Scholars in the Michigan Society of Fellows. They are expected to be in residence in Ann Arbor during the academic years of the fellowship, to teach for the equivalent of one academic year, to participate in the informal intellectual life of the Society, and to devote time to their independent research or artistic projects.

YEAR PROGRAM STARTED: 1970

PURPOSE:
To recognize and support academic and creative excellence in humanities and the arts, the social, physical, and life sciences, and the professions.

LEGAL BASIS:
Nonprofit, tax-exempt organization.

ELIGIBILITY:
Candidates should be near the beginning of their professional careers, but not more than three years beyond completion of their degrees. The Ph.D. degree or comparable professional or artistic degree, received prior to appointment, is required.

Applications from degree candidates and recipients of the Ph.D. from the University of Michigan will not be considered.

FINANCIAL DATA:
Amount of support per award: $55,000 annually plus health benefits for 2014-17 fellowships. $1,500 per year allowance toward travel and research expenses.

COOPERATIVE FUNDING PROGRAMS: Mellon Foundation.

NUMBER OF APPLICANTS MOST RECENT YEAR:
1,027 for the year 2013.

NUMBER OF AWARDS: 8 each year.

APPLICATION INFORMATION:
Applications will be reviewed by members of
the Society of Fellows and by faculty in
appropriate University of Michigan
departments. Final selection of candidates
will be made by the senior fellows of the
Society.

Duration: Three years.

Deadline: September 30. Final selections
made end of February.

PUBLICATIONS:
Application guidelines.

OFFICERS:
Donald S. Lopez, Jr., Chairperson of Society

*SPECIAL STIPULATIONS:
Fellows are expected to reside in Ann Arbor
during the academic years of the fellowship.

NATIONAL ENDOWMENT FOR
THE HUMANITIES   [378]
The Constitution Center
400 7th Street, S.W.
Washington, DC 20001
(202) 606-8424
Fax: (202) 606-8240

E-MAIL ADDRESS:
info@neh.gov

WEB SITE ADDRESS:
www.neh.gov

FOUNDED: 1965

AREAS OF INTEREST:
Scholarship, research, education and public
programs in the humanities. In the act that
established the Endowment, the term
humanities includes, but is not limited to, the
study of history, philosophy, languages,
linguistics, literature, archaeology,
jurisprudence, the history, theory and
criticism of the arts, ethics, comparative
religion and those aspects of the social
sciences that employ historical or
philosophical approaches.

NAME(S) OF PROGRAMS:
● **Research Program**

TYPE:
Research grants. Grants provide support for
collaborative research in the preparation for
publication of editions, translations and other
important works in the humanities and in the
conduct of large or complex interpretive
studies including archaeology projects and
the humanities studies of science and
technology. Grants also support research
opportunities offered through independent
research centers and scholarly organizations
and international research centers.

YEAR PROGRAM STARTED: 1967

PURPOSE:
To provide funding for research and the
publication of that research. The work must
be in a field of interest to the National
Endowment.

LEGAL BASIS:
Federal agency, established by act of
Congress: The National Foundation on the
Arts and Humanities Act of 1965, Public
Law 89-209, as amended.

ELIGIBILITY:
Applicants can be individuals, institutions of
higher education, nonprofit professional
associations, scholarly societies and other
nonprofit organizations.

GEOGRAPHIC RESTRICTIONS:
United States.

FINANCIAL DATA:
Amount of support per award: Varies.
Total amount of support: Varies.

APPLICATION INFORMATION:
Application can be downloaded from the web
site.
Duration: One year.
Deadline: November 5.

PUBLICATIONS:
Annual report; *Grant Programs; Humanities
Magazine.*

IRS IDENTIFICATION NUMBER: 52-1098584

ADDRESS INQUIRIES TO:
Paula Wasley, Public Affairs Specialist
(See address above.)

NATIONAL ENDOWMENT FOR
THE HUMANITIES   [379]
The Constitution Center
400 7th Street, S.W.
Washington, DC 20001
(202) 606-8424
Fax: (202) 606-8240

E-MAIL ADDRESS:
info@neh.gov

WEB SITE ADDRESS:
www.neh.gov

FOUNDED: 1965

AREAS OF INTEREST:
Scholarship, research, education and public
programs in the humanities. In the act that
established the Endowment, the term
humanities includes, but is not limited to, the
study of history, philosophy, languages,
linguistics, literature, archaeology,
jurisprudence, the history, theory and
criticism of the arts, ethics, comparative
religion and those aspects of the social
sciences that employ historical or
philosophical approaches.

NAME(S) OF PROGRAMS:
● **Office of Challenge Grants**

TYPE:
Capital grants; Challenge/matching grants;
Professorships; Residencies; Visiting
scholars. Nonprofit institutions interested in
developing new sources of long-term support
for educational, scholarly, preservation and
public programs in the humanities may be
assisted in these efforts by an NEH
Challenge Grant. Grantees are required to
raise three or four dollars in new or increased
donations for every federal dollar offered.

Both federal and nonfederal funds may be
used to establish or increase institutional
endowments and thus guarantee long-term
support for a variety of humanities needs.
Funds may also be used for limited direct
capital expenditures where such needs are
compelling and clearly related to
improvements in the humanities.

YEAR PROGRAM STARTED: 1977

PURPOSE:
To encourage long-range financial and
program planning within humanities

institutions and organizations; to provide
means for humanities organizations and
institutions to increase levels and kinds of
continuing financial support; to sustain or
develop high-quality work within the
humanities; to join federal with nonfederal
support so that those institutions in which
teaching, learning and research of the
humanities occur may achieve greater
financial stability.

LEGAL BASIS:
Federal agency, established by act of
Congress: The National Foundation on the
Arts and Humanities Act of 1965, Public
Law 89-209, as amended.

ELIGIBILITY:
Nonprofit postsecondary, educational,
research or cultural institutions and
organizations working within the humanities
are eligible for support.

GEOGRAPHIC RESTRICTIONS:
United States.

FINANCIAL DATA:
All funds may be used to establish or
increase institutional endowments.
Amount of support per award: Varies.
Total amount of support: Varies.
Matching fund requirements: A minimum of
three nonfederal dollars must match each
federal dollar received.

REPRESENTATIVE AWARDS:
$75,000 to Lenox Library Association,
Lenox, MA, to support construction of a
special collections research area, renovation
of archival storage facilities, collection
preservation, automation of acquisitions,
circulation and endowment expansion;
$150,000 to Saint Louis University, St.
Louis, MO, to support an endowment for
Saint Louis University's Center for Medieval
and Renaissance Studies that will provide
library materials, fellowships and a
professorship in Byzantine and classical
studies; $125,000 to Historical Society of
Cheshire County, Keene, NH, to support
renovation and expansion of a new site for a
consolidated museum and archival center.

APPLICATION INFORMATION:
Applications can be downloaded from the
above web site.
Duration: Varies.
Deadline: Late winter or early spring.

PUBLICATIONS:
Annual report; *Grant Programs; Humanities
Magazine.*

IRS IDENTIFICATION NUMBER: 52-1098584

ADDRESS INQUIRIES TO:
Paula Wasley, Public Affairs Specialist
(See address above.)

NATIONAL ENDOWMENT FOR
THE HUMANITIES   [380]
The Constitution Center
400 7th Street, S.W.
Washington, DC 20001
(202) 606-8424
Fax: (202) 606-8240

E-MAIL ADDRESS:
info@neh.gov

WEB SITE ADDRESS:
www.neh.gov

FOUNDED: 1965

AREAS OF INTEREST:
Scholarship, research, education and public programs in the humanities.

NAME(S) OF PROGRAMS:
- **Fellowships**
- **Summer Stipends**

TYPE:
Awards/prizes; Fellowships. Grants provide support for scholars to undertake full-time independent research and writing in the humanities. Grants are available for a maximum of one year and a minimum of six weeks to two months of summer study.

Grants also provide support for historically Black college and university faculty to undertake one year of full-time study leading to a doctoral degree in the humanities with preference given to those individuals who are at the dissertation stage of their work.

YEAR PROGRAM STARTED: 1967

PURPOSE:
To encourage continued research and study in the humanities discipline.

LEGAL BASIS:
Federal agency, established by act of Congress: The National Foundation on the Arts and Humanities Act of 1965, Public Law 89-209, as amended.

GEOGRAPHIC RESTRICTIONS:
United States.

FINANCIAL DATA:
Amount of support per award: Varies.
Total amount of support: Varies.

APPLICATION INFORMATION:
Application can be downloaded from the web site.
Duration: Up to one year.
Deadline: Fellowships: May 1; Summer Stipends: Late September.

PUBLICATIONS:
Annual report; *Grant Programs*; *Humanities Magazine*.

IRS IDENTIFICATION NUMBER: 52-1098584

ADDRESS INQUIRIES TO:
Paula Wasley, Public Affairs Specialist (See address above.)

NATIONAL ENDOWMENT FOR THE HUMANITIES   [381]
The Constitution Center
400 7th Street, S.W.
Washington, DC 20001
(202) 606-8424
Fax: (202) 606-8240

E-MAIL ADDRESS:
info@neh.gov

WEB SITE ADDRESS:
www.neh.gov

FOUNDED: 1965

AREAS OF INTEREST:
Scholarship, research, education and public programs in the humanities. In the act that established the Endowment, the term humanities includes, but is not limited to, the study of history, philosophy, languages, linguistics, literature, archaeology, jurisprudence, the history, theory and criticism of the arts, ethics, comparative religion and those aspects of the social sciences that employ historical or philosophical approaches.

NAME(S) OF PROGRAMS:
- **Seminars and Institutes Program**

TYPE:
Conferences/seminars. Grants support summer seminars and national institutes in the humanities for college and school teachers. These faculty development activities are conducted at colleges and universities across the country. Lists of pending seminars and institutes are available from the program.

YEAR PROGRAM STARTED: 1983

PURPOSE:
To provide opportunities for teachers to study under the direction of a master teacher and distinguished scholar in an area of mutual interest at a college or university during the summer.

LEGAL BASIS:
Federal agency, established by act of Congress: The National Foundation on the Arts and Humanities Act of 1965, Public Law 89-209, as amended.

ELIGIBILITY:
Applicants can be individuals or institutions of higher learning.

GEOGRAPHIC RESTRICTIONS:
United States.

FINANCIAL DATA:
Amount of support per award: Varies.
Total amount of support: Varies.

APPLICATION INFORMATION:
Complete application information can be found online. Participant application forms and instructions can be obtained from seminar directors at the host institutions. Those wishing to participate in seminars should submit their applications to the seminar director. Information about the program is publicized in the fall preceding the summer in question.
Duration: Seminars last four, five, or six weeks, depending on the choice of the director.
Deadline: Late February to early March.

PUBLICATIONS:
Annual report; *Grant Programs*; *Humanities Magazine*.

IRS IDENTIFICATION NUMBER: 52-1098584

ADDRESS INQUIRIES TO:
Paula Wasley, Public Affairs Specialist (See address above.)

NATIONAL ENDOWMENT FOR THE HUMANITIES   [382]
The Constitution Center
400 7th Street, S.W.
Washington, DC 20001
(202) 606-8424
Fax: (202) 606-8240

E-MAIL ADDRESS:
info@neh.gov

WEB SITE ADDRESS:
www.neh.gov

FOUNDED: 1965

AREAS OF INTEREST:
Scholarship, research, education and public programs in the humanities. In the act that established the Endowment, the term humanities includes, but is not limited to, the study of history, philosophy, languages, linguistics, literature, archaeology, jurisprudence, the history, theory and criticism of the arts, ethics, comparative religion and those aspects of the social sciences that employ historical or philosophical approaches.

NAME(S) OF PROGRAMS:
- **Preservation and Access**

TYPE:
Project/program grants. Support may be sought to preserve the intellectual content and aid bibliographic control of collections, to compile bibliographies, descriptive catalogs and guides to cultural holdings, to create dictionaries, encyclopedias, databases and other types of research tools and reference works and to stabilize material culture collections through the appropriate housing and storing of objects, improved environmental control and the installation of security, lighting and fire-prevention systems.

Applications may also be submitted for national and regional education and training projects, regional preservation field service programs and research and demonstration projects that are intended to enhance institutional practice and the use of technology for preservation and access.

YEAR PROGRAM STARTED: 1985

PURPOSE:
To advance study in the area indicated.

LEGAL BASIS:
Federal agency, established by act of Congress: The National Foundation on the Arts and Humanities Act of 1965, Public Law 89-209, as amended.

GEOGRAPHIC RESTRICTIONS:
United States.

FINANCIAL DATA:
Amount of support per award: Varies.
Total amount of support: Varies.

REPRESENTATIVE AWARDS:
$90,000 to Atlanta University Center, Atlanta, GA, to support a project to arrange and describe archival collections that document the African-American experience in the arts, religion, education, race relations and civil rights; $138,914 to Baltimore Museum of Industry, Baltimore, MD, to support the arrangement, description and preservation microfilming of the corporate records of the Canton Company of Baltimore, Maryland, dating from 1836 to 1981; $110,281 to Santa Barbara Museum of Natural History, Santa Barbara, CA, to support the computerization of the catalog and accession records of the museum's archaeological and ethnographic collections.

APPLICATION INFORMATION:
Application can be downloaded from the web site.
Duration: Usually one year.
Deadline: Beginning of May.

PUBLICATIONS:
Annual report; *Grant Programs*; *Humanities Magazine*.

IRS IDENTIFICATION NUMBER: 52-1098584

ADDRESS INQUIRIES TO:
Paula Wasley, Public Affairs Specialist (See address above.)

NATIONAL ENDOWMENT FOR THE HUMANITIES
1100 Pennsylvania Avenue, N.W.
Washington, DC 20506
(202) 606-8269
Fax: (202) 606-8557

E-MAIL ADDRESS:
publicpgms@neh.gov

WEB SITE ADDRESS:
www.neh.gov

TYPE:
Project/program grants. Grants support the planning and production of television and radio programs in the humanities intended for general audiences; the planning and implementation of exhibitions, the interpretation of historic sites and the production of related publications; multimedia components and educational programs and the planning and implementation of projects through the use of books, new technologies and other resources in the collections of libraries and archives in formats such as reading and discussion programs, lectures, symposia and interpretive exhibitions.

See entry 1947 for full listing.

NATIONAL HUMANITIES CENTER [383]
7 T.W. Alexander Drive
Research Triangle Park, NC 27709
(919) 549-0661
Fax: (919) 990-8535

E-MAIL ADDRESS:
nhc@nationalhumanitiescenter.org

WEB SITE ADDRESS:
www.nationalhumanitiescenter.org

FOUNDED: 1976

AREAS OF INTEREST:
History, literature, philosophy, classics, political theory, law, religion, anthropology, art history, folklore and other humanistic fields.

NAME(S) OF PROGRAMS:
• **National Humanities Center Fellowships**

TYPE:
Fellowships; Visiting scholars. Awards for advanced study in the humanities in residence at the Center.

YEAR PROGRAM STARTED: 1978

PURPOSE:
To support advanced study in the humanities; to encourage the exchange of ideas among humanist scholars; to enhance the influence of the humanities in the U.S.

LEGAL BASIS:
Privately incorporated nonprofit institute for advanced study.

ELIGIBILITY:
Open to scholars in the humanities. As a rule, the Center does not consider applications from candidates who have not yet completed the Doctorate. Fellowships for younger scholars are not intended for an immediate postdoctoral year but are awarded to individuals who have begun their professional careers and are undertaking research significantly beyond their dissertations.

FINANCIAL DATA:
Fellows receive travel expenses to and from the Center for themselves and their families.
Amount of support per award: Stipends up to $60,000.
Total amount of support: Varies.
Matching fund requirements: Stipulated with specific grants.

COOPERATIVE FUNDING PROGRAMS: Scholars who have financial support from university or other funding agencies are welcome to apply and receive from the Center the difference between that support and their normal academic salaries.

APPLICATION INFORMATION:
Applications accepted online only.
Duration: One academic year, September through May.
Deadline: October 15. Announcement in February.

PUBLICATIONS:
Annual report; application guidelines; semiannual newsletter.

IRS IDENTIFICATION NUMBER: 59-1735367

STAFF:
Elizabeth C. Mansfield, Vice President for Scholarly Programs

OFFICERS AND TRUSTEES:
Peter Benoliel, Chairman of the Board
William C. Jordan, Chairperson, Committee on Scholarly Programs

ADDRESS INQUIRIES TO:
Lois Whittington, Program Coordinator
Fellowship Program
(See address above.)

NEW YORK COUNCIL FOR THE HUMANITIES [384]
150 Broadway
Suite 1700
New York, NY 10038
(212) 233-1131
Fax: (212) 233-4607

E-MAIL ADDRESS:
nych@nyhumanities.org

WEB SITE ADDRESS:
www.nyhumanities.org

FOUNDED: 1975

AREAS OF INTEREST:
Humanities, public programs and education.

NAME(S) OF PROGRAMS:
• **Major Grants**
• **Reading and Discussion Grants**
• **Speakers in the Humanities Program**

TYPE:
Challenge/matching grants; Project/program grants; Seed money grants. Major Project Grants are generally awarded for large-scale projects in the form of matching grants.

Reading and Discussion Grants are awarded to involve community members in ongoing discussion of books and ideas.

Speakers in the Humanities Program allows local organizations to present distinguished lectures by a select group of scholars and professionals to community audiences on various topics.

YEAR PROGRAM STARTED: 1975

PURPOSE:
To help all New Yorkers become thoughtful participants in our communities by promoting critical inquiry, cultural understanding, and civic engagement.

LEGAL BASIS:
State humanities council, nonprofit under Internal Revenue Code 501(c)(3).

ELIGIBILITY:
Tax-exempt, nonprofit 501(c)(3) organizations in New York state.

GEOGRAPHIC RESTRICTIONS:
New York state.

FINANCIAL DATA:
Amount of support per award: Major Grants: Typically $500 to $3,000.
Total amount of support: $300,000.
Matching fund requirements: All program grants must be matched (at least dollar-for-dollar) with cash and/or in-kind contributions.

NUMBER OF APPLICANTS MOST RECENT YEAR:
Major Grants: 60; Speakers in the Humanities Awards: 350.

NUMBER OF AWARDS: Major Grants: 22; Speakers in the Humanities Awards: 349.

APPLICATION INFORMATION:
All applications are available online.

PUBLICATIONS:
Application guidelines.

IRS IDENTIFICATION NUMBER: 51-0152266

ADDRESS INQUIRIES TO:
Jane McNamara, Director of Grants
(See address and e-mail above.)

*SPECIAL STIPULATIONS:
Grants available only to New York-based, tax-exempt, nonprofit organizations.

THE NEWBERRY LIBRARY [385]
Office of Research and Academic Programs
60 West Walton Street
Chicago, IL 60610-7324
(312) 255-3666

E-MAIL ADDRESS:
research@newberry.org

WEB SITE ADDRESS:
www.newberry.org/fellowships

FOUNDED: 1887

AREAS OF INTEREST:
The humanities of Western Europe, England and the Americas from the late Middle Ages to the early 20th century.

NAME(S) OF PROGRAMS:
• **Newberry Library Short-Term Fellowships**

TYPE:
Fellowships; Residencies. Fellowships of one to two months for advanced research, including doctoral dissertations, in history and the humanities. Fellowships provide access to the Newberry's collections for those who live and work beyond commuting distance from Chicago.

YEAR PROGRAM STARTED: 1942

PURPOSE:
To give scholars engaged in research in the fields listed above the opportunity to utilize the specialized collections of the Newberry Library.

LEGAL BASIS:
Private research library.

ELIGIBILITY:
Applicants must have the Ph.D. or terminal degree in their field, or have completed all requirements except the dissertation. Preference will be given to applicants from outside the greater Chicago area whose research particularly requires study at the Newberry. Applicants must live and work outside of the Chicago area.

FINANCIAL DATA:
Amount of support per award: $2,500 per month.

NUMBER OF APPLICANTS MOST RECENT YEAR: 170.

NUMBER OF AWARDS: 40 to 45.

APPLICATION INFORMATION:
Applications must be submitted through the online webform.

Duration: One to two months.

Deadline: January 15.

STAFF:
Diane Dillon, Director of Scholarly and Undergraduate Programs

ADDRESS INQUIRIES TO:
See e-mail address above.

THE NEWBERRY LIBRARY [386]
Office of Research and Academic Programs
60 West Walton Street
Chicago, IL 60610-7324
(312) 255-3666

E-MAIL ADDRESS:
research@newberry.org

WEB SITE ADDRESS:
www.newberry.org/fellowships

FOUNDED: 1887

AREAS OF INTEREST:
Late Medieval and Renaissance studies.

NAME(S) OF PROGRAMS:
- **The Audrey Lumsden-Kouvel Fellowship**

TYPE:
Fellowships. The Audrey Lumsden-Kouvel Fellowship is for postdoctoral scholars conducting extended research in residence at the Newberry Library in the areas of late medieval and early modern literature.

LEGAL BASIS:
Private research library.

ELIGIBILITY:
Open to postdoctoral scholars who plan to be in continuous residence for at least three months. Preference will be given to those who plan longer stays during the academic year or who wish to use the Fellowship to extend a sabbatical. Project focus should be on Romance cultures.

FINANCIAL DATA:
Amount of support per award: $4,200 per month.

NUMBER OF APPLICANTS MOST RECENT YEAR: 40.

NUMBER OF AWARDS: 1.

APPLICATION INFORMATION:
Applications must be submitted through the online webform.

Duration: Four to six months.

Deadline: December 1, 11:59 P.M.

ADDRESS INQUIRIES TO:
See e-mail address above.

THE NEWBERRY LIBRARY [387]
Office of Research and Academic Programs
60 West Walton Street
Chicago, IL 60610-7324
(312) 255-3666

E-MAIL ADDRESS:
research@newberry.org

WEB SITE ADDRESS:
www.newberry.org/fellowships

FOUNDED: 1887

AREAS OF INTEREST:
The humanities of Western Europe, England and the Americas from the late Middle Ages to the early 20th century.

NAME(S) OF PROGRAMS:
- **National Endowment for the Humanities Fellowships**

TYPE:
Fellowships; Residencies. Support for projects in any field appropriate to the Library's collections.

YEAR PROGRAM STARTED: 1975

PURPOSE:
To encourage the individual scholar's research and to deepen and enrich the opportunities for serious intellectual exchange.

LEGAL BASIS:
Private research library.

ELIGIBILITY:
Established scholars at the postdoctoral level or its equivalent may apply. Awards are open to U.S. citizens and foreign nationals who have been living in the U.S. for at least three years. Preference is given to applicants who have not held major fellowships for three years preceding the proposed period of residency. An established scholar, as defined by the Awards Committee, is generally someone who has at least two published articles in refereed journals or the equivalent at the time of application.

Projects must be appropriate for research in the Newberry collection.

FINANCIAL DATA:
Applicants may combine grants with sabbaticals or other stipendiary support.
Amount of support per award: $4,200 per month.

NUMBER OF APPLICANTS MOST RECENT YEAR: 95.

NUMBER OF AWARDS: Approximately 4.

APPLICATION INFORMATION:
Applications must be submitted through the online webform.

Duration: Four to 12 months.

Deadline: December 1.

STAFF:
Diane Dillon, Director of Scholarly and Undergraduate Programs

ADDRESS INQUIRIES TO:
See e-mail address above.

THE NEWBERRY LIBRARY [388]
Office of Research and Academic Programs
60 West Walton Street
Chicago, IL 60610-7324
(312) 255-3666

E-MAIL ADDRESS:
research@newberry.org

WEB SITE ADDRESS:
www.newberry.org/fellowships

FOUNDED: 1887

AREAS OF INTEREST:
The humanities of Western Europe, England and the Americas from the late Middle Ages to the early 20th century.

NAME(S) OF PROGRAMS:
- **Arthur and Lila Weinberg Fellowship for Independent Scholars**

TYPE:
Fellowships; Residencies. Weinberg Fellowship is for scholars working outside traditional acedemic settings. The program seeks journalists, writers, filmmakers, visual and performing artists and scholars. Preference is given to scholars working on historical issues related to social justice or reform.

LEGAL BASIS:
Private research library.

ELIGIBILITY:
Candidates must have demonstrated excellence through publishing and are working in a field appropriate to the Newberry collections. Preference is given to scholars working on historical issues related to social justice and reform. Applicants for this fellowship need not be from outside the Chicago area.

FINANCIAL DATA:
Amount of support per award: $2,500 per month.

NUMBER OF APPLICANTS MOST RECENT YEAR: 8.

NUMBER OF AWARDS: 1.

APPLICATION INFORMATION:
Applications must be submitted through the online webform.

Duration: One to 12 months.

Deadline: January 15.

STAFF:
Diane Dillon, Director of Scholarly and Undergraduate Programs

ADDRESS INQUIRIES TO:
See e-mail address above.

THE NEWBERRY LIBRARY
Committee on Awards
60 West Walton Street
Chicago, IL 60610-7324
(312) 255-3666

E-MAIL ADDRESS:
research@newberry.org

WEB SITE ADDRESS:
www.newberry.org/fellowships

TYPE:
Fellowships. For scholars wishing to use the Newberry's collections to study the period 1660 to 1815.

See entry 623 for full listing.

THE NEWBERRY LIBRARY [389]
Office of Research and Academic Programs
60 West Walton Street
Chicago, IL 60610-7324
(312) 255-3666

E-MAIL ADDRESS:
research@newberry.org

WEB SITE ADDRESS:
www.newberry.org/fellowships

FOUNDED: 1887

AREAS OF INTEREST:
The humanities of Western Europe, England and the Americas from the late Middle Ages to the early 20th century.

NAME(S) OF PROGRAMS:
- **Lloyd Lewis Fellowship in American History**

TYPE:
Fellowships. The Lloyd Lewis Fellowship in American History is awarded to postdoctoral scholars pursuing projects in any area of American history appropriate to the Newberry's collections.

PURPOSE:
To further research in American history.

ELIGIBILITY:
Applicants must hold a Ph.D. at the time of application.

FINANCIAL DATA:
Applicants may combine these fellowship awards with sabbatical or other stipendiary support.
Amount of support per award: Monthly stipend of $4,200.

APPLICATION INFORMATION:
Applications must be submitted through the online webform.
Duration: Four to 12 months.
Deadline: December 1.

ADDRESS INQUIRIES TO:
See e-mail address above.

*PLEASE NOTE:
The Newberry's long-term fellowship grants support individual research and promote serious intellectual exchange through active participation in the Newberry's scholarly activities, including a biweekly fellows' seminar.

THE NEWBERRY LIBRARY [390]
Office of Research and Academic Programs
60 West Walton Street
Chicago, IL 60610-7324
(312) 255-3666

E-MAIL ADDRESS:
research@newberry.org

WEB SITE ADDRESS:
www.newberry.org/fellowships

FOUNDED: 1887

AREAS OF INTEREST:
The humanities of Western Europe, England and the Americas from the late Middle Ages to the early 20th century.

NAME(S) OF PROGRAMS:
- **Monticello College Foundation Fellowship for Women**

TYPE:
Fellowships. The Monticello College Foundation Fellowship for Women is intended to help a postdoctoral woman scholar at an early stage of her academic career.

PURPOSE:
To provide assistance to postdoctoral woman scholars at an early stage of their academic careers.

ELIGIBILITY:
Applicants must hold a Ph.D. at the time of application. This award is intended for a postdoctoral woman scholar at an early stage of her academic career. Preference will be given to proposals particularly concerned with the study of women.

FINANCIAL DATA:
Applicants may combine these fellowship awards with sabbatical or other stipendiary support.

Amount of support per award: Monthly stipend of $4,200 per month.

APPLICATION INFORMATION:
Applications must be submitted through the online webform.
Duration: Four to six months.
Deadline: December 1.

ADDRESS INQUIRIES TO:
See e-mail address above.

*PLEASE NOTE:
The Newberry's long-term fellowship grants support individual research and promote serious intellectual exchange through active participation in the Newberry's scholarly activities, including a biweekly fellows' seminar.

THE NEWBERRY LIBRARY [391]
Office of Research and Academic Programs
60 West Walton Street
Chicago, IL 60610-7324
(312) 255-3666

E-MAIL ADDRESS:
research@newberry.org

WEB SITE ADDRESS:
www.newberry.org/fellowships

FOUNDED: 1887

AREAS OF INTEREST:
The humanities of Western Europe, England and the Americas from the late Middle Ages to the early 20th century.

NAME(S) OF PROGRAMS:
- **Newberry Consortium in American Indian Studies Faculty Fellowship**

TYPE:
Fellowships.

PURPOSE:
To promote research in American Indian studies.

ELIGIBILITY:
This award is intended for faculty members at institutions participating in the Consortium. Preference is given to scholars at an early career stage.

FINANCIAL DATA:
Applicants may combine these fellowship awards with sabbatical or other stipendiary support.
Amount of support per award: Monthly stipend of $4,200.

APPLICATION INFORMATION:
Awardees must indicate in their applications how many months they intend to be in residence at the Newberry. Applications must be submitted through the online webform.
Duration: Four to six months.
Deadline: December 1.

ADDRESS INQUIRIES TO:
See e-mail address above.

*PLEASE NOTE:
The Newberry's long-term fellowship grants support individual research and promote serious intellectual exchange through active participation in the Newberry's scholarly activities, including a biweekly fellows' seminar.

THE NEWBERRY LIBRARY [392]
Office of Research and Academic Programs
60 West Walton Street
Chicago, IL 60610-7324
(312) 255-3666

E-MAIL ADDRESS:
research@newberry.org

WEB SITE ADDRESS:
www.newberry.org/fellowships

FOUNDED: 1887

AREAS OF INTEREST:
The humanities of Western Europe, England and the Americas from the late Middle Ages to the early 20th century.

NAME(S) OF PROGRAMS:
- **Sixteenth Century Society and Conference (SCSC) Fellowship**

TYPE:
Fellowships; Research grants; Residencies. Support for projects in any field appropriate to the Library's collection.

PURPOSE:
To support research in residence at The Newberry Library.

LEGAL BASIS:
Private research library.

ELIGIBILITY:
Applicants must have the Ph.D. or terminal degree in their field, or have completed all doctoral requirements except the dissertation. Preference will be given to those working in the early modern era, broadly defined (*circa* 1450 - *circa* 1660). Applicants must be members of the SCSC at the time of application and through the period of the fellowship. Applicants must be U.S. citizens or residents.

Applicants must live and work outside the greater Chicago area.

FINANCIAL DATA:
Amount of support per award: $2,000 for one month in residence.

APPLICATION INFORMATION:
Applications must be submitted through the online webform. Application form must be completed.
Deadline: January 15.

EXECUTIVE STAFF:
Diane Dillon, Director of Scholarly and Undergraduate Programs

ADDRESS INQUIRIES TO:
See e-mail address above.

THE NEWBERRY LIBRARY [393]
Office of Research and Academic Programs
60 West Walton Street
Chicago, IL 60610-7324
(312) 255-3666

E-MAIL ADDRESS:
research@newberry.org

WEB SITE ADDRESS:
www.newberry.org/fellowships

FOUNDED: 1887

AREAS OF INTEREST:
The humanities of Western Europe, England and the Americas from the late Middle Ages to the early 20th century.

NAME(S) OF PROGRAMS:
- **Newberry Library - Jack Miller Center Fellowship**

TYPE:
Fellowships; Residencies. Support for projects in any field appropriate to the Library's collection.

PURPOSE:
To advance scholarship in those fields of study that will contribute to a deeper understanding of America's founding principles and history and wider traditions that influenced its development.

LEGAL BASIS:
Private research library.

ELIGIBILITY:
Applicants must have the Ph.D. or terminal degree in their field, or have completed all doctoral requirements except the dissertation. Preference will be given to applicants whose research particularly requires study at the Newberry. Applicants must be U.S. citizens or residents.

Applicants must live and work outside the greater Chicago area.

FINANCIAL DATA:
Amount of support per award: $2,000 per month in residence.

APPLICATION INFORMATION:
Applications may be submitted through the online webform. Applicants must request one or two months of support at the time of application.
Deadline: January 15.

EXECUTIVE STAFF:
Diane Dillon, Director of Scholarly and Undergraduate Programs

ADDRESS INQUIRIES TO:
See e-mail address above.

*SPECIAL STIPULATIONS:
While in residence, fellows will deliver one public lecture based on research findings in the Newberry collection.

THE NEWBERRY LIBRARY [394]
Office of Research and Academic Programs
60 West Walton Street
Chicago, IL 60610-7324
(312) 255-3666

E-MAIL ADDRESS:
research@newberry.org

WEB SITE ADDRESS:
www.newberry.org/fellowships

FOUNDED: 1887

AREAS OF INTEREST:
The humanities of Western Europe, England and the Americas from the late Middle Ages to the early 20th century.

NAME(S) OF PROGRAMS:
● **Susan Kelly Power and Helen Hornbeck Tanner Fellowship**

TYPE:
Fellowships; Residencies. Support for projects in any field appropriate to the Library's collection.

PURPOSE:
To support Ph.D. candidates and postdoctoral scholars of American Indian heritage for one or two months of residential research in any field in the humanities using the Newberry collection.

LEGAL BASIS:
Private research library.

ELIGIBILITY:
Applicants must have the Ph.D. or terminal degree in their field, or have completed all doctoral requirements except the dissertation. Preference will be given to applicants whose

research particularly requires study at the Newberry. Applicants must be U.S. citizens or residents.

FINANCIAL DATA:
Amount of support per award: $2,000 for one month in residence.

APPLICATION INFORMATION:
Applications must be submitted through the online webform. Applicants must complete a supplementary application form, detailing American Indian heritage.
Deadline: January 15.

EXECUTIVE STAFF:
Diane Dillon, Director of Scholarly and Undergraduate Programs

ADDRESS INQUIRIES TO:
See e-mail address above.

THE NEWBERRY LIBRARY [395]
Office of Research and Academic Programs
60 West Walton Street
Chicago, IL 60610-7324
(312) 255-3666

E-MAIL ADDRESS:
research@newberry.org

WEB SITE ADDRESS:
www.newberry.org/fellowships

FOUNDED: 1887

AREAS OF INTEREST:
The humanities of Western Europe, England and the Americas from the late Middle Ages to the early 20th century.

NAME(S) OF PROGRAMS:
● **Society of Mayflower Descendants in the State of Illinois Fellowship**

TYPE:
Fellowships; Residencies. Support for projects in any field appropriate to the Library's collection.

PURPOSE:
To encourage research work, especially those working in early American history.

LEGAL BASIS:
Private research library.

ELIGIBILITY:
Applicants must have the Ph.D. or terminal degree in their field, or have completed all doctoral requirements except the dissertation. Preference will be given to applicants whose research particularly requires study at the Newberry, and whose research work is in early American history. Applicants have to be U.S. citizens or residents.

Applicants must live and work outside the greater Chicago area.

FINANCIAL DATA:
Amount of support per award: $2,000 for one month in residence.

APPLICATION INFORMATION:
Applications must be submitted through the online webform.
Deadline: January 15.

EXECUTIVE STAFF:
Diane Dillon, Director of Scholarly and Undergraduate Programs

ADDRESS INQUIRIES TO:
See e-mail address above.

THE NEWBERRY LIBRARY [396]
Office of Research and Academic Programs
60 West Walton Street
Chicago, IL 60610-7324
(312) 255-3666

E-MAIL ADDRESS:
research@newberry.org

WEB SITE ADDRESS:
www.newberry.org/fellowships

FOUNDED: 1887

AREAS OF INTEREST:
The humanities of Western Europe, England and the Americas from the late Middle Ages to the early 20th century.

NAME(S) OF PROGRAMS:
● **Charles Montgomery Gray Fellowship**

TYPE:
Fellowships; Residencies. Support for projects in any field appropriate to the Library's collection.

PURPOSE:
To encourage the individual scholar's research and to deepen and enrich the opportunities for serious intellectual exchange.

LEGAL BASIS:
Private research library.

ELIGIBILITY:
Applicants must have the Ph.D. or terminal degree in their field, or have completed all doctoral requirements except the dissertation. Applicants must also be U.S. citizens or residents. Projects must be appropriate for research in residence, within the Newberry's collection. Preference will be given to applicants whose research particularly requires study at the Newberry. Preference may be given to those working in the early modern period or Renaissance, as well as English history, legal history or European history.

Applicants must live and work outside the greater Chicago area.

FINANCIAL DATA:
Amount of support per award: $2,000 per month of residency.

APPLICATION INFORMATION:
Applications must be submitted through the online webform. Applicants may request one or two months of support at the time of application.
Deadline: January 15.

EXECUTIVE STAFF:
Diane Dillon, Director of Scholarly and Undergraduate Programs

ADDRESS INQUIRIES TO:
See e-mail address above.

THE NEWBERRY LIBRARY [397]
Office of Research and Academic Programs
60 West Walton Street
Chicago, IL 60610-7324
(312) 255-3666

E-MAIL ADDRESS:
research@newberry.org

WEB SITE ADDRESS:
www.newberry.org/fellowships

FOUNDED: 1887

AREAS OF INTEREST:
The humanities of Western Europe, England and the Americas from the late Middle Ages to the early 20th century.

138   HUMANITIES (GENERAL)

NAME(S) OF PROGRAMS:
- **Newberry Library - Kress Foundation Fellowship**

TYPE:
Fellowships; Residencies. Support for projects in any field appropriate to the Library's collection. The Newberry houses a variety of European art works and the history of art and architecture within its collection. Most of these works relate to subject areas for which the Library's holdings are particularly strong. Collection strengths include medieval manuscripts; post-1500 European manuscripts; book illustrations; printing and book arts; calligraphy; maps, views and topographical prints; caricatures and cartoons; and printed books and serials relating to the field of art history.

PURPOSE:
To offer support for qualified applicants working on a European art history project covering the period prior to 1830.

LEGAL BASIS:
Private research library.

ELIGIBILITY:
Applicants must have the Ph.D. or terminal degree in their field, or have completed all doctoral requirements except the dissertation. Preference will be given to applicants whose research particularly requires study at the Newberry. Applicants must also be U.S. citizens or residents.

Applicants must live and work outside the greater Chicago area.

FINANCIAL DATA:
Amount of support per award: $2,500 for one month in residence.

APPLICATION INFORMATION:
Applications must be submitted through the online webform.
Deadline: January 15.

EXECUTIVE STAFF:
Diane Dillon, Director of Scholarly and Undergraduate Programs

ADDRESS INQUIRIES TO:
See e-mail address above.

THE NEWBERRY LIBRARY [398]
Office of Research and Academic Programs
60 West Walton Street
Chicago, IL 60610-7324
(312) 255-3666

E-MAIL ADDRESS:
research@newberry.org

WEB SITE ADDRESS:
www.newberry.org/fellowships

FOUNDED: 1887

AREAS OF INTEREST:
The humanities of Western Europe, England and the Americas from the late Middle Ages to the early 20th century.

NAME(S) OF PROGRAMS:
- **Andrew W. Mellon Foundation Fellowship**

TYPE:
Fellowships; Residencies. Support for projects in any field appropriate to the Library's collection.

PURPOSE:
To encourage the individual scholar's research and to deepen and enrich the opportunities for serious intellectual exchange.

LEGAL BASIS:
Private research library.

ELIGIBILITY:
Established scholars at the postdoctoral level may apply. An established scholar, as defined by the Awards Committee, is generally someone who has at least two published articles in refereed journals or the equivalent at the time of application. Projects must be appropriate for research in residence, within the Newberry's collection. Applicants must be U.S. citizens or residents. There may be preference given for scholars who live and work outside of the Chicago area.

FINANCIAL DATA:
Amount of support per award: $4,200 per month of residency.

APPLICATION INFORMATION:
Applications may be submitted through the online webform. Applicants must request at least four and no more than 12 months of support at the time of application.
Deadline: December 1.

EXECUTIVE STAFF:
Diane Dillon, Director of Scholarly and Undergraduate Programs

ADDRESS INQUIRIES TO:
See e-mail address above.

THE PHI BETA KAPPA SOCIETY
1606 New Hampshire Avenue, N.W.
Washington, DC 20009
(202) 745-3287
Fax: (202) 986-1601

E-MAIL ADDRESS:
awards@pbk.org

WEB SITE ADDRESS:
www.pbk.org

TYPE:
Fellowships. Grant to women scholars made in alternate years for advanced research dealing with Greek language, literature, history or archaeology (odd-numbered years) or with French language or literature (even-numbered years).

See entry 1093 for full listing.

THE ROYAL SOCIETY OF CANADA
Walter House
282 Somerset Street West
Ottawa ON K2P 0J6 Canada
(613) 991-6990 ext. 107
Fax: (613) 991-6996

E-MAIL ADDRESS:
awards@rsc-src.ca

WEB SITE ADDRESS:
www.rsc-src.ca

TYPE:
Awards/prizes. The Award in Gender Studies is intended to recognize significant contributions by a Canadian scholar in the humanities and social sciences to furthering our understanding of issues concerning gender.

The Bancroft Award is given for publication, instruction and research in the earth sciences that have conspicuously contributed to public understanding and appreciation of the subject.

The Flavelle Medal is awarded for an outstanding contribution to biological science during the preceding 10 years or for significant additions to a previous outstanding contribution to biological science.

The McLaughlin Medal is awarded for important research of sustained excellence in any branch of the medical sciences.

The McNeil Medal for the Public Awareness of Science is awarded to a candidate who has demonstrated outstanding ability to promote and communicate science to students and the public (in the broadest sense of the latter term) within Canada.

The Lorne Pierce Medal is awarded for an achievement of special significance and conspicuous merit in imaginative or critical literature written in either English or French (critical literature dealing with Canadian subjects has priority over critical literature of equal merit that does not deal with Canadian subjects).

The Miroslaw Romanowski Medal is awarded for significant contributions to the resolution of scientific aspects of environmental problems or for important improvements to the quality of an ecosystem in all aspects - terrestrial, atmospheric and aqueous - brought about by scientific means.

The Rutherford Memorial Medals are awarded for outstanding research in any branch of physics and chemistry.

The J.B. Tyrrell Historical Medal is awarded for outstanding work in the history of Canada.

The Alice Wilson Award is given to a woman of outstanding academic qualifications who is entering a career in scholarship or research at the postdoctoral level.

See entry 1836 for full listing.

THE SCHOMBURG CENTER FOR RESEARCH IN BLACK CULTURE [399]
515 Malcolm X Boulevard
New York, NY 10037-1801
(212) 491-2228
Fax: (212) 491-2098

E-MAIL ADDRESS:
sir@nypl.org

WEB SITE ADDRESS:
www.nypl.org/locations/tid/64/node/131

FOUNDED: 1925

AREAS OF INTEREST:
African, African-American and Afro-Caribbean history and culture.

NAME(S) OF PROGRAMS:
- **Scholars-in-Residence**

TYPE:
Fellowships. Awarded to scholars and professionals whose research in the Black experience can benefit from extended access to the Center's collections. Seminars, colloquia, forums, symposia and conferences complement the residency program.

YEAR PROGRAM STARTED: 1986

PURPOSE:
To encourage research and writing in Black history and culture; to facilitate interaction among the participants, including fellows funded by other sources; to provide for

widespread dissemination of findings through lectures, publications and the Schomburg Center Seminars.

ELIGIBILITY:
Applicants must be professionals and/or scholars in the humanities studying Black history and culture and fields related to the Schomburg Center's collections and program activities, including librarianship, archives and museum administration, special collections, photographs, audiovisual materials and publications. Studies in the social sciences, the arts, science and technology, psychology, education and religion are also eligible if they utilize a humanistic approach and contribute to humanistic knowledge. Creative writing projects (works of poetry and fiction) and projects that result in a performance are not eligible.

Persons seeking support for research leading to degrees are not eligible under this program. Candidates for advanced degrees must have received the degree or completed all requirements for it by the application deadline. Foreign nationals are ineligible unless they will have resided in the U.S. for three years immediately preceding the award date of the fellowship.

FINANCIAL DATA:
Amount of support per award: Stipend of $30,000 per six months.

COOPERATIVE FUNDING PROGRAMS: Funded by the National Endowment for the Humanities, the Ford Foundation, the Samuel I. Newhouse Foundation, and the Andrew W. Mellon Foundation.

NUMBER OF APPLICANTS MOST RECENT YEAR: 100.

NUMBER OF AWARDS: 6.

APPLICATION INFORMATION:
Applications are accepted electronically only.
Duration: Six consecutive months.
Deadline: November 1.

PUBLICATIONS:
Program announcement.

STAFF:
Farah Griffin, Director

ADDRESS INQUIRIES TO:
Scholars-in-Residence Program
(See address or e-mail above.)

*PLEASE NOTE:
The Center will assist scholars in locating housing.

*SPECIAL STIPULATIONS:
Fellows may not be employed or hold other major fellowships or grants during period of residency.

SOCIAL SCIENCES AND HUMANITIES RESEARCH COUNCIL OF CANADA
350 Albert Street
Ottawa ON K1P 6G4 Canada
(613) 943-7777
Fax: (613) 943-1329

E-MAIL ADDRESS:
fellowships@sshrc-crsh.gc.ca

WEB SITE ADDRESS:
www.sshrc-crsh.gc.ca

TYPE:
Awards/prizes; Fellowships; Scholarships. Through its Doctoral Awards program,

SSHRC offers two types of funding for doctoral students:
(1) SSHRC Doctoral Fellowships and;
(2) Joseph-Armand Bombardier (JAB) Canada Graduate Scholarships (CGS) program–Doctoral Scholarships.

See entry 1871 for full listing.

SOCIAL SCIENCES AND HUMANITIES RESEARCH COUNCIL OF CANADA
350 Albert Street
Ottawa ON K1P 6G4 Canada
(613) 943-7777
Fax: (613) 943-1329

E-MAIL ADDRESS:
fellowships@sshrc-crsh.gc.ca

WEB SITE ADDRESS:
www.sshrc-crsh.gc.ca

TYPE:
Fellowships. For Canadian citizens or permanent residents of Canada, to support postdoctoral research in the humanities and social sciences.

See entry 1872 for full listing.

SOCIAL SCIENCES AND HUMANITIES RESEARCH COUNCIL OF CANADA
350 Albert Street
Ottawa ON K1P 6G4 Canada
(613) 943-7777
Fax: (613) 943-1329

E-MAIL ADDRESS:
fellowships@sshrc-crsh.gc.ca

WEB SITE ADDRESS:
www.sshrc-crsh.gc.ca

TYPE:
Fellowships. Awarded annually to encourage the development of expertise in the field of human rights. The research should emphasize themes and issues relevant to human rights in Canada. Research in all areas of the humanities and the social sciences, including journalism and law, is eligible. Of particular interest are multidisciplinary or interdisciplinary research projects. This award is intended for experienced researchers. It is not a research training fellowship.

See entry 1873 for full listing.

SOCIAL SCIENCES AND HUMANITIES RESEARCH COUNCIL OF CANADA
350 Albert Street
Ottawa ON K1P 6G4 Canada
(613) 943-7777
Fax: (613) 943-1329

E-MAIL ADDRESS:
fellowships@sshrc-crsh.gc.ca

WEB SITE ADDRESS:
www.vanier.gc.ca

TYPE:
Awards/prizes; Fellowships; Scholarships. For full-time doctoral students in the humanities and social sciences.

See entry 1875 for full listing.

SOCIAL SCIENCES AND HUMANITIES RESEARCH COUNCIL OF CANADA
350 Albert Street
Ottawa ON K1P 6G4 Canada
(613) 943-7777
Fax: (613) 943-1329

E-MAIL ADDRESS:
fellowships@sshrc-crsh.gc.ca

WEB SITE ADDRESS:
www.sshrc-crsh.gc.ca

TYPE:
Fellowships. For Canadian citizens, permanent residents of Canada and foreign citizens to support postdoctoral research in the humanities and social sciences.

See entry 1876 for full listing.

SOCIAL SCIENCES AND HUMANITIES RESEARCH COUNCIL OF CANADA
350 Albert Street
Ottawa ON K1P 6G4 Canada
(613) 943-7777
Fax: (613) 943-1329

E-MAIL ADDRESS:
fellowships@sshrc-crsh.gc.ca

WEB SITE ADDRESS:
www.sshrc-crsh.gc.ca

TYPE:
Awards/prizes; Fellowships; Scholarships.

See entry 1874 for full listing.

STANFORD HUMANITIES CENTER [400]
Stanford University
424 Santa Teresa Street
Stanford, CA 94305-4015
(650) 723-3052
Fax: (650) 723-1895

E-MAIL ADDRESS:
shc-fellowships@stanford.edu

WEB SITE ADDRESS:
shc.stanford.edu

FOUNDED: 1980

AREAS OF INTEREST:
History, literature, philosophy, classics, languages, social theory, political theory, law, religion, anthropology, art history, folklore and other areas of the humanities.

NAME(S) OF PROGRAMS:
● **External Faculty Fellowships**

TYPE:
Fellowships. Fellowships are awarded to support research projects in the humanities; creative arts projects are not eligible. The Humanities Center seeks candidates whose research is likely to contribute to intellectual exchange among a diverse group of scholars within the disciplines of the humanities.

YEAR PROGRAM STARTED: 1982

PURPOSE:
To promote the humanities and humanistic study at Stanford and nationally, primarily through a research fellowship program.

LEGAL BASIS:
Private, nonprofit research center at Stanford University.

ELIGIBILITY:
Postdoctoral level research in the humanities. Applicants are expected to be at least three years beyond receipt of their Ph.D. at the start of their fellowship year.

FINANCIAL DATA:
Amount of support per award: Stipend of $65,000, plus a moving and housing allowance.

Matching fund requirements: Applicants are encouraged to seek supplementary financial support.

NUMBER OF APPLICANTS MOST RECENT YEAR: 350.

NUMBER OF AWARDS: 10 for the year 2013-14.

APPLICATION INFORMATION:
Application is required and may be obtained directly from the Humanities Center web site.

Duration: Academic year. Normally September 15 to June 15. No renewals.

Deadline: October. Award announcement by late March.

ADVISORY BOARD:
Jayna Brown, Ethnic Studies, University of California, Riverside
Sally Haslanger, Linguistics and Philosophy, Massachusetts Institute of Technology
Michael Herzfield, Anthropology, Harvard University
Stephen Hinton, Music
Margaret Imber, Classical and Medieval Studies, Bates College
Gavin Jones, English
Harsha Ram, Slavic Languages and Literatures, University of California, Berkeley
Ben Wang, East Asian Languages and Cultures
Caroline Winterer, History
Connie Wolf, Cantor Arts Center

ADDRESS INQUIRIES TO:
See e-mail address above.

STIFTELSEN RIKSBANKENS JUBILEUMSFOND   [401]
Kungstradgardsg. 18
SE-114 86 Stockholm Sweden
46 08-50 62 64 00
Fax: 46 08-50 62 64 31

E-MAIL ADDRESS:
rj@rj.se

WEB SITE ADDRESS:
www.rj.se

FOUNDED: 1964

AREAS OF INTEREST:
Scientific research in humanities and social sciences.

NAME(S) OF PROGRAMS:
● **Europe and Global Challenges**
● **Flexit**
● **Pro Futura**

TYPE:
Conferences/seminars; Exchange programs; Fellowships; General operating grants; Project/program grants; Research grants; Travel grants; Visiting scholars.

YEAR PROGRAM STARTED: 1965

PURPOSE:
To support and promote scientific research in humanities and social sciences.

LEGAL BASIS:
Independent, non-governmental foundation.

ELIGIBILITY:
Open to single researchers or research groups. The Foundation is interested in supporting multidisciplinary or interdisciplinary research projects in which researchers from different disciplines, faculties, localities or countries collaborate with Swedish scholars.

FINANCIAL DATA:
Amount of support per award: Average SEK 3,600,000.

Total amount of support: Approximately SEK 400,000,000.

COOPERATIVE FUNDING PROGRAMS: Occasional co-financing for large projects.

NUMBER OF APPLICANTS MOST RECENT YEAR: Approximately 900.

APPLICATION INFORMATION:
Applicants should first submit a short outline sketch and a publication list. If the preliminary proposal is accepted, applicants will be required to send a complete application.

Duration: Three years average for projects; six to eight years for programs.

Deadline: End of January.

PUBLICATIONS:
Annual report; Information to Grant Applicants; yearbook.

STAFF:
Goran Blomquist, Managing Director
Bjorn Olsson, Finance Director
Dr. Jenny Bjorkman, Head of Communications
Hanna Kollerstrom, Public Relations Officer
Robert Hamren, Research Secretary, Economics, Law, and Political Science
Dr. Britta Lovgren, Research Secretary, Humanities
Dr. Maria Wikse, Research Secretary, Humanities
Dr. Torbjorn Eng, Research Secretary, Social Science
Dr. Fredrik Lundmark, Research Secretary, Social Science

ADDRESS INQUIRIES TO:
Dr. Jenny Bjorkman
Head of Communications
(See address above.)

SWANN FOUNDATION FOR CARICATURE AND CARTOON   [402]
Prints and Photographs Division
Library of Congress
101 Independence Avenue, S.E.
Washington, DC 20540-4730
(202) 707-9115
Fax: (202) 707-6647

E-MAIL ADDRESS:
swann@loc.gov

WEB SITE ADDRESS:
www.loc.gov/rr/print/swann/swann-fellow.html

FOUNDED: 1967

AREAS OF INTEREST:
Caricature and cartoons.

NAME(S) OF PROGRAMS:
● **Swann Foundation Fellowship**

TYPE:
Conferences/seminars; Fellowships; Internships; Project/program grants; Visiting

scholars. Small grants. Annual fellowship awarded to candidate for a Ph.D. or Master's degree.

YEAR PROGRAM STARTED: 1995

PURPOSE:
To support the documentation and understanding of caricature and cartoon as art, considering how theory developed in relation to other visual arts, social history and intellectual history.

LEGAL BASIS:
Nonprofit, federal agency.

ELIGIBILITY:
Fellowships are awarded to active Ph.D. candidates, M.A. candidates and those people who have received an advanced degree within the last three years.

GEOGRAPHIC RESTRICTIONS:
North America.

FINANCIAL DATA:
Amount of support per award: Up to $15,000.

Total amount of support: Varies.

NUMBER OF APPLICANTS MOST RECENT YEAR: Approximately 20.

NUMBER OF AWARDS: Varies.

APPLICATION INFORMATION:
Applicants should submit a project proposal and budget.

Duration: One academic year, generally fall through following late spring.

Deadline: February 15.

ADDRESS INQUIRIES TO:
Martha Kennedy
Curator, Popular and Applied Graphic Art
(See address above.)

*SPECIAL STIPULATIONS:
Must be a graduate student or a postgraduate within three years of receiving an M.A. or Ph.D. from a university in the U.S., Canada, or Mexico.

UCLA CHICANO STUDIES RESEARCH CENTER
193 Haines Hall
Box 951544
Los Angeles, CA 90095
(310) 794-9646
Fax: (310) 206-1784

E-MAIL ADDRESS:
csrcinfo@chicano.ucla.edu

WEB SITE ADDRESS:
www.chicano.ucla.edu

TYPE:
Fellowships; Visiting scholars.

See entry 1069 for full listing.

UNIVERSITY OF PENNSYLVANIA, PENN HUMANITIES FORUM   [403]
3260 South Street
Penn Museum
Philadelphia, PA 19104-6324
(215) 898-8220
Fax: (215) 746-5946

E-MAIL ADDRESS:
phf@sas.upenn.edu

WEB SITE ADDRESS:
www.phf.upenn.edu

FOUNDED: 1999

AREAS OF INTEREST:
Humanities.

NAME(S) OF PROGRAMS:
● **Andrew W. Mellon Postdoctoral Fellowships in the Humanities**

TYPE:
Fellowships. Fellows conduct research and teach one course.

YEAR PROGRAM STARTED: 1976

PURPOSE:
To support and encourage the intellectual development of untenured scholars in the humanities.

LEGAL BASIS:
Nonprofit, non-taxable university.

ELIGIBILITY:
Candidates must have research interests that relate to the forum's topic of study for the year of the fellowship. Preference is given to proposals that are interdisciplinary and to candidates who have not previously used the resources of the University of Pennsylvania and whose work would allow them to take advantage of the research strengths of the institution and to make a contribution to its intellectual life. Research proposals are invited in all areas of humanistic studies except educational curriculum-building and performing arts.

FINANCIAL DATA:
Fellowships include health insurance and a $2,500 research fund.
Amount of support per award: $46,500.

NUMBER OF AWARDS: 5.

APPLICATION INFORMATION:
Applications are available, commencing in May, on the web site. Applicants are expected to submit the application, which includes a description of their proposed project, as well as recommendations.
Duration: One year in residence at University of Pennsylvania.
Deadline: October 15 of the year preceding the fellowship. Announcement in January of the fellowship year.

STAFF:
James F. English, Director
Jennifer Conway, Associate Director
Sara Varney, Administrative Coordinator

ADDRESS INQUIRIES TO:
Jennifer Conway, Associate Director
(See address above.)

VILLA I TATTI: THE HARVARD UNIVERSITY CENTER FOR ITALIAN RENAISSANCE STUDIES
Via di Vincigliata, 26
50135 Florence Italy
+39.055.603251
+39.055.608909
Fax: +39.055.603383

E-MAIL ADDRESS:
info@itatti.harvard.edu

WEB SITE ADDRESS:
www.itatti.harvard.edu

TYPE:
Fellowships. Stipendiary and nonstipendiary fellowships for the academic year July 1 through June 30 in residence in Florence for study on any aspect of the Italian

Renaissance. There are a limited number of short-term Mellon Visiting Fellowships designed to reach out to Italian Renaissance scholars from areas that have been underrepresented at Villa I Tatti, especially those from Asia, Latin America, the Iberian Peninsula, the Mediterranean basin (except Italy and France), and the Islamic countries. There are also a limited number of short-term Craig Hugh Smyth Visiting Fellowships for scholars who do not have the benefit of sabbatical leave including curators, administrators, and conservators, as well as scholars who, having the primary responsibility of caring for young children, do not have easy access to major research libraries and research.

See entry 952 for full listing.

LEWIS WALPOLE LIBRARY   [404]
Yale University
P.O. Box 1408
Farmington, CT 06034
(860) 677-2140
Fax: (860) 677-6369

E-MAIL ADDRESS:
walpole@yale.edu

WEB SITE ADDRESS:
www.library.yale.edu/walpole

AREAS OF INTEREST:
18th century studies (mainly British), the study of Horace Walpole and Strawberry Hill.

NAME(S) OF PROGRAMS:
● **Visiting Research Fellowship Program**

TYPE:
Fellowships. 18th century studies (mainly British), including history, literature, theatre, drama, art, architecture, politics, philosophy or social history.

PURPOSE:
To fund study into any aspect of British 18th century studies in the Library's collection of 18th century British prints, paintings, books and manuscripts.

ELIGIBILITY:
Applicants should normally be pursuing an advanced degree or must be engaged in postdoctoral research or equivalent research. Study is at doctoral, postdoctoral, postgraduate and research levels.

FINANCIAL DATA:
Amount of support per award: Fellowship: $2,100, plus travel to and from the Library, and free accommodations on site.
Total amount of support: Varies.

NUMBER OF AWARDS: Up to 15.

APPLICATION INFORMATION:
Applicants must submit a curriculum vitae, a brief outline of research proposal of up to three pages and two confidential letters of recommendation.
Duration: One month.
Deadline: January 15.

ADDRESS INQUIRIES TO:
Margaret K. Powell, Librarian
(See address above.)

WOODROW WILSON INTERNATIONAL CENTER FOR SCHOLARS   [405]
One Woodrow Wilson Plaza
1300 Pennsylvania Avenue, N.W.
Washington, DC 20004-3027
(202) 691-4170
Fax: (202) 691-4001

E-MAIL ADDRESS:
fellowships@wilsoncenter.org

WEB SITE ADDRESS:
www.wilsoncenter.org

FOUNDED: 1968

AREAS OF INTEREST:
Social sciences, humanities and public policy.

NAME(S) OF PROGRAMS:
● **Fellowship Program at the Woodrow Wilson International Center for Scholars**

TYPE:
Fellowships; Research grants; Residencies; Scholarships; Visiting scholars. The Center seeks to commemorate, through its residential fellowship program of advanced research, both the scholarly depth and the public concerns of Woodrow Wilson. The Center welcomes outstanding project proposals in the social sciences and humanities on national and/or international issues - topics that intersect with questions of public policy or provide the historical framework to illume policy issues of contemporary importance. The Center especially welcomes projects likely to foster communication between the world of ideas and the world of public affairs.

Projects should have relevance to the world of public policy. Fellows should be prepared to interact with policymakers in Washington and with the Center's staff working on similar areas.

Fellowships are tenable in residence only at the Woodrow Wilson International Center for Scholars. The Center will not provide support for research to be carried out elsewhere. Fellows devote their full time to research and writing.

YEAR PROGRAM STARTED: 1970

LEGAL BASIS:
Government agency.

ELIGIBILITY:
The Center seeks individuals from throughout the world with superior projects representing diverse scholarly interests in the social sciences and humanities - topics that intersect with questions of public policy.

Academic participants are normally established scholars at the postdoctoral level but cannot be currently working on a Ph.D.

For nonacademic participants, namely those from careers in government, journalism, business, diplomacy and other professions, an equivalent degree of professional achievement is required.

Criteria for selection include scholarly capabilities, promise and achievements, the importance and originality of the proposed research, and the likelihood of the applicant being able to accomplish what he or she proposes.

Applicants should have a very good command of spoken English, since the Center is designed to encourage the exchange of ideas among its Fellows.

FINANCIAL DATA:
The Center tries to ensure that the stipend provided under the fellowship, together with fellow's other sources of funding (e.g., grants secured by applicant and sabbatical allowances), approximate a fellow's regular salary (up to a maximum of $85,000).

Amount of support per award: Varies.

Total amount of support: $1,000,000 for the year 2013.

NUMBER OF APPLICANTS MOST RECENT YEAR:
300.

NUMBER OF AWARDS: 20-22.

REPRESENTATIVE AWARDS:
"Business, Politics and Social Responsibility in Latin America;" "Fads and Fashions in Economic Policy Reform;" "Questions of Precedence: History, Ownership and Value in Contemporary West African Political Economies."

APPLICATION INFORMATION:
Applicant must submit:
(1) the two-page, single-sided Fellowship Application Form (preferably typed);
(2) a list of publications that includes exact titles, names of publishers, dates of publication and status of forthcoming publications (not to exceed three pages);
(3) a Project Proposal (not to exceed five single-spaced typed pages, using 12-point type). The Center reserves the right to omit from review applications that are longer than the requested page length;
(4) a bibliography for the project that includes primary sources and relevant secondary sources (not to exceed three pages) and;
(5) the one-page Financial Information Form.

All application materials must be submitted in English. Applications submitted via fax will not be considered.

Duration: Fellowships of usually nine months are tenable September 1 of the fellowship year.

Deadline: October 1 for receipt of applications. Decisions announced by early April of the following year.

PUBLICATIONS:
Annual report; application guidelines.

OFFICERS:
Jane Harman, Director, President and Chief Executive Officer

ADDRESS INQUIRIES TO:
Kim Connor, Fellowship Specialist
(See address above.)

WINTERTHUR MUSEUM, GARDEN & LIBRARY   [406]

5105 Kennett Pike
Winterthur, DE 19735
(302) 888-4600
(302) 888-4637
Fax: (302) 888-4870

E-MAIL ADDRESS:
rkrill@winterthur.org

WEB SITE ADDRESS:
www.winterthur.org

FOUNDED: 1951

AREAS OF INTEREST:
American decorative arts, American art, American cultural and social history and horticulture.

NAME(S) OF PROGRAMS:
- **Dissertation Fellowships**
- **NEH Fellowships**
- **Winterthur Fellowships**

TYPE:
Fellowships. Long-term and short-term fellowships to be held in residence at Winterthur Museum.

The Dissertation Fellowships are for doctoral candidates. The award is a nine-month fellowship or a semester-length fellowship.

NEH Fellowships consist of four- to 12-month fellowships for advanced research in American life into the early 20th century.

Winterthur Fellowships consist of one- to three-month fellowships designed to promote research and study in topics of relevance to Winterthur's collections.

All fellowships are residential, requiring research and writing at Winterthur.

YEAR PROGRAM STARTED: 1977

PURPOSE:
To promote research in any humanistic field related to Winterthur's collections (museum, library, garden), work of an interdisciplinary nature and/or research with both objects and documents.

LEGAL BASIS:
Tax-exempt, public charitable organization.

ELIGIBILITY:
Winterthur Fellowships are available to academic, museum and independent scholars and to support dissertation research.

NEH Fellowships are available to scholars, holding the Ph.D., pursuing advanced research. Must be U.S. citizen or resident of the U.S. three years prior to application.

Applicants for a Dissertation Fellowship must have completed coursework, passed qualifying exams, fulfilled language requirements, and have an approved prospectus. The fellowship is open to students in departments of history, anthropology, folklore, art history, American studies, African-American history, historic preservation, and related fields.

FINANCIAL DATA:
Applicants may hold sabbaticals and grants from their own institutions, but may not simultaneously hold other major fellowships. Housing is available in a cottage on the museum grounds (full housekeeping facilities and furnished rooms).

Amount of support per award: Dissertation Fellowships: $7,000 per semester; NEH Fellowships: Up to $40,000 for two semesters; Winterthur Fellowships: $1,750 per month.

Total amount of support: Varies.

REPRESENTATIVE AWARDS:
John Lardas Modern, Professor of Religious Studies, Franklin & Marshall College, Lancaster, PA, "Haunted Modernity; or, the Metaphysics of Secularism in Antebellum America;" Julia A. Sienkewicz, University of Illinois, *Citizenship by Design: the Creation of Identity through Art, Architecture and Landscape in the Early Republic*; Sarah Carter, Harvard University, *A Basket, A Needle, A Penknife: Object Lessons in Nineteenth-Century American Material and Visual Culture.*

APPLICATION INFORMATION:
Application instructions and materials are available online at the Winterthur web site.

Applicants for each fellowship should submit a three- to five-page statement of purpose, a curriculum vitae and two letters of recommendation. Supporting materials for dissertation research must include a letter from the dissertation advisor.

Duration: NEH Fellowships: Four to 12 months; Winterthur Fellowships: One to three months.

Deadline: January 15. Announcement by April 30.

IRS IDENTIFICATION NUMBER: 51-0066038

ADDRESS INQUIRIES TO:
Research Fellowship Program
Academic Programs Department
(See address and e-mail above.)

CARTER G. WOODSON INSTITUTE FOR AFRICAN-AMERICAN AND AFRICAN STUDIES   [407]

University of Virginia
McCormick Road, 108 Minor Hall
Charlottesville, VA 22903
(434) 924-3109
Fax: (434) 924-8820

E-MAIL ADDRESS:
woodson@virginia.edu

WEB SITE ADDRESS:
www.virginia.edu/~woodson

FOUNDED: 1981

AREAS OF INTEREST:
Those disciplines of the humanities and social sciences which concern themselves with Afro-American and African Studies.

NAME(S) OF PROGRAMS:
- **African-American and African Studies Fellowships**

TYPE:
Fellowships. The Woodson Institute offers residential fellowships to predoctoral and postdoctoral scholars. These fellowships are designed to facilitate the completion of works in progress by providing scholars with unencumbered leave.

Afro-American and African Studies is considered to cover Africa, Africans and peoples of African descent in North, Central and South America and the Caribbean, past and present.

YEAR PROGRAM STARTED: 1981

PURPOSE:
To help researchers complete dissertations, books and other research projects focusing on the Black experience.

LEGAL BASIS:
University.

ELIGIBILITY:
Applicants for the predoctoral fellowships must have completed all requirements for the Ph.D. except the dissertation prior to August 1. Applicants for the postdoctoral fellowship must have been awarded their Ph.D. by the time of application or furnish proof that it will have been received prior to June 30. There are no restrictions as to citizenship or current residence. Employees of the University of Virginia may not apply.

Proposals will be judged on the basis of the significance of the proposed work, the applicant's qualifications, familiarity with existing relevant research literature, the research design of the project and the promise of completion within the award period. Preference will be given to projects whose field research is already substantially completed.

Fellowship recipients must be in residence at the University of Virginia for the duration of the award period and are expected to contribute to the intellectual life of the University. In pursuit of these goals, predoctoral fellows will become visiting graduate students attached to their respective disciplinary departments, and postdoctoral fellows will receive the status of visiting scholars in their respective fields.

FINANCIAL DATA:
Amount of support per award: Predoctoral Fellowship: $20,000 per year; Postdoctoral Fellowship: $45,000.

NUMBER OF APPLICANTS MOST RECENT YEAR:
149; 58 predoctoral and 91 postdoctoral.

NUMBER OF AWARDS: 5.

APPLICATION INFORMATION:
Complete guidelines are available on the Institute web site.
Duration: Two years.
Deadline: December 1. Notification by mail early March.

PUBLICATIONS:
Program guidelines.

STAFF:
Deborah E. McDowell, Director

ADDRESS INQUIRIES TO:
Program Administrator
(See address above.)

*SPECIAL STIPULATIONS:
Fellows are required to present a formal paper to the University community at least once a year.

YALE CENTER FOR BRITISH ART [408]
1080 Chapel Street
New Haven, CT 06520-8280
(203) 432-9805
Fax: (203) 432-4538

E-MAIL ADDRESS:
ycba.research@yale.edu

WEB SITE ADDRESS:
www.britishart.yale.edu/research/visiting-scholars

FOUNDED: 1977

AREAS OF INTEREST:
British art, history and literature.

NAME(S) OF PROGRAMS:
● **Visiting Scholar Awards**

TYPE:
Fellowships; Research grants; Residencies; Visiting scholars. Short-term resident fellowships for scholars of literature, history, the history of art or related fields. The Center also offers predoctoral residential awards.

YEAR PROGRAM STARTED: 1978

PURPOSE:
To allow scholars of literature, history, the history of art or related fields to study the Center's holdings of paintings, drawings, prints and rare books and to make use of its research facilities (photograph archive and reference library).

LEGAL BASIS:
University-affiliated museum and research center.

ELIGIBILITY:
Open to scholars engaged in predoctoral and postdoctoral or equivalent research related to British art and to museum professionals whose responsibilities and research interests include British art.

FINANCIAL DATA:
Fellowships include the cost of travel to and from New Haven and also provide accommodation and a living allowance. Recipients will be required to be in residence in New Haven during the Fellowship period.
Amount of support per award: $1,800 plus travel expenses.

COOPERATIVE FUNDING PROGRAMS: One fellowship per annum is reserved for members of the American Society for Eighteenth-Century Studies; by arrangement with the Huntington Library and the Delaware Art Museum, scholars may apply for tandem awards.

NUMBER OF APPLICANTS MOST RECENT YEAR:
42 for the year 2012-13.

NUMBER OF AWARDS: 20.

REPRESENTATIVE AWARDS:
Diane Wolfthal, David and Caroline Minter Chair in the Humanities, Professor and Chair, Department of Art History, Rice University, Houston, "Toward a Visual History of Early Modern Workers: English Portraits of Female Domestic Servants;" Crystal B. Lake, Marion L. Brittain Postdoctoral Fellow, Georgia Institute of Technology, "Curious Things: Artifacts and Politics in British Literature and Culture, 1660-1840;" Patricia Mainardi, Professor of 18th- and 19th-Century Art, Doctoral Program in Art History, Graduate Center of the City University of New York, "British Precedents for French Illustrated Print Culture, 1800-1850;" Arnika Schmidt, Ph.D. candidate, History of Art Department, University of Dresden, "Giovanni 'Nino' Costa (1826-1903) - The National and International Context of a Roman Landscape Painter."

APPLICATION INFORMATION:
Complete application information is available on the web site.
Duration: One to four months.
Deadline: January.

PUBLICATIONS:
Brochure.

STAFF:
Amy Meyers, Director
Martina Droth, Head of Research
Lisa Ford, Associate Head of Research

ADDRESS INQUIRIES TO:
Lisa Ford, Associate Head of Research
P.O. Box 208280
New Haven, CT 06520
E-mail: lisa.ford@yale.edu

*SPECIAL STIPULATIONS:
Inquiries and application submissions must be by e-mail only.

Architecture

AMERICAN ARCHITECTURAL FOUNDATION [409]
c/o AAF-RMHF
2101 L Street, N.W., Suite 670
Washington, DC 20037
(202) 787-1001

E-MAIL ADDRESS:
info@archfoundation.org

WEB SITE ADDRESS:
www.archfoundation.org

FOUNDED: 1942

AREAS OF INTEREST:
Architecture, urban design and leadership development.

NAME(S) OF PROGRAMS:
● **The Richard Morris Hunt Fellowship**

TYPE:
Exchange programs; Fellowships; Research grants; Travel grants. Six-month professional study in France awarded in alternate years to midcareer American architects and urbanists pursuing careers with an emphasis on historic preservation topics.

YEAR PROGRAM STARTED: 1990

PURPOSE:
To study American and French architecture heritage.

ELIGIBILITY:
Open to architects and urban design professionals who have written and oral proficiency in French and are pursuing a career in historic preservation. In alternate years, open to French architects. Applicants must be U.S. or French citizens.

GEOGRAPHIC RESTRICTIONS:
United States and France.

FINANCIAL DATA:
Amount of support per award: $25,000.
Total amount of support: $25,000.

COOPERATIVE FUNDING PROGRAMS:
Co-sponsored by the AAF and the French Heritage Society.

NUMBER OF APPLICANTS MOST RECENT YEAR:
9.

NUMBER OF AWARDS: 1.

APPLICATION INFORMATION:
Applicants should submit a recent biography, three letters of recommendation, examples of professional work such as slides, sketches or photographs, a statement explaining how academic background and work experience relate to the Fellowship and how the Fellowship will benefit professionally. Applicants must demonstrate French language proficiency.
Duration: Six months.
Deadline: Mid-September.

PUBLICATIONS:
Program announcement.

STAFF:
Thom Minner, Program Director

ADDRESS INQUIRIES TO:
Thom Minner, Program Director
(See address above.)

THE AMERICAN INSTITUTE OF ARCHITECTS [410]
1735 New York Avenue, N.W.
Washington, DC 20006-5292
(202) 626-7539
Fax: (202) 626-7399

E-MAIL ADDRESS:
rhayes@aia.org
infocentral@aia.org

WEB SITE ADDRESS:
www.aia.org/aah

FOUNDED: 1952

AREAS OF INTEREST:
Health care, facility planning, design and
construction, facilities management, clinical
engineering, and safety and security.

NAME(S) OF PROGRAMS:
- **AIA Arthur N. Tuttle, Jr. Graduate
Fellowship in Health Facility Planning
and Design**

TYPE:
Fellowships; Research grants. The American
Institute of Architects and the American
Hospital Association sponsor this program
with additional support from the Steris
Corporation, which offers one or more
graduate fellowships.

YEAR PROGRAM STARTED: 1952

PURPOSE:
To increase the amount of research being
done in the area of health care facility design
and planning.

LEGAL BASIS:
Nonprofit organization.

ELIGIBILITY:
Open to graduate and postgraduate students
enrolled at an accredited school of
architecture. Applicants must be citizens of
Canada, Mexico or the U.S.

FINANCIAL DATA:
Amount of support per award: Varies.

APPLICATION INFORMATION:
Guidelines and application forms are
available on the Institute web site.
Duration: One to two years depending on
proposal.
Deadline: June.

PUBLICATIONS:
Guidelines.

ADDRESS INQUIRIES TO:
Richard L. Hayes, Ph.D., AIA, Director of
Knowledge Resources
(See address above.)

THE AMERICAN INSTITUTE OF ARCHITECTS   [411]

1735 New York Avenue, N.W.
Washington, DC 20006-5292
(202) 626-7529
(202) 626-7417
Fax: (202) 626-7399

E-MAIL ADDRESS:
divscholarships@aia.org

WEB SITE ADDRESS:
www.aia.org

FOUNDED: 1943

AREAS OF INTEREST:
Architecture.

NAME(S) OF PROGRAMS:
- **AIA/F Diversity Advancement
Scholarship**

TYPE:
Scholarships. Awards to provide an
opportunity for financially disadvantaged
and/or minority groups to pursue a
professional degree in architecture.

YEAR PROGRAM STARTED: 1973

PURPOSE:
To provide scholarships for those who would
not otherwise have the opportunity to be
enrolled in professional architecture studies.

ELIGIBILITY:
Applicants must be residents of the U.S.
High school seniors, technical school/junior
college students transferring to an NAAB
school of architecture or college freshmen
who are entering a program leading to a
professional degree (Bachelor, Master's of
Architecture or D.Arch.) are eligible to apply.
Students who have completed the first year
of a standard four-year curriculum are not
eligible.

GEOGRAPHIC RESTRICTIONS:
United States.

FINANCIAL DATA:
Scholarship awards vary according to
financial need. The amount of the award is
determined based on the financial information
and consultation with the Director of
Financial Aid at the student's school.
Amount of support per award: $3,000 to
$4,000.

NUMBER OF AWARDS: Approximately 2.

APPLICATION INFORMATION:
Candidates must submit:
(1) a letter of recommendation completed by
an architect, an AIA component, a
community design center representative, a
guidance counselor or teacher, a director of a
community, civic, or religious organization,
or the dean, administrative head, or professor
at an NAAB-accredited professional program;
(2) a completed application form;
(3) a copy of transcripts of all high school
and college records, including SAT or ACT
scores;
(4) a copy of a written acceptance from an
NAAB-accredited professional program in
architecture (can be provided at time of
acceptance);
(5) a personal statement outlining interests,
experience, and career plans related to
architecture;
(6) a statement describing the applicant's
disadvantaged circumstances;
(7) one freehand drawing on an 8 1/2 x
11-inch page depicting any subject; cannot be
drafted or done using computer-aided design
and;
(8) completed portion of the last page of the
application by the high school guidance
counselor or the administrative head at the
NAAB-accredited professional program.
Duration: One academic year. Renewable up
to five years.
Deadline: Postmarked by May 2.

OFFICERS:
Robert Ivey, Executive Vice President and
Chief Executive Officer, American Institute
of Architects

ADDRESS INQUIRIES TO:
Jamie Yeung, Manager
Professional Development and Resources
(See address above.)

THE AMERICAN SCHOOL OF CLASSICAL STUDIES AT ATHENS

6-8 Charlton Street
Princeton, NJ 08540-5232
(609) 683-0800
Fax: (609) 924-0578

E-MAIL ADDRESS:
ascsa@ascsa.org (for information)
application@ascsa.org (to apply)

WEB SITE ADDRESS:
www.ascsa.edu.gr

TYPE:
Fellowships.

See entry 432 for full listing.

AMERICAN SOCIETY OF INTERIOR DESIGNERS EDUCATIONAL FOUNDATION   [412]

608 Massachusetts Avenue, N.E.
Washington, DC 20002-6006
(202) 675-2351
Fax: (202) 546-3240

E-MAIL ADDRESS:
foundation@asid.org

WEB SITE ADDRESS:
www.asidfoundation.org

FOUNDED: 1931

AREAS OF INTEREST:
Interior design (commercial and residential)
and interior design-related industry.

NAME(S) OF PROGRAMS:
- **ASID Foundation Legacy Scholarship
for Graduate Students**
- **ASID Foundation Legacy Scholarship
for Undergraduates**
- **Irene Winifred Eno Grant**
- **Joel Polsky Academic Achievement
Award**
- **Joel Polsky Prize**

TYPE:
Awards/prizes; Research grants; Scholarships.
Irene Winifred Eno Grant provides financial
assistance to individuals or groups engaged
in the creation of an educational program(s)
or an interior design research project
dedicated to health, safety and welfare.

The Legacy Scholarship for Graduate
Students is awarded on the basis of
academic/creative accomplishment.

The Legacy Scholarship for Undergraduates
is given to a creatively outstanding student as
demonstrated through their portfolio.

The Polsky Academic Achievement Award is
given annually to recognize an outstanding
undergraduate or graduate student's interior
design research or thesis project.

The Joel Polsky Prize recognizes outstanding
academic contributions to the discipline of
interior design through literature or visual
communication.

PURPOSE:
To encourage excellence in the field of
interior design.

LEGAL BASIS:
Nonprofit foundation.

ELIGIBILITY:
The Legacy Scholarship for Graduate
Students is open to students who are enrolled
in or have applied for admission to a
graduate-level interior design program at a
degree-granting institution.

The Legacy Scholarship for Undergraduates
is open to all students in their junior or
senior year of undergraduate study and
enrolled in at least a three-year program of
interior design.

The Irene Winifred Eno Grant is open to students, educators, interior design practitioners, institutions or other interior design-related groups.

The Joel Polsky Academic Achievement Award judges interior design research or doctoral and Master's thesis projects.

The Joel Polsky Prize entrants should address the needs of the public, designers and students on such topics as educational research, behavioral science, business practice, design process, theory or other technical subjects.

High school students and college freshmen are not eligible.

GEOGRAPHIC RESTRICTIONS:
United States.

FINANCIAL DATA:
Amount of support per award: Irene Winifred Eno Grant, Joel Polsky Academic Achievement Award and Joel Polsky Prize: $5,000; Legacy Scholarship for graduate and undergraduate students: $4,000.

APPLICATION INFORMATION:
Complete details are available online.
Duration: One-time award.

PUBLICATIONS:
ASID ICON, magazine; *Access*, the student newsletter; application guidelines.

OFFICERS:
Valerie O'Keefe, Foundation Manager

ADDRESS INQUIRIES TO:
Valerie O'Keefe, Foundation Manager
(See address above.)

ARCHITECTURAL LEAGUE OF NEW YORK [413]
594 Broadway, Suite 607
New York, NY 10012
(212) 753-1722
Fax: (212) 486-9173

E-MAIL ADDRESS:
info@archleague.org

WEB SITE ADDRESS:
www.archleague.org

FOUNDED: 1881

AREAS OF INTEREST:
Architecture, architectural history and urban studies.

NAME(S) OF PROGRAMS:
● **Deborah J. Norden Fund**

TYPE:
Research grants; Travel grants. The Deborah J. Norden Fund, established in 1995 in memory of architect and arts administrator Deborah Norden, awards travel/study grants to students and recent graduates in the field of architecture, architectural history, and urban studies.

YEAR PROGRAM STARTED: 1995

PURPOSE:
To support genuinely independent projects that require travel.

ELIGIBILITY:
Students or recent graduates in the fields of architecture, architectural history and urban studies may apply.

The intention of the fund is to support genuinely independent projects. Grant funds cannot be used for tuition or for participation in an organized program, such as a university's summer abroad program.

FINANCIAL DATA:
Amount of support per award: Up to $5,000.
Total amount of support: $5,000.

NUMBER OF APPLICANTS MOST RECENT YEAR: 110.

NUMBER OF AWARDS: 2.

APPLICATION INFORMATION:
Applicants should submit a brief proposal in letter form, no more than three pages, which succinctly describes the objectives of the grant request and how it will assist the applicant's intellectual and creative development. The grant amount requested must be specified. The submission should also include a resume of not more than two pages, project schedule, and budget for travel and other project costs. Two letters of recommendation must be requested from individuals who are knowledgeable about the applicant's ability and project. The applicant's name and brief project title must appear on the first page of the proposal.
Deadline: Mid-April. Announcement in late May.

ADDRESS INQUIRIES TO:
Jessica Liss, Program Associate
(See address above.)

ARCHITECTURAL LEAGUE OF NEW YORK [414]
594 Broadway, Suite 607
New York, NY 10012
(212) 753-1722
Fax: (212) 486-9173

E-MAIL ADDRESS:
info@archleague.org

WEB SITE ADDRESS:
www.archleague.org

AREAS OF INTEREST:
Young architects.

NAME(S) OF PROGRAMS:
● **The League Prize for Young Architects and Designers**

TYPE:
Research grants; Travel grants. A catalogue of winning work will be published by the Architectural League and Princeton Architectural Press. An exhibition of the work will be held at the Architectural League each spring.

PURPOSE:
To recognize specific works of high quality and to encourage the exchange of ideas among young architects and designers who might otherwise not have a forum; to focus on the aesthetic, cultural, and social concerns of architecture and the allied arts; to help architects, artists, and the public enrich their understanding of the purposes and importance of the art of architecture.

ELIGIBILITY:
Entrants may submit work done independently. Entrants must be ten years or less out of graduate or undergraduate school; students are not eligible for this competition. Work completed for fulfillment of course requirements at academic institutions is not eligible.

GEOGRAPHIC RESTRICTIONS:
United States, Canada and Mexico.

FINANCIAL DATA:
Amount of support per award: $1,000.

NUMBER OF AWARDS: 6 per year.

APPLICATION INFORMATION:
A written statement (not to exceed 250 words) is requested, which defines and considers the work under the rubric of the competition theme. Significant weight is given to how an applicant's work addresses the theme. A single portfolio, which may include several projects, must be bound and no larger than 11x14 inches. The portfolio may not contain more than 30 double-sided pages. CDs, models, slides and transparencies will not be accepted.

Each submission must include an entry form and $25 entry fee. Insert form, intact, into an unsealed envelope attached to the inside back cover of the submission. To maintain anonymity, no identification of the entrant may appear on any part of the submission, except on the entry form and return envelope.

Portfolios will be returned by mail only if a self-addressed envelope with postage is also enclosed. The Architectural League assumes no liability for original drawings. The League will take every precaution to return submissions intact, but can assume no responsibility for loss or damage. Portfolios may be discarded after six months if no return envelope is provided.
Deadline: Varies.

ADDRESS INQUIRIES TO:
Anne Rieselbach, Program Director
(See address above.)

THE COMMUNITY FOUNDATION OF LOUISVILLE, INC.
325 West Main Street, Suite 1110
Louisville, KY 40202
(502) 585-4649
Fax: (502) 587-7484

E-MAIL ADDRESS:
gails@cflouisville.org

WEB SITE ADDRESS:
www.cflouisville.org

TYPE:
Endowments; Grants-in-aid; Scholarships.

See entry 441 for full listing.

ENTERPRISE COMMUNITY PARTNERS [415]
11000 Broken Land Parkway
Columbia, MD 21044
(781) 235-2006
Fax: (781) 235-4011

WEB SITE ADDRESS:
www.enterprisecommunity.org

AREAS OF INTEREST:
Architecture and community development.

NAME(S) OF PROGRAMS:
● **Rose Architectural Fellowship**

TYPE:
Fellowships.

YEAR PROGRAM STARTED: 2000

PURPOSE:
To promote architectural and community design in low-income communities and to encourage architects to become lifelong leaders in public service and community development.

ELIGIBILITY:
Applicants must possess a professional Baccalaureate degree in architecture from an accredited college or university, or expect to graduate from an accredited school of architecture before the Fellowship begins. A professional graduate degree in architecture from an accredited university is preferred. The expected minimum grade point average is "B" or 3.0 on a 4.0 scale for all undergraduate and graduate work.

Applicants with diverse educational, professional, and personal backgrounds are encouraged to apply.

GEOGRAPHIC RESTRICTIONS:
United States.

FINANCIAL DATA:
Compensation is provided to the partner organization to pay for its share of health insurance and payroll taxes which are paid on behalf of the employee.
Amount of support per award: $46,000 annual stipend.
Matching fund requirements:
Community-based organizations must match Rose Fellowship funds 2:1.

NUMBER OF APPLICANTS MOST RECENT YEAR: 25.

NUMBER OF AWARDS: Average of 3.

APPLICATION INFORMATION:
Contact Enterprise Community Partners.
Duration: One year.
Deadline: Mid-summer.

ADDRESS INQUIRIES TO:
Katie Swenson
Director, Rose Architectural Fellowship
(See address above.)

THE JAMES MARSTON FITCH CHARITABLE FOUNDATION [416]

c/o The Neighborhood Preservation Center
232 East 11th Street
New York, NY 10003
(212) 252-6809
Fax: (212) 471-9987

E-MAIL ADDRESS:
info@fitchfoundation.org

WEB SITE ADDRESS:
www.fitchfoundation.org

FOUNDED: 1988

AREAS OF INTEREST:
Architecture, engineering, environmental planning, and historic preservation.

NAME(S) OF PROGRAMS:
• **Richard Blinder Award**
• **Mid-Career Grant**

TYPE:
Research grants. Richard Blinder Award was created to promote studies that explore the architecture of cultural buildings which integrate historic preservation and new construction - past, present and future; presented biennially.

Mid-Career Grant Program: This grant is the primary mission and the signature grant of this Foundation. The grants are intended to support projects of innovative original research or creative design that advance the practice of historic preservation in the U.S.

PURPOSE:
To advance the study and practice of the preservation of the historic architectural

heritage of the U.S.; to support preservation through a research grant program as well as through such educational activities as publications, seminars and lectures.

ELIGIBILITY:
Richard Blinder Award proposal must demonstrate that it fosters architectural preservation in the U.S. Applicant must be an architect holding a professional degree or a valid license to practice architecture. Grants are awarded only to individuals, not organizations or university-sponsored research projects. Grants are not awarded for professional fees.

Mid-Career Grant is for college graduates with a postgraduate degree and at least 10 years of professional experience.

GEOGRAPHIC RESTRICTIONS:
United States.

FINANCIAL DATA:
Amount of support per award: Up to $15,000.

NUMBER OF AWARDS: Richard Blinder Award: 1; Mid-Career Grant: 1 to 3.

APPLICATION INFORMATION:
Contact the Foundation for guidelines and application.
Duration: One year.
Deadline: Mid-September.

ADDRESS INQUIRIES TO:
See e-mail address above.

GRAHAM FOUNDATION FOR ADVANCED STUDIES IN THE FINE ARTS [417]

4 West Burton Place
Chicago, IL 60610
(312) 787-4071

E-MAIL ADDRESS:
grantprograms@grahamfoundation.org

WEB SITE ADDRESS:
www.grahamfoundation.org

FOUNDED: 1956

AREAS OF INTEREST:
Architecture and related spatial practices that engage a wide range of cultural, social, political, technological, environmental and aesthetic issues. The Foundation is interested in projects that investigate the contemporary condition, expand historical perspectives, or explore the future of architecture and the designed environment.

NAME(S) OF PROGRAMS:
• **Carter Manny Award**
• **Production and Presentation Grants**
• **Research and Development Grants**

TYPE:
Awards/prizes; Project/program grants; Research grants. Grants to organizations, individuals and public programs.

Carter Manny Award: To support research for academic dissertations by promising scholars who are presently candidates for a doctoral degree, and whose dissertations focus on areas traditionally supported by the Foundation. Students must be nominated by their department to apply for this Award.

Production and Presentation Grants: To assist individuals and organizations with the production-related expenses that are necessary to take a project from conceptualization to realization and public

presentation. These projects may include, but are not limited to, publications, exhibitions, installations, conferences, films, new-media projects, and other public programs.

Research and Development Grants: To assist individuals with seed money for research-related expenses such as travel, documentation, materials, supplies and other development costs.

YEAR PROGRAM STARTED: 1956

PURPOSE:
To make project-based grants to individuals and organizations and to produce public programs to foster the development and exchange of diverse and challenging ideas about architecture and its role in the arts, culture and society.

LEGAL BASIS:
Private foundation.

ELIGIBILITY:
Individuals and institutions may apply. No grants for endowments, general operating expenses, capital projects, scholarship aid or for work in pursuit of an academic degree (except for the Carter Manny Award), debt or expenses incurred prior to the date of grant request.

APPLICATION INFORMATION:
Application to the Foundation involves a two-stage process and is open submission.

Stage One/Inquiry Form: Eligible candidates interested in applying for a grant must first submit an Inquiry Form. The Inquiry Form is available on the Foundation web site with each grant cycle and must be submitted online.

Stage Two/Proposal Form: Applicants whose projects best match the Foundation's priorities and interests are invited to submit a Proposal Form and supplementary materials. Applicants not invited to submit a Proposal Form are sent a decline letter at this stage. An invitation to submit a Proposal Form does not guarantee eventual funding.

Award Decision: Funding recommendations are presented to the Board of Trustees for consideration. If a grant is awarded, applicant will be asked to sign a Grant Agreement that outlines the conditions of the award, such as annual reporting. Funding decisions at all stages of the review are based on the priority of the proposed project as related to the Foundation's mission and interests, the project's fulfillment of the Foundation's criteria for evaluation, and availability of Foundation funds.
Duration: Varies.
Deadline: February 25 for organizations; September 15 for individuals.

PUBLICATIONS:
Annual report; guidelines.

OFFICERS:
Sarah Herda, Director
Ellen Hartwell Alderman, Managing Director
Stephanie Whitlock, Program Officer
Carolyn T. Kelly, Grants Manager

TRUSTEES:
Rena Conti
Jeanne Gang
Chandra Goldsmith
Sean Keller
Bruce Sagan
Elizabeth Smith
Hamza Walker
Ross Wimer

ADDRESS INQUIRIES TO:
See e-mail address above.

THE LEF FOUNDATION [418]
P.O. Box 382066
Cambridge, MA 02238-2066
(617) 492-5333
Fax: (617) 868-5603

E-MAIL ADDRESS:
sara@lef-foundation.org

WEB SITE ADDRESS:
www.lef-foundation.org

FOUNDED: 1985

AREAS OF INTEREST:
Film and video.

NAME(S) OF PROGRAMS:
● **Moving Image Fund**

TYPE:
Project/program grants; Seed money grants.
Program development.

PURPOSE:
To support the creation and presentation of
contemporary work.

ELIGIBILITY:
Grants are made to organizations that have
tax-exempt status under Section 501(c)(3) of
the Internal Revenue Code, as well as
individuals with 501(c)(3) fiscal sponsors.

GEOGRAPHIC RESTRICTIONS:
New England.

FINANCIAL DATA:
Amount of support per award: $5,000 to
$25,000.
Total amount of support: $165,000 annually.

NUMBER OF AWARDS: 300.

APPLICATION INFORMATION:
Application form and guidelines are available
on the Foundation web site.
Duration: Varies.
Deadline: Varies.

ADDRESS INQUIRIES TO:
Sara Archambault, Program Director
(See address above.)

THE PAUL MELLON CENTRE FOR STUDIES IN BRITISH ART [419]
16 Bedford Square
London WC1B 3JA England
44 (0) 20 7580 0311
Fax: 44 (0) 20 7636 6730

E-MAIL ADDRESS:
grants@paul-mellon-centre.ac.uk

WEB SITE ADDRESS:
www.paul-mellon-centre.ac.uk

FOUNDED: 1970

AREAS OF INTEREST:
British art and architectural history.

NAME(S) OF PROGRAMS:
● **Educational Programme Grants**
● **Junior Fellowships**
● **Paul Mellon Centre Rome Fellowship**
● **Postdoctoral Fellowships**
● **Research Support Grants**
● **Senior Fellowships**

TYPE:
Conferences/seminars; Fellowships;
Project/program grants; Research grants.

Educational Programme Grants for lectures,
symposia, seminars or conferences on British
art and architecture.

The Junior Fellowship is to pursue ongoing
doctoral research at an American or British
university.

The Paul Mellon Centre Rome Fellowship
offers fellowships to scholars working on
Grand Tour subjects or in the field of
Anglo-Italian cultural and artistic relations.

The Postdoctoral Fellowship works to
transform doctoral research into publishable
form such as a book, series of articles, or
exhibition catalogues.

Research Support Grants are for expenses in
pursuit of research.

The Senior Fellowship supports an
established scholar in the field of British art
and architectural history to complete a
manuscript or book for immediate
publication.

YEAR PROGRAM STARTED: 1998

PURPOSE:
To promote scholarship and publications.

LEGAL BASIS:
University-affiliated research center.

ELIGIBILITY:
Candidates for the Junior Fellowship may be
of any nationality but must be enrolled in a
graduate program at an American or other
non-British university for study in the U.K.
or at a non-American university for study in
the U.S.

The Postdoctoral fellowship is awarded
within four years of an applicant's doctoral
award. Applicants must have had their
doctoral theses successfully examined.

Applicants for the Rome Fellowship should,
preferably, be competent in spoken and
written Italian.

FINANCIAL DATA:
Amount of support per award: Varies.

APPLICATION INFORMATION:
Full details and application forms are
available online.
Duration: Junior Fellowship: Three months.
Postdoctoral Fellowship: Six months. Rome
Fellowship: Three months. Senior
Fellowship: 12 months.
Deadline: Fellowships and grants: January
15. Grants: September 15.

ADDRESS INQUIRIES TO:
Grants Administrator
(See e-mail address above.)

NATIONAL SOCIETY DAUGHTERS OF THE AMERICAN REVOLUTION [420]
1776 D Street, N.W.
Washington, DC 20006-5303
(202) 879-3292

WEB SITE ADDRESS:
www.dar.org

FOUNDED: 1895

AREAS OF INTEREST:
Historic preservation.

NAME(S) OF PROGRAMS:
● **J.E.R. Caldwell Centennial Scholarship**

TYPE:
Scholarships.

YEAR PROGRAM STARTED: 1985

PURPOSE:
To provide ways and means to aid students
in attaining higher education.

LEGAL BASIS:
Incorporated historical society.

ELIGIBILITY:
Applicants must be enrolled in the junior or
senior year of a fully accredited college or
university in the U.S. and pursuing a degree
in the field of historic preservation, may
reside in any state, and must be a U.S.
citizen. All applicants must be sponsored by
a local DAR chapter.

GEOGRAPHIC RESTRICTIONS:
United States.

FINANCIAL DATA:
Amount of support per award: $2,000.

APPLICATION INFORMATION:
To obtain a scholarship application packet,
send a self-addressed, stamped #10
business-size envelope to the Office of the
Reporter General, DAR Scholarship
Committee at the address listed above.

Included with the application packet is the
list of DAR State Scholarship Chairmen. All
scholarship applicants are required to have a
letter of sponsorship from a chapter.
Individuals interested in obtaining a letter of
sponsorship from a local chapter are
encouraged to contact the DAR State
Chairman.
Deadline: February 15.

PUBLICATIONS:
American Spirit, magazine.

ADDRESS INQUIRIES TO:
Office of the Reporter General
DAR Scholarship Committee
(See address above.)

ROTCH TRAVELLING SCHOLARSHIP IN ARCHITECTURE [421]
290 Congress Street, Suite 200
Boston, MA 02210
(617) 391-4000
Fax: (617) 951-0845

E-MAIL ADDRESS:
abey@architects.org

WEB SITE ADDRESS:
www.rotch.org

FOUNDED: 1883

AREAS OF INTEREST:
Architecture.

NAME(S) OF PROGRAMS:
● **Rotch Travelling Scholarship**
● **Rotch Travelling Studio**

TYPE:
Fellowships. Traveling Fellowships. Rotch
Travelling Scholarship awards a minimum of
eight months of foreign travel and study in
the field of architecture and allied subjects.

Rotch Travelling Studio allows faculty to
take architecture students for a one-month
travelling program.

YEAR PROGRAM STARTED: 1883

PURPOSE:
To provide young architects with the
opportunity to gain experience with other
cultures; to augment the architectural
education of students of architecture at the
highest level of scholarship within a studio
format.

LEGAL BASIS:
Private trust.

ELIGIBILITY:
Rotch Travelling Scholarship: Applicants must be U.S. citizens no more than 35 years of age who have a degree from an accredited school of architecture plus at least one year of experience in an architectural office in Massachusetts, or a degree from an accredited Massachusetts school of architecture and one year of experience in an architectural office not necessarily in Massachusetts.

Rotch Travelling Studio: Applicants are invited from faculty members in all NAAB-accredited schools of architecture in the U.S. for travel anywhere in the world during the following calendar year.

GEOGRAPHIC RESTRICTIONS:
United States.

FINANCIAL DATA:
Amount of support per award: Travelling Scholarship: $37,000 up; Travelling Studio: Up to $20,000.

APPLICATION INFORMATION:
Official application forms are available online.
Duration: Travelling Scholarship: Minimum eight months; Travelling Studio: One month.
Deadline: Travelling Scholarship: January; Travelling Studio: October.

*SPECIAL STIPULATIONS:
No Rotch scholar may hold simultaneously another travelling scholarship, nor may he or she be employed during the period of the scholarship without special permission.

ROYAL INSTITUTE OF BRITISH ARCHITECTS   [422]

RIBA Research Trusts
Education Department
66 Portland Place
London W1B 1AD England
44 (0) 20 7307 3678
Fax: 44 (0) 20 7307 3754

E-MAIL ADDRESS:
education@riba.org

WEB SITE ADDRESS:
www.architecture.com

FOUNDED: 1834

AREAS OF INTEREST:
Architecture, and the arts and sciences connected therewith, in the U.K.

NAME(S) OF PROGRAMS:
● **RIBA Research Trusts Awards**

TYPE:
Awards/prizes; Research grants; Seed money grants; Travel grants. Merit-based award to support recent architecture graduates who are pursuing research in the field of architecture.

PURPOSE:
To support individuals who are pursuing research in the field of architecture, with the anticipation that award winners may, in subsequent years, undertake a career as skilled researchers in the architectural field or be practicing architects developing a research trajectory.

ELIGIBILITY:
Open to applicants interested in a wide range of subject matter relevant to the advancement of architecture, and connected arts and sciences, in the U.K.

The Institute Research Trust Award is for a closely defined piece of architectural research. The committee will support practice-led or academic research, but it will not support course fees and subsistence costs for Ph.D./M.Phil. or Master's programmes. Awards are given only to named individuals, not organisations.

Applicants based outside the U.K. are also eligible to apply; however, the research work must in the main be undertaken within the U.K.

The Institute may support recent graduates or individuals who are already further into their careers. The committee will particularly welcome applications from practice-led researchers as this is an area from which it has historically received very few applications.

GEOGRAPHIC RESTRICTIONS:
United Kingdom.

FINANCIAL DATA:
The value of an award will be determined by the estimated requirements of the project.
Amount of support per award: Maximum award not to exceed GBP 10,000.

COOPERATIVE FUNDING PROGRAMS: A candidate may have funding from other sources.

NUMBER OF APPLICANTS MOST RECENT YEAR:
45.

NUMBER OF AWARDS: Up to 4.

APPLICATION INFORMATION:
Application forms are available from the Institute. Only requests up to GBP 10,000 will be considered.
Duration: Up to two years.
Deadline: Varies.

OFFICER:
Harry Rich, Chief Executive

ADDRESS INQUIRIES TO:
RIBA Education Projects
E-mail: hayley.russell@riba.org

SIR JOHN SOANE MUSEUM FOUNDATION   [423]

1040 First Avenue, Suite 311
New York, NY 10022
(212) 223-2012
Fax: (866) 841-1928

E-MAIL ADDRESS:
info@soanefoundation.com

WEB SITE ADDRESS:
www.soanefoundation.com

AREAS OF INTEREST:
Education of the public in architecture and the fine and decorative arts.

NAME(S) OF PROGRAMS:
● **Sir John Soane Museum Foundation Traveling Fellowship**

TYPE:
Fellowships. Designed to help graduate students and scholars pursue research projects related to the work of Sir John Soane's Museum and its collections.

PURPOSE:
To educate and inspire the general and professional public in architecture and the fine and decorative arts.

ELIGIBILITY:
Applicants must be enrolled in a graduate degree program in a field appropriate to the Foundation's purpose. Level of study is postgraduate.

FINANCIAL DATA:
Amount of support per award: $5,000.

NUMBER OF APPLICANTS MOST RECENT YEAR:
16.

NUMBER OF AWARDS: 2.

APPLICATION INFORMATION:
Applicants must submit a formal proposal of not more than one page describing the goal, scope and purpose of the research project, in addition to three letters of recommendation.
Duration: One year.
Deadline: March 1.

ADDRESS INQUIRIES TO:
Chas Miller, Executive Director
(See address above.)

SOCIETY OF ARCHITECTURAL HISTORIANS   [424]

1365 North Astor Street
Chicago, IL 60610-2144
(312) 573-1365
Fax: (312) 573-1141

E-MAIL ADDRESS:
beifrig@sah.org

WEB SITE ADDRESS:
www.sah.org

FOUNDED: 1940

AREAS OF INTEREST:
Architecture and its related arts.

NAME(S) OF PROGRAMS:
● **Sally Kress Tompkins Fellowship**

TYPE:
Fellowships; Internships; Travel grants. The Sally Kress Tompkins Fellowship, a joint program of the Society of Architectural Historians and the National Park Service's Historic American Buildings Survey, permits an architectural historian to work on a 12-week project during the summer. The Fellow will prepare a written history to become part of the permanent collection focusing on either a specific nationally significant building/site, or a broader architectural history topic. The Fellow will be stationed in the field working in conjunction with a measured drawings team, or in the Washington, DC office. The Fellow will be selected by a jury of two SAH members and one HABS representative.

PURPOSE:
To advance the knowledge and understanding of architecture, design, landscape and urbanism worldwide.

LEGAL BASIS:
Nonprofit professional organization.

ELIGIBILITY:
Graduate students and member of SAH.

FINANCIAL DATA:
Amount of support per award: $500 to $9,200.
Total amount of support: $10,000.

COOPERATIVE FUNDING PROGRAMS: National Park Service's Historic American Buildings Survey (HABS).

NUMBER OF APPLICANTS MOST RECENT YEAR:
5.

NUMBER OF AWARDS: 1.

APPLICATION INFORMATION:
Details are available online, for members.

Duration: One year.
Deadline: October 1.

PUBLICATIONS:
Newsletter; *Journal of the Society of Architectural Historians.*

ADDRESS INQUIRIES TO:
Beth Eifrig, Assistant Director of Programs
(See address above.)

THE SOCIETY OF NAVAL ARCHITECTS AND MARINE ENGINEERS
99 Canal Center Plaza, Suite 310
Alexandria, VA 22314
(703) 997-6709
Fax: (703) 997-6702

E-MAIL ADDRESS:
bgreer@sname.org

WEB SITE ADDRESS:
www.sname.org

TYPE:
Scholarships. The Society annually awards both graduate and undergraduate scholarships to encourage study in naval architecture, marine engineering, ocean engineering or marine industry-related fields.

Graduate Scholarships are made for one year of study leading to a Master's in naval architecture, marine engineering, ocean engineering or in fields directly related to the marine industry.

Undergraduate Scholarships are administered by schools offering undergraduate programs on grants given to the schools.

See entry 2663 for full listing.

VIRGINIA POLYTECHNIC INSTITUTE AND STATE UNIVERSITY
MAOP Office
110 Femoyer Hall
Blacksburg, VA 24061
(540) 231-5023
Fax: (540) 231-2618

E-MAIL ADDRESS:
maop@vt.edu

WEB SITE ADDRESS:
www.maop.vt.edu

TYPE:
Assistantships; Fellowships; Internships; Scholarships. The program assists with graduate school financing in exchange for assistance to MAOP administration. Graduate students assist with programming implementation such as mentoring to undergraduate students.

See entry 1022 for full listing.

WASHINGTON UNIVERSITY   [425]
School of Architecture
Campus Box 1079
One Brookings Drive
St. Louis, MO 63130-4899
(314) 935-6200
Fax: (314) 935-7656

E-MAIL ADDRESS:
ellis@samfox.wustl.edu

WEB SITE ADDRESS:
www.steedmancompetition.com

FOUNDED: 1925

AREAS OF INTEREST:
Architectural education.

NAME(S) OF PROGRAMS:
- **James Harrison Steedman Memorial Fellowship in Architecture**

TYPE:
Awards/prizes; Fellowships; Travel grants. An award made on the basis of a design competition that requires the recipient to travel and study abroad for nine months. Not to be used towards tuition.

YEAR PROGRAM STARTED: 1925

PURPOSE:
To assist well-qualified architectural graduates to benefit by travel and study of architecture in foreign countries.

ELIGIBILITY:
Open to graduates of an accredited school of architecture, regardless of age, for a period up to eight years after the receipt of their first professional degree. Candidates must have at least one year of practical experience in the office of a practicing architect. Citizens of all countries are eligible.

FINANCIAL DATA:
Amount of support per award: $30,000 stipend for nine months of travel abroad.
Total amount of support: $30,000.

NUMBER OF APPLICANTS MOST RECENT YEAR:
125.

NUMBER OF AWARDS: 1 awarded biennially.

APPLICATION INFORMATION:
Registration forms are available online. Applications are available in late October every odd year and fellowships are awarded in the spring every even year.
Duration: Nine months.

PUBLICATIONS:
Application guidelines.

GOVERNING BOARD:
William Wischmeyer

ADDRESS INQUIRIES TO:
Daphne Ellis, Assistant to Dean
(See address above.)

Arts (multiple disciplines)

ACADEMY FOUNDATION OF THE ACADEMY OF MOTION PICTURE ARTS AND SCIENCES
8949 Wilshire Boulevard
Beverly Hills, CA 90211-1972
(310) 247-3000 ext. 1131
Fax: (310) 859-9619

E-MAIL ADDRESS:
rmiller@oscars.org

WEB SITE ADDRESS:
www.oscars.org

TYPE:
Awards/prizes.

See entry 541 for full listing.

ACGG EDUCATION FOUNDATION   [426]
22 Vista View Lane
Cody, WY 82414-9606
(307) 587-4278
Fax: (307) 587-8296

E-MAIL ADDRESS:
jan@acggeducationfoundation.org

WEB SITE ADDRESS:
www.acggeducationfoundation.org

FOUNDED: 2006

AREAS OF INTEREST:
Custom gunmaking and gunsmithing.

NAME(S) OF PROGRAMS:
- **Gunsmithing Student Scholarships**
- **Trinidad State Gunsmithing Scholarship**

TYPE:
Scholarships.

PURPOSE:
To further the education and development of gunmakers.

LEGAL BASIS:
501(c)(3).

ELIGIBILITY:
Open to applicants that are gunsmithing students.

FINANCIAL DATA:
Amount of support per award: Trinidad State Gunsmithing Scholarship: $325.
Total amount of support: Trinidad State Gunsmithing Scholarship: $650.

NUMBER OF APPLICANTS MOST RECENT YEAR: 14.

NUMBER OF AWARDS: Trinidad State Gunsmithing Scholarship: 2.

APPLICATION INFORMATION:
Contact the Foundation for application.
Deadline: Trinidad State Gunsmithing Scholarship: June 1.

ADDRESS INQUIRIES TO:
Jan Billeb, Executive Director
(See address above.)

ALABAMA STATE COUNCIL ON THE ARTS   [427]
201 Monroe Street
Suite 110
Montgomery, AL 36104-3721
(334) 242-4076
Fax: (334) 240-3269

E-MAIL ADDRESS:
staff@arts.alabama.gov

WEB SITE ADDRESS:
www.arts.alabama.gov

FOUNDED: 1966

AREAS OF INTEREST:
Architecture, literature, fine arts, arts in education, museums and libraries, music, and creative and performing arts.

CONSULTING OR VOLUNTEER SERVICES:
Strengthens cultural activities already in existence, assists in formation of new cultural activities, works towards improving the quality of presentations by both professional and amateur organizations and offers assistance to culturally oriented groups.

NAME(S) OF PROGRAMS:
- **Art and Cultural Facilities**
- **Arts-in-Education**
- **Community Arts Development**
- **Folk Arts**
- **Literary Art**
- **Performing Arts**
- **Visual Arts and Crafts**

TYPE:
Awards/prizes; Challenge/matching grants; Conferences/seminars; Development grants; Fellowships; General operating grants; Internships; Project/program grants; Residencies; Technical assistance. Grants to various disciplines comprising technical and financial assistance to local organizations in sponsoring activities of quality and promise in the various arts disciplines of the visual and performing arts within communities throughout Alabama.

YEAR PROGRAM STARTED: 1967

PURPOSE:
To increase interest, participation and support in the arts by supplementing local initiatives and local funds in order to enable a greater number of quality activities to be seen or heard throughout the state.

LEGAL BASIS:
Alabama Law, Act No. 551, Regular Session 1967 and Act No. 1065, Regular Session, 1969.

ELIGIBILITY:
Applicants must be qualified organizations sponsoring arts events or programs for communities. Such groups include local arts councils, arts associations, museums, literary associations, colleges and universities, dance and theatre groups. Evidence of nonprofit status is required.

GEOGRAPHIC RESTRICTIONS:
Alabama.

FINANCIAL DATA:
Amount of support per award: $500 to $250,000 for the year 2013.
Total amount of support: $3,300,000 for the year ended September 30, 2013.
Matching fund requirements: Equal amounts from other sources with exception of Artists Fellowships.

APPLICATION INFORMATION:
A special application form can be obtained and submitted by using the Council eGRANT system which is available on their web site.
Duration: One year. Renewal by reapplication.
Deadline: March 1, June 1 and September 1.

PUBLICATIONS:
Guide to Programs; *Alabama Arts*, magazine; *Touring & Presenting Guide.*

IRS IDENTIFICATION NUMBER: 63-6000619

EXECUTIVE COUNCIL:
James Harrison, III, Chairman
Vaughan Morrissette, Vice Chairman
Lisa Weil, Secretary

ADDRESS INQUIRIES TO:
Albert B. Head, Executive Director
(See address above.)

ALASKA STATE COUNCIL ON THE ARTS   [428]
161 Klevin Street
Suite 102
Anchorage, AK 99508-1508
(907) 269-6610
Fax: (907) 269-6601

E-MAIL ADDRESS:
shannon.daut@alaska.gov

WEB SITE ADDRESS:
www.education.alaska.gov/aksca

FOUNDED: 1966

AREAS OF INTEREST:
Alaska native arts, visual, literary and performing arts.

CONSULTING OR VOLUNTEER SERVICES:
Technical assistance for grantees.

TYPE:
Conferences/seminars; General operating grants; Project/program grants; Residencies; Technical assistance; Travel grants. Services provided to arts organizations and individual artists statewide. Also, workshop grants and Master Artist/Apprentice grants.

Eight specific grant categories, responding to a variety of arts needs, are available to Alaskan nonprofit arts organizations and qualified individual artists.

YEAR PROGRAM STARTED: 1966

PURPOSE:
To promote general support of the arts in Alaska.

LEGAL BASIS:
State agency.

ELIGIBILITY:
Grant applicants must be Alaskan nonprofit organizations or individuals.

GEOGRAPHIC RESTRICTIONS:
Alaska.

FINANCIAL DATA:
Amount of support per award: Varies according to program.
Total amount of support: $600,000.
Matching fund requirements: All organizational grants require at least 1:1 match (cash).

APPLICATION INFORMATION:
Specific guidelines and applications are available online.
Duration: One year.
Deadline: Varies according to program.

PUBLICATIONS:
Annual report; individual grant program guidelines.

STAFF:
Shannon Daut, Executive Director
Andrea Noble-Pelant, Grants Administrator

ADDRESS INQUIRIES TO:
Shannon Daut, Executive Director
(See address above.)

THE ALLIANCE FOR YOUNG ARTISTS & WRITERS   [429]
557 Broadway
New York, NY 10012
(212) 343-7773
Fax: (212) 389-3939

E-MAIL ADDRESS:
kat@artandwriting.org

WEB SITE ADDRESS:
www.artandwriting.org

FOUNDED: 1923

AREAS OF INTEREST:
Art and writing.

NAME(S) OF PROGRAMS:
● **The Scholastic Art and Writing Awards**

TYPE:
Awards/prizes; Scholarships. The Alliance for Young Artists & Writers identifies teenagers with exceptional artistic and literary talent and brings their remarkable work to a national audience through The Scholastic Art & Writing Awards.

YEAR PROGRAM STARTED: 1923

PURPOSE:
To provide guidance and support for the next generation of artists and writers and reward outstanding achievement in the creative arts.

LEGAL BASIS:
Nonprofit.

ELIGIBILITY:
Individual awards are offered for students in grades 7-12. Scholarships are offered for seniors submitting portfolios.

GEOGRAPHIC RESTRICTIONS:
United States and Canada.

FINANCIAL DATA:
Scholarship recipients are additionally eligible for school-specific, tuition scholarships at more than 50 colleges.
Amount of support per award: $500 to $10,000.
Total amount of support: Varies.

NUMBER OF AWARDS: Approximately 100.

APPLICATION INFORMATION:
Contact the Alliance.
Duration: One year.
Deadline: Deadline varies by geographic location, approximately December 15 to January 15. See web site for details on specific regions.

IRS IDENTIFICATION NUMBER: 13-3780998

ADDRESS INQUIRIES TO:
Katherine Hendrix,
Associate Executive Director, Programs
(See address above.)

AMERICA-ISRAEL CULTURAL FOUNDATION
1140 Broadway
Suite 304
New York, NY 10001
(212) 557-1600
Fax: (212) 557-1611

E-MAIL ADDRESS:
admin@aicf.org

WEB SITE ADDRESS:
www.aicf.org

TYPE:
Awards/prizes; Endowments; Fellowships; Project/program grants; Scholarships. For study in the arts of music, painting and sculpture, dance and drama, film and television, to be pursued either in Israel or in other countries.

See entry 955 for full listing.

THE AMERICAN CERAMIC SOCIETY   [430]
600 North Cleveland Avenue, Suite 210
Westerville, OH 43082
(614) 794-5827
Fax: (614) 794-5817

E-MAIL ADDRESS:
tfreshour@ceramics.org

WEB SITE ADDRESS:
www.ceramics.org

FOUNDED: 1898

AREAS OF INTEREST:
Ceramic education and glass.

NAME(S) OF PROGRAMS:
- **Graduate Student Poster Contest**
- **Outstanding Educator Award**
- **Student Speaking Contest**
- **Undergraduate Student Poster Contest**

TYPE:
Awards/prizes.

PURPOSE:
To promote and encourage materials science and engineering studies in the discipline of glass and ceramics.

FINANCIAL DATA:
Amount of support per award: Varies.
Total amount of support: $2,000 for the year 2012.

APPLICATION INFORMATION:
Contact the Society.
Duration: One-time awards.
Deadline: Graduate Student Poster Contest: March; Outstanding Educator Award: April; Student Speaking and Undergraduate Student Poster Contests: September.

ADDRESS INQUIRIES TO:
Tricia Freshour, Membership Services Manager
(See address and e-mail above.)

AMERICAN FIDELITY FOUNDATION   [431]
2000 North Classen, Suite 7N
Oklahoma City, OK 73106
(405) 523-5111
Fax: (405) 523-5421

WEB SITE ADDRESS:
americanfidelityfoundation.org

AREAS OF INTEREST:
Education, arts, culture, health and human services, and civic and economic development.

TYPE:
Endowments; General operating grants; Research grants. Employment Matching Gifts.

ELIGIBILITY:
Organizations with 501(c)(3) status.

GEOGRAPHIC RESTRICTIONS:
Oklahoma County, Oklahoma.

FINANCIAL DATA:
Amount of support per award: Grants to a single charity are typically $500 to $5,000.
Total amount of support: Varies.

APPLICATION INFORMATION:
Organizations that wish to be considered for a grant are asked to submit a letter of interest. If the Foundation chooses to pursue the project or program described, a formal application will be sent for completion to the organization within two weeks.

ADDRESS INQUIRIES TO:
Jo Ella Ramsey, Administrator
(See address above.)

THE AMERICAN SCHOOL OF CLASSICAL STUDIES AT ATHENS   [432]
6-8 Charlton Street
Princeton, NJ 08540-5232
(609) 683-0800
Fax: (609) 924-0578

E-MAIL ADDRESS:
ascsa@ascsa.org (for information)
application@ascsa.org (to apply)

WEB SITE ADDRESS:
www.ascsa.edu.gr

FOUNDED: 1881

AREAS OF INTEREST:
Financial support for individuals involved in research.

NAME(S) OF PROGRAMS:
- **CAORC Multi-Country Research Fellowships**

TYPE:
Fellowships.

PURPOSE:
To provide support for individuals whose research has regional significance and requires travel to multiple countries, at least one of which hosts an American overseas research center such as the American School.

ELIGIBILITY:
Fellowship is limited to U.S. citizens. Open to U.S. doctoral candidates who have completed all Ph.D. requirements except the dissertation and U.S. postdoctoral scholars at all levels with research requiring travel to several countries with an American overseas research center.

School programs are generally open to qualified students and scholars at colleges or universities in the U.S. or Canada; restrictions may apply for specific fellowships and programs. The American School of Classical Studies at Athens does not discriminate on the basis of race, age, sex, sexual orientation, color, religion, ethnic origin, or disability when considering admission to any form of membership.

FINANCIAL DATA:
School fees are to be paid out of the fellowship stipend by the recipient. Fellowship does not include travel costs, housing, board, and other living expenses.
Amount of support per award: Doctoral candidates/postdoctoral scholars: $12,000 for all centers.

COOPERATIVE FUNDING PROGRAMS: Fellowships for Multi-Country Research are funded by the Bureau of Educational and Cultural Affairs of the U.S. Department of State through a grant to the Council of American Overseas Research Centers.

NUMBER OF APPLICANTS MOST RECENT YEAR:
8.

NUMBER OF AWARDS: 1.

APPLICATION INFORMATION:
Application guidelines are available at CAORC's web site. Associate Member application to ASCSA.
Duration: Doctoral and postdoctoral scholars: Minimum of 90 days.
Deadline: January 15. Awards announced on April 15.

STAFF:
James C. Wright, Director

ADDRESS INQUIRIES TO:
E-mail: ascsa@ascsa.org

*SPECIAL STIPULATIONS:
Research and reporting must be completed by October 31, 2014. Recipients may not hold any other federally funded grant at the same time, such as a Fulbright or NEH Fellowship.

Membership application to the ASCSA must be made online on the web site at the same time one applies to any outside funding organization for work at the School.

A final report is due at the end of the award period, and the ASCSA expects that copies of all publications that result from research conducted as a Fellow of the ASCSA be contributed to the relevant library of the School.

ARIZONA COMMISSION ON THE ARTS   [433]
417 West Roosevelt Street
Phoenix, AZ 85003
(602) 771-6502
Fax: (602) 256-0282

E-MAIL ADDRESS:
info@azarts.gov

WEB SITE ADDRESS:
www.azarts.gov

FOUNDED: 1967

AREAS OF INTEREST:
Performing arts, visual arts and literary arts.

TYPE:
Challenge/matching grants; Conferences/seminars; Development grants; General operating grants; Internships; Project/program grants; Research grants; Residencies; Technical assistance; Travel grants. Specialized library services to artists and arts organizations.

YEAR PROGRAM STARTED: 1967

PURPOSE:
To stimulate and encourage public interest in the arts. Dedicated to making quality arts opportunities available to its citizens, the Arts Commission takes a leadership role in broadening the support systems for the arts and demonstrating how the arts are integral to the vitality of our communities and citizens.

Commission goals are to increase opportunities for all residents of Arizona to experience the arts; assist individual artists and arts organizations in Arizona; stimulate support and visibility for the arts in Arizona; foster the preservation, promotion and availability of Arizona's diverse ethnic arts; make the arts fundamental to education.

LEGAL BASIS:
State agency.

GEOGRAPHIC RESTRICTIONS:
Arizona.

FINANCIAL DATA:
Amount of support per award: Varies.
Total amount of support: Varies.

APPLICATION INFORMATION:
Call for application or access from web site.
Duration: Varies.
Deadline: Varies.

ASIAN CULTURAL COUNCIL   [434]
6 West 48th Street, 12th Floor
New York, NY 10036-1802
(212) 843-0403
Fax: (212) 843-0343

E-MAIL ADDRESS:
acc@accny.org

WEB SITE ADDRESS:
www.asianculturalcouncil.org

FOUNDED: 1980

AREAS OF INTEREST:
Visual and performing arts of Asia.

TYPE:
Exchange programs; Fellowships;
Project/program grants; Research grants;
Residencies; Travel grants; Visiting scholars.
Support of cultural exchange in the visual
and performing arts between the U.S. and
those countries of Asia extending from
Afghanistan through Japan.

YEAR PROGRAM STARTED: 1980

PURPOSE:
To award fellowships to individuals and
grants to organizations to support projects
that foster exchange between Asia and the
U.S.; to fund regional travel within Asia.

LEGAL BASIS:
Public foundation organized under Section
501(c)(3).

ELIGIBILITY:
Grants are open to citizens and permanent
residents of the countries of Asia from
Afghanistan eastward through Japan and
Indonesia, and citizens and permanent
residents of the U.S. Individuals pursuing
projects in their home countries are not
supported. Priority consideration is generally
given to individuals who have not previously
received funding support from the Council.

FINANCIAL DATA:
The Asian Cultural Council's grant programs
are supported by endowment income and
annual contributions from foundations,
corporations, and individuals in the U.S. and
Asia. Levels of grant activity are based on
financial resources available.
Amount of support per award: Varies.
Total amount of support: Varies.

NUMBER OF APPLICANTS MOST RECENT YEAR:
500 for the year 2013.

NUMBER OF AWARDS: 100.

APPLICATION INFORMATION:
Grant applicants must first submit the
appropriate online Individual or Organization
Inquiry form. Applications are available
through the web site September 1 through
October 31 of each calendar year for grants
in the following year.
Duration: Three months to one year.
Renewals are rare.
Deadline: Full application: November 1
(postmarked).

PUBLICATIONS:
Annual report.

IRS IDENTIFICATION NUMBER: 13-3018822

OFFICERS:
Wendy O'Neill, Chairman
Hans Michael Jebsen, Vice Chairman
Valerie Rockefeller Wayne, Vice Chairman
Richard S. Lanier, President
Stephen B. Heintz, Vice President
Jonathan Fanton, Treasurer
Pauline R. Yu, Secretary

TRUSTEES:
Hope Aldrich
Jane DeBevoise
John H. Foster
Kenneth H.C. Fung
Curtis Greer
David Halpert
Douglas Tong Hsu
J. Christopher Kojima
Erh-fei Liu
Vincent Mai

Elizabeth J. McCormack
Ken Miller
Josie Cruz Natori
Abby M. O'Neill
Carol Rattray
David Rockefeller, Jr.
Lynne Rutkin
William G. Spears
Yuji Tsutsumi

ADDRESS INQUIRIES TO:
E-mail: applications@accny.org

ASTRAEA LESBIAN FOUNDATION FOR JUSTICE
116 East 16th Street, 7th Floor
New York, NY 10003
(212) 529-8021
Fax: (212) 982-3321

WEB SITE ADDRESS:
www.astraeafoundation.org

TYPE:
Awards/prizes.

See entry 980 for full listing.

THE WILLIAM G. BAKER, JR. MEMORIAL FUND   [435]
2 East Read Street, Ninth Floor
Baltimore, MD 21202
(410) 332-4171
Fax: (410) 837-4701

E-MAIL ADDRESS:
mwarlow@bcf.org

WEB SITE ADDRESS:
www.bcf.org/baker

FOUNDED: 1964

AREAS OF INTEREST:
Arts and culture.

TYPE:
Project/program grants.

YEAR PROGRAM STARTED: 1964

PURPOSE:
To strengthen Baltimore's arts and culture
sector.

LEGAL BASIS:
Private, nonprofit foundation.

ELIGIBILITY:
Cultural organizations (or their fiscal agents)
serving the Baltimore area that qualify as
public charities under Section 501(c)(3) of
the Internal Revenue Code.

The fund does not normally make grants to
endowment campaigns, annual appeals, event
sponsorships or services outside the greater
Baltimore area.

GEOGRAPHIC RESTRICTIONS:
Greater Baltimore area.

FINANCIAL DATA:
Amount of support per award: $2,500 to
$50,000.
Total amount of support: $1,027,362 for the
year 2013.

NUMBER OF APPLICANTS MOST RECENT YEAR:
50.

NUMBER OF AWARDS: 40 for the year 2013.

APPLICATION INFORMATION:
Applicants must complete the online
application and evaluation chart. Maryland
Cultural Data Project data profile is required.
Duration: Varies.

IRS IDENTIFICATION NUMBER: 52-6057178

GOVERNING BOARD:
Connie E. Imboden, President
Gwen Davidson
Steven G. Ziger

ADDRESS INQUIRIES TO:
Melissa Warlow, Director
(See address above.)

BATON ROUGE AREA FOUNDATION   [436]
402 North Fourth Street
Baton Rouge, LA 70802
(225) 387-6126
Fax: (225) 387-6153

E-MAIL ADDRESS:
jcarpenter@braf.org

WEB SITE ADDRESS:
www.braf.org

AREAS OF INTEREST:
Arts, cultural programs, education,
community development, human services,
environment, scholarships, medical and
health.

TYPE:
Capital grants; Challenge/matching grants;
Conferences/seminars; Demonstration grants;
Development grants; Matching gifts;
Project/program grants; Scholarships; Seed
money grants; Technical assistance; Training
grants; Visiting scholars.

PURPOSE:
To connect philanthropists with capable
nonprofits to make sure the needs of the
community are met; to invest in and manage
pivotal projects that can change the
community.

ELIGIBILITY:
Eligible organizations must be IRS 501(c)(3)
tax-exempt.

GEOGRAPHIC RESTRICTIONS:
Baton Rouge area, Louisiana.

FINANCIAL DATA:
Amount of support per award: Varies.
Total amount of support: Varies.

APPLICATION INFORMATION:
Application details are available online. All
applications must include a copy of the IRS
tax determination letter.
Duration: One year. Must reapply for
additional funding.

ADDRESS INQUIRIES TO:
John K. Carpenter, Director of Donor
Services
(See address above.)

CALIFORNIA ARTS COUNCIL   [437]
1300 I Street, Suite 930
Sacramento, CA 95814
(916) 322-6555
(800) 201-6201
Fax: (916) 322-6575

E-MAIL ADDRESS:
caitlin.fitzwater@arts.ca.gov

WEB SITE ADDRESS:
www.arts.ca.gov

FOUNDED: 1976

AREAS OF INTEREST:
Operating and creative support to art organizations, artists, visual and performing arts programs in schools and after-school programs.

CONSULTING OR VOLUNTEER SERVICES:
Sponsor conferences and technical assistance to art organizations.

NAME(S) OF PROGRAMS:
- **Artists in Schools**
- **Creating Places of Vitality**
- **State-Local Partnership Program in the Arts**
- **Statewide Service Networks in the Arts**

TYPE:
Challenge/matching grants; General operating grants; Project/program grants.

YEAR PROGRAM STARTED: 1976

PURPOSE:
To advance California in the arts and creativity.

LEGAL BASIS:
State arts agency, funded by state budget and other sources.

ELIGIBILITY:
To be eligible for funding, a California-based group or organization should be an incorporated nonprofit and have been in existence at least two years and be able to demonstrate fiscal and managerial responsibility. Grants are given to provide in-school and after-school arts educational activities, assistance for specific artistic services such as events, exhibitions and publications, to expand participation by segments of the public who have had limited access to cultural events, and to encourage and enhance communication among artists, organizations and the general public.

GEOGRAPHIC RESTRICTIONS:
California.

FINANCIAL DATA:
Amount of support per award: Varies according to program.
Total amount of support: Varies.

NUMBER OF APPLICANTS MOST RECENT YEAR: 300.

NUMBER OF AWARDS: Approximately 200.

APPLICATION INFORMATION:
Contact the Council.
Duration: Six months to one year.
Deadline: Varies according to program.

PUBLICATIONS:
Guide to programs; applications; newsletters.

COUNCIL MEMBERS:
Wylie Aitken, Chairperson
Susan Steinhauser, Vice Chairperson
Craig Watson, Director
Scott William Heckes, Deputy Director
Michael Alexander
Christopher Coppola
Andrew Green
Donn Harris
Charmaine Jefferson
Terry Lenihan
William Turner
Rosalind Wyman

ADDRESS INQUIRIES TO:
Caitlin Fitzwater
Public Information Officer
(See address above.)

CANADA COUNCIL FOR THE ARTS   [438]
150 Elgin Street
Ottawa ON K1P 5V8 Canada
(800) 263-5588 ext. 5060 (North America)
(613) 566-4414 ext. 5060
Fax: (613) 566-4390
TTY: (866) 585-5559

E-MAIL ADDRESS:
info@canadacouncil.ca

WEB SITE ADDRESS:
www.canadacouncil.ca

FOUNDED: 1957

AREAS OF INTEREST:
The arts in Canada (dance, music, inter-arts, theatre, visual arts, media arts, creative writing and publishing).

NAME(S) OF PROGRAMS:
- **Grants to Professional Canadian Artists and Arts Organizations**

TYPE:
Awards/prizes; Block grants; Development grants; Endowments; Fellowships; Formula grants; General operating grants; Project/program grants; Research grants; Residencies; Scholarships; Training grants; Travel grants; Visiting scholars. Several programs of support providing grants and services to professional Canadian artists and nonprofit arts organizations.

PURPOSE:
To provide grants and services to professional Canadian artists and arts organizations in dance, music, theatre, media arts (film video, audio, new media), inter-arts (including contemporary circus art), visual arts and creative writing to help them pursue professional development, independent artistic creation or production.

LEGAL BASIS:
Independent agency established by the Parliament of Canada in 1957.

ELIGIBILITY:
Individual professional artists must be Canadian citizens or permanent residents of Canada. They do not have to be living in Canada when they apply. The Canada Council defines a professional artist as someone who has specialized training in the field (not necessarily in academic institutions), who is recognized as such by her or his peers (artists working in the same artistic tradition) and who has a history of public presentation or publication.

Canadian arts organizations, such as theatre companies, art museums, public galleries, artist-run centres, dance companies, orchestras and film cooperatives, that are staffed by arts professionals who create artistic works or present them to the Canadian public, are also eligible, as are professional publishing houses.

Canadian arts organizations are assessed on the basis of criteria such as professionalism, artistic excellence, community support, stability and sound financial management.

GEOGRAPHIC RESTRICTIONS:
Canada.

FINANCIAL DATA:
Grants for Professional Artists contribute towards living expenses, cost of materials related to the project, professional development, or independent artistic creation or production. Funds may not be used for capital costs.

Amount of support per award: Grants for Professional Artists: $3,000 to $20,000 (CAN) in increments of $1,000 (CAN); Travel grants: $500 to $2,500 (CAN), depending on need.
Total amount of support: Varies.

NUMBER OF APPLICANTS MOST RECENT YEAR: 15,500.

NUMBER OF AWARDS: 6,100.

APPLICATION INFORMATION:
Prospective applicants should specify their citizenship and their field of interest and indicate whether they are professional. Further information and brochures are available on request.

The Council does not accept applications that are sent by fax or e-mail.

PUBLICATIONS:
Program information sheets.

ADDRESS INQUIRIES TO:
Christian Mondor, Information Officer
(See address above.)

CINTAS FOUNDATION   [439]
c/o Morrison, Brown, Argiz & Farra LLP
1450 Brickell Avenue, Suite 1800
Miami, FL 33131
(305) 373-5500 ext. 2202
Fax: (305) 373-0056

E-MAIL ADDRESS:
fgonzalez@mbafcpa.com

WEB SITE ADDRESS:
www.cintasfoundation.org

FOUNDED: 1981

AREAS OF INTEREST:
Architecture, creative writing, music composition and the visual arts.

NAME(S) OF PROGRAMS:
- **Cintas Fellowships in the Arts**

TYPE:
Awards/prizes; Fellowships. Awarded to persons of Cuban citizenship or lineage residing outside Cuba for achievement of a creative nature in architecture, painting, sculpture, printmaking, music composition and literature.

YEAR PROGRAM STARTED: 1964

PURPOSE:
To recognize outstanding creative work done by a person from Cuba or a person of Cuban descent.

LEGAL BASIS:
Private, not-for-profit agency.

ELIGIBILITY:
Applications are open to professionals in the creative arts, of Cuban citizenship or lineage, who can give evidence of their creative production by records of exhibitions, performances or (when appropriate) by published books or scores. Students wishing to pursue academic programs are not eligible for awards nor are performing artists as opposed to creative artists. Although there is no fixed age limit, the Fellowships are intended for young professionals in the arts who have completed their academic and technical training. The program focuses on one creative genre per grant cycle.

FINANCIAL DATA:
Amount of support per award: $10,000, paid in four equal quarterly stipends.
Total amount of support: Varies.

NUMBER OF APPLICANTS MOST RECENT YEAR:
150.

NUMBER OF AWARDS: 3 to 4 annually.

APPLICATION INFORMATION:
Eligible candidates may request application
forms and letter of reference forms from the
Foundation. Applications should be in
English and should be accompanied by
supporting documentation of an appropriate
nature, such as published books or music
scores or photographs and color slides of
paintings or sculpture.
Duration: 12 consecutive months beginning
October 10.
Deadline: July 1.

ADDRESS INQUIRIES TO:
Jessica Brodsky, Administrator
Miami Dade College
Museum of Art and Design
Tel: (305) 237-7722
E-mail: jbrodsky@mdc.edu.

ROBERT STERLING CLARK FOUNDATION
135 East 64th Street
New York, NY 10065
(212) 288-8900
Fax: (212) 288-1033

E-MAIL ADDRESS:
rscf@rsclark.org

WEB SITE ADDRESS:
www.rsclark.org

TYPE:
Project/program grants; Research grants.

See entry 1207 for full listing.

COLORADO CREATIVE INDUSTRIES   [440]
1625 Broadway, Suite 2700
Denver, CO 80202
(303) 892-3802
Fax: (303) 892-3848
TDD: (303) 894-2664

E-MAIL ADDRESS:
coloarts@state.co.us

WEB SITE ADDRESS:
www.coloradocreativeindustries.org

FOUNDED: 1967

AREAS OF INTEREST:
Visual arts, literature, performing arts, folk
arts and media arts, youth-at-risk and
economic benefits.

NAME(S) OF PROGRAMS:
* **Colorado Creates**
* **Creative Districts**
* **Jumpstart**
* **Start Schools**

TYPE:
Project/program grants.

PURPOSE:
To promote, support and expand the creative
industries to drive Colorado's economy, grow
jobs and enhance the quality of life.

LEGAL BASIS:
State government agency.

ELIGIBILITY:
Colorado artists and nonprofit tax-exempt
organizations and municipalities.

GEOGRAPHIC RESTRICTIONS:
Colorado.

FINANCIAL DATA:
Amount of support per award: Colorado
Creates: $4,000 to $10,000; Creative
Districts: $15,000 for certified, $8,000 for
prospective and $2,000 for emerging;
Jumpstart: Up to $1,000 for creative
businesses, whether nonprofit or commercial;
Start Schools: $2,000 to $15,000.
Total amount of support: Varies.
Matching fund requirements: Colorado
Creates: Based on cash operating income.
Creative Districts: 1:1 match; 50% can be
cash and 50% can be in-kind donations.
Jumpstart: 1:1 cash match. Start Schools:
Varies based on number of students enrolled
in district.

NUMBER OF APPLICANTS MOST RECENT YEAR:
380.

NUMBER OF AWARDS: 300; Creative Districts: 2
certified, 5 prospective and 8 emerging.

APPLICATION INFORMATION:
Contact Colorado Creative Industries.
Duration: Colorado Creates: Three years on,
one year off. Other programs: Generally one
year.

PUBLICATIONS:
Annual report; guidelines; press releases;
news clips; strategic plan.

OFFICERS:
John Hickenlooper, Governor
Robert Clasen, Chairperson
Margaret Hunt, Director

ADDRESS INQUIRIES TO:
Margaret Hunt, Director
(See address above.)

THE COMMUNITY FOUNDATION OF LOUISVILLE, INC.   [441]
325 West Main Street, Suite 1110
Louisville, KY 40202
(502) 585-4649
Fax: (502) 587-7484

E-MAIL ADDRESS:
gails@cflouisville.org

WEB SITE ADDRESS:
www.cflouisville.org

AREAS OF INTEREST:
Visual arts, crafts, theatre and historic
preservation.

TYPE:
Endowments; Grants-in-aid; Scholarships.

PURPOSE:
To enrich the quality of life for all citizens in
the Louisville area and to serve as a catalyst
for promoting philanthropy within the local
community.

ELIGIBILITY:
Grants are made to organizations that have
tax-exempt status under Section 501(c)(3) of
the Internal Revenue Code.

GEOGRAPHIC RESTRICTIONS:
Louisville, Kentucky and surrounding
communities.

FINANCIAL DATA:
Amount of support per award: Varies.
Total amount of support: Varies.

APPLICATION INFORMATION:
Contact the Foundation.
Duration: One year.
Deadline: Details are available on the web
site.

ADDRESS INQUIRIES TO:
Gail Sanders, Community Leadership Officer
(See address above.)

CONGRESSIONAL BLACK CAUCUS FOUNDATION, INC.
1720 Massachusetts Avenue, N.W.
Washington, DC 20036
(202) 263-2800
Fax: (202) 263-0846

E-MAIL ADDRESS:
scholarships@cbcfinc.org

WEB SITE ADDRESS:
www.cbcfinc.org

TYPE:
Scholarships. CBCS Performing Arts
Scholarship, developed in honor of the late
Curtis Mayfield, is intended to ensure that
students pursuing a career in the performing
arts receive the financial assistance to achieve
their goals.

CBCS Visual Arts Scholarship was
established for students who are pursuing a
career in the visual arts.

See entry 1026 for full listing.

CONSEIL DES ARTS DE MONTREAL   [442]
1210 East Sherbrooke Street
First Floor
Montreal QC H2L 2L9 Canada
(514) 280-3582
Fax: (514) 280-3784

E-MAIL ADDRESS:
nmaille.p@ville.montreal.qc.ca

WEB SITE ADDRESS:
www.artsmontreal.org

FOUNDED: 1956

AREAS OF INTEREST:
Visual arts, dance, theatre, music, literature,
cinema, new artistic practices, video and
electronic arts.

NAME(S) OF PROGRAMS:
* **Programme de tournees**
* **Programme General**

TYPE:
Awards/prizes; Development grants;
Exchange programs; General operating
grants; Project/program grants; Technical
assistance. Grants to nonprofit professional
organizations having their head offices in
Montreal.

YEAR PROGRAM STARTED: 1956

PURPOSE:
To assist Montreal's artistic and cultural
organizations.

LEGAL BASIS:
Regional organization.

ELIGIBILITY:
Professional, nonprofit organizations in
Montreal.

GEOGRAPHIC RESTRICTIONS:
Montreal, Quebec.

FINANCIAL DATA:
Amount of support per award: Varies.
Total amount of support: $11,201,120 (CAN)
for the year 2013.

NUMBER OF APPLICANTS MOST RECENT YEAR:
454.

NUMBER OF AWARDS: 379 for the year 2013.

APPLICATION INFORMATION:
Contact the Conseil des Arts.
Duration: One fiscal year.
Deadline: Programme de tournees:
September. Programme General: Varies by
type of grant.

PUBLICATIONS:
Annual report.

STAFF:
Sylviane Martineau, Cultural Advisor, Dance
Rejane Bouge, Cultural Advisor, Literature,
Cinema
Claire Metras, Cultural Advisor, Music
Christiane Bonneau, Cultural Advisor, New
Artist Practices, Multidisciplinary, Circus
Arts
Claude Des Landes, Cultural Advisor,
Theatre
Marie-Michele Cron, Cultural Advisor,
Visual Arts, Media Arts

ADDRESS INQUIRIES TO:
Cultural Advisor
(See address above.)

THE CORPORATION OF
YADDO   [443]
312 Union Avenue
Saratoga Springs, NY 12866
(518) 584-0746
Fax: (518) 584-1312

E-MAIL ADDRESS:
chwait@yaddo.org

WEB SITE ADDRESS:
www.yaddo.org

FOUNDED: 1900

AREAS OF INTEREST:
Literature, visual arts, music composition,
filmmaking, choreography, performance art
and other creative arts.

NAME(S) OF PROGRAMS:
● **Artist Residencies**

TYPE:
Residencies; Travel grants.

YEAR PROGRAM STARTED: 1926

PURPOSE:
To enable artists to work in a quiet, protected
and supportive environment.

LEGAL BASIS:
A publicly supported charity.

ELIGIBILITY:
For creative artists working at a professional
level in their field.

FINANCIAL DATA:
No cash grants. The award covers room,
board and studio costs. A small fund exists
to provide limited help towards the expenses
of travel or renting equipment to invited
guests of any discipline who otherwise might
not be able to visit.

NUMBER OF APPLICANTS MOST RECENT YEAR:
1,542 for the year 2013.

NUMBER OF AWARDS: 186 for the year 2013.

APPLICATION INFORMATION:
Applicants should apply to the Admissions
Panel that best represents the project they
wish to undertake should they be invited for
a residency. Applicants may apply to only
one admissions panel, in one genre, at a
time. Applicants with concerns about choice
of panel should contact the Program Director.

All application materials, including contact
information, resume, work sample, and
reference letters must be submitted
electronically.
Duration: Up to two months.
Deadline: January 1 and August 1.

PUBLICATIONS:
Annual report; newsletter; case statement.

IRS IDENTIFICATION NUMBER: 14-1343055

OFFICERS:
A.M. Homes, Chairperson
Susan Unterberg, Chairperson
Peter Kayafas, Vice Chairperson
Elaina Richardson, President
Patricia Sopp, Vice President, Finance and
Assistant Treasurer
Candace Weir, Treasurer
Gardner McFall, Corporate Secretary
Susan Brynteson, Recording Secretary

ADDRESS INQUIRIES TO:
Candace Wait, Program Director
The Corporation of Yaddo
P.O. Box 395
Saratoga Springs, NY 12886

THE COSTUME SOCIETY OF
AMERICA   [444]
390 Amwell Road, Suite 402
Hillsborough, NJ 08844
(908) 359-1471
(800) 272-9447 (U.S.)
Fax: (908) 450-1188

E-MAIL ADDRESS:
national.office@costumesocietyamerica.com

WEB SITE ADDRESS:
www.costumesocietyamerica.com

FOUNDED: 1973

AREAS OF INTEREST:
Costume, art history, research, textile and
fashion design, museum studies and
anthropology.

NAME(S) OF PROGRAMS:
● **Stella Blum Research Grant**
● **CSA Travel Research Grant**
● **Adele Filene Travel Award**

TYPE:
Awards/prizes; Conferences/seminars;
Development grants; Fellowships; General
operating grants; Project/program grants;
Research grants; Scholarships; Travel grants.
Stella Blum Research Grant is a merit award
for a student researching a North American
costume topic.

CSA Travel Research Grant aids in travel to
collections to any library, archive, museum or
site for research to further an ongoing
project.

Adele Filene Travel Award assists the travel
of a CSA student member to that year's CSA
national symposium to present either a juried
paper or poster.

YEAR PROGRAM STARTED: 1987

PURPOSE:
To advance the global understanding of all
aspects of dress and appearance.

ELIGIBILITY:
Must be a Costume Society of America
member for all awards.

CSA Travel Research Grant: Must be a CSA
nonstudent member. Proof must be given that
work on the project is already underway.

Adele Filene Travel Award: Must be
currently enrolled as a student with a juried
paper or poster accepted by the CSA
symposium.

FINANCIAL DATA:
Amount of support per award: Stella Blum
Research Grant: Up to $3,500; CSA Travel
Research Grant: $1,500; Adele Filene Travel
Award: Up to $500.
Total amount of support: Varies.

NUMBER OF APPLICANTS MOST RECENT YEAR:
6.

NUMBER OF AWARDS: Varies.

APPLICATION INFORMATION:
Information is available, under
"Opportunities," on the Society's web site.
Duration: One year.
Deadline: Stella Blum Research Grant: May
1; CSA Travel Research Grant: January 15;
Adele Filene Travel Award: March 1.

ADDRESS INQUIRIES TO:
Marie Cortsun, Executive Director
(See e-mail address above.)

DELAWARE DIVISION OF THE
ARTS   [445]
Carvel State Office Building
820 North French Street
Wilmington, DE 19801
(302) 577-8278
Fax: (302) 577-6561

E-MAIL ADDRESS:
delarts@state.de.us

WEB SITE ADDRESS:
www.artsdel.org

FOUNDED: 1969

AREAS OF INTEREST:
Performing arts, visual arts, literature and
media.

CONSULTING OR VOLUNTEER SERVICES:
Technical assistance to community groups
and arts organizations.

NAME(S) OF PROGRAMS:
● **Arts in Education**
● **Arts Organizations Grants**
● **Community Based Organizations
Grants**
● **Gallery Program**
● **Individual Artist Fellowships**
● **Opportunity Grants**

TYPE:
Challenge/matching grants;
Conferences/seminars; Fellowships; General
operating grants; Project/program grants;
Residencies; Technical assistance. Grants to
Delaware nonprofit, tax-exempt organizations
for projects in the arts. Fellowships program
for individual creative artists who reside in
Delaware.

YEAR PROGRAM STARTED: 1970

PURPOSE:
To nurture and support the arts to enhance
the quality of life for all Delawareans.

LEGAL BASIS:
State agency.

ELIGIBILITY:
Applicants must be nonprofit, tax-exempt
organizations in the state of Delaware.
Fellowship applicants are individual creative
artists who reside in Delaware.

GEOGRAPHIC RESTRICTIONS:
Delaware.

FINANCIAL DATA:
Amount of funds available is determined by state appropriation and funding from the National Endowment for the Arts.

Amount of support per award: Variable according to program.

Total amount of support: $3,100,000.

Matching fund requirements: Organization grants matching requirements vary according to program.

NUMBER OF APPLICANTS MOST RECENT YEAR:
253.

NUMBER OF AWARDS: 168.

APPLICATION INFORMATION:
Application must be made on forms available on the web site.

Duration: Varies.

Deadline: March 1 for most grants. Announcement July 1 for most grants.

ADDRESS INQUIRIES TO:
Paul Weagraff, Director
(See address above.)

DEPARTMENT OF ECONOMIC AND COMMUNITY DEVELOPMENT/CONNECTICUT OFFICE OF THE ARTS   [446]
One Constitution Plaza, 2nd Floor
Hartford, CT 06103
(860) 256-2722
(860) 256-2800
Fax: (860) 256-2811

E-MAIL ADDRESS:
acp.questions@ct.gov

WEB SITE ADDRESS:
www.cultureandtourism.org

FOUNDED: 1965

AREAS OF INTEREST:
Fine arts, literature, museums and libraries, music, creative and performing arts, theatre, dance, arts in education, community arts programs, artist slide bank, art in public spaces, history, tourism and colleges/universities.

CONSULTING OR VOLUNTEER SERVICES:
Volunteer Lawyers for the Arts program.

NAME(S) OF PROGRAMS:
• **Arts Catalyze Placemaking**

TYPE:
Awards/prizes; Challenge/matching grants; Conferences/seminars; Endowments; Fellowships; General operating grants; Internships; Project/program grants; Residencies; Technical assistance; Training grants. Grants are available to Connecticut artists, arts institutions, arts organizations and nonprofit arts-sponsoring organizations for program support and technical assistance.

YEAR PROGRAM STARTED: 1965

PURPOSE:
To invest in the state's art-based cultural activities and infrastructure in ways that will advance the attractiveness and competitiveness of Connecticut cities, towns and villages as meaningful communities in which to live, work, learn and play.

LEGAL BASIS:
The State of Connecticut Enabling Legislation, Public Act No. 78-187 created the original Connecticut Commission on the Arts.

ELIGIBILITY:
Connecticut artists, art institutions, units of state or local government, art organizations and nonprofit arts-sponsoring associations whose principle residence is in Connecticut. Ineligible programs are those which take place out of state, student projects, fund-raising benefits, social activities, membership activities, scholarships, underwriting of past deficits or capital expenditures.

GEOGRAPHIC RESTRICTIONS:
Connecticut.

FINANCIAL DATA:
Amount of support per award: $5,000 to $100,000 for the year 2013.

Total amount of support: $2,277,781 for the year 2013.

COOPERATIVE FUNDING PROGRAMS: Matching funds, Federal-state partnership and designated regional service organizations.

NUMBER OF APPLICANTS MOST RECENT YEAR:
250.

NUMBER OF AWARDS: 136.

APPLICATION INFORMATION:
A guidelines brochure may be requested from the Commission three to four months in advance to the project.

Duration: Varies.

Deadline: Varies.

PUBLICATIONS:
Copyright Law; *Non-Profit Incorporation-A Guide for Artists and Organizations*; *Contract Law for Artists and Organizations*; *Culture and Tourism Newsletter*; Bi-Monthly Bulletin; *Art in Public Spaces Program Guide*; *Hot Schools Transform Education*; *Economic Impact of the Nonprofit Arts Industry in Connecticut*; *Performing Artists*, online directories.

STAFF:
Christopher Bergstrom, Deputy Commissioner

ADDRESS INQUIRIES TO:
Rhonda Olisky, Special Projects Coordinator
(See address above.)

DISTRICT OF COLUMBIA COMMISSION ON THE ARTS AND HUMANITIES   [447]
200 I Street, S.E.
Suite 1400
Washington, DC 20003
(202) 724-5613
Fax: (202) 727-4135
TDD: (202) 727-3148

E-MAIL ADDRESS:
moshe.adams@dc.gov

WEB SITE ADDRESS:
www.dcarts.dc.gov

FOUNDED: 1968

AREAS OF INTEREST:
The arts and humanities in the District of Columbia.

NAME(S) OF PROGRAMS:
• **Artist Fellowship Program**
• **Arts Education Program**
• **City Arts Projects**
• **Community Arts Grant**
• **Cultural Facilities Program**
• **East of the River Arts Initiative**
• **Public Art Building Communities**
• **UPSTART Program**

TYPE:
Awards/prizes; Capital grants; Challenge/matching grants; Conferences/seminars; Exchange programs; Fellowships; General operating grants; Grants-in-aid; Project/program grants; Research grants; Residencies. Services provided to arts institutions and individual artists including inquiry services, technical assistance and funding.

YEAR PROGRAM STARTED: 1968

PURPOSE:
To administer funds to arts organizations, community organizations and individual artists to support arts endeavors within the District of Columbia.

LEGAL BASIS:
State arts agency authorized by executive order.

ELIGIBILITY:
Applicants must be residents of Washington, DC. Organizations must be located in Washington, DC and be nonprofit IRS 501(c)(3) arts organizations within the District of Columbia at least two years prior to application in some programs and one year in most others. Organizations are also required to participate in the DC Cultural Data Project.

Grant funds cannot be used for scholarships, reserve funds, or any food/receptions. Fiscal agents are strictly prohibited.

GEOGRAPHIC RESTRICTIONS:
Washington, DC.

FINANCIAL DATA:
Amount of support per award: $1,000 to $30,000. For capital funding projects and for organizations: Up to $100,000.

Total amount of support: $4,219,697.50 for fiscal year 2013.

Matching fund requirements: Matching funds are required for organizations.

COOPERATIVE FUNDING PROGRAMS: National Endowment for the Arts.

NUMBER OF APPLICANTS MOST RECENT YEAR:
844.

NUMBER OF AWARDS: 256.

REPRESENTATIVE AWARDS:
$5,000 to Thomas Circle Singers for general operating support; $15,000 to Kennedy Center for project support for its Millenium Stage; $11,162 to Shakespeare Theatre Company for a security camera.

APPLICATION INFORMATION:
Application information is available on the web site.

Duration: All expenses must be paid within the District's fiscal year of October 1 to September 30.

Deadline: Varies per grant cycle.

PUBLICATIONS:
Application guidelines.

STAFF:
Lionel Thomas, Executive Director

ADDRESS INQUIRIES TO:
Moshe Adams, Director of Grants and Legislative Affairs
(See address above.)

EAST TENNESSEE FOUNDATION

625 Market Street
Suite 1400
Knoxville, TN 37902
(865) 524-1223
(877) 524-1223
Fax: (865) 637-6039

E-MAIL ADDRESS:
etf@etf.org

WEB SITE ADDRESS:
www.easttennesseefoundation.org

TYPE:
Project/program grants; Scholarships; Seed money grants; Technical assistance. The Foundation administers 12 affiliate funds.

See entry 1121 for full listing.

THE FIELDSTONE FOUNDATION

14 Corporate Plaza, Suite 100
Newport Beach, CA 92660
(949) 873-2717
Fax: (949) 515-8520

E-MAIL ADDRESS:
janinem@fieldstonefoundation.org

WEB SITE ADDRESS:
www.fieldstonefoundation.org

TYPE:
Challenge/matching grants; General operating grants; Project/program grants.

See entry 369 for full listing.

FLORIDA DEPARTMENT OF STATE, DIVISION OF CULTURAL AFFAIRS [448]

500 South Bronough Street
Tallahassee, FL 32399-0250
(850) 245-6470
Fax: (850) 245-6497

E-MAIL ADDRESS:
info@florida-arts.org

WEB SITE ADDRESS:
www.florida-arts.org

FOUNDED: 1969

AREAS OF INTEREST:
The Division of Cultural Affairs administers the cultural grant programs of the Department of State and is responsible for planning and implementing arts programs statewide, providing technical assistance to artists and arts organizations, awarding, administering, monitoring and evaluating the grants program, disseminating arts-related information and encouraging cultural development in Florida.

CONSULTING OR VOLUNTEER SERVICES:
Facilitative services in all areas are available.

NAME(S) OF PROGRAMS:
• **Capitol Complex Exhibition Program**
• **Cultural Facilities Program**
• **Florida Cultural Endowment Program**
• **Florida Individual Artist Fellowship Program**
• **General Program Support Grants Program**
• **Specific Cultural Projects Grants Program**
• **State Touring Program**

TYPE:
Awards/prizes; Capital grants; Conferences/seminars; Endowments; Fellowships; Formula grants; General operating grants; Grants-in-aid; Project/program grants. Cultural facilities grants. State touring grants. Fellowships to individual artists residing in the state of Florida. Program provides a limited number of unmatched fellowships for creative artists in dance, folk arts, inter-disciplinary, literature, media arts, music, theatre and visual arts.

YEAR PROGRAM STARTED: 1969

PURPOSE:
To encourage the creation of projects that promote excellence in the arts and that strive to bring arts to a communitywide audience.

LEGAL BASIS:
State government agency.

ELIGIBILITY:
To apply for a grant, an organization must qualify as a political subdivision of a municipal, county or state government in Florida or be a not-for-profit, tax-exempt Florida corporation, meet specific budgetary and program requirements as outlined for the appropriate artistic disciplines, special programs and funding categories, match dollar-for-dollar, in most cases, the grant amount requested from the Division and meet all legal and financial requirements described in the *Guide to Cultural Programs.*

To apply for and retain a fellowship, an applicant must be a Florida citizen, at least 18 years old, and maintain Florida residency for the duration of the grant period. The applicant must not be a degree-seeking student at the time of application or at any time during the grant period. Applicant must not have received a Division fellowship during the past four years at the time of the application.

GEOGRAPHIC RESTRICTIONS:
Florida.

FINANCIAL DATA:
Cash grants are for program expenses rather than for capital improvements.
Amount of support per award: Varies depending upon grant program and specific eligibility.
Total amount of support: Varies by program.
Matching fund requirements: Fellowships: Unmatched. In most cases, grants are matched 1:1.

NUMBER OF APPLICANTS MOST RECENT YEAR:
More than 1,400.

NUMBER OF AWARDS: More than 100 awards for fiscal year 2012-13.

APPLICATION INFORMATION:
Program guidelines can be downloaded from the web site.
Duration: One year.
Deadline: June for General Program Support and Specific Cultural Projects grants. July for fellowships.

OFFICERS:
Sandy Shaughnessy, Director, Division of Cultural Affairs

STAFF:
Gaylen Phillips, Associate Director of Arts Resources and Services

ADDRESS INQUIRIES TO:
Tim Storhoff, Arts Consultant
(See address above.)

FONDATION DES ETATS-UNIS [449]

15, boulevard Jourdan
75014 Paris France
(33 1) 53 80 68 87
Fax: (33 1) 53 80 68 99

E-MAIL ADDRESS:
culture@feusa.org

WEB SITE ADDRESS:
www.feusa.org
www.harriet-hale-woolley.com

FOUNDED: 1929

AREAS OF INTEREST:
Graduate housing, artist ateliers, music studios, grants for musicians, artists, and interns in psychiatry.

CONSULTING OR VOLUNTEER SERVICES:
Office of Cultural Affairs.

NAME(S) OF PROGRAMS:
• **Harriet Hale Woolley Scholarships**

TYPE:
Awards/prizes; Development grants; Scholarships. Bequeathed to the Fondation des Etats-Unis, Cite Internationale Universitaire de Paris in the early 1930s, the Harriet Hale Woolley Scholarship is awarded annually to a select number of exceptional American artists and musicians who plan to pursue their studies in Paris.

A scholarship is also available to French, Swiss and American medical postgraduates specializing in psychiatry with an internship in a Parisian hospital.

YEAR PROGRAM STARTED: 1933

PURPOSE:
To promote artistic and cultural exchange between the U.S. and France.

LEGAL BASIS:
Fondation Reconnue d'Utilite Publique (FRUP).

ELIGIBILITY:
Requirements include:
(1) American citizenship;
(2) between 21 and 29 years of age (only single applicants can be considered, as the Fondation has no accommodations for couples);
(3) graduation with high academic standing from a college, university, or professional school of recognized standing;
(4) evidence of accomplishment in the candidate's field of expertise and;
(5) good moral character, personality and adaptability, plus good physical health and emotional stability.

Scholarship recipient must reside at the Fondation des Etats-Unis for the academic year.

FINANCIAL DATA:
The Scholarship is designed to assist with living expenses while in Paris.
Amount of support per award: Stipend of EUR 10,000, payable in five installments during the academic year (October 1 to June 30).

NUMBER OF APPLICANTS MOST RECENT YEAR:
15 to 20.

NUMBER OF AWARDS: Up to 4 annually.

APPLICATION INFORMATION:
Application should be made to the address above. Documents to be submitted include:
(1) a short yet detailed statement of the foreign study project including the Paris

school and/or instructor preferred by the candidate (candidates in the visual arts should be especially attentive to this point); (2) a Harriet Hale Woolley application (found on web site); all entries must be complete and accurate; (3) attestation of proficiency in the French language by a qualified teacher of French; (4) three letters of recommendation from professors familiar with the applicant's general qualifications, artistic ability and accomplishment (letters should be original copies on letterhead paper, and mailed by the issuer); it is highly recommended that candidates include a letter of admission to study at a French institution; (5) complete transcript of college or university record with embossed seal of the issuing institution; (6) a simple medical certificate of general health (successful candidates will be required to show proof of paid-up accident and health insurance before arrival); (7) four small identification photographs 1 inch x 1-1/4 inch (3 x 4 cm.), with applicant's name printed on the back of each one and; (8) examples of the applicant's work; for visual artists, a CD or DVD of works and/or photographs are suggested; for musicians, 10 to 15 minutes of music on audio CD showcasing three contrasting styles is suggested.

Application materials will not be returned. Please send all materials by mail. Faxes and e-mail attachments will not be accepted.

Duration: One academic year.

Deadline: All application dossiers and their supporting materials must be received no later than January 31, for the following academic year.

PUBLICATIONS:
Application guidelines.

OFFICER:
Terence Murphy, Director

ADDRESS INQUIRIES TO:
Harriet Hale Woolley Scholarship
(See address above.)

*SPECIAL STIPULATIONS:
As this project should include enrollment in a recognized institution, it is strongly suggested that the candidate establish a significant contact with a teacher or institution prior to arriving in France and to show evidence of this contact in his or her application dossier.

FORECAST PUBLIC ARTWORKS   [450]
2300 Myrtle Avenue
Suite 160
St. Paul, MN 55114
(651) 641-1128
Fax: (651) 641-1983

E-MAIL ADDRESS:
info@forecastart.org

WEB SITE ADDRESS:
www.forecastart.org

FOUNDED: 1978

AREAS OF INTEREST:
Public art.

CONSULTING OR VOLUNTEER SERVICES:
Consulting for public artists and communities.

NAME(S) OF PROGRAMS:
● **Jerome Planning Grant for Emerging Artists**
● **Jerome Project Grant for Emerging Artists**
● **McKnight Professional Development Grant for Mid-Career Artists**
● **McKnight Project Grant for Mid-Career Artists**
● **MN Regional Grant Program**

TYPE:
Development grants; Project/program grants; Research grants.

YEAR PROGRAM STARTED: 1988

PURPOSE:
To fund emerging and midcareer artists of all disciplines to develop and/or produce public art projects.

LEGAL BASIS:
Private nonprofit corporation.

ELIGIBILITY:
Open to emerging and midcareer artists of all disciplines. Minnesota residents only.

GEOGRAPHIC RESTRICTIONS:
Minnesota.

FINANCIAL DATA:
Amount of support per award: $2,000 for research and development; $7,000 or $50,000 for public projects; $5,000 for professional development.

NUMBER OF APPLICANTS MOST RECENT YEAR:
50 to 100 per competition.

APPLICATION INFORMATION:
Proposal forms available in September. There is no fee for the form. Generally five to 10 slides plus proposal for new work required.
Duration: Up to one year.
Deadline: November 15. Announcement February 15.

PUBLICATIONS:
Public Art Review, a semiannual publication focusing on public art projects and issues.

IRS IDENTIFICATION NUMBER: 41-1361351

STAFF:
Jack Becker, Executive Director
Stacey Holland, Associate Director
Melinda Childs, Director of Artist Services
Kirstin Wiegmann, Director of Education and Community Engagement
Amelia Foster, Program and Administrative Associate
Karen Olson, Executive Editor, *Public Art Review*

ADDRESS INQUIRIES TO:
Melinda Childs, Director of Artist Services
(See address above.)

CARL M. FREEMAN FOUNDATION   [451]
36097 Sand Cove Road
Selbyville, DE 19975
(302) 436-3015

E-MAIL ADDRESS:
info@freemanfoundation.org

WEB SITE ADDRESS:
www.freemanfoundation.org

FOUNDED: 1960

AREAS OF INTEREST:
Facilitating, supporting and promoting innovative community-based leadership and giving.

NAME(S) OF PROGRAMS:
● **FACES Grant**

TYPE:
Capital grants; Challenge/matching grants; General operating grants.

PURPOSE:
To provide funding and capacity-building support to nonprofit organizations in the communities served by the Carl M. Freeman Companies.

ELIGIBILITY:
Must be IRS-recognized 501(c)(3) tax-exempt, nonprofit organizations or public agencies serving the residents of the Companies' funding areas.

GEOGRAPHIC RESTRICTIONS:
Sussex County, Delaware and Montgomery County, Maryland.

FINANCIAL DATA:
Amount of support per award: $2,500 or $5,000.
Total amount of support: $50,000.

APPLICATION INFORMATION:
Guidelines available on the web site.
Duration: Six months; possible several-month renewal.
Deadline: Varies.

ADDRESS INQUIRIES TO:
Melissa Rizer, Administrative Associate
(See address above.)

FREER GALLERY OF ART AND ARTHUR M. SACKLER GALLERY   [452]
Smithsonian Institution, MRC 707
1050 Independence Avenue, S.W.
Washington, DC 20560
(202) 633-0401
Fax: (202) 633-0067

WEB SITE ADDRESS:
www.asia.si.edu/research/fellowships.asp

FOUNDED: 1923

AREAS OF INTEREST:
Asian art, 19th and early 20th century American art.

CONSULTING OR VOLUNTEER SERVICES:
Docent tours for the public through Freer Gallery of Art and Arthur M. Sackler Gallery.

NAME(S) OF PROGRAMS:
● **Forbes Fellowship**
● **The J.S. Lee Memorial Fellowship**
● **Smithsonian Fellowship**
● **Anne van Biema Fellowship**

TYPE:
Awards/prizes; Fellowships; Internships; Project/program grants; Research grants; Technical assistance; Visiting scholars. Forbes Fellowship is a competitive grant to further the scientific study of care, conservation and protection of works of art related to the Freer Collection.

The J.S. Lee Memorial Fellowship facilitates the international exchange of curatorial expertise and contributes to the professional development of Chinese art curators and academics.

Anne van Biema Fellowship is established to promote excellence in research and publication on the Japanese visual arts. One award is made each year to support a scholar at the postdoctoral level for a period of two to nine months.

YEAR PROGRAM STARTED: 1923

PURPOSE:
To advance scholarship of Asian art and 19th and early 20th century American art.

LEGAL BASIS:
U.S. government agency.

ELIGIBILITY:
Varies with each fellowship.

FINANCIAL DATA:
Amount of support per award: Senior and Postdoctoral: Up to $45,000 per year; Predoctoral: $30,000 per year.
Total amount of support: Varies.

COOPERATIVE FUNDING PROGRAMS:
Smithsonian Office of Fellowships and Grants, University of Michigan.

APPLICATION INFORMATION:
For Smithsonian Fellowship, write to Office of Fellowships and Grants in the Smithsonian. For Forbes Fellowship, write to Department of Conservation and Scientific Research, Freer/Sackler Galleries at the above address. For the J.S. Lee Memorial Fellowship, visit the fellowship page at www.jsleefellowship.org. Anne van Biema Fellowship information is available on the web site.

PUBLICATIONS:
Annual report.

OFFICERS:
Dr. Julian Raby, Director

THE DAVID GEFFEN FOUNDATION

12011 San Vicente Boulevard
Suite 606
Los Angeles, CA 90049
(310) 581-5955
Fax: (310) 581-5949

E-MAIL ADDRESS:
ddishman@geffenco.com

TYPE:
Capital grants; General operating grants; Project/program grants.

See entry 1432 for full listing.

GEORGIA COUNCIL FOR THE ARTS [453]

75 Fifth Street, N.W.
Suite 1200
Atlanta, GA 30308
(404) 962-4827

E-MAIL ADDRESS:
gaarts@gaarts.org

WEB SITE ADDRESS:
www.gaarts.org

FOUNDED: 1968

AREAS OF INTEREST:
The arts.

CONSULTING OR VOLUNTEER SERVICES:
Extensive technical assistance to nonprofit arts organizations in all disciplines on matters of artistic, administrative or technical concern.

NAME(S) OF PROGRAMS:
- **Georgia Masterpieces**
- **Literary Events Grants**
- **Poet Laureate**
- **Poetry Out Loud**
- **State Art Collection**

TYPE:
Awards/prizes; Challenge/matching grants; Conferences/seminars; Demonstration grants; Development grants; Formula grants; General operating grants; Grants-in-aid; Internships; Matching gifts; Project/program grants; Research grants; Residencies; Seed money grants; Technical assistance; Training grants; Visiting scholars; Research contracts. Capacity building; Poetry competitions; Traditional arts apprenticeships; Partner grants. Technical assistance and grants in categories including, but not limited to, architecture/environmental arts, dance, education (arts-related), filmmaking, folk arts/heritage arts and crafts, historic preservation (arts-related), literary arts, multimedia, museums, music, photography, public radio, television, theatre and visual arts.

YEAR PROGRAM STARTED: 1968

PURPOSE:
To cultivate the growth of Georgia communities through the arts.

LEGAL BASIS:
Government agency.

ELIGIBILITY:
Grants are made to nonprofit, tax-exempt arts organizations or units of government which are incorporated in the state of Georgia.

GEOGRAPHIC RESTRICTIONS:
Georgia.

FINANCIAL DATA:
Amount of support per award: $2,500 to $32,700 for the year 2013.
Total amount of support: $800,000 for the year 2013.
Matching fund requirements: Varies.

NUMBER OF APPLICANTS MOST RECENT YEAR: 250.

NUMBER OF AWARDS: 120.

APPLICATION INFORMATION:
Grant applications are available online.
Duration: One year. Must reapply for additional funding.

PUBLICATIONS:
Application guidelines; quarterly newsletter.

ADDRESS INQUIRIES TO:
Tina Lilly, Grants Program Manager
(See address above.)

NANCY GRAVES FOUNDATION [454]

450 West 31st Street, 2nd Floor
New York, NY 10001
(212) 560-0602
Fax: (212) 560-0604

E-MAIL ADDRESS:
mail@nancygravesfoundation.org

WEB SITE ADDRESS:
www.nancygravesfoundation.org

FOUNDED: 1996

AREAS OF INTEREST:
Visual arts.

NAME(S) OF PROGRAMS:
- **Grants for Visual Artists**

TYPE:
Grant for nominated visual artists for work in any medium other than their own.

YEAR PROGRAM STARTED: 2000

PURPOSE:
To give assistance to individual artists; to maintain an archive of the Founder's life and work and organize exhibitions of her art.

ELIGIBILITY:
Grantees must be residents of the U.S. who have been working as artists for at least five years beyond his or her schooling. Grants will not be awarded to students. Applications will be solicited from nominated visual artists who wish to have the opportunity to master a technique, medium or discipline that is different from the one in which he or she is primarily recognized.

GEOGRAPHIC RESTRICTIONS:
United States.

FINANCIAL DATA:
Amount of support per award: $5,000.

NUMBER OF AWARDS: 2 annually.

APPLICATION INFORMATION:
Artist applicants must be nominated by Foundation nominators and will subsequently receive an application for consideration by a second panel of jurors.

STAFF:
Christina Hunter, Director

ADDRESS INQUIRIES TO:
Christina Hunter, Director
(See address above.)

HAMBIDGE [455]

P.O. Box 339
Rabun Gap, GA 30568
(706) 746-5718
Fax: (706) 746-9933

E-MAIL ADDRESS:
center@hambidge.org

WEB SITE ADDRESS:
www.hambidge.org

FOUNDED: 1934

AREAS OF INTEREST:
Artist residency program.

NAME(S) OF PROGRAMS:
- **Hambidge Residency Program Fellowships**

TYPE:
Fellowships. The Hambidge Center awards residency fellowships to distinguished artists and scientists at its 600-acre creative sanctuary in the Blue Ridge Mountains. Fellowships apply to any field or discipline of creative work. They consist of the following:
(1) The Antinori Fellowship for Ceramic Artists awards a scholarship to a ceramic artist;
(2) The Bella Cucina (Art of Food) Fellowship awards a scholarship to a culinary artisan;
(3) The Elfster Fellowship awards a scholarship to a residency applicant in any discipline;
(4) The Neva Langley Fickling Fellowship for Piano awards a scholarship to a musician concentrating on work with the piano;
(5) The Friends of Hambidge Fellowship awards a scholarship to a residency applicant in any discipline;
(6) The Fulton County Arts & Culture Fellowship awards scholarships to three artists from Fulton County, GA;
(7) The Griffith Fellowship awards a scholarship to a residency applicant in any discipline;

(8) The Holland & Knight Fellowship awards a scholarship to a residency applicant in any discipline;

(9) The W.S. Hopkins Fellowship for Photography awards a scholarship to an applicant in the field of photography;

(10) The King & Spalding Fellowship awards a scholarship to a residency applicant in any discipline;

(11) The National Endowment for the Arts Fellowship awards scholarships to nine artists from across the U.S.;

(12) The Post Hope Fellowship awards a scholarship to a residency applicant in any discipline;

(13) The Joe Quattlebaum Fellowship awards a scholarship to a southern artist actively involved in sustainability, environmental consciousness or gardening and botany;

(14) The Rogers Fellowship for Textile Arts awards a scholarship to a textile or fiber artist;

(15) The Nellie Mae Rowe Fellowship, endowed by Judith Alexander, awards a scholarship to an African American artist of any discipline;

(16) The Ron Sanders Fellowship awards a scholarship to a residency applicant in any discipline;

(17) The Judith C. Simmons Fellowship for Visual Arts awards a scholarship to a visual artist and;

(18) The Lillian Thomas Fellowship awards a scholarship to a ceramic artist.

PURPOSE:
To provide applicants with an environment for creative work in the arts and sciences.

ELIGIBILITY:
Open to qualified applicants in all disciplines who can demonstrate seriousness, dedication and professionalism. International residents are welcome.

FINANCIAL DATA:
Each of the individuals in residence has private accommodations and studio space, and shares communal dinners prepared by an in-residence chef. Eight individuals are in residence at any given time.

Amount of support per award: Each artist receives:
(1) a two-week residency with no fees;
(2) a $700 stipend and;
(3) the honor of a Distinguished Fellowship.

APPLICATION INFORMATION:
Applicants should submit:
(1) completed application form (three pages);
(2) applicant statement;
(3) resume/professional summary;
(4) work examples (CDs and hard copies as outlined in the instruction pages);
(5) bio;
(6) two letters of reference included with the application or e-mailed by the application deadline (does not apply to returning Fellows);
(7) $30 check/processing fee (all applicants) and;
(8) stamped, self-addressed envelope for return of work samples (if desired).
Envelope should be marked "Attention Residency Program."

Duration: Two weeks.

Deadline: January 15, April 15 and September 15.

ADDRESS INQUIRIES TO:
Debra Sanders, Office Manager
(See address above.)

HANNAFORD CHARITABLE FOUNDATION
145 Pleasant Hill Road
Scarborough, ME 04074
(207) 885-3834
Fax: (207) 885-3051

WEB SITE ADDRESS:
www.hannaford.com

TYPE:
Capital grants; Project/program grants.

See entry 1550 for full listing.

HAWAII STATE FOUNDATION ON CULTURE AND THE ARTS   [456]
250 South Hotel Street
Second Floor
Honolulu, HI 96813
(808) 586-0305
Fax: (808) 586-0308
TTY: (808) 586-0740

E-MAIL ADDRESS:
jonathan.johnson@hawaii.gov

WEB SITE ADDRESS:
hawaii.gov/sfca

FOUNDED: 1965

AREAS OF INTEREST:
Arts education, community arts, heritage and preservation, presentation, folk arts and community arts.

NAME(S) OF PROGRAMS:
● **Biennium Grants Program**

TYPE:
Project/program grants.

YEAR PROGRAM STARTED: 1965

PURPOSE:
To stimulate, encourage and promote culture, the arts and humanities throughout the state of Hawaii.

LEGAL BASIS:
State arts agency.

ELIGIBILITY:
Hawaii Revised Statutes for organizations and individuals as defined in Section 9-11.

GEOGRAPHIC RESTRICTIONS:
Hawaii.

FINANCIAL DATA:
Limits on the amount of funding for any one project are established by the SFCA Board. Certain costs are not allowable for SFCA funding.

Amount of support per award: Varies.

Total amount of support: $600,000 for fiscal year 2013.

Matching fund requirements: 1:1 match required.

APPLICATION INFORMATION:
Applicants must complete the required application forms and attachments.

Duration: Funds are awarded on a biennial basis. No funds are awarded on a continuing basis.

Deadline: Varies.

PUBLICATIONS:
Annual Report; application guidelines.

BOARD MEMBERS:
Barbara Saromines-Ganne, Chairperson
Mary Begier
Leonard Chow
Joel Guy

Clifford P. Kapono
Michael Moore
Sharon Narimatsu
Peter Rosegg
Sheryl Seaman

ADDRESS INQUIRIES TO:
Jonathan Johnson, Executive Director
(See address above.)

HAYSTACK MOUNTAIN SCHOOL OF CRAFTS   [457]
22 Church Street
Deer Isle, ME 04627
(207) 348-2306
Fax: (207) 348-2307

E-MAIL ADDRESS:
haystack@haystack-mtn.org

WEB SITE ADDRESS:
www.haystack-mtn.org

FOUNDED: 1950

AREAS OF INTEREST:
Craft education and exploration in ceramics, metals, wood, fibers, graphics, glass and blacksmithing.

TYPE:
Conferences/seminars; Fellowships; Residencies; Scholarships; Visiting scholars; Work-study programs. Minority scholarships; Technical Assistant and Work Study Scholarships. Awards for study in diverse craft media and workshops in six studios including ceramics, metals, wood, fibers, graphics, glass and blacksmithing.

YEAR PROGRAM STARTED: 1950

PURPOSE:
To offer professional instruction and demonstration in crafts.

LEGAL BASIS:
Nonprofit educational organization.

ELIGIBILITY:
U.S. and foreign citizens who are capable of doing graduate-level work are eligible for technical assistant scholarships. Candidates must be at least 18 years of age.

FINANCIAL DATA:
Annual scholarships cover the cost of tuition, or tuition and room and board.

Amount of support per award: $1,270.

Total amount of support: $120,000.

NUMBER OF APPLICANTS MOST RECENT YEAR: 266.

NUMBER OF AWARDS: 109 (54 work-study students; 55 technical assistants).

APPLICATION INFORMATION:
Guidelines and application form are available at the web site.

Duration: One- to two-week sessions.

Deadline: Scholarship applications: March 1; Regular applications: April 1.

PUBLICATIONS:
Catalog; newsletter; scholarly monographs; regional program brochures; eNewsletters.

IRS IDENTIFICATION NUMBER: 01-0243548

TRUSTEES:
Claire Sanford, President
Matt Hutton, Vice President
Miguel Gómez-Ibáñez, Treasurer

ADDRESS INQUIRIES TO:
Stuart Kestenbaum, Director
Haystack Mountain School of Crafts

22 Church Street (November to April)
89 Haystack School Drive (May to October)
Deer Isle, ME 04627

MAXIMILIAN E. & MARION O. HOFFMAN FOUNDATION, INC.
970 Farmington Avenue, Suite 203
West Hartford, CT 06107
(860) 521-2949
Fax: (860) 561-5082

TYPE:
Project/program grants.

See entry 2270 for full listing.

HUTCHINSON COMMUNITY FOUNDATION   [458]
One North Main Street
Suite 501
Hutchinson, KS 67501
(620) 663-5293
Fax: (620) 663-9277

E-MAIL ADDRESS:
info@hutchcf.org

WEB SITE ADDRESS:
www.hutchcf.org

FOUNDED: 1989

AREAS OF INTEREST:
Arts, civic improvements, education, health
and human services.

TYPE:
Project/program grants; Seed money grants.

YEAR PROGRAM STARTED: 1989

PURPOSE:
To make Hutchinson area a better place to
work and live.

LEGAL BASIS:
501(c)(3) public foundation.

ELIGIBILITY:
Organizations that support innovative projects
located in Reno County, KS, and government
units that work in the Foundation's objective.

GEOGRAPHIC RESTRICTIONS:
Reno County, Kansas.

FINANCIAL DATA:
Amount of support per award: Varies.
Total amount of support: Varies.

NUMBER OF APPLICANTS MOST RECENT YEAR:
50.

NUMBER OF AWARDS: 23.

APPLICATION INFORMATION:
One copy of the applicant's current IRS
determination letter Section 501(c)(3) or
509(a) is required. Contact the Foundation
for application procedures.
Duration: One year. Reapplication possible.
Deadline: Early September. Contact
Foundation for exact date.

PUBLICATIONS:
Annual report; application guidelines.

OFFICERS AND STAFF:
Aubrey A. Patterson, President and Executive
Director
Terri L. Eisiminger, Vice President of
Administration
Janet Hamilton, Community Investment
Officer

ADDRESS INQUIRIES TO:
Aubrey A. Patterson
President and Executive Director
(See address above.)

IDAHO COMMISSION ON THE ARTS   [459]
2410 Old Penitentiary Road
Boise, ID 83712
(208) 334-2119
Fax: (208) 334-2488

E-MAIL ADDRESS:
info@arts.idaho.gov

WEB SITE ADDRESS:
www.arts.idaho.gov

FOUNDED: 1966

AREAS OF INTEREST:
All disciplines in the arts.

CONSULTING OR VOLUNTEER SERVICES:
Technical assistance in arts management.

NAME(S) OF PROGRAMS:
- **Arts Education Projects**
- **Directory of Teaching Artists**
- **Entry Track**
- **Fellowships**
- **Public Programs in the Arts**
- **Quick Fund$**
- **Traditional Arts Apprenticeship Program**
- **Tumblewords**
- **Writer-in-Residence Program**

TYPE:
Conferences/seminars; Fellowships; General
operating grants; Project/program grants;
Residencies; Technical assistance.
Fellowship/apprenticeship,
touring/sponsorship, immediate assistance.

YEAR PROGRAM STARTED: 1966

PURPOSE:
To develop the artistic and cultural life of
Idaho.

LEGAL BASIS:
State agency.

ELIGIBILITY:
Applicants must be nonprofit, tax-exempt
organizations or artists living in Idaho.

GEOGRAPHIC RESTRICTIONS:
Idaho.

FINANCIAL DATA:
Fiscal restrictions, non-cash benefits.
Amount of support per award: Up to
$25,000.
Total amount of support: $600,374 for fiscal
year 2012.
Matching fund requirements: 50:50, cash or
in-kind.

NUMBER OF APPLICANTS MOST RECENT YEAR:
274 for fiscal year 2012.

APPLICATION INFORMATION:
Applications must be on the appropriate
form, typed in 12-point, or neatly
handwritten. Do not use application forms
from previous years. Review the checklist
carefully because the panel will review the
application as submitted. Answer the required
narrative questions, paying close attention to
the page limitations, and check to see that
the application is complete, signed and dated.
Incomplete applications are subject to return.
Duration: 12 months.
Deadline: Varies.

PUBLICATIONS:
Application guidelines.

IRS IDENTIFICATION NUMBER: 82-6000952

OFFICERS:
Mark Hofflund, Chairman

Michelle Coleman, Community Development
Director
Barbara Robinson, Director of Artist Services
Ruth Piispanen, Education Program Director
Maria Carmen Gambliel, Folk Arts Program
Director
Cort Conley, Literature Director

ADDRESS INQUIRIES TO:
Executive Director
(See address above.)

ILLINOIS ARTS COUNCIL   [460]
James R. Thompson Center
100 West Randolph, Suite 10-500
Chicago, IL 60601
(312) 814-6750
Fax: (312) 814-1471

E-MAIL ADDRESS:
iac.info@illinois.gov

WEB SITE ADDRESS:
www.arts.illinois.gov

FOUNDED: 1965

AREAS OF INTEREST:
The arts.

TYPE:
General operating grants; Grants-in-aid;
Project/program grants.

PURPOSE:
To make the arts more widely available to
Illinois residents; to promote an environment
that is beneficial to artistic activities; to aid
the continuing development of the state's
cultural resources.

ELIGIBILITY:
Any nonprofit organization with 501(c)(3)
tax-exempt status actively servicing the
Illinois public for at least one year prior to
the date of application is eligible. Applicant
organizations should be involved in the
above-mentioned fields, although public and
private higher educational institutions may
apply for art programs that serve the wider
community and cannot be funded entirely
with regular institutional funds.

GEOGRAPHIC RESTRICTIONS:
Illinois.

FINANCIAL DATA:
Amount of support per award: Varies
depending on needs and nature of the
request.

APPLICATION INFORMATION:
Guidelines available on the Council web site.
Duration: Up to one year.

OFFICERS:
Shirley R. Madigan, Chairperson
Rhoda A. Pierce, Vice Chairperson
Andy Van Meter, Secretary

INDIANA ARTS COMMISSION   [461]
100 North Senate Avenue
Room N505
Indianapolis, IN 46204
(317) 232-1278
Fax: (317) 232-5595
TDD: (317) 233-3001

E-MAIL ADDRESS:
GrantsAdmin@iac.in.gov

WEB SITE ADDRESS:
www.in.gov/arts

FOUNDED: 1969

AREAS OF INTEREST:
The arts including crafts, dance, design, education, expansion arts, folk, literature, media, multiarts, museums, music, presenters, statewide arts service organizations, theatre and visual and local arts agencies.

CONSULTING OR VOLUNTEER SERVICES:
Consultation on a limited basis to Indiana organizations and artists.

TYPE:
Block grants; Conferences/seminars; Development grants; General operating grants; Project/program grants; Technical assistance. Arts in education; Arts organizations and services; Capacity building; Individual artist projects. Most grants are awarded through a network of regional partners which serve all 92 counties.

YEAR PROGRAM STARTED: 1969

PURPOSE:
To act as public catalyst, partner and investor that serves the citizens of Indiana by funding, encouraging, promoting and expanding all the arts.

LEGAL BASIS:
State agency.

ELIGIBILITY:
Applicants must be private tax-exempt, not-for-profit arts organizations or public agencies or individual artists. Eligible organizations without tax-exempt status should submit a fiscal year budget. IAC does not fund capital improvements, purchase of permanent equipment, costs of receptions, foods or beverages or agents fees for programs contracted through commercial agencies.

Must have impact on the state of Indiana.

GEOGRAPHIC RESTRICTIONS:
Indiana.

FINANCIAL DATA:
Amount of support per award: Varies.
Total amount of support: $3,600,000.
Matching fund requirements: Matching funds may include in-kind as well as cash.

APPLICATION INFORMATION:
Applicants must complete an application, grant agreement and any reporting required by the program guidelines. Program guidelines are available from the Commission. Potential applicants should contact the agency before applying.
Duration: July 1 through June 30, fiscal year.

PUBLICATIONS:
Monthy newsletters; press releases; grant/program guidelines.

IRS IDENTIFICATION NUMBER: 35-6000158

COMMISSION MEMBERS:
John Ford, Chairperson
Karen Ellerbrook, Vice Chairperson
Judy Hess, Secretary
Gilberto Cardenas
Linda W. Goad
Pam Hicks
Jeffrey Kirk
Linda S. Levell
Jeanne E. Mirro
Suzanne Rentschler
Kelly B. Schreckengast
Irene Smith-King
Richard Q. Stifel
Earl R. Williams
Trevor Yager

ADDRESS INQUIRIES TO:
Paige Sharp, Grants Manager
(See address above.)

INSTITUTE OF AMERICAN INDIAN ARTS (IAIA)
83 Avan Nu Po Road
Santa Fe, NM 87508
(505) 424-5724
(800) 804-6422
Fax: (505) 424-0909

E-MAIL ADDRESS:
lbarela@iaia.edu

WEB SITE ADDRESS:
www.iaia.edu

TYPE:
Awards/prizes; Scholarships.

See entry 1051 for full listing.

INTERNATIONAL DOCUMENTARY ASSOCIATION   [462]
3470 Wilshire Boulevard
Suite 980
Los Angeles, CA 90010
(213) 232-1660
Fax: (213) 232-1669

E-MAIL ADDRESS:
info@documentary.org

WEB SITE ADDRESS:
www.documentary.org

FOUNDED: 1982

AREAS OF INTEREST:
Documentary film.

NAME(S) OF PROGRAMS:
● **ABC News Videosource Award**
● **IDA/David L. Wolper Student Documentary Achievement Award**
● **Pare Lorentz Award**

TYPE:
Awards/prizes; Internships. ABC News Videosource Award is awarded for the best use of news footage as an integral component in a documentary.

IDA/David L. Wolper Student Documentary Achievement Award recognizes exceptional achievement in nonfiction film and video production at the university level and brings greater public and industry awareness to the work of students in the documentary field.

The Pare Lorentz Award is awarded for films that demonstrate exemplary filmmaking while focusing on the appropriate use of the natural environment, justice for all and the illumination of pressing social problems.

YEAR PROGRAM STARTED: 1984

PURPOSE:
To promote nonfiction film and video around the world by supporting and recognizing the efforts of documentary film and video makers, increasing public appreciation and demand for the documentary, and providing a forum for documentary makers, their supporters and suppliers.

LEGAL BASIS:
501(c)(3).

FINANCIAL DATA:
Amount of support per award: ABC News Videosource Award: $2,000 honorarium and research time at the ABC News Videosource; IDA/David L. Wolper Student Documentary

Achievement Award: $1,000 honorarium, production of 1,000 DVDs courtesy of Magic Rock Entertainment and $1,000 certificate toward purchase of motion picture film; Pare Lorentz Award: $2,500 honorarium.

NUMBER OF APPLICANTS MOST RECENT YEAR:
120.

NUMBER OF AWARDS: 4.

APPLICATION INFORMATION:
Guidelines and application form are available on the Association web site.
Duration: Annual awards.

IRS IDENTIFICATION NUMBER: 95-3911227

ADDRESS INQUIRIES TO:
Michael Lumpkin, Executive Director
(See address above.)

IOWA ARTS COUNCIL   [463]
600 East Locust Street
Des Moines, IA 50319-0290
(515) 281-4641
Fax: (515) 242-6498

E-MAIL ADDRESS:
matthew.harris@iowa.gov

WEB SITE ADDRESS:
www.iowaartscouncil.org

FOUNDED: 1967

AREAS OF INTEREST:
All arts disciplines, primarily in Iowa.

CONSULTING OR VOLUNTEER SERVICES:
Technical assistance in a variety of disciplines and subject areas, including information.

NAME(S) OF PROGRAMS:
● **Arts Resources and Artists Programs**
● **Funding and Arts in Education Programs**
● **Technical Assistance and Community Development Programs**

TYPE:
Challenge/matching grants; Conferences/seminars; Development grants; General operating grants; Project/program grants; Residencies; Scholarships; Technical assistance; Training grants. Seminars, technical assistance and funding. Services provided to institutions and individuals statewide.

YEAR PROGRAM STARTED: 1967

PURPOSE:
To enrich the quality of life for Iowans through support of the arts.

LEGAL BASIS:
State agency established under Chapter 304A, Code of Iowa.

ELIGIBILITY:
Applicants must be nonprofit, tax-exempt organizations or Iowa individuals, age 18 or older (and not a student, artist or arts educator), who have resided in Iowa at least one year prior to application deadline.

Nonprofit organizations located in states bordering Iowa are eligible for support if the project clearly demonstrates that Iowans are being served.

GEOGRAPHIC RESTRICTIONS:
Iowa.

FINANCIAL DATA:
Amount of support per award: Varies.
Matching fund requirements: One-to-one cash or in-kind match for most grant programs.

REPRESENTATIVE AWARDS:
$9,500 to University of Iowa, Iowa City, for City of Literature documentary; $6,700 to Quad City Symphony Orchestra for Midori Residency; $9,500 to Civic Center of Greater Des Moines to support the Dance Series project.

APPLICATION INFORMATION:
Completed application form must be submitted. Applicants must prepare a narrative section for all applications.
Duration: 12 months or less.

PUBLICATIONS:
Online e-newsletter (monthly); Online Teaching Artists Roster; Online Performing Artists Roster; Online Folk Arts Directory; Online Directory of Iowa Artists and Performing Groups.

IRS IDENTIFICATION NUMBER: 42-6004812

STAFF:
Matthew Harris, Division Administrator
Linda Lee, Grants Administrator

ADDRESS INQUIRIES TO:
Matthew Harris
Division Administrator
(See address above.)

JEROME FOUNDATION, INC.   [464]
400 Sibley Street, Suite 125
St. Paul, MN 55101
(651) 224-9431
(800) 995-3766 (MN and NYC only)
Fax: (651) 224-3439

E-MAIL ADDRESS:
info@jeromefdn.org

WEB SITE ADDRESS:
www.jeromefdn.org

FOUNDED: 1964

AREAS OF INTEREST:
Arts with a focus on film and video, literature, dance, music, theater and visual arts. Emphasis is on creation of new works by emerging artists.

TYPE:
Awards/prizes; Development grants; Fellowships; General operating grants; Project/program grants; Residencies; Seed money grants; Travel grants.

YEAR PROGRAM STARTED: 1964

PURPOSE:
To contribute to a dynamic and evolving culture by supporting the creation, development and production of new works by emerging artists.

LEGAL BASIS:
Tax-exempt, private foundation.

ELIGIBILITY:
Foundation grants are made primarily to not-for-profit arts organizations and to individual professional artists through specific programs. The Foundation accepts requests from new organizations. It also supports not-for-profit fiscal sponsors that apply on behalf of artists. The Foundation is flexible and will consider various funding mechanisms if they provide significant assistance to emerging artists.

The Foundation does not support capital (building and endowment) campaigns, nor does it offer travel grants other than the specific Travel and Study Grant Program it administers.

Foundation support is restricted to emerging artists who are legal residents of Minnesota and/or New York City, NY.

GEOGRAPHIC RESTRICTIONS:
Minnesota and the five boroughs of New York City, New York.

FINANCIAL DATA:
Amount of support per award: Average grant: $13,000.
Total amount of support: Average $2,900,000 annually.

NUMBER OF APPLICANTS MOST RECENT YEAR: 900.

NUMBER OF AWARDS: 145.

REPRESENTATIVE AWARDS:
$20,000 to Aaron Davis Hall, New York, NY, for fund for new works.

APPLICATION INFORMATION:
Guidelines and application forms are available on the web site.
Duration: One to two years. Renewal possible.
Deadline: Applications are accepted on an ongoing basis. Applicants should allow four to five months for evaluation of proposals.

PUBLICATIONS:
Annual report.

STAFF:
Cynthia A. Gehrig, President
Robert Byrd, Program Director
Eleanor Savage, Senior Program Officer

DIRECTORS:
Philip Bither
Carlyle Brown
Patricia Hampl
Barbara McLanahan
Gary Nan Tie
Calogero Salvo
Elizabeth Streb
Charles Zelle

ADDRESS INQUIRIES TO:
Cynthia A. Gehrig, President
(See address above.)

KENTUCKY ARTS COUNCIL   [465]
500 Mero Street, 21st Floor
Frankfort, KY 40601-1987
(502) 564-3757 ext. 469
Fax: (502) 564-2839

E-MAIL ADDRESS:
kyarts@ky.gov

WEB SITE ADDRESS:
artscouncil.ky.gov

FOUNDED: 1966

AREAS OF INTEREST:
Arts development (visual arts, performing arts, literature and media), community development, artists-in-education and individual artists.

CONSULTING OR VOLUNTEER SERVICES:
Staff available for assistance in planning in above areas and in applying for grants.

NAME(S) OF PROGRAMS:
● **Arts Education Programs**
● **Arts Organizations**
● **Community Arts**
● **Individual Artists**

TYPE:
Awards/prizes; Fellowships; General operating grants; Project/program grants; Residencies; Technical assistance. Arts development and artist support.

YEAR PROGRAM STARTED: 1966

PURPOSE:
To help sponsoring organizations and artists reach and develop new audiences or strengthen themselves artistically or managerially; to act as the funding and program coordinating organization for the arts in Kentucky.

LEGAL BASIS:
State Arts Agency of the Commonwealth of Kentucky.

ELIGIBILITY:
Nonprofit organizations incorporated in the state of Kentucky or Kentucky artists. Most grant programs require IRS tax-exempt status.

GEOGRAPHIC RESTRICTIONS:
Kentucky.

FINANCIAL DATA:
Amount of support per award: $200 to $135,000.
Total amount of support: $2,000,000 annually.
Matching fund requirements: Varies by program.

COOPERATIVE FUNDING PROGRAMS: Support for Kentucky arts partnership organizations through power2give.

NUMBER OF APPLICANTS MOST RECENT YEAR: 500.

NUMBER OF AWARDS: 175.

APPLICATION INFORMATION:
Guidelines and applications are found on the Council web site.
Duration: One fiscal year, July 1 through June 30.
Deadline: Varies.

PUBLICATIONS:
Bimonthly newsletter; guide to programs; *Kentucky Performing Arts Directory.*

IRS IDENTIFICATION NUMBER: 61-0600439

OFFICERS:
Lori Meadows, Executive Director

ADDRESS INQUIRIES TO:
Lori Meadows, Executive Director
(See address above.)

THE LEEWAY FOUNDATION
1315 Walnut Street
Suite 832
Philadelphia, PA 19107
(215) 545-4078
Fax: (215) 545-4021

E-MAIL ADDRESS:
info@leeway.org

WEB SITE ADDRESS:
www.leeway.org

TYPE:
Project/program grants. Art and Change Grants provide project-based grants to fund art for social change projects.

Leeway Transformation Award is an unrestricted award (not project-based) for women and trans people demonstrating a commitment to art for social change work.

See entry 1087 for full listing.

LEHIGH VALLEY COMMUNITY FOUNDATION [466]

968 Postal Road
Suite 100
Allentown, PA 18109-9521
(610) 266-4284
Fax: (610) 266-4285

E-MAIL ADDRESS:
lvcf@lehighvalleyfoundation.org

WEB SITE ADDRESS:
www.lehighvalleyfoundation.org

FOUNDED: 1967

AREAS OF INTEREST:
Arts and culture, community development, education, environment, health care, history and heritage, human services and science.

TYPE:
Project/program grants.

PURPOSE:
To promote philanthropy in order to improve the quality of life in the Foundation's region.

LEGAL BASIS:
Nonprofit, tax-exempt 501(c)(3) organization.

ELIGIBILITY:
Limited to nonprofit, tax-exempt organizations serving citizens within the geographic limits of its outreach.

GEOGRAPHIC RESTRICTIONS:
Lehigh and Northampton counties, Pennsylvania.

FINANCIAL DATA:
Amount of support per award: Average discretionary grant: $5,000.

Total amount of support: Approximately $1,750,000 from both discretionary and nondiscretionary funds for fiscal year ended June 30, 2012.

APPLICATION INFORMATION:
Application can be downloaded from the Foundation's web site. Financial sheet must be submitted with grant application.
Deadline: July 1. Notification December 15.

STAFF:
Bernard Story, Executive Director

ADDRESS INQUIRIES TO:
Bernard Story, Executive Director
(See address above.)

THE JOHN J. LEIDY FOUNDATION

c/o Pierson & Pierson
305 West Chesapeake Avenue, Suite 308
Towson, MD 21204
(410) 821-3006
Fax: (410) 821-3007

E-MAIL ADDRESS:
info@leidyfoundation.org

WEB SITE ADDRESS:
www.leidyfoundation.org

TYPE:
General operating grants; Scholarships.

See entry 1317 for full listing.

LOUISIANA DIVISION OF THE ARTS, DEPARTMENT OF CULTURE, RECREATION AND TOURISM [467]

1051 North Third Street, Room 420
Baton Rouge, LA 70802
(225) 342-8200
Fax: (225) 342-8173

E-MAIL ADDRESS:
arts@crt.state.la.us

WEB SITE ADDRESS:
www.crt.state.la.us/arts

FOUNDED: 1976

AREAS OF INTEREST:
Dance, design, folklife, literature, media, music, theater, visual arts and crafts, arts-in-education, and arts service organizations.

CONSULTING OR VOLUNTEER SERVICES:
Grants writing, program development, community development, and alternate funding sources.

NAME(S) OF PROGRAMS:
● **Decentralized Arts Funding Program**
● **Statewide Arts Grants Programs**

TYPE:
General operating grants; Technical assistance. Stabilization grants. Grants in a variety of programs are offered to arts organizations across the state.

Stabilization grants are offered in three levels of operating support to nonprofit arts organizations.

YEAR PROGRAM STARTED: 1977

PURPOSE:
To support established and emerging arts organizations; to stimulate public participation in the arts.

LEGAL BASIS:
Government agency (the official state arts agency of Louisiana).

ELIGIBILITY:
Grants are available for nonprofit arts organizations. Organizations domiciled in Louisiana are eligible to apply for grants to support arts activities taking place in Louisiana.

Eligible applicants generally fall into one of the following categories: nonprofit 501(c)(3) organizations, public or private educational institutions, colleges or universities sponsoring arts activities intended for community participation (not academic, credit-producing, or curriculum-oriented projects), agencies of local, parish, or state government such as state or parish libraries, units of municipal government, parish police juries and agencies of state government.

GEOGRAPHIC RESTRICTIONS:
Louisiana.

FINANCIAL DATA:
Amount of support per award: Decentralized Arts Funding Program: $500 to $15,000; Local Arts Agencies: $3,600 to $123,600; Stabilization: $2,500 to $45,000.

Matching fund requirements: Decentralized Arts Funding Program: No minimum match requirement; Stabilization and Local Arts Agencies: Dollar-for-dollar or as high as 3:1.

APPLICATION INFORMATION:
Applications are available online.
Duration: One year.
Deadline: Statewide Arts Grants Program: First business day in March. Decentralized Arts Funding Program: Varies by region.

ADDRESS INQUIRIES TO:
Director of Organization and Community Development
Tel: (225) 342-8175
E-mail: info@crt.state.la.us

THE MACDOWELL COLONY [468]

100 High Street
Peterborough, NH 03458
(603) 924-3886
(212) 535-9690
Fax: (603) 924-9142; (212) 737-3803

E-MAIL ADDRESS:
info@macdowellcolony.org
admissions@macdowellcolony.org

WEB SITE ADDRESS:
www.macdowellcolony.org

FOUNDED: 1907

AREAS OF INTEREST:
Writing, theatre, visual art, music composition, filmmaking, architecture and interdisciplinary art.

NAME(S) OF PROGRAMS:
● **Artist Residency Program**

TYPE:
Fellowships; Residencies; Travel grants. Residency fellowships awarded to emerging and established artists across a spectrum of disciplines - architecture, film, interdisciplinary practices, literature, music, visual art, and theatre - to support studio time and artistic exchange in an ideal environment for the creative process.

YEAR PROGRAM STARTED: 1907

PURPOSE:
To nurture the arts by offering creative individuals of the highest talent an inspiring environment in which they can produce enduring works of the imagination.

LEGAL BASIS:
Nonprofit corporation, certified by IRS as falling under Code Section 509(a)(2).

ELIGIBILITY:
Talent is the sole criterion for acceptance. Established artists as well as emerging artists of promising talent are encouraged to apply.

FINANCIAL DATA:
No residency fees. Fellowships cover costs of living accommodations, all meals, and use of an individual studio building. Travel reimbursement and stipends are available for artists who demonstrate need.

Amount of support per award: Stipends and travel grants up to $2,000.

Total amount of support: $2,600,000.

NUMBER OF APPLICANTS MOST RECENT YEAR: 2,534.

NUMBER OF AWARDS: Approximately 250 artists-in-residence.

APPLICATION INFORMATION:
Application forms are available on the web site. There is a $30 application fee. Work samples must be submitted digitally with the application. Read guidelines before applying.

Duration: Residence periods are from two weeks to two months. No more than one admission per 12-month period.

Deadline: January 15, April 15 and September 15.

PUBLICATIONS:
Application guidelines.

OFFICERS AND STAFF:
Michael Chabon, Chairman, Board of Directors
Susan Davenport Austin, President
Cheryl A. Young, Executive Director

ADDRESS INQUIRIES TO:
Courtney Bethel, Admissions Director
(See address above.)

MAINE ARTS COMMISSION   [469]
193 State Street
25 State House Station
Augusta, ME 04333-0025
(207) 287-2724
(207) 287-2750
Fax: (207) 287-2725
TTY: (877) 887-3878

E-MAIL ADDRESS:
kathy.shaw@maine.gov

WEB SITE ADDRESS:
www.mainearts.com

FOUNDED: 1966

AREAS OF INTEREST:
Arts.

CONSULTING OR VOLUNTEER SERVICES:
Opportunities for artists and arts organization.

NAME(S) OF PROGRAMS:
• **Arts and Humanities Grants**
• **Arts Learning**
• **CCED Grant**
• **Individual Artist Fellowship**
• **Jane Morrison Film Fund**
• **Partnership Grant**
• **Project Grant for Artists**
• **Project Grant for Organizations**
• **Traditional Arts Apprenticeship**
• **Traditional Arts Fellowship**

TYPE:
Fellowships; Project/program grants; Residencies.

YEAR PROGRAM STARTED: 1966

PURPOSE:
To encourage and stimulate public interest and participation in the cultural heritage and cultural programs of our state; to expand the state's cultural resources; to encourage and assist freedom of artistic expression for the well-being of the arts; to meet the needs and aspirations of persons in all parts of the state.

LEGAL BASIS:
Government agency.

ELIGIBILITY:
Applicants must be nonprofit Maine arts organizations, individual artists, schools and/or certain units of city/state or tribal government.

GEOGRAPHIC RESTRICTIONS:
Maine.

FINANCIAL DATA:
Amount of support per award: Generally $1,500 to $50,000.
Total amount of support: $508,965 for the year 2012.
Matching fund requirements: 1:1, cash or in-kind for most grants. No matching requirement for grants to individual artists.

COOPERATIVE FUNDING PROGRAMS: Maine Community Foundation; Maine Humanities Council.

NUMBER OF APPLICANTS MOST RECENT YEAR: 607.

NUMBER OF AWARDS: 132.

APPLICATION INFORMATION:
Applicant must speak with a staff member about the project before submitting an application. Failure to do so will disqualify the applicant.

Application forms must be submitted electronically through e-grants program.
Duration: Varies from 30 days to a full fiscal year period.
Deadline: Varies for all programs.

PUBLICATIONS:
Maine Arts Magazine; various program brochures.

IRS IDENTIFICATION NUMBER: 01-6000001

COMMISSION MEMBERS:
Charles Stanhope, Chairperson
Owen Smith, Vice Chairperson

ADDRESS INQUIRIES TO:
Kathy Ann Shaw
Senior Grants Associate
(See address above.)

ROBERT MAPPLETHORPE FOUNDATION, INC.   [470]
477 Madison Avenue, 15th Floor
New York, NY 10022-5835
(212) 755-3025
Fax: (212) 941-4764

E-MAIL ADDRESS:
joree@mapplethorpe.org

WEB SITE ADDRESS:
www.mapplethorpe.org

FOUNDED: 1988

AREAS OF INTEREST:
Photography as an art form; scientific study of AIDS and AIDS-related research in order to help find a cure.

NAME(S) OF PROGRAMS:
• **Photography Program**

TYPE:
Project/program grants. Funds medical research in the fight against AIDS and HIV infection and supports the promotion of photography as a fine art, embracing exhibitions, acquisitions, and publications.

YEAR PROGRAM STARTED: 1988

ELIGIBILITY:
The Foundation will not provide grants or scholarships to individual photographers. The Foundation will supply museums and other public institutions by assisting in the creation or expansion of photographic departments.

GEOGRAPHIC RESTRICTIONS:
United States.

FINANCIAL DATA:
Amount of support per award: Varies.
Total amount of support: Varies.

APPLICATION INFORMATION:
There is no formal application form.
Duration: Varies.
Deadline: Proposals are accepted on a continuing basis.

ADDRESS INQUIRIES TO:
Joree Adilman, Foundation Manager
(See address above.)

MARYLAND STATE ARTS COUNCIL   [471]
175 West Ostend Street
Suite E
Baltimore, MD 21230
(410) 767-6555
Fax: (410) 333-1062
TDD/TTY: (410) 333-4519

E-MAIL ADDRESS:
msac@msac.org

WEB SITE ADDRESS:
www.msac.org

FOUNDED: 1967

AREAS OF INTEREST:
Arts.

NAME(S) OF PROGRAMS:
• **Artists in Education**
• **Arts and Entertainment Districts Program**
• **Arts in Communities**
• **Community Arts Development**
• **Grants for Organizations**
• **Individual Artist Awards**
• **Maryland Folklife Program**
• **Public Art Program**

TYPE:
Awards/prizes; Block grants; Challenge/matching grants; General operating grants; Project/program grants; Residencies; Technical assistance. Arts program, arts project grants. Individual artist awards. The Council awards grants to county arts councils in Maryland through its Community Arts Development program.

The Maryland Folklife program is dedicated to the identification, documentation and presentation of Maryland traditional artists to general audiences through public life and educational activities.

The Artists in Education program is designed to increase access to a range of artistic disciplines and to assist schools in integrating the arts into the curriculum. Projects vary in length from one-day visits to four-week residencies.

The Arts in Communities program awards grants for up to $1,000 for arts activities undertaken by organizations not currently receiving MSAC funding.

The Grants for Organizations Program provides support to those who produce or present the arts to the public.

YEAR PROGRAM STARTED: 1967

PURPOSE:
To make the arts more widely available to all Maryland residents, to strengthen the state's cultural institutions and to encourage the development of resident artistic activity throughout the state.

LEGAL BASIS:
Article 41 of the Annotated Code of Maryland as amended, Sections 387 to 395, inclusive.

ELIGIBILITY:
Applying organizations must be not-for-profit, tax-exempt and incorporated in the state of Maryland. Individuals must be 18 years of age or older and a Maryland resident.

Funding is not provided for acquisition of capital assets, capital improvements, depreciation, deficits, capital debt reduction and contributions to endowments.

GEOGRAPHIC RESTRICTIONS:
Maryland.

FINANCIAL DATA:
Amount of support per award: Varies.
Total amount of support: Varies.
Matching fund requirements: 1:1

APPLICATION INFORMATION:
Guidelines and grant application forms may
be acquired by writing to the Council office.
Duration: Up to one year. No grants are
automatically renewable.

EXECUTIVE DIRECTOR:
Theresa Colvin

ADDRESS INQUIRIES TO:
Theresa Colvin, Executive Director
(See address above.)

MASSACHUSETTS CULTURAL
COUNCIL   [472]
10 St. James Avenue
3rd Floor
Boston, MA 02116-3803
(617) 727-3668
(800) 232-0960 (MA only)
Fax: (617) 727-0044
TTY: (617) 338-9153

E-MAIL ADDRESS:
mcc@art.state.ma.us

WEB SITE ADDRESS:
www.massculturalcouncil.org

FOUNDED: 1966

AREAS OF INTEREST:
The arts, humanities and interpretive sciences
in Massachusetts.

NAME(S) OF PROGRAMS:
- **John and Abigail Adams Arts Program
  for Cultural Economic Development**
- **Artist Fellowships**
- **The Big Yellow School Bus**
- **Cultural Investment Portfolio**
- **Local Cultural Council Program**
- **Massachusetts Cultural Facilities Fund**
- **STARS Residencies**
- **Traditional Arts Apprenticeship**
- **YouthReach Initiative**

TYPE:
Conferences/seminars; Fellowships; Formula
grants; General operating grants;
Project/program grants; Technical assistance.

LEGAL BASIS:
State agency.

ELIGIBILITY:
Applicants need to be either a nonprofit
organization in Massachusetts or a legal
resident of the state. Additional requirements
vary per program.

GEOGRAPHIC RESTRICTIONS:
Massachusetts.

FINANCIAL DATA:
Amount of support per award: Varies
according to program.

NUMBER OF APPLICANTS MOST RECENT YEAR:
Approximately 10,500.

NUMBER OF AWARDS: Approximately 5,000.

APPLICATION INFORMATION:
Contact the Council.
Duration: One or three years, depending on
program.
Deadline: Varies by program.

PUBLICATIONS:
Application guidelines.

STAFF:
Anita Walker, Executive Director
David Slatery, Deputy Director

BOARD:
Ira Lapidus, Chairperson
Barbara W. Grossman, Vice Chairperson

THE METROPOLITAN MUSEUM
OF ART   [473]
1000 Fifth Avenue
New York, NY 10028-0198
(212) 650-2763
Fax: (212) 396-5168

E-MAIL ADDRESS:
education.grants@metmuseum.org

WEB SITE ADDRESS:
www.metmuseum.org

FOUNDED: 1870

AREAS OF INTEREST:
Study or research in American visual and
decorative arts.

NAME(S) OF PROGRAMS:
- **The Douglass Foundation Fellowship in
  American Art**

TYPE:
Fellowships. Fellowship is awarded in honor
of John K. Howat. It is given to a promising
young scholar for one year's study or
research in the American Wing (in either the
Department of American Paintings and
Sculpture or the Department of American
Decorative Arts) on an aspect of the
Museum's collection.

PURPOSE:
To promote study and research in American
visual and decorative arts.

ELIGIBILITY:
Applicants should have been enrolled for at
least one year in an advanced degree
program in the field of American art or
culture.

FINANCIAL DATA:
Amount of support per award: $32,000, plus
up to $6,000 for travel and miscellaneous
expenses.
Total amount of support: Varies.

NUMBER OF AWARDS: 1.

APPLICATION INFORMATION:
Current application may be obtained from the
Museum's web site.
Duration: One year.
Deadline: First Friday in November.

ADDRESS INQUIRIES TO:
Marcie Karp, Managing Museum Educator
Academic Programs, Education Department
(See address above.)

MICHIGAN COUNCIL FOR
ARTS AND CULTURAL
AFFAIRS   [474]
300 North Washington Square
Lansing, MI 48913
(517) 241-4011
(888) 522-0103
Fax: (517) 241-3979

E-MAIL ADDRESS:
braceyj@michigan.org

WEB SITE ADDRESS:
www.michiganadvantage.org/arts

FOUNDED: 1966

AREAS OF INTEREST:
Arts.

CONSULTING OR VOLUNTEER SERVICES:
Consulting services in the arts, management,
development, consultations and workshops,
conferences, communications, media
development and artist services.

NAME(S) OF PROGRAMS:
- **Program for Operational and Projects
  Support**
- **School Bus Grants**

TYPE:
General operating grants; Project/program
grants. Grants and services to organizations
for the production, development, promotion
and support of the arts in Michigan.

School Bus Grants assist in covering school
bus transportation costs to visit museums,
musical or theatrical performances, zoos,
science centers, etc.

PURPOSE:
To develop and encourage programs and
projects that make music, painting, literature,
cinema, dance, sculpture, crafts, architecture
and all the arts available to the people of
Michigan, regardless of their age, location,
background or economic status; to support
activities of Michigan artists.

LEGAL BASIS:
State agency.

ELIGIBILITY:
Generally, grants will be awarded only for
activities within the state of Michigan. For
most programs, applicants should be
Michigan-based nonprofit tax-exempt
organizations residing in Michigan. The
Council ordinarily does not finance an
existing deficit, capital improvements,
curriculum-oriented activities or permanent
equipment.

GEOGRAPHIC RESTRICTIONS:
Michigan.

FINANCIAL DATA:
Amount of support per award: Varies.
Total amount of support: $2,300,000 for the
year 2013.
Matching fund requirements: Varies with
program.

COOPERATIVE FUNDING PROGRAMS:
Re-Granting and Partnership programs.

APPLICATION INFORMATION:
Guidelines and application forms for each
program are revised in the early fall each
year and are available upon request.
Duration: One year, October 1 through
September 30.

PUBLICATIONS:
Program guidelines; factsheet.

IRS IDENTIFICATION NUMBER: 38-6000134

OFFICERS:
Andrew Buchholz, Chairman
John Bracey, Executive Director

ADDRESS INQUIRIES TO:
John Bracey, Executive Director
(See address above.)

MID-AMERICA ARTS
ALLIANCE   [475]
2018 Baltimore Avenue
Kansas City, MO 64108
(816) 421-1388
Fax: (816) 421-3918

E-MAIL ADDRESS:
christine@maaa.org

WEB SITE ADDRESS:
www.maaa.org

FOUNDED: 1972

AREAS OF INTEREST:
Performing and visual arts (traveling exhibits) throughout the U.S.

NAME(S) OF PROGRAMS:
- **Regional Touring Program**
- **Touring Exhibits through ExhibitsUSA**

TYPE:
Project/program grants; Technical assistance. Support and project/program grants for community arts projects and touring performing arts.

YEAR PROGRAM STARTED: 1973

PURPOSE:
To increase the access to high-quality arts programs and to sponsor competency.

LEGAL BASIS:
Missouri corporation, 501(c)(3).

ELIGIBILITY:
Nonprofit organizations presenting M-AAA touring programs in Arkansas, Kansas, Missouri, Nebraska, Oklahoma and Texas may apply. Visual arts exhibitors throughout the country may request traveling exhibits.

GEOGRAPHIC RESTRICTIONS:
Arkansas, Kansas, Missouri, Nebraska, Oklahoma and Texas.

FINANCIAL DATA:
Amount of support per award: $500 to $15,000.
Total amount of support: Varies.
Matching fund requirements: Most grants require a dollar-for-dollar match.

COOPERATIVE FUNDING PROGRAMS: State arts agencies of Arkansas, Kansas, Missouri, Nebraska, Oklahoma, Texas, corporations and foundations, and the National Endowment for the Arts.

NUMBER OF APPLICANTS MOST RECENT YEAR: 129.

NUMBER OF AWARDS: 57.

APPLICATION INFORMATION:
Application information is available on the web site.

PUBLICATIONS:
Annual report; exhibit catalogs.

IRS IDENTIFICATION NUMBER: 23-7303693

OFFICERS:
Mary Kennedy, Executive Director

ADDRESS INQUIRIES TO:
Linda Gramse, Executive Assistant
(See address above.)

MID ATLANTIC ARTS FOUNDATION [476]
201 North Charles Street
Suite 401
Baltimore, MD 21201
(410) 539-6656 ext. 104
Fax: (410) 837-5517

E-MAIL ADDRESS:
maaf@midatlanticarts.org

WEB SITE ADDRESS:
www.midatlanticarts.org

FOUNDED: 1979

AREAS OF INTEREST:
Regional arts activities crossing state lines in Delaware, District of Columbia, Maryland, New Jersey, New York, Pennsylvania, Virginia, West Virginia and the U.S. Virgin Islands; national and international funding through Southern Exposure and USArtists International.

NAME(S) OF PROGRAMS:
- **ArtsConnect**
- **French-American Jazz Exchange**
- **Jazz Touring Network**
- **Living Legacy Jazz Award**
- **Mid Atlantic Creative Fellowships**
- **Mid Atlantic Folk Arts Outreach Program**
- **Mid Atlantic Tours**
- **On Screen/In Person**
- **Pennsylvania Performing Arts on Tour**
- **Southern Exposure**
- **Special Presenter Initiatives**
- **USArtists International**

TYPE:
Fellowships; Project/program grants; Residencies; Technical assistance.

YEAR PROGRAM STARTED: 1979

PURPOSE:
To promote the sharing of arts resources among the Foundation's partner states, regionally, nationally and internationally.

LEGAL BASIS:
Private, not-for-profit organization.

ELIGIBILITY:
Individuals and organizations must be based in the region for most programs. Other requirements vary according to the specific program.

ArtsConnect provides artist fee support to not-for-profit presenting networks comprised of at least three Mid Atlantic-based organizations.

French-American Jazz Exchange supports projects between French and American jazz artists.

Mid Atlantic Creative Fellowships places an artist from each member state in residence at selected organizations. A different artistic discipline is selected each year for foundation support.

Mid Atlantic Tours provide fee support for foundation-initiated performing arts tours.

On Screen/In Person provides fee subsidy to film series host sites.

Southern Exposure provides support to U.S. presenters working in consortia to present artists from Latin America.

USArtists International supports U.S. music, dance, and theatre artists at international festivals.

GEOGRAPHIC RESTRICTIONS:
Delaware, District of Columbia, Maryland, New Jersey, New York, Ohio, Pennsylvania, Virginia, West Virginia and the U.S. Virgin Islands for all programs except Southern Exposure and USArtists International.

FINANCIAL DATA:
Amount of support per award: $1,000 to $25,000.
Matching fund requirements: Varies according to program.

NUMBER OF APPLICANTS MOST RECENT YEAR: More than 1,000.

NUMBER OF AWARDS: More than 500.

APPLICATION INFORMATION:
Guidelines are available on the web site. The Foundation utilizes an electronic application process.
Duration: Varies.
Deadline: Varies.

PUBLICATIONS:
Guidelines; monthly e-mail newsletter; biennial report.

IRS IDENTIFICATION NUMBER: 52-1169382

STAFF:
Alan W. Cooper, Executive Director

THE MILLAY COLONY FOR THE ARTS, INC. [477]
454 East Hill Road
Austerlitz, NY 12017-0003
(518) 392-3103
Fax: (518) 392-4144 (call first)

E-MAIL ADDRESS:
apply@millaycolony.org

WEB SITE ADDRESS:
www.millaycolony.org

FOUNDED: 1973

AREAS OF INTEREST:
Writing, composing, music and visual arts.

TYPE:
Residencies. The Millay Colony offers one-month residencies from the months of April through November for visual artists, writers and composers in order to immerse themselves in creative work. The Colony accommodates a multidisciplinary group of six to seven artists each month.

YEAR PROGRAM STARTED: 1974

PURPOSE:
To provide space, studio and time for writers and composers to immerse themselves in their work.

ELIGIBILITY:
Residents are selected after undergoing an application and juried process. Juries make selections anonymously.

FINANCIAL DATA:
No cash grant is made, nor is any residency fee required. Meals are provided.

NUMBER OF APPLICANTS MOST RECENT YEAR: 1,000 for the year 2013.

NUMBER OF AWARDS: 52 for the year 2013.

APPLICATION INFORMATION:
Online application process is available. An application form may also be requested by sending a self-addressed, stamped envelope to the address above.

An application fee of $35 is required.
Duration: Residencies are for one month.
Deadline: October 1 for the following April through November.

DIRECTORS:
Caroline Crumpacker, Executive Director

ADDRESS INQUIRIES TO:
Calliope Nicholas, Residency Director
(See address above.)

JOAN MITCHELL FOUNDATION [478]
545 West 25th Street, 15th Floor
New York, NY 10001
(212) 524-0100
Fax: (212) 524-0101

E-MAIL ADDRESS:
info@joanmitchellfoundation.org

WEB SITE ADDRESS:
www.joanmitchellfoundation.org

AREAS OF INTEREST:
Art: painting and sculpture.

NAME(S) OF PROGRAMS:
- MFA Grant Program
- Painters and Sculptors Grant Program

TYPE:
Emerging grants. Stipends. Awarded in recognition of artistic merit and financial need, to further artistic careers.

PURPOSE:
To demonstrate that painting and sculpture are significant cultural necessities; to encourage the ambitions of developing artists.

ELIGIBILITY:
By nomination only.

GEOGRAPHIC RESTRICTIONS:
United States.

FINANCIAL DATA:
Amount of support per award: MFA Grants: $15,000; Painters and Sculptors Grants: $25,000.

Total amount of support: $850,000.

NUMBER OF AWARDS: MFA Grants: 15; Painters and Sculptors Grants: 25.

APPLICATION INFORMATION:
Candidates are nominated and contacted by the Foundation.

Duration: One-time award.

ADDRESS INQUIRIES TO:
Allison Hawkins, Grants Program Director
(See address above.)

THE MOODY FOUNDATION

2302 Post Office Street, Suite 704
Galveston, TX 77550
(409) 797-1525
Fax: (409) 763-5564

E-MAIL ADDRESS:
amatthews@moodyf.org

WEB SITE ADDRESS:
www.moodyf.org

TYPE:
Capital grants; Challenge/matching grants; Endowments; Grants-in-aid; Project/program grants; Research grants; Scholarships. Capital campaigns; Equipment; Matching funds; Building/renovation; Program development and research.

See entry 239 for full listing.

MARIETTA MCNEILL MORGAN AND SAMUEL TATE MORGAN, JR. FOUNDATION

Bank of America
Philanthropic Management VA2-300-12-99
1111 East Main Street, 12th Floor
P.O. Box 26688
Richmond, VA 23261-6688
(804) 887-8763
Fax: (804) 887-8854

TYPE:
Capital grants; Challenge/matching grants. Grants for capital only. No grants to individuals, for endowment funds or operating funds.

See entry 1496 for full listing.

WILLIAM MORRIS SOCIETY IN THE U.S.   [479]

P.O. Box 53263
Washington, DC 20009

E-MAIL ADDRESS:
us@morrissociety.org
ecmill@ucdavis.edu

WEB SITE ADDRESS:
www.morrissociety.org

FOUNDED: 1957

AREAS OF INTEREST:
The life and work of William Morris as a craftsman, designer and writer.

NAME(S) OF PROGRAMS:
- Joseph R. Dunlap Memorial Fellowship
- William Morris Society Award

TYPE:
Fellowships; Research grants; Scholarships; Travel grants; Visiting scholars; Research contracts. Supports scholarly, creative, and translation projects about William Morris and his designs, writings and other work.

YEAR PROGRAM STARTED: 1995

PURPOSE:
To support research projects that deal with any subject relating to William Morris.

LEGAL BASIS:
Society.

ELIGIBILITY:
Projects may deal with any subject - biographical, literary, historical, social, artistic, political, typographical - relating to Morris. They may be scholarly or creative, and may include translations or the preparation of educational materials. Applicants for all awards may be from any country. Applications are particularly encouraged from younger members of the Society and from those at the beginning of their careers. Recipients need not have an academic or institutional appointment and the Ph.D. is not required.

FINANCIAL DATA:
Amount of support per award: Up to $1,000.

APPLICATION INFORMATION:
Applicants are asked to submit a resume and a two-page description of their projects, including a timeline and an indication of where the results might be published. At least one recommendation should be sent separately. Submissions will not be accepted via e-mail.

For translation submissions, send one copy of the translation (of the published version, if relevant), with a letter of reference from someone acquainted with both languages assessing the quality of the translation. Translations should have been completed within the past five years.

For teaching materials, no letters of recommendation are needed, but enclose a cover letter describing the ways in which the materials might be (or already have been) used in learning situations.

Duration: One year.

Deadline: December 15. Announcement by January 15.

PUBLICATIONS:
Announcement.

ADDRESS INQUIRIES TO:
Linda K. Hughes, Vice President
(See address above.)

NATIONAL ENDOWMENT FOR THE ARTS   [480]

1100 Pennsylvania Avenue, N.W.
Washington, DC 20506
(202) 682-5400

E-MAIL ADDRESS:
webmgr@arts.gov

WEB SITE ADDRESS:
www.arts.gov

FOUNDED: 1965

AREAS OF INTEREST:
National artistic accomplishments of the past, present and future.

TYPE:
Fellowships; Project/program grants. The Arts Endowment offers assistance for a full range of arts disciplines, and types and sizes of organizations involved in the arts.

YEAR PROGRAM STARTED: 1966

PURPOSE:
To support artists, art forms, art events, art education, and to conserve highly significant works of art.

LEGAL BASIS:
The National Foundation on the Arts and Humanities Act of 1965, Public Law 89-209, as amended.

ELIGIBILITY:
Individuals who apply must be published (not self-published) authors or poets.

Grants are awarded only for specific projects. A project may consist of one or more specific events or activities. All phases of a project, from planning to implementation, are eligible. A project does not have to be new; existing projects are competitive. An organization must be nonprofit, 501(c)(3) tax-exempt, have a three-year history of programming (except for applicants for folk and traditional art projects), and have staff dedicated specifically to the project. The endowment welcomes projects that assist and involve individual artists or have national, regional or fieldwide impact or availability or that provide an unusual or especially valuable contribution because of geographic location.

Assistance is not available for elementary or secondary schools directly, avocational or student groups, new organizations, or for the purpose of construction, purchase or renovation of facilities. The endowment does not provide seasonal or general operating support.

GEOGRAPHIC RESTRICTIONS:
United States, American Samoa, Guam, the Northern Marianas, Puerto Rico or the U.S. Virgin Islands.

FINANCIAL DATA:
Amount of support per award: Varies.

Total amount of support: Varies.

Matching fund requirements: Grantee organizations must match with nonfederal funds on at least a one-to-one basis.

APPLICATION INFORMATION:
Each organization may apply on its own behalf only once, and under only one of the goals, each year. In addition to its own application, an organization may be part of a consortium application or as an independent component of a parent organization such as a

university or cultural complex. Applications will be reviewed on the basis of artistic excellence and artistic merit.

Duration: One year.

PUBLICATIONS:
The Grants to Organizations Guidelines.

ADDRESS INQUIRIES TO:
Nicki Jacobs, Grants Director
Tel: (202) 682-5546

NATIONAL FOUNDATION FOR ADVANCEMENT IN THE ARTS [481]

2100 Biscayne Boulevard
Miami, FL 33137
(305) 377-1140
(800) 970-2787
Fax: (305) 377-1149

E-MAIL ADDRESS:
dwebb@youngarts.org

WEB SITE ADDRESS:
www.youngarts.org

FOUNDED: 1981

AREAS OF INTEREST:
To identify emerging artists and assist them at critical junctures in their educational and professional development; to raise the appreciation for, and support of, the arts in American society.

CONSULTING OR VOLUNTEER SERVICES:
Offers the names of registrants and awardees of its YoungArts® program nationally to colleges, universities and performing arts institutions which subscribe to the Foundation's Scholarship List Service (SLS).

NAME(S) OF PROGRAMS:
- **Alumni Grant**
- **YoungArts Miami**
- **YoungArts New York**
- **YoungArts Week**

TYPE:
Awards/prizes; Conferences/seminars; Endowments; Fellowships; Internships; Project/program grants; Scholarships. Cash grants and scholarship opportunities to young artists.

YEAR PROGRAM STARTED: 1981

PURPOSE:
To recognize and support aspiring artists in their formative years and provide career entry opportunities.

LEGAL BASIS:
Private nonprofit, 501(c)(3), operating national foundation.

ELIGIBILITY:
YoungArts is open to all high school seniors or, if student has already graduated from high school, must be 17 or 18 years old on December 1, 2014 to participate in YoungArts 2015. Participants must be U.S. citizens or permanent residents.

NFAA does not make grants in response to unsolicited requests from individuals or organizations, but welcomes proposals for creation of formal or pilot programs in areas of its interest.

NFAA offers a conference for high school arts educators on preparing students for college auditions.

20 U.S. Presidential Scholars in the Arts are selected exclusively from YoungArts participants by the White House Commission on Presidential Scholars.

GEOGRAPHIC RESTRICTIONS:
United States.

FINANCIAL DATA:
Up to 150 national finalists attend YoungArts Week in Miami, all expenses paid.

Amount of support per award: YoungArts Gold Awards: $10,000 each; YoungArts Silver Awards: $5,000; YoungArts Award: Level I, $3,000; Level II, $1,500; Level III, $1,000; Level IV, $500; Level V, $250; Honorable Mention, $250.

Total amount of support: Over $525,000 annually.

COOPERATIVE FUNDING PROGRAMS: NFAA works in partnership with other arts organizations to offer workshops, internships and residencies to students in advanced stages of their arts training.

NUMBER OF APPLICANTS MOST RECENT YEAR:
YoungArts: 5,000 for the 2013 program.

NUMBER OF AWARDS: Approximately 800 cash awards per year.

APPLICATION INFORMATION:
There is a $35 registration fee per category. There is a $10 discount for registering early before June 30.

Deadline: YoungArts: Early registration June 30, regular registration through October 14. Audition/portfolio materials due late October.

IRS IDENTIFICATION NUMBER: 59-2141837

ADDRESS INQUIRIES TO:
Dale C. Webb
Vice President of Development
Tel: (305) 377-1140 ext. 1801
(See e-mail address above.)

NEBRASKA ARTS COUNCIL [482]

1004 Farnam Street, Lower Level
Omaha, NE 68102
(402) 595-2122
Fax: (402) 595-2334

E-MAIL ADDRESS:
nac.grants@nebraska.gov

WEB SITE ADDRESS:
www.nebraskaartscouncil.org

FOUNDED: 1965

AREAS OF INTEREST:
Architecture, visual arts, artists, art organizations, literature, museums and libraries, performing arts, aged, children and youth, community and rural development and services and education.

CONSULTING OR VOLUNTEER SERVICES:
Technical (staff) services for requesting organizations who desire assistance in arts programming efforts. Developmental aspects of assistance to arts organizations and/or individuals is predominant.

NAME(S) OF PROGRAMS:
- **Artists-in-Schools/Communities Grants**
- **Arts Learning Projects**
- **Arts Project Grants**
- **Basic Support Grants**
- **Individual Artist Fellowships**
- **Mini Grants**
- **Nebraska Touring Program**
- **School Bus for the Arts Grants**

TYPE:
Fellowships; General operating grants; Matching gifts; Project/program grants.

Grants to encourage growth and activity in the arts for the citizens of the state of Nebraska.

YEAR PROGRAM STARTED: 1965

PURPOSE:
To stimulate and encourage, throughout the state, the study and presentation of the visual and performing arts and public interest and participation therein; to promote the arts, cultivate resources and support excellence in artistic endeavors for all Nebraskans.

LEGAL BASIS:
Government agency under state legislation. Agency also accepts federal funds (from the National Endowment for the Arts) and private funds for purposes of its intent.

ELIGIBILITY:
Nonprofit, incorporated status is required of applying organizations. Applicant organizations must have federal tax-exempt status or proof of application for that status at the time of application. Individuals not connected with nonprofit organizations are eligible only for Individual Artist Fellowships and must be Nebraska residents. The NAC does not provide funding for capital expenditures or existing deficits.

GEOGRAPHIC RESTRICTIONS:
Nebraska.

FINANCIAL DATA:
Amount of support per award: Up to $7,500.

Total amount of support: $1,200,000.

Matching fund requirements: 1:1, at least half of the applicant match must be in cash, while the other may be in-kind.

COOPERATIVE FUNDING PROGRAMS: Support is provided for organizations desiring programming in the Mid-America Arts Alliance (six-state consortium consisting of Arkansas, Kansas, Missouri, Nebraska, Oklahoma and Texas).

APPLICATION INFORMATION:
Application form is available on the web site.

Duration: One year.

Deadline: March 1 and October 1.

PUBLICATIONS:
Guide to Programs and Services; Artist Directory.

STAFF:
Michael Markey, Grants Manager

ADDRESS INQUIRIES TO:
See e-mail address above.

*SPECIAL STIPULATIONS:
Please contact NAC prior to applying for the first time.

NEVADA ARTS COUNCIL [483]

716 North Carson Street
Suite A
Carson City, NV 89701
(775) 687-6680
Fax: (775) 687-6688

E-MAIL ADDRESS:
sboskoff@nevadaculture.org

WEB SITE ADDRESS:
nac.nevadaculture.org

FOUNDED: 1967

AREAS OF INTEREST:
Visual, literary, performing, design and folk arts, as well as community development.

CONSULTING OR VOLUNTEER SERVICES:
Consulting on arts management, resources in the arts, grants workshops, community arts and professional arts needs.

NAME(S) OF PROGRAMS:
- **Artist Services Program**
- **Arts Learning Program**
- **Community Arts Development**
- **Folklife Program**
- **Governor's Arts Awards**
- **Grants Program**

TYPE:
Awards/prizes; Challenge/matching grants; Conferences/seminars; Development grants; Fellowships; General operating grants; Project/program grants; Residencies; Technical assistance; Training grants; Work-study programs. Grants to Nevada nonprofit groups, individual artists, public institutions and for arts in education.

YEAR PROGRAM STARTED: 1967

PURPOSE:
To enrich the cultural life of the state through leadership that preserves, supports, strengthens and makes accessible excellence in the arts to all Nevadans.

LEGAL BASIS:
Government agency.

ELIGIBILITY:
Nevada nonprofit organizations with IRS tax-exempt status and individual artists with one-year minimum residency may apply for grants. Artists may also apply for artist residencies. Fellowships require residency.

GEOGRAPHIC RESTRICTIONS:
Nevada.

FINANCIAL DATA:
Amount of support per award: $250 to $10,000.
Matching fund requirements: Usually 1:1. Challenge grants 3:1.

APPLICATION INFORMATION:
Interested individuals or groups should check with the Council office for the latest information on grants policies and other programs. Applications are also available on the web site.
Duration: Length of project can usually be no longer than one fiscal year, July 1 to June 30, except for challenge grants and quarterly grants.
Deadline: Call for specific dates.

IRS IDENTIFICATION NUMBER: 88-6000022

OFFICERS:
Tim Jones, Chairperson
Susan Boskoff, Executive Director
Linda Ficklin, Administrative Services Officer

ADDRESS INQUIRIES TO:
Susan Boskoff, Executive Director
(See address above.)

NEW ENGLAND FOUNDATION FOR THE ARTS   [484]
145 Tremont Street
Seventh Floor
Boston, MA 02111-1254
(617) 951-0010
Fax: (617) 951-0016

E-MAIL ADDRESS:
info@nefa.org

WEB SITE ADDRESS:
www.nefa.org

FOUNDED: 1975

AREAS OF INTEREST:
Performing artists, ensembles, literary artists, composers, public art and Native American art.

NAME(S) OF PROGRAMS:
- **Center Stage**
- **Expeditions**
- **Fund for the Arts**
- **National Dance Project**
- **National Theater Pilot**
- **New England States Touring Program**
- **Presenter Travel Fund**

TYPE:
Awards/prizes; Development grants; Project/program grants; Travel grants. Production and touring grants.

PURPOSE:
To facilitate the movement of people, ideas and resources in the arts within New England and beyond; to make vital connections between artists and audiences; to build the strength, knowledge and leadership of the region's creative sector.

LEGAL BASIS:
Public/private partnership.

FINANCIAL DATA:
Amount of support per award: Varies by program.
Total amount of support: Varies.

NUMBER OF AWARDS: 450.

APPLICATION INFORMATION:
Contact the Foundation.
Duration: Varies.
Deadline: Varies.

NEW HAMPSHIRE STATE COUNCIL ON THE ARTS   [485]
19 Pillsbury Street
Concord, NH 03301
(603) 271-2789
Fax: (603) 271-3584

E-MAIL ADDRESS:
cassandra.mason@dcr.nh.gov

WEB SITE ADDRESS:
www.nh.gov/nharts

FOUNDED: 1965

AREAS OF INTEREST:
The arts in New Hampshire.

CONSULTING OR VOLUNTEER SERVICES:
Artists as Entrepreneurs Workshops, Fall Arts in Education Partnership Conference and Grants Information Services Workshops.

NAME(S) OF PROGRAMS:
- **Apprenticeships**
- **Artist Entrepreneurial Workshops**
- **Artist in Residence**
- **Artist Services**
- **Arts in Education**
- **Arts in Health Care Project Grants**
- **Cultural Conservation**
- **General Project Grants**
- **Operating Grants**
- **Percent for Art**
- **Public Value Partnerships**
- **Traditional Arts Apprenticeship**
- **Youth Arts Project Grants**

TYPE:
Awards/prizes; Challenge/matching grants; Conferences/seminars; Development grants; Fellowships; General operating grants; Project/program grants; Residencies;

Technical assistance. Grant assistance to New Hampshire organizations and individual artists.

YEAR PROGRAM STARTED: 1965

PURPOSE:
To support and promote excellence, education and community investment in the arts for people in New Hampshire.

LEGAL BASIS:
Agency of the state of New Hampshire.

ELIGIBILITY:
Organizations must be incorporated in New Hampshire. Individual artists must reside in New Hampshire for at least one year.

GEOGRAPHIC RESTRICTIONS:
New Hampshire.

FINANCIAL DATA:
Amount of support per award: $250 to $20,000.
Total amount of support: $695,421 for the year 2011.
Matching fund requirements: Varies.

NUMBER OF APPLICANTS MOST RECENT YEAR: 241 for the year 2011.

NUMBER OF AWARDS: 157 for the year 2011.

APPLICATION INFORMATION:
A completed application form is required for all grants. Support materials are required from all applicants; work sample required from individual artists. IRS tax-exempt 501(c)(3) letter is required from nonprofit organizations.
Deadline: Varies.

PUBLICATIONS:
E-News; *E-Opps*.

STAFF:
Lynn Graton, Acting Director

*SPECIAL STIPULATIONS:
Funding is restricted to New Hampshire artists, organizations, schools, libraries, branches of government and communities.

NEW JERSEY STATE COUNCIL ON THE ARTS   [486]
225 West State Street, 4th Floor
Trenton, NJ 08625
(609) 292-6130
Fax: (609) 989-1440

WEB SITE ADDRESS:
www.artscouncil.nj.gov

FOUNDED: 1966

AREAS OF INTEREST:
Dance, music, opera, musical theatre, theatre, visual arts, design arts, crafts, media arts, presenters, multi- and interdisciplinary, arts education, folk art, local arts, literary arts, stabilization and advancement.

NAME(S) OF PROGRAMS:
- **Arts Project Grants**
- **Folk Arts Apprenticeships**
- **General Operating Support Grants**
- **General Program Support Grants**
- **Long-Term Residencies**
- **Short-Term Residencies/Arts Education**
- **Special Project Grants**

TYPE:
Fellowships; General operating grants; Internships; Project/program grants; Residencies; Technical assistance. Apprenticeships; local arts grants. Fellowships and matching grants to provide money to New Jersey artists and

organizations. Local arts grants (for local arts) are available to designated county arts agencies only.

Arts Project Grants: awarded annually to New Jersey-based, nonprofit organizations and agencies to help support specific public arts events.

Folk Arts Apprenticeships: awarded to New Jersey residents to support an apprentice learning a traditional art form from a master in their shared community.

General Operating Support Grants: awarded every three years to New Jersey-based, nonprofit arts organizations to help underwrite the expense of their total operation including their expense of producing and presenting arts events.

General Program Support Grants: awarded every three years to other New Jersey-based, nonprofit organizations to help underwrite the expense of presenting major, ongoing arts programs.

Long-term Residencies: offered in several different arts disciplines and are applied for by the school or other sponsoring agency.

Short-term Residencies/Arts Education: offered in prose, poetry and playwriting with Council funds providing the artists' fees.

YEAR PROGRAM STARTED: 1966

PURPOSE:
To improve the quality of life of New Jersey, its people and communities by helping the arts to flourish.

LEGAL BASIS:
State governmental agency.

ELIGIBILITY:
The Council awards grants on a highly competitive basis, employing standardized criteria for eligibility and evaluation published in guidelines and convening panels of independent experts in the various fields of endeavor for objective feedback and recommendations. A New Jersey resident or a nonprofit organization incorporated in the State of New Jersey committed to professionalism in the arts may apply.

GEOGRAPHIC RESTRICTIONS:
New Jersey.

FINANCIAL DATA:
Amount of support per award: Varies.
Total amount of support: $15,000,000 for fiscal year 2013.
Matching fund requirements: Fellowships are non-matching. Matching grants to organizations must be on a basis of at least 1:1, 3:1 for operating and program support grants.

NUMBER OF APPLICANTS MOST RECENT YEAR:
Approximately 400 fellowship applications and 300 organization/project applications for fiscal year 2013.

APPLICATION INFORMATION:
Details available on the Council web site.
Duration: Annual.

STAFF:
Julie Ellen Prusinowski, Director of Programs and Services

ADDRESS INQUIRIES TO:
Julie Ellen Prusinowski, Director of Programs and Services
(See address above.)

NEW YORK FOUNDATION FOR THE ARTS   [487]
20 Jay Street, Suite 740
Brooklyn, NY 11201
(212) 366-6900
Fax: (212) 366-1778

E-MAIL ADDRESS:
dterry@nyfa.org

WEB SITE ADDRESS:
www.nyfa.org

FOUNDED: 1971

AREAS OF INTEREST:
The arts, with a primary focus on New York state.

NAME(S) OF PROGRAMS:
● **Artists' Fellowships**

TYPE:
Awards/prizes; Development grants; Fellowships; Grants-in-aid. Cash awards made to individual or pairs of originating artists living and working in the state of New York for use in career development. Funds are unrestricted.

YEAR PROGRAM STARTED: 1985

PURPOSE:
To provide the time and resources for the creative mind and the artistic spirit to think, work and prosper.

ELIGIBILITY:
Applicant must be 25 years of age or older and cannot be enrolled in a degree-granting program. Applicant must be a resident of New York state for the two years prior to the deadline.

GEOGRAPHIC RESTRICTIONS:
New York state.

FINANCIAL DATA:
Amount of support per award: $7,000 cash awards.
Total amount of support: Varies.

NUMBER OF APPLICANTS MOST RECENT YEAR:
Varies.

NUMBER OF AWARDS: Varies.

APPLICATION INFORMATION:
Contact the Foundation.
Deadline: Usually fall.

STAFF:
Michael Royce, Executive Director

NEW YORK STATE COUNCIL ON THE ARTS   [488]
300 Park Avenue South, 10th Floor
New York, NY 10010
(212) 459-8800
Fax: (212) 477-1471

E-MAIL ADDRESS:
public.affairs@arts.ny.gov

WEB SITE ADDRESS:
www.arts.ny.gov

FOUNDED: 1960

AREAS OF INTEREST:
Public support for the arts in New York state.

CONSULTING OR VOLUNTEER SERVICES:
Technical assistance is available for eligible nonprofit arts organizations.

TYPE:
Awards/prizes; Capital grants; Challenge/matching grants; Conferences/seminars; Development grants; General operating grants; Internships;

Residencies; Technical assistance. Grants are awarded to eligible New York state nonprofit organizations through 16 discipline-based funding programs: Architecture and Design; Facilities; Arts Education; Dance; Electronic Media and Film; Folk Arts; Individual Artists; Literature; Museum; Music; Presenting; Regional Economic Development; Special Arts Services; State and Local Partnerships; Theater; and Visual Arts. In addition, NYSCA support reaches an additional 1,500 community-based organizations each year in the form of regrants, which are administered by a statewide network of Local Arts Councils through NYSCA's Decentralization program.

YEAR PROGRAM STARTED: 1960

PURPOSE:
To ensure that the role of the arts in New York's communities will continue to grow and play a more significant part in the welfare and education of New York's citizens.

LEGAL BASIS:
State agency.

ELIGIBILITY:
Grants are awarded to nonprofit organizations incorporated in New York state, Indian tribes, and units of local government. Individuals and unincorporated groups may only apply through an eligible nonprofit organization.

GEOGRAPHIC RESTRICTIONS:
New York state.

FINANCIAL DATA:
Amount of support per award: Varies by program.
Matching fund requirements: Varies by program.

NUMBER OF AWARDS: Over 2,400 annually.

APPLICATION INFORMATION:
Applications and guidelines are available online. New applicants (except municipalities and Indian tribes) must submit proof of nonprofit status. Returning applicants who have applied in the past three years must certify that their nonprofit status remains valid.
Duration: One calendar year. Organizations may reapply each year.

PUBLICATIONS:
Program guidelines.

STAFF:
Aby Rosen, Chairperson
Dr. Barbaralee Diamonstein-Spielvogel, Vice Chairperson
Lisa Robb, Executive Director
Petra Maxwell, Deputy Executive Director of Agency Operations
Megan White, Deputy Executive Director of Programs

ADDRESS INQUIRIES TO:
Office of Public and Governmental Affairs
(See address above.)

NEW YORK STATE HISTORICAL ASSOCIATION   [489]
Lake Road
Cooperstown, NY 13326
(607) 547-1400
Fax: (607) 547-1404

E-MAIL ADDRESS:
publications@nysha.org

WEB SITE ADDRESS:
www.nysha.org

FOUNDED: 1899

AREAS OF INTEREST:
New York state and culture.

NAME(S) OF PROGRAMS:
● **Henry Allen Moe Prize**

TYPE:
Awards/prizes. Prizes for published catalogues treating collections located or exhibited in New York state.

YEAR PROGRAM STARTED: 1983

PURPOSE:
To foster and recognize scholarship in art history and decorative arts studies in the form of published catalogues located or exhibited in New York state.

LEGAL BASIS:
Private.

ELIGIBILITY:
Entries should add new information to what is known about the subject and may completely document an exhibition. Only catalogues treating collections located or exhibited in New York state qualify.

FINANCIAL DATA:
Amount of support per award: $250 to $1,000.

NUMBER OF APPLICANTS MOST RECENT YEAR: 7 for the year 2013.

NUMBER OF AWARDS: 1 for the year 2013.

APPLICATION INFORMATION:
Entries published in the previous two years only should be submitted in four copies accompanied by a letter of transmittal.
Deadline: On or before February 15 for awards in the current year.

PUBLICATIONS:
New York History; *Heritage Magazine*.

OFFICERS:
Dr. Douglas E. Evelyn, Chairman of the Board
Thomas O. Putnam, Vice Chairman
Stephen M. Duff, Treasurer
Glenn A. Perrone, Secretary

ADDRESS INQUIRIES TO:
Cynthia G. Falk
Assistant Professor of Material Culture
(See address above.)

NORTH CAROLINA ARTS COUNCIL   [490]
Department of Cultural Resources
109 East Jones Street
Raleigh, NC 27601
(919) 807-6500
Fax: (919) 807-6532

E-MAIL ADDRESS:
ncarts@ncdcr.gov

WEB SITE ADDRESS:
www.ncarts.org

FOUNDED: 1964

AREAS OF INTEREST:
Arts development throughout North Carolina.

CONSULTING OR VOLUNTEER SERVICES:
Consulting services to arts organizations.

NAME(S) OF PROGRAMS:
● **Artist Fellowships**
● **Arts and Audiences**
● **Arts in Education Grants**
● **Grassroots Arts Program**
● **Regional Artist Project Grants**

● **State Arts Resources**
● **Statewide Service Organizations**

TYPE:
Challenge/matching grants; Development grants; Fellowships; General operating grants; Internships; Project/program grants; Residencies; Technical assistance. Per capita distribution of funds for arts development, general operating support, project grants, local government challenge grants, arts-in-education grants, new works grants, discipline-development grants, individual artist fellowships, fee subsidy for touring groups, consultant grants, scholarship grants and workshops.

Artist Fellowships: To support the creative development of North Carolina artists. In even years, fellowships are awarded to writers, songwriters, composers, playwrights and screenwriters. In odd years, fellowships are awarded in the areas of visual art, craft, film/video and choreography.

Arts and Audiences: To help arts organizations broaden, deepen and diversify participation in their arts programs.

Arts in Education Grants: For schools and nonprofit organizations to strengthen the use of the arts in pre-K-through-12 settings.

Grassroots Arts Program: Distributes funds for arts programming, primarily through local arts councils, to all 100 North Carolina counties using a per capita-based formula.

Regional Artist Project Grants: For regional consortia of local arts councils, which award project grants to artists in their regions.

State Arts Resources: For mature arts organizations that, over time, have consistently produced strong arts programs and demonstrated strong management and financial accountability.

Statewide Service Organizations: Support is provided to organizations that provide programs and services to the arts community on a statewide or regional basis.

YEAR PROGRAM STARTED: 1967

PURPOSE:
To enrich cultural life in North Carolina by nurturing and supporting excellence in the arts and by providing opportunities for every North Carolinian to experience the arts.

LEGAL BASIS:
Agency of the state of North Carolina.

ELIGIBILITY:
Except for fellowships to individual artists who are North Carolina residents, the Council awards grants only to North Carolina organizations which qualify as tax-exempt and nonprofit under Section 501(c)(3) of the Internal Revenue Code of 1954.

GEOGRAPHIC RESTRICTIONS:
North Carolina.

FINANCIAL DATA:
Amount of support per award: $20,000 average grant. Project and challenge grants generally do not exceed $10,000. General operating support as much as $95,000, per capita distribution as much as $217,000 per grant and artist fellowships as much as $10,000.
Total amount of support: Varies.
Matching fund requirements: 1:1 cash match, except for fellowships.

APPLICATION INFORMATION:
Application form is available online.

Deadline: Organizational grant applications: March 1. Individuals: November 1.

STAFF:
Wayne Martin, Executive Director

ADDRESS INQUIRIES TO:
Mark Scaringelli, Grants and Finance Officer
(See address above.)

NORTH DAKOTA COUNCIL ON THE ARTS   [491]
1600 East Century Avenue
Suite 6
Bismarck, ND 58503
(701) 328-7590
Fax: (701) 328-7595

E-MAIL ADDRESS:
comserv@nd.gov

WEB SITE ADDRESS:
www.nd.gov/arts

FOUNDED: 1967

AREAS OF INTEREST:
Arts.

NAME(S) OF PROGRAMS:
● **Arts-in-Education/Artists in Residence**
● **Arts-in-Education/STE[A]M**
● **Arts-in-Education/Teacher Incentive**
● **Community Arts Access**
● **Individual Artists Fellowships**
● **Institutional Support**
● **Presenter Support**
● **Professional Development**
● **Special Projects**
● **Traditional Arts Apprenticeships**

TYPE:
Challenge/matching grants; Conferences/seminars; Exchange programs; Fellowships; General operating grants; Grants-in-aid; Project/program grants; Residencies; Technical assistance. Funding and technical assistance provided to institutions and organizations statewide for special projects and administration of special projects.

YEAR PROGRAM STARTED: 1967

PURPOSE:
To stimulate and encourage the study and presentation of and public participation in the performing and visual arts in North Dakota.

LEGAL BASIS:
North Dakota Legislative Assembly.

ELIGIBILITY:
Grants are awarded only to nonprofit organizations, schools, government subdivisions and individuals in North Dakota. Requirements vary according to program.

GEOGRAPHIC RESTRICTIONS:
North Dakota.

FINANCIAL DATA:
Amount of support per award: Varies by program.
Total amount of support: $880,454 for fiscal year 2014.
Matching fund requirements: Varies by grant.

COOPERATIVE FUNDING PROGRAMS: Institutional Support and Arts-in-Education.

NUMBER OF APPLICANTS MOST RECENT YEAR: 283 for the year 2013.

NUMBER OF AWARDS: 270 funded for the year 2013.

APPLICATION INFORMATION:
Contact the Council.
Duration: Up to one year.

Deadline: Varies.

PUBLICATIONS:
Newsletter; guidelines; brochures.

OFFICER:
David Trottier, Chairperson

ADDRESS INQUIRIES TO:
Jan Webb, Executive Director
(See address above.)

OHIO ARTS COUNCIL   [492]
30 East Broad Street
33rd Floor
Columbus, OH 43215
(614) 728-4429
Fax: (614) 466-4494
TDD: (800) 750-0750

E-MAIL ADDRESS:
dia.foley@oac.state.oh.us

WEB SITE ADDRESS:
www.oac.state.oh.us

FOUNDED: 1965

AREAS OF INTEREST:
Arts.

CONSULTING OR VOLUNTEER SERVICES:
Staff assistance related to applications and
program development.

NAME(S) OF PROGRAMS:
- **Artists with Disabilities Access**
- **Arts Access**
- **Arts Learning: Artist Express**
- **Arts Learning: Artist in
  Residence/Artists**
- **Arts Learning: Artist in
  Residence/Sponsors**
- **Arts Learning: Arts Partnership**
- **Building Cultural Diversity**
- **Individual Artist Grants and Services:
  Traditional Arts Apprenticeships**
- **Ohio Artists on Tour**
- **Ohio Heritage Fellowship Awards**
- **Project Support**
- **Sustainability**

TYPE:
Assistantships; Awards/prizes;
Conferences/seminars; Fellowships; Formula
grants; General operating grants; Internships;
Matching gifts; Project/program grants;
Residencies; Technical assistance. Special
projects and general programming.

YEAR PROGRAM STARTED: 1965

PURPOSE:
To fund and support quality arts experiences
to strengthen Ohio communities culturally,
educationally and economically.

LEGAL BASIS:
State agency.

ELIGIBILITY:
All applicants for grants must meet the
following legal requirements including
intending your project to be nonprofit, having
the fact that every tax-exempt organization
must have an Employer Identification
Number, every applicant having to be an
Ohio resident or Ohio-based to receive direct
grant support, producing projects of high
aesthetic quality and artistic merit, providing
at least one-half of the activity cost,
preferably in dollars (in-kind services may be
used as a part of the required match),
submitting accurate budgets that are
appropriate to the proposed project or
creative work, demonstrating financial
responsibility and methods to provide
community access and involvement.

No person or persons shall, on the grounds
of race, color, national origin, handicap, age,
sex or religion, be excluded from
participation in, be denied benefits of or be
otherwise subjected to discrimination under
any program, service or benefit advocated,
authorized or provided by the state of Ohio.

GEOGRAPHIC RESTRICTIONS:
Ohio.

FINANCIAL DATA:
Amount of support per award: $200 to
$400,000.

Total amount of support: $9,605,704 for
fiscal year 2013.

Matching fund requirements: Generally, 1:1
cash match.

COOPERATIVE FUNDING PROGRAMS: Ohio River
Border Initiative with West Virginia Arts
Commission.

REPRESENTATIVE AWARDS:
Cleveland Orchestra, Cleveland, OH;
Worthington Arts Council, Worthington, OH;
Lima Symphony Orchestra, Lima, OH;
Actor's Summer Theatre, Columbus, OH;
Southern Ohio Museum, Portsmouth, OH.

APPLICATION INFORMATION:
Applicants must use OAC's web-based
application system to submit an application.

Duration: July 1 through June 30.

Deadline: Artists with Disabilities Access:
Application accepted anytime; Arts Access:
March 1; Arts Learning-Artist Express:
Application due in six weeks prior to the
date of the visit; Arts Learning-Artist in
Residence/Artists: July 1; Arts
Learning-Artist in Residence/Sponsors:
February 1; Arts Learning-Arts Partnership:
March 1; Building Cultural Diversity: March
1, June 1, September 1 and December 1;
Individual Artist Grants and Services:
January 15 for Traditional Arts
Apprenticeships and September 1 for
Individual Excellence Awards; Ohio Artists
on Tour: May 15; Ohio Heritage Fellowship
Awards: January 15; Project Support: April
1; Sustainability: February 1.

PUBLICATIONS:
Guidelines; *Arts Ohio*; *Ohio Festivals &
Competitions Guide*; *Focusing the Light: The
Arts and Practice of Planning*; *Appreciative
Journey: A Guide to Developing
International Cultural Exchange.*

IRS IDENTIFICATION NUMBER: 31-1334820

OFFICERS:
Julie S. Henahan, Executive Director
Mary Campbell-Zopf, Deputy Director
Dia Foley, Grants Office Director

ADDRESS INQUIRIES TO:
Mary Campbell-Zopf, Deputy Director
(See address above.)

OKLAHOMA ARTS
COUNCIL   [493]
Jim Thorpe Building, Room 640
2101 North Lincoln Boulevard
Oklahoma City, OK 73105
(405) 521-2931
Fax: (405) 521-6418

E-MAIL ADDRESS:
okarts@arts.ok.gov

WEB SITE ADDRESS:
www.arts.ok.gov

FOUNDED: 1965

AREAS OF INTEREST:
Arts.

NAME(S) OF PROGRAMS:
- **Capitol Art Travel Subsidies**
- **Major Grant Support**
- **Organizational Support**
- **Small Grant Support**
- **Small Grant Support for Schools**

TYPE:
Challenge/matching grants;
Conferences/seminars; General operating
grants; Project/program grants; Residencies;
Technical assistance. State-appropriated funds
and federal funds from the National
Endowment for the Arts are disbursed to
nonprofit, tax-exempt and nonreligious
organizations for arts projects statewide.

YEAR PROGRAM STARTED: 1965

PURPOSE:
To further the arts in the state of Oklahoma.

LEGAL BASIS:
State agency.

ELIGIBILITY:
Nonprofit, tax-exempt and nonreligious
Oklahoma organizations are eligible to apply.

GEOGRAPHIC RESTRICTIONS:
Oklahoma.

FINANCIAL DATA:
Amount of support per award: Varies.

NUMBER OF APPLICANTS MOST RECENT YEAR:
Approximately 550.

APPLICATION INFORMATION:
Contact the Council.

Duration: Projects receiving funding must be
completed during the fiscal year.

PUBLICATIONS:
Program Guidelines; general brochures.

OFFICERS:
Kym Koch Thompson, Chairperson
Amber Sharples, Executive Director

ADDRESS INQUIRIES TO:
Whitney Moore, Grants Director
(See address above.)

OREGON ARTS
COMMISSION   [494]
775 Summer Street, N.E.
Suite 200
Salem, OR 97301-1280
(503) 986-0082
Fax: (503) 986-0260

E-MAIL ADDRESS:
oregon.artscomm@state.or.us

WEB SITE ADDRESS:
www.oregonartscommission.org

FOUNDED: 1967

AREAS OF INTEREST:
Arts.

NAME(S) OF PROGRAMS:
- **Access Reimbursement Grants**
- **Arts Build Communities**
- **Arts Learning Grants**
- **Arts Recognition Grants**
- **Arts Services Grants**
- **Capacity Building Grants**
- **Career Opportunity Grants**
- **Cultural Tourism Grants**
- **Individual Artists Fellowship Grants**
- **Operating Support Grants**
- **Oregon Media Arts Fellowship**

TYPE:
Awards/prizes; Conferences/seminars;
Fellowships; General operating grants;
Project/program grants; Technical assistance;
Training grants; Travel grants. Services
provided to arts institutions statewide.

YEAR PROGRAM STARTED: 1967

PURPOSE:
To provide grants and services to the arts,
offer developmental, consultative and
technical assistance, provide public
information and serve as a central resource
for the arts and collaborate in the
fiscal/financial management of arts
organizations.

LEGAL BASIS:
Agency of the state of Oregon.

ELIGIBILITY:
Grants are available to nonprofit
organizations and professional, nonstudent
artists.

GEOGRAPHIC RESTRICTIONS:
Oregon.

FINANCIAL DATA:
Amount of support per award: Varies.
Total amount of support: Approximately
$2,000,000 for the year 2012.
Matching fund requirements: Minimum 1:1.

NUMBER OF APPLICANTS MOST RECENT YEAR:
Varies.

NUMBER OF AWARDS: Varies.

APPLICATION INFORMATION:
Detailed information is available on the web
site.
Duration: One year.
Deadline: Varies.

PUBLICATIONS:
Program guide; monographs of Arts Build
Communities Program, Arts Learning
Program and Percent for Art Program;
guidelines for various grant programs;
Creative Vitality Index Report.

IRS IDENTIFICATION NUMBER: 93-0563386

PENNSYLVANIA COUNCIL ON THE ARTS [495]
216 Finance Building
Harrisburg, PA 17120
(717) 787-6883
Fax: (717) 783-2539

E-MAIL ADDRESS:
phorn@pa.gov

WEB SITE ADDRESS:
www.pacouncilonthearts.org

FOUNDED: 1966

AREAS OF INTEREST:
Arts.

NAME(S) OF PROGRAMS:
● **Arts Organization Grants**

TYPE:
General operating grants; Residencies.
General support grants, specific support
grants, and peer-to-peer consultation.

YEAR PROGRAM STARTED: 1966

PURPOSE:
To foster the excellence, diversity and vitality
of the arts in Pennsylvania; to broaden the
availability and appreciation of those arts
throughout the state.

LEGAL BASIS:
State agency.

ELIGIBILITY:
Incorporated nonprofit organizations located
in Pennsylvania and serving residents of the
state may apply.

GEOGRAPHIC RESTRICTIONS:
Pennsylvania.

FINANCIAL DATA:
Funding comes from state-appropriated funds
and federal grants.
Total amount of support: Varies.
Matching fund requirements: Usually a
dollar-for-dollar match for organizations.

APPLICATION INFORMATION:
Contact the Council.
Duration: One year.
Deadline: Varies.

PUBLICATIONS:
*Guide to Fellowship Programs; Guide to
Programs and Services; Guide to the
Arts-in-Education Program.*

STAFF:
Jewel Jones-Fulp, Program Associate

ADMINISTRATIVE STAFF:
Seth Poppy, Grants Manager

DIRECTORS:
Philip Horn, Executive Director
Amy Gabriele, Deputy Director for
Administration and Program Director for
Music
Heather Doughty, Deputy Director for
Communications
Charon Battles, Dance, Preserving Diverse
Cultures and Challenge Program
Jamie Dunlap, Arts in Education
Matt Serio, Entry Track, Partners in the Arts

ADDRESS INQUIRIES TO:
Program Director of Pertinent Arts Discipline
(See address above.)

RAGDALE FOUNDATION [496]
1260 North Green Bay Road
Lake Forest, IL 60045
(847) 234-1063 ext. 206
Fax: (847) 234-1063

E-MAIL ADDRESS:
admissions@ragdale.org

WEB SITE ADDRESS:
www.ragdale.org

FOUNDED: 1976

AREAS OF INTEREST:
Visual arts, poetry, fiction, nonfiction writing,
music composition, performance art,
play/screenwriting and interdisciplinary arts.

NAME(S) OF PROGRAMS:
● **Residencies at Ragdale Foundation**

TYPE:
Residencies. Low-cost subsidized residencies
at Ragdale Foundation, an artist's community,
providing a place to work undisturbed on
creative projects. Some financial aid and
fellowships are available upon acceptance.

YEAR PROGRAM STARTED: 1976

PURPOSE:
To provide a place for artists to work
undisturbed on creative projects.

LEGAL BASIS:
Not-for-profit, tax-exempt foundation.

ELIGIBILITY:
Residents are chosen by selections
committees composed of professionals in the
arts. Writers, composers, visual artists and
artists of other disciplines are accepted.
Couples are not accepted unless each
qualifies independently.

FINANCIAL DATA:
Amount of support per award: Residencies
with room and board provided. Standard fee
is $35 per day.
Total amount of support: Varies.

APPLICATION INFORMATION:
Completed application must be submitted
along with references, resume, work samples
and project description. Application process
is online through the ArtsApp portal. A $40
application fee is required. Financial aid
application must be completed after
acceptance.
Duration: Average 18 to 25 days.
Deadline: May 15.

PUBLICATIONS:
Application guidelines; two newsletters
annually.

IRS IDENTIFICATION NUMBER: 36-2937927

OFFICER:
Phoebe Turner, President

ADDRESS INQUIRIES TO:
Regin Igloria
Director of Residencies and Fellowships
(See address above.)

RHODE ISLAND STATE COUNCIL ON THE ARTS [497]
One Capitol Hill, 3rd Floor
Providence, RI 02908
(401) 222-3880
(401) 222-3882
Fax: (401) 222-3018

E-MAIL ADDRESS:
info@arts.ri.gov
lauren.faria@arts.ri.gov

WEB SITE ADDRESS:
www.arts.ri.gov

FOUNDED: 1967

AREAS OF INTEREST:
Arts.

NAME(S) OF PROGRAMS:
● **Arts Access Grant (AAG)**
● **Investments in Arts and Culture (IAC)**

TYPE:
Fellowships; General operating grants;
Project/program grants. Funding for Rhode
Island nonprofit organizations doing arts
programming and for Rhode Island artists.
Individual artist support includes Fellowships
and Folk Arts Apprenticeships.
Organizational support includes General
Operating Support.

YEAR PROGRAM STARTED: 1967

PURPOSE:
To support and develop increased and
substantial arts opportunities for Rhode
Island.

LEGAL BASIS:
Agency of the state of Rhode Island.

ELIGIBILITY:
Varies with each grant category.

GEOGRAPHIC RESTRICTIONS:
Rhode Island.

FINANCIAL DATA:
Amount of support per award: Varies.

Total amount of support: $1,800,000 for fiscal year 2012.

Matching fund requirements: Matching funds required for all grants, except for individual artists.

COOPERATIVE FUNDING PROGRAMS: State and local cooperative programs.

APPLICATION INFORMATION:
Contact the Council.
Duration: Varies with program.
Deadline: April 1 and October 1.

IRS IDENTIFICATION NUMBER: 05-6000523

OFFICERS:
Randall Rosenbaum, Executive Director
Sherilyn Brown, Arts-in-Education Director (Education Partnerships)
Elizabeth Keithline, Public Art Director
Cristina DiChiera, Individual Artists Coordinator
Daniel L. Kahn, Arts-in-Education Assistant (Grants)

ADDRESS INQUIRIES TO:
Lauren Faria
Project Grants for Organizations
(See street or e-mail address above.)
Tel: (401) 222-3882

THE SAN FRANCISCO FOUNDATION   [498]
225 Bush Street
Suite 500
San Francisco, CA 94104
(415) 733-8500
Fax: (415) 477-2783

E-MAIL ADDRESS:
info@sff.org

WEB SITE ADDRESS:
www.sff.org

FOUNDED: 1948

AREAS OF INTEREST:
Arts and artists.

NAME(S) OF PROGRAMS:
• **Art Awards**

TYPE:
Awards/prizes.

PURPOSE:
To foster individual artistic growth within the community.

LEGAL BASIS:
Community foundation.

ELIGIBILITY:
Poets, writers, sculptors, painters, filmmakers, media artists, photographers, printmakers and performing artists are eligible.

GEOGRAPHIC RESTRICTIONS:
Alameda, Contra Costa, Marin, San Francisco and San Mateo counties, California.

FINANCIAL DATA:
Amount of support per award: $2,000 to $10,000.
Total amount of support: Varies.

NUMBER OF AWARDS: Varies.

APPLICATION INFORMATION:
Details are available online.
Deadline: Varies.

ADDRESS INQUIRIES TO:
Art Awards Program
(See address above.)

THE GEORGE AND HELEN SEGAL FOUNDATION   [499]
136 Davidson Mill Road
North Brunswick, NJ 08902
(732) 951-0950
Fax: (732) 821-5877

E-MAIL ADDRESS:
segalfoundation@comcast.net

WEB SITE ADDRESS:
www.segalfoundation.org

FOUNDED: 2000

AREAS OF INTEREST:
Financial support to artists and sculptors.

TYPE:
Grants-in-aid. Biennial grant.

YEAR PROGRAM STARTED: 2000

PURPOSE:
To exhibit and display the works of George Segal, and to award grants to artists in order to enable them to pursue their artistic endeavors.

ELIGIBILITY:
Open to New Jersey sculptors only. Applicant must be 21 years of age or older. No students.

GEOGRAPHIC RESTRICTIONS:
New Jersey.

FINANCIAL DATA:
Amount of support per award: $5,000 to $10,000.

NUMBER OF AWARDS: Either ten $5,000 or five $10,000 awards.

APPLICATION INFORMATION:
The following items must be included with the application:
(1) cover letter describing how the grant funds will be used and how they will advance the applicant's artistic career;
(2) six images of current work on a CD. Place name, year the work was done, title, dimensions and medium used on the CD. The Foundation will not be returning any material and;
(3) current resume, including dates, listing exhibition record, grants, awards and other professional activities.

ADDRESS INQUIRIES TO:
Susan Kutliroff, Secretary/Treasurer
(See address above.)

SILICON VALLEY CREATES   [500]
4 North Second Street
Suite 500
San Jose, CA 95113-1305
(408) 998-2787 ext. 204
Fax: (408) 971-9458

E-MAIL ADDRESS:
audreys@svcreates.org

WEB SITE ADDRESS:
www.svcreates.org

FOUNDED: 1982

AREAS OF INTEREST:
Arts organizations, individual artists and community arts.

NAME(S) OF PROGRAMS:
• **Applied Materials Excellence in the Arts**
• **Artist Laureates**
• **Local Arts Grants**

TYPE:
Awards/prizes; Conferences/seminars; General operating grants; Project/program grants; Technical assistance. Laureate awards. Applied Materials Excellence in the Arts provides funding in two focus areas:
(1) project support for exceptional and unique projects conceived to enhance artistic and/or programmatic excellence and; (2) technical assistance for activities that support administrative development and organizational infrastructure.

Artist Laureate Awards provide awards to recognize the accomplishments of individual artists.

Local Arts Grants provide general operating support to arts organizations for activities that:
(1) promote artistic excellence while reflecting the dynamic diverse and innovative character of Santa Clara County;
(2) support the professional development of small and mid-sized arts organizations;
(3) recognize and encourage nonprofessional, volunteer involvement as an essential part of the county's cultural environment and;
(4) stimulate local support, particularly at the grassroots level.

LEGAL BASIS:
Private, nonprofit arts council.

GEOGRAPHIC RESTRICTIONS:
Santa Clara County, California.

FINANCIAL DATA:
Amount of support per award: Applied Materials Excellence in the Arts: $2,500 to $5,000; Artist Laureates: $5,000.
Total amount of support: $416,812 for fiscal year 2012-13.

COOPERATIVE FUNDING PROGRAMS: Applied Materials Excellence in the Arts.

NUMBER OF APPLICANTS MOST RECENT YEAR: 84 for the year 2012-13.

NUMBER OF AWARDS: Applied Materials Excellence in the Arts: 24; Artist Laureates: 6; Local Arts Grants: 72 for the year 2012-13.

PUBLICATIONS:
Annual report.

IRS IDENTIFICATION NUMBER: 94-2825213

ADDRESS INQUIRIES TO:
Audrey Struve, Program Manager
(See address above.)

SMITHSONIAN INSTITUTION
Office of Fellowships and Internships
470 L'Enfant Plaza, S.W., Suite 7102
MRC 902, P.O. Box 37012
Washington, DC 20013-7012
(202) 633-7070
Fax: (202) 633-7069

E-MAIL ADDRESS:
siofi@si.edu

WEB SITE ADDRESS:
www.si.edu/ofi

TYPE:
Fellowships. Offered to qualified scholars for research to be conducted in residence at the Smithsonian in association with the staff, using collections and research facilities.

See entry 1839 for full listing.

SOUTH DAKOTA ARTS COUNCIL   [501]

711 East Wells Avenue
Pierre, SD 57501-3369
(605) 773-3301
Fax: (605) 773-5977

E-MAIL ADDRESS:
sdac@state.sd.us

WEB SITE ADDRESS:
www.artscouncil.sd.gov

FOUNDED: 1966

AREAS OF INTEREST:
Statewide arts programming in all arts disciplines.

NAME(S) OF PROGRAMS:
● **Artist Grants**
● **Artist-in-Schools & Communities**
● **Arts Organization Challenge Grants**
● **Professional Development**
● **Project Grants**
● **Technical Assistance**
● **Touring Arts**

TYPE:
Challenge/matching grants; Fellowships; General operating grants; Grants-in-aid; Project/program grants; Residencies; Seed money grants; Technical assistance; Travel grants. Artist grants; arts challenge grants/general operating support.

YEAR PROGRAM STARTED: 1968

PURPOSE:
To support development of the arts.

LEGAL BASIS:
State agency.

ELIGIBILITY:
Requirements vary with projects. Most grants are available to South Dakota residents only, with the exception of Touring Arts and Artist-in-Schools & Communities.

GEOGRAPHIC RESTRICTIONS:
South Dakota.

FINANCIAL DATA:
Amount of support per award: $100 to $45,000.

Total amount of support: $1,200,000.

Matching fund requirements: Required except for Artist Grants.

NUMBER OF AWARDS: 500.

APPLICATION INFORMATION:
Applications are accepted through an online e-grant system.

Duration: Generally one fiscal year. Renewable.

Deadline: March 1 for Organizations and Artist Grants. September 1 for Touring Arts and Artist-in-Schools & Communities.

PUBLICATIONS:
Quarterly newsletter; strategic long-range plan; annual report.

STAFF:
Michael Pangburn, Director
Rebecca Cruse, Assistant Director
Paul Mehlhaff, Grants Officer
Sharon Winckler, Program Coordinator

ADDRESS INQUIRIES TO:
Michael Pangburn, Director
(See address above.)

H. CHASE STONE TRUST   [502]

c/o JPMorgan
370 17th Street, Suite 3200
Denver, CO 80202
(303) 607-7810
Fax: (303) 607-7761

E-MAIL ADDRESS:
julie.golden@jpmorgan.com

WEB SITE ADDRESS:
www.jpmorgan.com/onlinegrants

AREAS OF INTEREST:
Primarily performing, literary and fine arts.

TYPE:
Project/program grants.

PURPOSE:
To support, sustain and develop charitable organizations operating in the El Paso County community.

ELIGIBILITY:
Performing, literary and fine arts organizations serving the entire El Paso County community are eligible to apply. Must have 501(c)(3) not-for-profit status. No grants to individuals.

GEOGRAPHIC RESTRICTIONS:
El Paso County, Colorado.

FINANCIAL DATA:
Amount of support per award: $3,000 to $10,000.

APPLICATION INFORMATION:
Application and guidelines are available online. Organization must provide current copy of IRS determination letter showing tax-exempt status under Section 501(c)(3) and public charity status under Section 509(a).

Duration: One year. No renewals.

Deadline: March 31, June 30 and October 31.

ADDRESS INQUIRIES TO:
Julie Golden, Trust Advisor
(See address above.)

*SPECIAL STIPULATIONS:
JPMorgan will only accept applications submitted online.

THE FRANK M. TAIT FOUNDATION

1530 Kettering Tower
40 North Main Street
Dayton, OH 45423
(937) 222-2401
Fax: (937) 224-6015

E-MAIL ADDRESS:
taitfoundation@gmail.com

TYPE:
Project/program grants. Focus on youth development, particularly early childhood development.

See entry 1148 for full listing.

TENNESSEE ARTS COMMISSION   [503]

401 Charlotte Avenue
Nashville, TN 37243-0780
(615) 741-6395
Fax: (615) 741-8559

E-MAIL ADDRESS:
diane.williams@tn.gov

WEB SITE ADDRESS:
www.tn.gov/arts

FOUNDED: 1967

AREAS OF INTEREST:
All arts disciplines in Tennessee.

CONSULTING OR VOLUNTEER SERVICES:
Consultant, informational and developmental services are offered to arts groups, individual artists, museums and arts councils throughout the state.

NAME(S) OF PROGRAMS:
● **Division of Arts Programs**
● **Division of Communications, Information & Technology**

TYPE:
Conferences/seminars; Fellowships; General operating grants; Project/program grants; Residencies; Technical assistance; Training grants. Professional development. Matching grants. Arts Programs consist of grants to institutions, individuals, coordinating agencies and entities of government. Consultation information and development assistance to state arts constituency is also provided.

Grant Programs: Funds may not be used for capital improvements or for permanent equipment.

YEAR PROGRAM STARTED: 1967

PURPOSE:
To support and encourage the life and growth of the arts and craft in the state of Tennessee and preservation of the state's cultural heritage.

LEGAL BASIS:
Independent state agency.

ELIGIBILITY:
Grants categories are limited to residents, artists and organizations of Tennessee. Grants are made to individuals, nonprofit organizations and/or entities of government.

GEOGRAPHIC RESTRICTIONS:
Tennessee.

FINANCIAL DATA:
Amount of support per award: $200 to $100,000.

Matching fund requirements: Most grant awards require a 1:1 match.

NUMBER OF APPLICANTS MOST RECENT YEAR: 850.

NUMBER OF AWARDS: 800.

APPLICATION INFORMATION:
Details are available on the web site.

Duration: One fiscal year, July to June.

Deadline: Varies.

PUBLICATIONS:
Quarterly newsletters; weekly online newsletter.

COMMISSION MEMBERS:
Bob Wormsley, Chairperson
Rhea Condra, Secretary
Patsy White Camp
Gale Jones Carson
Donna Chase
Stephanie B. Conner
Lanis Cope
Ed Gerace
Lucia Gilliland
Waymon L. Hickman, Sr.
Chancellor Carol L. McCoy
Ann C. Smith
Connie S. Weathers

ADDRESS INQUIRIES TO:
Diane Williams, Director of Grants Management
(See address above.)

TEXAS COMMISSION ON THE ARTS [504]
E.O. Thompson Building
920 Colorado, 5th Floor
Austin, TX 78701
(512) 463-5535
(800) 252-9415 (Texas only)
Fax: (512) 475-2699

E-MAIL ADDRESS:
laura@arts.texas.gov

WEB SITE ADDRESS:
www.arts.texas.gov

FOUNDED: 1965

AREAS OF INTEREST:
Operational support and project support to nonprofit Texas arts organizations for ongoing programs and/or arts education, health and human services, economic development, public safety and criminal justice, and natural resources and agriculture; performance support for civic, cultural and other nonprofit organizations.

CONSULTING OR VOLUNTEER SERVICES:
Seminars, information services, technical assistance and funding. Services provided to institutions statewide.

NAME(S) OF PROGRAMS:
• **TCA Grant Programs**

TYPE:
Block grants; Challenge/matching grants; Conferences/seminars; Exchange programs; General operating grants; Project/program grants; Residencies; Technical assistance; Training grants; Travel grants; Visiting scholars. Organizational support, project support and touring support.

YEAR PROGRAM STARTED: 1965

PURPOSE:
To advance the state economically and culturally by investing in a creative Texas.

LEGAL BASIS:
Texas Government Code, Chapter 444, Section 021.

ELIGIBILITY:
Any 501(c)(3) organization, educational institution, or form of government may apply. Presenters and producers of performing arts whose programs are designed to stimulate artistic activity and to heighten awareness of and broaden public access to the arts in rural and underserved areas of the state are eligible to apply.

Award made according to project cost, program limits, ability to meet funding criteria and available funds.

GEOGRAPHIC RESTRICTIONS:
Texas.

FINANCIAL DATA:
Total amount of support: $5,400,000.
Matching fund requirements: Funds provided by the state through the grants process must be matched by the application organization. Matching funds are generally expected to be in cash or in cash and in kind.

NUMBER OF APPLICANTS MOST RECENT YEAR:
1,200.

APPLICATION INFORMATION:
Guidelines available online. All applications submitted electronically. Contact TCA staff to obtain user ID and password.
Duration: Up to one year.
Deadline: Varies.

PUBLICATIONS:
Guide to Programs and Services.

STAFF:
Dr. Gary Gibbs, Executive Director

COMMISSION MEMBERS:
Patricia A. Bryant, Chairperson
Linda Hatchel, Vice-Chairperson
Dale W. Brock, Treasurer
S. Shawn Stephens, Secretary
Liza Lewis, Parliamentarian
David Garza, At-Large
Molly Hipp Hubbard, At-Large
Rita E. Baca
Alphonse A. Dotson
Mila Gibson
Ronald Sanders

ADDRESS INQUIRIES TO:
Laura Wiegand
Director of Programs and Technology
(See address above.)

TOURISM CARES
275 Turnpike Street
Suite 307
Canton, MA 02021
(781) 821-5990
Fax: (781) 821-8949

WEB SITE ADDRESS:
www.tourismcares.org/grants

TYPE:
Project/program grants. Grants to nonprofit, tax-exempt organizations.

As part of its mission, Tourism Cares distributes charitable grants to worthy tourism-related 501(c)(3) nonprofit organizations worldwide to conserve, preserve or restore sites of exceptional cultural, historic or natural significance. The program goals call for a balanced distribution to U.S. and non-U.S. recipients.

See entry 2204 for full listing.

THE TRUST COMPANY [505]
Level 15, 20 Bond Street
G.P.O. Box 4270
Sydney N.S.W. 2000 Australia
(61)(2) 8295-8100

E-MAIL ADDRESS:
scholarships@thetrustcompany.com.au

WEB SITE ADDRESS:
www.thetrustcompany.com.au

FOUNDED: 1961

AREAS OF INTEREST:
Portrait painting.

NAME(S) OF PROGRAMS:
• **Portia Geach Memorial Award**

TYPE:
Awards/prizes. Cash award for the best portrait painted from life of a man or woman distinguished in Art, Letters or the Sciences, by any female artist resident in Australia.

YEAR PROGRAM STARTED: 1965

PURPOSE:
To recognize the portrait painted from life of the highest artistic merit.

LEGAL BASIS:
Trustees of the Portia Geach Memorial Fund.

ELIGIBILITY:
Entrants must be female Australian residents who are either Australian-born, naturalized, or British-born. Entries must be the original

work of the competitor. Works must have been executed entirely during the commenced year previously. Each entry must be a portrait painted from life of a man or woman distinguished in Art, Letters or the Sciences. Self-portraits are accepted. Works must be two-dimensional and must use the medium of paint.

Sculptures, photographic and video works are not eligible. There is no limit to the number of entries an artist can submit.

GEOGRAPHIC RESTRICTIONS:
Australia.

FINANCIAL DATA:
Amount of support per award: $18,000 (AUD) annually.

NUMBER OF APPLICANTS MOST RECENT YEAR:
312.

NUMBER OF AWARDS: 1.

APPLICATION INFORMATION:
Complete application information is available from The Trust Company.
Duration: One year.
Deadline: August.

ADDRESS INQUIRIES TO:
Scholarship and Awards
Portia Geach Memorial Award
(See e-mail address above.)

TWO TEN FOOTWEAR FOUNDATION
1466 Main Street
Waltham, MA 02451
(800) 346-3210 ext. 1512
Fax: (781) 736-1555

E-MAIL ADDRESS:
scholarship@twoten.org

WEB SITE ADDRESS:
www.twoten.org

TYPE:
Scholarships. Intended for students who are interested in pursuing a career in footwear design.

See entry 1768 for full listing.

UNITARIAN UNIVERSALIST ASSOCIATION OF CONGREGATIONS [506]
UU Funding Program
P.O. Box 301149
Jamaica Plain, MA 02130
(617) 971-9600
Fax: (617) 971-0029

E-MAIL ADDRESS:
uufunding@gmail.com

WEB SITE ADDRESS:
uua.org/care/scholarships/stanfield

FOUNDED: 1986

AREAS OF INTEREST:
Limited to the fine arts of painting, drawing, enameling, printmaking, photography and sculpture.

NAME(S) OF PROGRAMS:
• **Stanfield and D'Orlando Art Scholarship**

TYPE:
Scholarships. Annual scholarship to be awarded to an applicant majoring in art, for further study in that major, at an accredited school.

YEAR PROGRAM STARTED: 1980

PURPOSE:
To aid a Unitarian Universalist student majoring in fine arts.

LEGAL BASIS:
Religious organization.

ELIGIBILITY:
Applicants must be members in good standing for at least one year before date of application or sponsored by a member of a Unitarian Universalist Congregation and must be enrolled in an accredited school. Eligible art fields include drawing, painting, sculpture, enameling, printmaking and photography.

GEOGRAPHIC RESTRICTIONS:
United States.

FINANCIAL DATA:
Payment is made directly to the recipient.
Amount of support per award: Average $1,000.
Total amount of support: Varies.

NUMBER OF APPLICANTS MOST RECENT YEAR:
12 for the year 2013.

NUMBER OF AWARDS: Varies.

APPLICATION INFORMATION:
Applications should include a short essay on applicant, photos or slides of at least six works by applicant, a letter of recommendation, statement of tuition costs where applicant is enrolled and an application which has been signed.
Duration: One academic year.
Deadline: February 15. Announcements by May 15.

UNITED ARTS COUNCIL OF RALEIGH AND WAKE COUNTY, INC.   [507]
410 Glenwood Avenue, Suite 170
Raleigh, NC 27603
(919) 839-1498 ext. 203
Fax: (919) 839-6002

E-MAIL ADDRESS:
eoakley@unitedarts.org

WEB SITE ADDRESS:
www.unitedarts.org

FOUNDED: 1990

AREAS OF INTEREST:
Arts, arts education, music education, theatre arts education, humanities-community development, and teacher-preparation education.

NAME(S) OF PROGRAMS:
● **Artists-in-the-Schools Grants Program**
● **Community Arts Reach Program**
● **Program Support Grants**
● **Regional Artist Grants**

TYPE:
Awards/prizes; Project/program grants; Seed money grants.

YEAR PROGRAM STARTED: 1989

PURPOSE:
To enhance and strengthen arts and arts education in Wake County, NC.

ELIGIBILITY:
Funds are available to Wake County (NC) grades K-12 schools, individual artists, arts organizations and agencies with specific arts programming.

GEOGRAPHIC RESTRICTIONS:
Wake County, North Carolina.

FINANCIAL DATA:
Amount of support per award: $1,000 to $30,000.
Total amount of support: Varies.
Matching fund requirements: Required for some programs.

NUMBER OF APPLICANTS MOST RECENT YEAR:
Over 350.

NUMBER OF AWARDS: Over 350 for the year 2013-14.

APPLICATION INFORMATION:
Application information is available on the web site.
Duration: Varies by grant program.
Deadline: Varies by grant program.

PUBLICATIONS:
Guidelines.

IRS IDENTIFICATION NUMBER: 56-0770175

UNIVERSITY OF MINNESOTA
Room 113, Andersen Library
222 21st Avenue South
Minneapolis, MN 55455
(612) 624-4576

E-MAIL ADDRESS:
asc-clrc@umn.edu

WEB SITE ADDRESS:
special.lib.umn.edu/clrc/

TYPE:
Travel grants. Award to travel to Kerlan Collection, University of Minnesota, plus per diem.

See entry 702 for full listing.

UNIVERSITY OF MINNESOTA   [508]
Room 113, Andersen Library
222 21st Avenue South
Minneapolis, MN 55455
(612) 624-4576

E-MAIL ADDRESS:
clrc@umn.edu

WEB SITE ADDRESS:
special.lib.umn.edu/clrc/

AREAS OF INTEREST:
Research and children's literature.

NAME(S) OF PROGRAMS:
● **Marilyn Hollinshead Fellowship**

TYPE:
Travel grants. Award to travel to Kerlan Collection, University of Minnesota, as well as per diem.

PURPOSE:
To fund children's literature research with manuscripts and/or original illustrations.

FINANCIAL DATA:
Amount of support per award: $1,500.
Total amount of support: $1,500.

NUMBER OF AWARDS: 1.

APPLICATION INFORMATION:
Electronic application acceptable by deadline.
Duration: Grants are awarded annually and are nonrenewable.
Deadline: January 30 of research year.

ADDRESS INQUIRIES TO:
Fellowship Committee
(See address above.)

THE UNIVERSITY OF TEXAS AT AUSTIN AND THE TEXAS INSTITUTE OF LETTERS   [509]
The Graduate School
110 Inner Campus Drive, Main 101
Austin, TX 78705
(512) 232-3609
Fax: (512) 471-7620

E-MAIL ADDRESS:
adameve@mail.utexas.edu
gbarton@austin.utexas.edu

WEB SITE ADDRESS:
www.utexas.edu/ogs/Paisano

AREAS OF INTEREST:
Competitive writing fellowships.

NAME(S) OF PROGRAMS:
● **The Dobie Paisano Fellowship Program**

TYPE:
Project/program grants. Provides an opportunity for creative or nonfiction writers to live and write for an extended period in an environment that offers isolation and tranquility.

Ralph A. Johnston Memorial Fellowship is aimed at writers who have demonstrated some publishing and critical success.

Jesse H. Jones Writing Fellowship is aimed at, but not limited to, writers who are early in their careers.

Both fellowships provide and require free residence at the ranch.

YEAR PROGRAM STARTED: 1967

PURPOSE:
To stimulate creative writing by making it possible for a person to work without distractions in an environment that offers isolation and tranquility.

ELIGIBILITY:
Criteria for making the awards include quality of work, character of the proposed project, and suitability of the applicant for life at Paisano, the late J. Frank Dobie's ranch near Austin, TX.

At the time of application, the applicant must meet one of the following:
(1) be a native Texan;
(2) have lived in Texas at some time for at least three years or;
(3) have published significant work with a Texas subject.

FINANCIAL DATA:
Amount of support per award: Ralph A. Johnston Memorial Fellowship: $25,000 over four or five months; Jesse H. Jones Writing Fellowship: $18,000 over five-and-a-half months.

NUMBER OF APPLICANTS MOST RECENT YEAR:
Ralph A. Johnston Memorial Fellowship: 22; Jesse H. Jones Writing Fellowship: 67.

NUMBER OF AWARDS: 1 each annually.

APPLICATION INFORMATION:
Application fee of $20 for one fellowship or $30 for both fellowships is required. If applying for both fellowships, include the fee with the Johnston Memorial Fellowship application and check the appropriate box at the top of the Johnston application form. Application fees are nonrefundable.

Applicants must submit each application in triplicate and its accompanying materials in separate packets. Make checks or money orders payable to The University of Texas at Austin.

Both application forms can be downloaded and printed from the web site. To request a printed copy of either application, send a self-addressed, stamped envelope (2 ounces postage) to the address above.

Duration: Ralph A. Johnston Memorial Fellowship: Four or five months. Jesse H. Jones Writing Fellowship: Five-and-a-half months. Both nonrenewable.

Deadline: Mid-January.

ADDRESS INQUIRIES TO:
Michael Adams or
Gwen Barton
(See address above.)

*SPECIAL STIPULATIONS:
Applicant must demonstrate ability to live in a rustic secluded rural location. Fellows must reside at Paisano Ranch.

VCCA (VIRGINIA CENTER FOR THE CREATIVE ARTS)   [510]
154 San Angelo Drive
Amherst, VA 24521
(434) 946-7236
Fax: (434) 946-7239

E-MAIL ADDRESS:
vcca@vcca.com

WEB SITE ADDRESS:
www.vcca.com

FOUNDED: 1971

TYPE:
Exchange programs; Fellowships; Residencies. VCCA is a creative space offering exchange programs, fellowships and residencies. It is open to writers, visual artists and composers. VCCA enables these artists, both professional and upcoming, to concentrate on their work and take it to new heights.

YEAR PROGRAM STARTED: 1971

PURPOSE:
To provide visual artists, writers and composers with a creative space so they can pursue their projects with a minds-wide-open focus, free from the distractions and responsibilities of daily life.

LEGAL BASIS:
Nonprofit corporation.

ELIGIBILITY:
Achievement or outstanding promise within a field of art must be demonstrated.

FINANCIAL DATA:
All fellowships are for periods of residency. No cash awards are offered. Some fellowships do offer stipends.
Amount of support per award: Varies.
Total amount of support: Varies.

NUMBER OF AWARDS: Over 400.

APPLICATION INFORMATION:
Application must include two references from professionals in applicant's field, samples of applicant's work and a curriculum vitae. Residencies available for three composers, nine visual artists and 13 writers at any time.
Duration: Two to eight weeks.
Deadline: January 15 for fellowships running from June to September. May 15 for fellowships running from October to January. September 15 for fellowships running from February to May.

PUBLICATIONS:
Application form; annual report; newsletters.

STAFF:
Sheila Gulley Pleasants, Artists Services Director

ADDRESS INQUIRIES TO:
Sheila Gulley Pleasants, Artists Services Director
(See address above.)

VERMONT ARTS COUNCIL [511]
136 State Street
Montpelier, VT 05633
(802) 828-3293
Fax: (802) 828-3363

E-MAIL ADDRESS:
info@vermontartscouncil.org

WEB SITE ADDRESS:
www.vermontartscouncil.org

FOUNDED: 1964

AREAS OF INTEREST:
Visual arts including painting, sculpture, drawing, printmaking, architectural and cultural facilities design, crafts, film and photography; performing arts in music, theatre and dance; literature.

CONSULTING OR VOLUNTEER SERVICES:
Staff members may counsel and assist individuals and organizations in the development of arts projects and activities.

NAME(S) OF PROGRAMS:
• **Artist Development Grants**
• **Artists in Schools**
• **Arts Partnership Grants**
• **Creation Grants**
• **Cultural Facilities Grants**
• **Cultural Routes Grants**
• **Operating Support Grants**
• **Project Grants**

TYPE:
Conferences/seminars; Development grants; General operating grants; Project/program grants; Seed money grants; Technical assistance; Training grants; Travel grants. Professional development grants. Cultural facilities improvements. Arts partnerships.

YEAR PROGRAM STARTED: 1966

PURPOSE:
To advance and preserve the arts at the center of Vermont communities.

LEGAL BASIS:
Official state arts agency and a nonprofit membership corporation.

ELIGIBILITY:
Applicants must be nonprofit organizations, agencies of town, county, state government and/or individual artists of demonstrated ability who are residents of Vermont for at least one year.

Funding is not available for:
(1) academic tuition;
(2) activities in which artists are not appropriately compensated;
(3) construction of new facilities, renovation of existing facilities, or other capital improvements (exceptions in cases that comply with Cultural Facilities Grants);
(4) deficits and debts incurred from past activities;
(5) events that present faculty members on the campus of their own institutions;
(6) events which are predominantly religious or sectarian;
(7) events whose sponsors are not in compliance with the requirements of the Americans with Disabilities Act of 1990 and

Section 504 of the Rehabilitation Act of 1973;
(8) food and beverages;
(9) for-profit organizations;
(10) fund-raising events;
(11) international travel (airline tickets);
(12) lobbying expenses;
(13) private events to which the public is not invited and;
(14) purchase of permanent equipment (exceptions in cases that comply with Cultural Facilities Grants).

GEOGRAPHIC RESTRICTIONS:
Vermont.

FINANCIAL DATA:
Amount of support per award: Varies according to each program.
Total amount of support: $1,200,000 in grants and services and $579,000 in grants only for the fiscal year 2011.
Matching fund requirements: Generally 1:1.

COOPERATIVE FUNDING PROGRAMS: Cultural Facilities Grants with the state of Vermont.

NUMBER OF APPLICANTS MOST RECENT YEAR: 250.

NUMBER OF AWARDS: 135.

APPLICATION INFORMATION:
Interested applicants can view the *Arts Council Grant Guidelines* and application online. Individual artists are required to submit samples of work.
Duration: Typically one year.
Deadline: Varies.

PUBLICATIONS:
Grant guidelines; *Art Directory*; *ArtMail*.

IRS IDENTIFICATION NUMBER: 03-0218115

ADDRESS INQUIRIES TO:
Sonia Rae, Artist and Community Programs Manager or
Ben Doyle, Education Programs Manager
(See address above.)

VIRGIN ISLANDS COUNCIL ON THE ARTS   [512]
5070 Norre Gade, Suite 1
St. Thomas, VI 00802-6762
(340) 774-5984
Fax: (340) 774-6206

E-MAIL ADDRESS:
blmahoney@smartnet.vi

WEB SITE ADDRESS:
www.vicouncilonarts.org

FOUNDED: 1966

AREAS OF INTEREST:
Fine arts, language and literature, music, creative, visual and performing arts and crafts.

NAME(S) OF PROGRAMS:
• **Expanding Opportunities for Participation in the Arts**

TYPE:
General operating grants; Project/program grants; Residencies; Technical assistance. Professional development artist or art teacher grants. Grants and technical assistance to individual artists, arts organizations and arts institutions in the Virgin Islands.

YEAR PROGRAM STARTED: 1966

PURPOSE:
To encourage wider participation in the arts by means of individual creative development and the strengthening of cultural organizations.

LEGAL BASIS:
Government agency.

ELIGIBILITY:
Applicants must be residents of the Virgin Islands for at least two years. Grants are made to Virgin Island-based projects or applicants.

GEOGRAPHIC RESTRICTIONS:
Virgin Islands.

FINANCIAL DATA:
Amount of support per award: Up to approximately $10,000. Organizations can receive a maximum of $10,000 and individuals can receive a maximum of $5,000.
Total amount of support: Depends on government, local and federal funding.
Matching fund requirements: The amount varies depending on category of grant. Usually 1:1.

NUMBER OF APPLICANTS MOST RECENT YEAR:
109.

NUMBER OF AWARDS: 109.

REPRESENTATIVE AWARDS:
$10,000 to Reichhold Center for the Performing Arts; $5,000 to the Farmers Association.

APPLICATION INFORMATION:
Official application information is available from the Council.
Duration: One year. Renewable on reapplication and reconsideration by the Board of Directors.
Deadline: January 31 and August 31.

STAFF:
Betty L. Mahoney, Executive Director

ADDRESS INQUIRIES TO:
Betty L. Mahoney, Executive Director
(See address above.)

VIRGINIA COMMISSION FOR THE ARTS   [513]
1001 East Broad Street, Suite 330
Richmond, VA 23219
(804) 225-3132
Fax: (804) 225-4327

E-MAIL ADDRESS:
margaret.vanderhye@arts.virginia.gov

WEB SITE ADDRESS:
www.arts.virginia.gov

FOUNDED: 1968

AREAS OF INTEREST:
Arts activities including but not limited to performances, exhibitions, demonstrations, workshops, readings and other presentations or participatory experiences in the fields of crafts, dance, folk arts, literature, museum work, music, public media, theatre and visual arts, provided by artists or arts organizations located in the state of Virginia.

TYPE:
Fellowships; General operating grants; Project/program grants; Technical assistance. Touring grants; Residency, afterschool/arts programs, training programs for artists; Local government challenge grants; Cultural/arts tourism marketing program.

YEAR PROGRAM STARTED: 1968

PURPOSE:
To encourage participation and invest in the arts for all Virginians.

LEGAL BASIS:
State agency.

ELIGIBILITY:
Applicants must be nonprofit, tax-exempt organizations, schools or professional artists, government units.

GEOGRAPHIC RESTRICTIONS:
Virginia.

FINANCIAL DATA:
Amount of support per award: Varies.
Total amount of support: $3,700,000 for fiscal year 2013-14.
Matching fund requirements: Varies according to program.

NUMBER OF APPLICANTS MOST RECENT YEAR:
1,600 for fiscal year 2012-13.

NUMBER OF AWARDS: 700 for fiscal year 2012-13.

APPLICATION INFORMATION:
Contact the Commission.
Duration: One year.
Deadline: March 1 and April 1 for most programs. Varies for other programs.

PUBLICATIONS:
Tour directory.

IRS IDENTIFICATION NUMBER: 54-0843105

STAFF:
Margaret Vanderhye, Executive Director

ADDRESS INQUIRIES TO:
Margaret Vanderhye, Executive Director
(See address above.)

VIRGINIA MUSEUM OF FINE ARTS   [514]
Art and Education Division
200 North Boulevard
Richmond, VA 23220-4007
(804) 204-2685
Fax: (804) 204-2675

E-MAIL ADDRESS:
elizabeth.cruickshanks@vmfa.museum

WEB SITE ADDRESS:
www.vmfa.museum/fellowships

FOUNDED: 1940

AREAS OF INTEREST:
Education and careers in the visual arts.

NAME(S) OF PROGRAMS:
● **Professional Fellowship Program**
● **Student Fellowship Program**

TYPE:
Awards/prizes; Fellowships. Awards for undergraduate students, graduate students and professionals in the visual arts including painting, sculpture, crafts, photography, filmmaking, video, printmaking, mixed media, new/emerging media, and drawing. Art history is for graduate students only.

YEAR PROGRAM STARTED: 1940

PURPOSE:
To aid Virginians who seek financial aid for additional education or experience in the arts.

LEGAL BASIS:
State agency administering funds from an endowment and private foundations.

ELIGIBILITY:
All Applicants: Persons must be citizens or permanent residents of the U.S. and current legal residents of Virginia. A legal resident has a valid Virginia driver's license and/or pays income taxes in Virginia and/or is a registered Virginia voter. Applicants must be able to provide verification of residency upon request.

Student Applicants: Persons must be current legal residents of Virginia, and must have been legal residents for at least 12 consecutive months prior to the application deadline. Students paying in-state tuition to an accredited Virginia college, university or school of the arts qualify as legal residents of Virginia. Students must be enrolled full-time at an accredited college, university or school of the arts for the grant period of August 2015 to May 2016. Half-year fall semester Fellowship awards will be considered on a case-by-case basis for full-time students in the final year of a degree program who plan to graduate in December 2015.

Professional Applicants: Persons must be current legal residents of Virginia, and must have been legal residents for at least 24 consecutive months prior to the application deadline. Professional applicants must not be degree-seeking students at the time of the application deadline nor during the grant period of August 2015 to May 2016.

GEOGRAPHIC RESTRICTIONS:
Virginia.

FINANCIAL DATA:
Amount of support per award: Professional Fellowships: $8,000; Undergraduate Fellowships: $4,000; Graduate Fellowships: $6,000.
Total amount of support: $170,000 for the year 2014.

NUMBER OF APPLICANTS MOST RECENT YEAR:
798.

NUMBER OF AWARDS: 27.

APPLICATION INFORMATION:
Contact the Museum.
Duration: August 2015 to May 2016. No renewals.
Deadline: November 7, 2014. Notification in February 2015.

STAFF:
Elizabeth Cruickshanks, Coordinator, Fellowship Program

ADDRESS INQUIRIES TO:
Fellowship Program
(See address above.)

*PLEASE NOTE:
Awards are made to applicants of highest artistic merit whose education and/or careers will benefit from financial assistance.

KURT WEILL FOUNDATION FOR MUSIC   [515]
7 East 20th Street
New York, NY 10003-1106
(212) 505-5240
Fax: (212) 353-9663

E-MAIL ADDRESS:
kwfinfo@kwf.org

WEB SITE ADDRESS:
www.kwf.org

FOUNDED: 1962

AREAS OF INTEREST:
The study and performance of music by Kurt Weill and Marc Blitzstein.

TYPE:
Grants-in-aid; Project/program grants; Research grants; Travel grants. Broadcasts: Proposals are welcome from producers and not-for-profit broadcasters to support programs that feature Kurt Weill's or Marc Blitzstein's life and/or music.

College/University Performance: Grants to colleges and universities in support of general production expenses for performances of Kurt Weill's and Marc Blitzstein's stage works; grants are available to cover musical expenses in connection with performance of complete Weill and Blitzstein concert works.

Educational Outreach: Grants are awarded to performing and educational organizations which may request funding for educational activities (workshops, symposia, scholarly conferences, lectures in connection with performances, study days, secondary and college-level educational initiatives, etc.) focusing on Kurt Weill, Lotte Lenya and/or Marc Blitzstein, including payment of speakers' honoraria and travel expenses, preparation and printing of supporting materials, etc.

Professional Performance Grants: Funding may be requested by professional opera companies, theater companies, dance companies and concert groups in support of production expenses for performances of works by Kurt Weill or Marc Blitzstein.

Publication Assistance: Grants assist in expenses related to preparing manuscripts for publication in a recognized scholarly medium, including editing, indexing, design and reproduction fees. Not-for-profit publishing companies are encouraged to apply.

Research and Travel: Grants support research and travel expenses to locations of primary source material for applicants who are researching a topic related to Kurt Weill, Lotte Lenya and/or Marc Blitzstein.

Kurt Weill Dissertation Fellowship: Assists Ph.D. candidates in Weill-research activities.

Kurt Weill Mentors: Grants are awarded to aid in preparation of Weill or Blitzstein stage or concert performances, to present workshops or lectures or to participate in scholarly symposia; performing arts organizations and educational institutions may request support to engage performers, conductors, directors and scholars who have been designated "Weill Mentors" by the Kurt Weill Foundation.

PURPOSE:
To preserve and perpetuate the legacies of composer Kurt Weill (1900-1950) and actress-singer Lotte Lenya (1898-1981).

ELIGIBILITY:
Broadcasts: Proposals are welcome from producers and not-for-profit broadcasters to support programs that feature Kurt Weill's or Marc Blitzstein's life and/or music. A complete description of the project must be accompanied by a written commitment from the broadcaster.

College/University Performance: Stage Works - All works must be presented in their authorized versions and orchestrations. Performances of *Die sieben Todsonden* are fundable only in Weill's original orchestration and keys. Concert works - Grants are available to cover musical expenses in connection with performance of complete Weill and Blitzstein concert works. Compilation properties consisting solely of Weill's or Blitzstein's songs do not qualify for support.

Educational Outreach: Performing and educational organizations may request funding for educational activities (workshops, symposia, scholarly conferences, lectures in connection with performances, study days, secondary and college-level educational initiatives, etc.) focusing on Weill, Lenya and/or Blitzstein, including payment of speakers' honoraria and travel expenses, preparation and printing of supporting materials, etc.

Professional Performance: Funding may be requested by professional opera companies, theater companies, dance companies and concert groups. All works must be presented in their authorized versions and orchestrations. Applicants must furnish evidence (recordings, reviews) of the artistic merit of the organization's previous performances. Productions of *The Threepenny Opera* are not eligible for funding in the professional production and performance category, and performances of *Die sieben Todsunden* are fundable only in Weill's original orchestration and keys. Performances of *Kleine Dreigroschenmusik* alone are normally not eligible for funding, unless the piece is programmed as part of a group of Weill works. Compilation properties consisting solely of Weill's songs do not qualify for support.

Publication Assistance: Funds may be requested to assist in expenses related to preparing manuscripts for publication in a recognized scholarly medium, including editing, indexing, design and reproduction fees. Not-for-profit publishing companies are encouraged to apply. All proposals must have been subject to peer review. Normally conference proceedings are ineligible unless the essays have undergone significant revision and editing as components of a book.

Research and Travel: Applicants must be researching a topic related to Kurt Weill, Lotte Lenya and/or Marc Blitzstein.

Kurt Weill Dissertation Fellowship: Applicants must be writing their dissertation on a topic related to Kurt Weill.

Kurt Weill Mentors: To aid in preparation of Weill or Blitzstein stage or concert performances, to present workshops or lectures or to participate in scholarly symposia; performing arts organizations and educational institutions may request support to engage performers, conductors, directors and scholars who have been designated "Weill Mentors" by the Kurt Weill Foundation. Such requests may be considered even when the relevant performances would not otherwise be eligible for support under the Foundation's grant program. Applicants should contact the Foundation for further information.

FINANCIAL DATA:
Amount of support per award: Varies.
Total amount of support: Varies.

APPLICATION INFORMATION:
All applications must include the following:
(1) Application Cover Sheet, and
Performance Grant Fact Sheet (if applying for a performance grant) - available at the Foundation web site;
(2) a detailed description of the project;
(3) information about the applicant, including relevant qualifications and past achievements; performance grant applicants should also include a DVD or audio recording of a past performance and;
(4) a detailed and itemized budget specifying entire project expenses and income, including ticket revenue and income anticipated from other funding sources and date of determination; applicants must notify the Foundation if other grants are awarded.

In addition, specific items are requested for each category:
Broadcasts: a complete description of the project must be accompanied by a written commitment from the broadcaster;
College/University Performance: applicants must furnish evidence (recordings, reviews) of the artistic merit of the organization's previous performances;
Educational Outreach: applications must include detailed description of the educational activities and vitae for expert participants;
Professional Performance: applicants must furnish evidence (recordings, reviews) of the artistic merit of the organization's previous performances;
Publication Assistance: all proposals must have been subject to peer review; such reviews must be submitted in support of the application, along with a copy of the manuscript;
Research and Travel: grant applicants must submit a detailed outline of the proposed project, a writing sample, and at least one letter of recommendation;
Weill Dissertation Fellowship: applicants must include a copy of the dissertation proposal, at least one writing sample, and two letters of recommendation, one of which must be from the applicant's faculty advisor.

Deadline: November 1 for the following calendar year, academic year or cultural season. Applications for support of major professional productions/festivals/exhibitions, etc., will be evaluated on a case-by-case basis without application or performance deadlines. An additional application deadline of June 1 has been established, limited exclusively to College/University Performance grants for productions taking place in the fall semester of the current academic year.

ADDRESS INQUIRIES TO:
Carolyn Weber, Director
(See address above.)

WEST VIRGINIA DIVISION OF CULTURE AND HISTORY   [516]

The Culture Center
State Capitol Complex
1900 Kanawha Boulevard East
Charleston, WV 25305-0300
(304) 558-0220
Fax: (304) 558-3560

E-MAIL ADDRESS:
renee.margoce@wv.gov

WEB SITE ADDRESS:
www.wvculture.org

FOUNDED: 1967

AREAS OF INTEREST:
Artists and arts organizations, including community development, touring, institutions, special projects and support for artists, cultural facilities purchase and rehabilitation.

CONSULTING OR VOLUNTEER SERVICES:
Consultation in a variety of fields is available.

TYPE:
Capital grants; Challenge/matching grants; General operating grants; Internships; Project/program grants; Residencies; Technical assistance; Training grants; Travel grants. Long-range planning. Individual artists grants.

YEAR PROGRAM STARTED: 1967

PURPOSE:
To provide financial and technical assistance to further the promotion, presentation and development of the arts throughout the state of West Virginia.

LEGAL BASIS:
Government agency.

ELIGIBILITY:
Nonprofit organizations and public agencies may apply. Nonprofits must have been based in West Virginia one year prior to application. Individual artists must be residents of West Virginia one year prior to application.

GEOGRAPHIC RESTRICTIONS:
West Virginia.

FINANCIAL DATA:
Generally, grants cover 50% of project cost.
Amount of support per award: $125 to $100,000.
Total amount of support: Approximately $2,600,000 for the year 2013.
Matching fund requirements: Dollar-for-dollar.

COOPERATIVE FUNDING PROGRAMS: Ohio River Border Initiative (ORBI) with Ohio Arts Council.

NUMBER OF APPLICANTS MOST RECENT YEAR: 26.

NUMBER OF AWARDS: 12.

APPLICATION INFORMATION:
Copies of application guidelines and application forms are available upon request to the Commission or can be found on the Division web site.
Duration: One year. Must reapply for additional funding.
Deadline: Varies.

PUBLICATIONS:
Annual report; application guidelines; *ArtWorks*, newsletter.

OFFICERS:
Randall Reid-Smith, Commissioner
Karen Gresham, Deputy Commissioner

ADDRESS INQUIRIES TO:
Renée Margoce, Director of Arts
West Virginia Commission on the Arts
(See address above.)

WHITAKER FOUNDATION   [517]
308 North 21st Street
Suite 400
St. Louis, MO 63103
(314) 241-4352
Fax: (314) 241-4381

E-MAIL ADDRESS:
info@thewhitakerfoundation.org

WEB SITE ADDRESS:
www.thewhitakerfoundation.org

FOUNDED: 1975

AREAS OF INTEREST:
The arts, the use of and preservation of parks.

TYPE:
Project/program grants. Project/program grants are for urban parks and the arts.

PURPOSE:
To enrich lives through the arts; to encourage the preservation and use of parks.

LEGAL BASIS:
Private foundation.

ELIGIBILITY:
Organizations must be tax-exempt 501(c)(3). Project support is preferred. No support for social events.

The Foundation does not make grants to individuals.

GEOGRAPHIC RESTRICTIONS:
Metropolitan area of St. Louis, Missouri.

FINANCIAL DATA:
Amount of support per award: Varies.
Total amount of support: $1,053,361 for fiscal year 2013.

NUMBER OF APPLICANTS MOST RECENT YEAR: 150.

APPLICATION INFORMATION:
Detailed guidelines and application form can be obtained from the Foundation.
Duration: Varies.
Deadline: Letters of Inquiry: August 1, November 1 and February 1; Invited Proposals: December 1, March 1 and September 1, respectively.

PUBLICATIONS:
Guidelines.

ADDRESS INQUIRIES TO:
Christy Gray, Executive Director
(See address above.)

WISCONSIN ARTS BOARD   [518]
201 West Washington Avenue
2nd Floor
Madison, WI 53703
(608) 266-0190
Fax: (608) 267-0380

E-MAIL ADDRESS:
artsboard@wisconsin.gov

WEB SITE ADDRESS:
www.artsboard.wisconsin.gov

FOUNDED: 1973

AREAS OF INTEREST:
All arts disciplines in Wisconsin.

CONSULTING OR VOLUNTEER SERVICES:
Workshops and individual consultations.

NAME(S) OF PROGRAMS:
- **Creation & Presentation**
- **Creative Communities**
- **Folk Arts Apprenticeship Program**
- **Wisconsin Regranting Program**

TYPE:
Challenge/matching grants; Internships; Project/program grants; Technical assistance. Inquiry services, research and funding. Services provided to institutions and individuals statewide in Wisconsin.

Creative Communities Grants include Arts in Education, Local Arts and Folk Arts.

PURPOSE:
To provide support of arts projects and activities in the state of Wisconsin.

LEGAL BASIS:
Agency of the state of Wisconsin.

ELIGIBILITY:
Applicants must be organizations located in Wisconsin, operating for three years and have 501(c)(3) tax-exempt status.

GEOGRAPHIC RESTRICTIONS:
Wisconsin.

FINANCIAL DATA:
Amount of support per award: $1,500 to $20,000 depending on the program.
Total amount of support: $1,000,000 for fiscal year 2013.
Matching fund requirements: All grants must be matched.

NUMBER OF AWARDS: Varies.

APPLICATION INFORMATION:
Application form is available online.
Duration: One year.
Deadline: Varies.

STAFF:
George Tzougros, Executive Director

ADDRESS INQUIRIES TO:
Karen Goeschko, Assistant Director
Programs and Services
(See address above.)

WOMEN IN FILM
6100 Wilshire Boulevard
Suite 710
Los Angeles, CA 90048
(323) 935-2211
Fax: (323) 935-2212

E-MAIL ADDRESS:
foundation@wif.org

WEB SITE ADDRESS:
www.wif.org/fff

TYPE:
Project/program grants. Awards for completion of films or videotapes on subjects that meet the stated guidelines of WIF on an annual basis.

See entry 1100 for full listing.

WOMEN'S STUDIO WORKSHOP (WSW)   [519]
722 Binnewater Lane
Rosendale, NY 12472
(845) 658-9133
Fax: (845) 658-9031

E-MAIL ADDRESS:
info@wsworkshop.org

WEB SITE ADDRESS:
www.wsworkshop.org

FOUNDED: 1974

AREAS OF INTEREST:
Book arts.

NAME(S) OF PROGRAMS:
- **Artists' Book Residency Grants**

TYPE:
Project/program grants; Residencies.

YEAR PROGRAM STARTED: 1979

PURPOSE:
To enable artists to produce a limited edition artists' book while in residence at the Women's Studio Workshop.

ELIGIBILITY:
Women artists working in printmaking or the book arts.

FINANCIAL DATA:
Amount of support per award: $350 per week artist stipend, up to $750 materials, up to $250 travel costs within the continental U.S., access to all studios, and housing.

NUMBER OF APPLICANTS MOST RECENT YEAR:
100.

NUMBER OF AWARDS: 3 to 5.

APPLICATION INFORMATION:
Application must include:
(1) application form;
(2) 100-word description of the project (one copy), which should also include studios/media needed;
(3) a structural dummy to demonstrate how the book will appear; it does not have to be a complete representation of the finished piece; however, please include one to two spreads that are fully sketched out; the dummy should be actual size; (the Workshop anticipates that, if funded, applicant will refine her ideas before her residency);
(4) materials budget (two copies);
(5) resume;
(6) 10 images of recent work plus an image script, which should include title, media, dimensions and date and;
(7) self-addressed, stamped envelope or appropriate postage, if applicant wishes to have her application materials or dummy returned (please indicate if one wishes to have one's book dummy returned).
Duration: Six to eight weeks. Nonrenewable.
Deadline: November 15.

ADDRESS INQUIRIES TO:
Ann Kalmbach, Executive Director
(See address above.)

WOMEN'S STUDIO WORKSHOP (WSW) [520]
722 Binnewater Lane
Rosendale, NY 12472
(845) 658-9133
Fax: (845) 658-9031

E-MAIL ADDRESS:
info@wsworkshop.org

WEB SITE ADDRESS:
www.wsworkshop.org

FOUNDED: 1974

AREAS OF INTEREST:
Art-in-education.

NAME(S) OF PROGRAMS:
● **Art-in-Education Artists' Book Residency Grant**

TYPE:
Residencies. With National Endowment for the Arts (NEA) support, WSW awards two eight-week residencies to artists in the book arts. This is a residency grant.

PURPOSE:
To help grantees create new work while they simultaneously teach young people through the workshop's studio-based art-in-education program.

ELIGIBILITY:
Women artists working in printmaking or the book arts.

FINANCIAL DATA:
Amount of support per award: $400 per week stipend, $750 materials budget, housing, travel costs up to $250 within the continental U.S. and unlimited studio access.

APPLICATION INFORMATION:
Application should include:
(1) application form;
(2) 100-word description of the project, which should include media or studio needed to produce the edition;
(3) a one-page description of applicant's relevant experience working with children;
(4) a structural dummy to demonstrate how the book will be bound or function when handled; it does not have to be a complete representation of the finished piece; however, please include one to two spreads that are fully sketched out; the dummy should be actual size (the Workshop anticipates that, if funded, applicant will refine her ideas before her residency);
(5) materials budget (two copies);
(6) a CD with 10 clearly marked images of recent work; an image list should also be provided and include title, media, dimensions and date; check the Workshop Faq Sheet on its web site for digital specifications and;
(7) application materials/book dummies will not be returned unless requested; a self-addressed, stamped envelope or appropriate postage should be included if applicant wishes to have her application materials or dummy returned.
Duration: Eight to 10 weeks.
Deadline: November 15.

ADDRESS INQUIRIES TO:
Ann Kalmbach, Executive Director
(See address above.)

*PLEASE NOTE:
Normally, residencies are September to October and March to April. Specific dates are determined by the academic calendar and vary annually.

WOMEN'S STUDIO WORKSHOP (WSW) [521]
722 Binnewater Lane
Rosendale, NY 12472
(845) 658-9133
Fax: (845) 658-9031

E-MAIL ADDRESS:
info@wsworkshop.org

WEB SITE ADDRESS:
www.wsworkshop.org

FOUNDED: 1974

AREAS OF INTEREST:
Visual artists.

NAME(S) OF PROGRAMS:
● **Studio Residency**

TYPE:
Residencies.

YEAR PROGRAM STARTED: 1999

PURPOSE:
To provide artists with time and resources to create a new body of work.

ELIGIBILITY:
Women printmakers, papermakers, book artists, ceramists, photographers or artist collaborators can apply.

FINANCIAL DATA:
Amount of support per award: $350 per week artist stipend, up to $500 for materials, up to $250 for travel within the continental U.S., plus housing and unlimited studio use.

NUMBER OF APPLICANTS MOST RECENT YEAR:
125 in 2013.

NUMBER OF AWARDS: 2.

APPLICATION INFORMATION:
Applicants should submit:
(1) application form;
(2) a 100-word project description;
(3) resume/curriculum vitae;
(4) 10 numbered images of recent work, plus image script and;
(5) self-addressed, stamped envelope for return of materials.
Duration: Six to eight weeks. Nonrenewable.
Deadline: April 1.

ADDRESS INQUIRIES TO:
Ann Kalmbach, Executive Director
(See address above.)

THE HELENE WURLITZER FOUNDATION OF NEW MEXICO [522]
218 Los Pandos Road
Taos, NM 87571
(575) 758-2413
Fax: (575) 758-2559

E-MAIL ADDRESS:
hwf@taosnet.com

WEB SITE ADDRESS:
www.wurlitzerfoundation.org

FOUNDED: 1954

AREAS OF INTEREST:
Creative, not interpretive, work in all media and allied fields.

TYPE:
Residencies. Residence grants for national and international artists involved in creative work, including writing, painting, sculpture and musical composition.

YEAR PROGRAM STARTED: 1954

PURPOSE:
To encourage and stimulate creative work in all media, including visual arts, literary arts and musical composition.

LEGAL BASIS:
Tax-exempt under Section 501(c)(3) and Section 4945(j)(3), (g)(3) and (g)(1).

ELIGIBILITY:
No restrictions are made on the basis of race, sex, age or religious or ethnic background or national origin.

FINANCIAL DATA:
No direct monetary grants are made. Residences are located in Taos, NM and are furnished with free utilities and rent.
Amount of support per award: Varies.
Total amount of support: Varies.

COOPERATIVE FUNDING PROGRAMS: Robert Chesley Foundation.

NUMBER OF APPLICANTS MOST RECENT YEAR:
199.

NUMBER OF AWARDS: 33.

APPLICATION INFORMATION:
Application must include five samples maximum (photographs or digital images) from visual artists (please list medium and dimensions), writing sample not to exceed 35 double-spaced pages or six poems from literary artists, or one CD/DVD from

composers. Failure to comply with the guidelines will result in elimination from the review process. The Foundation will not retain samples of work and recommends a self-addressed, stamped envelope be included with samples if applicant wishes to have samples returned.

Applicant should also send self-addressed, stamped envelope if requesting application via mail.

Duration: Three-month residencies preferred. Grants can be shortened or extended under special circumstances.

Deadline: January 18.

IRS IDENTIFICATION NUMBER: 85-0128634

OFFICERS AND BOARD OF DIRECTORS:
Rena Rosequist, President
Peggy Nelson, Vice President
Bill Ebie, Treasurer
Harold Hahn, Secretary
Michael A. Knight, Executive Director
Joseph Caldwell
Tito Naranjo

ADDRESS INQUIRIES TO:
Michael A. Knight, Executive Director
(See address above.)

*SPECIAL STIPULATIONS:
Single occupancy only, no pets, no smoking, no outside employment while in residence.

WYOMING ARTS COUNCIL [523]

2320 Capitol Avenue
Cheyenne, WY 82002
(307) 777-7742
Fax: (307) 777-5499

WEB SITE ADDRESS:
wyoarts.state.wy.us

FOUNDED: 1967

AREAS OF INTEREST:
Arts within the state of Wyoming.

CONSULTING OR VOLUNTEER SERVICES:
Assistance for 501(c)(3) nonprofit and government organizations.

NAME(S) OF PROGRAMS:
- **Art Projects Grants**
- **Artists Across Wyoming Grants**
- **Arts Education Grants**
- **Capacity Building Grants**
- **Community Arts Partners Grants**
- **Grants to Organizations Grants**
- **Individual Artist Professional Development Grants**
- **Literary Arts Fellowships**
- **Operating Support Grants**
- **Performing Arts Fellowships**
- **Visual Arts Fellowships**

TYPE:
General operating grants; Project/program grants. Individual Artist Professional Development Grants, Literary Arts Fellowships, Performing Arts Fellowships and Visual Arts Fellowships are for individual artists. General operating support grants and project/program grants are for 501(c)(3) nonprofit and government organizations.

YEAR PROGRAM STARTED: 1967

PURPOSE:
To assist artistic programs of outstanding quality that serve the needs of Wyoming citizens, further public interest in the state's cultural heritage and resources and encourage artistic expression, essential for the well-being of the arts.

LEGAL BASIS:
Agency of the state of Wyoming.

ELIGIBILITY:
Grants are provided to 501(c)(3) nonprofit organizations, educational institutions and governmental entities within the state, including arts centers, museums, symphonies, schools, dance workshops, theatre and local arts councils. Individual Artist Professional Development Grants and the individual fellowships are provided in visual, literary and performing arts to Wyoming residents.

GEOGRAPHIC RESTRICTIONS:
Wyoming.

FINANCIAL DATA:
Amount of support per award: Varies.
Total amount of support: Varies.
Matching fund requirements: A one-to-one cash match is required on most grants.

NUMBER OF APPLICANTS MOST RECENT YEAR:
More than 300.

NUMBER OF AWARDS: Over 300 grants are awarded each year.

APPLICATION INFORMATION:
Apply online for most grant programs.
Duration: One fiscal year (July 1 to the following June 30).
Deadline: Varies.

PUBLICATIONS:
Artist roster; newsletter.

STAFF:
Rita Basom, Manager
Camilla El-Antably, Arts Education Specialist/Deputy Manager
Karen Merklin, Grants Manager
Michael Lange, Community Development of the Arts Specialist
Annie Hatch, Folk Arts Specialist
Michael Shay, Individual Arts Specialist
Katie Christensen, Arts Education Specialist

ADDRESS INQUIRIES TO:
Karen Merklin, Grants Manager
(See address above.)

Performing arts

ACADEMY FOUNDATION OF THE ACADEMY OF MOTION PICTURE ARTS AND SCIENCES [524]

1313 North Vine Street
Los Angeles, CA 90028
(310) 247-3010
Fax: (310) 247-3794

E-MAIL ADDRESS:
nicholl@oscars.org

WEB SITE ADDRESS:
www.oscars.org/nicholl

FOUNDED: 1927

AREAS OF INTEREST:
Motion picture arts and sciences.

NAME(S) OF PROGRAMS:
- **The Academy Nicholl Fellowships in Screenwriting**

TYPE:
Awards/prizes; Fellowships. Awards provide a portion of living expenses for one year for

promising new writers so that they may concentrate during that period on writing for the screen.

YEAR PROGRAM STARTED: 1985

PURPOSE:
To foster the development of the art of motion picture screenwriting.

LEGAL BASIS:
Nonpublic foundation.

ELIGIBILITY:
Applicants may not have earned more than $25,000 or any other consideration as a screenwriter for theatrical films or television or sold or optioned screen or television rights to any original story, treatment, outline screenplay or teleplay.

FINANCIAL DATA:
Amount of support per award: $35,000 each.
Total amount of support: $175,000 for the year 2013.

NUMBER OF APPLICANTS MOST RECENT YEAR:
7,251 for the year 2013.

NUMBER OF AWARDS: Up to 5 fellowships each year.

APPLICATION INFORMATION:
Applicants must submit one copy of an original screenplay in PDF format, approximately 90 to 120 pages in length, written in screenplay format standard to the U.S. motion picture industry. Submissions must have been written originally in English; translations will not be accepted. Submissions must be the original work of the applicant and may not be based, in whole or in part, on any other person's or persons' fictional or nonfictional material, published or unpublished, produced or unproduced. Sequels utilizing characters or storylines from produced motion pictures, television shows or published fiction are not eligible. Nor are adaptations eligible, unless the source material is solely the entrant's original work.

Applicants must also fill out an application form via an online account, completed in its entirety and pay a nonrefundable entry fee. This fee will be applied against judging and administrative costs. Applications and screenplays are accepted online only. Submitted materials will not be returned.
Duration: One year. Commencing around the first week of November.
Deadline: Uploaded by 5 P.M., April 10. Announcement in late October.

PUBLICATIONS:
Guidelines.

FELLOWSHIP COMMITTEE:
Gale Anne Hurd, Chairperson
John Bailey
Naomi Foner
Ron Mardigian
Dan Petrie, Jr.
Tom Rickman
Eric Roth
Eva Marie Saint
Peter Samuelson
Vicki Sanchez
Robert Shapiro
Buffy Shutt
Dana Stevens
Robin Swicord

ADDRESS INQUIRIES TO:
Academy Nicholl Fellowships
(See address above.)

*PLEASE NOTE:
Each fellowship is payable quarterly for one year. The first payment will be made at the

start of the fellowship year. The second, third, fourth and final payments will be made subject to satisfactory progress of the recipient's work, as judged by the Academy's Nicholl Fellowship Committee. The Academy reserves the right to grant no awards if, in the opinion of the Academy Nicholl Fellowship Committee, no application is of sufficient merit.

*SPECIAL STIPULATIONS:
Academy Nicholl Fellowships may not be held concurrently with other fellowships. During the fellowship year, Academy Nicholl Fellows are expected to complete an original screenplay approximately 90 to 120 pages in length.

AMERICAN DANCE FESTIVAL   [525]
Box 90772
Durham, NC 27708-0772
(919) 684-6402
Fax: (919) 684-5459

E-MAIL ADDRESS:
adf@americandancefestival.org

WEB SITE ADDRESS:
www.americandancefestival.org

NAME(S) OF PROGRAMS:
• Tuition Scholarships

TYPE:
Scholarships.

PURPOSE:
To offer assistance to promising students.

ELIGIBILITY:
Open to promising students who have a high level of technical ability, creative potential and who have experience in either performing and/or choreography.

GEOGRAPHIC RESTRICTIONS:
Primarily United States.

FINANCIAL DATA:
Amount of support per award: Quarter to full tuition.
Total amount of support: Varies.

APPLICATION INFORMATION:
Students must either submit their application before their audition date or be prepared to turn it in at the audition site. Students unable to attend an audition may submit a DVD containing two minutes of technique and a one-and-a-half-minute solo.
Duration: Six-and-a-half weeks.
Deadline: Details are available on the web site.

ADDRESS INQUIRIES TO:
Nicolle Wasserman Greenhood
Director of School Administration and Student Affairs
(See address above.)

AMERICAN SOCIETY FOR THEATRE RESEARCH (ASTR)   [526]
P.O. Box 1798
Boulder, CO 80306-1798
303-530-1838
Fax: 303-530-1839

E-MAIL ADDRESS:
fellowships@astr.org

WEB SITE ADDRESS:
www.astr.org

FOUNDED: 1956

AREAS OF INTEREST:
Theatre studies (history, criticism, theory) and performance studies.

NAME(S) OF PROGRAMS:
• **The ASTR Collaborative Research Award**
• **Biennial Sally Banes Publication Prize**
• **Oscar G. Brockett Essay Prize**
• **Cambridge University Press Prize**
• **Chinoy Dissertation Research Fellowships**
• **Co-sponsored Events Awards**
• **Selma Jeanne Cohen Conference Presentation Award**
• **Distinguished Scholar Award**
• **Grants for Researchers with Heavy Teaching Loads**
• **Barnard Hewitt Award**
• **Errol Hill Award**
• **Gerald Kahan Scholar's Prize**
• **David Keller Travel Grants**
• **Thomas F. Marshall Graduate Student Awards**
• **Brooks McNamara Publishing Subvention**
• **Research Fellowships**
• **Targeted Research Areas Grants**

TYPE:
Awards/prizes; Conferences/seminars; Development grants; Exchange programs; Fellowships; Research grants; Scholarships; Seed money grants; Travel grants; Visiting scholars. The ASTR Collaborative Research Award aims to foster the exchange of research across different academic and community contexts within the U.S. or between U.S. scholars/artists and those abroad. It also aims to foster long-term relationships benefiting faculty who work in different types of institutional environments and to foster the exchange of research in subject areas underrepresented in U.S. theatre scholarship, pedagogy, and performance practice.

Biennial Sally Banes Publication Prize is presented in even-numbered years for the publication (book or essay) that best explores the intersections of theatre and dance/movement in the previous two calendar years.

Oscar G. Brockett Essay Prize is jointly awarded by the Society and the Oscar G. Brockett Center for Theatre History and Criticism at the University of Texas - Austin for the best essay published in English in a refereed scholarly journal or volume published by a scholarly press. The essay can relate to any subject in theatre research, broadly construed.

The Cambridge University Press Prize is given for a Society conference plenary paper written by a first-time plenary presenter.

Chinoy Dissertation Research Fellowships assist Ph.D. candidates with travel to national and international collections to conduct research connected with their dissertations.

Co-sponsored Events Awards assist with events that fulfill ASTR's purpose through collaboration with other organizations and institutions and increase the visibility of the work of both ASTR and the award recipient within a wider professional context.

Selma Jeanne Cohen Conference Presentation Award goes to a scholar to participate in a plenary or working session at the ASTR

conference. The presentation must explore the intersections of theatre and dance/movement.

Distinguished Scholar Award is given each year to a scholar whose body of work has made a significant contribution to the field of theatre, dance, opera, and/or performance studies.

Grants for Researchers with Heavy Teaching Loads promote scholarly and practical exchange among theatre researchers by providing opportunities to faculty at institutions with heavy teaching loads and limited support for scholarship.

The Barnard Hewitt Award for Outstanding Research in Theatre History is awarded each year to the best book in "theatre history or cognate disciplines" published during the previous calendar year. The Department of Theatre at the University of Illinois, Urbana-Champaign, provides the monetary prize.

Errol Hill Award is given in recognition of outstanding scholarship in African American theatre, drama, and/or performance studies. The book or article must be published during the previous calendar year.

Gerald Kahan Scholar's Prize is awarded for the best essay written by a junior scholar and published in English in a refereed scholarly journal on any subject in theatre research, broadly construed.

David Keller Travel Grants encourage untenured scholars with terminal degrees to become active members of the Society by helping them to meet the expenses of attending the ASTR annual meeting in November.

Thomas F. Marshall Graduate Student Awards encourage active student membership in the Society by helping to meet the expenses of attending the ASTR annual meeting.

Brooks McNamara Publishing Subvention supports the costs of securing rights to reproduce illustrations for publication, costs of acquiring illustrations, and/or the costs of reproducing illustrations in conjunction with a book under contract for publication. (Electronic publications will also be considered.)

Research Fellowships underwrite some expenses associated with projects in the field of theatre and/or performance studies.

Targeted Research Areas Grants support specific projects in areas currently underrepresented. Such areas include, but are not limited to, pre-1900 research; Asian, African, Latin American, and Middle Eastern theatre, dance and performance. Translations of important theatre documents, including plays, are also considered.

YEAR PROGRAM STARTED: 1976

LEGAL BASIS:
Nonprofit learned society.

ELIGIBILITY:
The ASTR Collaborative Research Award: At least one participant from a host institution must be a current ASTR member.

Biennial Sally Banes Publication Prize: Any independent, tenured or untenured scholar; eligible books and articles must have been published in the previous two calendar years.

Oscar G. Brockett Essay Prize: Author must have been a member of ASTR for at least three years and be at least seven years beyond the Ph.D. Essays must have been published in the previous calendar year and may not have appeared elsewhere previously.

Cambridge University Press Prize: ASTR conference plenary paper written by a first-time plenary presenter.

Helen Krich Chinoy Dissertation Research Fellowships: Ph.D. candidates who have passed their qualifying exams within the last two years (or will have passed their qualifying exams by June of the current year) and have begun working on their dissertations. The project must be part of the dissertation research.

Co-sponsored Events Awards: Applications may come from individuals, institutions or a combination, to support events of regional, national or international significance in the form of conferences, colloquia, symposia, summits, etc. Events must foster scholarship on theatre and performance.

Selma Jeanne Cohen Conference Presentation Award: Tenured, untenured and contingent faculty, independent scholars and graduate students are eligible to apply.

Distinguished Scholar Award: Nominations are accepted from ASTR members and previous recipients of the award. In addition to contributions made to theatre, dance, opera and/or performance studies, involvement in ASTR is also a criterion of the award.

Grants for Researchers with Heavy Teaching Loads: Any full-time or contingent instructor at the college level, with a terminal degree and a heavy teaching load or the equivalent load based on heavy production and/or service obligations.

Barnard Hewitt Award: Eligible books must have been published in the previous calendar year. They must be written by a scholar or scholars residing in the Americas, or by a scholar or scholars located outside the Americas but writing on an American topic. Plays, edited collections and anthologies are not eligible for this prize.

Errol Hill Award: The book or article must have been published in the previous calendar year. Authors may nominate their own works; nominations from publishers and editors are also accepted.

Gerald Kahan Scholar's Prize: The author must be untenured and within seven years of the Doctorate, or must be enrolled in a doctoral program, at the time the essay is published.

David Keller Travel Grants: Any untenured scholars with terminal degrees, including independent scholars and tenure-track and adjunct faculty.

Thomas F. Marshall Graduate Student Awards: Any student majoring in theatre/performance studies in any academic department at any level of higher education.

Brooks McNamara Publishing Subvention: Any scholar holding a terminal degree and who has been a member of ASTR for at least three years. Applicant must hold a book contract to qualify. Preference is given to junior scholars.

Research Fellowships: Anyone who holds a terminal degree and has been a member of the Society for at least three years is eligible to apply.

Targeted Research Areas Grants: Any independent, tenured or untenured scholar who is currently a member of the Society

and holds a terminal degree, or any graduate student who is applying in support of a project that is not directly related to her/his dissertation.

FINANCIAL DATA:
Total amount of support: Varies.

APPLICATION INFORMATION:
Application information is available on the web site, under "Awards."
Duration: Varies.
Deadline: Varies.

ADDRESS INQUIRIES TO:
Director of Fellowships and Awards (See address above.)

ARTS MIDWEST   [527]
2908 Hennepin Avenue, Suite 200
Minneapolis, MN 55408-1954
(612) 341-0755
Fax: (612) 341-0902

E-MAIL ADDRESS:
christy@artsmidwest.org

WEB SITE ADDRESS:
www.artsmidwest.org

FOUNDED: 1985

AREAS OF INTEREST:
Performing arts booking conference and performing arts grants to presenting organizations.

NAME(S) OF PROGRAMS:
● **Arts Midwest Conference**
● **Arts Midwest Touring Fund**

TYPE:
Conferences/seminars. Performing arts grants.

YEAR PROGRAM STARTED: 1985

PURPOSE:
To connect people throughout the Midwest and the world to meaningful arts opportunities, sharing creativity, knowledge, and understanding across boundaries.

LEGAL BASIS:
Nonprofit.

ELIGIBILITY:
Nonprofit performing arts presenters within our nine-state region.

GEOGRAPHIC RESTRICTIONS:
Illinois, Indiana, Iowa, Michigan, Minnesota, North Dakota, Ohio, South Dakota and Wisconsin.

FINANCIAL DATA:
Amount of support per award: Up to 20% of the artist's contracted fee, $500 to $4,000.
Total amount of support: Varies.

NUMBER OF APPLICANTS MOST RECENT YEAR:
200.

APPLICATION INFORMATION:
Application information is available online. Only one application may be submitted.
Duration: Varies.
Deadline: Varies.

THE BANFF CENTRE   [528]
107 Tunnel Mountain Drive
Banff AB T1L 1H5 Canada
(403) 762-6180
Fax: (403) 762-6345

E-MAIL ADDRESS:
arts_info@banffcentre.ca

WEB SITE ADDRESS:
www.banffcentre.ca

FOUNDED: 1933

AREAS OF INTEREST:
Studio art, photography, ceramics, performance art, video art, theatre production and design, stage management and opera.

TYPE:
Conferences/seminars; Project/program grants; Residencies; Work-study programs.

PURPOSE:
To provide financial assistance to deserving artists for a residency at The Banff Centre.

ELIGIBILITY:
Open to advanced students who have been accepted for a residency at The Banff Centre.

FINANCIAL DATA:
Amount of support per award: Varies.
Total amount of support: Varies.

APPLICATION INFORMATION:
Applicants must submit a completed application form, accompanied by requested documentation.
Duration: Varies.
Deadline: Varies per program.

CAPEZIO/BALLET MAKERS DANCE FOUNDATION, INC. [529]
One Campus Road
Totowa, NJ 07512
(973) 595-9000 ext. 6203
Fax: (973) 595-0341

WEB SITE ADDRESS:
www.capeziodance.com

FOUNDED: 1952

AREAS OF INTEREST:
National, state and some local dance profession service organizations. Annual Capezio Dance Award in recognition of significant contribution to the art form.

NAME(S) OF PROGRAMS:
● **Capezio Dance Award**
● **Grants Program**

TYPE:
Awards/prizes; Development grants; General operating grants; Project/program grants. Grants to national, state and some local dance service organizations such as dance alliances, dance festivals and other organizations having a major impact on the field.

Capezio Dance Award is given annually by the Trustees to an individual, company or organization that brings respect, stature and distinction to dance in America.

YEAR PROGRAM STARTED: 1952

PURPOSE:
To create a greater awareness and appreciation of dance as an art form and support efforts which service and increase interest in the dance field.

LEGAL BASIS:
Private tax-exempt, corporate foundation.

ELIGIBILITY:
National, state and local organizations that provide essential services to the dance field may apply. Organization must have 501(c)(3) status. No support for individual dancers, companies or schools.

GEOGRAPHIC RESTRICTIONS:
United States.

FINANCIAL DATA:
Amount of support per award: $1,000 to $10,000.

Total amount of support: $50,000 to $100,000.

NUMBER OF APPLICANTS MOST RECENT YEAR: 200.

NUMBER OF AWARDS: 50 to 70.

APPLICATION INFORMATION:
Guidelines are available on the Foundation web site.

Duration: No limitations.

Deadline: April 1.

PUBLICATIONS:
Brochure of guidelines and criteria; listing of grantees and Capezio Award winners.

IRS IDENTIFICATION NUMBER: 13-6161198

*PLEASE NOTE:
Does not fund individuals, schools, colleges or universities, films or media or dance companies.

CHOPIN FOUNDATION OF THE U.S.

1440 79th Street Causeway, Suite 117
Miami, FL 33141
(305) 868-0624
Fax: (305) 865-5150

E-MAIL ADDRESS:
info@chopin.org

WEB SITE ADDRESS:
www.chopin.org

TYPE:
Scholarships. Scholarship program supporting young American pianists, 14 to 17 years of age.

See entry 758 for full listing.

COLONIAL PLAYERS, INC. THEATER-IN-THE-ROUND   [530]

108 East Street
Annapolis, MD 21401
(410) 268-7373 (Box Office)

E-MAIL ADDRESS:
treasurer@thecolonialplayers.org

WEB SITE ADDRESS:
thecolonialplayers.org

FOUNDED: 1949

AREAS OF INTEREST:
Theatre and the arts.

NAME(S) OF PROGRAMS:
• **Biennial Promising Playwright Award**

TYPE:
Awards/prizes. Monetary award and showcase for an outstanding script by an aspiring playwright.

YEAR PROGRAM STARTED: 1973

PURPOSE:
To foster the arts and to encourage aspiring playwrights and promising talent in every aspect of the theatre.

LEGAL BASIS:
501(c)(3) nonprofit.

ELIGIBILITY:
Competition is open to any aspiring playwright residing in any of the states descendant from the original 13 colonies (Connecticut, Delaware, Georgia, Maryland, Massachusetts, New Hampshire, New Jersey, New York, North Carolina, Pennsylvania, Rhode Island, South Carolina, Virginia, Washington, DC and West Virginia.)

Only full-length plays, suitable for arena production, with up to two settings, and running not less than 90 minutes and not more than two hours, excluding intermission, will be considered. Cast sizes are limited to 10 actors or fewer. Musicals and adaptations in copyright will not be considered. In addition, plays that have been previously produced professionally will not be considered.

Plays submitted must be free of royalty and copyright restrictions which would prevent Colonial Players from producing the play. Collaborations of two or more authors are acceptable. Musicals and adaptations in copyright will not be considered. The play must not have been professionally produced elsewhere at the time of submission. Nonprofessional productions, staged readings and/or workshop productions prior to submission are permitted. (Please list places and dates along with name, address, phone number of the playwright in a sealed envelope attached to the manuscript.) Only plays which receive Honorable Mention from previous Colonial Players' contests may be resubmitted for consideration.

GEOGRAPHIC RESTRICTIONS:
Connecticut, Delaware, Georgia, Maryland, Massachusetts, New Hampshire, New Jersey, New York, North Carolina, Pennsylvania, Rhode Island, South Carolina, Virginia, Washington, DC and West Virginia.

FINANCIAL DATA:
Amount of support per award: $1,000 and workshop reading of the play.

NUMBER OF APPLICANTS MOST RECENT YEAR: 200.

NUMBER OF AWARDS: 1.

APPLICATION INFORMATION:
Scripts must be typewritten and firmly bound in a cover (no brads, no staples and no ring binders). The first sheet must include only the title of the play. The second sheet must contain a description of the setting(s), characters and the time of action. In a separate packet, author should submit the same first two pages bound with a one-page synopsis of the play and a 10-page sample from the play. The author's name, address and phone number may not appear anywhere on the manuscripts (no headers or footers) but must be attached to the manuscript in a sealed envelope. Scripts will be numbered for judging.

Duration: Colonial Players reserves the right to work with the Director in a workshop production of the play within two years after the award is announced. Subsequent productions of the play at other theaters must give credit to Colonial Players, Inc. for premiering the play.

Deadline: Manuscripts will be accepted only if they bear postmarks between September 1 and December 31. Those received before or after will not be considered. Final decision of the judges will be announced no later than June 30 of the following year.

IRS IDENTIFICATION NUMBER: 23-7074203

OFFICERS:
Terry Averill, President

ADDRESS INQUIRIES TO:
Coordinator
The Colonial Players, Inc.
Promising Playwright Contest
(See address above.)

Manuscripts must be sent to
The Colonial Players, Inc.
Promising Playwright Contest
(See address above.)

*PLEASE NOTE:
The award-winning playwright will be invited to a weekend workshop devoted entirely to the winning play the summer after the contest winner is announced. The workshop will include intensive discussions with directors, designers and actors, and a rehearsed reading in front of an audience.

MARTHA GRAHAM SCHOOL OF CONTEMPORARY DANCE, INC.   [531]

55 Bethune Street, 11th Floor
New York, NY 10014
(212) 838-5886
(212) 229-9200 ext. 16
Fax: (212) 838-0339

E-MAIL ADDRESS:
info@marthagraham.org
talesson@marthagraham.org

WEB SITE ADDRESS:
marthagraham.org

FOUNDED: 1926

AREAS OF INTEREST:
Training professional dancers.

NAME(S) OF PROGRAMS:
• **Graham II Performing Group Scholarship**
• **Independent Program**
• **Professional Trainee Program**
• **Summer Intensive**
• **Teens Program**
• **Third Year Post Certificate Program**
• **Winter Intensive**

TYPE:
Conferences/seminars; General operating grants; Internships; Matching gifts; Project/program grants; Research grants; Residencies; Scholarships; Work-study programs. Awards for class tuition.

Scholarship students work at the school.

YEAR PROGRAM STARTED: 1966

PURPOSE:
To provide help to the most promising dance students who are studying at the Martha Graham School.

LEGAL BASIS:
Nonprofit private school.

ELIGIBILITY:
Proficiency in dancing with special proficiency in the Martha Graham Technique is required. On-site scholarship auditions.

FINANCIAL DATA:
Scholarships are full (minimum of eight classes a week) or partial (student pays approximately half tuition per quarter for a minimum of eight classes a week). Scholarships require regular attendance.

Amount of support per award: Full $5,000; Half $2,500. Both for a 10-month school year.

Total amount of support: Varies.

NUMBER OF APPLICANTS MOST RECENT YEAR: 210.

NUMBER OF AWARDS: 24.

APPLICATION INFORMATION:
Applicants are students at the School at the time they apply. Award is by competition judged by the School faculty.
Duration: Normally awarded on a 12-month basis, on the basis of competition.

IRS IDENTIFICATION NUMBER: 13-1834089

STAFF:
LaRue Allen, Executive Director
Virginie Mecene, Director of School
Tami Alesson, Director of Education

BOARD OF TRUSTEES:
Judith Schlosser, Chairman
Inger Witter, President
LaRue Allen
Peter Allstrom
Amy Blumenthal
Audra Cohen
Neila Fortino
Beau Gage
Inga Golay
Laura Gordon
Jon Gralnick
John Hotta
John R. Keller
Adam Klein
Lorraine Oler
Paul Szlard
Janis Tripodakis
Ronald Windisch

ADDRESS INQUIRIES TO:
Tami Alesson, Director of Education
(See address above.)

JACOB'S PILLOW DANCE FESTIVAL, INC.   [532]
358 George Carter Road
Becket, MA 01223
(413) 243-9919
Fax: (413) 243-4744

E-MAIL ADDRESS:
info@jacobspillow.org

WEB SITE ADDRESS:
www.jacobspillow.org

FOUNDED: 1932

AREAS OF INTEREST:
Nurturing and sustaining artistic creation, presentation, education and preservation as well as engaging and deepening public appreciation and support for dance.

NAME(S) OF PROGRAMS:
● **The Intern Program at Jacob's Pillow**
● **The School at Jacob's Pillow**

TYPE:
Assistantships; Awards/prizes; Exchange programs; Fellowships; Internships; Residencies; Scholarships; Training grants; Visiting scholars. The Intern Program at Jacob's Pillow has training in arts administration and technical theater production. The School at Jacob's Pillow has four intensive programs: Ballet, Cultural Traditions, Contemporary and Jazz/Musical Theatre Dance, all including awards/prizes/scholarships.

There are creative development residencies available.

PURPOSE:
The Intern Program at Jacob's Pillow: To train aspiring young professionals and career-changers in arts administration and technical theater production during the Festival season and in arts administrations during the fall/winter/spring. The School at

Jacob's Pillow: To provide professional development training to advanced dancers in summer dance programs.

ELIGIBILITY:
The Intern Program at Jacob's Pillow provides professional training experience in arts administration and technical theater production to aspiring young professionals and career-changers. The School at Jacob's Pillow is open to U.S. and foreign nationals who are 16 years of age or older and complete application requirements for the program(s) selected.

FINANCIAL DATA:
The School at Jacob's Pillow provides scholarships applicable toward tuition, room and board. Festival performances are an integral part of The School and Intern programs.
Amount of support per award: The School at Jacob's Pillow: Varies.
Total amount of support: Varies.

NUMBER OF APPLICANTS MOST RECENT YEAR:
Over 1,000 for both programs.

NUMBER OF AWARDS: 100 per year.

APPLICATION INFORMATION:
Intern Program at Jacob's Pillow: Applicants must write a cover letter explaining why they wish to intern at Jacob's Pillow, what position(s) they are applying for and in what priority order, their qualifications and interests, and their goals and expectations for the internship. Complete application instructions are downloadable from the web site.

The School at Jacob's Pillow: All applicants must audition. Initially, applicants must submit a complete, legible program application, assembled and mailed as instructed on the Application Checklist. Enclosures vary by program. Complete application instructions are downloadable from the web site.
Duration: The Intern Program at Jacob's Pillow: Up to three months. The School at Jacob's Pillow: One to three weeks.
Deadline: Intern Program: February; School: March.

ADDRESS INQUIRIES TO:
See e-mail address above.

THE JAPANESE AMERICAN CITIZENS LEAGUE (JACL)   [533]
New York JACL
75 Grove Street, Apartment No. 2
Bloomfield, NJ 07003
(973) 680-1441

E-MAIL ADDRESS:
lckimura@att.net

WEB SITE ADDRESS:
www.jacl.org

AREAS OF INTEREST:
Theatrical works of the Japanese American/Canadian experience.

NAME(S) OF PROGRAMS:
● **Ruby Yoshino Schaar Playwright Award**

TYPE:
Awards/prizes. Biennial playwright award.

YEAR PROGRAM STARTED: 1984

PURPOSE:
To encourage talented playwrights to tell the story of the Japanese American or Japanese Canadian experience in North America.

ELIGIBILITY:
Applicant must be a playwright of Japanese descent with American or Canadian citizenship, sponsored by an active member of JACL or a chapter of JACL, and have had at least one of his or her plays presented in a public forum, such as established theater, workshop or formal reading. Play submitted must not have been theatrically produced before January 1 of the two previous years. Manuscripts will be judged for dramatic excellence and insight into the Japanese American or Japanese Canadian experience.

FINANCIAL DATA:
Amount of support per award:
Approximately $3,000.

NUMBER OF AWARDS: 1 biennially.

APPLICATION INFORMATION:
Manuscripts are restricted to one per applicant. A clear copy of the typed manuscript in a professional format should be accompanied by a completed application form. Do not send an original manuscript.
Deadline: April 1.

ADDRESS INQUIRIES TO:
Lillian Kimura
(See address above.)

NATIONAL OPERA ASSOCIATION, INC.
2403 Russell Long Boulevard
Canyon, TX 79016
(806) 651-2857
Fax: (806) 651-2958

E-MAIL ADDRESS:
rhansen@noa.org

WEB SITE ADDRESS:
www.noa.org

TYPE:
Awards/prizes. Cash prizes awarded to Artist Division winners and Scholarship Division winners. Also scholarships to AIMS, awarded in both divisions. Productions of winning operas in Chamber Opera Competition will be scheduled for annual convention.

See entry 780 for full listing.

NEW DRAMATISTS   [534]
424 West 44th Street
New York, NY 10036
(212) 757-6960
Fax: (212) 265-4738

E-MAIL ADDRESS:
newdramatists@newdramatists.org

WEB SITE ADDRESS:
www.newdramatists.org

FOUNDED: 1949

AREAS OF INTEREST:
Service organization for member playwrights. Work with member writers on new plays, providing them with workshops, readings and staged readings. Involves directors and dramaturges in workshops.

TYPE:
Awards/prizes; Internships; Residencies. Resident playwrights are selected by an admissions panel which consists of current resident playwrights, alumni playwrights, and other theatre professionals. The panel changes completely from year to year.

YEAR PROGRAM STARTED: 1949

PURPOSE:
To provide playwrights with the tools and freedom to make lasting contributions to the theatre.

LEGAL BASIS:
Not-for-profit corporation.

ELIGIBILITY:
Open to U.S. citizens.

GEOGRAPHIC RESTRICTIONS:
United States.

FINANCIAL DATA:
Internships include college credit, where available. Full-time interns work 40 hours per week with a stipend of $50 to cover transportation and lunch. Part-time interns work a minimum of 15 hours per week with a stipend of $25.

NUMBER OF APPLICANTS MOST RECENT YEAR:
350 for the year 2013.

NUMBER OF AWARDS: 5 to 8 residencies per year.

APPLICATION INFORMATION:
Information is available online.
Deadline: Varies.

PUBLICATIONS:
Application guidelines; brochure.

OFFICERS:
Seth Gelblum, Chairman
Isobel Robins Konecky, President

ADDRESS INQUIRIES TO:
Rachel Hutt, Artistic Programs Administrator (See address above.)

NEW MUSIC USA
90 John Street, Suite 312
New York, NY 10038
(212) 645-6949
Fax: (646) 490-0998

E-MAIL ADDRESS:
info@newmusicusa.org

WEB SITE ADDRESS:
www.newmusicusa.org

TYPE:
Awards/prizes; Fellowships; Residencies.

See entry 783 for full listing.

PEN AMERICAN CENTER   [535]
588 Broadway, Suite 303
New York, NY 10012-5246
(212) 334-1660
Fax: (212) 334-2181

E-MAIL ADDRESS:
awards@pen.org

WEB SITE ADDRESS:
www.pen.org

FOUNDED: 1922

AREAS OF INTEREST:
American theater.

NAME(S) OF PROGRAMS:
• **PEN/Laura Pels Foundation Awards for Drama**

TYPE:
Awards/prizes. Honors a Grand Master of American Theater, Playwright in Mid-Career, and Emerging Playwright.

PURPOSE:
To honor the accomplishments of American playwrights.

ELIGIBILITY:
Candidates for the award to a senior American playwright are proposed by the judges. Candidates for the award to an American playwright in midcareer must be playwrights writing in English who have had a professional production of at least two full-length works mounted in a theatre of at least 299 seats and contracted specifically for either limited or open runs. Candidates for Emerging Playwright must have had a professional production of at least one full-length work.

Nominated playwrights must be U.S. citizens or permanent residents.

FINANCIAL DATA:
Amount of support per award: Emerging Playwright: cash prize of $2,500; Master American Dramatist: a specially commissioned art object; Mid-Career American Playwright: cash prize of $7,500.

NUMBER OF AWARDS: 3 annually.

APPLICATION INFORMATION:
Playwrights may not apply on their own behalf. They must be nominated by their peers - producers, agents, critics, or other playwrights who are expected to write a letter of support, describing in some detail the literary character of the candidate's work, accompanied by a list of the candidate's produced work. Do not send scripts.
Deadline: Fall 2014.

PEW FELLOWSHIPS AT THE PEW CENTER FOR ARTS & HERITAGE
1608 Walnut Street, 18th Floor
Philadelphia, PA 19103
(267) 350-4920
Fax: (267) 350-4997

E-MAIL ADDRESS:
pfa@pcah.us
mfranklin@pcah.us

WEB SITE ADDRESS:
www.pcah.us/fellowships

TYPE:
Fellowships. Opportunities for contemporary artists in the Philadelphia five-county area to concentrate on the development and creation of art. Fellowships to support artists at critical junctures in any stage of their career development. Fellows will be expected to participate annually in at least three meetings with other fellowship recipients.

See entry 564 for full listing.

PRINCESS GRACE FOUNDATION-USA   [536]
150 East 58th Street, 25th Floor
New York, NY 10155
(212) 317-1470
Fax: (212) 317-1473

E-MAIL ADDRESS:
grants@pgfusa.org

WEB SITE ADDRESS:
www.pgfusa.org

FOUNDED: 1982

AREAS OF INTEREST:
Theater, dance, choreography, film and playwriting.

NAME(S) OF PROGRAMS:
• **Princess Grace Awards**

TYPE:
Fellowships; Scholarships. Apprenticeships. Dedicated to identifying and assisting emerging artists in theater, dance and film through grants.

YEAR PROGRAM STARTED: 1984

PURPOSE:
To identify and assist emerging young artists in the fields of dance, theater and film within the U.S.

LEGAL BASIS:
Not-for-profit, tax-exempt, publicly supported charity.

ELIGIBILITY:
Must be a U.S. citizen or permanent resident.

GEOGRAPHIC RESTRICTIONS:
United States.

FINANCIAL DATA:
Amount of support per award: Theater, Dance and Film Awards: $5,000 to $25,000 average; Playwright Awards: $7,500.
Total amount of support: More than $7,000,000 since inception.

NUMBER OF AWARDS: Over 600 since inception.

APPLICATION INFORMATION:
All applicants, except playwrights, must be nominated by a school department chair/dean or company artistic director. The nominating organization must be a registered 501(c)(3). Detailed information is available online.
Duration: September 1 to August 31.
Deadline: Must be postmarked by March 31 for theater and playwriting; April 30 for dance and choreography; June 1 for film.

PUBLICATIONS:
Fact sheet; mission statement; press releases; newsletter.

IRS IDENTIFICATION NUMBER: 23-2218331

OFFICERS:
Hon. John F. Lehman, Chairman
Robert O. Marx, Vice Chairman
Toby E. Boshak, Secretary and Treasurer
Amy B. Desmond, Assistant Treasurer

ADDRESS INQUIRIES TO:
Diana Kemppainen, Program Manager (See address above.)

FOREST ROBERTS THEATRE   [537]
Northern Michigan University
1401 Presque Isle Avenue
Marquette, MI 49855-5364
(906) 227-2559
Fax: (906) 227-2567

E-MAIL ADDRESS:
newplays@nmu.edu

WEB SITE ADDRESS:
www.nmu.edu/theatre

FOUNDED: 1977

AREAS OF INTEREST:
Performing arts and playwriting.

NAME(S) OF PROGRAMS:
• **Mildred and Albert Panowski Playwriting Award**

TYPE:
Awards/prizes.

YEAR PROGRAM STARTED: 1977

PURPOSE:
To encourage and stimulate artistic growth among educational and professional

playwrights; to provide students with the creative opportunity to produce an original work on the university stage.

LEGAL BASIS:
Tax-exempt, nonprofit.

FINANCIAL DATA:
The award will include a fully mounted production and a trip to Marquette to act as Artist-in-Residence during the four-day run of the show. Room and board will be provided. Conducting informal seminars and workshops will be a part of this residency. A professional dramaturge will respond to the script and work with the playwright and director.
Amount of support per award: $2,000.

NUMBER OF APPLICANTS MOST RECENT YEAR:
18.

NUMBER OF AWARDS: Generally 1 award per school year.

REPRESENTATIVE AWARDS:
Mark Rigney for "Bears."

APPLICATION INFORMATION:
The contest has a different theme for each cycle. Applications are to be submitted online.
Duration: One year. Renewal possibilities on a year-to-year basis.
Deadline: Entries accepted in odd-numbered years. Entries must be received on or before September 1 to be considered for the current theme. Winner will be announced in December.

PUBLICATIONS:
Brochure.

ADDRESS INQUIRIES TO:
Playwriting Coordinator
(See address above.)

THE SHUBERT FOUNDATION, INC.   [538]
234 West 44th Street
New York, NY 10036
(212) 944-3777
Fax: (212) 944-3767

WEB SITE ADDRESS:
www.shubertfoundation.org

FOUNDED: 1945

AREAS OF INTEREST:
Arts-related organizations, dance, education, human services and theatre.

TYPE:
General operating grants.

YEAR PROGRAM STARTED: 1945

PURPOSE:
To sustain and advance the live performing arts, in particular the American theatre and secondarily dance.

LEGAL BASIS:
Private foundation.

ELIGIBILITY:
The Foundation supports not-for-profit theatre and dance companies, as well as some arts-related organizations that assist in the development of the theatre. Applicants must be nonprofit organizations with Internal Revenue Code 501(c)(3) status. Organizations must submit audited financial statements. No grants to individuals.

GEOGRAPHIC RESTRICTIONS:
United States.

FINANCIAL DATA:
All grants cover general operating support only.
Amount of support per award: $10,000 to $275,000.
Total amount of support: $22,500,000 for the year 2013.

NUMBER OF APPLICANTS MOST RECENT YEAR:
500.

REPRESENTATIVE AWARDS:
$20,000 to Open Stage of Harrisburg, Harrisburg, PA; $145,000 to La Jolla Playhouse, La Jolla, CA; $210,000 to Manhattan Theatre Club.

APPLICATION INFORMATION:
A comprehensive application form, including audited financial data, must be submitted to the Foundation in duplicate. Applications, guidelines and instructions can be downloaded from the web site August to December; however, applications cannot be requested or submitted via e-mail.
Duration: One year. Renewal only with reapplication.
Deadline: December 1 for theatre category; October 15 for dance and other categories. Announcement in May each year.

PUBLICATIONS:
Annual report with application guidelines.

OFFICERS:
Philip J. Smith, Chairman of the Board
Michael I. Sovern, President
Wyche Fowler, Jr.
Lee J. Seidler
Stuart Subotnick
Robert E. Wankel

ADDRESS INQUIRIES TO:
Vicki Reiss, Executive Director
(See address above.)

THE TRUST COMPANY   [539]
Level 15, 20 Bond Street
G.P.O. Box 4270
Sydney N.S.W. 2000 Australia
(61)(2) 8295-8100

E-MAIL ADDRESS:
scholarships@thetrustcompany.com.au

WEB SITE ADDRESS:
www.thetrustcompany.com.au

FOUNDED: 1979

AREAS OF INTEREST:
Personal management and furtherance of education of classical musicians in the arts (i.e., music, visual arts, literature, performing arts, etc.).

NAME(S) OF PROGRAMS:
• **Lady Mollie Isabelle Askin Ballet Scholarship**
• **Sir Robert William Askin Operatic Scholarship**
• **Kathleen Mitchell Award**

TYPE:
Awards/prizes; Scholarships. The scholarships shall be used for study, maintenance and travel either in Australia or overseas.

The Lady Mollie Isabelle Askin Ballet Scholarship is awarded every two years for outstanding ability and promise in ballet.

The Sir Robert William Askin Operatic Scholarship is awarded every two years for outstanding ability and promise as a male operatic singer.

The Kathleen Mitchell Award is awarded to young Australian writers aged under 30 at the time their novel is published.

The above scholarships and award are entirely separate and are from separate charitable bequests.

YEAR PROGRAM STARTED: 1996

PURPOSE:
Lady Mollie Isabelle Askin Ballet Scholarship and Sir Robert William Askin Operatic Scholarship: To augment a scholar's own resources affording him or her a cultural education by means of a travelling scholarship. Kathleen Mitchell Award: To advance the improvement of Australian literature; to improve the educational style of young authors, and to provide them with additional amounts to improve their literary efforts.

LEGAL BASIS:
Trust.

ELIGIBILITY:
Lady Mollie Isabelle Askin Ballet Scholarship: Must be Australian citizen 17 to 29 years of age; Sir Robert William Askin Operatic Scholarship: Must be male Australian citizen 18 to 29 years of age; Kathleen Mitchell Award: Born in Australia, British born or naturalized Australian who has been a resident in Australia for the 12 months preceding close of entries date, and 29 years of age or less.

FINANCIAL DATA:
Amount of support per award: Lady Mollie Isabelle Askin Ballet Scholarship and Sir Robert William Askin Operatic Scholarship: $20,000 (AUD) per year; Kathleen Mitchell Award: $15,000 (AUD).

NUMBER OF APPLICANTS MOST RECENT YEAR:
Lady Mollie Isabelle Askin Ballet Scholarship: 25; Sir Robert William Askin Operatic Scholarship: 20; Kathleen Mitchell Award: 12.

NUMBER OF AWARDS: Lady Mollie Isabelle Askin Ballet Scholarship and Sir Robert William Askin Operatic Scholarship: 3 each; Kathleen Mitchell Award: 1.

APPLICATION INFORMATION:
Applications must include a birth certificate, Australian citizenship certificate, a curriculum vitae, three references, work samples, and a summary of proposed aims and activities. Complete application information may be obtained from the address above.
Duration: Lady Mollie Isabelle Askin and Sir Robert William Askin Scholarships: Two years.
Deadline: Lady Mollie Isabelle Askin and Sir Robert William Askin Scholarships: Last Friday in November of preceding year.

PUBLICATIONS:
Application guidelines.

ADDRESS INQUIRIES TO:
Scholarship and Awards
(See e-mail address above.)

WAGNER COLLEGE   [540]
Wagner College Theater
One Campus Road
Staten Island, NY 10301
(718) 390-3223
Fax: (718) 390-3323

E-MAIL ADDRESS:
diane.catalano@wagner.edu

WEB SITE ADDRESS:
www.wagner.edu

FOUNDED: 1957

AREAS OF INTEREST:
Playwriting.

NAME(S) OF PROGRAMS:
● **Stanley Drama Award**

TYPE:
Awards/prizes; Project/program grants.
Annual award for the best play or musical
submitted to the competition.

YEAR PROGRAM STARTED: 1957

PURPOSE:
To call attention to and encourage new
playwrights.

LEGAL BASIS:
University.

ELIGIBILITY:
The Award is offered for an original
full-length play, musical or one-act play
sequence that has not been professionally
produced or received tradebook publication.
Writers of musicals are urged to submit
music on cassette tapes or CDs.

The Stanley Award competition will consider
only one submission (a single full-length
play, musical or one-act sequence) per
playwright. Plays entered previously in the
competition may not be resubmitted. Former
Stanley Award winners are not eligible to
compete.

FINANCIAL DATA:
Amount of support per award: $2,000.

NUMBER OF APPLICANTS MOST RECENT YEAR:
100.

NUMBER OF AWARDS: 3 (1 winner, 2 finalists).

APPLICATION INFORMATION:
Applications may be obtained by sending a
self-addressed, stamped envelope to the
address above or on the web site. All scripts
must be accompanied by a completed
application. A reading fee of $30 must
accompany the manuscript.
Deadline: October 31. Announcement the
following March.

PUBLICATIONS:
Application guidelines.

ADDRESS INQUIRIES TO:
Diane Catalano
Stanley Drama Award
(See address above.)

*SPECIAL STIPULATIONS:
Previous winners are ineligible.

THE LOREN L. ZACHARY SOCIETY FOR THE PERFORMING ARTS

2250 Gloaming Way
Beverly Hills, CA 90210-1717
(310) 276-2731
Fax: (310) 275-8245

E-MAIL ADDRESS:
peterhubner@earthlink.net

WEB SITE ADDRESS:
www.zacharysociety.org

TYPE:
Awards/prizes.

See entry 798 for full listing.

Fine arts

ACADEMY FOUNDATION OF THE ACADEMY OF MOTION PICTURE ARTS AND SCIENCES [541]

8949 Wilshire Boulevard
Beverly Hills, CA 90211-1972
(310) 247-3000 ext. 1131
Fax: (310) 859-9619

E-MAIL ADDRESS:
rmiller@oscars.org

WEB SITE ADDRESS:
www.oscars.org

AREAS OF INTEREST:
Filmmakers.

NAME(S) OF PROGRAMS:
● **Student Academy Awards Competition**

TYPE:
Awards/prizes.

PURPOSE:
To recognize outstanding achievements in
student filmmaking; to support and encourage
filmmakers with no previous professional
experience who are enrolled in accredited
colleges and universities.

ELIGIBILITY:
To be eligible, the filmmaker must be a
full-time student at an accredited U.S.
college, university, film school or art school.
The film must have been made in a
teacher-student relationship within the
curricular structure of that institution. The
film must be in one of the following
categories: Alternative, Animated,
Documentary and Narrative.

FINANCIAL DATA:
Amount of support per award: $5,000 Gold
Award, $3,000 Silver Award, and $2,000
Bronze Award.

NUMBER OF APPLICANTS MOST RECENT YEAR:
500.

NUMBER OF AWARDS: 12 maximum.

APPLICATION INFORMATION:
Regional juries have sole responsibility for
the determination of final selections for
submission to the Academy. Each regional
jury may consider only films from schools
within its own region.
Deadline: April 1.

ADDRESS INQUIRIES TO:
Richard Miller
Awards Administration Director
(See address above.)

AMERICAN ORIENTAL SOCIETY [542]

Hatcher Graduate Library, Room 110
University of Michigan
Ann Arbor, MI 48109-1205
(734) 764-7555
Fax: (734) 763-6743

E-MAIL ADDRESS:
jrodgers@umich.edu

WEB SITE ADDRESS:
www.umich.edu/~aos

FOUNDED: 1842

AREAS OF INTEREST:
Archaeology, fine arts, history, philosophy,
language, literature, religion and theology.

NAME(S) OF PROGRAMS:
● **Louise Wallace Hackney Fellowship**

TYPE:
Fellowships. Fellowship for the study of
Chinese art with special relation to painting.

YEAR PROGRAM STARTED: 1946

PURPOSE:
To encourage basic research in the languages
and literatures of Asia.

LEGAL BASIS:
Nonprofit.

ELIGIBILITY:
Graduate students who have successfully
completed at least three years of Chinese
language study at a recognized university and
have some knowledge or training in art.
Students must have completed all
requirements for the Ph.D. except research,
travel and the written dissertation. Applicants
should have the sponsorship of recognized
scholars in the fields of Chinese language
and culture.

U.S. citizenship is required.

GEOGRAPHIC RESTRICTIONS:
United States.

FINANCIAL DATA:
Amount of support per award: $8,000.
Total amount of support: $8,000 annually.

NUMBER OF APPLICANTS MOST RECENT YEAR:
Approximately 3.

NUMBER OF AWARDS: 1 annually.

APPLICATION INFORMATION:
Applicants should write to the secretary, at
the address given above, outlining the
proposed plan of study and accompany the
letter with a curriculum vitae, an academic
record and no less than three letters of
recommendation.

All materials must be submitted in duplicate
or application will be considered incomplete.
Duration: Renewals of appointment are
possible but not usually considered.
Deadline: Applications should be submitted
no later than March 1. Announcement at the
end of April.

PUBLICATIONS:
Application guidelines.

DIRECTORS AND OFFICERS:
Jonathan Rodgers, Secretary and Treasurer
Stephanie Jamison, Editor

ADDRESS INQUIRIES TO:
Jonathan Rodgers, Secretary and Treasurer
(See address above.)

BRUCEBO FINE ART SCHOLARSHIP FOUNDATION [543]

Department of Geography
McGill University
805 Sherbrooke West
Montreal QC H3A 2K6 Canada
(450) 672-6096
Fax: (514) 398-7437

E-MAIL ADDRESS:
jan.lundgren@mcgill.ca

WEB SITE ADDRESS:
www.bruceboscholarships.com

FOUNDED: 1971

AREAS OF INTEREST:
Promotion of fine arts; Canada-Sweden relationships.

CONSULTING OR VOLUNTEER SERVICES:
Evaluation Committee members provide free services.

NAME(S) OF PROGRAMS:
- **W.B. Bruce European Fine Art Travel Scholarship**
- **Brucebo Fine Art Summer Residency Scholarship**

TYPE:
Awards/prizes; Development grants; Residencies; Scholarships; Travel grants. Grant principally in the fields of fine arts, visual art and design. Grant is either for stay at the Brucebo Studio on the Island of Hanseatic Gotland, Sweden, in the Baltic Sea, for three months during the summer annually, or for undertaking a European Fine Art Travel-Study journey during a period of the fall term, or the following winter/spring term.

YEAR PROGRAM STARTED: 1971

PURPOSE:
To support talented Canadian fine arts graduated students and fine arts practitioners, B.F.A. or M.F.A. persons, in the early years of their respective careers.

LEGAL BASIS:
Private.

ELIGIBILITY:
Qualified Canadian artists (preferably painters) with appropriate project plans are eligible to apply. Must hold Canadian citizenship.

GEOGRAPHIC RESTRICTIONS:
Europe, with specific reference to the Nordic countries and Baltic Rim (coastal corridor).

FINANCIAL DATA:
Amount of support per award: SEK 30,000, the equivalent of approximately $5,000 (CAN).
Total amount of support: SEK 60,000.

NUMBER OF APPLICANTS MOST RECENT YEAR:
40.

NUMBER OF AWARDS: 2.

APPLICATION INFORMATION:
Application form and guidelines can be found on the Embassy of Sweden Ottawa web site.
Duration: Three months.
Deadline: January 31.

PUBLICATIONS:
Research reports.

STAFF:
Dr. Jan Lundgren, Liaison Officer, Brucebo Fine Art Scholarship Foundation of Gotland, Sweden

ADDRESS INQUIRIES TO:
Dr. Jan Lundgren, Liaison Officer
(See address above.)

*SPECIAL STIPULATIONS:
Canadian citizens only. Recipient submits a report on his or her activities engaged in after return to Canada.

THE CENTER FOR PHOTOGRAPHY AT WOODSTOCK   [544]
59 Tinker Street
Woodstock, NY 12498
(845) 679-9957
Fax: (845) 679-6337

E-MAIL ADDRESS:
info@cpw.org

WEB SITE ADDRESS:
www.cpw.org

FOUNDED: 1977

AREAS OF INTEREST:
Photography.

NAME(S) OF PROGRAMS:
- **Art Administration Interns**
- **The Photographers' Fund**
- **Woodstock A-I-R**
- **Workshop Interns**

TYPE:
Project/program grants; Residencies; Work-study programs. Photography Workshops. Photographers' Fund awards fellowships to regional photographers of vision and talent, selected by portfolio review by a panel of noted national artists.

Woodstock A-I-R is a residency program for artists of color working in the photographic arts.

YEAR PROGRAM STARTED: 1980

PURPOSE:
To support artists working in photography and related media and engaging their audiences through opportunities in which creation, discovery and learning are made possible.

LEGAL BASIS:
Not-for-profit arts and educational organization.

ELIGIBILITY:
Fellowship applicants must live and work in upstate New York.

FINANCIAL DATA:
Amount of support per award: Art Administration Interns and Woodstock A-I-R: Varies; Photographers' Fund: $2,500; Workshop Interns: $6,000 in-kind tuition.

COOPERATIVE FUNDING PROGRAMS: The Center receives funds from the National Endowment for the Arts and the New York State Council on the Arts and has received grants from IBM and the New York Council for the Humanities, The Avery Foundation, Eastman Kodak, Canon, U.S.A. and Andy Warhol Foundation.

NUMBER OF AWARDS: Art Administration Interns: Up to 4 seasonally; Photographers' Fund: 1 fellowship; Woodstock A-I-R: 8; Workshop Interns: 4.

APPLICATION INFORMATION:
Photographers must submit the following:
(1) portfolio of 10 prints (print portfolios strongly encouraged over slide or digital file submissions);
(2) image list detailing titles, medium, year and;
(3) artist statement and bio.

Submissions cannot be accepted via e-mail.

Full guidelines are available online.

IRS IDENTIFICATION NUMBER: 14-1592639

OFFICERS:
Ariel Shanberg, Executive Director

ADDRESS INQUIRIES TO:
Ariel Shanberg, Executive Director
(See address above.)

DALLAS MUSEUM OF ART   [545]
1717 North Harwood
Dallas, TX 75201
(214) 922-1334
Fax: (214) 922-1354

WEB SITE ADDRESS:
www.dallasmuseumofart.org

FOUNDED: 1903

AREAS OF INTEREST:
Contemporary art.

NAME(S) OF PROGRAMS:
- **Clare Hart DeGolyer Memorial Fund**

TYPE:
Awards/prizes.

YEAR PROGRAM STARTED: 1980

PURPOSE:
To support younger, emerging visual artists who reside in the southwestern part of the U.S.

LEGAL BASIS:
Nonprofit, tax-exempt arts organization.

ELIGIBILITY:
Applicants must be between 15 and 25 years of age, have lived in the southwestern part of the U.S. for the past four years and currently reside there.

Grants are not available for college or art school tuition.

GEOGRAPHIC RESTRICTIONS:
Arizona, Colorado, New Mexico, Oklahoma and Texas.

FINANCIAL DATA:
Amount of support per award:
Approximately $1,500.

NUMBER OF APPLICANTS MOST RECENT YEAR:
25.

NUMBER OF AWARDS: Varies.

APPLICATION INFORMATION:
Applications can be downloaded online.
Deadline: Mid-January.

PUBLICATIONS:
Bimonthly *DMAgenda*; permanent collection and exhibition catalogues.

ADDRESS INQUIRIES TO:
Awards to Artists
(See address above.)

DALLAS MUSEUM OF ART   [546]
1717 North Harwood
Dallas, TX 75201
(214) 922-1334
Fax: (214) 922-1354

WEB SITE ADDRESS:
www.dallasmuseumofart.org

FOUNDED: 1903

AREAS OF INTEREST:
Contemporary art.

NAME(S) OF PROGRAMS:
- **Arch and Anne Giles Kimbrough Fund**

TYPE:
Awards/prizes. Direct grants to artists.

YEAR PROGRAM STARTED: 1980

PURPOSE:
To support younger, emerging visual artists in Texas.

LEGAL BASIS:
Nonprofit, tax-exempt arts organization.

ELIGIBILITY:
Applicants must be under 30 years of age, have lived in Texas for the past three years and currently reside there.

Funds are not available for college or art school tuition.

GEOGRAPHIC RESTRICTIONS:
Texas.

FINANCIAL DATA:
Amount of support per award:
Approximately $3,500.

NUMBER OF APPLICANTS MOST RECENT YEAR:
35.

NUMBER OF AWARDS: Varies.

APPLICATION INFORMATION:
Applications can be downloaded online.
Deadline: Mid-January.

PUBLICATIONS:
Bimonthly *DMAgenda*; permanent collection and exhibition catalogues.

ADDRESS INQUIRIES TO:
Awards to Artists
(See address above.)

DALLAS MUSEUM OF ART [547]
1717 North Harwood
Dallas, TX 75201
(214) 922-1334
Fax: (214) 720-0862

E-MAIL ADDRESS:
cengle@DMA.org

WEB SITE ADDRESS:
www.dallasmuseumofart.org

FOUNDED: 1903

AREAS OF INTEREST:
Art. Collections include contemporary art, Pre-Columbian, Asian, African, American and European painting and sculpture, decorative arts and textiles.

NAME(S) OF PROGRAMS:
- **Otis and Velma Davis Dozier Travel Grant**

TYPE:
Awards/prizes; Travel grants.

YEAR PROGRAM STARTED: 1990

PURPOSE:
To recognize exceptional talent in professional artists who wish to expand their artistic horizons through domestic or foreign travel.

LEGAL BASIS:
Nonprofit, tax-exempt arts organization.

ELIGIBILITY:
Artists eligible for the grant must be practicing professionals, be 30 years of age or older, have lived in Texas for the past three years and be currently living in Texas. Financial need will be given consideration but will not be the determining factor in making the awards.

GEOGRAPHIC RESTRICTIONS:
Texas.

FINANCIAL DATA:
Amount of support per award: Varies.
Total amount of support: Approximately $6,000.

NUMBER OF APPLICANTS MOST RECENT YEAR:
40.

APPLICATION INFORMATION:
Applications can be downloaded online.

Deadline: March 29. Announcement in mid-April.

PUBLICATIONS:
Bimonthly *DMAgenda*; permanent collection and exhibition catalogues.

ADDRESS INQUIRIES TO:
Cheryl Engle, Arts Coordinator
(See address above.)

FINE ARTS WORK CENTER IN PROVINCETOWN [548]
24 Pearl Street
Provincetown, MA 02657
(508) 487-9960
Fax: (508) 487-8873

E-MAIL ADDRESS:
info@fawc.org

WEB SITE ADDRESS:
www.fawc.org

FOUNDED: 1968

AREAS OF INTEREST:
Visual arts and creative writing.

NAME(S) OF PROGRAMS:
- **Visual Arts Fellowship**
- **Writing Fellowship**

TYPE:
Fellowships; Residencies.

YEAR PROGRAM STARTED: 1968

PURPOSE:
To offer opportunities to emerging artists and writers.

LEGAL BASIS:
Nonprofit corporation.

ELIGIBILITY:
The Fine Arts Work Center offers seven-month Fellowships (October 1 to May 1) to selected writers and visual artists. Applicants must be in the emerging phase of their careers and must demonstrate significant talent and commitment. Fellows are provided with apartments, studios, and a monthly stipend, and have the support of a resident staff.

Applicants must be individuals (visual artists and creative writers) who have spent time working on their own and have created a considerable body of work which can be presented in the form of slides or manuscript.

FINANCIAL DATA:
Amount of support per award: Each Fellow receives a monthly stipend of $750 and is provided with an apartment and a studio in Provincetown, MA.

Each Residency includes a stipend of $750 per month plus private living and/or working studio in Provincetown, MA.
Total amount of support: $5,250, plus housing and work space.

NUMBER OF APPLICANTS MOST RECENT YEAR:
1,000.

NUMBER OF AWARDS: 20.

APPLICATION INFORMATION:
Forms and application information may be requested from the Center by sending a self-addressed, stamped envelope. Applications can also be downloaded at the web site. Application fee is $45.
Duration: Seven months. October 1 to May 1.
Deadline: Writers: December 1. Visual Arts: February 1. Announcement by May 15.

PUBLICATIONS:
Shankpainter, online literary magazine.

OFFICERS OF THE TRUSTEES:
Hatty Walker Fitts, Co-Chairperson
Lynne Kortenhaus, Co-Chairperson
Ted Chapin, President
Barbara Kapp, Vice President

ADDRESS INQUIRIES TO:
Melenie Flynn, Grant Writer
(See address above.)

*SPECIAL STIPULATIONS:
Fellowships are reserved for emerging writers and visual artists.

J. PAUL GETTY TRUST, GETTY FOUNDATION [549]
1200 Getty Center Drive
Suite 800
Los Angeles, CA 90049-1685
(310) 440-7320
Fax: (310) 440-7703

E-MAIL ADDRESS:
foundation@getty.edu

WEB SITE ADDRESS:
www.getty.edu/grants

FOUNDED: 1984

AREAS OF INTEREST:
Strengthening art history as a global discipline, promoting the interdisciplinary practice of conservation, increasing access to museums and archival collections, and developing current and future professionals and leaders.

TYPE:
Conferences/seminars; Internships; Matching gifts; Project/program grants; Training grants.

YEAR PROGRAM STARTED: 1984

PURPOSE:
To advance the understanding and preservation of the visual arts locally and throughout the world.

ELIGIBILITY:
Requirements vary according to grant category. Individuals at the undergraduate and graduate level may be eligible to apply for internships. Eligibility for all other grant categories is limited to nonprofit organizations.

Generally, grants are not made for operating or endowment purposes, for construction or maintenance of buildings or for acquisition of works of art.

FINANCIAL DATA:
Amount of support per award: Varies.
Total amount of support: $12,400,000 approved for fiscal year ended June 30, 2012.

NUMBER OF APPLICANTS MOST RECENT YEAR:
1,000.

NUMBER OF AWARDS: 546 for fiscal year ended June 30, 2012.

REPRESENTATIVE AWARDS:
$275,000 to Museum of Contemporary Art, Los Angeles, CA, for the exhibition and accompanying catalogue *A New Sculpturalism: Contemporary Architecture from Southern California*; $310,000 to Universidade do Estado do Rio de Janeiro, Brazil, for a series of research seminars and faculty and student exchanges; $231,000 to Courtauld Institute of Art, London, England, for training, condition assessments, and treatment related to four paintings in the

Courtauld Gallery; $1,950,000 to Claremont Graduate University, CA, for the Getty Leadership Institute.

APPLICATION INFORMATION:
Funding priorities and application information are available on the Foundation web site.
Duration: One to three years, depending upon the grant category.
Deadline: November 1. Internships: Varies.

PUBLICATIONS:
Annual report of J. Paul Getty Trust.

IRS IDENTIFICATION NUMBER: 95-1790021

OFFICERS:
Deborah Marrow, Director, The Getty Foundation
Rebecca Martin, Associate Director
Joan Weinstein, Deputy Director

ADDRESS INQUIRIES TO:
The Getty Foundation
(See address above.)

ADOLPH AND ESTHER GOTTLIEB FOUNDATION, INC. [550]

380 West Broadway
New York, NY 10012-5115
(212) 226-0581
Fax: (212) 226-0584

E-MAIL ADDRESS:
sross@gottliebfoundation.org

WEB SITE ADDRESS:
www.gottliebfoundation.org

FOUNDED: 1976

AREAS OF INTEREST:
Visual artists.

NAME(S) OF PROGRAMS:
• **Emergency Assistance Program**
• **Individual Support Program**

TYPE:
Grants-in-aid. Emergency Assistance Program provides cash award to mature creative painters, sculptors and printmakers who are experiencing financial hardship resulting from a current or recent emergency.

Individual Support Program was designed to encourage those artists who have dedicated their lives to developing their art, regardless of their level of commercial success.

YEAR PROGRAM STARTED: 1984

PURPOSE:
To provide interim financial assistance to qualified artists during times of emergencies (such as fire, flood, medical or other unexpected, catastrophic events), or to provide financial assistance as an encouragement to artists who have dedicated their lives to developing their art.

LEGAL BASIS:
Nonprofit corporation.

ELIGIBILITY:
Emergency Assistance Program: Applicant must be able to demonstrate a minimum involvement of 10 years in a mature phase of his or her work as a creative painter, sculptor or printmaker and his or her need must result from current or recent emergency beyond the artist's usual circumstances (medical, fire, flood, etc.). This Program does not consider requests for dental work, chronic situations, capital improvements, or projects of any

kind; nor can it consider situations resulting from general indebtedness or lack of employment.

Individual Support Program: Applicant will be able to demonstrate work in a mature phase of his or her art for at least 20 years. Eligibility is also determined by applicant's current financial need. The Foundation does not provide funding for organizations, projects of any type, educational institutions, students, graphic artists, or those working in crafts. The disciplines of photography, film, video or related forms are not eligible unless the work directly involves, or can be interpreted as, painting, printmaking or sculpture.

FINANCIAL DATA:
Amount of support per award: Emergency Assistance Program: Maximum $15,000; typical amount is $5,000. Individual Support Program: $25,000.
Total amount of support: $300,000.

NUMBER OF AWARDS: Individual Support Grants: 12.

APPLICATION INFORMATION:
Emergency Assistance Program: Application forms are available from the Foundation throughout the year and may be requested by telephone or in writing.

Individual Support Program: Application forms are available by mail in early September. Only written requests for application forms will be honored.
Deadline: Emergency Assistance Program: Available throughout the year, as budget permits. Individual Support Program: December 15.

PUBLICATIONS:
Information brochure.

BOARD OF DIRECTORS:
Sanford Hirsch, Executive Director
Lynda Benglis
Charlotta Kotik
Robert Mangold
Gordon Marsh

ADDRESS INQUIRIES TO:
Sheila Ross, Grants Manager
(See address above.)

*SPECIAL STIPULATIONS:
The Emergency Assistance Program is to assist individuals in emergency situations only.

THE ELIZABETH GREENSHIELDS FOUNDATION [551]

1814 Sherbrooke Street West, Suite 1
Montreal QC H3H 1E4 Canada
(514) 937-9225

E-MAIL ADDRESS:
greenshields@bellnet.ca

WEB SITE ADDRESS:
www.elizabethgreenshieldsfoundation.org

FOUNDED: 1955

AREAS OF INTEREST:
Art including painting, drawing, printmaking and sculpture.

NAME(S) OF PROGRAMS:
• **The Elizabeth Greenshields Foundation Grants**

TYPE:
Awards/prizes.

YEAR PROGRAM STARTED: 1955

PURPOSE:
To promote an appreciation of traditional expression in painting, drawing, sculpture and printmaking by aiding worthy art students, artists or sculptors who need further training or other assistance during their formative years.

LEGAL BASIS:
Charitable foundation.

ELIGIBILITY:
Awards are limited to candidates in the early stages of their careers who are working in a representational style in painting, drawing, sculpture and printmaking. Non-objective art is precluded by the Foundation's charter.

To be eligible for a grant, candidates must:
(1) have already started or completed training in an established school of art and/or;
(2) demonstrate, through past work and future plans, a commitment to making art a lifetime career.
The Foundation will not accept applications from commercial artists, photographers, video artists, filmmakers, craft-makers or any artist whose work falls primarily into these categories.

FINANCIAL DATA:
Funds may be used for any art-related purpose: study, travel, studio rental, purchase of materials, etc. Grants are made directly to the beneficiaries, and not through other organizations.

Amount of support per award: Normally, $15,000 (CAN). The Foundation reserves the right to award grants in other amounts.

APPLICATION INFORMATION:
Applications are available directly from the Foundation upon request. Grants are awarded to applicants of all nationalities and are made directly to the beneficiaries, not through other organizations. Grantees may reapply for a second grant one year after the first grant was awarded. Those applicants who are not awarded a grant may reapply two years after the last application was turned down.

Application instructions:
(1) return Foundation application form in a clear, complete and articulate manner, along with reproductions of six recent works (one image per work) - on CD only - preferably completed within the past two years but definitely no longer than three years ago;
(2) sculptors may send two images of six different works for a maximum of 12 images;
(3) images should be submitted in the best possible resolution (minimum 72 DPI, preferably 140 DPI or higher); images should be sized to fill the screen at a resolution of 1024 pixels wide by 768 pixels high;
(4) any digital treatment or manipulation of the initial picture may invalidate the entire application;
(5) digital art images should not be presented under separate cover;
(6) applications and reference letters must be signed and all documents must be sent together and;
(7) applications must be filled out on web page, printed and signed before sending with all documents by mail.

No Internet submissions are accepted. Submitted CD will not be returned. Slides are no longer accepted.

All completed applications are duly acknowledged and judged by a Selection Committee. Response time varies from one to six months. The decision of the trustees is final and not subject to review or appeal.

U.S. citizens sending applications should not enclose a self-addressed, stamped envelope because U.S. postage is not valid in Canada.

Duration: Award winners may reapply for another grant one year after a grant was awarded. Applicants who were declined a grant may reapply two years from the last decision.

Deadline: The Foundation welcomes applications throughout the year.

PUBLICATIONS:
Application guidelines.

ADDRESS INQUIRIES TO:
Claudette Bellemare, President
(See address above.)

SAMUEL H. KRESS FOUNDATION [552]
174 East 80th Street
New York, NY 10075
(212) 861-4993
Fax: (212) 628-3146

E-MAIL ADDRESS:
wyman.meers@kressfoundation.org

WEB SITE ADDRESS:
www.kressfoundation.org

FOUNDED: 1929

AREAS OF INTEREST:
Art history and art conservation.

NAME(S) OF PROGRAMS:
- **Fellowships in Art Conservation**
- **Interpretive Fellowships**
- **Research Fellowships in Art History**

TYPE:
Fellowships; Research grants; Travel grants. Program assistance is provided through Fellowship programs for predoctoral research in art history, advanced training and research in conservation of works of art, development of scholarly resources in museums and universities in support of art history and conservation, and restoration of monuments in Europe.

YEAR PROGRAM STARTED: 1963

PURPOSE:
To encourage the preservation and history of art, especially European art before 1800.

LEGAL BASIS:
Private foundation.

ELIGIBILITY:
Qualified institutions and organizations with appropriate interests are eligible to apply. The Foundation does not consider grants for films, art history programs below the predoctoral level or the purchase of works of art.

Research Fellowships in Art History provide travel grants to enable predoctoral candidates in the history of art to pursue essential research. They are available annually through a competitive program administered by any one of six affiliated European research centers, which vet applications and host the Kress Fellows each year. Applicants must anticipate completion of all requirements for the Ph.D. degree except the dissertation at the time the grant will be received.

Fellowships in Art Conservation provide recent graduates with a Master's degree in the conservation of works of art the opportunity to compete for funds to support professional studies or apprenticeship. Applicants must have completed a recognized training program and application must be from potential host institution. Fellowships are to be based at U.S. institutions or undertaken by an American if the organization is abroad.

FINANCIAL DATA:
Total amount of support: Approximately $3,900,000 for fiscal year 2012.

NUMBER OF APPLICANTS MOST RECENT YEAR:
Approximately 600.

NUMBER OF AWARDS: Approximately 300.

APPLICATION INFORMATION:
Prospective applicants should, as a first step, submit a brief letter outlining the scope of the proposed project and a budget describing the major anticipated expenses.
Duration: Varies.
Deadline: Fellowships in Art Conservation: March 10; Interpretive Fellowships: April 1; Predoctoral Fellowships: November 30; Research Fellowships in Art History: January 15, April 1 and October 1.

PUBLICATIONS:
Annual report.

IRS IDENTIFICATION NUMBER: 13-1624176

STAFF:
Wyman Meers, Program Administrator

OFFICERS AND TRUSTEES:
Frederick W. Beinecke, Chairman
David Rumsey, Vice Chairman
Max Marmor, President
Cheryl Hurley
Barbara A. Shailor

ADDRESS INQUIRIES TO:
Wyman Meers, Program Administrator
(See address above.)

*SPECIAL STIPULATIONS:
No applications accepted via fax or e-mail.

LIGHT WORK [553]
316 Waverly Avenue
Syracuse, NY 13244
(315) 443-1300
Fax: (315) 443-9516

E-MAIL ADDRESS:
info@lightwork.org

WEB SITE ADDRESS:
www.lightwork.org

FOUNDED: 1972

AREAS OF INTEREST:
Photography.

CONSULTING OR VOLUNTEER SERVICES:
All aspects of visual arts and programs for artists.

NAME(S) OF PROGRAMS:
- **Light Work Artist-in-Residence Program**

TYPE:
Project/program grants; Residencies; Visiting scholars. Artist-in-Residence, exhibitions, publications, sponsored projects, lectures and regrants.

YEAR PROGRAM STARTED: 1973

PURPOSE:
To support artists in photography.

LEGAL BASIS:
Not-for-profit organization.

ELIGIBILITY:
Applicants must be working in photography or related visual arts including video, installation and electronic media. Students are ineligible to apply.

FINANCIAL DATA:
Amount of support per award: $5,000.
Total amount of support: Varies.

COOPERATIVE FUNDING PROGRAMS: Yes.

NUMBER OF APPLICANTS MOST RECENT YEAR:
300 to 500.

NUMBER OF AWARDS: 12 to 15.

APPLICATION INFORMATION:
Applicants are encouraged to use the online application process.
Duration: One month.

STAFF:
Jeffrey Hoone, Executive Director

ADDRESS INQUIRIES TO:
Jeffrey Hoone, Executive Director
(See address above.)

THE ROBERTO LONGHI FOUNDATION FOR THE STUDY OF THE HISTORY OF ART [554]
Via Benedetto Fortini, 30
50125 Florence Italy
+39.055.6580794
Fax: +39.055.6580794

E-MAIL ADDRESS:
longhi@fondazionelonghi.it

WEB SITE ADDRESS:
www.fondazionelonghi.it

FOUNDED: 1971

AREAS OF INTEREST:
Italian painting from the 13th to the 18th centuries.

NAME(S) OF PROGRAMS:
- **Art History Fellowships in Florence**

TYPE:
Fellowships.

PURPOSE:
To promote and further the study of art history by keeping Roberto Longhi's cultural legacy and methods alive.

LEGAL BASIS:
Private foundation.

ELIGIBILITY:
Open to Italian citizens who possess a degree from an Italian university with a thesis in the history of art, and to non-Italian citizens who have fulfilled the preliminary requirements for a doctoral degree in the history of art at an accredited university or an institution of equal standing. Students who have reached their 32nd birthday before the application deadline are not eligible.

Designed for those who want to seriously dedicate themselves to research in the history of art. Fellowship holders may make use of the study materials available in the Institute. They must frequent the Institute and collaborate on a specific group research project selected by the Scientific Committee. In particular, successful candidates must give the assurance that they can dedicate their full time to the research for which the fellowship is assigned. They must live in Florence for the duration of the fellowship, except for travel required for their research. They may not exceed the periods of vacation fixed by the Institute. They are required to attend seminars, lectures and other activities arranged by the Institute. In addition, Fellows must submit a written report at the end of their stay in Florence, relating the findings of their individual research undertaken at the Longhi Foundation. The nonobservance of the above conditions will be considered sufficient grounds for the cancellation of a fellowship.

FINANCIAL DATA:
Amount of support per award: EUR 5,400 (paid in monthly installments over a period of nine months).

APPLICATION INFORMATION:
Applications should be addressed to the Secretariat of the Foundation at the address above and should contain the candidate's biographical data (place and date of birth, domicile, citizenship), a transcript of the candidate's undergraduate and graduate records, a copy of the degree thesis (if available) and other original works, published or unpublished, a "curriculum studiorum," also indicating the knowledge of foreign languages spoken and written, letters of reference from at least two persons of academic standing who are acquainted with the candidate's work, the subject of the research that the candidate is interested in pursuing within the range of the history of art and two passport photographs.

Recipients of fellowships are asked to communicate within 15 days of notification their acceptance and willingness to comply with the conditions and rules as stated.
Duration: Nine months beginning in October.
Deadline: May 15.

PUBLICATIONS:
Proporzioni, art review.

OFFICERS:
Mina Gregori, Chairman and President

MARYLAND INSTITUTE COLLEGE OF ART   [555]
Office of Graduate Admission
1300 West Mount Royal Avenue
Baltimore, MD 21217
(410) 225-2256
Fax: (410) 225-5275

E-MAIL ADDRESS:
graduate@mica.edu

WEB SITE ADDRESS:
www.mica.edu

FOUNDED: 1823

AREAS OF INTEREST:
Fine arts, design and art education.

NAME(S) OF PROGRAMS:
- **Art Education (Low-residency/online MA)**
- **Hoffberger School of Painting (MFA)**
- **MA in Critical Studies**
- **MA Social Design**
- **Master of Arts in Community Arts**
- **Master of Arts in Teaching**
- **MBA/MA**
- **MFA Community Arts**
- **MFA Curatorial Practice**
- **MFA Illustration Practice**
- **MFA in Graphic Design**
- **Mt. Royal School of Art (MFA)**
- **MPS in Art and Design**
- **MPS in Information Visualization**

- **Photographic and Electronic Media (MFA)**
- **Post-Baccalaureate Program**
- **Rinehart School of Sculpture (MFA)**
- **Studio Art (Low-residency MFA)**

TYPE:
Assistantships; Awards/prizes; Challenge/matching grants; Fellowships; Scholarships; Travel grants; Visiting scholars. Post-Baccalaureate Program awards certificates in fine arts and graphic design.

YEAR PROGRAM STARTED: 1896

LEGAL BASIS:
Nonprofit institution.

ELIGIBILITY:
For M.F.A. Summer programs: B.F.A. or B.A. degree with at least 48 studio credits is required plus 12 credits in art history. For M.F.A. Fall programs: Bachelor's degree is required.

FINANCIAL DATA:
Amount of support per award: M.I.C.A. scholarship awards for students in all graduate programs based on merit, up to half of tuition.
Total amount of support: Varies.

APPLICATION INFORMATION:
Submit completed application form, application fee of $60, three letters of recommendation, portfolio of 18 to 20 pieces of most recent work and college transcripts. Label each. CD-ROMs and DVDs accepted.
Duration: Two years. Renewable upon application for the second year.
Deadline: January 15. Announcement April 1.

ADDRESS INQUIRIES TO:
Scott G. Kelly
Associate Dean of Graduate Admission
(See address above.)

THE PAUL MELLON CENTRE FOR STUDIES IN BRITISH ART
16 Bedford Square
London WC1B 3JA England
44 (0) 20 7580 0311
Fax: 44 (0) 20 7636 6730

E-MAIL ADDRESS:
grants@paul-mellon-centre.ac.uk

WEB SITE ADDRESS:
www.paul-mellon-centre.ac.uk

TYPE:
Conferences/seminars; Fellowships; Project/program grants; Research grants. Educational Programme Grants for lectures, symposia, seminars or conferences on British art and architecture.

The Junior Fellowship is to pursue ongoing doctoral research at an American or British university.

The Paul Mellon Centre Rome Fellowship offers fellowships to scholars working on Grand Tour subjects or in the field of Anglo-Italian cultural and artistic relations.

The Postdoctoral Fellowship works to transform doctoral research into publishable form such as a book, series of articles, or exhibition catalogues.

Research Support Grants are for expenses in pursuit of research.

The Senior Fellowship supports an established scholar in the field of British art and architectural history to complete a manuscript or book for immediate publication.

See entry 419 for full listing.

THE METROPOLITAN MUSEUM OF ART   [556]
1000 Fifth Avenue
New York, NY 10028-0198
(212) 570-3710
Fax: (212) 570-3782

E-MAIL ADDRESS:
mmainterns@metmuseum.org

WEB SITE ADDRESS:
www.metmuseum.org

FOUNDED: 1870

AREAS OF INTEREST:
Internships in art museums.

TYPE:
Internships. Internships for graduate and undergraduate students.

YEAR PROGRAM STARTED: 1972

PURPOSE:
To provide pre-career training and experience for students and graduates in art museums.

ELIGIBILITY:
Most projects require strong preparation in the history of art. Applicants of diverse backgrounds and disciplines are encouraged to apply.

FINANCIAL DATA:
Amount of support per award: Varies by program.
Total amount of support: Varies.

NUMBER OF AWARDS: 42.

APPLICATION INFORMATION:
Applicants must submit:
(1) internship application form (available online);
(2) full resume of education and employment;
(3) two academic recommendations;
(4) official transcripts;
(5) a separate list of art history or other relevant courses taken, as well as knowledge of foreign languages taken; and
(6) a set of essays specific to the departmental placement.

After an initial review of the applications, a small number of students will be invited for a personal interview at the Museum, or on the phone.
Duration: Up to 12 months.
Deadline: Generally, early January.

ADDRESS INQUIRIES TO:
Internship Programs
(See address above.)

*PLEASE NOTE:
Final notification for all candidates will be mailed by late March or early April.

THE METROPOLITAN MUSEUM OF ART   [557]
1000 Fifth Avenue
New York, NY 10028-0198
(212) 650-2763
Fax: (212) 396-5168

E-MAIL ADDRESS:
education.grants@metmuseum.org

WEB SITE ADDRESS:
www.metmuseum.org

FOUNDED: 1870

AREAS OF INTEREST:
Museum conservation work.

NAME(S) OF PROGRAMS:
- **The Sherman Fairchild Foundation Fellowships**

TYPE:
Fellowships. Fellowships are awarded annually and make possible study and training in the following Museum conservation departments: Paintings Conservation, Objects Conservation (including sculpture, metalwork, glass, ceramics, furniture and archaeological objects), Musical Instruments, Arms and Armor, Paper Conservation, Textile Conservation, The Costume Institute Conservation.

The Museum offers junior-level and senior-level fellowships in conservation and scientific research. Junior fellowships are intended for those who have recently completed graduate-level training. Senior fellowships are intended for well-established professionals with advanced training in the field and a proven publication record.

All fellowships must take place between September 1 and the following August 31.

PURPOSE:
To make possible study and training in conservation departments of the Museum.

ELIGIBILITY:
Qualified candidates from the U.S. and abroad who have already reached an advanced level of training or experience.

FINANCIAL DATA:
Health care benefits are included.
Amount of support per award: $32,000 plus up to $6,000 for travel and miscellaneous expenses for Junior Conservation Fellow; $42,000 plus up to $6,000 for travel and miscellaneous expenses for Senior Conservation Fellow.
Total amount of support: Varies.

NUMBER OF AWARDS: Varies.

APPLICATION INFORMATION:
Application may be obtained from the Museum's web site.
Duration: Up to one year.
Deadline: First Friday in December.

ADDRESS INQUIRIES TO:
Marcie Karp
Managing Museum Educator
for Academic Programs
The Metropolitan Museum of Art
(See e-mail address above.)

THE METROPOLITAN MUSEUM OF ART [558]
1000 Fifth Avenue
New York, NY 10028-0198
(212) 650-2763
Fax: (212) 570-3972

E-MAIL ADDRESS:
education.grants@metmuseum.org

WEB SITE ADDRESS:
www.metmuseum.org

NAME(S) OF PROGRAMS:
- **Andrew W. Mellon Fellowships**

TYPE:
Fellowships. Awarded to promising young scholars with commendable research projects related to the Metropolitan Museum's collections and to distinguished visiting scholars from the U.S. and abroad who can serve as teachers and advisors making their expertise available to catalogue and refine the collections. Fellows are expected to spend most of their tenure at the Metropolitan Museum.

YEAR PROGRAM STARTED: 1974

PURPOSE:
To promote research in the fine arts.

ELIGIBILITY:
Applicants should have received the Doctorate or have completed substantial work toward it.

FINANCIAL DATA:
Amount of support per award: $42,000 stipend for senior fellows for one year, $32,000 for predoctoral fellows, and up to an additional $6,000 for travel and miscellaneous expenses.

APPLICATION INFORMATION:
Application may be obtained from the Museum's web site.
Duration: Normally, a fellow will be in residence at the Metropolitan for a maximum of one year. Fellowships for senior scholars are also available for as short a term as one month.
Deadline: Application and required letters of recommendation must be received by the first Friday in November. Announcement of awards will be made by late March.

ADDRESS INQUIRIES TO:
Marcie Karp, Managing Museum Educator Academic Programs, Education Department (See address above.)

*SPECIAL STIPULATIONS:
Predoctoral Fellows will generally be expected to assist the hosting curatorial departments up to one-half of their time during the fellowship period with projects that complement their approved scholarly project. They will be expected to participate in a fellows' colloquium in the second half of their fellowship term, in which they will give a 20-minute presentation on their work-in-progress. Senior Fellows will also be invited to participate in these activities.

THE METROPOLITAN MUSEUM OF ART [559]
1000 Fifth Avenue
New York, NY 10028-0198
(212) 650-2763
Fax: (212) 570-3972

E-MAIL ADDRESS:
education.grants@metmuseum.org

WEB SITE ADDRESS:
www.metmuseum.org

AREAS OF INTEREST:
Scholarly research in the fine arts.

NAME(S) OF PROGRAMS:
- **Chester Dale Fellowships**

TYPE:
Fellowships. Awarded for independent scholarly study or research related to the fine arts of the Western world at the Metropolitan Museum.

PURPOSE:
To promote research in the fine arts.

ELIGIBILITY:
Individuals whose fields of study are related to the fine arts of the Western world and who are preferably American citizens under the age of 40.

FINANCIAL DATA:
Fellowships are awarded as available funds permit.
Amount of support per award: $42,000 stipend for senior fellows, $32,000 for predoctoral fellows, and up to an additional $6,000 for travel and miscellaneous expenses.

APPLICATION INFORMATION:
Application may be obtained from the Museum's web site.
Duration: The grants typically cover periods from three months to one year.
Deadline: Application and required letters of recommendation must be received by the first Friday in November. Announcements of awards will be made by March.

ADDRESS INQUIRIES TO:
Marcie Karp, Managing Museum Educator Academic Programs, Education Department (See address above.)

*SPECIAL STIPULATIONS:
Predoctoral Fellows will generally be expected to assist the hosting curatorial department with projects that complement and are incidental to their approved scholarly project. They will be expected to participate in a fellows' colloquium in the second half of their fellowship term, in which they will give a 20-minute presentation on their work-in-progress. Senior Fellows will also be invited to participate in these activities.

THE METROPOLITAN MUSEUM OF ART [560]
1000 Fifth Avenue
New York, NY 10028-0198
(212) 650-2763
Fax: (212) 570-3972

E-MAIL ADDRESS:
education.grants@metmuseum.org

WEB SITE ADDRESS:
www.metmuseum.org

NAME(S) OF PROGRAMS:
- **J. Clawson Mills Scholarships**

TYPE:
Fellowships. Awarded to scholars interested in pursuing research projects at the Metropolitan Museum or abroad in any branch of the fine arts related to the Museum's collections.

PURPOSE:
To promote research in the fine arts.

ELIGIBILITY:
In general, these grants are reserved for mature scholars of demonstrated ability.

FINANCIAL DATA:
Scholarships are awarded as available funds permit.
Amount of support per award: $42,000 stipend for one year for senior fellows, $32,000 for predoctoral fellows, and up to an additional $6,000 for travel and miscellaneous expenses.

APPLICATION INFORMATION:
Application may be obtained from the Museum's web site.
Duration: One year.

Deadline: Application and required letters of recommendation must be received by the first Friday in November. Announcement of awards will be made by March 2.

ADDRESS INQUIRIES TO:
Marcie Karp, Managing Museum Educator Academic Programs, Education Department (See address above.)

*SPECIAL STIPULATIONS:
Predoctoral Fellows will generally be expected to assist the hosting curatorial departments up to one-half of their time during the fellowship period with projects that complement their approved scholarly project. They will be asked to give a gallery talk during their fellowship term and will be expected to participate in a fellows' colloquium in the second half of their term, in which they will give a 20-minute presentation on their work-in-progress. Senior Fellows will also be invited to participate in these activities.

THE METROPOLITAN MUSEUM OF ART [561]
1000 Fifth Avenue
New York, NY 10028-0198
(212) 650-2763
Fax: (212) 570-3972

E-MAIL ADDRESS:
education.grants@metmuseum.org

WEB SITE ADDRESS:
www.metmuseum.org

NAME(S) OF PROGRAMS:
● **The Bothmer Fellowship**

TYPE:
Fellowships. Awarded to an outstanding graduate student who has been admitted to the doctoral program of a university in the U.S., and who has submitted an outline of a thesis dealing with either Greek or Roman art.

YEAR PROGRAM STARTED: 1976

PURPOSE:
To promote research in the fine arts.

ELIGIBILITY:
An applicant must be an outstanding graduate student who has been admitted to the doctoral program of a university in the U.S. and who has submitted an outline of a thesis dealing with either Greek or Roman art. Preference will be given to the applicant who, in the opinion of the Grants Committee, would profit most from utilizing the resources of the Museum's Department of Greek and Roman Art: its collections, library, photographs and other archives with the guidance of its curatorial staff.

FINANCIAL DATA:
Amount of support per award: $32,000 for one year for predoctoral fellows with up to an additional $6,000 for travel and miscellaneous expenses.

APPLICATION INFORMATION:
Application may be obtained from the Museum's web site.
Duration: One academic year.
Deadline: Application and required letters of recommendation must be received by the first Friday in November. Announcements of awards will be made by late March.

ADDRESS INQUIRIES TO:
Marcie Karp, Managing Museum Educator Academic Programs, Education Department (See address above.)

*SPECIAL STIPULATIONS:
Predoctoral Fellows will generally be expected to assist the hosting curatorial departments up to one-half of their time during the fellowship period with projects that complement their approved scholarly project. They will be expected to participate in a fellows' colloquium in the second half of their term, in which they will give a 20-minute presentation on their work-in-progress.

MUSEUM OF EARLY SOUTHERN DECORATIVE ARTS (MESDA) [562]
924 South Main Street
Winston-Salem, NC 27101-5335
(336) 721-7360
Fax: (336) 721-7367

E-MAIL ADDRESS:
sgant@oldsalem.org

WEB SITE ADDRESS:
www.mesda.org

FOUNDED: 1965

AREAS OF INTEREST:
Decorative arts of the South before 1860.

NAME(S) OF PROGRAMS:
● **Horton Fellowship**

TYPE:
Fellowships.

YEAR PROGRAM STARTED: 1976

PURPOSE:
To combine the study of history and objects in a museum context.

LEGAL BASIS:
Nonprofit.

ELIGIBILITY:
Graduate student status or present employment in museum-related professions required.

FINANCIAL DATA:
Covers partial tuition for three credit hours.
Amount of support per award: $150 to $500.
Total amount of support: $7,550 for the year 2012.

NUMBER OF APPLICANTS MOST RECENT YEAR:
15 for the year 2013.

NUMBER OF AWARDS: 8 for the year 2013.

APPLICATION INFORMATION:
Applicant must submit a completed application form and letters of recommendation.
Duration: Four weeks.
Deadline: April 18. Notification May 1.

IRS IDENTIFICATION NUMBER: 56-0587289

STAFF:
Sally Gant, Director of Education

ADDRESS INQUIRIES TO:
Sally Gant, Director of Education
(See address above.)

MUSKINGUM COUNTY COMMUNITY FOUNDATION
534 Putnam Avenue
Zanesville, OH 43701
(740) 453-5192
Fax: (740) 453-5734

E-MAIL ADDRESS:
giving@mccf.org

WEB SITE ADDRESS:
www.mccf.org
zanesvilleprize.org

TYPE:
Awards/prizes; Challenge/matching grants; Conferences/seminars; Development grants; Endowments; Project/program grants; Scholarships; Seed money grants; Technical assistance; Visiting scholars. Scholarships for Muskingum County, OH residents and others designated in fund agreements. Support for contemporary ceramics through largest prize in the Western Hemisphere.

See entry 1334 for full listing.

NAMTA COUNCIL FOR ART ADVOCACY [563]
20200 Zion Avenue
Cornelius, NC 28031
(704) 892-6244
Fax: (704) 892-6247

E-MAIL ADDRESS:
lsiffringer@namta.org

WEB SITE ADDRESS:
www.namta.org

FOUNDED: 2005

AREAS OF INTEREST:
The fine arts industry.

TYPE:
Grants-in-aid; Project/program grants.

YEAR PROGRAM STARTED: 2012

PURPOSE:
To sustain, strengthen and support the art material industry through advocacy, awareness, increased funding of art and art education.

LEGAL BASIS:
501(c)(6) nonprofit corporation.

ELIGIBILITY:
The NAMTA Council for Art Advocacy provides grants in the following categories:
(1) the development of art education courses, programs or curricula and;
(2) any program that promotes and supports the visual and creative artists.

All grants are reviewed and selected by the NAMTA Council for Art Advocacy based on the following criteria:
(1) impact of the proposed project on the community and/or the promotion of the fine arts and art education;
(2) funds available;
(3) number of requested grants and;
(4) feasibility of any project proposed.

FINANCIAL DATA:
Amount of support per award: $500 to $5,000.

NUMBER OF AWARDS: Varies based on available funds.

APPLICATION INFORMATION:
Application information (including possible deadline changes) are available on the web site.
Deadline: Applications must be postmarked no later than October 15, 2013 in order to be considered.

ADDRESS INQUIRIES TO:
Leah Siffringer, Member Services
(See address above.)

PEW FELLOWSHIPS AT THE PEW CENTER FOR ARTS & HERITAGE [564]

1608 Walnut Street, 18th Floor
Philadelphia, PA 19103
(267) 350-4920
Fax: (267) 350-4997

E-MAIL ADDRESS:
pfa@pcah.us
mfranklin@pcah.us

WEB SITE ADDRESS:
www.pcah.us/fellowships

FOUNDED: 1991

AREAS OF INTEREST:
Fellowships are awarded for various art forms, including Choreography, Craft Arts, Folk and Traditional Arts, Literature (Fiction, Literary Non-Fiction and Poetry), Media Arts, Music Composition, Painting, Performance Art, Playwriting, Works on Paper and Visual Arts 3-D.

TYPE:
Fellowships. Opportunities for contemporary artists in the Philadelphia five-county area to concentrate on the development and creation of art. Fellowships to support artists at critical junctures in any stage of their career development. Fellows will be expected to participate annually in at least three meetings with other fellowship recipients.

YEAR PROGRAM STARTED: 1991

PURPOSE:
To provide financial support directly to artists so that they will have the opportunity to dedicate themselves wholly to the development of their artwork; to provide such support at a critical juncture in an artist's career, when a concentration on artistic development and exploration is most likely to contribute to personal and professional growth.

ELIGIBILITY:
Artists are nominated and invited to apply for the fellowship. Candidates must be residents of Bucks, Chester, Delaware, Montgomery or Philadelphia counties, PA, for two years or longer. Matriculated students, full or part-time, or immediate family members of a panelist for the year applied or of Pew Fellowships staff are not eligible.

There is no restriction as to citizenship.

GEOGRAPHIC RESTRICTIONS:
Bucks, Chester, Delaware, Montgomery and Philadelphia counties, Pennsylvania.

FINANCIAL DATA:
Fellowship includes stipend. Funds may be used to support costs such as equipment, materials, assistants, training and travel. The specific use of grant funds will be up to the recipient artist.
Amount of support per award: $60,000.
Total amount of support: Up to $720,000 each year.

COOPERATIVE FUNDING PROGRAMS: Program funded by the Pew Charitable Trusts.

NUMBER OF APPLICANTS MOST RECENT YEAR: Varies.

NUMBER OF AWARDS: Up to 12 each year.

APPLICATION INFORMATION:
Application by nomination only.

The application procedure involves a panel review by artists and arts professionals. The first level of review is discipline-based; the second level of review is interdisciplinary; the final selection of candidates is based on the applicant's accomplishments or promise in his or her discipline, and the degree to which the fellowship will address a critical juncture in the artist's career and/or artistic development.
Duration: Up to two years.

STAFF:
Melissa Franklin, Director
Jackie Liu, Senior Program Associate

ADDRESS INQUIRIES TO:
Melissa Franklin, Director
E-mail: mfranklin@pcah.us
(See address above.)

THE POLLOCK-KRASNER FOUNDATION, INC. [565]

863 Park Avenue
New York, NY 10075
(212) 517-5400
Fax: (212) 288-2836

E-MAIL ADDRESS:
grants@pkf.org

WEB SITE ADDRESS:
www.pkf.org

FOUNDED: 1985

AREAS OF INTEREST:
Visual arts.

TYPE:
Grants-in-aid. Grants to individual visual artists for personal and professional needs.

YEAR PROGRAM STARTED: 1985

PURPOSE:
To aid internationally working artists who have embarked on professional careers.

LEGAL BASIS:
Private foundation.

ELIGIBILITY:
Grants are made to painters, sculptors and artists who work on paper, including printmakers who have taken up art as a professional career. The Foundation will not accept applications from commercial artists, photographers, video artists, filmmakers, craft-makers or any artist whose work primarily falls into these categories. It does not make grants to students nor fund academic study.

The Foundation does not make grants to pay for past debts, legal fees, the purchase of real estate, moves to other cities or to pay for the costs of installations, commissions or projects ordered by others. With very few exceptions, the Foundation will not fund travel expenses.

FINANCIAL DATA:
Amount of support per award: The size of the grant is determined by the individual circumstances of the artist.
Total amount of support: Varies.

APPLICATION INFORMATION:
Artists are required to submit a cover letter, an application, and 10 images of current work. Applications are to be submitted online.
Duration: One year.
Deadline: Grants are awarded throughout the year.

PUBLICATIONS:
Biannual report; application guidelines.

OFFICERS:
Charles C. Bergman, Chairman of the Board and Chief Executive Officer
Samuel Sachs, II, President
Kerrie Buitrago, Executive Vice President

STAFF:
Caroline Black, Program Officer
Beth Cochems, Grants Manager

ADDRESS INQUIRIES TO:
Charles C. Bergman, Chairman of the Board and Chief Executive Officer
(See address above.)

ROSWELL ARTIST-IN-RESIDENCE PROGRAM [566]

P.O. Box One
Roswell, NM 88202
(575) 622-6037
Fax: (575) 623-5603

E-MAIL ADDRESS:
stephen@rair.org

WEB SITE ADDRESS:
www.rair.org

FOUNDED: 1967

AREAS OF INTEREST:
Studio-based, fine-art residencies.

TYPE:
Residencies. Roswell Artist-in-Residence Program is for artists who work in drawing, painting, sculpture, photography, printmaking and other fine art media.

YEAR PROGRAM STARTED: 1967

PURPOSE:
To provide time for artists to focus on their work, without distractions or interruptions.

FINANCIAL DATA:
Amount of support per award: $800 per month, plus housing, studio and utilities and $100 per dependent.
Matching fund requirements: Artists cover phone service, food, art materials and transportation.

NUMBER OF APPLICANTS MOST RECENT YEAR: Approximately 200 average.

NUMBER OF AWARDS: 6 each year.

APPLICATION INFORMATION:
Application information is available on the web site.
Duration: One year.
Deadline: Varies from year to year.

IRS IDENTIFICATION NUMBER: 33-0999247

STAFF:
Stephen Fleming, Director
Nancy Fleming, Programs and Publications and Co-Director

ADDRESS INQUIRIES TO:
Roswell Artist-in-Residence Program
(See address above.)

SAN DIEGO ART INSTITUTE [567]

1439 El Prado
House of Charm, Balboa Park
San Diego, CA 92101
(619) 236-0011
Fax: (619) 236-1974

E-MAIL ADDRESS:
admin@sandiego-art.org

WEB SITE ADDRESS:
www.sandiego-art.org

FOUNDED: 1941

AREAS OF INTEREST:
Visual arts.

NAME(S) OF PROGRAMS:
- **Annual International Juried Award Exhibition**
- **Southern California Regional Juried Award**
- **Youth Art**

TYPE:
Awards/prizes; Conferences/seminars; Internships. Monthly juried exhibitions; monthly youth art exhibitions; awarded member solo shows; annual international juried award exhibition; annual city/county youth art award show; quarterly informational lecture series; biannual art tours; newsletter/journal.

YEAR PROGRAM STARTED: 1954

PURPOSE:
To advance the visual arts through exhibition, outreach and education.

LEGAL BASIS:
Nonprofit organization.

ELIGIBILITY:
For the International Juried Award, the exhibition is open to any artist (digital entry only). There are no residency restrictions. Art must be original.

For the Southern California Regional Juried Award, southern California residency is required.

FINANCIAL DATA:
Awards include monetary compensation.

Amount of support per award: For the International Juried Award Exhibition, one award of $2,000; two awards of $1,000; one award of $500; two awards of $150; three awards of $100. For Southern California Regional Juried Award Exhibition: one award of $1,000; two awards of $500.

Total amount of support: $7,100.

NUMBER OF AWARDS: 13.

APPLICATION INFORMATION:
Work may be two- or three-dimensional. All media are welcome except crafts or functional art. For the Southern California Regional, one art work per artist. Entry fee required.

Duration: One-time awards.

PUBLICATIONS:
Journal; guidelines.

IRS IDENTIFICATION NUMBER: 95-1816068

ADDRESS INQUIRIES TO:
Ginger Shulick Porcella, Executive Director
(See address and e-mail above.)

*PLEASE NOTE:
All shows are juried by outside juror.

THE SAN FRANCISCO FOUNDATION   [568]
One Embarcadero Center, 14th Floor
San Francisco, CA 94111
(415) 733-8500
Fax: (415) 477-2783

E-MAIL ADDRESS:
tromo@sff.org

WEB SITE ADDRESS:
www.sff.org

FOUNDED: 1948

AREAS OF INTEREST:
Fine arts.

NAME(S) OF PROGRAMS:
- **Cadogan Fine Arts Scholarships**
- **Murphy Fine Arts Fellowships**

TYPE:
Fellowships; Scholarships.

YEAR PROGRAM STARTED: 1948

PURPOSE:
To assist San Francisco Bay Area students in pursuing graduate academic fine arts study at eight Bay Area institutions.

LEGAL BASIS:
Community foundation.

ELIGIBILITY:
Applicants must be graduate fine arts students in one of eight San Francisco Bay Area colleges and universities, which include John F. Kennedy University, Mills College, San Francisco State University, Stanford University, The California College of the Arts, The San Francisco Academy of Art University, The San Francisco Art Institute, and UC Berkeley. Students may self-nominate for the award.

Students must have completed at least one semester of graduate school by the time they apply, and must have at least one semester left to graduate. The work must have been completed within the past two years.

GEOGRAPHIC RESTRICTIONS:
San Francisco Bay Area, California.

FINANCIAL DATA:
Amount of support per award: $4,000 to underwrite tuition, paid directly to financial aid offices.

Total amount of support: $55,000 to $80,000 per year.

NUMBER OF APPLICANTS MOST RECENT YEAR:
120 for the year 2013.

NUMBER OF AWARDS: 26 for the year 2013.

APPLICATION INFORMATION:
Application information is available online.

Duration: One year.

Deadline: Spring. Announcement in early June.

ADDRESS INQUIRIES TO:
Arts and Culture Program Fellow
(See address above.)

SCHOOL OF THE MUSEUM OF FINE ARTS, BOSTON   [569]
230 The Fenway
Boston, MA 02115
(617) 369-3656
Fax: (617) 369-3856

WEB SITE ADDRESS:
www.smfa.edu

FOUNDED: 1876

AREAS OF INTEREST:
Studio fine arts.

NAME(S) OF PROGRAMS:
- **Traveling Fellowship Award**

TYPE:
Fellowships. Awarded for travel and study abroad.

YEAR PROGRAM STARTED: 1899

PURPOSE:
To further the professional development of the artist recipients.

LEGAL BASIS:
A part of the Museum of Fine Arts, a nonprofit Massachusetts corporation.

ELIGIBILITY:
Applicants must be alumni of the School of the Museum of Fine Arts and submit a body of work to the competition jury no later than the third year following graduation.

FINANCIAL DATA:
Amount of support per award: Up to $10,000.

Total amount of support: Approximately $100,000 annually.

NUMBER OF APPLICANTS MOST RECENT YEAR:
122.

APPLICATION INFORMATION:
Proposed plan of travel and study, including itinerary, must be submitted with a presentation of art work.

Duration: Varies according to proposal. Normally not more than one year. Nonrenewable.

Deadline: June. Announcement in September.

ADDRESS INQUIRIES TO:
Office of Exhibitions
(See address above.)

SKOWHEGAN SCHOOL OF PAINTING AND SCULPTURE   [570]
200 Park Avenue South
Suite 1116
New York, NY 10003-1503
(212) 529-0505
Fax: (212) 473-1342

E-MAIL ADDRESS:
mail@skowheganart.org

WEB SITE ADDRESS:
www.skowheganart.org

FOUNDED: 1946

AREAS OF INTEREST:
All visual arts.

TYPE:
Scholarships.

YEAR PROGRAM STARTED: 1946

PURPOSE:
To bring together a gifted and diverse group of individuals who have demonstrated a commitment to art-making and inquiry to create the most stimulating environment possible for a concentrated period of artistic creation, interaction and growth.

LEGAL BASIS:
Not-for-profit educational institution.

ELIGIBILITY:
Based on need. Candidate must be at least 21 years old.

FINANCIAL DATA:
Scholarships cover room, board and tuition.

Amount of support per award: Varies.

APPLICATION INFORMATION:
Application information is available online.

Duration: Nine-week summer program, mid-June to mid-August.

Deadline: February 1 for all applications. Notification in mid-April.

ADDRESS INQUIRIES TO:
Sarah Workneh, Director
(See address above.)

W. EUGENE SMITH MEMORIAL FUND [571]

c/o International Center of Photography
1114 Avenue of the Americas
New York, NY 10036
(212) 857-0064
Fax: (212) 857-0091

E-MAIL ADDRESS:
smithfund@icp.edu

WEB SITE ADDRESS:
www.smithfund.org

FOUNDED: 1979

AREAS OF INTEREST:
Photography.

NAME(S) OF PROGRAMS:
• **W. Eugene Smith Grant in Humanistic Photography**

TYPE:
Project/program grants.

PURPOSE:
To support a photographer working on a project in the humanistic tradition of W. Eugene Smith, in order to pursue the work.

ELIGIBILITY:
Open to outstanding photographers of any nationality.

FINANCIAL DATA:
Amount of support per award: $30,000 and a possible additional $5,000 fellowship.

NUMBER OF AWARDS: 1 annually.

APPLICATION INFORMATION:
Applicants should include a written proposal, resume of educational and professional qualifications, and 20 to 40 images. Entry fee of $50 is required.
Duration: One year.
Deadline: May 31.

*SPECIAL STIPULATIONS:
Grant recipients agree to give to the W. Eugene Smith Memorial Fund, Inc., as an unrestricted gift, 12 prints of work completed as part of the project proposed, within 18 months of the award and shall become part of the Legacy Collection.

SIR JOHN SOANE MUSEUM FOUNDATION

1040 First Avenue, Suite 311
New York, NY 10022
(212) 223-2012
Fax: (866) 841-1928

E-MAIL ADDRESS:
info@soanefoundation.com

WEB SITE ADDRESS:
www.soanefoundation.com

TYPE:
Fellowships. Designed to help graduate students and scholars pursue research projects related to the work of Sir John Soane's Museum and its collections.
See entry 423 for full listing.

THE JOHN F. AND ANNA LEE STACEY SCHOLARSHIP FUND [572]

c/o National Cowboy and
Western Heritage Museum
Oklahoma City, OK 73111
(405) 478-2250
Fax: (405) 478-4714

E-MAIL ADDRESS:
amorand@nationalcowboymuseum.org

WEB SITE ADDRESS:
www.nationalcowboymuseum.org

FOUNDED: 1955

AREAS OF INTEREST:
Drawing and painting in the conservative mode.

TYPE:
Awards/prizes. Cash awards to be used to further the development of young painters in the classical conservative tradition.

YEAR PROGRAM STARTED: 1975

PURPOSE:
To foster a high standard in the study of form, color, drawing, painting, design and technique, as these are expressed in modes showing patent affinity with the classical tradition of western culture.

LEGAL BASIS:
Nonprofit.

ELIGIBILITY:
Open to U.S. citizens between 18 and 35 years of age. Only those who are skilled and devoted to the painting or drawing of classical or conservative tradition of western culture should apply.

GEOGRAPHIC RESTRICTIONS:
United States.

FINANCIAL DATA:
Amount of support per award: $1,000 to $4,000.
Total amount of support: Varies.

NUMBER OF APPLICANTS MOST RECENT YEAR:
More than 200.

NUMBER OF AWARDS: 3 to 5.

APPLICATION INFORMATION:
Guidelines and application are posted online by November 1 for the following year. All applicants will be required to upload images to the Fund's FTP site. Not more than six images (clearly labeled with name, title, dimensions, medium and date of execution of the work) of their work in the following categories: painting from life, drawing from the figure (nude), composition, landscape and others.

Application forms must accompany all submissions.
Duration: One year.
Deadline: Entries need to be uploaded by February 1 of each year.

PUBLICATIONS:
Guidelines.

STAFF:
Anne Morand, Curator of Art

ADDRESS INQUIRIES TO:
See e-mail address above.

STUDIO ARTS CENTERS INTERNATIONAL (SACI) [573]

Palazzo dei Cartelloni
Via Sant' Antonino 11
50123 Florence Italy
(39) 055-289948
Fax: (39) 055-2776408

E-MAIL ADDRESS:
admissions@saci-florence.edu

WEB SITE ADDRESS:
www.saci-florence.edu

FOUNDED: 1975

AREAS OF INTEREST:
Studio art, art history, art conservation, Italian language and culture.

NAME(S) OF PROGRAMS:
• **Fall/Spring Study Abroad**
• **MFA in Photography**
• **MFA in Studio Art (Painting or Drawing)**
• **Post Baccalaureate Certificate Programs**

TYPE:
Scholarships. Fall/Spring Study Abroad: Undergraduate and graduate visiting students may attend for a term or more. SACI offers a wide variety of both traditional and cutting-edge studio art and design courses as well as classes in art history covering medieval and contemporary art. For conservation students, there is the unique opportunity to participate hands-on in the conservation of historic works in Florence. Studio Art courses include Fresco Painting, Serigraphy, Printmaking, Photography, Digital Multimedia, Video, Jewelry Making, Batik, Book Making, Sculpture, Ceramics, and many more.

MFA in Studio Art (Painting or Drawing)/MFA in Photography: SACI's MFAs are two-year programs in which students work in a creative environment of rigorous critical and technical inquiry utilizing the unique artistic and cultural resources of Florence to prepare for careers as artists and college instructors. Students pursue a curriculum integrating practical and critical skills that encourages individual innovation, creative collaboration, mentorships and instruction from SACI's outstanding faculty.

Post Baccalaureate Certificate Programs: SACI's Post Baccalaureate Certificate Programs are one-year programs of intensive graduate study in a selected major discipline within Art History, Conservation or Studio Art. The study program includes graduate seminars, reviews, field trips, lecture series and exhibitions.

YEAR PROGRAM STARTED: 1975

PURPOSE:
To study Studio Art, Art History or Conservation at a U.S.-accredited institution in Florence, Italy.

ELIGIBILITY:
Selection is based on academic/artistic merit as well as financial need.

FINANCIAL DATA:
Amount of support per award: $200 up to full tuition.

APPLICATION INFORMATION:
Application information is available on the web site.
Duration: Semester.
Deadline: Fall: March 15. Spring: October 15.

ADDRESS INQUIRIES TO:
Studio Arts Centers International (SACI)
New York Office
50 Broad Street, Suite 1617
New York, NY 10004-2372
Tel: (212) 248-7225
Fax: (212) 248-7222

UNIVERSITY OF ILLINOIS AT URBANA-CHAMPAIGN [574]
College of Fine and Applied Arts
608 East Lorado Taft Drive, Suite 100
Champaign, IL 61820
(217) 333-1661
(217) 333-1660
Fax: (217) 244-8381

E-MAIL ADDRESS:
faa@illinois.edu

WEB SITE ADDRESS:
www.faa.illinois.edu

FOUNDED: 1931

AREAS OF INTEREST:
Art, architecture, dance, landscape architecture, music, theatre, and urban and regional planning.

NAME(S) OF PROGRAMS:
● **Kate Neal Kinley Memorial Fellowship**

TYPE:
Fellowships. Awarded for advanced study in the fine arts in the U.S. or abroad, in an approved educational institution, with an approved private teacher or in independent study.

Three major Fellowships will be awarded:
(1) one in any field of music;
(2) one in architectural design and history, art and design, theatre, dance, or instrumental or vocal music and;
(3) one in art, architecture, dance, landscape architecture, theatre, or urban and regional planning.

YEAR PROGRAM STARTED: 1931

PURPOSE:
To help defray expenses of advanced study of the fine and applied arts in America or abroad.

Provides a meaningful opportunity for students to enhance their professional status, aid their pursuit of an advanced degree, or finance a special project within the field.

ELIGIBILITY:
Open to graduates of the College of Fine and Applied Arts of the University of Illinois at Urbana-Champaign and to graduates of similar institutions of equal educational standing whose principal or major studies have been in the fields of art, architecture, dance, landscape architecture, music, theatre, and urban and regional planning.

Although there is no age limitation for applicants, other factors being equal, preference will be given to applicants who have not reached their 25th birthday.

Fellowships will be awarded upon the basis of unusual promise in the fine arts as attested by:
(1) high attainment in the applicant's major field of study as evidenced by academic marks and quality of work submitted or performed;
(2) high attainment in related cultural fields as evidenced by academic marks;
(3) the character, merit and suitability of the program proposed by the applicant and;
(4) excellence of personality, seriousness of purpose and good moral character.

FINANCIAL DATA:
The fellowships are to be used by the recipients toward defraying the expenses of advanced study in America or abroad.

Amount of support per award: Major fellowships: Up to $20,000 in any field of music, up to $20,000 in architectural design

and history, art and design, theatre, dance, or instrumental or vocal music, and up to $9,000 in art, architecture, dance, landscape architecture, theatre, or urban and regional planning.

COOPERATIVE FUNDING PROGRAMS: Funded partially by the John Robert Gregg Fund at Community Funds, Inc. and the New York Community Trust.

NUMBER OF AWARDS: 3 major fellowships, plus up to 3 additional fellowships of lesser amounts, depending upon committee recommendations.

APPLICATION INFORMATION:
Application form and guidelines are available online.
Duration: Tenable for one academic year.
Deadline: December 1.

ADDRESS INQUIRIES TO:
Edward Feser, Dean
Kate Neal Kinley
Memorial Fellowship Committee
(See address above.)
Tel: (217) 333-1661

UNIVERSITY OF SOUTHERN CALIFORNIA ROSKI SCHOOL OF ART AND DESIGN [575]
Watt Hall 104
Los Angeles, CA 90089-0292
(213) 740-9153
Fax: (213) 740-8938

E-MAIL ADDRESS:
finearts@usc.edu

WEB SITE ADDRESS:
roski.usc.edu

FOUNDED: 1883

AREAS OF INTEREST:
Fine arts.

NAME(S) OF PROGRAMS:
● **M.F.A. Teaching Assistantships**

TYPE:
Assistantships; Travel grants. Tuition remission. Awards are for people pursuing M.F.A. degree, for experience in teaching art on a college level.

YEAR PROGRAM STARTED: 1960

PURPOSE:
To educate artists.

LEGAL BASIS:
Private university.

ELIGIBILITY:
Applicants must be accepted into the Roski School of Art and Design two-year M.F.A. program at University of Southern California.

All applicants to the program are considered for awards regardless of national origin.

FINANCIAL DATA:
Teaching Assistantship includes full tuition remission, generous monthly stipend and private studio.
Amount of support per award: Teaching Assistantship: $49,000 per year; Summer Travel Fellowship: Up to $5,000.
Total amount of support: $475,000.

NUMBER OF APPLICANTS MOST RECENT YEAR:
391.

NUMBER OF AWARDS: 8 Teaching Assistantships; 1 Travel Grant.

APPLICATION INFORMATION:
Applications are available online.
Duration: One year. Assistantships are renewable.
Deadline: January 20.

ADDRESS INQUIRIES TO:
Penelope Jones
Assistant Dean for Student Affairs
(See address above.)

History

AGRICULTURAL HISTORY SOCIETY [576]
MSU History Department
P.O. Box H
Mississippi State, MS 39762
(662) 268-2247

E-MAIL ADDRESS:
jgiesen@history.msstate.edu

WEB SITE ADDRESS:
www.aghistorysociety.org

AREAS OF INTEREST:
Agricultural and rural history.

NAME(S) OF PROGRAMS:
● **Everett E. Edwards Awards in Agricultural History**
● **Gilbert C. Fite Dissertation Award**
● **Wayne D. Rasmussen Award**
● **Theodore Saloutos Book Award**

TYPE:
Awards/prizes. The Everett E. Edwards Award is presented to the graduate student who submits the best manuscript on any aspect of agricultural history and rural studies during the current calendar year.

The Gilbert C. Fite Dissertation Award will be presented to the author of the best dissertation on any aspect of agricultural history completed during the current calendar year.

The Wayne D. Rasmussen Award is given to the author of the best article on agricultural history published by a journal other than *Agricultural History* during the current calendar year.

The Theodore Saloutos Book Award is presented to the author of a book on any aspect of agricultural history in the U.S. within the current year, broadly interpreted.

PURPOSE:
To promote research and publication in the field of agricultural and rural history.

FINANCIAL DATA:
Amount of support per award: Edwards Award: Honorarium of $200 and publication in *Agricultural History*; Fite Dissertation Award: Honorarium of $300 and a certificate; Rasmussen Award: Honorarium of $200 for the author and certificates for the author and publisher; Saloutos Book Award: $500 to the author.

APPLICATION INFORMATION:
Contact the Society for details.
Deadline: December 31.

AMERICAN ANTIQUARIAN SOCIETY (AAS)

185 Salisbury Street
Worcester, MA 01609-1634
(508) 755-5221
Fax: (508) 753-3311

E-MAIL ADDRESS:
cmcrell@mwa.org

WEB SITE ADDRESS:
www.americanantiquarian.org

TYPE:
Fellowships. Visiting fellowship for historical research by creative and performing artists, writers, filmmakers and journalists.

See entry 346 for full listing.

AMERICAN ANTIQUARIAN SOCIETY (AAS)

185 Salisbury Street
Worcester, MA 01609-1634
(508) 755-5221
Fax: (508) 754-9069

E-MAIL ADDRESS:
perickson@mwa.org

WEB SITE ADDRESS:
www.americanantiquarian.org

TYPE:
Conferences/seminars; Fellowships. Fellowships provide support for residence at the Society's library for research on any topic supported by the collections. All awards are for research and writing using the library's resources.

See entry 345 for full listing.

AMERICAN CATHOLIC HISTORICAL ASSOCIATION   [577]

Department of African & African-American Studies
Fordham University, Dealy Hall, Room 637
441 East Fordham Road
Bronx, NY 10458
(718) 817-3830
Fax: (718) 817-5690

E-MAIL ADDRESS:
acha@fordham.edu

WEB SITE ADDRESS:
www.achahistory.org

FOUNDED: 1919

AREAS OF INTEREST:
The history of Catholicism from antiquity to the present.

NAME(S) OF PROGRAMS:
• **The Howard R. Marraro Prize**

TYPE:
Awards/prizes. This Prize is given annually to the author of a book that is judged by a committee of experts to be the most distinguished work dealing with Italian history or Italo-American history or relations that has been published in a preceding 12-month period. It is named in memory of Howard A. Marraro (1879-1972), professor, Columbia University and the author of more than a dozen books on Italian literature, history and culture.

YEAR PROGRAM STARTED: 1973

PURPOSE:
To stimulate interest in the history of Catholicism among young scholars.

LEGAL BASIS:
An endowed fund owned by the Association.

ELIGIBILITY:
To be entered in the competition, a work must be of book length, in English, already published and must deal with Italian history or Italian-American history or relations. To be eligible for the prize, an author must be a citizen or resident of the U.S. or Canada. The work must have been published since June 1 of the previous year.

FINANCIAL DATA:
Amount of support per award: $750.

NUMBER OF AWARDS: 1 per annum.

APPLICATION INFORMATION:
Three copies, if possible, of the work to be considered should be sent, together with a brief curriculum vitae and bibliography of the author, to the American Historical Association, 400 A Street, S.E., Washington, DC 20003.
Deadline: May 15.

ADDRESS INQUIRIES TO:
Prize Administrator
Tel:(202) 544-2422
E-mail: dschaffer@historians.org

AMERICAN CATHOLIC HISTORICAL ASSOCIATION

Fordham University, Dealy Hall, Room 637
441 East Fordham Road
Bronx, NY 10458
(718) 817-3830
Fax: (718) 817-5690

E-MAIL ADDRESS:
acha@fordham.edu

WEB SITE ADDRESS:
www.achahistory.org

TYPE:
Awards/prizes; Challenge/matching grants; Conferences/seminars; Travel grants. A prize awarded annually to the author whose article, dealing with the history of the Catholic Church, is the first of his or her professional career and is judged to be the best of those in that category accepted for publication in any given year by the editors of the *Catholic Historical Review*.

See entry 803 for full listing.

AMERICAN CATHOLIC HISTORICAL ASSOCIATION

Fordham University, Dealy Hall, Room 637
441 East Fordham Road
Bronx, NY 10458
(718) 817-3830
Fax: (718) 817-5690

E-MAIL ADDRESS:
acha@fordham.edu

WEB SITE ADDRESS:
www.achahistory.org

TYPE:
Awards/prizes. This Prize is given annually to the author of a book, published during a preceding 12-month period, which is judged by a committee of experts to have made the most original and distinguished contribution to knowledge of the history of the Catholic Church.

See entry 804 for full listing.

AMERICAN CATHOLIC HISTORICAL ASSOCIATION

Fordham University, Dealy Hall, Room 637
441 East Fordham Road
Bronx, NY 10458
(718) 817-3830
Fax: (718) 817-5690

E-MAIL ADDRESS:
acha@fordham.edu

WEB SITE ADDRESS:
www.achahistory.org

TYPE:
Awards/prizes; Challenge/matching grants; Conferences/seminars; Research grants; Travel grants. ACHA Graduate Student Summer Research Grant is awarded to an ACHA graduate student member who has completed all requirements for the Doctorate except the dissertation.

ACHA Junior Faculty Grant is awarded to an ACHA tenure-track scholar to assist in summer travel to conduct research.

John Tracy Ellis Dissertation Award memorializes the scholarship and teaching of Monsignor Ellis (1905-1992).

Graduate Student Travel Grant was created in 2010 by the Association from donations from former presidents.

See entry 801 for full listing.

AMERICAN CATHOLIC HISTORICAL ASSOCIATION

Fordham University, Dealy Hall, Room 637
441 East Fordham Road
Bronx, NY 10458
(718) 817-3830
Fax: (718) 817-5690

E-MAIL ADDRESS:
acha@fordham.edu

WEB SITE ADDRESS:
www.achahistory.org

TYPE:
Awards/prizes. The Msgr. Harry C. Koenig Award for Catholic Biography is offered every two years (in even-numbered years) and recognizes outstanding biographies of members of the Catholic Church who have lived in any age or country.

See entry 802 for full listing.

THE AMERICAN HISTORICAL ASSOCIATION   [578]

400 A Street, S.E.
Washington, DC 20003
(202) 544-2422
Fax: (202) 544-8307

E-MAIL ADDRESS:
awards@historians.org

WEB SITE ADDRESS:
www.historians.org

FOUNDED: 1884

AREAS OF INTEREST:
Promotion of historical studies, the collection and preservation of historical manuscripts and the dissemination of historical research.

NAME(S) OF PROGRAMS:
• **The Herbert Baxter Adams Prize**
• **The George Louis Beer Prize**
• **The Jerry Bentley Prize**
• **The Albert J. Beveridge Award**
• **The Albert J. Beveridge Grant**
• **The Paul Birdsall Prize**

- The James Henry Breasted Prize
- The Albert B. Corey Prize in Canadian-American Relations
- The John H. Dunning Prize in United States History
- The John K. Fairbank Prize in East Asian History
- The Herbert Feis Award
- The Morris D. Forkosch Prize
- The Leo Gershoy Award
- The Clarence H. Haring Prize
- J. Franklin Jameson Award
- The Friedrich Katz Prize
- The Joan Kelly Memorial Prize in Women's History
- Martin A. Klein Prize in African History
- Michael Kraus Research Grant
- The Waldo G. Leland Prize
- Littleton-Griswold Grant
- The Littleton-Griswold Prize in American Law and Society
- The J. Russell Major Prize
- The Helen and Howard R. Marraro Prize in Italian History
- The George L. Mosse Prize
- The John E. O'Connor Film Award
- The Premio Del Rey
- The James A. Rawley Prize in Atlantic History
- John F. Richards Prize in South Asian History
- The James Harvey Robinson Prize
- Bernadotte Schmitt Grant
- The Wesley-Logan Prize

TYPE:
Awards/prizes; Fellowships; Research grants. Prizes and awards for distinguished scholarly publications written in English on historical subjects as follows:

Herbert Baxter Adams Prize: Awarded annually for a distinguished book by an American author in the field of European history.

Beer Prize: Awarded annually for the best work on European international history by a U.S. citizen.

Bentley Prize: Awarded annually for the best book in the field of world history.

Beveridge Award: Awarded annually for the best book in English on the history of the U.S., Canada, or Latin America from 1492 to the present.

Beveridge Grant: Given for research pertaining to the Western Hemisphere.

Birdsall Prize: For the best work in European military and strategic history. Awarded biennially in even years.

Breasted Prize: Awarded annually for an outstanding book in English in any field of history prior to 1000 A.D.

Corey Prize: Awarded biennially in even years for a book on the history of Canadian-U.S. relations, or on the history of both countries.

Dunning Prize: For a book on any subject relating to American history. Awarded biennially in odd years.

Fairbank Prize: Awarded annually for an outstanding book on the history of China proper, Vietnam, Chinese Central Asia, Mongolia, Manchuria, Korea or Japan since the year 1800.

Feis Award: Awarded for distinguished contributions to public history.

Forkosch Prize: Awarded annually in recognition of the best book in English in the field of British, British Imperial or British Commonwealth History.

Gershoy Prize: Awarded annually for an outstanding work published in English on any aspect of the fields of 17th and 18th century western European history.

Haring Prize: For a Latin American who, in the opinion of the committee, has published the most outstanding book on Latin American history during the preceding five years. Awarded every five years.

J. Franklin Jameson Award: Given for outstanding achievement in the editing of historical sources.

Friedrich Katz Prize: Awarded annually for the best book in Latin American and Caribbean history.

Kelly Memorial Prize: Awarded annually for the best work in women's history and/or feminist theory.

Martin A. Klein Prize: Awarded in the study of African history.

Michael Kraus Research Grant: Awarded for the study of colonial American history.

Leland Prize: Offered every five years for the outstanding reference tool in the field of history, i.e., bibliographies, indexes, encyclopedias and other scholarly apparatus.

Littleton-Griswold Grant: Awarded in U.S. legal history and law and society, broadly defined.

Littleton-Griswold Prize: Awarded annually for the best book in any subject on the history of American law and society, broadly defined.

J. Russell Major Prize: Awarded annually for the best work in English on any aspect of French history.

Marraro Prize: Awarded annually for the best work on any epoch of Italian history or Italian-American relations.

George L. Mosse Prize: Awarded annually for an outstanding major work of extraordinary scholarly distinction, creativity, and originality in the intellectual and cultural history of Europe since the Renaissance.

John E. O'Connor Film Award: Awarded annually to recognize outstanding interpretations of history through the medium of film.

Premio del Rey: Awarded biennially, in even years for the best book in English in the field of early Spanish history, 500 to 1516 A.D.

James A. Rawley Prize in Atlantic History: Awarded annually in recognition of outstanding historical writing that explores aspects of integration of Atlantic worlds before the 20th century.

John F. Richards Prize in South Asian History: Awarded annually for the most distinguished work of scholarship on South Asian history published in English.

Robinson Prize: Awarded biennially in even years for the teaching aid that has made the most outstanding contribution to the teaching of history in any field. Award encompasses textbooks, source materials, audio-visual and computer-assisted instruction programs/techniques.

Bernadette Schmitt Grant: Given for research of Europe, Asia and Africa.

Wesley-Logan Prize: Awarded annually for an outstanding book on African diaspora history.

PURPOSE:
To promote and honor good historical writing and scholarship.

LEGAL BASIS:
Nonprofit association.

ELIGIBILITY:
Applicant must be a member to apply for grants. Preference will be given to Ph.D. candidates and postgraduates.

FINANCIAL DATA:
Amount of support per award: Varies.

NUMBER OF AWARDS: 1 in each program on the yearly basis.

PUBLICATIONS:
Annual report; *American Historical Review; Perspectives in History.*

OFFICERS:
Jan E. Goldstein, President
James R. Grossman, Executive Director
Robert A. Schneider, Editor, *American Historical Review*
Randy B. Norell, Controller

ADDRESS INQUIRIES TO:
Prize or Grant Administrator
(See e-mail address above.)

THE AMERICAN HISTORICAL ASSOCIATION   [579]
400 A Street, S.E.
Washington, DC 20003
(202) 544-2422
Fax: (202) 544-8307

E-MAIL ADDRESS:
awards@historians.org

WEB SITE ADDRESS:
www.historians.org

FOUNDED: 1884

AREAS OF INTEREST:
Scholarly research.

NAME(S) OF PROGRAMS:
- The J. Franklin Jameson Fellowship

TYPE:
Fellowships. Award in American history offered annually by the Library of Congress and the American Historical Association.

YEAR PROGRAM STARTED: 1977

PURPOSE:
To support significant scholarly research in the collections of the Library of Congress by scholars at an early stage in their careers in history.

LEGAL BASIS:
Nonprofit association.

ELIGIBILITY:
At the time of application, applicants must hold the Ph.D. degree or equivalent, must have received this degree within the past seven years and must not have published or had accepted for publication a book-length historical work. The fellowship will not be awarded to complete a doctoral dissertation.

The applicant's project in American history must be one for which the general and special collections of the Library of Congress offer unique research support. Applicants should include a statement substantiating this relationship.

Before the conclusion of the fellowship, the Jameson fellow will summarize the results of his or her research at a professional gathering arranged by the American Historical Association and the Library of Congress. Jameson fellows are not required to complete their project during the tenure of the fellowship, nor need they necessarily have published the results as a discrete work.

The American Historical Association encourages nontenured faculty, public historians, independent scholars and two-year faculty to apply.

FINANCIAL DATA:
Amount of support per award: $5,000 stipend.

NUMBER OF APPLICANTS MOST RECENT YEAR: 5 to 10 annually.

NUMBER OF AWARDS: 1 annually.

APPLICATION INFORMATION:
Letter of application should include a vitae, statement concerning the proposed project and its relationship to Library of Congress holdings, tentative schedule for tenure of the fellowship and three letters of recommendation by persons qualified to judge the project and the applicant's fitness to undertake it.
Duration: Two to three months.
Deadline: April 1. Award announced in June.

PUBLICATIONS:
Annual report.

OFFICERS:
Jan E. Goldstein, President
James R. Grossman, Executive Director
Robert A. Schneider, Editor, American Historical Review
Randy B. Norell, Controller

ADDRESS INQUIRIES TO:
J. Franklin Jameson Fellowship
(See e-mail address above.)

THE AMERICAN HISTORICAL ASSOCIATION [580]
400 A Street, S.E.
Washington, DC 20003
(202) 544-2422
Fax: (202) 544-8307

E-MAIL ADDRESS:
awards@historians.org

WEB SITE ADDRESS:
www.historians.org

FOUNDED: 1884

AREAS OF INTEREST:
Scholarly research.

NAME(S) OF PROGRAMS:
● **Fellowship in Aerospace History**

TYPE:
Fellowships. The Association annually funds at least one fellow for a period of six to nine months, to undertake a proposed research project related to aerospace history. The Fellowship is supported by the National Aeronautics and Space Administration (NASA).

YEAR PROGRAM STARTED: 1986

PURPOSE:
To provide a fellow with an opportunity to engage in significant and sustained advanced research in all aspects of the history of aerospace from the earliest human interest in flight to the present, including cultural and

intellectual history, economic history, history of law and public policy and the history of science, engineering and management.

LEGAL BASIS:
Nonprofit association.

ELIGIBILITY:
Applicants must possess a Doctorate degree in history or in a closely related field or be enrolled as a student, having completed all course work, in a doctoral degree-granting program.

The Fellowship term is for a period of at least six months, but not more than nine months, and should commence no later than November 15. The fellow will be expected to devote the term entirely to the proposed research project. Office space is not provided with the Fellowship, and residency is not required; however, fellows are encouraged to take advantage of the resources of the National Aeronautics and Space Administration, the National Academies of Science, the Library of Congress, the Smithsonian Air and Space Museum and other collections in the Washington, DC area.

FINANCIAL DATA:
Amount of support per award: $20,000 stipend for a six- to nine-month fellowship. The stipend is adjustable to the length of the fellowship term.

NUMBER OF AWARDS: 1 per year.

APPLICATION INFORMATION:
Applicants must complete an application form, available online, and offer a specific and detailed research proposal that will be the basis of the fellow's research during the term. At the term's conclusion, the fellow will be expected to write a report and present a paper or public lecture on the Fellowship experience.
Duration: Six to nine months.
Deadline: April 1.

PUBLICATIONS:
Annual report.

OFFICERS:
Jan E. Goldstein, President
James R. Grossman, Executive Director
Robert A. Schneider, Editor, American Historical Review
Randy B. Norell, Controller

ADDRESS INQUIRIES TO:
Fellowship in Aerospace History
(See address above.)

*SPECIAL STIPULATIONS:
Funds may not be used to support tuition or fees. A fellow may not hold other major fellowships or grants during the fellowship term, except sabbatical and supplemental grants from their own institutions and small grants from other sources for specific research expenses. Sources of anticipated support must be listed in the application form.

AMERICAN INSTITUTE OF THE HISTORY OF PHARMACY
University of Wisconsin School of Pharmacy
Rennebohm Hall
777 Highland Avenue
Madison, WI 53705-2222
(608) 262-5378

E-MAIL ADDRESS:
gia@aihp.org

WEB SITE ADDRESS:
www.aihp.org

TYPE:
Grants-in-aid; Research grants.
See entry 2537 for full listing.

THE AMERICAN NUMISMATIC SOCIETY [581]
75 Varick Street, Floor 11
New York, NY 10013-1917
(212) 571-4470
Fax: (212) 571-4479

E-MAIL ADDRESS:
ans@numismatics.org

WEB SITE ADDRESS:
www.numismatics.org

FOUNDED: 1858

AREAS OF INTEREST:
Numismatics, history and archaeology.

NAME(S) OF PROGRAMS:
● **Frances M. Schwartz Fellowship**

TYPE:
Fellowships.

YEAR PROGRAM STARTED: 1994

PURPOSE:
To support work and the study of numismatic and museum methodology at the Society.

ELIGIBILITY:
Applicants must have a B.A. or equivalent.

FINANCIAL DATA:
Amount of support per award: The stipend will vary with the term of tenure (normally the academic year) but will not exceed $5,000.

NUMBER OF AWARDS: 1.

APPLICATION INFORMATION:
Detailed guidelines are available from the Society.
Duration: Up to one year.

ADDRESS INQUIRIES TO:
Board Secretary
(See address above.)

THE AMERICAN NUMISMATIC SOCIETY [582]
75 Varick Street, 11th Floor
New York, NY 10013
(212) 571-4470 ext. 110
Fax: (212) 571-4479

E-MAIL ADDRESS:
ans@numismatics.org

WEB SITE ADDRESS:
www.numismatics.org

FOUNDED: 1858

AREAS OF INTEREST:
Numismatics (coins and medals), history and archaeology.

NAME(S) OF PROGRAMS:
● **The Donald Groves Fund**

TYPE:
Fellowships.

YEAR PROGRAM STARTED: 1958

PURPOSE:
To promote publication in the field of early American numismatics involving material dating no later than 1800.

LEGAL BASIS:
Nonprofit.

GEOGRAPHIC RESTRICTIONS:
United States.

FINANCIAL DATA:
Groves funding is available for travel and other expenses in association with research as well as for publication costs.

Amount of support per award: Varies.

Total amount of support: Varies.

APPLICATION INFORMATION:
Applications should be addressed to the Secretary of the Society and should include an outline of the proposed research, the method of accomplishing the research, the funding requested and the specific uses to which funding will be put. Applications are reviewed periodically by a committee, which makes its recommendations to the Society's Board of Trustees.

Duration: Varies.

OFFICERS:
Dr. Ute Wartenberg Kagan, Executive Director

ADDRESS INQUIRIES TO:
Secretary of the Society
(See address above.)

BERKSHIRE CONFERENCE OF WOMEN HISTORIANS   [583]
11 Granite Street
Portland, ME 04101
(207) 780-4921

E-MAIL ADDRESS:
acameron@usm.maine.edu

WEB SITE ADDRESS:
www.berksconference.org

FOUNDED: 1930

AREAS OF INTEREST:
Women's history.

TYPE:
Awards/prizes. One prize awarded annually for the best first book and one for the best article of historical scholarship published by a woman historian in any field of history during the preceding year.

YEAR PROGRAM STARTED: 1972

PURPOSE:
To promote historical scholarship by women.

ELIGIBILITY:
The book or article must have been published in the year preceding the award date.

FINANCIAL DATA:
Amount of support per award: $1,000 for each book prize; $500 for each article prize.

Total amount of support: $1,500.

NUMBER OF APPLICANTS MOST RECENT YEAR: 150.

APPLICATION INFORMATION:
Detailed guidelines are available from Berkshire.

Deadline: January 15. Notification in June.

ADDRESS INQUIRIES TO:
Kathi Kern, Secretary
University of Kentucky
518 King Library
Lexington, KY 40506

JOHN CARTER BROWN LIBRARY   [584]
Brown University
Box 1894
Providence, RI 02912
(401) 863-2725
Fax: (401) 863-3477

E-MAIL ADDRESS:
jcbl_fellowships@brown.edu

WEB SITE ADDRESS:
www.jcbl.org

FOUNDED: 1846

AREAS OF INTEREST:
Historical studies pertaining to the Age of Exploration, Latin American history before 1830, North American history to approximately 1800, European impressions of America, New World travel, exploration and colonization. Also, Indian language, cartography, West Indies and Caribbean studies, maritime, slave trade, and the Jewish Experience in the colonial Americas, north and south.

NAME(S) OF PROGRAMS:
● **The John Carter Brown Library Research Fellowships**

TYPE:
Fellowships; Research grants. The John Carter Brown Library (JCB), an independently funded institution for advanced research at Brown University, contains one of the world's premier collections of primary materials related to the discovery, exploration, and settlement of the New World to 1825, including books, maps, newspapers and other printed objects.

The Library offers both Short-term and Long-term Fellowships.

YEAR PROGRAM STARTED: 1981

PURPOSE:
To promote scholarly research at the library.

LEGAL BASIS:
Independently funded and administered library and research center.

ELIGIBILITY:
Fellowships and grants will be awarded on the basis of the applicant's scholarly qualifications, the merits of the project, and the appropriateness of the inquiry in relation to the holdings of the John Carter Brown Library.

Fellowships are open to scholars and writers working on all aspects of the Americas in the early modern period.

Short-term Fellowships are open to U.S. and foreign citizens who are engaged in predoctoral or postdoctoral, or independent research. Graduate students must have passed their preliminary or general examinations at the time of application.

Long-term Fellowships, some of which are funded by the National Endowment for the Humanities (NEH), for which an applicant must be an American citizen or have been resident in the U.S. for the three years preceding the application deadline. There are other long-term JCB Fellowships for which all nationalities are eligible. Graduate students are not eligible for Long-term Fellowships.

FINANCIAL DATA:
Amount of support per award: Short-term Fellowships: $2,100 per month; Long-term Fellowships: $4,200 per month.

Total amount of support: Varies.

NUMBER OF AWARDS: Approximately 40 for the year 2013-14.

APPLICATION INFORMATION:
Application form is available online; only online applications will be accepted.

Duration: Short-term Fellowships: Two to four months; Long-term Fellowships: Five to 10 months.

Deadline: December 15. Announcements made by April 15.

PUBLICATIONS:
Application guidelines.

STAFF:
Valerie Andrews, Fellowship Coordinator

ADDRESS INQUIRIES TO:
See e-mail address above.

*PLEASE NOTE:
Recipients of all Fellowships must relocate to Providence and be in continuous residence at the John Carter Brown Library for the entire term of the award. Rooms are available for rent at Fiering House, the JCB Fellows' residence, a beautifully restored 1869 house just four blocks from the Library. Those living within commuting distance of the Library (approximately 45 miles distant) are ordinarily not eligible for JCB Fellowships.

CANADIAN INSTITUTE OF UKRAINIAN STUDIES   [585]
University of Alberta
430 Pembina Hall
Edmonton AB T6G 2H8 Canada
(780) 492-2972
Fax: (780) 492-4967

E-MAIL ADDRESS:
cius@ualberta.ca

WEB SITE ADDRESS:
www.cius.ca

FOUNDED: 1976

AREAS OF INTEREST:
Studies in history, literature, language, education, social sciences, library sciences and women's studies.

NAME(S) OF PROGRAMS:
● **The Helen Darcovich Memorial Doctoral Fellowship**
● **Marusia and Michael Dorosh Master's Fellowship**
● **Neporany Doctoral Fellowship**
● **Research Grants**

TYPE:
Fellowships; Research grants; Scholarships.

PURPOSE:
Fellowships: To aid students to complete a thesis on a Ukrainian or Ukrainian and Canadian topic in education, history, law, humanities, social sciences, women's studies or library sciences. Research grants: To aid scholars with research-related costs.

FINANCIAL DATA:
Total amount of support: Over $100,000 for the year 2012.

NUMBER OF APPLICANTS MOST RECENT YEAR: Over 100.

NUMBER OF AWARDS: Helen Darcovich Memorial Doctoral Fellowship: 3; Marusia and Michael Dorosh Master's Fellowship: 2; Neporany Doctoral Fellowship: 1; Research grants: 46.

APPLICATION INFORMATION:
Applicants should contact the Institute.
Deadline: March 1.

ADDRESS INQUIRIES TO:
Iryna Pak, Administrator
(See address above.)

COLLEGE OF PHYSICIANS OF PHILADELPHIA [586]

Francis Clark Wood Institute
for the History of Medicine
19 South 22nd Street
Philadelphia, PA 19103-3097
(215) 399-2305
Fax: (215) 561-6477

E-MAIL ADDRESS:
ssereda@collegeofphysicians.org

WEB SITE ADDRESS:
www.collegeofphysicians.org

FOUNDED: 1787

AREAS OF INTEREST:
The history of medicine.

NAME(S) OF PROGRAMS:
● **Wood Institute Travel Grants**

TYPE:
Travel grants; Visiting scholars. This program
allows scholars to conduct short-term
research in the College's Library and/or
Mutter Museum.

YEAR PROGRAM STARTED: 1983

PURPOSE:
To encourage the study and appreciation of
medicine in the broader historical and social
context in response to current health care
issues and public and professional interests.

LEGAL BASIS:
501(c)(3) not-for-profit educational
institution.

ELIGIBILITY:
Applicants must reside more than 75 miles
from Philadelphia to be eligible. Grants are
available to scholars and bona fide
researchers.

FINANCIAL DATA:
Amount of support per award: Up to $1,500.
Total amount of support: Up to $1,500.

NUMBER OF APPLICANTS MOST RECENT YEAR:
15.

NUMBER OF AWARDS: Varies.

APPLICATION INFORMATION:
Applicants should submit:
(1) one-page statement of the research project
and the applicability of the College's
resources;
(2) curriculum vitae (not to exceed three
pages in length);
(3) budget estimate of travel and lodging
needs and;
(4) one letter of reference (to be sent directly
from the source to the College).

Electronic applications are strongly
encouraged.
Duration: One to four weeks.

ADDRESS INQUIRIES TO:
Sofie Sereda
Assistant to the Director
(See address above.)

COLUMBIA UNIVERSITY [587]

517 Butler Library
535 West 114th Street
New York, NY 10027
(212) 854-2247
Fax: (212) 854-4972

E-MAIL ADDRESS:
jneal@columbia.edu

WEB SITE ADDRESS:
library.columbia.
edu/eguides/amerihist/bancroft.html

FOUNDED: 1754

NAME(S) OF PROGRAMS:
● **Bancroft Prizes**

TYPE:
Awards/prizes. Prizes of equal rank to be
awarded to the authors of distinguished
works in either or both American History,
including biography and diplomacy.

YEAR PROGRAM STARTED: 1948

PURPOSE:
To honor the authors of books of
distinguished merit and distinction, upon the
subject of American history in its broadest
sense.

LEGAL BASIS:
University.

ELIGIBILITY:
Awards are made for books first published in
the previous calendar year. The competition
is open to all persons whether connected with
Columbia University or not, and whether
citizens of the U.S. or any other country.

The word "American" is interpreted to
include all the Americas, North, Central and
South; however, the award is confined to
works originally written in English or of
which there is a published translation in
English. Volumes of papers, letters and
speeches of famous Americans, unless edited
by the author himself, are not eligible.
Autobiography comes within the terms of the
prize, but books reporting on recent personal
experiences of Americans, within a limited
area both in time and geography, are not
considered eligible.

Previous winners are eligible for an award in
a later year.

FINANCIAL DATA:
Amount of support per award: $10,000.
Total amount of support: $20,000 to $30,000
annually.

NUMBER OF APPLICANTS MOST RECENT YEAR:
225.

NUMBER OF AWARDS: 2 to 3.

APPLICATION INFORMATION:
Works submitted in competition may be sent
to the Bancroft Prize Committee at the
address above. It is requested that four copies
be furnished, three for jury members and one
for the Libraries of Columbia University. A
letter should accompany the books so that
acknowledgement may be made.
Deadline: Works may be submitted after
June 1 and before November 1. Page-proof
copy may be submitted after November 1
provided the work will be published after
that date and before December 31 of the year
preceding the award.

ADDRESS INQUIRIES TO:
Bancroft Prize Committee
(See address above.)

THE COORDINATING COUNCIL FOR WOMEN IN HISTORY, INC.

Department of History and Women's Studies
715 Zulauf Hall
Northern Illinois University
DeKalb, IL 60115
(815) 895-2624

E-MAIL ADDRESS:
execdir@theccwh.org

WEB SITE ADDRESS:
www.theccwh.org

TYPE:
Scholarships. The Catherine Prelinger Award
is given to a scholar, with a Ph.D. or A.B.D.,
whose career has not followed a traditional
academic path through secondary and higher
education and whose work has contributed to
women in the historical profession.

See entry 1078 for full listing.

THE COORDINATING COUNCIL FOR WOMEN IN HISTORY, INC. [588]

Department of History and Women's Studies
715 Zulauf Hall
Northern Illinois University
DeKalb, IL 60115
(815) 895-2624

E-MAIL ADDRESS:
execdir@theccwh.org

WEB SITE ADDRESS:
www.theccwh.org

AREAS OF INTEREST:
Women's history.

NAME(S) OF PROGRAMS:
● **Berkshire Conference of Women Historians Graduate Student Fellowship**
● **Nupur Chaudhuri First Article Prize**
● **National History Day Prize in Women's History, Junior Division**
● **Ida B. Wells Graduate Student Fellowship**

TYPE:
Awards/prizes; Fellowships.

PURPOSE:
To support the exploration of the diverse
experiences and histories of all women; to
educate men and women on the status of
women in the historical profession; to
promote research and interpretation in areas
of women's history.

ELIGIBILITY:
Berkshire Conference of Women Historians
Graduate Student Fellowship: Applicant must
be a woman graduate student completing a
dissertation in a history department.

Nupur Chaudhuri First Article Prize:
Applicant must be a CCWH member whose
first article is published in a refereed journal.

National History Day Prize in Women's
History, Jr. Division: Applicant must be a
precollegiate student participating in the
National History Day competition.

Ida B. Wells Graduate Student Fellowship:
Applicant must be an A.B.D. woman
graduate student working on a historical
dissertation, not necessarily in a history
department. Applicants in interdisciplinary
areas such as women's studies or ethnic
studies are particularly welcome.

GEOGRAPHIC RESTRICTIONS:
United States.

FINANCIAL DATA:
Amount of support per award: Berkshire Conference, Nupur Chaudhuri Prize and Wells Fellowships: $1,000; National History Day Prize: Varies.

ADDRESS INQUIRIES TO:
Sandra Trudgen Dawson, Executive Director (See e-mail address above.)

CUSHWA CENTER FOR THE STUDY OF AMERICAN CATHOLICISM   [589]
407 Geddes Hall
University of Notre Dame
Notre Dame, IN 46556
(574) 631-5441
Fax: (574) 631-8471

E-MAIL ADDRESS:
cushwa.1@nd.edu

WEB SITE ADDRESS:
www.cushwa.nd.edu

NAME(S) OF PROGRAMS:
● **Hibernian Research Award**

TYPE:
Research grants; Travel grants. The Hibernian Research Award is offered to further the scholarly study of Irish America by scholars of any academic discipline engaged in a research project studying the Irish experience in the U.S.

PURPOSE:
To promote the scholarly study of the Irish in the U.S.

ELIGIBILITY:
Awards are made to scholars in any academic discipline.

FINANCIAL DATA:
Amount of support per award: Maximum $2,000.

APPLICATION INFORMATION:
Applicants must include the following:
(1) a current curriculum vitae;
(2) a brief 1,000-word description of the research project;
(3) a proposed budget and;
(4) letters of recommendation from two people familiar with the applicant's work. These letters of recommendation should be sent directly to the Cushwa Center.
Deadline: December 31. Applicants will be notified in March.

DIRECTORS:
Kathleen Sprows Cummings

ADDRESS INQUIRIES TO:
Kathleen Sprows Cummings, Director (See address above.)

CUSHWA CENTER FOR THE STUDY OF AMERICAN CATHOLICISM   [590]
407 Geddes Hall
University of Notre Dame
Notre Dame, IN 46556
(574) 631-5441
Fax: (574) 631-8471

E-MAIL ADDRESS:
cushwa.1@nd.edu

WEB SITE ADDRESS:
www.cushwa.nd.edu

FOUNDED: 1980

AREAS OF INTEREST:
Catholicism in the U.S.

NAME(S) OF PROGRAMS:
● **Research Travel Grants**

TYPE:
Travel grants. Research Travel Grants support projects that require substantial use of the collection of the library and/or the archives of the University of Notre Dame and help to defray travel and lodging costs.

YEAR PROGRAM STARTED: 1980

PURPOSE:
To make it possible for scholars to make use of the Notre Dame archives.

LEGAL BASIS:
University.

ELIGIBILITY:
Grants are made to scholars in any academic discipline.

FINANCIAL DATA:
Amount of support per award: Typically, Research Travel Grants are $1,000 or less, unless extenuating circumstances necessitate greater funding. Assistance at finding affordable accommodations is available.
Total amount of support: Varies.

APPLICATION INFORMATION:
Applicant must include the following:
(1) one copy of the application form;
(2) current curriculum vitae;
(3) 1,000-word description of the project to be undertaken at the center and;
(4) proposed budget estimating lodging and research expenses.
Duration: Varies.
Deadline: December 31. Applicants will be notified in March.

STAFF:
Kathleen Sprows Cummings, Director

ADDRESS INQUIRIES TO:
Kathleen Sprows Cummings, Director (See address above.)

SHELBY CULLOM DAVIS CENTER FOR HISTORICAL STUDIES   [591]
Princeton University
129 Dickinson Hall
Princeton, NJ 08544-1017
(609) 258-4997
Fax: (609) 258-5326

E-MAIL ADDRESS:
jhoule@princeton.edu

WEB SITE ADDRESS:
www.princeton.edu/dav

FOUNDED: 1968

AREAS OF INTEREST:
Historical research.

TYPE:
Fellowships.

YEAR PROGRAM STARTED: 1969

LEGAL BASIS:
Center is part of a Charitable Educational Institution.

ELIGIBILITY:
Candidates must have a Ph.D. degree.

FINANCIAL DATA:
Fellowship includes salary plus research expenses.
Amount of support per award: Varies.

Total amount of support: Varies.

NUMBER OF APPLICANTS MOST RECENT YEAR: 130.

NUMBER OF AWARDS: 8 for the year 2012-13.

APPLICATION INFORMATION:
Contact the Center for application form and guidelines.
Duration: One semester or one academic year. Nonrenewable.
Deadline: December 1. Notification in early March.

EXECUTIVE COMMITTEE:
Philip Nord, Director

ADDRESS INQUIRIES TO:
Jennifer Goldman, Manager (See address above.)

THE DIRKSEN CONGRESSIONAL CENTER
2815 Broadway
Pekin, IL 61554
(309) 347-7113
Fax: (309) 347-6432

E-MAIL ADDRESS:
fmackaman@dirksencenter.org

WEB SITE ADDRESS:
www.dirksencongressionalcenter.org

TYPE:
Research grants; Seed money grants; Travel grants. Financial awards to individuals conducting research about the U.S. Congress and its leaders.
See entry 1995 for full listing.

GERMAN HISTORICAL INSTITUTE   [592]
1607 New Hampshire Avenue, N.W.
Washington, DC 20009-2562
(202) 387-3355
Fax: (202) 483-3430

E-MAIL ADDRESS:
info@ghi-dc.org
fellowships@ghi-dc.org

WEB SITE ADDRESS:
www.ghi-dc.org

FOUNDED: 1987

AREAS OF INTEREST:
German and U.S. history, transatlantic studies and comparative studies in economic, social, cultural and political history.

NAME(S) OF PROGRAMS:
● **Doctoral and Postdoctoral Fellowships**

TYPE:
Fellowships. The Institute awards short-term fellowships to German and American doctoral students as well as postdoctoral scholars/Habilitanden in the fields of German history, the history of German-American relations, and the role of Germany and the U.S. in international relations.

YEAR PROGRAM STARTED: 1989

PURPOSE:
To support research programme for doctoral students and postdoctoral scholars in the fields of German history, the history of German-American relations, the role of Germany and the U.S. in international relations and the history of consumption and consumerism.

ELIGIBILITY:
Open to German and U.S. doctoral and postdoctoral students.

FINANCIAL DATA:
Amount of support per award: Monthly
stipend for Europeans: EUR 1,700 for
doctoral students and EUR 3,000 for
postdoctoral scholars. Monthly stipend for
Americans: $1,900 for doctoral students and
$3,200 for postdoctoral scholars.

NUMBER OF APPLICANTS MOST RECENT YEAR:
150 annually.

NUMBER OF AWARDS: 40 to 50 annually.

APPLICATION INFORMATION:
Applications should include cover letter,
curriculum vitae, proof of academic degree
(or transcripts), project description (3,000
words), research schedule for the fellowship
period, and at least one letter of reference.
Although applicants may write in either
English or German, it is recommended that
they use the language in which they are most
proficient.
Duration: One to six months, but can be
extended one month.
Deadline: April 1 and October 1 annually.

ADDRESS INQUIRIES TO:
Bryan Hart, Research Associate
Prof. Dr. Britta Waldschmidt-Nelson
Deputy Director
(See address above.)

HAGLEY MUSEUM AND
LIBRARY   [593]
Center for the History of
Business, Technology and Society
298 Buck Road
Wilmington, DE 19807
(302) 658-2400 ext. 243
Fax: (302) 655-3188

E-MAIL ADDRESS:
clockman@hagley.org

WEB SITE ADDRESS:
www.hagley.org

FOUNDED: 1953

AREAS OF INTEREST:
American business, economic and labor
history and the history of technology and
science.

NAME(S) OF PROGRAMS:
● **Henry Belin du Pont Dissertation**
  Fellowship in Business, Technology, and
  Society
● **Henry Belin du Pont Fellowships**
● **Hagley Exploratory Research Grant**

TYPE:
Fellowships; Research grants; Travel grants;
Visiting scholars. Grants to support
short-term research in the imprint,
manuscript, pictorial and artifact collections
of the Hagley Museum and Library.

The Henry Belin du Pont Dissertation
Fellowship in Business, Technology, and
Society supports research and writing by
candidates for doctoral degrees. Projects
should demonstrate superior intellectual
quality and make substantial use of Hagley's
collections.

Henry Belin du Pont Fellowships support
research in the collections of the museum
and library.

Hagley Exploratory Research Grant supports
a one-week visit by scholars who believe that
their project will benefit from Hagley
research collections, but need the opportunity

to explore them on-site to determine if a
Henry Belin du Pont research grant
application is warranted.

YEAR PROGRAM STARTED: 1962

PURPOSE:
To encourage and support research in the
collections.

LEGAL BASIS:
Nonprofit educational institution.

ELIGIBILITY:
Degree candidates and advanced scholars
working in Hagley's areas of collecting and
research interest are invited to apply.
Applications should include research
proposals specifying the collections or
materials to be studied. Residential award,
not a scholarship for college or graduate
school.

Hagley Exploratory Research Grant: Priority
will be given to junior scholars with
innovative projects that seek to expand on
existing scholarships.

FINANCIAL DATA:
Amount of support per award: Hagley
Exploratory Research Grant: Stipend of $400;
Henry Belin du Pont Dissertation Fellowship:
Up to $6,500; Henry Belin du Pont
Fellowships: Average award of $800 for a
two-week period.
Total amount of support: Approximately
$50,000.

APPLICATION INFORMATION:
Application forms and guidelines are
available online.
Duration: Hagley Exploratory Research
Grant: One week; Henry Belin du Pont
Dissertation Fellowship: Up to four months;
Henry Belin du Pont Fellowships: Up to
eight weeks.
Deadline: Hagley Exploratory Research
Grant and Henry Belin du Pont Fellowships:
March 31, June 30 and October 31; Henry
Belin du Pont Dissertation Fellowship in
Business, Technology, and Society:
November 15.

PUBLICATIONS:
Guides to Collection; application; guidelines.

STAFF:
Philip Scranton, Executive Director
Roger Horowitz, Center Associate Director
Carol Ressler Lockman, Center Coordinator

RESEARCH STAFF:
Lynn Catanese, Chief Curator of Library
Collections
Max Moeller, Imprints Department
Jon Williams, Pictorial Collections
Department

ADDRESS INQUIRIES TO:
Carol Ressler Lockman, Center Coordinator
(See address above.)

THE HERITAGE
FOUNDATION/B. KENNETH
SIMON CENTER FOR
AMERICAN STUDIES
214 Massachusetts Avenue, N.E.
Washington, DC 20002
(202) 608-6203
Fax: (202) 675-1771

E-MAIL ADDRESS:
asjobs@heritage.org

WEB SITE ADDRESS:
www.heritage.org

TYPE:
Fellowships. The Research Fellowship in
American Studies is for recent college
graduates interested in political thought,
history and public philosophy and how those
ideas and principles relate to the issues and
debates of current American politics. The
Associate will work alongside Simon Center
staff at The Heritage Foundation in
Washington, DC.

See entry 2001 for full listing.

THE HISTORIC NEW ORLEANS
COLLECTION   [594]
533 Royal Street
New Orleans, LA 70130-2179
(504) 523-4662
Fax: (504) 598-7108

E-MAIL ADDRESS:
wrc@hnoc.org

WEB SITE ADDRESS:
www.hnoc.org

FOUNDED: 1966

AREAS OF INTEREST:
Louisana history and support of research in
the field.

NAME(S) OF PROGRAMS:
● **The Dianne Woest Fellowship in the**
  Arts and Humanities

TYPE:
Fellowships.

YEAR PROGRAM STARTED: 2005

PURPOSE:
To encourage research using The Historic
New Orleans Collection, as well as other
research facilities in the greater New Orleans
area.

ELIGIBILITY:
Open to doctoral candidates, academic and
museum professionals and independent
scholars. U.S. citizenship not required, but
applicants should be fluent in English.

Fellows will be expected to:
(1) present a public lecture during their term
of residence and;
(2) acknowledge The Collection in any
published work drawing on fellowship
research.

FINANCIAL DATA:
Amount of support per award:
Approximately $4,000 per month stipend.
Total amount of support: Varies.

NUMBER OF AWARDS: 1 to 3.

APPLICATION INFORMATION:
For information, call Dr. Alfred Lemmon at
(504) 598-7124 or Dr. Jessica Dorman at
(504) 598-7174.
Duration: One to three months.
Deadline: November 1. Announcement
February 1. Research to begin on or after
April 1.

ADDRESS INQUIRIES TO:
Priscilla Lawrence, Executive Director
(See address above.)

*SPECIAL STIPULATIONS:
Fellows may select their period of residence,
but all research must commence and
conclude during the specified calendar year.

THE HISTORIC NEW ORLEANS COLLECTION [595]

533 Royal Street
New Orleans, LA 70130-2179
(504) 523-4662
Fax: (504) 598-7108

E-MAIL ADDRESS:
wrc@hnoc.org

WEB SITE ADDRESS:
www.hnoc.org

FOUNDED: 1966

AREAS OF INTEREST:
Louisiana history and support of research in the field.

NAME(S) OF PROGRAMS:
● **Kemper and Leila Williams Prize in Louisiana History**

TYPE:
Awards/prizes.

YEAR PROGRAM STARTED: 1975

PURPOSE:
To encourage excellence in the writing and publishing of Louisiana history.

LEGAL BASIS:
Nonprofit foundation.

ELIGIBILITY:
Published books are eligible, but only in the year of their publication or completion.

FINANCIAL DATA:
Amount of support per award: $1,500.
Total amount of support: $1,500.

NUMBER OF APPLICANTS MOST RECENT YEAR:
29.

NUMBER OF AWARDS: 1.

APPLICATION INFORMATION:
Application forms are available on the web site. Four copies of each entry must be submitted.
Deadline: January 16. Announcement in March.

PUBLICATIONS:
Application guidelines.

OFFICERS:
Mrs. William K. Christovich, Chairperson
Fred M. Smith, President
Drew Jardine, Vice President
Hilton Bell
John Kallenborn
E. Alexandra Stafford
John E. Walker

STAFF:
Priscilla Lawrence, Executive Director

ADDRESS INQUIRIES TO:
John Lawrence, Chairman
Williams Prize Committee
(See address above.)

HISTORY OF SCIENCE SOCIETY [596]

440 Geddes Hall
University of Notre Dame
Notre Dame, IN 46556
(574) 631-1194
Fax: (574) 631-1533

E-MAIL ADDRESS:
info@hssonline.org

WEB SITE ADDRESS:
www.hssonline.org

FOUNDED: 1924

AREAS OF INTEREST:
History of science and its cultural influences.

NAME(S) OF PROGRAMS:
● **Derek Price/Rod Webster Prize**

TYPE:
Awards/prizes. Prize for the best scholarly article published in *Isis* during the past three years.

YEAR PROGRAM STARTED: 1979

PURPOSE:
To acknowledge the best scholarly work to appear in *Isis*.

LEGAL BASIS:
Nonprofit 501(c)(3).

ELIGIBILITY:
Applicant must have published an article in *Isis*.

FINANCIAL DATA:
Amount of support per award: $1,000.

NUMBER OF AWARDS: 1 per year.

PUBLICATIONS:
Syllabus samplers, Topical Essays for Teachers, Non-Western Science.

ADDRESS INQUIRIES TO:
Robert J. Malone, Executive Director
(See address above.)

HISTORY OF SCIENCE SOCIETY [597]

440 Geddes Hall
University of Notre Dame
Notre Dame, IN 46556
(574) 631-1194
Fax: (574) 631-1533

E-MAIL ADDRESS:
info@hssonline.org

WEB SITE ADDRESS:
www.hssonline.org

FOUNDED: 1924

AREAS OF INTEREST:
History of science, women in science and science service.

NAME(S) OF PROGRAMS:
● **Watson Davis and Helen Miles Davis Prize**
● **Joseph H. Hazen Education Prize**
● **Suzanne J. Levinson Prize**
● **Pfizer Prize**
● **Nathan Reingold Prize**
● **Margaret W. Rossiter History of Women in Science Prize**
● **Sarton Medal**

TYPE:
Awards/prizes. The Davis Prize honors books in the history of science directed to a wide public and was established through a long-term pledge from Miles and Audrey Davis.

The Joseph H. Hazen Education Prize recognizes excellence in teaching in the history of science.

The Levinson Prize is awarded in even-numbered years to an outstanding book in the life sciences and natural history.

The Pfizer Prize honors the best English-language work related to the history of science published in the preceding three years.

The Nathan Reingold Prize is given for an original essay in the history of science and its cultural influences. Essay must be no more than 8,000 words in length and thoroughly documented.

The Margaret W. Rossiter History of Women in Science Prize honors an outstanding book, or in even-numbered years an article, published in the preceding four years.

The Sarton Medal is given to an outstanding historian of science selected from the international scholarly community.

YEAR PROGRAM STARTED: 1955

PURPOSE:
To recognize and reward distinguished writing in the field of the history of science.

LEGAL BASIS:
Nonprofit.

ELIGIBILITY:
For the Davis Prize, books should be introductory in assuming no previous knowledge of the subject and be directed to audiences of beginning students and general readers. Books should introduce an entire field, a chronological period, a national tradition or the work of a noteworthy individual. Multi-authored or edited books are eligible, whereas unrevised reprints of previously published works are ineligible.

For the History of Women in Science Prize, books may take a biographical, institutional, theoretical or other approach. Include in the topic, "Women in Science," discussions of women's activities in science, analyses of past scientific practices that deal explicitly with gender and investigations regarding women as viewed by scientists. These may relate to medicine, technology and the social sciences as well as the natural sciences.

The Levinson Prize is open to all books in the life sciences and natural history published in the four years prior to the award year.

The Pfizer Prize is open to all books published in English. The quality of the work is the overriding criterion.

The Reingold Prize is open to graduate students at any American or Canadian college. Essays dealing with medical subjects are not accepted, though papers dealing with the relations between medicine and the natural sciences are welcome.

FINANCIAL DATA:
Amount of support per award: Davis, Hazen, Levinson and Rossiter History of Women in Science Awards: $1,000; Pfizer Prize: $2,500; Reingold Prize: $500 award, $500 in travel expenses.

APPLICATION INFORMATION:
Contact the Society for details.
Deadline: April 1.

PUBLICATIONS:
Newsletter.

OFFICERS:
Angela Creager, President
Janet Browne, Vice President
Adam Apt, Treasurer
Marsha Richmond, Secretary
Bernard Lightman, Editor

ADDRESS INQUIRIES TO:
Robert J. Malone, Executive Director
(See address above.)

*PLEASE NOTE:
Society does not give grants, scholarships or fellowships.

HOLLAND & KNIGHT CHARITABLE FOUNDATION, INC. [598]

P.O. Box 2877
Tampa, FL 33601-2877
(813) 227-8500

E-MAIL ADDRESS:
holocaust@hklaw.com

WEB SITE ADDRESS:
foundation.hklaw.com

AREAS OF INTEREST:
The study of the Holocaust.

NAME(S) OF PROGRAMS:
● **Holocaust Remembrance Project**

TYPE:
Awards/prizes; Scholarships. The Holocaust Remembrance Project is a national essay contest for high school students designed to encourage and promote the study of the Holocaust.

YEAR PROGRAM STARTED: 1995

PURPOSE:
To encourage and promote the study of the Holocaust; to recognize the moral imperative of teaching young people about this watershed event.

APPLICATION INFORMATION:
Application information is available on the web site.

ADDRESS INQUIRIES TO:
Holocaust Remembrance Project
(See address above.)

HERBERT HOOVER PRESIDENTIAL LIBRARY ASSOCIATION, INC.

302 Parkside Drive
West Branch, IA 52358
(800) 828-0475
Fax: (319) 643-2391

E-MAIL ADDRESS:
info@hooverassociation.org

WEB SITE ADDRESS:
www.hooverassociation.org

TYPE:
Travel grants. Money is only available for travel to the Hoover Presidential Library in West Branch, IA. The program seeks to encourage scholarly use of the holdings of the Herbert Hoover Presidential Library. It is specifically intended to promote the study of subjects of interest and concern to Herbert Hoover, Lou Henry Hoover, their associates and other public figures as reflected in the Library's 150 manuscript collections.

See entry 2002 for full listing.

IEEE [599]

IEEE History Center
Rutgers University
39 Union Street
New Brunswick, NJ 08901-8538
(732) 562-5468
Fax: (732) 932-1193

E-MAIL ADDRESS:
ieee-history@ieee.org

WEB SITE ADDRESS:
www.ieee.org/history_center

FOUNDED: 1884

AREAS OF INTEREST:
History of technology and sociology of technology.

NAME(S) OF PROGRAMS:
● **IEEE Fellowship in the History of Electrical and Computing Technology**
● **Internship in Electrical History**

TYPE:
Fellowships; Internships. Fellowship in the History of Electrical and Computing Technology: Award for one year of full-time doctoral or postdoctoral work in the history of electrical engineering and technology at a college or university of recognized standing.

Internship in Electrical History: Two-month internship for graduate research.

YEAR PROGRAM STARTED: 1980

ELIGIBILITY:
Fellowship in the History of Electrical and Computing Technology: Individuals doing graduate or postgraduate work in the history of electrical technology. Internship in Electrical History: Scholars at the beginning of their career studying the history of electrical technology and computing.

FINANCIAL DATA:
Total amount of support: Fellowship in the History of Electrical and Computing Technology: $17,000 annually; Internship in Electrical History: $3,500.

NUMBER OF APPLICANTS MOST RECENT YEAR:
12.

NUMBER OF AWARDS: Fellowship in the History of Electrical and Computing Technology: 1 annually; Internship in Electrical History: 1 annually.

APPLICATION INFORMATION:
Identification and description of a research project of value is an important part of the application procedure. Further information is available upon request to the Institute.

Duration: Fellowship in the History of Electrical and Computing Technology: One academic year; Internship in Electrical History: Two months.

Deadline: Fellowship in the History of Electrical and Computing Technology: February 1; Internship in Electrical History: March 1.

PUBLICATIONS:
Newsletter.

ADDRESS INQUIRIES TO:
Director, IEEE History Center
(See address above.)

IRISH AMERICAN CULTURAL INSTITUTE

P.O. Box 1716
Morristown, NJ 07962
(973) 605-1991

E-MAIL ADDRESS:
info@iaci-usa.org

WEB SITE ADDRESS:
www.iaci-usa.org

TYPE:
Awards/prizes; Exchange programs; Fellowships. Grants and awards available for authors of books written in Irish, for Irish artists and composers.

See entry 675 for full listing.

ISTITUTO ITALIANO PER GLI STUDI STORICI [600]

Via Benedetto Croce, 12
80134 Naples Italy
+39.081.5517159
+39.081.5512390
Fax: +39.081.5514813

E-MAIL ADDRESS:
istituto@iiss.it
info@iiss.it

WEB SITE ADDRESS:
www.iiss.it

FOUNDED: 1947

AREAS OF INTEREST:
Postgraduate institute for the study of history and philosophy.

NAME(S) OF PROGRAMS:
● **Federico II Scholarship**
● **Scholarships Istituto italiano per gli studi storici for Graduate Students and Young Postdocs, Italian and Foreign**

TYPE:
Awards/prizes; Conferences/seminars; Research grants; Scholarships. Awards for historical, literature and philosophical studies at the Istituto Italiano per gli Studi Storici in Naples.

Federico II Scholarship: Offered by the Universita di Napoli for graduates from Italian universities whose final thesis is in medieval studies.

YEAR PROGRAM STARTED: 1947

PURPOSE:
To promote historical studies.

LEGAL BASIS:
Private foundation.

ELIGIBILITY:
These annual scholarships are offered to young graduates and those with a Doctorate, both Italian and non-Italian, in the disciplines of history, philosophy and literature. Applicants must have presented their final university dissertation before the final application date and must be less than 32 years of age.

Applications will not be accepted from candidates who:
(1) already received a scholarship from the Istituto;
(2) will receive payment from another type of activity or;
(3) will be carrying out a research Doctorate or another scholarship (with financing).

FINANCIAL DATA:
The scholarship will be paid to the successful candidates in 12 monthly installments starting from November of the year of application.

Amount of support per award: Campania Region scholarships: EUR 9,300; for students residing outside of Campania: EUR 11,500; Federico II Scholarship: EUR 10,300.
Total amount of support: EUR 237,100.

NUMBER OF AWARDS: 1 for Federico II; 14 Scholarships for Graduate Students and Young Postdocs, Italian and Foreign.

APPLICATION INFORMATION:
Applications (including personal details, citizenship, residence, telephone numbers, e-mail address and a declaration of a clean police record) must be accompanied by the following documents:
(1) certificate of nationality (or photocopy of official identity card or passport);
(2) curriculum of studies, including

languages spoken;
(3) degree certificate showing marks for individual exams, or Doctorate degree (for non-Italians, an equivalent degree certificate is required);
(4) copy of graduation or doctoral dissertation and of publications, both in hard copy and digital file;
(5) research project that the student intends to carry out at the Institute, including aims and objectives, timing, materials to be used and the research location;
(6) academic letters of reference and;
(7) list of other applications already made or to be made for similar scholarships and grants by November 1 of the year in which one is applying.

Applications which do not conform to the above requirements will not be considered.

Candidates who are shortlisted on the basis of their curriculum may be called for an interview by a Board of Examiners. Scholarships will be assigned by the Commission on evaluation of curriculum and interview results.

Duration: Twelve months (November to June for courses and July to October for research). The scholarship can be renewed for a second year.

Deadline: Application materials must be received no later than September. (Postal dates will not be accepted.)

PUBLICATIONS:
Annali Dell' Istituto Italiano Per Gli Studi Storici; series of monographs; series of historical, philosophical and literary texts.

DIRECTORS:
Prof. Natalino Irti, President
Dr. Marta Herling, Secretary-General
Dr. Elli Catello, Librarian
Dr. Stefano Palmieri, Editor of Publications
Piero Craveri
Giulio de Caprariis
Melina Decaro Bonella
Paola Franchomme
Giuseppe Galasso
Roberto Giordano
Maurizio Mattioli
Federico Pepe
Gennaro Sasso
Fulvio Tessitore

ADDRESS INQUIRIES TO:
Dr. Marta Herling, General Secretary
(See address above.)

*SPECIAL STIPULATIONS:
Fellows must carry out their research project and attend lessons until the end of the academic year.

From December to May, fellows must reside in Naples in order to follow the courses and seminars organized by the Institute. In the five months that follow, they can carry out their research at another institution, either in Italy or abroad. They must make a first report about their research activities by July 31 and a final one by October 31.

The Institute reserves the right to withdraw funding should fellows prove themselves to be seriously inadequate.

ITALIAN AMERICAN STUDIES ASSOCIATION   [601]
P.O. Box 487
Millbrae, CA 94030
(408) 738-4564
Fax: (408) 864-5629

E-MAIL ADDRESS:
quinnroseanne@deanza.edu

WEB SITE ADDRESS:
www.italianamericanstudies.net

FOUNDED: 1966

AREAS OF INTEREST:
Encouragement of Italian-American studies, collection, preservation, study and popularization of materials that illuminate the Italian-American experience in the U.S. and Canada.

CONSULTING OR VOLUNTEER SERVICES:
Sponsors an annual national conference, resource depositories and maintains an information network.

NAME(S) OF PROGRAMS:
● **IASA Memorial Fellowship**

TYPE:
Fellowships.

YEAR PROGRAM STARTED: 1970

PURPOSE:
To promote understanding of the Italian experience in America.

LEGAL BASIS:
Nonprofit, tax-exempt organization.

FINANCIAL DATA:
Amount of support per award: $1,000.
Total amount of support: $1,000.

NUMBER OF AWARDS: 1.

APPLICATION INFORMATION:
Contact the Association for details.
Duration: One year.
Deadline: September 29.

PUBLICATIONS:
Annual Proceedings.

OFFICERS:
George Guida, President

ADDRESS INQUIRIES TO:
Dr. Roseanne Giannini Quinn
(See address above.)

THE LYNDON BAINES JOHNSON FOUNDATION
2313 Red River Street
Austin, TX 78705-5702
(512) 232-2266
Fax: (512) 232-2285

E-MAIL ADDRESS:
grants@lbjfoundation.org

WEB SITE ADDRESS:
www.lbjfoundation.org

TYPE:
Fellowships; Research grants.

See entry 2006 for full listing.

KENTUCKY HISTORICAL SOCIETY   [602]
100 West Broadway
Frankfort, KY 40601
(502) 564-1792
Fax: (502) 564-4701

E-MAIL ADDRESS:
darrell.meadows@ky.gov

WEB SITE ADDRESS:
history.ky.gov

FOUNDED: 1836

AREAS OF INTEREST:
Historical research and publishing.

NAME(S) OF PROGRAMS:
● **Scholarly Research Fellowship Program**

TYPE:
Fellowships; Research grants; Travel grants. Scholarly Research Fellowship Program encourages and promotes advanced research on all aspects of Kentucky-related local, regional, national and transnational history.

PURPOSE:
The fellowships are designed to assist researchers with travel and living expenses while using the Kentucky Historical Society research collections.

ELIGIBILITY:
These short-term fellowships are intended to support serious scholarly work. They enable individuals to pursue advanced study and research in the collections of the Kentucky Historical Society. Applications are welcome from independent scholars, as well as from college and university teachers, graduate students and scholars working in other related disciplines.

FINANCIAL DATA:
Amount of support per award: Typically $400 (for one week) to $1,600 (for four weeks).

NUMBER OF AWARDS: Typically 20-30 each year.

APPLICATION INFORMATION:
Applications are available on the Kentucky Historical Society web site. All applications are peer-reviewed by a panel of leading historians.
Deadline: March 15 and November 1.

ADDRESS INQUIRIES TO:
R. Darrell Meadows, Ph.D., Director
Division of Research and Interpretation
(See e-mail address above.)

LIBRARY COMPANY OF PHILADELPHIA   [603]
1314 Locust Street
Philadelphia, PA 19107
(215) 546-3181
Fax: (215) 546-5167

E-MAIL ADDRESS:
jgreen@librarycompany.org

WEB SITE ADDRESS:
www.librarycompany.org

FOUNDED: 1731

AREAS OF INTEREST:
American studies.

NAME(S) OF PROGRAMS:
● **Albert M. Greenfield Foundation Dissertation Fellowships**
● **NEH Postdoctoral Fellowships**
● **Program in African-American History**
● **Program in Early American Economy and Society**
● **Research Fellowships in American History and Culture**

TYPE:
Fellowships. Albert M. Greenfield Foundation Dissertation Fellowship: Supports dissertation research in residence at the Library Company on any subject relevant to its collections.

Program in Early American Economy and Society: Pre-1860 American economic and business history.

Research Fellowships in American History and Culture: 18th and 19th Century American social and cultural history.

YEAR PROGRAM STARTED: 1988

PURPOSE:
To promote early American historic studies.

ELIGIBILITY:
Both the short-term and long-term Fellowships support postdoctoral and dissertation research. Both also require that the project proposal demonstrate that the Library Company has a primary source central to the research topic. NEH fellows must be U.S. citizens or residents at least three years.

FINANCIAL DATA:
Amount of support per award: Long-term: $20,000 to $40,000; Short-term: $2,000.
Total amount of support: Approximately $170,000 annually.

NUMBER OF APPLICANTS MOST RECENT YEAR: 200.

NUMBER OF AWARDS: Long-term: 8; Short-term: 30.

APPLICATION INFORMATION:
For the short-term fellowships, applicants must complete the required electronic cover sheet and submit one portable document format (PDF) containing a resume and a two-to four-page description of the proposed research. One letter of recommendation should arrive under separate cover in PDF format as well. E-mail materials to fellowships@librarycompany.org.
Duration: Short-term: One month; Long-term: One semester.
Deadline: Program and Research Fellowships: March 1; Long-term Postdoctoral Fellowships: November 1.

ADDRESS INQUIRIES TO:
Jim Green, Fellowship Office
(See address above.)

JAMES MADISON MEMORIAL FELLOWSHIP FOUNDATION [604]

1613 Duke Street
Alexandria, VA 22314
(800) 525-6928
Fax: (319) 337-1204

E-MAIL ADDRESS:
madison@act.org

WEB SITE ADDRESS:
www.jamesmadison.gov

FOUNDED: 1986

AREAS OF INTEREST:
The roots, principles, framing and development of the U.S. Constitution.

NAME(S) OF PROGRAMS:
• **James Madison Fellowships**

TYPE:
Fellowships. The Foundation awards fellowships to college seniors and college graduates without teaching experience (Junior Fellows) and to experienced secondary school teachers in grades seven-12 (Senior Fellows) who will normally enroll respectively in full- and part-time graduate study leading to one of the following Master's degrees: Master's degree in American history or political science, a degree of Master of Arts in Teaching in history or political science, or a related

Master's degree in education that permits a concentration in American history, American government or social studies.

YEAR PROGRAM STARTED: 1992

PURPOSE:
To support the graduate study of the roots, principles, framing and development of the U.S. Constitution.

LEGAL BASIS:
Foundation.

ELIGIBILITY:
Each fellowship recipient must take at least 12 semester hours or their equivalent in topics directly related to the framing and history of the U.S. Constitution.

A James Madison Fellow must be a U.S. citizen or U.S. national, qualify for study toward one of the qualifying Master's degrees indicated and agree to teach full-time in a secondary school for no less than one year for each full academic year of study under a fellowship.

A Senior Fellow must be a full-time teacher of American history, American government, or social studies in grades seven through 12 during the previous year and be under contract or prospective contract to teach full-time as a secondary school teacher of the same subjects for the upcoming academic year.

A Junior Fellow must possess a Bachelor's degree or plan to receive a Bachelor's degree no later than August 31 of the year of application.

GEOGRAPHIC RESTRICTIONS:
United States and its territories.

FINANCIAL DATA:
Amount of support per award: Up to $24,000 for each award.

NUMBER OF APPLICANTS MOST RECENT YEAR: 400.

NUMBER OF AWARDS: 58 to 61.

APPLICATION INFORMATION:
Applicant must register online to complete the application process.
Duration: Up to five years for Senior Fellows. Up to two years for Junior Fellows.
Deadline: March 1, annually.

ADDRESS INQUIRIES TO:
James Madison Fellowship Program
327 2nd Street, Suite 103
Coralville, IA 52241

*SPECIAL STIPULATIONS:
No funding for Ph.D. programs.

JACOB RADER MARCUS CENTER OF THE AMERICAN JEWISH ARCHIVES

3101 Clifton Avenue
Cincinnati, OH 45220-2488
(513) 221-1875
Fax: (513) 221-7812

E-MAIL ADDRESS:
kproffitt@huc.edu

WEB SITE ADDRESS:
www.americanjewisharchives.org

TYPE:
Fellowships. The Marcus Center's Fellowship Program provides recipients with month-long fellowships for research and writing at The Jacob Rader Marcus Center of the American

Jewish Archives. Fellowship stipends will be sufficient to cover transportation and living expenses while in residence. Applicants must be conducting serious research in some area relating to the history of North American Jewry.

See entry 818 for full listing.

THE MASSACHUSETTS HISTORICAL SOCIETY [605]

1154 Boylston Street
Boston, MA 02215
(617) 536-1608
(617) 646-0557
Fax: (617) 859-0074

E-MAIL ADDRESS:
education@masshist.org

WEB SITE ADDRESS:
www.masshist.org

FOUNDED: 1791

AREAS OF INTEREST:
Massachusetts, New England and U.S. history.

NAME(S) OF PROGRAMS:
• **Swensrud Teacher Fellowships at MHS**

TYPE:
Fellowships. Swensrud Teacher Fellowships are offered to public and/or parochial schoolteachers and library media specialists for on-site research at the Society.

YEAR PROGRAM STARTED: 2001

PURPOSE:
To support four weeks of research at the Society for a specific project.

ELIGIBILITY:
Applications are welcome from any K-12 teacher or library media specialist who has a serious interest in using the collections at the MHS to prepare primary-source-based curricula, supported by documents and visual aids, in the fields of American history, world history or English/language arts.

The fellowship process is competitive. Awards are made on the strength of:
(1) project design;
(2) the plan for using the Society collections;
(3) the creativity of the proposed classroom activities;
(4) usability in other classrooms and;
(5) recommendations.

Open to national and international applicants.

FINANCIAL DATA:
Amount of support per award: Stipend of $4,000.

NUMBER OF AWARDS: Minimum of 3.

APPLICATION INFORMATION:
Application information is available on the web site.
Duration: Four weeks.
Deadline: March 5.

ADDRESS INQUIRIES TO:
Kathleen Barker, Assistant Director of Education and Public Programs

THE MASSACHUSETTS HISTORICAL SOCIETY [606]

1154 Boylston Street
Boston, MA 02215
(617) 646-0512
Fax: (617) 859-0074

E-MAIL ADDRESS:
cwright@masshist.org

WEB SITE ADDRESS:
www.masshist.org

FOUNDED: 1791

AREAS OF INTEREST:
Civil War history, Massachusetts, New England, and U.S. history.

NAME(S) OF PROGRAMS:
● **Suzanne and Caleb Loring Research Fellowship**

TYPE:
Fellowships; Research grants; Visiting scholars. Fellowship funds research on the Civil War, its origins, and consequences, for projects that use the resources at the Massachusetts Historical Society and the Boston Athenaeum. Research must be conducted for at least four weeks at each of the two participating institutions.

YEAR PROGRAM STARTED: 2008

PURPOSE:
To encourage projects that draw on the Civil War resources of the participating organizations.

ELIGIBILITY:
Open to independent scholars, advanced graduate students and holders of a Ph.D. or equivalent.

FINANCIAL DATA:
Amount of support per award: $4,000.

NUMBER OF APPLICANTS MOST RECENT YEAR:
11.

NUMBER OF AWARDS: 1.

APPLICATION INFORMATION:
Applicants must submit the following materials:
(1) cover letter;
(2) current curriculum vitae;
(3) project proposal, approximately 1,000 words in length, which includes a description of the project, a statement explaining the historiographical significance of the project, and an indication of the specific Massachusetts Historical Society and Boston Athenaeum collections the applicant wishes to consult and;
(4) letter of recommendation from a faculty member familiar with the student's work and with the project being proposed (graduate students only).
Duration: Minimum of 20 days at each of the two institutions, for a total of 40 days.
Deadline: February 15.

ADDRESS INQUIRIES TO:
Katheryn P. Viens, Research Coordinator (See address above.)

THE MASSACHUSETTS HISTORICAL SOCIETY   [607]
1154 Boylston Street
Boston, MA 02215
(617) 646-0512
Fax: (617) 859-0074

E-MAIL ADDRESS:
cwright@masshist.org

WEB SITE ADDRESS:
www.masshist.org

FOUNDED: 1791

AREAS OF INTEREST:
Massachusetts, New England and U.S. history.

NAME(S) OF PROGRAMS:
● **Short-Term Research Fellowship**

TYPE:
Fellowships; Research grants; Visiting scholars. Research fellowship to use the Society's collection to complete a major project.

YEAR PROGRAM STARTED: 1983

PURPOSE:
To support at least 20 days of research at the Society for a specific project.

ELIGIBILITY:
Must be U.S. citizens or foreign nationals holding appropriate U.S. government status. Open to independent scholars, advanced graduate students, and holders of a Ph.D. or equivalent.

FINANCIAL DATA:
Amount of support per award: Stipend of $1,500 to $2,500.

NUMBER OF APPLICANTS MOST RECENT YEAR:
116.

NUMBER OF AWARDS: 20.

APPLICATION INFORMATION:
Applicants must submit the following materials:
(1) cover letter;
(2) current curriculum vitae;
(3) project proposal, approximately 1,000 words in length, which includes a description of the project, a statement explaining the historiographical significance of the project, and an indication of the specific MHS collections the applicant wishes to consult and;
(4) letter of recommendation from a faculty member familiar with the student's work and with the project being proposed (graduate students only).
Duration: Minimum of 20 days.
Deadline: March 1.

ADDRESS INQUIRIES TO:
Katheryn P. Viens, Research Coordinator (See address above.)

THE MASSACHUSETTS HISTORICAL SOCIETY   [608]
1154 Boylston Street
Boston, MA 02215
(617) 646-0512
Fax: (617) 859-0074

E-MAIL ADDRESS:
cwright@masshist.org

WEB SITE ADDRESS:
www.masshist.org

FOUNDED: 1791

AREAS OF INTEREST:
Massachusetts, New England and U.S. history.

NAME(S) OF PROGRAMS:
● **Long-Term Research Fellowship**

TYPE:
Fellowships; Research grants; Visiting scholars. Research fellowship to use the Society's collection to complete a major project.

YEAR PROGRAM STARTED: 1983

PURPOSE:
To support four to 12 months of research at the Society for a specific project.

ELIGIBILITY:
Applicants must be U.S. citizens or foreign nationals who have lived in the U.S. for at least three years prior to the application deadline. Applicants must have completed their professional training. Fellowship is not available to graduate students. Awards committee will pay special attention both to the quality of proposed projects and to their relationship to the Society's collections. Preference will be given to candidates who have not held a long-term grant during the preceding three years.

FINANCIAL DATA:
Amount of support per award: $4,200 per month stipend with up to $500 per month housing allowance. Up to $750 for professional expenses.

NUMBER OF APPLICANTS MOST RECENT YEAR:
37.

NUMBER OF AWARDS: 2 to 4.

APPLICATION INFORMATION:
Applicants must submit the following materials:
(1) cover letter;
(2) current curriculum vitae;
(3) project proposal, approximately 1,000 words in length, which includes a description of the project, a statement explaining the historiographical significance of the project, and an indication of the specific MHS collections the applicant wishes to consult;
(4) Certification for Participants form and;
(5) two letters of recommendation.
Duration: Four to 12 months of continuous tenure.
Deadline: January 15.

ADDRESS INQUIRIES TO:
Katheryn P. Viens, Research Coordinator (See address above.)

THE MASSACHUSETTS HISTORICAL SOCIETY   [609]
1154 Boylston Street
Boston, MA 02215
(617) 646-0512
Fax: (617) 859-0074

E-MAIL ADDRESS:
cwright@masshist.org

WEB SITE ADDRESS:
www.masshist.org

FOUNDED: 1791

AREAS OF INTEREST:
Massachusetts, New England and U.S. history.

NAME(S) OF PROGRAMS:
● **New England Regional Fellowship Consortium**

TYPE:
Fellowships; Research grants; Travel grants; Visiting scholars. Research fellowship to use the resources at a minimum of three different participating institutions.

YEAR PROGRAM STARTED: 1999

PURPOSE:
To encourage projects that draw on the resources of the participating organizations.

ELIGIBILITY:
Open to individuals with a serious need to use the collections and facilities of the participating organizations.

Fellows must work at each of at least three chosen organizations for at least two weeks.

FINANCIAL DATA:
Amount of support per award: Stipend of $5,000 for eight weeks of research at participating institutions.

NUMBER OF APPLICANTS MOST RECENT YEAR: 67.

NUMBER OF AWARDS: 11.

APPLICATION INFORMATION:
Guidelines and fellowship applications are available on the New England Regional Fellowship Consortium (NREFC) web site.
Duration: Minimum of eight weeks.
Deadline: February 1.

ADDRESS INQUIRIES TO:
Katheryn P. Viens, Research Coordinator
(See address above.)

## THE MEDIEVAL ACADEMY OF AMERICA				[610]
104 Mount Auburn Street
5th Floor
Cambridge, MA 02138-5019
(617) 491-1622
Fax: (617) 492-3303

E-MAIL ADDRESS:
info@themedievalacademy.org

WEB SITE ADDRESS:
www.medievalacademy.org

FOUNDED: 1925

AREAS OF INTEREST:
Any aspect of medieval studies, 500 to 1500 A.D.

NAME(S) OF PROGRAMS:
- **Birgit Baldwin Fellowship**
- **John Nicholas Brown Prize**
- **Van Courtlandt Elliott Prize**
- **Haskins Medal**
- **Schallek Fellowship**

TYPE:
Awards/prizes; Fellowships. Cash prizes for publications of material on medieval topics.

Birgit Baldwin Fellowship supports a graduate student studying in a North American university researching and writing a significant dissertation for a Ph.D. on any subject in French medieval history. Research must be in archives and libraries of France.

The Brown Prize is awarded annually to a first book or monograph on a medieval topic.

The Elliott Prize is awarded annually for a first published article in the medieval field, judged by the selection committee to be of outstanding quality.

The Haskins Medal is awarded to the author of a book of outstanding quality and contribution to the field of medieval studies. This prize usually goes to a senior scholar.

Schallek Fellowship supports Ph.D. dissertation research in any relevant discipline dealing with late-Medieval Britain (circa. 1350-1500).

YEAR PROGRAM STARTED: 1940

PURPOSE:
To promote publication on medieval topics.

LEGAL BASIS:
Nonprofit corporation.

GEOGRAPHIC RESTRICTIONS:
North America.

FINANCIAL DATA:
Amount of support per award: Birgit Baldwin Fellowship: $20,000; Brown Prize: $1,000; Elliott Prize: $500; Schallek Fellowship: $30,000.

NUMBER OF APPLICANTS MOST RECENT YEAR: 30.

NUMBER OF AWARDS: 1 each annually.

APPLICATION INFORMATION:
For Brown Prize, candidates must submit three offprints of an article or book and a letter stating that the submission is the author's first published article or book respectively on a medieval topic. The Brown Prize also requires submission of any reviews that have appeared.

For the Elliott Prize, candidates must submit a first published article on a medieval topic, bearing a publication date of two years before the prize. Articles must be at least five pages in length and the author's primary residence must be in North America.

For the Haskins Medal, submit three copies of the book accompanied by copies of any major reviews that have appeared.
Duration: Fellowships: One year. Baldwin Fellowship is renewable for a second year.
Deadline: November 15. Announcement in April.

ADDRESS INQUIRIES TO:
Sheryl Mullane-Corvi
Assistant to the Executive Director
(See address above.)

## MOUNT VERNON HOTEL MUSEUM & GARDEN				[611]
421 East 61st Street
New York, NY 10065
(212) 838-6878
Fax: (212) 838-7390

E-MAIL ADDRESS:
e.wilcox@mvhm.org

WEB SITE ADDRESS:
www.mvhm.org

AREAS OF INTEREST:
American social history, material culture, historic preservation and museum education.

NAME(S) OF PROGRAMS:
- **William Randolph Hearst Foundation Fellowship**

TYPE:
Fellowships. Provides fellowships to graduate or undergraduate students who are interested in American social history, material culture, historic preservation and museum education.

YEAR PROGRAM STARTED: 1984

PURPOSE:
To promote the study of American history.

ELIGIBILITY:
Applicants must currently be enrolled in a college, university or graduate program.

FINANCIAL DATA:
Amount of support per award: $2,750.
Total amount of support: $5,500.

NUMBER OF AWARDS: 2.

APPLICATION INFORMATION:
Students must submit the completed application form, an essay explaining the applicant's interest in the fellowship, and two letters of recommendation. Applications are available on the web site.

Duration: Nine weeks in June and July.
Deadline: Second Friday in March.

ADDRESS INQUIRIES TO:
Dana Settles
Curator of Education
(See address above.)

## NANTUCKET HISTORICAL ASSOCIATION				[612]
P.O. Box 1016
Nantucket, MA 02554-1016
(508) 228-1655
Fax: (508) 325-7968

E-MAIL ADDRESS:
btyler@nha.org

WEB SITE ADDRESS:
www.nha.org/library/verney.html

AREAS OF INTEREST:
History.

NAME(S) OF PROGRAMS:
- **E. Geoffrey and Elizabeth Thayer Verney Fellowship**

TYPE:
Fellowships; Residencies. To pursue historical research pertaining to Nantucket, MA. This is a residency.

The Verney Fellowship encourages research in the collections of the Nantucket Historical Association Research Library. The Association is the principal repository of Nantucket history, with extensive archives, collections of historic properties, and art and artifacts that broadly illustrate Nantucket's past.

YEAR PROGRAM STARTED: 1999

PURPOSE:
To enhance the public's knowledge and understanding of the heritage of Nantucket, MA.

ELIGIBILITY:
Open to graduate students, independent scholars and academics in any field to conduct research in the collections of the Association.

FINANCIAL DATA:
Amount of support per award: $300 per week stipend; housing will be provided. Travel is reimbursed up to $600.

NUMBER OF AWARDS: 1.

REPRESENTATIVE AWARDS:
Verney Fellows: (2011) Brigid Harmon, "Feasts, Flogging and Famine: Complex Foodways on Nantucket Whaleships;" (2012) Seth Bruggeman, "Ships in a Bottle: The History of American Maritime Museums in the Twentieth Century;" (2013) Edward D. Melillo, "Out of the Blue: Nantucket and the Pacific World."

APPLICATION INFORMATION:
Applicants must send a full description of the proposed project, a curriculum vitae, the names of three references, and an estimate of anticipated time and duration of stay. Send application packet to: Betsy Tyler, Obed Macy Research Chair and Editor of *Historic Nantucket*, Nantucket Historical Association, at the address above.
Duration: Up to three weeks.
Deadline: January 1.

ADDRESS INQUIRIES TO:
Betsy Tyler, Obed Macy Research Chair
(See address above.)

*PLEASE NOTE:
The Verney Fellow resides in the Thomas Macy House, a historic property owned by the Association, for up to a three-week period.

*SPECIAL STIPULATIONS:
NHA Visiting Research Scholars are expected to produce an article suitable for publication in *Historic Nantucket*, the NHA's biannual journal, and to deliver a public lecture on the subject of their research, as well as a presentation to NHA staff. Projects resulting in the publication of a book, article, conference paper, or other media, are looked upon favorably.

NATIONAL HISTORICAL PUBLICATIONS AND RECORDS COMMISSION   [613]
National Archives and Records Administration
700 Pennsylvania Avenue, N.W., Room 114
Washington, DC 20408-0001
(202) 357-5010
Fax: (202) 357-5914

E-MAIL ADDRESS:
nhprc@nara.gov

WEB SITE ADDRESS:
www.archives.gov/nhprc

FOUNDED: 1934

AREAS OF INTEREST:
Archives and historical manuscripts relating to American history.

TYPE:
Project/program grants; Research grants; Technical assistance; Training grants. Grants to support the collection, preservation, digitization, arrangement, description, editing and publishing of documentary source material relating to the history of the U.S., the papers of American leaders and documents treating major subjects and events in American history.

YEAR PROGRAM STARTED: 1964

PURPOSE:
To promote the preservation and use of historical records important for an understanding and appreciation of the history of the U.S.

LEGAL BASIS:
44 U.S.C. 2501-2506.

ELIGIBILITY:
Tribal, state and local government agencies, nonprofit organizations and institutions.

GEOGRAPHIC RESTRICTIONS:
United States and its territories.

FINANCIAL DATA:
Amount of support per award: Average $70,000.
Total amount of support: $5,000,000 for fiscal year 2012.
Matching fund requirements: Generally, 1:1.

NUMBER OF APPLICANTS MOST RECENT YEAR: 240 for fiscal year 2012.

NUMBER OF AWARDS: 77 for fiscal year 2012.

REPRESENTATIVE AWARDS:
$148,000 to the Massachusetts Historical Society to edit *The Papers of John Adams*; $112,693 to Appalachian State University, Boone, NC to process and provide online access to primary research materials within the W.L. Eury Appalachian Collection.

APPLICATION INFORMATION:
All applications must be submitted through Grants.gov.
Duration: Up to three years, depending on the individual project.
Deadline: Varies by program.

PUBLICATIONS:
Newsletter and special reports.

NATIONAL SOCIETY DAUGHTERS OF THE AMERICAN REVOLUTION   [614]
1776 D Street, N.W.
Washington, DC 20006-5303
(202) 879-3292
Fax: (202) 879-3348

E-MAIL ADDRESS:
scholarships@dar.org

WEB SITE ADDRESS:
www.dar.org

FOUNDED: 1895

AREAS OF INTEREST:
American history.

NAME(S) OF PROGRAMS:
- **Dr. Aura-Lee A. and James Hobbs Pittenger American History Scholarship**

TYPE:
Scholarships. The American History Scholarship is awarded to graduating high school students in the upper one-fifth of the class or home schooled who will have a concentrated study of a minimum of 24 credit hours in American History and American Government.

PURPOSE:
To provide ways and means to help students to attain higher education; to perpetuate the memory and spirit of men and women who achieved American independence by acquisition and protection of historical spots and erection of monuments; to carry out injunction of Washington in his farewell address to American people; to maintain institutions of American Freedom; to aid liberty.

LEGAL BASIS:
Incorporated historical society.

ELIGIBILITY:
Scholarships are awarded without regard to race, religion, sex or national origin. All four-year, or more, scholarships must be for consecutive years and are renewable only upon review and approval of annual transcript. Candidates must be U.S. citizens and must attend an accredited college or university in the U.S. No affiliation or relationship to DAR is required for qualification, but candidate must be sponsored by a local DAR Chapter. Awards are judged on the basis of academic excellence, commitment to field of study, as required, and financial need.

GEOGRAPHIC RESTRICTIONS:
United States.

FINANCIAL DATA:
Amount of support per award: $2,000 per year for maximum of $8,000.
Total amount of support: Varies.

NUMBER OF AWARDS: Varies.

APPLICATION INFORMATION:
Application information is available online. The application package must be completed.

All transcripts, letters of recommendation and other required documents must be in a single package.

Included with the application packet is the list of DAR State Scholarship Chairmen. All scholarship applicants are required to have a letter of sponsorship from a chapter. Individuals interested in obtaining a letter of sponsorship from a local chapter are encouraged to contact the DAR State Chairman.
Duration: One academic year. Renewable for up to four years upon annual transcript review and approval.
Deadline: February 15.

PUBLICATIONS:
American Spirit, magazine.

ADDRESS INQUIRIES TO:
Office of the Reporter General
DAR Scholarship Committee
(See address above.)

NATIONAL TRUST FOR HISTORIC PRESERVATION [615]
2600 Virginia Avenue, Suite 1000
Washington, DC 20037
(202) 588-6277
Fax: (202) 588-6223

E-MAIL ADDRESS:
grants@savingplaces.org

WEB SITE ADDRESS:
www.preservationnation.org/funding

FOUNDED: 1949

AREAS OF INTEREST:
To encourage public participation in the preservation of sites, buildings and objects significant in American history and culture.

NAME(S) OF PROGRAMS:
- **National Trust Preservation Funds (NTPF)**

TYPE:
Challenge/matching grants; Project/program grants; Seed money grants; Technical assistance; Training grants. Education program curricula. Project grants to support consultants with professional expertise in areas such as architecture, law, planning, economics, archeology and graphic design. Conferences that address subjects of particular importance to historic preservation also are funded. In addition, grants are made for curriculum development in preservation education directed at select audiences.

YEAR PROGRAM STARTED: 1979

PURPOSE:
To increase the flow of information and ideas in the field of preservation by helping stimulate public discussion, enabling local groups to gain the technical expertise needed for particular projects, introducing students to preservation concepts and crafts and encouraging participation by the private sector in preservation.

LEGAL BASIS:
Nonprofit corporation.

ELIGIBILITY:
Applicants must be nonprofit incorporated organizations or public agencies. Applicants are eligible for no more than three NTPF grants in any two-year period.

Activities eligible for National Trust Preservation Funds grants include hiring consultants to undertake preservation planning or design projects, obtaining professional advice to strengthen management capabilities, sponsoring preservation conferences, designing and implementing innovative preservation education programs targeted to a specific audience and undertaking other planning activities that will lead to implementation of a specific preservation project.

Grants can be used for professional consultant services, preservation education programs and conferences and rehabilitation feasibility studies. Projects, programs and conferences are not funded retroactively.

Bricks-and-mortar construction projects and the funding of ongoing staff positions are not eligible activities. In addition, historic resource surveys to create inventories or to list resources on local, state or national registers are generally not eligible for funding.

GEOGRAPHIC RESTRICTIONS:
United States and its territories.

FINANCIAL DATA:
Amount of support per award: $2,500 to $5,000.

Total amount of support: $3,900,000 for fiscal year 2012.

Matching fund requirements: Each grantee must match the funds on at least a dollar-for-dollar basis using cash contributions.

NUMBER OF AWARDS: 225 grants for fiscal year 2012.

APPLICATION INFORMATION:
Guidelines and application forms may be found on the web site. Applications must be completed and submitted online by the appropriate deadline. Incomplete applications will not be considered.

Duration: Usually a one-time award.

Deadline: Applicants should contact the National Trust Grants Office to obtain information regarding application deadlines.

PUBLICATIONS:
Annual report; brochures.

IRS IDENTIFICATION NUMBER: 53-0210807

ADDRESS INQUIRIES TO:
Grants Coordinator
National Trust Preservation Funds
(See address above.)

NEW JERSEY HISTORIC TRUST [616]
101 South Broad Street
Trenton, NJ 08608-2401
(609) 984-0473
Fax: (609) 984-7590

E-MAIL ADDRESS:
njht@dca.state.nj.us

WEB SITE ADDRESS:
www.njht.org

FOUNDED: 1967

AREAS OF INTEREST:
Historic preservation.

NAME(S) OF PROGRAMS:
● **Discover New Jersey History License Plate Fund for Heritage Tourism**
● **Garden State Historic Preservation Trust Fund (GSHPTF)**

TYPE:
Challenge/matching grants;
Conferences/seminars; Demonstration grants;

Project/program grants; Technical assistance; Training grants. Planning Grants. Provides funding for the preservation of historic properties.

The Discover New Jersey History License Plate Fund awards small grants for projects that develop and promote visitor-ready sites as heritage tourism destinations.

Under the Garden State Historic Preservation Fund (GSHPTF) matching historic site management grants are awarded.

Activities eligible for Historic Site Management Grants include those intended to aid historic property owners and managers to gain a better understanding of preservation needs for a particular site or structure, to enhance long-term planning for the operations and programs of historic sites, and to broaden public awareness and enjoyment of historic sites.

YEAR PROGRAM STARTED: 1989

PURPOSE:
To advance the preservation of the state's historic properties through financial, educational and stewardship programs.

LEGAL BASIS:
Government agency, established by the New Jersey Legislature. Statutory Citation, N.J.S.A. 13:1B-15.111 and NJSCA 13:8C-1 et seq.

ELIGIBILITY:
Applicants must be state, county or municipal governments or nonprofit organizations who either own or operate property that is listed or eligible for listing in the New Jersey or National Register of Historic Places.

GEOGRAPHIC RESTRICTIONS:
New Jersey.

FINANCIAL DATA:
Amount of support per award: Discover New Jersey History License Plate Fund: Up to $3,000; Garden State Historic Preservation Trust Fund: $5,000 to $50,000.

Matching fund requirements: Under the GSHPTF, applicants must provide matching funds.

COOPERATIVE FUNDING PROGRAMS: Program is funded through a state sales tax set aside.

REPRESENTATIVE AWARDS:
$50,000 to Wayne Township, Passaic County, to fund roof restoration study and construction documents of multigenerational home dating to 1695; $529,035 to Cranbury Township, Middlesex County, to fund restoration and adoptive use of school for municipal offices and community space; $574,378 to Monmouth County Parks Commission for rehabilitation of early 18th century house for Bayshore Park Visitors' Center.

APPLICATION INFORMATION:
Applicants must submit a Declaration of Intent to Apply prior to submitting an application for funding, thus allowing grant applicants to receive technical assistance from the Trust's preservation specialists prior to the application deadline.

Duration: Varies.
Deadline: Varies.

PUBLICATIONS:
Annual report; program announcement; *Economic Impact of Historic Preservation in New Jersey* (1997), funding resources for history; *Economic and Fiscal Impacts of Heritage Tourism in New Jersey.*

IRS IDENTIFICATION NUMBER: 22-3113979

STAFF:
Dorothy Guzzo, Executive Director

NEW JERSEY HISTORIC TRUST [617]
101 South Broad Street
Trenton, NJ 08608-2401
(609) 984-0473
Fax: (609) 984-7590

E-MAIL ADDRESS:
njht@dca.state.nj.us

WEB SITE ADDRESS:
www.njht.org

FOUNDED: 1967

AREAS OF INTEREST:
Capital preservation of historic properties.

NAME(S) OF PROGRAMS:
● **Emergency Loans**

TYPE:
Capital grants; Matching gifts; Project/program grants. Loans. Activities which qualify for funding include emergency repair or stabilization, planning or research necessary to preserve an endangered property, limited rehabilitation, restoration or improvement, acquisition of a historic property or the purchase of an option to acquire a historic property.

PURPOSE:
To provide emergency funding for capital preservation projects of historic properties.

LEGAL BASIS:
Government-approved program. Statutory Citation: P.L. 1967, c. 124.

ELIGIBILITY:
Applicants must be nonprofit, tax-exempt organizations or agencies of county or municipal governments. All properties must be listed or eligible for listing in the State and National Registers of Historic Places. For all requests other than acquisition, applicants must demonstrate control of the property through a deed or a valid lease.

GEOGRAPHIC RESTRICTIONS:
New Jersey.

FINANCIAL DATA:
Awards may take the form of matching grants and/or short-term low-interest loans.
Amount of support per award: $1,000 to $10,000.

Total amount of support: Approximately $15,000.

Matching fund requirements: All grants must be matched on a dollar-for-dollar basis. Matching funds for loans are encouraged but not required.

REPRESENTATIVE AWARDS:
$10,000 to Newark Museum for stabilization of skylight in historic Polhemus House.

APPLICATION INFORMATION:
A nonrefundable application fee of $25 must be submitted with each application. Applicants must consult with Trust staff before making application for these funds.
Duration: Varies.

Deadline: Notification two months after submission of complete application.

PUBLICATIONS:
Program announcement.

IRS IDENTIFICATION NUMBER: 21-6000928

ADDRESS INQUIRIES TO:
Lauren Giannullo
(See address above.)

NEW JERSEY HISTORICAL COMMISSION   [618]
New Jersey Department of State
225 West State Street, Fifth Floor
Trenton, NJ 08625-0305
(609) 292-6062
Fax: (609) 633-8168

E-MAIL ADDRESS:
skylar.harris@sos.state.nj.us

WEB SITE ADDRESS:
www.newjerseyhistory.org

FOUNDED: 1969

AREAS OF INTEREST:
New Jersey history.

NAME(S) OF PROGRAMS:
● **General Operating Support Grants**

TYPE:
General operating grants. Provide general assistance to historical organizations, museums, historic sites, archives, libraries and similar organizations with collections or programming relating to the history of New Jersey.

YEAR PROGRAM STARTED: 2000

PURPOSE:
To provide operating support for New Jersey history organizations.

LEGAL BASIS:
Agency within the Department of State, State of New Jersey.

ELIGIBILITY:
To be eligible to apply for a General Operating Support Grant, an organization must:
(1) be a not-for-profit corporation or government (municipal or county) agency, commission or other organization;
(2) be based in New Jersey;
(3) be governed by a board responsible for the programs and policies of the organization;
(4) have a clearly stated mission of service to the promotion, preservation, research, interpretation or public presentation of New Jersey history and;
(5) have a two-year track record of providing programs and services to the public that fulfill that mission.

Eligible applicants include a wide variety of organizations, both public and private.

GEOGRAPHIC RESTRICTIONS:
New Jersey.

FINANCIAL DATA:
Amount of support per award: General Operating Support: $5,000 to $10,000 (budgets under $30,000); up to 33% of the nonstate operating income for either the current or next fiscal year (budgets of $30,000 and up).
Total amount of support: $3,000,000 for fiscal year 2012.
Matching fund requirements: Matching fund ratio of 3:1 (grantee: Commission) for organizations with budgets over $30,000.

NUMBER OF APPLICANTS MOST RECENT YEAR:
202 for fiscal year 2012.

NUMBER OF AWARDS: 116 for fiscal year 2012.

REPRESENTATIVE AWARDS:
$53,000 to Friends at the Hermitage; $46,800 to Alice Paul Institute Inc.; $107,000 to Historic Cold Spring Village; $105,000 to Monmouth County Historical Association; $101,000 to Union County Division of Cultural and Heritage Affairs.

APPLICATION INFORMATION:
The Commission offers assistance to applicants in the technical aspects of completing the application. Applicants may call the Grants Director at (609) 943-3306 for information or check the web site.
Duration: Two-year funding cycle. Successful applicants will receive a grant for fiscal year 2014, and a commitment to support in fiscal year 2015 if funds are available and all reporting obligations are met.
Deadline: Applicants must notify the Commission of their intent to apply for the grant by March 1. Full proposals must be received in the Commission office by April 5.

PUBLICATIONS:
Annual report; application guidelines.

ADMINISTRATION:
Skylar Harris, Grants Manager

ADDRESS INQUIRIES TO:
Skylar Harris
Grants Manager
P.O. Box 305
Trenton, NJ 08625-0305

*SPECIAL STIPULATIONS:
All funding is based on state appropriations.

NEW JERSEY HISTORICAL COMMISSION   [619]
New Jersey Department of State
225 West State Street, Fifth Floor
Trenton, NJ 08625-0305
(609) 292-6062
Fax: (609) 633-8168

E-MAIL ADDRESS:
sara.cureton@sos.state.nj.us

WEB SITE ADDRESS:
www.history.nj.gov

FOUNDED: 1969

AREAS OF INTEREST:
New Jersey history.

NAME(S) OF PROGRAMS:
● **Alfred E. Driscoll Dissertation Prize**
● **Mildred Barry Garvin Prize**
● **Richard P. McCormick Prize for Scholarly Publication**

TYPE:
Awards/prizes. The Driscoll Dissertation Prize is awarded in even years to the author of an outstanding doctoral dissertation on any topic on New Jersey history.

The Garvin Prize is awarded annually to a New Jersey teacher, guidance counselor or school librarian for outstanding teaching of Black American history or related activity at any grade, K-12.

The McCormick Prize is awarded in odd years for an outstanding scholarly work on any aspect of New Jersey history.

YEAR PROGRAM STARTED: 1981

PURPOSE:
To stimulate the study and public knowledge of the history of New Jersey.

LEGAL BASIS:
Agency within the Department of State, State of New Jersey.

ELIGIBILITY:
Driscoll Prize: Doctoral dissertations in New Jersey history are eligible.

Garvin Prize: Applicant must be a New Jersey teacher, guidance counselor or school librarian.

McCormick Prize: Scholarly books published in the preceding two years are eligible.

FINANCIAL DATA:
Amount of support per award: $1,500 for each prize.

NUMBER OF AWARDS: Garvin Prize: 1 per year. Driscoll and McCormick Prizes alternate; each year the Historical Commission may award either 1 Driscoll Prize or 1 McCormick Prize.

APPLICATION INFORMATION:
Guidelines and application forms are available on the web site.
Duration: One-time award. Not renewable.
Deadline: McCormick (2015) and Driscoll (2016) Prizes: March; Garvin Prize: September/October.

PUBLICATIONS:
Annual report; application guidelines.

ADMINISTRATION:
Sara R. Cureton, Director, New Jersey Historical Commission

ADDRESS INQUIRIES TO:
For the Driscoll or Garvin Prize:
Niquole Primiani, Chief Programs Officer
For the McCormick Prize:
Sara Cureton, Director, Grants Program
(See address above.)

NEW JERSEY HISTORICAL COMMISSION   [620]
New Jersey Department of State
225 West State Street, Fifth Floor
Trenton, NJ 08625-0305
(609) 292-6062
Fax: (609) 633-8168

E-MAIL ADDRESS:
skylar.harris@sos.state.nj.us

WEB SITE ADDRESS:
www.history.nj.gov

FOUNDED: 1967

AREAS OF INTEREST:
New Jersey history.

NAME(S) OF PROGRAMS:
● **Minigrants**
● **Project Grants**

TYPE:
Project/program grants. Minigrants: Support for smaller projects of the type covered by special projects and research, publication and media.

Projects: Funding for expenses of specific projects relating to New Jersey history. Eligible categories include conservation of historical materials (manuscripts, books, costumes, historical visuals), editorial and publication projects, educational initiatives, exhibitions, media (films, radio, videotape, digital media), public programs, and research (including archaeological projects, fellowships, oral history, and national and New Jersey registers of historic places nominations).

YEAR PROGRAM STARTED: 1975

PURPOSE:
To stimulate the study and popularization of New Jersey history.

LEGAL BASIS:
Agency within the New Jersey Department of State.

ELIGIBILITY:
Grants are available for both individuals and organizations. There are general standards of eligibility, as well as specific requirements for programs.

FINANCIAL DATA:
Amount of support per award: Minigrants: Up to $3,000; Projects: $3,000 to $15,000.
Matching fund requirements: Organizations only, depending on budget.

NUMBER OF AWARDS: 22 for fiscal year 2012.

REPRESENTATIVE AWARDS:
$11,600 to fund an exhibition on Rock and Roll in New Jersey; $7,877 to fund a cataloging project at Newark Library.

APPLICATION INFORMATION:
Applicants must submit a Declaration of Intent online prior to submitting an application for either general operating or project support. Minigrant applicants do not need to do so.
Deadline: Varies.

PUBLICATIONS:
Annual report; application guidelines.

ADMINISTRATION:
Skylar Harris, Grants Manager

ADDRESS INQUIRIES TO:
Skylar Harris, Grants Manager
P.O. Box 305
Trenton, NJ 08625-0305

NEW YORK LANDMARKS CONSERVANCY [621]
One Whitehall Street, 21st Floor
New York, NY 10004-2127
(212) 995-5260
Fax: (212) 995-5268

E-MAIL ADDRESS:
nylandmarks@nylandmarks.org

WEB SITE ADDRESS:
www.nylandmarks.org

FOUNDED: 1973

AREAS OF INTEREST:
Historic preservation and restoration of buildings.

NAME(S) OF PROGRAMS:
• **City Ventures Fund**
• **EZ (Empowerment Zone) Consulting Grants**
• **Historic Properties Fund**
• **Sacred Sites Program**
• **Technical Services Program**

TYPE:
Project/program grants.

PURPOSE:
To provide financial and technical services to nonprofit housing corporations, community development organizations, social service agencies, homesteading groups, and mutual housing associations.

LEGAL BASIS:
501(c)(3) not-for-profit.

ELIGIBILITY:
Eligible organizations must be IRS 501(c)(3) tax-exempt.

GEOGRAPHIC RESTRICTIONS:
New York.

FINANCIAL DATA:
Amount of support per award: Varies.
Total amount of support: Varies.

APPLICATION INFORMATION:
Prospective applicants should first contact the Conservancy. Applications must include a copy of the IRS tax determination letter.
Duration: Varies.
Deadline: Varies.

IRS IDENTIFICATION NUMBER: 23-7181785

ADDRESS INQUIRIES TO:
See e-mail address above.

NEW YORK STATE HISTORICAL ASSOCIATION [622]
5798 State Highway 80
Cooperstown, NY 13326
(607) 547-1416
Fax: (607) 547-1404

E-MAIL ADDRESS:
c.miosek@nysha.org

WEB SITE ADDRESS:
www.nysha.org

FOUNDED: 1899

AREAS OF INTEREST:
The history of New York state.

NAME(S) OF PROGRAMS:
• **The Dixon Ryan Fox Manuscript Prize of the New York State Historical Association**

TYPE:
Awards/prizes. Annual cash prize and publication assistance.

YEAR PROGRAM STARTED: 1973

PURPOSE:
To award the best unpublished, book-length monograph dealing with the history of New York state, as judged by an editorial committee.

LEGAL BASIS:
Private nonprofit association.

ELIGIBILITY:
Manuscripts may deal with any aspect of New York state history. Biographies of individuals whose careers illuminate aspects of the history of the state are also eligible, as are manuscripts dealing with such cultural matters as literature and the arts, provided that in such cases the methodology used is historical. Works of fiction are not eligible.

FINANCIAL DATA:
Amount of support per award: $3,000.
Total amount of support: $3,000.

NUMBER OF APPLICANTS MOST RECENT YEAR:
14.

NUMBER OF AWARDS: 1 annually.

APPLICATION INFORMATION:
Manuscripts must be typed, double-spaced, with at least one-inch margins. Please send two copies. Clear, readable photocopies or computer printouts are acceptable.
Duration: One-time award. Nonrenewable.
Deadline: February 1. Announcement by July 30 annually.

PUBLICATIONS:
Application guidelines.

ADDRESS INQUIRIES TO:
Caitlin Miosek, Administrative Assistant
Curatorial and Publications
(See address above.)

NEW YORK STATE HISTORICAL ASSOCIATION
Lake Road
Cooperstown, NY 13326
(607) 547-1400
Fax: (607) 547-1404

E-MAIL ADDRESS:
publications@nysha.org

WEB SITE ADDRESS:
www.nysha.org

TYPE:
Awards/prizes. Prizes for published catalogues treating collections located or exhibited in New York state.
See entry 489 for full listing.

THE NEWBERRY LIBRARY [623]
Committee on Awards
60 West Walton Street
Chicago, IL 60610-7324
(312) 255-3666

E-MAIL ADDRESS:
research@newberry.org

WEB SITE ADDRESS:
www.newberry.org/fellowships

FOUNDED: 1887

AREAS OF INTEREST:
The humanities of Western Europe, England and the Americas from the late Middle Ages to the early 20th century.

NAME(S) OF PROGRAMS:
• **American Society for Eighteenth-Century Studies Fellowships**

TYPE:
Fellowships. For scholars wishing to use the Newberry's collections to study the period 1660 to 1815.

PURPOSE:
To help provide access to Newberry resources for people who live beyond commuting distance.

LEGAL BASIS:
Private research library.

ELIGIBILITY:
Applicants must have received their Ph.D. or equivalent degree, or be a Ph.D. candidate at dissertation level.

Applicants must be members of the ASECS at the time of award.

Applicants must live outside the Chicago area.

FINANCIAL DATA:
Amount of support per award: $2,000 per month.

NUMBER OF APPLICANTS MOST RECENT YEAR: 15.

NUMBER OF AWARDS: 1 per year.

APPLICATION INFORMATION:
Applications must be submitted through the online webform.
Duration: One month.
Deadline: January 15.

STAFF:
Diane Dillon, Director of Scholarly and Undergraduate Programs

ADDRESS INQUIRIES TO:
See e-mail address above.

OMOHUNDRO INSTITUTE OF EARLY AMERICAN HISTORY AND CULTURE [624]
400 Landrum Drive, Ground Floor
Swem Library
Williamsburg, VA 23185
(757) 221-1116
Fax: (757) 221-1047

E-MAIL ADDRESS:
nizimmerli@wm.edu

WEB SITE ADDRESS:
oieahc.wm.edu/pub/bookprize.html

FOUNDED: 1943

AREAS OF INTEREST:
Manuscripts about any area of early American studies.

NAME(S) OF PROGRAMS:
● Jamestown Prize

TYPE:
Awards/prizes. Prize to the author of the best book-length scholarly manuscript pertaining to the early American period. Subject of the manuscript must pertain to America circa 1450 to 1815 or to the related history of the British Isles, Europe, West Africa or the Caribbean. The award also guarantees publication by the Institute in association with the University of North Carolina Press.

YEAR PROGRAM STARTED: 1957

LEGAL BASIS:
Independent, nonprofit research institution.

ELIGIBILITY:
The competition is open only to authors who have not previously published a book. Previous and current holders of Institute postdoctoral fellowships are not eligible.

FINANCIAL DATA:
Amount of support per award: $3,000, plus publication.

NUMBER OF AWARDS: 1 every two years.

APPLICATION INFORMATION:
Potential entrants should write to the Editor of Publications at the Institute for detailed instructions before sending in any work.
Deadline: April 30, 2015.

STAFF:
Karin A. Wulf, Director

ADDRESS INQUIRIES TO:
Assistant Editor of Publications
Jamestown Prize
(See e-mail address above.)

*SPECIAL STIPULATIONS:
Past holders of Institute postdoctoral fellowships are ineligible.

OMOHUNDRO INSTITUTE OF EARLY AMERICAN HISTORY AND CULTURE [625]
400 Landrum Drive, Ground Floor
Swem Library
Williamsburg, VA 23185
(757) 221-1110
Fax: (757) 221-1047

E-MAIL ADDRESS:
ieahc1@wm.edu

WEB SITE ADDRESS:
oieahc.wm.edu/fellowship

FOUNDED: 1943

AREAS OF INTEREST:
Research leading to book publication on any area of early American studies.

NAME(S) OF PROGRAMS:
● Omohundro Institute Postdoctoral Fellowship

TYPE:
Fellowships. The Omohundro Institute of Early American History and Culture, located on the campus of The College of William and Mary, annually offers one postdoctoral fellowship to a promising young scholar in any area of early American studies whose dissertation shows potential for making a significant book-length contribution to scholarship.

Fellows have the opportunity of teaching at the College of William and Mary with a concurrent appointment as visiting assistant professor in the appropriate department.

YEAR PROGRAM STARTED: 1945

LEGAL BASIS:
Independent, nonprofit research institution.

ELIGIBILITY:
Fellows must have successfully defended their dissertation and completed all requirements for the Doctorate by the time they begin the fellowship and may not have previously published a book or have a book under contract. Applications are due by November 1 for the term beginning the following July. Foreign nationals are eligible to apply.

FINANCIAL DATA:
Amount of support per award: $50,400 per year stipend.

COOPERATIVE FUNDING PROGRAMS: The fellowships are supported by the Omohundro Institute and the College of William and Mary.

NUMBER OF APPLICANTS MOST RECENT YEAR: 53 for the 2014-16 fellowship.

NUMBER OF AWARDS: 1 annually.

APPLICATION INFORMATION:
Applicants should write the Director of the Institute for application forms and instructions. Information is also available on the web site.
Duration: Two years.
Deadline: October 31 for the term beginning the following July 1.

PUBLICATIONS:
William and Mary Quarterly, scholarly journal; Uncommon Sense, newsletter; books.

STAFF:
Karin A. Wulf, Director

ADDRESS INQUIRIES TO:
Karin A. Wulf, Director
(See address above.)

*SPECIAL STIPULATIONS:
The Institute holds first rights to publishing the resulting book manuscript.

OMOHUNDRO INSTITUTE OF EARLY AMERICAN HISTORY AND CULTURE [626]
400 Landrum Drive, Ground Floor
Swem Library
Williamsburg, VA 23185
(757) 221-1114
(757) 221-1110
Fax: (757) 221-1047

E-MAIL ADDRESS:
ieahc1@wm.edu

WEB SITE ADDRESS:
oieahc.wm.edu/fellowship

FOUNDED: 1943

AREAS OF INTEREST:
Graduate student research related to Early American and transatlantic print culture.

NAME(S) OF PROGRAMS:
● Lapidus-OIEAHC Fellowship

TYPE:
Fellowships. The Lapidus-OIEAHC Fellowship is offered annually to support advanced graduate student research related to Early American and transatlantic print culture, including authorship, production, circulation and reception.

LEGAL BASIS:
Independent, nonprofit research institution.

FINANCIAL DATA:
Amount of support per award: $500.

COOPERATIVE FUNDING PROGRAMS: Fellowships are made possible through the generous support of Sid Lapidus.

NUMBER OF AWARDS: Up to 4 annually.

APPLICATION INFORMATION:
Duration: Application information is available on the web site.
Deadline: January 15. Fellowship recipients may expect to be notified of the award by early spring.

STAFF:
Karin A. Wulf, Director

ADDRESS INQUIRIES TO:
Fellowship Program
(See address above.)

*SPECIAL STIPULATIONS:
Fellowship recipients must provide a one-page report of their progress no more than 12 months after notification of their award.

PHI ALPHA THETA HISTORY HONOR SOCIETY [627]
University of South Florida, SOC107
4202 East Fowler Avenue
Tampa, FL 33620-8100
(800) 394-8195
(813) 974-8212
Fax: (813) 974-8215

E-MAIL ADDRESS:
info@phialphatheta.org

WEB SITE ADDRESS:
www.phialphatheta.org

FOUNDED: 1921

AREAS OF INTEREST:
History.

NAME(S) OF PROGRAMS:
- **Member's First Book Award**
- **Member's Subsequent Book Award**

TYPE:
Awards/prizes. Awards for the best books published by members of Phi Alpha Theta, one for his or her first book, one for subsequent books (second, third, etc.), published in the field of history.

PURPOSE:
To encourage the publication of distinctive books in history.

LEGAL BASIS:
Nonprofit, 501(c)(3).

ELIGIBILITY:
Books to be judged must be published during the previous calendar year. Awards restricted to society members.

FINANCIAL DATA:
Amount of support per award: $1,000.
Total amount of support: $2,000.

NUMBER OF APPLICANTS MOST RECENT YEAR:
15 to 20.

NUMBER OF AWARDS: 2 for the year 2013.

APPLICATION INFORMATION:
Six copies of each book and a completed application must be forwarded to the Society.
Deadline: July 1 (postmark).

OFFICERS:
Dr. Graydon A. Tunstall, Jr., Executive Director

ADDRESS INQUIRIES TO:
Dr. Graydon A. Tunstall, Jr.
Executive Director
(See address above.)

PHI ALPHA THETA HISTORY HONOR SOCIETY [628]
University of South Florida
4202 East Fowler Avenue, SOC107
Tampa, FL 33620-8100
(800) 394-8195
(813) 974-8212
Fax: (813) 974-8215

E-MAIL ADDRESS:
info@phialphatheta.org

WEB SITE ADDRESS:
www.phialphatheta.org

FOUNDED: 1921

AREAS OF INTEREST:
History.

NAME(S) OF PROGRAMS:
- **Thomas S. Morgan Scholarship**
- **William P. Parrish Scholarship**
- **Phi Alpha Theta Scholarship**
- **John Pine Memorial Award**
- **Graydon A. Tunstall, Jr. Scholarship**
- **A.F. Zimmerman Scholarship**

TYPE:
Awards/prizes; Scholarships. The Thomas S. Morgan, William P. Parrish and A.F. Zimmerman Scholarships are given to student members entering graduate school for the first time for work leading to a Master's degree in history.

The Phi Alpha Theta Scholarship, the John Pine Memorial Award and two additional awards are given to graduate student members for work leading to a Ph.D. in history.

The Graydon A. Tunstall, Jr. Scholarship is given to exceptional junior-year students majoring in Modern European History (1815 to present).

PURPOSE:
To promote the study of history at the graduate level.

LEGAL BASIS:
Nonprofit, 501(c)(3).

ELIGIBILITY:
Applicants must be initiated members of the Phi Alpha Theta History Honor Society.

For the Phi Alpha Theta Scholarship and the John Pine Memorial Award, students must have passed general examinations and be ready to start dissertations.

For the Graydon A. Tunstall, Jr. Scholarship, students must be entering the senior year in September.

FINANCIAL DATA:
Amount of support per award: Morgan and Parrish Scholarships, Phi Alpha Theta Scholarship, Pine Memorial and Graydon A. Tunstall, Jr. Scholarship: $1,000 each; Zimmerman Award: $1,250. In some years, there may be two additional awards of $750 each for Doctoral Scholarships.
Total amount of support: Varies.

NUMBER OF APPLICANTS MOST RECENT YEAR:
Pine Memorial Award: 90; Scholarship Grants: 120; Zimmerman Award: 80.

NUMBER OF AWARDS: Master's degree: 3; Ph.D. in history: 4; Undergraduate: 1.

APPLICATION INFORMATION:
Applications may be obtained by writing to the Executive Director or downloaded from the Society web site.
Duration: One year.
Deadline: Applications must be received on or before March 1.

OFFICERS:
Dr. Graydon A. Tunstall, Jr., Executive Director

ADDRESS INQUIRIES TO:
Dr. Graydon A. Tunstall, Jr.
Executive Director
(See address above.)

*SPECIAL STIPULATIONS:
Applicants must be members of Phi Alpha Theta.

PHI ALPHA THETA HISTORY HONOR SOCIETY [629]
University of South Florida, SOC107
4202 East Fowler Avenue
Tampa, FL 33620-8100
(800) 394-8195
(813) 974-8212
Fax: (813) 974-8215

E-MAIL ADDRESS:
info@phialphatheta.org

WEB SITE ADDRESS:
www.phialphatheta.org

FOUNDED: 1921

AREAS OF INTEREST:
History.

NAME(S) OF PROGRAMS:
- **The Nels Andrew N. Cleven Founder's Paper Prize Awards**
- **Dr. George P. Hammond Paper Prize**
- **Dr. Lynn W. Turner Paper Prize**

TYPE:
Awards/prizes. The George P. Hammond Prize award is for the best paper by a graduate student member of the Society.

The Dr. Lynn W. Turner Prize is awarded for the best paper by an undergraduate student member of the Society.

The four Founder's Paper Prizes are awarded to two graduate and two undergraduate student members of the Society.

PURPOSE:
To promote historical research.

LEGAL BASIS:
501(c)(3).

ELIGIBILITY:
All students must be initiated members. All manuscripts must carry a letter of recommendation from either the faculty advisor or the chair of the department of history. Papers should not exceed 25 typewritten pages in length.

FINANCIAL DATA:
Amount of support per award: Founder's Awards: $350; Hammond Prize and Turner Award: $500 each.

NUMBER OF APPLICANTS MOST RECENT YEAR:
50.

NUMBER OF AWARDS: 6.

APPLICATION INFORMATION:
Essay should combine original historical research on significant subjects, based on source material and manuscripts if possible, with good English composition and superior style. Papers should not exceed 25 typewritten double-spaced pages in length, excluding bibliography. Entries received that do not comply with these guidelines will be disqualified.

Title page of the paper must include the applicant's name, mailing address, phone number and e-mail address, as well as the college/university and year at which he or she joined Phi Alpha Theta.

Entrants must submit five copies of each manuscript and a letter of recommendation from either the Faculty Advisor or History Department Chair indicating the applicant's chapter affiliation and whether the individual is a graduate or an undergraduate student.
Send to:
Dr. Clayton Drees
Department of History
Virginia Wesleyan College
1584 Wesleyan Drive
Norfolk, VA 23502-5599
E-mail: cdrees@vwc.edu.
Deadline: July 1.

OFFICERS:
Dr. Graydon A. Tunstall, Jr., Executive Director

ADDRESS INQUIRIES TO:
Dr. Graydon A. Tunstall, Jr.
Executive Director
(See address above.)

PONTIFICAL INSTITUTE OF MEDIAEVAL STUDIES [630]
59 Queen's Park Crescent East
Toronto ON M5S 2C4 Canada
(416) 926-7142
Fax: (416) 926-7292

E-MAIL ADDRESS:
allan.smith@utoronto.ca

WEB SITE ADDRESS:
www.pims.ca

FOUNDED: 1929

AREAS OF INTEREST:
Medieval studies.

NAME(S) OF PROGRAMS:
● **Mellon Postdoctoral Fellowships**

TYPE:
Fellowships.

PURPOSE:
To develop a candidate's personal research in the context of the Institute's mission.

ELIGIBILITY:
Open to scholars engaged in medieval studies. Level of study is postdoctoral.

FINANCIAL DATA:
Total amount of support: Approximately $35,000 (CAN).

NUMBER OF APPLICANTS MOST RECENT YEAR:
29 for the year 2012.

NUMBER OF AWARDS: 4.

APPLICATION INFORMATION:
Application must include official confirmation that the Ph.D. has been examined and that its award has been approved by the appropriate authority.
Duration: One year.
Deadline: February 1.

ROCK ISLAND ARSENAL MUSEUM   [631]

Rock Island Arsenal Historical Society
R. Maguire Scholarship Committee
One Rock Island Arsenal
Rock Island, IL 61299-5000
(309) 782-5021
Fax: (309) 782-3598

E-MAIL ADDRESS:
rimahoch@aol.com

WEB SITE ADDRESS:
www.arsenalhistoricalsociety.com

AREAS OF INTEREST:
Postgraduate, Master's or Doctorate studies in history and museum study.

NAME(S) OF PROGRAMS:
● **Richard C. Maguire Scholarship**

TYPE:
Scholarships.

PURPOSE:
To provide financial support to a student working for a Master's or Doctorate degree in the fields of history, archaeology or museum study.

ELIGIBILITY:
Applicants must be U.S. citizens. Grants will be awarded on an objective and nondiscriminatory basis without regard to age, sex, race, religion or affiliation. Level of study is postdoctoral and postgraduate.

GEOGRAPHIC RESTRICTIONS:
United States.

FINANCIAL DATA:
Amount of support per award: $1,000.

APPLICATION INFORMATION:
Write to the Museum for an application form. Applicant must enclose a self-addressed, stamped envelope.
Duration: One year.
Deadline: May 2.

ADDRESS INQUIRIES TO:
Dick Hochstetler
(See e-mail address above.)

ROCKEFELLER ARCHIVE CENTER   [632]

15 Dayton Avenue
Pocantico Hills
Sleepy Hollow, NY 10591
(914) 366-6309
Fax: (914) 366-6395

E-MAIL ADDRESS:
archive@rockarch.org

WEB SITE ADDRESS:
www.rockarch.org

FOUNDED: 1974

AREAS OF INTEREST:
Preservation of and research in the records of The Rockefeller University, the Rockefeller Foundation, the Rockefeller Brothers Fund, the Rockefeller family and associated organizations and individuals which include major concentrations in philanthropy, education, health, science, social science, agriculture, Black history, international relations and the arts.

CONSULTING OR VOLUNTEER SERVICES:
Reports on holdings and their relevance to research topics and provides assistance to visiting scholars.

NAME(S) OF PROGRAMS:
● **Grants-in-Aid for Research at the Rockefeller Archive Center**

TYPE:
Grants-in-aid. Grants-in-Aid to individual scholars to defray costs of travel and accommodation expenses while doing research at the Rockefeller Archive Center in the Center's collections.

YEAR PROGRAM STARTED: 1977

PURPOSE:
To foster, promote and support research by serious scholars in the collections located at the Rockefeller Archive Center, which includes the records of the Rockefeller Family, the Rockefeller University, the Rockefeller Foundation and other philanthropies and associated individuals.

LEGAL BASIS:
Nonprofit and educational.

ELIGIBILITY:
Grants will be made on a competitive basis to applicants from any discipline, usually graduate students or postdoctoral scholars, who are engaged in research that requires use of the collections at the Center.

FINANCIAL DATA:
Grants are for receipted, approved expenses. Expenses are reimbursed after the completion of the research visit.
Amount of support per award: Up to $4,000.
Total amount of support: $120,000 for the year 2014.

NUMBER OF APPLICANTS MOST RECENT YEAR:
67 for the year 2012.

NUMBER OF AWARDS: 41 for the year 2014.

APPLICATION INFORMATION:
Two letters supporting the Grant-in-Aid application are required.
Duration: Applications for second- and third-year support will be considered, but preference is given to new applicants.

Deadline: November 1. Announcement of awards at the beginning of March.

PUBLICATIONS:
Research Reports OnLine from the Rockefeller Archive Center; guides to manuscripts and photograph collections; surveys of holdings on specific subjects.

OFFICERS AND STAFF:
Jack Meyers, President
James A. Smith, Vice President

ADDRESS INQUIRIES TO:
Norine Hochman, Executive Assistant
(See address above.)

SANTA BARBARA MISSION ARCHIVE-LIBRARY   [633]

2201 Laguna Street
Santa Barbara, CA 93105
(805) 682-4713 ext. 152
Fax: (805) 682-9323

E-MAIL ADDRESS:
director@sbmal.org

WEB SITE ADDRESS:
www.sbmal.org

FOUNDED: 1786

AREAS OF INTEREST:
California Mission history.

NAME(S) OF PROGRAMS:
● **Geiger Memorial Internship**

TYPE:
Internships; Residencies.

YEAR PROGRAM STARTED: 1978

PURPOSE:
To support scholarly research related to the American Southwest prior to 1846, with preferential consideration being given to studies relating to Alta and Baja California.

ELIGIBILITY:
Consideration will be given to graduate and undergraduate students furthering their studies in public history.

FINANCIAL DATA:
Amount of support per award: $2,500 stipend.

NUMBER OF AWARDS: 1 annually.

APPLICATION INFORMATION:
Application information is available online.
Duration: Three months during the summer.
Deadline: May 1. Announcement June 1.

ADDRESS INQUIRIES TO:
Chair of the Award Committee or
Dr. Monica Orozco, Director
(See address and e-mail above.)

SMITHSONIAN NATIONAL AIR AND SPACE MUSEUM

601 Independence Avenue, S.W.
Washington, DC 20560
(202) 633-2540
Fax: (202) 633-8928

E-MAIL ADDRESS:
banksscottm@si.edu

WEB SITE ADDRESS:
airandspace.si.edu

TYPE:
Internships. Full-time interns work 40 hours per week from approximately the first week in June until the second week in August.

See entry 2629 for full listing.

SOCIETY FOR FRENCH HISTORICAL STUDIES [634]

Department of History, University of Vermont
201 Wheeler House
133 South Prospect Street
Burlington, VT 05405-0164

E-MAIL ADDRESS:
steven.zdatny@uvm.edu

WEB SITE ADDRESS:
www.societyforfrenchhistoricalstudies.net

FOUNDED: 1955

AREAS OF INTEREST:
French history.

NAME(S) OF PROGRAMS:
- **The Gilbert Chinard Prize**
- **Marjorie M. and Lancelot L. Farrar Awards**
- **The William Koren, Jr. Prize**
- **The David Pinkney Prize**
- **Research Travel Award**
- **John B. and Theta H. Wolf Travel Fellowship**

TYPE:
Awards/prizes. The Chinard Prize is for a recent book on historical relations between France and the Americas.

Farrar Award is for dissertation research.

The Koren Prize is for a recent article written on French history.

The Pinkney Prize is for a recent book written on French history.

Research Travel Award is for recent recipients of doctorates (awarded jointly with Western Society for French History).

Wolf Travel Fellowship is for research travel pertaining to a dissertation.

YEAR PROGRAM STARTED: 1955

PURPOSE:
To further the study of French history in the U.S. and Canada.

ELIGIBILITY:
Gilbert Chinard Prize: Historical studies of any area or period are acceptable.

Marjorie M. and Lancelot L. Farrar Awards: Must be a doctoral student in French history at a North American university.

William Koren, Jr. Prize: Must be a North American scholar who published an article on any era of French History in an American, European or Canadian journal.

David Pinkney Prize: Must be a citizen of the U.S. or Canada or an author with a full-time appointment at a U.S. or Canadian college or university. Books on any aspect and period of French history will be considered.

Research Travel Award: Granted to an outstanding American or Canadian scholar who has received the Doctorate in History in the five-year period prior to the award.

John B. and Theta H. Wolf Travel Fellowship: Must be a doctoral student at a university in the U.S. or Canada.

FINANCIAL DATA:
Amount of support per award: Chinard and Koren Prize: $1,000; Farrar Awards: $2,500 each; Pinkney Prize: $1,500; Research Travel Award and Wolf Travel Fellowship: $2,000.

NUMBER OF AWARDS: Chinard Prize, Koren Prize, Pinkney Prize, Research Travel Award and Wolf Travel Fellowship: 1; Farrar Awards: 2.

APPLICATION INFORMATION:
Application information is available on the web site.

ADDRESS INQUIRIES TO:
Dr. Steven Zdatny, Executive Director
(See address above.)

THE SOCIETY OF AMERICAN HISTORIANS, INC. [635]

Columbia University
Graduate School of Journalism
2950 Broadway
New York, NY 10027
(212) 854-6495

E-MAIL ADDRESS:
amhistsociety@columbia.edu

WEB SITE ADDRESS:
www.sah.columbia.edu

FOUNDED: 1939

AREAS OF INTEREST:
American history and biography.

NAME(S) OF PROGRAMS:
- **James Fenimore Cooper Prize**
- **Allan Nevins Prize**
- **Francis Parkman Prize**

TYPE:
Awards/prizes. James Fenimore Cooper Prize: Biennial award in odd-numbered years for a book of historical fiction on an American subject that makes a significant contribution to historical understanding, portrays authentically the people and events of the historical past, and displays skills in narrative construction and prose style copyrighted in the previous two years.

Allan Nevins Prize: Award for the best written doctoral dissertation on an American subject completed in the previous year.

Francis Parkman Prize: Award for the best nonfiction book in American history published the previous year.

YEAR PROGRAM STARTED: 1960

PURPOSE:
To encourage literary distinction in the writing of history and biography.

LEGAL BASIS:
Nonprofit.

ELIGIBILITY:
Allan Nevins Prize: Eligible doctoral dissertation manuscripts must be submitted by the university at which the doctoral studies were undertaken.

FINANCIAL DATA:
Amount of support per award: $2,000 per prize.

NUMBER OF AWARDS: James Fenimore Cooper Prize: 1 biennially in odd-numbered years; Allan Nevins and Francis Parkman Prizes: 1 each annually.

APPLICATION INFORMATION:
Application information and guidelines are available online.
Deadline: January 31.

OFFICERS:
Patricia Nelson Limerick, President
Andie Tucher, Executive Secretary

ADDRESS INQUIRIES TO:
See e-mail address above.

THE SONS OF THE REPUBLIC OF TEXAS [636]

SRT Office
1717 Eighth Street
Bay City, TX 77414
(979) 245-6644
Fax: (979) 244-3819

E-MAIL ADDRESS:
srttexas@srttexas.org

WEB SITE ADDRESS:
www.srttexas.org

FOUNDED: 1893

AREAS OF INTEREST:
Republic of Texas (1836-1846).

NAME(S) OF PROGRAMS:
- **Summerfield G. Roberts Award**

TYPE:
Awards/prizes. Cash award to the author of a work of creative writing on the Republic of Texas.

PURPOSE:
To encourage literary effort and research about historical events and personalities during the days of the Republic of Texas (1836-1846), and to stimulate interest in this period.

LEGAL BASIS:
Nonprofit organization.

ELIGIBILITY:
The competition is open to all writers everywhere; they need not reside in Texas nor must the publishers be in Texas. Manuscripts may be either fiction or nonfiction, poems, essays, plays, short stories, novels, or biographies.

FINANCIAL DATA:
Amount of support per award: $2,500.
Total amount of support: $2,500 annually.

NUMBER OF AWARDS: 1 annually.

APPLICATION INFORMATION:
Manuscripts must be written or published during the calendar year for which the award is given. No entry may be submitted more than one time. There is no word limit on the material submitted for the award. The title page must have the contestant's full name, address and phone number. Five copies of each entry must be mailed to the General Office of The Sons of the Republic of Texas at the address above. No copies will be returned.
Duration: One-time award.
Deadline: Postmarked no later than January 15 of the year following the qualifying year of the award.

THE SONS OF THE REPUBLIC OF TEXAS [637]

SRT Office
1717 Eighth Street
Bay City, TX 77414
(979) 245-6644
Fax: (979) 244-3819

E-MAIL ADDRESS:
srttexas@srttexas.org

WEB SITE ADDRESS:
www.srttexas.org

FOUNDED: 1893

AREAS OF INTEREST:
Spanish colonial period of Texas history.

NAME(S) OF PROGRAMS:
- **Presidio La Bahia Award**

TYPE:
Awards/prizes. Presidio La Bahia Award is intended to promote suitable preservation of relics, appropriate dissemination of data, and research into Texas heritage, with particular emphasis on the Spanish colonial period.

PURPOSE:
To encourage literary effort and research about historical events and personalities during the days of the Spanish colonial period of Texas history, and to stimulate interest in this period.

ELIGIBILITY:
Open to all persons interested in the Spanish colonial influence on Texas culture.

Research writings have proved in the past to be the most successful type of entry. However, careful consideration will be given to other literary forms, as well as to art, architecture, and archaeological discovery.

FINANCIAL DATA:
Amount of support per award: First place: a minimum of $1,200 for the best published book. At its discretion, the organization may award a second-place book prize. There is a separate category with a prize for the best published paper, article published in a periodical, or project of a nonliterary nature.
Total amount of support: A total of $2,000 is available annually for winning participants in the competition.

APPLICATION INFORMATION:
Applicants must submit four copies of published writings to the office. Galley proofs are not acceptable.
Deadline: Entries are accepted from June 1 to September 30.

THE SUMMERLEE FOUNDATION
5556 Caruth Haven Lane
Dallas, TX 75225
(214) 363-9000
Fax: (214) 363-1941

E-MAIL ADDRESS:
info@summerlee.org

WEB SITE ADDRESS:
www.summerlee.org

TYPE:
Project/program grants; Research grants; Technical assistance.

See entry 1384 for full listing.

HARRY S. TRUMAN LIBRARY INSTITUTE
500 West U.S. Highway 24
Independence, MO 64050
(816) 268-8248
Fax: (816) 268-8299

E-MAIL ADDRESS:
sullivan.hstli@gmail.com

WEB SITE ADDRESS:
www.trumanlibrary.org

TYPE:
Awards/prizes; Fellowships; Grants-in-aid; Research grants; Travel grants. The Dissertation Year Fellowships are given to encourage historical scholarship of the public career of Harry S. Truman or the Truman era. Support is given annually to one or two graduate students who have completed the dissertation research and are in the writing stage. Preference will be given to projects

based on extensive research at the Truman Library. Successful applicants will be expected to deposit one copy of their completed dissertation, or any publication resulting therefrom, with the Truman Library.

Research Grants are intended to enable graduate students as well as postdoctoral scholars to come to the Library for one to three weeks to use its archival facilities.

The Scholar's Award is given every other year, even-numbered years only, to a scholar engaged in a study of either the public career of Harry S. Truman or some aspect of the history of the Truman administration or of the U.S. during that administration. The scholar's work must be based on extensive research at the Truman Library and must be designed to result in the publication of a book-length manuscript. One copy of such book (and/or any other publication resulting from work done under this award) shall be deposited by the author with the Harry S. Truman Library.

The Harry S. Truman Book Award is given in even years for the best book dealing with some aspect of history of the U.S. between April 12, 1945 and January 20, 1953 or with the public career of Harry S. Truman.

See entry 2018 for full listing.

U.S. ARMY CENTER OF MILITARY HISTORY   [638]
103 Third Avenue
Fort McNair
Washington, DC 20319-5058
(202) 685-2393
Fax: (202) 685-2077

E-MAIL ADDRESS:
cmhonline@us.army.mil

WEB SITE ADDRESS:
www.army.mil/cmh-pg

FOUNDED: 1942

AREAS OF INTEREST:
History of warfare on land, with special emphasis on the history of the U.S. Army.

NAME(S) OF PROGRAMS:
● **Dissertation Year Fellowships**

TYPE:
The Center offers two Dissertation Fellowships each year and sometimes awards a third fellowship to exceptional dissertations on museum-related topics. The Center will consider dissertations on the history of land warfare; preference is given to topics on the history of the U.S. Army.

YEAR PROGRAM STARTED: 1970

PURPOSE:
To encourage scholarship in military history.

LEGAL BASIS:
Government agency.

ELIGIBILITY:
Applicants must be civilian citizens or nationals of the U.S. that have demonstrated ability and special aptitude for advanced training and study in military history, be enrolled in a recognized graduate school and have successfully completed by September of the year of the award all requirements for the Ph.D. except the dissertation.

FINANCIAL DATA:
Amount of support per award: Stipend of $10,000.
Total amount of support: Up to $30,000.

NUMBER OF APPLICANTS MOST RECENT YEAR:
26 for the year 2013.

NUMBER OF AWARDS: Up to 3 annually.

REPRESENTATIVE AWARDS:
"A Crisis of Faith: Chaplains, Vietnam and Religion in the American Military;" "Conflict and Change during the U.S. Occupation of Cuba, 1898-1902;" "Creature Comforts: The Exchange and Consumption of Sugar, Tobacco, and Other Everyday Stimulants during the Great War."

APPLICATION INFORMATION:
Applicants must submit by mail or fax the following materials:
(1) completed, typed application form;
(2) proposed research plan and reasons for interest in this topic (not to exceed 10 double-spaced, typed pages);
(3) letter from dissertation director confirming dissertation proposal has been accepted by the committee;
(4) letters of recommendation;
(5) a writing sample of approximately 25 double-spaced, typed pages (e.g., seminar paper, published scholarly article, excerpt from M.A. thesis or Ph.D. dissertation) and;
(6) transcripts from all undergraduate and graduate schools attended.
Duration: One year.
Deadline: January 15. Announcement April 1.

ADDRESS INQUIRIES TO:
Brian F. Neumann
CMH Dissertation Fellowship Committee
(See address above.)

U.S. ARMY MILITARY HISTORY INSTITUTE   [639]
U.S. Army Heritage and Education Center
U.S. Army War College
950 Soldiers Drive
Carlisle, PA 17013-5021
(717) 245-4240 (office)
Fax: (717) 245-4370

E-MAIL ADDRESS:
thomas.hendrix@us.army.mil

WEB SITE ADDRESS:
www.carlisle.army.mil/ahec/USAMHI/grants.cfm

FOUNDED: 1967

AREAS OF INTEREST:
Military history with emphasis on the U.S. Army.

NAME(S) OF PROGRAMS:
● **General and Mrs. Matthew B. Ridgway Research Grant**

TYPE:
Research grants; Travel grants. Research and travel fellowships to cover expenses incurred while conducting individual research in USAMHI holdings. These grants may not be used to cover costs for travel to and research at other institutions.

YEAR PROGRAM STARTED: 1977

PURPOSE:
To stimulate utilization of holdings of the Institute in preparation of scholarly, mature publications in military history (theses, dissertations or books).

LEGAL BASIS:
U.S. Department of the Army.

ELIGIBILITY:
Applicants must be scholars at the graduate, postgraduate, or instructor/professor level; or be other professional scholars or authors; or have comparable qualifications based on experience who are pursuing research topics on significant subjects in the field of military history which are well represented in USAMHI holdings.

Government historians researching for official projects are not eligible. No recipient is eligible for more than one grant.

FINANCIAL DATA:
Amount of support per award: Up to $2,500.

NUMBER OF APPLICANTS MOST RECENT YEAR: 26.

NUMBER OF AWARDS: 13 for the year 2012-13 (2 to professors, 9 to graduate students, and 2 to authors).

APPLICATION INFORMATION:
Applications can be downloaded online.
Duration: Until December 31 of the following year.
Deadline: Postmarked by December 31, to be considered when review panel meets in January.

ADDRESS INQUIRIES TO:
Ridgway Research Grants
(See address above.)

*SPECIAL STIPULATIONS:
Must do research in U.S. Army Military History Institute holdings.

U.S. MARINE CORPS [640]
Marine Corps History Division
3078 Upshur Avenue
Quantico, VA 22134
(703) 432-5058
Fax: (703) 432-5054

E-MAIL ADDRESS:
paul.j.weber1@usmc.mil

WEB SITE ADDRESS:
www.history.usmc.mil

FOUNDED: 1919

AREAS OF INTEREST:
U.S. military and naval history and history-based studies in the social and behavioral sciences with a direct relationship to the USMC.

NAME(S) OF PROGRAMS:
• **Marine Corps Historical Program Research Grants**

TYPE:
Research grants. Grants in areas of tangible benefit to the Marine Corps to support research that will add materially to the sum of knowledge regarding the Marine Corps and will not duplicate official projects.

YEAR PROGRAM STARTED: 1975

PURPOSE:
To promote the scholarly study of the USMC from 1775 to the present.

LEGAL BASIS:
Funds provided by the Marine Corps Heritage Foundation, a nonprofit, educational organization.

ELIGIBILITY:
Graduate students, postdoctoral scholars and others with demonstrated professional competence to pursue research projects.

FINANCIAL DATA:
Grants ordinarily will be paid in two installments. Half on the initiation of the approved project and half on its successful conclusion. There are no restrictions on how the recipients apply these funds.
Amount of support per award: $400 to $3,000.

NUMBER OF APPLICANTS MOST RECENT YEAR: 8.

NUMBER OF AWARDS: 2 for the year 2012.

APPLICATION INFORMATION:
A letter should be submitted prior to formal application if the applicant feels that the project involved is within the scope of the program as outlined in the brochure describing the program. This letter should describe concisely the project and its intended purpose and will serve to initiate a request for formal application if deemed appropriate.
Duration: Varies.
Deadline: Applications accepted throughout the year. Decisions on applicants are announced as soon as possible.

PUBLICATIONS:
Brochure describing program.

OFFICER:
Paul J. Weber, Deputy Director

ADDRESS INQUIRIES TO:
Paul J. Weber, Deputy Director
Marine Corps History Division
(See address above.)

U.S. MARINE CORPS [641]
Marine Corps History Division
3078 Upshur Avenue
Quantico, VA 22134
(703) 432-5058
Fax: (703) 432-5054

E-MAIL ADDRESS:
paul.j.weber1@usmc.mil

WEB SITE ADDRESS:
www.history.usmc.mil

FOUNDED: 1919

AREAS OF INTEREST:
U.S. military and naval history and history-based studies in the social and behavioral sciences with a direct relationship to the history of the USMC.

NAME(S) OF PROGRAMS:
• **Dissertation Fellowships in Marine Corps History**

TYPE:
Fellowships. Awarded to a qualified graduate student working on a doctoral dissertation pertinent to U.S. Marine Corps history. Topics in U.S. military and naval history and history-based topics in the social and behavioral sciences with a direct relationship to the history of the U.S. Marine Corps will be considered.

YEAR PROGRAM STARTED: 1975

PURPOSE:
To promote the scholarly study of the USMC from 1775 to the present.

LEGAL BASIS:
Funds provided by the Marine Corps Heritage Foundation, a nonprofit, educational organization.

ELIGIBILITY:
Applicants must be enrolled in a recognized graduate school, have completed all

requirements for the Ph.D. degree except the dissertation and have a university-approved dissertation topic pertinent to U.S. Marine Corps history.

FINANCIAL DATA:
Stipend will be provided directly to the recipient in two equal payments. The first upon acceptance of the award and the second at the completion of the program.
Amount of support per award: $10,000.
Total amount of support: Varies.

NUMBER OF APPLICANTS MOST RECENT YEAR: 4 for the year 2012.

NUMBER OF AWARDS: 1 for the year 2012.

APPLICATION INFORMATION:
Applications may be obtained from the chairman of the history department of the applicant's institution or from the Coordinator, Grants and Fellowships, at the address above.
Duration: One year. No renewals.
Deadline: May 1.

PUBLICATIONS:
Brochure.

OFFICER:
Paul J. Weber, Deputy Director

ADDRESS INQUIRIES TO:
Paul J. Weber, Deputy Director
Marine Corps History Division
(See address above.)

U.S. MARINE CORPS [642]
Marine Corps History Division
3078 Upshur Avenue
Quantico, VA 22134
(703) 432-5058
Fax: (703) 432-5054

E-MAIL ADDRESS:
paul.j.weber1@usmc.mil

WEB SITE ADDRESS:
www.history.usmc.mil

FOUNDED: 1919

AREAS OF INTEREST:
U.S. military and naval history and history-based studies in the social and behavioral sciences with a direct relationship to the history of the USMC.

NAME(S) OF PROGRAMS:
• **Master's Thesis Fellowships in Marine Corps History**

TYPE:
Fellowships. Awarded to qualified graduate students with university-approved thesis topics pertinent to U.S. Marine Corps history. Topics may be in U.S. military and naval history or in history-based studies in the social and behavioral sciences, with a direct relationship to the history of the U.S. Marine Corps.

YEAR PROGRAM STARTED: 1986

PURPOSE:
To promote the scholarly study of all aspects of Marine Corps activities from 1775 to the present.

LEGAL BASIS:
Funds provided by the Marine Corps Heritage Foundation, a nonprofit, educational organization.

ELIGIBILITY:
Applicants must be actively enrolled in an accredited Master's degree program requiring a Master's thesis and have a university-approved topic pertinent to U.S.

Marine Corps history. Applicants must be U.S. citizens or nationals and must not have held or accepted an equivalent fellowship from any other Department of Defense agency.

FINANCIAL DATA:
Stipend will be provided directly to the recipient in two equal payments. The first upon acceptance of the award and the second upon completion.
Amount of support per award: $3,000.
Total amount of support: Varies.

NUMBER OF APPLICANTS MOST RECENT YEAR: 2 for the year 2012.

NUMBER OF AWARDS: 2 for the year 2012.

APPLICATION INFORMATION:
Applications may be obtained from the chairman of the history department of the applicant's institution or from the Coordinator, Grants and Fellowships, at the address above.
Duration: One year. No renewal; however, thesis fellows are eligible to apply for the Marine Corps Historical Program's doctoral dissertation fellowship when qualified.
Deadline: May 1.

PUBLICATIONS:
Brochure.

OFFICER:
Paul J. Weber, Deputy Director

ADDRESS INQUIRIES TO:
Paul J. Weber, Deputy Director
Marine Corps History Division
(See address above.)

UNITED STATES HOLOCAUST MEMORIAL MUSEUM, CENTER FOR ADVANCED HOLOCAUST STUDIES [643]
100 Raoul Wallenberg Place, S.W.
Washington, DC 20024-2126
(202) 314-7829
Fax: (202) 479-9726

E-MAIL ADDRESS:
vscholars@ushmm.org

WEB SITE ADDRESS:
www.ushmm.org

FOUNDED: 1993

AREAS OF INTEREST:
Holocaust and genocide studies.

NAME(S) OF PROGRAMS:
• Visiting Scholar Program

TYPE:
Exchange programs; Fellowships. The Center for Advanced Holocaust Studies is an integral part of the United States Holocaust Memorial Museum, which serves as America's national institution for Holocaust education and remembrance. The Center awards fellowships to support significant research and writing about the Holocaust. Awards are granted on a competitive basis. The Center welcomes proposals from scholars in all relevant academic disciplines, including history, political science, literature, Jewish studies, philosophy, religion, psychology, comparative genocide studies, law and others.

Visiting scholars at the Center have access to more than 60,000,000 pages of Holocaust-related archival documentation; the

Museum's extensive library; oral history, film, photo, art, artifacts and memoir collections; and Holocaust survivor database.

YEAR PROGRAM STARTED: 1994

PURPOSE:
To support scholarship and publication in the field of Holocaust studies; to promote the growth of Holocaust studies at American universities; to seek to foster strong relationships between American and international scholars; to organize programs to ensure the ongoing training of future generations of scholars specializing in the Holocaust.

ELIGIBILITY:
Fellowships are awarded to candidates working on their dissertations (ABD), postdoctoral researchers, and senior scholars. Immediate postdoctorals and faculty between appointments will also be considered.

FINANCIAL DATA:
Amount of support per award: Up to $3,500 monthly.
Total amount of support: Varies.

NUMBER OF APPLICANTS MOST RECENT YEAR: 111.

NUMBER OF AWARDS: Approximately 30.

APPLICATION INFORMATION:
Application forms can be obtained by contacting Visiting Scholar Programs at the address above.
Duration: Three to eight months. Must be a minimum of three consecutive months.
Deadline: November of each year.

PUBLICATIONS:
Program announcement.

ADDRESS INQUIRIES TO:
Jo-Ellyn Decker, Program Coordinator
(See address above.)

THE UNIVERSITY OF DELAWARE-HAGLEY GRADUATE PROGRAM [644]
Department of History, John Munroe Hall
University of Delaware
Newark, DE 19716
(302) 831-8226
Fax: (302) 831-1538

E-MAIL ADDRESS:
dianec@udel.edu

WEB SITE ADDRESS:
www.udel.edu/hagley

FOUNDED: 1954

AREAS OF INTEREST:
Technology, business, consumption, and work in industrial and post-industrial societies.

TYPE:
Fellowships. The University of Delaware, in association with the Hagley Museum, sponsors a premier graduate resident program for the study of technology, business, consumption, and work in industrial and post-industrial societies leading to a Master of Arts or Ph.D. in History. Students have access to faculty with international reputations in American, European and non-Western history, and benefit from strong interdisciplinary ties to museum studies and material culture programs, as well as the Hagley Museum and Library.

YEAR PROGRAM STARTED: 1954

PURPOSE:
To prepare students planning careers as college teachers and as professionals in museums and historical agencies.

LEGAL BASIS:
Not-for-profit organization classified by IRS as 501(c)(3) organization.

ELIGIBILITY:
All Hagley Fellows are required to complete 30 credits (ten classes). Some of these classes must be selected to fulfill History Department requirements. Hagley Fellows also must take two "Hagley courses" which reflect student and faculty interests. These are offered every semester. Ph.D. students take a written comprehensive examination and write a dissertation. A thesis is optional for M.A. students.

FINANCIAL DATA:
All Hagley Fellows receive a stipend and tuition remission. M.A. students are supported for two years. Ph.D. students receive four years of funding. In exchange, Fellows work as teaching assistants during half the semesters in which they are funded. Hagley Fellows also receive an allowance of $600 a year for travel and research expenses. The Program and the History Department also have additional funds which can be used to support internships and Ph.D. research.
Amount of support per award: $16,650 stipend plus full tuition and a $600 research and travel budget.

APPLICATION INFORMATION:
Interested applicants should complete the online application for the UD History Graduate Program. Applicant should clearly indicate on the top of the personal statement that he or she wishes to be considered for the Hagley Program.
Duration: Nine-month fellowships may be renewed once for those seeking a terminal Master's degree and up to three times for those seeking a Ph.D.
Deadline: January 15.

ADDRESS INQUIRIES TO:
Diane Clark, Administrative Assistant
(See address above.)

*SPECIAL STIPULATIONS:
This is a resident graduate program.

UNIVERSITY OF DELAWARE, DEPARTMENT OF HISTORY [645]
46 West Delaware Avenue
Newark, DE 19716
(302) 831-8226
Fax: (302) 831-1538

E-MAIL ADDRESS:
dianec@udel.edu

WEB SITE ADDRESS:
www.udel.edu

AREAS OF INTEREST:
Professional training in historical studies.

NAME(S) OF PROGRAMS:
• E. Lyman Stewart Fellowship

TYPE:
Fellowships. Residential program in history.

PURPOSE:
To provide a program of graduate study leading to an M.A. or Ph.D. degree for students who plan careers as museum professionals, historical agency administrators or seek careers in college teaching and public history.

ELIGIBILITY:
Open to nationals of any country.

FINANCIAL DATA:
Amount of support per award: $16,650, plus tuition.
Total amount of support: Varies.

NUMBER OF AWARDS: Varies.

APPLICATION INFORMATION:
Applications must be submitted online using the University of Delaware application form and include transcripts, Graduate Record Examination scores, TOEFL scores (where applicable), plus three letters of recommendation and a writing sample.
Duration: Two to four years.
Deadline: January 15.

ADDRESS INQUIRIES TO:
Diane Clark, Administrative Assistant
(See address above.)

WISCONSIN HISTORICAL SOCIETY PRESS   [646]
816 State Street
Madison, WI 53706-1482
(608) 264-6582
Fax: (608) 264-6486

E-MAIL ADDRESS:
whspress@wisconsinhistory.org

WEB SITE ADDRESS:
www.wisconsinhistory.org/whspress

FOUNDED: 1846

AREAS OF INTEREST:
Wisconsin history and culture.

NAME(S) OF PROGRAMS:
● **D.C. Everest Fellowship**
● **Amy Louise Hunter Fellowship**
● **Alice E. Smith Fellowship**

TYPE:
Fellowships; Research grants. Fellowships awarded for research and writing for publication in book form by the Society press on Wisconsin history topics.

YEAR PROGRAM STARTED: 2000

PURPOSE:
To promote research and writing on Wisconsin history topics.

LEGAL BASIS:
Agency of the state of Wisconsin.

ELIGIBILITY:
Fellowships are awarded to individuals. Organizations are not eligible to apply.

FINANCIAL DATA:
Amount of support per award: $1,000 to $2,000.

NUMBER OF AWARDS: 3.

APPLICATION INFORMATION:
Application form available online.
Duration: One-time award.

PUBLICATIONS:
Program announcement.

ADDRESS INQUIRIES TO:
Kathy Borkowski, Editorial Director
(See address above.)

YIVO INSTITUTE FOR JEWISH RESEARCH   [647]
15 West 16th Street, 3rd Floor
New York, NY 10011-6301
(917) 606-8290
Fax: (212) 292-1892

E-MAIL ADDRESS:
jyoung@yivo.cjh.org

WEB SITE ADDRESS:
www.yivo.org

FOUNDED: 1925

AREAS OF INTEREST:
Yiddish, East European and American Jewish history and culture.

NAME(S) OF PROGRAMS:
● **Fellowship in American Jewish Studies**

TYPE:
Fellowships. Fellowship in American Jewish Studies is dedicated to doctoral or postdoctoral research in American Jewish history, with special consideration given to scholars working on some aspect of the Jewish labor movement. This Fellowship is for research at the YIVO Library and Archives.

YEAR PROGRAM STARTED: 1990

PURPOSE:
To further research of American Jewish history, based on resources from the YIVO Library and Archives.

LEGAL BASIS:
Tax-exempt 501(c)(3) organization.

ELIGIBILITY:
Applicants must be working in American Jewish history with special consideration toward the Jewish Labor Movement. The research must be conducted at YIVO in New York City.

FINANCIAL DATA:
Amount of support per award: Stipend of $5,500.
Total amount of support: $5,500.

NUMBER OF AWARDS: 1.

APPLICATION INFORMATION:
Application materials should be sent by regular mail, fax or e-mail to:
Chairperson, Fellowship Committee
YIVO Institute for Jewish Research.

Applicants should include the following materials:
(1) curriculum vitae, including all contact information and detailing education, publications, other scholarly activity (papers presented, etc.), teaching and other relevant work experience, knowledge of relevant languages, honors, awards and fellowships, etc.;
(2) research proposal of no more than four pages, including aims for research during the period of fellowship; whether the proposed work is part of a larger project, such as a dissertation, book, etc.; how the resources of YIVO will contribute to the work and;
(3) two letters of support, which discuss the importance of the applicant's work for the relevant field, as well as the applicant's ability to carry out the proposed work.

Applicants may apply for only one fellowship.
Deadline: January 15, 2015.

PUBLICATIONS:
YIVO-bleter; *Yedies fun YIVO.*

ADDRESS INQUIRIES TO:
Jennifer Young, Director of Education
Max Weinreich Center for Advanced Jewish Studies
(See address above.)

*PLEASE NOTE:
Each fellowship requires up to three months' research stay and at least one public lecture by the holder.

YIVO INSTITUTE FOR JEWISH RESEARCH   [648]
15 West 16th Street, 3rd Floor
New York, NY 10011-6301
(917) 606-8290
Fax: (212) 292-1892

E-MAIL ADDRESS:
jyoung@yivo.cjh.org

WEB SITE ADDRESS:
www.yivo.org

FOUNDED: 1925

AREAS OF INTEREST:
Yiddish, East European and American Jewish history and culture.

NAME(S) OF PROGRAMS:
● **Fellowship in East European Jewish Literature and Arts**

TYPE:
Fellowships. Fellowship in East European Jewish Literature and Arts is designed to assist an undergraduate, graduate or postgraduate researcher in Eastern European Jewish music, art and theater or Yiddish literature. The stipend is intended to defray expenses connected with research in YIVO's music, art and theater collections and library.

YEAR PROGRAM STARTED: 1994

PURPOSE:
To further research in Yiddish Studies, based on resources from the YIVO Library and Archives.

LEGAL BASIS:
Tax-exempt 501(c)(3) organization.

FINANCIAL DATA:
Amount of support per award: Stipend of $6,500.

NUMBER OF AWARDS: 1.

APPLICATION INFORMATION:
Application materials should be sent by regular mail, fax or e-mail to:
Chairperson, Fellowship Committee
YIVO Institute for Jewish Research.

Applicants should include the following materials:
(1) curriculum vitae, including all contact information and detailing education; publications; other scholarly activity (papers presented, etc.); teaching and other relevant work experience; knowledge of relevant languages; honors, awards and fellowships, etc.;

(2) research proposal of no more than four pages, including aims for research during the period of fellowship; whether the proposed work is part of a larger project, such as a dissertation, book, etc.; how the resources of YIVO will contribute to the work and; (3) two letters of support, which discuss the importance of the applicant's work for the relevant field, as well as the applicant's ability to carry out the proposed work.

Applicants may apply for one fellowship only.

Deadline: January 15.

PUBLICATIONS:
Yedies fun YIVO; *YIVO-bleter.*

BOARD OF DIRECTORS:
Ruth Levine, Chairman
Jonathan Mishkin, Chairman
Rosina Abramson
Jack Bendheim
Martin Flumenbaum
Fanya Gottesfeld Heller
Solomon Krystal
Dr. Chava Lapin
Leo Melamed
Jacob Morowitz
Bernard Nussbaum
Doris Payson
Martin Peretz
Irena Pletka
Dr. Arnold Richards
Bruce Slovin
Joseph S. Steinberg
Michael Trock

ADDRESS INQUIRIES TO:
Jennifer Young, Director of Education
Max Weinreich Center for
Advanced Jewish Studies
(See address above.)

*PLEASE NOTE:
Each fellowship requires up to three months' research stay and at least one public lecture by the holder.

YIVO INSTITUTE FOR JEWISH RESEARCH   [649]
15 West 16th Street
New York, NY 10011-6301
(212) 294-6139
Fax: (212) 292-1892

E-MAIL ADDRESS:
pglasser@yivo.cjh.org

WEB SITE ADDRESS:
www.yivo.org

FOUNDED: 1925

AREAS OF INTEREST:
Eastern European Jewish studies.

NAME(S) OF PROGRAMS:
• **Fellowship in Baltic Jewish Studies**
• **Fellowship in Polish Jewish Studies**

TYPE:
Fellowships. Fellowship in Baltic Jewish Studies supports original doctoral or postdoctoral research in the field of Lithuanian Jewish history at the YIVO Library and Archives or travel for Ph.D. dissertation research in archives and libraries of the Baltic states.

Fellowship in Polish Jewish Studies supports doctoral or postdoctoral research on Polish-Jewish history in the modern period, particularly Jewish-Polish relations, including the Holocaust period, and Jewish

contributions to Polish literature and culture. This Fellowship is for research at the YIVO Library and Archives.

PURPOSE:
To advance Eastern European Jewish studies.

FINANCIAL DATA:
Amount of support per award: Fellowship in Baltic Jewish Studies: $5,000. Fellowship in Polish Jewish Studies: $4,000.

APPLICATION INFORMATION:
Applications should include a curriculum vitae, a research proposal (four-page maximum), and two letters of support.
Duration: Varies.
Deadline: December 31.

ADDRESS INQUIRIES TO:
Dr. Paul Glasser
Chairman, Fellowship Committee
(See address above.)

*PLEASE NOTE:
Each fellowship requires up to three months' research stay and at least one public lecture by the holder.

*SPECIAL STIPULATIONS:
Applicants may apply for one fellowship only.

YIVO INSTITUTE FOR JEWISH RESEARCH   [650]
15 West 16th Street
New York, NY 10011-6301
(212) 294-6139
Fax: (212) 292-1892

E-MAIL ADDRESS:
pglasser@yivo.cjh.org

WEB SITE ADDRESS:
www.yivo.org

FOUNDED: 1925

AREAS OF INTEREST:
Eastern European Jewish studies.

NAME(S) OF PROGRAMS:
• **The Dina Abramowicz Emerging Scholar Fellowship**
• **Fellowship in East European Jewish Studies**
• **The Workmen's Circle/Dr. Emanuel Patt Visiting Professorship**

TYPE:
Fellowships; Visiting scholars. The Dina Abramowicz Emerging Scholar Fellowship is intended for postdoctoral research on a topic in Eastern European Jewish studies. The work should lead to a significant scholarly publication and may encompass the revision of a doctoral dissertation. The Fellowship carries a stipend for the holder to conduct research at the YIVO Library and Archives.

Fellowship in East European Jewish Studies supports original doctoral or postdoctoral research in the field of East European Jewish studies. This Fellowship is for research at the YIVO Library and Archives, as well as two public lectures by the holder.

The Workmen's Circle/Dr. Emanuel Patt Visiting Professorship in Eastern European Jewish Studies, established by the Van Cortlandt Workmen's Circle Community House, is designed to support postdoctoral research at the YIVO Library and Archives.

PURPOSE:
To advance Eastern European Jewish studies.

FINANCIAL DATA:
Amount of support per award: Abramowicz Fellowships: $3,000; Fellowship in East European Jewish Studies: $9,000; Workmen's Circle: $5,000.

APPLICATION INFORMATION:
Applications should include a cover letter indicating one choice of fellowship, a curriculum vitae, a research proposal (four-page maximum), and two letters of support.
Duration: Varies.
Deadline: December 31.

ADDRESS INQUIRIES TO:
Dr. Paul Glasser
Chairman, Fellowship Committee
(See address above.)

*PLEASE NOTE:
Each fellowship requires up to three months' research stay and at least one public lecture by the holder.

*SPECIAL STIPULATIONS:
Applicants may apply for one fellowship only.

Languages

THE AMERICAN CLASSICAL LEAGUE   [651]
Miami University
422 Wells Mill Drive
Oxford, OH 45056
(513) 529-7741
Fax: (513) 529-7742

E-MAIL ADDRESS:
info@aclclassics.org

WEB SITE ADDRESS:
www.aclclassics.org

FOUNDED: 1919

AREAS OF INTEREST:
Latin and Classical Studies of ancient Rome and Greece.

CONSULTING OR VOLUNTEER SERVICES:
Placement service for teachers of Latin.

NAME(S) OF PROGRAMS:
• **McKinlay Scholarship**

TYPE:
Grants-in-aid; Scholarships.

YEAR PROGRAM STARTED: 1975

PURPOSE:
To assist high school teachers of Latin to further their educational background.

LEGAL BASIS:
Nonprofit.

ELIGIBILITY:
Applicant must be a member of American Classical League for the preceding three years and current year and teaching high school Latin courses.

GEOGRAPHIC RESTRICTIONS:
United States.

FINANCIAL DATA:
Amount of support per award: Varies.
Total amount of support: Varies.

APPLICATION INFORMATION:
The application form and guidelines are available on the League web site.
Duration: One-time award.
Deadline: January 15. Award announcement March 15.

ADDRESS INQUIRIES TO:
Geri Dutra, Administrative Secretary
(See address above.)

AMERICAN INSTITUTE OF INDIAN STUDIES [652]

1130 East 59th Street
Chicago, IL 60637
(773) 702-8638
Fax: (773) 702-6636

E-MAIL ADDRESS:
aiis@uchicago.edu

WEB SITE ADDRESS:
www.indiastudies.org

FOUNDED: 1961

AREAS OF INTEREST:
Indian studies.

NAME(S) OF PROGRAMS:
● Advanced Language Program in India

TYPE:
Fellowships. Awards for graduate studies in India in an Indian language.

YEAR PROGRAM STARTED: 1969

PURPOSE:
To provide advanced language training in India.

LEGAL BASIS:
Cooperative, nonprofit organization of 47 American colleges and universities.

ELIGIBILITY:
Open to graduate students in U.S. colleges and universities who have had a minimum of two years or 240 class hours of classroom instruction in Bengali, Hindi or Tamil and intend to pursue teaching degrees. Applicants for other Indian languages may be considered, but they should contact the AIIS for further information and advice. Applicants must be U.S. citizens.

FINANCIAL DATA:
Grants will be awarded on a competitive basis and will include round-trip airfare to India and a maintenance allowance sufficient to cover living expenses. No funding will be provided for dependents.

APPLICATION INFORMATION:
Application forms are available from the address above. All applications must include a $25 processing fee.
Duration: Nine months.
Deadline: January 31.

OFFICERS:
Frederick Asher, President
Elise Auerbach, Administrator

ADDRESS INQUIRIES TO:
Fellowship Coordinator
(See address above.)

AMERICAN RESEARCH INSTITUTE IN TURKEY, INC.

c/o The University of Pennsylvania Museum
3260 South Street
Philadelphia, PA 19104-6324
(215) 898-3474
Fax: (215) 898-0657

E-MAIL ADDRESS:
leinwand@sas.upenn.edu

WEB SITE ADDRESS:
ccat.sas.upenn.edu/ARIT

TYPE:
Fellowships. Bogazici University Summer Language Program: For summer study in Turkey. Also offer travel, stipend and tuition grants. This intensive program offers the equivalent of one full academic year of study in advanced Turkish language at the college level.

See entry 882 for full listing.

AXE-HOUGHTON FOUNDATION [653]

c/o Foundation Source
55 Walls Drive, 3rd Floor
Fairfield, CT 06824
(800) 839-1754
Fax: (800) 421-6579

WEB SITE ADDRESS:
www.foundationcenter.org/grantmaker/axehoughton

FOUNDED: 1965

AREAS OF INTEREST:
Improvement of English speech and its uses in the areas of public affairs, education, theatre, poetry and debate. A portion of available funds may be devoted to speech remediation.

TYPE:
Project/program grants.

YEAR PROGRAM STARTED: 1965

PURPOSE:
To foster and encourage an appreciation of the English language, with emphasis on the spoken language.

LEGAL BASIS:
Tax-exempt eleemosynary foundation.

ELIGIBILITY:
Applicant institutions must have tax-exempt status. No grants to individuals or for operating budgets, general purposes, continuing support, annual campaigns, emergency funds, deficit financing, capital funds, endowment funds, loans, matching gifts, scholarships, fellowships or publications.

Grants are rarely made to organizations outside of the New York City metropolitan area.

GEOGRAPHIC RESTRICTIONS:
Primarily New York City.

FINANCIAL DATA:
Amount of support per award: $2,000 to $6,000; Average: $4,000.

APPLICATION INFORMATION:
Applications are only accepted by organizations who have been invited to apply.
Duration: One year. Renewals generally of no more than three years.
Deadline: Submit invited proposals between June 1 and September 1. Award announcements are made in late December.

PUBLICATIONS:
Program policy statement; application guidelines.

OFFICERS AND TRUSTEES:
Lynn Angelson, President
Robert B. von Mehren, Vice President
Bruce D. Haims, Treasurer
Suzanne Schwartz Davidson, Secretary

ADDRESS INQUIRIES TO:
John Johnson
(See address above.)

*PLEASE NOTE:
Communications by mail only.

INSTITUTE OF INTERNATIONAL EDUCATION [654]

U.S. Student Programs
809 United Nations Plaza
New York, NY 10017-3580
(212) 984-5525

WEB SITE ADDRESS:
www.us.fulbrightonline.org

FOUNDED: 1919

AREAS OF INTEREST:
Educational, art and cultural exchange programs.

NAME(S) OF PROGRAMS:
● Padagogischer Austauschdienst Teaching Assistantships

TYPE:
Assistantships. The Fulbright U.S. Student Program provides an opportunity for young teachers and university students of German to serve as English language teaching assistants in secondary schools in Germany.

YEAR PROGRAM STARTED: 1951

PURPOSE:
To provide English teaching assistantships to foreign language students.

LEGAL BASIS:
Private, not-for-profit agency.

ELIGIBILITY:
Open to students who possess a Bachelor's degree from a U.S. university.

FINANCIAL DATA:
Assistants receive a 10-month maintenance allowance and international travel.

NUMBER OF APPLICANTS MOST RECENT YEAR:
300.

NUMBER OF AWARDS: Approximately 140 for the year 2015-16.

APPLICATION INFORMATION:
Applications and additional information may be obtained from the address above.
Duration: Tenable for one academic year.
Deadline: Mid-October.

ADDRESS INQUIRIES TO:
Walter Jackson, Manager
(See address above.)

THE JAPAN FOUNDATION

152 West 57th Street
17th Floor
New York, NY 10019
(212) 489-0299
Fax: (212) 489-0409

E-MAIL ADDRESS:
info@jfny.org

WEB SITE ADDRESS:
www.jfny.org

TYPE:
Conferences/seminars; Development grants; Fellowships; Grants-in-aid; Product donations; Professorships; Project/program grants; Research grants; Training grants; Travel grants.

See entry 852 for full listing.

KOBE COLLEGE CORPORATION-JAPAN EDUCATION EXCHANGE

540 West Frontage Road, Suite 3335
Northfield, IL 60093
(847) 386-7661
Fax: (847) 386-7662

E-MAIL ADDRESS:
kccjee@comcast.net

WEB SITE ADDRESS:
www.kccjee.org

TYPE:
Awards/prizes. The KCC-JEE High School Essay Contest includes a one-month trip to Japan. It incorporates intensive language study, college credit and a home stay with a Japanese family.

See entry 924 for full listing.

LUSO-AMERICAN EDUCATION FOUNDATION   [655]

7080 Dolon Way
Suite 200
Dublin, CA 94568
(925) 828-3883
Fax: (925) 828-4554

E-MAIL ADDRESS:
education@luso-american.org

WEB SITE ADDRESS:
www.luso-american.org

FOUNDED: 1963

AREAS OF INTEREST:
Perpetuation of the Portuguese language and culture in the U.S.

NAME(S) OF PROGRAMS:
• **Luso-American Education**

TYPE:
Scholarships.

LEGAL BASIS:
Tax-exempt corporation.

ELIGIBILITY:
Applicants must be under 21 years of age and a graduate of an accredited high school by the summer of the year of the award with a grade point average of at least 3.0 on a 4.0 scale. Must also be one of the following:
(1) of Portuguese descent;
(2) enrolled in Portuguese classes in a four-year college or university or;
(3) a member of an organization whose scholarships are administered by the Luso-American Education Foundation.

GEOGRAPHIC RESTRICTIONS:
California, Connecticut, Idaho, Massachusetts, Nevada, New Jersey, Pennsylvania and Rhode Island.

FINANCIAL DATA:
Amount of support per award: $300 to $4,000.

NUMBER OF APPLICANTS MOST RECENT YEAR:
112.

APPLICATION INFORMATION:
Application form required. SAT scores should be forwarded to the Foundation along with application form, transcript and letters of recommendation.
Duration: Nonrenewable.
Deadline: Must be postmarked by February 15. Announcement prior to June 1.

PUBLICATIONS:
Program announcement.

ADDRESS INQUIRIES TO:
Bela Ferreira-Goncalves
Administrative Director
(See address above.)

LUSO-AMERICAN EDUCATION FOUNDATION   [656]

7080 Donlon Way, Suite 200
Dublin, CA 94568
(925) 828-3883
Fax: (925) 828-3883

E-MAIL ADDRESS:
education@luso-american.org

WEB SITE ADDRESS:
www.luso-american.org

FOUNDED: 1963

AREAS OF INTEREST:
Perpetuation of the Portuguese language and culture in the U.S., Portuguese education and the teaching of Portuguese in California schools and universities.

CONSULTING OR VOLUNTEER SERVICES:
Provides advisory and reference services, assists teachers and school districts in setting up Portuguese language and literature courses, choosing texts, etc., makes referrals to other sources of information, permits on-site use of collection and holds annual Conference on Portuguese-American Education for educators, administrators and community persons. Services are free and available to California residents only.

NAME(S) OF PROGRAMS:
• **Educational Grant Program**

TYPE:
Grants-in-aid; Scholarships. Educational grants in three categories:
(1) Financial Aid - A limited number of grants for the development of Portuguese curriculum and materials for schools;
(2) Grant to participate in the summer program at universities and colleges in California and;
(3) Grant to participate in the summer program at a Portuguese university.

YEAR PROGRAM STARTED: 1970

PURPOSE:
To foster, sponsor and perpetuate in the U.S. as part of its culture the ethnicity and national culture of Portugal brought to America by Portuguese emigrants; to help students and teachers become qualified to teach and promote the Portuguese language and culture at all levels of education.

LEGAL BASIS:
Tax-exempt corporation.

ELIGIBILITY:
For all programs, candidates must be residents of California.

For category 1, all projects will be judged on how relevant they are to the goals and objectives of the Luso-American Education Foundation and the Portuguese Heritage in California.

For category 2, candidates for the grant to participate in the summer program at universities and colleges in California must demonstrate a desire to study the Portuguese language and culture, be of Portuguese descent or be working in a school setting with Portuguese children and be enrolled in an accredited California university or college and will qualify only if these courses are not offered at their school.

For category 3, candidates for the grant to participate in the summer program at a Portuguese university must be a teacher of Portuguese in grades K-12 in an accredited California school, hold a B.A. or higher degree with emphasis in the Portuguese language, culture and literature, have been admitted to a teaching credential program at an accredited California university or college and must demonstrate a desire to teach the Portuguese language and culture, have been admitted to an advanced degree program at an accredited California university or college in which the study of Portuguese is an integral part, direct or indirect, of the program and must demonstrate a desire to teach the Portuguese language and/or culture.

GEOGRAPHIC RESTRICTIONS:
California.

FINANCIAL DATA:
Amount of support per award: Grants vary in amount, depending on the applicant's need and Foundation funds allocated.
Total amount of support: Varies.

APPLICATION INFORMATION:
Call and request application form.
Deadline: Applications are accepted during January and February only. For completed application, postmark by February 15.

PUBLICATIONS:
The Luso-American, annual; *Portuguese Presence in California; Literatura de Expressao Portuguesa Nos Estados Unidos;* bibliographies; annual report.

ADDRESS INQUIRIES TO:
Anthony Pio
Administrative Director
(See address above.)

MODERN LANGUAGE ASSOCIATION OF AMERICA   [657]

26 Broadway, 3rd Floor
New York, NY 10004-1789
(646) 576-5141
Fax: (646) 458-0030

E-MAIL ADDRESS:
awards@mla.org

WEB SITE ADDRESS:
www.mla.org

FOUNDED: 1883

AREAS OF INTEREST:
Literary studies, languages and education.

NAME(S) OF PROGRAMS:
• **Katherine Singer Kovacs Prize**
• **Fenia and Yaakov Leviant Memorial Prize in Yiddish Studies**
• **James Russell Lowell Prize**
• **Howard R. Marraro Prize**
• **MLA Prize for a Distinguished Bibliography**
• **MLA Prize for a First Book**
• **MLA Prize in United States Latina and Latino and Chicana and Chicano Literary and Cultural Studies**
• **Lois Roth Award for a Translation of a Literary Work**
• **Aldo and Jeanne Scaglione Prize for a Translation of a Literary Work**
• **Aldo and Jeanne Scaglione Prize for a Translation of a Scholarly Study of Literature**
• **Aldo and Jeanne Scaglione Prize for Comparative Literary Studies**

- **Aldo and Jeanne Scaglione Prize for French and Francophone Studies**
- **Aldo and Jeanne Scaglione Prize for Italian Studies**
- **Aldo and Jeanne Scaglione Prize for Slavic Studies**
- **Aldo and Jeanne Scaglione Prize for Studies in Germanic Languages and Literatures**
- **Aldo and Jeanne Scaglione Publication Award for a Manuscript in Italian Literary Studies**
- **William Sanders Scarborough Prize**

TYPE:
Awards/prizes. To recognize outstanding scholarly works in the fields of English, French, Italian, Germanic languages and Slavic languages, Yiddish literature and culture, Black American literature and culture, Latino/Latina and Chicana/Chicano literature and culture. Germanic languages include Danish, Dutch, German, Icelandic, Norwegian, Swedish and Yiddish.

MLA Prize in United States Latina and Latino and Chicana and Chicano Literary and Cultural Studies is offered biennially. All others are awarded annually.

PURPOSE:
To recognize outstanding scholarly work.

LEGAL BASIS:
Membership association.

ELIGIBILITY:
For all awards, works of literary history, literary criticism, philology or literary theory are eligible. Except for translation prizes, books that are primarily translations are ineligible. For French, Germanic, Italian, Lowell, First Book and Marraro Prizes, books must be written by a current member of the Association.

FINANCIAL DATA:
Amount of support per award: Varies.

APPLICATION INFORMATION:
To enter books into competition for prizes, no special form or procedure is needed. Four to six copies of each work are required, depending upon the prize. Shipments of books should be preceded or accompanied by letters identifying the works and where necessary, confirming the author's membership in the MLA.
Duration: One-time awards.
Deadline: James Russell Lowell Prize: March 1. Prize for a First Book, Scaglione Prize for a Translation of a Literary Work and Lois Roth Award: April 1. Scaglione Publication Award for a Manuscript in Italian Literary Studies: August 1. All other awards: May 1.

ADDRESS INQUIRIES TO:
Annie Reiser, Coordinator of Book Prizes
(See address above.)

MODERN LANGUAGE ASSOCIATION OF AMERICA   [658]

26 Broadway, 3rd Floor
New York, NY 10004-1789
(646) 576-5141
Fax: (646) 458-0030

E-MAIL ADDRESS:
awards@mla.org

WEB SITE ADDRESS:
www.mla.org

FOUNDED: 1883

AREAS OF INTEREST:
Literary studies, languages and education.

NAME(S) OF PROGRAMS:
- **Morton N. Cohen Award**
- **Kenneth W. Mildenberger Prize**
- **Modern Language Association Prize for a Scholarly Edition**
- **Modern Language Association Prize for Independent Scholars**
- **Mina P. Shaughnessy Prize**

TYPE:
Awards/prizes.

PURPOSE:
To recognize outstanding scholarly work.

LEGAL BASIS:
Membership association.

ELIGIBILITY:
Authors are not required to be members of the Association.

The Morton N. Cohen Award is presented biennially in odd-numbered years for important collections of letters published in either of the two preceding years. A multivolume edition is eligible if at least one volume was published during that period. Editors can apply regardless of the fields they and the authors of the letters represent. The winning collection will be one that provides a clear, accurate and readable text, necessary background information, and succinct and eloquent introductory material and annotations. The collection should be in itself a work of literature.

The Kenneth W. Mildenberger Prize is presented biennially in odd-numbered years for an outstanding publication in the field of teaching foreign languages and literatures.

The Modern Language Association Prize for a Scholarly Edition will be given biennially in odd-numbered years to a book published in either of the two preceding years without regard to the field or language either of the editor or of the text presented in the edition. To qualify for the award, an edition should be based on an examination of all available relevant textual sources; the source texts and the edited text's deviations from them should be fully described; the edition should employ editorial principles appropriate to the materials edited, and those principles should be clearly articulated in the volume; the text should be accompanied by appropriate textual and other historical contextual information; the edition should exhibit the highest standards of accuracy in the presentation of its text and apparatus; and the text and apparatus should be presented as accessibly and elegantly as possible.

The Modern Language Association Prize for Independent Scholars is awarded biennially in even-numbered years for a distinguished scholarly book published in the field of English or another modern language or literature. Authors enrolled in a program leading to an academic degree and authors holding a tenured, tenure-accruing or tenure-track position in a postsecondary institution at the time of publication of the book are not eligible. Tenure is understood to include any comparable provision for job security in a postsecondary educational institution.

The Mina P. Shaughnessy Prize is presented biennially in even-numbered years for an outstanding research publication in the field of teaching English language, literature, rhetoric and composition.

FINANCIAL DATA:
Amount of support per award: Varies.
Total amount of support: Varies.

APPLICATION INFORMATION:
Application form is required for submissions to the Prize for Independent Scholars. To enter book into competition for other prizes, no special form or procedure is needed. Shipments of books should be preceded or accompanied by letters identifying the works.
Duration: One-time award.
Deadline: May 1.

ADDRESS INQUIRIES TO:
Annie Reiser, Coordinator of Book Prizes
(See address above.)

NATIONAL SCIENCE FOUNDATION   [659]

Linguistics Program
Division of Behavioral and Cognitive Sciences
4201 Wilson Boulevard, Suite 995
Arlington, VA 22230
(703) 292-8046
Fax: (703) 292-9068

E-MAIL ADDRESS:
jmaling@nsf.gov

WEB SITE ADDRESS:
www.nsf.gov

FOUNDED: 1950

NAME(S) OF PROGRAMS:
- **Doctoral Dissertation Research Improvement Grants (DDRIG)**
- **Documenting Endangered Languages (DEL)**
- **Linguistics Program**

TYPE:
Research grants. Conferences/workshops. Awards provide support for research into the syntactic, morphological, semantic, phonological and phonetic properties of individual languages and of language in general. Research into the acquisition of language, the psychological processes in the production and perception of language, the biological foundations of language, the social influences on and effects of language and dialect variation, and the formal and mathematical properties of language models are also supported.

YEAR PROGRAM STARTED: 1975

PURPOSE:
To support scientific research and education to strengthen research potential in language sciences.

LEGAL BASIS:
National Science Foundation Act of 1950.

ELIGIBILITY:
Applicants may be U.S. colleges and universities on behalf of their staff members, nonprofit, nonacademic research institutions, such as independent museums, observatories, research laboratories, stock centers and similar organizations, private profit organizations and, under special circumstances, unaffiliated U.S. scientists.

FINANCIAL DATA:
Support may cover salaries, research assistantships, staff benefits if a direct cost, permanent equipment, travel, publication costs, computer costs and certain other direct and indirect costs.
Amount of support per award: Averages $335,000 over three-year grant period.

Total amount of support: Approximately $6,000,000 for fiscal year 2013; $3,100,000 for DEL.

COOPERATIVE FUNDING PROGRAMS: DEL in partnership with the National Endowment for the Humanities.

NUMBER OF APPLICANTS MOST RECENT YEAR: Approximately 223 for the year 2012; 80 for DEL.

NUMBER OF AWARDS: Approximately 50 (23 dissertation improvements, 27 standard) plus 10 conference workshops for fiscal year 2012.

APPLICATION INFORMATION:
A proposal should include information about the institution, principal investigator and business administrator, title and description of proposed research, desired effective date of grant, duration of support, facilities, personnel, biographical sketches, current support and pending applications and budget.
Duration: Research grants may be for periods of up to five years. Most grants are for three years, except dissertation awards which are typically for two years.
Deadline: Linguistics Program: Target dates are July 15 for Fall review and January 15 for Spring review. Proposals received too late for one round of review will be reviewed in the following round with a corresponding delay in the availability of funding. Documenting Endangered Languages Program: September 15 annually.

PUBLICATIONS:
NSF grant proposal guide.

STAFF:
Joan Maling, Program Director

ADDRESS INQUIRIES TO:
Joan Maling, Program Director
(See address above.)

PEN AMERICAN CENTER   [660]
588 Broadway, Suite 303
New York, NY 10012-5246
(212) 334-1660
Fax: (212) 334-2181

E-MAIL ADDRESS:
awards@pen.org

WEB SITE ADDRESS:
www.pen.org

FOUNDED: 1922

AREAS OF INTEREST:
Intellectual cooperation among men and women of letters in all countries in the interests of literature, the exchange of ideas, freedom of expression and goodwill.

NAME(S) OF PROGRAMS:
● **PEN Translation Prize**

TYPE:
Awards/prizes. Translation prize awarded for a distinguished translation into English from any language published in the U.S. in 2014.

YEAR PROGRAM STARTED: 1962

PURPOSE:
To promote the art of translation; to pay tribute to the profession.

LEGAL BASIS:
Nonprofit organization affiliated with International PEN.

ELIGIBILITY:
Although all eligible books must have been published in the U.S. in 2014, translators

may be of any nationality; U.S. residency or citizenship is not required. There are no restrictions on the subject matter of translated works, although eligible titles should be of a literary character; technical, scientific, or bibliographical translations will not be considered.

FINANCIAL DATA:
Amount of support per award: $3,000.
Total amount of support: $3,000 annually.

NUMBER OF APPLICANTS MOST RECENT YEAR: 100.

NUMBER OF AWARDS: 1 each year.

REPRESENTATIVE AWARDS:
Tiina Nunnally, translator of *Kristin Lavransdottir,* by Sigrid Undset.

APPLICATION INFORMATION:
Online application form can be found on the Center web site. One copy of a book-length literary translation published during the calendar year under consideration may be submitted by publishers, agents, or the translators themselves. Self-published books are not eligible. Early submissions are strongly recommended.
Duration: One year.
Deadline: Fall 2014.

BOARD OF TRUSTEES:
Peter Godwin, President

ADDRESS INQUIRIES TO:
PEN Literary Awards
(See address above.)

THE PHI BETA KAPPA SOCIETY
1606 New Hampshire Avenue, N.W.
Washington, DC 20009
(202) 745-3287
Fax: (202) 986-1601

E-MAIL ADDRESS:
awards@pbk.org

WEB SITE ADDRESS:
www.pbk.org

TYPE:
Fellowships. Fellowship for at least six months of study in France. One award given annually.

See entry 935 for full listing.

SOUTH ATLANTIC MODERN LANGUAGE ASSOCIATION   [661]
Georgia State University
Department of English, GCB 923
38 Peachtree Center Avenue
Atlanta, GA 30303
(404) 413-5816
Fax: (404) 413-5830

E-MAIL ADDRESS:
samla@gsu.edu

WEB SITE ADDRESS:
samla.memberclicks.net

FOUNDED: 1928

AREAS OF INTEREST:
All humanities.

NAME(S) OF PROGRAMS:
● **Graduate Student Essay Prize**
● **Harper Fund Award**
● **SAMLA Studies Award**
● **SAR Prize**

TYPE:
Assistantships; Awards/prizes;
Conferences/seminars; Internships;

Professorships; Travel grants. SAMLA Studies Award is for the best scholarly book written by a SAMLA member. Presses and individual members may nominate their recent publications in the year prior to the year of the convention.

YEAR PROGRAM STARTED: 1934

PURPOSE:
To encourage and honor distinguished scholarship in the modern languages and literatures.

LEGAL BASIS:
Nonprofit organization.

ELIGIBILITY:
Open to SAMLA members.

GEOGRAPHIC RESTRICTIONS:
Alabama, District of Columbia, Florida, Georgia, Kentucky, Maryland, North Carolina, South Carolina, Tennessee, Virginia, and West Virginia.

FINANCIAL DATA:
Amount of support per award: Graduate Student Essay Prize: $250; Harper Fund Award: Up to $500; SAMLA Studies Award: $1,000; SAR Prize: $500.
Total amount of support: Varies.

NUMBER OF APPLICANTS MOST RECENT YEAR: SAMLA Studies Award: 8; SAR Prizes: 25.

NUMBER OF AWARDS: SAMLA Studies Award, SAR Prizes and Graduate Student Essay Prize: 4. Harper Fund Award: Varies.

APPLICATION INFORMATION:
SAMLA Studies Award: Applicants must be SAMLA members who have had a scholarly book published in the preceding year. No bibliographies or editions. Must be written in English. Presses and individuals may nominate their recent publications.
Duration: One-time award. Nonrenewable.
Deadline: May 1.

PUBLICATIONS:
South Atlantic Review, quarterly journal; *SAMLA News,* newsletter.

IRS IDENTIFICATION NUMBER: 62-0800246

OFFICERS:
Kathleen Blake Yancey, President
Lynn Ramey, First Vice President
H.R. Stoneback, Second Vice President

EXECUTIVE COMMITTEE:
Tony Grooms
Stuart Noel
Michael Rice
Giovanna Summerfield
Freddy L. Thomas
Katherine Weiss

ADDRESS INQUIRIES TO:
Diana Eidson
Editorial and Production Manager
(See address above.)

U.S. DEPARTMENT OF EDUCATION   [662]
International and Foreign Language Education (IFLE)
1990 K Street, N.W., Suite 6000
Washington, DC 20006-8521
(202) 502-7631
(202) 502-7700
Fax: (202) 502-7860

E-MAIL ADDRESS:
OPE_NRC-FLAS@ed.gov

WEB SITE ADDRESS:
www.ed.gov/programs/iegpsflasf/index.html

AREAS OF INTEREST:
Foreign language and area studies.

NAME(S) OF PROGRAMS:
- **Foreign Language and Area Studies Fellowships**

TYPE:
Fellowships. The Foreign Language and Area Studies program provides allocations of academic year and summer fellowships to institutions of higher education or consortia of institutions of higher education to assist meritorious undergraduate students and graduate students undergoing training in modern foreign languages and related international studies.

YEAR PROGRAM STARTED: 1959

LEGAL BASIS:
Section 602, Title VI of the Higher Education Act of 1965, as amended.

ELIGIBILITY:
FLAS grants are awarded to institutions for a four-year project period. Institutions conduct competitions to select eligible undergraduate and graduate students to receive fellowships.

Funds may be used overseas with prior approval from IFLE.

GEOGRAPHIC RESTRICTIONS:
United States.

FINANCIAL DATA:
Each fellowship includes an institutional payment and a subsistence allowance.
Amount of support per award: The estimated institutional payment for 2014-15 academic year fellowship is $18,000 for a graduate student and $10,000 for an undergraduate student. The estimated institutional payment for summer 2015 fellowship is $5,000 for graduate and undergraduate students.

The estimated subsistence allowance for academic year 2014-15 fellowship is $15,000 for a graduate student and $5,000 for an undergraduate student. The subsistence allowance for summer 2015 fellowship is $2,500 for graduate and undergraduate students.

APPLICATION INFORMATION:
An electronic application form is available at the web site.
Duration: Varies.
Deadline: March.

ADDRESS INQUIRIES TO:
Cheryl E. Gibbs, Senior Program Officer (See address above.)

U.S. DEPARTMENT OF EDUCATION [663]
International and Foreign Language Education (IFLE)
Advanced Training & Research Group
Room 6084, 6th Floor
1990 K Street, N.W.
Washington, DC 20006-8521
(202) 502-7589
(202) 502-7700 (main office)
Fax: (202) 502-7860

E-MAIL ADDRESS:
ddra@ed.gov

WEB SITE ADDRESS:
www.ed.gov/programs/iegpsddrap/index.html

AREAS OF INTEREST:
Foreign languages.

NAME(S) OF PROGRAMS:
- **Fulbright-Hays Doctoral Dissertation Research Abroad**

TYPE:
Fellowships. Fellowships to support doctoral dissertation research abroad in modern foreign languages and related area studies. For the purpose of these programs, area studies is defined as a program of comprehensive study of the aspects of a society or societies, including the study of their geography, history, culture, economy, politics, international relations and languages. The program is designed to develop research knowledge and capability in world areas not widely included in American curricula. Awards will not be available for projects focusing on Western Europe.

YEAR PROGRAM STARTED: 1964

PURPOSE:
To enable graduate students who plan to teach in the U.S. to undertake doctoral dissertation research in the field of modern foreign languages and area studies; to assist with the development of language and area studies specialists.

LEGAL BASIS:
The Mutual Educational and Cultural Exchange Act of 1961, Public Law 87-256, as amended (commonly known as the Fulbright-Hays Act), Section 102(b)(6).

ELIGIBILITY:
A student is eligible to receive a fellowship if he or she:
(1) is a citizen or national of the U.S. or is a permanent resident of the U.S.;
(2) is a graduate student in good standing at an institution of higher education who, when the fellowship begins, is admitted to candidacy in a doctoral program in modern foreign languages and area studies at that institution;
(3) is planning a teaching career in the U.S. upon graduation and;
(4) possesses adequate skills in the language(s) necessary to carry out the dissertation project.

FINANCIAL DATA:
Travel expenses, including excess baggage to and from the residence of the fellow to the host country of research. Maintenance allowance based on the cost of living in country(ies) of research for the fellow and his or her dependent(s). Project allowance for research-related expenses such as books, affiliation fees, local travel and other incidental expenses. Health and accident insurance premiums. $100 administrative fee to applicant institution.
Amount of support per award: $39,000 average for the year 2012.
Total amount of support: $3,239,776 for the year 2012.

NUMBER OF APPLICANTS MOST RECENT YEAR: 380.

NUMBER OF AWARDS: 84.

REPRESENTATIVE AWARDS:
$19,303 for "Testing AIDS Treatment Efficacy by a Northern Thai Community;" $28,565 for "Rethinking Community Through Suburban Nepal;" $22,364 for "Culture, Nationalism and Ethnicity in Twentieth Century Lesotho."

APPLICATION INFORMATION:
Official application materials are available from college and university graduate schools

concerned with the fellowship program. Prospective applicants must apply electronically through their institutions. The completed materials are then forwarded electronically by the institution to the U.S. Education Department's Application Control Center (ACC) in accordance with instructions published in the *Federal Register*.
Duration: Fellowships provide support for a minimum period of six months and a maximum period of 12 months.

U.S. DEPARTMENT OF EDUCATION
International and Foreign Language Education
1990 K Street, N.W., 6th Floor
Washington, DC 20006-8521
(202) 502-7709
(202) 502-7700
Fax: (202) 502-7860

E-MAIL ADDRESS:
loveen.bains@ed.gov

WEB SITE ADDRESS:
www2.ed.gov/programs/iegpsgpa/index.html

TYPE:
Exchange programs; Project/program grants; Seed money grants; Training grants; Travel grants. Also, study grants and grants for foreign language and area study programs of educational development for projects to be undertaken abroad. Grants are awarded to higher education institutions, nonprofit educational organizations, state department of education and consortium of such institutions, departments, organizations and institutions which, in turn, enable professors, college and elementary and secondary school teachers and advanced students to attend seminars abroad and to travel and study in foreign countries in order to strengthen the institution's programs in foreign languages, area studies and world affairs.

See entry 943 for full listing.

U.S. DEPARTMENT OF EDUCATION
Office of Postsecondary Education
International and Foreign Language Education
1990 K Street, N.W., 6th Floor
Washington, DC 20006-8521
(202) 502-7589
(202) 502-7700
Fax: (202) 502-7859

E-MAIL ADDRESS:
stephanie.mckissic@ed.gov

WEB SITE ADDRESS:
www2.ed.gov/programs/iegpsfra/index.html

TYPE:
Fellowships; Research grants. This program funds fellowships through institutions of higher education (IHEs) to faculty members who propose to conduct research abroad in modern foreign languages and area studies to improve their skill in language and their knowledge of the culture of the people of these countries.

See entry 944 for full listing.

U.S. DEPARTMENT OF EDUCATION

International and Foreign Language
Education Office
1990 K Street, N.W., Sixth Floor
Washington, DC 20006-8521
(202) 502-7626
Fax: (202) 502-7860

E-MAIL ADDRESS:
tanyelle.richardson@ed.gov

WEB SITE ADDRESS:
www.ed.gov/ope/iegps

TYPE:
Project/program grants; Seed money grants.
Grants to plan, develop, and carry out a
program to strengthen and improve
undergraduate instruction in international
studies and foreign languages. Projects
primarily focus on curriculum and faculty
development. Institutions of higher education
and public and private nonprofit agencies and
organizations may apply for funds to develop
projects which have the potential for making
an especially significant contribution to the
improvement of undergraduate instruction in
international and foreign language studies in
the U.S.

See entry 1644 for full listing.

U.S. DEPARTMENT OF EDUCATION　[664]

International and Foreign Language Education
(IFLE)
1990 K Street, N.W., Suite 6000
Washington, DC 20006-8521
(202) 502-7631
(202) 502-7700
Fax: (202) 502-7860

WEB SITE ADDRESS:
www.ed.gov/ope/iegps

AREAS OF INTEREST:
Foreign language and area studies.

NAME(S) OF PROGRAMS:
● **National Resource Centers (NRC)
Program**

TYPE:
Project/program grants; Training grants. The
NRC Program provides grants to institutions
of higher education and consortia of
institutions to establish, strengthen and
operate comprehensive and undergraduate
centers that will be national resources for:
(1) teaching of any modern foreign language;
(2) instruction in fields needed to provide full
understanding of areas, regions or countries
in which the modern foreign language is
commonly used;
(3) research and training in international
studies and the international and foreign
language aspects of professional and other
fields of study and;
(4) instruction and research on issues in
world affairs that concern one or more
countries.

LEGAL BASIS:
Authorized under Section 602, Title VI of the
Higher Education Act, as amended.

ADDRESS INQUIRIES TO:
Cheryl E. Gibbs, Senior Program Officer
(See address above.)

*PLEASE NOTE:
The NRC Program competes every four
years. This is not a matching or cost-share
grant program.

YIVO INSTITUTE FOR JEWISH RESEARCH

15 West 16th Street, 3rd Floor
New York, NY 10011-6301
(917) 606-8290
Fax: (212) 292-1892

E-MAIL ADDRESS:
jyoung@yivo.cjh.org

WEB SITE ADDRESS:
www.yivo.org

TYPE:
Fellowships. Fellowship in East European
Jewish Literature and Arts is designed to
assist an undergraduate, graduate or
postgraduate researcher in Eastern European
Jewish music, art and theater or Yiddish
literature. The stipend is intended to defray
expenses connected with research in YIVO's
music, art and theater collections and library.

See entry 648 for full listing.

Literature

THE AMERICAN-SCANDINAVIAN FOUNDATION　[665]

58 Park Avenue
New York, NY 10016
(212) 879-9779
(212) 847-9728
Fax: (212) 249-3444

E-MAIL ADDRESS:
grants@amscan.org

WEB SITE ADDRESS:
www.amscan.org

FOUNDED: 1910

AREAS OF INTEREST:
Translations of poetry, fiction or drama by
Danish, Finnish, Icelandic, Norwegian or
Swedish authors born after 1800.

NAME(S) OF PROGRAMS:
● **American-Scandinavian Foundation
Translation Prize**

TYPE:
Awards/prizes. Prize for translation of fiction
(50 double-spaced manuscript pages) or
poetry (25 double-spaced manuscript pages).

YEAR PROGRAM STARTED: 1980

PURPOSE:
To encourage English translation of
contemporary Scandinavian literature.

LEGAL BASIS:
Nonprofit educational institution qualifying
under statutes 501(c)(3), 509(a)(1) and
170(c)(2) of the IRS code.

ELIGIBILITY:
Entry must be work by one author, though
not necessarily from a single work. It should
be conceived as part of a book manuscript. A
table of contents for the proposed book
should also be included.

FINANCIAL DATA:
Amount of support per award: First prize:
$2,500; Second Prize: $2,000.
Total amount of support: $4,500.

NUMBER OF APPLICANTS MOST RECENT YEAR:
20.

NUMBER OF AWARDS: 2.

APPLICATION INFORMATION:
Request rules for Translation Prize
Competition. Applicants should submit one
copy of work in original language and four
copies of translation, including title page and
table of contents. Name, address and phone
number of translator and title and author of
the manuscript with the original language
specified should be on a separate page.
Translator must include written permission
from author or author's agent for translation
to be entered in competition and published in
Scandinavian Review. Manuscripts
accompanied by self-addressed, stamped
envelope will be returned.

Duration: One-time award.

Deadline: June 1. Awards announced by
November 1.

PUBLICATIONS:
Competition rules.

OFFICER:
Edward P. Gallagher, President

ADDRESS INQUIRIES TO:
Translation Prize Committee
(See address above.)

AMERICAN SOCIETY OF COMPOSERS, AUTHORS AND PUBLISHERS (ASCAP)　[666]

1900 Broadway, 7th Floor
New York, NY 10023
(212) 621-6318
Fax: (212) 595-3342

E-MAIL ADDRESS:
jsteinblatt@ascap.com

WEB SITE ADDRESS:
www.ascap.com

FOUNDED: 1914

AREAS OF INTEREST:
Music, creative and performing arts.

NAME(S) OF PROGRAMS:
● **ASCAP Deems Taylor Awards**

TYPE:
Awards/prizes. The ASCAP Deems Taylor
Awards program recognizes books, articles,
broadcasts and web sites on the subject of
music selected for their excellence.

YEAR PROGRAM STARTED: 1967

PURPOSE:
To encourage, recognize and reward
excellence in a field that is vital to the health
and growth of America's musical heritage.

LEGAL BASIS:
Membership association.

ELIGIBILITY:
Any written works published anywhere in the
U.S. (the 50 states and Puerto Rico) in
English during the calendar year preceding
the award will be eligible. The subject matter
may be biographical or critical, reportorial or
historical - almost any form of nonfiction
prose about music and/or its creators - not an
instructional textbook, how-to guide, or a
work of fiction.

Paperbacks that were originally published in
hardcover are not eligible. Reprints or
translations of works that were previously
published outside of the U.S. and are now
being published in the U.S. for the first time
are eligible. Program notes, recording liner
notes, and online publications are also
eligible.

GEOGRAPHIC RESTRICTIONS:
United States.

FINANCIAL DATA:
Amount of support per award: Several categories of cash prizes, from $200 to $500. Plaques are also presented to the authors and journalists as well as to their respective publishers.

Total amount of support: Varies.

NUMBER OF AWARDS: 12.

APPLICATION INFORMATION:
Application may be made online. All submissions must include a cover letter containing the following information:
(1) title of the book, article, program or liner notes;
(2) copyright date of book or date of publication for the article (or issue date for recording liner notes);
(3) name, street address, e-mail address and daytime phone number of all authors of the book or article and;
(4) contact name, address and daytime phone number of the publisher or publication in which the article appeared.

Four copies of each entry are required. Submissions will not be returned. For articles and liner notes, submissions are limited to three entries per author. Those articles that were published as a series of articles on a single, specific topic may be considered as one entry. When submitting one or more articles, be sure that a copy of every article is put into each of four letter-sized file folders. Label each folder with one's full name only. (This is for the competition judges who will review the entries.) Liner notes should be limited to 4,500 words and include four copies of each recording.

Submissions should be addressed to ASCAP Deems Taylor Awards; American Society of Composers, Authors and Publishers at the address listed above.

Duration: Annual award.

Deadline: May 31.

DIRECTORS:
Paul Williams, Chairman and President
Irwin Z. Robinson, Publisher Vice Chairman
Jimmy Webb, Writer Vice Chairman
James M. Kendrick, Treasurer
Martin Bandier
Richard Bellis
Marilyn Bergman
Caroline Bienstock
Bruce Broughton
Desmond Child
Alf Clausen
Barry Coburn
Dan Foliart
Wayland Holyfield
Zach Horowitz
Laurent Hubert
Dean Kay
Leeds Levy
Mary Megan Peer
Matt Pincus
Alex Shapiro
Valerie Simpson
Cameron Strang
Doug Wood

ADDRESS INQUIRIES TO:
Jim Steinblatt
ASCAP-Deems Taylor Awards
(See address above.)

THE ASSOCIATION OF WRITERS & WRITING PROGRAMS [667]
Mail Stop 1E3, 4400 University Drive
George Mason University
Fairfax, VA 22030
(703) 993-4301
Fax: (703) 993-4302

E-MAIL ADDRESS:
supriya@awpwriter.org

WEB SITE ADDRESS:
www.awpwriter.org

FOUNDED: 1967

AREAS OF INTEREST:
Creative writing; four genres: short fiction, poetry, creative nonfiction and the novel.

CONSULTING OR VOLUNTEER SERVICES:
The office provides information on curricula for courses or programs in creative writing and members of the Board of Directors occasionally visit campuses in order to consult with departments wishing to establish or improve creative writing programs. The office also sponsors the INTRO Journals Project, an annual competition of fiction, nonfiction and poetry by students of creative writing; runs job placement service for members interested in obtaining teaching and writing-oriented positions.

NAME(S) OF PROGRAMS:
- **AWP Award Series in Creative Nonfiction**
- **AWP Award Series in the Novel**
- **Donald Hall Prize in Poetry**
- **Grace Paley Prize in Short Fiction**

TYPE:
Awards/prizes. Annual open competitions for book-length manuscripts: a collection of short stories, a collection of poems, or a work of creative nonfiction of more than 60,000 words. The award in each case is the publication of the winning manuscript by a university press and a cash honorarium from AWP in addition to royalties from the publisher.

YEAR PROGRAM STARTED: 1974

PURPOSE:
To support American writers and creative writing programs in U.S. colleges and universities; to encourage the publication and distribution of good fiction, poetry and other creative writing; to improve the quality of literary education primarily at the college level, as well as at the public school level; to disseminate information useful to writers and students of writing.

LEGAL BASIS:
Nonprofit, tax-exempt corporation.

ELIGIBILITY:
Original works written in English are eligible.

Only book-length manuscripts are eligible (poetry: 48 pages minimum; short story collection and creative nonfiction: 150 to 300 manuscript pages; novel: at least 60,000 words).

The AWP Award Series is open to all authors writing original works in English. No mixed-genre manuscripts can be accepted. Criticism and scholarly monographs are not acceptable for creative nonfiction, which the Award Series defines as factual and literary writing that has the narrative, dramatic, meditative and lyrical elements of novels, plays, poetry, and memoirs.

To avoid conflict of interest and to avoid the appearance of a conflict of interest, former students of a judge (former students who studied with a judge in an academic degree-conferring program or its equivalent) are ineligible to enter the competition in the genre for which their former teacher is serving as judge.

FINANCIAL DATA:
Negotiations regarding book royalties are left to the author and publisher, but AWP has established minimum standards.

Amount of support per award: AWP Prize for Creative Fiction and AWP Prize for the Novel: $2,500 each; Donald Hall Prize in Poetry and Grace Paley Prize in Short Fiction: $5,500 each.

Total amount of support: $14,000.

COOPERATIVE FUNDING PROGRAMS: Donald Hall Prize in Poetry and Grace Paley Prize for Short Fiction are made possible by the generous support of amazon.com.

NUMBER OF APPLICANTS MOST RECENT YEAR:
Nonfiction: 129; Novel: 251; Poetry: 794; Short Fiction: 335.

NUMBER OF AWARDS: 1 winner per genre; 2 finalists per genre.

APPLICATION INFORMATION:
For the Award Series, submissions are only accepted via Submittable (online submissions manager).

Manuscripts must be uploaded between January 1 and February 28. If the author's name appears anywhere except the cover page, the manuscript will be disqualified. Do not attach acknowledgement of previous publications or a biographical note. No manuscripts will be returned. There is a $30 entry/reading fee for nonmembers, $20 for AWP members. Please read guidelines on Association's web site before uploading one's manuscript through Submittable.

Deadline: Manuscripts are accepted only with postmark between January 1 and February 28.

PUBLICATIONS:
Guidelines; *The Writer's Chronicle*, six times per year.

IRS IDENTIFICATION NUMBER: 05-0314999

EXECUTIVE DIRECTOR:
D.W. Fenza

ADDRESS INQUIRIES TO:
Supriya Bhatnagar
Director of Publications
(See address above.)

BREAD LOAF WRITERS' CONFERENCE [668]
Middlebury College
204 College Street
Middlebury, VT 05753
(802) 443-5286
Fax: (802) 443-2087

E-MAIL ADDRESS:
blwc@middlebury.edu

WEB SITE ADDRESS:
www.middlebury.edu/blwc

FOUNDED: 1926

AREAS OF INTEREST:
Poetry, fiction and nonfiction.

NAME(S) OF PROGRAMS:
- **Fellowship and Scholarship Program for Writers**

TYPE:
Fellowships; Scholarships; Work-study programs. Fellowships and scholarships pay all or part of conference fees.

YEAR PROGRAM STARTED: 1926

PURPOSE:
To encourage writers at the beginning of their careers.

LEGAL BASIS:
Nonprofit.

ELIGIBILITY:
Fellowship candidates must have had one or two original books published. Privately printed books are not considered.

Candidates for tuition scholarships must have had their work published in recognized literary periodicals, but will not have published in book form.

Working scholarships as waiters and waitresses are available for people who have not had their work published but who show promise as writers.

People under 18 are not eligible.

FINANCIAL DATA:
Fellowships pay all conference fees, tuition, room and board. Tuition scholarships pay full tuition but not room and board. Working scholarships pay part of tuition and room and board; recipients earn the remainder.
Amount of support per award: Varies.
Total amount of support: Varies.

NUMBER OF APPLICANTS MOST RECENT YEAR: 1,400.

NUMBER OF AWARDS: 60.

APPLICATION INFORMATION:
Information is available online.
Duration: Usually one-time award.
Deadline: March 1. Announcement in May.

DIRECTORS:
Michael Collier, Director
Jennifer Grotz, Assistant Director

ADDRESS INQUIRIES TO:
Megan Fitzgerald, Administrative Associate (See address above.)

THE WITTER BYNNER FOUNDATION FOR POETRY, INC.   [669]
P.O. Box 10169
Santa Fe, NM 87504-0169
(505) 988-3251
Fax: (505) 986-8222

E-MAIL ADDRESS:
witterb123@gmail.com

WEB SITE ADDRESS:
bynnerfoundation.org

FOUNDED: 1972

AREAS OF INTEREST:
Poetry, with special interest in developing the poetry audience, the process of poetry translation, uses of poetry (including but not limited to dramatic, educational, therapeutic, etc.) and the support of individual poets through existing institutional programs.

TYPE:
Project/program grants; Residencies; Scholarships.

YEAR PROGRAM STARTED: 1972

PURPOSE:
To develop the poetic art through grant support to nonprofit organizations and individuals represented by such organizations.

LEGAL BASIS:
Exempt, private foundation.

ELIGIBILITY:
Only applications from nonprofit tax-exempt organizations will be accepted. No grants to individuals. Publication projects, endowment funds, capital improvements, continued support and operating expenses are not generally funded.

GEOGRAPHIC RESTRICTIONS:
United States.

FINANCIAL DATA:
Amount of support per award: $1,000 to $10,000.
Total amount of support: $67,600 for the year 2012-13.

NUMBER OF APPLICANTS MOST RECENT YEAR: 127 letters of intent for the year 2014.

NUMBER OF AWARDS: 12 grant programs for the year 2013-14.

REPRESENTATIVE AWARDS:
Library of Congress/Fellowships in Poetry; Santa Fe Art Institute/Translator Residencies; Santa Fe Girls School/Poetry Workshops; Santa Fe Arts Commission/Poetry Works; Academy of Technology and Classics Charter School; Teatro Paraguas; New Mexico Culture Net; Santa Fe Playhouse; Forest Woods Media Productions.

APPLICATION INFORMATION:
Upon request, the Foundation's guidelines, an annual report, and a list of the most recent grants will be provided. Applicants must submit a letter of intent prior to application.
Duration: One-year grants only. May be renewed at the discretion of the Board of Directors.
Deadline: February 15 annually. Announcement in May. Letters of intent accepted from August 1 to December 31 annually.

PUBLICATIONS:
Annual report; application guidelines.

IRS IDENTIFICATION NUMBER: 23-7169999

BOARD OF DIRECTORS:
Dr. Douglas Schwartz, Chairman
Robert Kurth, Vice President
Fletcher Catron, Secretary/Treasurer
Dr. Mark McDaniel

ADMINISTRATIVE STAFF:
Steven D. Schwartz, Executive Director
Nanci Caldwell, Business Manager

ADDRESS INQUIRIES TO:
Steven D. Schwartz, Executive Director (See address above.)

*SPECIAL STIPULATIONS:
The Foundation is interested particularly in using its limited funds as a means to help attract additional monies from other sources to advance the art of poetry. Applications to support the development of seed-money proposals in each of the above areas, therefore, are especially encouraged. While the Foundation has traditionally been supportive of the four areas listed above, it may consider the support of other creative and innovative projects in poetry.

CANADA COUNCIL FOR THE ARTS   [670]
350 Albert Street
Ottawa ON K1P 5V8 Canada
(613) 566-4414 ext. 5060
(800) 263-5588 ext. 5060 (CAN only)
Fax: (613) 566-4390
TTY: (613) 565-5194 (hearing-impaired)

E-MAIL ADDRESS:
info@canadacouncil.ca

WEB SITE ADDRESS:
www.canadacouncil.ca/writing

FOUNDED: 1957

AREAS OF INTEREST:
The arts in Canada (dance, media arts, music, theatre, creative writing and publishing, inter-arts and visual arts).

NAME(S) OF PROGRAMS:
● **Writing and Publishing Section Grants**

TYPE:
Development grants; General operating grants; Grants-in-aid; Project/program grants; Residencies; Travel grants. Council grants support the following types of activities:
(1) Grants for Individual Professional Writers: These grants can help one create new work or travel to events important to one's career.
(2) Operating Funding: These grants offer operating support to book and periodical publishers and nonprofit arts service organizations.
(3) Project Funding: Project grants are available to nonprofit arts organizations, magazine and book publishers, artists' collectives or groups to cover some of the costs of specific, time-limited activities.

PURPOSE:
To provide support for the creation, translation, publication and promotion of Canadian literature.

LEGAL BASIS:
Independent agency established by the Parliament of Canada in 1957.

ELIGIBILITY:
Council grants cannot be used to start a business or to buy capital items, such as computers, musical instruments, film and video equipment, or printing presses.

GEOGRAPHIC RESTRICTIONS:
Canada.

FINANCIAL DATA:
Amount of support per award: Varies depending on project.
Total amount of support: Varies.

APPLICATION INFORMATION:
The Council does not send or accept applications by fax or e-mail.
Deadline: Varies.

PUBLICATIONS:
Program information sheets.

ADDRESS INQUIRIES TO:
Christian Mondor, Information Officer (See address above.)

CARNEGIE FUND FOR AUTHORS   [671]
P.O. Box 409
Lenox Hill Post Office
New York, NY 10021

FOUNDED: 1942

AREAS OF INTEREST:
Literary interests.

TYPE:
Grants-in-aid.

YEAR PROGRAM STARTED: 1942

PURPOSE:
To award grants to authors in need in order to tide over an author whose need has come about because of illness or other emergency.

ELIGIBILITY:
Applicants must be authors who have had at least one book of reasonable length published by a mainstream publisher. Applicants cannot use any publication they paid to have published.

Grants are made to individuals who must be U.S. citizens or residents.

GEOGRAPHIC RESTRICTIONS:
Applicants must live in the United States.

FINANCIAL DATA:
Amount of support per award: No fixed sum; based on need.

APPLICATION INFORMATION:
Applicants request application form, fill it out, and provide whatever supporting documentation may be needed, and send form with supporting data. Trustees vote on grant and, if any, how much should be awarded.
Duration: Lump-sum grant. Must reapply.
Deadline: Grants are voted on and given all year-round. There is no annual meeting.

IRS IDENTIFICATION NUMBER: 13-6084244

CHILDREN'S LITERATURE ASSOCIATION   [672]
1301 West 22nd Street
Suite 202
Oak Brook, IL 60523
(630) 571-4520
Fax: (708) 876-5598

E-MAIL ADDRESS:
info@childlitassn.org

WEB SITE ADDRESS:
www.childlitassn.org

FOUNDED: 1973

AREAS OF INTEREST:
All aspects of children's literature scholarship, research and criticism.

NAME(S) OF PROGRAMS:
● **ChLA Diversity Research Grant**

TYPE:
Project/program grants; Research grants. ChLA Diversity Research Grant is a grant to support research related to children's and young adult cultural artifacts (including media, culture and texts) about populations that have been traditionally underrepresented or marginalized culturally and/or historically. Applications for this grant are to be considered annually and will be awarded as warranted.

YEAR PROGRAM STARTED: 2013

PURPOSE:
To promote scholarship and criticism in children's literature.

LEGAL BASIS:
International; tax-exempt 501(c)(3), nonprofit scholarly organization.

ELIGIBILITY:
Applications will be evaluated based upon the quality of the proposal and the potential of the project to enhance or advance Children's Literature studies. Funds may be used for - but are not restricted to - research-related expenses such as travel to special collections, subvention funds, or purchasing materials and supplies. The awards may not be used for obtaining advanced degrees, for researching or writing a thesis or dissertation, for textbook writing or for pedagogical projects. Winners must be members of the Children's Literature Association before they receive any funds. Winners must acknowledge ChLA in any publication or other presentation resulting from the grant.

The following general guidelines apply:
(1) members of the ChLA Diversity Committee are not eligible to apply; recipients of a Diversity Research Grant are not eligible to reapply until the third year . from the date of the first award; (in the event the ChLA Board institutes another time interval - whether longer or shorter - the vote of the Board shall supersede the three-year interval rule;) and;
(2) in a given year, if there are no proposals for the Diversity Research Grant that the Diversity and/or Grants Committee deems of sufficient quality to support ChLA's aims, no grants will be given; conversely, if there are multiple Diversity Research Grant proposals of high quality, it is possible that multiple grants will be made, in which case the award may be less than the proposed budget.

FINANCIAL DATA:
Amount of support per award: $500 to $1,000, depending upon the winning proposal's projected budgetary considerations.

APPLICATION INFORMATION:
Proposals should take the form of a single Word document and include the following information:
(1) cover page including name, telephone number, mailing address and e-mail address, as well as academic institution and status/rank (student, professor, librarian, etc.) or institution applicant is affiliated with (library, publisher, etc.), if any;
(2) a detailed description of the research proposal (not to exceed three single-spaced pages), indicating the nature and significance of the project, where it will be carried out, rough budget and the expected date of completion and;
(3) a vitae that includes a bibliography of major publications and scholarly achievements (degrees, honors, etc.). E-mail the completed proposal as an attachment to: ChLA Association Manager at the e-mail address above. Subject line should read: "ChLA Diversity Research Grant Application." A confirmation e-mail will be sent to acknowledge receipt of proposal.

The following general guidelines apply:
(1) e-mail the proposal as an attachment dated within the application period (January 1 - February 1 annually); incomplete or late applications will not be considered; applications and supporting materials should be written in, or translated into, English; if applicant is applying for both a Diversity Research Grant and a general ChLA Research Grant, applicant must state this in the application;
(2) The ChLA Diversity Committee will screen all proposals and select the

awardee(s);
(3) The ChLA Diversity Committee is encouraged to communicate openly with the Grants Committee since some submissions could be appropriate for both submission processes and;
(4) winners are urged to attend the annual conference if at all possible to receive the award.
Deadline: Only applications that are complete and received as of midnight on February 1 will be considered. Winners will be notified in April, and the awards will be announced at the ChLA annual conference.

IRS IDENTIFICATION NUMBER: 38-2005828

ADDRESS INQUIRIES TO:
ChLA Grants Committee
(See address above.)

*SPECIAL STIPULATIONS:
Grant recipients are required to submit a progress report of the project to the chair of the Diversity Committee by April/May of the year following the award and a summary report of the completed project to the chair of the Diversity Committee by April/May of the second year, prior to the presentation of the ideas at the conference.

Each grant will be awarded with the expectation that the undertaking will lead to publication and make a significant contribution to the field of children's literature scholarship or criticism. Within two years of receiving the grant, the recipient will be asked to submit a paper proposal based upon the project for presentation at a ChLA annual conference.

CHILDREN'S LITERATURE ASSOCIATION   [673]
1301 West 22nd Street
Suite 202
Oak Brook, IL 60523
(630) 571-4520
Fax: (708) 876-5598

E-MAIL ADDRESS:
info@childlitassn.org

WEB SITE ADDRESS:
www.childlitassn.org

FOUNDED: 1973

AREAS OF INTEREST:
All aspects of children's literature scholarship, research and criticism.

NAME(S) OF PROGRAMS:
● **ChLA Beiter Graduate Student Research Grants**
● **ChLA Faculty Research Grants**

TYPE:
Conferences/seminars; Grants-in-aid; Project/program grants; Research grants. ChLA Beiter Graduate Student Research Grants are awarded for proposals of original scholarship with the expectation that the undertaking will lead to publication or a conference presentation and contribute to the field of children's literature criticism.

ChLA Faculty Research Grants are awarded for proposals dealing with criticism or original scholarship with the expectation that the undertaking will lead to publication and make a significant contribution to the field of children's literature in the area of scholarship or criticism. Proposals that deal with critical or original work in the areas of fantasy or science fiction for children or adolescents will be awarded the Margaret P. Esmonde Memorial Scholarship.

YEAR PROGRAM STARTED: 1978

PURPOSE:
To promote scholarship and criticism in children's literature.

LEGAL BASIS:
International; tax-exempt 501(c)(3), nonprofit scholarly organization.

ELIGIBILITY:
ChLA Beiter Research Grants for Graduate Students: Grant funds are not intended as income to assist in the completion of a graduate degree, but as support for research that may be related to the dissertation or Master's thesis. The grant may be used to purchase supplies and materials (e.g., books, videos, equipment), as research support (photocopying, etc.), or to underwrite travel to special collections or libraries. Winners must either be members of the Children's Literature Association or join the Association before they receive any funds. Students of ChLA Executive Board members or Scholarship Committee members are not eligible to apply.

ChLA Faculty Research Grants: Applications will be evaluated based upon the quality of the proposal and the potential of the project to enhance or advance children's literature studies. Funds may be used for (but are not restricted to) research-related expenses such as travel to special collections or purchasing materials and supplies. The awards may not be used for obtaining advanced degrees, for researching or writing a thesis or dissertation, for textbook writing, or for pedagogical projects. Winners must either be members of the Children's Literature Association or join the Association before they receive any funds. Members of the Executive Board of ChLA and of the Scholarship Committee are not eligible to apply.

FINANCIAL DATA:
ChLA Faculty Research Grants may be used for such expenses as transportation, living expenses or materials and supplies, but not for obtaining advanced degrees.
Amount of support per award: $500 to $1,500.
Total amount of support: Up to $10,000 annually for both grants.

NUMBER OF APPLICANTS MOST RECENT YEAR:
Faculty: 21; Graduate student: 10 for the year 2011.

NUMBER OF AWARDS: Varies.

APPLICATION INFORMATION:
E-mail proposals as an attachment dated within the application period of January 1 to February 1. Incomplete or late applications will not be considered. Subject line should read: ChLA Faculty Research Grant Application or ChLA Beiter Graduate Research Grant Application. Applications should include name, mailing address, phone, e-mail address, academic institution, academic status or institution applicant is affiliated with (library, publisher, etc.), a detailed description of the research proposal, a vita that includes a bibliography of major publications and scholarly achievements (for Beiter Grants, just a curriculum vitae), and two letters of reference (for Beiter Grant applicants only). One letter must be from applicant's dissertation or thesis advisor. For more information, write to the address listed above.
For a printed copy of guidelines, please send a self-addressed, stamped envelope.

Duration: Varies. Usually a one-time award to run the length of the project or course of study.
Deadline: February 1. Announcement at the annual conference.

PUBLICATIONS:
Application guidelines.

IRS IDENTIFICATION NUMBER: 38-2005828

ADDRESS INQUIRIES TO:
ChLA Grants Committee
(See address above.)

*SPECIAL STIPULATIONS:
Winners should acknowledge ChLA in any publication resulting from the award.

GREAT LAKES COLLEGES ASSOCIATION NEW WRITERS AWARDS   [674]
535 West William Street
Suite 301
Ann Arbor, MI 48103
(734) 661-2350
Fax: (734) 661-2349

E-MAIL ADDRESS:
wegner@glca.org

WEB SITE ADDRESS:
www.glca.org

FOUNDED: 1962

AREAS OF INTEREST:
Education.

NAME(S) OF PROGRAMS:
● **New Writers Awards**

TYPE:
Awards/prizes. Winners invited to tour up to 13 Great Lakes Colleges. Honorarium and expenses included. Awards are made for yearly, first published best book of fiction, best book of poetry and best book of creative nonfiction. Judges of the awards are faculty members of literature and creative writing at member colleges.

YEAR PROGRAM STARTED: 1970

PURPOSE:
To promote new writers, literature and colleges.

LEGAL BASIS:
Association of independent, liberal arts colleges in Michigan, Indiana, Ohio and Pennsylvania.

ELIGIBILITY:
The book must be the first published volume in fiction, poetry, or creative nonfiction by the author. Only publishers may submit, on behalf of the author, one book in each category, four copies.

Entries submitted must be written in English and published in the U.S. or Canada.

GEOGRAPHIC RESTRICTIONS:
United States and Canada.

FINANCIAL DATA:
Amount of support per award: At least $500 per college visited.

NUMBER OF APPLICANTS MOST RECENT YEAR:
117.

NUMBER OF AWARDS: 1 each for creative nonfiction, fiction and poetry.

APPLICATION INFORMATION:
Applicants should send for rules and enclose self-addressed, stamped envelope or visit the GLCA web site to download submission packet.

Deadline: July 25.

ADDRESS INQUIRIES TO:
New Writers Awards
(See address above.)

IRISH AMERICAN CULTURAL INSTITUTE   [675]
P.O. Box 1716
Morristown, NJ 07962
(973) 605-1991

E-MAIL ADDRESS:
info@iaci-usa.org

WEB SITE ADDRESS:
www.iaci-usa.org

FOUNDED: 1962

AREAS OF INTEREST:
Promotion of better understanding of Ireland through publications and educational programs such as the Institute's IRISH WAY Program for high school students and its Irish Perceptions Series which brings Irish lecturers and performers to the U.S. to tour.

NAME(S) OF PROGRAMS:
● **IACI Visiting Fellowship in Irish Studies at NUI-G**

TYPE:
Awards/prizes; Exchange programs; Fellowships. Grants and awards available for authors of books written in Irish, for Irish artists and composers.

YEAR PROGRAM STARTED: 1966

PURPOSE:
To stimulate, develop and disseminate information pertinent to the Irish culture.

LEGAL BASIS:
Public foundation under IRS code 501(c)(3).

ELIGIBILITY:
Fellowship is open to scholars of all disciplines relating to Irish studies. Art awards to residents of Ireland only.

FINANCIAL DATA:
Lecturers receive expenses, honoraria and services in arranging tours.
Amount of support per award: Fellowship: $4,000.

NUMBER OF APPLICANTS MOST RECENT YEAR:
40.

NUMBER OF AWARDS: 1 fellowship.

REPRESENTATIVE AWARDS:
$5,000 to painter Basil Blackshaw; $5,000 to author Michael Davitt; $5,000 to poet Patrick Galvin.

APPLICATION INFORMATION:
Projects are generally initiated by the Institute with pertinent announcements distributed when necessary. However, brief descriptive statements of appropriate proposed projects are welcomed. Such requests should outline the objectives to be accomplished, the proposed means of accomplishment and the type and amount of assistance desired.
Duration: One-time awards.
Deadline: December 31.

PUBLICATIONS:
Eire-Ireland, magazine.

OFFICERS:
Peter Halas, Chairman
Brian Stack, Vice Chairman
Barbara Lyons, Treasurer
Edward F. Ginty, Secretary

ITALIAN AMERICAN STUDIES ASSOCIATION

P.O. Box 487
Millbrae, CA 94030
(408) 738-4564
Fax: (408) 864-5629

E-MAIL ADDRESS:
quinnroseanne@deanza.edu

WEB SITE ADDRESS:
www.italianamericanstudies.net

TYPE:
Fellowships.

See entry 601 for full listing.

JEWISH BOOK COUNCIL   [676]

520 Eighth Avenue, 4th Floor
New York, NY 10018-4393
(212) 201-2920
Fax: (212) 532-4952

E-MAIL ADDRESS:
jbc@jewishbooks.org

WEB SITE ADDRESS:
www.jewishbookcouncil.org

FOUNDED: 1943

AREAS OF INTEREST:
Jewish literature.

NAME(S) OF PROGRAMS:
- **National Jewish Book Award-American Jewish Studies**
- **National Jewish Book Award-Anthologies and Collections**
- **National Jewish Book Award-Biography, Autobiography and Memoir**
- **National Jewish Book Award-Children's and Young Adult Literature**
- **National Jewish Book Award-Contemporary Jewish Life**
- **National Jewish Book Award-Education and Jewish Identity**
- **National Jewish Book Award-Fiction**
- **National Jewish Book Award-History**
- **National Jewish Book Award-Holocaust**
- **National Jewish Book Award-Illustrated Children's Book**
- **National Jewish Book Award-Modern Jewish Thought and Experience**
- **National Jewish Book Award-Outstanding Debut Fiction**
- **National Jewish Book Award-Poetry**
- **National Jewish Book Award-Scholarship**
- **National Jewish Book Award-Sephardic Culture**
- **National Jewish Book Award-Visual Arts**
- **National Jewish Book Award-Women's Studies**
- **National Jewish Book Award-Writing Based on Archival Materials**

TYPE:
Awards/prizes. National Jewish Book Awards:
(1) Award to the author of a nonfiction book about the Jewish experience in North America;
(2) Award to the author of a book of essays, biographies, short stories, or other collected works by more than one author;
(3) Award to the author of a biography, autobiography, personal memoir or family history. The subject need not be a Jewish person or family, but must have significant relevance to the Jewish experience;
(4) Award to the author of a book on a Jewish theme for ages 7-16;
(5) Award to the author of a nonfiction book about current tools and resources of Jewish living within the greater Ashkenazic and Sephardic communities. These include, but are not limited to, cookbooks, holiday how-to books and life-cycle books;
(6) Award to the author of a nonfiction work that focuses on theory, history and/or practice of Jewish education. Textbooks are not eligible;
(7) Award to the author of a novel or short-story collection with Jewish content;
(8) Award to the author of a nonfiction work about the Jewish historical experience. Books focusing primarily on the Holocaust do not belong in this category;
(9) Award to the author of a nonfiction book concerning the Holocaust including autobiographies, memoirs and academic studies;
(10) Award to the author of a picture or illustrated book with Jewish theme for children from infancy to age 10. The award is shared by the author and illustrator;
(11) Award to the author of a nonfiction work addressing Sephardic and/or Ashkenazic Jewish thought and experience;
(12) Award to the author of a debut novel or short-story collection with Jewish content;
(13) Award to the author of a book of verse consisting primarily of poems of Jewish concern;
(14) Award to the author of a nonfiction selection that makes an original contribution to Jewish learning. This includes, but is not limited to, works on Bible, Rabbinics and Jewish Law;
(15) Award to the author of a book that explores the traditions and practices unique to Sephardic Jews;
(16) Award to the author of a work of one or more visual artists (painters, weavers, sculptors, photographers, etc.) which includes illustrations and images of Jewish content as a dominant component and;
(17) Award to the author of a nonfiction book about women's role in the Jewish experience.

YEAR PROGRAM STARTED: 1949

PURPOSE:
To promote greater awareness of works of Jewish literature and scholarship.

LEGAL BASIS:
Not-for-profit organization.

ELIGIBILITY:
Books published during the current calendar year will be eligible, except anthologies of previously published material or collections of writings by various authors or reprints and revised editions, unless otherwise specified. No manuscripts are accepted.

Books must be published in the English language unless otherwise specified. This includes books translated into English from any other language.

FINANCIAL DATA:
Amount of support per award: Varies.
Total amount of support: Varies.

NUMBER OF APPLICANTS MOST RECENT YEAR: 400.

NUMBER OF AWARDS: 18 to 20 each year.

APPLICATION INFORMATION:
Guidelines and submission forms are available online in June.
Duration: One year.
Deadline: Submissions accepted early summer to late September.

PUBLICATIONS:
Application guidelines.

EXECUTIVE DIRECTOR:
Carolyn Starman Hessel

ADDRESS INQUIRIES TO:
Carolyn Starman Hessel
Executive Director
(See address above.)

JEWISH BOOK COUNCIL   [677]

520 Eighth Avenue, 4th Floor
New York, NY 10018
(212) 201-2920
Fax: (212) 532-4952

E-MAIL ADDRESS:
carolynhessel@jewishbooks.org

WEB SITE ADDRESS:
www.jewishbookcouncil.org

AREAS OF INTEREST:
Jewish literature.

NAME(S) OF PROGRAMS:
- **Sami Rohr Prize for Jewish Literature**

TYPE:
Awards/prizes. In celebration of Sami Rohr's 80th birthday, his children and grandchildren instituted the Sami Rohr Prize for Jewish Literature to honor his lifelong love of Jewish writing. The annual award recognizes the unique role of contemporary writers in the transmission and examination of Jewish values, and is intended to encourage and promote outstanding writing of Jewish interest.

In conjunction with this award, the Rohr family has established the Sami Rohr Jewish Literary Institute, a forum devoted to the continuity of Jewish Literature. The Prize and Institute are coordinated and administered under the exclusive auspices of the Jewish Book Council. Winners will be selected by an independent panel of judges.

YEAR PROGRAM STARTED: 2006

PURPOSE:
To reward an emerging writer of Jewish literature whose work has demonstrated a fresh vision and evidence of future potential.

ELIGIBILITY:
Recipients must have written a book of exceptional literary merit that stimulates an interest in themes of Jewish concern. Fiction and nonfiction books will be considered in alternate years. Books published during the current calendar year and previous publishing year are eligible. Books must be published in the English language unless otherwise specified. This includes books translated into English from any other language.

FINANCIAL DATA:
Amount of support per award: $100,000.

NUMBER OF AWARDS: 1.

APPLICATION INFORMATION:
An author may not submit directly to the Prize, but may submit their title for review in the Jewish Book Council publication *Jewish Book World* or in National Jewish Book Awards so that the Rohr committee can be made aware of their title.

STAFF:
Carolyn Starman Hessel, Director

ADDRESS INQUIRIES TO:
Carolyn Starman Hessel, Director
Sami Rohr Prize for Jewish Literature
(See address above.)

ROBERT F. KENNEDY CENTER FOR JUSTICE AND HUMAN RIGHTS [678]

1300 19th Street, N.W.
Suite 750
Washington, DC 20036
(202) 463-7575
Fax: (202) 463-6606

E-MAIL ADDRESS:
info@rfkcenter.org

WEB SITE ADDRESS:
www.rfkcenter.org

FOUNDED: 1968

NAME(S) OF PROGRAMS:
- Robert F. Kennedy Book Award
- Robert F. Kennedy Journalism Award

TYPE:
Awards/prizes. Annual prize for the book which most faithfully and forcefully reflects Robert Kennedy's purposes, namely, his concern for the poor and the powerless, his struggle for honest and even-handed justice, his convictions that a decent society must assure all young people a fair chance and his faith that a free democracy can act to remedy disparities of power and opportunity.

YEAR PROGRAM STARTED: 1980

PURPOSE:
To carry forward the mission of Robert F. Kennedy.

LEGAL BASIS:
Tax-exempt public charity.

ELIGIBILITY:
Fiction and nonfiction books published in the U.S. in the previous calendar year are eligible.

FINANCIAL DATA:
Amount of support per award: Grand prize: $2,500.
Total amount of support: Varies.

NUMBER OF APPLICANTS MOST RECENT YEAR: 75.

NUMBER OF AWARDS: Varies.

APPLICATION INFORMATION:
Entries may be made by either individual authors or publishers. There is a handling fee of $75 per entry. Books must be submitted in quadruplicate with an entry form clipped inside the front cover of each book.
Duration: One-time award.
Deadline: Varies.

PUBLICATIONS:
Rules for entry.

ADDRESS INQUIRIES TO:
Christina Taylor, Coordinator
(See address above.)

KNIGHTS OF COLUMBUS VATICAN FILM LIBRARY AT ST. LOUIS UNIVERSITY [679]

Pius XII Memorial Library
St. Louis University
3650 Lindell Boulevard
St. Louis, MO 63108-3302
(314) 977-3090
Fax: (314) 977-3108

E-MAIL ADDRESS:
vfl@slu.edu

WEB SITE ADDRESS:
libraries.slu.
edu/special_collections/vfl_fellowships

AREAS OF INTEREST:
Classical languages and literature, palaeography, scriptural and patristic studies, history, philosophy and sciences in the Middle Ages and the Renaissance, early Romance literature, history of music, manuscript illumination, mathematics and technology, theology, liturgy, Roman and canon law or political theory.

NAME(S) OF PROGRAMS:
- Vatican Film Library Mellon Fellowship

TYPE:
Travel grants.

YEAR PROGRAM STARTED: 1976

PURPOSE:
To assist scholars wishing to conduct research in the manuscript collections in the Vatican Film Library at St. Louis University.

ELIGIBILITY:
Applicants must be at the postdoctoral level or be a graduate student formally admitted to Ph.D. candidacy and working on their dissertation.

FINANCIAL DATA:
Fellowship provides the cost of air travel within the continental U.S.
Amount of support per award: $2,250 per month living allowance.
Total amount of support: Varies.

NUMBER OF AWARDS: Varies.

APPLICATION INFORMATION:
Applicants must write a brief project description and notify of the manuscripts to be consulted (for availability), including dates of proposed study, a curriculum vitae, as well as a select bibliography on titles related to project. Proposals should not exceed more than two to three pages. Doctoral applicants must include a letter of recommendation from their advisor.
Duration: Two to eight weeks. Nonrenewable.
Deadline: March 1 for June to August. June 1 for September to December. October 1 for January to May.

STAFF:
Gregory A. Pass, Assistant University Librarian for Special Collections

ADDRESS INQUIRIES TO:
See e-mail address above.

STEPHEN LEACOCK ASSOCIATION [680]

R.R. 2
4223 Line 12 North
Coldwater ON L0K 1E0 Canada
(705) 835-3218
Fax: (705) 835-5171

E-MAIL ADDRESS:
judith.rapson@gmail.com

WEB SITE ADDRESS:
www.leacock.ca

FOUNDED: 1946

AREAS OF INTEREST:
Writing of humour by Canadians.

NAME(S) OF PROGRAMS:
- Stephen Leacock Memorial Medal for Humour

TYPE:
Awards/prizes. Stephen Leacock Memorial Medal for Humour is presented for a book of humour published in the current calendar year and written by a Canadian. A cash prize from the TD Bank Financial Group accompanies this award.

YEAR PROGRAM STARTED: 1947

PURPOSE:
To promote the writing of Canadian humour.

LEGAL BASIS:
Nonprofit charitable organization.

ELIGIBILITY:
Author must be a Canadian citizen or landed immigrant. Books to be published in year current to year award given. Content to be humour. No e-books are eligible.

FINANCIAL DATA:
Amount of support per award: Awardee receives a sterling silver medal plus a $15,000 (CAN) cash prize; four finalists receive $1,500 (CAN) each.

COOPERATIVE FUNDING PROGRAMS: The T.D. Financial Group of Canada provides the major sponsorship for the prize money.

NUMBER OF AWARDS: 1.

APPLICATION INFORMATION:
There is an entry fee of $150. Send 10 copies of each title plus author biography and 8 x 10-inch photo to Stephen Leacock Associates. Photographs may be sent electronically. Work must be published in previous calendar year. Not more than two authors. All authors must be Canadian citizens or landed immigrants. Books are nonreturnable.
Deadline: November 30. (No submissions until June 15.) Short list announced April 1. Winner announced end of April. Presentation of cash prize and medal in early June.

PUBLICATIONS:
Newspacket.

BOARD OF DIRECTORS:
Michael Hill, President
Don Reid, Vice President
Judith Rapson, Chairman, Award Committee

ADDRESS INQUIRIES TO:
Judith Rapson
Chairman, Award Committee
(See address above.)

WILLIAM MORRIS SOCIETY IN THE U.S.

P.O. Box 53263
Washington, DC 20009

E-MAIL ADDRESS:
us@morrissociety.org
ecmill@ucdavis.edu

WEB SITE ADDRESS:
www.morrissociety.org

TYPE:
Fellowships; Research grants; Scholarships; Travel grants; Visiting scholars; Research contracts. Supports scholarly, creative, and translation projects about William Morris and his designs, writings and other work.

See entry 479 for full listing.

NATIONAL FEDERATION OF STATE POETRY SOCIETIES, INC. [681]

22614 North Santiam Highway
Lyons, OR 97358
(503) 859-3045

E-MAIL ADDRESS:
eberry@wvi.com

WEB SITE ADDRESS:
www.nfsps.com

AREAS OF INTEREST:
Poetry.

NAME(S) OF PROGRAMS:
- **The Edna Meudt Memorial Award & The Florence Kahn Memorial Award**
- **NFSPS College University Level Poetry Competition Awards**

TYPE:
Awards/prizes.

YEAR PROGRAM STARTED: 1989

PURPOSE:
To encourage the study and writing of poetry.

ELIGIBILITY:
All undergraduate levels of study at an accredited university or college are eligible (freshman through senior).

GEOGRAPHIC RESTRICTIONS:
Canada and United States.

FINANCIAL DATA:
Amount of support per award: $500 plus 75 copies of published manuscript and an additional $300 stipend for travel to the NFSPS Convention to give a reading.

NUMBER OF APPLICANTS MOST RECENT YEAR:
50.

NUMBER OF AWARDS: 2.

APPLICATION INFORMATION:
Applicant must submit an official NFSPS application that has been notarized and a manuscript of 10 original poems (four copies). Manuscript must be titled and have a cover page with name, address, and phone number in the upper left corner and the title of the manuscript in the center of the page. One poem to each page, single-spaced, is permitted and each poem must be titled. Each poem must be no more than 46 lines and have no more than 50 characters per line (including spaces between words and punctuation). No identification on any page other than the cover page. A dedication page, however, may be included.

Send via First Class Mail only. No special deliveries or e-mail submissions.

Deadline: Applications are accepted January 1 to February 14. Three anonymous, highly qualified judges will evaluate, judge and select scholarship winners on or before April 15.

ADDRESS INQUIRIES TO:
Eleanor Berry, Chairperson
College/University Level Poetry Awards
(See address above.)

THE NATIONAL POETRY SERIES [682]

57 Mountain Avenue
Princeton, NJ 08540
(609) 430-0999
Fax: (609) 430-9933

WEB SITE ADDRESS:
www.nationalpoetryseries.org

FOUNDED: 1978

AREAS OF INTEREST:
Poetry.

NAME(S) OF PROGRAMS:
- **National Poetry Series Open Competition**

TYPE:
Awards/prizes.

YEAR PROGRAM STARTED: 1978

PURPOSE:
To publish five books of poetry each year through sponsorship of a contest and arrangement for publication through two trade publishing houses, two small presses and one university press.

LEGAL BASIS:
Nonprofit, private.

ELIGIBILITY:
The National Poetry Series seeks book-length manuscripts of poetry written by American citizens. All manuscripts must be previously unpublished, although some or all of the individual poems may have appeared in periodicals. Translations, chapbooks, small groups of poems and books previously self-published are not eligible. Manuscript length is not limited; however, a length of 48 to 64 pages is suggested.

GEOGRAPHIC RESTRICTIONS:
United States.

FINANCIAL DATA:
Financial arrangements are between author and publisher.
Amount of support per award: $1,000 and book publication.
Total amount of support: $5,000.

NUMBER OF APPLICANTS MOST RECENT YEAR:
1,850.

NUMBER OF AWARDS: 5.

APPLICATION INFORMATION:
Each manuscript must be accompanied by an entrance fee of $30.

Manuscripts must include two cover pages:
(1) title of manuscript, author's name, address and telephone number (this should be the only page with author's identification) and;
(2) title of manuscript only.

Manuscripts must be typed on standard white paper, on one side of the page only, paginated (include a table of contents), and bound only by a clip as more permanent bindings are very difficult to handle. Do not include acknowledgments, explanatory statements, resumes, autobiographical statements, photographs, illustrations or artwork. These will not be considered.

Manuscripts cannot be returned.

Please include a self-addressed, stamped postcard if you would like confirmation of receipt of the manuscript. Include a self-addressed, stamped envelope if you would like to be notified of the NPS winners (announced in August).

Duration: One-time award.

Deadline: Postmarked between January 1 and February 16.

PUBLICATIONS:
Guidelines.

STAFF:
Daniel Halpern, Director
Stephanie Stio, Coordinator

ADDRESS INQUIRIES TO:
Coordinator, National Poetry Series
(See address above.)

PEN AMERICAN CENTER [683]

588 Broadway, Suite 303
New York, NY 10012-5246
(212) 334-1660 ext. 108
Fax: (212) 334-2181

E-MAIL ADDRESS:
awards@pen.org

WEB SITE ADDRESS:
www.pen.org

FOUNDED: 1922

AREAS OF INTEREST:
Promoting the professional development of talented fiction writers.

NAME(S) OF PROGRAMS:
- **PEN/Robert W. Bingham Prize**

TYPE:
Awards/prizes. The PEN/Robert W. Bingham Prize is awarded annually and honors an exceptionally talented fiction writer whose debut work - a first novel or collection of short stories published in the prior year - represents distinguished literary achievement and suggests great promise.

YEAR PROGRAM STARTED: 1990

PURPOSE:
To promote the professional careers of exceptionally talented fiction writers.

LEGAL BASIS:
Nonprofit organization affiliated with International PEN.

ELIGIBILITY:
Candidate's first (and only the first) novel or first collection of short fiction must have been published by a U.S. trade publisher between January 1 and December 31 of the prior year. Candidates must be U.S. residents. American citizenship is not required. There are no restrictions on the candidate's age or on the style of his or her work.
Self-published books are not eligible.

FINANCIAL DATA:
Amount of support per award: Stipend of $25,000.

NUMBER OF AWARDS: 1.

APPLICATION INFORMATION:
Nominations are welcome from writers, editors, literary agents, and members of the literary community. Describe the literary character of the candidate's work, and the degree of promise evident in his or her first book of literary fiction. Send three copies of the candidate's book with nomination.

Deadline: Submissions: October 15 to February 1.

ADDRESS INQUIRIES TO:
Paul W. Morris
Director, Membership, Marketing and Literary Awards
(See address above.)

PEN AMERICAN CENTER [684]

588 Broadway, Suite 303
New York, NY 10012-5246
(212) 334-1660
Fax: (212) 334-2181

E-MAIL ADDRESS:
awards@pen.org

WEB SITE ADDRESS:
www.pen.org

FOUNDED: 1922

AREAS OF INTEREST:
Fiction, literary nonfiction, biography/memoir
and poetry.

NAME(S) OF PROGRAMS:
● **PEN Open Book Award**

TYPE:
Awards/prizes. Invites submissions of
book-length writings by authors of color,
published during the calendar year.

PURPOSE:
To encourage racial and ethnic diversity
within the literary and publishing
communities.

ELIGIBILITY:
Open to authors of color who have not
received wide media coverage. U.S. residency
or citizenship is not required. Works of
fiction, literary nonfiction, biography/memoir
and other works of literary character are
strongly preferred.

FINANCIAL DATA:
Amount of support per award: $5,000.

NUMBER OF AWARDS: 1.

APPLICATION INFORMATION:
Online application form can be found on the
Center web site. Publishers and agents may
submit one copy of a book-length writing by
an author of color published during the
calendar year under consideration, with an
official letter of recommendation.
Self-published books are not eligible. Early
submissions are strongly recommended.
Deadline: Fall 2014.

ADDRESS INQUIRIES TO:
See e-mail address above.

PEN AMERICAN CENTER   [685]
588 Broadway, Suite 303
New York, NY 10012-5246
(212) 334-1660 ext. 126
Fax: (212) 334-2181

E-MAIL ADDRESS:
awards@pen.org

WEB SITE ADDRESS:
www.pen.org

FOUNDED: 1922

AREAS OF INTEREST:
Poetry.

NAME(S) OF PROGRAMS:
● **PEN/Joyce Osterweil Award for Poetry**

TYPE:
Awards/prizes. Recognizes the high literary
character of the published work to date of a
new and emerging American poet of any age
and the promise of further literary
achievement.

PURPOSE:
To recognize the achievements of new and
emerging American poets.

ELIGIBILITY:
Poets nominated for the Award have to be
selected by a PEN member.

FINANCIAL DATA:
Amount of support per award: $5,000
awarded in odd-numbered years.

NUMBER OF AWARDS: 1.

APPLICATION INFORMATION:
Letters of nomination are accepted from PEN
members only.
Deadline: February 1 in odd-numbered years.

ADDRESS INQUIRIES TO:
See e-mail address above.

PEN AMERICAN CENTER   [686]
588 Broadway, Suite 303
New York, NY 10012-5246
(212) 334-1660 ext. 126
Fax: (212) 334-2181

E-MAIL ADDRESS:
awards@pen.org

WEB SITE ADDRESS:
www.pen.org

FOUNDED: 1922

AREAS OF INTEREST:
Children's/young adult fiction.

NAME(S) OF PROGRAMS:
● **PEN/Phyllis Naylor Working Writer
Fellowship**

TYPE:
Awards/prizes; Fellowships. The Fellowship
is offered annually to an author of children's
or young adult fiction.

PURPOSE:
To recognize the fact that many writers' work
is of high literary caliber but has not yet
attracted a broad readership.

ELIGIBILITY:
A candidate is a writer of children's or young
adult fiction demonstrating financial need.
Candidates have published at least two novels
for children or young adults which have been
warmly received by literary critics, but have
not generated sufficient income to support the
author. The writer's books must be published
by a U.S. publisher.

FINANCIAL DATA:
Amount of support per award: $5,000.

NUMBER OF AWARDS: 1.

APPLICATION INFORMATION:
Writers must be nominated by an editor or a
fellow writer. It is strongly recommended
that the nominator write a letter of support,
describing in some detail how the candidate
meets the criteria for the Fellowship. The
nominator should provide the following:
(1) a list of the candidate's published work
(preferably accompanied by copies of
reviews, where possible);
(2) three copies of the outline of the current
novel in progress, together with 50 to 75
pages of the text (picture books not eligible)
and;
(3) on a separate paper, a brief description of
the candidate's recent earnings and a
statement about why monetary support will
make a particular difference in the applicant's
writing life at this time. If the candidate is
married or living with a domestic partner,
please include a brief description of total
family income and expenses.
Deadline: Fall 2014.

ADDRESS INQUIRIES TO:
See e-mail address above.

PEN AMERICAN CENTER   [687]
588 Broadway, Suite 303
New York, NY 10012-5246
(212) 334-1660 ext. 126
Fax: (212) 334-2181

E-MAIL ADDRESS:
awards@pen.org

WEB SITE ADDRESS:
www.pen.org

FOUNDED: 1922

AREAS OF INTEREST:
Poetry in translation.

NAME(S) OF PROGRAMS:
● **PEN Award for Poetry in Translation**

TYPE:
Awards/prizes. The award recognizes
book-length translations of poetry from any
language into English published during the
current calendar year and is judged by a
single translator of poetry appointed by the
PEN Translation Committee. The award was
made possible originally by a bequest from
the late translator and PEN member Rae
Dalven, and has received current support
from The Kaplen Foundation. It is conferred
every spring in New York.

YEAR PROGRAM STARTED: 1963

PURPOSE:
To recognize book-length translations of
poetry from any language into English
published during the current calendar year.

ELIGIBILITY:
Although all eligible books must have been
published in the U.S., translators may be of
any nationality; U.S. residency or citizenship
is not required.

Self-published books or books with more
than two translators are not eligible.

FINANCIAL DATA:
Amount of support per award: $3,000.

NUMBER OF AWARDS: 1.

APPLICATION INFORMATION:
Three copies of book-length translations of
poetry published during the calendar year
under consideration may be submitted by
publishers, agents, or the translators
themselves. Early submissions are strongly
recommended.
Deadline: Fall 2014.

ADDRESS INQUIRIES TO:
See e-mail address above.

PEN AMERICAN CENTER   [688]
588 Broadway, Suite 303
New York, NY 10012-5246
(212) 334-1660 ext. 126
Fax: (212) 334-2181

E-MAIL ADDRESS:
awards@pen.org

WEB SITE ADDRESS:
www.pen.org

FOUNDED: 1922

AREAS OF INTEREST:
Poetry.

NAME(S) OF PROGRAMS:
● **PEN/Voelcker Award for Poetry**

TYPE:
Awards/prizes. The Award, established by a
bequest from Hunce Voelcker, will be
presented to an American poet whose
distinguished and growing body of work to
date represents a notable and accomplished
presence in American literature, for whom
the promise seen in earlier work has been
fulfilled, and who has matured with each
successive volume of poetry.

PURPOSE:
To honor an American poet whose distinguished and growing body of work to date represents a notable and accomplished presence in American literature.

ELIGIBILITY:
Candidates must be American residents and can be nominated only by members of PEN. It is understood that all nominations made for the Award supplement internal nominations made by the panel of judges. There are no restrictions whatsoever to the age of the poet or to the style of his or her work.

FINANCIAL DATA:
Amount of support per award: $5,000 awarded in even-numbered years.

NUMBER OF AWARDS: 1.

APPLICATION INFORMATION:
All letters of nomination (one to two pages is expected) should describe the scope and literary caliber of the candidate's work, and summarize the candidate's publications. Most importantly, nominations should articulate the degree of accomplishment the nominated poet has attained, and the esteem in which the candidate's work is held within the American literary community.
Deadline: Offered in even-numbered years. The next application cycle begins in the fall of 2015.

ADDRESS INQUIRIES TO:
See e-mail address above.

PEN AMERICAN CENTER   [689]
588 Broadway, Room 303
New York, NY 10012-5246
(212) 334-1660 ext. 103/117
Fax: (212) 334-2181

E-MAIL ADDRESS:
prisonwriting@pen.org

WEB SITE ADDRESS:
www.pen.org

FOUNDED: 1922

AREAS OF INTEREST:
Writing of literature and poetry.

NAME(S) OF PROGRAMS:
• **PEN Prison Writing Program**

TYPE:
Awards/prizes.

YEAR PROGRAM STARTED: 1973

PURPOSE:
To help incarcerated writers develop their writing talents and to promote writing as a means of rehabilitation.

LEGAL BASIS:
Tax-exempt, nonprofit organization.

ELIGIBILITY:
U.S. federal, state or county prisoners may apply. Only unpublished manuscripts will be considered, except those that have appeared in a prison publication.

GEOGRAPHIC RESTRICTIONS:
United States.

FINANCIAL DATA:
Amount of support per award: Four first prizes at $200 each, four second prizes at $100 each and four third prizes at $50 each. One prize is given for each of four categories: Poetry, Fiction, Drama and Nonfiction to first, second and third prize winners.
Total amount of support: $1,400 annually.

NUMBER OF APPLICANTS MOST RECENT YEAR:
1,500.

NUMBER OF AWARDS: 12 annually.

APPLICATION INFORMATION:
Manuscripts must be typewritten (double-spaced) or clearly printed on standard letter-size paper. Also accept alternative submissions. Authors must not submit more than one entry in each category. Name, inmate number and address must appear on each submission.
Duration: One-time award.
Deadline: September 1. Winners announced in March.

PUBLICATIONS:
PEN Handbook for Writers in Prison (lists resources available to inmates and journals interested in prison writing).

STAFF:
Jackson Taylor, Prison Writing Program Director
Tim Small, Prison Writing Mentorship Program Coordinator

ADDRESS INQUIRIES TO:
Director
PEN Writing Award for Prisoners
(See address above.)

PEN AMERICAN CENTER   [690]
588 Broadway, Suite 303
New York, NY 10012-5246
(212) 334-1660 ext. 126
Fax: (212) 334-2181

E-MAIL ADDRESS:
info@pen.org

WEB SITE ADDRESS:
www.pen.org

FOUNDED: 1922

AREAS OF INTEREST:
Literature, free expression and international literary fellowship.

NAME(S) OF PROGRAMS:
• **PEN Writers' Fund**

TYPE:
Grants-in-aid. Emergency fund for professional (published or produced) writers in acute, emergency financial crisis.

YEAR PROGRAM STARTED: 1958

PURPOSE:
To assist professional literary writers in times of short-term financial emergency and also to assist writers and editors with AIDS or HIV; to advance literature, defend free expression and foster international literary fellowship.

LEGAL BASIS:
Nonprofit organization affiliated with International PEN.

ELIGIBILITY:
The fund aims to assist professional (published or produced) writers facing unexpected financial and medical emergencies, and those who are HIV-positive. The fund does not exist for research purposes, for completing projects or to support publications or organizations. Must be a U.S. resident. Self-published writers are not eligible.

GEOGRAPHIC RESTRICTIONS:
United States.

FINANCIAL DATA:
Amount of support per award: Up to $2,000.

APPLICATION INFORMATION:
Applicants should submit a completed application form, published writing samples, documentation of financial emergency and professional resume. Applications are accepted year-round and are reviewed every three months by the Writers' Fund Committee.

Applications are available online.
Deadline: Mid-March, mid-June, mid-September and mid-December.

PUBLICATIONS:
Application; guidelines.

STAFF:
Arielle Anema, Writers' Fund Associate

ADDRESS INQUIRIES TO:
Arielle Anema, Writers' Fund Associate
(See address above.)

*SPECIAL STIPULATIONS:
Applicants may only receive a grant every three years.

PEN NEW ENGLAND   [691]
Massachusetts Institute of Technology,
14N-221A
77 Massachusetts Avenue
Cambridge, MA 02139
(617) 324-1729

E-MAIL ADDRESS:
pen-newengland@mit.edu

WEB SITE ADDRESS:
www.pen-ne.org

FOUNDED: 1975

AREAS OF INTEREST:
Authors.

NAME(S) OF PROGRAMS:
• **PEN New England Awards**

TYPE:
Awards/prizes. Three prizes will be awarded annually for best book of fiction, nonfiction and poetry by New England authors or books with a New England topic or setting.

YEAR PROGRAM STARTED: 1975

PURPOSE:
To recognize literary excellence and honor works of fiction, nonfiction and poetry by New England authors.

LEGAL BASIS:
Nonprofit organization affiliated with International PEN.

ELIGIBILITY:
Books of fiction, nonfiction and poetry by New England authors or with a New England topic or setting.

FINANCIAL DATA:
Amount of support per award: $1,000 in each category.
Total amount of support: $3,000.

NUMBER OF APPLICANTS MOST RECENT YEAR:
Approximately 500.

NUMBER OF AWARDS: 3; 1 for fiction, 1 for nonfiction and 1 for poetry.

APPLICATION INFORMATION:
Full guidelines available on web site. Submit three copies of eligible books and an entry fee of $40 per title to the PEN New England Award, at the address above.
Deadline: December 31, 2014. Awards ceremony in April 2015 held at the John F. Kennedy Library, Boston.

ADDRESS INQUIRIES TO:
See e-mail address above.

*SPECIAL STIPULATIONS:
Self-published books, electronic submissions
or e-books are not eligible for consideration.

PEN NEW ENGLAND   [692]

Massachusetts Institute of Technology,
14N-221A
77 Massachusetts Avenue
Cambridge, MA 02139
(617) 324-1729

E-MAIL ADDRESS:
pen-newengland@mit.edu

WEB SITE ADDRESS:
www.pen-ne.org

NAME(S) OF PROGRAMS:
● PEN/Hemingway Award for Debut
   Fiction

TYPE:
Awards/prizes. Awarded annually for the first
published book-length work of fiction by an
American writer.

YEAR PROGRAM STARTED: 1976

PURPOSE:
PEN New England: To celebrate literature
and free expression. PEN/Hemingway Award:
To recognize literary excellence and to honor
debut fiction.

LEGAL BASIS:
Nonprofit organization affiliated with
International PEN.

ELIGIBILITY:
First published book-length work of fiction (a
novel or book of short stories) by an
American citizen or resident, published in the
U.S. in 2014, may be submitted by
publishers, agents or the authors themselves.
Authors are not disqualified by the previous
publication of nonfiction, poetry, drama or
books for children.

GEOGRAPHIC RESTRICTIONS:
United States.

FINANCIAL DATA:
Amount of support per award: $10,000.
Total amount of support: $10,000.

NUMBER OF APPLICANTS MOST RECENT YEAR:
450.

NUMBER OF AWARDS: 1 winner, 2 finalists, and
2 honorable mentions.

APPLICATION INFORMATION:
Full guidelines are available on the web site.
Submit four copies of eligible books and an
entry fee of $40 per title to the PEN
Hemingway Award, at the address above.
Duration: One-time award.
Deadline: December 31, 2014. Awards
ceremony in April 2015 held at the John F.
Kennedy Library, Boston.

ADDRESS INQUIRIES TO:
See e-mail address above.

*SPECIAL STIPULATIONS:
Self-published books, electronic submissions
or e-books are not eligible for consideration.

PEN/FAULKNER
FOUNDATION   [693]

PEN/Faulkner Foundation
201 East Capitol Street, S.E.
Washington, DC 20003
(202) 898-9063
Fax: (202) 675-0360

E-MAIL ADDRESS:
esnyder@penfaulkner.org

WEB SITE ADDRESS:
www.penfaulkner.org

FOUNDED: 1980

AREAS OF INTEREST:
Fiction.

NAME(S) OF PROGRAMS:
● PEN/Faulkner Award for Fiction

TYPE:
Awards/prizes. Cash awards for a published
winning author and four nominees.

YEAR PROGRAM STARTED: 1981

PURPOSE:
To honor literary excellence.

LEGAL BASIS:
Nonprofit 501(c)(3) organization.

ELIGIBILITY:
Candidates must be American citizens. Books
must be published within the calendar year of
the award. No self-published books.

GEOGRAPHIC RESTRICTIONS:
United States.

FINANCIAL DATA:
Amount of support per award: $15,000 for
the winner. $5,000 to each of four finalists.
Total amount of support: $35,000.

NUMBER OF APPLICANTS MOST RECENT YEAR:
350.

NUMBER OF AWARDS: 5.

APPLICATION INFORMATION:
Candidates should submit four copies of their
book.
Deadline: October 31. Announcement by
mid-March.

IRS IDENTIFICATION NUMBER: 52-1431622

OFFICERS:
Susan Richards Shreve, Co-Chairman
Robert Stone, Co-Chairman

ADDRESS INQUIRIES TO:
Executive Director
(See address above.)

*PLEASE NOTE:
This is not a grant program, but a prize for
published work.

THE PHI BETA KAPPA
SOCIETY   [694]

1606 New Hampshire Avenue, N.W.
Washington, DC 20009
(202) 745-3287
Fax: (202) 986-1601

E-MAIL ADDRESS:
awards@pbk.org

WEB SITE ADDRESS:
www.pbk.org

FOUNDED: 1776

NAME(S) OF PROGRAMS:
● Ralph Waldo Emerson Award
● Christian Gauss Award
● Phi Beta Kappa Award in Science

TYPE:
Awards/prizes. Three book awards given
annually to outstanding scholarly books that
have been published in the U.S. in the fields
of the humanities, the social sciences, the
natural sciences and mathematics.

The Ralph Waldo Emerson Book Award is
offered annually for scholarly studies that
contribute significantly to interpretations of
the intellectual and cultural condition of
humanity. This award may recognize work in
the fields of history, philosophy and religion;
these fields are conceived in sufficiently
broad terms to permit the inclusion of
appropriate work in related fields such as
anthropology and the social sciences.
Biographies of public figures may be eligible
if their critical emphasis is primarily on the
intellectual and cultural condition of
humanity.

The Christian Gauss Award is offered for
books in the field of literary scholarship or
criticism. The prize honors the late Christian
Gauss, the distinguished Princeton University
scholar, teacher, and dean, who also served
as president of the Phi Beta Kappa Society.
To be eligible, a literary biography must have
a predominantly critical emphasis.

Phi Beta Kappa Book Award in Science is
offered for outstanding contributions by
scientists to the literature of science. The
Award's intent is to encourage literate and
scholarly interpretations of the physical and
biological sciences and mathematics;
monographs and compendiums are not
eligible. To be eligible, biographies of
scientists must have a substantial critical
emphasis on their scientific research.

YEAR PROGRAM STARTED: 1950

PURPOSE:
To recognize outstanding printed work in
several fields including the social sciences,
humanities, natural science and math.

LEGAL BASIS:
National scholarly honorary society.

ELIGIBILITY:
Awards are given for works published in the
U.S. during the previous calendar year.
Entries must be original publications.
Translations and works previously published
as a whole are not eligible. Books that
contain chapters or sections previously
published as articles in periodicals will be
considered only if they have very clear,
unifying themes and are not random
collections. Books that consist entirely of
previously published articles are unlikely to
qualify.

Entries ordinarily will be the work of a
single writer. Exceptions may be made for
books written by small teams of scholars
working in close collaboration. Books that
are collections of chapters by several
different authors are not eligible. Entries
should not be highly technical in character,
nor should they treat subjects of narrowly
limited interest. Monographs and reports on
research as such are not eligible. In all cases,
the subject and style of the entries should be
accessible to the general, literate reader.

Authors must be citizens or residents of the
U.S. Entries must have been published
originally in the U.S. A book may not be
entered for more than one of the awards. All
entries must be submitted by the publisher.
Publishers may submit no more than one
entry for each award.

GEOGRAPHIC RESTRICTIONS:
United States.

FINANCIAL DATA:
Amount of support per award: $10,000 to the
winning author.
Total amount of support: $30,000 annually.

NUMBER OF APPLICANTS MOST RECENT YEAR:
80 for each program for the year 2013.

NUMBER OF AWARDS: 1 award in each category
each year.

APPLICATION INFORMATION:
Inquiries and entries should be addressed to
the appropriate award committee at the
address above. Entries must be submitted by
the publisher.
Duration: No renewal.
Deadline: February 15.

PUBLICATIONS:
Application guidelines.

OFFICERS:
Kate Soule, President
John Churchill, Secretary

ADDRESS INQUIRIES TO:
Laura Hartnett
Coordinator of Administration
(See address above.)

PITT POETRY SERIES   [695]
University of Pittsburgh Press
7500 Thomas Boulevard
Pittsburgh, PA 15260
(412) 383-2456
Fax: (412) 383-2466

E-MAIL ADDRESS:
info@upress.pitt.edu

WEB SITE ADDRESS:
www.upress.pitt.edu

FOUNDED: 1967

AREAS OF INTEREST:
Contemporary American poetry.

NAME(S) OF PROGRAMS:
• **Agnes Lynch Starrett Poetry Prize**

TYPE:
Awards/prizes. Cash prize, plus publication in
the Pitt Poetry Series.

YEAR PROGRAM STARTED: 1980

LEGAL BASIS:
University.

ELIGIBILITY:
Starrett Prize awarded annually for a
manuscript in English by a writer who has
not previously published a full-length book
of poetry.

FINANCIAL DATA:
Amount of support per award: $5,000, plus
book publication.
Total amount of support: $5,000.

NUMBER OF APPLICANTS MOST RECENT YEAR:
750.

NUMBER OF AWARDS: 1 each year.

REPRESENTATIVE AWARDS:
Michael McGriff, *Dismantling the Hills.*

APPLICATION INFORMATION:
Send one copy of manuscript on good quality
white paper, with no fewer than 48 and no
more than 100 typescript pages. Clean,
legible photocopies are acceptable. Name,
address, phone number, and e-mail address
should be on the title page. Also include
curriculum vitae. A $25 reading fee per
manuscript is required.
Deadline: Between March 1 and April 30
only. Announcement in the fall.

PUBLICATIONS:
Competition rules.

OFFICERS:
Ed Ochester, Editor, Pitt Poetry Series

ADDRESS INQUIRIES TO:
See e-mail address above.

*SPECIAL STIPULATIONS:
Competition for the Starrett Prize is severe.
Casual submissions are not encouraged.
Publisher cannot provide critiques of
manuscripts.

Manuscripts will not be returned.

THE PLAYWRIGHTS'
CENTER   [696]
2301 Franklin Avenue East
Minneapolis, MN 55406
(612) 332-7481
Fax: (612) 332-6037

E-MAIL ADDRESS:
info@pwcenter.org

WEB SITE ADDRESS:
www.pwcenter.org

FOUNDED: 1971

AREAS OF INTEREST:
Playwriting.

CONSULTING OR VOLUNTEER SERVICES:
Advice on career development, jobs and
production for playwrights.

NAME(S) OF PROGRAMS:
• **Affiliated Writer Program**
• **Core Writer Program**
• **Jerome Fellowships**
• **Many Voices Fellowships**
• **McKnight Advancement Grants**
• **McKnight National Residency and
  Commission**
• **McKnight Theater Artist Fellowships**
• **New Plays on Campus**

TYPE:
Awards/prizes; Conferences/seminars;
Development grants; Fellowships;
Internships; Residencies. Core Writer
Program confers additional membership
benefits to committed professional
playwrights.

Jerome Fellowships provide grants to
emerging playwrights, who receive access to
Center's developmental services.

Many Voices Fellowships are awarded to
playwrights of color.

McKnight Advancement Grants provide
grants to midcareer Minnesota playwrights.

McKnight National Residency and
Commission aids in the creation and
development of new works from nationally
recognized playwrights not residing in
Minnesota.

McKnight Theater Artist Fellowships are
awarded to Minnesota theater artists (other
than playwrights).

YEAR PROGRAM STARTED: 1971

PURPOSE:
To assist playwrights.

LEGAL BASIS:
Tax-exempt and nonprofit.

ELIGIBILITY:
Core Writer Program is open to professional
playwrights in the U.S.

Jerome Fellowships are open to emerging
playwrights in the U.S. (citizens or
permanent residents).

Many Voices Fellowships are available to
national and local writers of color.

McKnight Advancement Grants and
McKnight Theater Artist Fellowships are for
Minnesota residents only.

McKnight National Residency and
Commission is for playwrights residing
outside of Minnesota.

Additional criteria vary for each program.

FINANCIAL DATA:
Amount of support per award: Varies.
Total amount of support: Over $250,000.

NUMBER OF APPLICANTS MOST RECENT YEAR:
200 for fellowships. 500 for all programs.

NUMBER OF AWARDS: For the year 2014-15:
Core Writer: Varies; Jerome Fellowships: 4;
Many Voices Fellowships: 2; Many Voices
Mentorship: 2; McKnight Advancement
Grants: 2; McKnight National Residency and
Commission: 1; McKnight Theater Artist
Fellowships: 3.

APPLICATION INFORMATION:
Application information is available on the
web site.
Duration: One year.

PUBLICATIONS:
Annual report; newsletter.

IRS IDENTIFICATION NUMBER: 41-6170139

STAFF:
Jeremy Cohen, Producing Artistic Director
Hayley Finn, Associate Artistic Director
Amanda Robbins-Butcher, Artistic
Administrator
Christina Ham, Many Voices Program
Coordinator

ADDRESS INQUIRIES TO:
Sarah Chaplin, Development Manager
(See address above.)

*SPECIAL STIPULATIONS:
Playwright must be in residence in Minnesota
for one year for Jerome Fellowship.
Recipients of McKnight Advancement
Grants, McKnight Theater Artist Fellowships,
and Many Voices Fellowships must maintain
residence in Minnesota during program year.

SOCIETY OF CHILDREN'S
BOOK WRITERS AND
ILLUSTRATORS   [697]
8271 Beverly Boulevard
Los Angeles, CA 90048
(323) 782-1010
Fax: (323) 782-1892

E-MAIL ADDRESS:
scbwi@scbwi.org

WEB SITE ADDRESS:
www.scbwi.org

FOUNDED: 1968

AREAS OF INTEREST:
Writers, editors and illustrators of children's
books.

NAME(S) OF PROGRAMS:
• **Don Freeman Memorial Grant-in-Aid**
• **Work-In-Progress Grants**

TYPE:
Grants-in-aid; Project/program grants. The
Freeman Memorial Grant-In-Aid has been
established to enable picture-book artists to
further their understanding, training and work
in any aspect of the picture-book genre.

Work-In-Progress Grants have been established to assist children's book writers to complete a specific project. Grants are given in four categories: General Work-in-Progress Grant; Grant for a Contemporary Novel for Young People; Nonfiction Research Grant; and Grant for a work whose author has never had a book published.

YEAR PROGRAM STARTED: 1974

PURPOSE:
To encourage continuing excellence in the creation of children's literature and to provide assistance and support to those working in the children's book field.

LEGAL BASIS:
Corporation.

ELIGIBILITY:
Both grants are available to full and associate members of the Society of Children's Book Writers. The SCBW Grant Committee reserves the right to withhold the grants for any given year.

FINANCIAL DATA:
Amount of support per award: Freeman Memorial Grant-In-Aid: $2,000, plus a runner-up grant of $500; Work-in-Progress Grants: $2,000 in each category, plus runner-up grants of $500 in each category.

NUMBER OF APPLICANTS MOST RECENT YEAR: 285.

NUMBER OF AWARDS: 1 Freeman Memorial Grant-In-Aid and 4 Work-In-Progress Grants are awarded each year. Runner-up grants are made in each category.

APPLICATION INFORMATION:
Applications may be obtained by sending a self-addressed, stamped envelope to the address above beginning October 1 of each year. Instructions for mailing the completed applications and written materials will be sent with the application.

Applicants for the Freeman Memorial Grant-In-Aid must enclose either (a) a rough picture-book dummy, the picture-book text in manuscript form and two finished illustrations (one color and one black-and-white); or (b) 10 finished illustrations that would make a suitable portfolio presentation expressly intended for picture books. Specifications will be sent with the application.

Applicants for the Work-In-Progress Grants must enclose three clearly reproduced copies of a synopsis of the work for which the grant will be used and a two- to 10-page writing sample from that work.
Duration: One-time grant.
Deadline: Freeman Memorial Grant-In-Aid: applications accepted between February 1 and May 1. Announcement on June 15. Work-In-Progress Grants: applications accepted between February 1 and May 1. Announcement the following September.

PUBLICATIONS:
Grants brochure.

OFFICERS:
Stephen Mooser, President
Lin Oliver, Executive Director

ADDRESS INQUIRIES TO:
For the Freeman Memorial Grant-In-Aid:
SCBW Don Freeman Grant-In-Aid
(See address above.)

For the Work-In-Progress Grants:
SCBW Grant Committee
(See address above.)

SYRACUSE UNIVERSITY   [698]
Department of English
420 Hall of Languages
Syracuse, NY 13244-1170
(315) 443-3755
Fax: (315) 443-3660

E-MAIL ADDRESS:
ckennedy@syr.edu

WEB SITE ADDRESS:
english.syr.edu

FOUNDED: 1861

AREAS OF INTEREST:
Creative writing in poetry and fiction.

NAME(S) OF PROGRAMS:
● **Graduate Program in Creative Writing**

TYPE:
Assistantships; Awards/prizes; Fellowships; Scholarships; Travel grants. Fellowships and teaching assistantships in creative writing.

YEAR PROGRAM STARTED: 1963

PURPOSE:
To assist talented writers to pursue graduate degrees at Syracuse University.

ELIGIBILITY:
Applicant must have a B.A. or B.S. degree.

FINANCIAL DATA:
Fellowships and assistantships include remission of tuition costs for graduate study.
Amount of support per award: University Fellowships: $17,220; Cornelia Carhart Award: $16,480 (fiction only); Mead Fellowship: $16,480 (poetry only); Teaching Assistantships: $14,455; Creative Writing Scholarships: $13,040 (fiction and poetry).
Total amount of support: Varies.

APPLICATION INFORMATION:
An applicant must submit a writing sample (poetry or fiction), statement of purpose, teaching statement, official transcripts, and letters of recommendation.
Duration: Three years.
Deadline: January 1 for writing sample; January 9 for complete application.

ADDRESS INQUIRIES TO:
Christopher Kennedy
Director, Creative Writing Program
(See address above.)

TOWSON UNIVERSITY   [699]
College of Liberal Arts
8000 York Road
Towson, MD 21252
(410) 704-2128
Fax: (410) 704-6392

E-MAIL ADDRESS:
cla@towson.edu

WEB SITE ADDRESS:
www.towson.edu/cla

FOUNDED: 1866

NAME(S) OF PROGRAMS:
● **Towson University Prize for Literature**

TYPE:
Awards/prizes. Awarded to Maryland writer of a single book or book-length manuscript of fiction, poetry, drama or imaginative nonfiction.

YEAR PROGRAM STARTED: 1980

PURPOSE:
To honor a published work of fiction, poetry or imaginative nonfiction by a Maryland resident.

LEGAL BASIS:
Special endowment.

ELIGIBILITY:
Applicant must be a Maryland resident for at least three years at the time of the award. Prize is awarded on the basis of literary and aesthetic excellence. Book must have been published in the three years prior to the award.

The winning author must be willing to be present at the awards ceremony and to grant to Towson State University the right to quote from the winning work in any publicity related to the prize.

GEOGRAPHIC RESTRICTIONS:
Maryland.

FINANCIAL DATA:
Amount of support per award: Generally $1,000.
Total amount of support: $1,000.

NUMBER OF APPLICANTS MOST RECENT YEAR: 14.

NUMBER OF AWARDS: 1 annually.

APPLICATION INFORMATION:
Any individual, institution, group or publisher may nominate one or more works for the prize. Submit three copies of the work by certified mail, bound if published or typewritten if manuscript. If manuscript, proof of acceptance by a publisher and proposed date of publication must be provided. A completed nomination form must accompany entry.
Duration: One-time award.
Deadline: June 15 each year. Announcement in December.

ADDRESS INQUIRIES TO:
Dean, College of Liberal Arts, LA 2213
Towson University
(See address above.)

THE TRUST COMPANY   [700]
Level 15, 20 Bond Street
G.P.O. Box 4270
Sydney N.S.W. 2000 Australia
(61)(2) 8295-8100

E-MAIL ADDRESS:
scholarships@thetrustcompany.com.au

WEB SITE ADDRESS:
www.thetrustcompany.com.au

FOUNDED: 1954

AREAS OF INTEREST:
The advancement, improvement and betterment of Australian literature.

NAME(S) OF PROGRAMS:
● **Miles Franklin Literary Award**

TYPE:
Awards/prizes. Annual cash award for a published book on Australian life.

YEAR PROGRAM STARTED: 1957

PURPOSE:
To improve the educational style of authors; to help and give incentive to authors and to provide them with additional monetary support to enable them to improve their literary efforts.

LEGAL BASIS:
Trustees of estate of the late Miles Franklin.

ELIGIBILITY:
No special requirements as regards nationality, age, etc. The book must be published in the year of entry of the award and be of the highest literary merit and must present Australian life in any of its phases. More than one entry may be submitted by each author. Novels or plays written by two or more authors in collaboration are eligible.

Biographies, collections of short stories, young adult/children's books, poetry, farce or musical comedy are not eligible.

FINANCIAL DATA:
There is an entry fee of $90 (AUD).
Amount of support per award: $60,000 (AUD).

NUMBER OF APPLICANTS MOST RECENT YEAR:
50.

NUMBER OF AWARDS: 1 per year.

APPLICATION INFORMATION:
Conditions of entry including copies of proposed entries are to be submitted by the entrant to The Trust Company including completed application form and six copies of novel. All packages containing entries should be clearly marked "Miles Franklin Literary Award Entry."
Duration: Annual.
Deadline: Second Friday in December of preceding year. Announcement of award in May/June.

PUBLICATIONS:
Application guidelines.

ADDRESS INQUIRIES TO:
Scholarship and Awards
Miles Franklin Literary Award
(See e-mail address above.)

THE UNIVERSITY OF IOWA [701]

Iowa Writers' Workshop
102 Dey House
507 North Clinton Street
Iowa City, IA 52242-1000
(319) 335-0416
Fax: (319) 335-0420

E-MAIL ADDRESS:
kelly-a-smith@uiowa.edu

WEB SITE ADDRESS:
www.uiowa.edu/~iww

AREAS OF INTEREST:
Short story collection.

NAME(S) OF PROGRAMS:
- **The Iowa Short Fiction Award**
- **The John Simmons Short Fiction Award**

TYPE:
Awards/prizes. Publication of short story collection/manuscript.

YEAR PROGRAM STARTED: 1969

PURPOSE:
To encourage writing of short stories.

ELIGIBILITY:
Any writer who has not previously published a volume of prose fiction is eligible. Revised manuscripts which have been previously entered may be resubmitted. Writers who have published a volume of poetry are eligible.

The manuscript must be a collection of short stories of at least 150 word-processed, double-spaced pages. Stories previously published in periodicals are eligible.

COOPERATIVE FUNDING PROGRAMS: The awards are provided with cooperation of the Iowa Writers' Workshop and the University of Iowa Press.

NUMBER OF APPLICANTS MOST RECENT YEAR:
Over 500.

NUMBER OF AWARDS: 1 of each annually.

APPLICATION INFORMATION:
No application forms are necessary. Manuscripts should be mailed to: Iowa Short Fiction Award, Iowa Writers' Workshop, at the address listed above. Do not send the only copy of the manuscript. Xeroxed copies are encouraged. Stamped, self-addressed packaging may be included for return of the manuscript, but is not required.
Deadline: Entries should be postmarked between August 1 and September 30. Announcement of the winners will be made early in the following year.

STAFF:
Lan Samantha Chang, Director

ADDRESS INQUIRIES TO:
Connie Brothers, Program Associate
(See address above.)

UNIVERSITY OF MINNESOTA [702]

Room 113, Andersen Library
222 21st Avenue South
Minneapolis, MN 55455
(612) 624-4576

E-MAIL ADDRESS:
asc-clrc@umn.edu

WEB SITE ADDRESS:
special.lib.umn.edu/clrc/

AREAS OF INTEREST:
Children's book artist development.

NAME(S) OF PROGRAMS:
- **Ezra Jack Keats/Kerlan Collection Memorial Fellowship**

TYPE:
Travel grants. Award to travel to Kerlan Collection, University of Minnesota, plus per diem.

PURPOSE:
To fund the artist development of a talented writer and/or illustrator of children's books.

ELIGIBILITY:
Grants are awarded to individuals based on need. Special consideration will be given to those who would find it difficult to finance a visit to the Kerlan Collection. Candidates do not have to be U.S. citizens or residents.

FINANCIAL DATA:
Recipient will receive transportation cost and a per diem allotment.
Amount of support per award: Up to $1,500.
Total amount of support: Up to $1,500.

NUMBER OF AWARDS: 1.

APPLICATION INFORMATION:
Electronic application acceptable by deadline.
Duration: Grants are awarded annually and are nonrenewable.
Deadline: January 30 (postmark).

ADDRESS INQUIRIES TO:
Ezra Jack Keats/Kerlan Collection
Memorial Fellowship Committee
(See address above.)

UNIVERSITY OF NEW MEXICO [703]

MSC03 2170
One University of New Mexico
Albuquerque, NM 87131-0001
(505) 277-5572
Fax: (505) 277-2950

E-MAIL ADDRESS:
taosconf@unm.edu

WEB SITE ADDRESS:
www.unm.edu/~taosconf

FOUNDED: 1999

AREAS OF INTEREST:
Fiction, nonfiction and poetry workshops.

NAME(S) OF PROGRAMS:
- **Taos Summer Writers' Conference**

TYPE:
Assistantships; Awards/prizes; Conferences/seminars; Fellowships; Scholarships; Work-study programs. The Taos Summer Writers' Conference has a number of scholarships to provide support for talented writers.

The D.H. Lawrence Fellowship is intended for emerging writers with one book in print. It provides tuition remission and the cost of lodging.

The Taos Resident Writer Award provides tuition remission for one workshop to a resident of the Taos area.

The Hispanic Writer Award is open to any New Mexican resident of Hispanic, Latino, or Spanish heritage. The award provides tuition remission for one workshop and the cost of lodging.

The Leo Love Merit Scholarships are available to any potential conference participant. It pays tuition for a weeklong workshop or partial tuition for a master class. Recipient is responsible for her or his transportation and/or lodging costs.

The Native Writer Award is open to any Native American writer who is a resident of New Mexico. It provides tuition remission for one workshop and the cost of lodging.

YEAR PROGRAM STARTED: 1999

PURPOSE:
To help up-and-coming writers hone their skills by continuing to take courses to advance their writing career.

LEGAL BASIS:
University.

ELIGIBILITY:
Qualified individuals involved in the fields listed above are eligible to apply.

FINANCIAL DATA:
Recipients receive tuition remission, lodging, breakfast and lunch. Lodging costs are excluded from the Leo Love Merit Scholarships.
Amount of support per award: Up to $650.
Total amount of support: Varies.

NUMBER OF APPLICANTS MOST RECENT YEAR:
50.

NUMBER OF AWARDS: 6 annually.

APPLICATION INFORMATION:
Application information is available on the web site.
Duration: 10 to 12 days.
Deadline: April 15 to May 1 as per award.

IRS IDENTIFICATION NUMBER: 85-6000642

STAFF:
Sharon Oard Warner, Director
Eva Lipton-Ormand, Assistant Director

ADDRESS INQUIRIES TO:
Eva Lipton-Ormand, Assistant Director
Taos Summer Writers' Conference
(See address above.)

THE UNIVERSITY OF SOUTHERN MISSISSIPPI [704]
118 College Drive
Box 5148
Hattiesburg, MS 39406
(601) 266-4349
Fax: (601) 266-6269

E-MAIL ADDRESS:
ellen.ruffin@usm.edu

WEB SITE ADDRESS:
www.lib.usm.edu/~degrum/html/research/re-
fellowships.shtml

FOUNDED: 1966

AREAS OF INTEREST:
American and British children's literature.

NAME(S) OF PROGRAMS:
● **Ezra Jack Keats Children's Literature Research Fellowship Program**

TYPE:
Fellowships; Research grants.

PURPOSE:
To support research in children's literature.

FINANCIAL DATA:
Amount of support per award: Varies.
Total amount of support: Varies.

NUMBER OF APPLICANTS MOST RECENT YEAR: 7
for the year 2012.

NUMBER OF AWARDS: 1 for the year 2012.

APPLICATION INFORMATION:
Application information is available on the
web site.
Duration: One year. Grants not renewable.
Deadline: November 30. Announcement in
mid-December.

ADDRESS INQUIRIES TO:
Ellen H. Ruffin, Curator
de Grummond Children's Literature
Collection
(See address above.)

UNIVERSITY OF VIRGINIA PRESS [705]
P.O. Box 400318
Charlottesville, VA 22904-4318
(434) 924-3468
Fax: (434) 982-2655

E-MAIL ADDRESS:
arh2h@virginia.edu

WEB SITE ADDRESS:
www.upress.virginia.edu

FOUNDED: 1989

AREAS OF INTEREST:
18th century studies.

NAME(S) OF PROGRAMS:
● **Walker Cowen Memorial Prize**

TYPE:
Awards/prizes.

YEAR PROGRAM STARTED: 1989

LEGAL BASIS:
University.

ELIGIBILITY:
Author of work in 18th century studies (i.e.,
the "long" 18th century, from the 1690s to
1815) in history (including the history of
science), literature, philosophy or the arts.
The work may cover Europe, the Americas,
or the Atlantic world.

New manuscripts: Any unpublished,
book-length (60,000 to 150,000 words)
manuscript in English. The author may be of
any nationality. Only manuscripts that are not
under review (i.e., not being considered for
publication at another press) elsewhere will
be considered.

Translation candidates: Books published
within the last three years in a European
language may be submitted.

Contact the Press for complete details.

FINANCIAL DATA:
Amount of support per award: $5,000, plus
publication by The University of Virginia
Press.

NUMBER OF APPLICANTS MOST RECENT YEAR:
10.

NUMBER OF AWARDS: 1 annually.

APPLICATION INFORMATION:
Include three copies of applicant's curriculum
vitae and a description (one to two typescript
pages) of the manuscript's content, scope and
intended readership. New manuscripts:
Submit three identical copies of the
manuscript simultaneously. Translation
candidates: Submit one copy of the work in
the original language together with copies of
any published reviews.

Submissions should be mailed to the address
given above, or, if mailing by courier, to the
following:
Cowen Award Judges
c/o The University of Virginia Press
210 Sprigg Lane
Charlottesville, VA 22904-4318.
Deadline: November 1 (postmark). Award
announcement in the following March.

ADDRESS INQUIRIES TO:
Angie Hogan, Assistant Editor
(See address above.)

THE WORD WORKS, INC. [706]
P.O. Box 42164
Washington, DC 20015
(301) 581-9439

E-MAIL ADDRESS:
editor@wordworksbooks.org

WEB SITE ADDRESS:
www.wordworksbooks.org

FOUNDED: 1974

AREAS OF INTEREST:
Poetry and literature.

NAME(S) OF PROGRAMS:
● **The Washington Prize**

TYPE:
Awards/prizes.

YEAR PROGRAM STARTED: 1981

PURPOSE:
To encourage and promote contemporary
American poetry.

LEGAL BASIS:
Nonprofit corporation.

ELIGIBILITY:
The Washington Prize is awarded for a
volume of original poetry in English by a
living American or Canadian writer.

GEOGRAPHIC RESTRICTIONS:
Canada and United States.

FINANCIAL DATA:
Amount of support per award: $1,500 plus
book publication.

NUMBER OF AWARDS: 1 each year.

APPLICATION INFORMATION:
Application may be submitted online. There
is an entry fee of $25 (U.S.) drawn on a U.S.
bank only, payable to The Word Works.
Deadline: January 15 to March 15. Decision
by August.

IRS IDENTIFICATION NUMBER: 52-1042022

BOARD OF DIRECTORS:
Karren L. Alenier, Chairperson of the Board
Nancy White, President
J.H. Beall
Todd Ibrahim
Rebecca Kutzer-Rice

ADDRESS INQUIRIES TO:
Nancy White, Executive Director
The Word Works Washington Prize
Adirondack Community College
640 Bay Road
Queensbury, NY 12804

*PLEASE NOTE:
The Washington Prize is for support of poets.
It is not an academic scholarship for higher
education.

THE WORD WORKS, INC. [707]
P.O. Box 42164
Washington, DC 20015
(301) 581-9439

E-MAIL ADDRESS:
editor@wordworksbooks.org

WEB SITE ADDRESS:
www.wordworksbooks.org

FOUNDED: 1974

AREAS OF INTEREST:
Poetry.

NAME(S) OF PROGRAMS:
● **Tenth Gate Prize**

TYPE:
Awards/prizes. Award is given to a living
poet with at least two full-length collections
of poetry published by literary presses.

PURPOSE:
To encourage and promote contemporary
American poetry.

ELIGIBILITY:
Submitted work must be a volume of original
poetry written in English. Applicant must
have had at least two full-length collections
of poetry published by literary presses.

FINANCIAL DATA:
Amount of support per award: $1,000 plus
book publication.

APPLICATION INFORMATION:
Application may be made online. There is an
entry fee of $25 (U.S.).
Deadline: June 1 to July 15. Decision by
November 15.

Museums and libraries

ALABAMA LIBRARY ASSOCIATION SCHOLARSHIP LOAN FUND, INC. [708]

Alabama Library Association
6030 Monticello Drive
Montgomery, AL 36117
(334) 414-0113

E-MAIL ADDRESS:
allanet.org@gmail.com

WEB SITE ADDRESS:
www.allanet.org

FOUNDED: 1904

AREAS OF INTEREST:
Library science.

NAME(S) OF PROGRAMS:
- **Scholarships in Library Science**

TYPE:
Scholarships. Scholarships for graduate study in library science/library media.

YEAR PROGRAM STARTED: 1945

PURPOSE:
To provide professional training for librarians and prospective librarians.

LEGAL BASIS:
Nonprofit corporation.

ELIGIBILITY:
Residents of Alabama who have been accepted by an accredited institution offering a graduate course in library science are eligible to apply.

GEOGRAPHIC RESTRICTIONS:
Alabama.

FINANCIAL DATA:
Amount of support per award: ALLA Centennial Memorial Scholarship and ALLA Memorial Scholarship: Up to $1,000 per award.
Total amount of support: Up to $2,000.

NUMBER OF AWARDS: 2.

APPLICATION INFORMATION:
Application forms are available online or from the Association Administrator. Three references are required and proof of admission to school.
Duration: One academic year.
Deadline: June 1.

PUBLICATIONS:
Brochure; application guidelines.

OFFICERS:
Dena Luce, President

ADDRESS INQUIRIES TO:
See e-mail address above.

AMERICAN ASSOCIATION OF LAW LIBRARIES [709]

105 West Adams Street
Suite 3300
Chicago, IL 60603
(312) 939-4764
Fax: (312) 431-1097

E-MAIL ADDRESS:
membership@aall.org

WEB SITE ADDRESS:
www.aallnet.org

FOUNDED: 1906

AREAS OF INTEREST:
Librarianship, law librarianship and law.

NAME(S) OF PROGRAMS:
- **Library Degree for Law School Graduates**
- **Library Degree for Non-Law School Graduates**
- **Library School Graduates Attending Law School**
- **Library School Graduates Seeking a Non-Law Degree**

TYPE:
Scholarships. For study of law or librarianship, with support intended for prospective law librarians.

YEAR PROGRAM STARTED: 1966

PURPOSE:
To assist qualified persons who are interested in becoming professional law librarians.

LEGAL BASIS:
Not-for-profit corporation.

ELIGIBILITY:
Preference is given to AALL members, but scholarships are not restricted to members. Evidence of financial need must be submitted.

GEOGRAPHIC RESTRICTIONS:
United States.

FINANCIAL DATA:
Amount of support per award: $1,000 to $3,000. Amounts vary according to available funds and may be limited at the discretion of the Scholarships Committee.
Total amount of support: Varies.

NUMBER OF APPLICANTS MOST RECENT YEAR:
40.

NUMBER OF AWARDS: Varies.

APPLICATION INFORMATION:
Application information is available on the web site.
Duration: Varies by scholarship.
Deadline: April 1.

ADDRESS INQUIRIES TO:
Hannah Phelps Proctor
Membership Services Coordinator
(See address above.)

AMERICAN ASSOCIATION OF LAW LIBRARIES [710]

105 West Adams Street
Suite 3300
Chicago, IL 60603
(312) 939-4764
Fax: (312) 431-1097

E-MAIL ADDRESS:
membership@aall.org

WEB SITE ADDRESS:
www.aallnet.org

FOUNDED: 1906

AREAS OF INTEREST:
Librarianship, law librarianship and minorities.

NAME(S) OF PROGRAMS:
- **George A. Strait Minority Stipend Scholarship Endowment**

TYPE:
Scholarships. Stipend for graduate study leading to a degree at an accredited school of library or information science or an accredited law school. Preference will be given to individuals with previous service to, or interest in, law librarianship.

YEAR PROGRAM STARTED: 1966

PURPOSE:
To assist qualified persons who are interested in becoming professional law librarians.

LEGAL BASIS:
Not-for-profit corporation.

ELIGIBILITY:
Application is limited to minority group members defined by current guidelines of the U.S. government. Applicant must be a degree candidate in an ALA-accredited library school or ABA-accredited law school and intend to have a career in law librarianship.

GEOGRAPHIC RESTRICTIONS:
United States.

FINANCIAL DATA:
Amount of support per award: Up to $2,500.
Total amount of support: Varies.

NUMBER OF APPLICANTS MOST RECENT YEAR:
25.

NUMBER OF AWARDS: Varies.

APPLICATION INFORMATION:
Application packet must include:
(1) an official transcript from the school where applicant completed most recent degree;
(2) a letter from the Admissions Officer of the library school, stating the program for which the applicant has been accepted and the date the courses begin, or, if applicant has already begun pursuing the degree, a transcript showing they are a degree candidate in good standing, or, if the applicant is attending law school, a transcript showing they are a degree candidate in good standing;
(3) three letters of recommendation from persons who have knowledge of the applicant's abilities and who can evaluate and comment upon law library employment experience;
(4) a personal statement discussing the applicant's interest in law librarianship, reason for applying for this scholarship, career goals as a law librarian, and any other pertinent information and;
(5) a resume.
Duration: One year.
Deadline: April 1.

ADDRESS INQUIRIES TO:
Hannah Phelps Proctor
Membership Services Coordinator
(See address above.)

AMERICAN ASSOCIATION OF SCHOOL LIBRARIANS [711]

50 East Huron Street
Chicago, IL 60611
(800) 545-2433 ext. 4382
Fax: (312) 280-5276

E-MAIL ADDRESS:
aasl@ala.org

WEB SITE ADDRESS:
www.ala.org/aasl

FOUNDED: 1951

AREAS OF INTEREST:
Libraries and librarianship.

NAME(S) OF PROGRAMS:
- **AASL Collaborative School Library Award**
- **AASL Frances Henne Award**
- **AASL Innovative Reading Grant**

- **AASL National School Library Program of the Year Award**
- **ABC-CLIO Leadership Grant**

TYPE:
Awards/prizes; Development grants; Project/program grants.

PURPOSE:
To honor distinguished service and foster professional growth in the school library profession.

ELIGIBILITY:
Frances Henne Award: The applicant must be a full-time student preparing to be a school librarian at the preschool, elementary or secondary level.

Applicants for awards/grants must be members of the American Association of School Librarians.

FINANCIAL DATA:
Amount of support per award: $1,000 to $10,000.

Total amount of support: Varies.

NUMBER OF APPLICANTS MOST RECENT YEAR:
50.

NUMBER OF AWARDS: Varies.

APPLICATION INFORMATION:
Application form and information are available from the Association.

Deadline: AASL National School Library Program of the Year Award: January 1; AASL Collaborative School Library Award, AASL Frances Henne Award, and ABC-CLIO Leadership Grant: February 1.

EXECUTIVE DIRECTOR:
Julie Walker

ADDRESS INQUIRIES TO:
See e-mail address above.

AMERICAN ASSOCIATION OF SCHOOL LIBRARIANS   [712]
50 East Huron Street
Chicago, IL 60611
(800) 545-2433 ext. 4382
Fax: (312) 280-5276

E-MAIL ADDRESS:
aasl@ala.org

WEB SITE ADDRESS:
www.ala.org/aasl

FOUNDED: 1951

AREAS OF INTEREST:
Libraries.

NAME(S) OF PROGRAMS:
- **Distinguished Service Award**

TYPE:
Awards/prizes. Baker and Taylor provides funding for this award.

YEAR PROGRAM STARTED: 1978

PURPOSE:
To honor distinguished service and foster professional growth in the school library field.

ELIGIBILITY:
Nominator must be a member of AASL.

FINANCIAL DATA:
Amount of support per award: $3,000 and a citation.

Total amount of support: $3,000.

NUMBER OF AWARDS: 1.

APPLICATION INFORMATION:
Application form and information are available from the Association.

Deadline: February 1.

ADDRESS INQUIRIES TO:
See e-mail address above.

AMERICAN LIBRARY ASSOCIATION (ALA)   [713]
50 East Huron Street
Chicago, IL 60611-2795
(312) 280-3247
(800) 545-2433 ext. 3247
Fax: (312) 280-5014

E-MAIL ADDRESS:
awards@ala.org

WEB SITE ADDRESS:
www.ala.org

FOUNDED: 1876

AREAS OF INTEREST:
Librarianship.

NAME(S) OF PROGRAMS:
- **ALA Awards**

TYPE:
Awards/prizes; Conferences/seminars; Development grants; Fellowships; Research grants; Scholarships; Seed money grants; Travel grants. Cash and noncash awards for achievement/distinguished service, authors/illustrators/publishers, exhibits, funding, intellectual freedom, literacy, professional development, public relations, publications/articles and special services, as well as scholarships, fellowships and research grants sponsored by ALA and its units.

PURPOSE:
To honor distinguished service and foster professional growth.

FINANCIAL DATA:
Amount of support per award: Awards: $250 to $10,000; Research Grants and Fellowships: $500 to $10,000.

Total amount of support: Varies.

COOPERATIVE FUNDING PROGRAMS: Some grants are sponsored by Baker and Taylor, H.W. Wilson Company and Voice of Youth Advocates.

NUMBER OF AWARDS: More than 150 annually.

REPRESENTATIVE AWARDS:
Academic or Research Librarian of the Year Award for outstanding contribution to academic and research librarianship and library development, $3,000 (donated by Baker & Taylor); The H.W. Wilson Library Staff Development Grant to library organization for a program to further its goals and objectives, $3,500 (donated by The H.W. Wilson Company); Frances Henne Research Grant to provide seed money to an individual, institution or group for a project to encourage research on library service to young adults, $500 minimum (donated by Voice of Youth Advocates); David H. Clift Scholarship to worthy U.S. or Canadian citizen to begin an M.L.S. degree in an ALA-accredited program, $3,000 (donated by scholarship endowment interest, individual contributions).

APPLICATION INFORMATION:
Application information is available on the web site.

Duration: Varies.

Deadline: December 1.

ADDRESS INQUIRIES TO:
Cheryl Malden, Program Officer
(See address above.)

ASSOCIATION FOR LIBRARY AND INFORMATION SCIENCE EDUCATION   [714]
65 East Wacker Place, Suite 1900
Chicago, IL 60601-7246
(312) 795-0996
Fax: (312) 419-8950

E-MAIL ADDRESS:
contact@alise.org

WEB SITE ADDRESS:
www.alise.org

FOUNDED: 1915

AREAS OF INTEREST:
Library and information science education.

NAME(S) OF PROGRAMS:
- **ALISE Research Awards**

TYPE:
Awards/prizes; Research grants. Award for an outstanding research proposal in the field of librarianship and information science.

YEAR PROGRAM STARTED: 1976

PURPOSE:
To provide support for research which will help to promote excellence in education for librarianship and information science.

LEGAL BASIS:
Nonprofit 501(c)(3) corporation.

ELIGIBILITY:
Eligibility is determined on the basis of the project's appropriateness to the goals of the ALISE, evidence of an established methodology and a viable research design, likelihood of completion in 12 to 18 months and on the qualifications of the researcher, who should be an ALISE member. Evidence that other funds are not available for the project should be presented.

The award cannot be used to support a doctoral dissertation. At least one applicant in a group submitting a proposal must be a personal member of the Association as of the deadline date. Staff training, general operating or overhead expenses, and other indirect costs are not funded.

Recipients of the award must present a progress report at the ALISE Annual Conference, submit written quarterly reports to the Executive Director of ALISE, who will pay the grant in periodic installments as the research progresses, submit the results of the funded study to the Association's Journal of Education for Library and Information Science (JELIS) for possible publication prior to submission to other publications, that is, the Journal will have first option on publication, acknowledge the support of ALISE in any publicity or presentation based on the funded study and inform the Executive Director if they receive research funding in addition to that provided by ALISE.

FINANCIAL DATA:
Allowable expenses include salaries for secretarial and research assistance, purchasing, processing and duplicating of print and nonprint materials, mailing, telephone and other communications costs and travel and per diem directly related to the research project.

Expenses normally not allowed include living expenses to supplement the investigator's salary, institutional overhead and other expenses not normally supported by research grants awarded by the U.S. Department of Education.

Amount of support per award: Up to $5,000.

Total amount of support: $5,000 annually.

NUMBER OF AWARDS: 1.

REPRESENTATIVE AWARDS:
Joan Cherry, Lusanne Freund and Wendy Duff, University of Toronto for "Learning From Our Student: Assessing Student Perceptions of Information Studies Programs and The Information Professions."

APPLICATION INFORMATION:
Proposals should be succinct and precise. No more than 20 double-spaced, typed pages. If necessary, supporting information may be included in an appendix. Proposals must include the following information to be considered in the competition:
(1) abstract of the project in no greater than 200 words;
(2) problem statement and literature review including justification and need for the research;
(3) project objectives;
(4) project description;
(5) research design, methodology and analysis techniques;
(6) detailed budget (including institutional or departmental contributions, if any);
(7) expected benefits and impact from the research;
(8) vita(e) of project investigator(s) and;
(9) ten copies of the proposal and an e-mail/postal return address should be submitted to ALISE, Attn.: ALISE Res Com Awards, c/o Information International Associates, see address above.

Duration: One year.

Deadline: July 15. Announcement the following January.

PUBLICATIONS:
Application guidelines.

IRS IDENTIFICATION NUMBER: 51-0193882

STAFF:
Kathleen Combs, Executive Director

BOARD OF DIRECTORS AND OFFICERS:
Clara Chu, President
Steven MacCall, Secretary/Treasurer
Carol Tilly, Director for External Relations
Laurie Bonnici, Director for Membership Services
Don Latham, Director for Special Interest Groups

ADDRESS INQUIRIES TO:
ALISE Awards
(See address above.)

*SPECIAL STIPULATIONS:
The Research Grant award cannot be used to support a doctoral dissertation.

ASSOCIATION FOR LIBRARY AND INFORMATION SCIENCE EDUCATION [715]

65 East Wacker Place, Suite 1900
Chicago, IL 60601-7246
(312) 795-0996
Fax: (312) 419-8950

E-MAIL ADDRESS:
contact@alise.org

WEB SITE ADDRESS:
www.alise.org

FOUNDED: 1915

AREAS OF INTEREST:
Library and information science education.

NAME(S) OF PROGRAMS:
● **ALISE/ProQuest Methodology Paper Competition**
● **The Eugene Garfield/ALISE Doctoral Dissertation Competition**
● **Bohdan S. Wynar Research Paper Competition**

TYPE:
Awards/prizes. Awards for an outstanding unpublished research paper, methodology paper and for each of two outstanding doctoral dissertations, respectively.

YEAR PROGRAM STARTED: 1977

PURPOSE:
To encourage research in the field of library and information science education and related areas.

LEGAL BASIS:
Nonprofit 501(c)(3) corporation.

ELIGIBILITY:
ALISE/ProQuest Methodology Paper Competition is open to all types of methodology. Papers must be limited to description and discussion of a research method or a technique associated with a particular research method. Papers must explain the particular method/technique, including methodological implications for library and information science. Examples to illustrate its value can come from LIS-related published studies, proposed studies, and works in progress. Papers that stress findings are not eligible.

The Eugene Garfield/ALISE Doctoral Dissertation Competition is open to doctoral students who have recently graduated in any field of study, or who will have completed their dissertations by the deadline. Dissertations must deal with substantive issues related to library and information science, but applicants may be from within or outside LIS programs.

Bohdan S. Wynar Research Paper Competition is open to research papers concerning any aspect of library and information science. This competition is not limited to research regarding LIS education. Any research methodology is acceptable.

FINANCIAL DATA:
Amount of support per award:
ALISE/ProQuest Methodology Paper and The Eugene Garfield/ALISE Doctoral Dissertation Competitions: $500 each; Bohdan S. Wynar Research Paper Competition: $2,500.

NUMBER OF AWARDS: ALISE/ProQuest Methodology Paper Competition: 1; The Eugene Garfield/ALISE Doctoral Dissertation and Bohdan S. Wynar Research Paper Competitions: Up to 2 each.

APPLICATION INFORMATION:
Application information is available on the web site.

Deadline: ALISE/ProQuest Methodology Paper and Bohdan S. Wynar Research Paper Competitions: July 15; The Eugene Garfield/ALISE Doctoral Dissertation Competition: June 30.

IRS IDENTIFICATION NUMBER: 51-0193882

STAFF:
Kathleen Combs, Executive Director

BOARD OF DIRECTORS AND OFFICERS:
Clara Chu, President
Steven MacCall, Secretary/Treasurer
Carol Tilly, Director for External Relations
Laurie Bonnici, Director for Membership Services
Don Latham, Director for Special Interest Groups

ADDRESS INQUIRIES TO:
ALISE Awards
(See address above.)

BETA PHI MU [716]

Drexel University
College of Computing and Informatics
3141 Chestnut Street
Philadelphia, PA 19104
(215) 895-2492
Fax: (215) 895-2494

E-MAIL ADDRESS:
betaphimu@drexel.edu

WEB SITE ADDRESS:
www.beta-phi-mu.org

FOUNDED: 1948

AREAS OF INTEREST:
Library and information studies.

NAME(S) OF PROGRAMS:
● **Eugene Garfield Doctoral Dissertation Fellowship**
● **Harold Lancour Scholarship for Foreign Study**
● **Sarah Rebecca Reed Scholarship**
● **Frank B. Sessa Scholarship for Continuing Education of a Beta Phi Mu Member**
● **Blanche E. Woolls Scholarship for School Media Service**

TYPE:
Fellowships; Scholarships. Eugene Garfield Doctoral Dissertation Fellowship is funded through the generosity of Eugene Garfield, and provides fellowships for up to six students per year. They are awarded to foster high-quality research in the field and to expedite the movement of new Doctorates into teaching positions.

The Harold Lancour Scholarship is given for foreign study.

The Sarah Rebecca Reed Scholarship is given to a beginning student at the Master's level accepted in an American Library Association-accredited program.

The Frank B. Sessa Scholarship is given for Continuing Education for a Beta Phi Mu member.

The Blanche Woolls Scholarship is given to a beginning student at the Master's level accepted in an American Library Association-Accredited Program majoring in School Media Services.

PURPOSE:
To assist qualified persons who are interested in completing a course of advanced study in library and information studies.

LEGAL BASIS:
Nonprofit organization.

FINANCIAL DATA:
Amount of support per award: Garfield Doctoral Dissertation Fellowship: $3,000; Lancour Scholarship: $1,750; Reed and Woolls Scholarships: $2,250 each; Sessa Scholarship: $1,500.

Total amount of support: Up to $28,000.

NUMBER OF APPLICANTS MOST RECENT YEAR: 85.

NUMBER OF AWARDS: 10.

APPLICATION INFORMATION:
Forms are available on the Society's web site.
Duration: One-time award. Nonrenewable.
Deadline: March 15.

PUBLICATIONS:
The Pipeline, online newsletter.

STAFF:
Alison M. Lewis, Ph.D., Executive Director
Erin Gabriele, Program Director

ADDRESS INQUIRIES TO:
Erin Gabriele, Program Director
(See address above.)

GLADYS BROOKS FOUNDATION

1055 Franklin Avenue
Suite 208
Garden City, NY 11530-2903
(516) 746-6103

WEB SITE ADDRESS:
www.gladysbrooksfoundation.org

TYPE:
Capital grants; Challenge/matching grants; Demonstration grants; Development grants; Endowments; Matching gifts; Project/program grants; Scholarships. Grants to private, not-for-profit publicly supported libraries, educational institutions, hospitals and clinics in the eastern U.S.

See entry 1188 for full listing.

CALIFORNIA LIBRARY ASSOCIATION   [717]

2471 Flores Street
San Mateo, CA 94403
(650) 376-0886
Fax: (650) 539-2341

E-MAIL ADDRESS:
info@cla-net.org

WEB SITE ADDRESS:
www.cla-net.org

FOUNDED: 1896

AREAS OF INTEREST:
Librarianship.

NAME(S) OF PROGRAMS:
● **Begun Scholarship**
● **CLA Scholarship for Minority Students in Memory of Edna Yelland**
● **Reference Service Press Fellowship**

TYPE:
Fellowships; Scholarships. Support for minority library school students. Support for graduate students in reference/information service librarianship.

YEAR PROGRAM STARTED: 1973

PURPOSE:
To help support the educational goals of minority students in the library service field.

LEGAL BASIS:
Nonprofit.

ELIGIBILITY:
Applicant must be accepted by a graduate library school in California, accredited by the American Library Association, be of ethnic origin and show financial need. California residents and U.S. citizens or permanent U.S. residents may apply. For fellowships, applicants must be preparing for a career in reference or information service librarianship. Students pursuing an M.L.S. on a part-time or full-time basis are equally eligible.

GEOGRAPHIC RESTRICTIONS:
California.

FINANCIAL DATA:
Amount of support per award: Generally $2,500 per Edna Yelland Scholarship; $3,000 for Begun Scholarship; $3,000 for fellowship.
Total amount of support: $10,500 for scholarships; $3,000 for fellowship.

NUMBER OF APPLICANTS MOST RECENT YEAR:
25.

NUMBER OF AWARDS: 4 scholarships and 1 fellowship each year.

APPLICATION INFORMATION:
Application includes academic record, essay and letters of recommendation.
Duration: One-time award.
Deadline: Mid-March.

ADDRESS INQUIRIES TO:
Natalie Cole, Interim Executive Director
(See address above.)

CAMBRIDGE UNIVERSITY LIBRARY   [718]

West Road
Cambridge CB3 9DR England
(01223) 333083
Fax: (01223) 339973

E-MAIL ADDRESS:
sm683@cam.ac.uk

WEB SITE ADDRESS:
www.lib.cam.ac.uk

FOUNDED: 1400

AREAS OF INTEREST:
Bibliographic research.

NAME(S) OF PROGRAMS:
● **The Munby Fellowship in Bibliography**

TYPE:
Fellowships. Graduate fellowships for bibliographical research based on the collections of Cambridge libraries.

YEAR PROGRAM STARTED: 1977

LEGAL BASIS:
University.

ELIGIBILITY:
Open to university graduates of postdoctoral or equivalent level, of any nationality or age. Research must be bibliographical.

FINANCIAL DATA:
Amount of support per award: GBP 32,267 for the year 2012-13.

NUMBER OF APPLICANTS MOST RECENT YEAR:
50.

NUMBER OF AWARDS: 1.

APPLICATION INFORMATION:
Applicants must send a completed cover sheet (available from the Library), curriculum vitae and statement of proposed research.
Duration: One year.

PUBLICATIONS:
Application guidelines.

ADDRESS INQUIRIES TO:
The Deputy Librarian
(See address above.)

CANADIAN LIBRARY ASSOCIATION/ASSOCIATION CANADIENNE DES BIBLIOTHEQUES   [719]

1150 Morrison Drive, Suite 400
Ottawa ON K2H 8S9 Canada
(613) 232-9625 ext. 301
Fax: (613) 563-9895

E-MAIL ADDRESS:
membership@cla.ca

WEB SITE ADDRESS:
www.cla.ca

FOUNDED: 1946

AREAS OF INTEREST:
Development and promotion of excellence in librarianship and library information services.

NAME(S) OF PROGRAMS:
● **Library Research and Development Grants**

TYPE:
Awards/prizes. Grants are awarded annually, when merited, to personal members of the Canadian Library Association, in support of theoretical and applied research in library and information services.

PURPOSE:
To support theoretical and applied research in the field of library and information services; to encourage and support research undertaken by practitioners in the field of library and information services; to promote research in the field of library and information services by and/or about Canadians.

LEGAL BASIS:
Nonprofit organization.

ELIGIBILITY:
Proposals for funding are judged on originality or necessity of research, appropriateness of proposed project to the goals and objectives of the Canadian Library Association, cost-effectiveness of research in terms of the expected influence and ramifications of the results, timeliness of the research, assurance of project management and control, appropriateness of the proposed research method and design, completeness of application and availability of other funding to researcher.

Preference will be given to submissions from practitioners in the field of library and information services.

FINANCIAL DATA:
Total amount of support: Maximum $1,000 per year.

NUMBER OF AWARDS: Varies.

APPLICATION INFORMATION:
Grant applicants should submit their proposal via e-mail as an MS Word document in either French or English to the Chair, Research and Development Grant. Grant applications should be submitted in the form of a letter, four pages or less, containing the following:
(1) title of the research project;
(2) name and address of applicant, mailing address and date of application (this information should be listed on a separate page from the body of the application);
(3) a reasonable description of the research project identifying methodology and design;
(4) duration of the project, including a detailed project timetable;
(5) assessment of the potential utility of research results to the Canadian library community;

(6) a detailed assessment of costs and statement of other grants/awards received and;
(7) an assessment of relevance of the research to the goals and objectives of the Canadian library community.

Applications that do not follow submission guidelines and headers will not be considered.

ADDRESS INQUIRIES TO:
Library Research and Development Committee
(See address above.)

CANADIAN LIBRARY ASSOCIATION/ASSOCIATION CANADIENNE DES BIBLIOTHEQUES [720]

1150 Morrison Drive, Suite 400
Ottawa ON K2H 8S9 Canada
(613) 232-9625
Fax: (613) 563-9895

E-MAIL ADDRESS:
info@cla.ca

WEB SITE ADDRESS:
www.cla.ca

FOUNDED: 1946

AREAS OF INTEREST:
Development and promotion of excellence in librarianship and library/information services.

CONSULTING OR VOLUNTEER SERVICES:
Continuing education and professional development for library and information personnel.

NAME(S) OF PROGRAMS:
- **CLA/ACB Dafoe Scholarship**
- **The H.W. Wilson Scholarship**

TYPE:
Scholarships. Awarded for advanced study in the field of librarianship. Award is tenable at an accredited library school in either Canada or the U.S.

YEAR PROGRAM STARTED: 1969

PURPOSE:
To support programs of study or series of courses either leading to a further library degree or related to library work.

LEGAL BASIS:
Nonprofit organization.

ELIGIBILITY:
Canadian citizens or individuals holding landed immigrant status are eligible to apply. Candidates must be commencing studies for their first professional library degree at an ALA-accredited institution.

FINANCIAL DATA:
Amount of support per award: CLA/ACB Dafoe Scholarship: $5,000; H.W. Wilson Scholarship: $2,000.

COOPERATIVE FUNDING PROGRAMS: Programs supported by H.W. Wilson Company and the CLA Scholarship Fund.

NUMBER OF AWARDS: 1 annually.

APPLICATION INFORMATION:
Official application materials are available upon request to the address above.
Duration: The award is tenable for one academic year consisting of two semesters or three quarters.
Deadline: May 1.

ADDRESS INQUIRIES TO:
Scholarships and Awards Committee
(See address above.)

CONNECTICUT LIBRARY ASSOCIATION [721]

234 Court Street
Middletown, CT 06457
(860) 346-2444
Fax: (860) 344-9199

E-MAIL ADDRESS:
cla@ctlibrarians.org

WEB SITE ADDRESS:
www.ctlibraryassociation.org

NAME(S) OF PROGRAMS:
- **Connecticut Library Association's Program for Educational Grants**

TYPE:
Grants-in-aid. Grants for personnel at all levels of library work.

YEAR PROGRAM STARTED: 1976

PURPOSE:
To support the educational goals of library science students in Connecticut.

LEGAL BASIS:
Nonprofit organization.

ELIGIBILITY:
Grants are made to CLA members only.

GEOGRAPHIC RESTRICTIONS:
Connecticut.

FINANCIAL DATA:
Amount of support per award: Up to $400.
Total amount of support: Varies.

NUMBER OF AWARDS: Up to 4 or 5 grants per year.

APPLICATION INFORMATION:
Apply to the Chairperson, Program for Educational Grants, at the address above.
Duration: One year. Not renewable.
Deadline: Reviewed at quarterly meetings.

ADDRESS INQUIRIES TO:
Peter F. Ciparelli, PEG Chairman
Killingly Public Library
25 Westcott Road
Danielson, CT 06239-2928
E-mail: pciparelli@biblio.org
Tel: (860) 779-5383

*PLEASE NOTE:
Only for continuing education, workshops and seminars. Any other applications will be considered at the discretion of the committee.

GEORGIA LIBRARY ASSOCIATION [722]

P.O. Box 793
Rex, GA 30273
(678) 466-4325
Fax: (678) 466-4349

E-MAIL ADDRESS:
gordonbaker@clayton.edu

WEB SITE ADDRESS:
gla.georgialibraries.org/scholarship.htm

FOUNDED: 1897

AREAS OF INTEREST:
Library professional development.

NAME(S) OF PROGRAMS:
- **Beard Scholarship**
- **Hubbard Scholarship**

TYPE:
Scholarships. Awards for graduate study of library science.

PURPOSE:
To recruit excellent librarians for Georgia.

LEGAL BASIS:
Professional association.

ELIGIBILITY:
Applicants must be accepted for admission to a Master's program at an ALA-accredited library school and must indicate intention to complete the Master's program within three years. Recipient must work in a library in Georgia for at least one year after graduation from ALA-accredited library school. Beard Scholarship is for candidates who demonstrate leadership potential.

GEOGRAPHIC RESTRICTIONS:
Georgia.

FINANCIAL DATA:
Amount of support per award: Beard Scholarship: $1,000; Hubbard Scholarship: $3,000.
Total amount of support: $4,000 annually.

NUMBER OF AWARDS: 1 each annually.

APPLICATION INFORMATION:
Applicant must submit to the Chair the following:
(1) one official application form (applicant may be considered for both scholarships via one form and other accompanying documentation; do not submit duplicate materials);
(2) proof of admission to an American Library Association-accredited Master's program/library school, i.e., a letter from the dean of the school/program certifying acceptance (photocopy is acceptable);
(3) three letters of reference sent directly from the reference to the Committee Chair and;
(4) official transcripts of all academic work sent directly to the Chair from each college or university attended.
Duration: Beard Scholarship: Up to two semesters; Hubbard Scholarship: Up to four semesters. Both are nonrenewable.
Deadline: Beard and Hubbard Scholarships: May 21.

ADDRESS INQUIRIES TO:
Karen Viars
GLA Scholarship Committee
GPC Alpharetta Center Library
3705 Brookside Parkway
Alpharetta, GA 30022

*SPECIAL STIPULATIONS:
The scholarship winners must agree to work in Georgia for one year following receipt of the Master's degree or agree to pay back a prorated amount of the award plus interest. Repayment must be made within two years.

HARTFORD PUBLIC LIBRARY [723]

500 Main Street
Hartford, CT 06103-3075
(860) 695-6330
Fax: (860) 722-6897

E-MAIL ADDRESS:
lmcclure@hplct.org

WEB SITE ADDRESS:
www.hplct.org

FOUNDED: 1774

NAME(S) OF PROGRAMS:
- **The Caroline M. Hewins Scholarship**

TYPE:
Scholarships. Awarded to candidates for
M.L.S. who will work with children.

YEAR PROGRAM STARTED: 1926

PURPOSE:
To assist in graduate Library Science study,
leading to a career in library service with
children.

ELIGIBILITY:
Students who plan to specialize in library
work with children, who have received or are
about to receive a four-year undergraduate
degree and who have been admitted to or are
attending an ALA-accredited library school
are eligible. Preference is given to applicants
who plan to pursue a career in public library
service.

FINANCIAL DATA:
Amount of support per award: Up to $4,000.
Total amount of support: Up to $4,000
annually.

NUMBER OF AWARDS: 1 annually.

APPLICATION INFORMATION:
The application form can be downloaded
from the web site or obtained by writing to
the Library, at the above address.
Deadline: Completed applications must be
submitted by May 1.

ADDRESS INQUIRIES TO:
Lisa McClure
Youth and Family Services Director
(See address above.)

HARVARD UKRAINIAN RESEARCH INSTITUTE [724]

34 Kirkland Street
Cambridge, MA 02138
(617) 495-4053
Fax: (617) 495-8097

E-MAIL ADDRESS:
huri@fas.harvard.edu

WEB SITE ADDRESS:
www.huri.harvard.edu

FOUNDED: 1980

AREAS OF INTEREST:
Ukrainian studies.

NAME(S) OF PROGRAMS:
● **Eugene and Daymel Shklar Fellowships in Ukrainian Studies**

TYPE:
Fellowships.

YEAR PROGRAM STARTED: 1980

PURPOSE:
To promote scholarship in history, literature,
philology and other disciplines relating to the
Ukraine.

LEGAL BASIS:
Nonprofit organization.

ELIGIBILITY:
Individuals who hold a Doctorate in
Ukrainian history, literature, linguistics,
philology or culture and other fields in the
humanities and social sciences and have
demonstrated scholarship in Ukrainian studies
are eligible to apply.

FINANCIAL DATA:
Amount of support per award: $3,300 per
month.
Total amount of support: Average: $13,200.

APPLICATION INFORMATION:
Application information is available on the
web site.
Duration: Four months average.
Deadline: March 11 for following academic
year. Announcement after May 1.

ADDRESS INQUIRIES TO:
Harvard Ukrainian Research Institute
(See address above.)

HERITAGE PRESERVATION [725]

1012 14th Street, N.W., Suite 1200
Washington, DC 20005
(202) 233-0800
Fax: (202) 233-0807

E-MAIL ADDRESS:
cap@heritagepreservation.org

WEB SITE ADDRESS:
www.heritagepreservation.org

FOUNDED: 1973

AREAS OF INTEREST:
Conservation assessment of museum
collections.

CONSULTING OR VOLUNTEER SERVICES:
Professional consulting services.

NAME(S) OF PROGRAMS:
● **Conservation Assessment Program**

TYPE:
Technical assistance. Provides funds for an
independent, professional conservation
assessment of a museum's collections and
environmental conditions and, where
appropriate, historic structures. The assessor's
resulting report will identify conservation
priorities to assist the museum in developing
a long-term plan for collections care and
management.

YEAR PROGRAM STARTED: 1990

PURPOSE:
To make collections care and conservation a
fundamental priority of museums and
historical societies.

LEGAL BASIS:
Private and nonprofit.

ELIGIBILITY:
Institutions including museums, zoos,
aquariums, botanical gardens and arboreta are
eligible for assistance. For museums located
in historic structures, CAP will also support
the on-site participation of an architectural
assessor. Zoos and aquariums that do not
have an assessment of the animals' physical
conditions and habitats can use the program
for a general assessment of those collections.

GEOGRAPHIC RESTRICTIONS:
United States.

FINANCIAL DATA:
Amount of support per award: $3,390 to
$7,190, depending on institution and
collections.
Total amount of support: Varies.

NUMBER OF APPLICANTS MOST RECENT YEAR:
132.

NUMBER OF AWARDS: 83 participants for the
2013 program year.

APPLICATION INFORMATION:
Notification of the release of CAP application
online will be emailed to all museums on
CAP's e-mail list on October 1, 2014. To
receive this notification, museums should
submit their e-mail address to
cap@heritagepreservation.org. Institutions

should submit application materials as soon
as possible as applications are reviewed as
they are received.
Duration: One year.
Deadline: December 1.

PUBLICATIONS:
Sample CAP application with guidelines;
CAP brochure; *Heritage Preservation*,
publications brochure; annual report.

STAFF:
Teresa Martinez, Director, Conservation
Assessment Program
Melanie Zucker, Assistant, Conservation
Assessment Program

ADDRESS INQUIRIES TO:
Conservation Assessment Program
(See address above.)

INDIANA LIBRARY FEDERATION [726]

941 East 86th Street
Suite 260
Indianapolis, IN 46240
(317) 257-2040
Fax: (317) 257-1389

E-MAIL ADDRESS:
askus@ilfonline.org

WEB SITE ADDRESS:
www.ilfonline.org

FOUNDED: 1891

AREAS OF INTEREST:
Librarian education and training.

NAME(S) OF PROGRAMS:
● **The Esther Schlundt Fund**
● **The Sue Marsh Weller Fund**

TYPE:
Scholarships. Awards for graduate study of
library science at ALA-Accredited schools.

PURPOSE:
To aid students in financial need who have
strong undergraduate records and who show
unusual ability in the library field either
public or academic.

LEGAL BASIS:
Professional association.

ELIGIBILITY:
Applicants must be legal residents of Indiana
who intend to work in an Indiana library for
at least one year after completing library
education and must be enrolled in an
ALA-Accredited graduate program of library
science.

GEOGRAPHIC RESTRICTIONS:
Indiana.

FINANCIAL DATA:
Amount of support per award: Up to $1,100.
Total amount of support: Varies.

APPLICATION INFORMATION:
Application must be made in writing. Further
information may be requested from the
Federation.
Deadline: June 30.

ADDRESS INQUIRIES TO:
Susan Akers, Executive Director
(See address above.)

INSTITUTE OF MUSEUM AND LIBRARY SERVICES [727]
1800 M Street, N.W., 9th Floor
Washington, DC 20036
(202) 653-4657
Fax: (202) 653-4600
TTY: (202) 606-8636

E-MAIL ADDRESS:
imlsinfo@imls.gov

WEB SITE ADDRESS:
www.imls.gov

FOUNDED: 1996

AREAS OF INTEREST:
Museums in all disciplines including art, history, science, as well as aquariums and zoological parks, botanical gardens, arboretums, planetariums, nature centers, natural history and children's museums.

Libraries, including public libraries, archives, public elementary or secondary school libraries, academic libraries, and research libraries (which make publicly available library services and materials suitable for scholarly research and not otherwise available to the public and are not an integral part of institutions of higher education) and private libraries (only if determined by the state in which they are located that they are libraries for the purposes of the Library Services and Technology Act). Special funding categories for state library administrative agencies, tribal libraries and organizations providing library services to Native Hawaiians.

NAME(S) OF PROGRAMS:
- **Conservation Assessment Program**
- **Museum Assessment Program**
- **National Leadership Grants**
- **National Medal for Museum and Library Services**
- **Native American Library Services: Basic Grants**
- **Native Hawaiian Library Services Grant**
- **Sparks! Ignition Grants for Libraries**
- **Sparks! Ignition Grants for Museums**

TYPE:
Awards/prizes; Challenge/matching grants; Conferences/seminars; Demonstration grants; Development grants; Fellowships; Formula grants; Internships; Project/program grants; Research grants; Scholarships; Seed money grants; Technical assistance; Training grants; Research contracts. Conservation Assessment Program, which is funded by IMLS and administered by Heritage Preservation, provides a general conservation assessment of a museum's collection, environmental conditions and site.

Museum Assessment Program (MAP) provides eligible museums noncompetitive grants of technical assistance in one of the following three categories: institutional assessment, collections management assessment, and a public dimension assessment.

National Leadership Grants enhance the quality of library and museum services nationwide in several categories of funding. The competitive grants support model projects that can be widely replicated.

National Medal for Museum and Library Services is the nation's highest honor for libraries and museums and is awarded by IMLS to outstanding institutions that make exceptional contributions to their communities.

Native American Library Services grants provide funds for core library operations, technical assistance, and innovative project grants for libraries serving Native Americans and Alaska Native villages.

A Native Hawaiian Library Services Grant is awarded annually to an organization providing library services to Native Hawaiians.

Sparks! Ignition Grants for Libraries provide an opportunity to expand and test the boundaries of library and archive services and practices.

Sparks! Ignition Grants for Museums provide an opportunity to expand and test the boundaries of museum services and practices.

YEAR PROGRAM STARTED: 1977

PURPOSE:
To foster leadership, innovation and lifetime learning by supporting museums and libraries.

LEGAL BASIS:
Federal independent agency within the Executive Branch.

ELIGIBILITY:
All types of museums, large and small, are eligible for funding. An eligible museum must be a public or private nonprofit institution that exists on a permanent basis for educational or aesthetic purposes.

All types of libraries and archives, except federal and for-profit libraries, are eligible for National Leadership Grants. Restricted funding categories exist for state library administrative agencies and for library services to Native Americans and Native Hawaiians.

Funds cannot be used for construction, renovation of facilities, endowment or acquisition of objects. Contact IMLS for program-specific eligibility.

GEOGRAPHIC RESTRICTIONS:
United States, American Samoa, Guam, the Marshall Islands, Micronesia, Northern Mariana Islands, Palau, Puerto Rico or the Virgin Islands.

APPLICATION INFORMATION:
Grant program guidelines and application instructions are available at IMLS web site.
Deadline: Varies.

PUBLICATIONS:
Annual report.

INSTITUTE OF MUSEUM AND LIBRARY SERVICES [728]
1800 M Street, N.W., 9th Floor
Washington, DC 20036
(202) 653-4657
Fax: (202) 653-4600

E-MAIL ADDRESS:
imlsinfo@imls.gov

WEB SITE ADDRESS:
www.imls.gov

FOUNDED: 1996

AREAS OF INTEREST:
Museums in all disciplines including art, history, science, as well as aquariums and zoological parks, botanical gardens, arboretums, planetariums, nature centers, natural history and children's museums.

Libraries, including public libraries, archives, public elementary or secondary school libraries, academic libraries, and research libraries (which make publicly available library services and materials suitable for scholarly research and not otherwise available to the public and are not an integral part of institutions of higher education) and private libraries (only if determined by the state in which they are located that they are libraries for the purposes of the Library Services and Technology Act). Special funding categories for state library administrative agencies, tribal libraries and organizations providing library services to Native Hawaiians.

NAME(S) OF PROGRAMS:
- **Laura Bush 21st Century Librarian Program**
- **Museum Grants for African American History and Culture**
- **Museums for America**
- **Native American Library Services: Enhancement Grants**
- **Native American/Native Hawaiian Museum Services Program**

TYPE:
Project/program grants. Laura Bush 21st Century Librarian Program: Project types of collections management, community engagement, conservation, formal education, informal learning, partnerships, professional development/continuing education, research.

Museum Grants for African American History and Culture: Project types of professional development/continuing education.

Museums for America: Project types of collections management, community engagement, demonstration, digital collections/tools, formal education, informal learning, partnerships, professional development/continuing education, public programs, research.

Native American Library Services: Enhancement Grants: Project types of collections management, community engagement, digital collections/tools, informal learning, partnerships, professional development/continuing education, public programs.

Native American/Native Hawaiian Museum Services Program: Project types of collections management, community engagement, conservation, digital collections/tools, formal education, informal learning, partnerships, professional development/continuing education, public programs, research.

PURPOSE:
To foster leadership, innovation and lifetime learning by supporting museums and libraries.

LEGAL BASIS:
Federal independent agency within the Executive Branch.

ELIGIBILITY:
All types of museums, large and small, are eligible for funding. An eligible museum must be a public or private nonprofit institution that exists on a permanent basis for educational or aesthetic purposes.

Restricted funding categories exist for state library administrative agencies and for library services to Native Americans and Native Hawaiians.

Funds cannot be used for construction, renovation of facilities, endowment or acquisition of objects. Contact IMLS for program-specific eligibility.

GEOGRAPHIC RESTRICTIONS:
United States and territories.

FINANCIAL DATA:
Amount of support per award: Varies.
Total amount of support: Varies.

NUMBER OF APPLICANTS MOST RECENT YEAR:
Varies.

NUMBER OF AWARDS: Varies.

APPLICATION INFORMATION:
Application information is available online.
Duration: Varies per award.
Deadline: Varies.

MEDICAL LIBRARY ASSOCIATION   [729]
65 East Wacker Place
Suite 1900
Chicago, IL 60601-7246
(312) 419-9094
Fax: (312) 419-8950

E-MAIL ADDRESS:
grants@mlahq.org

WEB SITE ADDRESS:
www.mlanet.org/awards

FOUNDED: 1898

AREAS OF INTEREST:
Health sciences librarianship.

NAME(S) OF PROGRAMS:
● **MLA Scholarship**
● **Thomson Reuters/MLA Doctoral Fellowship**

TYPE:
Fellowships; Scholarships. Awarded for study and doctoral work in health sciences librarianship.

Thomson Reuters/MLA Doctoral Fellowship is awarded biennially. It was established by the Institute for Scientific Information (ISI) and is administered by the MLA.

YEAR PROGRAM STARTED: 1986

PURPOSE:
To support and encourage individuals who are qualified to make a contribution to librarianship.

LEGAL BASIS:
Nonprofit.

ELIGIBILITY:
Citizens or permanent residents of the U.S. or Canada are eligible to apply.

Applicants for the MLA Scholarship must be entering an ALA-Accredited graduate library school or, at the time of the granting of the scholarship (February), have completed no more than one-half of the academic requirements of the graduate program. An applicant who is a past recipient of the MLA Scholarship or the MLA Scholarship for Minority Students is ineligible.

For the Thomson Reuters/MLA Doctoral Fellowship, applicants must be graduates of an ALA-Accredited library school. They must also have been accepted to candidacy in a Ph.D. program in health sciences librarianship with an emphasis on biomedical and health-related information science. A past recipient of the MLA Doctoral Fellowship is ineligible.

GEOGRAPHIC RESTRICTIONS:
United States and Canada.

FINANCIAL DATA:
Amount of support per award: MLA Scholarship: Up to $5,000; Thomson Reuters/MLA Doctoral Fellowship: Up to $2,000.

NUMBER OF AWARDS: MLA Scholarships: 1 each per year; Thomson Reuters/MLA Doctoral Fellowship: 1 every two years.

APPLICATION INFORMATION:
For the MLA Scholarship, applicant must submit an application form, essay, and all related documents plus a single copy of transcripts and three letters of reference.

For the Thomson Reuters/MLA Doctoral Fellowship, applicant must submit the following:
(1) application form and pertinent documentation;
(2) signed statement of terms and conditions;
(3) two letters of reference, submitted by the reference directly to MLA, Professional Development Department;
(4) transcripts of graduate work or proof of enrollment in the graduate program and a list of courses completed and;
(5) name, title, address, phone and e-mail of doctoral advisor.

Application and all supporting documents must be received by the deadline to be valid.
Duration: One year.
Deadline: December 1.

STAFF:
Maria Lopez, Grants and Scholarships Coordinator

ADDRESS INQUIRIES TO:
Grants and Scholarships Coordinator
(See address above.)

MEDICAL LIBRARY ASSOCIATION   [730]
65 East Wacker Place
Suite 1900
Chicago, IL 60601-7298
(312) 419-9094
Fax: (312) 419-8950

E-MAIL ADDRESS:
mlapd2@mlahq.org

WEB SITE ADDRESS:
www.mlanet.org/awards

FOUNDED: 1898

AREAS OF INTEREST:
Health sciences librarianship.

NAME(S) OF PROGRAMS:
● **Award for Excellence and Achievement in Hospital Librarianship**
● **Estelle Brodman Award for Academic Medical Librarian of the Year**
● **Louise Darling Medal for Distinguished Achievement in Collection Development in the Health Sciences**
● **Janet Doe Lectureship**
● **Ida and George Eliot Prize**
● **Murray Gottlieb Prize**
● **Marcia C. Noyes Award**
● **Rittenhouse Award**
● **Frank Bradway Rogers Information Advancement Award**

TYPE:
Awards/prizes; Visiting scholars. Awards to honor service to libraries and librarianship.

The Award for Excellence and Achievement in Hospital Librarianship is given to an MLA-member who has made significant contributions to the profession in the area of hospital librarianship.

The Estelle Brodman Award for Academic Medical Librarian of the Year recognizes an academic medical librarian at the midcareer level who demonstrates significant achievement or the potential for leadership and continuing excellence.

The Louise Darling Medal for Distinguished Achievement in Collection Development in the Health Sciences is given annually for outstanding collection development in the health sciences.

The Janet Doe Lectureship chooses an individual to present the lecture at the MLA's annual meeting. Recipients are chosen for their unique perspective on the history or philosophy of medical librarianship.

The Ida and George Eliot Prize is presented annually for a work published in the preceding calendar year that has been judged most effective in furthering medical librarianship.

The Murray Gottlieb Prize is awarded annually for the best unpublished essay on the history of medicine and allied health science written by a health science librarian.

The Marcia C. Noyes Award is the highest professional distinction of the MLA. It recognizes a career that has resulted in lasting contributions to medical librarianship.

The Rittenhouse Award recognizes an outstanding paper written by a library student or intern.

The Frank Bradway Rogers Information Advancement Award is presented annually to recognize the application of technology to the delivery of health sciences information.

Fellows and Honorary Members are selected for outstanding lifetime contributions to the advancement of the purposes of the MLA and are ordinarily chosen from members at or near the close of an active professional career. Honorary members are nonmembers who have made outstanding contributions to the advancement of the purposes of the Association.

PURPOSE:
To honor those who have rendered distinguished service to libraries and medical librarianship.

LEGAL BASIS:
Nonprofit organization.

ELIGIBILITY:
Applicants must be health science librarians. Essays submitted must be on the history of medicine or the allied sciences and must be unpublished.

FINANCIAL DATA:
Amount of support per award: Award for Achievement and Excellence in Hospital Librarianship, Rittenhouse Award and Rogers Award: $500 each; Janet Doe Lectureship: $250; Eliot Prize: $200; Gottlieb Prize: $100.

COOPERATIVE FUNDING PROGRAMS: The Rittenhouse Award established and sponsored by the Rittenhouse Book Distributors, Philadelphia, PA. The Murray Gottlieb Prize is given by the MLA History of the Health Sciences Section.

NUMBER OF AWARDS: 1 per award each year.

APPLICATION INFORMATION:
Nominations forms and guidelines are available on the web site.
Deadline: November 1.

PUBLICATIONS:
Honors and awards program announcement.

STAFF:
Carla J. Funk, Executive Director

ADDRESS INQUIRIES TO:
Grants and Scholarships Coordinator
(See address above.)

MEDICAL LIBRARY ASSOCIATION
65 East Wacker Place
Suite 1900
Chicago, IL 60601-7298
(312) 419-9094
Fax: (312) 419-8950

E-MAIL ADDRESS:
mlapd2@mlahq.org

WEB SITE ADDRESS:
www.mlanet.org/awards/grants/index.html

TYPE:
Fellowships; Travel grants; Work-study programs. Work-study program for medical librarians from countries other than the U.S. or Canada for a time period of at least two weeks.

See entry 962 for full listing.

MEDICAL LIBRARY ASSOCIATION
65 East Wacker Place
Suite 1900
Chicago, IL 60601-7298
(312) 419-9094
Fax: (312) 419-8950

E-MAIL ADDRESS:
mlapd2@mlahq.org

WEB SITE ADDRESS:
www.mlanet.org/awards/grants/index.html

TYPE:
Awards/prizes; Scholarships. Awarded for study in health sciences librarianship.

See entry 999 for full listing.

THE METROPOLITAN MUSEUM OF ART [731]
1000 Fifth Avenue
New York, NY 10028-0198
(212) 650-2763
Fax: (212) 570-3972

E-MAIL ADDRESS:
education.grants@metmuseum.org

WEB SITE ADDRESS:
www.metmuseum.org

NAME(S) OF PROGRAMS:
● **Theodore Rousseau Fellowships**

TYPE:
Fellowships. Awarded for the training of students whose goal is to enter museums as curators of painting, by enabling them to undertake related study in Europe, made possible by a bequest from the late Curator-in-Chief of the Metropolitan Museum of Art.

PURPOSE:
To develop the skills of connoisseurship by supporting firsthand examination of paintings

in major European collections, rather than by supporting library research for the completion of degree requirements.

ELIGIBILITY:
Applicants should have been enrolled for at least one year in an advanced degree program in the field of art history.

FINANCIAL DATA:
Amount of support per award: Stipends vary in amount. For one year: $32,000 for predoctoral fellows, and up to an additional $6,000 for travel and miscellaneous expenses.

APPLICATION INFORMATION:
Current application information may be obtained from the Museum's web site.
Duration: Three to 12 months.
Deadline: Application and required letters of recommendation must be received by the first Friday in November. Announcement of awards will be made by late March.

ADDRESS INQUIRIES TO:
Marcie Karp, Managing Museum Educator Academic Programs, Education Department
(See address above.)

THE METROPOLITAN MUSEUM OF ART [732]
1000 Fifth Avenue
New York, NY 10028-0198
(212) 650-2763
Fax: (212) 570-3972

E-MAIL ADDRESS:
education.grants@metmuseum.org

WEB SITE ADDRESS:
www.metmuseum.org

NAME(S) OF PROGRAMS:
● **Andrew W. Mellon Conservation Fellowship**

TYPE:
Fellowships. The Fellowship is awarded for training in one or more of the following Departments of the Metropolitan Museum: Arms and Armor, Asian Art Conservation, The Costume Institute, Musical Instruments, Objects Conservation (including sculpture, metalwork, glass, ceramics, furniture and archaeological objects), Paintings Conservation, Paper Conservation, Photograph Conservation, Scientific Research, or Textile Conservation, and made possible by the Andrew W. Mellon Foundation.

All fellowship recipients will be expected to spend the fellowship in residence in the department with which they are affiliated.

The Museum offers junior-level and senior-level fellowships in conservation and scientific research. Junior fellowships are intended for those who have recently completed graduate-level training. Senior fellowships are intended for well-established professionals with advanced training in the field and a proven publication record.

All fellowships must take place between September 1 and the following August 31.

ELIGIBILITY:
Applicants should have reached an advanced level of experience or training.

FINANCIAL DATA:
Health care benefits are included.

Amount of support per award: Stipend: $32,000 per year for junior-level conservators and researchers, $42,000 for senior-level, plus $6,000 for travel and miscellaneous expenses.

APPLICATION INFORMATION:
Current application may be obtained from the Museum's web site.
Duration: Usually one year in duration. Shorter-term fellowships for senior scholars are also available.
Deadline: Application and required letters of recommendation must be received by the first Friday in December.

ADDRESS INQUIRIES TO:
Marcie Karp
Managing Museum Educator
for Academic Programs
The Metropolitan Museum of Art
E-mail: education.grants@metmuseum.org

*SPECIAL STIPULATIONS:
All fellowship recipients will be expected to spend the fellowship in residence in the department with which they are affiliated.

MINNESOTA DEPARTMENT OF EDUCATION [733]
State Library Services
1500 Highway 36 West
Roseville, MN 55113
(651) 582-8791
Fax: (651) 582-8752

E-MAIL ADDRESS:
mde.lst@state.mn.us

WEB SITE ADDRESS:
education.state.mn.
us/MDE/StuSuc/Lib/StateLibServ/index.html

FOUNDED: 1899

AREAS OF INTEREST:
Supporting innovation in library services, cooperation among all types of libraries, public library accessibility, library technology and resource sharing.

CONSULTING OR VOLUNTEER SERVICES:
Consultant assistance provided on a range of library issues.

NAME(S) OF PROGRAMS:
● **Library Accessibility and Improvement Grants**
● **Library Services and Technology Act Competitive Grants**
● **Multi-Type Library Cooperation Aid**
● **Regional Library Telecommunications Aid**
● **Regional Public Libraries Systems Support**

TYPE:
Capital grants; Development grants; Formula grants; General operating grants; Project/program grants; Seed money grants; Technical assistance; Training grants. Matching capital grants for library accessibility and improvement. Competitive grants that address activities and priorities in the Minnesota Five-Year Plan.

YEAR PROGRAM STARTED: 1957

PURPOSE:
To extend and improve library and information services for the people of Minnesota through public libraries and cooperation among all types of libraries.

LEGAL BASIS:
Government agency..

ELIGIBILITY:
Specific requirements vary by program, and
include local public libraries, Minnesota
county and regional public library systems,
and multicounty, multitype library systems
meeting minimum support requirements,
academic libraries and school library media
centers are eligible to apply. Contact the
Department for details.

GEOGRAPHIC RESTRICTIONS:
Minnesota.

FINANCIAL DATA:
Amount of support per award: Varies by
grant program.
Total amount of support: $17,200,000 for the
year 2012.
Matching fund requirements: Varies by
program.

NUMBER OF APPLICANTS MOST RECENT YEAR:
Varies by grant program.

NUMBER OF AWARDS: Varies by grant program.

APPLICATION INFORMATION:
Applications available online.
Duration: Varies by grant program.
Deadline: Varies by grant program.

ADDRESS INQUIRIES TO:
Jennifer R. Nelson, Director and State
Librarian
(See address above.)

NATIONAL HOME LIBRARY
FOUNDATION   [734]
3804 Williams Lane, Lower Level
Chevy Chase, MD 20815
(301) 986-4854
Fax: (301) 986-4855

E-MAIL ADDRESS:
natlhomelibrary@yahoo.com

WEB SITE ADDRESS:
www.homelibraryfoundation.com

FOUNDED: 1932

AREAS OF INTEREST:
Literacy.

TYPE:
Project/program grants. Grants in support of
libraries, books and publications.

PURPOSE:
To assist in the distribution of books and
other literacy-related resources to libraries
and community groups with limited access to
sources of specific areas of information; to
assist in support, promotion and development
of programs with the goal of combating
illiteracy and/or encouraging an interest in
reading and the literacy arts among all ages;
to encourage development of programs
relating primarily to literary or cultural topics
that utilize various means of
communications.

ELIGIBILITY:
Applicants must be tax-exempt groups with
appropriate interests and activities.

GEOGRAPHIC RESTRICTIONS:
United States, with preference to Maryland,
Virginia and Washington, DC, areas.

FINANCIAL DATA:
Amount of support per award: $500 to
$5,000.

REPRESENTATIVE AWARDS:
$1,000 to the city of Coffman Cove, AK, to
fund fledgling community library; $2,000 to
Calvin Coolidge High, DC, to purchase

contemporary books for school library;
$5,000 to Washington Jesuit Academy, DC,
to fund books for the tuition-free middle
school for disadvantaged minority students.

APPLICATION INFORMATION:
Application takes the form of a proposal
stating the nature of the project and its
sponsors, along with a budget and financial
statement.
Duration: Grants are usually awarded for one
year.
Deadline: Applications may be submitted at
any time and are reviewed at thrice-annual
board meetings.

IRS IDENTIFICATION NUMBER: 52-6051013

OFFICERS:
Lynda J. Robb, President
Ervin S. Duggan, Secretary and Treasurer

TRUSTEES:
Vandna Wendy Bhagat
Ervin S. Duggan
Michael R. Gardner
Alice B. Popkin
Lynda J. Robb
Ricardo Urbino
Kathleen M. Vance

ADDRESS INQUIRIES TO:
Joan Smith Sahlgren, Executive Director
(See address above.)

NEW HAMPSHIRE LIBRARY
ASSOCIATION   [735]
c/o NH State Library
20 Park Street
Concord, NH 03301-6314
(603) 673-2288
Fax: (603) 672-6063

E-MAIL ADDRESS:
sleonardi@amherstlibrary.org

WEB SITE ADDRESS:
www.nhlibrarians.org

FOUNDED: 1889

AREAS OF INTEREST:
Library and information science education.

NAME(S) OF PROGRAMS:
● **Rosalie Norris Scholarship**
● **F. Mabel Winchell Loan Fund**

TYPE:
Scholarships. The Norris Scholarship is
awarded to New Hampshire residents or
individuals working in a New Hampshire
library for graduate library study. The
Winchell Loan Fund provides for interest-free
loans to New Hampshire residents or
individuals working in a New Hampshire
library to attend graduate library schools.

YEAR PROGRAM STARTED: 1949

PURPOSE:
To promote good library service from all
types of libraries to all people of the state.

LEGAL BASIS:
Nonprofit.

ELIGIBILITY:
An applicant must be a member of the New
Hampshire Library Association and have
been accepted into the appropriate program.
Applicant must live in New Hampshire or be
employed by a New Hampshire library and
must be enrolled in an ALA- accredited
program.

GEOGRAPHIC RESTRICTIONS:
New Hampshire.

FINANCIAL DATA:
Amount of support per award: Scholarship
grant provides a maximum of $1,000. Loan
provides $1,500 (interest-free) to be repaid in
five years.
Total amount of support: Varies.

NUMBER OF APPLICANTS MOST RECENT YEAR: 6
for the year 2013.

NUMBER OF AWARDS: 3 Norris Scholarships and
1 F. Mabel Winchell Loans for the year
2013.

APPLICATION INFORMATION:
Applications are approved by the New
Hampshire Library Association Scholarship
Committee. Mail applications to: Sarah
Leonardi, Scholarship Chairperson, New
Hampshire Library Association, c/o Amherst
Town Library, 14 Main Street, Amherst, NH
03031.
Duration: One year.
Deadline: April 1 and September 1.

ADDRESS INQUIRIES TO:
Sarah Leonardi, Scholarship Chairperson
(See address above.)

NEW JERSEY LIBRARY
ASSOCIATION   [736]
P.O. Box 1534
Trenton, NJ 08607
(609) 394-8032
Fax: (609) 394-8164

E-MAIL ADDRESS:
ptumulty@njla.org

WEB SITE ADDRESS:
www.njla.org

FOUNDED: 1890

AREAS OF INTEREST:
Education, training of members and
recruitment into the profession.

NAME(S) OF PROGRAMS:
● **Scholarships for Study in Library
Service**

TYPE:
Scholarships. Offered to residents of New
Jersey for study leading to a degree in library
science at a graduate library school with an
ALA-accredited degree program.

YEAR PROGRAM STARTED: 1926

PURPOSE:
To give financial support for tuition to
worthy candidates, of New Jersey residency,
desiring to work toward a graduate degree in
library service as a profession.

LEGAL BASIS:
Nonprofit status.

ELIGIBILITY:
Applicants for scholarships must:
(1) be residents of New Jersey at the time of
application or have worked in any New
Jersey library for at least 12 months on a
full-time or part-time basis;
(2) show substantial financial need and;
(3) present worthy scholarship, as shown by
official transcript, a written essay describing
what the applicant can contribute to
librarianship, and two recommendations by
people in the field of librarianship if possible.

FINANCIAL DATA:
Scholarships are awarded in the spring for
the following school year for full- or
part-time study. Funds must be used for
tuition only and are sent directly to the

college. Any unused monies are refunded to the treasurer of the New Jersey Library Association.

Amount of support per award: Varies.

Total amount of support: $8,000 for the year 2014-15.

NUMBER OF AWARDS: 8 for the year 2014-15.

APPLICATION INFORMATION:
Applications and guidelines are available on the Association web site.

Duration: One year. Renewal by reapplication.

Deadline: Approximately February 15.

ADDRESS INQUIRIES TO:
Patricia Tumulty, Executive Director
(See address above.)

NEW MEXICO LIBRARY ASSOCIATION   [737]

P.O. Box 26074
Albuquerque, NM 87125
(505) 400-7309

E-MAIL ADDRESS:
contact@nmla.org

WEB SITE ADDRESS:
nmla.org

FOUNDED: 1923

AREAS OF INTEREST:
Promoting libraries and librarianship in New Mexico.

NAME(S) OF PROGRAMS:
● **College Scholarship Fund**
● **Continuing Education Grants**
● **Marion Dorroh Memorial Scholarship**

TYPE:
Scholarships. The scholarships support study in an accredited library school program. The continuing grants support attending workshops, conferences and educational activities of practicing New Mexico librarians.

YEAR PROGRAM STARTED: 1953

PURPOSE:
To support and promote libraries and the development of library personnel.

LEGAL BASIS:
Nonprofit corporation.

ELIGIBILITY:
College Scholarship Fund: Applicant must be a resident of New Mexico and currently accepted or enrolled in an undergraduate or graduate program culminating in a degree and/or in Library Science certification. Preference will be given to those currently employed in a New Mexico library and to members of the New Mexico Library Association.

Marion Dorroh Memorial Scholarship: Applicant must have resided in New Mexico during the preceding year and must be accepted or currently enrolled in an ALA-Accredited school as a full- or part-time student.

The Continuing Education Grants support is based upon financial need. Applicants must be a member of the New Mexico Library Association.

GEOGRAPHIC RESTRICTIONS:
New Mexico.

FINANCIAL DATA:
Amount of support per award: College Scholarship: $1,000; Marion Dorroh Memorial Scholarship: $1,500; Continuing Education Grants: Up to $200.

APPLICATION INFORMATION:
Application forms are available upon request. The Education Committee Chair must receive the following:
(1) application form;
(2) resume;
(3) statement of professional goals;
(4) transcript of completed college courses and;
(5) three letters of reference, one of which is from a librarian (for the Dorroh Scholarship only).
For the Continuing Education Fund, a copy of the workshop brochure, conference agenda or registration form should accompany the completed application form.

Incomplete applications cannot be considered.

Duration: One year.

Deadline: College Scholarship: January 31 for summer and fall term grants. Marion Dorroh Memorial Scholarship: January 15.

IRS IDENTIFICATION NUMBER: 23-7024820

ADDRESS INQUIRIES TO:
Kevin Comerford, Chairperson
NMLA Education Committee
(See address above.)

NEW YORK STATE HISTORICAL ASSOCIATION   [738]

SUNY College at Oneonta
Cooperstown Graduate Program in History Museum Studies
P.O. Box 800, Lake Road
Cooperstown, NY 13326
(607) 547-2586
Fax: (607) 547-8926

E-MAIL ADDRESS:
rosemary.craig@oneonta.edu
gretchen.sorin@oneonta.edu

WEB SITE ADDRESS:
www.oneonta.edu/academics/cgp

FOUNDED: 1964

AREAS OF INTEREST:
History museum studies.

NAME(S) OF PROGRAMS:
● **The Cooperstown Graduate Program**

TYPE:
Assistantships; Fellowships; Scholarships. Awards for museum studies for Cooperstown Graduate Program students only.

YEAR PROGRAM STARTED: 1964

PURPOSE:
To provide professionally trained individuals for the museum field.

ELIGIBILITY:
Applicants must have a strong academic record, an interest in public service, excellent writing skills and a demonstrated commitment to the field through museum work in either staff or volunteer capacity.

FINANCIAL DATA:
Amount of support per award: $4,000 to $12,000 per year.

Total amount of support: $150,000.

COOPERATIVE FUNDING PROGRAMS:
Co-sponsored with SUNY College at Oneonta.

NUMBER OF APPLICANTS MOST RECENT YEAR:
80 to 90.

NUMBER OF AWARDS: Approximately 15 to 19 awards for students.

APPLICATION INFORMATION:
Applications and further information may be obtained from the web site. Applications are to be submitted online.

Duration: Tenable in Cooperstown, NY, for 24 months.

Deadline: Applications must be received by January 10. Notification in April.

PUBLICATIONS:
Viewbook.

ADDRESS INQUIRIES TO:
Rosemary Craig
Assistant to Program Director
(See address above.)

NORTH CAROLINA LIBRARY ASSOCIATION   [739]

c/o Scholarships Committee
1841 Capital Boulevard
Raleigh, NC 27604
(919) 839-6252
Fax: (919) 839-6253

E-MAIL ADDRESS:
nclaonline@gmail.com

WEB SITE ADDRESS:
www.nclaonline.org

FOUNDED: 1904

AREAS OF INTEREST:
The promotion of libraries and library service in North Carolina.

NAME(S) OF PROGRAMS:
● **Appalachian Scholarship**
● **McLendon Scholarship**
● **The Query-Long Scholarship**

TYPE:
Scholarships. Scholarships and loans to promote the education of qualified librarians.

PURPOSE:
To promote library science education.

LEGAL BASIS:
Professional association.

ELIGIBILITY:
Applicants must have been a legal resident of North Carolina for two years, have a genuine interest in professional library work, demonstrate need of financial assistance, hold an undergraduate degree and be accepted by a library school.

GEOGRAPHIC RESTRICTIONS:
North Carolina.

FINANCIAL DATA:
Amount of support per award: Appalachian and Query-Long Scholarships: $1,000; McLendon Scholarship: $400.

APPLICATION INFORMATION:
Application and three letters of reference required.

Duration: One year.

Deadline: May 30. Notification in the summer. Awarded biennially in Conference years.

ADDRESS INQUIRIES TO:
Libby Hayes
Chairperson for Scholarships
North Carolina Library Association
(See address above.)

ROCK ISLAND ARSENAL MUSEUM
Rock Island Arsenal Historical Society
R. Maguire Scholarship Committee
One Rock Island Arsenal
Rock Island, IL 61299-5000
(309) 782-5021
Fax: (309) 782-3598

E-MAIL ADDRESS:
rimahoch@aol.com

WEB SITE ADDRESS:
www.arsenalhistoricalsociety.com

TYPE:
Scholarships.

See entry 631 for full listing.

STATE LIBRARY AND ARCHIVES OF FLORIDA   [740]
R.A. Gray Building
500 South Bronough Street
Tallahassee, FL 32399-0250
(850) 245-6600
Fax: (850) 245-6643

E-MAIL ADDRESS:
marian.deeney@dos.myflorida.com

WEB SITE ADDRESS:
info.florida.gov/bld/grants/Lsta/LSTA.html

FOUNDED: 1925

AREAS OF INTEREST:
Public libraries, public elementary school or secondary school libraries, academic libraries, research libraries, private libraries, or library consortium.

CONSULTING OR VOLUNTEER SERVICES:
Consultant advice to public and institution libraries and libraries for the blind and handicapped.

NAME(S) OF PROGRAMS:
• **Library Services and Technology Act**

TYPE:
Project/program grants. Project grants congruent with the state long-range plan.

YEAR PROGRAM STARTED: 1997

PURPOSE:
To stimulate excellence and promote access to learning and information resources in all types of libraries for individuals of all ages; to promote library services that provide all users access to information through state, regional, national, and international electronic networks; to provide linkages among and between libraries; to promote targeted library services to people of diverse geographic, cultural, and socioeconomic backgrounds, to individuals with disabilities and to people with limited functional literacy or information skills.

LEGAL BASIS:
Based on U.S. Library Services and Technology Act (P.L. 104-208, as amended) and Florida Statutes 257.12, 257.191 and 257.192.

ELIGIBILITY:
Applicants must be Florida libraries that provide free library service or institution libraries that are operated or substantially supported by the state.

GEOGRAPHIC RESTRICTIONS:
Florida.

FINANCIAL DATA:
Amount of support per award: Varies.

Total amount of support: $7,571,343 for fiscal year 2013; $7,967,170 for fiscal year 2014.
Matching fund requirements: Matching funds must equal at least one-third of the grant request or award.

NUMBER OF APPLICANTS MOST RECENT YEAR: 45.

NUMBER OF AWARDS: 22.

APPLICATION INFORMATION:
Application must be submitted online. Applicants should supply project proposal.
Duration: One year. Must reapply for each year.
Deadline: March 15.

PUBLICATIONS:
Grant guidelines.

IRS IDENTIFICATION NUMBER: 59-3466865

ADDRESS INQUIRIES TO:
Dorothy Frank, Library Program Administrator
(See address above.)

TEXAS LIBRARY ASSOCIATION   [741]
3355 Bee Cave Road, Suite 401
Austin, TX 78746
(512) 328-1518
(800) 580-2852
Fax: (512) 328-8852

E-MAIL ADDRESS:
tla@txla.org

WEB SITE ADDRESS:
www.txla.org

FOUNDED: 1902

AREAS OF INTEREST:
Library and information science.

NAME(S) OF PROGRAMS:
• **Walter H. Escue Memorial Scholarship**
• **Vivian Greenfield Education Award**
• **Ray C. Janeway Scholarship**
• **TLA Summer School Scholarship**
• **Van Dusen-Tobin-Kaiser Scholarship**

TYPE:
Scholarships. Awards for graduate study leading to a Master's degree in library science.

YEAR PROGRAM STARTED: 1998

PURPOSE:
To help support the educational goals of students who want to get an advanced degree in library science.

LEGAL BASIS:
Professional association.

ELIGIBILITY:
Applicants must be members of TLA.

Walter Escue Scholars must be Texas residents concentrating studies in technical services, system administration or library automation.

Graduate student scholars must be Texas residents, attained at least a "B" average during the last two years of a Baccalaureate degree program and have been accepted as a graduate student to a Texas ALA-accredited library education program.

Vivian Greenfield Award applicants must reside in Texas and write a goal statement outlining a desired educational endeavor revolving around youth services.

TLA Summer School Scholar must be a Texas resident, attain at least a "B" average during the last two years of a Baccalaureate degree program, and must be registered for MLS degree courses during a summer session of a TLA-accredited library education program.

Van Dusen-Tobin-Kaiser Scholars must be pursuing graduate studies leading to a career as an elementary school or children's librarian.

Contact the Association for complete details.

GEOGRAPHIC RESTRICTIONS:
Texas.

FINANCIAL DATA:
Amount of support per award: Escue Scholarship: $1,000; Greenfield Award: $1,500; Janeway Scholarship: $2,000, awarded annually; TLA Summer School Scholarship: $500; Van Dusen-Tobin-Kaiser Scholarship: $1,000, awarded biennially in even-numbered years.
Total amount of support: Varies.

NUMBER OF AWARDS: Varies.

APPLICATION INFORMATION:
Application must be submitted online.
Duration: One year.
Deadline: Completed applications must be postmarked by January 31 postmark date of year to be awarded.

IRS IDENTIFICATION NUMBER: 74-6014110

ADDRESS INQUIRIES TO:
Glenda Genchur, Director of Administration
(See address above.)

*SPECIAL STIPULATIONS:
Scholarships and grants are to be awarded to Texas residents only and only to applicants attending an institution of higher learning in Texas with an accredited School of Library Science.

UNITED STATES HOLOCAUST MEMORIAL MUSEUM, CENTER FOR ADVANCED HOLOCAUST STUDIES
100 Raoul Wallenberg Place, S.W.
Washington, DC 20024-2126
(202) 314-7829
Fax: (202) 479-9726

E-MAIL ADDRESS:
vscholars@ushmm.org

WEB SITE ADDRESS:
www.ushmm.org

TYPE:
Exchange programs; Fellowships. The Center for Advanced Holocaust Studies is an integral part of the United States Holocaust Memorial Museum, which serves as America's national institution for Holocaust education and remembrance. The Center awards fellowships to support significant research and writing about the Holocaust. Awards are granted on a competitive basis. The Center welcomes proposals from scholars in all relevant academic disciplines, including history, political science, literature, Jewish studies, philosophy, religion, psychology, comparative genocide studies, law and others.

Visiting scholars at the Center have access to more than 60,000,000 pages of Holocaust-related archival documentation; the

Museum's extensive library; oral history, film, photo, art, artifacts and memoir collections; and Holocaust survivor database.

See entry 643 for full listing.

UNIVERSITY OF ARIZONA SCHOOL OF INFORMATION RESOURCES AND LIBRARY SCIENCE [742]

University of Arizona
1515 East First Street, Room 3
Tucson, AZ 85719
(520) 621-3565
Fax: (520) 621-3279

E-MAIL ADDRESS:
sirls@email.arizona.edu

WEB SITE ADDRESS:
www.sirls.arizona.edu

FOUNDED: 1963

AREAS OF INTEREST:
Promoting new knowledge and practice in the library and information professions with research, education, and public service through degree programs at the Master's, doctoral, and certificate levels.

TYPE:
Assistantships; Internships; Scholarships. Graduate assistantships; Research assistantships; Undergraduate internships and scholarships. Awarded to qualified students to attend SIRLS.

YEAR PROGRAM STARTED: 1963

PURPOSE:
To educate students in the area of information resources and library science.

LEGAL BASIS:
Nonprofit, tax-exempt.

ELIGIBILITY:
Any student receiving financial aid must be accepted into the SIRLS degree program. Awards are made to students who meet the criteria set by the School. (This includes students participating in the program online.) The School requires that the student be enrolled for the required number of hours for the semester of award. Assistance is awarded on a semester basis.

A new financial aid form must be completed each semester that a student wishes to be considered for aid. To be considered for financial assistance, an applicant must meet the deadlines posted. Criteria for financial aid are: stellar academic performance, financial status, and other qualifications as defined by specific scholarships.

FINANCIAL DATA:
Amount of support per award: Varies by program.
Total amount of support: Varies.

APPLICATION INFORMATION:
Applicant must complete the Financial Assistance Application section of Library Science Application for Admission.
Duration: One or two semesters.
Deadline: March 1.

THE UNIVERSITY OF DELAWARE-HAGLEY GRADUATE PROGRAM

Department of History, John Munroe Hall
University of Delaware
Newark, DE 19716
(302) 831-8226
Fax: (302) 831-1538

E-MAIL ADDRESS:
dianec@udel.edu

WEB SITE ADDRESS:
www.udel.edu/hagley

TYPE:
Fellowships. The University of Delaware, in association with the Hagley Museum, sponsors a premier graduate resident program for the study of technology, business, consumption, and work in industrial and post-industrial societies leading to a Master of Arts or Ph.D. in History. Students have access to faculty with international reputations in American, European and non-Western history, and benefit from strong interdisciplinary ties to museum studies and material culture programs, as well as the Hagley Museum and Library.

See entry 644 for full listing.

THE UNIVERSITY OF SOUTHERN MISSISSIPPI [743]

118 College Drive, Box 5148
Hattiesburg, MS 39406
(601) 266-4349
Fax: (601) 266-6269

E-MAIL ADDRESS:
ellen.ruffin@usm.edu

WEB SITE ADDRESS:
www.lib.usm.edu/legacy/degrum/public_html/
html/research/re-fellowships.shtml

NAME(S) OF PROGRAMS:
- **Ezra Jack Keats/Janina Domanska Research Fellowship**
- **H.A. and Margret Rey Translation Fellowship**

TYPE:
Fellowships. Keats/Domanska Research Fellowship awards grants to scholars engaged in projects based substantially on the holdings of the de Grummond Children's Literature Collection.

Rey Translation Fellowship is awarded to hire translators (French, German, Portuguese or Russian) for the purpose of translating the H.A. and Margret Rey documents into English to further facilitate use in research.

ELIGIBILITY:
Keats/Domanska Research Fellowship: Applicants can be of any discipline who engage in projects that require substantial use of the de Grummond Collection. Awards are based on the applicant's scholarly qualifications, the merits of the proposal submitted and the appropriateness of the proposal to the resources of the de Grummond Collection.

Rey Translation Fellowship: Applicant must demonstrate through formal education or other experience expertise in translating material.

FINANCIAL DATA:
Amount of support per award:
Keats/Domanska Research Fellowship: $1,582 for 2013. Rey Translation Fellowship: $1,664 for 2013.

NUMBER OF AWARDS: Keats/Domanska Research Fellowship: 1-2 awards per year. Rey Translation Fellowship: 1-2 awards per year.

APPLICATION INFORMATION:
Application information is available on the web site.
Duration: Keats/Domanska Research Fellowship: Up to eight months; nonrenewable. Rey Translation Fellowship: One year; nonrenewable.
Deadline: Keats/Domanska Research Fellowship: Late September to early October. Rey Translation Fellowship: July 31; decision by August 15.

ADDRESS INQUIRIES TO:
Ellen H. Ruffin, Curator, de Grummond Children's Literature Collection
The University of Southern Mississippi
(See address above.)

UNIVERSITY OF TORONTO [744]

Faculty of Information
140 St. George Street, Room 211
Toronto ON M5S 3G6 Canada
(416) 978-8589
Fax: (416) 978-5762

E-MAIL ADDRESS:
inquire.ischool@utoronto.ca

WEB SITE ADDRESS:
www.ischool.utoronto.ca

FOUNDED: 1928

AREAS OF INTEREST:
Education.

NAME(S) OF PROGRAMS:
- **Patricia Fleming Visiting Fellowship in Bibliography and Book History**

TYPE:
Fellowships; Research grants; Visiting scholars.

YEAR PROGRAM STARTED: 1928

PURPOSE:
To encourage outstanding scholars to conduct research in the field of bibliographical studies or book history.

LEGAL BASIS:
University.

GEOGRAPHIC RESTRICTIONS:
Canada.

FINANCIAL DATA:
Amount of support per award: $1,000 (CAN).

NUMBER OF AWARDS: 1.

APPLICATION INFORMATION:
Applicants should submit a resume, two letters of recommendation, and a one- to two-page research proposal describing the project.
Duration: One month.
Deadline: February/March annually.

ADDRESS INQUIRIES TO:
Adriana Rossini, Registrar and Director of Student Services
Faculty of Information
(See address above.)

Music

ACCADEMIA MUSICALE CHIGIANA [745]
Via di Città, 89
53100 Siena Italy
+39.0577.22091
Fax: +39.0577.288124

E-MAIL ADDRESS:
allievi@chigiana.it
accademia.chigiana@chigiana.it

WEB SITE ADDRESS:
www.chigiana.it

FOUNDED: 1932

AREAS OF INTEREST:
Music.

NAME(S) OF PROGRAMS:
- **Scholarships for Summer Music Courses**

TYPE:
Awards/prizes; Scholarships. Merit scholarships to those who are registered as active students at the Academy, which offers various summer music master courses in orchestral conducting, composition, voice and various instruments.

In addition, there are other scholarships financed by public institutions or private donors and are awarded at the discretion of the Accademia Chigiana Direction.

YEAR PROGRAM STARTED: 1932

PURPOSE:
To allow young musicians from all over the world to perfect themselves in the principal instruments, studying with many world famous musicians.

ELIGIBILITY:
Applicants can be students of any nationality. Active students must hold an Italian music diploma or an equivalent foreign certificate (exception made for the courses of guitar and singing) and must pass an entrance examination. Age limits are as follows: Conducting, 30 years for the session dedicated to the classical orchestral repertoire; 40 years for the session dedicated to the modern symphonic repertoire; Voice, 32 years (sopranos and tenors), 34 years (mezzo sopranos, baritones and basses); Instruments, 30 years; Chamber Music, average of 30 years. The Italian government also finances scholarships for attendance of summer master classes at the Accademia Chigiana.

Scholarships offered by the Accademia Musicale Chigiana are awarded on the basis of the results of the entrance examination and student merit.

No scholarship will be granted to students already benefiting from financial help from other institutions or to those who do not take the entrance examination on the established date.

FINANCIAL DATA:
Amount of support per award: Scholarships consist of reimbursement of tuition fees (after detraction of the added value tax) plus a daily grant of EUR 35 gross.
Total amount of support: EUR 60,000 (with funds of the Academy) plus EUR 30,000 (by public institutions or private donors).

NUMBER OF APPLICANTS MOST RECENT YEAR:
507 for the year 2010.

NUMBER OF AWARDS: 83 scholarships financed with funds of the Accademia Chigiana and 38 scholarships by public institutions or private donors for the year 2010.

APPLICATION INFORMATION:
Detailed information and application forms are available from the address above. For details of requirements and application formalities about scholarships awarded by the Italian government, candidates should write directly to the Italian Culture Institute or to the Italian Embassy in their own country.
Deadline: May 15 for the Orchestral Conducting Course; May 31 for Composition; June 10 for all other courses.

PUBLICATIONS:
Courses booklet (information and application form).

OFFICERS:
Gabriello Mancini, President
Aldo Bennici, Artistic Director
Angelo Armienta, Administration Manager

ADDRESS INQUIRIES TO:
Fondazione Accademia Musicale Chigiana
(See address above.)

AMERICAN ACADEMY OF ARTS AND LETTERS [746]
633 West 155th Street
New York, NY 10032-7599
(212) 368-5900
Fax: (212) 491-4615

E-MAIL ADDRESS:
academy@artsandletters.org

WEB SITE ADDRESS:
www.artsandletters.org

FOUNDED: 1898

NAME(S) OF PROGRAMS:
- **The Richard Rodgers Awards**

TYPE:
Awards/prizes. Completed musical scripts are accepted by the Academy for this annual competition. The award subsidizes staged readings, studio productions or productions in New York City by a not-for-profit theater group of a musical play by composers and writers who are not already established in this field.

YEAR PROGRAM STARTED: 1978

PURPOSE:
To further the art of the musical theater in the U.S.

LEGAL BASIS:
Nonprofit Internal Revenue Code 501(c)(3).

ELIGIBILITY:
Open only to U.S. citizens or permanent residents of any age. While students may enter the competition, it is primarily intended for work at a professional level.

GEOGRAPHIC RESTRICTIONS:
United States.

FINANCIAL DATA:
Award money is given to the not-for-profit theater for production expenses.
Amount of support per award: Varies.

NUMBER OF APPLICANTS MOST RECENT YEAR:
133.

NUMBER OF AWARDS: 1 to 4.

APPLICATION INFORMATION:
Application form can be downloaded from the Academy web site. The name(s) of the author(s) must be blocked out on each of the items submitted, with the exception of the application form. Write only the title of the work on the script, plot summary and CD. Entries must include the following items: (1) script with lyrics, preferably with no binders or metal clips. Do not send score, videos or visuals; (2) half-page synopsis of the action and a list of characters; (3) CD which must contain at least 45 minutes of music, including a minimum of eight songs, recorded in chronological order. Orchestrations are not necessary; piano and vocals are sufficient. Songs must be in sequence on the CD and each song clearly keyed into the script. Please include a separate track sheet of recorded songs with page numbers indicating where they appear in the script, and specify the total number of minutes recorded. Audio tapes will not be accepted and; (4) application form signed by all collaborators in a sealed envelope with the title of the work on the outside. Applicants submitting work which has already been produced must give full information concerning these productions, including programs. A work is not eligible if one of the collaborators is deceased.

If the submitted work (or a portion thereof) is an adaptation of material which is not in the public domain, candidates must submit licenses, permissions, or authorizations necessary to permit the work to be produced in conformity with applicable copyright laws. The music must be original.

Materials will be returned if a self-addressed, stamped mailer is enclosed. Addresses must be valid for at least six months. The Academy will take all due care of materials, but it cannot be held responsible for their safe return.
Deadline: November 3. Notification by March.

PUBLICATIONS:
Application guidelines.

STAFF:
Virginia Dajani, Executive Director
Jane Bolster, Coordinator, Richard Rodgers Awards

ADDRESS INQUIRIES TO:
The Richard Rodgers Awards
(See address above.)

*SPECIAL STIPULATIONS:
Musical submitted may not be entered again, even if revised.

AMERICAN ACCORDION MUSICOLOGICAL SOCIETY [747]
322 Haddon Avenue
Westmont, NJ 08108
(856) 854-6628

E-MAIL ADDRESS:
accordion.1@verizon.net

WEB SITE ADDRESS:
www.aamsaccordionfestival.com

FOUNDED: 1968

AREAS OF INTEREST:
Research and symposiums on accordion history in the U.S.

CONSULTING OR VOLUNTEER SERVICES:
Library services, books and music on the accordion, and records, CDs and DVDs for rental.

NAME(S) OF PROGRAMS:
- **Annual Symposium and Festival**

TYPE:
Awards/prizes; Work-study programs. The Annual Symposium and Festival is held on a weekend in March.

YEAR PROGRAM STARTED: 1970

PURPOSE:
To help and stimulate young composers to write for the accordion.

LEGAL BASIS:
Nonprofit professional association.

ELIGIBILITY:
Composer must be acquainted with the various types of accordions.

FINANCIAL DATA:
Amount of support per award: $600.

NUMBER OF AWARDS: 1.

APPLICATION INFORMATION:
Applicants should write for entry forms or send an e-mail to the address above.
Deadline: Contact the Society.

PUBLICATIONS:
Annual news bulletin on classical/folk accordion; annual booklet of accordion information.

ADDRESS INQUIRIES TO:
Joanna Darrow, Director
(See address above.)

THE AMERICAN BANDMASTERS ASSOCIATION   [748]
Westlake High School
4100 Westbank Drive
Austin, TX 78746
(512) 732-9280 ext. 33820

E-MAIL ADDRESS:
ktaylor@eanesisd.net
colburnmj@mac.com

WEB SITE ADDRESS:
www.americanbandmasters.org

FOUNDED: 1929

AREAS OF INTEREST:
Concert band and band music.

NAME(S) OF PROGRAMS:
- **Sousa/Ostwald Award**

TYPE:
Awards/prizes. Prize sponsored by the American Bandmasters Association and Sousa Foundation, involving cash award and performance of the winning band or wind ensemble composition. One award is presented in odd years for grades 1-4; one award is presented in even years for grades 5-6.

YEAR PROGRAM STARTED: 1955

PURPOSE:
To enrich the spectrum of concert band activity.

ELIGIBILITY:
Details are available on the Association web site.

FINANCIAL DATA:
Amount of support per award: $5,000.
Total amount of support: $5,000.

NUMBER OF APPLICANTS MOST RECENT YEAR: 91.

NUMBER OF AWARDS: 1.

APPLICATION INFORMATION:
Send scores (PDFs only) and recordings (mp3 of live performances only) and direct all inquiries to the Chairman of the Contest Committee at the e-mail address above.
Deadline: October 1.

PUBLICATIONS:
Journal of Band Research.

IRS IDENTIFICATION NUMBER: 36-6112860

OFFICERS:
Dennis J. Zeisler, President
Terry Austin, President-Elect
Dr. Timothy Rhea, Vice President
William J. Moody, Secretary-Treasurer
Thomas G. Leslie, Chairperson, Nominating Committee

BOARD OF DIRECTORS:
David Waybright, Chairman
Col. Michael J. Colburn
Jay Gephart
William Johnson
Linda Moorhouse
Bruce Moss
Timothy Rhea
Gary Smith
Ray Toler

ADDRESS INQUIRIES TO:
Kerry Taylor, Co-Chairperson
ABA/Ostwald Committee (Grades 1-4)
Michael Colburn, Co-Chairperson
ABA/Ostwald Committee (Grades 5-6)
(See e-mail addresses above.)

*SPECIAL STIPULATIONS:
All inquiries and correspondence must be in the form of an e-mail.

AMERICAN CONSERVATORY OF MUSIC   [749]
252 Wildwood Road
Hammond, IN 46324
(219) 931-6000
Fax: (219) 931-6089

E-MAIL ADDRESS:
registrar@americanconservatory.edu

WEB SITE ADDRESS:
www.americanconservatory.edu

FOUNDED: 1886

AREAS OF INTEREST:
Music performance, conducting, composition, theory and music technology.

NAME(S) OF PROGRAMS:
- **Leo Heim Presidential Scholarships**

TYPE:
Scholarships.

YEAR PROGRAM STARTED: 1984

PURPOSE:
To provide excellent musical instruction for talented students at all levels of ability.

LEGAL BASIS:
Not-for-profit corporation since 1941; partnership, multiple partners.

ELIGIBILITY:
Applicants must be students with strong musical background.

FINANCIAL DATA:
Award to be applied solely towards tuition at the Conservatory.
Amount of support per award: Varies based on merit and need.
Total amount of support: Varies.

APPLICATION INFORMATION:
Applicants should submit a standard application form and audition.
Duration: One year.

IRS IDENTIFICATION NUMBER: 84-1454666

ADDRESS INQUIRIES TO:
Admissions
(See address above.)

AMERICAN MATTHAY ASSOCIATION   [750]
405 East Hermosa Circle
Tempe, AZ 85282
(480) 829-0228
Fax: (480) 829-0228 (notice required)

E-MAIL ADDRESS:
mcpiano2@aol.com

WEB SITE ADDRESS:
www.matthay.org

FOUNDED: 1925

AREAS OF INTEREST:
Piano performance and teaching.

NAME(S) OF PROGRAMS:
- **Clara Wells Scholarships for Piano Study**

TYPE:
Conferences/seminars; Scholarships; Work-study programs. Prize funds for study of piano with member of the Association, emphasizing the performance and teaching principles of Tobias Matthay. The Clara Wells Scholarships are awarded biennially.

The next Clara Wells Auditions will be held in June 2016 at the Festival of the American Matthay Association for Piano. Contact the Association for the specific date and time.

YEAR PROGRAM STARTED: 1970

PURPOSE:
To foster the teaching principles of Tobias Matthay.

LEGAL BASIS:
Nonprofit organization.

ELIGIBILITY:
Entrants must submit CD recordings for the preliminary phases. Finals require live performance.

FINANCIAL DATA:
Funds must be used to study piano with a member of the Association.
Amount of support per award: First prize: $2,000. Second Prize: $1,500.
Total amount of support: Varies.

NUMBER OF APPLICANTS MOST RECENT YEAR: 6 to 10 per year.

NUMBER OF AWARDS: 2.

APPLICATION INFORMATION:
Contact the Association.

PUBLICATIONS:
The Matthay News.

ADDRESS INQUIRIES TO:
Dr. Mary Pendleton Hoffer
Competition Chairperson
(See address and e-mail above.)

AMERICAN MUSICOLOGICAL SOCIETY   [751]
6010 College Station
Brunswick, ME 04011-8451
(207) 798-4243
(877) 679-7648
Fax: (207) 798-4254

E-MAIL ADDRESS:
ams@ams-net.org

WEB SITE ADDRESS:
www.ams-net.org

FOUNDED: 1934

AREAS OF INTEREST:
Scholastic work in musicology published in any country, any language.

NAME(S) OF PROGRAMS:
- **The Philip Brett Award**
- **The Alfred Einstein Award**
- **Noah Greenberg Award**
- **Thomas Hampson Award**
- **The Otto Kinkeldey Award**
- **Lewis Lockwood Award**
- **Music in American Culture Award**
- **Claude V. Palisca Award**
- **Paul A. Pisk Prize**
- **H. Colin Slim Award**
- **Ruth A. Solie Award**
- **Robert M. Stevenson Award**

TYPE:
Awards/prizes. The Philip Brett Award honors exceptional musicological work in the field of gay, lesbian, bisexual, transgender/transsexual studies completed during the previous two academic years (ending June 30), in any country and in any language. By "work" is meant a published article, book, edition, annotated translation, a paper read at a conference, teaching materials (course descriptions and syllabi), and other scholarly work accepted by the award committee that best exemplifies the highest qualities of originality, interpretation, theory and communication in this field of study.

The Alfred Einstein Award honors a musicological article of exceptional merit, published during the previous year in any language and in any country, by a scholar in the early stages of his or her career.

The Noah Greenberg Award is intended as a grant-in-aid to stimulate active cooperation between scholars and performers by recognizing and fostering outstanding contributions to historical performing practices. Both scholars and performers may apply, since the Award may subsidize the publication costs of articles, monographs, or editions, as well as public performance, recordings, or other projects.

The Thomas Hampson Award is dedicated to fostering editions and scholarship on classic song in all its contexts as well as new and innovative technologies for promoting and understanding classic song via interactive media and the Internet.

The Otto Kinkeldey Award will honor each year a musicological book of exceptional merit published during the previous year in any language and in any country by a scholar who is past the early stages of his or her career.

The Lewis Lockwood Award honors each year a musicological book of exceptional merit published during the previous year in any language and in any country by a scholar in the early stages of his or her career who is a member of the AMS or a citizen or permanent resident of Canada or the U.S.

The Music in American Culture Award honors each year a book of exceptional merit that both illuminates some important aspect of the music of the U.S. and places that music in a rich cultural context. Books published in the previous year in any language and in any country are eligible. The author must be a citizen or permanent resident of the U.S. or Canada.

The Claude V. Palisca Award honors each year a scholarly edition or translation in the field of musicology published during the previous year in any language and in any country by a scholar who is a member of the AMS or a citizen or permanent resident of Canada or the U.S., deemed by a committee of scholars to best exemplify the highest qualities of originality, interpretation, logic and clarity of thought, and communication.

The Paul A. Pisk Prize is awarded annually to a graduate music student for a scholarly paper to be presented at the Annual Meeting of the Society.

The H. Colin Slim Award honors each year a musicological article of exceptional merit, published during the previous year in any language and in any country by a scholar who is past the early stages of his or her career and who is a member of the AMS or a citizen or permanent resident of Canada or the U.S.

The Ruth A. Solie Award honors each year a collection of musicological essays of exceptional merit published during the preceding calendar year in any language and in any country and edited by a scholar or scholars who are members of the AMS or citizens or permanent residents of Canada or the U.S.

The Robert M. Stevenson Award recognizes outstanding scholarship in Iberian music. The prize will be awarded annually to a book, monograph, edition, or journal article by a member of the AMS. The publication must be written in English and must have been published during the preceding three calendar years.

Winners of all awards receive a monetary prize, conferred at the Annual Business Meeting and Awards Presentation of the Society by the chair of the committee.

YEAR PROGRAM STARTED: 1967

LEGAL BASIS:
Private.

GEOGRAPHIC RESTRICTIONS:
United States and Canada.

FINANCIAL DATA:
Amount of support per award: Varies.
Total amount of support: Maximum $1,000 (U.S.).

APPLICATION INFORMATION:
Application information is available on the web site.
Deadline: Philip Brett Award: July 1. Noah Greenburg Award: August 15. Paul A. Pisk Prize: October 1. All others: May 1.

IRS IDENTIFICATION NUMBER: 23-1577392

AMERICAN MUSICOLOGICAL SOCIETY [752]
6010 College Station
Brunswick, ME 04011-8451
(207) 798-4243
(877) 679-7648
Fax: (207) 798-4254

E-MAIL ADDRESS:
ams@ams-net.org

WEB SITE ADDRESS:
www.ams-net.org

FOUNDED: 1934

AREAS OF INTEREST:
Research in the various fields of music as a branch of learning and scholarship.

NAME(S) OF PROGRAMS:
- **Howard Mayer Brown Fellowship**
- **Alvin H. Johnson AMS 50 Dissertation Fellowships**

TYPE:
Fellowships; Grants-in-aid. The Publications Committee of the American Musicological Society makes available funds to help individuals with expenses involved in the publication of works of musical scholarship, including books, articles and works in nonprint media.

The Howard Mayer Brown Fellowship is intended to increase the presence of minority scholars and teachers in musicology. The fellowship supports one year of graduate work for a member of a group historically underrepresented in the discipline.

The Alvin H. Johnson AMS Dissertation Fellowships are intended for full-time study. It is expected that the recipient's dissertation be completed within the fellowship year.

YEAR PROGRAM STARTED: 1989

PURPOSE:
To support the advancement of research in various fields of music.

LEGAL BASIS:
Nonprofit organization.

ELIGIBILITY:
For the AMS Fellowship, applicants must be registered for a doctorate at a North American university and have completed all formal degree requirements except the dissertation.

The Howard Mayer Brown Fellowship will be awarded to a student who has completed at least one year of graduate work, and who intends to complete a Ph.D. in the field. Applications are encouraged from African-Americans, Native Americans, Latinos, Asian-Americans and, in Canada, visible minorities. There are no restrictions as to age or sex.

FINANCIAL DATA:
Amount of support per award: $17,000 stipend.
Total amount of support: Varies.

APPLICATION INFORMATION:
Applications must be submitted electronically.
Duration: One year. No individual can receive a subvention more than once in a three-year period.
Deadline: December 15.

IRS IDENTIFICATION NUMBER: 23-1577392

AMERICAN SOCIETY OF COMPOSERS, AUTHORS AND PUBLISHERS (ASCAP)
1900 Broadway, 7th Floor
New York, NY 10023
(212) 621-6318
Fax: (212) 595-3342

E-MAIL ADDRESS:
jsteinblatt@ascap.com

WEB SITE ADDRESS:
www.ascap.com

xTYPE:
Awards/prizes. The ASCAP Deems Taylor Awards program recognizes books, articles, broadcasts and web sites on the subject of music selected for their excellence.

See entry 666 for full listing.

ARD INTERNATIONAL MUSIC COMPETITION   [753]
Internationaler Musikwettbewerb der ARD
Bayerischer Rundfunk
Rundfunkplatz 1
D-80335 Munich Germany
0049 89 5900 42471
Fax: 0049 89 5900 3573

E-MAIL ADDRESS:
ard.musikwettbewerb@br.de

WEB SITE ADDRESS:
www.ard-musikwettbewerb.de

FOUNDED: 1952

AREAS OF INTEREST:
International music competition.

NAME(S) OF PROGRAMS:
● **Music Competition**

TYPE:
Awards/prizes. Cash prizes; Competition for music.

Intended for a selection of young musicians who are interested in following an international career. The standards are, therefore, high and the prizes are awarded only for outstanding performances. Program categories differ each year. For 2015: voice, flute, trombone and piano duo.

YEAR PROGRAM STARTED: 1952

PURPOSE:
To create gifted musicians and international soloists.

ELIGIBILITY:
Instrumentalists should be born between 1986 and 1998.

FINANCIAL DATA:
Amount of support per award: Soloists: First prize, EUR 10,000; Second prize, EUR 7,500; Third prize, EUR 5,000. Wind Quintet (2014): First prize, EUR 25,000; Second prize, EUR 20,000; Third prize, EUR 15,000. Piano Duo (2015): First prize, EUR 12,000; Second prize, EUR 9,000; Third prize, EUR 6,000. String Quartet (2016): First prize, EUR 24,000; Second prize, EUR 18,000; Third prize, EUR 12,000. Piano Trio (2017): First Prize, EUR 18,000; Second prize, EUR 13,500; Third prize, EUR 9,000.
Total amount of support: EUR 127,500 for the year 2015.

COOPERATIVE FUNDING PROGRAMS: Theodor - Rogler - Foundation, Alice - Rosner - Foundation, and others.

NUMBER OF APPLICANTS MOST RECENT YEAR:
Approximately 400 each year.

NUMBER OF AWARDS: 12.

APPLICATION INFORMATION:
A valid statement of type and duration of study should accompany the entry form. Students must have permission from their current teacher to participate. A list of the applicant's complete repertoire is required. Upon arrival in Munich, each competitor should present a birth certificate or a valid passport at the Competition Office.

Preselections with CD are obligatory for all categories.

PUBLICATIONS:
Annual prospectus with application guidelines and programs.

OFFICERS:
Axel Linstaedt, Artistic Director

ADDRESS INQUIRIES TO:
Competition Office
(See address above.)

THE ASCAP FOUNDATION   [754]
1900 Broadway, 7th Floor
New York, NY 10023
(212) 621-6588
Fax: (212) 595-3276

E-MAIL ADDRESS:
concertmusic@ascap.com

WEB SITE ADDRESS:
www.ascapfoundation.org

FOUNDED: 1975

AREAS OF INTEREST:
Music, music composition and music education.

NAME(S) OF PROGRAMS:
● **The Morton Gould Young Composer Awards**

TYPE:
Awards/prizes.

YEAR PROGRAM STARTED: 1978

PURPOSE:
To encourage talented young American composers.

LEGAL BASIS:
Publicly supported foundation, 501(c)(3) organization.

ELIGIBILITY:
Individuals must have not reached their 30th birthday as of January 1 of the year of application and must be U.S. citizens, permanent residents or enrolled students with student visas.

Previous recipients are eligible to reapply for the award.

GEOGRAPHIC RESTRICTIONS:
United States.

FINANCIAL DATA:
Amount of support per award: $500 to $2,500, at discretion of judges.
Total amount of support: $45,000.

NUMBER OF APPLICANTS MOST RECENT YEAR:
Approximately 700.

NUMBER OF AWARDS: 39 or more.

APPLICATION INFORMATION:
A completed application form must be submitted along with one reproduction of an original manuscript or score, a listing of music studies and compositions to date, and biographical information.
Deadline: February 1.

PUBLICATIONS:
Annual report; contributions policy; application guidelines.

BOARD OF DIRECTORS:
Paul Williams, President
Irwin Z. Robinson, Vice President
Dean Kay, Treasurer
Ginny Mancini, Secretary
Marilyn Bergman
Charles Bernstein

Bruce Broughton
Tita Cahn
Alf Clausen
Dan Foliart
Arthur Hamilton
Wayland Holyfield
James M. Kendrick
Robert Kimball
Ed London
Johnny Mandel
James McBride
Jay R. Morgenstern
Mary Rodgers
Stephen Schwartz
Valerie Simpson
Charles Strouse
Doug Wood

ADMINISTRATION:
Karen Sherry, Executive Director
Colleen McDonough, Director
Julie Lapore, Program Manager

ADDRESS INQUIRIES TO:
Cia Toscanini, Vice President
Concert Music ASCAP
(See address above.)

BRANDON UNIVERSITY   [755]
School of Music
270 18th Street
Brandon MB R7A 6A9 Canada
(204) 727-7388
Fax: (204) 728-6839

E-MAIL ADDRESS:
music@brandonu.ca

WEB SITE ADDRESS:
www.brandonu.ca/music

AREAS OF INTEREST:
Music education, performance and literature (piano, collaborative piano, strings, composition, clarinet, trumpet, conducting and jazz).

TYPE:
Assistantships; Scholarships.

YEAR PROGRAM STARTED: 1980

PURPOSE:
To afford graduate students the opportunity to gain professional experience while studying and to provide monetary assistance.

ELIGIBILITY:
Open to candidates with a Bachelor's degree in music or music education with a minimum grade point average of 3.0 during the final year.

FINANCIAL DATA:
Amount of support per award: Up to $5,000 per year.
Total amount of support: $20,000 per year.

NUMBER OF APPLICANTS MOST RECENT YEAR:
15.

NUMBER OF AWARDS: 11.

APPLICATION INFORMATION:
Applications available both online and from the Graduate Music Office.
Deadline: April 1.

ADDRESS INQUIRIES TO:
T. Patrick Carrabré
Chairperson
Graduate Music Department
(See address above.)

CHAMBER MUSIC AMERICA [756]

UPS Box 458
243 Fifth Avenue
New York, NY 10016
(212) 242-2022 ext. 5082

E-MAIL ADDRESS:
sdadian@chamber-music.org

WEB SITE ADDRESS:
www.chamber-music.org

FOUNDED: 1977

AREAS OF INTEREST:
The promotion of public interest in and appreciation of chamber music and the promotion of cooperation among and advancement of professional American chamber music ensembles and presenters.

CONSULTING OR VOLUNTEER SERVICES:
Technical assistance provided in such areas as fund-raising, marketing and residency design and implementation.

NAME(S) OF PROGRAMS:
● **Residency Partnership Program**

TYPE:
Project/program grants. Direct grants for ensembles and concert presenters.

YEAR PROGRAM STARTED: 1978

PURPOSE:
To stimulate the establishment of chamber music residencies.

LEGAL BASIS:
Nonprofit arts service organization.

ELIGIBILITY:
Candidates must be an ensemble member or a presenter in good standing of CMA, have a minimum of two years of continuous public performance and operation, and have experience in touring, workshops or other residency-related activities.

GEOGRAPHIC RESTRICTIONS:
United States.

FINANCIAL DATA:
Amount of support per award: $2,500 to $12,000.

Total amount of support: Varies.

Matching fund requirements: CMA funds up to 75% of the requested amount.

NUMBER OF APPLICANTS MOST RECENT YEAR:
65.

NUMBER OF AWARDS: 8.

APPLICATION INFORMATION:
Telephone consultations and workshops held by teleconference with CMA staff are available for organizations with questions about the application process.

Duration: Three days to one year.

Deadline: October 31, 2014.

PUBLICATIONS:
Chamber Music, magazine; *CMA Matters*, newsletter; application guidelines.

ADDRESS INQUIRIES TO:
Susan Dadian, Program Director
CMA Classical/Contemporary
(See address above.)

*SPECIAL STIPULATIONS:
Residencies must take place within the U.S.

CHAMBER MUSIC AMERICA [757]

UPS Box 458
243 Fifth Avenue
New York, NY 10016
(212) 242-2022 ext. 5082

E-MAIL ADDRESS:
sdadian@chamber-music.org

WEB SITE ADDRESS:
www.chamber-music.org

FOUNDED: 1977

AREAS OF INTEREST:
The promotion of public interest in and appreciation of chamber music and the promotion of cooperation among and advancement of professional American chamber music ensembles and presenters.

NAME(S) OF PROGRAMS:
● **Chamber Music America Classical Commissioning Program**

TYPE:
Project/program grants. Classical Commissioning provides support to U.S. member ensembles and presenters for commissions of new chamber works. Grants are made for commissioning fees, copying costs and ensemble rehearsal honoraria.

YEAR PROGRAM STARTED: 1983

PURPOSE:
To stimulate the composition of new works for chamber ensembles.

LEGAL BASIS:
Nonprofit arts service organization.

ELIGIBILITY:
Ensembles and presenters must be organizational members of Chamber Music America. Compositions must be written for small ensembles (two to 10 musicians) performing one to a part, and may represent a diverse musical spectrum, including contemporary art music, world music, and works that include electronics.

GEOGRAPHIC RESTRICTIONS:
United States.

FINANCIAL DATA:
Amount of support per award: Up to $20,000 for composer fee, copying allotment of $1,000 and subsidy of $1,000 per musician.

Total amount of support: Varies.

NUMBER OF APPLICANTS MOST RECENT YEAR:
102.

NUMBER OF AWARDS: 10 to 12.

APPLICATION INFORMATION:
Guidelines may be obtained in the fall from the address above.

Duration: Applicants may reapply after one cycle.

Deadline: March 20, 2015.

PUBLICATIONS:
Guidelines and applications.

ADDRESS INQUIRIES TO:
Susan Dadian, Program Director
CMA Classical/Contemporary
(See address above.)

CHOPIN FOUNDATION OF THE U.S. [758]

1440 79th Street Causeway, Suite 117
Miami, FL 33141
(305) 868-0624
Fax: (305) 865-5150

E-MAIL ADDRESS:
info@chopin.org

WEB SITE ADDRESS:
www.chopin.org

FOUNDED: 1977

AREAS OF INTEREST:
Chopin and the promotion of classical music in the community by the support of young American pianists.

NAME(S) OF PROGRAMS:
● **Scholarship Program for Young Pianists**

TYPE:
Scholarships. Scholarship program supporting young American pianists, 14 to 17 years of age.

YEAR PROGRAM STARTED: 1997

PURPOSE:
To support talented young American musicians in their struggle for career recognition; to make classical music available to the community.

ELIGIBILITY:
Open to any qualified American pianists (citizens or legal residents) not younger than 14 and not older than 17 years of age on the application deadline, whose field of study is music and whose major is piano. If applicant is older than 17 years of age, he or she may only be accepted if currently in this scholarship program.

GEOGRAPHIC RESTRICTIONS:
United States.

FINANCIAL DATA:
Amount of support per award: $1,000.

Total amount of support: $12,000 for the year 2012.

NUMBER OF APPLICANTS MOST RECENT YEAR:
25.

NUMBER OF AWARDS: 12 for the year 2012.

APPLICATION INFORMATION:
Submit application along with the following documents:
(1) statement of career goals;
(2) minimum of two references from piano teachers or performers;
(3) video recording of 20 to 30 minutes of Chopin's works. Each piece must be an unedited performance on the DVD media. Recording must be clearly labeled, including applicant's name, address and works performed and;
(4) $25 registration fee.

Duration: One year. Renewable up to four years as long as the recipient continues to study piano, maintains satisfactory progress, and each year submits an audiocassette, CD or DVD recording of unedited performances of Chopin's works for evaluation as per renewal information.

Deadline: April 15.

IRS IDENTIFICATION NUMBER: 59-1778404

ADDRESS INQUIRIES TO:
Jadwiga Gewert, Executive Director
(See address above.)

*SPECIAL STIPULATIONS:
Registration fee of $25 must be included with application.

CIVIC ORCHESTRA OF CHICAGO [759]

220 South Michigan Avenue
Chicago, IL 60604
(312) 294-3422
Fax: (312) 294-3450

E-MAIL ADDRESS:
civic@cso.org

WEB SITE ADDRESS:
www.cso.org/civic

FOUNDED: 1919

AREAS OF INTEREST:
Training young musicians for professional work in the orchestral field at the highest level with an emphasis on artistic excellence, community engagement and advocacy.

NAME(S) OF PROGRAMS:
● **Civic Orchestra Lesson Scholarship Stipends**

TYPE:
Fellowships; Scholarships. Stipends to help defray cost of private study with Chicago Symphony members and additional music training-related costs. Scholarship funds may be used for full-time two-year graduate-level study at a local academic institution.

YEAR PROGRAM STARTED: 1919

PURPOSE:
The development of aesthetic sensitivity and playing technique through personal instruction with skilled pedagogues.

LEGAL BASIS:
The Civic Orchestra is a training orchestra under the auspices of the Chicago Symphony Orchestra, which is incorporated as a nonprofit, tax-exempt organization.

ELIGIBILITY:
Scholarships are available to all Civic Orchestra members.

FINANCIAL DATA:
Amount of support per award: $6,900 average for 30-week season.
Total amount of support: Varies.

NUMBER OF APPLICANTS MOST RECENT YEAR:
604.

NUMBER OF AWARDS: 90 for the 2011-12 season.

APPLICATION INFORMATION:
Application forms can be filled out when auditioning for the Civic Orchestra. Membership application forms are available from the Civic Orchestra office. Auditions are held in February and March.
Duration: 30 weeks, September to May or June. Renewal possible for up to two years.
Deadline: Mid-January.

OFFICERS:
William A. Osborn, Chairperson
Deborah Rutter, President, Chicago Symphony Orchestra

ADDRESS INQUIRIES TO:
Yoo-Jin Hong, Manager
(See address above.)

CLEVELAND INSTITUTE OF MUSIC [760]

11021 East Boulevard
Cleveland, OH 44106
(216) 791-5000 ext. 262
Fax: (216) 791-3063

E-MAIL ADDRESS:
kxg26@case.edu

WEB SITE ADDRESS:
www.cim.edu

FOUNDED: 1920

NAME(S) OF PROGRAMS:
● **Cleveland Institute of Music Scholarships**

TYPE:
Scholarships.

PURPOSE:
To provide talented students with a professional, world-class education in the art of music.

ELIGIBILITY:
Candidates for the Teaching Fellowships should have a Bachelor of Music degree or equivalent and must be proficient in English.

FINANCIAL DATA:
Amount of support per award: Varies.

NUMBER OF APPLICANTS MOST RECENT YEAR:
1,400 for the year 2011-12.

APPLICATION INFORMATION:
Students must apply online.
Deadline: Returning students: March 1. New students: February 15.

ADDRESS INQUIRIES TO:
Kristie Gripp, Director of Financial Aid
(See address above.)

COLUMBIA UNIVERSITY

709 Pulitzer Hall
2950 Broadway
New York, NY 10027
(212) 854-3841
Fax: (212) 854-3342

E-MAIL ADDRESS:
pulitzer@pulitzer.org

WEB SITE ADDRESS:
www.pulitzer.org

TYPE:
Awards/prizes; Fellowships. Awards in journalism, books and music.

Pulitzer Prizes in Journalism are awarded based on material appearing in a text-based U.S. newspaper or news site that publishes at least once a week during the year. Awards given for:
(1) meritorious public service by a newspaper through the use of its journalistic resources which may include editorials, cartoons, photographs, graphics and online material;
(2) local reporting of breaking news;
(3) investigative reporting by an individual or team, presented as a single article or series;
(4) explanatory journalism that illuminates a significant or complex subject, demonstrating mastery of the subject, lucid writing and clear presentation;
(5) local reporting;
(6) reporting on national affairs;
(7) reporting on international affairs, including United Nations correspondence;
(8) feature writing giving prime consideration to high literary quality and originality;
(9) commentary;
(10) criticism;
(11) editorial writing;
(12) cartoon or portfolio of cartoons;
(13) breaking news photography in black and white or color, which may consist of a photograph or photographs, a sequence or an album and;
(14) feature photography in black and white or color with the same stipulations as above.

Prizes in Letters are restricted to works first published in the U.S. during the year in book form and available for purchase by the general public. Awards given for:
(1) fiction by an American author, preferably dealing with American life;
(2) a play by an American author, preferably original in its source and dealing with American life, produced in the U.S. January 1 to December 31;
(3) appropriately documented book on the history of the U.S.;
(4) appropriately documented biography or autobiography by an American author;
(5) volume of original verse by an American author and;
(6) appropriately documented book of nonfiction by an American author that is not eligible for consideration in any other category.

A prize in music is given for distinguished musical composition by an American that has had its first performance in the U.S. during the year.

Four fellowships enable outstanding graduates to travel, report and study abroad. One fellowship is given to an outstanding graduate who wishes to specialize in drama, music, literary, film or television criticism.

See entry 1926 for full listing.

CONCOURS OSM STANDARD LIFE [761]

260 de Maisonneuve Boulevard West
2nd Floor
Montreal QC H2X 1Y9 Canada
(514) 840-7415
Fax: (514) 842-0728

E-MAIL ADDRESS:
concoursosm@osm.ca

WEB SITE ADDRESS:
www.osm.ca/competition

FOUNDED: 1937

AREAS OF INTEREST:
Music.

NAME(S) OF PROGRAMS:
● **OSM Standard Life Competition**

TYPE:
Awards/prizes; Scholarships. Prizes include money prizes, a performance with the Orchestre symphonique de Montreal, concert opportunities with various organizations throughout Canada, scholarships at Canada's leading summer academies and a professional recording in one of Radio-Canada's studios. For musicians of the following categories: strings and harp.

YEAR PROGRAM STARTED: 1937

PURPOSE:
To encourage young Canadian musicians.

LEGAL BASIS:
Symphony orchestra.

ELIGIBILITY:
Open to Canadian citizens or landed immigrants in the following categories: Piano and Strings, up to 25 years of age; Woodwinds and Brass, 16 to 25 years of age (except tuba, 16 to 30 years of age); Percussion, 16 to 30 years of age; Voice, 22 to 30 years of age.

Each year is for a different category.

FINANCIAL DATA:
Amount of support per award: Three first prizes: $10,000 (CAN). Three second prizes: $5,000 (CAN). Three third prizes: $2,500 (CAN). Three prizes for the best interpretation of a Canadian work: $2,500 (CAN). The Paul Merkelo Scholarship: $2,000 (CAN).

Total amount of support: More than $100,000 (CAN) in prizes, scholarships and concert opportunities.

NUMBER OF APPLICANTS MOST RECENT YEAR: 85 to 95.

NUMBER OF AWARDS: Approximately 20 annually.

APPLICATION INFORMATION:
Include application form, registration fee, proof of age and of Canadian citizenship and curriculum vitae. Applicants must contact OSM Competition to acquire full details of application process.
Deadline: September 30.

ADDRESS INQUIRIES TO:
Daniele LeBlanc, Head
Concours OSM Standard Life Competition
(See address above.)

*PLEASE NOTE:
Musical program approved by the jury members of the competition.

CONTEMPORARY MUSIC FESTIVAL   [762]
School of Music
Indiana State University
Terre Haute, IN 47809
(812) 237-2743
Fax: (812) 237-3009

E-MAIL ADDRESS:
kurt.fowler@indstate.edu

WEB SITE ADDRESS:
www.indstate.edu/music/cmf

FOUNDED: 1966

AREAS OF INTEREST:
Contemporary orchestra music.

NAME(S) OF PROGRAMS:
● **Competition for Orchestral Compositions**

TYPE:
Conferences/seminars; Residencies. Performance of new music by the Indianapolis Chamber Orchestra. Winning composers will take part in seminars that are part of the festival and will receive an honorarium to cover expenses.

YEAR PROGRAM STARTED: 1966

PURPOSE:
Performance of new orchestral music.

ELIGIBILITY:
Contestants must be citizens or legal residents of the U.S. Winners of the competition within the last five years are not eligible.

FINANCIAL DATA:
Amount of support per award: First place: $1,000.

NUMBER OF APPLICANTS MOST RECENT YEAR: 85.

NUMBER OF AWARDS: 1.

APPLICATION INFORMATION:
Guidelines are available on the web site.
Deadline: June 15.

ADDRESS INQUIRIES TO:
Indianapolis Chamber Orchestra
4603 Clarendon Road, Suite 36
Indianapolis, IN 46208
Tel: (317) 940-9607

AARON COPLAND FUND FOR MUSIC, INC.   [763]
254 West 31st Street, 15th Floor
New York, NY 10001
(212) 461-6956
Fax: (212) 810-4567

E-MAIL ADDRESS:
info@coplandfund.org

WEB SITE ADDRESS:
www.coplandfund.org

FOUNDED: 1992

AREAS OF INTEREST:
Music.

NAME(S) OF PROGRAMS:
● **Performing Ensembles Program**
● **Recording Program**
● **Supplemental Program**

TYPE:
General operating grants; Project/program grants. Performing Ensembles Program: To support performing organizations whose artistic excellence encourages and improves public knowledge and appreciation of serious contemporary American music. Organizations whose principal function is to support a specific performing ensemble should apply to this program.

Recording Program: To document and provide wider exposure for the music of contemporary American composers; to develop audiences for contemporary American music through record distribution and other retail markets; to support the release and dissemination of recordings of previously unreleased contemporary American music and the reissuance of recordings that are no longer available.

Supplemental Program: To support nonprofit organizations that have a history of substantial commitment to contemporary American music but whose needs are not addressed by the Fund's programs of support for performing organizations and recording projects, such as presenters and music service organizations.

YEAR PROGRAM STARTED: 1992

PURPOSE:
To encourage and improve public knowledge and appreciation of contemporary American music.

LEGAL BASIS:
Foundation.

ELIGIBILITY:
For the Performing Ensembles Program, applicants must be nonprofit professional performing ensembles with a history of substantial commitment to contemporary American music and with plans to continue that commitment. Ensembles must have been in existence for at least two years at the time of application. Festivals are only eligible to apply for their professional core ensembles. Individuals, student ensembles, presenters without a core ensemble are not eligible. Grants will not be made for the purpose of commissions to composers.

For the Recording Program, applicants must be nonprofit performance ensembles, presenting institutions or nonprofit or commercial recording companies. Any applicant who, as of the deadline date, has one or more Recording Program grants that have been paid but that have not been released within two years after receiving funds will not be eligible to apply for a Recording Program grant. Grants will not be made for the purpose of commissions to composers.

Supplemental Program: Applications may be submitted by nonprofit organizations that have a history of substantial commitment to contemporary American music but whose needs are not addressed by the Fund's programs of support for performing organizations and recording projects. Organizations must have been in existence for at least two years at the time of application.

FINANCIAL DATA:
Grants for recordings of orchestral works may cover up to 50% of the total project costs, including musicians' recording fees, production, marketing and distribution.
Amount of support per award: $1,000 to $20,000 for Performing Ensembles and Supplemental Program; $2,000 to $20,000 for the Recording Program.
Total amount of support: $1,500,000.

NUMBER OF APPLICANTS MOST RECENT YEAR: Approximately 500.

NUMBER OF AWARDS: 261 for calendar year 2013.

APPLICATION INFORMATION:
Fund guidelines and application procedures are available to prospective applicants on the Fund's web site.
Duration: Varies depending on needs and nature of the request.
Deadline: October 31, 2014 for Supplemental Program. Notification by February 2015. January 15, 2015 for Recording Program. Notification by June 30, 2015 for Performing Ensembles. Notification by November.

ADDRESS INQUIRIES TO:
Grants Manager
E-mail: grantsmanager@coplandfund.org
(See address above.)

THE CURTIS INSTITUTE OF MUSIC   [764]
1726 Locust Street
Philadelphia, PA 19103
(215) 717-3117
Fax: (215) 893-7900

E-MAIL ADDRESS:
admissions@curtis.edu

WEB SITE ADDRESS:
www.curtis.edu

FOUNDED: 1924

AREAS OF INTEREST:
Musical performance.

NAME(S) OF PROGRAMS:
● **Bachelor of Music Degree Program**
● **Diploma Program**
● **Master of Music in Opera**

TYPE:
Scholarships. The training of young performing musicians, admitted by competitive audition for a tuition-free musical education.

YEAR PROGRAM STARTED: 1924

PURPOSE:
To train exceptionally gifted young musicians for careers as performing artists on the highest professional level.

LEGAL BASIS:
The school is operated under a Charter granted by the Commonwealth of Pennsylvania and is also included in the list of "Colleges and Universities in Pennsylvania approved by the State Council of Education for the Granting of Degrees."
The U.S. Government has duly approved the Curtis Institute of Music as an institution of learning for the attendance of nonimmigrant students, under the Immigration and Nationality Act.

ELIGIBILITY:
All are eligible for the competitive audition, regardless of race, origin or geographic distribution. There are maximum ages for applicants which vary by instrument.

For Bachelor of Music Degree Program and Diploma Program, eligibility requirements consist of a competitive audition, high school diploma or GED, SAT Scores, English achievement scores and TOEFL for foreign students.

For Master of Music Degree Programs, eligibility requirements consist of a competitive audition and previous Bachelor's degree.

FINANCIAL DATA:
All students are on a scholarship basis exclusively and pay no tuition fees.
Amount of support per award: Varies depending upon award program.
Total amount of support: Varies.

APPLICATION INFORMATION:
An application form with requested information completed in detail and transcript of high school, college and other academic records should be submitted to the Admissions Officer.
Duration: One-time award.
Deadline: December 15, 2014.

PUBLICATIONS:
The Curtis Institute of Music Catalogue (includes application form).

IRS IDENTIFICATION NUMBER: 23-1585611

ADDRESS INQUIRIES TO:
Christopher Hodges, Admissions Officer
(See address above.)

EASTMAN SCHOOL OF MUSIC OF THE UNIVERSITY OF ROCHESTER   [765]
26 Gibbs Street
Rochester, NY 14604
(585) 274-1560
Fax: (585) 274-1088

E-MAIL ADDRESS:
gdean@esm.rochester.edu

WEB SITE ADDRESS:
www.rochester.edu/eastman

AREAS OF INTEREST:
Music.

NAME(S) OF PROGRAMS:
- **Eastman School of Music Graduate Awards**

TYPE:
Assistantships; Fellowships; Scholarships; Visiting scholars.

PURPOSE:
To support the School's academic programs.

ELIGIBILITY:
Open to nationals of all countries. Candidates should have the qualifications necessary for admission to the Eastman School of Music. Non-U.S. citizens are usually offered service scholarships in ensemble work at graduate level.

FINANCIAL DATA:
Amount of support per award: Up to $21,000 in stipend and $36,000 in tuition scholarship per year.

NUMBER OF AWARDS: 300.

APPLICATION INFORMATION:
Applicants must complete an application form. In addition, awards require an interview in Rochester or at one of the regional auditions.
Duration: One academic year. Renewable.
Deadline: December 1.

ADDRESS INQUIRIES TO:
Admissions Office
Eastman School of Music
(See address above.)

AVERY FISHER ARTIST PROGRAM   [766]
c/o M.L. Falcone
155 West 68th Street, Suite 1114
New York, NY 10023
(212) 580-4302
Fax: (212) 787-9638

WEB SITE ADDRESS:
www.averyfisherartistprogram.org

FOUNDED: 1974

AREAS OF INTEREST:
Music, specifically classical instrumentalists.

NAME(S) OF PROGRAMS:
- **The Avery Fisher Career Grants**
- **The Avery Fisher Prize**

TYPE:
Awards/prizes; Grants-in-aid. Awards for excellence and help in launching major careers.

YEAR PROGRAM STARTED: 1974

PURPOSE:
To recognize outstanding classical instrumentalists and chamber ensembles.

LEGAL BASIS:
Not-for-profit, tax-exempt.

ELIGIBILITY:
Instrumentalists who are U.S. citizens or permanent residents may be nominated.

FINANCIAL DATA:
Amount of support per award: Avery Fisher Career Grants: $25,000 each; Avery Fisher Prize: $75,000.

NUMBER OF AWARDS: Up to 5 Career Grants per year. Avery Fisher Prize considered every year, but not necessarily awarded.

APPLICATION INFORMATION:
Individual artists may not apply directly. Nominations are made by the Recommendation Board, which comprises nationally known instrumentalists, conductors, music educators and presenters. Final selections are made by the Executive Committee. The Program is administered by the Lincoln Center for the Performing Arts, Inc.

Deadline: Varies.

EXECUTIVE COMMITTEE:
Emanuel Ax
Jed Bernstein
David Finckel
Henry Fogel
Anthony Fogg
Pamela Frank
Ara Guzelimian
Wu Han
Nathan Leventhal
Yo-Yo Ma
Jane S. Moss
Chad Smith
Matias Tarnopolsky
Matthew VanBesien

ADDRESS INQUIRIES TO:
Nathan Leventhal, Chairman
(See address above.)

FROMM MUSIC FOUNDATION AT HARVARD   [767]
Department of Music
Harvard University
Cambridge, MA 02138
(617) 495-2791
Fax: (617) 496-8081

E-MAIL ADDRESS:
moncrief@fas.harvard.edu

WEB SITE ADDRESS:
www.fas.harvard.edu/~musicdpt/fromm.html

FOUNDED: 1972

AREAS OF INTEREST:
Commissioning and performance of contemporary music.

TYPE:
Commission and grant-in-aid.

YEAR PROGRAM STARTED: 1952

PURPOSE:
To bring contemporary music closer to the public by providing support to composers and performers.

LEGAL BASIS:
Private foundation.

ELIGIBILITY:
Composers must be citizens or residents of the U.S. For these purposes, "residents" shall be deemed to include only lawful permanent residents, temporary residents, asylees, refugees and nonimmigrants who have lawfully been admitted to the U.S. for a term of one year or more.

FINANCIAL DATA:
Amount of support per award: $12,000.

NUMBER OF APPLICANTS MOST RECENT YEAR: 200.

NUMBER OF AWARDS: 12.

APPLICATION INFORMATION:
Applicants must contact the Foundation for an application.
Deadline: June 1 for consideration in following fall. Commissions will be awarded in December.

PUBLICATIONS:
Application guidelines.

STAFF:
Jean Moncrieff, Administrator

DIRECTORS:
Alex Rehding, Chairperson
Tania Leon
Marilyn Nonken

ADDRESS INQUIRIES TO:
Jean Moncrieff, Administrator
(See address above.)

*SPECIAL STIPULATIONS:
For those who have previously received a
Fromm Commission, there is a 15-year
waiting period before you can apply again.
The Fromm Commission cannot be applied
to projects that have been awarded other
commissions.

THE GRAMMY FOUNDATION [768]

3030 Olympic Boulevard
Santa Monica, CA 90404
(310) 581-8788
Fax: (310) 392-2188

E-MAIL ADDRESS:
grant@grammy.com

WEB SITE ADDRESS:
www.grammy.org/grammy-foundation/grants

FOUNDED: 1989

AREAS OF INTEREST:
Music research, archiving and preserving and
the medical and occupational well-being of
music professionals.

TYPE:
Challenge/matching grants; Project/program
grants; Research grants. The GRAMMY
Foundation Grant Program funds the
following areas:
(1) Scientific Research Projects - Grants to
organizations and individuals to support
efforts that advance the research and/or broad
reaching implementations of original
scientific research projects related to the
impact of music on the human condition,
such as the links between music study and
early childhood development, the effects of
music therapy and the medical and
occupational well-being of music
professionals.
(2) Archiving and Preservation Projects -
Grants to organizations and individuals to
support efforts that advance the archiving and
preservation of the music and recorded sound
heritage of the Americas. The Archiving and
Preservation area has two funding categories:
(a) Preservation Implementation and (b)
Planning, Assessment and/or Consultation.

YEAR PROGRAM STARTED: 1989

PURPOSE:
To cultivate the understanding, appreciation
and advancement of the contribution of
recorded music to American culture.

ELIGIBILITY:
Priority is given to music projects of national
significance, that achieve a broad reach and
whose final results are accessible to the
general public.

The GRAMMY Foundation, Inc., will not
fund:
(1) chapters, trustees, officers or staff;
(2) organizations that discriminate on the
basis of race, sex, religion, national origin,
disability or age;
(3) recording projects, demo tapes or live
performances designed to promote the career
of an individual or group;
(4) faculty and staff salaries unrelated to the
project;
(5) performance events;
(6) purchase or repairs of music instruments
or equipment;
(7) competitions and related expenses;

(8) work toward academic degrees;
(9) regular ongoing business activities of
corporate clients;
(10) organizations or individuals for more
than three consecutive years;
(11) organizations not based in the U.S. or;
(12) documentaries, endowments and web
sites.

FINANCIAL DATA:
Amount of support per award: $5,000 to
$20,000.

NUMBER OF APPLICANTS MOST RECENT YEAR:
200 for the year 2013.

NUMBER OF AWARDS: 14 for the year 2013.

APPLICATION INFORMATION:
Letters of inquiry are only accepted online.
Guidelines are available on the Foundation
web site. Applicants must use current grant
application only and should also include:
(1) evidence of organization's nonprofit status
and copy of IRS tax determination letter;
(2) general description, history and
accomplishments of the organization;
(3) current resume for individual applicants
and organization's key personnel;
(4) two letters of support for the project and;
(5) an itemized budget.
Late or incomplete applications will not be
reviewed.
Duration: Six to 24 months.
Deadline: October 1. Invitation to submit full
proposal sent in November. Notification by
March 15.

*SPECIAL STIPULATIONS:
Projects must be completed and a final report
submitted within 12 to 24 months of project
start date. A full set of the completed project
is due to The GRAMMY Foundation within
90 days of the project completion date.
Grantees must formally credit The
GRAMMY Foundation in all published
materials and announcements.

GUITAR FOUNDATION OF AMERICA [769]

4500 Williams Drive
Suite 212-301
Georgetown, TX 78633
(877) 570-1651
Fax: (877) 570-3409

E-MAIL ADDRESS:
info@guitarfoundation.org

WEB SITE ADDRESS:
www.guitarfoundation.org

FOUNDED: 1973

AREAS OF INTEREST:
Classical guitar.

NAME(S) OF PROGRAMS:
● **International Concert Artists Competition**
● **International Youth Competition**

TYPE:
Awards/prizes. International Youth
Competition awarded in two divisions:
Division I for ages 15 to 18 years old and
Division II for ages 14 years old and under.

PURPOSE:
To support the serious study of the guitar in
its historic and performance aspects; to
promote the guitar as an ensemble
instrument; to encourage composition and
arrangements of ensemble music involving
the guitar; to preserve and make available
literature on the guitar.

LEGAL BASIS:
501(c)(3).

ELIGIBILITY:
Open to competitors worldwide.

FINANCIAL DATA:
Amount of support per award: Varies.
Total amount of support: Varies.

NUMBER OF AWARDS: 12 annually.

IRS IDENTIFICATION NUMBER: 51-0147668

EXECUTIVE DIRECTOR:
Galen Wixson

THE KOSCIUSZKO FOUNDATION, INC. [770]

15 East 65th Street
New York, NY 10065
(212) 734-2130
Fax: (212) 628-4552

E-MAIL ADDRESS:
info@thekf.org
kharanczyk@thekf.org

WEB SITE ADDRESS:
www.thekf.org/programs/competitions/chopin/

FOUNDED: 1925

NAME(S) OF PROGRAMS:
● **Chopin Piano Competition**

TYPE:
Awards/prizes.

YEAR PROGRAM STARTED: 1949

PURPOSE:
To encourage gifted young pianists to further
their studies and perform the works of
Chopin, Szymanowski and other Polish
composers.

LEGAL BASIS:
Public foundation.

ELIGIBILITY:
The competition is open to citizens and
permanent residents of the U.S., Polish
citizens, and to international full-time
students with valid student visas. Applicants
must be between the ages of 16 and 26. It is
expected that applicants will have
demonstrated exceptional talent and artistic
achievement. Contestants may apply to
compete in the preliminaries in New York.
Each contestant should have a program of at
least 60 minutes and is expected to perform
complete works from memory.

FINANCIAL DATA:
Amount of support per award: $5,000 first
prize; $2,500 second prize; $1,500 third
prize.
Total amount of support: $9,000.

NUMBER OF APPLICANTS MOST RECENT YEAR:
10.

NUMBER OF AWARDS: 3.

APPLICATION INFORMATION:
Official application materials are available
upon request to the Foundation. Send
business-size, self-addressed, stamped
envelope. These materials are also available
on the web site.
Deadline: October 3.

OFFICERS:
Alex Storozynski, President

ADDRESS INQUIRIES TO:
Chopin Piano Competition
(See address above.)

THE LEEDS INTERNATIONAL PIANOFORTE COMPETITION [771]

The Piano Competition Office
The University of Leeds
Leeds LS2 9JT England
(44) 0 113 244 6586
Fax: (44) 0 113 234 6106

E-MAIL ADDRESS:
info@leedspiano.com

WEB SITE ADDRESS:
www.leedspiano.com

FOUNDED: 1961

AREAS OF INTEREST:
Piano.

NAME(S) OF PROGRAMS:
● **Leeds International Pianoforte Competition**

TYPE:
Awards/prizes. Prizes in pianoforte awarded every third year.

YEAR PROGRAM STARTED: 1963

PURPOSE:
To provide a competition for professional pianists.

LEGAL BASIS:
Charity.

ELIGIBILITY:
The Competition is open to professional pianists of all nationalities up to 30 years of age.

FINANCIAL DATA:
Amount of support per award: GBP 200 to GBP 18,000.
Total amount of support: Prize money in excess of GBP 70,000.

APPLICATION INFORMATION:
Application information and forms are available from the Administrator at the address above. The official application form must be completed in English.
Deadline: The application form, with enclosures, must arrive no later than February 1 of the year of the competition.

ADDRESS INQUIRIES TO:
Administrator
(See address above.)

THE LESCHETIZKY ASSOCIATION, INC. [772]

880 West 181st Street
Apartment 3H
New York, NY 10033
(212) 222-2733

E-MAIL ADDRESS:
alison.thomas@verizon.net

WEB SITE ADDRESS:
www.leschetizky.org

FOUNDED: 1942

AREAS OF INTEREST:
Organization founded by Theodore Leschetizky's pupils to honor the memory of a great and beloved master and to perpetuate his principles in piano playing, teaching and composing.

CONSULTING OR VOLUNTEER SERVICES:
Offers teaching and consulting services in piano playing and piano education.

NAME(S) OF PROGRAMS:
● **Gifted Young Pianists Concerto Competition**

TYPE:
Awards/prizes. Competition for a debut recital in New York.

YEAR PROGRAM STARTED: 1942

PURPOSE:
To perpetuate Theodore Leschetizky's principles in playing and teaching.

LEGAL BASIS:
Tax-exempt organization under the IRS code 501(c)(3).

ELIGIBILITY:
Open to pianists ages 13 to 17.

FINANCIAL DATA:
Amount of support per award: $300 to $1,000.
Total amount of support: $9,000.

NUMBER OF APPLICANTS MOST RECENT YEAR:
50.

NUMBER OF AWARDS: 1 to 3.

APPLICATION INFORMATION:
Information is available online. Entry materials may be mailed to Mara Waldman at the address below.
Deadline: Biennial competition in odd-numbered years. Next competition in 2015. Application entry deadline information is available online.

PUBLICATIONS:
Annual bulletin.

OFFICERS:
Mara Waldman, Chairperson
Dr. Alison Thomas, President

ADDRESS INQUIRIES TO:
Mara Waldman, Chairperson
884 West End Avenue, Suite 105
New York, NY 10025-3517

LIEDERKRANZ FOUNDATION, INC. [773]

6 East 87 Street
New York, NY 10128
(212) 534-0880
Fax: (212) 828-5372

E-MAIL ADDRESS:
info@liederkranzny.org

WEB SITE ADDRESS:
www.liederkranzny.org

FOUNDED: 1947

AREAS OF INTEREST:
Vocal music.

NAME(S) OF PROGRAMS:
● **Annual Awards for Voice**

TYPE:
Awards/prizes. Musicals, concerts, operettas, operas, general opera.

Annual Awards for Voice consist of three divisions: General Opera, Wagner and Art Song.

YEAR PROGRAM STARTED: 1960

PURPOSE:
To encourage and provide financial assistance to deserving singers selected in an annual competition.

LEGAL BASIS:
Tax-exempt, nonprofit.

ELIGIBILITY:
Only singers may apply.

FINANCIAL DATA:
Amount of support per award: $2,000 to $10,000.

Total amount of support: $63,000.

NUMBER OF APPLICANTS MOST RECENT YEAR:
365.

NUMBER OF AWARDS: 17.

APPLICATION INFORMATION:
Applicants may apply in one division only. Application forms are available in September. In order to consider the application complete, applicants must submit:
(1) a completed application form (do not include resume, photo or cover letter);
(2) a stamped, self-addressed business (9 1/2 x 4 1/8) envelope with the Liederkranz address as the return address;
(3) a $60 (non-refundable) application fee (with the applicant's name clearly indicated on the check) and;
(4) proof of age (a copy of the applicant's passport, driver's license or photo ID) with the date of birth highlighted.

Failure to enclose all four items will void the application.

Alternatively, all materials can be submitted online through www.yaptracker.com by clicking on the link listed on the Liederkranz web site.
Duration: Nonrenewable.
Deadline: November 15. Award announcement in January.

OFFICERS:
Joseph Pfeifer, President

ADDRESS INQUIRIES TO:
Liederkranz Competition
(See address above.)

LONG-THIBAUD-CRESPIN COMPETITION [774]

32, avenue Matignon
75008 Paris France
33 (1) 42 66 66 80
Fax: 33 (1) 42 66 06 43

E-MAIL ADDRESS:
contact@long-thibaud-crespin.org

WEB SITE ADDRESS:
www.long-thibaud-crespin.org

FOUNDED: 1943

AREAS OF INTEREST:
Music.

TYPE:
Awards/prizes. International competition for piano, violin and voice. The competition varies yearly: The Thibaud Violin Competition (2014); The Crespin Singing Competition (2015); The Long Piano Competition (2016).

ELIGIBILITY:
Candidate maximum age of 30 years on January 1 of the year of the contest.

FINANCIAL DATA:
Amount of support per award: First Grand Prize: EUR 25,000. There are other prizes also in each competition.

NUMBER OF APPLICANTS MOST RECENT YEAR:
57.

NUMBER OF AWARDS: Varies with the competition.

APPLICATION INFORMATION:
Information about the various competitions can be found on the web site.

Duration: One week, November 14 to November 20.
Deadline: Varies.

PUBLICATIONS:
Brochures.

OFFICERS:
Jean-Philippe Schweitzer, President

ADDRESS INQUIRIES TO:
Delegate General
Long-Thibaud-Crespin Competition
(See address above.)

E. NAKAMICHI FOUNDATION [775]

5013 Maytime Lane
Culver City, CA 90230
(714) 771-9677
Fax: (866) 879-2140

E-MAIL ADDRESS:
yas@enfoundation.com

WEB SITE ADDRESS:
www.enfoundation.com

FOUNDED: 1985

AREAS OF INTEREST:
Music.

TYPE:
Project/program grants. Performance of baroque or early classical music.

YEAR PROGRAM STARTED: 1986

PURPOSE:
To support appreciation of early, baroque, classical and similar music.

LEGAL BASIS:
Private foundation.

ELIGIBILITY:
Eligible organizations must be 501(c)(3) tax-exempt. Individuals and religious organizations are ineligible.

GEOGRAPHIC RESTRICTIONS:
Japan and United States.

FINANCIAL DATA:
Amount of support per award: $3,000 to $20,000.
Total amount of support: Generally $350,000 to $400,000 per year.

NUMBER OF APPLICANTS MOST RECENT YEAR:
100.

NUMBER OF AWARDS: 35.

APPLICATION INFORMATION:
Contact the Foundation for application procedures.
Duration: Single/multiple performances.
Deadline: March 15 and October 15.

IRS IDENTIFICATION NUMBER: 95-3870341

ADDRESS INQUIRIES TO:
Yas Yamazaki, President and Executive Director
(See address above.)

*PLEASE NOTE:
The Foundation is only accepting grant applications from those organizations that were successfully awarded a grant in the years 2000 through 2007.

NATIONAL ASSOCIATION OF COMPOSERS, USA (NACUSA) [776]

P.O. Box 49256
Barrington Station
Los Angeles, CA 90049
(541) 765-2406

E-MAIL ADDRESS:
gsteinke9@gmail.com
nacusa@music-usa.org

WEB SITE ADDRESS:
www.music-usa.org/nacusa

FOUNDED: 1932

AREAS OF INTEREST:
The performance, publication, broadcasting and archiving of new American concert hall music.

NAME(S) OF PROGRAMS:
● **Young Composers' Competition**

TYPE:
Awards/prizes; Conferences/seminars. Cash awards and guaranteed performances.

YEAR PROGRAM STARTED: 1978

PURPOSE:
To recognize and encourage young talent.

LEGAL BASIS:
501(c)(3) nonprofit organization.

ELIGIBILITY:
Open to all NACUSA members between the ages of 18 and 30. Compositions submitted should not exceed 15 minutes in length. Compositions should not require more than five players; an additional person for tape playback will not be counted as a performer. Compositions submitted must not have been previously published nor won any other musical competition. Instrumentation will be specified on a yearly basis.

GEOGRAPHIC RESTRICTIONS:
United States.

FINANCIAL DATA:
Amount of support per award: First prize: $400 and a guaranteed performance at a Los Angeles NACUSA concert; Second prize: $100 and a guaranteed performance at a NACUSA concert.

COOPERATIVE FUNDING PROGRAMS: Contest is supported, in part, by grants from ASCAP and BMI.

NUMBER OF APPLICANTS MOST RECENT YEAR:
63.

NUMBER OF AWARDS: Varies.

APPLICATION INFORMATION:
Complete information and electronic application submission is available on the Association web site. One copy of the score is to be submitted. Recordings of the entire composition are highly desirable, but not mandatory. Return postage must accompany each score if the composer wishes to maintain possession of the music. Scores will be judged, in part, on clear and legible music copying. Composers may submit up to two compositions. Scores should be submitted anonymously with an envelope attached containing the name of the work, the name of the composer and the composer's address and phone number.
Deadline: October 31.

PUBLICATIONS:
Composer/USA, newsletter.

IRS IDENTIFICATION NUMBER: 51-0166704

ADDRESS INQUIRIES TO:
Dr. Greg A. Steinke, President
(See address above.)

NATIONAL FEDERATION OF MUSIC CLUBS [777]

1646 Smith Valley Road
Greenwood, IN 46142
(317) 882-4003
Fax: (317) 882-4019

E-MAIL ADDRESS:
info@nfmc-music.org

WEB SITE ADDRESS:
www.nfmc-music.org

FOUNDED: 1898

AREAS OF INTEREST:
Vocal and instrumental music, dance and composition.

NAME(S) OF PROGRAMS:
● **NFMC Competitions and Awards**

TYPE:
Awards/prizes. Competitions. Awards for students and adults who show proficiency in the fields of voice, instrumental performance, dance, composition, etc. The Federation provides a wide range of awards.

PURPOSE:
To support performance and promotion of American music.

LEGAL BASIS:
Nonprofit.

ELIGIBILITY:
Competitions cover a wide range of age groups from age 10 through adult. In general, applicants must be native-born or naturalized American citizens and must be members or become members of the National Federation of Music Clubs either by individual or group affiliation before applications are accepted.

GEOGRAPHIC RESTRICTIONS:
United States.

FINANCIAL DATA:
Amount of support per award: $50 to $15,000.

APPLICATION INFORMATION:
Except in a few instances, applicants must become members of the NFMC on or before application either through individual or group affiliation before applications are considered. Application forms and information may be obtained from the NFMC at the address above. Enclose a self-addressed, stamped envelope. All requests for information must include $2 for material, postage and handling.
Duration: One-time award.

PUBLICATIONS:
Competitions and awards chart; *Junior Keynotes Magazine; Music Club Magazine.*

OFFICERS:
Carolyn Nelson, President
Barbara Hildebrand, Treasurer
Melanie Perez, Recording Secretary

STAFF:
Jennifer Griffin, Administrative Manager

ADDRESS INQUIRIES TO:
Jennifer Griffin, Administrative Manager
(See address above.)

NATIONAL FEDERATION OF MUSIC CLUBS [778]

1646 Smith Valley Road
Greenwood, IN 46142
(317) 882-4003
Fax: (317) 882-4019

E-MAIL ADDRESS:
info@nfmc-music.org

WEB SITE ADDRESS:
www.nfmc-music.org

FOUNDED: 1898

AREAS OF INTEREST:
Vocal and instrumental music and
composition.

NAME(S) OF PROGRAMS:
- **Award Program for Summer Music
  Festivals and Music Centers**

TYPE:
Awards/prizes. Prizes for the performance
and promotion of American music at summer
music festivals.

PURPOSE:
To support performance and promotion of
American music.

LEGAL BASIS:
Nonprofit.

ELIGIBILITY:
Program open to summer music festivals,
centers and camps in the U.S. and its
territories. In general, applicants must be
native-born or naturalized American citizens
and must be members or become members of
the National Federation of Music Clubs
either by individual or group affiliation
before applications are accepted.

GEOGRAPHIC RESTRICTIONS:
United States.

FINANCIAL DATA:
Amount of support per award: Average $150
to $2,700.

NUMBER OF AWARDS: Over 39.

OFFICERS:
Carolyn Nelson, President
Barbara Hildebrand, Treasurer
Melanie Perez, Recording Secretary

STAFF:
Jennifer Griffin, Administrative Manager

ADDRESS INQUIRIES TO:
Jennifer Griffin, Administrative Manager
(See address above.)

NATIONAL FEDERATION OF
MUSIC CLUBS   [779]

1646 Smith Valley Road
Greenwood, IN 46142
(317) 882-4003
Fax: (317) 882-4019

E-MAIL ADDRESS:
info@nfmc-music.org

WEB SITE ADDRESS:
www.nfmc-music.org

FOUNDED: 1898

AREAS OF INTEREST:
Dedicated to finding and fostering young
musical talent.

NAME(S) OF PROGRAMS:
- **Dorothy Dann Bullock Music Therapy
  Award**

TYPE:
Grants-in-aid. Financial assistance.

PURPOSE:
To support performance and promotion of
American music.

LEGAL BASIS:
Nonprofit.

ELIGIBILITY:
Offered to Music Therapy Majors (college
sophomores, juniors or seniors) in accredited
schools offering Music Therapy degrees
approved by American Music Therapy
Association. Applicants must be native-born
or naturalized American citizens and must be
members or become members of NFMC
either by individual or group affiliation
before applications are accepted.

GEOGRAPHIC RESTRICTIONS:
United States.

FINANCIAL DATA:
Amount of support per award: $1,350.
Total amount of support: $1,350 annually.

NUMBER OF AWARDS: 1 annually.

APPLICATION INFORMATION:
Application information is available on the
web site.
Deadline: March 1.

OFFICERS:
Carolyn Nelson, President
Barbara Hildebrand, Treasurer
Melanie Perez, Recording Secretary

STAFF:
Jennifer Griffin, Administrative Manager

ADDRESS INQUIRIES TO:
Bullock Music Therapy Award
(See address above.)

NATIONAL OPERA
ASSOCIATION, INC.   [780]

2403 Russell Long Boulevard
Canyon, TX 79016
(806) 651-2857
Fax: (806) 651-2958

E-MAIL ADDRESS:
rhansen@noa.org

WEB SITE ADDRESS:
www.noa.org

FOUNDED: 1955

AREAS OF INTEREST:
Opera production, opera composition,
promotion of operatic talent, opera education
and opera for youth.

CONSULTING OR VOLUNTEER SERVICES:
Distinguished members available for
consultation and workshops.

NAME(S) OF PROGRAMS:
- **Biennial Dissertation Competition**
- **Chamber Opera Competition**
- **Collegiate Opera Scenes Competition**
- **Opera Production Competition**
- **Sacred in Opera**
- **Scholarly Paper Competition**
- **Student and Artist Vocal Auditions**

TYPE:
Awards/prizes. Cash prizes awarded to Artist
Division winners and Scholarship Division
winners. Also scholarships to AIMS, awarded
in both divisions. Productions of winning
operas in Chamber Opera Competition will
be scheduled for annual convention.

YEAR PROGRAM STARTED: 1977

PURPOSE:
To assist young opera singers in furthering
their training for an operatic career and to
honor the best of the new chamber operas
and the outstanding opera productions by
universities and colleges.

LEGAL BASIS:
Nonprofit organization.

ELIGIBILITY:
All applicants must submit an entrance fee
depending on category and membership
status.

FINANCIAL DATA:
Amount of support per award: $500 to
$2,000 for singing competitors.
Total amount of support: $10,000.

NUMBER OF APPLICANTS MOST RECENT YEAR:
150 for vocal competition, 25 for opera
production competition and over 100 for
chamber opera competition.

NUMBER OF AWARDS: Approximately 10.

APPLICATION INFORMATION:
Application information is available on the
web site.
Duration: Nonrenewable.
Deadline: Varies by contest.

PUBLICATIONS:
Opera Journal; NOA Newsletter.

ADDRESS INQUIRIES TO:
Robert Hansen, Executive Director
(See address above.)

NATIONAL ORCHESTRAL
INSTITUTE   [781]

2110 Clarice Smith Performing Arts Center
University of Maryland School of Music
College Park, MD 20742
(301) 405-2317
Fax: (301) 314-9504

E-MAIL ADDRESS:
noi@umd.edu

WEB SITE ADDRESS:
www.noi.umd.edu

FOUNDED: 1988

AREAS OF INTEREST:
Orchestral music.

TYPE:
Residencies; Scholarships; Training grants;
Visiting scholars. Advanced orchestral
training program offering talented musicians
on the threshold of their professional careers
a four-week opportunity to study and perform
under internationally renowned conductors
and principal musicians from leading
American orchestras.

YEAR PROGRAM STARTED: 1988

PURPOSE:
To prepare musicians for professional
orchestral careers.

LEGAL BASIS:
University.

ELIGIBILITY:
Applicants must be between the ages of 18
and 28 with appropriate orchestral music
skill.

FINANCIAL DATA:
Support includes tuition at the Institute and
housing.
Amount of support per award: Over $4,000.
Total amount of support: Varies.

NUMBER OF APPLICANTS MOST RECENT YEAR:
750 for the year 2013.

NUMBER OF AWARDS: 90 for the year 2013.

APPLICATION INFORMATION:
Applicants should submit an application,
resume and one letter of recommendation.

They should also audition at one of the audition centers in cities across the U.S. between January and March.

Duration: May 30 to June 29.

Deadline: Varies by audition location.

PUBLICATIONS:
Program announcement.

ADDRESS INQUIRIES TO:
Richard Scerbo, General Manager
(See address above.)

THE WALTER W. NAUMBURG FOUNDATION, INC.   [782]
120 Claremont Avenue
New York, NY 10027
(212) 362-9877

WEB SITE ADDRESS:
www.naumburg.org

FOUNDED: 1925

AREAS OF INTEREST:
Sponsorship of international competitions for violin, cello, piano, voice, chamber music and composition.

TYPE:
Awards/prizes.

ELIGIBILITY:
Requirements differ with various categories of violin, cello, piano, voice, chamber music and composition. This competition is open to musicians and composers of every nationality. The competitors may not be under 17 years of age or more than 31 years of age, and may not have had a birthday before 1984 for the 2014 Violin, Cello and Chamber Music Competitions. Voice applicants may not be under 20 years of age or more than 35 years of age.

FINANCIAL DATA:
Solo Competition: First prize award includes two fully subsidized New York Recitals - Debut in Weill Hall, Carnegie Hall, recital and orchestral performances, in addition to a cash award. Chamber Music Award: Recital with commission work.

Amount of support per award: Solo Competition: $15,000 first prize, $10,000 second prize and $5,000 third prize.

APPLICATION INFORMATION:
Application forms may be obtained online.

Duration: One-time award.

Deadline: Application forms and a CD of no less than 30 minutes of satisfactory audible quality must be received at the Naumburg office by the deadline. Contact the Foundation for exact date.

BOARD OF DIRECTORS AND OFFICERS:
Robert Mann, President
David Geber, Vice President
Nicholas Mann, Vice President
Lucy Rowan Mann, Assistant Treasurer
Marshall Gibson
Bonnie Hampton
Joel Krosnick
Claude Mann
Judith Naumburg
Charles Neidich
Anton Nel
Ursula Oppens
Julius Rudel
Robert Sherman
Benita Valente

ADDRESS INQUIRIES TO:
Lucy Rowan Mann, Executive Director
(See address above.)

NEW MUSIC USA   [783]
90 John Street, Suite 312
New York, NY 10038
(212) 645-6949
Fax: (646) 490-0998

E-MAIL ADDRESS:
info@newmusicusa.org

WEB SITE ADDRESS:
www.newmusicusa.org

FOUNDED: 1974

AREAS OF INTEREST:
Living composers and contemporary music of all kinds.

NAME(S) OF PROGRAMS:
● **Cary New Music Performance Fund**
● **Music Alive**
● **New Music USA Project Grants**

TYPE:
Awards/prizes; Fellowships; Residencies.

YEAR PROGRAM STARTED: 1974

PURPOSE:
To increase opportunities for composers by fostering the creation, performances, dissemination, and appreciation for their music; to fund the creation of new work; to support direct contact between composers and audiences; to create education programs that deepen the understanding of composers and their work; to establish innovative private- and public-sector partnerships that create new opportunities.

LEGAL BASIS:
Nonprofit corporation.

GEOGRAPHIC RESTRICTIONS:
United States.

FINANCIAL DATA:
Amount of support per award: Varies by program.
Total amount of support: Average $1,000,000 annually.

NUMBER OF APPLICANTS MOST RECENT YEAR:
500.

NUMBER OF AWARDS: 100.

APPLICATION INFORMATION:
Application information is available on the web site.

Duration: Varies.

Deadline: Varies.

PUBLICATIONS:
Commissioning Music: A Basic Guide; *Composer in Residence: Meet The Composer's Orchestra Residencies Program, 1982-92; An Individual's Guide to Commissioning Music.*

IRS IDENTIFICATION NUMBER: 13-2928942

OFFICERS AND BOARD OF DIRECTORS:
Frederick Peters, Chairman
Joseph Walker, Secretary and Treasurer
Rae Alexander-Minter
Theodore Chapin
Edward Harsh
Harriet Kaufman
Alan Kornberg
Marya Martin
Gayle Morgan
Frances Richard

ADDRESS INQUIRIES TO:
Scott Winship, Director of Grant Programs
(See address above.)

PERCUSSIVE ARTS SOCIETY   [784]
110 West Washington
Suite A
Indianapolis, IN 46204
(317) 974-4488
Fax: (317) 974-4499

E-MAIL ADDRESS:
percarts@pas.org

WEB SITE ADDRESS:
www.pas.org

FOUNDED: 1961

AREAS OF INTEREST:
Percussive arts, including music education, performance and literature related to percussion instruments.

CONSULTING OR VOLUNTEER SERVICES:
Consulting committees on acoustics, education curricula, literature, etc.

NAME(S) OF PROGRAMS:
● **Annual Composition Contest**
● **Fred Hoey Scholarship**
● **Internship Program**
● **Larrie Londin Scholarship**
● **PASIC International Scholarship**
● **PASIC Scholarships**
● **Yamaha Terry Gibbs Scholarship**
● **Armand Zildjian Scholarship**
● **Zildjian Family Opportunity Fund**

TYPE:
Awards/prizes; Internships; Project/program grants; Scholarships.

YEAR PROGRAM STARTED: 1961

PURPOSE:
To promote percussion education, research, performance and appreciation.

LEGAL BASIS:
Not-for-profit corporation.

ELIGIBILITY:
Internships are open to enrolled music business major students in an accredited university program.

FINANCIAL DATA:
Amount of support per award: Varies.
Total amount of support: Varies.

NUMBER OF APPLICANTS MOST RECENT YEAR:
135.

NUMBER OF AWARDS: 12.

APPLICATION INFORMATION:
Application may be submitted online.

Duration: One year.

Deadline: Varies.

PUBLICATIONS:
Percussive Notes, magazine; *Percussion News*, newsletter.

IRS IDENTIFICATION NUMBER: 73-1385751

STAFF:
Jeff Hartsough, Executive Director

ADDRESS INQUIRIES TO:
Jeff Hartsough, Executive Director
(See address above.)

THE PITTSBURGH NEW MUSIC ENSEMBLE, INC.   [785]
P.O. Box 14577
Pittsburgh, PA 15234
(512) 785-6255

E-MAIL ADDRESS:
pamurchison@gmail.com

WEB SITE ADDRESS:
www.pnme.org

FOUNDED: 1975

AREAS OF INTEREST:
New music.

NAME(S) OF PROGRAMS:
- **Harvey Gaul Music Composition Contest**

TYPE:
Awards/prizes.

YEAR PROGRAM STARTED: 1975

PURPOSE:
To promote new music and support composers.

LEGAL BASIS:
Nonprofit corporation.

ELIGIBILITY:
Contestants must be U.S. citizens.

FINANCIAL DATA:
Amount of support per award: $6,000 commission.

NUMBER OF AWARDS: 1.

APPLICATION INFORMATION:
An entry form is required. An entry fee of $20 must accompany each composition. Contestants should send a score and CD of a representative instrumental work, along with a current biography and contact information. No MIDI realizations.
Deadline: January 1 of odd-numbered years.

PUBLICATIONS:
Application guidelines.

IRS IDENTIFICATION NUMBER: 25-1364030

OFFICERS:
Pamela Murchison, Executive Director
Kevin Noe, Executive Artistic Director

ADDRESS INQUIRIES TO:
Kevin Noe, Executive Artistic Director
(See address above.)

*PLEASE NOTE:
Contest is biennial.
The Ensemble does not award scholarships.

PRESSER FOUNDATION   [786]
385 Lancaster Avenue
Room 205
Haverford, PA 19041
(610) 658-9030

E-MAIL ADDRESS:
mfrank@presserfoundation.org

WEB SITE ADDRESS:
www.presserfoundation.org

FOUNDED: 1916

AREAS OF INTEREST:
Music education at the postsecondary level.

NAME(S) OF PROGRAMS:
- **Presser Undergraduate Scholar Award**

TYPE:
Fellowships; Project/program grants; Scholarships.

YEAR PROGRAM STARTED: 1916

PURPOSE:
To provide awards to worthy candidates to pursue a higher level of music education at the college level.

LEGAL BASIS:
Private foundation.

ELIGIBILITY:
Only college and university music departments. Institution must have a minimum of 40 undergraduate music majors. Awarded to students at end of his/her junior year or beginning of senior year. Awards are granted to institutions, not individuals. Institution shall select its outstanding candidate for award. Candidate must take at least one-third course credits in subjects not related to music.

GEOGRAPHIC RESTRICTIONS:
United States.

FINANCIAL DATA:
Amount of support per award: Cash stipend of approximately $4,000 payable at the beginning of the student's senior year.

NUMBER OF AWARDS: 1 per institution.

APPLICATION INFORMATION:
Application form can be downloaded from the Foundation web site.
Duration: One year. Nonrenewable.
Deadline: September 1.

ADDRESS INQUIRIES TO:
Mariel Frank, Executive Director
(See address above.)

THE QUEEN ELISABETH INTERNATIONAL MUSIC COMPETITION OF BELGIUM   [787]
20, rue aux Laines
B-1000 Brussels Belgium
(32 2) 213 40 50
Fax: (32 2) 514 32 97

E-MAIL ADDRESS:
info@qeimc.be

WEB SITE ADDRESS:
www.qeimc.be
www.cmireb.be/en

FOUNDED: 1951

AREAS OF INTEREST:
Voice, violin, and piano.

TYPE:
Awards/prizes.

PURPOSE:
To support young artists and thus help to establish their reputations with both professionals and the public through an international competition for music interpretation.

LEGAL BASIS:
Nonprofit organization.

ELIGIBILITY:
Programs alternate each year. The competition is reserved for violin in 2015, piano in 2016 and for voice in 2017.

The competition is open to musicians of all nationalities. The minimum age for applicants is 18. Maximum age is 30 for piano, violin and singers. Instrumental competitors play both assigned works and pieces of their own selection. The competition is divided into selection rounds and final round.

FINANCIAL DATA:
Amount of support per award: Varies.

NUMBER OF APPLICANTS MOST RECENT YEAR:
214 singers for the year 2014.

NUMBER OF AWARDS: 12 for the year 2014.

APPLICATION INFORMATION:
Applications for registration should be downloaded online and accompanied by the following:
(1) a copy of birth certificate;
(2) proof of nationality;
(3) two photographs (passport size);
(4) one 9 x 12-inch photograph;
(5) curriculum vitae;
(6) documentation providing proof of his or her skill (for example, higher diplomas, repertoire list with works performed in public, prizes and diplomas received from other competitions, press reviews, etc.) and;
(7) a DVD recording (image and sound) with appropriate music programme.
Deadline: January 15 of the year of the competition.

PUBLICATIONS:
Competition announcement and rules; brochures.

OFFICERS:
Count Jean-Pierre de Launoit, Chairman
Michel-Etienne Van Neste, Secretary General

ADDRESS INQUIRIES TO:
The Secretariat of the Competition
(See address above.)

SAN FRANCISCO CONSERVATORY OF MUSIC   [788]
50 Oak Street
San Francisco, CA 94102
(415) 503-6214
Fax: (415) 503-6299

E-MAIL ADDRESS:
dbh@sfcm.edu

WEB SITE ADDRESS:
www.sfcm.edu

FOUNDED: 1917

AREAS OF INTEREST:
Music.

NAME(S) OF PROGRAMS:
- **Performance Scholarships in Music for Students in Bachelor and Master of Music Programs**

TYPE:
Assistantships; Scholarships; Work-study programs. Awards for the study of music at the Conservatory.

YEAR PROGRAM STARTED: 1917

PURPOSE:
To enable talented, needy students to attend the Conservatory.

LEGAL BASIS:
Conservatory of Music.

ELIGIBILITY:
U.S. and foreign citizens may apply. Candidates must have had considerable experience in musical performance and must attend the Conservatory on a full-time basis.

FINANCIAL DATA:
Scholarships are to be applied toward tuition at the Conservatory.
Amount of support per award: $1,000 and up.
Total amount of support: $5,620,000 for the year 2011.

NUMBER OF APPLICANTS MOST RECENT YEAR:
950.

NUMBER OF AWARDS: 356.

APPLICATION INFORMATION:
Applicants must submit the San Francisco Conservatory of Music Application and either the Free Application for Federal Student Aid or the International Student Financial Aid Application and International Student Certification of Finances. CSS/Financial Aid Profile is required for all international students and domestic students under the age of 26.

Duration: Tenable for one year and may be renewed.

Deadline: February 15.

OFFICER:
Doris Howard, Director of Financial Aid

ADDRESS INQUIRIES TO:
Financial Aid
finaid@sfcm.edu
(See address and e-mail above.)

SAN FRANCISCO OPERA CENTER [789]

War Memorial Opera House
301 Van Ness Avenue
San Francisco, CA 94102-4509
(415) 565-3277
Fax: (415) 255-6774

E-MAIL ADDRESS:
merolaauditions@sfopera.com

WEB SITE ADDRESS:
www.sfopera.com/auditions

FOUNDED: 1954

AREAS OF INTEREST:
Young professional singers, pianists/accompanists and stage directors interested in a sequence of opera performance and career development opportunities.

CONSULTING OR VOLUNTEER SERVICES:
Board of Directors of Merola Opera Program and a full staff of conductors, coaches, stage directors and instructors in singing, acting, movement, stage combat, auditioning, career development and other activities.

NAME(S) OF PROGRAMS:
• **Adler Fellowships**
• **Merola Opera Program**
• **Schwabacher Debut Recitals**

TYPE:
Assistantships; Awards/prizes; Fellowships; Internships; Technical assistance. Auditions by application are held in the fall of each year for the following summer's Merola Opera Program in various cities throughout the U.S. Participants will also be considered for Adler Fellowships (singers/pianists).

YEAR PROGRAM STARTED: 1954

PURPOSE:
To provide professional opera training and performance opportunities for talented young opera professionals.

LEGAL BASIS:
Nonprofit.

ELIGIBILITY:
Open to all singers, pianists/accompanists and stage directors. All voice types are eligible, between the ages of 20 and 34.

FINANCIAL DATA:
Merola Opera Program participants receive shared housing accommodations, weekly allowance and round-trip airfare from place of residence to San Francisco. Adler Fellowships are for a salaried 12-month contract.

Amount of support per award: Contracted salary varies.

Total amount of support: Varies.

APPLICATION INFORMATION:
Application form is required. Details available on the web site.

Duration: Adler Fellowships: 12-month contract. Merola Opera Program: June to August.

Deadline: Fall of each year.

PUBLICATIONS:
Application guidelines.

OFFICERS:
Sheri Greenawald, Director
Mark Morash, Director of Musical Studies

ADDRESS INQUIRIES TO:
Jo Ann McStravick, Artists' Services and Audition Administrator
(See address above.)

SIGMA ALPHA IOTA PHILANTHROPIES, INC. [790]

One Tunnel Road
Asheville, NC 28805-1229
(828) 251-0606
Fax: (828) 251-0644

E-MAIL ADDRESS:
nh@sai-national.org

WEB SITE ADDRESS:
www.sai-national.org

FOUNDED: 1903

AREAS OF INTEREST:
Music, new compositions.

CONSULTING OR VOLUNTEER SERVICES:
Local volunteers in music.

NAME(S) OF PROGRAMS:
• **Inter-American Music Awards**

TYPE:
Awards/prizes. Music composition contest. The 2015 prize will go to an SATB adult choral piece.

YEAR PROGRAM STARTED: 1948

PURPOSE:
To give to the fraternity, and to the public, compositions of high musical merit; to bring distinction to winning composers; to offer royalties and other benefits coincident with publication of winning music.

LEGAL BASIS:
Nonprofit corporation.

ELIGIBILITY:
Requirements change each triennium; however, applicants must be residents of North, Central or South America.

FINANCIAL DATA:
Amount of support per award: $2,500 prize, plus winning composition published by a major music publisher.

NUMBER OF APPLICANTS MOST RECENT YEAR: 50.

NUMBER OF AWARDS: 1.

APPLICATION INFORMATION:
Application information is available on the web site.

Duration: One-time award.

Deadline: September 1.

PUBLICATIONS:
Brochure.

STAFF:
Ruth Sieber Johnson, Executive Director

ADDRESS INQUIRIES TO:
SAI Philanthropies, Inc.
(See address above.)

SYMPHONY OF THE MOUNTAINS [791]

Kingsport Renaissance Center
1200 East Center Street
Kingsport, TN 37660
(423) 392-8423
Fax: (423) 392-8428

E-MAIL ADDRESS:
melissa@symphonyofthemountains.org

WEB SITE ADDRESS:
www.symphonyofthemountains.org

FOUNDED: 1946

AREAS OF INTEREST:
Symphonic concerts and educational and social activities.

NAME(S) OF PROGRAMS:
• **Elizabeth Harper Vaughn Concerto Competition**

TYPE:
Awards/prizes. Cash prize and appearance with the Symphony of the Mountains Orchestra.

YEAR PROGRAM STARTED: 1969

PURPOSE:
Career advancement and recognition of excellence in music performance.

LEGAL BASIS:
Not-for-profit corporation.

ELIGIBILITY:
Open to musicians 25 years of age and under, with recommendation of private instructor.

FINANCIAL DATA:
Amount of support per award: $750.
Total amount of support: $750.

NUMBER OF APPLICANTS MOST RECENT YEAR: 10.

NUMBER OF AWARDS: 1.

APPLICATION INFORMATION:
Requires recommendation of private instructor and CD or DVD of performance (full concerto or other appropriate musical arrangement with orchestral accompaniment).

Duration: One-time award.

Deadline: September 1.

PUBLICATIONS:
Posters, postcards, programs for subscription concerts.

IRS IDENTIFICATION NUMBER: 62-0534228

STAFF:
Cornelia Laemmli Orth, Music Director/Chief Operating Officer

ADDRESS INQUIRIES TO:
Cornelia Laemmli Orth
Music Director/Chief Operating Officer
(See address above.)

THE RICHARD TUCKER MUSIC FOUNDATION, INC. [792]

1790 Broadway
Suite 715
New York, NY 10019-1412
(212) 757-2218
Fax: (212) 757-2347

E-MAIL ADDRESS:
info@richardtucker.org

WEB SITE ADDRESS:
www.richardtucker.org

FOUNDED: 1975

AREAS OF INTEREST:
Financial aid to American opera singers and opera companies with development programs for American singers.

NAME(S) OF PROGRAMS:
- **Richard Tucker Award**
- **Richard Tucker Career Grants**
- **Sara Tucker Study Grants**

TYPE:
Awards/prizes.

YEAR PROGRAM STARTED: 1978

PURPOSE:
To help further the careers of young American singers.

LEGAL BASIS:
Tax-exempt, not-for-profit organization.

ELIGIBILITY:
Nominees must already be performing in opera. Open to males and females in all vocal categories. Singers cannot apply; they must be recommended by a professional in the field. Applicants must also be American-born or a naturalized citizen by the age of 18.

GEOGRAPHIC RESTRICTIONS:
United States.

FINANCIAL DATA:
Amount of support per award: Richard Tucker Award: $50,000; Richard Tucker Career Grants: $10,000; Sara Tucker Study Grants: $5,000.
Total amount of support: Approximately $105,000.

NUMBER OF APPLICANTS MOST RECENT YEAR:
100 to 120.

NUMBER OF AWARDS: Richard Tucker Award: 1; Richard Tucker Career Grants and Sara Tucker Study Grants: 3 to 5 each.

APPLICATION INFORMATION:
Information on the nominating process for the awards is available on the web site or by telephoning the Foundation. Application is via a confidential anonymous nomination process.
Duration: Varies, but most of the awards are one-time awards.
Deadline: Recommendations are due December 31.

IRS IDENTIFICATION NUMBER: 23-7431029

BOARD OF DIRECTORS:
Jeffrey Manocherian, Chairman
Barry Tucker, President
Sherrill Milnes, Vice President
John A. Petts, Vice President
Samuel Ramey, Vice President
Robert S. Tucker, Vice President
Peter H. Carwell, Executive Director

ADDRESS INQUIRIES TO:
Peter H. Carwell, Executive Director
(See address above.)

THE VIOLIN SOCIETY OF AMERICA [793]

341 North Maitland Avenue
Suite 260
Maitland, FL 32751
(407) 647-8839
Fax: (407) 629-2502

E-MAIL ADDRESS:
info@vsaweb.org

WEB SITE ADDRESS:
www.vsaweb.org

FOUNDED: 1973

AREAS OF INTEREST:
Making and restoring stringed instruments and their bows, the history of stringed instruments and performers, technique, performance practice, repertory and the acoustics of bowed stringed instruments. The Society also sponsors conventions that include lectures, demonstrations, symposia and concerts, biennial international competitions for new stringed instruments and their bows, a Music Fair and a periodical covering all aspects of bowed string instruments.

NAME(S) OF PROGRAMS:
- **Kaplan-Goodkind Memorial Scholarship Fund**
- **Kun Scholarship Fund**
- **Aram and Rose Nigogosian Fund**

TYPE:
Scholarships. Tuition grants to students of violin-making and bow-making enrolled in a full-time violin-making school.

YEAR PROGRAM STARTED: 1982

PURPOSE:
To bring together people from various fields to exchange ideas and skills and to help people learn about the making of bows and stringed instruments.

LEGAL BASIS:
Tax-exempt educational organization.

ELIGIBILITY:
Students must be U.S. citizens, have satisfactorily completed at least one full year of study in the program, have shown serious effort, talent and future promise, and have financial need.

GEOGRAPHIC RESTRICTIONS:
United States.

FINANCIAL DATA:
Tuition grants are made to the school in student's name.
Amount of support per award: $500 average.
Total amount of support: Varies.

NUMBER OF AWARDS: 8 to 12 annually.

APPLICATION INFORMATION:
Apply by letter of recommendation from school to main office of VSA.
Duration: One-time tuition grant.
Deadline: Grants made on a continuing basis.

PUBLICATIONS:
The Journal, newsletter.

OFFICERS:
Chris Germain, President
Laurie Kirr, President-Elect
Jerry Pasewicz, Vice President
Richard Dodson, Treasurer
Ted White, Secretary

ADDRESS INQUIRIES TO:
Phil Pyster, Executive Director
(See address above.)

THE WORLD PIANO COMPETITION [794]

1241 Elm Street
Cincinnati, OH 45202
(513) 744-3501
Fax: (513) 744-3504

E-MAIL ADDRESS:
wpc@cincinnatiwpc.org

WEB SITE ADDRESS:
www.cincinnatiwpc.org

FOUNDED: 1956

AREAS OF INTEREST:
Musical education and identification of piano talent worldwide.

CONSULTING OR VOLUNTEER SERVICES:
Development of piano artistry and education directed by well renowned artists.

NAME(S) OF PROGRAMS:
- **World Piano Competition**

TYPE:
Awards/prizes; Challenge/matching grants; Development grants; Internships; Scholarships; Visiting scholars; Work-study programs. Annual awards.

YEAR PROGRAM STARTED: 1956

PURPOSE:
To develop talent of young piano prodigies and artists.

LEGAL BASIS:
Nonprofit association.

FINANCIAL DATA:
Amount of support per award: Gold: $20,000 cash prize, solo performance with the Cincinnati Symphony Orchestra, and recital in New York, NY. Silver: $15,000 cash prize. Bronze: $10,000 cash prize.

NUMBER OF APPLICANTS MOST RECENT YEAR:
38 for the 2013 competition.

NUMBER OF AWARDS: 3.

APPLICATION INFORMATION:
Applications available upon request.
Duration: One-time awards.
Deadline: April 1.

BOARD OF DIRECTORS:
George H. Musekamp, III, Chairman
Mark Ernster, Executive Director
Gary Smith, Treasurer
Mrs. Kirk Polking, Secretary
Jerome Eichert, Finance Officer
Susan Plageman, Fundraising Officer
Joe Shields, Public Relations Officer
Sam Ross, Branding Officer
Mary Jo Barnett, Volunteer Coordinator
Mrs. Jackie Lett Brown
Trish Bryan
Brent Ludwick
Pamela E. McDonald
Christine Neyer
Mrs. Laure Quinlivan
Ernest L. Robinson
Mrs. Mazal Rosenblatt
Jack Rouse

ADDRESS INQUIRIES TO:
Mark Ernster, Chief Executive Officer
(See address above.)

YOUNG CONCERT ARTISTS, INC. [795]

250 West 57th Street
Suite 1222
New York, NY 10107
(212) 307-6655
Fax: (212) 581-8894

E-MAIL ADDRESS:
yca@yca.org

WEB SITE ADDRESS:
www.yca.org

FOUNDED: 1961

AREAS OF INTEREST:
Young composers, young solo classical musicians (instruments and voice) and string quartets.

NAME(S) OF PROGRAMS:
● **Young Concert Artists International Auditions**

TYPE:
Awards/prizes. Artist management. YCA sponsors the Young Concert Artists Series in New York City at Carnegie's Zankel Hall, Lincoln Center's Alice Tully Hall, The Kaufman Music Merkin Hall, and in Washington, DC at the Kennedy Center; books concert engagements in the U.S. and abroad; offers career guidance and development; and provides all promotion and publicity materials, at no cost to the artists. YCA membership generally continues until the artists are signed by commercial management. The organization's work is made possible by contributions from corporations, foundations, individuals and government agencies.

YEAR PROGRAM STARTED: 1961

PURPOSE:
To discover and launch the careers of exceptional young musicians.

LEGAL BASIS:
Nonprofit, tax-exempt.

ELIGIBILITY:
Instrumentalists and singers must perform required repertoire and have letters of recommendation.

NUMBER OF APPLICANTS MOST RECENT YEAR:
214.

NUMBER OF AWARDS: Varies. Winners are selected only against a standard of excellence; any number can win who are selected by the jury.

APPLICATION INFORMATION:
Auditions dates, application form and requirements are available online.
Duration: Each winner signs a multiyear renewable contract with Young Concert Artists, which may be extended by mutual consent.

PUBLICATIONS:
Brochure.

OFFICER:
Susan Wadsworth, Director

ADDRESS INQUIRIES TO:
Susan Wadsworth, Director

Auditions:
Jennifer DeCinque
(See address above.)

YOUNG MUSICIANS FOUNDATION (YMF) [796]

244 South San Pedro Street
Suite 506
Los Angeles, CA 90012
(310) 859-7668
Fax: (310) 859-1365

E-MAIL ADDRESS:
info@ymf.org

WEB SITE ADDRESS:
www.ymf.org

FOUNDED: 1955

AREAS OF INTEREST:
Young musicians, ages eight to 25, aspiring to careers in professional classical music.

NAME(S) OF PROGRAMS:
● **Arts Management Internship**
● **Debut Concerto Competition**
● **Debut Orchestra**
● **Music Director**
● **Music Mentors Program**
● **Music 360 Degrees**
● **Scholarship Program**

TYPE:
Awards/prizes; Development grants; General operating grants; Internships; Project/program grants; Scholarships; Training grants. Mentor program. Financial assistance for private study and/or tuition at recognized musical institutions. Significant performance opportunity may be offered.

YEAR PROGRAM STARTED: 1955

PURPOSE:
To assist needy, exceptionally gifted students to continue their classical musical education.

LEGAL BASIS:
Nonprofit organization.

ELIGIBILITY:
Music students eight to 25 years of age.

GEOGRAPHIC RESTRICTIONS:
Southern California.

FINANCIAL DATA:
Amount of support per award: $500 to $2,500.
Total amount of support: Over $15,000.

NUMBER OF APPLICANTS MOST RECENT YEAR:
79 for the year 2011-12.

NUMBER OF AWARDS: 14 for the year 2011-12.

APPLICATION INFORMATION:
A complete application and financial information form must be accompanied by a letter of recommendation from applicant's music teacher. Applicants must audition in person for an adjudicating panel.
Duration: One year. Recipient must reapply for renewal.
Deadline: June; check online for exact date.

IRS IDENTIFICATION NUMBER: 95-2250007

EXECUTIVE OFFICERS:
J.D. Hornberger, Chairman of the Board
David Regan, Treasurer
Julia Gaskill, Executive Director

ADDRESS INQUIRIES TO:
Sarah Thomas, Programs Manager
(See address above.)

YOUNG MUSICIANS FOUNDATION (YMF) [797]

244 South San Pedro Street
Suite 506
Los Angeles, CA 90012
(213) 617-7707
Fax: (213) 617-7706

E-MAIL ADDRESS:
info@ymf.org

WEB SITE ADDRESS:
www.ymf.org

FOUNDED: 1955

AREAS OF INTEREST:
Young musicians, ages 11 to 18, seeking training in chamber music.

NAME(S) OF PROGRAMS:
● **Chamber Music Series (CMS)**

TYPE:
Grants-in-aid; Scholarships. Each year, young musicians are selected through auditions to receive a grant for a series of coaching sessions with leading professional musicians from the Los Angeles (CA) area.

PURPOSE:
To promote chamber music training for young musicians.

LEGAL BASIS:
Nonprofit organization.

ELIGIBILITY:
The program is open to talented piano, string, harp, woodwind and brass players through age 18, and auditions are held annually in the fall. Each student receives a scholarship to pay for coaching sessions with one of Los Angeles' finest master teachers.

NUMBER OF AWARDS: 30.

IRS IDENTIFICATION NUMBER: 95-2250007

ADDRESS INQUIRIES TO:
Delores Stevens, Artistic Director
(See address above.)

THE LOREN L. ZACHARY SOCIETY FOR THE PERFORMING ARTS [798]

2250 Gloaming Way
Beverly Hills, CA 90210-1717
(310) 276-2731
Fax: (310) 275-8245

E-MAIL ADDRESS:
peterhubner@earthlink.net

WEB SITE ADDRESS:
www.zacharysociety.org

FOUNDED: 1972

AREAS OF INTEREST:
Performing arts, operatic vocal only.

NAME(S) OF PROGRAMS:
● **Annual Loren L. Zachary National Vocal Competition for Young Opera Singers**

TYPE:
Awards/prizes.

YEAR PROGRAM STARTED: 1973

PURPOSE:
To discover and help launch the careers of young opera singers and to assist in career development through financial support.

LEGAL BASIS:
Educational, tax-exempt, nonprofit corporation.

ELIGIBILITY:
Open to singers between the ages of 21 and 35, who have completed proper operatic training and are prepared to pursue professional stage careers. Awards are available only through participation in the annual vocal competition in New York and Los Angeles. All singers with completed applications are guaranteed an audition.

GEOGRAPHIC RESTRICTIONS:
United States and Canada.

FINANCIAL DATA:
Amount of support per award: First prize: $12,000 to $15,000; remaining distributed amongst the finalists with a guaranteed minimum of $1,000 to $2,000.
Total amount of support: Approximately $50,000 to $55,000.

NUMBER OF APPLICANTS MOST RECENT YEAR: 195.

NUMBER OF AWARDS: 10 for the year 2013.

APPLICATION INFORMATION:
Application and rules are available at the web site, or submit a letter requesting audition information and applications in November. Singers must be present in Los Angeles or New York for all phases of the Auditions. Recordings are not acceptable. No fax or e-mail requests.

For more information, contact the Competition Director at the phone number above.

Deadline: January (for New York Auditions) and February to March (for Los Angeles Auditions); exact date varies each year.

PUBLICATIONS:
Application; guidelines.

IRS IDENTIFICATION NUMBER: 95-2800160

OFFICERS:
Nedra Zachary, President and Founder
Peter Hubner, Vice President
Sharron Levey, Secretary
Carl Mengert, Treasurer

ADVISORY BOARD:
Licia Albanese
Tito Capobianco
John DeMain
Stephen De Maio
Michael Hampe
Ioan Holender
Marilyn Horne
David Hulme
Mrs. George London
Peter Mark
Thea Musgrave
Julius Rudel
William Wiemhoff
Nedra Zachary

ADDRESS INQUIRIES TO:
Mrs. Nedra Zachary, Director of Competition
(See address above.)

Religion and theology

AMERICAN ACADEMY OF RELIGION [799]
825 Houston Mill Road, N.E.
Suite 300
Atlanta, GA 30329
(404) 727-3049
Fax: (404) 727-7959

E-MAIL ADDRESS:
info@aarweb.org

WEB SITE ADDRESS:
www.aarweb.org

FOUNDED: 1909

AREAS OF INTEREST:
Religion and theology.

NAME(S) OF PROGRAMS:
- **Collaborative Research Grants**
- **Individual Research Grants**
- **International Dissertation Research Grant**

TYPE:
Research grants. Collaborative Research Grants and Individual Research Grants provide support for important aspects of research such as travel to archives and libraries, research assistance, field work and released time. However, funds are not provided for dissertation research.

International Dissertation Research Grants support AAR student members whose dissertation research requires them to travel outside of the country in which their school or university is located. Grants are intended to help candidates complete their doctoral degrees by offsetting costs of travel, lodging, and other dissertation research-related expenses.

YEAR PROGRAM STARTED: 1989

PURPOSE:
To promote research and scholarship in the field of religion; to foster excellence in teaching in the field of religion; to support and encourage members' professional development; to develop programming and participation in AAR regional groups; to advance publication and scholarly communication in the field of religion; to contribute to the public understanding of religion; to welcome the various voices in the field of religion and to support and encourage diversity within the AAR; to help to advance and secure the future of the academic study of religion.

LEGAL BASIS:
501(c)(3).

ELIGIBILITY:
Applicants must be current AAR members who have been in good standing for the previous three years and have not received an AAR Research Award in the previous five years.

FINANCIAL DATA:
Amount of support per award: $500 to $5,000.

APPLICATION INFORMATION:
Individual or Collaborative grant applicants should submit through the Academy's electronic system:
(1) cover page that includes the following: (a) name, (b) institutional affiliation, (c) title of the project and, (d) grant type - Individual or Collaborative;
(2) abstract of 50 words or fewer describing the project;
(3) project budget;
(4) two-page focused description of the research project that details its aims and significance and explains how the award would be used. Collaborative project descriptions should include brief descriptions of the scholarly role of each collaborator and a plan to have the research published and;
(5) curriculum vitae of no more than two pages.

International Dissertation Research Grant applicants must submit:
(1) letter of application (no longer than three pages) that describes their research project and how support for on-site research is critical for the completion of their dissertation;
(2) current curriculum vitae;

(3) proposed budget and project timeline and;
(4) letter of support from their dissertation supervisor.
Duration: Individual or Collaborative Grant: Research projects may be undertaken any time within that academic year and up to the end of the following calendar year. International Dissertation Research Grant: Funds must be expended by the end of the calendar year awarded.
Deadline: Individual or Collaborative Grant: August 1; International Dissertation Grant: December 1.

IRS IDENTIFICATION NUMBER: 25-6063005

STAFF:
Elizabeth Hardcastle, Service Coordinator

ADDRESS INQUIRIES TO:
Elizabeth Hardcastle, Service Coordinator
(See address above.)

AMERICAN ACADEMY OF RELIGION [800]
825 Houston Mill Road, N.E.
Suite 300
Atlanta, GA 30329
(404) 727-3049
Fax: (404) 727-7959

E-MAIL ADDRESS:
dminor@aarweb.org

WEB SITE ADDRESS:
www.aarweb.org

FOUNDED: 1909

AREAS OF INTEREST:
To support projects within the regions that promise to benefit the scholarly and professional life of AAR members and the work of the regions.

NAME(S) OF PROGRAMS:
- **Regional Development Grants**

TYPE:
Development grants. Workshops, special programs, training events and other innovative regional projects may be funded through this source.

PURPOSE:
To promote research and scholarship in the field of religion; to foster excellence in teaching in the field of religion; to support and encourage members' professional development; to develop programming and participation in AAR regional groups; to advance publication and scholarly communication in the field of religion; to contribute to the public understanding of religion; to welcome into our conversation the various voices in the field of religion and to support and encourage diversity within the AAR; to help to advance and secure the future of the academic study of religion.

LEGAL BASIS:
501(c)(3).

GEOGRAPHIC RESTRICTIONS:
United States.

FINANCIAL DATA:
Amount of support per award: Maximum $4,000.
Total amount of support: $10,000.

NUMBER OF APPLICANTS MOST RECENT YEAR: 15.

NUMBER OF AWARDS: 4.

APPLICATION INFORMATION:
Applications should include a narrative description of the project, not to exceed two

pages, detailing how the project promises to benefit the scholarly and professional life of AAR members and the work of the region. Please include comments on how these projects or activities may be adapted to other regional groups. The application should state the time period covered by the project and provide a detailed budget (office expenses, travel expenses, honoraria, stipend and other expenses).

Duration: One year.

Deadline: August 1.

IRS IDENTIFICATION NUMBER: 20-5478525

ADDRESS INQUIRIES TO:
Deborah B. Minor
Director of Business and Finance
(See address above.)

AMERICAN CATHOLIC HISTORICAL ASSOCIATION   [801]

Fordham University, Dealy Hall, Room 637
441 East Fordham Road
Bronx, NY 10458
(718) 817-3830
Fax: (718) 817-5690

E-MAIL ADDRESS:
acha@fordham.edu

WEB SITE ADDRESS:
www.achahistory.org

FOUNDED: 1919

AREAS OF INTEREST:
The history of Catholicism from antiquity to the present.

NAME(S) OF PROGRAMS:
● **ACHA Graduate Student Summer Research Grant**
● **ACHA Junior Faculty Grant**
● **John Tracy Ellis Dissertation Award**
● **Graduate Student Travel Grant**

TYPE:
Awards/prizes; Challenge/matching grants; Conferences/seminars; Research grants; Travel grants. ACHA Graduate Student Summer Research Grant is awarded to an ACHA graduate student member who has completed all requirements for the Doctorate except the dissertation.

ACHA Junior Faculty Grant is awarded to an ACHA tenure-track scholar to assist in summer travel to conduct research.

John Tracy Ellis Dissertation Award memorializes the scholarship and teaching of Monsignor Ellis (1905-1992).

Graduate Student Travel Grant was created in 2010 by the Association from donations from former presidents.

PURPOSE:
To stimulate interest in the history of Catholicism among young scholars.

LEGAL BASIS:
Learned society.

ELIGIBILITY:
ACHA Graduate Student Summer Research Grant: Awarded to an ACHA graduate student member who has completed all requirements for the Doctorate except the dissertation and is attending an accredited institution of higher learning.

Graduate Student Travel Grant: Given on a competitive basis to two graduate students who are current members of the Association and who have papers accepted at either the Annual or Spring meetings.

FINANCIAL DATA:
Amount of support per award: ACHA Graduate Student Summer Research Grant and ACHA Junior Faculty Grant: $1,000 per award; John Tracy Ellis Dissertation Award: A purse of $1,500; Graduate Student Travel Grant: $500.

APPLICATION INFORMATION:
Graduate Student Travel Grant: Applicants should provide a letter formally applying for the grant and detailing the content of his/her paper, and a mini-curriculum vitae (one page), and a letter of recommendation from a faculty member - preferably the dissertation director.

Deadline: ACHA Graduate Student Summer Research Grant: Early 2015 (for applying), with notification no later than March 31; ACHA Junior Faculty Grant: Early 2015 (for applying); John Tracy Ellis Dissertation Award: September 30; Graduate Student Travel Grant: Applications should be submitted two months prior to either the Annual or Spring meeting.

ADDRESS INQUIRIES TO:
R. Bentley Anderson, S.J.
Executive Secretary-Treasurer
(See e-mail address above.)

AMERICAN CATHOLIC HISTORICAL ASSOCIATION   [802]

Fordham University, Dealy Hall, Room 637
441 East Fordham Road
Bronx, NY 10458
(718) 817-3830
Fax: (718) 817-5690

E-MAIL ADDRESS:
acha@fordham.edu

WEB SITE ADDRESS:
www.achahistory.org

FOUNDED: 1919

AREAS OF INTEREST:
The history of Catholicism from antiquity to the present.

NAME(S) OF PROGRAMS:
● **The Msgr. Harry C. Koenig Award for Catholic Biography**

TYPE:
Awards/prizes. The Msgr. Harry C. Koenig Award for Catholic Biography is offered every two years (in even-numbered years) and recognizes outstanding biographies of members of the Catholic Church who have lived in any age or country.

ELIGIBILITY:
The Prize is awarded in even-numbered years to the author of the book deemed by the Prize Committee to be the best such work published in the two previous calendar years. Entries must have first been published in English.

FINANCIAL DATA:
Amount of support per award: $1,500.

APPLICATION INFORMATION:
Application information is available on the web site.

Deadline: June 1, 2016. Prize is presented in January at the Association's annual meeting.

ADDRESS INQUIRIES TO:
R. Bentley Anderson, S.J.
Executive Secretary-Treasurer
(See e-mail address above.)

AMERICAN CATHOLIC HISTORICAL ASSOCIATION   [803]

Fordham University, Dealy Hall, Room 637
441 East Fordham Road
Bronx, NY 10458
(718) 817-3830
Fax: (718) 817-5690

E-MAIL ADDRESS:
acha@fordham.edu

WEB SITE ADDRESS:
www.achahistory.org

FOUNDED: 1919

AREAS OF INTEREST:
The history of Catholicism from antiquity to the present.

NAME(S) OF PROGRAMS:
● **The Peter Guilday Prize**

TYPE:
Awards/prizes; Challenge/matching grants; Conferences/seminars; Travel grants. A prize awarded annually to the author whose article, dealing with the history of the Catholic Church, is the first of his or her professional career and is judged to be the best of those in that category accepted for publication in any given year by the editors of the *Catholic Historical Review*.

YEAR PROGRAM STARTED: 1972

PURPOSE:
To stimulate interest in the history of Catholicism among young scholars.

LEGAL BASIS:
Learned society.

ELIGIBILITY:
The article must deal with some aspect of the history of the Catholic Church broadly considered. Anyone who has already published an historical book or an article in a learned journal will not be eligible for competition. Articles based on doctoral dissertations will be welcome, provided they are self-contained studies. Manuscripts must not exceed 30 typewritten pages (footnotes included). The author must be a citizen or permanent resident of the U.S. or Canada.

GEOGRAPHIC RESTRICTIONS:
United States and Canada.

FINANCIAL DATA:
Amount of support per award: $250.
Total amount of support: $250 per annum.

NUMBER OF APPLICANTS MOST RECENT YEAR:
3.

NUMBER OF AWARDS: 1 per annum.

APPLICATION INFORMATION:
Inquiries and manuscripts should be sent to the address above.

Deadline: September 1.

ADDRESS INQUIRIES TO:
R. Bentley Anderson, S.J.
Executive Secretary-Treasurer
(See e-mail address above.)

AMERICAN CATHOLIC HISTORICAL ASSOCIATION   [804]

Fordham University, Dealy Hall, Room 637
441 East Fordham Road
Bronx, NY 10458
(718) 817-3830
Fax: (718) 817-5690

E-MAIL ADDRESS:
acha@fordham.edu

WEB SITE ADDRESS:
www.achahistory.org

FOUNDED: 1919

AREAS OF INTEREST:
The history of Catholicism from antiquity to the present.

NAME(S) OF PROGRAMS:
- **The John Gilmary Shea Prize**

TYPE:
Awards/prizes. This Prize is given annually to the author of a book, published during a preceding 12-month period, which is judged by a committee of experts to have made the most original and distinguished contribution to knowledge of the history of the Catholic Church.

YEAR PROGRAM STARTED: 1945

PURPOSE:
To stimulate interest in the history of Catholicism among young scholars.

LEGAL BASIS:
Learned society.

ELIGIBILITY:
Any author who is a citizen or permanent resident of the U.S. or Canada is eligible to apply. The work submitted must have been published within the calendar year preceding the May 1 submission deadline.

GEOGRAPHIC RESTRICTIONS:
United States and Canada.

FINANCIAL DATA:
Amount of support per award: $1,500.
Total amount of support: $1,500 per annum.

NUMBER OF AWARDS: 1 per annum.

APPLICATION INFORMATION:
No formal application is required. Publishers or authors may enter by sending three copies of the work to be considered. Write or e-mail to the above address for further details.
Deadline: The prize is presented each January at the Association's annual meeting.

ADDRESS INQUIRIES TO:
R. Bentley Anderson, S.J.
Executive Secretary-Treasurer
American Catholic Historical Association
(See e-mail address above.)

THE AMY FOUNDATION [805]
P.O. Box 16091
Lansing, MI 48901
(517) 323-6233

E-MAIL ADDRESS:
amyawards@worldmag.com

WEB SITE ADDRESS:
www.amyfound.org
www.worldmag.com/amyawards

FOUNDED: 1976

AREAS OF INTEREST:
Moral and spiritual renewal in America.

NAME(S) OF PROGRAMS:
- **Amy Writing Awards**

TYPE:
Awards/prizes. Program is designed to recognize creative, skillful writing that presents in a sensitive, thought-provoking manner the biblical position on issues affecting the world today.

PURPOSE:
To present biblical truth reinforced with scripture in secular, nonreligious publications.

ELIGIBILITY:
Submitted articles must be published in a secular, journalistic outlet such as a city or college newspaper, a local or national magazine, or a news web site. Articles from personal blogs, newsletters, or religious publications are ineligible, as are books, manuscripts, and works of poetry or fiction. World News Group is the final determiner of eligibility.

Submissions must be published during the calendar year and must contain at least one verse of scripture quoted from an accepted and popular edition of the Bible.

FINANCIAL DATA:
Amount of support per award: First prize: $10,000; second prize: $5,000; third prize: $4,000; fourth prize: $3,000; fifth prize: $2,000; plus 10 prizes of $1,000 each.
Total amount of support: $34,000.

APPLICATION INFORMATION:
A PDF of the article, as published, must be submitted using the online submission form. The PDF must have the byline blacked out (redacted). Complete instructions are available online.
Deadline: Entries must be submitted on or before July 15 for the preceding January to June, and January 15 for the preceding July to December.

ADDRESS INQUIRIES TO:
See e-mail address above.

ATLANTIC SCHOOL OF THEOLOGY [806]
660 Francklyn Street
Halifax NS B3H 3B5 Canada
(902) 423-5592
Fax: (902) 492-4048

E-MAIL ADDRESS:
academicoffice@astheology.ns.ca

WEB SITE ADDRESS:
www.astheology.ns.ca

FOUNDED: 1971

AREAS OF INTEREST:
Any subject offered at the Atlantic School of Theology.

NAME(S) OF PROGRAMS:
- **The Evelyn Hilchie Betts Memorial Fellowship**

TYPE:
Fellowships. The Atlantic School of Theology is an ecumenical university committed to excellence in graduate-level theological education and research. The school is also committed to the provision of training for Christian ministries, both lay and ordained, in church and society, primarily in Atlantic Canada.

PURPOSE:
To enable ordained clergy from the developing world to study at the school for one year and thereby to introduce persons from other Christian communities to the church and theological education in Canada and to share their context with the school.

ELIGIBILITY:
Applicants must be nominated by their denomination. Open to ordained clergy (male or female) from developing countries, who

are interested in theological education in an ecumenical atmosphere and are able to speak and write in the English language.

Applicants must be interested in living and working in a Christian community and willing to share their work and experience with the Canadian church. Since the Atlantic School of Theology is a postgraduate school, applicants with university training are encouraged to apply.

FINANCIAL DATA:
Amount of support per award: Up to $18,000 for transportation, tuition, room and board.
Total amount of support: Varies.

NUMBER OF AWARDS: 1 award every one to two years.

APPLICATION INFORMATION:
Applicants must submit a completed application form along with a letter of support.
Duration: One year.
Deadline: Varies.

ADDRESS INQUIRIES TO:
Academic Office
Atlantic School of Theology
(See address above.)

*SPECIAL STIPULATIONS:
Must return to own country after scholarship year.

THE CHATLOS FOUNDATION, INC. [807]
P.O. Box 915048
Longwood, FL 32791-5048
(407) 862-5077

E-MAIL ADDRESS:
info@chatlos.org

WEB SITE ADDRESS:
www.chatlos.org

FOUNDED: 1953

AREAS OF INTEREST:
Bible colleges, seminaries, religion, liberal arts colleges, medical and social concerns.

TYPE:
General operating grants; Project/program grants; Scholarships; Technical assistance; Training grants. Scholarships are not provided directly to individuals but rather to colleges and seminaries which in turn provide monies to the students of their choice.

YEAR PROGRAM STARTED: 1953

LEGAL BASIS:
Private foundation.

ELIGIBILITY:
The Foundation only funds nonprofit organizations which are tax-exempt for U.S. federal income tax purposes around the globe. Less emphasis on grant requests for bricks and mortar, endowments, conference and administrative expenses and multiyear grants. No grants for medical research, individual church congregations, primary/secondary schools, organizations in existence for less than two years, arts organizations or individuals. Contributions cannot be made to organizations which discriminate on the basis of race, color, sex, creed, age or national origin.

FINANCIAL DATA:
Amount of support per award: Bible colleges: $5,000 to $20,000; Religious causes

and medical concerns: $5,000 to $15,000;
Liberal arts colleges: $2,500 to $7,500;
Social concerns: $2,000 to $5,000.

Initially, the Foundation tends to fund
requests for amounts around $10,000.
Total amount of support: $1,972,976 in
grants for the year 2013.

NUMBER OF APPLICANTS MOST RECENT YEAR:
848 for the year 2013.

NUMBER OF AWARDS: 293 for the year 2013.

APPLICATION INFORMATION:
All requests must be submitted in writing and
include the following:
(1) cover letter which includes the specific
request amount and project description;
(2) complete proposal (kept brief);
(3) one copy of U.S. IRS tax-exempt status
letter;
(4) most recent budget for the organization
and;
(5) completed Chatlos Foundation
application.

All requests are answered by the Foundation
in writing.
Duration: Varies, although multiyear grants
are rarely considered.
Deadline: Applications are accepted
throughout the year.

PUBLICATIONS:
Application guideline brochure.

IRS IDENTIFICATION NUMBER: 13-6161425

BOARD OF DIRECTORS:
Kathryn A. Randle, Chairman of the Board
William J. Chatlos, President
Michele C. Roach, Senior Vice President and
Secretary
William J. Chatlos, III, Vice President
Cindee Random, Treasurer and Trustee
Janet A. Chatlos, Trustee
Cherlyn Dannhaeuser, Trustee
Kimberly Grimm, Trustee
Charles O. Morgan, Jr., Trustee
Brianne Ortt, Trustee

ADDRESS INQUIRIES TO:
Grants Administrator
(See address above.)

CHRISTIAN CHURCH
(DISCIPLES OF CHRIST)   [808]
P.O. Box 1986
Indianapolis, IN 46204
(317) 635-3100
(800) 458-3318
Fax: (317) 635-3700
TDD: (317) 635-4717

E-MAIL ADDRESS:
mail@dhm.disciples.org

WEB SITE ADDRESS:
www.discipleshomemissions.org

NAME(S) OF PROGRAMS:
● **African-American Scholarship Fund
   (Star Supporter)**
● **Disciple Chaplains' Scholarship Fund**
● **David Tamotsu Kagiwada Memorial
   Fund**
● **Edwin G. & Lauretta M. Michael
   Scholarship for Minister's Spouses**
● **James M. Philputt Memorial Loan
   Fund**
● **Rowley/Wolfe Ministerial Education
   Scholarship**
● **Katherine J. Schutze Memorial
   Scholarship for Women Seminary
   Students**

TYPE:
Scholarships. Scholarship funds for Disciples
of Christ students preparing for vocational
ministry.

PURPOSE:
To help individuals pursue education in the
Disciples of Christ.

LEGAL BASIS:
Religious nonprofit organization.

ELIGIBILITY:
The general eligibility requirements are as
follows:
(1) the applicant must be a member of a
congregation in the Christian Church
(Disciples of Christ) in the U.S. and Canada;
(2) plan to prepare for a professional ministry
in the Christian Church (Disciples of Christ)
in the U.S. and Canada;
(3) applicant must be aware that grade point
average may be a determining factor in the
awarding of scholarships;
(4) provide evidence of financial need;
(5) be enrolled in an ATS-accredited graduate
school or seminary as a full-time student (at
least nine credit hours per semester);
(6) be enrolled in an M.Div., or equivalent
degree program;
(7) provide official transcript(s) of academic
work;
(8) provide references from (a) a regional
minister of the Christian Church (Disciples of
Christ) in the U.S. and Canada from the
region with which one is under care, (b) the
pastor of one's home Christian Church
(Disciples of Christ) congregation or the
Christian Church (Disciples of Christ)
congregation in which one is a member, and
(c) a professor (seminary or undergraduate)
and;
(9) be under care of a regional Commission
on the Ministry or in the process of coming
under care.
Contact the Christian Church (Disciples of
Christ) for full details.

Applicants must apply or reapply each year
to receive scholarships. There are no
automatic renewals.

Additional requirements are as follows:
(1) African-American Scholarship Fund (Star
Supporter) is limited to Black or
Afro-American ministerial students;
(2) Michael Scholarship is limited to
minister's spouses;
(3) James M. Philputt Memorial Loan Fund
is limited to seminary or graduate students
enrolled in one of the following seminaries
including Divinity School of the University
of Chicago, Union Theological Seminary,
Vanderbilt Divinity School or Yale Divinity
School;
(4) Disciple Chaplains' Scholarship Fund is
limited to first-year seminarians;
(5) David Tamotsu Kagiwada Memorial Fund
is limited to North American Pacific/Asian
ministerial students;
(6) Rowley/Wolfe Ministerial Education
Scholarship has no additional eligibility
limitations and;
(7) Schutze Memorial Scholarship for women
seminary students.

FINANCIAL DATA:
Funds issued in the form of a
scholarship/loan call for a promissory note to
be signed by the recipient. Two options of
repayment are provided:
(1) a service option in which each year of
full-time professional ministry reduces the
scholarship/loan by one-third. Three years of
service with the Christian Church (Disciples

of Christ) will repay the entire
scholarship/loan and;
(2) those not entering the ministry in the
Christian Church (Disciples of Christ) are
expected to repay the scholarship/loan either
in one cash payment or on a monthly
installment basis of $100 at the rate of six
percent annual interest on the principal.
These payments would begin three months
after leaving school.
Amount of support per award: $1,500 to
$2,000.

APPLICATION INFORMATION:
Application information is available on the
web site.
Duration: Varies.
Deadline: Applications: March 15; Reference
material: April 15. No exceptions to
deadlines.

ADDRESS INQUIRIES TO:
Kelly Harris
(See address above.)

COLLEGEVILLE INSTITUTE
FOR ECUMENICAL AND
CULTURAL RESEARCH   [809]
2475 Ecumenical Drive
Collegeville, MN 56321
(320) 363-3366
Fax: (320) 363-3313

E-MAIL ADDRESS:
staff@collegevilleinstitute.org

WEB SITE ADDRESS:
www.collegevilleinstitute.org

FOUNDED: 1967

AREAS OF INTEREST:
Religion, ecumenism, faith and writing, faith
and scholarship, faith and culture.

NAME(S) OF PROGRAMS:
● **Hoyt Fellowship**
● **Kilian McDonnell Fellowship**
● **Pastoral Fellowship**
● **Post-Doctoral Fellowship**
● **Resident Scholars Program**
● **Seminars on Vocation**
● **Summer Writing Workshops**

TYPE:
Awards/prizes; Conferences/seminars;
Fellowships; Research grants; Residencies;
Visiting scholars. Grant equivalencies are
given in the form of living accommodations
for Resident Scholars and their families in
well-maintained apartments and excellent
study facilities, privileges at Saint John's
University and dialogue and community
experience.

Post-Doctoral Fellowship offers a cash
stipend for living expenses.

YEAR PROGRAM STARTED: 1967

PURPOSE:
To facilitate constructive thought and
research which bear upon Christianity,
ecumenically understood, and its relation to
the cultures of our world.

LEGAL BASIS:
Incorporated in Minnesota.

ELIGIBILITY:
Criteria include completion of graduate work
and submission of a research or writing
project proposal acceptable to the admissions
committee. Award normally made to research
scholars who already have the Doctorate,

though persons writing doctoral dissertations can be considered. Oriented by tradition and conviction to Christian faith, the Institute welcomes people from other religions.

Applicant for Hoyt Fellowship must be a North American person of color who is writing a doctoral dissertation.

FINANCIAL DATA:
Residency fees include housing for self and family, utilities, spacious private study and Institute program. Fellowships cover residency fees, travel, research and, in some cases, living expenses.
Amount of support per award: Varies by program.

NUMBER OF APPLICANTS MOST RECENT YEAR: 45.

NUMBER OF AWARDS: 15.

APPLICATION INFORMATION:
Applicants must include application form, three letters of recommendation and statement of project.
Duration: September to December semester, January to April semester or full academic year (September to April).
Deadline: November 1. Announcement December 1. Post-Doctoral Fellowship: January 15.

PUBLICATIONS:
Bearings Magazine; annual report; application forms and provisions for Resident Scholars; informational brochures.

IRS IDENTIFICATION NUMBER: 41-6059644

STAFF:
Donald B. Ottenhoff, Executive Director

OFFICERS AND BOARD OF DIRECTORS:
Father Kilian McDonnell, O.S.B., President
Mary Bednarowski, Chairperson
Darrell H. Jodock, Vice Chairperson
Linda Hoeschler, Secretary and Treasurer

ADDRESS INQUIRIES TO:
Carla Durand, Program Manager
(See address above.)

EPISCOPAL CHURCH FOUNDATION [810]

815 Second Avenue, Seventh Floor
New York, NY 10017
(212) 697-2858
(800) 697-2858
Fax: (212) 297-0142

E-MAIL ADDRESS:
all@episcopalfoundation.org

WEB SITE ADDRESS:
www.episcopalfoundation.org

FOUNDED: 1949

AREAS OF INTEREST:
Innovative programs in leadership development, education and philanthropy for the clergy and laity of the Episcopal Church.

CONSULTING OR VOLUNTEER SERVICES:
Capital campaigns, planned giving and endowment management services.

NAME(S) OF PROGRAMS:
● **ECF Fellowship Partners Program**

TYPE:
Fellowships. Religious studies. Fellowships under two categories:
(a) Academic Fellowships and;
(b) Transformational Ministries.

YEAR PROGRAM STARTED: 1964

PURPOSE:
To support doctoral study for Episcopalians planning teaching careers in theological education in the Episcopal Church in the U.S.

ELIGIBILITY:
Applications from both lay and clergy are welcome.

Fellowship applicants on the academic track must be engaged in or embarking on a course of study at the graduate level, except for first professional degrees (e.g., M.Div., J.D., M.D.). Acceptable courses of study include doctoral- and Master's-level programs, as well as clinical study or training at the postundergraduate level.

Transformational ministry applicants will be asked to demonstrate how their ministry has the potential to transform community at the grassroots level, and special consideration will be given to programs in locations with limited resources or among underserved communities.

GEOGRAPHIC RESTRICTIONS:
United States.

FINANCIAL DATA:
Amount of support per award: $3,000 to $15,000 per year.
Total amount of support: Approximately $100,000 annually.

NUMBER OF APPLICANTS MOST RECENT YEAR: 4.

NUMBER OF AWARDS: 3.

APPLICATION INFORMATION:
Application information is available on the web site.
Duration: One year. Fellowship is renewable for two more years.
Deadline: March 15. Notification by May 15.

PUBLICATIONS:
ECF Vital Practices.

ADDRESS INQUIRIES TO:
Miguel Escobar, Program Director
(See address above.)

EVANGELICAL LUTHERAN CHURCH IN AMERICA [811]

Congregation and Synodical Mission Unit
8765 West Higgins Road
Chicago, IL 60631-4101
(773) 380-2874
Fax: (773) 380-2750

E-MAIL ADDRESS:
melinda.valverde@elca.org

WEB SITE ADDRESS:
www.elca.org

FOUNDED: 1988

AREAS OF INTEREST:
Theological education.

NAME(S) OF PROGRAMS:
● **Educational Grant Program**

TYPE:
Scholarships. Educational grants for members of the Evangelical Lutheran Church in America in advanced academic theological education degrees with intent to teach in seminary or university.

YEAR PROGRAM STARTED: 1988

PURPOSE:
To provide support to members of the Evangelical Lutheran Church in America in

graduate study that would prepare them to teach in a seminary or college department of religion.

LEGAL BASIS:
Nonprofit religious organization.

ELIGIBILITY:
Applicant church members must have been accepted into an accredited graduate institution, Ph.D. and Th.D. programs in theological areas appropriate to seminary teaching and research. Priority is given to women and Asians, Hispanics, Blacks and Native Americans preparing for leadership in the church and applicants with high potential for making substantial contributions to ministry in the Evangelical Lutheran Church in America.

FINANCIAL DATA:
Amount of support per award: $250 to $3,000.

APPLICATION INFORMATION:
Application information is available on the web site.
Duration: Up to five years. Must reapply each year.
Deadline: April.

STAFF:
Jonathan Strandjord, Director for Seminaries

ADDRESS INQUIRIES TO:
Melinda Valverde, Grant Administrator
(See address above.)

GENERAL BOARD OF HIGHER EDUCATION AND MINISTRY, THE UNITED METHODIST CHURCH [812]

1001 19th Avenue South
Nashville, TN 37212
(615) 340-7338
Fax: (615) 340-7529

E-MAIL ADDRESS:
mbigord@gbhem.org

WEB SITE ADDRESS:
www.gbhem.org

AREAS OF INTEREST:
Religion.

NAME(S) OF PROGRAMS:
● **Georgia Harkness Scholarships**

TYPE:
Awards/prizes; Scholarships. Awards to encourage women over age 35 to prepare for ordained ministry as an Elder in the United Methodist Church as a second career. The scholarship is to be used for study toward the basic seminary degree in an accredited school of theology.

YEAR PROGRAM STARTED: 1975

PURPOSE:
To support and encourage women for ordained ministry as an Elder in the United Methodist Church.

LEGAL BASIS:
Nonprofit organization.

ELIGIBILITY:
An applicant must be a certified candidate for Elder in the United Methodist Church in the year they are applying. Women over age 35 who have received a Bachelor of Arts or equivalent degree, have been accepted in an accredited school of theology, and have

affirmed a specific interest in preparation for ordination as an Elder in the United Methodist Church are eligible.

FINANCIAL DATA:
  Amount of support per award: $5,000.
  Total amount of support: $55,000 annually.

NUMBER OF APPLICANTS MOST RECENT YEAR:
  60.

NUMBER OF AWARDS: 11.

APPLICATION INFORMATION:
  Applicants must submit one copy of the application and four copies of the reference letter. Application packets may be obtained from any United Methodist or University Senate-approved seminary financial aid office or the Division of Ordained Ministry at the address or e-mail above. Applications may be requested between November 1 and February 15.
  Duration: One year.
  Deadline: March 1.

ADDRESS INQUIRIES TO:
  Allyson Collinsworth
  Director of Loans and Scholarships
  (See address above.)

GENERAL COMMISSION ON ARCHIVES AND HISTORY OF THE UNITED METHODIST CHURCH   [813]
36 Madison Avenue
Madison, NJ 07940
(973) 408-3189
Fax: (973) 408-3909

E-MAIL ADDRESS:
  rwilliams@gcah.org

WEB SITE ADDRESS:
  www.gcah.org

FOUNDED: 1968

AREAS OF INTEREST:
  History of the United Methodist Church and antecedent bodies.

NAME(S) OF PROGRAMS:
  • **John Harrison Ness Memorial Award**

TYPE:
  Awards/prizes. Awards to the students of accredited seminaries who submit the best papers on various aspects of United Methodist denominational history. In general, comprehensive subjects on the history of some phase of the denomination will be preferred, but papers on local church or annual conference subjects will be accepted if approved by the professor advising the project.

YEAR PROGRAM STARTED: 1979

PURPOSE:
  To stimulate interest in history of the United Methodist Church.

LEGAL BASIS:
  Private church-related organization.

ELIGIBILITY:
  The paper must have been appraised by the professor of church history under whom the student has been studying and who will submit the paper. The paper must be properly annotated and be a minimum length of 3,000 words. It is desired that the project be undertaken only after the student has had a course in United Methodist history or at least during the enrollment in such.

FINANCIAL DATA:
  Amount of support per award: First prize: $500; Second prize: $300.
  Total amount of support: $800 annually.

NUMBER OF AWARDS: 2.

APPLICATION INFORMATION:
  Three copies of the paper will be submitted for judging, two of which will be retained by the Commission.
  Duration: Annual. A recipient may resubmit if he or she is still in seminary.
  Deadline: February 1. Announcement approximately three months later.

OFFICERS:
  Dr. Robert J. Williams, General Secretary

ADDRESS INQUIRIES TO:
  Dr. Robert J. Williams, General Secretary
  (See address above.)

THE STEWART HUSTON CHARITABLE TRUST   [814]
50 South First Avenue
Coatesville, PA 19320
(610) 384-2666
Fax: (610) 384-3396

E-MAIL ADDRESS:
  admin@stewarthuston.org

WEB SITE ADDRESS:
  www.stewarthuston.org

FOUNDED: 1989

AREAS OF INTEREST:
  Health and human services, civic affairs and religion.

TYPE:
  Capital grants; Challenge/matching grants; General operating grants; Matching gifts; Project/program grants.

YEAR PROGRAM STARTED: 1989

PURPOSE:
  To provide funds, technical assistance and collaboration on behalf of nonprofit organizations engaged exclusively in religious, charitable or educational work; to extend opportunities to deserving needy persons.

LEGAL BASIS:
  Private foundation.

ELIGIBILITY:
  Applicants must be tax-exempt and address a particular community need. Grants are not awarded for scholarship support to individuals, endowment purposes, purchase of tickets or advertising for benefit purposes, coverage of continuing operating deficits, and document publication costs. Support is not provided to intermediate or pass-through organizations (other than United Way), groups such as fraternal organizations, political campaigns, veterans, labor or local civic groups, volunteer fire companies, and groups engaged in influencing legislation.

  According to Stewart Huston's Indenture of Trust, 60% of distributions go to Trinitarian/Evangelical organizations as defined by the Chester County Orphans Court: "The grant applicant must be organized and operated exclusively to further religious and charitable activities carried on by Protestant churches, other than Unitarian churches, and affiliated or related organizations; grant proceeds must be used exclusively for one or both of the following two activities: dissemination of the Christian

Gospel by preaching and conducting religious services, offering a Christian education, etc.; and promotion of Christian principles through charity."

  The remaining 40% is to be distributed for secular purposes.

GEOGRAPHIC RESTRICTIONS:
  Chester County, Pennsylvania and Savannah, Georgia areas.

FINANCIAL DATA:
  Amount of support per award: Maximum grant: $50,000; Average $5,000 to $10,000.
  Total amount of support: $608,000 for the year ended December 31, 2013.

NUMBER OF APPLICANTS MOST RECENT YEAR:
  116.

NUMBER OF AWARDS: 45.

REPRESENTATIVE AWARDS:
  $35,000 to Calvary Day School; $20,000 to Christ Church; $50,000 to Episcopal Academy; $15,000 to Good Works; $4,000 to Habitat for Humanity of Chester County.

APPLICATION INFORMATION:
  Applications must be submitted online. Applicants are encouraged to call and discuss their project with the staff. The application form should be submitted with a grant proposal and include the following attachments:
  (1) IRS tax-exemption letter;
  (2) Pennsylvania charitable organizations registration certificate (any organization with gross revenue over $25,000, regardless of location). Churches exempt;
  (3) by-laws;
  (4) last independent financial audit;
  (5) list of the organization's major public and private funding sources;
  (6) list of the Board of Directors with their community/professional affiliations;
  (7) agency's current operating budget;
  (8) most recent Form 990 filed with the IRS;
  (9) latest annual report;
  (10) list of the public and private sources being solicited to fund the project;
  (11) detailed project budget;
  (12) statement that there has been no change in purpose, character or method of operation since the agency's IRS tax ruling was issued and;
  (13) a few examples of media reviews about your agency program.
  Duration: No multiyear commitments.
  Deadline: March 1 and September 1 for religious organizations; March 1 for health and civic organizations.

PUBLICATIONS:
  Program announcement; guidelines; annual report.

IRS IDENTIFICATION NUMBER: 23-2612599

TRUSTEES:
  Charles L. Huston, III
  Elinor Lashley
  Shelton Sanford

ADDRESS INQUIRIES TO:
  Scott G. Huston, Executive Director
  (See address above.)

IMMANUEL BIBLE FOUNDATION   [815]
1301 South Fell Avenue
Normal, IL 61761
(309) 452-6710
Fax: (309) 862-4121

E-MAIL ADDRESS:
immanuelbiblefoundation@yahoo.com

WEB SITE ADDRESS:
www.ibfoundation.org

FOUNDED: 1944

AREAS OF INTEREST:
Local charities and youth-serving
organizations.

TYPE:
General operating grants. Special needs
grants.

YEAR PROGRAM STARTED: 1949

PURPOSE:
To promote the gospel and serve as a
resource for the Christian community.

LEGAL BASIS:
Tax-exempt private foundation.

ELIGIBILITY:
Tax-exempt organizations, entirely local to
the Foundation's immediate area. Out-of-state
applications not accepted. No grants to
individuals.

GEOGRAPHIC RESTRICTIONS:
McLean County, Illinois.

FINANCIAL DATA:
Amount of support per award: $500.
Total amount of support: Up to $7,500.

APPLICATION INFORMATION:
By letter. Must get form and attach
appropriate documentation.
Duration: Varies by need.
Deadline: Applications accepted January 1 to
May 1. Announcement by September 1.

IRS IDENTIFICATION NUMBER: 37-0688539

ADDRESS INQUIRIES TO:
Jan Godbey, Executive Director
(See address above.)

KOCH FOUNDATION, INC.   [816]

4421 N.W. 39th Avenue
Building 1, Suite 1
Gainesville, FL 32606
(352) 373-7491
Fax: (352) 337-1548

E-MAIL ADDRESS:
staff@thekochfoundation.org

WEB SITE ADDRESS:
www.thekochfoundation.org

FOUNDED: 1979

AREAS OF INTEREST:
Roman Catholic evangelization.

TYPE:
Development grants; Fellowships;
Grants-in-aid; Project/program grants;
Training grants. Grants are made for direct
evangelization programs, preparation of
evangelists, resource-poor Catholic schools
that are the principal means of evangelization
in the community, a Catholic presence in the
media, and capital expenditures such as
construction and repair of churches or
formation centers.

YEAR PROGRAM STARTED: 1979

PURPOSE:
To provide financial support for
evangelization efforts to Catholic
organizations throughout the world that
propagate the Roman Catholic faith.

LEGAL BASIS:
Not-for-profit corporation.

ELIGIBILITY:
U.S. Catholic organizations must be
501(c)(3) and appear in the Official Catholic
Directory. Non-U.S. Catholic organizations
must have a fiscal agent in the U.S. who is
willing to disburse grant funds for them,
should a grant be awarded.

FINANCIAL DATA:
Amount of support per award: Varies
depending on needs and nature of the
request; typical grant $15,000.
Total amount of support: $8,000,000 for
fiscal year 2013.

APPLICATION INFORMATION:
Application forms are available January 1 to
May 1. Briefly describe the project when
writing for a grant application. All requests
must be in English to assure appropriate
attention. Faxed requests are not accepted.
Completed applications must be returned
within 90 days. Applications must include a
budget, a statement of the desired impact on
evangelization and, if international, the
country and diocese where the program will
take place and the U.S. fiscal agent who will
be responsible for distributing the funds.
Applications for a continuing project must be
accompanied by a six-month progress report
or yearly evaluation.
Duration: Varies.
Deadline: August 31. Announcement in late
March.

PUBLICATIONS:
Application guidelines.

IRS IDENTIFICATION NUMBER: 59-1885997

BOARD OF DIRECTORS:
William A. Bomberger, President
Inge L. Vraney, Vice President
Dorothy C. Bomberger, Treasurer
Lawrence E. Vraney, Jr., Assistant Treasurer
Rachel A. Bomberger, Secretary
Michelle H. Bomberger, Assistant Secretary
Carolyn Bomberger
Matthew A. Bomberger
Charlotte L. Spacinsky
Jeffrey Vraney
Lori Vraney
Maura J. Vraney

ADDRESS INQUIRIES TO:
Executive Director
(See address above.)

LUTHERAN FOUNDATION OF ST. LOUIS   [817]

8860 Ladue Road
Suite 200
St. Louis, MO 63124
(314) 231-2244
Fax: (314) 727-7688

E-MAIL ADDRESS:
info@lutheranfoundation.org

WEB SITE ADDRESS:
www.lutheranfoundation.org

FOUNDED: 1984

AREAS OF INTEREST:
Christian voluntarism, congregation social
service outreach, Lutheran education, services
to ex-offenders and their families,
foreign-born populations, and older adults
maintaining independence.

TYPE:
Project/program grants.

YEAR PROGRAM STARTED: 1984

PURPOSE:
To provide grant awards in the areas of
Christian voluntarism, congregation social
service outreach ministry, Lutheran
education, prevention and early intervention
in children's mental health, and services to
prisoners, ex-offenders and their families.

LEGAL BASIS:
Religious foundation.

ELIGIBILITY:
Applicant must be a 501(c)(3), serve the St.
Louis metropolitan area, address one or more
of the funding focus areas, and complement
the Foundation's core values.

The Foundation does not make grants to
individuals.

GEOGRAPHIC RESTRICTIONS:
Metropolitan St. Louis, Missouri area.

FINANCIAL DATA:
Amount of support per award: Varies.
Total amount of support: $3,263,969 for the
year 2013.
Matching fund requirements: Varies
depending on the grant.

NUMBER OF AWARDS: 158 for the year 2013.

APPLICATION INFORMATION:
Applicant must submit:
(1) organization and contact information;
(2) relationship to The Lutheran
Church-Missouri Synod;
(3) statement of community need;
(4) project description: plan to help who?
help how? (expected objectives, measurable
outcomes, number of people served),
difference in lives of those helped?, any
collaborating partners?;
(5) evaluation plan (tie to evidence-based,
best or promising practices);
(6) project budget and budget narrative
justifying expenditures;
(7) copy of most recent audited financial
statements;
(8) bids for capital funding requests;
(9) copy of IRS Letter of Determination
indicating 501(c)(3) status and;
(10) list of current board members.

See Foundation web site for complete
application information.
Duration: Varies.
Deadline: June 1 and December 1.
Announcement in August and February,
respectively.

IRS IDENTIFICATION NUMBER: 43-1379359

BOARD OF DIRECTORS:
Karl A. Dunajcik, Chairperson
Robert E. Beumer, Vice Chairperson
Elizabeth A. Goad, Secretary
Jeffrey A. Craig-Meyer
James R. Dankenbring
Robert P. Ensor
Carl J. Fruend
Sarah A. Kramer
Linda L. Moen
Bruce Pompe
Rev. Dr. Ronald D. Rall
Catherine Rodgers-Edmonds
Sharon Rohrbach
Rev. Dr. Scott K. Seidler
Paul N. Tice
Ann L. Vazquez

ADDRESS INQUIRIES TO:
Program Director
(See address above.)

JACOB RADER MARCUS CENTER OF THE AMERICAN JEWISH ARCHIVES [818]

3101 Clifton Avenue
Cincinnati, OH 45220-2488
(513) 221-1875
Fax: (513) 221-7812

E-MAIL ADDRESS:
kproffitt@huc.edu

WEB SITE ADDRESS:
www.americanjewisharchives.org

FOUNDED: 1947

AREAS OF INTEREST:
American and western hemisphere Jewish history.

NAME(S) OF PROGRAMS:
* **The American Jewish Archives Fellowship Program**

TYPE:
Fellowships. The Marcus Center's Fellowship Program provides recipients with month-long fellowships for research and writing at The Jacob Rader Marcus Center of the American Jewish Archives. Fellowship stipends will be sufficient to cover transportation and living expenses while in residence. Applicants must be conducting serious research in some area relating to the history of North American Jewry.

YEAR PROGRAM STARTED: 1977

PURPOSE:
To collect, preserve and publish the history of the American Jewish experience.

LEGAL BASIS:
A division of the Hebrew Union College, Jewish Institute of Religion; tax-exempt.

ELIGIBILITY:
Doctoral and postdoctoral applicants working in the field are eligible. For the Rabbi Frederic A. Doppelt Memorial Fellowship, preference will be given to candidates from Eastern Europe or those working on a topic related to East European Jewry in the American context.

FINANCIAL DATA:
Grant amount is based upon the individual's research. Fellowship stipends will be sufficient to cover transportation and living expenses while in residence in Cincinnati.
Amount of support per award: Varies.
Total amount of support: Varies.

REPRESENTATIVE AWARDS:
Dr. William Pencak, Pennsylvania State University, "Popular and Political Anti-Semitism in Early America;" Dr. Leonard W. Rogoff, Jewish Heritage Foundation of North Carolina, "A Tale of Two Cities: Race, Riots and Religion in North Carolina, 1898;" Dr. David Dalin, Ave Maria University, FL, "American Jewry and the Republican Party before 1932;" Dr. Raphael Medoff, The David Wyman Institute for Holocaust Studies, "American Jewish Efforts to Solve the Dilemma of Arab-Jewish Relations."

APPLICATION INFORMATION:
Fellowship applicants should provide an up-to-date curriculum vitae, a research proposal (no more than five typewritten, double-spaced pages), and two recommendations, preferably from academic colleagues (for Ph.D. students, one of these recommendations should be from the candidate's dissertation advisor). Research must be done for one month on campus through the archives.

Application should not be made to individually named fellowship funds of the Center. Applicants will be considered for all available Center fellowships.

Prior to completion of the Fellowship applications, the Center strongly recommends that applicants familiarize themselves with its collection. The American Jewish Archives web site contains a list of holdings and a number of finding aids for applicant to peruse. An archivist can be contacted directly for information at the number above (ext. 403).
Duration: Up to one month.
Deadline: February 8. Announcement by May 15.

PUBLICATIONS:
Program description.

STAFF:
Dr. Gary P. Zola, Executive Director
Kevin Proffitt, Director

ADDRESS INQUIRIES TO:
Kevin Proffitt
Director of Fellowship Programs
(See address above.)

VERNE CATT MCDOWELL CORPORATION [819]

P.O. Box 1336
Albany, OR 97321-0440
(541) 924-0976

FOUNDED: 1963

AREAS OF INTEREST:
Graduate theological education.

NAME(S) OF PROGRAMS:
* **Verne Catt McDowell Scholarship**

TYPE:
Scholarships. Financial assistance for men and women attending an approved seminary to become ordained in the Christian Church (Disciples of Christ) denomination and work actively in that church.

YEAR PROGRAM STARTED: 1966

PURPOSE:
To train men and women to become pastors in the Christian Church (Disciples of Christ) Denomination.

LEGAL BASIS:
Private nonprofit corporation.

ELIGIBILITY:
A graduate from an accredited college and/or university who plans to enter an approved seminary of the Christian Church (Disciples of Christ) is eligible to apply. Study must take place in the U.S. Candidates must plan to be ordained in the Christian Church (Disciples of Christ) Denomination and work actively in that church.

Preference given to students from Oregon.

FINANCIAL DATA:
Amount of support per award: Varies.
Approximately $200 to $400 per school month.
Total amount of support: Varies.

NUMBER OF APPLICANTS MOST RECENT YEAR:
4.

NUMBER OF AWARDS: 1 to 3 per year.

APPLICATION INFORMATION:
Write for application and include eligibility and where information regarding program was found.
Duration: Varies with each student; continues support until completion of seminary.
Deadline: May 1. Awards are usually announced after annual meeting in June.

IRS IDENTIFICATION NUMBER: 93-6022991

OFFICERS:
Chet Houser, President
Nadine Wood, Business Manager

ADDRESS INQUIRIES TO:
Nadine Wood, Business Manager
(See address above.)

MEMORIAL FOUNDATION FOR JEWISH CULTURE [820]

50 Broadway, 34th Floor
New York, NY 10004
(212) 425-6606
Fax: (212) 425-6602

E-MAIL ADDRESS:
office@mfjc.org

WEB SITE ADDRESS:
www.mfjc.org

FOUNDED: 1964

AREAS OF INTEREST:
Support for Jewish cultural and educational programs all over the world, in cooperation with universities and established scholarly organizations. Also, annual scholarship and fellowship program.

NAME(S) OF PROGRAMS:
* **International Doctoral Scholarship for Studies Specializing in Jewish Fields**
* **International Fellowship in Jewish Studies and Jewish Culture**

TYPE:
Fellowships; Scholarships. Doctoral scholarships, post-rabbinic scholarships, Fellowships in Jewish culture and Jewish studies.

PURPOSE:
To help assure a creative Jewish future throughout the world by encouraging Jewish scholarship, Jewish education and Jewish cultural creativity; to support communities that are struggling to maintain their Jewish identity; to make possible the training of Jewish men and women for professional careers in communal service in Jewishly deprived communities.

LEGAL BASIS:
IRS Section 501(c)(3) charity; not a private foundation.

ELIGIBILITY:
Individual requirements vary according to the scholarship or fellowship.

FINANCIAL DATA:
Amount of support per award: Up to $10,000 per year. Scholarships and fellowships are given to individuals in amounts which vary according to the cost of living in the grantee's country of residence.

APPLICATION INFORMATION:
Guidelines and application forms for scholarships and fellowships are available on written request to the Foundation at the address above.
Duration: One academic year.
Deadline: October 31 for doctoral scholarships and fellowships.

OFFICERS:
Dr. Jerry Hochbaum, Executive Vice
President

ADDRESS INQUIRIES TO:
Dr. Jerry Hochbaum
Executive Vice President
(See address above.)

THE MUSTARD SEED FOUNDATION

7115 Leesburg Pike, Suite 304
Falls Church, VA 22043
(703) 524-5620

E-MAIL ADDRESS:
ljackson@msfdn.org

WEB SITE ADDRESS:
www.msfdn.org

TYPE:
Fellowships.

See entry 1566 for full listing.

PONTIFICAL INSTITUTE OF MEDIAEVAL STUDIES

59 Queen's Park Crescent East
Toronto ON M5S 2C4 Canada
(416) 926-7142
Fax: (416) 926-7292

E-MAIL ADDRESS:
allan.smith@utoronto.ca

WEB SITE ADDRESS:
www.pims.ca

TYPE:
Fellowships.

See entry 630 for full listing.

PRESBYTERIAN CHURCH (U.S.A.) [821]

Office of Financial Aid for Service
100 Witherspoon Street
Louisville, KY 40202-1396
(502) 569-5224
(800) 728-7228 ext. 5224
Fax: (502) 569-8766

E-MAIL ADDRESS:
finaid@pcusa.org

WEB SITE ADDRESS:
www.pcusa.org/financialaid

NAME(S) OF PROGRAMS:
• **Presbyterian Study Grants**

TYPE:
Grants-in-aid.

PURPOSE:
To assist graduate students who are
communicant members of the Presbyterian
Church (U.S.A.) in their preparation for
professional church occupations.

ELIGIBILITY:
Applicants must demonstrate financial need
beyond that which they are able to meet
through other grants, scholarships, savings
and employment, be enrolled on a full-time
basis, be in good academic standing, be
recommended by the financial aid officer at
their theological institution, be studying in a
Presbyterian Church (U.S.A.) seminary, and
must be studying in one of the two categories
listed below:

(1) students preparing for ordination must be
full-time M.Div. and must be enrolled as an
inquirer with or received as a candidate by a
Presbyterian Church (U.S.A.) presbytery for
a church occupation or;

(2) students preparing for occupations as a
Christian educator must be full-time
M.A.C.E. students.

FINANCIAL DATA:
Grants are meant to be supplemental to other
assistance a student has sought and is
receiving from presbytery, seminary, home
church, etc. Grants are not available for
summer study, intern year or studying
abroad.
Amount of support per award: Up to $4,000
for the academic year, depending upon
demonstrated need and availability of funds.
Total amount of support: Varies.

APPLICATION INFORMATION:
Detailed information and forms are available
on the web site.
Duration: One academic year. Renewals
possible (annually).
Deadline: Varies.

*SPECIAL STIPULATIONS:
No grants are available for doctoral study.

RASKOB FOUNDATION FOR CATHOLIC ACTIVITIES [822]

P.O. Box 4019
Wilmington, DE 19807
(302) 655-4440
Fax: (302) 655-3223

WEB SITE ADDRESS:
www.rfca.org

FOUNDED: 1945

AREAS OF INTEREST:
Catholic activities.

TYPE:
Challenge/matching grants; Development
grants; General operating grants;
Project/program grants; Seed money grants;
Training grants.

YEAR PROGRAM STARTED: 1945

PURPOSE:
To engage in such exclusively religious,
charitable, literary and educational activities
as will aid the Roman Catholic Church and
institutions and organizations identified with
it.

LEGAL BASIS:
Nonprofit foundation.

ELIGIBILITY:
Applicants must be Catholic organizations
with nonprofit status.

FINANCIAL DATA:
Amount of support per award: $15,000 for
the year 2013.
Total amount of support: $5,215,882 for the
year 2013.

NUMBER OF APPLICANTS MOST RECENT YEAR:
948 for the year 2013.

NUMBER OF AWARDS: 302 for the year 2013.

APPLICATION INFORMATION:
To be considered for review, organizations
within the U.S. must submit an application
with the following required documents:
(1) a fully completed application form;
(2) a detailed breakdown of the budget of the
project/program;

(3) financial statements of the incorporated
Catholic organization that will conduct the
proposed project;
(4) a letter from the Ordinary of the Diocese
where the project will take place,
commenting upon the applicant's request to
the Raskob Foundation and;
(5) a narrative (optional).

Any application lacking any of the first three
items will not be considered.

Organizations located outside the U.S. must
submit an application with the following
required documents:
(1) a fully completed application form;
(2) a detailed breakdown of the budget of the
project/program and;
(3) a letter from the Ordinary where project
will take place, verifying the organization is
Catholic, not-for-profit, and located in
Diocese.

Organizations can apply online at the web
site listed above.
Duration: Varies.
Deadline: Applications will only be accepted
for the spring from December 8 to January
15 and for the fall from June 8 to July 15.
Announcement follows May and November
Board meetings.

PUBLICATIONS:
Application guidelines.

IRS IDENTIFICATION NUMBER: 51-0070060

STAFF:
L. Charles Rotunno, Jr., Executive Vice
President-Grants and External Affairs
Theresa G. Robinson, Executive Vice
President-Operations and Finance

ADDRESS INQUIRIES TO:
L. Charles Rotunno, Jr.
Executive Vice President
(See address above.)

DAVID AND SYLVIA STEINER CHARITABLE TRUST [823]

Steiner Equities Group
75 Eisenhower Parkway
Roseland, NJ 07068
(973) 228-5800
Fax: (973) 228-5817

FOUNDED: 1987

AREAS OF INTEREST:
Jewish organizations and higher education.

TYPE:
Project/program grants.

YEAR PROGRAM STARTED: 1987

LEGAL BASIS:
Private foundation.

ELIGIBILITY:
Applicants must be nonprofit entities. Grants
are given to religious organizations and for
religious education.

GEOGRAPHIC RESTRICTIONS:
New Jersey and New York.

FINANCIAL DATA:
Amount of support per award: Varies.

REPRESENTATIVE AWARDS:
$55,000 to United Jewish Appeal of
Metrowest, East Orange, NJ; $20,000 to
American Associates of Ben Gurion
University of the Negev, New York, NY;
$5,000 to National Council of Jewish
Women, New York, NY.

APPLICATION INFORMATION:
Applications should be in letter form and must include a statement of purpose, amount requested and a description of the organization.
Duration: One year.

ADDRESS INQUIRIES TO:
Robert Testa, Chief Financial Officer
(See address above.)

SUBCOMMITTEE ON THE HOME MISSIONS   [824]
United States Conference of Catholic Bishops
3211 4th Street, N.E.
Washington, DC 20017-1194
(202) 541-5400
Fax: (202) 541-3473

E-MAIL ADDRESS:
homemissions@usccb.org

WEB SITE ADDRESS:
www.usccb.org

FOUNDED: 1924

AREAS OF INTEREST:
Catholic missions in America, including evangelization, catechesis, parish life and personnel training.

TYPE:
General operating grants; Project/program grants; Seed money grants; Training grants. Annual grants to fund home mission activities, such as evangelization through proclamation of the Word, pastoral services, personnel training and the formation of faith communities in the U.S. and its territories. Home mission activities may be centered at the national, regional, diocesan or local level and may address the country as a whole, a particular group of people or a particular place.

YEAR PROGRAM STARTED: 1924

ELIGIBILITY:
Eligible applicants may come from three sources, including (in order of priority) diocesan bishops of home mission dioceses for activities that serve to establish or strengthen the church in their dioceses, heads of national, regional or interdiocesan Catholic organizations for home mission activities that serve the church at a supra-diocesan level and provincials of religious institutes for home mission activities that form part of their apostolate. No funds are available for endowments or loans.

GEOGRAPHIC RESTRICTIONS:
United States and its Caribbean and Pacific territories.

FINANCIAL DATA:
Amount of support per award: Varies depending on needs and nature of the request.
Total amount of support: $8,400,000 for the year 2013.

APPLICATION INFORMATION:
Application materials are available January of each year. Contact office for other requirements.
Duration: Grants are renewable.
Deadline: April 1. Announcement in October. Disbursements are made quarterly January to December.

PUBLICATIONS:
Annual report; guidelines; *Neighbors*, quarterly newsletter.

OFFICERS:
Most Rev. Michael W. Warfel, Chairman
Dr. David J. Suley, Director

ADDRESS INQUIRIES TO:
Dr. David J. Suley, Director
Tel: (202) 541-5400
E-mail: dsuley@usccb.org
(See address above.)

*PLEASE NOTE:
Currently considering grants from dioceses only.

UNITARIAN UNIVERSALIST ASSOCIATION OF CONGREGATIONS   [825]
24 Farnsworth Street
Boston, MA 02210
(617) 742-2100
Fax: (617) 367-3237

E-MAIL ADDRESS:
scarey@uua.org

WEB SITE ADDRESS:
www.uua.org

FOUNDED: 1961

AREAS OF INTEREST:
Religious liberalism, philosophy, social change, child and family welfare, and ethics.

NAME(S) OF PROGRAMS:
● **Frederic G. Melcher Book Award**

TYPE:
Awards/prizes. Award for the book published in the U.S. during the last calendar year which is judged to make the most significant contribution to religious liberal thought.

YEAR PROGRAM STARTED: 1964

PURPOSE:
To encourage writing in liberal religion.

LEGAL BASIS:
Nonprofit association.

ELIGIBILITY:
Books must be published in the U.S. Any serious book-length publication in the tradition of free inquiry is eligible. Any publisher may submit a candidate. Entries are judged on the basis of scholarship, competence, responsibility and devotion to the ideals of religious liberalism which include freedom, reason and tolerance.

GEOGRAPHIC RESTRICTIONS:
United States.

FINANCIAL DATA:
Amount of support per award: $1,000 and a citation.
Total amount of support: $1,000.

NUMBER OF AWARDS: 1.

APPLICATION INFORMATION:
Publishers should contact office for information.
Deadline: December 31.

ADDRESS INQUIRIES TO:
Stephanie Carey Maron
Executive Assistant for the
Office of the President
(See address above.)

*SPECIAL STIPULATIONS:
Recipient is expected to come to Boston to accept the award and make a public appearance, including a speech. Expenses paid.

UNITED JEWISH APPEAL-FEDERATION OF JEWISH PHILANTHROPIES OF NEW YORK   [826]
130 East 59th Street
New York, NY 10022
(212) 980-1000
(212) 836-1321
Fax: (212) 836-1353

E-MAIL ADDRESS:
snersonj@ujafedny.org

WEB SITE ADDRESS:
www.ujafedny.org

FOUNDED: 1917

AREAS OF INTEREST:
Human services, Jewish identity and education, rescue and resettlement of Jewish communities in distress.

CONSULTING OR VOLUNTEER SERVICES:
Offers numerous opportunities to volunteer. Please call Resource Line: (212) 836-1447.

TYPE:
Capital grants; Challenge/matching grants; Conferences/seminars; Demonstration grants; Development grants; General operating grants; Internships; Project/program grants; Technical assistance; Travel grants.

YEAR PROGRAM STARTED: 1917

PURPOSE:
To care for people in need; to inspire a passion for Jewish life and learning; to strengthen Jewish communities in New York, in Israel, and around the world.

LEGAL BASIS:
501(c)(3).

ELIGIBILITY:
No grants to individuals. Applicants must be 501(c)(3) organizations.

GEOGRAPHIC RESTRICTIONS:
New York including the five boroughs, Nassau, Suffolk and Westchester counties.

FINANCIAL DATA:
Amount of support per award: Varies depending upon needs and nature of the request.
Total amount of support: Approximately $131,300,000 for the year 2013-14.

APPLICATION INFORMATION:
Application form required. Organizations must include documentation of IRS nonprofit status with their application.
Duration: One year. Renewal possible.

PUBLICATIONS:
Annual Report to the Community.

IRS IDENTIFICATION NUMBER: 51-0172429

ADDRESS INQUIRIES TO:
Jed Snerson
Executive Director of Grants Program
(See address above.)

UNITED METHODIST COMMUNICATIONS
810 12th Avenue South
Nashville, TN 37203-4704
(888) 278-4862
Fax: (615) 742-5777

E-MAIL ADDRESS:
scholarships@umcom.org

WEB SITE ADDRESS:
www.umcom.org

TYPE:
Fellowships. Assists one United Methodist student in graduate study at an accredited U.S. college or university who intends to pursue a career in religious journalism.

See entry 1961 for full listing.

THE WABASH CENTER FOR TEACHING AND LEARNING IN THEOLOGY AND RELIGION [827]

301 West Wabash Avenue
Crawfordsville, IN 47933
(765) 361-6047
Fax: (765) 361-6051

E-MAIL ADDRESS:
wabashcenter@wabash.edu

WEB SITE ADDRESS:
www.wabashcenter.wabash.edu

FOUNDED: 1995

AREAS OF INTEREST:
Teaching religion and theology, higher education pedagogy in theology and religion.

NAME(S) OF PROGRAMS:
- **Educational Environments**
- **Faculty Practices and Vocation**
- **Teaching and Learning Resources**

TYPE:
Conferences/seminars; Fellowships; Project/program grants; Research grants.

YEAR PROGRAM STARTED: 1995

PURPOSE:
To strengthen and enhance the teaching of religion and theology in North American theological schools, colleges and universities.

ELIGIBILITY:
Full-time faculty members in religion departments of colleges and universities in North America and in theological schools accredited by the Association of Theological Schools are eligible to apply for these grants.

GEOGRAPHIC RESTRICTIONS:
United States and Canada.

FINANCIAL DATA:
Amount of support per award: Up to $20,000.

NUMBER OF APPLICANTS MOST RECENT YEAR:
77.

NUMBER OF AWARDS: 68.

APPLICATION INFORMATION:
Grant proposals should consist of an application form, project proposal (including budget) and letter of support. Specific format for grant proposals is explained in detail on the Center's web site.

Deadline: March 1 and October 1 annually.

PUBLICATIONS:
Teaching Theology and Religion, published quarterly by Wiley-Blackwell Publishers.

ADDRESS INQUIRIES TO:
Paul Myhre, Associate Director
(See address above.)

INTERNATIONAL AFFAIRS AND AREA STUDIES

International affairs and area studies

AMERICAN INSTITUTE OF PAKISTAN STUDIES [828]

University of Wisconsin-Madison
B488 Medical Sciences Center
1300 University Avenue
Madison, WI 53706
(608) 265-1471
Fax: (608) 265-3302

E-MAIL ADDRESS:
aips@pakistanstudies-aips.org

WEB SITE ADDRESS:
www.pakistanstudies-aips.org

FOUNDED: 1973

AREAS OF INTEREST:
All fields of humanities and social sciences if engaged in research on Pakistan and relations between Pakistan and other countries.

NAME(S) OF PROGRAMS:
- **AIPS Post Doctoral Fellowship**
- **AIPS Pre-Doctoral Fellowship**

TYPE:
Awards/prizes; Conferences/seminars; Fellowships; Travel grants; Visiting scholars. Awarded in several categories including predoctoral research, postdoctoral study, library service and professional development.

YEAR PROGRAM STARTED: 1973

PURPOSE:
To promote research on Pakistan.

ELIGIBILITY:
Applicants must be scholars and advanced graduate students who are American citizens and are engaged in research on Pakistan in ancient, medieval and modern times, in all fields of the humanities and social sciences. Research topics comparing aspects of Pakistan with other Muslim countries are especially encouraged.

Graduate student applicants must have fulfilled all residence, language and preliminary examination requirements for the Doctorate and have an approved dissertation topic.

See web site for current restrictions.

FINANCIAL DATA:
The award will provide a maintenance allowance for the scholar and dependents, plus travel and other benefits.
Amount of support per award: Varies.
Total amount of support: $65,000.

NUMBER OF APPLICANTS MOST RECENT YEAR:
15.

NUMBER OF AWARDS: Varies.

APPLICATION INFORMATION:
Predoctoral applications should include a proposal (five pages), curriculum vitae, a transcript, a letter from the dissertation advisor and contact information for two references. Postdoctoral applications should include a proposal (five pages), curriculum vitae, and contact information for two referees.

A nonrefundable processing fee of $30 must be included with the completed application form. Any forms that are incomplete will be returned without refund of the application fee.
Duration: Two to nine months.

Deadline: Varies.

STAFF:
Laura Hammond, U.S. Director

ADDRESS INQUIRIES TO:
Laura Hammond, U.S. Director
(See address above.)

THE KATHRYN AMES FOUNDATION [829]

c/o Pierson & Pierson
305 West Chesapeake Avenue, Suite 308
Towson, MD 21204
(410) 821-3006
Fax: (410) 821-3007

E-MAIL ADDRESS:
info@kathrynames.org

WEB SITE ADDRESS:
www.kathrynames.org

FOUNDED: 1993

AREAS OF INTEREST:
Israel, education, health care, poverty relief and pluralism.

TYPE:
General operating grants; Project/program grants.

YEAR PROGRAM STARTED: 1993

PURPOSE:
To benefit organizations located in Israel which are working for charitable and benevolent purposes.

LEGAL BASIS:
Private foundation.

ELIGIBILITY:
Eligible organizations must be nonprofit and located in Israel.

GEOGRAPHIC RESTRICTIONS:
Israel.

FINANCIAL DATA:
Amount of support per award: $5,000 to $40,000.
Total amount of support: $527,000 for the year 2012.

NUMBER OF AWARDS: 33 for the year 2011.

APPLICATION INFORMATION:
Application form is available online.
Duration: Typically one year.

PUBLICATIONS:
Application guidelines.

ADDRESS INQUIRIES TO:
Lu Pierson, Grants Administrator
(See address above.)

ARCHAEOLOGICAL INSTITUTE OF AMERICA [830]

656 Beacon Street, 6th Floor
Boston, MA 02215
(617) 358-4184
Fax: (617) 353-6550

E-MAIL ADDRESS:
fellowships@aia.bu.edu

WEB SITE ADDRESS:
www.archaeological.org

FOUNDED: 1879

AREAS OF INTEREST:
Archaeological research and publication.

NAME(S) OF PROGRAMS:
- **The Archaeology of Portugal Fellowship**

TYPE:
Fellowships. The Fellowship supports projects pertaining to the archaeology of Portugal. These include, but are not limited to, research projects, colloquia, symposia, publication, research-related travel, or travel to academic meetings for the purpose of presenting papers on the archaeology of Portugal.

PURPOSE:
To promote archaeological studies pertaining to Portugal.

ELIGIBILITY:
Portuguese, American and other international scholars are invited to apply.

FINANCIAL DATA:
Amount of support per award: Award may vary based on the merit of the proposal. Typically $4,000.
Total amount of support: $4,000 to $8,000.

NUMBER OF APPLICANTS MOST RECENT YEAR:
6.

NUMBER OF AWARDS: 2.

APPLICATION INFORMATION:
Application information is available on the web site.
Duration: One year.
Deadline: November 1. Announcement by February 1.

ADDRESS INQUIRIES TO:
Laurel Nilsen Sparks
Lecture and Fellowship Coordinator
(See address above.)

ASHBURN INSTITUTE INC. [831]

198 Okatie Village Drive
Suite 103, PMB 301
Bluffton, SC 29909
Fax: (843) 705-7643

E-MAIL ADDRESS:
info@ashburninstitute.org

WEB SITE ADDRESS:
www.ashburninstitute.org

FOUNDED: 1940

AREAS OF INTEREST:
International affairs, international federalism, and political science.

NAME(S) OF PROGRAMS:
- **Frank Educational Fund**

TYPE:
Research grants; Scholarships.

YEAR PROGRAM STARTED: 1991

PURPOSE:
To support the study of federalism and international integration at the graduate and postgraduate level.

ELIGIBILITY:
Open to graduate students of good academic standing working on a thesis or dissertation relating to international integration and federalism, doing coursework that places major weight on international integration and federalism or an independent project relating to international integration and federalism. International (foreign institutions) graduate students are eligible, as well as U.S. students.

FINANCIAL DATA:
Amount of support per award: $1,000 to $3,000.
Total amount of support: $40,000.

APPLICATION INFORMATION:
Applicants must complete the FEF
Application Form and submit it along with
the following materials:
(1) a description of any courses planned to
be completed by the applicant during the
period of the proposed grant;
(2) a concise, yet complete description of the
project relating to international integration
and federalism and how this will fit the
requirements of the Fund;
(3) a brief writing sample and;
(4) a copy of the applicant's graduate
transcripts if currently enrolled in a graduate
program (or have it sent separately by the
institution, if so, indicate), or a copy of the
applicant's undergraduate transcript if
enrolled in a graduate program but has not
yet started it.

Only complete applications will be
considered for a scholarship.

Deadline: April 1 for Fall term awards and
October 1 for Spring term awards.

ADDRESS INQUIRIES TO:
Frank Fund Manager
(See address above.)

AUSTRO-AMERICAN ASSOCIATION OF BOSTON [832]

67 Bridle Path
Sudbury, MA 01776
(978) 579-2191

E-MAIL ADDRESS:
scholarship@austria-boston.org

WEB SITE ADDRESS:
www.austria-boston.org

FOUNDED: 1944

AREAS OF INTEREST:
All aspects of Austrian society, especially
culture; Austrian-American relations.

TYPE:
Awards/prizes; Research grants; Scholarships.
Support for a project relating to Austrian
literature, music, art, history or other aspects
of the Austrian contribution to culture.

YEAR PROGRAM STARTED: 1976

PURPOSE:
To further interest in Austrian culture and
foster Austro-American friendship.

LEGAL BASIS:
Legally organized and established as of July
6, 1970 by the Secretary of the
Commonwealth.

ELIGIBILITY:
The project must be related to Austria.

Undergraduate or graduate students are
eligible:
(1) whose project is related to Austria;
(2) who reside or study in New England and;
(3) who are willing to present the results of
their project at an event of the
Austro-American Association.

GEOGRAPHIC RESTRICTIONS:
New England.

FINANCIAL DATA:
The stipend does not support tuition or other
expenses related to a course of study.
However, it may be used to travel to Europe
or within the U.S., to purchase books and
other materials or to facilitate publications.
Amount of support per award: $3,000.
Total amount of support: $3,000.

NUMBER OF APPLICANTS MOST RECENT YEAR:
5.

NUMBER OF AWARDS: 1 per year (when funds
are available).

APPLICATION INFORMATION:
Applications should include a curriculum
vitae, a detailed description of the proposed
project and two letters of recommendation
from faculty members well acquainted with
the applicant's background and potential.
Applicants may be invited to present the
results of their project at a meeting of the
Association. A personal interview may be
required.
Deadline: March 2, 2015.

OFFICERS:
David Acker, Board Chairman
Traude Schieber-Acker, President
Marta Stasa, Vice President
Hana Sittler, Treasurer
Judy Zohn, Secretary

ADDRESS INQUIRIES TO:
Traude Schieber-Acker, President and
Chairperson, Scholarship Panel
Austro-American Association of Boston, Inc.
(See address and e-mail above.)

*PLEASE NOTE:
E-mail correspondence and electronic
submission are requested.

CENTER FOR COMPARATIVE IMMIGRATION STUDIES AT THE UNIVERSITY OF CALIFORNIA-SAN DIEGO

9500 Gilman Drive, MC 0548
La Jolla, CA 92093-0548
(858) 822-4447
Fax: (858) 822-4432

E-MAIL ADDRESS:
ccis@ucsd.edu

WEB SITE ADDRESS:
ccis-ucsd.org

TYPE:
Fellowships.

See entry 1622 for full listing.

CENTER FOR INTERNATIONAL SECURITY AND COOPERATION (CISAC)   [833]

Freeman Spogli Institute for
International Studies
Encina Hall, E200
Stanford University
Stanford, CA 94305-6165
(650) 723-9625
Fax: (650) 724-5683

E-MAIL ADDRESS:
cisacfellowship@stanford.edu

WEB SITE ADDRESS:
cisac.stanford.edu/fellowships

FOUNDED: 1970

AREAS OF INTEREST:
CISAC fellows may focus on any of the
following topics: nuclear weapons policy and
nonproliferation; nuclear energy;
cybersecurity, cyberwarfare, and the future of
the Internet; biosecurity and global health;
implications of geostrategic shifts;
insurgency, terrorism, and homeland security;
war and civil conflict; consolidating peace
after conflict; as well as global governance,
migration, and transnational flows, from

norms to criminal trafficking. Also, other
research proposals on international security
topics are welcomed.

NAME(S) OF PROGRAMS:
• **Cybersecurity and International
Security Fellowship**
• **Law and International Security
Fellowship**
• **The MacArthur Foundation Nuclear
Security Fellowship**
• **Natural Sciences or Engineering
International Security Fellowship**
• **The William J. Perry Fellowship in
International Security**
• **Social Sciences or Humanities
International Security Fellowship**
• **The Stanton Nuclear Security
Fellowship**

TYPE:
Fellowships.

PURPOSE:
To train predoctoral, postdoctoral, junior
faculty and professionals in international
security policy areas.

LEGAL BASIS:
University.

ELIGIBILITY:
Must be in Ph.D. program, have a Ph.D. or
equivalent, or extraordinary professional
experience.

FINANCIAL DATA:
Amount of support per award: Varies.
Total amount of support: Varies.

NUMBER OF APPLICANTS MOST RECENT YEAR:
Over 200.

NUMBER OF AWARDS: 10-20.

APPLICATION INFORMATION:
Contact the Center.
Deadline: February 1.

ADDRESS INQUIRIES TO:
CISAC Fellowship Program
(See address above.)

CENTER FOR U.S. - MEXICAN STUDIES, UNIVERSITY OF CALIFORNIA, SAN DIEGO   [834]

School of International Relations
and Pacific Studies
9500 Gilman Drive, No. 0519
La Jolla, CA 92093-0519
(858) 534-4503
Fax: (858) 534-6447

E-MAIL ADDRESS:
usmex@ucsd.edu

WEB SITE ADDRESS:
usmex.ucsd.edu

FOUNDED: 1979

AREAS OF INTEREST:
The study of U.S. and Mexico relations and
the study of Mexico within the social
sciences and history.

NAME(S) OF PROGRAMS:
• **USMEX Visiting Scholars Program**

TYPE:
Fellowships; Professorships.

YEAR PROGRAM STARTED: 1980

PURPOSE:
To support the write-up of a Ph.D.
dissertation or the write-up of a postdoctoral
research project.

ELIGIBILITY:
Open to Mexican citizens, advanced graduate students, recent Ph.D. recipients, junior faculty and advanced faculty members from any campus of the University of California system, as well as other institutions.

GEOGRAPHIC RESTRICTIONS:
United States and Mexico.

FINANCIAL DATA:
Amount of support per award: Predoctoral Fellows: $2,500 per month; Visiting Professors: $3,500 per month.
Total amount of support: $150,000.

APPLICATION INFORMATION:
Applications should be submitted online.
Duration: Up to nine months. Former Visiting Fellows are eligible to apply again after five years.
Deadline: January.

ADDRESS INQUIRIES TO:
Greg Mallinger, Program Coordinator
(See address above.)

THE CHRISTENSEN FUND
260 Townsend Street
Suite 600
San Francisco, CA 94107
(415) 644-1630
Fax: (415) 644-1670

E-MAIL ADDRESS:
info@christensenfund.org

WEB SITE ADDRESS:
www.christensenfund.org

TYPE:
General operating grants; Project/program grants; Research grants.

See entry 64 for full listing.

COUNCIL FOR EUROPEAN STUDIES AT COLUMBIA UNIVERSITY [835]
420 West 118th Street, MC 3307
New York, NY 10027
(212) 854-4172
Fax: (212) 854-8808

E-MAIL ADDRESS:
ces@columbia.edu

WEB SITE ADDRESS:
councilforeuropeanstudies.org

FOUNDED: 1970

AREAS OF INTEREST:
The study of Europe.

NAME(S) OF PROGRAMS:
● **Book Award**
● **Council for European Studies Pre-Dissertation Research Fellowships**
● **First Article Prize in Humanities and Social Sciences**
● **Mellon-CES Dissertation Completion Fellowship in European Studies**

TYPE:
Awards/prizes; Fellowships. The CES Book Award honors talented emerging scholars with an award for the best first book on any subject in European studies. The award is given every two years.

Council for European Studies Pre-Dissertation Research Fellowships are intended to fund student's first major research project in Europe.

First Article Prize awards one prize to a scholar working in the humanities and one to a scholar working in the social sciences. These prizes will honor the writers of the best first articles on European studies published within a two-year period.

Mellon-CES Dissertation Completion Fellowships are intended to facilitate the timely completion of the doctoral degree by late-stage graduate students focused on topics in European studies.

YEAR PROGRAM STARTED: 1971

ELIGIBILITY:
Book Award: Must be scholar's first book on any subject in European studies. Books may be nominated by the author, a CES member, or by a publisher.

Pre-Dissertation Research Fellowships are limited to graduate students currently enrolled in a doctoral program at a university that is a member of the Council for European Studies Academic Consortium. Member universities and additional eligibility requirements can be found online.

First Article Prize nominees meet the following criteria:
(1) be the first article published by the nominee in the field of European studies in a peer-reviewed journal;
(2) be published between January 1, 2012 and December 31, 2013;
(3) be the work of one author only or be an article on which the nominee is the first author and;
(4) be authored by a member of the Council for European Studies or a faculty/student of an institution that is a member. Nominations may be submitted by the publisher, editor, author, or admiring colleagues.

To be eligible for the Mellon-CES Dissertation Completion Fellowship, the applicant must be ABD, be enrolled at a higher education institution in the U.S., and can have no more than one full year of dissertation work remaining at the start of the fellowship year as certified by his or her dissertation advisor. The applicant must also have exhausted the dissertation completion funding normally provided by his or her academic department or university, and he or she must be working on a topic within or substantially overlapping European studies. To be eligible to receive the fellowship, applicants must also be enrolled in an institution that is a member of the CES Academic Consortium. However, students whose universities are not currently members of the CES consortium may apply, but they are encouraged to apply early in the application season so that every effort may be made to enroll the institution in the CES member consortium and, thus, establish the student's eligibility by the application deadline.

FINANCIAL DATA:
Book Award recipient receives a certificate, $1,000 and all-expenses-paid trip to International Conference and award ceremony. Fellowship recipients receive a stipend, travel support for attending and presenting at the CES International Conference of Europeanists, and the opportunity to publish in *Perspectives on Europe.*
Amount of support per award: Book Award: $1,000; First Article Prize: $500; Mellon-CES Dissertation Completion

Fellowship: $25,000 stipend to be paid in six bimonthly installments; Pre-Dissertation Research Fellowship: $4,000 stipend.
Total amount of support: Varies.

APPLICATION INFORMATION:
Applications and guidelines are available online.
Deadline: Book Award: Early October; First Article Prize: Nomination mid-April or before; Mellon-CES Dissertation Completion Fellowship: January 19; Pre-Dissertation Research Fellowship: February 1.

COUNCIL FOR INTERNATIONAL EXCHANGE OF SCHOLARS (CIES) [836]
1400 K Street, N.W.
Suite 700
Washington, DC 20005
(202) 686-6252
Fax: (202) 362-3442

E-MAIL ADDRESS:
asquitieri@iie.org

WEB SITE ADDRESS:
www.iie.org/cies

FOUNDED: 1947

AREAS OF INTEREST:
Humanities or social sciences, or any field that will benefit from an international perspective.

NAME(S) OF PROGRAMS:
● **Fulbright Scholar-in-Residence Program**

TYPE:
Awards/prizes; Exchange programs; Visiting scholars. Grants support a visiting lecturer from outside the U.S. to teach regular courses or develop new ones, team teach or participate in special seminars or serve as a resource to faculty and students and, through outreach, to the community at large.

PURPOSE:
To initiate or develop international programs at colleges and universities by using a foreign scholar-in-residence to internationalize the curriculum, set up global studies or area-specific programs or otherwise expand contacts of students and faculty with other cultures and to strengthen or enrich existing international or area studies programs.

LEGAL BASIS:
Public Law 87-256, as amended, The Mutual Educational and Cultural Exchange Act of 1961.

ELIGIBILITY:
U.S. colleges and universities, including community colleges, are invited to submit proposals to obtain a foreign scholar-in-residence. Preference is given to proposals in the humanities or social sciences, although other fields focusing on international issues will be considered.

GEOGRAPHIC RESTRICTIONS:
United States.

FINANCIAL DATA:
Monthly stipend as well as round-trip international travel, excess baggage allowance, accident and sickness insurance, and allowances for books, professional development and dependents.
Amount of support per award:
Approximately $2,710 to $3,145 per month, depending on the cost of living in the city where the scholar will reside.

Total amount of support: Over $1,000,000 for the year 2012.

Matching fund requirements: Some cost sharing by the host institution is required, either supplementary funding or in-kind support, such as housing.

COOPERATIVE FUNDING PROGRAMS: U.S. Department of State.

NUMBER OF AWARDS: 46.

APPLICATION INFORMATION:
Guidelines are available in March. Application must be submitted online.
Duration: One semester to one academic year.
Deadline: October 15.

PUBLICATIONS:
Directory of Visiting Scholars; descriptive brochure; annual report.

STAFF:
Anna Valiante, Program Coordinator

ADDRESS INQUIRIES TO:
Anna Valiante, Program Coordinator
(See address above.)

COUNCIL FOR INTERNATIONAL EXCHANGE OF SCHOLARS (CIES)

1400 K Street, N.W.
Suite 700
Washington, DC 20005
(202) 686-6232
Fax: (202) 686-4029

E-MAIL ADDRESS:
jmcpeek@iie.org

WEB SITE ADDRESS:
www.cies.org

TYPE:
Awards/prizes. There are approximately 40 distinguished chair awards in 18 countries. Awards available in a wide variety of disciplines.

See entry 1623 for full listing.

COUNCIL FOR INTERNATIONAL EXCHANGE OF SCHOLARS (CIES)   [837]

1400 K Street, N.W.
Suite 700
Washington, DC 20005-2403
(202) 898-0600
Fax: (202) 686-4029

E-MAIL ADDRESS:
fulspec@iie.org

WEB SITE ADDRESS:
www.cies.org/specialist

FOUNDED: 1947

AREAS OF INTEREST:
Scholarly exchange.

NAME(S) OF PROGRAMS:
● **Fulbright Specialist Program**

TYPE:
Exchange programs; Project/program grants. The Fulbright Specialist Program is designed to provide short-term project opportunities for U.S. faculty and professionals. Grant recipients have a chance to participate in a variety of new and exciting activities: collaborate with counterparts in other countries on curriculum and faculty

development, assist in institutional planning, deliver a series of lectures or provide other expertise, etc.

YEAR PROGRAM STARTED: 2001

PURPOSE:
To promote mutual understanding and scholarship.

LEGAL BASIS:
Private, nonprofit organization that receives funding from the U.S. State Department.

ELIGIBILITY:
The Fulbright Specialist Program is open to qualified U.S. scholars and professionals in various fields. Applicants will be considered without regard to race, color, religion, sex, age, national origin and/or physical impairment.

Applicants must meet all of the following minimum eligibility requirements:
(1) U.S. citizen at the time of application; permanent resident status is not sufficient;
(2) for academics, a Ph.D. or equivalent professional/terminal degree at the time of application plus a minimum of five years of postdoctoral teaching or professional experience in the field in which person is applying;
(3) for professionals and artists outside academe, recognized professional standing and substantial professional accomplishments plus a minimum of five years of professional experience in the field in which person is applying;
(4) disclosure of prior conviction, current indictment or arrest for commission of a felony or misdemeanor (excluding minor traffic violations); prior conviction or current indictment may result in disqualification and;
(5) U.S. residency required at the time of selection for a grant.

In matching candidates with grant opportunities, preference will be given to candidates with the most relevant professional experience.

FINANCIAL DATA:
Grants awarded will include travel and per diem plus a $200 per day honorarium. Per diem costs, which are in-country costs for lodging, meals and in-country transportation, will be covered by the host institution.
Amount of support per award: Varies.

NUMBER OF APPLICANTS MOST RECENT YEAR: 600.

NUMBER OF AWARDS: Approximately 300 to 400 per year.

APPLICATION INFORMATION:
Qualified U.S. scholars and professionals apply throughout the calendar year for candidacy on the Fulbright Specialists Roster. Peer review is conducted six times each year. CIES builds lists of qualified Specialist candidates for each eligible discipline and facilitates matching Specialist candidates with project requests. There is a two-tier application process for U.S. scholars.
Non-U.S. postsecondary degree-granting academic institutions and other eligible institutions with education-focused programming submit Specialist project requests through the appropriate Fulbright agency in their country. Once approved by the Fulbright Commission or U.S. Embassy, the Specialist project request is forwarded to the U.S. Department of State for final approval.
Duration: Two to six weeks.

ADDRESS INQUIRIES TO:
See e-mail address above.

COUNCIL ON FOREIGN RELATIONS   [838]

58 East 68th Street
New York, NY 10065
(212) 434-9740
Fax: (212) 434-9870

E-MAIL ADDRESS:
fellowships@cfr.org

WEB SITE ADDRESS:
www.cfr.org/fellowships

FOUNDED: 1921

AREAS OF INTEREST:
International relations, international affairs, Japan, U.S.-Japan relations, U.S.-Japan politics, Japanese studies, Japanese-American relations, foreign policy, policymaking, and public service.

NAME(S) OF PROGRAMS:
● **International Affairs Fellowship in Japan (IAF-J)**

TYPE:
Fellowships. The International Affairs Fellowship in Japan (IAF-J), sponsored by Hitachi, Ltd., provides a selected group of midcareer U.S. citizens the opportunity to expand their professional horizons by spending a period of research or other professional activity in Japan. Fellows are drawn from academia, business, government, media, NGOs and think tanks. In cooperation with the Council on Foreign Relations (CFR), the program's sponsor, Hitachi, Ltd., assists fellows in finding suitable host organizations in Japan.

YEAR PROGRAM STARTED: 1997

PURPOSE:
To strengthen mutual understanding and cooperation between the rising generations of leaders in the U.S. and Japan.

ELIGIBILITY:
The IAF-J is only open to U.S. citizens between the ages of 27 and 45. The program is intended primarily for those without substantial prior experience in Japan, although the selection committee has made exceptions when it considered that the fellowship would allow an individual to add a significant new dimension to his or her career. Knowledge of the Japanese language is not a requirement.

FINANCIAL DATA:
The program awards a stipend in yen, which covers travel and living expenses in Japan. Fellows are considered independent contractors rather than employees of CFR, and are not eligible for employment benefits, including health insurance.

COOPERATIVE FUNDING PROGRAMS: Hitachi, Ltd.

NUMBER OF AWARDS: Approximately 3 to 5 per year.

APPLICATION INFORMATION:
Interested candidates who meet the program's eligibility requirements can apply online via the CFR web site between June 1 and October 1 on an annual basis. Candidates who are selected as IAF-J finalists will be notified between December and January, with finalist interviews scheduled in Washington, DC, and New York, NY, between January

and February. Official selections and announcement of IAF-J awards will be made between February and March.

Duration: Three to 12 months.

Deadline: October 2013.

ADDRESS INQUIRIES TO:
See telephone or e-mail address above.

COUNCIL ON FOREIGN RELATIONS

58 East 68th Street
New York, NY 10065
(212) 434-9740
Fax: (212) 434-9870

E-MAIL ADDRESS:
fellowships@cfr.org

WEB SITE ADDRESS:
www.cfr.org/fellowships

TYPE:
Fellowships. The Edward R. Murrow Press Fellow spends nine months full-time in residence at the Council on Foreign Relations' (CFR) headquarters in New York. The program enables the fellow to engage in sustained analysis and writing, expand his or her intellectual and professional horizons, and extensively participate in CFR's active program of meetings and events. The Fellow will be part of the David Rockefeller Studies Program, CFR's think tank, alongside the program's full-time, adjunct and visiting fellows, whose expertise extends across the broad range of significant foreign policy issues facing the U.S. and the international community.

See entry 1931 for full listing.

COUNCIL ON FOREIGN RELATIONS [839]

58 East 68th Street
New York, NY 10065
(212) 434-9740
Fax: (212) 434-9800

E-MAIL ADDRESS:
fellowships@cfr.org

WEB SITE ADDRESS:
www.cfr.org/fellowships

FOUNDED: 1921

AREAS OF INTEREST:
International affairs, international relations, policymaking, U.S. foreign policy, foreign affairs, public service, government, and academia.

NAME(S) OF PROGRAMS:
● **International Affairs Fellowship (IAF)**

TYPE:
Fellowships. The International Affairs Fellowship (IAF) Program aims to strengthen career development by helping outstanding individuals acquire and apply foreign policy skills beyond the scope of their professional and scholarly achievements. The distinctive character of the IAF Program lies in the contrasting professional experiences fellows obtain through their 12-month appointment. Selected fellows from academia and the private sector spend fellowship tenures in public service and policy-oriented settings, while government officials spend their tenures in a scholarly atmosphere free from operational pressure.

YEAR PROGRAM STARTED: 1967

PURPOSE:
To assist midcareer scholars and professionals in advancing their analytic capabilities and broadening their foreign policy experience.

ELIGIBILITY:
The IAF Program is only open to U.S. citizens and permanent residents between the ages of 27 and 35 who are eligible to work in the U.S. CFR does not sponsor for visas. While a Ph.D. is not a requirement, selected fellows generally hold an advanced degree and possess a strong record of work experience as well as a firm grounding in the field of foreign policy. The program does not fund pre- or postdoctoral research, work toward a degree, or the completion of projects for which substantial progress has been made prior to the Fellowship period.

FINANCIAL DATA:
Fellows are considered independent contractors rather than employees of CFR, and are not eligible for employment benefits, including health insurance.

Amount of support per award: Stipend of $85,000.

NUMBER OF AWARDS: Approximately 10 annually.

APPLICATION INFORMATION:
Interested candidates who meet the program's eligibility requirements can apply online via the Council web site between June 1 and October 1 on an annual basis. Candidates who are selected as IAF finalists will be notified between December and January, with finalist interviews scheduled in Washington, DC, and New York, NY, between January and February. Official selections and announcement of IAF awards will be made between February and March.

Duration: 12 months, preferably beginning in September. Though deferment is not an option, requests to do so, for up to one year only, will be considered on a case-by-case basis and under special circumstances.

Deadline: October 31.

ADDRESS INQUIRIES TO:
See telephone or e-mail address above.

COUNCIL ON FOREIGN RELATIONS [840]

58 East 68th Street
New York, NY 10065
(212) 434-9740
Fax: (212) 434-9870

E-MAIL ADDRESS:
fellowships@cfr.org

WEB SITE ADDRESS:
www.cfr.org/fellowships

FOUNDED: 1921

AREAS OF INTEREST:
International relations, international affairs, South Korea, U.S.-South Korea relations, South Korean-American relations, Korean studies, U.S.-South Korea politics, foreign policy, policymaking, and public service.

NAME(S) OF PROGRAMS:
● **International Affairs Fellowship in South Korea (IAF-SK)**

TYPE:
Fellowships. The International Affairs Fellowship in South Korea (IAF-SK), sponsored by the Asan Institute for Policy Studies, assists midcareer scholars and

professionals from the public and private sectors to advance their analytic capabilities and broaden their foreign policy experience in South Korea. The Council on Foreign Relations (CFR) awards several fellowships annually to highly accomplished individuals who have a capacity for independent work and who are eager to undertake serious foreign policy analysis while affiliated with the Asan Institute for Policy Studies in South Korea. Fellows are drawn from academia, business, government, media, NGOs and think tanks.

YEAR PROGRAM STARTED: 2010

PURPOSE:
To strengthen mutual understanding and cooperation between the rising generations of leaders in the U.S. and South Korea by expanding cultural exchange and enhancing communication between both countries on global issues.

ELIGIBILITY:
The IAF-SK is only open to U.S. citizens. Applicants do not have to be Korea specialists, and knowledge of the Korean language is not a requirement. While a Ph.D. is not a requirement, selected fellows generally hold an advanced degree and possess a strong record of work experience as well as a firm grounding in the field of foreign policy. The program does not fund pre- or postdoctoral research, work toward a degree, or the completion of projects for which substantial progress has been made prior to the fellowship period.

FINANCIAL DATA:
The program awards a stipend which covers living expenses in Seoul, South Korea, plus international travel and necessary research expenses. Fellows are considered independent contractors rather than employees of CFR, and are not eligible for employment benefits, including health insurance.

COOPERATIVE FUNDING PROGRAMS: The program is sponsored by the Asan Institute for Policy Studies.

NUMBER OF AWARDS: Approximately 2 to 3.

APPLICATION INFORMATION:
Interested candidates who meet the program's eligibility requirements must submit an application form, a CV, and a proposal (as specified on the CFR web site). Each applicant should arrange to have two letters of recommendation sent assessing the policy relevance of the applicant's proposed project as well as the applicant's qualifications for carrying it out.

All application materials must be submitted to the e-mail address above.

Duration: Four to 12 months.

Deadline: October 2013.

ADDRESS INQUIRIES TO:
See telephone or e-mail address above.

COUNCIL ON FOREIGN RELATIONS [841]

58 East 68th Street
New York, NY 10065
(212) 434-9740
Fax: (212) 434-9870

E-MAIL ADDRESS:
fellowships@cfr.org

WEB SITE ADDRESS:
www.cfr.org/fellowships

FOUNDED: 1921

AREAS OF INTEREST:
Nuclear security, nuclear weapons, nuclear proliferation, nuclear terrorism, nuclear energy, nuclear arms, nuclear force posture, international relations, international affairs, foreign affairs, government, and public policy.

NAME(S) OF PROGRAMS:
● **International Affairs Fellowship in Nuclear Security (IAF-NS)**

TYPE:
Fellowships. The International Affairs Fellowship in Nuclear Security (IAF-NS), sponsored by the Stanton Foundation, offers university-based scholars valuable hands-on experience in the nuclear security policymaking field and places selected fellows in U.S. government positions or international organizations for a period of 12 months to work with practitioners. The Fellowships will be awarded on the basis of academic and professional accomplishments, and on the merits of the specific research projects proposed.

YEAR PROGRAM STARTED: 2011

PURPOSE:
To close the gap between research and practice and to enrich the teaching and scholarship of academics, while also benefiting policymakers by exposing them to cutting-edge scholarly research.

ELIGIBILITY:
The IAF-NS is only open to faculty members with tenure or on tenure-track lines at accredited universities and who propose to conduct policy-relevant research on nuclear security issues. Qualified candidates must be U.S. citizens or permanent residents who are eligible to work in the U.S. and be between the ages of 29 and 40. CFR does not sponsor for visas.

Potential topics appropriate for the Fellowship include nuclear terrorism, nuclear proliferation, nuclear weapons, nuclear force posture, and the security implications of nuclear energy.

FINANCIAL DATA:
Fellows are considered independent contractors rather than employees of CFR, and are not eligible for employment benefits, including health insurance.
Amount of support per award: Stipend of $125,000.

COOPERATIVE FUNDING PROGRAMS: The Fellowship is sponsored by the Stanton Foundation.

NUMBER OF AWARDS: Approximately 2 fellowships annually.

APPLICATION INFORMATION:
Interested candidates who meet the program's eligibility requirements must submit a cover letter, a CV, and a proposal (maximum 1,000 words in length). Each applicant should arrange to have two letters of recommendation sent assessing the policy relevance of the applicant's proposed project as well as the applicant's qualifications for carrying it out.

All application materials must be submitted to the e-mail address above.
Duration: 12 months, preferably beginning in September.
Deadline: November 2013.

ADDRESS INQUIRIES TO:
See telephone or e-mail address above.

COUNCIL ON FOREIGN RELATIONS [842]
58 East 68th Street
New York, NY 10065
(212) 434-9740
Fax: (212) 434-9870

E-MAIL ADDRESS:
fellowships@cfr.org

WEB SITE ADDRESS:
www.cfr.org/fellowships

FOUNDED: 1921

AREAS OF INTEREST:
Nuclear security, nuclear weapons, nuclear proliferation, nuclear terrorism, nuclear energy, nuclear force posture, nuclear arms, international relations, international affairs, foreign affairs, government, and public policy.

NAME(S) OF PROGRAMS:
● **Stanton Nuclear Security Fellowship Program (SNSF)**

TYPE:
Fellowships. The Stanton Nuclear Security Fellowship (SNSF) Program, made possible by a grant from the Stanton Foundation, offers younger scholars studying nuclear security issues the opportunity to spend a period of 12 months at the Council on Foreign Relations' (CFR) offices in New York or Washington, DC, conducting policy-relevant research. The Fellowships will be awarded on the basis of academic and professional accomplishments and promise, and on the merits of the specific research projects proposed.

YEAR PROGRAM STARTED: 2009

PURPOSE:
To stimulate the development of the next generation of thought leaders in nuclear security. The fellows could work on a wide range of issues, including nuclear terrorism, nuclear proliferation, nuclear weapons, nuclear force posture, and nuclear energy.

ELIGIBILITY:
Qualified candidates must be junior (non-tenured) faculty, postdoctoral fellows, or predoctoral candidates from any discipline who are working on a nuclear security-related issue. The program is only open to U.S. citizens and permanent residents who are eligible to work in the U.S. CFR does not sponsor for visas.

FINANCIAL DATA:
Payment will be made in 12 equal monthly installments. Fellows are considered independent contractors rather than employees of CFR, and are not eligible for employment benefits, including health insurance.
Amount of support per award: A stipend of $100,000 for junior (non-tenured) faculty, $75,000 for postdoctoral, and $50,000 for predoctoral fellows.

COOPERATIVE FUNDING PROGRAMS: The SNSF Program is made possible by a generous grant from the Stanton Foundation.

NUMBER OF AWARDS: Up to 3 Fellowships annually.

APPLICATION INFORMATION:
Interested candidates who meet the program's eligibility requirements must submit an application form, a cover letter, a CV, and a proposal outlining the work proposed to conduct (as specified on the CFR web site). Each applicant should arrange to have two letters of recommendation sent assessing the policy relevance of the applicant's proposed project as well as the applicant's qualifications for carrying it out.

All application materials must be sent to the e-mail address above.
Duration: 12 months, preferably beginning in September.

ADDRESS INQUIRIES TO:
See telephone or e-mail address above.

CULTURAL VISTAS [843]
440 Park Avenue South, 2nd Floor
New York, NY 10016
(212) 497-3510
Fax: (212) 497-3587

E-MAIL ADDRESS:
alfa@culturalvistas.org

WEB SITE ADDRESS:
www.culturalvistas.org/alfa

FOUNDED: 2004

AREAS OF INTEREST:
Culture, business, law, politics, public policy, government, journalism, mass communications, finance and economics.

NAME(S) OF PROGRAMS:
● **Alfa Fellowship Program**

TYPE:
Exchange programs; Fellowships; Internships. A high-level professional development exchange program placing qualified American and British citizens in work assignments at leading organizations in Russia in the fields of business, economics, journalism, law and public policy. The program includes language training, seminar programs, and extended professional work experience. Fellows receive a stipend, travel, housing and insurance.

YEAR PROGRAM STARTED: 2004

PURPOSE:
To foster a new generation of future American and British leaders with in-depth practical experience in the modern business and public policy environment of the Russian Federation.

ELIGIBILITY:
Open to U.S. and U.K. citizens with a graduate degree, work experience and professional interest or background in above fields. Russian language proficiency preferred, but not required.

Applicants must:
(1) have U.S. or U.K. citizenship;
(2) be 25 to 35 years of age at time of application;
(3) have a graduate degree or equivalent training in business, economics, journalism, law or public policy and;
(4) have at least two years relevant work experience in their field of expertise.

Russian proficiency is preferred but not required at the time of application.

GEOGRAPHIC RESTRICTIONS:
United States, United Kingdom and Russia.

FINANCIAL DATA:
Monthly stipend, free accommodations in Russia, all in-country program-related travel, round-trip flight to Moscow, and limited international health, accident and liability insurance during the program in Russia.

Amount of support per award: Varies.

Total amount of support: Varies.

NUMBER OF APPLICANTS MOST RECENT YEAR:
Approximately 180.

NUMBER OF AWARDS: 15.

APPLICATION INFORMATION:
Candidates must submit application online with all supporting materials by the deadline.

Duration: 11 months, June to April.

Deadline: December 1, 2014 for 2015-16 program year.

ADDRESS INQUIRIES TO:
Melissa Graves, Program Director
(See address above.)

J.W. DAFOE FOUNDATION   [844]
Department of Political Studies
University of Manitoba
University College, Room 351
Winnipeg MB R3T 2M8 Canada
(204) 474-6606
Fax: (204) 474-7645

E-MAIL ADDRESS:
james.fergusson@ad.umanitoba.ca

WEB SITE ADDRESS:
www.dafoefoundation.ca

AREAS OF INTEREST:
International relations, economics, history and political science.

TYPE:
Awards/prizes; Conferences/seminars; Fellowships; Project/program grants; Research grants. Fellowships for graduate study in international relations, economics, history or political studies.

PURPOSE:
To support graduate study in international relations, economics, history and political science.

LEGAL BASIS:
University association.

ELIGIBILITY:
Master's students enrolled at the University of Manitoba in the Departments of Economics, History, Political Studies, Faculty of Law or Conflict Resolution.

GEOGRAPHIC RESTRICTIONS:
Canada.

FINANCIAL DATA:
Amount of support per award: $10,000 (CAN).

Total amount of support: $10,000 (CAN); can be held in conjunction with other awards.

NUMBER OF AWARDS: 1 per year.

APPLICATION INFORMATION:
Application information is available from the Awards Officer, Faculty of Graduate Studies, at the University of Manitoba.

Duration: Fellowships are for one year and are nonrenewable.

Deadline: February 28 for applications for tenure beginning with the fall term. The Award is announced following the Annual General Meeting of the Board in May.

TRUSTEES:
Keith Findlay, Chairperson

*SPECIAL STIPULATIONS:
A submission fee of $50 per entry is required for the J.W. Dafoe Book Prize.

THE EAST-WEST CENTER   [845]
1601 East West Road
Honolulu, HI 96848-1601
(808) 944-7735
Fax: (808) 944-7730 (Award Service Center)

E-MAIL ADDRESS:
scholarships@eastwestcenter.org

WEB SITE ADDRESS:
www.eastwestcenter.org/studentprograms

FOUNDED: 1960

AREAS OF INTEREST:
Economics; environmental change, vulnerability and governance; population and health; politics, governance and security, at a local, national and/or regional level in the Asia Pacific region.

NAME(S) OF PROGRAMS:
● **East-West Center Graduate Degree Fellowship**

TYPE:
Fellowships.

YEAR PROGRAM STARTED: 1960

PURPOSE:
To strengthen relations and understanding among the peoples and nations of Asia, the Pacific and the U.S.; to serve as a vigorous hub for cooperative research, education and dialogue on critical issues of common concern to the Asia Pacific region and the U.S.

LEGAL BASIS:
Public, nonprofit educational corporation established in Hawaii in 1960 by the U.S. Congress.

ELIGIBILITY:
Candidates must have obtained a four-year Bachelor's degree or its equivalent, must be a citizen or permanent resident of the U.S. or a country in Asia or the Pacific, and must come to the Center on the exchange visitor (J-1) visa.

Priority in the student selection process is given to applicants seeking degrees in fields of study related to research themes at the East-West Center.

GEOGRAPHIC RESTRICTIONS:
Hawaii.

FINANCIAL DATA:
Award may include housing, stipend, tuition, health insurance, when relevant, and book allowance as approved. Costs may be shared by collaborating institutions.

Amount of support per award: Varies.

Total amount of support: Varies.

Matching fund requirements: Cost-sharing on any Center award is actively sought.

COOPERATIVE FUNDING PROGRAMS: Funding for the Center comes from the U.S. government, with additional support provided by private agencies, individuals, foundations, corporations, and the governments of the region.

NUMBER OF APPLICANTS MOST RECENT YEAR:
Over 300.

NUMBER OF AWARDS: Varies based on funding.

APPLICATION INFORMATION:
Applications are available online.

Duration: Initially 12 months with possible renewal up to two years for Master's Degree or doctoral studies, contingent upon funding, performance and academic progress.

Deadline: November 1 for forwarding to the Award Services Office.

ADDRESS INQUIRIES TO:
Award Services Office
(See address above.)

*SPECIAL STIPULATIONS:
Study must be at the University of Hawaii at Manoa.

THE EAST-WEST CENTER   [846]
1601 East West Road
Honolulu, HI 96848-1601
(808) 944-7744
Fax: (808) 944-7070 (Attn: APLP)

E-MAIL ADDRESS:
aplp@eastwestcenter.org

WEB SITE ADDRESS:
www.eastwestcenter.org/aplp

FOUNDED: 1960

AREAS OF INTEREST:
Issues related to the Asia Pacific region.

NAME(S) OF PROGRAMS:
● **Asia Pacific Leadership Program Fellowship**

TYPE:
Fellowships.

YEAR PROGRAM STARTED: 2001

PURPOSE:
To create a network of action focused on building a peaceful, prosperous and just Asia Pacific community.

LEGAL BASIS:
Public, nonprofit educational corporation.

ELIGIBILITY:
Candidates must have a four-year Bachelor's degree or its equivalent from an accredited U.S. college or university or from a recognized institution of higher learning abroad.

Priority in the student selection process is given to candidates with professional work experience:
(1) international experience and aptitude, including overseas residence, language skills, intercultural and diversity exposure;
(2) leadership track record in professional, public and/or personal realms;
(3) volunteer and community service experience;
(4) Asia Pacific engagement and evidence of interest in the region, as well as commitment to its future prosperity; this might include classes taken at university, time spent in the region, languages spoken, membership and fellowships, specific projects, field studies and areas of research interest and;
(5) experience working collaboratively in small teams or in large groups.

GEOGRAPHIC RESTRICTIONS:
Hawaii.

FINANCIAL DATA:
Award may include program fees, living expenses, field study costs, and other academic expenses.

Amount of support per award: Varies.

Total amount of support: Varies.

NUMBER OF AWARDS: 39.

APPLICATION INFORMATION:
Application form is available online.

Duration: Mid-August to mid-May.

Deadline: Priority Deadline: December 1.
Final Deadline: March 1.

PUBLICATIONS:
Annual report.

ADDRESS INQUIRIES TO:
Award Services Office
(See address above.)

THE EISENHOWER
INSTITUTE   [847]
818 Connecticut Avenue, N.W.
Suite 800
Washington, DC 20006
(202) 628-4444
Fax: (202) 628-4445

E-MAIL ADDRESS:
ei@eisenhowerinstitute.org

WEB SITE ADDRESS:
www.eisenhowerinstitute.org

FOUNDED: 1983

AREAS OF INTEREST:
World affairs.

NAME(S) OF PROGRAMS:
● **Eisenhower Institute Scholarship
   Programs**

TYPE:
Conferences/seminars; Endowments;
Fellowships; Internships; Scholarships.

PURPOSE:
To promote sound and forward-looking
policies that lay the intellectual and civic
groundwork for the next generation of
opinion-leaders, policy-shapers and public
servants.

ELIGIBILITY:
Open to American high school,
undergraduate, and graduate students.

FINANCIAL DATA:
Amount of support per award: Scholarships
and fellowships: $4,000 to $10,000.

APPLICATION INFORMATION:
Application procedures are available online.

IRS IDENTIFICATION NUMBER: 52-1306218

ADDRESS INQUIRIES TO:
Rick Farwell, Program Coordinator
(See address above.)

GRADUATE INSTITUTE OF
INTERNATIONAL AND
DEVELOPMENT STUDIES   [848]
Rue de Lausanne 132
P.O. Box 136
CH - 1211 Geneva 21 Switzerland
41 22 908 57 00
Fax: 41 22 908 57 10

E-MAIL ADDRESS:
prospective@graduateinstitute.ch

WEB SITE ADDRESS:
graduateinstitute.ch

FOUNDED: 1927

AREAS OF INTEREST:
Development, anthropology and sociology of
development, and international relations.

NAME(S) OF PROGRAMS:
● **Financial Aid for Study at The
   Graduate Institute of International and
   Development Studies**

TYPE:
Assistantships; Awards/prizes; Exchange
programs; Fellowships; Residencies;
Scholarships; Visiting scholars. Financial aid
in advanced study in international relations

including intensive research and study
towards the Master's degree and the Ph.D.
Tenable at the Institute.

PURPOSE:
To support the scientific study of
contemporary international relations and
development studies and the pursuit of
advanced studies based on personal work and
research.

LEGAL BASIS:
Foundation.

ELIGIBILITY:
Each year, financial assistance is awarded by
the Institute in the form of scholarships
covering the minimum needs of students.
They are allocated on the basis of applicants'
academic performance and financial needs.

Scholarships also awarded for young
lecturers from the global south.

FINANCIAL DATA:
Scholars are exempted from Institute fees,
but not from the obligatory fees of the
University of Geneva which confers the
Doctorate.
Amount of support per award: Full
scholarship: CHF 18,000 per academic year.

NUMBER OF AWARDS: 250 scholarships annually.

APPLICATION INFORMATION:
Applications are available upon request.
Duration: One year. Renewable.
Deadline: January 15.

PUBLICATIONS:
Annual report.

ADDRESS INQUIRIES TO:
E-mail: prospective@graduateinstitute.ch

INSTITUTE OF CURRENT
WORLD AFFAIRS   [849]
1779 Massachusetts Avenue, N.W.
Suite 615
Washington, DC 20036
(202) 364-4068

E-MAIL ADDRESS:
icwa@icwa.org

WEB SITE ADDRESS:
www.icwa.org

FOUNDED: 1925

AREAS OF INTEREST:
Current world affairs.

TYPE:
Fellowships. Fellowships are not
scholarships, and are not awarded to support
work toward academic degrees or for
collaborative research projects, or to write
books.

PURPOSE:
To provide talented and promising individuals
with an opportunity to develop a deep
understanding of an issue, country or region
outside the U.S. and to share that
understanding with a wider public.

ELIGIBILITY:
Fellowships are for self-designed independent
study only. Applicants must have a good
command of written and spoken English and
be women and men under 36 years of age
who demonstrate initiative, integrity,
outstanding character, good communications
skills, seriousness of purpose and enthusiasm
for their chosen fields.

FINANCIAL DATA:
Amount of support per award: Varies.

Total amount of support: Varies.

NUMBER OF AWARDS: 2.

APPLICATION INFORMATION:
Applicants should write an initial letter of
interest to the Executive Director explaining
the personal background and professional
experience that would qualify them for the
fellowship they have in mind. They should
describe the activities they would like to
carry out during two years overseas and
enclose a resume or curriculum vitae. Select
candidates will be invited to submit a more
detailed application.

Initial letter should be by e-mail, although
regular mail will be accepted. Further
information may be obtained from the
Institute's web site.
Duration: Minimum period of two years.
Deadline: March 1 and September 1.

ADDRESS INQUIRIES TO:
Ellen Kozak, Program Manager
(See address above.)

THE INTERNATIONAL
FOUNDATION   [850]
1700 Route 23 North
Suite 300
Wayne, NJ 07470
(973) 406-3970
Fax: (973) 406-3969

E-MAIL ADDRESS:
info@intlfoundation.org

WEB SITE ADDRESS:
intlfoundation.org

FOUNDED: 1948

AREAS OF INTEREST:
Agriculture, health, education, social
development, the environment and
community development.

TYPE:
Development grants; Project/program grants;
Seed money grants; Technical assistance;
Training grants.

YEAR PROGRAM STARTED: 1948

PURPOSE:
To help people of the developing world in
their endeavors to solve some of their
problems, to attain a better standard of living,
and to obtain a reasonable degree of
self-sufficiency.

LEGAL BASIS:
Private foundation.

ELIGIBILITY:
The Foundation funds only projects of
U.S.-based, IRS-certified philanthropies.

GEOGRAPHIC RESTRICTIONS:
United States.

FINANCIAL DATA:
Amount of support per award:
Approximately $5,000 to $15,000.

NUMBER OF AWARDS: Approximately 100.

APPLICATION INFORMATION:
Applications are to be submitted on the
Foundation's web site. Proposals must
include a statement from IRS of not-for-profit
status, a brief overview of the proposal,
amount of funds requested from The
Foundation, a brief background of
organization applying, a statement of the
problem addressed by project, objectives of
the project, plan of operation/method of

achieving objectives, beneficiaries of the project, methods of project evaluation and report, project budget, sources of other funding applied for or received and date.

All appropriate communications will be answered.

Duration: One year. Must reapply.

Deadline: Grant applications are reviewed twice monthly by the Grants Committee.

PUBLICATIONS:
Brochure, includes application guidelines.

IRS IDENTIFICATION NUMBER: 13-1962255

OFFICERS:
Frank H. Madden, President
John D. Carrico, Secretary and Treasurer
William M. McCormack, M.D., Grants Chairman

BOARD OF TRUSTEES:
John D. Carrico
Gary Dicovitsky
Edward A. Holmes, Ph.D.
Frank H. Madden
William M. McCormack, M.D.
Douglas P. Walker

IRISH AMERICAN CULTURAL INSTITUTE [851]
P.O. Box 1716
Morristown, NJ 07962
(973) 605-1991
Fax: (973) 605-8875

E-MAIL ADDRESS:
info@iaci-usa.org

WEB SITE ADDRESS:
www.iaci-usa.org

FOUNDED: 1962

AREAS OF INTEREST:
Ireland and Irish affairs.

NAME(S) OF PROGRAMS:
● IACI/NUI-G

TYPE:
Fellowships; Research grants; Research contracts.

YEAR PROGRAM STARTED: 1992

PURPOSE:
To stimulate, develop and disseminate information pertinent to the Irish culture.

LEGAL BASIS:
Public foundation under IRS Code 501(c)(3).

ELIGIBILITY:
Projects from all disciplines, regardless of historic period or geographic focus, can be considered for these grants. All projects must deal with significant research matters, relate to any aspect of Irish studies and be directed by competent scholars.

The Fellowship is tenable at NUI-G to scholars normally residents in the U.S. who wish to spend a semester (not less than four months) at NUI-G, and whose work relates to any aspect of Irish studies.

FINANCIAL DATA:
Amount of support per award: Fellowship stipend $4,000; Research fund support varies depending on the project.

NUMBER OF APPLICANTS MOST RECENT YEAR:
Varies.

NUMBER OF AWARDS: Fellowship: 1.

APPLICATION INFORMATION:
Application requirements and guidelines are available online.

Duration: Varies.
Deadline: February 28.

OFFICERS:
Peter Halas, Chairman
Brian Stack, Vice Chairman
Michael Farrell, Treasurer
Edward F. Ginty, Secretary

THE JAPAN FOUNDATION [852]
152 West 57th Street
17th Floor
New York, NY 10019
(212) 489-0299
Fax: (212) 489-0409

E-MAIL ADDRESS:
info@jfny.org

WEB SITE ADDRESS:
www.jfny.org

FOUNDED: 1972

AREAS OF INTEREST:
Cultural exchange and Japanese studies.

NAME(S) OF PROGRAMS:
● **Doctoral Fellowship**
● **Institutional Project Support Program for Japanese Studies**
● **JFNY Grant for Japanese Studies**
● **JFNY Grant Program - Arts and Culture**
● **Performing Arts Japan Program**
● **Research Fellowship**
● **Short-Term Research Fellowship**
● **Support Program for Translation and Publication on Japan**

TYPE:
Conferences/seminars; Development grants; Fellowships; Grants-in-aid; Product donations; Professorships; Project/program grants; Research grants; Training grants; Travel grants.

YEAR PROGRAM STARTED: 1973

PURPOSE:
To conduct international cultural exchange; to assist Japanese studies programs in the U.S.

LEGAL BASIS:
Independent administrative institution.

FINANCIAL DATA:
For Fellowships, the Foundation will provide a round-trip, economy class airfare to and from Japan. The stipend is determined in accordance with the grantee's professional status. A dependent allowance will be provided in some cases to Fellows whose dependents (spouse and children) reside in Japan continuously for more than six months.
Amount of support per award: Varies according to program.

APPLICATION INFORMATION:
Program announcements and application forms are available at the web site. Applications from the western states of Alaska, Arizona, California, Colorado, Hawaii, Idaho, Montana, Nevada, New Mexico, Oregon, Utah, Washington and Wyoming should be sent to the Japan Foundation, Los Angeles Office, 333 South Grand Avenue, Suite 2250, Los Angeles, CA 90071, Tel: (213) 621-2267, Fax: (213) 621-2590. Applications from all other states should be sent directly to the Japan Foundation New York Office at the address above.
Duration: Varies.
Deadline: Varies.

PUBLICATIONS:
Annual report.

IRS IDENTIFICATION NUMBER: 13-2974222

STAFF:
Junichi Chano, Director General
Yoshihiro Wada, Deputy Director General
Yukihiro Ohira, Program Director, Arts and Culture
Noriko Yamamoto, Program Director, Japanese Studies
Kanako Shirasaki, Program Associate, Arts and Culture
Tomomi Tanikawa, Program Associate, Japanese Studies

ADDRESS INQUIRIES TO:
See e-mail address above.

JAPAN-U.S. FRIENDSHIP COMMISSION [853]
1201 15th Street, N.W.
Suite 330
Washington, DC 20005
(202) 653-9800
Fax: (202) 653-9802

E-MAIL ADDRESS:
jusfc@jusfc.gov

WEB SITE ADDRESS:
www.jusfc.gov

FOUNDED: 1976

AREAS OF INTEREST:
Cultural and educational activities between Japan and the U.S., including language and area studies, economic relations, media and public education.

TYPE:
Project/program grants. Programs of institutional support. Grants for projects of research, training and exchange with Japan.

YEAR PROGRAM STARTED: 1977

PURPOSE:
To enhance reciprocal people-to-people understanding and friendship between the U.S. and Japan.

LEGAL BASIS:
Independent agency of the U.S. government.

ELIGIBILITY:
Grants are offered to cultural and educational institutions in the U.S. and Japan.

GEOGRAPHIC RESTRICTIONS:
United States and Japan.

FINANCIAL DATA:
U.S. government trust fund of $43,000,000.
Amount of support per award: Varies.
Total amount of support: Varies.

COOPERATIVE FUNDING PROGRAMS: NEA.

NUMBER OF APPLICANTS MOST RECENT YEAR:
Approximately 100.

NUMBER OF AWARDS: Approximately 30 annually.

APPLICATION INFORMATION:
Application forms are available upon request.
Duration: One year.
Deadline: August 1. Notification in October.

PUBLICATIONS:
Biennial report; program information/guidelines; application form.

OFFICERS:
Harry Hill, Chairman
Dr. Sheila Smith, Vice Chairman
Hon. Brenda Dann-Messier

Dr. Edward Lincoln
Dr. Patricia Maclachlan
Dr. Deanna Marcum
Rep. James McDermott
Dr. Anne Nishimura Morse
Hon. Lisa Murkowski
Dr. T.J. Pempel
Rep. Thomas Petri
Sen. John D. Rockefeller, IV
Daniel Russel
Hon. Evan Ryan
Dr. Leonard J. Schoppa, Jr.
Joan Shigekawa
Dr. David Sneider
Carol M. Watson

ADDRESS INQUIRIES TO:
Paige Cottingham-Streater, Executive
Director
(See address above.)

*SPECIAL STIPULATIONS:
Institution grants only.

A.J. MUSTE MEMORIAL INSTITUTE

339 Lafayette Street
New York, NY 10012
(212) 533-4335

E-MAIL ADDRESS:
info@ajmuste.org

WEB SITE ADDRESS:
www.ajmuste.org

TYPE:
Grants-in-aid. The Institute's regular grant
fund annually funds international, national
and local projects in the U.S. and around the
world. It gives priority to those with small
budgets and little chance of funding from
more traditional sources. The Institute does
not provide academic scholarships.

See entry 1497 for full listing.

THE NATIONAL COUNCIL FOR EURASIAN AND EAST EUROPEAN RESEARCH   [854]

910 17th Street, N.W.
Suite 300
Washington, DC 20006
(202) 296-1677
Fax: (866) 937-9872

E-MAIL ADDRESS:
info@nceeer.org

WEB SITE ADDRESS:
www.nceeer.org

FOUNDED: 1978

AREAS OF INTEREST:
The program is limited to research designed
to contribute to knowledge of current
developments and analysis of their
significance in Eastern Europe and the
successor states of the former Soviet Union.

TYPE:
Research grants; Research contracts.
Institutional grants and research contracts and
policy research scholarships and related
activities, such as meetings and conferences,
research-specific training, contact among
scholars and specialists in government and
private enterprise, development of databanks
and other reference aids and dissemination of
research data, methodology and findings,
both in scholarly forms and through public
media.

YEAR PROGRAM STARTED: 1978

PURPOSE:
To encourage and sustain high-quality
research on Eastern Europe, the former
Soviet Union and its successor states, in the
social sciences (including geography,
demography and environmental studies) and
history.

LEGAL BASIS:
Incorporated, nonprofit, autonomous
academic body.

ELIGIBILITY:
Limited to scholars at the postdoctoral level
for academic participants and to an
equivalent degree of maturity and
professional employment for those from other
fields. Applicant must be a U.S. citizen.
Applications must be submitted to the
Council by U.S. nonprofit institutions in the
form of grant or contract proposals.

GEOGRAPHIC RESTRICTIONS:
United States.

FINANCIAL DATA:
Amount of support per award: Varies;
normally not more than $70,000 for any
individual project.
Matching fund requirements: Cost sharing at
a minimum of 20% from non-federal funds is
mandatory.

COOPERATIVE FUNDING PROGRAMS: NEH
Collaborative Research Fellowship; Carnegie
Research Fellowship Program.

APPLICATION INFORMATION:
Application guidelines, compliance with
which is required, should be obtained from
the Council, at the address above. Required
documentation includes:
(1) identification form;
(2) one-page summary;
(3) detailed description of project;
(4) curriculum vitae and bibliographies for
principal personnel;
(5) description of proposed written or other
products and dissemination methods;
(6) budget and;
(7) letters of recommendation.
Duration: Varies.
Deadline: Spring of each year.

PUBLICATIONS:
Guidelines.

STAFF:
Dana Ponte, Senior Program Officer

BOARD OF DIRECTORS:
Maria Carlson, Chairperson
Bruce Grant, Vice Chairperson
Valerie Bunce
Ted Gerber
Nancy Kollmann
Martha Lampland
Susan Linz
Mieke Meurs
Douglas Northrup
Joanna Regulska
James Richter
Edward Schatz
Elizabeth Wood

ADDRESS INQUIRIES TO:
President
(See address above.)

NUCLEAR AGE PEACE FOUNDATION   [855]

PMB 121
1187 Coast Village Road, Suite 1
Santa Barbara, CA 93108
(805) 965-3443
Fax: (805) 568-0466

E-MAIL ADDRESS:
wagingpeace@napf.org

WEB SITE ADDRESS:
www.wagingpeace.org

FOUNDED: 1982

AREAS OF INTEREST:
Achieving a nuclear weapon-free world,
international law, international relations,
liberty, justice, human dignity, human rights,
nonviolence, responsible use of technology,
peace education, and youth empowerment.

NAME(S) OF PROGRAMS:
● **Barbara Mandigo Kelly Peace Poetry
Awards**

TYPE:
Awards/prizes; Internships. An annual series
of awards to encourage poets to explore and
illuminate positive visions of peace and the
human spirit.

PURPOSE:
To play an important role in making the 21st
century a time of peace and justice, and a
time in which the rights of all individuals to
peace, security and a healthy environment
will be realized.

FINANCIAL DATA:
Amount of support per award: Adults:
$1,000; Youth (13-18): $200; Youth (12 and
under): $200.
Total amount of support: $1,400.

APPLICATION INFORMATION:
Application information is available on the
web site.
Deadline: Postmarked by July 1.

ADDRESS INQUIRIES TO:
Carol Warner, Awards Coordinator
(See address above.)

ORGANIZATION OF AMERICAN STATES   [856]

1889 F Street, N.W.
Seventh Floor
Washington, DC 20006
(202) 370-9771
Fax: (202) 458-3897

E-MAIL ADDRESS:
scholarships@oas.org

WEB SITE ADDRESS:
www.oas.org/scholarships

FOUNDED: 1890

AREAS OF INTEREST:
To promote the economic, social, scientific
and cultural development of the Member
States in order to achieve a stronger bond
and better understanding among the peoples
of the Americas through the advanced
training of its citizens in the priority areas
requested by the countries.

NAME(S) OF PROGRAMS:
● **Academic Studies**
● **Professional Development**

TYPE:
Fellowships; Scholarships; Technical
assistance. Awarded for graduate academic
studies and/or research, and last two years of
undergraduate studies for students in the
English-speaking Caribbean, for training in
areas contributing to the economic, social,
technical and cultural development of OAS
member countries.

YEAR PROGRAM STARTED: 1958

PURPOSE:
Program of Scholarships and Training: to assist the member states with their domestic efforts in pursuit of integral development goals by supporting human resource development in the priority areas established by the member countries.

ELIGIBILITY:
Candidates must be citizens or permanent residents of an OAS member country, with a university degree in the case of academic studies, or who have demonstrated ability to pursue advanced training in the field chosen for professional development courses. Scholarships are for graduate or undergraduate studies, research, or professional training in any field, with the exception of the medical sciences and related areas and introductory language studies. Candidates must know the language of the study country. Studies must be undertaken at an institution in a member country of the OAS, with the exception of the country of which the candidate is a citizen or permanent resident.

Graduate scholarships are offered for study towards a Master's or Doctorate degree. They may also be used for research, if required by a specific academic program. Scholarships are awarded for an initial period of one academic year and may be extended subsequently for up to one additional year. Under the Self-Placed in an OAS Non-Consortium University, candidates apply directly for admission to the universities or educational institutions of their choice, and present their application for an OAS scholarship. Only one candidate per country will be awarded with this type of scholarship. In the Self-Placed in an OAS Consortium University, candidates apply directly to up to three programs in different universities, part of the OAS Consortium University, located in three different countries. Applying to this type of scholarship increases the applicant's chances of being offered an OAS scholarship. Undergraduate scholarships are available only to citizens of the English-speaking Caribbean member countries for the last two years of study for an undergraduate degree.

No fellowships will be awarded retroactively, and no benefits will be provided to the family of the fellowship holder.

FINANCIAL DATA:
Fellowship may include, depending upon the circumstances of each fellow, a round-trip ticket, tuition fees, study materials, health insurance, and partial subsistence allowance (which varies from country to country).
Amount of support per award: Not to exceed U.S. $30,000.
Matching fund requirements: Students are responsible for covering a portion of their subsistence costs.

APPLICATION INFORMATION:
Application materials are available at the web site. Except for applicants in the U.S., applications must be presented to the National Liaison Offices (ONEs) of the applicant's country of origin or permanent residence. The ONE is the official channel identified by each government for submission of applications for OAS scholarships. U.S. citizens can send applications directly to the Organization's mailing address.
Duration: Fellowships are tenable for not less than one year nor more than two years.

Deadline: Deadline for presentation of applications to the National Liaison Office (ONE) differs from country to country and should therefore be confirmed with the National Liaison Office (ONE) in the applicant's country of origin or permanent residence.

OFFICERS:
Marie Levens, Director

ADDRESS INQUIRIES TO:
Department of Human Development, Education and Employment
(See address above.)

*SPECIAL STIPULATIONS:
For countries other than the U.S., the fellowship form must be presented to the General Secretariat of the OAS in Washington, DC, through the official channels established by each government.

HERBERT SCOVILLE, JR., PEACE FELLOWSHIP [857]

322 Fourth Street, N.E.
Washington, DC 20002
(202) 446-1565

E-MAIL ADDRESS:
info@scoville.org

WEB SITE ADDRESS:
www.scoville.org

FOUNDED: 1987

AREAS OF INTEREST:
Arms control research and/or advocacy for disarmament, international security, nuclear and conventional arms control and peace organizations.

NAME(S) OF PROGRAMS:
● **Herbert Scoville Jr. Peace Fellowship Program**

TYPE:
Fellowships.

YEAR PROGRAM STARTED: 1987

PURPOSE:
To provide an opportunity for college graduates to gain practical knowledge and experience by contributing to the efforts of nonprofit, public-interest organizations working on peace and security issues.

LEGAL BASIS:
Nonprofit program.

ELIGIBILITY:
Prospective Fellows are expected to demonstrate excellent academic accomplishments and a strong interest in issues of peace and security. Graduate study, a college major, course work, or substantial independent reading that reflects the substantive focus of the Fellowship is also a plus. Prior experience with public-interest activism or advocacy is highly desirable. It is preferred, but not required, that such activities be focused on peace and security issues.

Candidates are required to have completed a Baccalaureate degree by the time the Fellowship commences. Preference is given to U.S. citizens, although a Fellowship to a foreign national residing in the U.S. is awarded periodically based on availability of funding. The Scoville Fellowship is not intended for students or scholars interested in pursuing independent research in Washington, DC.

Preference will be given to individuals who have not had substantial prior public-interest or government experience in the Washington, DC area.

FINANCIAL DATA:
Amount of support per award: $2,700 per month, plus $1,000 in travel expenses to the Washington, DC area and health insurance.
Total amount of support: Varies.

NUMBER OF APPLICANTS MOST RECENT YEAR:
300 to 350.

NUMBER OF AWARDS: 6 to 8 per year.

APPLICATION INFORMATION:
Information is available on the web site. All application materials must be submitted by e-mail to apply@scoville.org.
Duration: Six to nine months.
Deadline: Spring Fellowship: October 1; Fall Fellowship: January 13.

PUBLICATIONS:
Application guidelines; organization description.

ADDRESS INQUIRIES TO:
Paul Revsine, Program Director
(See address above.)

SOCIAL SCIENCE RESEARCH COUNCIL [858]

One Pierrepont Plaza
15th Floor
Brooklyn, NY 11201
(212) 377-2700 ext. 3640
Fax: (212) 377-2727

E-MAIL ADDRESS:
japan@ssrc.org

WEB SITE ADDRESS:
www.ssrc.org/fellowships/jsps-fellowship

FOUNDED: 1923

AREAS OF INTEREST:
Social sciences and humanities.

NAME(S) OF PROGRAMS:
● **SSRC/JSPS Long-Term Fellowship**
● **SSRC/JSPS Short-Term Fellowship**

TYPE:
Fellowships; Research grants. The Japan Society for the Promotion of Science (JSPS) Postdoctoral Fellowship for Foreign Researchers provides promising and highly qualified recent Ph.Ds. and ABDs with funding to conduct research in Japan. JSPS guidelines target the applicant who wishes to conduct cooperative research under the leadership of a host researcher, thereby advancing the Fellow's own research and at the same time stimulating Japanese academic circles through close collaboration with young Japanese researchers.

YEAR PROGRAM STARTED: 1967

PURPOSE:
To stimulate Japanese academic circles through close collaboration with young foreign researchers.

LEGAL BASIS:
Not-for-profit organization.

ELIGIBILITY:
Applicants must be U.S. citizens or permanent residents at the time of application and not be of Japanese descent. Citizens of other countries are eligible for short-term fellowships if they have completed a Master's or Ph.D. course at an institution of higher education in the U.S. and, upon completing the course, have for at least three continuous

years conducted high-level research at a university in the U.S. Japanese nationals are not eligible for a fellowship regardless of current residency status. Applicants currently in Japan are not eligible for short-term fellowships.

Applicants for long-term fellowships must submit a copy of a Ph.D. diploma from a university outside Japan dated no more than six years prior to April 1, 2015.

Applicants for short-term fellowships must submit a copy of a Ph.D. diploma from a university outside Japan dated no more than six years prior to April 1, 2015 or a letter from their institution stating that the applicant is a Ph.D. candidate within two years of receiving a Ph.D.

Scholars who have previously received funding from JSPS for the Short-Term Fellowship are eligible to apply for the JSPS Long-Term Fellowship.

FINANCIAL DATA:
Grants are to be used for maintenance, travel and research expenses.
Amount of support per award: Varies based on length of research term and doctoral status.
Total amount of support: Varies.

NUMBER OF APPLICANTS MOST RECENT YEAR: Long-Term and Short-Term Fellowships: 45.

NUMBER OF AWARDS: Long-Term and Short-Term Fellowships: Up to 20 (10 in each category).

APPLICATION INFORMATION:
Application information is available on the web site.
Duration: Long-Term Fellowships: 12 to 24 months; Short-Term Fellowships: One to 12 months.
Deadline: December 1.

PUBLICATIONS:
Annual report; *Items*, newsletter; *Fellowships and Grants for Training and Research*, brochure.

STAFF:
Nicole Restrick, Japan Program Coordinator
Fernando Rojas, Fellowships Coordinator

ADDRESS INQUIRIES TO:
Fernando Rojas, Fellowships Coordinator
Japan Program
Social Science Research Council
(See address above.)

SOCIAL SCIENCE RESEARCH COUNCIL   [859]
One Pierrepont Plaza
15th Floor
Brooklyn, NY 11201
(212) 377-2700
Fax: (212) 377-2727

E-MAIL ADDRESS:
idrf@ssrc.org

WEB SITE ADDRESS:
www.ssrc.org/programs/idrf

FOUNDED: 1923

AREAS OF INTEREST:
Fellowships in the humanities and humanistic social sciences.

NAME(S) OF PROGRAMS:
● **International Dissertation Research Fellowship Program (IDRF)**

TYPE:
Fellowships. Support to graduate students in the humanities and humanistic social sciences who are enrolled in doctoral programs in the U.S. and conducting dissertation research outside of the U.S.

YEAR PROGRAM STARTED: 1997

PURPOSE:
To support the advancement of social science and humanistic research.

LEGAL BASIS:
Not-for-profit corporation.

ELIGIBILITY:
Applicants must be enrolled in a full-time doctoral program at a U.S. university. Research must be conducted outside of the U.S.

FINANCIAL DATA:
Amount of support per award: Average $20,000.

NUMBER OF APPLICANTS MOST RECENT YEAR: More than 1,100.

NUMBER OF AWARDS: 80.

APPLICATION INFORMATION:
Application information is available on the web site.
Duration: Nine to 12 months.
Deadline: November 2014.

ADDRESS INQUIRIES TO:
See e-mail address above.

SOCIAL SCIENCE RESEARCH COUNCIL   [860]
One Pierrepont Plaza
15th Floor
Brooklyn, NY 11201
(212) 377-2700
Fax: (212) 377-2727

E-MAIL ADDRESS:
abe@ssrc.org

WEB SITE ADDRESS:
www.ssrc.org/fellowships/abe-fellowship

FOUNDED: 1923

AREAS OF INTEREST:
Issues of global concern.

NAME(S) OF PROGRAMS:
● **Abe Fellowship Program**

TYPE:
Fellowships; Research grants. The program encourages international multidisciplinary research on topics of pressing global concern and fosters the development of a new generation of researchers interested in policy-relevant topics of long-range importance and willing to become key members of a bilateral and global research network built around such topics.

The Abe Fellowship Program administers an annual fellowship competition that provides scholars and nonacademic research professionals in the social sciences and related disciplines with support for research projects addressing one or more of three themes: (1) traditional and nontraditional approaches to security and diplomacy; (2) global and regional economic issues and; (3) social and cultural issues.

YEAR PROGRAM STARTED: 1991

PURPOSE:
To encourage international multidisciplinary research on topics of pressing global concern.

ELIGIBILITY:
Competition is open to citizens of the U.S. and Japan as well as to nationals of other countries who can demonstrate strong and serious long-term affiliations with research communities in Japan or the U.S. Applicants must hold the Ph.D. or the terminal degree in their field, or have attained an equivalent level of professional experience. Applications from researchers in professions other than academia are encouraged. Previous language training is not a prerequisite for this Fellowship. However, if the research project requires language ability, the applicant should provide evidence of adequate proficiency to complete the project. Projects proposing to address key policy issues or seeking to develop a concrete policy proposal must reflect nonpartisan positions.

GEOGRAPHIC RESTRICTIONS:
Japan and United States.

FINANCIAL DATA:
Awards may be used for maintenance, travel and research expenses.
Amount of support per award: Varies.
Total amount of support: Varies.

NUMBER OF AWARDS: 12 to 15.

APPLICATION INFORMATION:
Applications must be submitted online at applications.ssrc.org.
Duration: Three to 12 months of full-time support over a 24-month period. Fellowship tenure must begin between April 1 and December 31 of a given year.
Deadline: Applications are available by early summer. Receipt of applications: September 1.

STAFF:
Nicole Levit, Associate Director
Fernando Rojas, Fellowships Coordinator

ADDRESS INQUIRIES TO:
Abe Fellowship Program
Social Science Research Council
(See address above.)

SOCIETY FOR FRENCH HISTORICAL STUDIES
Department of History, University of Vermont
201 Wheeler House
133 South Prospect Street
Burlington, VT 05405-0164

E-MAIL ADDRESS:
steven.zdatny@uvm.edu

WEB SITE ADDRESS:
www.societyforfrenchhistoricalstudies.net

TYPE:
Awards/prizes. The Chinard Prize is for a recent book on historical relations between France and the Americas.

Farrar Award is for dissertation research.

The Koren Prize is for a recent article written on French history.

The Pinkney Prize is for a recent book written on French history.

Research Travel Award is for recent recipients of doctorates (awarded jointly with Western Society for French History).

Wolf Travel Fellowship is for research travel pertaining to a dissertation.

See entry 634 for full listing.

SWEDISH WOMEN'S EDUCATIONAL ASSOCIATION INC. [861]
P.O. Box 4128
Fort Lauderdale, FL 33338-4128

E-MAIL ADDRESS:
office@swea.org

WEB SITE ADDRESS:
www.swea.org

AREAS OF INTEREST:
Sweden's culture, history and language.

NAME(S) OF PROGRAMS:
- **SWEA Scholarship in Literature, Language and Area Studies**

TYPE:
Scholarships. Funds may be used to study in Sweden. Previous trips to Sweden, or lack thereof, are of no consideration. Willingness to travel to Sweden for dissertation work is a plus, but not a requirement.

PURPOSE:
To promote and preserve the Swedish language, cultures and traditions.

ELIGIBILITY:
The applicant must:
(1) be a well-merited doctoral candidate, studying at a non-Swedish university and reside permanently outside of Sweden;
(2) have filed a dissertation topic and;
(3) have a good knowledge of the Swedish language (written and spoken).

FINANCIAL DATA:
Amount of support per award: $10,000.
Total amount of support: $10,000.

NUMBER OF AWARDS: 1.

APPLICATION INFORMATION:
The applicant must submit an application, curriculum vitae, a detailed description of the dissertation project, a statement explaining how the scholarship money will be used, a presentation of himself or herself in Swedish, and three letters of recommendation. Applications are available online.
Duration: One year. Recipients may reapply.
Deadline: November 1.

ADDRESS INQUIRIES TO:
Administrator
(See address above.)

*SPECIAL STIPULATIONS:
There is no discrimination on the basis of gender, race, color, age, religion or nationality.

TINKER FOUNDATION INC. [862]
55 East 59th Street
New York, NY 10022
(212) 421-6858
Fax: (212) 223-3326

E-MAIL ADDRESS:
tinker@tinker.org

WEB SITE ADDRESS:
www.tinker.org

FOUNDED: 1959

AREAS OF INTEREST:
Institutional grants for projects addressing democratic governance, sustainable resource management, and education, with a geographic focus on the Spanish- and Portuguese-speaking countries of Latin America.

NAME(S) OF PROGRAMS:
- **Tinker Field Research Grants**

TYPE:
Travel grants. Travel grants (issued to universities) are to be used to support brief periods of individual research in Latin America by graduate students. There are also Institutional Grants for charitable organizations.

YEAR PROGRAM STARTED: 1979

PURPOSE:
To enable emerging scholars to work in the Spanish- and Portuguese-speaking countries of Latin America, enabling them to acquire a comprehensive knowledge of language, cultures and terrain, and to gather research data and develop contacts with scholars and institutions in their respective fields.

LEGAL BASIS:
Private foundation.

ELIGIBILITY:
Open to all recognized Centers or Institutes of Ibero-American or Latin American Studies with graduate doctoral programs at accredited U.S. universities. Field Research Grants, awarded to individuals by the appropriate university institutes/centers, are to reflect the Foundation's broad areas of interest.

The Foundation's selection criteria include the quality of the overall graduate program in Ibero-American studies, the immediate benefits to the Ibero-American studies program that will result from the availability of Field Research Grants at the university and the level of general university support for Ibero-American studies as demonstrated by past commitments and future projects.

Institutional Grants: Open to any 501(c)(3) (or equivalent foreign) organization doing work in and on the Spanish- and Portuguese-speaking countries of Latin America.

GEOGRAPHIC RESTRICTIONS:
Latin America, excluding Puerto Rico.

FINANCIAL DATA:
Amount of support per award: $10,000 and $15,000. Institutional Grants: $50,000 to $150,000.
Total amount of support: Approximately $75,000 in new grants annually.
Matching fund requirements: Field Research Grant applicants are required to match the award on a 1:1 ratio.

NUMBER OF APPLICANTS MOST RECENT YEAR: 11.

NUMBER OF AWARDS: Up to 6 new annually; more than 6 annually for Institutional Grants.

APPLICATION INFORMATION:
Application instructions and forms can be accessed via the web site.
Duration: Maximum of three years.
Deadline: Field Research Grants: October 1. Institutional Grants: March 1 and September 15.

PUBLICATIONS:
Annual report; application guidelines.

STAFF:
Margaret J. Cushing, Senior Program Officer
Kirsten Cowal, Program Officer
Jessica Tomb, Director of Administration and Finance
Karen Nassi, Grants and Information Officer
Rachel Fagiano, Program Assistant

DIRECTORS AND OFFICERS:
Renate Rennie, Chairman and President
Kathleen Waldron, Treasurer
Alan Stoga, Secretary
John H. Coatsworth
Sally Grooms Cowal
Arturo C. Porzecanski
Luis Rubio
Susan Segal

ADDRESS INQUIRIES TO:
Renate Rennie, Chairman and President
(See address above.)

U.S. DEPARTMENT OF EDUCATION
International and Foreign Language Education (IFLE)
1990 K Street, N.W., Suite 6000
Washington, DC 20006-8521
(202) 502-7631
(202) 502-7700
Fax: (202) 502-7860

E-MAIL ADDRESS:
OPE_NRC-FLAS@ed.gov

WEB SITE ADDRESS:
www.ed.gov/programs/iegpsflasf/index.html

TYPE:
Fellowships. The Foreign Language and Area Studies program provides allocations of academic year and summer fellowships to institutions of higher education or consortia of institutions of higher education to assist meritorious undergraduate students and graduate students undergoing training in modern foreign languages and related international studies.

See entry 662 for full listing.

U.S. DEPARTMENT OF EDUCATION
International and Foreign Language Education (IFLE)
Advanced Training & Research Group
Room 6084, 6th Floor
1990 K Street, N.W.
Washington, DC 20006-8521
(202) 502-7589
(202) 502-7700 (main office)
Fax: (202) 502-7860

E-MAIL ADDRESS:
ddra@ed.gov

WEB SITE ADDRESS:
www.ed.gov/programs/iegpsddrap/index.html

TYPE:
Fellowships. Fellowships to support doctoral dissertation research abroad in modern foreign languages and related area studies. For the purpose of these programs, area studies is defined as a program of comprehensive study of the aspects of a society or societies, including the study of their geography, history, culture, economy, politics, international relations and languages. The program is designed to develop research knowledge and capability in world areas not widely included in American curricula. Awards will not be available for projects focusing on Western Europe.

See entry 663 for full listing.

U.S. DEPARTMENT OF EDUCATION

International and Foreign Language Education (IFLE)
1990 K Street, N.W., Suite 6000
Washington, DC 20006-8521
(202) 502-7631
(202) 502-7700
Fax: (202) 502-7860

WEB SITE ADDRESS:
www.ed.gov/ope/iegps

TYPE:
Project/program grants; Training grants. The NRC Program provides grants to institutions of higher education and consortia of institutions to establish, strengthen and operate comprehensive and undergraduate centers that will be national resources for:
(1) teaching of any modern foreign language;
(2) instruction in fields needed to provide full understanding of areas, regions or countries in which the modern foreign language is commonly used;
(3) research and training in international studies and the international and foreign language aspects of professional and other fields of study and;
(4) instruction and research on issues in world affairs that concern one or more countries.

See entry 664 for full listing.

U.S. DEPARTMENT OF EDUCATION   [863]

International and Foreign Language Education (IFLE)
1990 K Street, N.W., Suite 6000
Washington, DC 20006-8521
(202) 502-7631
(202) 502-7700
Fax: (202) 502-7860

WEB SITE ADDRESS:
www.ed.gov/ope/iegps

AREAS OF INTEREST:
Area studies.

NAME(S) OF PROGRAMS:
● **American Overseas Research Centers (AORC) Program**

TYPE:
Project/program grants; Research grants; Training grants. The AORC Program provides grants to consortia of U.S. institutions of higher education to establish or operate an AORC that promotes postgraduate research, exchanges and area studies.

LEGAL BASIS:
Authorized under Section 609 of the Higher Education Act of 1965, as amended.

ELIGIBILITY:
Any American overseas research center can qualify that meets the following conditions:
(1) be a consortium of U.S. institutions of higher education that receives more than 50% of its funding from public or private U.S. sources;
(2) have a permanent presence in the country in which the center is located and;
(3) be an organization described in Section 501(c)(3) of the Internal Revenue Code of 1993, which is exempt from taxation under Section 501(a) of the Code.

FINANCIAL DATA:
AORC grants may be used to pay all or a portion of the cost of establishing or operating a center or program including:

(1) the cost of operation and maintenance of overseas facilities;
(2) the cost of organizing and managing conferences;
(3) the cost of teaching and research materials;
(4) the cost of acquisition, maintenance and preservation of library collections;
(5) the cost of bringing visiting scholars and faculty to the center to teach or to conduct research;
(6) the cost of faculty and staff stipends and salaries;
(7) the cost of faculty, staff and student travel and;
(8) the cost of publication and dissemination of materials for the scholarly and general public.

NUMBER OF AWARDS: In 2012 10 AORC grants for fiscal years 2012-15 were awarded.

ADDRESS INQUIRIES TO:
Cheryl E. Gibbs, Senior Program Officer
(See address above.)

*PLEASE NOTE:
The AORC Program competes every four years. The U.S. Department of Education will announce the competition for awards for fiscal years 2016-19 sometime in calendar year 2015, contingent upon federal funds.

U.S. INSTITUTE OF PEACE   [864]

Jennings Randolph Fellowship
Programs for International Peace
2301 Constitution Avenue, N.W.
Washington, DC 20037-2900
(202) 429-4746
Fax: (202) 429-6063

E-MAIL ADDRESS:
jrprogram@usip.org

WEB SITE ADDRESS:
www.usip.org

FOUNDED: 1984

AREAS OF INTEREST:
Topics and disciplines related to international peace, conflict and conflict management.

NAME(S) OF PROGRAMS:
● **Jennings Randolph Fellowship Programs for International Peace**

TYPE:
Fellowships; Residencies. Program is generally residential, but may vary. The U.S. Institute of Peace is an independent, nonpartisan institution created by Congress to strengthen the nation's capacity to promote the peaceful resolution of international conflict.

Under the Jennings Randolph Fellowship Programs for International Peace, Senior Fellowships and Peace Scholar Dissertation Fellowships are awarded on a competitive basis.

Senior Fellowships are awarded annually to scholars and practitioners from a variety of professions, including college and university faculty, journalists, diplomats, writers, educators, military officers, international negotiators and lawyers, and staff of civil society organizations. Fellows are supported for varying periods of time to conduct research on themes defined by USIP's five centers in their Calls for Applications, which will be published on USIP's web site, consult with staff and contribute to the ongoing work

of the Institute. Some Senior Fellowships may be partially residential or possibly even nonresidential.

Peace Scholar program supports doctoral dissertations that explore the sources and nature of international conflict, and strategies to prevent or end conflict and to sustain peace. Peace Scholars work at their university or appropriate field research sites. Successful applicants must demonstrate that their work is relevant for policy and/or practice in the field of conflict analysis, prevention and management, and postconflict peacebuilding.

YEAR PROGRAM STARTED: 1987

PURPOSE:
To enable outstanding scholars, practitioners and doctoral students to focus their efforts on critical problems of international peace and conflict.

Fellows undertake research and education projects that will increase knowledge and spread awareness among the public and policymakers and the public about topics concerning the sources and nature of international conflict and the full range of ways to end or prevent conflict and to sustain peace.

LEGAL BASIS:
Independent, nonpartisan and educational institution created by the U.S. Congress.

ELIGIBILITY:
Senior Fellowships: The competition is open to citizens of all nations. Women and members of minorities are especially encouraged to apply. Fellowship topics will vary.

Peace Scholar Dissertation Fellowships: Citizens of all countries are eligible, but must be enrolled in an accredited college or university in the U.S. Applicants must have completed all requirements for the degree except the dissertation by the commencement of the award (September 1). Priority will be given to projects that contribute knowledge relevant to the formulation of policy or to understanding of best practices on international peace and conflict issues.

FINANCIAL DATA:
Senior Fellows receive a stipend that will vary according to the particular call for applications.
Amount of support per award: Senior Fellows can receive up to $100,000 each for a 10-month period. Peace Scholar Dissertation Fellows receive a $20,000 flat stipend, which may be used to support writing or field research.
Total amount of support: Varies each year.

NUMBER OF APPLICANTS MOST RECENT YEAR:
140 for Peace Scholar Awards.

NUMBER OF AWARDS: Senior Fellowships: Varies; Peace Scholar Awards: 5 to 7 per year.

APPLICATION INFORMATION:
For application forms for either the Senior Fellowships or the Peace Scholar Dissertation Fellowships, please visit the Institute's web site or contact the Jennings Randolph Fellowship Programs at the address above.
Duration: Senior Fellowships: Varies; Peace Scholar Dissertation Fellowships: 10 months.
Deadline: Jennings Randolph Senior Fellowships: Varies. There may be up to four competitions per year. Peace Scholar Fellows:

December 12, 2014. Please note that the applications for both competitions are online only.

PUBLICATIONS:
Program Description with guidelines; application form; brochure.

STAFF:
Elizabeth Cole, Ph.D., Senior Program Officer

ADDRESS INQUIRIES TO:
Jennings Randolph Fellowship Programs for International Peace (See address above.) No phone calls please.

*PLEASE NOTE:
Research on conflict within the U.S. may not be supported under the terms of the Institute's mandate.

U.S. INSTITUTE OF PEACE [865]
2301 Constitution Avenue, N.W.
Washington, DC 20037
(202) 429-3842
Fax: (202) 833-1741

E-MAIL ADDRESS:
grants@usip.org

WEB SITE ADDRESS:
www.usip.org/grants-fellowships

FOUNDED: 1984

AREAS OF INTEREST:
International peace and conflict management and related fields. Topic areas of interest include, but are not restricted to, international conflict resolution, diplomacy, negotiation theory, functionalism and "track two" diplomacy, methods of third-party dispute settlement, international law, international organizations and collective security, deterrence and balance of power, arms control, psychological theories about international conflict, the role of nonviolence and nonviolent sanctions, moral and ethical thought about conflict and conflict resolution and theories about relationships among political institutions, human rights and conflict.

NAME(S) OF PROGRAMS:
• **U.S. Institute of Peace Grant Program**

TYPE:
Conferences/seminars; Project/program grants; Research grants; Research contracts. Support for research, education and training and the dissemination of information on international peace and conflict resolution.

YEAR PROGRAM STARTED: 1986

PURPOSE:
To carry out basic and applied research on the causes of war and other international conflicts; to develop curricula and texts for high school through postgraduate study and to conduct teacher-training institutes, workshops and seminars; to conduct training, symposia and continuing education programs for practitioners, policymakers, policy implementers and the public; to undertake public information efforts; to increase the store of information on international peace and conflict resolution.

LEGAL BASIS:
Independent, nonpartisan federal institution created and funded by the U.S. Congress.

ELIGIBILITY:
Grant applicants must be nonprofit organizations, official public institutions and individuals, both U.S. and foreign nationals, including the following: institutions of postsecondary, community and secondary education, public and private education, training or research institutions and libraries and public departments and agencies (including state and territorial departments of education and commerce).

Individuals requesting support for degree work are not eligible.

FINANCIAL DATA:
Amount of support per award: The amount of any grant is based on the proposed budget and on negotiations with successful applicants. Average $107,000.

Total amount of support: $5,371,683 for fiscal year 2013.

NUMBER OF APPLICANTS MOST RECENT YEAR:
385 for the year 2012.

NUMBER OF AWARDS: 63 for the year 2012.

APPLICATION INFORMATION:
Application information is available on the web site.

Duration: One to two years.

Deadline: Priority Grant Competition applications are accepted on an ongoing basis, or as advertised on the Institute's web site.

PUBLICATIONS:
Program announcement.

ADDRESS INQUIRIES TO:
The Grant Program
United States Institute of Peace
(See address above.)

*SPECIAL STIPULATIONS:
The Institute does not support funding for degree work.

UNITED STATES-JAPAN FOUNDATION [866]
145 East 32nd Street
12th Floor
New York, NY 10016
(212) 481-8753
(212) 481-8757
Fax: (212) 481-8762

E-MAIL ADDRESS:
info@us-jf.org

WEB SITE ADDRESS:
www.us-jf.org

FOUNDED: 1980

AREAS OF INTEREST:
Precollege education and policy studies, communication and public opinion.

NAME(S) OF PROGRAMS:
• **Grants**
• **Elgin Heinz Award**
• **U.S.-Japan Leadership Program**

TYPE:
Awards/prizes; General operating grants; Project/program grants; Research grants; Travel grants. In the area of Precollege Education, the Foundation supports the improvement and enhancement of instruction of Japan in the U.S. and on the U.S. in Japan in secondary and elementary schools through programs which foster the creative use of the Internet in education, teacher training, professional development, intensive study tours, and curriculum design. The Foundation also supports the improvement of Japanese language instruction.

In the area of Policy Studies, the Foundation supports joint policy research and has established several nongovernmental channels for ongoing discussions between small groups of prominent experts. Policy projects have been active in such fields as trade and international finance, the environment, multilateral crisis management, and Northeast Asian security.

The Foundation will consider communication/public opinion projects that not only raise awareness about Japan in the U.S. and of the U.S. in Japan, but also deal with concrete issues that affect the bilateral relationship. Using creative approaches, these programs should reach broad audiences to stimulate balanced, in-depth and quality media coverage of issues that are central to U.S.-Japan relations.

Projects that link civil society organizations in the two countries are also supported.

YEAR PROGRAM STARTED: 1980

PURPOSE:
To promote stronger ties between Americans and Japanese through education, communication, policy studies and similar activities that foster greater mutual knowledge and understanding regarding each other and issues of common concern.

LEGAL BASIS:
Not-for-profit private foundation.

ELIGIBILITY:
Certain types of programs fall outside the Foundation's current interests. These include undergraduate education, cultural performances or exhibitions, sports exchanges, publication subsidies, scientific research and research conferences. As a rule, grants cannot be made to individuals applying on their own behalf for independent study, research, travel or participation in meetings; grants also cannot be made to for-profit organizations.

Because the Foundation is interested primarily in supporting program activities, it does not award grants as contributions to capital campaigns, endowment funds or deficit operations. In addition, it does not award grants for the construction or maintenance of buildings or other physical premises or for the purchase of equipment.

The Foundation does not administer programs which it supports. Foundation grants may not be used to influence legislation or election to public office.

GEOGRAPHIC RESTRICTIONS:
United States or Japan.

FINANCIAL DATA:
Amount of support per award: $10,000 to $100,000.

Total amount of support: Approximately $2,000,000 annually.

NUMBER OF APPLICANTS MOST RECENT YEAR:
150 to 200.

NUMBER OF AWARDS: Approximately 40.

REPRESENTATIVE AWARDS:
Pre-College Education: $7,500 to Lincoln Memorial University, Harrogate, TN, to enable students from Kanto International Senior High School in Tokyo, Japan, to visit primary and secondary schools in Tennessee; Policy Studies: $75,103 to Pacific Forum CSIS, Honolulu, HI, to support the second year of a three-year focused policy dialogue on U.S.-Japan-China relations that will draw attention to the long-term strategic goals of

the three countries, and how current policy positions and pronouncements on all three sides impact the realization of those goals; Communications/Public Opinion: $110,000 to Japan Society, New York, NY, to support the 11th year of an intensive fellowship program for American media professionals, allowing them to reside, study and work for six weeks in Japan, focused on research topic of their choice.

APPLICATION INFORMATION:
Applicants should submit a preproposal letter of inquiry, including a brief description of the proposed project and its objectives, any necessary background information on the project and applicant, and a brief budget estimate. If there is interest, the applicant will be invited to prepare a full proposal.
Duration: 12 months. Annual renewal possible.
Deadline: Preproposals are accepted on a rolling basis.

BOARD OF TRUSTEES:
James W. Lintott, Chairman
George R. Packard, President
Jane Mack Gould
Akinari Horii
Yoriko Kawaguchi
Dr. Shin'ichi Kitaoka
Taro Kono
Dr. Alexander Munroe
Satoru Murase
Dr. Richard J. Samuels
Thomas W. Strauss
Daniel Tani
Takeshi Ueshima

OFFICERS AND STAFF:
Maria Cristina Manapat-Sims, Assistant Secretary, Treasurer of the Corporation
David P. Janes, Director of Foundation Grants
Kelly Nixon, Program Officer
Aya Tsujita, Program Officer, Tokyo Office
Tomoyuki Watanabe, Japan Representative

ADDRESS INQUIRIES TO:
David P. Janes
Director of Foundation Grants
(See address above.)

International studies and research abroad

AFS INTERCULTURAL PROGRAMS/USA [867]
120 Wall Street, 4th Floor
New York, NY 10005
(800) 237-4636
(212) 299-9000
Fax: (212) 299-9090

E-MAIL ADDRESS:
afsinfo@afsusa.org

WEB SITE ADDRESS:
www.afsusa.org

FOUNDED: 1947

AREAS OF INTEREST:
International exchange of high school students and secondary teachers who live with host families and attend local schools. Participants go to and from 55 countries, including the former Soviet Union and Eastern Europe.

CONSULTING OR VOLUNTEER SERVICES:
More than 100,000 volunteers around the world.

NAME(S) OF PROGRAMS:
• **AFS Cultural Studies Program**
• **AFS Faces of America Diversity Scholarship Program**
• **AFS Gap Year Program**
• **AFS Language Studies Program**
• **AFS Semester Program**
• **AFS Summer Home Stay Program**
• **AFS Volunteer Development Program**
• **AFS Year Program**

TYPE:
Exchange programs; Scholarships; Visiting scholars. Assistance for summer and school year programs. Exchanges are for high school students and secondary school teachers, community service programs, and ages 18 and above.

YEAR PROGRAM STARTED: 1947

PURPOSE:
To provide cross-cultural learning experiences for young people in another environment.

LEGAL BASIS:
Incorporated under the Not-for-Profit Corporation Laws of the state of New York. Exempt from New York state, New York City and federal taxes.

ELIGIBILITY:
Age, health, academic background, motivation and personality are considered.

FINANCIAL DATA:
Amount of support per award: Varies depending on merit and need.
Total amount of support: Approximately $3,000,000.

NUMBER OF AWARDS: 40% of all participants receive financial aid. AFS deals with 4,400 students each year.

APPLICATION INFORMATION:
Candidate must submit health record, school record, applicant essay, screening group recommendation, interview forms and parental essay.
Duration: Two to six weeks to one year. Nonrenewable.
Deadline: Dependent on program.

PUBLICATIONS:
Annual report; application forms; AFS program catalog; *Partnerships*, newsletter.

IRS IDENTIFICATION NUMBER: 39-1711417

ADDRESS INQUIRIES TO:
See e-mail address above.

ALBRIGHT INSTITUTE OF ARCHAEOLOGICAL RESEARCH (AIAR) [868]
Department of Art and Art History
Providence College
Providence, RI 02918
(401) 865-1789
Fax: (401) 865-2410

E-MAIL ADDRESS:
jbranham@providence.edu

WEB SITE ADDRESS:
www.aiar.org

FOUNDED: 1900

AREAS OF INTEREST:
Fellowships are open to those in Near Eastern studies from prehistory through the early Islamic period, including the fields of

anthropology, archaeology, art history, Bible, epigraphy, historical geography, history, language, literature, philology and religion, and related disciplines.

NAME(S) OF PROGRAMS:
• **Fellowships at the Albright Institute of Archaeological Research in Jerusalem**

TYPE:
Fellowships; Professorships; Scholarships; Travel grants; Visiting scholars. The ACLS Recent Doctoral Recipients Fellowship is available to awardees and alternates of the Mellon/ACLS Dissertation Completion Fellowships the prior year.

The Annual Professorship is awarded to postdoctoral scholars who are U.S. citizens.

The George A. Barton Fellowship is awarded for two months and is open to all doctoral students or recent Ph.D. recipients.

The Council of American Overseas Research Centers (CAORC) Multi-Country Research Fellowships are open to U.S. doctoral candidates and scholars who have already earned their Ph.D. in fields in the humanities, social sciences, or allied natural sciences and wish to conduct research of regional or transregional significance. Fellowships require scholars to conduct research in more than one country, at least one of which hosts a participating American overseas research center. (Apply at www.caorc.org/programs/index.html.)

Educational and Cultural Affairs Fellowships (ECA): (1) Junior Research Fellowships consist of two fellowships of nine months each; these fellowships are open to doctoral students and recent Ph.D. recipients who are U.S. citizens and; (2) Associate Fellowships consist of 13 administrative fee awards for senior and junior fellows (one or two semesters).

Ernest S. Frerichs Fellow and Program Coordinator is for nine months and is open to doctoral and postdoctoral scholars of all nationalities. Recipient is expected to assist the Albright's Director in planning and implementing the Ernest S. Frerichs Program for Albright Fellows, which requires a working knowledge of living and traveling in Israel.

The Seymour Gitin Distinguished Professorship is open to internationally recognized senior scholars of all nationalities who have made significant contributions to their field of study.

Glassman Holland Research Fellowship is open to all European postdoctoral researchers who are permanently resident in Europe.

Carol and Eric Meyers Doctoral Dissertation Fellowship provides two months of study for doctoral students whose research involves the study of archaeology and society in the biblical or early postbiblical periods. Topics dealing with society at the household level are encouraged.

National Endowment for the Humanities (NEH) Fellowships are awarded for up to 12 months. Open to postdoctoral scholars who are U.S. citizens or alien residents in the U.S. for at least three years.

The Noble Group Fellowships are open to Chinese citizens who are doctoral students and postdoctoral candidates and are either studying or in residence in China or doing research at institutions in other countries.

YEAR PROGRAM STARTED: 1940

PURPOSE:
To help scholars undertake high-quality research and field projects in the Near East; to encourage interdisciplinary study and communication among scholars.

LEGAL BASIS:
Nonprofit, archaeological research corporation.

ELIGIBILITY:
Fellowships are open to those in Near Eastern studies from prehistoric through the early Islamic period, including the fields of archaeology, anthropology, art history, Bible, epigraphy, gender studies, historical geography, history, language, literature, philology and religion and related disciplines. The research period should be continuous, without frequent trips outside the country. Residence at the Albright is required. The option to accommodate dependents is subject to space available at the Albright.

FINANCIAL DATA:
Amount of support per award: Varies.
Total amount of support: $325,000 in fellowships and awards.

COOPERATIVE FUNDING PROGRAMS: With various organizations and foundations, such as the NEH.

NUMBER OF AWARDS: 60 for all programs: 28 in fellowships and awards from the Institute; 32 Associate Fellows receive funding from other sources.

APPLICATION INFORMATION:
All eligible persons are encouraged to apply for as many awards as they wish, but each awardee can hold only one AIAR award at a time. Persons who have received an award in one year can reapply for the same or other awards the following year, but new applicants will be given priority.
Duration: Up to one year.
Deadline: October 1 and January 15.

PUBLICATIONS:
Applications.

ADDRESS INQUIRIES TO:
Dr. Joan R. Branham, Chair
Albright Fellowship Committee
(See address above.)

THE AMERICAN ACADEMY IN BERLIN [869]
Am Sandwerder 17-19
D-14109 Berlin Germany
+49 30 804 83 106
Fax: +49 30 804 83 111

E-MAIL ADDRESS:
cs@americanacademy.de

WEB SITE ADDRESS:
www.americanacademy.de

FOUNDED: 1994

AREAS OF INTEREST:
History, political science, literature, economics, German studies, art history, musicology, anthropology, law, linguistics, writing, composing, and visual arts.

NAME(S) OF PROGRAMS:
● Berlin Prize Fellowship

TYPE:
Fellowships; Residencies. Academic semester fellowship in Berlin with residence at the Hans Arnhold Center.

YEAR PROGRAM STARTED: 1998

PURPOSE:
To further scholarly professional development.

LEGAL BASIS:
Private, independent, nonprofit center.

ELIGIBILITY:
Must be either a U.S. citizen or permanent resident, and have completed their Doctorate or equivalent professional degree. Open to scholars, artists, and professionals who wish to engage in independent study in Berlin for an academic semester or, in very rare cases, for an entire academic year. Candidates need not work on German topics, but their project descriptions should explain how a residency in Berlin will contribute to further professional development. Writers must have published at least one book at time of application.

FINANCIAL DATA:
Amount of support per award: Stipend of $5,000 per month, round-trip airfare, and an apartment and partial board at the Hans Arnhold Center.

NUMBER OF APPLICANTS MOST RECENT YEAR: 300 to 400.

NUMBER OF AWARDS: Approximately 24 (12 each semester) annually.

APPLICATION INFORMATION:
General Application is available online.
Duration: One academic semester.
Deadline: Beginning of September.

STAFF:
Carol Scherer, Manager of Fellows Selection

ADDRESS INQUIRIES TO:
Carol Scherer
Manager of Fellows Selection
(See address above.)

AMERICAN ACADEMY IN ROME
7 East 60th Street
New York, NY 10022-1001
(212) 751-7200
Fax: (212) 751-7220

E-MAIL ADDRESS:
info@aarome.org

WEB SITE ADDRESS:
www.aarome.org

TYPE:
Awards/prizes; Fellowships; Residencies. Fellowships for independent work in architecture, landscape architecture, design, musical composition, visual arts, historic preservation/conservation, ancient studies, medieval studies, renaissance and early modern studies, and modern Italian studies. Supported projects must be conducted at American Academy in Rome facilities.

See entry 344 for full listing.

AMERICAN ACADEMY IN ROME
7 East 60th Street
New York, NY 10022
(212) 751-7200
Fax: (212) 751-7220

E-MAIL ADDRESS:
info@aarome.org

WEB SITE ADDRESS:
www.aarome.org

TYPE:
Awards/prizes; Fellowships; Residencies. Provides a residential year at the American Academy in Rome for an American landscape architect for advanced study, travel and association with other fellows in the arts and humanities.

See entry 2166 for full listing.

AMERICAN CENTER OF ORIENTAL RESEARCH [870]
656 Beacon Street
5th Floor
Boston, MA 02215-2010
(617) 353-6571
Fax: (617) 353-6575

E-MAIL ADDRESS:
acor@bu.edu

WEB SITE ADDRESS:
www.bu.edu/acor

FOUNDED: 1968

AREAS OF INTEREST:
The study of humanistic disciplines, such as art and architecture, literature, philology, prehistory and topography, relating in particular to the Middle East from prehistoric times to the modern era. Projects involving Islamic studies are especially encouraged.

The American Center of Oriental Research in Amman, Jordan serves as a center of operations for scholars of all nationalities wishing to conduct research in Jordan.

NAME(S) OF PROGRAMS:
● ACOR-CAORC Fellowship
● ACOR-CAORC Postgraduate Fellowships
● Pierre and Patricia Bikai Fellowship
● Bert and Sally de Vries Fellowship
● Jennifer C. Groot Fellowships in the Archaeology of Jordan
● Harrell Family Fellowship
● MacDonald/Sampson Fellowship
● National Endowment for the Humanities (NEH) Fellowship
● James A. Sauer Fellowship

TYPE:
Fellowships; Research grants; Visiting scholars. ACOR-CAORC Fellowships are for M.A. and doctoral students. Fields of study include all areas of the humanities and the natural and social sciences. Topics should contribute to scholarship in Near Eastern studies; U.S. citizenship required.

ACOR-CAORC Postgraduate Fellowships are for postdoctoral scholars and scholars with a terminal degree in their field, pursuing research or publication projects in the natural and social sciences, humanities, and associated disciplines relating to the Near East; U.S. citizenship required.

Pierre and Patricia Bikai Fellowship is for a residency at ACOR in Amman and is open to enrolled graduate students of any nationality, except Jordanian citizens, participating in an archaeological project or conducting archaeological work in Jordan.

Bert and Sally de Vries Fellowship supports a student for participation on an archaeological project or research in Jordan. Senior project staff members whose expenses are being borne largely by the project are ineligible. Open to enrolled undergraduate or graduate students of any nationality except Jordanian citizens.

The Jennifer C. Groot Fellowships support beginners in archaeological fieldwork who have been accepted as team members on archaeological projects with ASOR/CAP affiliation in Jordan. Open to undergraduate or graduate students of U.S. or Canadian citizenship.

Harrell Family Fellowship supports a graduate student for participation on an archaeological project or research in Jordan. Senior project staff members whose expenses are being borne largely by the project are ineligible. Open to enrolled graduate students of any nationality except Jordanian citizens.

MacDonald/Sampson Fellowship is for a residency at ACOR for research in the fields of Ancient Near Eastern languages and history, archaeology, Bible studies, or comparative religion, or a travel grant to assist with participation in an archaeological field project in Jordan. Open to enrolled undergraduate or graduate students of Canadian citizenship or landed immigrant status.

The National Endowment for the Humanities (NEH) Fellowship is for scholars who have a Ph.D. or have completed their professional training. Fields of research include modern and classical languages, linguistics, literature, history, jurisprudence, philosophy, archaeology, comparative religion, ethics, and the history, criticism and theory of the arts. Social and political scientists are encouraged to apply. Applicants must be U.S. citizens or foreign nationals living in the U.S. three years immediately preceding the application deadline.

James A. Sauer Fellowship is open to enrolled graduate students of U.S. or Canadian citizenship participating on an archaeological project or research in Jordan.

YEAR PROGRAM STARTED: 1968

PURPOSE:
To help scholars undertake high-quality research and field projects in the Middle East; to encourage interdisciplinary study and communication among scholars.

LEGAL BASIS:
Nonprofit, archaeological research corporation.

ELIGIBILITY:
Most fellowships are restricted to U.S. or Canadian citizens.

CAORC, NEH, MacDonald/Sampson and Bikai Fellows will reside at the ACOR facility in Amman while conducting their research. Recipients are expected to participate actively in the formal and informal activities of the Center.

FINANCIAL DATA:
Amount of support per award:
ACOR-CAORC Fellowships: $22,600 maximum; ACOR-CAORC Postgraduate Fellowships: $31,800 maximum; Pierre and Patricia Bikai Fellowship: $600 monthly stipend plus room and board at ACOR; Bert and Sally de Vries Fellowship: $1,200; Groot Fellowships and Harrell Family Fellowship: $1,800; MacDonald/Sampson Fellowship: $600 stipend, plus room and board at ACOR, or travel grant of $1,800 to help with any project-related expenses; National Endowment for the Humanities (NEH) Fellowship: $25,200 maximum (for six months); James A. Sauer Fellowship: Room and board at ACOR and a stipend of $400.
Total amount of support: Varies.

COOPERATIVE FUNDING PROGRAMS: With various organizations and foundations, such as the NEH.

NUMBER OF APPLICANTS MOST RECENT YEAR: 45 for all programs.

NUMBER OF AWARDS: ACOR-CAORC Fellowships, ACOR-CAORC Postgraduate Fellowships and Groot Fellowships: 2 or more each; Bikai Fellowship and NEH Fellowship: 1 to 2 each; Bert and Sally de Vries, Harrell Family, MacDonald/Sampson and Sauer Fellowships: 1 each.

APPLICATION INFORMATION:
Prospective applicants are encouraged to consult with the ACOR Administrative Director about application procedures, the competitiveness of their applications, or any other questions they might have about the awards program.

All eligible persons are encouraged to apply for as many awards as they wish, but each awardee can hold only one ACOR award at a time. Persons who have received an award in one year can reapply for the same or other awards the following year, but new applicants will be given priority.
Duration: ACOR-CAORC Fellowships/Postgraduate Fellowships: Two to six months; Bikai Fellowship: One to two months; National Endowment for the Humanities (NEH) Fellowship: Four to six months; Sauer Fellowship: One month.
Deadline: February 1.

PUBLICATIONS:
Program announcements.

IRS IDENTIFICATION NUMBER: 23-7084091

ADDRESS INQUIRIES TO:
ACOR Fellowship Committee
(See address above.)

AMERICAN FRIENDS OF THE ALEXANDER VON HUMBOLDT FOUNDATION   [871]
1101 17th Street, N.W.
Suite 603
Washington, DC 20036
(202) 783-1907

E-MAIL ADDRESS:
info@americanfriends-of-avh.org

WEB SITE ADDRESS:
www.humboldt-foundation.de
americanfriends-of-avh.org

FOUNDED: 1953

AREAS OF INTEREST:
Postgraduate research in Germany.

NAME(S) OF PROGRAMS:
● **Humboldt Research Fellowship for Experienced Researchers**

TYPE:
Fellowships. This program allows a researcher to carry out a long-term research project (six to 18 months) at a research institution in Germany which the applicant has selected in cooperation with an academic host.

PURPOSE:
To support highly qualified scholars and scientists of all nationalities and disciplines so that they may carry out a long-term research project.

ELIGIBILITY:
Open to scientists and scholars from outside Germany with above-average qualifications,

who:
(1) have completed their Doctorate less than 12 years ago;
(2) already have his or her own research profile and;
(3) are working at least at the level of Assistant Professor or Junior Research Group Leader or have a record of several years of independent academic work.

Fellowships are awarded on the basis of academic achievement, the quality and feasibility of the proposed research and the candidate's publications.

FINANCIAL DATA:
In addition to a monthly stipend, special allowances are available for accompanying family members, travel expenses, and German language instruction.
Amount of support per award: EUR 3,150 monthly stipend.
Total amount of support: Varies.

NUMBER OF AWARDS: Approximately 600.

APPLICATION INFORMATION:
Those interested must use application documents which can be downloaded from www.humboldt-foundation.de.
Duration: Six to 18 months. Fellowships may be divided into a maximum of three visits of at least three months each.
Deadline: Applications may be submitted at any time to the Humboldt Foundation in Bonn, Germany. The review process takes four to seven months, and the selection committee meets three times a year to review applications.

ADDRESS INQUIRIES TO:
Program Coordination
(See address above.) or

Alexander von Humboldt Stiftung
Jean-Paul-Strasse 12
D-53173 Bonn
Germany
Tel: 49 (0228) 833-0
Fax: 49 (0228) 833-199
E-mail: info@avh.de

AMERICAN FRIENDS OF THE ALEXANDER VON HUMBOLDT FOUNDATION   [872]
1101 17th Street, N.W.
Suite 603
Washington, DC 20036
(202) 783-1907

E-MAIL ADDRESS:
info@americanfriends-of-avh.org

WEB SITE ADDRESS:
www.humboldt-foundation.de
www.americanfriends-of-avh.org

FOUNDED: 1953

AREAS OF INTEREST:
Intercultural exchange.

NAME(S) OF PROGRAMS:
● **German Chancellor Fellowship**

TYPE:
Exchange programs; Fellowships. Fellowship for one-year stay in Germany for professional development, study or research. Applicants design individual projects specific to Germany and decide at which institutions to pursue them.

YEAR PROGRAM STARTED: 1990

PURPOSE:
To strengthen ties between Germany and the U.S. through fellowship recipient's profession or studies.

ELIGIBILITY:
Intended for career-oriented individuals from any profession or field of study who show outstanding potential for U.S. leadership. Selected fellows represent the private, public, not-for-profit, cultural and academic sectors. U.S. citizenship is required.

FINANCIAL DATA:
Stipend covers housing and living expenses. In addition, the Fellowship also covers travel expenses to and from Germany and the costs of a German language course, introductory seminar, study tour, and final meeting in Bonn.
Amount of support per award: Monthly stipend of EUR 2,150 to 2,750.
Total amount of support: Varies.

NUMBER OF AWARDS: 10 annually.

APPLICATION INFORMATION:
Applications must be submitted to the Foundation's Bonn, Germany office.
Duration: One year.
Deadline: October 15. Fellowship period begins the following year on September 1.

ADDRESS INQUIRIES TO:
Margot Pfefferly, Program Coordinator
(See address above.)

*SPECIAL STIPULATIONS:
Prior to submitting an application, applicants are expected to have established contact with a mentor in Germany who agrees to provide professional and/or scholarly assistance throughout the program year.

AMERICAN INSTITUTE FOR SRI LANKAN STUDIES (AISLS) [873]

155 Pine Street
Belmont, MA 02478

E-MAIL ADDRESS:
rogersjohnd@aol.com

WEB SITE ADDRESS:
www.aisls.org

FOUNDED: 1996

AREAS OF INTEREST:
The promotion of scholarly excellence in Sri Lankan studies.

NAME(S) OF PROGRAMS:
● **AISLS Fellowship Program**

TYPE:
Fellowships. Program supports research in Sri Lanka by U.S. citizens who already hold a Ph.D. or the equivalent at the time they begin their fellowship tenure.

PURPOSE:
To foster excellence in American research and teaching on Sri Lanka; to promote the exchange of scholars and scholarly information between the U.S. and Sri Lanka.

ELIGIBILITY:
Applicants must hold U.S. citizenship and a Ph.D. or equivalent academic degree, or show that they will hold such a degree before taking up the fellowship. Scholars at all ranks are eligible. Applicants must plan to spend at least two months in Sri Lanka and complete the fellowship within the time frame listed under eligibility guidelines. Projects in all fields in the social sciences and humanities are eligible.

GEOGRAPHIC RESTRICTIONS:
United States.

FINANCIAL DATA:
Fellowship includes reimbursement up to $2,000 for round-trip airfare between the U.S. and Colombo via U.S. carriers, and a limited budget for research expenses, to be negotiated.
Amount of support per award: Stipend of $3,500 per month.

APPLICATION INFORMATION:
The completed application should contain the following items:
(1) AISLS Fellowship Application Cover Sheet;
(2) curriculum vitae, not to exceed three pages;
(3) description of the proposed study, not to exceed three single-spaced pages. This is the most important part of the application. It should cover the questions to be addressed by the project, the approach to be taken, work done to date, work to be accomplished during the fellowship period, the applicant's competence to carry out the project, how the project addresses the criteria of the competition, and a statement of other support received or being sought for the project and;
(4) one-page bibliography, including a selected list of publications by other scholars or primary sources that have been or will be used in the project.
Duration: Two to nine months.
Deadline: December 1.

ADDRESS INQUIRIES TO:
John Rogers, Chairperson
AISLS Selection Committee
(See address above.)

AMERICAN INSTITUTE FOR SRI LANKAN STUDIES (AISLS) [874]

155 Pine Street
Belmont, MA 02478

E-MAIL ADDRESS:
rogersjohnd@aol.com

WEB SITE ADDRESS:
www.aisls.org

FOUNDED: 1996

AREAS OF INTEREST:
The promotion of scholarly excellence in Sri Lankan studies.

NAME(S) OF PROGRAMS:
● **AISLS Dissertation Planning Grant**

TYPE:
Research grants. Grant to assist graduate students intending to do dissertation research in Sri Lanka.

YEAR PROGRAM STARTED: 2006

PURPOSE:
To enable graduate students to make a pre-dissertation visit to Sri Lanka to investigate the feasibility of their topic, to sharpen their research design, or to make other practical arrangements for future research.

ELIGIBILITY:
Applicants must be enrolled in a Ph.D. program (or equivalent) in a U.S. university. There are no citizenship requirements. Applicants should have completed most of their graduate coursework by the time they take up their grant. The grant is especially intended for students who are in the process of completing their dissertation proposals and

preparing applications for funds to support their dissertation research, but other purposes may be proposed. Applicants should plan to spend at least six weeks in Sri Lanka.

GEOGRAPHIC RESTRICTIONS:
United States.

FINANCIAL DATA:
Grant includes reimbursement up to $2,000 for round-trip airfare between U.S. and Colombo, reimbursement for any visa fees paid to the Sri Lankan government, and a per diem for six to eight weeks.
Amount of support per award: Per diem of $400 per week.

APPLICATION INFORMATION:
The completed application should contain the following items:
(1) AISLS Dissertation Planning Grant Application Cover Sheet;
(2) curriculum vitae, not to exceed two pages, which should include the name and e-mail address of the applicant's dissertation supervisor;
(3) copy of the applicant's graduate transcript. An unofficial copy is acceptable;
(4) project narrative, not to exceed two single-spaced pages. This is the most important part of the application and should contain a summary of the proposed dissertation project, or, if the purpose of the planning grant is to define a dissertation project, a summary of the more general questions the applicant hopes to address in his or her dissertation, a description of what the applicant intends to do during the grant period, and the applicant's competence to carry out his or her proposed project, including language training;
(5) one-page project bibliography, including a selected list of publications by other scholars or primary sources that have been or will be used in the project and;
(6) a confidential letter of recommendation from the applicant's dissertation supervisor. This letter should cover the applicant's academic record and be specific about the applicant's progress to date within the graduate program concerned. This letter should be sent directly to John Rogers at the address listed above.
Duration: Six to eight weeks.
Deadline: December 1. Early submission is encouraged.

ADDRESS INQUIRIES TO:
John Rogers, Chairperson
AISLS Selection Committee
(See address above.)

AMERICAN INSTITUTE FOR YEMENI STUDIES [875]

232 Bay State Road
Room 426
Boston, MA 02215
(617) 358-4649
Fax: (617) 358-4650

E-MAIL ADDRESS:
aiys.us@aiys.org

WEB SITE ADDRESS:
www.aiys.org

FOUNDED: 1977

AREAS OF INTEREST:
Study and research in or about Yemen.

NAME(S) OF PROGRAMS:
● **General Fellowship Program**

TYPE:
Fellowships. Fellowship program for graduate and postgraduate scholars for Arabic language study, feasibility studies or research projects in Yemen.

PURPOSE:
To foster research in and about Yemen; to utilize American academic talent to strengthen Yemeni scholarship; to promote U.S.-Yemeni understanding.

ELIGIBILITY:
Limited to U.S. citizens who are enrolled as full-time graduate students in recognized degree programs or who are postgraduate researchers. Awards are made on the basis of merit. Collaborative or group projects are eligible for funding. It is permissible to combine Arabic language study with a research or feasibility project.

FINANCIAL DATA:
Amount of support per award: Up to $10,000.

NUMBER OF AWARDS: Approximately 10.

APPLICATION INFORMATION:
There is a $25 processing fee for applications to the U.S. fellowship program. The fee is waived for applicants who are individual AIYS members.

All applicants must submit the original, plus five copies, of each of the following:
(1) completed application form;
(2) curriculum vitae and;
(3) application narrative consisting of a short statement explaining their interest in Yemen and their background in Arabic language (for applicants of Arabic language training grants) or a project description, four to six double-spaced pages, plus a proposed budget and schedule (for all other applicants).

Three letters of recommendation, preferably on institutional stationery, must be sent directly to AIYS postmarked by the deadline. Predoctoral applicants must have both undergraduate and graduate transcripts sent; recent Ph.D. recipients are encouraged to provide a graduate transcript.
Duration: Two months minimum.
Deadline: December 31.

ADDRESS INQUIRIES TO:
Michael Carroll, U.S. Director
(See address above.)

*SPECIAL STIPULATIONS:
If applicant is not an individual AIYS member, a $25 processing fee for application will apply. Named fellows must become AIYS members before starting their fellowship tenure.

AMERICAN INSTITUTE OF BANGLADESH STUDIES [876]
B488 Medical Sciences Center
1300 University Avenue
Madison, WI 53706
(608) 265-1471

E-MAIL ADDRESS:
aibsinfo@aibs.net

WEB SITE ADDRESS:
www.aibs.net

FOUNDED: 1989

AREAS OF INTEREST:
Bangladesh culture and society.

NAME(S) OF PROGRAMS:
● **Junior Fellowship**

● **Pre-Dissertation Fellowships**
● **Seminar, Workshop and Conference Support**
● **Senior Fellowship**
● **Undergraduate Research Initiative**

TYPE:
Awards/prizes; Conferences/seminars; Fellowships; Research grants; Travel grants. Junior Fellowship is for those who are in the ABD phase of their Ph.D. program. Applicants must be prepared to commence field research at the start of the fellowship period.

Pre-Dissertation Fellowships are short-term grants offered to graduate students pursuing studies of Bangladesh. The grant provides a stay of between two and four months in Bangladesh that may be used for language study, resource assessment, or network building to aid the completion of a competitive dissertation proposal.

The Senior Fellowship is for those who have a Ph.D. They may already have research experience in Bangladesh or may be interested in developing a research area on Bangladesh.

YEAR PROGRAM STARTED: 1989

PURPOSE:
To improve the scholarly understanding of Bangladesh culture and society in the U.S. and to promote educational exchange between the U.S. and Bangladesh.

ELIGIBILITY:
Applicants must be U.S. citizens or permanent residents and have their Ph.D.

Pre-Dissertation Fellowship: At the time of application, students must have completed at least one year of graduate study in a recognized Ph.D.-granting institution.

GEOGRAPHIC RESTRICTIONS:
United States.

FINANCIAL DATA:
Amount of support per award: Junior Fellowship: $920 monthly allowance; Senior Fellowship: $1,150 plus research and dependents' allowances per month in non-convertible Bangladesh Taka. Round-trip air transportation will be provided via the most direct route and using the Bangladesh carrier whenever possible.
Total amount of support: Varies.

APPLICATION INFORMATION:
Application forms and complete details are available online.
Duration: Junior Fellowship: Six to 10 months; Pre-Dissertation Fellowship: Two to four months; Senior Fellowship: Four to 12 months.
Deadline: Varies depending upon program.

ADDRESS INQUIRIES TO:
See e-mail address above.

AMERICAN INSTITUTE OF INDIAN STUDIES [877]
1130 East 59th Street
Chicago, IL 60637
(773) 702-8638
Fax: (773) 702-6636

E-MAIL ADDRESS:
aiis@uchicago.edu

WEB SITE ADDRESS:
www.indiastudies.org

FOUNDED: 1961

AREAS OF INTEREST:
Indian studies.

NAME(S) OF PROGRAMS:
● **AIIS Fellowships**

TYPE:
Fellowships; Research grants. Senior (postdoctoral) Research Fellowships are awarded to academic specialists in Indian studies who possess the Ph.D. or equivalent. While in India, each Senior Research Fellow will be formally affiliated with an Indian university.

Fellowships for Senior Scholarly Development are awarded to established scholars who have not previously specialized in Indian studies and to established professionals who have not previously worked or studied in India. Proposals in this category should have a substantial research or project component and the anticipated results should be clearly defined. While in India, each Fellow will be formally affiliated with an Indian university.

Junior (dissertation) Fellowships are awarded to graduate students from all academic disciplines whose dissertation research requires study in India. Junior Fellows will have formal affiliation with Indian universities and Indian research supervisors.

Senior Performing Arts Fellowships are awarded to accomplished practitioners of the performing arts of India who demonstrate that studying in India will enhance their skills, develop their capabilities to teach or perform in the U.S., enhance American involvement with India's artistic traditions and strengthen their links with peers in India.

YEAR PROGRAM STARTED: 1962

PURPOSE:
To support the advancement of knowledge and understanding of India, its people and culture, primarily through research conducted in India by American scholars.

LEGAL BASIS:
Cooperative, nonprofit organization of 47 American colleges and universities.

ELIGIBILITY:
U.S. citizens are eligible for AIIS grants, as are foreign nationals enrolled or teaching full-time at American colleges or universities. U.S. and Indian government employees are ineligible for AIIS grants. Eligible applicants who are unaffiliated or who are from nonmember institutions are encouraged to apply.

FINANCIAL DATA:
Fellowships include a maintenance allowance and international travel. Fellowships for four months or less have significant travel restrictions. Fellowships for six months or more may include limited dependent coverage if funds are available. Award funds are generally made available in foreign currency only. An administrative overhead charge will be assessed to each AIIS Fellowship; this is not an application fee and is incurred only when a fellowship is awarded.

COOPERATIVE FUNDING PROGRAMS: Fellowship programs of the AIIS have been supported by foreign currency funds received from the Smithsonian Institution and the National Science Foundation. Funding was also provided by the U.S. Information Agency and the AIIS member institutions.

Additionally, the Institute receives a continuing grant from the National Endowment for the Humanities (NEH).

NUMBER OF AWARDS: Determined by the amount of support received by AIIS.

APPLICATION INFORMATION:
Application materials are available upon request from the address above.

Duration: Up to nine months for Senior Research Fellowships, Fellowships for Senior Scholarly Development and Senior Performing Arts Fellowships; up to 11 months for Junior Fellowships.

Deadline: July 1. Awards are announced the following spring or summer. Awards begin in July of the following year.

OFFICERS:
Frederick Asher, President
Elise Auerbach, Administrator

ADDRESS INQUIRIES TO:
Elise Auerbach, Administrator
(See address above.)

*PLEASE NOTE:
A limited number of Senior Fellows will be selected to receive $1,000 per month of their fellowship award in U.S. dollars (with the remainder of their award still being in Indian rupees) due to a grant from the National Endowment for the Humanities. Awards will be assigned to those scholars who appear most likely to carry out "distinguished work in the humanities" in India.

*SPECIAL STIPULATIONS:
All AIIS-sponsored research projects and programs must receive the approval of the Indian government.

AMERICAN INSTITUTE OF INDIAN STUDIES

1130 East 59th Street
Chicago, IL 60637
(773) 702-8638
Fax: (773) 702-6636

E-MAIL ADDRESS:
aiis@uchicago.edu

WEB SITE ADDRESS:
www.indiastudies.org

TYPE:
Fellowships. Awards for graduate studies in India in an Indian language.

See entry 652 for full listing.

THE AMERICAN JEWISH JOINT DISTRIBUTION COMMITTEE   [878]

711 Third Avenue
New York, NY 10017-4104
(212) 687-6200
Fax: (212) 370-5467

E-MAIL ADDRESS:
globalservice@jdcny.org

WEB SITE ADDRESS:
www.jdc.org

AREAS OF INTEREST:
International Jewish communal service.

NAME(S) OF PROGRAMS:
• **The Ralph I. Goldman Fellowship**

TYPE:
Fellowships. Offers work-study fellowship in overseas locations where JDC is active.

YEAR PROGRAM STARTED: 1987

PURPOSE:
To provide young Jewish leaders with an insider's perspective on JDC's global programs, while also giving them the opportunity to participate in the life of international Jewish communities.

ELIGIBILITY:
Candidates should have the following credentials:
(1) Master's degree or equivalent and proven academic excellence;
(2) some work experience in the candidate's chosen career;
(3) demonstrated exceptional leadership skills;
(4) strong interest in international Jewish communal affairs and social welfare;
(5) knowledge of foreign language(s) is a plus, but not a requirement and;
(6) formal and/or informal Jewish education.

FINANCIAL DATA:
Amount of support per award: $35,000 stipend plus international travel expenses.

NUMBER OF AWARDS: 1 annually.

APPLICATION INFORMATION:
Candidates should send an e-mail to the address above.
Duration: One year, beginning in September.
Deadline: Letter of Intent: December 30. Application: January 15.

AMERICAN RESEARCH CENTER IN EGYPT, INC.   [879]

8700 Crownhill Boulevard, Suite 507
San Antonio, TX 78209
(210) 821-7000
Fax: (210) 821-7007

E-MAIL ADDRESS:
info@arce.org
fellows@arce.org

WEB SITE ADDRESS:
www.arce.org

FOUNDED: 1948

AREAS OF INTEREST:
Research on Egypt and in Egypt on all phases of Egyptian civilization and culture from earliest times to the present.

NAME(S) OF PROGRAMS:
• **Fellowships for Research in Egypt**

TYPE:
Awards/prizes; Fellowships; Research grants. Fellowships awarded to doctoral students in the all-but-dissertation (ABD) stage as well as to postdoctoral scholars. Topics for research fellowship encompass the humanities, social sciences and art and archaeology and cover periods from ancient times to the present.

YEAR PROGRAM STARTED: 1974

PURPOSE:
To obtain a fresh and more profound knowledge of Egypt and the Near East through scholarly research; to train American specialists in Near Eastern Studies in academic disciplines which require familiarity with Egypt; to disseminate knowledge of Egypt and thus understanding of the whole Near East and promote American-Egyptian cultural relations.

LEGAL BASIS:
Nonprofit organization.

ELIGIBILITY:
Criteria for selections rest on the Committee's judgment of the applicant's

intellectual capacity and maturity, fitness for field work in Egypt, the significance and relevance of the proposed topic and its potential contribution to scholarly research in Egypt. No special consideration is given to applicants from member institutions and candidates need not be members of the ARCE. Awards are open to all qualified candidates without regard to sex, race and religion. All applicants, pre- and postdoctoral, must be U.S. citizens due to funding guidelines. Under certain circumstances, funding is available through the NEH for non-U.S. postdoctoral scholars living in the U.S. for more than three consecutive years to receive funding. Therefore, it is advisable to contact fellows@arce.org for further clarification.

GEOGRAPHIC RESTRICTIONS:
Egypt.

FINANCIAL DATA:
Monthly per diem plus round-trip airfare between the U.S. and Cairo. Fellows may receive stipends only for the period of time during which they are present in Egypt. A small dependent allowance for accompanying family members is available.

Amount of support per award: $2,200 to $3,650 monthly per diem; NEH all-inclusive award: $4,200 per month.

Total amount of support: Varies.

COOPERATIVE FUNDING PROGRAMS: NEH and CAORC/ECA.

NUMBER OF APPLICANTS MOST RECENT YEAR: 18 for the year 2013-14.

NUMBER OF AWARDS: 5.

APPLICATION INFORMATION:
Electronic submission is preferred. Original letters of recommendation and transcripts, if applicable, may also be scanned and sent electronically.

All applicants must submit three letters of recommendation. Predoctoral applicants must submit a fourth recommendation attesting to their capacity in ancient or modern languages as related to their proposed research.
Duration: CAORC/ECA: Three to 12 months; NEH all-inclusive award: Four to 10 months.
Deadline: Mid-January.

PUBLICATIONS:
Annual report; application guidelines; journal; bulletin; e-newsletter.

IRS IDENTIFICATION NUMBER: 04-2319500

GOVERNING BOARD:
Sameh Iskander, President
Melinda Hartwig, Vice President
Janet Irwine, Treasurer

ADDRESS INQUIRIES TO:
Djodi Deutsch
Academic Programs Coordinator
E-mail: fellows@arce.org

AMERICAN RESEARCH CENTER IN SOFIA (ARCS) - U.S. OFFICE   [880]

120 Goldwin Smith Hall
Department of Classics
Cornell University
Ithaca, NY 14853
(917) 572-2491

E-MAIL ADDRESS:
sofiadirector@arcsofia.org

WEB SITE ADDRESS:
arcsofia.org/en/home

NAME(S) OF PROGRAMS:
- **Academic Program Fellowship Competition**

TYPE:
Fellowships. The American Research Center in Sofia (ARCS), Bulgaria, offers three programs with accompanying fellowships: a fall term program (September-November) focusing on the history and archaeology of Bulgaria and neighboring countries, from prehistory to the present; a spring term program (February-April) focusing on the history of religion in Bulgaria and neighboring countries; and a nine-month program (September-May) which incorporates the material of both fall and spring terms. The programs combine a formal academic curriculum with independent research. The Center hosts the programs' lectures and seminars, organizes related study trips, facilitates opportunities for taking Bulgarian and other Balkan language classes, and provides logistical support and access to local libraries, museums and other educational institutions. The Center engages the participants with eminent local scholars relevant to the field of their study and makes arrangements for specialized research at local institutions.

ELIGIBILITY:
Graduate students at North American academic institutions engaged in research on ancient, medieval or modern Bulgaria or the Balkan peninsula, in any field of the humanities and social sciences. Non-U.S. applicants are expected to maintain an affiliation with an educational institution in the U.S. or Canada.

FINANCIAL DATA:
The Fellowship includes free housing in Sofia, Bulgaria; monthly stipend ($600/month); language instruction; travel expenses within the academic program; and travel expenses between North America and Bulgaria (up to $1,000).

NUMBER OF AWARDS: 7 (3 for fall semester; 3 for spring semester; 1 full academic year).

APPLICATION INFORMATION:
A complete application consists of the following:
(1) the ARCS application form;
(2) a project proposal describing how participation in the ARCS academic program will serve one's research interests (not to exceed three double-spaced pages);
(3) a current curriculum vitae;
(4) academic transcripts and;
(5) two letters of reference from scholars familiar with applicant's work.

Applications should be submitted by e-mail to Professor Kevin Clinton (kmc1@cornell.edu), Chair of the ARCS Fellowship Committee.

Deadline: February 15. Notification date: April 1.

ADDRESS INQUIRIES TO:
U.S. Office of ARCS:
Eric De Sena, Director and Chief Executive Officer
(See address above.)

AMERICAN RESEARCH INSTITUTE IN TURKEY, INC.   [881]
c/o The University of Pennsylvania Museum
3260 South Street
Philadelphia, PA 19104-6324
(215) 898-3474
Fax: (215) 898-0657

E-MAIL ADDRESS:
leinwand@sas.upenn.edu

WEB SITE ADDRESS:
ccat.sas.upenn.edu/ARIT/ARITFellowships.html

FOUNDED: 1964

AREAS OF INTEREST:
Research and study in Turkey, including all fields of the humanities and social sciences.

NAME(S) OF PROGRAMS:
- **ARIT Fellowship Program**

TYPE:
Fellowships. ARIT offers a number of fellowships for research in Turkey in humanities and social sciences. Grants for tenures of up to one academic year will be considered; some preference is given to projects of shorter duration. ARIT operates hostel, research and study facilities for researchers in Turkey at its branch centers in Istanbul and Ankara.

YEAR PROGRAM STARTED: 1964

PURPOSE:
To support research in humanities and social sciences in Turkey.

LEGAL BASIS:
Funded in part by grants from U.S. Department of State, Bureau of Educational and Cultural Affairs.

ELIGIBILITY:
Scholars and advanced graduate students engaged in research on ancient, medieval or modern times in Turkey, in any field of the humanities and social sciences, are eligible. Student applicants must have fulfilled all preliminary requirements for the Doctorate except the dissertation by June of the program year, and before beginning any ARIT-sponsored research. Non-U.S. applicants who currently reside in the U.S. or Canada are expected to maintain an affiliation with an educational institution in the U.S. or Canada. For questions of eligibility and procedures, please check with the ARIT office in Philadelphia.

FINANCIAL DATA:
Awards cover international travel to and from Turkey and provide a stipend based on Turkish living standards and the fellow's academic status.
Amount of support per award: $4,000 to $16,000, depending on length of stay in Turkey.
Total amount of support: Varies.

COOPERATIVE FUNDING PROGRAMS: The Fellowship program is supported in part by a grant from the U.S. Department of State, Bureau of Educational and Cultural Affairs.

NUMBER OF APPLICANTS MOST RECENT YEAR: 90 for the year 2014-15.

NUMBER OF AWARDS: 4 for the year 2014.

APPLICATION INFORMATION:
Turkish law requires foreign scholars to obtain formal permission for any research to be carried out at institutions in Turkey. ARIT fellowship applicants are responsible for

obtaining the appropriate research permissions and visas. In general, researchers should seek permission to carry out research directly from the director(s) of the institution(s) where they intend to work; this includes researchers who wish to work in libraries housed in Turkish museums. For short-term research tenures some foreign scholars may enter Turkey on a tourist visa and apply for the research permit and visa from within Turkey, or scholars may choose to procure a research visa from the Turkish embassy in advance of their arrival. Scholars wishing to carry out research in Turkey for terms longer than three months should apply for the research permit and in addition secure a research visa prior to entering Turkey. Non-U.S. researchers should consult the Turkish Consulate for specific procedures.

Researchers who wish to work with collections housed in the Turkish archaeological museums, however, should make their applications through the Ministry of Culture and Tourism, General Directorate for Cultural Heritage and Museums. In addition, if the material they wish to work with is part of an excavation, researchers must submit a letter with their application signed by the excavation director giving permission to carry out the research. The research permit application regulations and format for researchers are posted on the ARIT web site. ARIT reserves the right to withhold payment of fellowship stipends if appropriate research permission is not obtained.

Please include letters of reference with one's application. Graduate student applicants must provide a copy of their graduate transcript.
Duration: Stipends are provided for a period determined by each Fellow's research requirements, but not exceeding 12 months. Some preference will be given to projects of shorter duration.
Deadline: Applications and three letters of recommendation must be received by November 1 to ARIT, c/o University of Pennsylvania Museum.

OFFICERS:
A. Kevin Reinhart, President
Nick Cahill, Vice President
Maria de Jong Ellis, Treasurer
Linda Darling, Secretary

ADDRESS INQUIRIES TO:
Nancy W. Leinwand
(See telephone and e-mail above.)

AMERICAN RESEARCH INSTITUTE IN TURKEY, INC.   [882]
c/o The University of Pennsylvania Museum
3260 South Street
Philadelphia, PA 19104-6324
(215) 898-3474
Fax: (215) 898-0657

E-MAIL ADDRESS:
leinwand@sas.upenn.edu

WEB SITE ADDRESS:
ccat.sas.upenn.edu/ARIT

FOUNDED: 1964

AREAS OF INTEREST:
Turkey.

NAME(S) OF PROGRAMS:
- **Bogazici University Summer Language Program for Intensive Advanced Turkish Language Study**

TYPE:
Fellowships. Bogazici University Summer Language Program: For summer study in Turkey. Also offer travel, stipend and tuition grants. This intensive program offers the equivalent of one full academic year of study in advanced Turkish language at the college level.

YEAR PROGRAM STARTED: 1981

PURPOSE:
To support the study of advanced Turkish language.

LEGAL BASIS:
Consortium of universities. Funding from the U.S. Department of Education.

ELIGIBILITY:
Full-time students and scholars affiliated at academic institutions are eligible to apply. To be a fellowship applicant, one must:
(1) be a citizen, national or permanent resident of the U.S.;
(2) be enrolled in an undergraduate- or graduate-level academic program, or be faculty;
(3) have a minimum B average in one's studies, if still a student; and
(4) perform at the high-intermediate level on a proficiency-based admissions examination.

FINANCIAL DATA:
Fellowships cover round-trip airfare to Istanbul, application and tuition fees, and a maintenance stipend.

COOPERATIVE FUNDING PROGRAMS: Funded by U.S. Department of Education, Fulbright-Hays Group Projects Abroad Program.

NUMBER OF APPLICANTS MOST RECENT YEAR: Approximately 50.

NUMBER OF AWARDS: 15.

APPLICATION INFORMATION:
Application information is available on the web site.
Duration: Approximately eight weeks (late June through early August).
Deadline: February 1.

OFFICERS:
A. Kevin Reinhart, President
Nick Cahill, Vice President
Maria de Jong Ellis, Treasurer
Linda Darling, Secretary

ADDRESS INQUIRIES TO:
Dr. Sylvia Onder
Eastern Mediterranean Languages
Department of Arabic and Islamic Studies
Georgetown University
210 North Poulton Hall
1437 37th Street, N.W.
Washington, DC 20007
E-mail: aritfellowship@georgetown.edu or

Nancy Leinwand
American Research Institute in Turkey
(See address and e-mail above.)

AMERICAN RESEARCH INSTITUTE IN TURKEY, INC.   [883]
c/o The University of Pennsylvania Museum
3260 South Street
Philadelphia, PA 19104-6324
(215) 898-3474
Fax: (215) 898-0657

E-MAIL ADDRESS:
leinwand@sas.upenn.edu

WEB SITE ADDRESS:
ccat.sas.upenn.edu/ARIT/

FOUNDED: 1964

AREAS OF INTEREST:
Turkey covering all periods of history in the general range of the humanities and including humanistically oriented aspects of the social sciences, prehistory, history, art, archaeology, literature and linguistics, as well as interdisciplinary aspects of cultural history.

NAME(S) OF PROGRAMS:
- **NEH Fellowships for Research in Turkey**

TYPE:
Fellowships. These advanced fellowships are made possible by support from the National Endowment for the Humanities. The fields of study cover all periods of history in the general range of the humanities and include humanistically oriented aspects of the social sciences, prehistory, history, art, archaeology, literature and linguistics, as well as interdisciplinary aspects of cultural history.

ARIT maintains two research institutes in Turkey. ARIT in Istanbul has a research library concentrated on Byzantine and Ottoman Turkey. The ARIT Ankara center focuses on art, archaeology, and ancient history in its library, and serves Turkish and American archaeologists through its programs. Both institutes have residential facilities for fellows and provide general assistance as well as introductions to colleagues, institutions and authorities in Turkey.

YEAR PROGRAM STARTED: 1991

PURPOSE:
To support long-term postdoctoral research in Turkey in the humanities.

LEGAL BASIS:
Consortium of universities. Funding from the National Endowment for the Humanities.

ELIGIBILITY:
Scholars who have completed their formal academic training by the application deadline and plan to carry out research in Turkey may apply. Applicants may be U.S. citizens or three-year residents of the U.S. Please consult ARIT headquarters on questions of eligibility. Advanced scholars may also apply for ARIT Fellowships in the Humanities and Social Sciences.

FINANCIAL DATA:
Amount of support per award: $16,800 to $50,400 stipend, depending on individual proposals.

NUMBER OF APPLICANTS MOST RECENT YEAR: 15.

NUMBER OF AWARDS: 1 to 3 advanced fellowships for the 2015-16 academic year.

APPLICATION INFORMATION:
Turkish law requires foreign scholars to obtain formal permission to carry out research at institutions in Turkey. ARIT fellowship applicants are responsible for obtaining the appropriate research permissions and visas. In general, researchers should seek permission to carry out research from the director(s) of the institution(s) where they intend to work; this includes researchers who wish to work in libraries housed in Turkish museums. For short-term research tenures some foreign scholars may enter Turkey on a tourist visa and apply for the research permit and visa from within

Turkey; or they may choose to procure a research visa via the Turkish Embassy in advance of their arrival. Scholars wishing to carry out research in Turkey for terms longer than three months should apply for the research permit and in addition secure a research visa prior to entering Turkey. Non-U.S. researchers should consult the Turkish Consulate for specific procedures.

Researchers who wish to work with collections housed in the Turkish archaeological museums, however, should make their applications through the Ministry of Culture and Tourism, General Directorate for Cultural Heritage and Museums. In addition, if the material they wish to work with is part of an excavation, researchers must submit a letter with their application signed by the excavation director giving permission to carry out the research. The research permit application regulations and format for researchers are posted on the ARIT web site (ccat.sas.upenn.edu/ARIT/Research Permit.htm). ARIT reserves the right to withhold payment of fellowship stipends if appropriate research permission is not obtained.

Duration: Four to 12 continuous months.
Deadline: Applications and three letters of recommendation must be received by ARIT by November 1 for the following academic year. Please use the ARIT application format accessible on its web site and submit all materials to the above address. Applicants will be notified by the end of January of that following year.

PUBLICATIONS:
Program announcement.

OFFICERS:
A. Kevin Reinhart, President
Nick Cahill, Vice President
Maria de Jong Ellis, Treasurer
Linda Darling, Secretary

ADDRESS INQUIRIES TO:
Nancy W. Leinwand
(See telephone number above.)

THE AMERICAN-SCANDINAVIAN FOUNDATION   [884]
58 Park Avenue
New York, NY 10016
(212) 879-9779

E-MAIL ADDRESS:
grants@amscan.org

WEB SITE ADDRESS:
www.amscan.org

FOUNDED: 1910

AREAS OF INTEREST:
Advanced study in Scandinavia.

NAME(S) OF PROGRAMS:
- **ASF Awards for Study in Scandinavia**

TYPE:
Fellowships; Research grants. Short-term project grants and long-term fellowships for advanced study in a field which may be pursued with particular merit in one of the Scandinavian countries (Denmark, Finland, Iceland, Norway or Sweden).

Fellowships are intended to support an academic year-long stay. Priority is given to candidates at the graduate level for dissertation-related study or research.

Grants are considered especially suitable for postgraduate scholars, professionals and candidates in the arts to carry out research or study visits of one to three months' duration.

YEAR PROGRAM STARTED: 1911

PURPOSE:
To advance cultural and intellectual understanding between the U.S. and Scandinavia, primarily through exchange programs, cultural programs and publications.

LEGAL BASIS:
Nonprofit educational institution qualifying under statutes 501(c)(3), 509(a)(1) and 170(c)(2) of the IRS code.

ELIGIBILITY:
Applicants must have a well-defined research or study project that makes a stay in Scandinavia essential. Applicants must be U.S. citizens or permanent residents who will have completed their undergraduate education by the start of their project in Scandinavia. Team projects are eligible, but each member must apply as an individual, submitting a separate, fully documented application. First priority will be given to applicants who have not previously received an ASF award. Only in exceptional cases will a third award be considered. The ASF considers it desirable that all candidates have at least some ability in the language of the host country, even if it is not essential for the execution of the research plan. For projects that require a command of one or more Scandinavian (or other) languages, candidates should defer application until they have the necessary proficiency. Evidence of a confirmed invitation or affiliation is an important factor in award consideration.

ASF does not fund the following:
(1) travel for attendance at professional meetings, conferences, seminars or conventions;
(2) performances or exhibitions;
(3) publication costs;
(4) equipment purchases, including personal computers, software and cell phones;
(5) research assistants;
(6) institutional overhead costs;
(7) tuition fees from U.S. home institution;
(8) foregone salary;
(9) supplementation of substantial sabbatical support;
(10) support for dependents;
(11) repayment of loans or other personal obligations;
(12) acquisition of language skills;
(13) study in programs especially designed for English-speaking students, or at English-language institutions;
(14) beginning studies in any subject or;
(15) retroactive program support.

Projects must be undertaken in Denmark, Finland, Iceland, Norway or Sweden.

GEOGRAPHIC RESTRICTIONS:
Scandinavia.

FINANCIAL DATA:
The awards support project-related costs, including maintenance, transatlantic round-trip travel, in-country travel, tuition and fees (where applicable) and materials expenditures (e.g., books, photocopying, art supplies).

Amount of support per award: Grants normally up to $5,000, especially suited for short visits of one to three months and fellowships of up to $23,000, intended for a full academic year of study or research.

Total amount of support: Varies annually. Over $300,000 is available for the 2015-16 competition.

NUMBER OF APPLICANTS MOST RECENT YEAR:
132.

NUMBER OF AWARDS: Varies each year according to total funds available. Awards were made to 25 Americans in the 2014-15 competition.

APPLICATION INFORMATION:
Only applications on current official ASF forms will be considered. Such applications are available online. Incomplete applications cannot be processed. Unsuccessful applications will be discarded.

Applicants for Awards for Study in Scandinavia are urged to arrange their academic or professional affiliations as far in advance as possible. Applicants must secure these placements or affiliations on their own; the ASF cannot assist in establishing contacts. The ASF requires confirmation of invitation or affiliation from the institution or individuals detailed in the proposal. Since July and August are traditionally holiday months in Scandinavia, many people may not be available for consultation. Applicants are cautioned to plan their projects accordingly. Applicants are expected to devote full-time to their proposed study or research, and must justify the length of time needed to complete their project. Awards are based on the application submitted; subsequent changes in the proposal are discouraged and may not be considered.

Duration: Grants: One to three months. Fellowships: One academic year.

Deadline: November 1 for receipt of fully documented applications. Awards announced by the following March 15.

PUBLICATIONS:
Annual report; fellowship and grant application guidelines; *Scandinavian Review*; *Scan*, newsletter; *Study in Scandinavia*, guide.

ADMINISTRATION:
Edward P. Gallagher, President
Lynn Carter, Executive Vice President
Matthew Walters, Director, Fellowships and Grants

ADDRESS INQUIRIES TO:
Fellowships and Grants
(See address above.)

*SPECIAL STIPULATIONS:
ASF awards may require supplementation from other sources, but they should not duplicate the benefits of additional awards (and vice versa). Candidates must notify the ASF if they have received other award offers. The ASF will not provide funds if, in its judgment, a proposal can be carried out without its assistance.

THE AMERICAN SCHOOL OF CLASSICAL STUDIES AT ATHENS   [885]
6-8 Charlton Street
Princeton, NJ 08540-5232
(609) 683-0800
Fax: (609) 924-0578

E-MAIL ADDRESS:
ascsa@ascsa.org (for information)
application@ascsa.org (to apply)

WEB SITE ADDRESS:
www.ascsa.edu.gr

FOUNDED: 1881

AREAS OF INTEREST:
Classical studies.

NAME(S) OF PROGRAMS:
● **National Endowment for the Humanities Fellowships**

TYPE:
Fellowships. Fellowships for postdoctoral scholars and professionals in the humanities.

YEAR PROGRAM STARTED: 1881

LEGAL BASIS:
Graduate research and teaching center.

ELIGIBILITY:
Applicants must be U.S. citizens or foreign nationals who have been U.S. residents for three years prior to application deadline. Candidates must hold their Ph.D. or equivalent terminal degree at time of application.

School programs are generally open to qualified students and scholars at colleges or universities in the U.S. or Canada; restrictions may apply for specific fellowships and programs. The American School of Classical Studies at Athens does not discriminate on the basis of race, age, sex, sexual orientation, color, religion, ethnic origin, or disability when considering admission to any form of membership.

FINANCIAL DATA:
Amount of support per award: Stipend up to $21,000 (for a five-month project) and up to $42,000 (for a 10-month project).

NUMBER OF APPLICANTS MOST RECENT YEAR:
21.

NUMBER OF AWARDS: 2 to 4.

APPLICATION INFORMATION:
Correspondence about fellowships and admission to membership in the school should be directed to the address above. Applicants must submit an online application form and letters of reference.

Duration: Five to 10 months during academic year, September 1 to June 1.

Deadline: October 31.

STAFF:
James C. Wright, Director

ADDRESS INQUIRIES TO:
E-mail: ascsa@ascsa.org

*SPECIAL STIPULATIONS:
Membership application to the ASCSA must be made online on the web site at the same time one applies to any outside funding organization for work at the School.

THE AMERICAN SCHOOL OF CLASSICAL STUDIES AT ATHENS   [886]
6-8 Charlton Street
Princeton, NJ 08540-5232
(609) 683-0800
Fax: (609) 924-0578

E-MAIL ADDRESS:
ascsa@ascsa.org (for information)
application@ascsa.org (to apply)

WEB SITE ADDRESS:
www.ascsa.edu.gr

FOUNDED: 1881

AREAS OF INTEREST:
Classical studies, archaeology, art history, post-classical, Byzantine and post-Byzantine, Late Antiquity and Modern Greek Studies.

NAME(S) OF PROGRAMS:
- **M. Alison Frantz Fellowship in Post-Classical Studies at the Gennadius Library**
- **The Jacob Hirsch Fellowship in Archaeology**

TYPE:
Fellowships. The M. Alison Frantz Fellowship and The Jacob Hirsch Fellowship are part of the Student Associate Program, which is open to advanced graduate students in the same fields as the Regular Academic Program (classical studies and ancient Mediterranean studies and related fields such as history of art, anthropology, prehistory, studies in postclassical Greece, etc.), who plan to pursue independent research projects and who do not wish to commit to the full Regular Academic Program.

The Jacob Hirsch Fellowship is also open to students from Israel.

YEAR PROGRAM STARTED: 1963

PURPOSE:
To provide financial assistance to advanced graduate students who plan to pursue independent research projects and who do not wish to commit to the American School's full Regular Academic Program.

LEGAL BASIS:
Graduate educational institution (non-degree granting).

ELIGIBILITY:
Frantz Fellowship: Awarded to Ph.D. candidates at a U.S. or Canadian institution or college or a recent Ph.D. from a U.S. or Canadian institution. Applicants must demonstrate their need to work in the Gennadius Library. Fields of study include late antiquity, Byzantine or modern Greek studies.

Hirsch Fellowship: Awarded to a Ph.D. candidate from U.S. or Israel (Israeli citizens) writing a dissertation, or a recent Ph.D. revising a dissertation for publication, for projects carried out in Greece.

School programs are generally open to qualified students and scholars at colleges or universities in the U.S. or Canada; restrictions may apply for specific fellowships and programs. The American School of Classical Studies at Athens does not discriminate on the basis of race, age, sex, sexual orientation, color, religion, ethnic origin, or disability when considering admission to any form of membership.

FINANCIAL DATA:
In addition to stipend, room and board is provided at the American School of Classical Studies in Athens.
Amount of support per award: Stipend of $11,500, plus room, board and waiver of School fees.

NUMBER OF APPLICANTS MOST RECENT YEAR: 24.

NUMBER OF AWARDS: 1 of each annually.

APPLICATION INFORMATION:
Application must be made online on the ASCSA web site.

Frantz Fellowship: Applicants must submit a full curriculum vitae, a project description showing the need for using the Gennadius Library and three supporting letters from qualified scholars. Send application to Chairperson, Gennadius Library Committee.

Hirsch Fellowship: Online application for admission to the American School should be made in conjunction with application for the Hirsch Fellowship. Transcripts of record, three letters of recommendation and a detailed description of the project to be pursued in Greece should be submitted to Chair, Committee on Admissions and Fellowships.

Duration: One academic year (September to June).

Deadline: January 15, with announcement by March 15.

STAFF:
James C. Wright, Director

ADDRESS INQUIRIES TO:
Frantz Fellowship:
Chair,
Committee on Libraries and Archives
(See address above.)

Hirsch Fellowship:
Chair,
Committee on Admissions and Fellowships
(See address above.)

*SPECIAL STIPULATIONS:
Membership application to the ASCSA must be made online on the web site at the same time one applies to any outside funding organization for work at the School.

Hirsch and Frantz Fellowship recipients must maintain residence in Athens and work at the Gennadius Library during the full term of the Fellowship.

THE AMERICAN SCHOOL OF CLASSICAL STUDIES AT ATHENS [887]
6-8 Charlton Street
Princeton, NJ 08540-5232
(609) 683-0800
Fax: (609) 924-0578

E-MAIL ADDRESS:
application@ascsa.org

WEB SITE ADDRESS:
www.ascsa.edu.gr

FOUNDED: 1881

AREAS OF INTEREST:
Research at the ASCSA excavations at Ancient Corinth in Greece.

NAME(S) OF PROGRAMS:
- **Henry S. Robinson Corinth Research Fellowship**

TYPE:
Fellowships. Fellowship for research on a doctoral dissertation or primary publication specifically on Corinth.

PURPOSE:
To revive field work at Corinth.

ELIGIBILITY:
Ph.D. candidate or recent Ph.D. (within five years), for research on a doctoral dissertation or primary publication specifically on Corinth, requiring the use of the resources, archaeological site and collections at the ASCSA excavations at Ancient Corinth in Greece. Open to all nationalities.

FINANCIAL DATA:
The Fellowship does not allow travel costs (to and from country of origin or within Greece). Availability of rooms and work space is limited during the excavation season from April to June.
Amount of support per award: Up to $4,500 for one or more individuals. Funding is for research activities at Corinth, to be used to cover living expenses, including room, board, fees and other costs associated with the study, such as photography and drawings.

APPLICATION INFORMATION:
Submit Associate Membership application online, including curriculum vitae and proposal statement, which should have the following items:
(1) project outline;
(2) explanation of goals;
(3) statement of the significance of the project;
(4) work completed to date;
(5) schedule for completion;
(6) dates for project;
(7) budget and;
(8) two letters of support, including one from dissertation advisor if applicant is a Ph.D. candidate.

Duration: Up to three months within the 12-month period July 1 to June 30; nonrenewable.

Deadline: January 15; announcement mid-March.

*SPECIAL STIPULATIONS:
The Robinson Fellowship may not be held concurrently with another School fellowship. Preference is given to candidates who have not previously held the Robinson Fellowship or received substantial ASCSA funding for the same project.

THE AMERICAN SCHOOL OF CLASSICAL STUDIES AT ATHENS [888]
6-8 Charlton Street
Princeton, NJ 08540-5232
(609) 683-0800
Fax: (609) 924-0578

E-MAIL ADDRESS:
application@ascsa.org

WEB SITE ADDRESS:
www.ascsa.edu.gr

FOUNDED: 1881

AREAS OF INTEREST:
Research in the art and architecture of antiquity.

NAME(S) OF PROGRAMS:
- **Kress Publication Fellowships**

TYPE:
Fellowships. Fellowships are aimed at supporting scholars who are assigned material for publication from the School's excavations at Ancient Corinth or the Athenian Agora.

ELIGIBILITY:
Senior postdoctoral scholars working on a Corinth or Agora publication assignment. Preference will be given to those working on a Corinth or Agora excavation volume and to those applicants who have not previously received the Kress Publications Fellowship. Applications from current staff of the School are not eligible.

FINANCIAL DATA:
School fees, travel costs, housing, board and other living expenses are to be paid out of the stipend by the recipient.

Total amount of support: A total of $30,000 is available for each grant cycle, defined as the School's fiscal year (July 1 - June 30).

NUMBER OF AWARDS: The School awards up to three grants each cycle.

APPLICATION INFORMATION:
Application and requirements are available on the web site.

Duration: Grants are for a minimum of three months (up to $10,000) to a maximum of nine months (up to $30,000). Grants are not renewable.

Deadline: Approximately December 1.

THE AMERICAN SCHOOL OF CLASSICAL STUDIES AT ATHENS   [889]

6-8 Charlton Street
Princeton, NJ 08540-5232
(609) 683-0800
Fax: (609) 924-0578

E-MAIL ADDRESS:
application@ascsa.org

WEB SITE ADDRESS:
www.ascsa.edu.gr

FOUNDED: 1881

AREAS OF INTEREST:
Modern Greek political and social history.

NAME(S) OF PROGRAMS:
● **The George Papaioannou Fellowship**

TYPE:
Fellowships. Research fellowship. Fellows are required to make use of and refer to the George Papaioannou Papers housed at the Archives of the Gennadius Library.

PURPOSE:
The Fellowship was established to honor George Papaioannou, leader of the Trichonis subdivision of EDES.

ELIGIBILITY:
Ph.D. candidates or recent Ph.Ds. researching Greece in the 1940s and the postwar period. Open to all nationalities.

FINANCIAL DATA:
The Fellowship does not include travel costs, housing, board and other living expenses.
Amount of support per award: Grant of EUR 1,000. School fees are covered by the award for a maximum of two months.

APPLICATION INFORMATION:
Submit application, curriculum vitae, project description (up to two pages) and two letters of reference online.
Duration: Up to two months; nonrenewable.
Deadline: January 15; announcement in mid-March.

*SPECIAL STIPULATIONS:
The recipient should not plan to work at the Archives of the Gennadius Library during the month of August.

THE AMERICAN SCHOOL OF CLASSICAL STUDIES AT ATHENS   [890]

6-8 Charlton Street
Princeton, NJ 08540-5232
(609) 683-0800
Fax: (609) 924-0578

E-MAIL ADDRESS:
ascsa@ascsa.org (for information)
application@ascsa.org (to apply)

WEB SITE ADDRESS:
www.ascsa.edu.gr

FOUNDED: 1881

AREAS OF INTEREST:
Classical studies, history of art, history of architecture, pottery, Mycenaean archaeology, Athenian architecture and archaeology.

NAME(S) OF PROGRAMS:
● **Advanced Fellowships**

TYPE:
Fellowships. Several Fellowships awarded by the School for the full academic year: the Samuel H. Kress Fellowship in art and architecture of antiquity; the Gorham Phillips Stevens Fellowship in the history of architecture; the Ione Mylonas Shear Fellowship in Mycenaean archaeology or Athenian architecture and/or archaeology; the Homer A. and Dorothy B. Thompson Fellowship in the study of pottery. Additionally, three Fellowships are unrestricted as to field: the Edward Capps, the Doreen Canaday Spitzer, and the Eugene Vanderpool Fellowships.

PURPOSE:
To support work on a specific project by students who wish to study at the School for a year.

ELIGIBILITY:
Students who have completed the Regular Program or one year as a Student Associate Member at the ASCSA and plan to return to the School to pursue independent research, usually for the Ph.D. dissertation, may apply. Given only if candidates meet a standard acceptable to the Director and the Committee.

School programs are generally open to qualified students and scholars at colleges or universities in the U.S. or Canada; restrictions may apply for specific fellowships and programs. The American School of Classical Studies at Athens does not discriminate on the basis of race, age, sex, sexual orientation, color, religion, ethnic origin, or disability when considering admission to any form of membership.

GEOGRAPHIC RESTRICTIONS:
United States and Canada.

FINANCIAL DATA:
Amount of support per award: Stipend of $11,500, plus room, board and waiver of School fees.

NUMBER OF APPLICANTS MOST RECENT YEAR:
23.

NUMBER OF AWARDS: 7.

APPLICATION INFORMATION:
Submit application form, curriculum vitae, transcripts, letters of recommendation and a detailed statement of the project to be pursued in Greece. Application must be made online on the ASCSA web site.
Duration: One year.
Deadline: February 15.

STAFF:
James C. Wright, Director

ADDRESS INQUIRIES TO:
Committee Chair
(See address above.)

*SPECIAL STIPULATIONS:
Membership application to the ASCSA must be made online on the web site at the same time one applies to any outside funding organization for work at the School.

THE AMERICAN SCHOOL OF CLASSICAL STUDIES AT ATHENS   [891]

6-8 Charlton Street
Princeton, NJ 08540-5232
(609) 683-0800
Fax: (609) 924-0578

E-MAIL ADDRESS:
ascsa@ascsa.org (for information)
application@ascsa.org (to apply)

WEB SITE ADDRESS:
www.ascsa.edu.gr

FOUNDED: 1881

AREAS OF INTEREST:
Ancient Greek law.

NAME(S) OF PROGRAMS:
● **The Harry Bikakis Fellowship**

TYPE:
Fellowships. Research fellowship awarded periodically, but not more frequently than once a year.

PURPOSE:
To promote research.

ELIGIBILITY:
North American or Greek graduate students researching ancient Greek law, or Greek graduate students working on a School excavation.

School programs are generally open to qualified students and scholars at colleges or universities in the U.S. or Canada; restrictions may apply for specific fellowships and programs. The American School of Classical Studies at Athens does not discriminate on the basis of race, age, sex, sexual orientation, color, religion, ethnic origin, or disability when considering admission to any form of membership.

GEOGRAPHIC RESTRICTIONS:
North America.

FINANCIAL DATA:
Amount of support per award: $1,875.

NUMBER OF APPLICANTS MOST RECENT YEAR:
2.

NUMBER OF AWARDS: 1.

APPLICATION INFORMATION:
Submit Associate Member application, including an outline of the proposed project, and one letter of reference online on the ASCSA web site.
Deadline: January 15.

STAFF:
James C. Wright, Director

ADDRESS INQUIRIES TO:
Committee Chair
(See address above.)

*SPECIAL STIPULATIONS:
Membership application to the ASCSA must be made online on the web site at the same time one applies to any outside funding organization for work at the School.

THE AMERICAN SCHOOL OF CLASSICAL STUDIES AT ATHENS   [892]

6-8 Charlton Street
Princeton, NJ 08540-5232
(609) 683-0800
Fax: (609) 924-0578

E-MAIL ADDRESS:
ascsa@ascsa.org (for information)
application@ascsa.org (to apply)

WEB SITE ADDRESS:
www.ascsa.edu.gr

FOUNDED: 1881

AREAS OF INTEREST:
Gennadeion collections.

NAME(S) OF PROGRAMS:
• **Cotsen Traveling Fellowship for Research in Greece**

TYPE:
Fellowships. Short-term travel-to-collections award.

PURPOSE:
To assist students and scholars in the pursuit of research topics requiring the use of Gennadeion collections.

ELIGIBILITY:
Senior scholars and graduate students for projects and research at the Gennadius Library. Requires residency in Athens of at least one month during the academic year and recipient to take part in the life of the Library and of the School in addition to pursuing research.

School programs are generally open to qualified students and scholars at colleges or universities in the U.S. or Canada; restrictions may apply for specific fellowships and programs. The American School of Classical Studies at Athens does not discriminate on the basis of race, age, sex, sexual orientation, color, religion, ethnic origin, or disability when considering admission to any form of membership.

FINANCIAL DATA:
Amount of support per award: $2,000 towards cost of travel, school fees and living expenses while in Athens.

NUMBER OF APPLICANTS MOST RECENT YEAR:
7.

NUMBER OF AWARDS: 1.

APPLICATION INFORMATION:
Application must be made online and should include the following:
(1) curriculum vitae;
(2) letter (up to three pages) describing the project, proposed dates, budget, and explanation of the relation of the Gennadius Library's collection to the research project and;
(3) two letters of recommendation.
Deadline: January 15.

STAFF:
Dr. Maria Georgopoulou, Director, Gennadius Library

ADDRESS INQUIRIES TO:
Committee Chair, Libraries and Archives
(See address above.)

*SPECIAL STIPULATIONS:
Membership application to the ASCSA must be made online on the web site at the same time one applies to any outside funding organization for work at the School.

THE AMERICAN SCHOOL OF CLASSICAL STUDIES AT ATHENS [893]
6-8 Charlton Street
Princeton, NJ 08540-5232
(609) 683-0800
Fax: (609) 924-0578

E-MAIL ADDRESS:
ascsa@ascsa.org (for information)
application@ascsa.org (to apply)

WEB SITE ADDRESS:
www.ascsa.edu.gr

FOUNDED: 1881

AREAS OF INTEREST:
Medieval Greek language and philology.

NAME(S) OF PROGRAMS:
• **Medieval Greek Summer Session at the Gennadius Library**

TYPE:
Scholarships. Four-week program in intermediate-level Medieval Greek language and philology at the Gennadius Library, with site and museum trips. Seminar given every other year. Next seminar to be held in 2015.

YEAR PROGRAM STARTED: 2005

PURPOSE:
To promote the study of Medieval Greek language and philology.

ELIGIBILITY:
Graduate students and professors in any field of late antiquity, post-antiquity, Byzantine or medieval studies from any university or graduate center worldwide.

School programs are generally open to qualified students and scholars at colleges or universities in the U.S. or Canada; restrictions may apply for specific fellowships and programs. The American School of Classical Studies at Athens does not discriminate on the basis of race, age, sex, sexual orientation, color, religion, ethnic origin, or disability when considering admission to any form of membership.

GEOGRAPHIC RESTRICTIONS:
North America.

FINANCIAL DATA:
The Leventis scholarships cover tuition, travel within Greece, lodging but no meals.

NUMBER OF APPLICANTS MOST RECENT YEAR:
38.

NUMBER OF AWARDS: Up to 10 scholarships.

APPLICATION INFORMATION:
Application information is available on the web site. Application fee of $25 is required.
Duration: One full month.
Deadline: January 15.

STAFF:
Dr. Maria Georgopoulou, Director, Gennadius Library

ADDRESS INQUIRIES TO:
Committee Chair, Libraries and Archives
(See address above.)

*SPECIAL STIPULATIONS:
Membership application to the ASCSA must be made online on the web site at the same time one applies to any outside funding organization for work at the School.

THE AMERICAN SCHOOL OF CLASSICAL STUDIES AT ATHENS [894]
6-8 Charlton Street
Princeton, NJ 08540-5232
(609) 683-0800
Fax: (609) 924-0578

E-MAIL ADDRESS:
ascsa@ascsa.org (for information)
application@ascsa.org (to apply)

WEB SITE ADDRESS:
www.ascsa.edu.gr

FOUNDED: 1881

AREAS OF INTEREST:
Skeletal, faunal, geoarchaeological, environmental studies and archaeological science.

NAME(S) OF PROGRAMS:
• **Wiener Laboratory Fellowships**
• **Wiener Laboratory Research Associateships**
• **Wiener Laboratory Travel Grants**

TYPE:
Fellowships; Research grants; Travel grants. Fellowships for projects in skeletal, faunal, geoarchaeological or environmental studies.

Research Associateships for well-defined research projects.

Travel Grants for projects in archaeological science research in Greece.

PURPOSE:
To promote laboratory research pertinent to the American School of Classical Studies at Athens.

ELIGIBILITY:
Fellowships: Graduate students or postdoctoral scholars working on well-defined projects in skeletal, faunal, geoarchaeological or environmental studies.

Research Associateships: For well-defined research projects at the Wiener Laboratory.

Travel Grants: Graduate students or postdoctoral scholars from North American institutions working on projects in archaeological science in Greece.

School programs are generally open to qualified students and scholars at colleges or universities in the U.S. or Canada; restrictions may apply for specific fellowships and programs. The American School of Classical Studies at Athens does not discriminate on the basis of race, age, sex, sexual orientation, color, religion, ethnic origin, or disability when considering admission to any form of membership.

FINANCIAL DATA:
Amount of support per award: Fellowships: Stipend of $15,500 to $27,000; Research Associateships: Up to $7,000; Travel Grants: $2,000.

NUMBER OF APPLICANTS MOST RECENT YEAR:
25.

NUMBER OF AWARDS: Fellowships: 1 to 2 annually; Associateships: 4 to 6; Travel Grant: 1 to 2.

APPLICATION INFORMATION:
Application must be made online on the ASCSA web site.

Applicants for the Fellowships and Research Associateships must submit the following:
(1) cover letter (Fellowship) or application (Research Associateship) naming the applicant and title of the project;
(2) project description, no more than 2,500 words, describing the purpose, nature and methodology of the research project;
(3) copies of permits or letters from relevant authorities to study proposed materials, and copies of permission(s) from relevant excavation or project directors to study the proposed materials;
(4) budget (itemize in as much detail as

possible);
(5) curriculum vitae and;
(6) two letters of recommendation.

Applicants seeking the Travel Grant must submit application, curriculum vitae, statement of the project to be pursued (up to 2,000 words), and budget.

Deadline: Research Associateships and Travel Grants: September 1 and January 15, annually. Fellowships: January 15.

STAFF:
Sherry Fox, Director of the Wiener Laboratory

ADDRESS INQUIRIES TO:
Committee Chair, Wiener Laboratory
(See address above.)

*SPECIAL STIPULATIONS:
Membership application to the ASCSA must be made online on the web site at the same time one applies to any outside funding organization for work at the School.

AMERICAN SCHOOLS OF ORIENTAL RESEARCH (ASOR)   [895]
656 Beacon Street, Fifth Floor
Boston, MA 02215
(617) 353-6570
Fax: (617) 353-6575

E-MAIL ADDRESS:
asor@bu.edu

WEB SITE ADDRESS:
www.asor.org

FOUNDED: 1900

AREAS OF INTEREST:
The study of humanistic disciplines, such as anthropology, archaeology, Biblical studies, epigraphy, history, history of art and architecture, literature, philology, prehistory and topography, relating in particular to the Middle East from prehistoric times to the modern era.

NAME(S) OF PROGRAMS:
● **Harris Grants**
● **Heritage Fellowships**
● **Mesopotamian Fellowship**
● **Platt Fellowships**

TYPE:
Conferences/seminars; Fellowships; Research grants; Scholarships; Travel grants.

YEAR PROGRAM STARTED: 1940

PURPOSE:
To encourage scholars to undertake study and research about the ancient Near East.

LEGAL BASIS:
Nonprofit, archaeological research corporation.

ELIGIBILITY:
The Fellowship is open to qualified students and scholars from any country. Applicants must be or become individual professional members of ASOR, or must be affiliated with an institution that is a member of ASOR.

FINANCIAL DATA:
Amount of support per award: Harris Grants: Approximately $500 to $1,000; Heritage and Platt Fellowships: $1,000 each; Mesopotamian Fellowship: $9,000.
Total amount of support: Approximately $64,000 for the year 2013.

NUMBER OF APPLICANTS MOST RECENT YEAR:
Varies.

NUMBER OF AWARDS: Harris Grants: 14; Heritage Fellowships: 24; Mesopotamian Fellowship: 1; Platt Fellowships: 15.

APPLICATION INFORMATION:
All eligible persons are encouraged to apply for as many fellowships and professorships as they wish, but a person can hold only one award at a time. Persons who have received an award in one year can reapply for the same or other awards the following year, but new applicants will have priority.
Deadline: Harris Grants, Heritage Fellowships and Platt Fellowships: Mid-February; Mesopotamian Fellowship: March 1.

PUBLICATIONS:
Application forms.

STAFF:
Andrew Vaughn, Executive Director

ADDRESS INQUIRIES TO:
Office Coordinator
(See address above.)

*SPECIAL STIPULATIONS:
Applicants must be or become members of ASOR or attend an ASOR-affiliated institution.

THE AMERICAN SWEDISH INSTITUTE   [896]
2600 Park Avenue
Minneapolis, MN 55407
(612) 871-4907
Fax: (612) 871-8682

E-MAIL ADDRESS:
info@asimn.org

WEB SITE ADDRESS:
www.asimn.org

FOUNDED: 1929

AREAS OF INTEREST:
Swedish culture.

NAME(S) OF PROGRAMS:
● **Lilly Lorénzen Scholarship**

TYPE:
Scholarships; Travel grants.

YEAR PROGRAM STARTED: 1980

PURPOSE:
To foster and preserve Swedish culture in America.

ELIGIBILITY:
Must be a Minnesota resident or a student attending a Minnesota school with working knowledge of the Swedish language that presents a creditable plan of study for the next academic year.

FINANCIAL DATA:
Amount of support per award: $1,000.
Total amount of support: $1,000.

NUMBER OF APPLICANTS MOST RECENT YEAR:
11.

APPLICATION INFORMATION:
Submit application form and college transcript. If transcript is not available, include a statement of professional and community achievement. Contact the Institute at the address above for an application, or visit the Institute web site.
Duration: One-time award.
Deadline: May 1.

ADDRESS INQUIRIES TO:
Karin Krull, Adult Programs Coordinator
(See address above.)

THE AMERICAN SWEDISH INSTITUTE   [897]
2600 Park Avenue
Minneapolis, MN 55407
(612) 871-4907
Fax: (612) 871-8682

E-MAIL ADDRESS:
info@asimn.org

WEB SITE ADDRESS:
www.asimn.org

FOUNDED: 1929

AREAS OF INTEREST:
Swedish culture.

NAME(S) OF PROGRAMS:
● **The Malmberg Scholarship for Study in Sweden**

TYPE:
Scholarships; Travel grants. The Malmberg Scholarship is awarded for up to one academic year of study in Sweden.

PURPOSE:
To support intellectual connections between the U.S. and Sweden by providing grants to students and scholars.

ELIGIBILITY:
Enrolled undergraduate and graduate students and qualified scholars are eligible. The recipient must be a U.S. resident.

FINANCIAL DATA:
Amount of support per award: Up to $10,000.

NUMBER OF APPLICANTS MOST RECENT YEAR:
9.

NUMBER OF AWARDS: 2.

APPLICATION INFORMATION:
Application forms are available on the web site.
Deadline: November 15.

ADDRESS INQUIRIES TO:
Karin Krull
Adult Programs Coordinator
(See address above.)

ASIAN CULTURAL COUNCIL   [898]
6 West 48th Street, 12th Floor
New York, NY 10036-1802
(212) 843-0403
Fax: (212) 843-0343

E-MAIL ADDRESS:
acc@accny.org

WEB SITE ADDRESS:
www.asianculturalcouncil.org

FOUNDED: 1980

AREAS OF INTEREST:
Cultural exchange between Asia and the U.S. in the performing and visual arts.

NAME(S) OF PROGRAMS:
● **Asian Cultural Council Fellowships**

TYPE:
Exchange programs; Fellowships. Grants are awarded to individuals for research and creative projects across a wide spectrum of the performing and visual arts, and across both traditional and contemporary concentrations. Some grants are also made to educational and cultural organizations engaged in projects of special significance to Asian-American exchange. The ACC is both

a grantmaking and grant-seeking organization, raising funding from corporate, foundation and individual donors in both the U.S. and Asia.

YEAR PROGRAM STARTED: 1963

PURPOSE:
To support cultural exchange between the U.S. and Asia and within the countries of Asia.

ELIGIBILITY:
Applicants from Asia must live and work in their home countries and be committed to pursuing professional careers there. The same is true of American applicants. Priority is generally given to individuals with little or no previous opportunity for study and research in the country for which travel assistance is being sought from the ACC.

GEOGRAPHIC RESTRICTIONS:
United States and Asia.

FINANCIAL DATA:
Amount of support per award: $1,000 to $35,000.

Total amount of support: Varies.

NUMBER OF AWARDS: 150.

APPLICATION INFORMATION:
Applicant must complete an inquiry form online. If project meets ACC's requirements, an application is then e-mailed.

Duration: Generally, one to 12 months.

Deadline: Varies.

AUSTRIAN CULTURAL FORUM [899]
11 East 52nd Street
New York, NY 10022
(212) 319-5300
Fax: (212) 644-8660

E-MAIL ADDRESS:
desk@acfny.org

WEB SITE ADDRESS:
www.acfny.org

TYPE:
Research grants; Scholarships. The Forum serves as a contact point for correspondence about grants.

PURPOSE:
To enable students to carry out research or study projects on contemporary Austrian topics.

LEGAL BASIS:
Agency of the Republic of Austria.

ADDRESS INQUIRIES TO:
Christian Ebner, Deputy Director
(See address above.)

BELGIAN AMERICAN EDUCATIONAL FOUNDATION, INC. [900]
195 Church Street
New Haven, CT 06510
(203) 785-4055
Fax: (203) 777-5765

E-MAIL ADDRESS:
emile.boulpaep@yale.edu

WEB SITE ADDRESS:
www.baef.us
www.baef.be

FOUNDED: 1920

AREAS OF INTEREST:
Educational exchange between the U.S. and Belgium.

NAME(S) OF PROGRAMS:
● **B.A.E.F. Fellowships for Study in Belgium**

TYPE:
Fellowships. Predoctoral and postdoctoral fellowships for advanced study in most fields of knowledge with supported work to be undertaken at a Belgian university or an institution of higher learning. Fellowships for Belgian students are also available.

YEAR PROGRAM STARTED: 1920

PURPOSE:
To allow American candidates to pursue independent study and research in Belgium on projects for which Belgium provides special advantages.

LEGAL BASIS:
Public foundation.

ELIGIBILITY:
The applicant must be a citizen or permanent resident of the U.S. and either have a Master's degree or equivalent degree, or be working towards a Ph.D. or equivalent degree. Preference is given to applicants under the age of 30. Knowledge of Dutch, French or German is optional.

FINANCIAL DATA:
Fellowships carry a fixed stipend for living expenses, travel and tuition, if any. This stipend is judged adequate for a single person, but additional funds must be provided from other sources if the fellow is to be accompanied by spouse or by spouse and family. Health insurance coverage is also provided.

Amount of support per award: $25,000 for 12 months.

Total amount of support: $3,675,000 for the academic year 2013-14.

NUMBER OF APPLICANTS MOST RECENT YEAR:
50 U.S. applicants per academic year.

NUMBER OF AWARDS: 9 awards to American students per academic year.

APPLICATION INFORMATION:
Applicant shall furnish a completed application form with all its appropriate attachments. Application blanks are available on www.baef.us. Completed applications must be submitted electronically with attachments in PDF format to the e-mail address above.

Duration: 12 months preferred; no less than six months.

Deadline: October 31, for the following academic year. Fellowship starting as early as July 1 of that following year.

DIRECTORS:
Dr. Emile L. Boulpaep, President and Chairman
Olivier Trouveroy, Treasurer
L. Gilles Sion, Secretary
Maryan Ainsworth
Luc Coene
Marcel Crochet
Jacques de Groote
Diego du Monceau
Susan Friberg
Margaret Hoover
Daniel Janssen
Filip Moerman
William S. Moody
Dirk Wauters
Jacques Willems

ADDRESS INQUIRIES TO:
Dr. Emile L. Boulpaep, President
(See address above.)

THE BRITISH INSTITUTE IN EASTERN AFRICA [901]
Laikipia Road
Kileleshwa
Nairobi Kenya
(254) (0)20 43 43190/43 43330
Fax: (254) (0)20 43 43365

E-MAIL ADDRESS:
office@biea.ac.uk

WEB SITE ADDRESS:
www.biea.ac.uk

FOUNDED: 1960

AREAS OF INTEREST:
Any field of the humanities and social sciences in Eastern Africa, including South Sudan, Tanzania and Uganda.

NAME(S) OF PROGRAMS:
● **Minor Research Grant Program**

TYPE:
Research grants. Ad hoc grants are made for research in the field of pre-colonial history and archaeology in Eastern Africa.

YEAR PROGRAM STARTED: 1960

PURPOSE:
To facilitate original research in Eastern African countries.

LEGAL BASIS:
Self-governing institute with Governing Council in London, sponsored by the British Academy.

ELIGIBILITY:
Applicants should have a B.A. or equivalent degree and graduate or undergraduate training in African studies, archaeology or social anthropology, with ability to undertake independent research. Priority is given to researchers based in the U.K. or Eastern Africa.

GEOGRAPHIC RESTRICTIONS:
Eastern Africa, including South Sudan, Tanzania and Uganda

FINANCIAL DATA:
Size of support dependent on Institute's discretion. Funding does not include institutional overheads, stipendiary element or publication costs.

Amount of support per award: GBP 500 to GBP 1,000 (or its equivalent in local currency).

NUMBER OF AWARDS: 15 for the year 2012.

APPLICATION INFORMATION:
Applications are available online. All applications and references should be submitted electronically by e-mail to grants@biea.ac.uk.

Duration: Research must commence within six months of award.

Deadline: January 30.

PUBLICATIONS:
Azania, annual BIEA journal; annual reports; BIEA memoirs; *Journal of Eastern African Studies*.

STAFF:
Dr. Ambreena Manji, Director

ADDRESS INQUIRIES TO:
Dr. Ambreena Manji, Director
The British Institute in Eastern Africa
E-mail: ambreena.manji@biea.ac.uk or director@biea.ac.uk

BRUCEBO FINE ART SCHOLARSHIP FOUNDATION

Department of Geography
McGill University
805 Sherbrooke West
Montreal QC H3A 2K6 Canada
(450) 672-6096
Fax: (514) 398-7437

E-MAIL ADDRESS:
jan.lundgren@mcgill.ca

WEB SITE ADDRESS:
www.brucebosscholarships.com

TYPE:
Awards/prizes; Development grants;
Residencies; Scholarships; Travel grants.
Grant principally in the fields of fine arts,
visual art and design. Grant is either for stay
at the Brucebo Studio on the Island of
Hanseatic Gotland, Sweden, in the Baltic
Sea, for three months during the summer
annually, or for undertaking a European Fine
Art Travel-Study journey during a period of
the fall term, or the following winter/spring
term.

See entry 543 for full listing.

CANADIAN BUREAU FOR INTERNATIONAL EDUCATION (CBIE)   [902]

220 Laurier Avenue West, Suite 1550
Ottawa ON K1P 5Z9 Canada
(613) 237-4820
Fax: (613) 237-1073

E-MAIL ADDRESS:
scholarships-bourses@cbie.ca

WEB SITE ADDRESS:
www.scholarships.gc.ca

FOUNDED: 1981

AREAS OF INTEREST:
All disciplines at the Master's, doctoral or
postdoctoral levels.

NAME(S) OF PROGRAMS:
● **Foreign Government Awards**

TYPE:
Scholarships. Scholarships for study or
research.

PURPOSE:
To provide opportunities for Canadians to
pursue studies or research at institutions of
higher education abroad.

ELIGIBILITY:
Candidates must be Canadian citizens by the
competition deadline and must have obtained
the equivalent of a Canadian Bachelor's
degree from a recognized university. Studies
must take place in Korea or Mexico.

FINANCIAL DATA:
Funding includes tuition and monthly living
allowances, with additional benefits provided
by varying countries. These scholarships are
subject to the availability of funding.
Amount of support per award: Varies by
geographical location.

NUMBER OF APPLICANTS MOST RECENT YEAR:
40.

NUMBER OF AWARDS: 2 to 15 per year,
depending on geographical location.

APPLICATION INFORMATION:
Further information and application forms are
available on the web site above.
Duration: One academic year.

ADDRESS INQUIRIES TO:
Program Coordinator
International Scholarship Programs
(See address above.)

*SPECIAL STIPULATIONS:
Candidates may not hold other awards
concurrently.

CANADIAN BUREAU FOR INTERNATIONAL EDUCATION (CBIE)   [903]

220 Laurier West, Suite 1550
Ottawa ON K1P 5Z9 Canada
(613) 237-4820
Fax: (613) 237-1073

E-MAIL ADDRESS:
scholarships-bourses@cbie.ca

WEB SITE ADDRESS:
www.scholarships.gc.ca

AREAS OF INTEREST:
Higher education.

NAME(S) OF PROGRAMS:
● **Commonwealth Scholarship Plan**

TYPE:
Scholarships. Under the Commonwealth
Scholarship and Fellowship Plan,
scholarships are available for Canadians to
pursue studies and/or research at higher
education institutions in the Commonwealth.

PURPOSE:
To provide opportunities for candidates to
pursue studies and/or research at higher
education institutions in the Commonwealth.

ELIGIBILITY:
Candidates must be Canadian citizens by the
competition deadline and must have obtained
the equivalent of a Canadian Master's or
Ph.D. degree from a recognized university.
Studies must take place in India or New
Zealand. Candidates studying in New
Zealand must have a Ph.D. degree.

FINANCIAL DATA:
Funding includes tuition and monthly living
allowances, with additional benefits provided
by varying countries. These scholarships are
subject to the availability of funding.
Amount of support per award: Varies by
geographical location.

NUMBER OF APPLICANTS MOST RECENT YEAR:
150.

NUMBER OF AWARDS: 1 to 3.

APPLICATION INFORMATION:
Further information and application forms are
available on the web site above.
Duration: Up to five years.

ADDRESS INQUIRIES TO:
Program Coordinator
International Scholarship Programs
(See address above.)

CANADIAN INSTITUTE FOR ADVANCED LEGAL STUDIES

P.O. Box 43538, Leaside Post Office
1601 Bayview Avenue
Toronto ON M4G 4G8 Canada
(416) 429-3292
Fax: (416) 429-9805

E-MAIL ADDRESS:
info@canadian-institute.com

WEB SITE ADDRESS:
www.canadian-institute.com

TYPE:
Scholarships.

See entry 1972 for full listing.

CANADIAN INSTITUTE IN GREECE/L'INSTITUT CANADIEN EN GRECE

330 Albert Street
Waterloo ON N2L 3T8 Canada
(519) 886-4428

E-MAIL ADDRESS:
gschaus@wlu.ca

WEB SITE ADDRESS:
www.cig-icg.gr

TYPE:
Conferences/seminars; Endowments;
Fellowships; Internships. Intended to support
the graduate work of a person who needs to
study in Greece.

See entry 355 for full listing.

WINSTON CHURCHILL FOUNDATION OF THE UNITED STATES   [904]

600 Madison Avenue, 16th Floor
New York, NY 10022-1737
(212) 752-3200
Fax: (212) 246-8330

E-MAIL ADDRESS:
info@winstonchurchillfoundation.org

WEB SITE ADDRESS:
www.winstonchurchillfoundation.org

FOUNDED: 1959

AREAS OF INTEREST:
Science, math and engineering.

NAME(S) OF PROGRAMS:
● **Churchill Scholarship**

TYPE:
Research grants; Scholarships; Travel grants.
Scholarship for one year of graduate work at
University of Cambridge. Churchill
Scholarship may also include a Special
Research Grant and Travel Award.

YEAR PROGRAM STARTED: 1963

PURPOSE:
To encourage Anglo-American cooperation
and American scientific and technological
talent.

LEGAL BASIS:
Public charity.

ELIGIBILITY:
Candidate must be a citizen of the U.S.,
between 19 and 26 years of age, have a
Bachelor's degree from an accredited U.S.
college or university and be enrolled at one
of 103 participating American institutions.

FINANCIAL DATA:
Amount of support per award: Churchill
Scholarship: Tuition, plus GBP 11,000 to
GBP 13,000 living allowance, $1,100 travel
allowance and reimbursement of visa
application fees. Total individual package is
approximately $50,000; Churchill Scholars
may also receive a Travel Award of $500, as
well as a Special Research Grant of up to
$2,000.
Total amount of support: Approximately
$750,000 in total grants for the year 2013.

NUMBER OF APPLICANTS MOST RECENT YEAR:
100.

NUMBER OF AWARDS: 14 scholarships for the year 2013.

APPLICATION INFORMATION:
Application forms are available from Foundation representatives at participating institutions. Information also available on Foundation's web site.
Duration: One year.
Deadline: Early November.

OFFICERS:
John L. Loeb, Jr., Chairman
Patrick A. Gerschel, President
Peter Patrikis, Executive Director
David D. Burrows, Treasurer
James A. Fitzpatrick, Jr., Secretary

ADDRESS INQUIRIES TO:
Peter Patrikis, Executive Director
(See address above.)

CORPUS CHRISTI COLLEGE [905]
Trumpington Street
Cambridge, CB2 1RH England
44 01223 338038
Fax: 44 01223 765589

E-MAIL ADDRESS:
graduate-tutor@corpus.cam.ac.uk

WEB SITE ADDRESS:
www.corpus.cam.ac.uk

FOUNDED: 1352

AREAS OF INTEREST:
All subjects of postgraduate research at the University of Cambridge.

NAME(S) OF PROGRAMS:
● **Postgraduate Research at the University of Cambridge**

TYPE:
Scholarships.

PURPOSE:
To enable the candidate to pursue, as a member of the college, research in any subject leading to a research degree of Cambridge University.

LEGAL BASIS:
University College.

ELIGIBILITY:
Applicants must have a first degree from a recognized university and name Corpus Christi College as their college of first preference on GAF. Candidates must become registered as University of Cambridge graduate students.

FINANCIAL DATA:
Amount of support per award: Varies.
Matching fund requirements: It is a requirement that individuals who are eligible apply to other funding bodies, e.g. Cambridge Trusts.

APPLICATION INFORMATION:
Application forms for graduate study are available from the Board of Graduate Studies, 4 Mill Lane, Cambridge CB2 1YP, England, or online at www.admin.cam.ac.uk/univ/gsprospectus.
Duration: Up to three years.
Deadline: November 15.

ADDRESS INQUIRIES TO:
Tutor for Advanced Students
(See e-mail address above.)

COUNCIL FOR INTERNATIONAL EXCHANGE OF SCHOLARS (CIES) [906]
1400 K Street, N.W.
Suite 700
Washington, DC 20005-2403
(202) 686-4000
Fax: (202) 686-4029

E-MAIL ADDRESS:
scholars@iie.org

WEB SITE ADDRESS:
www.iie.org/cies

FOUNDED: 1947

AREAS OF INTEREST:
Fulbright Scholar grants to more than 125 countries for teaching, research or a combination of both.

NAME(S) OF PROGRAMS:
● **Fulbright Scholar Program**

TYPE:
Awards/prizes. Awards to university faculty and professionals outside academe for teaching and/or advanced research worldwide. Awards are available in 45 disciplines from agriculture to urban planning.

YEAR PROGRAM STARTED: 1947

PURPOSE:
To promote mutual understanding and scholarship.

LEGAL BASIS:
Private, nonprofit organization that receives funding from the U.S. State Department.

ELIGIBILITY:
Applicant must be a U.S. citizen at the time of application and hold a Ph.D. or equivalent professional/terminal degree. Recognized professional standing for artists and professionals outside of academe is required.

FINANCIAL DATA:
Amount of support per award: Award benefits vary by country. Usually a base stipend, in-country maintenance and travel.
Total amount of support: Varies.

NUMBER OF APPLICANTS MOST RECENT YEAR:
Approximately 3,000.

NUMBER OF AWARDS: Approximately 800.

APPLICATION INFORMATION:
Application forms and detailed awards information are available February 1 from the Council. Applications will be screened by CIES peer review committees. Recommendations will be made by the binational Fulbright Commissions or U.S. Information Service posts overseas, with final selection by the J. William Fulbright Foreign Scholarship Board. See web site for complete information.
Duration: Two weeks to 10 months.
Deadline: August 1 for most programs. Rolling deadline for the short-term Fulbright Specialist Program.

PUBLICATIONS:
Annual awards; catalog; descriptive brochure; annual report.

ADDRESS INQUIRIES TO:
See e-mail address above.

COUNCIL FOR INTERNATIONAL EXCHANGE OF SCHOLARS (CIES) [907]
1400 K Street, N.W.
Suite 700
Washington, DC 20005
(202) 686-4013
Fax: (202) 362-3442

E-MAIL ADDRESS:
scholars@iie.org

WEB SITE ADDRESS:
www.iie.org/cies

AREAS OF INTEREST:
Academic/professional field in Middle East and North Africa.

NAME(S) OF PROGRAMS:
● **Middle East, North Africa and Regional Research Programs and Country Grants**

TYPE:
Fellowships; Research grants; Scholarships.

ELIGIBILITY:
Applicants must be U.S. citizens with a Ph.D. or equivalent professional/terminal degree at the time of application.

GEOGRAPHIC RESTRICTIONS:
Middle East and North Africa.

FINANCIAL DATA:
Awards include travel, stipend, and monthly payments.
Amount of support per award: Varies.

NUMBER OF AWARDS: U.S. Scholars Grantees: 51 lecturing and 19 research.

APPLICATION INFORMATION:
Applicants must use the Council's application form, which is available online.
Duration: Three to 10 months of research, lecturing one or two semesters.
Deadline: August 1.

ADDRESS INQUIRIES TO:
Caroline Proulx, Assistant Director for Middle East and North Africa
(See address above.)

COUNCIL OF AMERICAN OVERSEAS RESEARCH CENTERS (CAORC) [908]
P.O. Box 37012
MRC 178
Washington, DC 20013-7012
(202) 633-1599
Fax: (202) 786-2430

E-MAIL ADDRESS:
fellowships@caorc.org

WEB SITE ADDRESS:
www.caorc.org

FOUNDED: 1981

AREAS OF INTEREST:
Promoting the work of American overseas research centers.

NAME(S) OF PROGRAMS:
● **Multi-Country Research Fellowship Program**

TYPE:
Fellowships; Research grants. Requires scholars to conduct research in more than one country, at least one of which hosts a participating American overseas research center.

PURPOSE:
To advance higher learning and scholarly research by providing a forum for communication and cooperation among American overseas advanced research centers; to provide general and continuing publicity about the importance and contributions of the centers; to exchange operational and administrative information among the centers; to exchange scholarly and research information among the centers; to encourage joint research projects.

LEGAL BASIS:
501(c)(3) organization.

ELIGIBILITY:
Program is open to U.S. doctoral candidates and scholars who have already earned their Ph.D. in fields in the humanities, social sciences, or allied natural sciences and wish to conduct research of regional or trans-regional significance. Must be U.S. citizen or permanent resident.

U.S. State Department travel restrictions apply.

FINANCIAL DATA:
Amount of support per award: Up to $10,500.

NUMBER OF AWARDS: Ph.D./Postdoctoral: 9.

APPLICATION INFORMATION:
A complete application consists of:
(1) application form;
(2) project description (1,500 words or less) describing the nature of the proposal and competence to carry out the required research;
(3) project bibliography/literature review (one page maximum);
(4) two signed letters of recommendation;
(5) curriculum vitae (three pages maximum) and;
(6) graduate transcripts (Ph.D. candidates only).

Applicants are urged to review the Application Instructions before submitting the application.
Duration: Ph.D./Postdoctoral: Minimum of 90 days.
Deadline: Mid-January.

ADDRESS INQUIRIES TO:
Monica Clark, Program Manager
(See address above.)

*SPECIAL STIPULATIONS:
Fellows must complete their research within a specific time.

COUNCIL ON FOREIGN RELATIONS
58 East 68th Street
New York, NY 10065
(212) 434-9740
Fax: (212) 434-9870

E-MAIL ADDRESS:
fellowships@cfr.org

WEB SITE ADDRESS:
www.cfr.org/fellowships

TYPE:
Fellowships. The International Affairs Fellowship in South Korea (IAF-SK), sponsored by the Asan Institute for Policy Studies, assists midcareer scholars and professionals from the public and private sectors to advance their analytic capabilities and broaden their foreign policy experience in South Korea. The Council on Foreign

Relations (CFR) awards several fellowships annually to highly accomplished individuals who have a capacity for independent work and who are eager to undertake serious foreign policy analysis while affiliated with the Asan Institute for Policy Studies in South Korea. Fellows are drawn from academia, business, government, media, NGOs and think tanks.

See entry 840 for full listing.

COUNCIL ON FOREIGN RELATIONS
58 East 68th Street
New York, NY 10065
(212) 434-9740
Fax: (212) 434-9870

E-MAIL ADDRESS:
fellowships@cfr.org

WEB SITE ADDRESS:
www.cfr.org/fellowships

TYPE:
Fellowships. The International Affairs Fellowship in Japan (IAF-J), sponsored by Hitachi, Ltd., provides a selected group of midcareer U.S. citizens the opportunity to expand their professional horizons by spending a period of research or other professional activity in Japan. Fellows are drawn from academia, business, government, media, NGOs and think tanks. In cooperation with the Council on Foreign Relations (CFR), the program's sponsor, Hitachi, Ltd., assists fellows in finding suitable host organizations in Japan.

See entry 838 for full listing.

CULTURAL SERVICES OF THE FRENCH EMBASSY [909]
972 Fifth Avenue
New York, NY 10075
(212) 439-1463
Fax: (212) 439-1455

E-MAIL ADDRESS:
puf.scac@ambafrance-us.org

WEB SITE ADDRESS:
www.facecouncil.org/puf

NAME(S) OF PROGRAMS:
● **Partner University Fund**

TYPE:
Project/program grants; Research grants. Grants provided by this Fund support research and graduate education partnerships between French and American universities with emphasis placed on novel, innovative and interdisciplinary projects when relevant.

YEAR PROGRAM STARTED: 2007

PURPOSE:
To promote the exchange of ideas between France and the U.S.

ELIGIBILITY:
Grants are not given to individuals.

GEOGRAPHIC RESTRICTIONS:
United States and France.

FINANCIAL DATA:
Amount of support per award: Up to $80,000 (U.S.) per year per project (up to 30% of the total cost of the project); and up to $160,000 (U.S.) per year per project in the humanities (up to 60% of the total cost of the project).

APPLICATION INFORMATION:
There is an application form to complete. Details are available online.
Duration: Up to three years, with an annual review.

CULTURAL VISTAS [910]
440 Park Avenue South, Second Floor
New York, NY 10016
(212) 497-3522
Fax: (212) 497-3588

E-MAIL ADDRESS:
wisp@culturalvistas.org

WEB SITE ADDRESS:
www.wispgermany.org

FOUNDED: 1968

AREAS OF INTEREST:
Culture and vocational fields.

NAME(S) OF PROGRAMS:
● **Baden-Wuerttemberg-STIPENDIUM Work Immersion Study Program**

TYPE:
Fellowships; Internships; Scholarships. Language learning. Cultural Vistas partners with the Baden-Wuerttemberg Stiftung and the American Association of Teachers of German (AATG) to offer the Baden-Wuerttemberg Stipendium for Vocationally Qualified People "Work Immersion Study Program" exclusively to college students in vocational fields. The Work Immersion Study Program is a three-month work/study immersion program in Germany that includes a one-month intensive German language course and a two-month internship in the state of Baden-Wuerttemberg.

YEAR PROGRAM STARTED: 2001

PURPOSE:
To provide college students in vocational fields with the unique opportunity to gain practical work experience in their career field, improve their German language skills and experience German culture firsthand.

ELIGIBILITY:
Candidate must:
(1) be a U.S. citizen or permanent resident;
(2) be a minimum age of 18, maximum age of 27;
(3) have at least one semester of German instruction completed upon departure to Germany;
(4) be studying in a vocational field and have completed at least four semesters of study by the start of the program;
(5) have practical experience in the desired field and;
(6) be enrolled at a U.S. college both before and after the program.

FINANCIAL DATA:
Scholarship includes transatlantic round-trip to Germany, free housing, monthly stipend, one-month intensive language course, and health and accident insurance while abroad.

NUMBER OF APPLICANTS MOST RECENT YEAR: 35.

NUMBER OF AWARDS: Up to 10.

APPLICATION INFORMATION:
Electronic submission of the application is preferred. All supporting materials must be sent to Cultural Vistas by the deadline.
Duration: Three months, summer.
Deadline: December 1.

PUBLICATIONS:
General information and applications.

ADDRESS INQUIRIES TO:
Max Flescher, Program Assistant or
Nele Feldmann, Assistant Program Officer
(See address above.)

*SPECIAL STIPULATIONS:
This program is exclusively for students in
vocational fields.

CULTURAL VISTAS [911]
440 Park Avenue South, Second Floor
New York, NY 10016
(212) 497-3522
Fax: (212) 497-3588

E-MAIL ADDRESS:
cbyx@culturalvistas.org

WEB SITE ADDRESS:
www.cbyx.info

FOUNDED: 1968

AREAS OF INTEREST:
All areas of culture, business, technical, and
engineering.

NAME(S) OF PROGRAMS:
 • **Congress-Bundestag Youth Exchange
   for Young Professionals**

TYPE:
Exchange programs; Fellowships; Internships;
Scholarships; Work-study programs.
Language learning. Scholarship program with
a strong focus on cultural exchange.
One-year scholarship for work/study program
to Germany including German language
training, academic semester in Germany and
internship component.

YEAR PROGRAM STARTED: 1983

PURPOSE:
To give participants understanding for
everyday life, education and professional
training in Germany.

ELIGIBILITY:
Requirements include:
(1) U.S. citizenship or permanent residency;
(2) 18 to 24 years of age at start of program;
(3) at least high school diploma or equivalent
and;
(4) clear career goals, a solid academic
background, and relevant work experience or
internships in field strongly preferred.

No German language proficiency
requirements.

FINANCIAL DATA:
Funding provided for international airfare,
language training and study costs, living
expenses during study phases, all seminars,
and sickness and accident insurance while
abroad.

COOPERATIVE FUNDING PROGRAMS: Funded in
U.S. by the Bureau of Educational and
Cultural Affairs of the Department of State
and through the Administration of the
Bundestag in Germany.

NUMBER OF APPLICANTS MOST RECENT YEAR:
710.

NUMBER OF AWARDS: 75.

APPLICATION INFORMATION:
Electronic submission only.
Duration: One year (July to July).
Deadline: December 1 for the following
program year.

ADDRESS INQUIRIES TO:
Congress-Bundestag Youth Exchange
for Young Professionals
(See address above.)

*SPECIAL STIPULATIONS:
Must be U.S. citizens or permanent residents,
18 to 24 years of age at the start of the
program. Previous recipients of
Congress-Bundestag scholarships are not
eligible for this program.

CULTURAL VISTAS [912]
440 Park Avenue South, 2nd Floor
New York, NY 10016
(212) 497-3500
Fax: (212) 497-3586

E-MAIL ADDRESS:
bosch@culturalvistas.org

WEB SITE ADDRESS:
www.culturalvistas.org

FOUNDED: 1968

AREAS OF INTEREST:
Business administration, cultural management
(for example, of a museum, theater or
orchestra), law, public policy, journalism,
nonprofit, and urban planning.

NAME(S) OF PROGRAMS:
 • **The Robert Bosch Foundation
   Fellowship Program**

TYPE:
Fellowships. Graduate fellowships for
extended career training opportunities in
Germany.

YEAR PROGRAM STARTED: 1984

PURPOSE:
To provide international professional
experience through high-level work
placements within German industry, business,
government and media.

LEGAL BASIS:
Program funded by Robert Bosch Stiftung, a
private German foundation.

ELIGIBILITY:
Applicants must be U.S. citizens under the
age of 40 years old at the time of application
deadline. Graduate degree is preferred and
applicant should have a minimum of five
years of relevant experience. Applicants must
show evidence of outstanding professional
performance and community involvement.
German language is not required at the time
of application.

FINANCIAL DATA:
Includes transatlantic flights, language
training, three European seminars, travel,
health, accident and liability insurance, etc.
Amount of support per award: EUR 3,000
stipend per month; monthly summer stipend
EUR 1,000.
Total amount of support: Varies.

NUMBER OF APPLICANTS MOST RECENT YEAR:
600.

NUMBER OF AWARDS: 15 for the 2014-15
academic year.

APPLICATION INFORMATION:
Candidates must submit an application form,
personal statement, transcripts, letters of
recommendation and resume.
Duration: Six to nine months.
Deadline: November 1.

PUBLICATIONS:
General information and applications.

STAFF:
Carolina Solms-Baruth, Assistant Program
Officer

ADDRESS INQUIRIES TO:
See e-mail address above.

CYPRUS AMERICAN ARCHAEOLOGICAL RESEARCH INSTITUTE [913]
656 Beacon Street, 5th Floor
Boston, MA 02215
(617) 353-6571
Fax: (617) 353-6575

E-MAIL ADDRESS:
caari@bu.edu

WEB SITE ADDRESS:
www.caari.org

FOUNDED: 1900

AREAS OF INTEREST:
The study of humanistic disciplines, such as
anthropology, archaeology, Biblical studies,
epigraphy, history, history of art and
architecture, literature, philology, prehistory
and topography, relating in particular to the
Middle East from prehistoric times to the
modern era.

Cyprus American Archaeological Research
Institute is the only residential archaeological
institute on the island of Cyprus and serves
as a center for the dissemination of
information about the archaeology of Cyprus.

NAME(S) OF PROGRAMS:
 • **The Anita Cecil O'Donovan Fellowship**
 • **The Danielle Parks Memorial
   Fellowship**
 • **The Helena Wylde Swiny and Stuart
   Swiny Fellowship**

TYPE:
Fellowships; Research grants; Residencies;
Travel grants. There are a large variety of
fellowships available through the Near
Eastern Fellowship Program for the
American Schools of Oriental Research and
affiliated overseas research centers. Besides
The Cyprus American Archaeological
Research Institute in Nicosia, Cyprus
(CAARI), there are also The American
Center of Oriental Research in Amman,
Jordan (ACOR) and the W.F. Albright
Institute of Archaeological Research in
Jerusalem, Israel (AIAR). Contact the
American Schools of Oriental Research for
full details.

The Anita Cecil O'Donovan Fellowship is an
award to a graduate student of any
nationality, enrolled in a graduate program in
any nation, to pursue research on a project
relevant to the archaeology and/or culture of
Cyprus.

The Danielle Parks Memorial Fellowship is
for a graduate student of any nationality who
needs to work in Cyprus to further his or her
research on a subject of relevance to Cypriot
archaeology and culture.

The Helena Wylde Swiny and Stuart Swiny
Fellowship is a grant to a graduate student of
any nationality in a U.S. or Canadian
university or college to pursue a research
project relevant to an ongoing field project in
Cyprus or that requires work on Cyprus
itself.

YEAR PROGRAM STARTED: 1940

PURPOSE:
To help scholars undertake high-quality
research and field projects in the Middle East
and to encourage interdisciplinary study and
communication among scholars.

LEGAL BASIS:
Nonprofit, archaeological research corporation.

ELIGIBILITY:
All ASOR awards are open to qualified students and scholars from any country. Applicants must be affiliated with an institution that is a member of the ASOR corporation or must be an individual professional member. Prime consideration is given to applicants whose projects are affiliated with ASOR.

ASOR does not conduct the competition nor take part in the selection process for the Fulbright Fellowships, but encourages qualified scholars to apply for these awards.

FINANCIAL DATA:
The Anita Cecil O'Donovan Fellowship and The Helena Wylde Swiny and Stuart Swiny Fellowship will be used to fund research time in residence at CAARI and to help defray costs of travel.

The Danielle Parks Memorial Fellowship covers travel to and living expenses in Cyprus.

Amount of support per award: $1,000 each.

Total amount of support: $3,000.

NUMBER OF APPLICANTS MOST RECENT YEAR: 11.

NUMBER OF AWARDS: 1 each.

APPLICATION INFORMATION:
Application form is available on the Institute web site. All eligible persons are encouraged to apply for as many fellowships and professorships as they wish, but a person can hold only one award at a time. Persons who have received an award in one year can reapply for the same or other awards the following year, but new applicants will have priority.

Duration: One-time awards.

Deadline: November 1.

STAFF:
Donald Keller, Administrator

ADDRESS INQUIRIES TO:
See e-mail address above.

*SPECIAL STIPULATIONS:
For the O'Donovan, Parks and Swiny Fellowships, residence at CAARI is mandatory.

For the Danielle Parks Memorial Fellowship, the fellow is expected during his or her stay to give a presentation at CAARI on a subject related to his or her research. The fellow will periodically keep the Director of CAARI apprised of his or her research activities and will acknowledge CAARI and the Danielle Parks Memorial Fellowship in any publication that emerges from the research carried during the Fellowship.

THE LADY DAVIS FELLOWSHIP TRUST [914]
Hebrew University
Givat Ram
Jerusalem 91904 Israel
972-2-651-2306 (voice mail)
972-2-658-4723
Fax: 972-2-566-3848

E-MAIL ADDRESS:
ld.fellows@mail.huji.ac.il

WEB SITE ADDRESS:
ldft.huji.ac.il

FOUNDED: 1973

NAME(S) OF PROGRAMS:
- **Postdoctoral Researchers Fellowship**
- **Visiting Professorships Fellowship**

TYPE:
Fellowships.

YEAR PROGRAM STARTED: 1973

LEGAL BASIS:
University association.

APPLICATION INFORMATION:
Prospective candidates must establish contact with the relevant department at the Hebrew University, and ensure that there is a faculty member willing to sponsor the application.

Duration: Postdoctoral researchers and doctoral students may request an extension of one year to their fellowships. Deadlines are the same as for initial application. There is no need to submit all the information again. A letter from the researcher/student explaining the request for the extension together with a supporting letter from the scholar is sufficient.

Visiting professorships and associate professorships last from three to nine months during the academic year.

Deadline: Hebrew University: Visiting Professorships, November 30; Postdoctoral Researchers, December 31.

*SPECIAL STIPULATIONS:
Fellowships may not be deferred from one year to the next.

Fellows who have won another concurrent fellowship must disclose this to the Trust, whereupon the amount of the award will be reviewed.

A Fellow is expected to take up the Fellowship within the period of the academic year for which he has applied (in other words, between October 1 and September 30 in the following year). Attempts are made to be as elastic as possible should a Fellow expect to arrive before or after October 1.

FLANDERS HOUSE [915]
620 Eighth Avenue, 44th Floor
New York, NY 10018
(212) 584-2200 ext. 2004
Fax: (212) 575-3606

E-MAIL ADDRESS:
info@flandershouse.org

WEB SITE ADDRESS:
www.flandershouse.org

AREAS OF INTEREST:
Belgium.

NAME(S) OF PROGRAMS:
- **Fellowship of the Flanders House**

TYPE:
Fellowships. Granted for study or research at universities, conservatories of music, or art academies recognized by the Flemish Community and encompasses the studies of art, music, humanities, social and political sciences, law, economics, sciences and medicine.

PURPOSE:
To assist American college students who wish to continue their postgraduate education in Flanders, Belgium.

ELIGIBILITY:
Open to U.S. citizens (in case of dual citizenship, please include proof) of no more than 35 years of age at the time of application deadline, who hold a Bachelor's or Master's degree, and who have no other Belgian sources of income.

FINANCIAL DATA:
Includes a monthly stipend, tuition fees at a Flemish institution, health insurance and public liability insurance in accordance with Belgian law. There is no reimbursement of travel expenses.

Amount of support per award: Monthly stipend approximately EUR 770; tuition fees maximum EUR 540. The amount of the stipend is subject to change without notice.

Total amount of support: Varies.

NUMBER OF AWARDS: 5.

APPLICATION INFORMATION:
Application information is available on the web site.

Duration: 10 months.

Deadline: January 31. Notification by July.

ADDRESS INQUIRIES TO:
Nicolas Polet, Policy Officer
(See address above.)

*PLEASE NOTE:
The academic year, for most institutes of higher learning in Flanders, starts at the end of September.

THE GARDEN CLUB OF AMERICA
14 East 60th Street, Third Floor
New York, NY 10022
(212) 753-8287
Fax: (212) 753-0134

E-MAIL ADDRESS:
scholarships@gcamerica.org

WEB SITE ADDRESS:
www.gcamerica.org

TYPE:
Exchange programs; Fellowships. A graduate academic year in the U.S. for a British student and a work-study program for an American at universities and botanical gardens in the U.K. in fields related to horticulture, botany and landscape design.

See entry 2178 for full listing.

THE GARDEN CLUB OF AMERICA
14 East 60th Street, Third Floor
New York, NY 10022
(212) 753-8287
Fax: (212) 753-0134

E-MAIL ADDRESS:
scholarships@gcamerica.org

WEB SITE ADDRESS:
www.gcamerica.org

TYPE:
Research grants. Anne S. Chatham Fellowship in Medicinal Botany: Grant to enable study in medicinal botany.

GCA Awards in Tropical Botany: Grants to enable field study in tropical botany.

Frances M. Peacock Scholarship for Native Bird Habitat: Financial assistance to college seniors and graduate students to study habitat-related issues that will benefit threatened or endangered bird species and lend useful information for land management decisions.

See entry 2179 for full listing.

GERMAN ACADEMIC EXCHANGE SERVICE [916]

871 United Nations Plaza, 14th Floor
New York, NY 10017
(212) 758-3223
Fax: (212) 755-5780

E-MAIL ADDRESS:
daadny@daad.org

WEB SITE ADDRESS:
www.daad.org

FOUNDED: 1925

AREAS OF INTEREST:
International exchanges in education, research in higher education, and academic teaching staff; scholarships to German and foreign students.

CONSULTING OR VOLUNTEER SERVICES:
DAAD serves on a consultancy service in the field of international academic mobility.

NAME(S) OF PROGRAMS:
- **DAAD Emigre Memorial German Internship Program (EMGIP-Bundestag)**
- **DAAD German Studies Summer Seminar**
- **DAAD Intensive Language Grant**
- **DAAD Research Grant**
- **DAAD Research Internships in Science and Engineering (RISE)**
- **DAAD Research Visit for Faculty**
- **DAAD RISE Pro**
- **DAAD Study Scholarship**
- **DAAD Undergraduate Scholarship**
- **DAAD University Summer Language Grant**
- **DAAD Visiting Professorship**

TYPE:
Awards/prizes; Conferences/seminars; Exchange programs; Fellowships; Internships; Professorships; Project/program grants; Research grants; Scholarships; Visiting scholars. The German Academic Exchange Service is the New York office of the Deutscher Akademischer Austausch Dienst (DAAD), a German organization with its head office in Bonn. DAAD offers a wide range of opportunities to students, scholars and higher education institutions of the U.S. and Canada, from undergraduate students to faculty, for study and research in Germany.

YEAR PROGRAM STARTED: 1971

PURPOSE:
To provide information on study and research opportunities in higher education at home and abroad; to promote international higher education and research through scholarships; to recruit and place German academic teaching staff from all disciplines at foreign institutions of higher education; to maintain a network of former scholarship holders abroad.

LEGAL BASIS:
Registered association under private law.

ELIGIBILITY:
DAAD grants are available to faculty and students in the U.S. and Canada to participate in a wide variety of academic activities. Funding is restricted to travel to Germany, including German higher education institutions, research institutions and archives in Germany.

GEOGRAPHIC RESTRICTIONS:
United States and Canada.

FINANCIAL DATA:
Amount of support per award: Varies.

Total amount of support: Varies.

APPLICATION INFORMATION:
Application information is available on the web site.
Duration: Varies.
Deadline: Varies.

PUBLICATIONS:
Grants for Study and Research in Germany.

ADDRESS INQUIRIES TO:
Jane Fu, Information Officer
(See address above.)

GERMAN HISTORICAL INSTITUTE

1607 New Hampshire Avenue, N.W.
Washington, DC 20009-2562
(202) 387-3355
Fax: (202) 483-3430

E-MAIL ADDRESS:
info@ghi-dc.org
fellowships@ghi-dc.org

WEB SITE ADDRESS:
www.ghi-dc.org

TYPE:
Fellowships. The Institute awards short-term fellowships to German and American doctoral students as well as postdoctoral scholars/Habilitanden in the fields of German history, the history of German-American relations, and the role of Germany and the U.S. in international relations.

See entry 592 for full listing.

THE HAGUE ACADEMY OF INTERNATIONAL LAW

Peace Palace
Carnegieplein 2
2517 KJ The Hague The Netherlands
(31-70) 302-4242

E-MAIL ADDRESS:
registration@hagueacademy.nl

WEB SITE ADDRESS:
www.hagueacademy.nl

TYPE:
Project/program grants. Study programs. Residential scholarships for doctoral candidates from developing countries whose thesis, in private international law or public international law, is in the process of completion, who reside in their home country and who do not have access to scientific sources.

See entry 1976 for full listing.

THE HAGUE ACADEMY OF INTERNATIONAL LAW

Peace Palace
Carnegieplein 2
2517 KJ The Hague The Netherlands
(31-70) 302-4242

E-MAIL ADDRESS:
registration@hagueacademy.nl

WEB SITE ADDRESS:
www.hagueacademy.nl

TYPE:
Project/program grants; Scholarships. Study programs. A limited number of scholarships are given to cover tuition and living expenses while studying at the three-week summer session of the Hague Academy of

International Law. Because of the limited number, granting of scholarships to attendees from every country is not possible.

See entry 1977 for full listing.

THE HAGUE ACADEMY OF INTERNATIONAL LAW

Peace Palace
Carnegieplein 2
2517 KJ The Hague The Netherlands
(31-70) 302 4242

E-MAIL ADDRESS:
registration@hagueacademy.nl

WEB SITE ADDRESS:
www.hagueacademy.nl

TYPE:
Project/program grants.

See entry 1978 for full listing.

THE HAGUE ACADEMY OF INTERNATIONAL LAW

Peace Palace
Carnegieplein 2
2517 KJ The Hague The Netherlands
(31-70) 302 4242

E-MAIL ADDRESS:
registration@hagueacademy.nl

WEB SITE ADDRESS:
www.hagueacademy.nl

TYPE:
Project/program grants. External Programme is held each year, in turn in Africa, Asia and Latin America, upon the invitation of host governments or international organizations. It is designed for approximately 20 participants from the countries in the region (who are resident in their own country), whose traveling expenses are usually financed by the Academy and whose accommodation is financed by the government of the host state or organization. In addition, a number of participants come from the host state itself.

See entry 1979 for full listing.

HEINRICH HERTZ-STIFTUNG [917]

Ministry of Innovation, Science and Research des Landes Nordrhein-Westfalen
Heinrich Hertz-Stiftung
Voelklinger Strasse 49
40221 Duesseldorf Germany
(0211) 896 4266
Fax: (0211) 896 4407

E-MAIL ADDRESS:
martina.schoeler@miwf.nrw.de
heinrich-hertz-stiftung@miwf.nrw.de

WEB SITE ADDRESS:
www.heinrich-hertz-stiftung.de

FOUNDED: 1961

AREAS OF INTEREST:
International exchange of scientists.

TYPE:
Exchange programs; Scholarships. Scholarships to promote the sciences through the exchange of university teachers and young scientists (without special restrictions).

YEAR PROGRAM STARTED: 1962

PURPOSE:
To promote sciences.

LEGAL BASIS:
Public foundation.

ELIGIBILITY:
University teachers and young scientists are eligible. Non-German citizens should have a working knowledge of German and German citizens a working knowledge of the language of the host country.

GEOGRAPHIC RESTRICTIONS:
Land Nordrhine-Westphalia.

FINANCIAL DATA:
Amount of support per award: Award values are dependent upon individual needs.
Total amount of support: Varies.

NUMBER OF AWARDS: 21 for the year 2012.

APPLICATION INFORMATION:
Applications should be submitted only by third persons. A curriculum vitae, examination record, two references and a full description of the planned project with a timetable are to be included. Further information may be obtained on request.
Duration: Dependent upon individual needs. Two years maximum.

PUBLICATIONS:
Hinweise auf die Antragstellung; *Die Heinrich Hertz-Stiftung*, booklet; Heinrich Hertz-Stiftung, folder.

ADDRESS INQUIRIES TO:
Ministry of Innovation, Science and Research des Landes Nordrhein-Westfalen
Heinrich Hertz-Stiftung
E-mail: heinrich-hertz-stiftung@miwf.nrw.de

INSTITUTE FOR THE INTERNATIONAL EDUCATION OF STUDENTS (IES)
33 West Monroe Street
Suite 2300
Chicago, IL 60603-5405
(312) 944-1750
(800) 995-2300
Fax: (312) 944-1448

E-MAIL ADDRESS:
info@IESabroad.org

WEB SITE ADDRESS:
www.IESabroad.org

TYPE:
Awards/prizes; Scholarships. The IES Abroad Boren and Gilman Scholarship Support Grants offer recipients of these prestigious scholarships the opportunity to apply for additional financial support.

IES Merit-Based Scholarships supplement U.S. college and university awards for undergraduates studying with IES Abroad in Argentina, Australia, Austria, Chile, China, Costa Rica, Ecuador, England, France, Germany, India, Ireland, Italy, Japan, Morocco, the Netherlands, New Zealand, South Africa, Spain and Turkey. Merit-Based Scholarships are available for proven strength and interest in fine arts, foreign language, high achievement, international business, international relations, leadership, science and urban issues. Diversity Scholarships are also available as are scholarships for students who attend historically Black colleges/universities.

Need-based grants available to students with demonstrated financial need.

All IES Abroad aid is available only to students from schools within the IES Abroad Consortium and who attend an IES Abroad program.

See entry 1700 for full listing.

INSTITUTE OF INTERNATIONAL EDUCATION   [918]
U.S. Department of State
Fulbright U.S. Student Program
U.S. Student Programs Division
809 United Nations Plaza
New York, NY 10017-3580
(212) 984-5525

WEB SITE ADDRESS:
www.us.fulbrightonline.org

FOUNDED: 1919

AREAS OF INTEREST:
International educational and cultural exchange on all levels.

NAME(S) OF PROGRAMS:
● **U.S. Department of State Fulbright U.S. Student Program**

TYPE:
Exchange programs; Scholarships. Grants for graduate study, research or English Teaching Assistantships abroad.

YEAR PROGRAM STARTED: 1946

PURPOSE:
To give U.S. students the opportunity to live, study, teach or do research in a foreign country for one academic year and to increase mutual understanding between the people of the U.S. and other countries through the exchange of persons, knowledge and skills.

LEGAL BASIS:
Nonprofit, as described under Internal Revenue Code 501(c)(3).

ELIGIBILITY:
Candidates must possess U.S. citizenship, a B.A. degree by the beginning date of the grant, language proficiency sufficient to carry out the project overseas and good health. Preference in selecting candidates is for those who have had the majority of high school and undergraduate college education at educational institutions in the U.S. Candidates may not hold a doctoral degree at the time of application.

FINANCIAL DATA:
Fulbright Grants provide round-trip transportation, language or orientation course (where appropriate), tuition, books, maintenance for one academic year in only one country and health and accident insurance. The maintenance allowance is based on living costs in the host country and is sufficient to meet normal expenses of a single person.

COOPERATIVE FUNDING PROGRAMS: Funds from other scholarships, fellowships or grants in dollars or foreign currency received concurrently with a Fulbright Grant will be deducted if they duplicate the Fulbright benefits. No deduction is made if other grants are for assistance in meeting family expenses of grantees or other expenses not covered by the grant.

NUMBER OF APPLICANTS MOST RECENT YEAR: 10,023.

NUMBER OF AWARDS: Approximately 1,800 for the year 2015-16.

APPLICATION INFORMATION:
Enrolled students should contact the Fulbright Program Adviser on their campus. Candidates who are not enrolled in an educational institution should contact IIE, U.S. Student Programs Division, at the address above.

Duration: One academic year.
Deadline: Enrolled students should submit their applications to their campus Fulbright Program Advisers by the dates set by them. At-large candidates must submit their applications to the IIE office in October.

INTERNATIONAL DEVELOPMENT RESEARCH CENTRE (IDRC)   [919]
150 Kent Street
Ottawa ON K1P 0B2 Canada
(613) 696-2098
Fax: (613) 236-4026

E-MAIL ADDRESS:
awards@idrc.ca

WEB SITE ADDRESS:
www.idrc.ca/awards

FOUNDED: 1970

AREAS OF INTEREST:
Agriculture, forestry and biology.

NAME(S) OF PROGRAMS:
● **The Bentley Cropping Systems Fellowship**

TYPE:
Awards/prizes; Fellowships. This fellowship provides assistance to Canadian and developing-country graduate students with a university degree in agriculture, forestry or biology who wish to undertake postgraduate, applied, on-farm research in a developing country with cooperating farmers.

PURPOSE:
To promote applied, on-farm research in a developing country with cooperating farmers.

ELIGIBILITY:
Applicants must be citizens, permanent residents of Canada, or citizens of a developing country who are registered in a Canadian university or in a recognized university in a developing country in agriculture, forestry or biology for a Master's or Ph.D. degree. Those involved in postdoctoral research are also eligible.

Program can involve research in any developing region of the world, excluding Central Asia, Cuba, Eastern Europe, Iran, Iraq, Korea (Democratic People's Republic of) and Somalia.

FINANCIAL DATA:
Amount of support per award: $30,000 (CAN).

NUMBER OF APPLICANTS MOST RECENT YEAR: Varies.

NUMBER OF AWARDS: 1 biennially.

APPLICATION INFORMATION:
Applications must be submitted online from the IDRC's competitions page.
Duration: 18 to 24 months. Renewable upon reapplication.
Deadline: October 1 in even-numbered years.

ADDRESS INQUIRIES TO:
Fellowships and Awards
(See address above.)

INTERNATIONAL DEVELOPMENT RESEARCH CENTRE (IDRC)

150 Kent Street
Ottawa ON K1P 0B2 Canada
(613) 696-2098
Fax: (613) 236-4026

E-MAIL ADDRESS:
awards@idrc.ca

WEB SITE ADDRESS:
www.idrc.ca/awards

TYPE:
Awards/prizes. Program provides training in research management and grant administration under the guidance of Centre program staff. Approximately 50% of the time spent on own research project.

See entry 1305 for full listing.

INTERNATIONAL FEDERATION OF UNIVERSITY WOMEN

10, rue du Lac
CH 1207 Geneva Switzerland
+4122 731 23 80

E-MAIL ADDRESS:
fellowships@ifuw.org

WEB SITE ADDRESS:
www.ifuw.org

TYPE:
Awards/prizes; Capital grants; Fellowships; Research grants; Training grants. IFUW fellowships and grants are awarded biennially to encourage and enable women graduates to undertake original research or obtain further training in the humanities, social sciences and natural sciences.

See entry 1085 for full listing.

INTERNATIONAL RESEARCH & EXCHANGES BOARD (IREX)   [920]

1275 K Street, N.W.
Suite 600
Washington, DC 20005
(202) 628-8188
Fax: (202) 628-8189

E-MAIL ADDRESS:
irex@irex.org

WEB SITE ADDRESS:
www.irex.org

FOUNDED: 1968

AREAS OF INTEREST:
Academic research exchanges and professional training programs in Europe, Eurasia, the Middle East and North Africa, and Asia.

NAME(S) OF PROGRAMS:
- **ECA Alumni Small Grants Program**
- **Eurasia/South Asia Teaching Excellence and Achievement Program (TEA)**
- **Global Undergraduate Exchange Program in Eurasia and Central Asia (UGRAD)**
- **Individual Advanced Research Opportunities (IARO)**
- **International Leaders in Education Program (ILEP)**
- **Edmund S. Muskie Graduate Fellowship Program**
- **Short-Term Travel Grants**

TYPE:
Conferences/seminars; Exchange programs; Fellowships; Project/program grants; Research grants; Training grants; Travel grants; Visiting scholars. IARO: Grants to Master's, predoctoral and postdoctoral U.S. scholars for research at institutions in Europe and Eurasia.

ILEP: Grants to secondary teachers from around the globe to the U.S. to further develop expertise in their subject areas, enhance their teaching skills, and increase their knowledge about the U.S.

Muskie: Grants to graduate students and professionals from Armenia, Azerbaijan, Belarus, Georgia, Kazakhstan, Kyrgyzstan, Moldova, Russia, Tajikistan, Turkmenistan, Ukraine and Uzbekistan for one-year non-degree, one-year degree or two-year degree study in the U.S. in business administration, economics, education, environmental management, international affairs, journalism and mass communication, law, library and information science, public administration, public health and public policy.

Short-Term Travel Grants (two to eight weeks) to U.S. researchers for scholarly projects focusing on Eurasia and Europe.

Small Grants: Grants to NIS alumni of ECA-sponsored programs for professional development activities.

TEA: Grants to secondary-school teachers from Eurasia and South Asia with unique opportunities to develop expertise in their subject areas, enhance their teaching skills, and increase their knowledge about the U.S.

UGRAD: Fellowships for first-, second- and third-year undergraduate students from Eurasia to study at a U.S. undergraduate institution for one year.

YEAR PROGRAM STARTED: 1968

PURPOSE:
To promote advanced field research and professional training programs between the U.S. and the countries of Europe, Eurasia, Asia and the Middle East and North Africa.

LEGAL BASIS:
Nonprofit organization.

GEOGRAPHIC RESTRICTIONS:
United States, Europe, Eurasia, the Middle East, Asia and North Africa.

FINANCIAL DATA:
Amount of support per award: Varies per program.

APPLICATION INFORMATION:
Application information is available upon request.

PUBLICATIONS:
Policy papers, application materials.

ADDRESS INQUIRIES TO:
Program Coordinator
(See address above.)

ISTITUTO ITALIANO PER GLI STUDI STORICI

Via Benedetto Croce, 12
80134 Naples Italy
+39.081.5517159
+39.081.5512390
Fax: +39.081.5514813

E-MAIL ADDRESS:
istituto@iiss.it
info@iiss.it

WEB SITE ADDRESS:
www.iiss.it

TYPE:
Awards/prizes; Conferences/seminars; Research grants; Scholarships. Awards for historical, literature and philosophical studies at the Istituto Italiano per gli Studi Storici in Naples.

Federico II Scholarship: Offered by the Universita di Napoli for graduates from Italian universities whose final thesis is in medieval studies.

See entry 600 for full listing.

JAPAN INFORMATION CENTER   [921]

Consulate General of Japan
299 Park Avenue, 18th Floor
New York, NY 10171-0025
(212) 418-4452
Fax: (212) 371-1294

E-MAIL ADDRESS:
scholarship@ny.mofa.go.jp

WEB SITE ADDRESS:
www.ny.us.emb-japan.go.jp

FOUNDED: 1955

AREAS OF INTEREST:
Japanese language and cultural studies.

NAME(S) OF PROGRAMS:
- **Japanese Government (Monbukagakusho) Scholarships for Japanese Studies**

TYPE:
Scholarships. Undergraduate scholarships awarded to foreign students who wish to pursue Japanese language and cultural studies in Japan. The program offers students an intensive course of Japanese language and introduction to Japanese studies in various aspects.

YEAR PROGRAM STARTED: 1955

PURPOSE:
To provide funding for non-Japanese students who want to pursue a course of Japanese and cultural studies in Japan.

LEGAL BASIS:
Japanese government agency.

ELIGIBILITY:
Applicants must:
(1) be nationals of the country to which the scholarships are offered;
(2) be at least 18 years and less than 30 years of age as of April 1 of the year of application;
(3) be regular students who follow an undergraduate course at a university in their own country or a third country and who are mainly second- or third-year students or above in that course;
(4) be specializing in a field concerning Japanese language or Japanese culture at their university;
(5) have good knowledge of the Japanese language and;
(6) be in good health.

Applicants must have a background in Japanese studies to qualify. A written Japanese examination will be given to selected applicants before being considered by the government offices in Japan.

FINANCIAL DATA:
Amount of support per award: JPY 117,000 per month (subject to change), plus tuition, fees and round-trip transportation costs.
Total amount of support: Varies.

NUMBER OF AWARDS: Varies.

APPLICATION INFORMATION:
Applicants should contact the appropriate Japanese consulate. Consulates General are located in Anchorage, Atlanta, Boston, Chicago, Denver, Detroit, Guam, Honolulu, Houston, Los Angeles, Miami, Nashville, New York City, Portland, San Francisco and Seattle.
Duration: One academic year.
Deadline: Varies.

PUBLICATIONS:
Application guidelines.

ADDRESS INQUIRIES TO:
Local Japanese Consulate General

*PLEASE NOTE:
Placement of grantees to universities will be decided by Monbukagakusho after consultation with the universities concerned.

JAPAN INFORMATION CENTER   [922]
Consulate General of Japan
299 Park Avenue, 18th Floor
New York, NY 10171-0025
(212) 371-8222
Fax: (212) 371-1294

E-MAIL ADDRESS:
scholarship@ny.mofa.go.jp

WEB SITE ADDRESS:
www.ny.us.emb-japan.go.jp

FOUNDED: 1955

AREAS OF INTEREST:
Humanities and social sciences: literature, history, aesthetics, law, politics, economics, commerce, pedagogy, psychology, sociology, music, fine arts, natural sciences, pure science, engineering, agriculture, fisheries, pharmacology, medicine, dentistry and home economics.

NAME(S) OF PROGRAMS:
● **Japanese Government (Monbukagakusho) Scholarships for Research Students**

TYPE:
Scholarships. Graduate scholarships awarded to foreign students who wish to study at Japanese universities as nondegree research students.

PURPOSE:
To help students wishing to pursue Japan-related studies.

LEGAL BASIS:
Japanese government agency.

ELIGIBILITY:
Applicants must:
(1) be nationals of the country to which the scholarships are offered;
(2) be under 35 years of age as of April 1 of the year of the award;
(3) be university or college graduates;
(4) be willing to study the Japanese language and to receive instruction in that language and;
(5) be in good health.

The study area must be in the same field as the applicant has studied (or is now studying) or a related one.

FINANCIAL DATA:
Amount of support per award: JPY 143,000 per month.
Total amount of support: Varies.

NUMBER OF AWARDS: Varies.

APPLICATION INFORMATION:
Applicants should contact the appropriate Japanese consulate. Consulates General are located in Anchorage, Atlanta, Boston, Chicago, Denver, Detroit, Hagatna (Guam), Honolulu, Houston, Los Angeles, Miami, Nashville, New York City, Portland, San Francisco and Seattle.
Duration: Up to two years, with possibility of extension.
Deadline: Varies.

PUBLICATIONS:
Application guidelines.

ADDRESS INQUIRIES TO:
Local Japanese Consulate General

*PLEASE NOTE:
Field of study must be one of those available at the Japanese universities and practical training given by factories or companies is excluded.

HERBERT D. KATZ CENTER FOR ADVANCED JUDAIC STUDIES   [923]
420 Walnut Street
Philadelphia, PA 19106
(215) 238-1290
Fax: (215) 238-1540

E-MAIL ADDRESS:
carrielo@sas.upenn.edu

WEB SITE ADDRESS:
katz.sas.upenn.edu

AREAS OF INTEREST:
Advanced research in Judaic and related studies.

NAME(S) OF PROGRAMS:
● **Judaic and Related Studies Postdoctoral Fellowships**

TYPE:
Fellowships.

PURPOSE:
To support education in Judaic and related studies.

ELIGIBILITY:
Individuals are eligible to apply.

FINANCIAL DATA:
Amount of support per award: Up to $50,000.

APPLICATION INFORMATION:
Application information is available on the web site.
Duration: One year. Grants are not renewable.
Deadline: November 10.

ADDRESS INQUIRIES TO:
Carrie Love
Fellowship Program Administrator
(See address above.)

MACKENZIE KING SCHOLARSHIP TRUST
c/o J. Blom, Faculty of Law
1822 East Mall, University of British Columbia
Vancouver BC V6T 1Z1 Canada
(604) 822-4564
Fax: (604) 822-8108

E-MAIL ADDRESS:
mkingscholarships@law.ubc.ca

WEB SITE ADDRESS:
www.mkingscholarships.ca

TYPE:
Scholarships. For graduate study, either in the U.S. or the U.K., in the field of international or industrial relations (including the international or industrial aspects of law, history, politics or economics).

See entry 1706 for full listing.

KOBE COLLEGE CORPORATION-JAPAN EDUCATION EXCHANGE   [924]
540 West Frontage Road, Suite 3335
Northfield, IL 60093
(847) 386-7661
Fax: (847) 386-7662

E-MAIL ADDRESS:
kccjee@comcast.net

WEB SITE ADDRESS:
www.kccjee.org

AREAS OF INTEREST:
Japanese culture and language.

NAME(S) OF PROGRAMS:
● **The KCC-JEE High School Essay Contest**

TYPE:
Awards/prizes. The KCC-JEE High School Essay Contest includes a one-month trip to Japan. It incorporates intensive language study, college credit and a home stay with a Japanese family.

YEAR PROGRAM STARTED: 1995

PURPOSE:
To provide American high school students the opportunity to experience Japanese culture firsthand, enhancing their Japanese language skills and deepening their appreciation of Japanese culture and values by living in Japan for one month.

ELIGIBILITY:
Applicant must meet the following requirements:
(1) be an American citizen or permanent resident alien, 16 years of age by July 1 of the year contest is held;
(2) must have had at least one year of accredited Japanese language study;
(3) attend a public or private high school in the U.S. and;
(4) be available to study during the four weeks established for this program.

GEOGRAPHIC RESTRICTIONS:
United States.

FINANCIAL DATA:
Prize includes round-trip airfare, tuition, and room and board in a Japanese home.
Amount of support per award: Approximately $4,000.

NUMBER OF AWARDS: 1 award given annually.

APPLICATION INFORMATION:
Application and complete information can be found online.
Duration: One summer month (typically July); nonrenewable.
Deadline: February.

THE KOSCIUSZKO FOUNDATION, INC. [925]

15 East 65th Street
New York, NY 10065
(212) 734-2130
Fax: (212) 628-4552

E-MAIL ADDRESS:
APieski@aol.com

WEB SITE ADDRESS:
www.thekf.
org/programs/teaching_english_in_poland

FOUNDED: 1925

AREAS OF INTEREST:
Educational and cultural exchange program
in Poland.

NAME(S) OF PROGRAMS:
● **Teaching English in Poland**

TYPE:
Summer educational and cultural exchange
program for American teachers and teaching
assistants in Poland.

YEAR PROGRAM STARTED: 1991

PURPOSE:
To provide Polish students with English
language experiences within an American
cultural context; to familiarize Polish students
with various aspects of American life and
culture; to introduce American teachers and
teaching assistants to Polish culture, history,
traditions and people of Poland so that their
knowledge and impressions will be shared.

LEGAL BASIS:
501(c)(3) not-for-profit organization.

ELIGIBILITY:
Experienced teachers/administrators certified
in the U.S., educators with private/parochial
school or other verifiable teaching
experience, college/university faculty, and
those engaged in student services (school
nurse, social worker, guidance counselor,
school psychologist, etc.) are eligible for
participation. Group flight arrangements will
be made by the Foundation. Participants are
encouraged to travel to Poland with the
group.

GEOGRAPHIC RESTRICTIONS:
United States.

FINANCIAL DATA:
Registration fee of $250 for teachers and
$200 for teaching assistants. Medical
insurance, required by The Kosciuszko
Foundation, is covered. This is a volunteer
opportunity. Applicant pays for airfare. Room
and board during the teaching program as
well as sightseeing in Poland after the
program's end are covered by Polish hosts.
Amount of support per award: Varies.
Matching fund requirements: In-kind
donations such as art and sport equipment
towards the program are accepted.

COOPERATIVE FUNDING PROGRAMS: Delta
Kappa Gamma support in the amount of
$14,000.

NUMBER OF APPLICANTS MOST RECENT YEAR:
70.

NUMBER OF AWARDS: 31.

APPLICATION INFORMATION:
Faxed applications are not acceptable.
Duration: Approximately one month. May
reapply by letter requesting reactivation of
application.
Deadline: January 13.

PUBLICATIONS:
KF Newsletter; Annual Report.

IRS IDENTIFICATION NUMBER: 13-1628179

STAFF:
Mary Kay Pieski, Ph.D.

ADDRESS INQUIRIES TO:
Teaching English in Poland Program
315 Fawnwood Drive
Tallmadge, OH 44278

THE KOSCIUSZKO FOUNDATION, INC. [926]

15 East 65th Street
New York, NY 10065
(212) 734-2130 ext. 210

E-MAIL ADDRESS:
addy@thekf.org

WEB SITE ADDRESS:
www.thekf.org/programs/study

FOUNDED: 1925

AREAS OF INTEREST:
Strengthening of cultural and educational
bonds between the U.S. and Poland through
an exchange program to Poland for the
purpose of Polish language, culture and
history studies.

NAME(S) OF PROGRAMS:
● **Summer Study Abroad Programs**

TYPE:
Exchange programs; Scholarships. Summer
programs. The Summer Study Abroad
Programs offer a variety of courses from July
through August at the Jagiellonian University
in Krakow and at the John Paul II Catholic
University of Lublin, Poland. Polish
language, culture, history, art and many other
subjects are available. The Foundation
sponsors this program mainly for paying
students; however, some scholarship awards
are available for the program at the
Jagiellonian University in Krakow.

YEAR PROGRAM STARTED: 1970

PURPOSE:
To enable American students to pursue a
short-term course of Polish language, culture,
history and art studies abroad.

LEGAL BASIS:
501(c)(3) not-for-profit organization.

ELIGIBILITY:
The Summer Study Abroad Programs are
open to U.S. undergraduate and graduate
students as well as graduating high school
students who will be 18 years of age by the
first day of the program.

Students of Polish descent can apply for
funding to attend the Foundation's
three-week program at the Jagiellonian
University via the Foundation's
Tomaszkiewicz-Florio Scholarship.

GEOGRAPHIC RESTRICTIONS:
United States.

FINANCIAL DATA:
Program fee includes tuition, cultural events
and sightseeing trips, a language placement
test, language classes, a choice of history,
literature and sociology classes, shared
dormitory room, three meals a day and
assistance from Polish university students. A
Kosciuszko Foundation representative is
available in Poland during the program. The
scholarships which are available cover
program fees for three-week programs at the
Jagiellonian University in Krakow.

Amount of support per award: $1,865 for the
year 2014.
Total amount of support: $31,770 awarded
towards Summer Studies in Krakow for the
year 2013.

NUMBER OF APPLICANTS MOST RECENT YEAR:
80.

NUMBER OF AWARDS: 16 for the year 2013.

APPLICATION INFORMATION:
Official application materials and other
pertinent information are available online.
Application is available from January to May.
When requesting forms and additional
information via e-mail, please indicate
"Summer Study Abroad Programs" in the
subject line.
Duration: Two- to eight-week programs are
available.
Deadline: March 31 for scholarship
applicants. May 15 for students who wish to
pay their own way.

PUBLICATIONS:
KF Newsletter; annual report.

IRS IDENTIFICATION NUMBER: 13-1628179

ADDRESS INQUIRIES TO:
Addy Tymczyszyn, Coordinator
Summer Study Abroad Programs
(See address above.)

*PLEASE NOTE:
Students submit scholarship applications to
the Foundation's chapters. Pay-to-go
applicants must submit application materials
to Kosciuszko Foundation's headquarters in
New York City.

*SPECIAL STIPULATIONS:
Students who receive scholarships are
required to submit a report upon completion
of the program. The report is forwarded to
the donors of the scholarship.

THE KOSCIUSZKO FOUNDATION, INC. [927]

15 East 65th Street
New York, NY 10065
(212) 734-2130 ext. 210

E-MAIL ADDRESS:
addy@thekf.org

WEB SITE ADDRESS:
www.thekf.org/scholarships/exchange-
poland/year-abroad

FOUNDED: 1925

AREAS OF INTEREST:
Strengthening of cultural and educational
bonds between the U.S. and Poland through
an exchange program to Poland for the
purpose of Polish language, culture and
history studies.

NAME(S) OF PROGRAMS:
● **The Kosciuszko Foundation Year
Abroad Program**

TYPE:
Exchange programs; Scholarships; Visiting
scholars. The Year Abroad Program at the
Center for Polish Language and Culture in
the World, Jagiellonian University (Krakow)
offers American students the opportunity to
study Polish language, history, literature and
culture for one academic year or one
semester. This program allows students to
spend their undergraduate junior or senior
year in Poland. Undergraduate credit may be
transferred. Students at the Master's level
may also apply.

PURPOSE:
To enable American students to pursue an undergraduate course of Polish language, literature, history and culture at the Center for Polish Language and Culture, Jagiellonian University, Krakow.

LEGAL BASIS:
501(c)(3) not-for-profit organization.

ELIGIBILITY:
U.S. citizens enrolled at a U.S. college or university who will be entering their junior or senior year can apply. Graduate students, with the exception of those at the dissertation level, can also apply. Minimum grade point average of 3.0 is required.

Polish citizens are not eligible.

Scholarship does not cover second majors.

GEOGRAPHIC RESTRICTIONS:
United States.

FINANCIAL DATA:
Scholarship offers a tuition waiver, housing and a monthly stipend of 1,350 Polish zloty per month towards living expenses. Recipients also receive $200 per month from the Foundation for living expenses. Transportation to and from Poland is not included.
Amount of support per award: $900 per semester plus additional funding from the Polish Ministry in the amount of 1,350 Polish zloty per month of study.
Total amount of support: Varies.

NUMBER OF AWARDS: Varies.

APPLICATION INFORMATION:
Applications are available on the Foundation web site from October to December 31. When requesting information and/or forms, please specify "Year Abroad Program" in the subject line of your e-mail. Applications and supporting materials must be accompanied by a nonrefundable $50 application fee. The Foundation does not accept faxed applications.
Duration: One semester or one academic year.
Deadline: January 5. Notification in June. Funding is for the following academic year.

PUBLICATIONS:
Guidelines; *KF Newsletter*; annual report.

IRS IDENTIFICATION NUMBER: 13-1628179

ADDRESS INQUIRIES TO:
Year Abroad Program
(See address above.)

THE KOSCIUSZKO FOUNDATION, INC.   [928]
15 East 65th Street
New York, NY 10065
(212) 734-2130 ext. 210

E-MAIL ADDRESS:
addy@thekf.org

WEB SITE ADDRESS:
www.thekf.org/scholarships/exchange-poland/research

FOUNDED: 1925

AREAS OF INTEREST:
Strengthening of cultural and educational bonds between the U.S. and Poland through this exchange program for graduate-level students and scholars who wish to conduct research programs in Poland.

NAME(S) OF PROGRAMS:
- **The Kosciuszko Foundation Graduate Studies and Research in Poland**

TYPE:
Exchange programs; Research grants; Scholarships; Visiting scholars. This program enables American students and scholars to pursue a course of graduate or postgraduate study and research in Poland. It is also open to university faculty who wish to spend a sabbatical conducting research in Poland.

Research may be conducted during the Polish academic year, October through June only. No funding during the summer months of July, August and September.

YEAR PROGRAM STARTED: 1925

PURPOSE:
To assist Americans in continuing their graduate and postgraduate studies and research at institutions of higher learning in Poland.

LEGAL BASIS:
501(c)(3) not-for-profit organization.

ELIGIBILITY:
U.S. citizens with strong Polish language skills who wish to conduct research in Poland can apply. Funds can only be used at institutions of higher learning in Poland which fall under the jurisdiction of the Polish Ministry of Education and Science.

Polish citizens are not eligible.

GEOGRAPHIC RESTRICTIONS:
United States.

FINANCIAL DATA:
Scholarship does not cover tuition costs. Participants receive a stipend from the Polish government towards housing and living expenses. No provisions are made for dependents. Transportation to and from Poland is at the expense of the participant. The scholarship does not cover second majors.
Amount of support per award: $300 per month of approved study/research, plus 1,350 zloty per month from the Polish government.
Total amount of support: Varies.

NUMBER OF AWARDS: Varies.

APPLICATION INFORMATION:
Official application materials are available upon request to the Foundation at the address above. Please specify "Graduate Study and Research in Poland" when requesting application materials and/or information. Applications are available online at the Foundation's web site from October through December 31. Nonrefundable application fee of $50 is required.

Applicants must submit a letter of invitation from the host university's International Student Office specifying terms of the research including start and end dates of the research project, whether dormitory housing will be provided to the candidate, and provisions for access to university libraries, archives, and/or equipment as needed. A letter from the professor or department chairperson with whom research is to be conducted indicating the feasibility of the research proposal, agreement to act as the candidate's Academic Advisor and provision for letters of introduction as may be necessary for the research proposal. The host institution must fall under jurisdiction of the Polish Ministry of Education and Science in order to be considered.

The Foundation does not accept faxed applications.
Duration: Maximum of nine months. Research may be conducted from October to June. No funding from July through September.
Deadline: January 5. Notification in June/July for funding in the following academic year.

PUBLICATIONS:
KF Newsletter; annual report.

IRS IDENTIFICATION NUMBER: 13-1628179

ADDRESS INQUIRIES TO:
Studies and Research in Poland
(See address above.)

THE ROBERTO LONGHI FOUNDATION FOR THE STUDY OF THE HISTORY OF ART
Via Benedetto Fortini, 30
50125 Florence Italy
+39.055.6580794
Fax: +39.055.6580794

E-MAIL ADDRESS:
longhi@fondazionelonghi.it

WEB SITE ADDRESS:
www.fondazionelonghi.it

TYPE:
Fellowships.
See entry 554 for full listing.

MARSHALL AID COMMEMORATION COMMISSION   [929]
ACU
Woburn House
20-24 Tavistock Square
London WC1H 9HF England
020 7380 6700
Fax: 020 7387 2655

E-MAIL ADDRESS:
macc@acu.ac.uk

WEB SITE ADDRESS:
www.marshallscholarship.org

FOUNDED: 1953

NAME(S) OF PROGRAMS:
- **Marshall Scholarships**

TYPE:
Scholarships. Tenable at any university in the U.K. in any subject leading to the award of a British university degree, which recipients are required to take.

Marshall Scholarships finance young Americans of high ability to study for a degree in the U.K. in a system of higher education recognized for its excellence. These grants have been established to express British gratitude for the European Recovery Program (the Marshall Plan) instituted by General of the Army George C. Marshall.

YEAR PROGRAM STARTED: 1954

PURPOSE:
To enable citizens of the U.S., both men and women who are graduates of U.S. colleges and universities, to study for a degree from a university in the U.K. for a period of at least one academic year.

LEGAL BASIS:
Programme established by British Parliamentary Act.

ELIGIBILITY:
Scholarships are offered to U.S. citizens for study in the United Kingdom. Graduates of a degree-granting college or university who have graduated from their undergraduate college or university no more than three years before the year the award will be taken up are eligible (e.g., for awards tenable from October 2014, candidates must have graduated after April 2011). Candidates must be American citizens at the time of application and must have obtained a grade point average of not less than 3.7 (or A-). (Exceptions will be considered only on the specific recommendation of the sponsoring college.)

FINANCIAL DATA:
Scholarships include a personal allowance, tuition fees, grants for books, travel, thesis and fares to and from Britain.
Amount of support per award: Currently GBP 917 per month (GBP 1,134 for those studying at Central London institutions) for 12 or 22 months, plus book grants and fares to/from the U.K., plus payment of university tuition fees to GBP 25,000 per year.
Total amount of support: GBP 2,000,000 for the year ended March 31, 2013.

NUMBER OF APPLICANTS MOST RECENT YEAR:
Approximately 800.

NUMBER OF AWARDS: Up to 40 awards annually.

APPLICATION INFORMATION:
Application should be made to a British Consulate-General (in Atlanta, Boston, Chicago, Houston, Los Angeles, New York and San Francisco) or to the British Embassy in Washington.
Duration: One to two years. May be extended for a third year.
Deadline: Early October of the year preceding the award.

OFFICERS:
John Kirkland, Executive Secretary
Mary C. Denyer, Assistant Secretary

COMMISSION MEMBERS:
Dr. John Hughes, Chairperson
Michael Birshan
Prof. Bob Deacon
Richard Dendy
Timothy Hornsby
Ruth Kosmin
Carol Madison-Graham
Simon Morris
Eric Thomas
Nigel Thrift

THE MATSUMAE INTERNATIONAL FOUNDATION [930]
4-14-46, Kamiogi, Suginami-ku
Tokyo 167-0043 Japan
+81-3-3301-7600
Fax: +81-3-3301-7601

E-MAIL ADDRESS:
contact2mif@mist.dti.ne.jp

WEB SITE ADDRESS:
www.mars.dti.ne.jp/mif

FOUNDED: 1979

AREAS OF INTEREST:
First priority: Natural sciences, engineering and medicine.

NAME(S) OF PROGRAMS:
● **Fellowship Program**

TYPE:
Fellowships; Research grants.

YEAR PROGRAM STARTED: 1980

PURPOSE:
To provide opportunity to foreign scientists to conduct research at Japanese institutions.

LEGAL BASIS:
Private foundation.

ELIGIBILITY:
Citizenship is unrestricted. Those of non-Japanese nationality who meet all of the following eligibility requirements are invited to submit the required application documents:
(1) Applicants must hold a Ph.D. degree, or be recognized by the Foundation as possessing equivalent academic qualifications;
(2) Applicants must be under 49 years of age at the time of application;
(3) Applicants must have sufficient conversational ability in English or Japanese to prevent insurmountable difficulties during their research activities in Japan;
(4) Applicants should not have been in Japan in the past and/or in the present;
(5) Applicants should have firm positions and professions in their home countries and should return to their countries on completion of their fellowship stay by the Foundation and;
(6) Applicants must be of sound health and not physically handicapped in any way which would prevent them from carrying out research in Japan.

Fields of study such as natural science, engineering and medicine are given first priority.

FINANCIAL DATA:
Awards include stipend for research and stay, lump sum on arrival, round-trip travel and insurance.
Amount of support per award: Monthly stipend of JPY 200,000.

NUMBER OF APPLICANTS MOST RECENT YEAR:
129 from 33 countries for the year 2014.

NUMBER OF AWARDS: 24 from 19 countries for the year 2014. From 1980 to 2013, there have been 698 Research Fellows from 112 countries.

APPLICATION INFORMATION:
Application form required. Application must be submitted from the applicant's home country. Under no circumstances will an application be accepted from a person already in Japan. The Foundation does not accept applications by fax or e-mail.

All documents must be typewritten in English. The following documents (A4 in size) must be included and submitted on one occasion by the applicant:
(1) a photograph (taken within the last three months) along with the fully completed application form (signed and dated);
(2) a description of the research project by the applicant;
(3) complete list of publications;
(4) reprint(s) of what the applicant considers to be his or her most important publication(s);
(5) a personal history (curriculum vitae);
(6) a letter of recommendation from the applicant's employer and/or supervisor testifying to academic ability and achievements and confirming the availability of study leave covering the grant period;
(7) a certified copy of the applicant's

academic certificates (Ph.D., Master's, Bachelor's) issued by the university concerned (in English, or document with English translation attached) and;
(8) an invitation letter with signature from the host scientist confirming the period of stay, the research project and the availability of research facilities/materials, and the arrangement of lodging accommodation under the Foundation Fellowship Program.

Submitted applications which do not contain all of the required documents will automatically be rejected.

The Foundation will not be responsible for costs incurred in submitting an application and reserves the right to request additional documents if necessary. All documents received become the property of the Foundation and will not be returned. The Foundation will not respond to individual inquiry concerning the status/arrival of application documents.
Duration: Three to six months; extension/reduction of the granted period is not allowed.
Deadline: Applications must be received by the Foundation by August 31 for the following year's fellowship.

PUBLICATIONS:
Program announcement.

ADDRESS INQUIRIES TO:
Fellowship Program
(See address above.)

*PLEASE NOTE:
To promote deeper understanding of Japan, the Foundation organizes a Study Tour during the invitation period in Japan.

Each year, the Foundation issues a "Research Report" containing summaries of research activities or results which are kindly submitted by the Fellows.

In order to keep in touch with Fellows after their return home, the Foundation issues a "Newsletter" and "Fellowship Directory" annually.

MICHIGAN STATE UNIVERSITY [931]
Office of Study Abroad
International Center
427 North Shaw Lane, Room 109
East Lansing, MI 48824-1035
(517) 353-8920
Fax: (517) 432-2082

E-MAIL ADDRESS:
osapa@isp.msu.edu

WEB SITE ADDRESS:
www.studyabroad.msu.edu

NAME(S) OF PROGRAMS:
● **MSU Study Abroad Scholarships**

TYPE:
Scholarships. Academic study abroad scholarships for college-level credit. The program includes over 270 overseas study programs in more than 60 countries in a wide variety of academic fields.

PURPOSE:
To assist Michigan State University students who will benefit from study abroad.

LEGAL BASIS:
University.

ELIGIBILITY:
Applicants must be MSU students. Participation in study abroad program is:

(1) based on financial need. Applicant must have FAFSA application on file with MSU office of financial aid and have a minimum 2.5 grade point average and;
(2) based on academic performance. Applicant must have a minimum 3.5 grade point average and submit an essay explaining how study abroad would enhance the student's education.

FINANCIAL DATA:
Amount of support per award: $500 to $2,000 available per student.
Total amount of support: Approximately $400,000 annually.

NUMBER OF APPLICANTS MOST RECENT YEAR: 1,200.

APPLICATION INFORMATION:
Application information is available on the web site.
Duration: Varies.
Deadline: October 15 and March 1.

STAFF:
Lynn Aguado, Study Abroad Program Coordinator

ADDRESS INQUIRIES TO:
Lynn Aguado
Study Abroad Program Coordinator
(See address above.)

THE NANSEN FUND, INC.   [932]
5219 Pine Arbor Drive
Houston, TX 77066-2548
(281) 682-4327
Fax: (281) 587-9284

E-MAIL ADDRESS:
anne-brith@nacchouston.org

WEB SITE ADDRESS:
www.noram.no

FOUNDED: 1979

AREAS OF INTEREST:
International educational exchange, international relations, classics, political science and Norwegian culture.

NAME(S) OF PROGRAMS:
● **John Dana Archbold Fellowships**

TYPE:
Fellowships; Scholarships; Travel grants. Stipends for subsistence and quarters. One-year graduate fellowships for study at the University of Oslo in Norway, offered in even-numbered years; in odd-numbered years offered to Norwegians for study in the U.S.

YEAR PROGRAM STARTED: 1981

PURPOSE:
To promote better understanding among peoples for peace among nations and to support educational exchange between the U.S. and Norway.

LEGAL BASIS:
509(a)(2) organization.

ELIGIBILITY:
Fellowships are open to Norwegians and Americans for a year of graduate, postdoctoral or professional study and research. Eligibility is limited to persons 20 to 35 years old, in good health, of good character, and citizens of the U.S. or Norway. Qualified applicants must show evidence of real ability in their chosen field, indicate seriousness of purpose, and have a record of social adaptability. Undergraduate applicants must have a B.A. or B.S. degree (or equivalent) before their departure date.

GEOGRAPHIC RESTRICTIONS:
Norway and United States.

FINANCIAL DATA:
Maintenance stipend is sufficient to meet basic expenses for a single person. Some travel allowance.
Amount of support per award: Up to $10,000, depending on projected costs of tuition, maintenance, travel and rate of exchange.
Total amount of support: Up to $10,000.

COOPERATIVE FUNDING PROGRAMS: The University of Oslo charges no tuition to fellows.

NUMBER OF APPLICANTS MOST RECENT YEAR: Average 6.

NUMBER OF AWARDS: 1 annually.

APPLICATION INFORMATION:
Application forms are available from the address above until December 1 of the year preceding the award period. Completed applications require a statement of the proposed study, curriculum vitae, three academic references, foreign language report and transcripts, international relations, classics, political science and Norwegian culture.
Duration: One year, including Oslo International Summer School.
Deadline: February 1. Announcement by March 1.

PUBLICATIONS:
Program description.

IRS IDENTIFICATION NUMBER: 74-6043421

OFFICERS AND DIRECTORS:
Anne-Brith Berge

ADDRESS INQUIRIES TO:
For further information about the University of Oslo, contact:
Ms. Torild Homstad
The University of Oslo International Summer School
North American Branch Office
St. Olaf College
1520 St. Olaf Avenue
Northfield, MN 55057
Tel: (507) 786-3269 or (800) 639-0058
Fax: (507) 786-3732
E-mail: iss@stolaf.edu
Web site: www.uio.no/iss/

*SPECIAL STIPULATIONS:
Successful applicant(s) will be recommended to the University of Oslo by the Nansen Fund, but he or she must make application to, and be accepted by, the University as a graduate student in a particular department. The University of Oslo International Summer School offers orientation and Norwegian language courses for six weeks before the start of the regular academic year. For Americans, tuition is paid. Attendance is required.

NATIONAL SECURITY EDUCATION PROGRAM   [933]
Boren Scholarships
Institute of International Education
1400 K Street, N.W., 7th Floor
Washington, DC 20005-2403
(800) 618-6737
Fax: (202) 326-7672

E-MAIL ADDRESS:
boren@iie.org

WEB SITE ADDRESS:
www.borenawards.org

FOUNDED: 1991

AREAS OF INTEREST:
Languages and cultures of world regions that are critical to U.S. interests and underrepresented in study abroad, including Africa, Asia, Central and Eastern Europe, Eurasia, Latin America, and the Middle East.

NAME(S) OF PROGRAMS:
● **Boren Scholarships**

TYPE:
Scholarships. Boren Scholarships provide funding for U.S. undergraduate students to study abroad in areas of the world that are critical to U.S. interests and underrepresented in study abroad.

PURPOSE:
To provide American undergraduates with the resources and encouragement they need to acquire language skills and cultural experiences in areas of the world critical to national security, broadly defined. In exchange for funding, recipients commit to working in the federal government for a minimum of one year after graduation.

ELIGIBILITY:
Must be a U.S. citizen at the time of application. Open to high school graduates, or those who have earned a GED, and are matriculated as a freshman, sophomore, junior, or senior in a U.S. postsecondary institution, including universities, colleges, and community colleges. Applicant must plan to study abroad in Africa, Asia, Central and Eastern Europe, Eurasia, or the Middle East. The countries of Western Europe, Canada, Australia, and New Zealand are excluded. The study abroad program must meet home institution standards and end prior to graduation.

FINANCIAL DATA:
Amount of support per award: Summer: Up to $8,000; Semester: Up to $10,000; Full academic year: Up to $20,000.

NUMBER OF APPLICANTS MOST RECENT YEAR: 947.

NUMBER OF AWARDS: 161.

APPLICATION INFORMATION:
Complete details and application information can be found on the Boren Awards web site.
Duration: Summer (minimum eight weeks), fall or spring semester, and full academic year.
Deadline: National Application: January or February 2015.

ADDRESS INQUIRIES TO:
See e-mail address or phone number above.

*SPECIAL STIPULATIONS:
In exchange for funding, recipients agree to the National Security Education Program (NSEP) Service Requirement. The NSEP Service Requirement stipulates that an award recipient work for a minimum of one year in the federal government in a position with national security responsibilities. The Departments of Defense, Homeland Security, State, or any element of the Intelligence Community are priority agencies.

NATIONAL SECURITY EDUCATION PROGRAM [934]

Boren Fellowships
Institute of International Education
1400 K Street, N.W., 7th Floor
Washington, DC 20005-2403
(800) 618-6737
Fax: (202) 326-7672

E-MAIL ADDRESS:
boren@iie.org

WEB SITE ADDRESS:
www.borenawards.org

FOUNDED: 1991

AREAS OF INTEREST:
Boren Fellowships support study and research in areas of the world that are critical to U.S. interests, including Africa, Asia, Central and Eastern Europe, Eurasia, Latin America, and the Middle East.

NAME(S) OF PROGRAMS:
● **Boren Fellowships**

TYPE:
Fellowships. Fellowships for U.S. graduate students to provide support for overseas study or a combination of overseas and domestic study.

PURPOSE:
To encourage U.S. graduate students to add an important international and language component to their graduate education through specialization in area study, language study, or increased language proficiency; to support study and research in areas of the world that are critical to U.S. interests, including Africa, Asia, Central and Eastern Europe, Eurasia, Latin America, and the Middle East.

ELIGIBILITY:
Must be a U.S. citizen at the time of application. Applicants must be matriculated in or applying to a graduate degree program at an accredited U.S. college or university located within the U.S. Boren Fellows must remain matriculated in their graduate programs for the duration of the fellowship. Applicant must plan an overseas program that meets home institution standards in Africa, Asia, Central and Eastern Europe, Eurasia, Latin America, and the Middle East. The countries of Western Europe, Canada, Australia, and New Zealand are excluded.

FINANCIAL DATA:
Amount of support per award: Up to $24,000 for overseas study; Up to $30,000 for a combination of domestic and overseas study.

NUMBER OF APPLICANTS MOST RECENT YEAR: 526.

NUMBER OF AWARDS: 110.

APPLICATION INFORMATION:
Complete details and application information can be found on the Boren Awards web site.
Duration: Maximum two years for domestic and overseas study. Minimum 12 weeks for overseas study. Preference will be given to programs of six to 12 months.
Deadline: January or February 2015.

ADDRESS INQUIRIES TO:
See e-mail address or phone number above.

*SPECIAL STIPULATIONS:
In exchange for funding, recipients agree to the National Security Education Program (NSEP) Service Requirement. The NSEP Service Requirement stipulates that an award recipient work for a minimum of one year in the federal government in a position with national security responsibilities. The Departments of Defense, Homeland Security, State, or any element of the Intelligence Community are priority agencies.

THE PHI BETA KAPPA SOCIETY [935]

1606 New Hampshire Avenue, N.W.
Washington, DC 20009
(202) 745-3287
Fax: (202) 986-1601

E-MAIL ADDRESS:
awards@pbk.org

WEB SITE ADDRESS:
www.pbk.org

AREAS OF INTEREST:
French language, literature and culture.

NAME(S) OF PROGRAMS:
● **The Walter J. Jensen Fellowship for French Language, Literature and Culture**

TYPE:
Fellowships. Fellowship for at least six months of study in France. One award given annually.

YEAR PROGRAM STARTED: 2001

PURPOSE:
To help educators and researchers improve education in standard French language, literature and culture, and in the study of standard French in the U.S.

ELIGIBILITY:
Candidates must be U.S. citizens under 40 years of age who can demonstrate their career does or will involve active use of the French language. They must have earned a Baccalaureate degree from an accredited four-year institution, and have a 3.0 minimum grade point average in French language and literature as a major. They must demonstrate superior competence in French, according to the standards established by the American Association of Teachers of French. Preference may be given to members of Phi Beta Kappa and educators at the secondary school level or above.

GEOGRAPHIC RESTRICTIONS:
United States.

FINANCIAL DATA:
Includes single round-trip, economy-class ticket for travel to France.
Amount of support per award: Minimum $10,000 stipend.

NUMBER OF APPLICANTS MOST RECENT YEAR: 6.

NUMBER OF AWARDS: Minimum 1 annually.

APPLICATION INFORMATION:
The application booklet contains:
(1) the Application for the Walter J. Jensen Fellowship;
(2) two Transcript Request forms and;
(3) the Letter of Recommendation Form.

Applicant must submit three complete sets of documents. The Letter of Recommendation and Transcript Request forms may be duplicated. Please indicate the Fellowship name on all correspondence.

Applicant should send the application, official transcripts, and confidential letters of recommendation (in sealed envelopes) to the Walter J. Jensen Fellowship Committee in care of the Phi Beta Kappa Society.

Duration: At least six months.
Deadline: October. Contact Society for exact date.

ADDRESS INQUIRIES TO:
Laura Hartnett
Coordinator of Administration
(See address above.)

THE ROTARY FOUNDATION OF ROTARY INTERNATIONAL [936]

One Rotary Center
1560 Sherman Avenue
Evanston, IL 60201-3698
(866) 976-8279
(847) 866-3000
Fax: (847) 556-2141

E-MAIL ADDRESS:
rotarypeacecenters@rotary.org

WEB SITE ADDRESS:
www.rotary.org/en/peace-fellowships

FOUNDED: 2002

AREAS OF INTEREST:
Higher education.

NAME(S) OF PROGRAMS:
● **Rotary Peace Fellowships**

TYPE:
Fellowships. The Rotary Peace Centers offer individuals committed to peace and cooperation the opportunity to pursue a one- to two-year Master's-level degree or a three-month professional certificate in international studies, peace studies and conflict resolution at one of the six Rotary Peace Centers. The university partners are: Duke University and the University of North Carolina at Chapel Hill (North Carolina, U.S.A.); International Christian University (Tokyo, Japan); University of Bradford (West Yorkshire, England); University of Queensland (Brisbane, Queensland, Australia); Uppsala University (Uppsala, Sweden); and Chulalongkorn University (Bangkok, Thailand).

YEAR PROGRAM STARTED: 2002

PURPOSE:
To further peace and international understanding.

LEGAL BASIS:
Incorporated not-for-profit foundation.

ELIGIBILITY:
Applicants must have:
(1) the academic background, training and work experience required for a Master's-level program at the partner universities;
(2) proficiency in more than one language (even if they propose to study in a country where their native language is spoken);
(3) excellent leadership skills;
(4) a demonstrated commitment to peace and international understanding through their personal and community service activities and/or academic and professional achievements and;
(5) endorsement of their local rotary district office.

Persons with disabilities and members of Rotaract clubs are eligible and encouraged to apply.

FINANCIAL DATA:
Fellowship will include funding for tuition and required fees, room and board, transportation, contingency expenses and other funding, including paid internship experience.

Amount of support per award: Master's Program: Average $75,000; Professional Development Certificate: Average $12,000.

Total amount of support: Varies.

NUMBER OF APPLICANTS MOST RECENT YEAR: 325.

NUMBER OF AWARDS: Approximately 100 each year.

APPLICATION INFORMATION:
All Rotary districts around the world are invited to nominate an unlimited number of candidates for the world-competitive selection each year. Applications generally need to be completed approximately 18 months in advance of the planned study period. Applications are available from the Rotary web site or from local Rotary clubs (listed under "Club Locator" on the Foundation web site). Interested applicants must contact a local Rotary club to ask about local application deadlines. Club deadlines may be as early as January or as late as June of the year prior to the study period.

Duration: Master's Program: One to two years; Professional Development Certificate: Three months.

Deadline: July 1.

PUBLICATIONS:
Application; brochure.

ADDRESS INQUIRIES TO:
Local Rotary Club or Contact Center (See e-mail address above.)

THE ROYAL SOCIETY OF EDINBURGH   [937]

22-26 George Street
Edinburgh EH2 2PQ Scotland
44 0131 240 5000
44 0131 240 5013
Fax: 44 0131 240 5024

E-MAIL ADDRESS:
info@royalsoced.org.uk
afraser@royalsoced.org.uk

WEB SITE ADDRESS:
www.royalsoced.org.uk

FOUNDED: 1783

AREAS OF INTEREST:
Physical, computational, biological, medical, natural and social disciplines.

NAME(S) OF PROGRAMS:
● **Royal Society of Edinburgh Scottish Government Personal Research Fellowships**

TYPE:
Fellowships. Postdoctoral fellowships for research in science and technology disciplines in any Scottish higher education institution.

YEAR PROGRAM STARTED: 1983

PURPOSE:
To enhance the transfer of ideas and technology from the research community to wealth creation and improvement of the quality of life in Scotland.

ELIGIBILITY:
Applicants must possess a Doctorate, or equivalent higher education qualification, and should have two to six years of relevant postdoctoral academic research experience at the time of the application closing date. Only applicants who meet these criteria by the date of application will be considered. Applicants must show that they have an outstanding

capacity for innovative research with a strong publication record relevant to their proposed field of study. Preference will be given to those not holding a permanent position in an academic or research institution.

Research fellows must be based in Scotland during the fellowship, but can travel outside the U.K. for up to one year.

FINANCIAL DATA:
Salary, national insurance and pension costs covered, plus GBP 10,000 support funds and up to GBP 8,000 for travel, attendance at approved meetings and cost of minor equipment.

Amount of support per award: Stipend approximately GBP 24,766 to GBP 37,382.

COOPERATIVE FUNDING PROGRAMS: Fellowships are made with the support of the Scottish government. Funding is also provided by the EU Marie Curie Co-Fund under FP7, to allow research fellows to spend up to one year outside the U.K.

NUMBER OF APPLICANTS MOST RECENT YEAR: 60.

NUMBER OF AWARDS: 6.

APPLICATION INFORMATION:
Application form and guidelines are available from the Research Fellowships secretary. Applicant can also consult online.

Duration: Up to five years.

Deadline: March 25.

OFFICERS:
Sir John Arbuthnott, President
Gerald Wilson, Treasurer

ADDRESS INQUIRIES TO:
Anne Fraser, Research and International Awards Manager
The Royal Society of Edinburgh
Tel: 44 0131 240 5013
E-mail: afraser@royalsoced.org.uk
(See address above.)

ST. ANDREW'S SOCIETY OF THE STATE OF NEW YORK [938]

150 East 55th Street, 3rd Floor
New York, NY 10022
(212) 223-4248
Fax: (212) 233-0748

E-MAIL ADDRESS:
office@standrewsny.org

WEB SITE ADDRESS:
www.standrewsny.org

FOUNDED: 1756

AREAS OF INTEREST:
Charitable support of needy persons of Scottish descent and scholarship program.

NAME(S) OF PROGRAMS:
● **Scholarship Program for Graduate Study in Scotland**

TYPE:
Scholarships. Scholarships for American students of Scottish descent for one year of graduate study in any Scottish university.

YEAR PROGRAM STARTED: 1956

PURPOSE:
To promote cultural interchange and goodwill between Scotland and the U.S.

LEGAL BASIS:
Tax-exempt charitable organization.

ELIGIBILITY:
An applicant must have a Bachelor's degree, exhibit financial need, possess an outstanding

scholastic and activity record, provide evidence of Scottish descent, and reside within a 250-mile radius of New York state.

GEOGRAPHIC RESTRICTIONS:
New Jersey, New York, Pennsylvania and the New England states.

FINANCIAL DATA:
Award is to be used initially against tuition, then board, room, transportation and other expenses.

Amount of support per award: Up to $30,000.

Total amount of support: Varies each year.

NUMBER OF APPLICANTS MOST RECENT YEAR: 100.

NUMBER OF AWARDS: 2 per year (for U.S. applicants).

APPLICATION INFORMATION:
The applicant must contact St. Andrew's Society in writing with a request for an application. When the application is completed, it should be submitted to the college/university from/at which the student graduated or is due to graduate. Each college or university is invited to send only one candidate forward to the St. Andrew's Society Selection Committee. Referral must be by president of the institution the applicant is attending.

Duration: One year. Nonrenewable.

Deadline: December 15. Announcement in early March.

PUBLICATIONS:
Quarterly newsletter.

IRS IDENTIFICATION NUMBER: 13-5602329

OFFICERS:
Samuel F. Abernethy, President
Derek Anderson, Treasurer
Heath McLendon, Chairman, Finance Committee

ADDRESS INQUIRIES TO:
Peter Lawrie, Scholarship Chairman
(See address above.)

*SPECIAL STIPULATIONS:
Candidates must be from northeastern U.S. and of Scottish descent, and must be U.S. citizens.

SCAC (FRENCH CULTURAL AND EDUCATIONAL OFFICE)   [939]

4101 Reservoir Road, N.W.
Washington, DC 20007
(202) 944-6000
Fax: (202) 944-6268

E-MAIL ADDRESS:
hss.coordinator@chateaubriand-fellowship.org

WEB SITE ADDRESS:
frenchculture.org

FOUNDED: 1980

NAME(S) OF PROGRAMS:
● **Chateaubriand Fellowships Program**
● **Culture Lab**
● **Benjamin Franklin Travel Grant for Undergraduate Students**
● **Teacher Training in France**
● **Teaching Assistant Program in France**

TYPE:
Assistantships; Exchange programs; Fellowships; Grants-in-aid; Project/program grants; Research grants; Training grants;

Travel grants. Chateaubriand Fellowships Program: Offered by the embassy of France in the U.S., each year this program allows doctoral students enrolled in American universities to conduct research in France for up to nine months.

Culture Lab: Participants will travel to France, immerse themselves in the French language and culture, and take part in a unique summer program.

Benjamin Franklin Travel Grant: Allows sophomore, junior and senior students enrolled in an American university, who are enrolled in a double major including one major in French and one major in another discipline, the opportunity to discover France. Consideration will also be given to students enrolled in a minor/certificate in French and majoring in another subject.

Teacher Training in France: Each year the Cultural Services Department of the French Embassy offers a number of two-week grants to qualified primary and secondary school teachers of French who would like to enhance their knowledge of French culture and improve their language and teaching skills.

Teaching Assistant Program in France: The French Ministry of Education and the Cultural Services Department of the French Embassy in Washington, DC offer over 1,100 teaching assistantships each year for American citizens and permanent residents of the U.S. to teach English in French schools. Assistants may work in primary schools or secondary schools.

YEAR PROGRAM STARTED: 1980

PURPOSE:
To promote the exchange of ideas between France and the U.S.

LEGAL BASIS:
Embassy.

ELIGIBILITY:
Details are available online.

FINANCIAL DATA:
Amount of support per award: Assistantships in France: EUR 780 monthly; Chateaubriand Fellowships Program: EUR 1,500 monthly, a round-trip ticket to France and health insurance; Culture Lab: The travel grant covers airfare to and from France, and program expenses for participants including housing, meals, transportation, activities and insurance while in France; Benjamin Franklin Travel Grant: One-time support for airfare for travel; Teacher Training in France: Program includes tuition and training fees for two weeks, a round-trip train ticket from Paris to the destination city; program participants receive a grant for two weeks covering a portion of their accommodation and food expenses; round-trip airfare is not included; Teaching Assistant Program in France: EUR 964.88 per month.

NUMBER OF APPLICANTS MOST RECENT YEAR: Chateaubriand Fellowships Program: 120; Teacher Training in France: 90; Teaching Assistant Program in France: 2,350.

NUMBER OF AWARDS: Chateaubriand Fellowships Program: 15; Culture Lab: 1 for the year 2014; Teacher Training in France: 40 for the year 2014; Teaching Assistant Program in France: 1,100.

APPLICATION INFORMATION:
Details are available online.

Duration: Chateaubriand Fellowships Program: Up to eight months (a full university year in France); Culture Lab: 10 days; Benjamin Franklin Travel Grant: Up to 90 days during the summer; Teacher Training in France: Two weeks; Teaching Assistant Program in France: One school year (October 1-April 30).
Deadline: Details are available online.

ADDRESS INQUIRIES TO:
Culture Lab and
Teacher Training in France:
E-mail:
scule.washington-amba@diplomatie.gouv.fr.
Benjamin Franklin Travel Grant:
E-mail: prudence.barbera@diplomatie.gouv.fr
Teaching Assistant Program in France:
E-mail: assistant.washington-amba@diplomatie.gouv.fr.

SCUOLA NORMALE SUPERIORE [940]
Area Didattica
Palazzo del Castelletto in Pisa
via del Castelletto n. 11
56100 Pisa Italy
+39.050.509237
+39.050.509111
Fax: +39.050.563513

E-MAIL ADDRESS:
m.landucci@sns.it

WEB SITE ADDRESS:
www.sns.it

FOUNDED: 1813

AREAS OF INTEREST:
Classical philology, linguistics and history, modern philology and linguistics, history, art history, philosophy, mathematics and physics and their applications in chemistry and biology.

NAME(S) OF PROGRAMS:
● **Graduate School Scholarships for Study in Italy**

TYPE:
Scholarships. Scholarships for study at the Scuola Normale Superiore, Pisa, Italy, for postgraduate study in the disciplinary areas of the humanities and of mathematics, physics and natural sciences listed above.

PURPOSE:
Research and study leading to Diploma di Perfezionamento (Ph.D.); three years of scholarship. Research and study for a one-year scholarship.

LEGAL BASIS:
State-owned university.

ELIGIBILITY:
Citizens of all countries who have an M.A. degree and know Italian may apply. Students over 30 at the time of application cannot be admitted to the graduate courses. Applicants may not be receiving other forms of assistance.

FINANCIAL DATA:
Amount of support per award:
Perfezionamento (Ph.D.): Study grant of EUR 13,000 per year. One-year scholarship: Study grant of EUR 9,200 per year.

NUMBER OF APPLICANTS MOST RECENT YEAR: 8 for both sciences and humanities.

APPLICATION INFORMATION:
Information is available online. The new announcement appears around May-June each year.

Duration: Up to three years, fellowship may be extended for an additional year for justified academic and/or scientific reasons if possible within the budget.
Deadline: Faculty of Sciences: March 20 for spring session, September 20 for autumn session; Faculty of Arts: August 1.

ADDRESS INQUIRIES TO:
Student Secretariat
Dott. Mario Landucci
(See address above.)

SHASTRI INDO-CANADIAN INSTITUTE (SICI) [941]
Room 1402, Education Tower
2500 University Drive, N.W.
Calgary AB T2N 1N4 Canada
(403) 220-7467
Fax: (403) 289-0100

E-MAIL ADDRESS:
sici@ucalgary.ca

WEB SITE ADDRESS:
www.sici.org

AREAS OF INTEREST:
Understanding of India in Canada.

NAME(S) OF PROGRAMS:
● **India Studies Fellowship Competition**

TYPE:
Fellowships. India Studies Fellowship Competition is intended to support candidates wishing to undertake research or training in India. The focus of study is subjects relating to India in the social sciences and humanities, including education, law, management, the arts, science, and technology.

YEAR PROGRAM STARTED: 1968

PURPOSE:
To promote understanding between Canada and India, mainly through facilitating academic activities.

ELIGIBILITY:
Applicants must be Canadian citizens or permanent residents.

FINANCIAL DATA:
Amount of support per award: Varies.

COOPERATIVE FUNDING PROGRAMS: Department of Education, Ministry of Human Resources, Government of India.

NUMBER OF AWARDS: Approximately 32.

APPLICATION INFORMATION:
Application information is available on the web site.
Duration: Three months to one year.
Deadline: June 30.

ADDRESS INQUIRIES TO:
See e-mail address above.

SOMMERHOCHSCHULE-UNIVERSITY OF VIENNA [942]
Alser Strasse 4/Hof 1/Tuer 1.16
1090 Vienna Austria
43-1-4277-24131
Fax: 43-1-4277-9241

E-MAIL ADDRESS:
sommerhochschule@univie.ac.at

WEB SITE ADDRESS:
shs.univie.ac.at/shs

FOUNDED: 1949

AREAS OF INTEREST:
European Studies (with focus on the legal, economic, political and cultural aspects) taught in English; German Language Courses (A1, A2, B1, B2).

NAME(S) OF PROGRAMS:
- **International Summer Program (Summer Campus Strobl/St. Wolfgang/Austria)**

TYPE:
Scholarships. The European Studies courses focus on the political, economic and legal, but also historical and cultural, aspects of Europe and the EU. The German language courses are offered at four different levels of proficiency (beginners to advanced).

YEAR PROGRAM STARTED: 1949

PURPOSE:
To contribute to an increased understanding of the EU and its possible future shape and to create an environment which encourages intercultural and social exchange and favors mutual understanding among participants.

LEGAL BASIS:
A subcompany of the University of Vienna; nonprofit status; state supported.

ELIGIBILITY:
Applicants have to be at least 18 years old and must have completed at least two years of studies at college or university level in their countries of residence or have an educational background equivalent to one year at a European university before the beginning of the program.

FINANCIAL DATA:
A limited number of partial scholarships are available for the European Studies section of the program. The scholarships are awarded on the basis of academic excellence and financial need.
Amount of support per award: EUR 300 to 2,400.
Total amount of support: Approximately EUR 40,000 for the year 2013.

NUMBER OF APPLICANTS MOST RECENT YEAR:
80 to 100.

NUMBER OF AWARDS: Varies based on the size of the scholarships.

APPLICATION INFORMATION:
Applicants must submit the following documents:
(1) completed application form;
(2) transcript of grades;
(3) two letters of recommendation (academic or professional);
(4) official proof of proficiency in English;
(5) statement of purpose (one page maximum);
(6) two passport-size photos taken within the past year and;
(7) application for financial assistance.

All documents have to be submitted either in original or as a certified copy and have to be translated into English or German.

Application material must be sent to the office of the Sommerhochschule (faxed or e-mailed applications cannot be accepted).
Duration: Four weeks, middle of July to middle of August.
Deadline: February 28 for scholarship applications; April 30 for regular applications.

PUBLICATIONS:
Annual brochures and leaflets for the International Summer Program of the Sommerhochschule.

OFFICERS:
Dr. Franz-Stefan Meissel, Director
Nina Gruber, Program Coordinator

ADDRESS INQUIRIES TO:
Nina Gruber, Program Coordinator
(See address above.)

U.S. DEPARTMENT OF EDUCATION [943]

International and Foreign Language Education
1990 K Street, N.W., 6th Floor
Washington, DC 20006-8521
(202) 502-7709
(202) 502-7700
Fax: (202) 502-7860

E-MAIL ADDRESS:
loveen.bains@ed.gov

WEB SITE ADDRESS:
www2.ed.gov/programs/iegpsgpa/index.html

FOUNDED: 1967

AREAS OF INTEREST:
Foreign languages and area studies.

NAME(S) OF PROGRAMS:
- **Fulbright-Hays Group Projects Abroad Program**

TYPE:
Exchange programs; Project/program grants; Seed money grants; Training grants; Travel grants. Also, study grants and grants for foreign language and area study programs of educational development for projects to be undertaken abroad. Grants are awarded to higher education institutions, nonprofit educational organizations, state department of education and consortium of such institutions, departments, organizations and institutions which, in turn, enable professors, college and elementary and secondary school teachers and advanced students to attend seminars abroad and to travel and study in foreign countries in order to strengthen the institution's programs in foreign languages, area studies and world affairs.

YEAR PROGRAM STARTED: 1967

PURPOSE:
To contribute to the development and improvement of the study of foreign languages and area studies in the U.S. by providing opportunities for faculty, teachers, upperclassmen and/or graduate students to travel to foreign countries in group projects for research, training and curriculum development.

LEGAL BASIS:
The Mutual Educational and Cultural Exchange Act of 1961, Public Law 87-256 (Fulbright Hays Act), Section 102(b)(6).

ELIGIBILITY:
Under the program, grants are awarded to institutions of higher education, state departments of education, private nonprofit educational organizations and consortiums of such institutions, departments and organizations to conduct overseas group projects in research, training and curriculum development, by groups of individuals engaged in a common endeavor.

A participant must be a citizen, national or permanent resident of the U.S. and either a faculty member in modern foreign languages or area studies, an experienced educator responsible for planning, conducting or supervising programs in modern foreign languages or area studies at the elementary,

secondary or postsecondary levels, a graduate student or upperclassman who plans a teaching career in modern foreign languages or area studies.

The grant does not provide funds for project-related expenses within the U.S. Funds may be used only for a maintenance stipend based on 50% of the amount established in the U.S. Department of State publication, *Maximum Travel Per Diem Allowances for Foreign Areas*, round-trip international travel, a local travel allowance for necessary project-related transportation within the country of study, exclusive of the purchase of transportation equipment, the purchase of project-related artifacts, books and other teaching materials in the country of study, rent for instructional facilities in the country of study, and clerical and professional services performed by resident instructional personnel in the country of study.

FINANCIAL DATA:
Amount of support per award: $50,000 to $375,000.
Total amount of support: $2,990,000 in U.S. funds for fiscal year 2012.

NUMBER OF APPLICANTS MOST RECENT YEAR:
88.

NUMBER OF AWARDS: 23.

APPLICATION INFORMATION:
Application information is available on the web site.
Duration: Four weeks to one year. No renewal.
Deadline: Fall.

ADDRESS INQUIRIES TO:
Carly Borgmeier, Program Office
(See address above.)

U.S. DEPARTMENT OF EDUCATION [944]

Office of Postsecondary Education
International and Foreign Language Education
1990 K Street, N.W., 6th Floor
Washington, DC 20006-8521
(202) 502-7589
(202) 502-7700
Fax: (202) 502-7859

E-MAIL ADDRESS:
stephanie.mckissic@ed.gov

WEB SITE ADDRESS:
www2.ed.gov/programs/iegpsfra/index.html

NAME(S) OF PROGRAMS:
- **Fulbright-Hays Faculty Research Abroad Program**

TYPE:
Fellowships; Research grants. This program funds fellowships through institutions of higher education (IHEs) to faculty members who propose to conduct research abroad in modern foreign languages and area studies to improve their skill in language and their knowledge of the culture of the people of these countries.

YEAR PROGRAM STARTED: 1964

PURPOSE:
To strengthen college and university programs of international studies by helping key faculty members remain current in their specialties and by assisting institutions in updating curriculums and improving teaching methods and materials.

LEGAL BASIS:
U.S. Government agency.

ELIGIBILITY:
Faculty members must apply through their employing institution. A candidate must be a U.S. citizen, national or permanent resident, an educator experienced in foreign languages and/or area studies, must have engaged in teaching during the two years preceding the date of award and possess adequate skills in the language of the country or in a language germane to the project or region.

GEOGRAPHIC RESTRICTIONS:
United States.

APPLICATION INFORMATION:
Applications must be submitted electronically using e-grants.ed.gov.
Duration: Three to 12 months.
Deadline: Late October of the year preceding the year of study.

PUBLICATIONS:
Guidelines.

ADDRESS INQUIRIES TO:
Program Officer
(See address above.)

UNIVERSITY OF BRISTOL   [945]
Senate House
Tyndall Avenue
Bristol BS8 1TH England
44 (0) 117 928 9000
Fax: 44 (0) 117 925 1424

E-MAIL ADDRESS:
student-funding@bris.ac.uk

WEB SITE ADDRESS:
www.bris.ac.uk

FOUNDED: 1909

AREAS OF INTEREST:
Faculties of arts, engineering, medical and veterinary sciences, medicine and dentistry, science, social sciences and law.

NAME(S) OF PROGRAMS:
● **Postgraduate Research Scholarships**

TYPE:
Scholarships. Postgraduate research scholarships for study toward the Ph.D. degree in one of the departments of the University of Bristol.

YEAR PROGRAM STARTED: 1989

PURPOSE:
To attract excellent research students.

LEGAL BASIS:
University.

ELIGIBILITY:
Scholarships are available for the U.K., Europe and overseas students.

FINANCIAL DATA:
Amount of support per award: 27.

APPLICATION INFORMATION:
Information is available from the Student Funding Office at the University of Bristol or online.
Duration: Up to three years, subject to satisfactory academic progress.
Deadline: February and March.

PUBLICATIONS:
Annual report; research prospectus.

STAFF:
Jane Fitzwalter, Student Funding Manager

ADDRESS INQUIRIES TO:
Student Funding Office
(See address above.)

UNIVERSITY OF ILLINOIS AT URBANA-CHAMPAIGN
College of Fine and Applied Arts
608 East Lorado Taft Drive, Suite 100
Champaign, IL 61820
(217) 333-1661
(217) 333-1660
Fax: (217) 244-8381

E-MAIL ADDRESS:
faa@illinois.edu

WEB SITE ADDRESS:
www.faa.illinois.edu

TYPE:
Fellowships. Awarded for advanced study in the fine arts in the U.S. or abroad, in an approved educational institution, with an approved private teacher or in independent study.

Three major Fellowships will be awarded:
(1) one in any field of music;
(2) one in architectural design and history, art and design, theatre, dance, or instrumental or vocal music and;
(3) one in art, architecture, dance, landscape architecture, theatre, or urban and regional planning.

See entry 574 for full listing.

UNIVERSITY OF LEEDS   [946]
Postgraduate Scholarships Office
Level 9, Marjorie & Arnold Ziff Building
University of Leeds
Leeds LS2 9JT England
44 (0) 113 343 4007
44 (0) 113 343 4077
Fax: 44 (0) 113 343 3941

E-MAIL ADDRESS:
pg_scholarships@leeds.ac.uk

WEB SITE ADDRESS:
www.scholarships.leeds.ac.uk

AREAS OF INTEREST:
Education abroad.

NAME(S) OF PROGRAMS:
● **Tetley and Lupton Scholarships for International Students**

TYPE:
Scholarships. Awarded for Master's degree study. Tenable at University of Leeds.

YEAR PROGRAM STARTED: 1982

PURPOSE:
To help defray the cost of education for international students.

LEGAL BASIS:
University.

ELIGIBILITY:
Open to international students who are applying to begin courses leading to a postgraduate degree at the University of Leeds. Scholarships will be awarded only to students who are liable to pay the tuition fees at the full-cost rate for international students, accepted for admission as a full-time student for a Master's degree at the University of Leeds, but not holding another award which covers the payment of tuition fees in full. Applicants must be of high academic standard.

FINANCIAL DATA:
Scholarships provide partial contribution to academic fees. Refer to postgraduate scholarships information on the web site.

APPLICATION INFORMATION:
Application information is available on the web site.
Duration: One academic year. May be held concurrently with other awards, except those providing full payment of fees.

ADDRESS INQUIRIES TO:
Postgraduate Scholarships Office
(See e-mail address above.)

UNIVERSITY OF LEEDS   [947]
Postgraduate Scholarships Office
Level 9, Marjorie & Arnold Ziff Building
University of Leeds
Leeds LS2 9JT England
44 (0) 113 343 4007
44 (0) 113 343 4077
Fax: 44 (0) 113 343 3941
pg_scholarships@leeds.ac.uk

E-MAIL ADDRESS:
www.scholarships.leeds.ac.uk

AREAS OF INTEREST:
Education abroad.

NAME(S) OF PROGRAMS:
● **Leeds International Research Scholarship**

TYPE:
Scholarships. Awarded for Ph.D. study. Tenable at University of Leeds.

YEAR PROGRAM STARTED: 2012

PURPOSE:
To help defray the cost of education for international students.

LEGAL BASIS:
University.

ELIGIBILITY:
Open to applicants who would be liable to pay academic fees at the University's international rate for full-time Ph.D. study.

FINANCIAL DATA:
Covers the cost of academic fees at the University's standard international rate and provides a maintenance stipend.

ADDRESS INQUIRIES TO:
See e-mail address above.

THE UNIVERSITY OF MANCHESTER   [948]
Manchester Doctoral College
Research Office, 2nd Floor
Christie Building
Manchester M13 9PL England
44 0161 275 8792

E-MAIL ADDRESS:
mdc@manchester.ac.uk

WEB SITE ADDRESS:
www.mdc.manchester.ac.uk/resources/contact/

FOUNDED: 1824

AREAS OF INTEREST:
Arts, economic, social and legal studies, education, science, engineering, medicine and biological sciences.

NAME(S) OF PROGRAMS:
● **British Marshall Scholarships**
● **Fulbright - University of Manchester Award**
● **North American Foundation Awards**
● **President's Doctoral Scholar Award**

TYPE:
Assistantships; Awards/prizes; Block grants;
Conferences/seminars; Endowments;
Exchange programs; Fellowships; Research
grants; Scholarships; Training grants; Travel
grants; Visiting scholars. Research
studentships for postgraduate-taught and
research programmes in the fields above.
North American Foundation Awards are for
postgraduate study at the University of
Manchester (NAFUM).
The University of Manchester is also a
recognized institution for the purpose of U.S.
federal loans and Canadian student loans.

FINANCIAL DATA:
Studentships include payment of fees at U.K.
level and/or maintenance allowance.
Amount of support per award: Varies.

ADDRESS INQUIRIES TO:
Student Services Centre
E-mail: ssc@manchester.ac.uk

UNIVERSITY OF OSLO INTERNATIONAL SUMMER SCHOOL [949]

Oslo International Summer School
c/o St. Olaf College
1520 St. Olaf Avenue
Northfield, MN 55057-1098
(507) 786-3269
(800) 639-0058

E-MAIL ADDRESS:
iss@stolaf.edu

WEB SITE ADDRESS:
www.uio.no/summerschool

FOUNDED: 1947

AREAS OF INTEREST:
The International Summer School offers
undergraduate and graduate courses in the
following areas:
General course offerings - Norwegian
language, Norwegian art history, Norwegian
architecture and design, Norwegian literature,
history, political science, culture and society,
international relations and gender equality in
Nordic countries;
Graduate courses - special education, peace
research, international development, media
and communications, international
community health, energy and sustainable
development, human rights, and a changing
Arctic.

TYPE:
Scholarships.

YEAR PROGRAM STARTED: 1947

PURPOSE:
To offer academic instruction to a gathering
of many nationalities in the hope of a modest
but concrete increase in understanding and
goodwill among nations.

LEGAL BASIS:
Part of the University of Oslo.

ELIGIBILITY:
Scholarships awarded only to students
accepted into the Oslo International Summer
School program. Scholarship applicants must
meet the entrance requirements of the
International Summer School and must
present evidence of attending or having
attended a recognized university and have a
good academic record. One year or more of
college or university is required. In addition,
seriousness of academic purpose and personal
qualities likely to make the applicant a good
representative of his or her country.

FINANCIAL DATA:
Amount of support per award: Varies.
Total amount of support: Varies.

NUMBER OF APPLICANTS MOST RECENT YEAR:
Approximately 30.

NUMBER OF AWARDS: Varies.

APPLICATION INFORMATION:
A financial aid application form and the
application for admission to the International
Summer School and the supporting letters of
recommendation are used by the Financial
Aid Committee to choose financial aid
recipients.
Duration: Six weeks during the summer,
from late June to early August. No renewal
possibilities.
Deadline: Papers are due by February 1.
Results are announced the first week in
April.

PUBLICATIONS:
ISS catalog.

ADMINISTRATION:
Einar Vannebo, Director, International
Summer School Norwegian Office
Torild Homstad, Administrator, North
American Admissions Office

ADDRESS INQUIRIES TO:
Non-North American students should request
information from:
International Summer School
Postbox 1082
N-0317 Oslo, Norway
Tel: (011) 47 2285-6385
Fax: (011) 47 2285-4199

All other applicants can use the North
American address above.

THE UNIVERSITY OF SYDNEY [950]

Scholarships Office
Level 5, Jane Foss Russell Building G02
The University of Sydney N.S.W. 2006
Australia
(02) 8627 8112
Fax: (02) 8627 8485

E-MAIL ADDRESS:
research.training@sydney.edu.au

WEB SITE ADDRESS:
www.sydney.edu.au/scholarships/research

FOUNDED: 1850

NAME(S) OF PROGRAMS:
● **Australian Postgraduate Awards (APA)**
● **International Postgraduate Research
Scholarships (IPRS)**

TYPE:
Scholarships. Awarded for research leading to
a higher degree. Tenable at the University of
Sydney.

LEGAL BASIS:
University.

ELIGIBILITY:
The scholarships are awarded on academic
merit and research ability to qualified
candidates. Open to qualified foreign
graduates from any country eligible to
commence a higher degree by research.
Australian and New Zealand citizens or
permanent residents are not eligible.

FINANCIAL DATA:
Amount of support per award: APA: $24,653
AUD per annum for the year 2013; IPRS:
Tuition fees.

NUMBER OF AWARDS: 33 for the year 2013.

APPLICATION INFORMATION:
Contact the International Office at the
University of Sydney between May and July.
Duration: Two years for a Master's research
degree and three years for a Ph.D.
Deadline: July 31 for semester one
commencement and December 15 for
semester two commencement.

ADDRESS INQUIRIES TO:
International Office
Level 4, Jane Foss Russell Building G02
The University of Sydney
N.S.W. 2006 Australia
Tel: (02) 8627 8300
Fax: (02) 8627 8387
E-mail: infoschol@io.usyd.edu.au
Web site:
www.sydney.edu.au/internationaloffice

UNIVERSITY OF VIRGINIA [951]

120 Vincennes Road
Charlottesville, VA 22911
(434) 924-3192
(434) 977-1868
Fax: (434) 924-3359

E-MAIL ADDRESS:
al4u@virginia.edu

FOUNDED: 1976

AREAS OF INTEREST:
International law and politics, international
economics, international institutions and
international development.

NAME(S) OF PROGRAMS:
● **Gallatin Fellowships**

TYPE:
Exchange programs; Fellowships.

YEAR PROGRAM STARTED: 1976

PURPOSE:
To support advanced doctoral study in
international affairs.

LEGAL BASIS:
University.

ELIGIBILITY:
Ph.D. students in international affairs at the
dissertation stage of their work. Applicants
must be U.S. citizens or permanent residents.
Intended for students who plan to study at
the Graduate Institute of International
Studies, Geneva, Switzerland.

GEOGRAPHIC RESTRICTIONS:
United States.

FINANCIAL DATA:
Amount of support per award: $26,000
stipend plus transatlantic airfare up to $1,500.
Total amount of support: $55,000 to $60,000.

NUMBER OF APPLICANTS MOST RECENT YEAR:
7.

NUMBER OF AWARDS: 1 or more annually.

APPLICATION INFORMATION:
Applicants should submit the following in
five paper copies:
(1) personal data form;
(2) academic record to include a
chronological list of all educational
institutions attended above high school level,
naming institutions, fields of study, years of
study and degree, a transcript of graduate
work completed, listing courses and grades, a
list of published works, articles or topics of
research papers undertaken during graduate
study including a copy of a published work

or research paper, a list of academic distinctions, fellowships, etc., including those currently held or applied for;
(3) international experience, which should consist of a list of the countries, other than the U.S., in which applicant has lived or traveled, with the dates, duration and purpose of these stays (business, education and/or pleasure) indicated and a description, of not more than 300 words, of any aspect of these experiences, or others, which is believed to have contributed notably to applicant's academic career or to their proposed professional interests, including language training;
(4) proficiency in foreign language, in which the applicant should list those foreign languages of which he or she has a speaking, reading and writing knowledge, indicating under each of these headings if knowledge is elementary, medium or advanced and provide among the references an individual who can be consulted on applicant's language competence;
(5) study program, which should consist of an essay of up to 1,500 words describing applicant's research program, showing how the Institute's curriculum of research, seminars, etc., as well as institutions located in Geneva, will contribute to it. Candidates are advised to study the Institute's catalogue in formulating their programs;
(6) career intentions, in which the applicant should briefly describe his or her professional objectives and how he or she sees their current studies and those proposed at the Institute contributing to them. Any professional work which applicant may have already undertaken in the international field should be described, including teaching assistantships, participation in research programs, publications and awards and;
(7) references, which should consist of the above information further supplemented by letters from four individuals who are familiar with the applicant's proposed research program, including thesis supervisor. If possible, one should be able to judge applicant's competence in the French language. These letters of reference should be sent directly to the address above when completed application is submitted. These letters should include the office addresses and telephone numbers of those sending them.

Duration: One academic year. Shorter term grants are also available.

Deadline: March 1.

PUBLICATIONS:
Application guidelines.

STAFF:
Allen C. Lynch, Supervisor, Gallatin Fellowship Program

ADDRESS INQUIRIES TO:
Allen C. Lynch, Supervisor
Gallatin Fellowship Program
(See address above.)

*SPECIAL STIPULATIONS:
Applicant must be engaged in the dissertation phase of Ph.D. work in international affairs.

VILLA I TATTI: THE HARVARD UNIVERSITY CENTER FOR ITALIAN RENAISSANCE STUDIES [952]
Via di Vincigliata, 26
50135 Florence Italy
+39.055.603251
+39.055.608909
Fax: +39.055.603383

E-MAIL ADDRESS:
info@itatti.harvard.edu

WEB SITE ADDRESS:
www.itatti.harvard.edu

FOUNDED: 1961

AREAS OF INTEREST:
All aspects of the Italian Renaissance: fine arts, literature, music, science, philosophy, religion and political, intellectual, economic and social history.

CONSULTING OR VOLUNTEER SERVICES:
Library, photographic collection and archive.

NAME(S) OF PROGRAMS:
- **Fellowships for Independent Study on the Italian Renaissance**
- **Mellon Visiting Fellowships**
- **Craig Hugh Smyth Visiting Fellowships**

TYPE:
Fellowships. Stipendiary and nonstipendiary fellowships for the academic year July 1 through June 30 in residence in Florence for study on any aspect of the Italian Renaissance. There are a limited number of short-term Mellon Visiting Fellowships designed to reach out to Italian Renaissance scholars from areas that have been underrepresented at Villa I Tatti, especially those from Asia, Latin America, the Iberian Peninsula, the Mediterranean basin (except Italy and France), and the Islamic countries. There are also a limited number of short-term Craig Hugh Smyth Visiting Fellowships for scholars who do not have the benefit of sabbatical leave including curators, administrators, and conservators, as well as scholars who, having the primary responsibility of caring for young children, do not have easy access to major research libraries and research.

YEAR PROGRAM STARTED: 1961

PURPOSE:
To promote advanced interdisciplinary study in Renaissance fields.

LEGAL BASIS:
Part of Harvard University.

ELIGIBILITY:
I Tatti Fellowship applicants can be scholars of any nationality, and must be postdoctoral and in the earlier stages of their careers and free to devote full-time to study.

FINANCIAL DATA:
Stipends will be given in accord with the individual needs of the approved applicants and the availability of funds.
Amount of support per award: For a yearlong fellowship, the maximum stipend is $50,000.
Total amount of support: $852,500 for the yearlong fellowships for the year 2012-13.

COOPERATIVE FUNDING PROGRAMS: Deborah Loeb Brice Fellowship, Committee to Rescue Italian Art, Francesco E. de Dombrowski Bequest, Florence Gould Foundation, Hanna Kiel Fellowship, Melville J. Kahn Fellowship Fund, Samuel H. Kress Foundation, Robert Lehman Fellowship, Jean Francois Malle

Fellowship Fund, Andrew W. Mellon Foundation, Ahmanson Foundation, Lila Wallace - Reader's Digest Endowment Fund.

NUMBER OF APPLICANTS MOST RECENT YEAR:
100 for the year 2013-14.

NUMBER OF AWARDS: 15 for the 2013-14 academic year.

APPLICATION INFORMATION:
Application forms are available online. Applications by fax are not accepted.
Duration: July 1 to June 30.
Deadline: I Tatti Fellowships: To be received by October 15. Announcement by early spring.

Mellon Visiting Fellowships and Craig Hugh Smyth Visiting Fellowships: February 1. Announcement by early spring.

IRS IDENTIFICATION NUMBER: 04-2103580

ADDRESS INQUIRIES TO:
Lino Pertile, Director
(See address above.)

THOMAS J. WATSON FELLOWSHIP PROGRAM
11 Park Place, Suite 1503
New York, NY 10017
(212) 245-8859
Fax: (212) 245-8860

E-MAIL ADDRESS:
tjw@tjwf.org

WEB SITE ADDRESS:
watsonfellowship.org

TYPE:
Fellowships. The Foundation provides Fellows an opportunity for a focused and disciplined "Wanderjahr" of their own devising or design-time in which to explore with thoroughness a particular interest, test their aspirations and abilities, view their lives and American society in greater perspective and concomitantly, to develop a more informed sense of international concern. The Fellowship experience is intended to provide Fellows an opportunity to immerse themselves in cultures other than their own for an entire year. The candidate's proposed project should involve investigation into an area of demonstrated concern and personal interest.

See entry 1648 for full listing.

WEIZMANN INSTITUTE OF SCIENCE [953]
Feinberg Graduate School of the Weizmann Institute of Science
P.O. Box 26
Rehovot 76100 Israel
(972-8) 9343843
(972-8) 9342924
Fax: (972-8) 9344114

E-MAIL ADDRESS:
postdoc@weizmann.ac.il

WEB SITE ADDRESS:
www.fgs.org.il

FOUNDED: 1934

AREAS OF INTEREST:
Life sciences, chemistry, physics, mathematics and computer science.

NAME(S) OF PROGRAMS:
- **Postdoctoral Fellowships Program at the Weizmann Institute of Science**

TYPE:
Fellowships. The Feinberg Graduate School of the Weizmann Institute of Science offers a limited number of postdoctoral fellowships in all areas of research in which the Weizmann Institute is engaged. The fellowships are offered in various fields of biology, chemistry, physics, biochemistry-biophysics, mathematics and computer science.

YEAR PROGRAM STARTED: 1976

PURPOSE:
To train postgraduate research students to senior positions in academia, scientific research, medical research, industry, education, and government systems.

LEGAL BASIS:
Research institute.

ELIGIBILITY:
Postdoctoral fellowship applicants must have received a Ph.D. or equivalent degree within four years of the submission deadline. Candidates may be citizens of any country.

FINANCIAL DATA:
The annual stipend is adjusted periodically in accordance with living costs. Also offered is a small relocation allowance and a one-way, economy-class airfare (round-trip airfare in case the fellowship is extended to two years).
Amount of support per award: Approximately $28,000 per year.

APPLICATION INFORMATION:
Application forms and additional information may be obtained from the Feinberg Graduate School, Weizmann Institute of Science and from the web site.
Duration: 12 months. Possible renewal for a second and third year.
Deadline: Applications may be submitted year-round.

OFFICERS:
Prof. Daniel Zajfman, President
Prof. Yuval Eshed, Head, Postdoctoral Program

ADDRESS INQUIRIES TO:
Feinberg Graduate School
(See address above.)

YOUTH FOR UNDERSTANDING USA   [954]
6400 Goldsboro Road
Suite 100
Bethesda, MD 20817
(240) 235-2100
(800) 833-6243
(866) 493-8872
Fax: (240) 235-2188

E-MAIL ADDRESS:
admissions@yfu.org

WEB SITE ADDRESS:
www.yfu-usa.org

FOUNDED: 2002

AREAS OF INTEREST:
The exchange of U.S. and international high school students in over 60 countries.

CONSULTING OR VOLUNTEER SERVICES:
Intercultural education and training and research.

NAME(S) OF PROGRAMS:
● **Americans Overseas Summer, Semester and Year Programs**
● **Congress-Bundestag Youth Exchange Program**
● **Corporate Scholarship Program**
● **Finland-U.S. Senate Youth Exchange Program**
● **International Semester and Year Programs**
● **Japan-U.S. Senate Youth Exchange Program**

TYPE:
Exchange programs; Grants-in-aid; Scholarships; Travel grants. Students on summer semester and year programs live with volunteer host families overseas. Students on semester and academic year programs also attend school. International students live and study at U.S. high schools or community colleges. Competitive, full and partial scholarships for Corporate, Finland-U.S. Senate, Japan-U.S. Senate Programs and Japan-America Friendship Scholars Program.

YEAR PROGRAM STARTED: 2002

PURPOSE:
To prepare young people for their responsibilities and opportunities in a changing, interdependent world.

LEGAL BASIS:
Tax-exempt, 501(c)(3) international educational organization.

ELIGIBILITY:
Applicants must be U.S. or international high school students between the ages of 15 and 18. Full scholarships for special programs are awarded through merit competition. Partial scholarships (10 to 25%) are awarded on the basis of need.

FINANCIAL DATA:
Amount of support per award: From $500 to full support.

COOPERATIVE FUNDING PROGRAMS: Funding sources for scholarships include a multitude of governments, corporations, foundations and individuals.

NUMBER OF AWARDS: Approximately 2,500.

APPLICATION INFORMATION:
Applicants for programs involving full scholarships must complete special application materials. For corporate programs, applicants must meet special eligibility requirements. Applicants for partial scholarships must complete financial aid forms.
Duration: Scholarships awarded for the program period.
Deadline: Between September and March, depending on program. Announcement between February and April.

IRS IDENTIFICATION NUMBER: 02-0557010

OFFICERS:
Michael Finnell, President and Chief Executive Officer
Margie Ott, Director of Programs and Contracts

BOARD OF TRUSTEES:
Ulrich Zahllen, Chairman
David Bachner
Michael Finnell
William Schupp

ADDRESS INQUIRIES TO:
Alicia Kubert Smith, Communications Manager
(See address and toll-free telephone number above.)

Programs for foreign scholars

AMERICA-ISRAEL CULTURAL FOUNDATION   [955]
1140 Broadway
Suite 304
New York, NY 10001
(212) 557-1600
Fax: (212) 557-1611

E-MAIL ADDRESS:
admin@aicf.org

WEB SITE ADDRESS:
www.aicf.org

FOUNDED: 1939

AREAS OF INTEREST:
Music, dance, theater, visual arts, film and television.

NAME(S) OF PROGRAMS:
● **Scholarship Program for Israelis**

TYPE:
Awards/prizes; Endowments; Fellowships; Project/program grants; Scholarships. For study in the arts of music, painting and sculpture, dance and drama, film and television, to be pursued either in Israel or in other countries.

YEAR PROGRAM STARTED: 1952

PURPOSE:
To further Israeli talent in the fields of music, visual arts, dance and drama, film and television.

ELIGIBILITY:
Only Israeli nationals that live and study in Israel are eligible to apply for domestic scholarships. Israeli nationals studying abroad are able to apply for scholarships to any international location of study.

FINANCIAL DATA:
Amount of support per award: $600 to $10,000.
Total amount of support: $1,300,000 per year.

NUMBER OF APPLICANTS MOST RECENT YEAR: Approximately 2,500.

NUMBER OF AWARDS: Approximately 600.

APPLICATION INFORMATION:
Application materials are available upon request to America-Israel Cultural Foundation, 8 Shaul Hamelech Boulevard, Tel Aviv 64733, Israel.
Duration: Grants are awarded for one to two years of study. Teachers of the arts may also apply for up to six-month fellowships.
Deadline: Varies.

IRS IDENTIFICATION NUMBER: 13-1664048

ADDRESS INQUIRIES TO:
Scholarships: Lee Perlman
Executive Director
8 Shaul Hamelech Boulevard, Tel Aviv 64733, Israel

AMERICAN ASSOCIATION OF FAMILY AND CONSUMER SCIENCES (AAFCS)   [956]
400 North Columbus Street
Suite 202
Alexandria, VA 22314-2752
(703) 706-4600
(800) 424-8080
Fax: (703) 706-4663

E-MAIL ADDRESS:
rayona@aafcs.org

WEB SITE ADDRESS:
www.aafcs.org/awards/index.asp

FOUNDED: 1909

AREAS OF INTEREST:
Family and consumer sciences.

NAME(S) OF PROGRAMS:
● **National and International Fellowships**

TYPE:
Fellowships. AAFCS awards fellowships to individuals who have exhibited the potential to make contributions to the family and consumer sciences profession.

YEAR PROGRAM STARTED: 1962

PURPOSE:
To support graduate study in the field of family and consumer sciences.

LEGAL BASIS:
501(c)(3) nonprofit charity.

FINANCIAL DATA:
Amount of support per award: $3,500 to $5,000 for each fellowship, plus up to $1,000 of support.
Total amount of support: Varies.

NUMBER OF AWARDS: Up to 10 annually.

APPLICATION INFORMATION:
Application information is available on the web site.
Duration: One academic year.
Deadline: Varies.

PUBLICATIONS:
Brochure.

ADDRESS INQUIRIES TO:
Roxana Marissa Ayona
Senior Manager, Awards and Governance
(See e-mail address above.)

AMERICAN ASSOCIATION OF UNIVERSITY WOMEN EDUCATIONAL FOUNDATION [957]

327 Second Street, Suite 103
Coralville, IA 52241
(319) 688-4334

E-MAIL ADDRESS:
aauw@scholarshipamerica.org

WEB SITE ADDRESS:
www.aauw.org

FOUNDED: 1958

AREAS OF INTEREST:
Advancement of educational and professional opportunities for women in the U.S. and around the globe.

NAME(S) OF PROGRAMS:
● **AAUW Educational Foundation International Fellowships**

TYPE:
Fellowships. Awards for women who are not citizens or permanent residents of the U.S. for full-time graduate or postgraduate study or research in the U.S.

A limited number of project grants are available to successful applicants who wish to implement a community-based project in the year immediately following the fellowship. Eligible project proposals must demonstrate that they will be implemented in the applicant's home country and will have a direct impact on women and girls. Only

applicants who are selected to receive an International Fellowship will be considered for project grant funding.

YEAR PROGRAM STARTED: 1917

PURPOSE:
To provide advanced study and training for non-American women (i.e., women who are not U.S. citizens or permanent residents) of outstanding academic ability who may be expected to give effective leadership in their homelands.

ELIGIBILITY:
Women from countries other than the U.S. who hold the equivalent of an American Bachelor's degree at the time of application and have scored a minimum of 550 (paper-based), 213 (computer-based) or 79 (Internet-based) on the TOEFL within the past two years. Strong preference is given to women whose credentials demonstrate prior commitment to improving the lives of other women and girls through civic, community or professional work, whose study or research proposals show a continued interest in the advancement of women.

Upon completion of study, fellowship recipients are expected to return to their home countries to pursue professional careers. Preference is given to applicants who can verify that they have definite positions to which they will return.

Applicants are judged on their professional potential and on the importance of their projects in relation to their country of origin. Previous and current recipients of AAUW fellowships are not eligible to apply.

Applicants must be accepted to or have applied to an accredited institution of study.

FINANCIAL DATA:
Amount of support per award: $18,000 to $30,000 for fellowships.
Total amount of support: Approximately $978,000 for the year 2012-13.

NUMBER OF APPLICANTS MOST RECENT YEAR: 1,220.

NUMBER OF AWARDS: 40 to 50 annually.

APPLICATION INFORMATION:
Guidelines are posted on the web site. Applications become available August 1 and must be submitted online.
Duration: Fellowships are awarded for one academic year, beginning July 1.
Deadline: December 1.

ADDRESS INQUIRIES TO:
See e-mail address above.

THE AMERICAN SOCIETY OF MECHANICAL ENGINEERS AUXILIARY, INC.

2 Park Avenue, MS-RB
New York, NY 10016-5990
(212) 591-7650
Fax: (212) 591-7739

E-MAIL ADDRESS:
bigleyr@asme.org

WEB SITE ADDRESS:
go.asme.org/scholarships

TYPE:
Scholarships. ASME/ASME Auxiliary Clarke Scholarship is for incoming freshman enrolling in a mechanical engineering program.

ASME/ASME Auxiliary FIRST Clarke Scholarship is for high school seniors participating on a FIRST team.

Baldwin, Cartwright, Farny, Kezios and Scharp Scholarships are for undergraduate students in mechanical engineering.

Parsons and Rothermel Scholarships are for graduate students with a degree in mechanical engineering, to be used to pursue a Master's degree in mechanical engineering.

Rice-Cullimore Scholarship is for foreign students at the graduate level.

Student Loan Fund is for juniors, seniors or graduate students enrolled as degree candidates in good standing.

See entry 2646 for full listing.

BELGIAN AMERICAN EDUCATIONAL FOUNDATION, INC.

195 Church Street
New Haven, CT 06510
(203) 785-4055
Fax: (203) 777-5765

E-MAIL ADDRESS:
emile.boulpaep@yale.edu

WEB SITE ADDRESS:
www.baef.us
www.baef.be

TYPE:
Fellowships. Predoctoral and postdoctoral fellowships for advanced study in most fields of knowledge with supported work to be undertaken at a Belgian university or an institution of higher learning. Fellowships for Belgian students are also available.

See entry 900 for full listing.

THE ENGLISH-SPEAKING UNION [958]

Dartmouth House
37 Charles Street
London W1J 5ED England
44 (0) 20 7529 1550
44 (0) 20 7529 1590
Fax: 44 (0) 20 7495 6108

E-MAIL ADDRESS:
education@esu.org

WEB SITE ADDRESS:
www.esu.org

FOUNDED: 1918

AREAS OF INTEREST:
Education.

NAME(S) OF PROGRAMS:
● **The British Morehead-Cain Scholarship to the University of North Carolina at Chapel Hill**
● **The Chautauqua Institution Scholarships**
● **The Lindemann Trust Fellowships**
● **Walter Hines Page Scholarships**

TYPE:
Exchange programs; Fellowships; Scholarships; Travel grants.

YEAR PROGRAM STARTED: 1923

PURPOSE:
To enable teachers and students in Great Britain to observe teaching methods in the U.S. The same applies for U.S. and Canadian students spending time in the U.K.

LEGAL BASIS:
Educational charity.

ELIGIBILITY:
The Chautauqua Institution Scholarships are open to all qualified teachers. The award covers the cost of attendance at the Institution and includes lectures, classes, board, lodging, and entertainment for up to six weeks' stay.

The Lindemann Trust Fellowships are awarded for research in the U.S. to graduates of exceptional promise in both the pure and applied physical sciences, who have shown capacity for achieving original research.

The British Morehead-Cain Scholarship is open to all secondary schools in the United Kingdom. All nominees should show evidence of outstanding achievement in four criteria: leadership, scholarship, moral force of character and physical vigor.

Walter Hines Page Scholarships are awarded to teachers and educators from the U.K. and are intended to promote the exchange of educational ideas between Britain and America. Scholars travel to the United States to study a specific aspect of American education which interests them and which is relevant to their own professional responsibilities.

GEOGRAPHIC RESTRICTIONS:
Canada, United Kingdom and United States.

FINANCIAL DATA:
Amount of support per award: Varies.
Total amount of support: Varies.

COOPERATIVE FUNDING PROGRAMS: Sponsored by the English-Speaking Union and various teaching unions.

NUMBER OF AWARDS: Chautauqua Institution Scholarships: 2; Lindemann Trust Fellowships and Walter Hines Page Scholarships: Varies; Morehead-Cain Scholarship: Up to 4.

APPLICATION INFORMATION:
Applications must be made to the address above.
Duration: Chautauqua Institution Scholarships: Two to four weeks; Lindemann Trust Fellowships: One year; Morehead-Cain: Full four-year scholarship; Walter Hines Page Scholarships: One academic year.
Deadline: Varies.

PUBLICATIONS:
Annual report; *Concord*, newsletter.

ADDRESS INQUIRIES TO:
Mary Greer
Education Programmes Team Leader
(See address above.)

INTERNATIONAL ROAD FEDERATION   [959]
500 Montgomery Street, Suite 525
Alexandria, VA 22314
(703) 535-1001
Fax: (703) 535-1007

E-MAIL ADDRESS:
eninova@irfnews.org
info@irfnews.org

WEB SITE ADDRESS:
www.irfnews.org

FOUNDED: 1948

AREAS OF INTEREST:
Highway engineering and management.

NAME(S) OF PROGRAMS:
● **IRF Fellowship Program**

TYPE:
Fellowships; Scholarships. Annual awards for graduate study in highway and traffic engineering for graduate engineers.

YEAR PROGRAM STARTED: 1949

PURPOSE:
To train personnel in the field of highways and highway transport.

LEGAL BASIS:
Private foundation.

ELIGIBILITY:
Open to non-U.S. graduate students. Qualified civil engineers must return to home country following completion of program.

FINANCIAL DATA:
Amount of support per award: $2,500 to $15,000 to defray partially one year of graduate study.
Total amount of support: Approximately $90,000 for the year 2013-14.
Matching fund requirements: Home country donors must make up differential.

NUMBER OF APPLICANTS MOST RECENT YEAR:
45 for the year 2011.

NUMBER OF AWARDS: 5 to 10.

APPLICATION INFORMATION:
Application must be made to the National Road Association or Ministry in one's home country.
Duration: One year.
Deadline: September 30.

PUBLICATIONS:
Annual Report; *Directory of Students*.

IRS IDENTIFICATION NUMBER: 52-0793883

STAFF:
C. Patrick Sankey, President and Chief Executive Officer

ADDRESS INQUIRIES TO:
Emilia Ninova
Fellowship Program Coordinator
(See address above.)

THE KENNEDY MEMORIAL TRUST   [960]
3 Birdcage Walk
Westminster
London SW1H 9JJ England
(020) 7222 1151
Fax: (020) 7222 7189

E-MAIL ADDRESS:
annie@kennedytrust.org.uk

WEB SITE ADDRESS:
www.kennedytrust.org.uk

FOUNDED: 1966

NAME(S) OF PROGRAMS:
● **Kennedy Scholarships**

TYPE:
Scholarships. Awarded for postgraduate work for one year at Harvard or the Massachusetts Institute of Technology. Field of study is unrestricted.

YEAR PROGRAM STARTED: 1966

LEGAL BASIS:
Private.

ELIGIBILITY:
Those applying for awards must be British citizens at the time of application, ordinarily

resident in the U.K., and wholly or mainly educated there. All applicants must have studied at a U.K. university or university college. Applicants may be studying for a first degree and due to graduate in the academic year 2014-15, studying for a higher degree and due to graduate in the academic year 2014-15, or a graduate of a U.K. university or university college who has completed a first degree not earlier than 2010, and who has spent two of the seven academic years prior to January 9, 2015 at a U.K. university or university college.

Awards are tenable either at Harvard University or the Massachusetts Institute of Technology. Kennedy Scholars are not required to study for a degree in the U.S., but are free to do so if they are eligible and able to complete the necessary requirements.

FINANCIAL DATA:
Full tuition and health insurance fees, plus a stipend for living costs.
Amount of support per award: Minimum $25,000 stipend.

NUMBER OF APPLICANTS MOST RECENT YEAR:
298.

NUMBER OF AWARDS: 10 for the year 2014.

APPLICATION INFORMATION:
Applications must be submitted online via the Trust's web site.
Duration: One year.
Deadline: Late October.

OFFICERS AND TRUSTEES:
Tony Badger, Chairman
Annie Thomas, Secretary
Daniel Alexander, QC
Dr. Peter Englander
J.J. Grimond
Prof. Kay-Tee Khaw
Prof. Anthony Saich
Dr. Martin Weale
Prof. Andrew Whittle

ADDRESS INQUIRIES TO:
Secretary
(See address above.)

LASPAU: ACADEMIC AND PROFESSIONAL PROGRAMS FOR THE AMERICAS   [961]
25 Mount Auburn Street
Suite 300
Cambridge, MA 02138-6095
(617) 495-5255
Fax: (617) 495-8990

E-MAIL ADDRESS:
laspau-webmaster@calists.harvard.edu

WEB SITE ADDRESS:
www.laspau.harvard.edu

FOUNDED: 1964

AREAS OF INTEREST:
Designing and administering academic and professional exchange programs in Latin America, the Caribbean, Canada and the U.S.

CONSULTING OR VOLUNTEER SERVICES:
Specialized educational consulting services are offered by LASPAU.

TYPE:
Conferences/seminars; Exchange programs; Fellowships; Project/program grants; Scholarships; Technical assistance; Training grants; Travel grants. LASPAU administers school programs, institutional development programs through executive training, and graduate admission tests. LASPAU is

involved in these exchange areas: professional/business, students/educators and training.

YEAR PROGRAM STARTED: 1964

PURPOSE:
To empower citizens through education and professional development as a necessity in today's global context.

LEGAL BASIS:
Nonprofit corporation.

ELIGIBILITY:
In most cases, individuals wishing to apply for an award must be nominated through the program sponsor by a participating Latin American, Caribbean or other institution. (Similarly, all scholarship and loan recipients agree to return promptly to their home institutions.)

LASPAU gives special priority to regional, socio-economic and ethnic diversity in order to broaden opportunities for underserved populations. Independent applications are accepted only for certain programs; details are available at the Programs section on the web site.

GEOGRAPHIC RESTRICTIONS:
Latin America and the Caribbean.

FINANCIAL DATA:
LASPAU provides grantees and their sponsors with comprehensive financial services, disbursement of scholarship grants and regular reports to sponsoring agencies.

Amount of support per award: Varies.

Total amount of support: Approximately $13,000,000.

APPLICATION INFORMATION:
Application procedures vary by program. Check the Programs section on the web site for details.

PUBLICATIONS:
eNewsletter, annual report; newsletter; brochures; grantee guides.

OFFICERS:
Peter DeShazo, Executive Director
Angelica Natera, Deputy Director
Cindy Bowen, Associate Director for Finance and Administration

TRUSTEES:
Jeff Coburn, Chairperson
Fernando Reimers, Vice Chairperson
John Knutson, Treasurer
Jeffrey Davidow
Luiz Felipe D'Avila
Everett Egginton
Margot Gill
Merilee Grindle
James Honan
Mauricio Lopez
Felipe Medina
Aldo Musacchio
Douglas Orane
Lygia Pereira
Francisco Sananez
Ned Strong
Alexander Watson

ADDRESS INQUIRIES TO:
Peter DeShazo, Executive Director
(See address above.)

MEDICAL LIBRARY ASSOCIATION [962]

65 East Wacker Place
Suite 1900
Chicago, IL 60601-7298
(312) 419-9094
Fax: (312) 419-8950

E-MAIL ADDRESS:
mlapd2@mlahq.org

WEB SITE ADDRESS:
www.mlanet.org/awards/grants/index.html

FOUNDED: 1898

AREAS OF INTEREST:
Health sciences librarianship.

NAME(S) OF PROGRAMS:
● **Cunningham Memorial International Fellowship**

TYPE:
Fellowships; Travel grants; Work-study programs. Work-study program for medical librarians from countries other than the U.S. or Canada for a time period of at least two weeks.

YEAR PROGRAM STARTED: 1971

PURPOSE:
To educate and train medical librarians from countries outside the continental U.S. and Canada in areas where improved medical library service is essential to the health and welfare of the people through the education of physicians and scientists.

LEGAL BASIS:
Nonprofit.

ELIGIBILITY:
Candidate must be working in a medical library or be preparing to work in one in his country and must have an undergraduate and library degree. Candidate must have a statement from a responsible official of the institution where he is working or plans to work that he will be guaranteed a position in a medical library when he returns to his country, he must pass the TOEFL exam to demonstrate competence in English and he must present three letters of recommendation and a health certificate.

FINANCIAL DATA:
Amount of support per award: Varies.

Matching fund requirements: Candidate may need additional resources during the period of his fellowship.

NUMBER OF AWARDS: 1 per year.

APPLICATION INFORMATION:
Applicant must submit the following:
(1) three letters of reference, in English, from responsible persons who are familiar with the applicant's qualifications;
(2) a signed statement, in English, from a responsible official of the institution where he or she is working or plans to work, guaranteeing a position in a health sciences library upon his or her return;
(3) a TOEFL score of 500 or greater, except for applicants whose native language is English or whose language of instruction at the university level was English;
(4) a project overview in accordance to the guidelines described in the "Project Goals" and;
(5) a certificate of good physical health, written in English, from a licensed physician.

Duration: At least two weeks.

Deadline: December 1. Announcement in March.

STAFF:
Maria Lopez, Grants and Scholarships Coordinator

ADDRESS INQUIRIES TO:
Coordinator
Grants, Scholarships and Awards
(See address above.)

NATIONAL INSTITUTES OF HEALTH

Division of International Services
31 Center Drive, B2BO7
MSC-2028
Bethesda, MD 20892-2028
(301) 496-6166
Fax: (301) 496-0847

E-MAIL ADDRESS:
dis@mail.nih.gov

WEB SITE ADDRESS:
www.training.nih.gov
dis.ors.od.nih.gov

TYPE:
Exchange programs; Fellowships.

See entry 1455 for full listing.

ORGANIZATION OF AMERICAN STATES [963]

Department of Human Development, Education and Employment
1889 F Street, N.W., Seventh Floor
Washington, DC 20006
(202) 370-9760
Fax: (202) 458-3897

E-MAIL ADDRESS:
rowefund@oas.org

WEB SITE ADDRESS:
www.oas.org/en/rowefund

FOUNDED: 1948

AREAS OF INTEREST:
Education.

NAME(S) OF PROGRAMS:
● **The Leo S. Rowe Pan American Fund**

TYPE:
Assistantships; Awards/prizes; Scholarships; Visiting scholars. Loan program. The Leo S. Rowe Pan American Fund awards interest-free student loans to citizens from Latin America and the Caribbean countries, to help them finance their higher studies or research in accredited universities across the U.S. Program is available to foreign students and foreign scholars in U.S. universities.

YEAR PROGRAM STARTED: 1948

PURPOSE:
To provide a loan program to qualified citizens from Latin America and the Caribbean countries to help them finance their higher education or research at accredited institutions in the U.S. by awarding interest-free loans.

ELIGIBILITY:
Rowe Fund loans are granted to individuals currently studying or wishing to pursue graduate, postgraduate or the last two years of undergraduate studies. Additionally, professionals or university faculty who are currently pursuing, or wish to pursue, advanced training, research or technical certificates at accredited institutions in the U.S. are also eligible. This includes

semester-abroad programs and professional development courses, with the exception of English-as-a-Second-Language courses.

Candidates must:
(1) be nationals of a Latin American or Caribbean member state of the OAS (U.S. and Canadian citizens are not eligible);
(2) have an international student visa (F, J or M) allowing them to study full-time in the U.S.;
(3) be accepted as a full-time student in an accredited institution of higher learning in the U.S.;
(4) have adequate academic records;
(5) be able to demonstrate other sources of financing (such as savings, employment, fellowship, funds supplied by the university or relatives, etc.) to cover the greater portion of their academic expenses;
(6) ensure that loans are underwritten by a guarantor (citizen or permanent resident of the U.S.) and;
(7) promise that upon completion of his or her studies, he or she will repay the loan in full and return to his or her country; (if OPT is granted, the return date can be extended up to a year upon completion of studies).

FINANCIAL DATA:
Loans can be used to cover a portion of the tuition and other university fees, essential books and supplies, room and board and/or emergencies not covered by their principal source of funding. No application or processing fees. Funding is sent directly to the student after approval.

Amount of support per award: Loan: Up to U.S. $7,500 per academic period. Loan recipients may apply for additional loans for subsequent academic periods, providing the total amount of loans granted does not exceed U.S. $15,000 over the course of the studies for which the loan is granted.

Total amount of support: $15,000 (U.S.) per Rowe Fund recipient.

Matching fund requirements: The prospective applicant must demonstrate other sources of financing (such as savings, employment, a fellowship, funds supplied by the university or relatives, etc.), to cover the greater part of their academic expenses and must present a guarantor.

NUMBER OF AWARDS: Averaging 100.

APPLICATION INFORMATION:
Applicants must be citizens of the following countries: Antigua and Barbuda, Argentina, Barbados, Belize, Bolivia, Brazil, Chile, Colombia, Costa Rica, Dominica (Commonwealth of), Dominican Republic, Ecuador, El Salvador, Grenada, Guatemala, Guyana, Haiti, Honduras, Jamaica, Mexico, Nicaragua, Panama, Paraguay, Peru, Saint Kitts and Nevis, Saint Lucia, Saint Vincent and the Grenadines, Suriname, The Bahamas (Commonwealth of), Trinidad and Tobago, Uruguay, Venezuela (Bolivarian Republic of).

Loan applications are usually submitted directly from students to the OAS-Rowe Fund Secretariat and are accepted and reviewed year-round at any time during the academic year in the U.S. by the Rowe Fund Committee. Loan applications that comply with the eligibility requirements will be reviewed and evaluated by the Committee; however, this is not to be defined as automatic approval. The decision of the Committee, which is final, will be communicated to the applicant by the Secretariat of the Fund. Eligible candidates

may find the application forms, eligibility requirement and FAQs at the web site, or may send an e-mail requesting the application forms at the e-mail address above.

Duration: Two years maximum.

STAFF:
Lina M. Sevillano, Program Manager

ADDRESS INQUIRIES TO:
Leo S. Rowe Pan American Fund
(See address above.)

*SPECIAL STIPULATIONS:
Repayment is deferred while the loan recipient is in school. Loans must be repaid within 50 months of completion of the degree.

These loans are made with the understanding that, upon completing those studies, loan recipients commit to repay the loan in full and return to their home countries within a year to apply their knowledge and training as well as continue fostering friendship and communication among the peoples of the Americas.

ORGANIZATION OF AMERICAN STATES
1889 F Street, N.W.
Seventh Floor
Washington, DC 20006
(202) 370-9771
Fax: (202) 458-3897

E-MAIL ADDRESS:
scholarships@oas.org

WEB SITE ADDRESS:
www.oas.org/scholarships

TYPE:
Fellowships; Scholarships; Technical assistance. Awarded for graduate academic studies and/or research, and last two years of undergraduate studies for students in the English-speaking Caribbean, for training in areas contributing to the economic, social, technical and cultural development of OAS member countries.

See entry 856 for full listing.

P.E.O. SISTERHOOD   [964]
P.E.O. Executive Office
3700 Grand Avenue
Des Moines, IA 50312
(515) 255-3153
Fax: (515) 255-3820

E-MAIL ADDRESS:
ips@peodsm.org

WEB SITE ADDRESS:
www.peointernational.org

FOUNDED: 1869

NAME(S) OF PROGRAMS:
● **P.E.O. International Peace Scholarships**

TYPE:
Grants-in-aid; Scholarships. Awards for selected women from countries other than the U.S. and Canada to pursue graduate study in the U.S. or Canada. Support is available for advanced study in any field except for research. No new applications at the dissertation level.

YEAR PROGRAM STARTED: 1949

PURPOSE:
To promote world peace and understanding through scholarship aid to selected women from other countries to further their education in the U.S. and Canada.

LEGAL BASIS:
Nonprofit organization.

ELIGIBILITY:
Prerequisites for applicants:
(1) Applicant must be qualified for admission to full-time graduate study, working toward a graduate degree in the college or university she will attend;
(2) A copy of the applicant's confirmation of admission must be received by the IPS office by April 1 in order to complete the application. This notice must specify the graduate degree program. No consideration will be given to applicants lacking evidence of admission and;
(3) Prerequisites 1 and 2 do not apply to the applicant who enrolls at Cottey College (Nevada, MO), which is owned and operated by the P.E.O. Sisterhood. The applicant shall present evidence of admission to Cottey.

In order to qualify for her first scholarship, an applicant must have a full year of coursework remaining and be enrolled and on campus for the entire school year. Doctoral students who have completed coursework and are working on dissertations only are not eligible as first-time applicants. Doctoral students in medicine or dentistry will be considered only in the final two years of study.

Upon completion of the degree program or Optional Practical Training, the applicant must promise to return to her home country or to a location outside the U.S. or Canada within 60 days, depending on visa status.

A student holding citizenship or permanent residency in the U.S. or Canada is ineligible. Scholarships are not given for research, internships or for practical training if not combined with coursework. Scholarships are not awarded for travel, repayment of past debt, or to fund online courses.

FINANCIAL DATA:
Scholarships to students studying in Canadian universities will be paid in Canadian dollars.

Amount of support per award: $10,000 maximum per year.

NUMBER OF APPLICANTS MOST RECENT YEAR: 425.

NUMBER OF AWARDS: 149 for the 2013-14 academic year.

APPLICATION INFORMATION:
In order to be considered for an IPS Scholarship, a student must submit an eligibility form electronically through the P.E.O. International web site. Paper forms sent to the P.E.O. International office will not be accepted. The online eligibility form can be submitted from September 15 to December 15.

Duration: Initial support is for a period not to exceed one year (two semesters and one summer session or the equivalent), with one renewal possible. Not to exceed a total of two years.

Deadline: To establish eligibility: December 15. Final date for receipt of confirmation of admission from university: April 1. Notification of scholarships: May 1. Final date for student acceptance of scholarships: June 1.

No eligibility information will be accepted before September 15 or after December 15.

PUBLICATIONS:
Information sheet.

ADDRESS INQUIRIES TO:
Carolyn Larson, Project Supervisor
(See address above.)

*SPECIAL STIPULATIONS:
Applicant must have round-trip or return travel expense guaranteed at the time of application.

THE UNIVERSITY OF SYDNEY [965]

Scholarships Office
Level 5, Jane Foss Russell Building G02
The University of Sydney N.S.W. 2006
Australia
(02) 8627 8112
Fax: (02) 8627 8485

E-MAIL ADDRESS:
research.training@sydney.edu.au

WEB SITE ADDRESS:
www.sydney.edu.au/scholarships/research

FOUNDED: 1850

NAME(S) OF PROGRAMS:
● **Walter Mersh Strong Scholarship**

TYPE:
Scholarships. Awarded for studies at postgraduate level. Tenable at the University of Sydney. The scholarship is available for a Master by coursework program in agriculture, education and social work, or public health.

PURPOSE:
To provide opportunities for graduate students from Papua New Guinea to attend the University of Sydney to undertake a Master by coursework program in agriculture, education and social work, or public health.

LEGAL BASIS:
University.

ELIGIBILITY:
Open to graduates from Papua New Guinea who qualify for admission to the University of Sydney.

GEOGRAPHIC RESTRICTIONS:
Papua New Guinea.

FINANCIAL DATA:
Amount of support per award: Tuition fees and living allowance of $24,653 AUD per annum for the year 2013.

NUMBER OF AWARDS: 1 for the year 2013.

APPLICATION INFORMATION:
Application information is available on the web site.
Deadline: As advertised, when funds are available.

ADDRESS INQUIRIES TO:
The International Office
Level 4, Jane Foss Russell Building G02
The University of Sydney
N.S.W. 2006 Australia
Tel: (02) 8627 8302
Fax: (02) 8627 8387
E-mail: io.studentadvisers@sydney.edu.au

WENNER-GREN FOUNDATION FOR ANTHROPOLOGICAL RESEARCH, INC.

470 Park Avenue South, 8th Floor
New York, NY 10016-6819
(212) 683-5000
Fax: (212) 683-9151

E-MAIL ADDRESS:
internationalprograms@wennergren.org

WEB SITE ADDRESS:
www.wennergren.org

TYPE:
Fellowships; Scholarships. Wadsworth International Fellowship is for scholars and students from developing countries undertaking study leading to a Ph.D. or equivalent doctoral degree at universities where they can receive international-level training in anthropology and its related subdisciplines. The main goals of these Fellowships are to expand and strengthen international ties and enhance anthropological infrastructure in countries where anthropology is underrepresented and where there are limited resources to send students overseas for training.

See entry 2027 for full listing.

Technical assistance and cooperative research

JOHN E. FOGARTY INTERNATIONAL CENTER

Division of International Training and Research
Building 31, B2C39
31 Center Drive, MSC 2220
Bethesda, MD 20892-2220
(301) 496-1653
Fax: (301) 402-0779

WEB SITE ADDRESS:
www.fic.nih.gov

TYPE:
Research grants. A small grants program to support biomedical, behavioral and social sciences health research.

See entry 2146 for full listing.

NATIONAL INSTITUTES OF HEALTH [966]

Division of International Relations
Fogarty International Center
Building 31, Room B2C39
31 Center Drive, MSC 2220
Bethesda, MD 20892-2220
(301) 496-4784

E-MAIL ADDRESS:
chungt@mail.nih.gov
mili.ferreira@nih.gov

WEB SITE ADDRESS:
www.fic.nih.gov/programs/pages/japan-fellowships.aspx

AREAS OF INTEREST:
Biomedical and behavioral sciences.

NAME(S) OF PROGRAMS:
● **Japan Society for the Promotion of Science Postdoctoral Research Fellowships (Extramural)**

TYPE:
Fellowships. A limited number of postdoctoral research fellowships are provided by the Japan Science and Technology Agency (JSTA) to U.S. scientists to conduct research in Japan. Types of activity supported include collaboration in basic or clinical research and familiarization with or utilization of special techniques and equipment not otherwise available to the applicant.

YEAR PROGRAM STARTED: 1987

PURPOSE:
To provide a research experience in the biomedical, clinical and behavioral sciences in Japanese laboratories.

LEGAL BASIS:
Government agency.

ELIGIBILITY:
Applicants for the program must be U.S. citizens or permanent U.S. residents, hold a Doctorate in one of the clinical, behavioral or biomedical sciences and make prior arrangements with the appropriate Japanese host researcher as to the research plan.

The program does not provide support for activities that have as their principal purpose brief observational visits, attendance at scientific meetings or independent study.

NUMBER OF AWARDS: Up to 10 short-term, 5 long-term.

APPLICATION INFORMATION:
Application information is available on the web site.
Duration: Short-term: Under 12 months; Long-term: 12 to 24 months.
Deadline: Varies.

ADDRESS INQUIRIES TO:
Tina Chung, M.P.H., Program Officer
(See address above.)

NORTH ATLANTIC TREATY ORGANIZATION [967]

Emerging Security Challenges Division (ESCD)
NATO HQ, Boulevard Leopold III
B-1110 Brussels Belgium
Fax: 32 2 707 4232

E-MAIL ADDRESS:
science@hq.nato.int

WEB SITE ADDRESS:
www.nato.int/science

FOUNDED: 1958

AREAS OF INTEREST:
Scientific cooperation between NATO Allies and partner countries.

NAME(S) OF PROGRAMS:
● **Science for Peace and Security (SPS) Programme**

TYPE:
Multiyear projects; workshops and training.

Offers grants to scientists in NATO and Partner countries to collaborate on priority research topics, which include NATO priorities and additional Partner country priorities. Grants are also offered to assist the academic community in Partner countries to set up computer networking infrastructure and to optimize their use of electronic communication.

In addition to activities funded by the NATO international budget, the Science for Peace and Security Programme also engages in activities funded directly by one or more nations. These consist of pilot studies, short-term projects and topical workshops which are aligned with NATO's Strategic Objectives and are in areas of priority to NATO or Partner countries. Any NATO or Partner country can initiate a new proposal. The initiating nation seeks the participation of other NATO and Partner nations and this participation is always voluntary. Support Grant Programme is open to experts from both NATO countries and those Partner countries eligible for support.

YEAR PROGRAM STARTED: 1960

PURPOSE:
To stimulate collaboration between laboratories in different countries and thus enhance the effectiveness of research.

GEOGRAPHIC RESTRICTIONS:
NATO countries: Albania, Belgium, Bulgaria, Canada, Croatia, Czech Republic, Denmark, Estonia, France, Germany, Greece, Hungary, Iceland, Italy, Latvia, Lithuania, Luxembourg, Netherlands, Norway, Poland, Portugal, Romania, Slovak Republic, Slovenia, Spain, Turkey, United Kingdom and United States.

FINANCIAL DATA:
Covering project-related costs and organizational costs.
Amount of support per award: EUR 5,000 to EUR 50,000 depending on the type of support mechanism.

APPLICATION INFORMATION:
Applications should be presented on the official application forms that can be downloaded from the Science for Peace and Security web site. Applications should be submitted via e-mail (sps.applications@hq.nato.int) to the Emerging Security Challenges/SPS Staff.
Duration: Depends on the mechanism. Up to three years for the multiyear projects.
Deadline: October 1. Applications may be submitted at any time. Applications received later than this deadline date will be considered during the next evaluation cycle.

PUBLICATIONS:
NATO Science Series.

ADDRESS INQUIRIES TO:
E-mail: science@hq.nato.int

U.S.-ISRAEL BINATIONAL SCIENCE FOUNDATION (BSF)   [968]
P.O. Box 45086 (Hamarpeh Street, No. 8)
Har Hotzvim
Jerusalem 91450 Israel
972-2-5828239
Fax: 972-2-5828306

E-MAIL ADDRESS:
bsf@bsf.org.il

WEB SITE ADDRESS:
www.bsf.org.il

FOUNDED: 1972

AREAS OF INTEREST:
Science.

TYPE:
Research grants. Workshops.

Promotes cooperation between the countries in research concerned with science and technology for peaceful purposes through grants to cooperative research projects. Grants are for bilateral, cooperative research between U.S. and Israeli scientists for research conducted in either country.

YEAR PROGRAM STARTED: 1974

PURPOSE:
To strengthen U.S.-Israel science cooperation.

LEGAL BASIS:
Established by government-to-government agreement.

ELIGIBILITY:
Any scientist on the staff of a U.S. or Israel nonprofit research institution may apply by submitting a cooperative research proposal.

Eligible research areas are health sciences, life sciences, physics, chemistry, mathematical sciences, atmospheric and earth sciences, oceanography and limnology, materials research, environmental research, energy research, biomedical engineering, economics, sociology, social and developmental psychology.

Submission of grant applications is on a split-program basis; namely, eligibility is limited, in alternate years, to either health and life sciences or to exact, natural and social sciences.

FINANCIAL DATA:
Awards are made to cover the direct cost of executing the approved research, i.e., salaries for research assistants, supplies, travel, etc. Salaries of principal investigators are not included.
Amount of support per award: Up to $230,000. Average $40,000 per year.
Total amount of support: Approximately $17,000,000.

APPLICATION INFORMATION:
Proposals are unsolicited and should be submitted jointly by the collaborating scientists via the prospective grantee institution where the research will be performed.
Duration: Up to four years.
Deadline: The completed application form must reach the BSF by November 15 for a grant to be awarded in the following year. Awards are made annually and are announced in July.

OFFICERS:
Dr. Yair Rotstein, Director
Dr. Rachel Haring, Assistant Director

ADDRESS INQUIRIES TO:
Dr. Yair Rotstein, Director
(See address above.)

SPECIAL POPULATIONS

Special Populations

THE ABLE TRUST [969]

3320 Thomasville Road
Suite 200
Tallahassee, FL 32308
(888) 838-2253
(850) 224-4493
Fax: (850) 224-4496

E-MAIL ADDRESS:
info@abletrust.org

WEB SITE ADDRESS:
www.abletrust.org

FOUNDED: 1991

AREAS OF INTEREST:
Disabilities and handicapped persons.

NAME(S) OF PROGRAMS:
● **Organization Grant Program**
● **Special Projects Program**
● **Strategic Employment Grant Program**

TYPE:
Project/program grants. The Organization Grant Program funds innovative employment programs for people with disabilities from organizations in Florida.

The Special Projects Program solicits proposals which focus on the employment of people with disabilities in Florida and provide innovative approaches on service delivery or new concept. These special projects often are pilot or demonstration projects.

The Strategic Employment Grant Program addresses the employment placement of Floridians with disabilities.

YEAR PROGRAM STARTED: 1990

PURPOSE:
To provide Floridians with disabilities fair employment opportunities through fund-raising grant programs, public awareness and education.

LEGAL BASIS:
501(c)(3) public-private partnership foundation.

ELIGIBILITY:
Proposals will be accepted from Florida-based nonprofit organizations with 501(c)(3) status serving disabled Florida citizens. Each organization may have only one active grant in any one-year time period.

GEOGRAPHIC RESTRICTIONS:
Florida.

FINANCIAL DATA:
Amount of support per award: Average award is $40,000 for organizations. Organization Grant Program: Up to $65,000. Strategic Employment Grant Program: Up to $250,000.
Total amount of support: $1,200,000.

NUMBER OF APPLICANTS MOST RECENT YEAR:
150.

NUMBER OF AWARDS: 74.

APPLICATION INFORMATION:
Application guidelines are available on the Trust web site.
Duration: Organization Grants: One year. Strategic Employment Grants: Up to three years.
Deadline: Organization Grants: April 5 and July 5. Strategic Employment Grants: September 5.

IRS IDENTIFICATION NUMBER: 59-3052307

STAFF:
Dr. Susanne Homant, President and Chief Executive Officer

ADDRESS INQUIRIES TO:
Dr. Susanne Homant
President and Chief Executive Officer
(See address above.)

THE ACTUARIAL FOUNDATION

475 North Martingale Road
Suite 600
Schaumburg, IL 60173-2226
(847) 706-3500
Fax: (847) 706-3599

E-MAIL ADDRESS:
Scholarships@ActFnd.org

WEB SITE ADDRESS:
www.actuarialfoundation.org

TYPE:
Scholarships. The Actuarial Diversity Scholarship was formed in 1977 as a joint effort of the Casualty Actuarial Society and the Society of Actuaries. In 2008, the scholarship was transferred to The Actuarial Foundation.

The scholarship promotes diversity in the profession through an annual scholarship program for Black/African American, Hispanic, Native North American and Pacific Islander students. The scholarship award recognizes and encourages academic achievements by awarding scholarships to full-time undergraduate students pursuing a degree that may lead to a career in the actuarial profession.

See entry 2091 for full listing.

ALZHEIMER'S DRUG DISCOVERY FOUNDATION

57 West 57th Street
Suite 904
New York, NY 10019
(212) 901-8000
Fax: (212) 901-8010

E-MAIL ADDRESS:
hfillit@alzdiscovery.org

WEB SITE ADDRESS:
www.alzdiscovery.org

TYPE:
Awards/prizes; Conferences/seminars; Research grants.

See entry 2216 for full listing.

THE AMERICAN ACADEMY OF ESTHETIC DENTISTRY

303 West Madison Street
Suite 2650
Chicago, IL 60606
(312) 981-6770
Fax: (312) 265-2908

E-MAIL ADDRESS:
info@estheticacademy.org

WEB SITE ADDRESS:
www.estheticacademy.org

TYPE:
Research grants.

See entry 2340 for full listing.

AMERICAN ASSOCIATION OF LAW LIBRARIES

105 West Adams Street
Suite 3300
Chicago, IL 60603
(312) 939-4764
Fax: (312) 431-1097

E-MAIL ADDRESS:
membership@aall.org

WEB SITE ADDRESS:
www.aallnet.org

TYPE:
Scholarships. Stipend for graduate study leading to a degree at an accredited school of library or information science or an accredited law school. Preference will be given to individuals with previous service to, or interest in, law librarianship.

See entry 710 for full listing.

AMERICAN BAR FOUNDATION [970]

750 North Lake Shore Drive
Fourth Floor
Chicago, IL 60611
(312) 988-6517
Fax: (312) 988-6579

E-MAIL ADDRESS:
fellowships@abfn.org

WEB SITE ADDRESS:
www.americanbarfoundation.org

FOUNDED: 1952

AREAS OF INTEREST:
Law and social science.

NAME(S) OF PROGRAMS:
● **Summer Research Diversity Fellowships in Law and Social Science for Undergraduate Students**

TYPE:
Fellowships; Internships.

YEAR PROGRAM STARTED: 1988

PURPOSE:
To interest undergraduate students from diverse backgrounds in pursuing graduate study in the social sciences; to introduce students to the rewards and demands of a research-oriented career in the field of law and social science.

LEGAL BASIS:
Private foundation.

ELIGIBILITY:
Must be a U.S. citizen or permanent resident. The program is open, but not limited to, persons who are African-American, Hispanic/Latino, Native American, or Puerto Rican. Applicants must be sophomores or juniors in college with a grade point average of at least 3.0 on a scale of 4.0 and must be moving toward an academic major in one of the social science or humanities disciplines.

GEOGRAPHIC RESTRICTIONS:
United States.

FINANCIAL DATA:
Amount of support per award: $3,600.
Total amount of support: $14,400.

NUMBER OF APPLICANTS MOST RECENT YEAR:
200.

NUMBER OF AWARDS: 4 each year.

APPLICATION INFORMATION:
Application form is available online.
Duration: Eight weeks during the summer.
Deadline: Late March to April 15.

PUBLICATIONS:
Annual report, application guidelines and forms.

ADDRESS INQUIRIES TO:
Amanda Ehrhardt
(See address above.)

AMERICAN COUNCIL FOR POLISH CULTURE (ACPC)

812 Lombard Street, No. 12
Philadelphia, PA 19147-1308
(215) 627-1391

E-MAIL ADDRESS:
dziecko2@comcast.net

WEB SITE ADDRESS:
www.polishcultureacpc.org

TYPE:
Scholarships.

See entry 1655 for full listing.

AMERICAN COUNCIL OF THE BLIND

2200 Wilson Boulevard, Suite 650
Arlington, VA 22201
(202) 467-5081
(800) 424-8666
Fax: (703) 465-5085

E-MAIL ADDRESS:
info@acb.org

WEB SITE ADDRESS:
www.acb.org

TYPE:
Assistantships; Awards/prizes; Internships; Scholarships. Scholarships for outstanding blind students enrolled in academic, vocational, technical or professional training programs beyond the high school level.

See entry 1656 for full listing.

AMERICAN FOUNDATION FOR THE BLIND, INC. [971]

1000 Fifth Avenue, Suite 350
Huntington, WV 25701
(212) 502-7600
(800) 232-5463
Fax: (888) 545-8331
TDD: (212) 502-7662

E-MAIL ADDRESS:
afbinfo@afb.net

WEB SITE ADDRESS:
www.afb.org/scholarships.asp

FOUNDED: 1921

AREAS OF INTEREST:
Blindness, education, vocational and social services, public education, consultation and publications related to blindness and visual impairment.

NAME(S) OF PROGRAMS:
- **Gladys C. Anderson Memorial Scholarship**
- **The Karen D. Carsel Memorial Scholarship**
- **The Delta Gamma Foundation Florence Margaret Harvey Memorial Scholarship**
- **The Rudolph Dillman Memorial Scholarship**
- **The R.L. Gillette Scholarship**
- **The Paul and Ellen Ruckes Scholarship**

TYPE:
Scholarships. Undergraduate and graduate scholarships for students who are legally blind.

The Gladys C. Anderson Memorial Scholarship is offered to a female undergraduate or graduate student studying classical or religious music.

The Karen D. Carsel Memorial Scholarship provides a grant to a full-time graduate student who is legally blind and who presents evidence of economic need.

The Delta Gamma Foundation Florence Margaret Harvey Memorial Scholarship is offered to an undergraduate or graduate student who is legally blind, has exhibited academic excellence, and is studying in the field of rehabilitation and/or education of persons who are visually impaired or blind.

The Rudolph Dillman Memorial Scholarship provides four grants to undergraduate or graduate students who are legally blind and studying in the field of rehabilitation and/or education of persons who are blind or visually impaired.

The R.L. Gillette Scholarship offers two scholarships to women who are legally blind and are enrolled in a four-year undergraduate degree program in literature or music.

The Paul and Ellen Ruckes Scholarship is offered to an undergraduate or graduate student who is legally blind and studying engineering, computer, physical or life sciences.

LEGAL BASIS:
Not-for-profit corporation.

ELIGIBILITY:
Applicants must be U.S. citizens or residents who are, by definition, legally blind. Other criteria vary depending on the specific scholarship.

GEOGRAPHIC RESTRICTIONS:
United States.

FINANCIAL DATA:
Amount of support per award: Gladys C. Anderson Memorial, Delta Gamma Foundation Florence Margaret Harvey Memorial, R.L. Gillette, and Paul and Ellen Ruckes Scholarships: $1,000 each; Karen D. Carsel Memorial Scholarship: $500; Rudolph Dillman Memorial Scholarship: $2,500.
Total amount of support: $15,500.

NUMBER OF AWARDS: 6 scholarships with 10 total awards.

APPLICATION INFORMATION:
Applications must be submitted online. No paper applications will be accepted.

In general, applicants must submit a completed scholarship application form, evidence of legal blindness (or official letter from a state or private agency for the blind), certified transcripts, proof of acceptance in a postsecondary school, proof of U.S. citizenship, two letters of reference and typewritten statement of educational and personal goals, the field of study applicant is pursuing and why he or she has chosen it, the applicant's work experience, extracurricular activities and how the award will be used.
Duration: One academic year.
Deadline: Usually April 30, but can vary.

OFFICERS:
Carl R. Augusto, President and Chief Executive Officer

ADDRESS INQUIRIES TO:
Information Specialist
American Foundation for the Blind, Inc.
(See address above.)

THE AMERICAN GEOSCIENCES INSTITUTE (AGI)

4220 King Street
Alexandria, VA 22302-1502
(703) 379-2480 ext. 227
Fax: (703) 379-7563

E-MAIL ADDRESS:
wallacescholarship@agiweb.org

WEB SITE ADDRESS:
www.agiweb.org/scholarships/wallace

TYPE:
Scholarships. The Harriet Evelyn Wallace Scholarship is available for female students pursuing a Master's or Doctorate degree at an accredited institution of higher education in a recognized geoscience program.

See entry 2072 for full listing.

THE AMERICAN HELLENIC EDUCATIONAL PROGRESSIVE ASSOCIATION [972]

1909 Q Street, N.W.
Suite 500
Washington, DC 20009
(202) 232-6300
Fax: (202) 232-2140

E-MAIL ADDRESS:
ahepa@ahepa.org

WEB SITE ADDRESS:
www.ahepa.org

FOUNDED: 1922

AREAS OF INTEREST:
Culture, history, and issues relating to Greece and Cyprus.

TYPE:
Scholarships.

PURPOSE:
To promote, encourage, induce and advance education at the college, university and graduate school level.

ELIGIBILITY:
Applicants must be of Hellenic heritage, although their ancestry does not have to be 100% Greek. The applicant must be a member in good standing of AHEPA or affiliated organizations, demonstrate financial need and have no criminal record.

FINANCIAL DATA:
Amount of support per award: $500 to $2,000.
Total amount of support: $100,000 for the year 2011.

NUMBER OF AWARDS: 77.

APPLICATION INFORMATION:
Contact the Organization for application procedures.
Duration: One year. Renewal possible.
Deadline: March 31.

ADDRESS INQUIRIES TO:
Basil Mossaidis, Executive Director
(See address above.)

THE AMERICAN INSTITUTE OF ARCHITECTS

1735 New York Avenue, N.W.
Washington, DC 20006-5292
(202) 626-7529
(202) 626-7417
Fax: (202) 626-7399

E-MAIL ADDRESS:
divscholarships@aia.org

WEB SITE ADDRESS:
www.aia.org

TYPE:
Scholarships. Awards to provide an opportunity for financially disadvantaged and/or minority groups to pursue a professional degree in architecture.

See entry 411 for full listing.

AMERICAN INSTITUTE OF CHEMICAL ENGINEERS (AICHE)

120 Wall Street, Floor 23
New York, NY 10005-4020
(646) 495-1384
Fax: (646) 495-1503

E-MAIL ADDRESS:
awards@aiche.org

WEB SITE ADDRESS:
www.aiche.org

TYPE:
Scholarships.

See entry 2633 for full listing.

AMERICAN PLANNING ASSOCIATION   [973]

205 North Michigan Avenue
Suite 1200
Chicago, IL 60601
(202) 349-1027

E-MAIL ADDRESS:
mgroh@planning.org

WEB SITE ADDRESS:
www.planning.org

FOUNDED: 1909

AREAS OF INTEREST:
Urban and regional planning and the promotion of the art and science of planning.

NAME(S) OF PROGRAMS:
• **Judith McManus Fellowship**

TYPE:
Fellowships; Scholarships.

YEAR PROGRAM STARTED: 1970

PURPOSE:
To celebrate planning by providing partial funding for all women and minority (African American, Hispanic American or Native American) students.

LEGAL BASIS:
Private, nonprofit educational association.

ELIGIBILITY:
Applicants must be citizens of the U.S. and enrolled or accepted for enrollment in a planning program accredited by the Planning Accreditation Board (PAB). Applicants must document the need for financial assistance.

GEOGRAPHIC RESTRICTIONS:
United States.

FINANCIAL DATA:
Fellowship provides partial funding for tuition and living expenses. One-year student membership in the American Planning Association. Scholarship provides partial tuition funding.
Amount of support per award: Judith McManus Fellowship: $1,500 to $4,000.
Total amount of support: Varies.

NUMBER OF APPLICANTS MOST RECENT YEAR:
40.

NUMBER OF AWARDS: Varies.

APPLICATION INFORMATION:
Contact the Association.
Duration: One academic year.
Deadline: April 30.

PUBLICATIONS:
Program announcement.

ADDRESS INQUIRIES TO:
Monica Groh, Director of Early Career Programs
(See address above.)

AMERICAN POLITICAL SCIENCE ASSOCIATION

1527 New Hampshire Avenue, N.W.
Washington, DC 20036
(202) 483-2512
Fax: (202) 483-2657

E-MAIL ADDRESS:
minority@apsanet.org

WEB SITE ADDRESS:
www.apsanet.org

TYPE:
Fellowships; Grants-in-aid; Scholarships. Awards to aid prospective African American, Asian Pacific, Latino/Latina and Native American political science students beginning the doctoral study of political science.

See entry 1988 for full listing.

AMERICAN PSYCHOLOGICAL ASSOCIATION

Minority Fellowship Program/APA
750 First Street, N.E.
Washington, DC 20002-4242
(202) 336-6127
Fax: (202) 336-6012

E-MAIL ADDRESS:
mfp@apa.org

WEB SITE ADDRESS:
www.apa.org/pi/mfp

TYPE:
Fellowships. Fellowship is geared to those pursuing careers as practitioners and as researchers specializing in the delivery of mental health services to ethnic minority populations. Students specializing in clinical, school and counseling psychology are encouraged to apply.

See entry 2567 for full listing.

AMERICAN PSYCHOLOGICAL ASSOCIATION   [974]

Minority Fellowship Program/APA
750 First Street, N.E.
Washington, DC 20002-4242
(202) 336-6127
Fax: (202) 336-6012

E-MAIL ADDRESS:
mfp@apa.org

WEB SITE ADDRESS:
www.apa.org/pi/mfp

FOUNDED: 1892

AREAS OF INTEREST:
Mental health and substance abuse services.

NAME(S) OF PROGRAMS:
• **Mental Health and Substance Abuse Services Fellowship**

TYPE:
Fellowships. Geared to those pursuing careers in substance abuse treatment and prevention as practitioners and as researchers specializing in the delivery of mental health services to ethnic minority populations.

YEAR PROGRAM STARTED: 1974

PURPOSE:
To increase the knowledge of issues related to ethnic minority mental health and to improve the quality of mental health treatment delivered to ethnic minority populations by providing financial support and professional guidance to individuals pursuing doctoral degrees in psychology.

LEGAL BASIS:
Nonprofit.

ELIGIBILITY:
A U.S. citizen, permanent resident or noncitizen national who makes a commitment to a career in ethnic minority behavioral health services. No fellowship during internship year.

FINANCIAL DATA:
Amount of support per award: Varies.
Total amount of support: Varies.

NUMBER OF AWARDS: 5 to 15.

APPLICATION INFORMATION:
Complete details are available on the Association web site.
Duration: Maximum three years. Must renew each year.
Deadline: January 15. Announcement by April.

ADDRESS INQUIRIES TO:
Andrew Austin-Daley, Director
Minority Fellowship Program/APA
(See address above.)

*SPECIAL STIPULATIONS:
Applicants may apply for only one Fellowship at a time.

AMERICAN SOCIETY FOR MICROBIOLOGY

Education Department
1752 N Street, N.W.
Washington, DC 20036
(202) 942-9283
Fax: (202) 942-9329

E-MAIL ADDRESS:
fellowships@asmusa.org

WEB SITE ADDRESS:
www.asm.org/cdcfellowship
www.asm.org/urc
www.asm.org/postdocs

TYPE:
Fellowships. ASM/CDC Postdoctoral Research Fellowship Program: The American Society for Microbiology and Centers for Disease Control and Prevention (ASM/CDC) Postdoctoral Research Fellowship Program is

a comprehensive training program which provides opportunities to participate in interdisciplinary training on global public health issues. Fellows will perform research at one of the Centers for Disease Control and Prevention (CDC) locations.

Undergraduate Research Capstone Program: This fellowship encourages students to pursue careers or advanced degrees in the microbiological sciences by providing an opportunity to participate in a research project at their institution and gain experience in presenting their results. The fellowship allows students to conduct research in the summer with an ASM member faculty mentor and present the results at the ASM General Meeting the following year.

See entry 2139 for full listing.

AMERICAN SOCIETY FOR MICROBIOLOGY
Education Department
1752 N Street, N.W.
Washington, DC 20036
(202) 942-9283
Fax: (202) 942-9329

E-MAIL ADDRESS:
fellowships@asmusa.org

WEB SITE ADDRESS:
www.asm.org/watkins

TYPE:
Fellowships. This fellowship encourages underrepresented and historically excluded graduate students to conduct research in the microbiological sciences.

See entry 2140 for full listing.

AMERICAN SOCIOLOGICAL ASSOCIATION   [975]
1430 K Street, N.W.
Suite 600
Washington, DC 20005
(202) 383-9005 ext. 321
TDD: (202) 638-0981
Fax: (202) 638-0882

E-MAIL ADDRESS:
minority.affairs@asanet.org

WEB SITE ADDRESS:
www.asanet.org

FOUNDED: 1905

AREAS OF INTEREST:
All areas of sociology.

NAME(S) OF PROGRAMS:
● **Minority Fellowship Program**

TYPE:
Fellowships. Predoctoral training fellowships for minority-group members studying sociology.

YEAR PROGRAM STARTED: 1974

PURPOSE:
To provide predoctoral students with financial support, academic and research training, and mentoring, in coordination with university graduate programs, in order to increase the talent pool of minority sociologists in the U.S.

LEGAL BASIS:
Nonprofit professional association.

ELIGIBILITY:
Applicants must be citizens, noncitizen nationals of the U.S. or have been lawfully

admitted to the U.S. for permanent residence and have in their possession an Alien Registration Card, and they must be accepted and/or enrolled in a full-time sociology doctoral program in the U.S. at the time of appointment.

In addition, applicants must be members of an underrepresented racial and ethnic group, including African Americans, Latinos (e.g., Chicano, Cuban, Puerto Rican), American Indians or Alaskan Natives and Asians (e.g., Chinese, Japanese, Korean, Southeast Asian) or Pacific Islanders (e.g., Hawaiian, Guamanian, Samoan, Filipino) and who are college or university seniors and/or students in Master's-only programs who have been accepted or are applying to doctoral programs and have strong interests in sociology. If, however, an applicant is selected for an award, but not enrolled in an appropriate doctoral program by the time the funding year begins, the applicant will not be eligible to receive the award.

GEOGRAPHIC RESTRICTIONS:
United States.

FINANCIAL DATA:
Award includes stipend and some tuition assistance.
Amount of support per award: $18,000 for ASA-funded students.
Total amount of support: Varies.

NUMBER OF APPLICANTS MOST RECENT YEAR:
60.

NUMBER OF AWARDS: Up to 5 annually.

APPLICATION INFORMATION:
Applicants must submit completed application forms, transcripts, letters of recommendation and goal statement. Selection is based upon evidence of scholarship, writing ability, research potential, financial need and racial and ethnic minority identification.
Duration: Fellowships are tenable for one calendar year.
Deadline: January 31. Announcement by April 30.

STAFF:
Jean H. Shin, Program Director
Beth Floyd, Program Assistant

ADDRESS INQUIRIES TO:
Beth Floyd, Program Assistant
(See address above.)

ARMENIAN GENERAL BENEVOLENT UNION
55 East 59th Street
New York, NY 10022-1112
(212) 319-6383
Fax: (212) 319-6507

E-MAIL ADDRESS:
scholarship@agbu.org

WEB SITE ADDRESS:
www.agbu-scholarship.org

TYPE:
Fellowships; Scholarships.

See entry 1666 for full listing.

ARMENIAN RELIEF SOCIETY OF EASTERN U.S.A., INC.   [976]
80 Bigelow Avenue
Suite 200
Watertown, MA 02472
(617) 926-3801
Fax: (617) 924-7238

E-MAIL ADDRESS:
arseastus@aol.com

WEB SITE ADDRESS:
www.arseastusa.org

FOUNDED: 1910

NAME(S) OF PROGRAMS:
● **A.R.S. Lazarian Graduate Scholarship**
● **A.R.S. Undergraduate Scholarship**

TYPE:
Awards/prizes; Scholarships. Scholarships to assist students of Armenian ancestry in their higher education studies.

PURPOSE:
To aid Armenian students residing in the U.S.

LEGAL BASIS:
Nonprofit organization.

ELIGIBILITY:
Undergraduate or graduate students of Armenian ancestry attending a four-year college or university may apply.

For the Undergraduate Scholarship, the applicant must:
(1) be an undergraduate student attending an accredited four-year college or university in the U.S. and;
(2) be a full-time matriculated student having completed at least one college semester and who is presently enrolled.
These Undergraduate Scholarships are awarded on the basis of financial need, merit and involvement in the Armenian community.

The Lazarian Graduate Scholarships are open to students who intend to pursue their studies at the Master's or Doctorate level in the fields of law, history, political science, international relations, journalism, government, economics, business administration, medicine and public service. Selection is based on scholastic qualifications, financial need and involvement in the Armenian community. Must have an undergraduate degree from an accredited university in the U.S.

FINANCIAL DATA:
Amount of support per award: Varies, according to donations.

NUMBER OF APPLICANTS MOST RECENT YEAR:
Undergraduate: 25; Graduate: 20.

APPLICATION INFORMATION:
To receive an application, send a self-addressed, stamped envelope to the ARS office, and state undergraduate or graduate status. Scholarships are awarded based on merit, need and involvement in the Armenian community.

For Undergraduate Scholarships, the following information must accompany the application:
(1) financial aid forms filed with a testing service or school's financial aid office or a copy of a recent income tax return of the applicant's parents;
(2) a recent official transcript of college grades with a raised seal (no faxes or copies will be accepted) and;
(3) three letters of recommendation from a college professor or advisor, affiliate(s) of Armenian organization(s) of which the student is a member, and a personal acquaintance other than a relative.

For the Lazarian Graduate Scholarship:
(1) applicants must be currently enrolled in a graduate program or provide proof of acceptance and entrance into a program within the coming six months;
(2) applicants must provide official, sealed transcripts as requested (unofficial, unsealed transcripts will not be accepted);
(3) applications and all required documents must be postmarked by April 1 to be considered;
(4) applicants will not be considered for a scholarship if they have already received it twice;
(5) applicants must provide a copy of the most recent income tax return and tuition bill to be considered for a scholarship;
(6) applications will not be considered without the required three recommendations (if from an institution/organization, it should be on official letterhead) and;
(7) incomplete applications will not be considered under any circumstance.

Deadline: April 1.

STAFF:
Vart Chiloyan, Executive Secretary

ADDRESS INQUIRIES TO:
Scholarship Committee
(See address above.)

ASSOCIATION OF UNIVERSITIES AND COLLEGES OF CANADA [977]

350 Albert Street, Suite 600
Ottawa ON K1R 1B1 Canada
(613) 563-1236
Fax: (613) 563-9745

E-MAIL ADDRESS:
awards@aucc.ca

WEB SITE ADDRESS:
www.aucc.ca

FOUNDED: 1911

AREAS OF INTEREST:
Financial aid for disabled students.

NAME(S) OF PROGRAMS:
● **Mattinson Scholarship Program for Students with Disabilities**

TYPE:
Scholarships. These scholarships are applicable towards full-time studies for applicants entering the first year or already enrolled in a first Bachelor's-degree program.

PURPOSE:
To encourage Canadian students with permanent disabilities to pursue university studies with the ultimate objective of obtaining a first university degree.

LEGAL BASIS:
Nonprofit association.

ELIGIBILITY:
All candidates must be Canadian citizens or permanent residents who have lived in Canada for at least two years and be diagnosed with a documented permanent disability that is the primary disability for which they are applying.

Eligible applicants must have a minimum cumulative average of 75% (or equivalent) over the last three semesters of available marks. Nonacademic courses such as career- or personal development-related courses will not be considered.

All disciplines are eligible. The program must be of a minimum three-year duration.

GEOGRAPHIC RESTRICTIONS:
Canada.

FINANCIAL DATA:
Amount of support per award: $2,500 (CAN).

Total amount of support: Varies.

NUMBER OF AWARDS: Up to 6 scholarships: 1 in physical disability; 1 in sensory disability; 1 in mental health disability; 1 in learning disability; and 2 additional in any of the preceding disciplines listed.

APPLICATION INFORMATION:
Eligible applicants must provide:
(1) an official transcript of the last three semesters of available marks;
(2) two signed reference letters with the references' original signatures (one from a teacher and one from a person familiar with their volunteer/community involvement and/or extracurricular activities);
(3) one page (maximum 250 words) describing their volunteer/community involvement and/or extracurricular activities and their future goals and;
(4) proof of disability in one of the following forms: medical certificate, documentation showing receipt of federal and/or provincial disability assistance, or a letter, signed and on a letterhead, confirming the permanent disability from an official from the institution's centre for students with disabilities.

Note that a transcript will be considered acceptable only if it meets the following criteria:
(1) it is presented on the official paper of the institution and;
(2) it bears the appropriate signature(s) and/or seal of the institution.

Duration: One academic year. Renewable upon reapplication.

Deadline: Postmarked paper application must be sent to the Association no later than May 15. Applicant is responsible for ensuring that the post office postmarks his or her envelope by the due date.

PUBLICATIONS:
Program announcement.

ADDRESS INQUIRIES TO:
Fatim Chaki, Program Officer or Christine Paramanoss, Program Officer
(See address above.)

ASTRAEA LESBIAN FOUNDATION FOR JUSTICE [978]

116 East 16th Street, 7th Floor
New York, NY 10003
(212) 529-8021
Fax: (212) 982-3321

WEB SITE ADDRESS:
www.astraeafoundation.org

FOUNDED: 1977

AREAS OF INTEREST:
Social, racial, and economic justice for lesbian, gay, bisexual, transgender, and intersex (LGBTI) peoples in the global south and east.

NAME(S) OF PROGRAMS:
● **International Fund**

TYPE:
General operating grants; Grants-in-aid; Project/program grants.

PURPOSE:
To provide critically needed financial support to lesbian-led, LGBTI and progressive organizations striving to eliminate oppression based on race, age, sex, religion, sexual orientation, gender identity, economic exploitation, physical and mental ability, anti-semitism, and other such factors.

ELIGIBILITY:
Must be charitable nongovernmental organizations and meet the criteria used in determining 501(c)(3) status in the U.S. Those eligible to apply are:
(1) groups led by and/or for LGBTI communities;
(2) groups doing work towards social change on issues affecting LGBTI people;
(3) nongovernmental, not-for-profit groups with organizational budgets of $500,000 (U.S.) or less and;
(4) groups active for at least one year at the time of proposal.

Organizations applying must not have a budget of over $500,000 (U.S.).

GEOGRAPHIC RESTRICTIONS:
Africa, Asia and the Pacific, Eastern Europe/Commonwealth of Independent States, Latin America and the Caribbean, and the Middle East.

FINANCIAL DATA:
Amount of support per award: $5,000 to $10,000.

Total amount of support: Varies.

APPLICATION INFORMATION:
Organizations must submit letter of interest. Full applications are by invitation only.

Duration: One year. Must reapply.

Deadline: Letter of interest accepted throughout the year.

ADDRESS INQUIRIES TO:
Mai Kiang, Director of Grantmaking
(See address above.)

ASTRAEA LESBIAN FOUNDATION FOR JUSTICE [979]

116 East 16th Street, 7th Floor
New York, NY 10003
(212) 529-8021
Fax: (212) 982-3321

WEB SITE ADDRESS:
www.astraeafoundation.org

FOUNDED: 1977

AREAS OF INTEREST:
Social change organizations and projects (including film, video, media and cultural projects) that directly address the depth and complexity of critical issues in LGBTI communities.

NAME(S) OF PROGRAMS:
● **U.S. General Fund**

TYPE:
General operating grants; Grants-in-aid; Project/program grants.

PURPOSE:
To provide critically needed financial support to lesbian-led, LGBTI and progressive organizations striving to eliminate oppression based on race, age, sex, religion, sexual orientation, gender identity, economic exploitation, physical and mental ability, anti-semitism, and other such factors.

ELIGIBILITY:
501(c)(3) organizations. No grants to
individuals.

GEOGRAPHIC RESTRICTIONS:
United States and its territories.

FINANCIAL DATA:
Amount of support per award: $5,000 to
$10,000.
Total amount of support: Varies.

APPLICATION INFORMATION:
Organizations must be invited to apply. Faxed
proposals are not accepted. IRS letter
certifying organization's or fiscal sponsor's
nonprofit tax-exempt status is required.
Duration: One year. Must reapply.

ADDRESS INQUIRIES TO:
Mai Kiang, Director of Grantmaking
(See address above.)

ASTRAEA LESBIAN
FOUNDATION FOR
JUSTICE   [980]
116 East 16th Street, 7th Floor
New York, NY 10003
(212) 529-8021
Fax: (212) 982-3321

WEB SITE ADDRESS:
www.astraeafoundation.org

FOUNDED: 1977

AREAS OF INTEREST:
Impactful art by LGBTQI people and
organizations.

NAME(S) OF PROGRAMS:
● **Global Arts Fund**

TYPE:
Awards/prizes.

PURPOSE:
To recognize the work of LGBTQI artists
and organizations by providing support to
those who show artistic merit and whose art
and perspective reflect a commitment to
Astraea's mission and efforts to promote
LGBTQI visibility and social justice in
marginalized LGBTQI communities in the
face of exploitations wrought by
globalization, imperialism, and
neocolonialism.

ELIGIBILITY:
LGBTQI people and organizations with
limited access to resources are eligible. The
Fund will consider submissions, requested
through a nomination process, in many
artistic expressions: video, film, poetry,
fictional prose, photography, painting,
performance, dance, theater, music and other
interdisciplinary expressions.

GEOGRAPHIC RESTRICTIONS:
United States, the Global East and the Global
South.

FINANCIAL DATA:
Amount of support per award: $5,000 to
$10,000.

NUMBER OF AWARDS: 4 to 10.

APPLICATION INFORMATION:
The Fund only considers submissions
through a nomination process, nominators
having been grantees.
Deadline: Varies.

ADDRESS INQUIRIES TO:
Mai Kiang, Director of Grantmaking
(See address above.)

ALEXANDER GRAHAM BELL
ASSOCIATION FOR THE DEAF
AND HARD OF HEARING   [981]
3417 Volta Place, N.W.
Washington, DC 20007
(202) 337-5220
Fax: (202) 337-8314

E-MAIL ADDRESS:
financialaid@agbell.org

WEB SITE ADDRESS:
www.listeningandspokenlanguage.org

FOUNDED: 1890

AREAS OF INTEREST:
All areas of study.

NAME(S) OF PROGRAMS:
● **Alexander Graham Bell College
Scholarship Awards**

TYPE:
Scholarships.

YEAR PROGRAM STARTED: 1967

PURPOSE:
To assist students with pre-lingual, bilateral
hearing loss to attend mainstream colleges.

ELIGIBILITY:
Based on age of diagnosis, degree of hearing
loss and grade point average.

FINANCIAL DATA:
Amount of support per award: $1,000 to
$10,000.
Total amount of support: Varies.

NUMBER OF APPLICANTS MOST RECENT YEAR:
141.

NUMBER OF AWARDS: 20.

APPLICATION INFORMATION:
Applicants must download the application or
request via e-mail. Photocopies are not
accepted.
Duration: One year. Nonrenewable.
Deadline: Varies. Details posted online in
January.

ADDRESS INQUIRIES TO:
College Scholarships
(See address and e-mail above.)

*PLEASE NOTE:
E-mail recommended, as staff for this
program are not located in Washington, DC,
and mail and fax requests are significantly
delayed.

BEN & JERRY'S
FOUNDATION   [982]
30 Community Drive
South Burlington, VT 05403-6828
(802) 846-1500
Fax: (802) 846-1610

E-MAIL ADDRESS:
info@benandjerrysfoundation.org

WEB SITE ADDRESS:
www.benandjerrysfoundation.org

FOUNDED: 1985

AREAS OF INTEREST:
Economic, environmental, social justice and
grassroots organizing.

TYPE:
General operating grants; Project/program
grants. Grants to nonprofit organizations
which facilitate progressive social change by
addressing the underlying conditions of
societal and/or environmental problems using
organizing as a strategy to create change.

YEAR PROGRAM STARTED: 1986

PURPOSE:
To support and encourage organizations that
facilitate progressive social change by
addressing the underlying conditions of
societal and environmental problems.

LEGAL BASIS:
Private foundation.

ELIGIBILITY:
The Foundation generally funds organizations
with budgets less than $500,000. Applicant
must be a nonprofit 501(c)(3) organization or
have a sponsoring agent that has this status.
No grants to support basic services.
Applicants need to demonstrate that their
projects will lead to societal, institutional or
environmental change, help ameliorate an
unjust or destructive situation by empowering
constituents and address the root causes of
social and/or environmental problems.

No funding for discretionary or emergency
requests, colleges or universities, individuals
or scholarships, research projects, religious
projects, state agencies, international or
foreign programs or direct-service programs.

GEOGRAPHIC RESTRICTIONS:
United States and its territories.

FINANCIAL DATA:
Amount of support per award: $1,000 to
$20,000.
Total amount of support: $2,300,000 for the
year 2013.

REPRESENTATIVE AWARDS:
$10,000 to Ohio Valley Environmental
Coalition to continue funding to support their
work organizing broad-based opposition to
mountaintop removal/valley fill coal mining
practices as well as unsafe coal waste ponds;
$10,000 to Little Village Environmental
Justice Organization to continue funding for
the People United for Dignity, Democracy
and Justice project.

APPLICATION INFORMATION:
Contact the Foundation.
Duration: One year. Must reapply.
Deadline: Letters of Interest: March 15 and
September 15.

PUBLICATIONS:
Annual report; application guidelines; grant
recipients list.

IRS IDENTIFICATION NUMBER: 03-0300865

STAFF:
Lisa Pendolino, Managing Director
Rebecca Golden, Director of Programs

JACOB AND HILDA BLAUSTEIN
FOUNDATION   [983]
10 East Baltimore Street
Suite 1111
Baltimore, MD 21202
(410) 347-7201

E-MAIL ADDRESS:
info@blaufund.org

WEB SITE ADDRESS:
www.blaufund.org

FOUNDED: 1957

AREAS OF INTEREST:
Jewish life and Israel, education, human
rights, health and mental health.

TYPE:
General operating grants; Matching gifts;
Project/program grants.

ELIGIBILITY:
Grants are made to organizations that have
tax-exempt status under Section 501(c)(3) of
the Internal Revenue Code. No grants are
made to individuals.

GEOGRAPHIC RESTRICTIONS:
United States (primarily in Baltimore,
Maryland) and Israel.

FINANCIAL DATA:
Amount of support per award: Varies.
Total amount of support: $6,000,000 for the
year 2012.

APPLICATION INFORMATION:
Send a letter of inquiry outlining the
organization's goal and purposes, and the
intended use and amount of the grant
requested.
Duration: Typically one to two years.

ADDRESS INQUIRIES TO:
Michael Hirschhorn, President
(See address above.)

CALIFORNIA LIBRARY
ASSOCIATION

2471 Flores Street
San Mateo, CA 94403
(650) 376-0886
Fax: (650) 539-2341

E-MAIL ADDRESS:
info@cla-net.org

WEB SITE ADDRESS:
www.cla-net.org

TYPE:
Fellowships; Scholarships. Support for
minority library school students. Support for
graduate students in reference/information
service librarianship.

See entry 717 for full listing.

THE CENTER FOR LESBIAN
AND GAY STUDIES   [984]

The Graduate Center/CUNY
365 Fifth Avenue, Room 7115
New York, NY 10016
(212) 817-1958
Fax: (212) 817-1567

E-MAIL ADDRESS:
clagsfellowships@gmail.com

WEB SITE ADDRESS:
www.clags.org

AREAS OF INTEREST:
Scholarly research on the lesbian, gay,
bisexual, transgender, and queer experience.

NAME(S) OF PROGRAMS:
● **The Martin Duberman Fellowship**

TYPE:
Awards/prizes; Fellowships.

PURPOSE:
To promote the study of historical, cultural,
and political issues of vital concern to
lesbian, gay, bisexual, and transgendered
individuals.

ELIGIBILITY:
Senior scholars (tenured university professors
or advanced independent scholars) from any
country doing scholarly research on the
lesbian, gay, transgender, bisexual, or queer
(LGBTQ) experience. University affiliation is

not necessary, but the applicant must be able
to show a prior contribution to the field of
LGTBQ studies.

FINANCIAL DATA:
Amount of support per award: $7,500.
Total amount of support: $7,500 annually.

NUMBER OF AWARDS: 1.

APPLICATION INFORMATION:
Electronic submission by e-mail is preferred
by CLAGS. Guidelines and application form
are available at the web site.
Deadline: November 15.

PUBLICATIONS:
CLAGS News.

ADDRESS INQUIRIES TO:
Noam Parness
Membership and Fellowships Coordinator
(See address above.)

CINTAS FOUNDATION

c/o Morrison, Brown, Argiz & Farra LLP
1450 Brickell Avenue, Suite 1800
Miami, FL 33131
(305) 373-5500 ext. 2202
Fax: (305) 373-0056

E-MAIL ADDRESS:
fgonzalez@mbafcpa.com

WEB SITE ADDRESS:
www.cintasfoundation.org

TYPE:
Awards/prizes; Fellowships. Awarded to
persons of Cuban citizenship or lineage
residing outside Cuba for achievement of a
creative nature in architecture, painting,
sculpture, printmaking, music composition
and literature.

See entry 439 for full listing.

COLAGE   [985]

4509 Interlake Avenue North
No. 180
Seattle, WA 98103
(855) 426-5243

E-MAIL ADDRESS:
colage@colage.org

WEB SITE ADDRESS:
www.colage.org

AREAS OF INTEREST:
Children, youth and adults with LGBT
parents.

NAME(S) OF PROGRAMS:
● **Lee Dubin Memorial Scholarship**

TYPE:
Awards/prizes; Scholarships. Grants and
awards are offered to foster the growth of
children, youth and adults of lesbian, gay,
bisexual and transgender parents of all racial,
ethnic and class backgrounds, by providing
education, support and community on local
and international levels.

YEAR PROGRAM STARTED: 1993

PURPOSE:
To engage, connect, and empower people to
make the world a better place for children of
lesbian, gay, bisexual, and transgender
parents and families.

ELIGIBILITY:
Post-secondary students who have one or
more lesbian, gay, bisexual or transgender
parent/guardian, and have demonstrated

ability and commitment to effecting change
in the LGBTQ community and the
community at large.

GEOGRAPHIC RESTRICTIONS:
United States.

FINANCIAL DATA:
Amount of support per award: $1,000.

NUMBER OF AWARDS: 4 for the year 2010.

APPLICATION INFORMATION:
Guidelines and application forms are
available at COLAGE web site.

PUBLICATIONS:
Just For Us.

IRS IDENTIFICATION NUMBER: 94-3316616

STAFF:
Beth Teper, Executive Director
Carlos Uribe, Program Director

ADDRESS INQUIRIES TO:
Carlos Uribe, Program Director
(See address above.)

THE CONSORTIUM FOR
GRADUATE STUDY IN
MANAGEMENT

229 Chesterfield Business Parkway
Chesterfield, MO 63005
(636) 681-5553
(888) 658-6814
Fax: (636) 681-5499

WEB SITE ADDRESS:
www.cgsm.org

TYPE:
Fellowships. Graduate fellowships for
minority students interested in management
careers in business.

See entry 1892 for full listing.

COUNCIL ON SOCIAL WORK
EDUCATION   [986]

1701 Duke Street, Suite 200
Alexandria, VA 22314-3457
(703) 683-8080
Fax: (703) 683-8099

E-MAIL ADDRESS:
gmeeks@cswe.org

WEB SITE ADDRESS:
www.cswe.org/mfp

FOUNDED: 1952

AREAS OF INTEREST:
Improvement of social services and mental
health.

NAME(S) OF PROGRAMS:
● **The Mental Health and Substance
Abuse Fellowship Program**

TYPE:
Fellowships. Awards for minority
doctoral-level studies in social work,
specializing in mental health and substance
abuse-related education, research, policy and
practice.

YEAR PROGRAM STARTED: 1974

PURPOSE:
To equip ethnic minority individuals for the
provision of leadership, teaching,
consultation, training, policy development
and administration in mental health and/or
substance abuse programs and to enhance the
development and dissemination of knowledge
requisite for the provision of relevant clinical
and social services to ethnic minority
individuals and communities.

LEGAL BASIS:
Nonprofit organization.

ELIGIBILITY:
Applicants must be American citizens or non-citizen nationals of the U.S. or have permanent residence status, including but not limited to persons who are American Indian/Alaskan Native, Asian/Pacific Islander (e.g., Chinese, East Indian and other South Asians, Filipino, Hawaiian, Japanese, Korean, Samoan), Black and Hispanic (e.g., Mexican/Chicano, Cuban, Central or South American).

The Fellowship is open to students with a Master's degree in social work who will begin full-time study leading to a doctoral degree in social work or who are currently enrolled as full-time students in a doctoral social work program. Applicants should demonstrate potential for assuming leadership roles, potential for success in doctoral studies and commitment to a career in providing mental health and/or substance abuse services to ethnic/racial/social/cultural minority clients and communities.

FINANCIAL DATA:
Fellowship awards include a monthly stipend for one year to help meet living and doctoral study expenses.
Amount of support per award: Varies.
Total amount of support: Varies.

COOPERATIVE FUNDING PROGRAMS: Funded by the Substance Abuse and Mental Health Services Administration (SAMHSA), Department of Health and Human Services.

NUMBER OF AWARDS: Up to 25.

APPLICATION INFORMATION:
Complete information is available at the Council web site.
Duration: Three years maximum. Renewable each year subject to availability of funds and progress in program.
Deadline: February 28.

ADDRESS INQUIRIES TO:
E-mail: mfp@cswe.org
(See telephone number above.)

DARTMOUTH COLLEGE   [987]
Office of Graduate Studies
Chavez/Eastman/Marshall
6062 Wentworth Hall
Hanover, NH 03755-3526
(603) 646-6578
Fax: (603) 646-8762

E-MAIL ADDRESS:
jane.b.seibel@dartmouth.edu

WEB SITE ADDRESS:
www.dartmouth.
edu/~gradstdy/funding/fellowships

FOUNDED: 1769

AREAS OF INTEREST:
Fellowships for underrepresented minority scholars (including African-American, Latina/o and Native American scholars) and other graduate scholars with a demonstrated commitment and ability to advance educational diversity.

NAME(S) OF PROGRAMS:
● **Chavez/Eastman/Marshall Dissertation Fellowships**

TYPE:
Exchange programs; Fellowships.

YEAR PROGRAM STARTED: 1991

PURPOSE:
To increase the number of underrepresented minority faculty in American higher education by supporting African-American, Latina/o, Native American and other scholars with a demonstrated commitment to the advancement of educational diversity.

LEGAL BASIS:
University.

ELIGIBILITY:
Applicants will be chosen on the basis of academic achievement and promise, membership in a racial or ethnic group that is currently underrepresented among faculty in the applicant's academic field, demonstrated commitment to increasing opportunities for underrepresented minorities and increasing cross-racial understanding, and potential for serving as an advocate and mentor for minority undergraduate and graduate students.

GEOGRAPHIC RESTRICTIONS:
United States and Canada.

FINANCIAL DATA:
Fellowship provides stipend, office space, library privileges, research assistance and housing.
Amount of support per award: $26,000 stipend and $2,500 research assistance.
Total amount of support: $85,500 annually.

NUMBER OF AWARDS: 3.

APPLICATION INFORMATION:
Application form required. Contact the Office of Graduate Studies. Supporting documentation includes abstract of dissertation prospectus, statement of academic career plan, curriculum vitae, transcripts and three letters of reference.
Duration: One year.
Deadline: February 1. Announcement April 1.

PUBLICATIONS:
Program announcement.

ADDRESS INQUIRIES TO:
Jane Seibel, Assistant Dean
(See address above.)

*SPECIAL STIPULATIONS:
Fellows are expected to complete the dissertation during the tenure of the Fellowship and may have the opportunity to participate in teaching, either as a primary instructor or as part of a team.

DAUGHTERS OF ITALY LODGE #2825
14 South Jupiter Avenue
Clearwater, FL 33755
(727) 447-6890

E-MAIL ADDRESS:
vincenzad@verizon.net

WEB SITE ADDRESS:
www.daughtersofitaly.com

TYPE:
Scholarships. Open to full-time students at a Florida-accredited junior college, college or university or students graduating from high school.

See entry 1681 for full listing.

DAUGHTERS OF PENELOPE FOUNDATION, INC.   [988]
1909 Q Street, N.W., Suite 500
Washington, DC 20009
(202) 234-9741
Fax: (202) 483-6983

E-MAIL ADDRESS:
president@dopfoundationinc.com
dophq@ahepa.org

WEB SITE ADDRESS:
www.dopfoundationinc.com

FOUNDED: 1983

AREAS OF INTEREST:
Philanthropic, educational and cultural activities pertaining to Greek culture.

NAME(S) OF PROGRAMS:
● **Daughters of Penelope National Scholarship Awards**

TYPE:
Scholarships. Academic and Financial Need.

YEAR PROGRAM STARTED: 1984

PURPOSE:
To promote the social, ethical and intellectual interests of members; to perpetuate the study of American ideals and to encourage Hellenic study; to cultivate citizenship and patriotism.

ELIGIBILITY:
Applicant must be a woman and have a current member of their immediate family or legal guardian (court-appointed) in the Daughters of Penelope or the Order of Ahepa, in good standing for a minimum of two years, or be a member in good standing for two years in the Daughters of Penelope or the Maids of Athena.

FINANCIAL DATA:
Amount of support per award: $500 to $2,500 depending on scholarship.

NUMBER OF APPLICANTS MOST RECENT YEAR:
Varies.

NUMBER OF AWARDS: Varies.

APPLICATION INFORMATION:
Contact the Foundation for application procedures.
Duration: One year.
Deadline: May 1.

EDUCATIONAL TESTING SERVICE
660 Rosedale Road, MS 19-T
Princeton, NJ 08541
(609) 734-5543
Fax: (609) 734-5010

E-MAIL ADDRESS:
internfellowships@ets.org

WEB SITE ADDRESS:
www.ets.org/research/fellowships

TYPE:
Fellowships.

See entry 1539 for full listing.

EDUCATIONAL TESTING SERVICE
660 Rosedale Road, MS 19-T
Princeton, NJ 08541
(609) 734-5543
Fax: (609) 734-5010

E-MAIL ADDRESS:
internfellowships@ets.org

WEB SITE ADDRESS:
www.ets.org/research/fellowships.html

TYPE:
   Internships. Interns in this eight- or 12-week
   program participate in research under the
   guidance of a senior ETS staff member in
   one of the areas of interest listed above.
   Interns also participate in seminars and
   workshops on a variety of topics.

   See entry 1540 for full listing.

LOIS & RICHARD ENGLAND FAMILY FOUNDATION
P.O. Box 341077
Bethesda, MD 20827
(301) 657-7737
Fax: (301) 657-7738

E-MAIL ADDRESS:
   englandfamilyfdn@verizon.net

WEB SITE ADDRESS:
   fdncenter.org/grantmaker/england

TYPE:
   Capital grants; Challenge/matching grants;
   Development grants; General operating
   grants; Matching gifts; Project/program
   grants; Seed money grants; Technical
   assistance; Training grants.

   See entry 1123 for full listing.

EVANGELICAL LUTHERAN CHURCH IN AMERICA
Congregation and Synodical Mission Unit
8765 West Higgins Road
Chicago, IL 60631-4101
(773) 380-2874
Fax: (773) 380-2750

E-MAIL ADDRESS:
   melinda.valverde@elca.org

WEB SITE ADDRESS:
   www.elca.org

TYPE:
   Scholarships. Educational grants for members
   of the Evangelical Lutheran Church in
   America in advanced academic theological
   education degrees with intent to teach in
   seminary or university.

   See entry 811 for full listing.

FEDERAL HIGHWAY ADMINISTRATION
Technology Partnerships Program
1310 North Courthouse Road, Suite 300
Arlington, VA 22201
(703) 235-0536
Fax: (703) 235-0593

E-MAIL ADDRESS:
   fawn.thompson@dot.gov

WEB SITE ADDRESS:
   www.fhwa.dot.gov/ugp

TYPE:
   Fellowships; Internships; Research grants.
   Dwight David Eisenhower Transportation
   Fellowship Program's objectives are to attract
   the nation's brightest minds to the field of
   transportation, to enhance the careers of
   transportation professionals by encouraging
   them to seek advanced degrees, and to retain
   top talent in the transportation industry of the
   U.S. This Program encompasses all areas of
   transportation. The Program has seven award
   categories:
   (1) Eisenhower Graduate (GRAD)
   Fellowships enable students to pursue
   Master's degrees or Doctorates in

transportation-related fields at the university
of their choice;
(2) Eisenhower Grants for Research (GRF)
Fellowships acquaint undergraduate and
graduate students with transportation
research, development and
technology-transfer activities at the U.S.
Department of Transportation facilities;
(3) Eisenhower Historically Black Colleges
and Universities (HBCU) Fellowships
provide HBCU students with additional
opportunities to enter careers in
transportation. The Fellowships also serve as
a feeder for other Eisenhower fellowships;
(4) Eisenhower Hispanic Serving Institutions
(HSI) Fellowships provide HSI students with
additional opportunities to enter careers in
transportation. The Fellowships also serve as
a feeder for other Eisenhower fellowships;
(5) Eisenhower Tribal College Fellowships
(TC) identify transportation-related activities
and provide student fellowship opportunities
at tribal colleges. The Fellowships also serve
as a feeder for other Eisenhower fellowships;
(6) Eisenhower Intern Fellowships (EIF);
(7) Eisenhower People with Disabilities
(PWD) Fellowships and;
(8) Eisenhower Community College
Fellowship.

See entry 2607 for full listing.

FEEA SCHOLARSHIP PROGRAM
3333 South Wadsworth Boulevard
Suite 300
Lakewood, CO 80227
(303) 933-7580
Fax: (303) 933-7587

E-MAIL ADDRESS:
   ngleason@feea.org

WEB SITE ADDRESS:
   www.feea.org

TYPE:
   Scholarships. Merit-based scholarship
   competition program open exclusively to
   federal employees, their spouses and their
   children.

   See entry 1685 for full listing.

FOUNDATION FOR SCIENCE AND DISABILITY   [989]
503 N.W. 89th Street
Gainesville, FL 32607
(352) 374-5774
Fax: (352) 374-5781

E-MAIL ADDRESS:
   rmankin1@ufl.edu

WEB SITE ADDRESS:
   stemd.org

FOUNDED: 1978

AREAS OF INTEREST:
   Science, mathematics, medicine, engineering
   and computer science.

TYPE:
   Grants-in-aid; Research grants.

YEAR PROGRAM STARTED: 1978

PURPOSE:
   To assist disabled students who are interested
   in obtaining a graduate degree in one of the
   above fields.

LEGAL BASIS:
   Affiliate of American Association for
   Advancement of Science.

ELIGIBILITY:
   Open to college seniors and graduate students
   who have some physical or sensory disability
   and who have been accepted to graduate or
   professional school. Selection is based on
   sincerity of purpose and scholarship and/or
   research ability.

FINANCIAL DATA:
   Funds may be used for an assistive device or
   instrument, or as financial support to work
   with a professor on an individual research
   project, or for some other special need.
   Amount of support per award: $1,000.

NUMBER OF APPLICANTS MOST RECENT YEAR:
   8.

NUMBER OF AWARDS: Varies, depending on
   funds available.

APPLICATION INFORMATION:
   Application forms may be obtained by
   writing or e-mailing Dr. Richard Mankin, as
   listed above, or can be downloaded from the
   Foundation web site.

   Applicants should submit a copy of college
   transcript, two letters of recommendation,
   250-word summary of educational goals
   including what the funds will be used for, if
   awarded, and a copy of a U.S. birth or
   naturalization certificate.
   Deadline: December 1.

ADDRESS INQUIRIES TO:
   Dr. Richard Mankin, Chairperson
   Science Student Grant Committee
   (See address above.)

THE FOUNDATION OF THE AMERICAN COLLEGE OF HEALTHCARE EXECUTIVES
One North Franklin Street
Suite 1700
Chicago, IL 60606-3529
(312) 424-9400
Fax: (312) 424-9405

E-MAIL ADDRESS:
   contact@ache.org

WEB SITE ADDRESS:
   www.ache.org/scholarships

TYPE:
   Scholarships. Offered annually, the Albert W.
   Dent and the Foster G. McGaw Graduate
   Student Scholarships are designated for
   students enrolled in their final year of
   classroom work in a health care management
   graduate program.

   Albert W. Dent Graduate Student Scholarship
   is only available to minority students.

   See entry 1431 for full listing.

4A'S   [990]
1065 Avenue of the Americas, 16th Floor
New York, NY 10018
(212) 682-2500
Fax: (212) 867-8329

E-MAIL ADDRESS:
   maip@aaaa.org

WEB SITE ADDRESS:
   maip.aaaa.org

FOUNDED: 1917

AREAS OF INTEREST:
   Advertising.

NAME(S) OF PROGRAMS:
   ● **Multicultural Advertising Intern
   Program**

TYPE:
Internships.

YEAR PROGRAM STARTED: 1973

PURPOSE:
To assist minority students in attaining skills and knowledge necessary for careers in advertising and to assist advertising agencies in recruiting minorities for the professional level.

LEGAL BASIS:
Nonprofit organization.

ELIGIBILITY:
Open to any Black, Asian, Hispanic, Native American, multiracial or multiethnic student. Students must be currently enrolled in an undergraduate or graduate program and have completed at least their junior year by the time of the internship. Applicants must have a grade point average minimum of 3.0 on a scale of 4.0 and must be citizens or permanent residents of the U.S.

Students have the opportunity to work in one of the basic career areas of advertising including account management, media, research and creative (art direction or copywriting), broadcast and print production, traffic, strategic and account planning.

GEOGRAPHIC RESTRICTIONS:
United States.

FINANCIAL DATA:
Students who do not live in the metropolitan area of their host agency are housed in 4A's-arranged housing. MAIP interns requesting travel/housing assistance will be responsible for paying $1,000 to the 4A's toward summer housing and transportation cost, payable in two installments during the internship period.
Amount of support per award: $10 per hour.
Total amount of support: Varies.

NUMBER OF APPLICANTS MOST RECENT YEAR:
325.

NUMBER OF AWARDS: 100 to 150.

APPLICATION INFORMATION:
Candidates must submit an application, resume, letters of recommendation, school transcripts and supporting materials (such as artwork). $25 application fee required. Semi-finalists are interviewed before final selections are made.
Duration: 10 weeks during the summer.
Deadline: End of November.

ADDRESS INQUIRIES TO:
Carl Desir
Manager of Diversity and Inclusions
(See address above.)

THE GAMBLE FOUNDATION
1660 Bush Street, Suite 300
San Francisco, CA 94109
(415) 561-6540 ext. 222
Fax: (415) 561-6477

WEB SITE ADDRESS:
www.pfs-llc.net/gamble/gamble.html

TYPE:
Project/program grants.

See entry 1547 for full listing.

GILL FOUNDATION   [991]
2215 Market Street
Denver, CO 80205
(303) 292-4455
Fax: (303) 292-2155

E-MAIL ADDRESS:
grantsmanager@gillfoundation.org

WEB SITE ADDRESS:
www.gillfoundation.org

FOUNDED: 1994

AREAS OF INTEREST:
Lesbian, gay, bisexual, and transgender (LGBT).

NAME(S) OF PROGRAMS:
● **Gill Foundation General Fund**

TYPE:
Challenge/matching grants; General operating grants; Project/program grants.

YEAR PROGRAM STARTED: 1994

PURPOSE:
To secure equal opportunity for all people, regardless of sexual orientation or gender expression.

ELIGIBILITY:
Grants are by invitation only. Unsolicited grant requests will not be accepted. 501(c)(3) organizations with a copy of an official nondiscrimination policy for your organization including sexual orientation and gender expression.

GEOGRAPHIC RESTRICTIONS:
United States.

FINANCIAL DATA:
Amount of support per award: Varies.
Total amount of support: $12,582,536 for the year 2011.

NUMBER OF APPLICANTS MOST RECENT YEAR:
220 for the year 2013.

NUMBER OF AWARDS: 220 for the year 2013.

APPLICATION INFORMATION:
Contact the Foundation.
Duration: One year.

PUBLICATIONS:
Annual report.

IRS IDENTIFICATION NUMBER: 84-1264186

ADDRESS INQUIRIES TO:
Grants Department
(See address above.)

GRADUATE EDUCATION OPPORTUNITY PROGRAM [992]
Michigan State University
The Graduate School, 479 West Circle Drive
116 Linton Hall
East Lansing, MI 48824-1044
(517) 353-3262
Fax: (517) 353-3355

E-MAIL ADDRESS:
gradschool@grd.msu.edu

WEB SITE ADDRESS:
www.grad.msu.edu

FOUNDED: 1855

AREAS OF INTEREST:
Higher education.

NAME(S) OF PROGRAMS:
● **Academic Achievement Graduate Assistantships**
● **Education Opportunity Program**
● **University Distinguished Fellowships**
● **University Enrichment Fellowships**

TYPE:
Assistantships; Fellowships.

YEAR PROGRAM STARTED: 1970

PURPOSE:
To increase participation by all U.S. students in graduate programs leading to advanced degrees in fields that do not yet reflect the inclusive diversity of the U.S. population; to enhance their retention and degree completion.

LEGAL BASIS:
University.

ELIGIBILITY:
Candidates are considered for the Academic Achievement Graduate Assistantship if nominated by the academic unit of the graduate program. Candidates for the Education Opportunity Fellowship may apply directly upon admission into a graduate program.

Candidate must be admitted to or enrolled in a graduate/professional degree-granting program at Michigan State University. Some programs require a student to demonstrate financial need. To be considered for financial support under the Graduate Education Opportunity Programs (GEOP), all recipients must be able to prove U.S. citizenship or permanent residency. Funding based on financial need.

University Distinguished Fellowship and University Enrichment Fellowship are merit-based recruitment fellowships. Students must be nominated by a department/college.

GEOGRAPHIC RESTRICTIONS:
United States.

FINANCIAL DATA:
Amount of support per award: Academic Achievement Graduate Assistantship (AAGA): Level I, half-time, $12,488 to $21,290, plus nine credits (Fall/Spring), including health care; Education Opportunity Program (EOP): $1,500 per semester plus $100 to $200 per dependent for each semester; University Distinguished Fellowships (UDF) and University Enrichment Fellowships (UEF): $25,000, plus six to 10 credits (Fall/Spring) or three to five credits (Summer), including health care.
Total amount of support: Education Opportunity Program: Approximately $270,000.

APPLICATION INFORMATION:
Contact the Graduate Education Opportunity Program.
Duration: Five to 11 semesters.
Deadline: Academic Achievement Graduate Assistantship and Education Opportunity Program: April 15; University Distinguished and Enrichment Fellowships: Varies.

ADDRESS INQUIRIES TO:
Karen Klomparens
Dean of the Graduate School
Associate Provost for Graduate Education
(See address above.)

*SPECIAL STIPULATIONS:
Students must be enrolled in a graduate/professional program at Michigan State University.

GSBA SCHOLARSHIP FUND   [993]
400 East Pine Street, Suite 322
Seattle, WA 98122
(206) 363-9188
Fax: (206) 568-3123

E-MAIL ADDRESS:
jessicaw@thegsba.org

WEB SITE ADDRESS:
www.thegsba.org

FOUNDED: 1991

AREAS OF INTEREST:
Leadership and service in the gay and lesbian community.

NAME(S) OF PROGRAMS:
- **GSBA Scholarships**

TYPE:
Awards/prizes; Scholarships. Scholarships are intended for college, creative study, vocational training and postsecondary education.

YEAR PROGRAM STARTED: 1991

PURPOSE:
To invest in tomorrow's LGBTQA leaders today.

LEGAL BASIS:
501(c)(3) nonprofit.

ELIGIBILITY:
Applicants must demonstrate academic ability, a commitment to diversity and potential leadership in the lesbian, gay, bisexual & transgender community, and must be a resident of Washington state.

Scholarships are available for:
(1) gay, lesbian, bisexual, transgender and allied students;
(2) LGBTQA students of color;
(3) students raised by lesbian or gay parents and;
(4) potential leaders in the sexual minority community.

GEOGRAPHIC RESTRICTIONS:
Washington state.

FINANCIAL DATA:
Amount of support per award: $4,000 to $13,000.
Total amount of support: $240,000 for the year 2014.

NUMBER OF APPLICANTS MOST RECENT YEAR:
300.

NUMBER OF AWARDS: 44 for the year 2013.

APPLICATION INFORMATION:
Applicants must submit the online application form, letters of recommendation, transcript and an essay.
Duration: One-time award; can reapply.
Deadline: January 15.

PUBLICATIONS:
Guide/Directory, business listing and resources; *Perspective*, monthly newsletter.

IRS IDENTIFICATION NUMBER: 94-3138514

STAFF:
Louise Chernin, President and Chief Executive Officer
Rachael Brister, Deputy Director
Rachel Chernin, Business Officer
Amy Burdick, Business Development Manager
Scott Walden, Events and Community Outreach Manager
Matt Landers, Public Policy and Communications Coordinator
Randy Bowren, Office and Events Coordinator
Jessica Wootten, Development Associate and Scholarship Manager
Holly Teige, Membership Services Coordinator

BOARD OF DIRECTORS:
Martha Davis, Chairperson
Kevin Gaspari, Vice President
Lillian McDonell, Treasurer
Elaine DuCharme, Secretary
Mark Rosen, Scholarship Chairperson
Roen Ako
Allan Aquila
Kim Bogucki
Carrie Carson
Stephanie Dallas
Ryan Digges
Lori Friedt
Calvin Goings
Jenny Harding
David Hernandez
Frank Huguenin
Jeff Kinney
Robin Larmer
Dena Levine
Rene Neidhart
Drew Ness
Jay Petterson
Kurt Sarchet
Mona Smith
Monique Szyszka-Ramos
Paul Villa

ADDRESS INQUIRIES TO:
Jessica Wootten
Development Associate
and Scholarship Manager
(See address above.)

THE DONALD D. HAMMILL FOUNDATION [994]

8700 Shoal Creek Boulevard
Austin, TX 78757-6897
Fax: (512) 451-1888

E-MAIL ADDRESS:
jvoress@hammillfoundation.org

WEB SITE ADDRESS:
www.hammillfoundation.org

FOUNDED: 1987

AREAS OF INTEREST:
Financially disadvantaged, disabled people, chronically ill and aged.

NAME(S) OF PROGRAMS:
- **Organizational Grants**

TYPE:
Project/program grants. Fund nonprofit organizations that provide direct services to meet basic needs of clients in the Austin community.

YEAR PROGRAM STARTED: 1987

PURPOSE:
To improve the quality of life for people who have disabilities or who are financially disadvantaged, including those who are indigent, chronically ill, and aged.

LEGAL BASIS:
Private foundation.

GEOGRAPHIC RESTRICTIONS:
Austin, Texas.

FINANCIAL DATA:
Amount of support per award: Up to $15,000.
Total amount of support: $580,000 for the year 2013.

NUMBER OF APPLICANTS MOST RECENT YEAR:
Approximately 75 for the year 2013.

NUMBER OF AWARDS: 48 for the year 2013.

REPRESENTATIVE AWARDS:
$15,000 to Capital Area Food Bank of Texas; $15,000 to Hospice Austin; $3,000 to Mobile Loaves and Fishes.

APPLICATION INFORMATION:
Guidelines available at the web site.
Deadline: March 15.

PUBLICATIONS:
Application guidelines.

IRS IDENTIFICATION NUMBER: 74-2499947

OFFICERS:
Judith K. Voress, Ph.D., President
Cindy Thigpen, Treasurer
Nils Pearson, Ph.D., Secretary

BOARD OF TRUSTEES:
Donald D. Hammill, Ed.D.
Phyllis L. Newcomer, Ed.D.
Jim Patton, Ed.D.
Nils Pearson, Ph.D.
Judith K. Voress, Ph.D.

ADDRESS INQUIRIES TO:
Judith K. Voress, Ph.D., President
(See address above.)

*PLEASE NOTE:
Programs are only funded locally in Austin, TX. The Foundation does not fund directly to individuals.

WILLIAM G. AND MYRTLE E. HESS CHARITABLE TRUST [995]

c/o JPMorgan Chase Bank, NA
1116 West Long Lake Road
Bloomfield Hills, MI 48302
Fax: (248) 645-5742

E-MAIL ADDRESS:
nayda.schwartz@jpmorgan.com

WEB SITE ADDRESS:
www.jpmorgan.com/onlinegrants

FOUNDED: 1985

AREAS OF INTEREST:
Catholic charitable organizations located in Oakland County, MI; Catholic charitable, educational and scientific objectives.

TYPE:
Capital grants; Development grants; Endowments; General operating grants; Project/program grants.

YEAR PROGRAM STARTED: 1985

PURPOSE:
To provide funds in perpetuity for charitable purposes.

LEGAL BASIS:
Private foundation.

ELIGIBILITY:
Limited to Catholic organizations with charitable, educational and scientific objectives. Particular preference being given to such objectives within the confines of Waterford and White Lake Townships.

GEOGRAPHIC RESTRICTIONS:
Oakland County, Michigan.

FINANCIAL DATA:
Amount of support per award: $2,500 to $25,000.

NUMBER OF APPLICANTS MOST RECENT YEAR:
28.

NUMBER OF AWARDS: 26.

APPLICATION INFORMATION:
Only online applications are accepted.
Duration: One year. Renewals possible.
Deadline: April 30.

ADDRESS INQUIRIES TO:
   Nayda Schwartz
   (See address above.)

IMMUNE DEFICIENCY
FOUNDATION   [996]
40 West Chesapeake Avenue
Suite 308
Towson, MD 21204
(800) 296-4433
Fax: (410) 321-9165

E-MAIL ADDRESS:
   dgill@primaryimmune.org

WEB SITE ADDRESS:
   www.primaryimmune.org

FOUNDED: 1980

AREAS OF INTEREST:
   Immunodeficiency diseases.

TYPE:
   Scholarships.

YEAR PROGRAM STARTED: 1986

ELIGIBILITY:
   Open to those with diagnosis of primary
   immunodeficiency that are attending
   undergraduate college. Must be resident of
   the U.S.

GEOGRAPHIC RESTRICTIONS:
   United States.

FINANCIAL DATA:
   Amount of support per award: $500 to
   $1,000.

NUMBER OF AWARDS: 60.

APPLICATION INFORMATION:
   Contact the Foundation for application
   procedures.
   Duration: Renewable yearly based on
   financial need and academic participation.
   Deadline: March 31.

ADDRESS INQUIRIES TO:
   Diana Gill
   Director of Program Services
   (See address above.)

INSTITUTE OF INDUSTRIAL
ENGINEERS (IIE)
3577 Parkway Lane, Suite 200
Norcross, GA 30092
(770) 449-0461
Fax: (770) 441-3295

E-MAIL ADDRESS:
   bcameron@iienet.org

WEB SITE ADDRESS:
   www.iienet.org

TYPE:
   Fellowships; Scholarships. The Institute
   supports the advancement of engineering
   education and research through scholarships
   and fellowships to recognize and support
   these types of endeavors.

See entry 2653 for full listing.

THE JAPANESE AMERICAN
CITIZENS LEAGUE (JACL)
New York JACL
75 Grove Street, Apartment No. 2
Bloomfield, NJ 07003
(973) 680-1441

E-MAIL ADDRESS:
   lckimura@att.net

WEB SITE ADDRESS:
   www.jacl.org

TYPE:
   Awards/prizes. Biennial playwright award.

See entry 533 for full listing.

JEWISH COMMUNITY
FOUNDATION OF LOS
ANGELES
6505 Wilshire Boulevard
Suite 1200
Los Angeles, CA 90048
(323) 761-8700
Fax: (323) 761-8666

E-MAIL ADDRESS:
   thecenter@jewishfoundationla.org

WEB SITE ADDRESS:
   www.jewishfoundationla.org

TYPE:
   Awards/prizes; Capital grants;
   Project/program grants; Seed money grants.

See entry 1308 for full listing.

MARCUS AND THERESA LEVIE
EDUCATION FUND
Jewish Vocational Service
216 West Jackson Boulevard, Suite 700
Chicago, IL 60606-6921
(312) 673-3444
Fax: (312) 553-5544
TTY: (312) 444-2877

E-MAIL ADDRESS:
   jvsscholarship@jvschicago.org

WEB SITE ADDRESS:
   www.jvschicago.org

TYPE:
   Awards/prizes; Scholarships. Awards to
   individuals for the academic year.

See entry 1711 for full listing.

THE LUCIUS N. LITTAUER
FOUNDATION, INC.   [997]
220 Fifth Avenue, 19th Floor
New York, NY 10001-7708
(212) 697-2677

E-MAIL ADDRESS:
   info@littauerfoundation.org

WEB SITE ADDRESS:
   www.littauerfoundation.org

FOUNDED: 1929

AREAS OF INTEREST:
   Education, social welfare, health care, the
   environment, arts and culture, with a
   geographic focus on New York and Israel.

TYPE:
   Endowments; General operating grants;
   Project/program grants; Research grants;
   Seed money grants; Training grants; Loan
   forgiveness programs.

YEAR PROGRAM STARTED: 1929

PURPOSE:
   To support research, education, health care
   and social welfare in the Jewish world and
   beyond.

LEGAL BASIS:
   Independent foundation.

ELIGIBILITY:
   Funds are awarded to nonprofit institutions.
   No grants to individuals.

FINANCIAL DATA:
   Total amount of support: $2,700,000 for the
   year 2013.

NUMBER OF AWARDS: 175.

APPLICATION INFORMATION:
   All grant requests must be made online
   through the Foundation web site. Application
   includes a full description of project, budget
   request, curriculum vitae, timetable for
   completion, institution which will administer
   grant without deductions and contact person.
   Duration: Varies. Renewal possible.
   Deadline: Applications are accepted on a
   rolling basis.

PUBLICATIONS:
   Guidelines.

IRS IDENTIFICATION NUMBER: 13-1688027

TRUSTEES AND OFFICERS:
   Robert D. Frost, President
   Geula R. Solomon, Treasurer
   Noah Perlman, Secretary
   Charles Berlin
   Berthald Bilski
   Mark A. Bilski
   George Harris
   Sarah Levy
   Henry A. Lowet
   Peter J. Soloman

LUSO-AMERICAN EDUCATION
FOUNDATION
7080 Dolon Way
Suite 200
Dublin, CA 94568
(925) 828-3883
Fax: (925) 828-4554

E-MAIL ADDRESS:
   education@luso-american.org

WEB SITE ADDRESS:
   www.luso-american.org

TYPE:
   Scholarships.

See entry 655 for full listing.

MARINE BIOLOGICAL
LABORATORY
Office of Research and Programs
7 MBL Street
Woods Hole, MA 02543
(508) 289-7173
Fax: (508) 289-7934

E-MAIL ADDRESS:
   researchprograms@mbl.edu

WEB SITE ADDRESS:
   www.mbl.edu

TYPE:
   Research grants.

See entry 2151 for full listing.

THURGOOD MARSHALL
COLLEGE FUND
901 F Street, N.W., Suite 300
Washington, DC 20004
(202) 507-4851
Fax: (202) 448-1017

E-MAIL ADDRESS:
   scholarships@tmcfund.org

WEB SITE ADDRESS:
   www.thurgoodmarshallcollegefund.org

TYPE:
Scholarships. Program for underrepresented minority students who intend to enter the intellectual property law field, to attend law school.

See entry 1983 for full listing.

MAURICE J. MASSERINI CHARITABLE TRUST [998]
c/o Wells Fargo Private Bank
4475 Executive Drive, Suite 100
San Diego, CA 92121
(888) 234-1999
Fax: (877) 746-5889

E-MAIL ADDRESS:
grantadministration@wellsfargo.com

WEB SITE ADDRESS:
www.wellsfargo.
com/privatefoundationgrants/masserini

AREAS OF INTEREST:
Underprivileged children, the elderly, religious, human services, health, environment/animals, education, and arts and culture.

TYPE:
Project/program grants.

ELIGIBILITY:
Eligible organizations must be IRS 501(c)(3) tax-exempt and be located in San Diego County, CA. Start-up organizations or salaries are generally not supported.

GEOGRAPHIC RESTRICTIONS:
San Diego County, California.

FINANCIAL DATA:
Amount of support per award: Generally $5,000 to $20,000.
Total amount of support: Varies.

NUMBER OF APPLICANTS MOST RECENT YEAR:
200.

NUMBER OF AWARDS: More than 60 per year.

APPLICATION INFORMATION:
Applications are submitted through an online application process.
Duration: One year. Renewable by reapplication.
Deadline: April 30, August 31 and December 31.

ADDRESS INQUIRIES TO:
Wells Fargo Philanthropic Services
(See e-mail address above.)

MEDICAL LIBRARY ASSOCIATION [999]
65 East Wacker Place
Suite 1900
Chicago, IL 60601-7298
(312) 419-9094
Fax: (312) 419-8950

E-MAIL ADDRESS:
mlapd2@mlahq.org

WEB SITE ADDRESS:
www.mlanet.org/awards/grants/index.html

FOUNDED: 1898

AREAS OF INTEREST:
Health sciences librarianship.

NAME(S) OF PROGRAMS:
● **MLA Scholarship for Minority Students**

TYPE:
Awards/prizes; Scholarships. Awarded for study in health sciences librarianship.

YEAR PROGRAM STARTED: 1964

PURPOSE:
To contribute to the support of minority individuals who are qualified to make a contribution to health sciences librarianship.

LEGAL BASIS:
Nonprofit.

ELIGIBILITY:
Applicant must be:
(1) a member of a minority group. A minority group is defined as African-American, Asian, Hispanic, Native American or Pacific Islander;
(2) entering an ALA-accredited graduate library school or must have completed no more than half of his or her graduate program at the time the award is made and;
(3) a citizen of or have permanent residence status in the U.S. or Canada.

A past recipient of the MLA Scholarship for Minority Students is ineligible.

FINANCIAL DATA:
Amount of support per award: Up to $5,000.

NUMBER OF AWARDS: 1 per year.

APPLICATION INFORMATION:
Applicant must submit the following:
(1) a copy of the completed application;
(2) two to three letters of reference from persons not related to the applicant who are knowledgeable about the applicant's character, education and abilities;
(3) official transcript from each college or university attended, sent directly from the respective institution that grants either Baccalaureate degree or library study degree and;
(4) statement of career objectives.
Duration: One year.
Deadline: December 1.

EXECUTIVE DIRECTOR:
Carla J. Funk

ADDRESS INQUIRIES TO:
Grants and Scholarships Coordinator
(See address above.)

MITSUBISHI ELECTRIC AMERICA FOUNDATION
1560 Wilson Boulevard
Suite 1150
Arlington, VA 22209
(703) 276-8240

E-MAIL ADDRESS:
mea.foundation@meus.mea.com

WEB SITE ADDRESS:
www.meaf.org

TYPE:
Demonstration grants; General operating grants; Internships; Matching gifts; Project/program grants; Seed money grants; Technical assistance; Training grants. Grants are offered to make a better world for all by helping young people with disabilities to maximize their potential and participation in society.

See entry 1606 for full listing.

NATIONAL ACTION COUNCIL FOR MINORITIES IN ENGINEERING, INC. (NACME) [1000]
440 Hamilton Avenue
Suite 302
White Plains, NY 10601-1813
(914) 539-4010 ext. 222
Fax: (914) 539-4032

E-MAIL ADDRESS:
scholars@nacme.org

WEB SITE ADDRESS:
www.nacme.org

FOUNDED: 1974

CONSULTING OR VOLUNTEER SERVICES:
NACME communicates and cooperates with the precollege, college and industry communities that are involved in the minority engineering effort.

NAME(S) OF PROGRAMS:
● **NACME Pre-Engineering Student Scholarship**

TYPE:
Block grants; Endowments; Fellowships; Scholarships. NACME encourages students to consider engineering as a career and to pursue the requisite preparation in mathematics and science. It motivates high school students and channels them to engineering schools and provides scholarship support and leadership development seminars to its university scholars. The retention of minority students in engineering is a priority issue for NACME.

YEAR PROGRAM STARTED: 1975

PURPOSE:
To enhance awareness of the engineering profession among students, parents, teachers, and guidance counselors; to recognize high school graduating seniors who have achieved exemplary academic performance and have decided to pursue an engineering education.

LEGAL BASIS:
Nonprofit organization incorporated in New York.

ELIGIBILITY:
Selected graduating underrepresented minority high school seniors must satisfy the following criteria:
(1) be an African-American, Latino, or American-Indian;
(2) be in the top 10 percent of the graduating class;
(3) have demonstrated leadership qualities both in and outside high school and;
(4) have been accepted as a full-time student to an ABET-accredited engineering program.

GEOGRAPHIC RESTRICTIONS:
United States.

FINANCIAL DATA:
Each NACME Pre-Engineering Student Scholarship winner receives a certificate of recognition and a $1,500 scholarship award to be used toward the cost of attending an engineering school.
Amount of support per award: $1,500.

NUMBER OF AWARDS: Approximately 1,000 annually.

APPLICATION INFORMATION:
Each high school may submit one nomination per school year. Guidelines and nomination form are available on the Council's web site.
Duration: Students selected by participating schools for NACME awards will be funded until graduation or a maximum of five years.

Deadline: April 1.

ADDRESS INQUIRIES TO:
Melonia Simpson, Program Manager
(See address above.)

NATIONAL ASSOCIATION OF HISPANIC JOURNALISTS   [1001]

1050 Connecticut Avenue, N.W.
10th Floor
Washington, DC 20036
(202) 662-7145
Fax: (202) 662-7144

E-MAIL ADDRESS:
alopez@nahj.org

WEB SITE ADDRESS:
www.nahj.org

FOUNDED: 1984

AREAS OF INTEREST:
English or Spanish language print, photo, broadcast or online journalism.

NAME(S) OF PROGRAMS:
- **Ford Motor Scholarship**
- **Gannett Foundation Scholarship**
- **NAHJ General Scholarships (Ruben Salazar Fund)**
- **NBC Fellowship**
- **News Corporation Scholarship**
- **Soledad O'Brien Scholarship**
- **PepsiCo Scholarships/Internship**
- **Geraldo Rivera Scholarship**
- **Maria Elena Salinas Scholarship**

TYPE:
Awards/prizes; Conferences/seminars; Fellowships; General operating grants; Internships; Matching gifts; Project/program grants; Research grants; Scholarships; Seed money grants; Training grants; Travel grants.

YEAR PROGRAM STARTED: 1986

PURPOSE:
To encourage the study and practice of journalism and mass communications by Hispanics.

ELIGIBILITY:
Open to high school seniors, college undergraduates and first-year graduate students pursuing careers in print, photo, broadcast or online journalism.

Gannett Foundation Scholarship applicant must be Florida International University student.

GEOGRAPHIC RESTRICTIONS:
United States and Puerto Rico.

FINANCIAL DATA:
Amount of support per award: Ford Motor Scholarship: Up to $2,000; Gannett Foundation Scholarship, Soledad O'Brien Scholarship and Geraldo Rivera Scholarship: $5,000; NAHJ General Scholarships: $1,000 to $2,000; Maria Elena Salinas Scholarship: $2,000.

NUMBER OF APPLICANTS MOST RECENT YEAR:
Approximately 230.

NUMBER OF AWARDS: 50 scholarships.

APPLICATION INFORMATION:
Scholarship applications are available online in January of each year.
Duration: One year.
Deadline: March.

IRS IDENTIFICATION NUMBER: 95-3927141

ADDRESS INQUIRIES TO:
Scholarships Department
(See address above.)

NATIONAL FEDERATION OF THE BLIND   [1002]

NFB Scholarship Program
200 East Wells Street at Jernigan Place
Baltimore, MD 21230
(410) 659-9314 ext. 2415

E-MAIL ADDRESS:
scholarships@nfb.org

WEB SITE ADDRESS:
www.nfb.org/scholarships

FOUNDED: 1940

AREAS OF INTEREST:
Improving the quality of life for blind persons by creating opportunity and combating discrimination.

CONSULTING OR VOLUNTEER SERVICES:
Major programs in scholarships, promoting employment for the blind, civil rights litigation, helping parents of blind children, public education, etc.

NAME(S) OF PROGRAMS:
- **National Federation of the Blind Scholarship Program**

TYPE:
Scholarships. Awarded on the basis of academic excellence and service to the community. Provides a one-time grant plus a continuing program of mentors and seminars for blind college students.

PURPOSE:
To create opportunities for blind persons residing in and attending college or university in the U.S. or Puerto Rico.

LEGAL BASIS:
Nonprofit, tax-deductible, nationwide membership organization of the blind.

ELIGIBILITY:
Applicants residing in the U.S. or Puerto Rico must be legally blind and pursuing or planning to pursue a full-time postsecondary course of study in the upcoming fall semester in the U.S or Puerto Rico. One scholarship, however, may be given to a person working full-time while attending school part-time. In addition, some scholarships have been further restricted by the donor. Recipients of Federation scholarships need not be members of the National Federation of the Blind. International students are not eligible unless they reside in the U.S. or Puerto Rico.

GEOGRAPHIC RESTRICTIONS:
United States and Puerto Rico.

FINANCIAL DATA:
Scholarship includes financial assistance to attend the NFB Annual Convention and other gifts.
Amount of support per award: $3,000 to $12,000; other gifts vary in value.

NUMBER OF APPLICANTS MOST RECENT YEAR:
470.

NUMBER OF AWARDS: 30 (1 $12,000 scholarship, 1 $10,000 scholarship, 2 $7,000 scholarships, 4 $5,000 scholarships and 22 $3,000 scholarships).

APPLICATION INFORMATION:
Application information is available on the web site. Those interested in applying should read the rules of eligibility, the timeline, the Submission Checklist and the Scholarship FAQ, then fill in the online Scholarship Application Form. Supply the required documents and complete one telephone interview with the NFB representative.

Duration: One year. Renewals possible upon reapplication.
Deadline: Scholarship applications are accepted from November 1 of the previous year to March 31 of the year in which the scholarship is to be awarded. All documentation and the interview request must be received by the deadline. Notification in early May.

ADDRESS INQUIRIES TO:
Scholarship Committee
(See address above.)

*SPECIAL STIPULATIONS:
Applicants must be legally blind in both eyes. Winners are assisted to attend the NFB Annual Convention in July. Attendance is required and a part of the prize awarded to each winner.

THE NATIONAL GEM CONSORTIUM   [1003]

1430 Duke Street
Alexandria, VA 22314
(703) 562-3646
Fax: (202) 207-2518

E-MAIL ADDRESS:
info@gemfellowship.org

WEB SITE ADDRESS:
www.gemfellowship.org

FOUNDED: 1976

AREAS OF INTEREST:
Engineering at the Master's and Doctorate levels and science at the Doctorate level.

CONSULTING OR VOLUNTEER SERVICES:
Mentor/protege training, graduate study preparedness training, success training, programs and publications designed to promote graduate education in engineering and science.

NAME(S) OF PROGRAMS:
- **The GEM M.S. Engineering Fellowship**
- **The GEM Ph.D. Engineering Fellowship**
- **The GEM Ph.D. Science Fellowship**
- **Grad Lab**
- **Graduate and Faculty Development Program**

TYPE:
Internships; Matching gifts; Project/program grants; Scholarships. All-expense fellowship for graduate study (tuition and stipend) and paid summer work experience in a scientific or engineering environment.

YEAR PROGRAM STARTED: 1976

PURPOSE:
To increase the number of minorities with graduate degrees in engineering and science.

LEGAL BASIS:
Incorporated in the State of Indiana; 501(c)(3) tax-exempt.

ELIGIBILITY:
Must be a U.S. citizen or permanent resident and an American Indian, Black American, Mexican American or Hispanic American.

FINANCIAL DATA:
Amount of support per award: M.S. Fellowship: Tuition and fees, plus a $16,000 stipend over entire M.S. program. Master's-level students also are assigned to a paid internship. Ph.D. Fellowships: $16,000

stipend applied in one academic year. Additional stipend support from GEM University.

Total amount of support: Varies.

NUMBER OF APPLICANTS MOST RECENT YEAR: 1,000.

NUMBER OF AWARDS: 100 for the year 2013.

APPLICATION INFORMATION:
Three recommendations, GRE scores, and unofficial transcript of all college work.

Duration: Average three semesters or four quarters for Master's; five years renewable for Doctorate.

Deadline: November 15. Announcement April 15.

PUBLICATIONS:
Annual report; application brochure.

OFFICERS:
Eric Evans, Ph.D., President

ADDRESS INQUIRIES TO:
Valerie Washington, Coordinator of Information
(See address above.)

NATIONAL INSTITUTE OF GENERAL MEDICAL SCIENCES

National Institutes of Health
45 Center Drive, MSC 6200
Bethesda, MD 20892-6200
(301) 496-7301
Fax: (301) 402-0224

E-MAIL ADDRESS:
info@nigms.nih.gov

WEB SITE ADDRESS:
www.nigms.nih.gov

TYPE:
Fellowships; Project/program grants; Research grants; Training grants; Research contracts. Grants to support research on the structure and function of cells and cell organelles. Research to gain knowledge that will lead to the prevention, therapy and control of genetic diseases, as well as research to increase knowledge of drug action in order to increase safety of administration and diminish toxicity. Grants also given for research in biophysics and the physiological sciences and in certain clinical areas, particularly anesthesiology and trauma and burns. All of the research programs also support research training.

In addition, the Institute has special research training programs designed to increase the diversity of the biomedical and behavioral research workforce.

See entry 2289 for full listing.

NATIONAL INSTITUTE OF GENERAL MEDICAL SCIENCES

Division of Training, Diversity
& Workforce Development
45 Center Drive, Room 2AS-37
MSC 6200
Bethesda, MD 20892-6200
(301) 594-3900
Fax: (301) 480-2753

E-MAIL ADDRESS:
zlotnikh@nigms.nih.gov

WEB SITE ADDRESS:
www.nigms.nih.gov

TYPE:
Development grants; Research grants; Technical assistance. Grants to assist eligible institutions to strengthen the institutions' biomedical research capabilities and provide opportunities to students to engage in biomedical or behavioral research and other activities in preparation for Ph.D. training in these areas.

See entry 2290 for full listing.

NATIONAL INSTITUTE ON MINORITY HEALTH AND HEALTH DISPARITIES [1004]

6707 Democracy Boulevard, Suite 800
MSC 5465
Bethesda, MD 20892-5465
(301) 402-1366
Fax: (301) 480-4049

WEB SITE ADDRESS:
www.nimhd.nih.gov

AREAS OF INTEREST:
Minority opportunities in biomedical and behavioral science.

NAME(S) OF PROGRAMS:
● **Minority Health and Health Disparities International Research Training Grant (MIRT)**

TYPE:
Research grants; Training grants. Awards to U.S. colleges and universities to encourage students to pursue careers and degrees in the biological sciences by broadening their undergraduate and graduate education through international experiences.

Award provides support for undergraduates to undertake research and course work for 10 to 12 weeks during the summer or one semester during the academic year.

YEAR PROGRAM STARTED: 1993

PURPOSE:
To provide research training opportunities for minority undergraduate students, minority graduate students and minority faculty members in biomedical and behavioral research; to support faculty members to conduct independent research abroad and to serve as mentors to students abroad.

ELIGIBILITY:
Minority participants must be from underrepresented minority groups including African Americans, Native Americans, Hispanic Americans, Alaskan Natives and Pacific Islanders.

Applicants must be undergraduate students pursuing life science curricula, students pursuing doctoral degrees in the biomedical or behavioral sciences and/or faculty members in the biomedical and behavioral sciences.

GEOGRAPHIC RESTRICTIONS:
United States and its territories.

FINANCIAL DATA:
Amount of support per award: Up to $250,000 in direct costs.

Total amount of support: Approximately $5,000,000.

NUMBER OF AWARDS: Up to 24.

APPLICATION INFORMATION:
Contact the Institute.

Duration: Up to five years.

Deadline: Varies.

PUBLICATIONS:
Program announcement; guidelines.

ADDRESS INQUIRIES TO:
Nathaniel Stinson, Ph.D., Acting Director
Division of Scientific Programs
(See address above.)

THE NATIONAL ITALIAN AMERICAN FOUNDATION

1860 19th Street, N.W.
Washington, DC 20009-5501
(202) 939-3116
Fax: (202) 483-2618

E-MAIL ADDRESS:
scholarships@niaf.org

WEB SITE ADDRESS:
www.niaf.org/scholarships

TYPE:
Scholarships. The National Italian American Foundation (NIAF) will award scholarships and grants to outstanding students for use during the following academic year. The awards will be made on the basis of academic merit and divided between two groups of students.

See entry 1720 for full listing.

NATIONAL MEDICAL FELLOWSHIPS, INC.

347 Fifth Avenue, Suite 510
New York, NY 10016
(212) 483-8880
Fax: (212) 483-8897

E-MAIL ADDRESS:
scholarships@nmfonline.org

WEB SITE ADDRESS:
www.nmfonline.org

TYPE:
Awards/prizes; Fellowships; Scholarships. Aetna Foundation/NMF Healthcare Leadership Program is a highly successful national program that awards 10 second- and third-year minority medical students who demonstrate leadership potential through commitment to service. Target cities are Los Angeles, Chicago and New York City.

GE/NMF International Medical Scholars Program supports for the next three years in Ghana and Kenya a mentored service-learning clinical experience for U.S. fourth-year medical students to improve patient care in district hospitals, including a new focus on building site capacity on public health/disease-prevention issues.

GE-NMF Primary Care Leadership Program (PCLP) is a transformational, multiyear, multimillion-dollar program that will provide community service scholarships for medical students, nursing and health professions students in eight key U.S. states during its first two program years.

Monash/Scott Medical Student Scholarship Program was, with funding and leadership from The Chicago Community Trust, conceived to help Chicago meet its need for culturally competent physician-leaders by 2040. Service scholarships are provided to second- and third-year students in Chicago medical schools, and residency scholarships to students who have completed medical school and matched as residents in the Chicago area.

See entry 2296 for full listing.

NATIONAL RESEARCH COUNCIL OF THE NATIONAL ACADEMIES [1005]

The Fellowship Office-KECK576
500 Fifth Street, N.W.
Washington, DC 20001
(202) 334-2872
Fax: (202) 334-3419

E-MAIL ADDRESS:
infofell@nas.edu

WEB SITE ADDRESS:
www.nationalacademies.org/ford

FOUNDED: 1979

AREAS OF INTEREST:
Behavioral and social sciences, humanities, engineering, mathematics, physical sciences, biological sciences, (postdoctoral) education and interdisciplinary programs comprised of two or more eligible disciplines.

NAME(S) OF PROGRAMS:
● **Ford Foundation Fellowship Program**

TYPE:
Fellowships. Awards for study in research-based doctoral programs leading to the Ph.D. or Sc.D. degrees, as well as postdoctoral studies.

YEAR PROGRAM STARTED: 1986

PURPOSE:
To increase the diversity of the nation's college and university faculties and to encourage students to achieve their full potential as scholars who will inspire others to follow an academic career in teaching and research.

LEGAL BASIS:
Private foundation.

ELIGIBILITY:
Applicants to these Ford Foundation Fellowships must be citizens, permanent residents or nationals of the U.S. at the time of application.

Predoctoral Fellowships are intended for students who plan to work toward the Ph.D. or Sc.D. degree in selected academic disciplines that lead to careers in teaching and research at the college or university level, and who are at or near the beginning of their graduate study or Sc.D. program. They may be college seniors, or individuals who have completed undergraduate study, or who have completed some graduate study, or who have already enrolled in a Ph.D. or Sc.D. program.

Dissertation Fellowships are intended for Ph.D. or Sc.D. degree candidates who have finished all required course work and examinations except for the writing and defense of the dissertation. Fellowship support is intended for the final year of dissertation writing.

Predoctoral and Dissertation Fellowships: Persons holding a doctoral degree earned at any time and in any field are not eligible to apply. Applicants must be Ph.D. or Sc.D. degree candidates studying one of the fields in the behavioral sciences, humanities, social sciences, life sciences, chemistry, earth sciences, physics and astronomy, engineering, mathematics, or computer science. They must aspire to a teaching and research career. Awards are not made for work leading to degrees in such areas as business administration and management, health sciences, public health, home economics, library science, speech pathology and audiology, personnel and guidance, social work, fine arts and performing arts and education.

Postdoctoral Fellowships: Intended for fellows to engage in a year of postdoctoral research and scholarship in an environment free from the interference of their normal professional duties. Applicants are required to have earned a Ph.D. or Sc.D. degree from a U.S. educational institution within a specified time period. Only those individuals already engaged in a teaching and research career or those planning such a career are eligible to apply in this program. Previous Foundation postdoctoral fellows may not reapply. Awards will be made in research-based areas of the behavioral and social sciences, humanities, engineering, mathematics, physical sciences, life sciences, education, or for interdisciplinary programs composed of two or more eligible disciplines.

FINANCIAL DATA:
Amount of support per award: Dissertation Fellowships: $25,000 for one year and expenses paid to attend one Conference of Ford Fellows; Predoctoral Fellowships: Annual $24,000 stipend, expenses paid to attend at least one Conference of Ford Fellows; Postdoctoral Fellowships: $45,000 stipend and expenses paid to attend one Conference of Ford Fellows.

COOPERATIVE FUNDING PROGRAMS: Program funded by the Ford Foundation.

NUMBER OF APPLICANTS MOST RECENT YEAR: 2,165.

NUMBER OF AWARDS: Approximately 60 Predoctoral Fellowships, 30 Dissertation Fellowships, and 18 Postdoctoral Fellowships.

APPLICATION INFORMATION:
Applications are to be submitted online.
Duration: Predoctoral Fellowships: Up to three years; Dissertation Fellowships: Nine to 12 months; Postdoctoral Fellowships: Nine or 12 months.
Deadline: Predoctoral Fellowships: November 19, 2014; Dissertation and Postdoctoral Fellowships: November 14, 2014.

PUBLICATIONS:
Program announcement.

NATIONAL SOCIETY OF HISPANIC MBAS (NSHMBA) [1006]

450 East John Carpenter Freeway
Suite 200
Irving, TX 75062
(214) 596-9338
(877) 467-4622
Fax: (214) 596-9325

E-MAIL ADDRESS:
scholarships@nshmba.org

WEB SITE ADDRESS:
www.nshmba.org

AREAS OF INTEREST:
Business administration.

NAME(S) OF PROGRAMS:
● **NSHMBA Scholarship Program**

TYPE:
Scholarships.

YEAR PROGRAM STARTED: 1989

PURPOSE:
To foster Hispanic leadership through graduate management education and professional development.

LEGAL BASIS:
501(c)(3) organization.

ELIGIBILITY:
Applicants must:
(1) be U.S. citizen or legal permanent resident;
(2) be of Hispanic heritage;
(3) have a minimum grade point average of 3.0 on a 4.0 scale from either a Bachelor's degree or Master's degree, or have a minimum grade point average of 2.75 on a 4.0 scale from a Bachelor's degree in combination with two years of full-time work experience;
(4) be a current NSHMBA member and;
(5) be enrolled in a graduate business program in a college or university in the U.S. or Puerto Rico, accredited by the AACSB at the time of award.

GEOGRAPHIC RESTRICTIONS:
United States and Puerto Rico.

FINANCIAL DATA:
Amount of support per award: Up to $10,000.

NUMBER OF APPLICANTS MOST RECENT YEAR: 346 for the year 2012.

NUMBER OF AWARDS: 102 for the year 2012.

APPLICATION INFORMATION:
Interested students must submit an online application, available March 1 to April 30, and mail all supporting documentation to Scholarship Management Services.
Application must include:
(1) all undergraduate and graduate official transcripts (grade reports are not acceptable). Online transcripts must display student name, school name, grade and credit hours earned for each course, and the term in which each course was taken and;
(2) two letters of recommendation from professors, advisors, or employers addressing current academic achievement, personal qualities, potential for future success and contributions to the community.
Duration: One academic year.
Deadline: April 30.

NATIONAL TAXIDERMISTS ASSOCIATION [1007]

108 Branch Road
Slidell, LA 70461
(985) 641-4682
(866) 662-9054
Fax: (985) 641-9463

E-MAIL ADDRESS:
ntahq@aol.com

WEB SITE ADDRESS:
nationaltaxidermists.com

AREAS OF INTEREST:
Taxidermy and education.

NAME(S) OF PROGRAMS:
● **Charlie Fleming Scholarship**

TYPE:
Scholarships.

PURPOSE:
To promote higher education and taxidermy education.

ELIGIBILITY:
Students must be a member, spouse or dependent of the NTA for three consecutive years.

FINANCIAL DATA:
Amount of support per award: Generally $500.
Total amount of support: Generally $1,000.

APPLICATION INFORMATION:
Contact the Organization for application procedures.
Duration: One year.
Deadline: April 30.

ADDRESS INQUIRIES TO:
Cindy Crain, Membership Management
(See address above.)

NEW JERSEY OFFICE OF THE SECRETARY OF HIGHER EDUCATION

P.O. Box 542
Trenton, NJ 08625-0542
(609) 984-2709
Fax: (609) 633-8420

E-MAIL ADDRESS:
audrey.bennerson@njhe.state.nj.us

WEB SITE ADDRESS:
www.state.nj.us/highereducation/EOF/EOF_Description.shtml

TYPE:
Grants-in-aid. The Higher Education Student Assistance Authority (HESAA) is a New Jersey authority that provides students and families with the financial and informational resources for students to pursue their education beyond high school. With roots dating back to 1959, HESAA's singular focus has always been to benefit the students it serves. HESAA provides state supplemental loans, grants and scholarships. HESAA also administers the state's college savings plan.

Educational Opportunity Fund Grants (EOF) provide financial aid to eligible students from educationally and economically disadvantaged backgrounds at participating in-state institutions.

See entry 1730 for full listing.

ORDER SONS OF ITALY IN AMERICA, GRAND LODGE OF FLORIDA

18281 Fresh Lake Way
Boca Raton, FL 33498
(561) 479-2096

E-MAIL ADDRESS:
nana3028@aol.com

WEB SITE ADDRESS:
osiafl.org

TYPE:
Awards/prizes; Grants-in-aid; Scholarships. Scholarships are provided to high school students entering college.

Financial aid is given in support of charitable programs, such as Alzheimer's disease, Cooley's anemia, autism, and cancer.

See entry 1742 for full listing.

PEN AMERICAN CENTER

588 Broadway, Suite 303
New York, NY 10012-5246
(212) 334-1660
Fax: (212) 334-2181

E-MAIL ADDRESS:
awards@pen.org

WEB SITE ADDRESS:
www.pen.org

TYPE:
Awards/prizes. Invites submissions of book-length writings by authors of color, published during the calendar year.

See entry 684 for full listing.

PRIDE FOUNDATION [1008]

2014 East Madison Street
Suite 300
Seattle, WA 98122
(206) 323-3318
Fax: (206) 323-1017

E-MAIL ADDRESS:
grants@pridefoundation.org

WEB SITE ADDRESS:
www.pridefoundation.org

FOUNDED: 1985

AREAS OF INTEREST:
Arts and recreation; education outreach and advocacy; HIV/AIDS; lesbian health; youth and family; and other health and community services.

TYPE:
Endowments; General operating grants; Project/program grants; Scholarships; Seed money grants.

YEAR PROGRAM STARTED: 1987

PURPOSE:
To strengthen the lesbian, gay, bisexual and transgender community today and build an endowment fund for tomorrow.

ELIGIBILITY:
Projects must support lesbian, gay, bisexual and transgender causes. Organizations applying for funds must have 501(c)(3) nonprofit tax status, or be affiliated with an organization that has 501(c)(3) status that will assume responsibility for administering all funds received and expended. Grants to individuals cannot be considered.

GEOGRAPHIC RESTRICTIONS:
Alaska, Idaho, Montana, Oregon and Washington.

FINANCIAL DATA:
Amount of support per award: Maximum $5,000; some rare special projects exceptions.

REPRESENTATIVE AWARDS:
$3,000 to Causa for LGBT Spanish language radio show; $4,200 to Youth Suicide Prevention Program for suicide and bias-based bullying prevention activities in Spokane, WA; $5,000 to Cedar River Clinics for training medical staff to create a safer, more culturally competent and compassionate environment for lesbians, bisexual women and transgendered people.

APPLICATION INFORMATION:
Contact the Foundation.
Duration: One year.
Deadline: Varies.

PUBLICATIONS:
Newsletter.

IRS IDENTIFICATION NUMBER: 91-1325007

ADDRESS INQUIRIES TO:
Gunner Scott, Director of Programs
(See address above.)

THE RETIREMENT RESEARCH FOUNDATION [1009]

8765 West Higgins Road
Suite 430
Chicago, IL 60631-4170
(773) 714-8080
Fax: (773) 714-8089

E-MAIL ADDRESS:
info@rrf.org

WEB SITE ADDRESS:
www.rrf.org

FOUNDED: 1950

AREAS OF INTEREST:
Aging.

NAME(S) OF PROGRAMS:
- **Accessible Faith**
- **Grants Program**
- **Organizational Capacity Building**

TYPE:
Challenge/matching grants; Demonstration grants; Project/program grants; Research grants; Technical assistance; Training grants. For the Grants Program, awards are generally limited to projects directly related to the Foundation's interests.

Funding of service/service development projects which do not have potential for national or regional impact are limited to the six midwestern states (Illinois, Indiana, Iowa, Kentucky, Missouri, Wisconsin) and Florida. The Foundation has strong interest in serving the Chicago metropolitan area.

Accessible Faith is designed to assist Chicago-area houses of worship make their facilities more accessible for elder adults and individuals with disabilities.

Organizational Capacity Building is designed to strengthen the effectiveness of Chicago-area nonprofit groups serving the elderly. Grants are available to help these organizations make long-term improvements in their management and governance, and by doing so, to sustain and enhance their services to the elderly.

YEAR PROGRAM STARTED: 1979

PURPOSE:
The Foundation is devoted exclusively to improving the quality of life for the nation's older population. Its funding is directed to efforts that:
(1) improve the availability and quality of community-based and long-term services and supports;
(2) provide new and expanded opportunities for older adults to engage in meaningful roles in society;
(3) seek causes and solutions to significant problems of older adults and;
(4) increase the number of professionals and paraprofessionals adequately prepared to serve the elder population.

LEGAL BASIS:
Private foundation.

ELIGIBILITY:
To be eligible for support, organizations, congregations and institutions must qualify under the regulations of the IRS.

To achieve its goals, the Foundation supports education and training, advocacy, direct service, replications of evidence-based programs, models and practices, and applied clinical, policy and social science research.

The Foundation is particularly interested in innovative projects that develop and/or demonstrate new approaches to the problems of older Americans and that have the potential for national or regional impact.

The Foundation normally does not provide support for construction of facilities, general operating expenses, computers, endowment or developmental campaigns, scholarships or loans, grants to individuals, projects outside the U.S., conferences, publications and travel unless components of a larger Foundation-funded project, dissertation research or the production of films and videos.

Requests for research, advocacy and training are considered from eligible organizations anywhere in the U.S.

GEOGRAPHIC RESTRICTIONS:
Florida, Illinois, Iowa, Kentucky, Michigan, Missouri and Wisconsin.

FINANCIAL DATA:
Assets of $121,919,399 for the year 2012.

Amount of support per award: $1,000 to $187,542; $46,800 average for the year 2013.

Total amount of support: $5,070,553 for the year 2013.

NUMBER OF APPLICANTS MOST RECENT YEAR:
248 for the year 2013.

NUMBER OF AWARDS: 97 for the year 2013.

REPRESENTATIVE AWARDS:
$75,000 to Brown University for research on the prevalence and impact of billing Medicare beneficiary stays as outpatient observation; $186,012 (over two years) to Easter Seals National Office for a training program to transform the culture of adult day services to deliver person-centered care; $40,000 to Swedish Covenant Hospital to expand a home telehealth monitoring program for congestive heart failure patients; $34,962 to Provena Mercy Medical Center for an Advance Practice Nurse to coordinate care and services to patients with dementia and their caregivers; $60,000 to the Center for Medicare Advocacy to train the National Medicare Alliance and to maintain an electronic searchable database of Medicare appeals decisions.

APPLICATION INFORMATION:
The Foundation does not have a standard grant application form. Visit the Foundation web site to find information about submitting a proposal.

Deadline: February 1, May 1 and August 1, with award announcement three to six months after submission date.

TRUSTEES AND OFFICERS:
Nathaniel P. McParland, M.D., Chairman of the Board
Irene Frye, Executive Director
Downey R. Varey, Treasurer
Ruth Ann Watkins, Secretary
Marilyn Hennessy
Marvin Meyerson
Thomas R. Prohaska, Ph.D.
Cheryl E. Woodson, M.D.

ADDRESS INQUIRIES TO:
Irene Frye, Executive Director
(See address above.)

RIGHTEOUS PERSONS FOUNDATION [1010]

400 South Beverly Drive, Suite 420
Beverly Hills, CA 90212
(310) 314-8393
Fax: (310) 314-8396

E-MAIL ADDRESS:
grants@righteouspersons.org

WEB SITE ADDRESS:
www.righteouspersons.org

FOUNDED: 1994

AREAS OF INTEREST:
Primarily Jewish organizations.

TYPE:
General operating grants; Matching gifts; Project/program grants; Seed money grants; Technical assistance.

PURPOSE:
To strengthen Jewish life in America.

LEGAL BASIS:
Nonprofit.

ELIGIBILITY:
Applicants must be tax-exempt organizations. Priority is given to national organizations and projects which create meaningful experiences for Jewish youth, promote Jewish learning, provide leadership training grounded in Jewish tradition, employ the arts and media to explore the relevance of modern Jewish identity, promote tolerance and understanding between Jews and non-Jews, and encourage Jews to participate in the work of social justice.

The Foundation does not make grants to individuals. Also, the Foundation does not support university faculty chairs, individual synagogues or day schools, research, the publication of books or magazines, or organizations or projects based outside of the U.S. In addition, the Foundation generally does not support endowments, capital campaigns, building funds, or social service projects.

GEOGRAPHIC RESTRICTIONS:
United States.

FINANCIAL DATA:
Amount of support per award: Varies.
Total amount of support: Varies.

APPLICATION INFORMATION:
Applicants should submit a two- to three-page letter of inquiry including:
(1) a description of the proposed project including the issues the project will address and the target population(s);
(2) a brief description of the organization's mission, activities and history;
(3) the total amount of the organization's operating budget;
(4) the total amount requested from the Foundation;
(5) the name, mailing address and telephone number of a contact person;
(6) a detailed project budget;
(7) a list of the organization's board of directors;
(8) documentation of the organization's 501(c)(3) status;
(9) the total amount requested from the Foundation and;
(10) a list of the organization/project's primary sources of support over the last two years including names of foundations and amounts provided each year.

If there is a fiscal sponsor for the project, include a current copy of the sponsor's tax-exempt letter from the IRS as well as a

letter of support from the sponsor acknowledging their responsibilities. Do not send full proposals or video or audio tapes unless otherwise requested. Faxed applications will not be considered.

Duration: Varies.

PUBLICATIONS:
Program announcement; guidelines.

STAFF:
Rachel Levin, Executive Director
Margery Tabankin, Senior Advisor

BOARD OF DIRECTORS:
Steven Spielberg, Chairman
Gerald Breslauer, President
Tammy Anderson

ADDRESS INQUIRIES TO:
Rebecca Lehrer, Program Officer
(See address above.)

JACKIE ROBINSON FOUNDATION [1011]

75 Varick Street, 2nd Floor
New York, NY 10013-1917
(212) 290-8600
Fax: (212) 290-8081

E-MAIL ADDRESS:
general@jackierobinson.org

WEB SITE ADDRESS:
www.jackierobinson.org

FOUNDED: 1973

AREAS OF INTEREST:
Providing college education for academically gifted students of color with financial need.

NAME(S) OF PROGRAMS:
● **Mentoring and Leadership Development Program**

TYPE:
Conferences/seminars; Internships; Scholarships.

PURPOSE:
To award four-year college scholarships to academically gifted students of color with financial need, enabling them to attend the college of their choice.

ELIGIBILITY:
Foundation Scholar applicants must meet all of the following criteria:
(1) have U.S. citizenship;
(2) be a minority student;
(3) be a high school senior enrolling in college in the coming fall;
(4) have an SAT score of 1,000 or above, an ACT of 21 or above;
(5) have leadership potential and;
(6) be in financial need.

FINANCIAL DATA:
Amount of support per award: Scholarships: Up to $7,500 per year; maximum $30,000.

NUMBER OF APPLICANTS MOST RECENT YEAR:
1,730.

APPLICATION INFORMATION:
Application information is available at the Foundation web site. Scholarship application is available for online review on October 15, and goes live on November 1.

Duration: Four years.

Deadline: The application is due February 15. Applicants are notified of status April 30; final selection of Scholars is announced on June 15.

SANTA FE COMMUNITY FOUNDATION [1012]

501 Halona Street
Santa Fe, NM 87505
(505) 988-9715
Fax: (505) 988-1829

E-MAIL ADDRESS:
foundation@santafecf.org

WEB SITE ADDRESS:
www.santafecf.org

FOUNDED: 1981

AREAS OF INTEREST:
Arts, animal welfare, education, economic opportunity, environment, health, human services, lesbian, gay, bisexual and transgender community and Native American.

CONSULTING OR VOLUNTEER SERVICES:
Online directories for consultants and for organizations needing volunteers.

NAME(S) OF PROGRAMS:
• **MoGro**
• **NM Health Equity Partnership**
• **Root2Fruit**

TYPE:
General operating grants; Project/program grants. Emergency funds.

YEAR PROGRAM STARTED: 1981

PURPOSE:
Charitable.

LEGAL BASIS:
Community foundation.

ELIGIBILITY:
The Foundation awards grants to nonprofit organizations only. The Foundation does not award grants for religious or political purposes, capital outlay, endowment or to individuals.

GEOGRAPHIC RESTRICTIONS:
Santa Fe and northern New Mexico.

FINANCIAL DATA:
Amount of support per award: $5,000 to $15,000.
Total amount of support: $5,000,000 (including donor-advised funds) for the year 2013.

COOPERATIVE FUNDING PROGRAMS: Hispanics in Philanthropy.

NUMBER OF APPLICANTS MOST RECENT YEAR:
Approximately 200 for the year 2013.

NUMBER OF AWARDS: 43 for the year 2013.

APPLICATION INFORMATION:
Applicants must submit proof of IRS 501(c)(3) status.
Duration: One year.
Deadline: Varies.

PUBLICATIONS:
Giving Together catalogues; *Guide to Giving* materials.

IRS IDENTIFICATION NUMBER: 85-0303044

OFFICER:
Brian Byrnes, President and Chief Executive Officer

ADDRESS INQUIRIES TO:
Christa Coggins
Vice President for Community Philanthropy
(See address above.)

ALFRED P. SLOAN FOUNDATION [1013]

630 Fifth Avenue, Suite 2550
New York, NY 10111
(212) 649-1649
Fax: (212) 757-5117

E-MAIL ADDRESS:
boylan@sloan.org

WEB SITE ADDRESS:
www.sloanphds.org

FOUNDED: 1934

AREAS OF INTEREST:
Multiple special purpose.

NAME(S) OF PROGRAMS:
• **Minority Ph.D. Program**

TYPE:
Fellowships; Scholarships. Offers substantial scholarship support to underrepresented minority (African American, Hispanic American or Native American) students who are U.S. citizens and who are beginning their doctoral work in engineering, natural science and mathematics in selected departments at selected U.S. universities.

YEAR PROGRAM STARTED: 1995

PURPOSE:
To increase the number of Ph.Ds. among underrepresented minorities.

ELIGIBILITY:
African Americans, Hispanic Americans and American Indians/Alaskan Natives. Candidates must first apply for and be accepted at one of the academic departments in their discipline supported by the Foundation. Those accepted qualify as a candidate for a Foundation scholarship.

GEOGRAPHIC RESTRICTIONS:
United States.

FINANCIAL DATA:
Amount of support per award: Varies.
Total amount of support: $3,500,000.
Matching fund requirements: Universities must provide balance of support needed by students.

NUMBER OF AWARDS: Varies.

ADDRESS INQUIRIES TO:
Program Director
Minority Ph.D. Program
(See address above.)

ALFRED P. SLOAN FOUNDATION [1014]

630 Fifth Avenue, Suite 2550
New York, NY 10111
(212) 649-1649
Fax: (212) 757-5117

E-MAIL ADDRESS:
boylan@sloan.org

WEB SITE ADDRESS:
www.sloanphds.org

FOUNDED: 1934

AREAS OF INTEREST:
Multiple special purpose.

NAME(S) OF PROGRAMS:
• **Sloan Indigenous Graduate Partnership**

TYPE:
Fellowships; Scholarships. Offers substantial scholarship support to indigenous students (Native Americans, including American Indians, Native Alaskans and Native Hawaiians) who are beginning their Master's or doctoral work in engineering, natural science and mathematics in selected departments at selected U.S. universities.

YEAR PROGRAM STARTED: 2003

PURPOSE:
To increase the number of Master's and Ph.D. degrees among indigenous people.

ELIGIBILITY:
American Indians/Alaskan Natives/Hawaiian Natives. Candidates must first apply for and be accepted at one of the academic departments in their discipline at a university in the program. Those accepted qualify as a candidate for a Foundation scholarship.

GEOGRAPHIC RESTRICTIONS:
United States.

FINANCIAL DATA:
Amount of support per award: Varies.
Matching fund requirements: Universities must provide balance of support needed by students.

ADDRESS INQUIRIES TO:
Program Director
Sloan Indigenous Graduate Partnership
(See address above.)

SONS OF ITALY FOUNDATION [1015]

219 E Street, N.E.
Washington, DC 20002
(202) 547-2900
Fax: (202) 546-8168

E-MAIL ADDRESS:
scholarships@osia.org

WEB SITE ADDRESS:
www.osia.org

FOUNDED: 1959

AREAS OF INTEREST:
Cultural preservation and advancement for Italian Americans; education.

NAME(S) OF PROGRAMS:
• **National Leadership Grant Competition**

TYPE:
Awards/prizes; Scholarships. The Foundation provides Italian language scholarships, study-abroad scholarships and merit-based higher education scholarships.

YEAR PROGRAM STARTED: 1959

PURPOSE:
To help educate Italian Americans and improve their lives.

LEGAL BASIS:
Public, tax-exempt organization as defined by Section 501(c)(3) and Section 509(a)(1) of the Internal Revenue Code.

ELIGIBILITY:
Open to high school seniors, undergraduate and graduate students. Applicants must be U.S. citizens of Italian heritage.

FINANCIAL DATA:
Amount of support per award: Scholarships: $4,000 to $20,000.
Total amount of support: Varies.

NUMBER OF APPLICANTS MOST RECENT YEAR:
1,000.

NUMBER OF AWARDS: 10 to 12.

APPLICATION INFORMATION:
Contact the Foundation.
Duration: One year.
Deadline: February 28.

PUBLICATIONS:
Annual report; *Grant Priorities, Guidelines and Procedures*, booklet.

STAFF:
Philip R. Piccigallo, Ph.D., National Executive Director

OFFICERS OF THE TRUSTEES:
Vincent Sarno, President
Joseph DiTrapani, Chairman

ADDRESS INQUIRIES TO:
Laura Kelly, Scholarship Coordinator
(See address above.)

THE SOSLAND FOUNDATION   [1016]
4800 Main Street, Suite 100
Kansas City, MO 64112
(816) 756-1000
Fax: (816) 756-0494

E-MAIL ADDRESS:
debbie@sosland.com

WEB SITE ADDRESS:
www.soslandfoundation.org

FOUNDED: 1954

AREAS OF INTEREST:
Jewish organizations, cultural arts, social welfare, education, health and civic concerns.

TYPE:
Capital grants; Development grants; Endowments; General operating grants; Project/program grants.

YEAR PROGRAM STARTED: 1954

PURPOSE:
To carry on a family tradition of helping the community to help themselves; to make sure the community continues to grow and meet the needs of its residents.

LEGAL BASIS:
Family foundation.

ELIGIBILITY:
Grants to 501(c)(3) organizations only. No grants to individuals.

GEOGRAPHIC RESTRICTIONS:
Metropolitan Kansas City area.

FINANCIAL DATA:
Amount of support per award: Varies.
Total amount of support: Varies.
Matching fund requirements: Family members only.

APPLICATION INFORMATION:
Guidelines are available at the Foundation's web site.
Duration: One year. Renewal possible.

PUBLICATIONS:
Application guidelines.

IRS IDENTIFICATION NUMBER: 44-6007129

STAFF:
Debbie Sosland-Edelman, Executive Director

BOARD OF DIRECTORS:
Neil N. Sosland, President
Blanche E. Sosland
Charles S. Sosland
L. Joshua Sosland
Morton I. Sosland

ADDRESS INQUIRIES TO:
Debbie Sosland-Edelman
Executive Director
(See above address.)

*PLEASE NOTE:
The Foundation does not accept unsolicited requests for funding.

THE SPECIAL HOPE FOUNDATION   [1017]
2225 East Bayshore Road, Suite 200
Palo Alto, CA 94303
(650) 644-5376
Fax: (650) 320-1716

E-MAIL ADDRESS:
info@specialhope.org

WEB SITE ADDRESS:
www.specialhope.org

FOUNDED: 2002

AREAS OF INTEREST:
Health care access and health care research benefiting adults with developmental disabilities.

TYPE:
Challenge/matching grants; Conferences/seminars; General operating grants; Project/program grants; Research grants; Technical assistance.

YEAR PROGRAM STARTED: 2002

PURPOSE:
To provide financial support to organizations that promote the establishment of comprehensive health care for adults with developmental disabilities.

ELIGIBILITY:
Organizations must be nonprofit 501(c)(3). Only grant proposals consistent with the Foundation's mission statement will be eligible for funding. No grants are made to individuals.

GEOGRAPHIC RESTRICTIONS:
United States.

FINANCIAL DATA:
Amount of support per award: $20,000 to $50,000.
Matching fund requirements: By invitation only.

NUMBER OF APPLICANTS MOST RECENT YEAR: 50.

NUMBER OF AWARDS: 10.

APPLICATION INFORMATION:
Pre-application questionnaire must be completed online.
Duration: One to three years.

ADDRESS INQUIRIES TO:
Shannon Cully, Director of Programs
(See address above.)

U.S. DEPARTMENT OF EDUCATION
Office of English Language Acquisition, Language Enhancement and Academic Achievement
LBJ Education Building, Room 5C-140, MS-6510
400 Maryland Avenue, S.W.
Washington, DC 20202
(202) 401-1436
Fax: (202) 260-5496

E-MAIL ADDRESS:
libia.gill@ed.gov

WEB SITE ADDRESS:
www.ed.gov/offices/oela

TYPE:
Formula grants. National Professional Development Program provides professional development activities intended to improve instruction for students with limited English proficiency (LEP) and assists education personnel working with such children to meet high professional standards.

Native American and Alaska Native Children in School Program provides grants to eligible entities that support language instruction education projects for limited English proficient (LEP) children from Native American, Alaska Native, native Hawaiian, and Pacific Islander backgrounds. The program is designed to ensure that LEP children master English and meet the same rigorous standards for academic achievement that all children are expected to meet. Funds may support the study of Native American languages.

See entry 1595 for full listing.

UCLA INSTITUTE OF AMERICAN CULTURES (IAC)   [1018]
2329 Murphy Hall, Box 957244
Los Angeles, CA 90095-7244
(310) 825-6815
Fax: (310) 825-3994

E-MAIL ADDRESS:
iaccoordinator@conet.ucla.edu

WEB SITE ADDRESS:
www.iac.ucla.edu

FOUNDED: 1969

AREAS OF INTEREST:
Advancing knowledge, strengthening and integrating interdisciplinary research and enriching instruction on African Americans, American Indians, Asian Americans and Chicanos.

NAME(S) OF PROGRAMS:
• **UCLA IAC Visiting Scholar/Researcher Program in Ethnic Studies**

TYPE:
Fellowships. Deals with arts and humanities, education and teacher training, fine arts, applied arts, law, social sciences, and sciences. The IAC, in cooperation with UCLA's four Ethnic Studies Research Centers (American Indian Studies Center, Asian American Studies Center, Bunche Center for African American Studies, and Chicano Studies Research Center), offers awards to visiting scholars to support research on African Americans, American Indians, Asian Americans and Chicanas/os.

PURPOSE:
To enable Ph.D. scholars wishing to work in association with the American Indian Studies Center, the Bunche Center for African American Studies, the Asian American Studies Center, and the Chicano Studies Research Center, in order to conduct research and publish books or manuscripts.

ELIGIBILITY:
Open to U.S. citizens or permanent residents of the U.S. who hold a Ph.D. from an accredited college or university (or, in the case of the arts, a terminal degree) in the appropriate field at the time of appointment. UCLA faculty, staff and currently enrolled students are not eligible to apply.

FINANCIAL DATA:
Amount of support per award: $32,000 to $35,000 stipend, plus health benefits and up

to $4,000 in research support. Amount contingent upon rank, experience and date of completion of Ph.D.

NUMBER OF AWARDS: Up to 4.

APPLICATION INFORMATION:
Applicants are encouraged to contact the Studies Research Center of interest prior to applying.
Duration: Up to one year.
Deadline: February 1.

ADDRESS INQUIRIES TO:
Megan Odegaard, Coordinator
(See address above.)

UNITED METHODIST COMMUNICATIONS [1019]
810 12th Avenue South
Nashville, TN 37203-4704
(888) 278-4862
Fax: (615) 742-5777

E-MAIL ADDRESS:
rjames@umcom.org

WEB SITE ADDRESS:
www.umcom.org

FOUNDED: 1948

AREAS OF INTEREST:
Religious communications.

NAME(S) OF PROGRAMS:
● **The Leonard M. Perryman Communications Scholarship for Ethnic Minority Students**

TYPE:
Fellowships; Scholarships. Award for junior or senior undergraduate study in religion journalism or mass communications. The term *communications* is meant to cover various media as audio-visual, electronic and print journalism.

PURPOSE:
To enable the recipient to continue his or her studies in communication; to promote a level of excellence in communication on the undergraduate level by an ethnic minority student.

ELIGIBILITY:
Applicants must be members of The United Methodist Church and must be racial ethnic minority undergraduate students, junior or senior, who have an intention to pursue a career in religion journalism or mass communications and are enrolled in an accredited U.S. college or university.

FINANCIAL DATA:
Amount of support per award: $2,500.
Total amount of support: $2,500 per academic year.

NUMBER OF AWARDS: 1.

APPLICATION INFORMATION:
Applicant must submit:
(1) an application form (completed and submitted electronically or printed and mailed);
(2) official transcripts from the current institution of higher education and any others attended. Transcripts should be mailed by the school directly to the address listed in the application packet;
(3) three letters of recommendation, one from the local church pastor or a denominational official, one from the chairperson of the department in which the applicant is majoring as an undergraduate student, and one from an employer or supervisor in a

position to evaluate the applicant's communications skills;
(4) an essay (no more than 500 words) about the applicant's commitment to the Christian faith and interest in communications, and how the applicant sees the two intersecting in their life presently and in the future;
(5) three examples of journalistic work (audiovisual, electronic, print). If requested in writing, these materials will be returned after the committee has completed its selection and;
(6) a recent photograph, preferably head and shoulders, suitable for publicity use if awarded the scholarship.
Duration: One academic year.
Deadline: March 15 (postmarked).

PUBLICATIONS:
Application guidelines.

ADDRESS INQUIRIES TO:
Scholarships Coordinator
(See address above.)

*SPECIAL STIPULATIONS:
Candidates must be in their junior or senior year to qualify.

UNIVERSITY OF CALIFORNIA [1020]
President's Postdoctoral Fellowship Program
102 California Hall
UC Berkeley
Berkeley, CA 94720-1508
(510) 643-8235

E-MAIL ADDRESS:
ppfpinfo@berkeley.edu

WEB SITE ADDRESS:
ppfp.ucop.edu/info

FOUNDED: 1869

AREAS OF INTEREST:
Education and research.

NAME(S) OF PROGRAMS:
● **University of California President's Postdoctoral Fellowship Program**

TYPE:
Fellowships. Awarded for research conducted under faculty sponsorship on any one of the University of California's 10 campuses.

YEAR PROGRAM STARTED: 1984

PURPOSE:
To encourage outstanding women and minority Ph.D. recipients to pursue academic careers at the University of California; to offer research fellowships to all qualified candidates who are committed to university careers in research, teaching and service that will enhance the diversity of the academic community at the University of California.

LEGAL BASIS:
University.

ELIGIBILITY:
Applicants must be U.S. citizens or permanent residents and must hold or receive a Ph.D. from an accredited university. Applicants should expect to have earned their Ph.D. degree by June 30 of the year for which they are applying.

The program will prefer candidates who have research interests focusing on underserved populations and understanding issues of racial or gender inequalities.

The program also prefers candidates with a record of leadership or significant experience teaching and mentoring students from groups that have been historically underrepresented in higher education.

FINANCIAL DATA:
The award includes salary, health, vision and dental benefits, and up to $5,000 for research-related and program travel expenses.
Amount of support per award:
Approximately $45,000 per fellow, depending upon the field and level of experience, plus benefits for self and dependents.

NUMBER OF APPLICANTS MOST RECENT YEAR:
519 for the year 2014-15.

NUMBER OF AWARDS: 16 for the year 2014-15.

APPLICATION INFORMATION:
Application consists of curriculum vitae, research proposal, dissertation abstract, personal statement, writing sample, mentor support letter and thesis advisor letter.
Duration: Initially one academic year beginning July 1. Renewal for a second year will be granted upon demonstration of academic productivity and participation in program events.
Deadline: November 1. Announcement of awardees in the spring.

STAFF:
Kimberly M. Adkinson, Program Manager

ADDRESS INQUIRIES TO:
Kimberly M. Adkinson, Manager
President's Postdoctoral Fellowship Program
(See address above.)

UNIVERSITY OF CALIFORNIA, LOS ANGELES [1021]
Asian American Studies Center
3230 Campbell Hall
405 Hilgard Avenue, Box 951546
Los Angeles, CA 90095-1546
(310) 825-2974
Fax: (310) 206-9844

E-MAIL ADDRESS:
dkyoo@ucla.edu

WEB SITE ADDRESS:
www.aasc.ucla.edu

FOUNDED: 1969

AREAS OF INTEREST:
Asian American studies, policy research on Asian Americans, and arts and humanities on Asian Americans.

NAME(S) OF PROGRAMS:
● **Ethnic Studies Fellowships**

TYPE:
Awards/prizes; Conferences/seminars; Fellowships; Research grants; Scholarships; Visiting scholars; Work-study programs. Support for visiting scholars and researchers.

YEAR PROGRAM STARTED: 1969

PURPOSE:
To provide funding for studies in the field of Asian American arts, humanities, social sciences and applied research.

LEGAL BASIS:
University.

ELIGIBILITY:
Applicants must have the Ph.D. in place at the time Fellowship is awarded. UCLA faculty members are not eligible for support.

FINANCIAL DATA:
Visiting Scholars may use the funds to supplement sabbatical support, though the total available will not exceed the maximum stipend levels, and when combined with sabbatical funds may not exceed the candidate's current institutional salary.

Visiting Scholars will be paid through their home institutions and will be expected to continue their health benefits through that source; Visiting Researchers receive health benefits and will be paid directly by UCLA. Awardees may receive up to $4,000 in research support (through reimbursements of research expenses), $1,000 of which may be applied toward relocation expenses.
Amount of support per award: Maximum stipend of $32,000 to $35,000, contingent upon rank, experience and date of completion of terminal degree.
Total amount of support: Varies.

NUMBER OF APPLICANTS MOST RECENT YEAR:
30.

NUMBER OF AWARDS: 1.

APPLICATION INFORMATION:
Contact the University.
Duration: Nine months.
Deadline: February 2015.

STAFF:
Melany Dela Cruz-Viesca, Assistant Director/IAC Coordinator

ADDRESS INQUIRIES TO:
Melany Dela Cruz-Viesca
Assistant Director/IAC Coordinator
Asian American Studies Center
(See address above.)

UNIVERSITY OF SOUTHERN CALIFORNIA
USC Graduate School
3601 Watt Way, GFS 315
Los Angeles, CA 90089-1695
(213) 740-9033
Fax: (213) 740-9048

E-MAIL ADDRESS:
gradfllw@usc.edu

WEB-SITE ADDRESS:
www.usc.edu/schools/GraduateSchool/

TYPE:
Fellowships. Merit fellowships. Fellowships will be combined with matching funds from individual schools to provide four or more years of funding toward the Ph.D.

See entry 1797 for full listing.

VIRGINIA POLYTECHNIC INSTITUTE AND STATE UNIVERSITY   [1022]
MAOP Office
110 Femoyer Hall
Blacksburg, VA 24061
(540) 231-5023
Fax: (540) 231-2618

E-MAIL ADDRESS:
maop@vt.edu

WEB SITE ADDRESS:
www.maop.vt.edu

AREAS OF INTEREST:
Graduate programs particularly in science, math and technology.

NAME(S) OF PROGRAMS:
● **Multicultural Academic Opportunity Graduate Student Scholars Program**

TYPE:
Assistantships; Fellowships; Internships; Scholarships. The program assists with graduate school financing in exchange for assistance to MAOP administration. Graduate students assist with programming implementation such as mentoring to undergraduate students.

YEAR PROGRAM STARTED: 1973

PURPOSE:
To improve professional and educational opportunities for minority students in architecture, planning, public and international affairs, and landscape architecture.

ELIGIBILITY:
Grade point average of 3.0 during the last two years of undergraduate school is required along with an essay focusing upon their commitment to academic diversity at Virginia Tech and admission to the Graduate School. Scholars must maintain a 3.0 grade point average to remain qualified for the program.

FINANCIAL DATA:
Amount of support per award: Varies.
Total amount of support: Varies.

APPLICATION INFORMATION:
Contact the Institute.
Duration: One year. Renewable.
Deadline: April 1.

ADDRESS INQUIRIES TO:
Dr. Jody Thompson-Marshall
Director, MAOP Office
(See address above.)

WIDENER MEMORIAL FOUNDATION IN AID OF HANDICAPPED CHILDREN   [1023]
4060 Butler Pike
Suite 225
Plymouth Meeting, PA 19462
(610) 825-8900
Fax: (610) 825-8904

E-MAIL ADDRESS:
jhagerty@erdixon.com

FOUNDED: 1912

AREAS OF INTEREST:
Handicapped children and education.

TYPE:
Capital grants; Project/program grants.

PURPOSE:
To benefit orthopedically handicapped children.

LEGAL BASIS:
Special interest foundation.

ELIGIBILITY:
Applicants must be 501(c)(3) organizations that are not classified as private foundations. Organizations must benefit orthopedically handicapped children in some way.

GEOGRAPHIC RESTRICTIONS:
Greater Delaware Valley area (including the city of Philadelphia, Pennsylvania), and Bucks, Burlington, Camden, Chester, Delaware, Gloucester, Montgomery and Philadelphia counties.

FINANCIAL DATA:
Amount of support per award: Varies.

Total amount of support: Approximately $900,000.

NUMBER OF APPLICANTS MOST RECENT YEAR:
26.

NUMBER OF AWARDS: 17.

APPLICATION INFORMATION:
Applicant should include a letter describing the purpose for which grant would be used, persons who would benefit from the activity for which the grant is requested, specifically orthopedically handicapped children, and statements showing that the organization is exempt under 501(c)(3) of the Internal Revenue Code and also not classified as a private foundation.
Duration: Typically one year. Must reapply.
Deadline: May 15 and October 15.

OFFICERS:
Edith D. Miller, President
Peter M. Mattoon, Esq., Vice President and Trustee
Edith R. Dixon, Treasurer and Trustee
George W. Dixon, Secretary and Treasurer
Bruce L. Castor, Esq., Trustee
Michael Clancy, M.D., Trustee
Mark S. DePillis, Esq., Trustee
Linda Grobman, Ed.D., Trustee
John Keleher, Trustee

ADDRESS INQUIRIES TO:
Edith D. Miller, President
P.O. Box 178
Lafayette Hill, PA 19444-0178

African-American

AFRICAN AMERICAN FUND OF NEW JERSEY   [1024]
132 South Harrison Street
East Orange, NJ 07018
(908) 561-0123
Fax: (908) 561-4710

E-MAIL ADDRESS:
lclark@aafnj.org

WEB SITE ADDRESS:
www.aafnj.org

FOUNDED: 1980

AREAS OF INTEREST:
Primarily African-American communities in the state of New Jersey.

TYPE:
Conferences/seminars; Demonstration grants; General operating grants; Project/program grants; Seed money grants; Training grants. The African American Fund of New Jersey is a philanthropic organization that funds community-based agencies and programs in and for, but not limited to, African-American communities in the state of New Jersey.

The Fund supports social programs that are important to its donors. Its goal is to provide more extensive educational programs that cater to all age groups. The focus of the grants is to agencies that provide services in the following areas: Early Childhood and Youth Education, Healthcare, Teen Pregnancy Prevention, Substance Abuse, Aid to the Homeless, Adult Literacy, Child Abuse Prevention, AIDS Education, Recreation, Arts and Culture and Leadership Development.

YEAR PROGRAM STARTED: 1980

PURPOSE:
To develop and perpetuate the empowerment of the African-American community through fund-raising and volunteerism for the purpose of Black philanthropy.

LEGAL BASIS:
Private 501(c)(3).

ELIGIBILITY:
Applicants may be any 501(c)(3) nonprofit, tax-exempt organization, agency or community-based organization operating in the state of New Jersey.

GEOGRAPHIC RESTRICTIONS:
New Jersey.

FINANCIAL DATA:
Amount of support per award: $500 to $5,000.

Total amount of support: $60,000 to $100,000.

NUMBER OF APPLICANTS MOST RECENT YEAR:
60.

NUMBER OF AWARDS: 20.

APPLICATION INFORMATION:
Request for Proposal (RFP) application required. Forms must be typed and complete. Information and/or technical assistance is available by contacting BUF/NJ State Office in East Orange.
Duration: One year.
Deadline: Letter of Intent: July; Request for Proposal: September.

PUBLICATIONS:
Annual report.

IRS IDENTIFICATION NUMBER: 22-2349446

BOARD OF DIRECTORS AND OFFICERS:
Sondra Clark, President and Chief Executive Officer
Robert T. Pickett, Chairperson
Hon. Charles Craig, Treasurer/Secretary

ADDRESS INQUIRIES TO:
Lisa Clark, Grants Coordinator
(See address above.)

CONGRESSIONAL BLACK CAUCUS FOUNDATION, INC.   [1025]
1720 Massachusetts Avenue, N.W.
Washington, DC 20036
(202) 263-2800
Fax: (202) 263-0846

E-MAIL ADDRESS:
internships@cbcfinc.org

WEB SITE ADDRESS:
www.cbcfinc.org

FOUNDED: 1976

AREAS OF INTEREST:
Health policies and politics.

NAME(S) OF PROGRAMS:
● **The Louis Stokes Urban Health Policy Fellows Program**

TYPE:
Fellowships. The Louis Stokes Urban Health Policy Fellows Program is a 20-month policy training and leadership development program that targets early to mid-level policy professionals who are committed to eliminating health disparities nationally and globally. Fellows receive health policy training while working in a CBC Member's office as well as on a congressional committee. They spend 10 months working

in a congressional Member's office and the remaining 10 months working on a congressional committee that focuses on health-related issues.

The program also includes educational enrichment opportunities through seminars on policy and politics.

YEAR PROGRAM STARTED: 2003

PURPOSE:
To increase the pool of qualified minority health policy professionals who are committed to eliminating health disparities in the United States and abroad.

ELIGIBILITY:
Applicants must be U.S. citizens or persons permitted to work in the U.S. for the duration of the program (September 2014 through May 2016). Applicants must meet the following additional requirements:
(1) have a graduate or professional degree in a health-related field (behavioral sciences, social sciences, biological sciences and health professions) from an accredited institution completed prior to the fellowship start date;
(2) have a familiarity with the federal legislative process, Congress and the Congressional Black Caucus (CBC) and;
(3) have a demonstrated interest in public policy and a commitment to creating and implementing policy to improve the living conditions for underserved and underrepresented individuals.

Selection for the program is based on a combination of the following criteria:
(1) record of academic and professional achievement and;
(2) evidence of leadership skills and the potential for further growth.

GEOGRAPHIC RESTRICTIONS:
Washington, District of Columbia.

FINANCIAL DATA:
Amount of support per award: Varies.

NUMBER OF AWARDS: 2.

APPLICATION INFORMATION:
The online application form will be available on the Foundation web site in 2014. Complete application details and guidelines are also available on the web site.
Duration: 20 months (September 2014 through May 2016).

ADDRESS INQUIRIES TO:
See e-mail address above.

*SPECIAL STIPULATIONS:
All Fellows must be able to participate for the full term of the program. If selected, applicants are expected to complete all professional qualifying exams.

CONGRESSIONAL BLACK CAUCUS FOUNDATION, INC.   [1026]
1720 Massachusetts Avenue, N.W.
Washington, DC 20036
(202) 263-2800
Fax: (202) 263-0846

E-MAIL ADDRESS:
scholarships@cbcfinc.org

WEB SITE ADDRESS:
www.cbcfinc.org

FOUNDED: 1976

NAME(S) OF PROGRAMS:
● **CBCS Performing Arts Scholarship**
● **CBCS Visual Arts Scholarship**

TYPE:
Scholarships. CBCS Performing Arts Scholarship, developed in honor of the late Curtis Mayfield, is intended to ensure that students pursuing a career in the performing arts receive the financial assistance to achieve their goals.

CBCS Visual Arts Scholarship was established for students who are pursuing a career in the visual arts.

PURPOSE:
To encourage education in the performing and visual arts among minority students.

ELIGIBILITY:
Applicants must:
(1) be preparing to pursue an undergraduate degree full-time, or be a current full-time student in good academic standing at a U.S. accredited college or university;
(2) have a minimum 2.5 grade point average and;
(3) exhibit leadership ability and participate in community service activities.

The scholarships do not have a residency requirement.

GEOGRAPHIC RESTRICTIONS:
United States.

FINANCIAL DATA:
Amount of support per award: $3,000.
Total amount of support: $60,000.

NUMBER OF AWARDS: 10 annually.

APPLICATION INFORMATION:
The Foundation utilizes an online application process.
Duration: One year. Must reapply.
Deadline: May 1.

ADDRESS INQUIRIES TO:
Leadership Institute for Public Service
(See address above.)

CONGRESSIONAL BLACK CAUCUS FOUNDATION, INC.   [1027]
1720 Massachusetts Avenue, N.W.
Washington, DC 20036
(202) 263-2800
Fax: (202) 263-0846

E-MAIL ADDRESS:
info@cbcfinc.org

WEB SITE ADDRESS:
www.cbcfinc.org

FOUNDED: 1976

AREAS OF INTEREST:
Promoting educational and leadership opportunities for African Americans.

NAME(S) OF PROGRAMS:
● **CBC Spouses Cheerios Brand Health Initiative Scholarship**
● **CBC Spouses Education Scholarship Fund**
● **The CBCF Congressional Fellows Program**
● **The CBCF Congressional Internship Program**

TYPE:
Fellowships; Internships; Scholarships. The CBC Spouses Cheerios Brand Health Initiative Scholarship is intended to increase the number of minority students pursuing degrees in the fields of medicine, engineering, technology, nutrition and other health-related professions.

The CBC Spouses Education Scholarship Fund is a national program that awards scholarships to academically talented and highly motivated students who intend to pursue full-time undergraduate, graduate or doctoral degrees.

The CBCF Congressional Fellows Program helps participants gain invaluable experience as they assist in the development of legislative and public policy initiatives while working as congressional staff for a year. This program targets early career policy professionals who have completed a professional and/or graduate degree and have demonstrated commitment to improving the lives and services for individuals living in underserved communities. Fellows work on Capitol Hill in the office of a Congressional Black Caucus member.

The CBCF Congressional Internship Program provides undergraduate students with an in-depth orientation to Capitol Hill and the legislative process through actual work experience in the offices of Congressional Black Caucus Members. In this way interns prepare to become decision makers in the policymaking process.

YEAR PROGRAM STARTED: 1983

PURPOSE:
To increase the number of African Americans on congressional committees and subcommittees by providing students the opportunity to participate in all aspects of the legislative process.

LEGAL BASIS:
Nonpartisan, nonprofit foundation.

ELIGIBILITY:
CBC Spouses Cheerios Brand Health Initiative Scholarship is for students pursuing career in a health profession, who must reside or attend school in district represented by CBC member.

CBC Spouses Education Scholarship is for undergraduate or graduate students residing or attending school in district of CBC member.

Fellows Program applicants must have completed graduate coursework.

Internship Program applicants must be college undergraduates.

FINANCIAL DATA:
Fellows are responsible for their own travel arrangements, expenses and housing accommodations. CBCF provides health and dental insurance coverage during term of fellowship. Interns receive a stipend and housing at a local university.
Amount of support per award: Fellows Program: $40,000 annual stipend; Internship Program: $3,000 stipend.
Total amount of support: Varies.

APPLICATION INFORMATION:
Submit a completed application with detailed resume, certificate of academic standing and/or faculty certification, a writing sample of up to 10 pages, three letters of recommendation, one of which must be from the dean, department chairperson, faculty or advisor and an official transcript from each school attended.
Duration: All Fellows serve 20 months. Internships occur during the Spring, Fall and Summer.

Deadline: CBC Spouses Cheerios Brand Health Initiative Scholarship and CBC Spouses Education Scholarship: June 1; Fellows Program: April; Internship Program: February, May and November.

PUBLICATIONS:
Policy review; annual report.

IRS IDENTIFICATION NUMBER: 52-1160561

BOARD OF DIRECTORS:
Rep. Chaka Fattah, Chairman
A. Shaunise Washington, President and Chief Operating Officer
Marcus Mason, Treasurer
Amy Goldson, Counsel

ADDRESS INQUIRIES TO:
Leadership Institute and Scholarships Programs
(See address above.)

FREDERICK DOUGLASS INSTITUTE FOR AFRICAN AND AFRICAN-AMERICAN STUDIES

University of Rochester
Morey Hall 302
Rochester, NY 14627-0440
(585) 276-5744
Fax: (585) 256-2594

E-MAIL ADDRESS:
fdi@mail.rochester.edu

WEB SITE ADDRESS:
www.rochester.edu/college/aas/grad_programs

TYPE:
Awards/prizes; Conferences/seminars; Fellowships.

See entry 1538 for full listing.

FLORIDA DEPARTMENT OF EDUCATION   [1028]

Office of Student Financial Assistance
325 West Gaines Street, Suite 1314
Tallahassee, FL 32399-0400
(888) 827-2004
Fax: (850) 487-1809

E-MAIL ADDRESS:
osfa@fldoe.org

WEB SITE ADDRESS:
www.FloridaStudentFinancialAid.org

NAME(S) OF PROGRAMS:
● **Rosewood Family Scholarship Program**

TYPE:
Scholarships. Financial assistance for descendants of the Rosewood family affected by the incidents of January 1923, to attend a state university, public community college or public postsecondary vocational-technical school.

PURPOSE:
To encourage and assist minority students to continue on to higher education.

LEGAL BASIS:
Governmental agency.

ELIGIBILITY:
To receive funding, the applying student must meet the following initial eligibility requirements:
(1) not owe a repayment or be in default under any state or federal grant, loan or scholarship program unless satisfactory arrangements to repay have been made;
(2) not have previously received a baccalaureate degree;

(3) enroll full-time at an eligible participating postsecondary institution in a program of study leading to an undergraduate degree, a certificate or a diploma and;
(4) must provide copies of documents of ancestry by April 1; mail copies to Florida Department of Education, Office of Student Financial Assistance, State Scholarship and Grant Programs, at the address above.

NUMBER OF AWARDS: Up to 25.

APPLICATION INFORMATION:
Detailed program information can be found on the web site.
Duration: One academic year; renewable.
Deadline: April 1 for submitting a fully completed, error-free Initial Student Florida Financial Aid Application. Florida residents must complete and submit the Free Application for Federal Student Aid (FAFSA) online in time to be processed error-free by the U.S. Department of Education on or before May 15. Florida nonresidents must complete and submit the FAFSA in time to receive the Student Aid Report (SAR) from the processor and postmark a copy of the SAR to OSFA by May 15.

ADDRESS INQUIRIES TO:
State Scholarship and Grant Programs
(See address above.)

THE JACK AND JILL OF AMERICA FOUNDATION   [1029]

1930 17th Street, N.W.
Washington, DC 20009-6207
(202) 232-5290
Fax: (202) 232-1747

E-MAIL ADDRESS:
administration@jackandjillfoundation.org

WEB SITE ADDRESS:
www.jackandjillfoundation.org

FOUNDED: 1968

AREAS OF INTEREST:
Cultural, social, educational, civic and recreational activities for children; youth leadership development.

CONSULTING OR VOLUNTEER SERVICES:
Volunteer services.

NAME(S) OF PROGRAMS:
● **Violet D. Greer Grant Awards**
● **Independent Grant Awards**
● **Jacqueline Robinson Regional Competition Grant Awards**

TYPE:
Project/program grants; Scholarships. Volunteer opportunities.

YEAR PROGRAM STARTED: 1968

PURPOSE:
To influence the ongoing positive development of children.

LEGAL BASIS:
Public charity.

ELIGIBILITY:
Independent Grant Awards are awarded to nonprofit organizations when their project's thematic emphasis corresponds to the Foundation's focus.

For the Jacqueline Robinson Regional Competition Grant Awards, applications are submitted by adult or teen members of local chapters to their region for programs that benefit youth outside the organization.

GEOGRAPHIC RESTRICTIONS:
United States.

FINANCIAL DATA:
Amount of support per award: $2,000 to $5,000.
Total amount of support: Varies.

NUMBER OF APPLICANTS MOST RECENT YEAR: 40.

NUMBER OF AWARDS: Varies.

APPLICATION INFORMATION:
Applicant should carefully read the Information for Grant Applicants on the Foundation web site, before submitting an application on the designated form. Furthermore, answers on the application coversheet must be given in the space provided; no additional sheets can be attached. Type the application (using at least 10-point type). Applications may not be faxed. All signatures should be signed in blue ink. A complete application consists of an application coversheet along with the following materials:
(1) proposal;
(2) copy of IRS 501(c)(3) letter or documentation of 501(c)(4) status, whichever is applicable;
(3) most recent audited income statement or 990 tax return, if 501(c)(3) organization, or most recent year-end statement of income and expenses, if 501(c)(4) organization and;
(4) brief resume or bio of your Project Director and other relevant supporting material.
Duration: One year.
Deadline: Violet D. Greer and Independent Grant Awards: December 1; Jacqueline Robinson Regional Competition Grant Awards: February 15.

PUBLICATIONS:
Newsletter; annual report; application guidelines.

IRS IDENTIFICATION NUMBER: 51-0224656

STAFF:
Pier A.H. Blake, Executive Director

ADDRESS INQUIRIES TO:
Pier A.H. Blake, Executive Director
(See address above.)

THE NAACP LEGAL DEFENSE AND EDUCATIONAL FUND, INC. [1030]
40 Rector Street
5th Floor
New York, NY 10006
(212) 965-2225
Fax: (212) 226-7592

E-MAIL ADDRESS:
scholarships@naacpldf.org
mcorro@naacpldf.org

WEB SITE ADDRESS:
www.naacpldf.org/scholarships

FOUNDED: 1964

AREAS OF INTEREST:
Financial assistance for African-American undergraduates and for law students with a demonstrable interest in civil rights.

NAME(S) OF PROGRAMS:
- **LDF Herbert Lehman Education Fund Scholarship Program**
- **LDF Earl Warren Legal Training Program**

TYPE:
Awards/prizes; Grants-in-aid; Internships; Scholarships. LDF Herbert Lehman Education Fund Scholarship Program: Scholarships for African-American high school seniors, high school graduates and college freshmen to attend four-year accredited colleges and universities.
LDF Earl Warren Legal Training Program: Scholarships for law students to attend three-year accredited law schools.

YEAR PROGRAM STARTED: 1964

PURPOSE:
To encourage students to continue the work of the Legal Defense Fund; to encourage young people to be involved in public service; to increase the presence of African-American students in colleges, universities and law schools in the U.S.

LEGAL BASIS:
501(c)(3) corporation.

ELIGIBILITY:
Applicants must be U.S. citizens. Candidates must have outstanding potential evidenced by their recommendations, high school academic records, test scores and essays. They must understand their educational goals and academic abilities. Candidates should have a clear commitment to working in the public service as exemplified by their community and school involvements. Candidates should have exceptional leadership potential with an ability to work well in diverse settings.

Law students already enrolled in law school are not eligible to apply for the LDF Earl Warren Legal Training Program.

GEOGRAPHIC RESTRICTIONS:
United States.

FINANCIAL DATA:
Amount of support per award: $3,000 to $5,000 per year.

NUMBER OF APPLICANTS MOST RECENT YEAR: Over 2,000.

NUMBER OF AWARDS: 50 to 100 annually.

APPLICATION INFORMATION:
Applications will be available for online submission by November 1 of each year. Applicants who do not meet the basic criteria for eligibility or do not satisfy program requirements for the completion of applications will not be considered.
Duration: Up to four years depending upon availability of funds. Renewable during undergraduate career, if student remains in good standing with their college or university.
Deadline: March 31 for the Lehman Scholarship and April 30 for the Warren Legal Training Program. Notification normally takes place at the end of July, prior to the fall semester of the student's first academic year.

STAFF:
Maruja Corro, Program Assistant

ADDRESS INQUIRIES TO:
Maruja Corro, Program Assistant
(See address above.)

NATIONAL ASSOCIATION FOR EQUAL OPPORTUNITY IN HIGHER EDUCATION (NAFEO) [1031]
209 Third Street, S.E.
Washington, DC 20003
(202) 552-3300
Fax: (202) 552-3330

E-MAIL ADDRESS:
admin@nafeo.org

WEB SITE ADDRESS:
www.nafeointernships.net

FOUNDED: 1969

AREAS OF INTEREST:
Equal opportunity in higher education.

NAME(S) OF PROGRAMS:
- **NAFEO Internship Program**

TYPE:
Internships. NAFEO Internship Program offers full-time paid internships in the summer.

ELIGIBILITY:
Preference will be given to students enrolled in undergraduate or graduate programs at historically or predominantly black colleges and universities. A grade point average of 3.0 or above on a 4.0 scale is required. (Some internships require U.S. citizenship.)

FINANCIAL DATA:
Stipends are paid according to a student's classification at the time of application. Round-trip travel: Students selected for summer internships only who reside outside of the Washington, DC, metropolitan area will receive a travel allowance. A housing stipend will be provided. Local travel: Interns receive an allowance to subsidize daily travel to and from their work assignments.
Amount of support per award: Undergraduate students, $11 per hour; graduate students, $13 per hour.

NUMBER OF AWARDS: Approximately 50.

APPLICATION INFORMATION:
Application requirements are as follows:
(1) U.S. citizen;
(2) complete application;
(3) current resume;
(4) unofficial transcript - by request only;
(5) official transcript - by request only and;
(6) two completed faculty recommendation forms - by request only.

In conjunction with NAFEO member institutions, NAFEO staff reviews applications to ensure that applicants are eligible and that the applications are complete. NAFEO staff then refers applications to employing agencies based on the academic disciplines they are seeking. Employing agencies review the applications, conduct interviews if necessary, and make all final selections.

Selected students will be notified by NAFEO staff and provided with an official internship offer.
Duration: Summer: 10 weeks; fall and spring: 15 weeks.
Deadline: March 25.

ADDRESS INQUIRIES TO:
Internship Coordinator
(See address above.)

THE NATIONAL ASSOCIATION OF BLACK SOCIAL WORKERS [1032]
2305 Martin Luther King Jr. Avenue, S.E.
Washington, DC 20020
(202) 678-4570
Fax: (202) 678-4572

E-MAIL ADDRESS:
harambee@nabsw.org

WEB SITE ADDRESS:
www.nabsw.org

FOUNDED: 1968

AREAS OF INTEREST:
Social work and community advocacy.

NAME(S) OF PROGRAMS:
- **Dr. Joyce Beckett Scholarship**
- **Selena Danette Brown Book Scholarship**
- **Guynn Family Book Scholarship**
- **Emma Meloid and Algood Tuition Scholarship (Undergraduate)**
- **Cenie Jomo Williams Tuition Scholarship**

TYPE:
Scholarships.

YEAR PROGRAM STARTED: 1968

PURPOSE:
To promote the welfare, survival and liberation of communities of African ancestry.

LEGAL BASIS:
Nonprofit membership association.

ELIGIBILITY:
Student must be a member of NABSW. For the Emma and Meloid Algood Tuition Scholarship, student must have a 3.0 grade point average on a 4.0 scale. For all other scholarships, students must have a 2.5 grade point average on a 4.0 scale. Student must express research interest in African Americans or those of African ancestry. Student must be enrolled for full-time study at an accredited U.S. social work program for the semester that the award will be granted.

GEOGRAPHIC RESTRICTIONS:
United States.

FINANCIAL DATA:
Amount of support per award: $250 to $2,000.
Total amount of support: Varies.

NUMBER OF AWARDS: Varies.

APPLICATION INFORMATION:
Scholarship applications can be obtained from the National Office.
Duration: One-time award. May reapply for the Emma Meloid and Algood Tuition Scholarship.
Deadline: Third Friday of December.

PUBLICATIONS:
Quarterly newsletters.

IRS IDENTIFICATION NUMBER: 13-2779773

ADDRESS INQUIRIES TO:
Terrence Bradford, National Office Manager
(See address above.)

NATIONAL BLACK NURSES ASSOCIATION, INC.

8630 Fenton Street
Suite 330
Silver Spring, MD 20910
(301) 589-3200
Fax: (301) 589-3223

E-MAIL ADDRESS:
info@nbna.org

WEB SITE ADDRESS:
www.nbna.org

TYPE:
Scholarships.

See entry 2492 for full listing.

NATIONAL SOCIETY OF BLACK ENGINEERS

205 Daingerfield Road
Alexandria, VA 22314
(703) 549-2207
Fax: (703) 683-5312

E-MAIL ADDRESS:
scholarships@nsbe.org

WEB SITE ADDRESS:
www.nsbe.org

TYPE:
Awards/prizes; Scholarships. The Society offers a variety of NSBE and corporate-sponsored scholarship and award opportunities to its precollege, collegiate undergraduate and graduate student members as well as technical professional members.

See entry 1725 for full listing.

NEED [1033]

The Law and Finance Building
429 Fourth Avenue, 20th Floor
Pittsburgh, PA 15219
(412) 566-2760
Fax: (412) 471-6643

E-MAIL ADDRESS:
info@needld.org

WEB SITE ADDRESS:
www.needld.org

FOUNDED: 1963

AREAS OF INTEREST:
Higher education, college access services.

CONSULTING OR VOLUNTEER SERVICES:
Counseling for postsecondary education; assistance to students and parents needing help with the completion of financial aid forms; mentoring services.

NAME(S) OF PROGRAMS:
- **Access to College and Career Education (ACE) Program**
- **African American Male Mentoring Initiative (AAMMI)**
- **Science Technology Engineering & Math (STEM) Female Mentoring Program**
- **Unmet NEED Grants and Scholarships**

TYPE:
Internships; Matching gifts; Scholarships. Supplemental grants for postsecondary education at colleges and business, trade and technical schools.

YEAR PROGRAM STARTED: 1963

PURPOSE:
To provide career and college access services which empower youth from the Pittsburgh region to aspire to, learn about, prepare for, and complete higher education.

LEGAL BASIS:
Incorporated nonprofit, tax-exempt.

ELIGIBILITY:
Applicant must be African American, with a high school diploma or GED, resident in Allegheny, Armstrong, Beaver, Butler, Fayette, Greene, Lawrence, Washington or Westmoreland counties in Pennsylvania and enrolled in or planning to enroll in a state-approved program.

GEOGRAPHIC RESTRICTIONS:
Allegheny, Armstrong, Beaver, Butler, Fayette, Greene, Lawrence, Washington and Westmoreland counties, Pennsylvania.

FINANCIAL DATA:
Amount of support per award: $1,000 to $1,500.
Total amount of support: $953,982 for the 2012-13 academic year.

NUMBER OF APPLICANTS MOST RECENT YEAR:
1,022 for the year 2012-13.

NUMBER OF AWARDS: 571 for the 2012-13 academic year.

APPLICATION INFORMATION:
Applicant must submit:
(1) NEED application;
(2) high school, college, or school transcript (whichever is most recent) and;
(3) photo.
Duration: Academic year. May reapply in subsequent years.
Deadline: May 31.

PUBLICATIONS:
Annual report.

OFFICERS:
Candi Castleberry-Singleton, Chairman of the Board

ADDRESS INQUIRIES TO:
Student Services Department
(See address above.)

SACHS FOUNDATION [1034]

90 South Cascade Avenue
Suite 1410
Colorado Springs, CO 80903
(719) 633-2353
Fax: (719) 633-3663

E-MAIL ADDRESS:
lisa@sachsfoundation.org

WEB SITE ADDRESS:
sachsfoundation.org

FOUNDED: 1931

AREAS OF INTEREST:
Education.

NAME(S) OF PROGRAMS:
- **Financial Aid for Education of Black Residents of Colorado**

TYPE:
Grants-in-aid; Scholarships.

YEAR PROGRAM STARTED: 1931

PURPOSE:
To promote education of Black residents of Colorado.

LEGAL BASIS:
Private foundation.

ELIGIBILITY:
Applicants must be U.S. citizens, Black, residents of the state of Colorado for five or more years and high school seniors with about a 3.5 grade point average or better, on a 4.0 scale, depending on the number of applications. Awardees may attend any accredited college or university.

GEOGRAPHIC RESTRICTIONS:
Colorado.

FINANCIAL DATA:
Amount of support per award: $5,000 maximum per annum for undergraduates; $6,000 for graduate grants.
Total amount of support: Varies.

NUMBER OF APPLICANTS MOST RECENT YEAR:
400.

NUMBER OF AWARDS: Approximately 35 for the year 2013.

APPLICATION INFORMATION:
Application forms are only available online.
Duration: Four years for undergraduate and some graduate degrees, if requirements are met.
Deadline: March 15.

PUBLICATIONS:
Annual report; other printed materials available upon written request.

OFFICERS AND DIRECTORS:
Craig S. Ralston, President
Lisa M. Harris, Secretary/Treasurer
Wilton Cogswell, III, Director

TRUSTEE:
Wilton Cogswell, III
Thomas James

ADDRESS INQUIRIES TO:
Lisa M. Harris, Secretary/Treasurer
(See address above.)

*SPECIAL STIPULATIONS:
Must be Black Colorado resident for five years.

THE SCHOMBURG CENTER FOR RESEARCH IN BLACK CULTURE
515 Malcolm X Boulevard
New York, NY 10037-1801
(212) 491-2228
Fax: (212) 491-2098

E-MAIL ADDRESS:
sir@nypl.org

WEB SITE ADDRESS:
www.nypl.org/locations/tid/64/node/131

TYPE:
Fellowships. Awarded to scholars and professionals whose research in the Black experience can benefit from extended access to the Center's collections. Seminars, colloquia, forums, symposia and conferences complement the residency program.

See entry 399 for full listing.

UNITED NEGRO COLLEGE FUND   [1035]
1805 Seventh Street, N.W.
Washington, DC 20001
(800) 331-2244

E-MAIL ADDRESS:
scholarships@uncf.org

WEB SITE ADDRESS:
www.uncf.org

FOUNDED: 1944

TYPE:
Fellowships; Internships; Scholarships; Technical assistance. The Fund, since its founding, has raised money for 39 private, historically Black colleges.

Faculty fellowship programs make it possible for hundreds of instructors to earn doctoral degrees.

Mentoring and internship opportunities are provided for hundreds of UNCF students.

Scholarships are offered to a pool of more than 60,000 talented students attending UNCF colleges and universities. The Fund oversees more than 450 scholarship programs in the following general categories:
(1) geographically based scholarships;
(2) scholarships based on academic major;
(3) scholarships based on merit and need and;
(4) financial aid for graduate study.

PURPOSE:
To provide low-cost quality education in an environment that enables students to excel.

FINANCIAL DATA:
Amount of support per award: Scholarships: $500 to $10,000.

APPLICATION INFORMATION:
Contact the Fund for detailed information.

OFFICERS:
Michael L. Lomax, Ph.D, President and Chief Executive Officer

ADDRESS INQUIRIES TO:
Kimberly Hall, Director Program Services
(See address above.)

Native American

AMERICAN INDIAN COLLEGE FUND   [1036]
8333 Greenwood Boulevard
Denver, CO 80221
(303) 426-8900
Fax: (303) 426-1200

E-MAIL ADDRESS:
scholarships@collegefund.org

WEB SITE ADDRESS:
collegefund.org

FOUNDED: 1989

AREAS OF INTEREST:
Scholarship funding for Native American and Alaska Native students.

NAME(S) OF PROGRAMS:
● **Full Circle Scholarship Program**
● **TCU Scholarship Program**

TYPE:
Scholarships.

YEAR PROGRAM STARTED: 1989

PURPOSE:
To educate the mind and spirit of Native American communities by providing undergraduate and graduate Native student scholarships and programmatic support for the nation's 34 accredited tribal colleges and universities to provide access to an affordable, quality higher education while preserving Native cultures and languages; to make scholarships available to undergraduate and graduate Native students at any accredited public or private (nonprofit) college.

ELIGIBILITY:
Minimum requirements for all American Indian College Fund Full Circle Scholarships include:
(1) U.S. citizenship;
(2) enrollment full-time in an accredited tribal, public or private (nonprofit) college or university;
(3) ability to trace Indian ancestry; registered as a member of a federal- or state-recognized tribe, or a descendant of at least one grandparent or parent who is an enrolled tribal member; Alaska Natives may use Native Corporation membership;
(4) minimum grade point average of 2.0 mandatory (many Full Circle Scholarships funded by Fund's partners are more competitive) and;
(5) submission of a completed online application.

Eligible organizations have to be 501(c)(3) not-for-profit. No grants are made to religious organizations.

GEOGRAPHIC RESTRICTIONS:
United States.

FINANCIAL DATA:
Amount of support per award: Scholarships: $1,000 to $18,000 per year.

APPLICATION INFORMATION:
Guidelines and application form are available on the web site.
Deadline: Applications accepted January 1 to May 31 each year.

ADDRESS INQUIRIES TO:
See e-mail address above.

AMERICAN INDIAN GRADUATE CENTER   [1037]
3701 San Mateo Boulevard, N.E.
Suite 200
Albuquerque, NM 87110
(505) 881-4584
Fax: (505) 884-0427

E-MAIL ADDRESS:
fellowships@aigcs.org

WEB SITE ADDRESS:
www.aigcs.org

FOUNDED: 1969

AREAS OF INTEREST:
Graduate-level education in any field.

NAME(S) OF PROGRAMS:
● **Fellowships for American Indians or Alaskan Natives**

TYPE:
Fellowships; Grants-in-aid; Scholarships. Grants on an academic year basis. Summer funding available to continuing students only; these are students who are currently in the fellowship program.

YEAR PROGRAM STARTED: 1969

PURPOSE:
To help open doors to graduate education and help tribes obtain the educated professionals they need to become more self-sufficient and exercise their rights to self-determination.

LEGAL BASIS:
IRS status 501(c)(3), tax-exempt, incorporated in New Mexico.

ELIGIBILITY:
An applicant must be an enrolled member of a U.S. federally recognized American Indian tribe or Alaska Native group, or possess one-fourth degree Indian blood from a federally recognized tribe. Applicant must be pursuing a Master's, Doctorate or professional degree as a full-time graduate student at an accredited graduate school in the U.S. and must be in financial need. They must submit an essay as described in application packet. Applicants must apply for federal financial and campus-based aid at the financial aid office of the university they plan to attend.

GEOGRAPHIC RESTRICTIONS:
United States.

FINANCIAL DATA:
Awards are based on each applicant's unmet financial need as verified by the applicant's college financial aid office. Fellowships are

supplementary grants and are only a percentage of a student's total unmet financial need.

Amount of support per award: Varies.

Total amount of support: Varies.

Matching fund requirements: Universities are encouraged to provide assistance.

COOPERATIVE FUNDING PROGRAMS: The organization works with other scholarship agencies to assure that there will be no overfunding of students.

NUMBER OF APPLICANTS MOST RECENT YEAR: Over 600 for the year 2013.

NUMBER OF AWARDS: Over 500 for the year 2013.

APPLICATION INFORMATION:
Application must be submitted online.

Duration: One academic year at a time. Students may reapply each year.

Deadline: June 1.

PUBLICATIONS:
Annual report; newsletter; brochure.

IRS IDENTIFICATION NUMBER: 85-0222386

ADDRESS INQUIRIES TO:
See e-mail address above.

AMERICAN INDIAN SCIENCE AND ENGINEERING SOCIETY (AISES)   [1038]
2305 Renard, S.E.
Suite 200
Albuquerque, NM 87106
(505) 765-1052 ext. 103
(720) 552-6123

E-MAIL ADDRESS:
kcristiano@aises.org

WEB SITE ADDRESS:
www.aises.org/scholarships

FOUNDED: 1977

AREAS OF INTEREST:
American Indian education in the science and engineering fields.

NAME(S) OF PROGRAMS:
● **A.T. Anderson Memorial Scholarship**

TYPE:
Scholarships. AISES scholarships are intended to partially defray tuition and other educational expenses, thereby increasing access to higher education and improving college retention rates for AISES members.

AISES scholarships are made possible by corporations, government agencies, foundations, and individuals who wish to support the advancement of American Indians/Alaskan Natives. Scholarships are distributed in two disbursements and awarded for one academic year, unless otherwise specified. Recipients cannot receive more than one scholarship in any of the six programs.

Scholarships are also awarded to members of AISES who are American Indian/Alaskan Native college students who meet the eligibility requirements for each scholarship.

YEAR PROGRAM STARTED: 1983

PURPOSE:
To significantly increase the number of American Indian/Alaskan Native scientists and engineers, and develop knowledgeable leaders within native communities; to foster

the building of community by bridging science and technology with traditional native values.

LEGAL BASIS:
Private, nonprofit corporation.

ELIGIBILITY:
Applicant must be a current member of AISES and a full-time undergraduate or graduate student at an accredited four-year college/university, or a full-time student at a two-year college enrolled in a program leading to an academic degree, with a 3.0 minimum, cumulative grade point average. Candidate must major in Math, Science, Engineering, Physical Science, Medicine, or Natural Resources. Candidate must be at least one-quarter American Indian/Alaskan Native or otherwise considered American Indian by a member with which affiliation is claimed.

GEOGRAPHIC RESTRICTIONS:
United States and Canada.

FINANCIAL DATA:
Amount of support per award: $1,000 undergraduate and $2,000 graduate per year.

Total amount of support: Varies.

NUMBER OF AWARDS: 20 to 40 for the year 2014-15.

APPLICATION INFORMATION:
Guidelines and application are available on the web site after April 11, or can be requested from the Society.

Duration: One academic year.

Deadline: May 26 (postmark).

PUBLICATIONS:
AISES Scholarship Program brochure.

IRS IDENTIFICATION NUMBER: 73-1023474

STAFF:
Tina Farrenkopf, Director of Programs

ADDRESS INQUIRIES TO:
Katherine Cristiano, Programs Coordinator
American Indian Science
and Engineering Society
1630 Main Street, Suite 201
Longmont, CO 80501
Tel: (720) 552-6123

AMERICAN INDIAN SCIENCE AND ENGINEERING SOCIETY (AISES)   [1039]
P.O. Box 9828
Albuquerque, NM 87119-9828
(505) 765-1052

E-MAIL ADDRESS:
info@aises.org

WEB SITE ADDRESS:
www.aises.org/Programs/
ScholarshipsandInternships/Scholarships

FOUNDED: 1977

AREAS OF INTEREST:
American Indian education in the science, engineering and other related technical fields.

NAME(S) OF PROGRAMS:
● **AISES Google Scholarship**

TYPE:
Scholarships.

PURPOSE:
To aid in the education of American Indians and Alaskan Natives in the science, engineering fields and other related technical fields.

ELIGIBILITY:
Applicant must:
(1) be a current AISES member;
(2) be a member of an American Indian tribe, Alaska Native or Native Hawaiian or otherwise considered to be an American Indian by the tribe with which affiliation is claimed; or is at least one-fourth American Indian blood; or is at least one-fourth Alaskan Native or considered to be an Alaskan Native by an Alaskan Native group by which affiliation is claimed. Proof of tribal enrollment is required;
(3) be a full-time undergraduate or graduate student at an accredited four-year college or university, or in the second year at a two-year college leading to a four-year degree and have a minimum cumulative grade point average of 3.5 and;
(4) be majoring in one of the following disciplines: computer science or computer engineering.

GEOGRAPHIC RESTRICTIONS:
United States and Canada.

FINANCIAL DATA:
Amount of support per award: $10,000.

Total amount of support: $100,000 for the year 2012.

APPLICATION INFORMATION:
Complete information is available online.

Duration: One year.

Deadline: March 31.

ADDRESS INQUIRIES TO:
Deleana Otherbull, Programs Officer
(See address above.)

AMERICAN PHILOSOPHICAL SOCIETY   [1040]
104 South Fifth Street
Philadelphia, PA 19106-3387
(215) 440-3429

E-MAIL ADDRESS:
lmusumeci@amphilsoc.org

WEB SITE ADDRESS:
www.amphilsoc.org

FOUNDED: 1743

AREAS OF INTEREST:
Scholarly research.

NAME(S) OF PROGRAMS:
● **Phillips Fund Grants for Native American Research**

TYPE:
Grants-in-aid; Research grants. Postgraduate grants for research on North American Indian linguistics, ethnohistory and the history of studies of Native Americans in the continental U.S. and Canada. The Committee prefers supporting the work of younger scholars/graduate students for research on Master's or doctoral dissertations. Grants are for travel costs, tapes and consultants' fees.

YEAR PROGRAM STARTED: 1940

LEGAL BASIS:
Nonprofit learned society.

ELIGIBILITY:
Open to graduate students and postdoctoral candidates.

The grants described above are for research in Native American linguistics and ethnohistory, as well as in the history of studies of Native Americans. There are no ethnic restrictions on applicants. Work must be on groups located north of the U.S.-Mexican border.

The Committee will seldom approve more than two awards to the same person within a five-year period. Grants are not made for projects in archaeology, ethnography, psycholinguistics, or for the preparation of pedagogical materials, general maintenance or purchase of permanent equipment (tape recorders, books, etc.).

FINANCIAL DATA:
The grants are intended for such extra costs as travel, tapes, films, consultants' fees, etc., but not for the purchase of permanent equipment (tape recorders, books, etc.)
Amount of support per award: Awards average $2,500; grants do not exceed $3,500.
Total amount of support: $56,600 for the year 2013.

NUMBER OF APPLICANTS MOST RECENT YEAR:
49 for the year 2011.

NUMBER OF AWARDS: 23 for the year 2013.

APPLICATION INFORMATION:
Application must be submitted electronically through the Society's online portal. Up to two additional pages may be submitted for the project statement.

Two letters of support are required.

The application and both letters of reference must be received by the deadline.
Duration: One year.
Deadline: March 1. Notification by May.

ADDRESS INQUIRIES TO:
Linda Musumeci
Director of Grants and Fellowships
(See address above.)

ASSOCIATION ON AMERICAN INDIAN AFFAIRS [1041]

966 Hungerford Drive, Suite 12-B
Rockville, MD 20850
(240) 314-7155
Fax: (240) 314-7159

E-MAIL ADDRESS:
lw.aaia@indian-affairs.org

WEB SITE ADDRESS:
www.indian-affairs.org

FOUNDED: 1922

AREAS OF INTEREST:
Advocates for the well-being of Indian people. Primary focus on cultural preservation, youth/education and sovereignty.

NAME(S) OF PROGRAMS:
● **David Risling Emergency Aid Scholarships**

TYPE:
Grants-in-aid; Scholarships. Emergency Aid Scholarships are for full-time graduate and undergraduate students who are seeking a degree in any curriculum. This program is limited by the availability of scholarship funds.

YEAR PROGRAM STARTED: 1922

PURPOSE:
To promote the welfare of American Indians and Alaska Natives by supporting efforts to sustain and perpetuate their cultures and languages; to protect their sovereignty, constitutional, legal and human rights and natural resources; to improve their health, education and economic and community development.

ELIGIBILITY:
The applicant must meet the following basic requirements:
(1) be enrolled in one's tribe;
(2) be attending an accredited school full-time both fall and spring semesters and;
(3) be seeking an Associate's degree or higher.

Scholarship is open to college freshman, sophomores, juniors, seniors and graduate students from federally recognized tribes and tribes not recognized by the federal government. Funding is limited to eviction, utility disconnection, removal of children from daycare for nonpayment or some extreme car repairs for commuting students. Other extreme hardship may be considered on a case-by-case basis.

Expected expenses such as tuition, books and computers will not be funded. Expenses incurred over the summer months will not be funded.

GEOGRAPHIC RESTRICTIONS:
Continental United States and Alaska.

FINANCIAL DATA:
Amount of support per award: $100 to $400, pending availability and whether the emergency qualifies. Dollars and types of situations funded are very limited.

NUMBER OF AWARDS: Varies.

APPLICATION INFORMATION:
Students must call AAIA's Director of Scholarship Programs in its Rockville, MD office prior to applying.
Deadline: Acceptance period is mid-October to early May, pending availability of funds. Turnaround time may be up to two weeks from time of first contacting AAIA office.

ADDRESS INQUIRIES TO:
Lisa Wyzlic
Director of Scholarship Programs
(See address above.)

ASSOCIATION ON AMERICAN INDIAN AFFAIRS [1042]

966 Hungerford Drive, Suite 12-B
Rockville, MD 20850
(240) 314-7155
Fax: (240) 314-7159

E-MAIL ADDRESS:
lw.aaia@indian-affairs.org

WEB SITE ADDRESS:
www.indian-affairs.org

FOUNDED: 1922

AREAS OF INTEREST:
Advocates for the well-being of Indian people. Primary focus on cultural preservation, youth/education and sovereignty.

NAME(S) OF PROGRAMS:
● **Graduate Scholarships**

TYPE:
Scholarships.

PURPOSE:
To promote the welfare of American Indians and Alaska Natives by supporting efforts to sustain and perpetuate their cultures and languages; to protect their sovereignty, constitutional, legal and human rights and natural resources; to improve their health, education and economic and community development.

LEGAL BASIS:
Charitable nonprofit foundation.

ELIGIBILITY:
The applicant must meet the following basic requirements:
(1) be enrolled in one's tribe;
(2) be attending an accredited school full-time both fall and spring semesters and;
(3) be seeking a Master's degree in any curriculum, Ph.D., law degree or medical degree.

GEOGRAPHIC RESTRICTIONS:
Continental United States and Alaska.

FINANCIAL DATA:
Amount of support per award: $1,500.

NUMBER OF AWARDS: Varies.

APPLICATION INFORMATION:
Application information is available on the web site each February.
Duration: One year.
Deadline: Acceptance period changes from year to year.

ADDRESS INQUIRIES TO:
Lisa Wyzlic
Director of Scholarship Programs
(See address above.)

ASSOCIATION ON AMERICAN INDIAN AFFAIRS [1043]

966 Hungerford Drive, Suite 12-B
Rockville, MD 20850
(240) 314-7155
Fax: (240) 314-7159

E-MAIL ADDRESS:
lw.aaia@indian-affairs.org

WEB SITE ADDRESS:
www.indian-affairs.org

FOUNDED: 1922

AREAS OF INTEREST:
Advocates for the well-being of Indian people. Primary focus on cultural preservation, youth/education and sovereignty.

NAME(S) OF PROGRAMS:
● **Undergraduate Scholarships**

TYPE:
Scholarships.

PURPOSE:
To promote the welfare of American Indians and Alaska Natives by supporting efforts to sustain and perpetuate their cultures and languages; to protect their sovereignty, constitutional, legal and human rights and natural resources; to improve their health, education and economic and community development.

ELIGIBILITY:
The applicant must meet the following basic requirements:
(1) be enrolled in one's tribe;
(2) be attending an accredited school full-time both fall and spring semesters and;
(3) be seeking an Associate's or Bachelor's degree.
These Scholarships are open to high school seniors who will be entering college in the fall, college freshman, sophomores, juniors and seniors.

GEOGRAPHIC RESTRICTIONS:
Continental United States and Alaska.

FINANCIAL DATA:
Amount of support per award: $1,500.

NUMBER OF AWARDS: Varies.

APPLICATION INFORMATION:
Application information is available on the web site each February.

Duration: One year.

Deadline: Acceptance period changes from year to year.

PUBLICATIONS:
Brochure.

ADDRESS INQUIRIES TO:
Lisa Wyzlic
Director of Scholarship Programs
(See address above.)

ASSOCIATION ON AMERICAN INDIAN AFFAIRS   [1044]
966 Hungerford Drive, Suite 12-B
Rockville, MD 20850
(240) 314-7155
Fax: (240) 314-7159

E-MAIL ADDRESS:
lw.aaia@indian-affairs.org

WEB SITE ADDRESS:
www.indian-affairs.org

FOUNDED: 1922

AREAS OF INTEREST:
Advocates for the well-being of Indian people. Primary focus on cultural preservation, youth/education and sovereignty.

NAME(S) OF PROGRAMS:
● **Allogan Slagle Memorial Scholarship**

TYPE:
Scholarships. Offered to American Indian and Alaskan Native graduate and undergraduate students in any curriculum who are members of tribes that are not federally recognized.

PURPOSE:
To promote the welfare of American Indians and Alaska Natives by supporting efforts to sustain and perpetuate their cultures and languages; to protect their sovereignty, constitutional, legal and human rights and natural resources; to improve their health, education and economic and community development.

ELIGIBILITY:
Applicants must be American Indian and Native Alaskan graduate or undergraduate students in any curriculum who are members of tribes that are not federally recognized. This Scholarship is open to high school seniors who will be entering college in the fall, college freshman, sophomores, juniors, seniors and graduate students.

The applicant must meet the following basic requirements:
(1) be enrolled in one's tribe;
(2) be attending an accredited school full-time both fall and spring semesters and;
(3) be seeking an Associate's degree or higher.

FINANCIAL DATA:
Amount of support per award: $1,500 ($750 each for fall and spring semesters).

NUMBER OF AWARDS: Varies.

APPLICATION INFORMATION:
Application information is available on the web site.

Duration: One year. Students are eligible to apply on a yearly basis.

Deadline: Acceptance period changes from year to year.

ADDRESS INQUIRIES TO:
Lisa Wyzlic
Director of Scholarship Programs
(See address above.)

BNSF RAILWAY FOUNDATION   [1045]
2650 Lou Menk Drive
Fort Worth, TX 76131-2830
(817) 867-6458
Fax: (817) 352-7925

E-MAIL ADDRESS:
bnsffoundation@bnsf.com

WEB SITE ADDRESS:
www.bnsffoundation.org

NAME(S) OF PROGRAMS:
● **Native American Scholarship Program**

TYPE:
Scholarships. Awarded annually to outstanding Native American high school seniors from funds provided by the Foundation, for up to four years or until undergraduate degree requirements are completed, whichever occurs first. Scholarship winners may attend any accredited college (two-year leading to a four-year degree) or university in the U.S.

LEGAL BASIS:
Corporate foundation.

ELIGIBILITY:
High school seniors having one-fourth or more Indian blood are eligible. Applicants need not be related to Burlington Northern Santa Fe personnel to qualify. Two scholarships are provided exclusively for members of the Navajo Tribe and the other three are available to any Native American high school students residing in Arizona, California, Colorado, Kansas, Minnesota, Montana, New Mexico, North Dakota, Oklahoma, Oregon, South Dakota, or Washington.

Winners are selected on the basis of strong academic performance in high school, with award preference being given to the study of any of the sciences such as medicine, engineering, natural and physical sciences, as well as business, education and health administration.

GEOGRAPHIC RESTRICTIONS:
Arizona, California, Colorado, Kansas, Minnesota, Montana, New Mexico, North Dakota, Oklahoma, Oregon, South Dakota and Washington.

FINANCIAL DATA:
Amount of support per award: $1,000 to $2,500 annually for up to four years or until undergraduate degree requirements are completed, whichever occurs first (but not to exceed five years). Financial need determines the amount awarded.

NUMBER OF AWARDS: 5.

APPLICATION INFORMATION:
The scholarship is administered by the American Indian Science and Engineering Society (AISES) and all winners are selected by the organization. Applications may be obtained by writing American Indian Science and Engineering Society, P.O. Box 9828, Albuquerque, NM 87119-9828. All correspondence and questions should be directed to AISES.

ADDRESS INQUIRIES TO:
Lisa Wyzlic
Director of Scholarship Programs
(See address above.)

Duration: Up to four years or until undergraduate degree requirements are completed, whichever occurs first, but not to exceed five years.

ADDRESS INQUIRIES TO:
American Indian Science and Engineering Society
(See address above.)

BUREAU OF INDIAN EDUCATION   [1046]
1849 C Street, N.W.
MS 3609 MIB
Washington, DC 20240
(202) 208-6123
Fax: (202) 208-3312

WEB SITE ADDRESS:
www.bie.edu

FOUNDED: 1824

AREAS OF INTEREST:
Elementary and secondary education tribal colleges.

NAME(S) OF PROGRAMS:
● **Higher Education Grant Program for American Indians**

TYPE:
Fellowships; Scholarships.

YEAR PROGRAM STARTED: 1949

PURPOSE:
To provide financial aid to eligible Indian students enabling them to attend accredited institutions of higher education.

LEGAL BASIS:
Snyder Act.

ELIGIBILITY:
Applicant must be a member of a tribe eligible for services from the Bureau, enrolled or accepted for enrollment in an accredited college and have financial need as determined by the institution's financial aid office.

FINANCIAL DATA:
The grants are intended to supplement the financial aid package prepared by the educational institution's financial aid officer. The grant meets the unmet need portion of the package.

Amount of support per award: Varies.

Total amount of support: Varies.

Matching fund requirements: Meets the unmet need portion of the institution's financial aid package.

COOPERATIVE FUNDING PROGRAMS: Other donor's funding programs are a part of the financial aid package.

NUMBER OF APPLICANTS MOST RECENT YEAR: 20,000.

NUMBER OF AWARDS: 15,000.

APPLICATION INFORMATION:
Candidates should request an application from a home agency or tribal Higher Education Grant Program (HEGP). Contact the BIA/Tribal census office to obtain a Certificate of Degree of Indian Blood (CDIB) and tribal enrollment and submit with the application. Write to the admissions office of the chosen school for an application. Request a financial aid packet from the school's Financial Aid Officer, who will prepare a financial aid package based on the applicant's need. Then submit all these forms to the appropriate offices well in advance of the deadline.

Duration: One academic year. Must renew annually.

Deadline: Varies.

PUBLICATIONS:
Newsletter for prospective college students.

ADDRESS INQUIRIES TO:
Home agency or tribally administered Higher Education Grant Program

CATCHING THE DREAM   [1047]

8200 Mountain Road, N.E.
Suite 203
Albuquerque, NM 87110
(505) 262-2351
Fax: (505) 262-0534

E-MAIL ADDRESS:
NScholarsh@aol.com

WEB SITE ADDRESS:
www.catchingthedream.org

FOUNDED: 1986

AREAS OF INTEREST:
Scholarships for Native college students and improvement of Indian schools and postsecondary education for Native American students in the fields of math, engineering, science, business, education and computers.

CONSULTING OR VOLUNTEER SERVICES:
The Fund assists Native American students who need help in locating other sources of funding and provides fund-raising, management training, conferences, and seminars.

NAME(S) OF PROGRAMS:
• **Math and Science Teaching (MAST)**
• **MESBEC (Math, Engineering, Science, Business, Education and Computers) Program**
• **Native American Leadership in Education (NALE) Program**
• **Reading Award Program (RAP)**
• **Tribal Business Management (TBM) Program**

TYPE:
Conferences/seminars; Fellowships; Scholarships; Technical assistance. CTD also works to improve Indian schools through a program of grants and technical assistance. This work has led to the development of 40 Exemplary Programs in Indian education since 1988. The annual Exemplary Institute is a meeting of these Exemplary Programs, where they teach other people how to develop similar programs.

MAST program makes grants of $5,000 to Indian high schools to improve their math and science teaching.

MESBEC Program consists of competitive scholarships for high-potential Native Americans studying in math, engineering, science, business, education and computers.

NALE Program consists of competitive scholarships for high-potential paraprofessional Native Americans who plan to complete their degrees and obtain credentials as teachers, counselors or administrators.

RAP makes grants to Indian schools to improve the reading ability of their students.

Tribal Business Management (TBM) Program consists of competitive scholarships for Native students in all fields of business.

YEAR PROGRAM STARTED: 1986

PURPOSE:
To help tribes prepare young people to work in the fields which are critical for economic, social, business and political development in Indian Country.

LEGAL BASIS:
Nonprofit organization.

ELIGIBILITY:
Applicants must be at least one-quarter blood member of a federally recognized, state recognized or terminated Indian tribe. They must have high potential for the field of study and work for which they are preparing. They must attend an accredited U.S. college or university. They must have clear goals in mind and have done some work toward accomplishing these goals. The goals must be related to the betterment of Indian people or the betterment of an Indian tribe or community. Progress toward accomplishing a goal may be demonstrated by study, by work, by volunteer work or by other means.

Students with no clear goals are discouraged from applying. Normally, successful applicants will plan to earn a four-year degree or a graduate degree. In a few cases, associate degrees are approved. Applicants must apply for all other sources of funding for which they are eligible, including private scholarship sources, corporate traineeships, federal funds, loans, jobs, grants and so forth.

Students can contact CTD up to three years in advance.

GEOGRAPHIC RESTRICTIONS:
United States.

FINANCIAL DATA:
Amount of support per award: $500 to $5,000.

Total amount of support: $254,000 for the year 2014.

NUMBER OF AWARDS: MAST: 6; RAP: 17; All other programs: 189 for the year 2014.

APPLICATION INFORMATION:
Contact Catching the Dream.

Duration: Until completion of degree.

Deadline: March 15 for summer school. September 15 for winter quarter and spring semester. April 15 for fall semester.

PUBLICATIONS:
The National Indian Grant Directory; *Preparing Indian Students for College*; *Exemplary Programs in Indian Education*; *Reading for College*; *Racism in Indian Country*; *Modern American Indian Leaders*; *The Secret of No Face*; *Basics of Fund Raising*; *How to Write Winning Proposals*; *Literacy in Indian Country.*

IRS IDENTIFICATION NUMBER: 85-0360858

BOARD OF DIRECTORS:
James Lujan, President
Darrell Jeanotte, Vice President
Gloria Hale, Treasurer
Jodie Palmer, Secretary
Dr. Dean Chavers
Ed Harris
Kelvin Sampson
Dr. Lester Sandoval
Ms. Lynn Okon Scholnick
John Tohtsoni, Jr.
Lindsay Wagner

CHEROKEE NATION   [1048]

P.O. Box 948
Tahlequah, OK 74465
(918) 453-5000
(918) 453-5465
Fax: (918) 458-6286

E-MAIL ADDRESS:
mandy-scott@cherokee.org

WEB SITE ADDRESS:
www.cherokee.org

FOUNDED: 1904

AREAS OF INTEREST:
Planning and development (individual and tribal), health, education and welfare.

CONSULTING OR VOLUNTEER SERVICES:
Tribal government administration consultants and volunteers in all interest areas available to eligible tribal members.

NAME(S) OF PROGRAMS:
• **College Resource Center**

TYPE:
Project/program grants; Scholarships; Technical assistance. Financial and other support through all programs to eligible tribal members.

YEAR PROGRAM STARTED: 1964

PURPOSE:
To serve its tribes and members in the areas indicated.

LEGAL BASIS:
Federally recognized Indian tribe.

ELIGIBILITY:
Tribal membership is required.

GEOGRAPHIC RESTRICTIONS:
Primarily northeast Oklahoma.

FINANCIAL DATA:
Tribe operates $300,000,000 in social and economic programs.

Amount of support per award: Varies.

Total amount of support: Varies.

APPLICATION INFORMATION:
Guidelines and application form are available on the web site.

Duration: Varies.

Deadline: Varies.

ADDRESS INQUIRIES TO:
Mandy Scott
Manager, College Resource Center
(See e-mail address above.)

FIRST NATIONS DEVELOPMENT INSTITUTE   [1049]

2432 Main Street, Second Floor
Longmont, CO 80501
(303) 774-7836
Fax: (303) 774-7841

E-MAIL ADDRESS:
info@firstnations.org

WEB SITE ADDRESS:
www.firstnations.org

FOUNDED: 1980

AREAS OF INTEREST:
Native American-owned business, small business development and capacity building.

CONSULTING OR VOLUNTEER SERVICES:
Yes.

NAME(S) OF PROGRAMS:
• **The Eagle Staff Fund**

TYPE:
Program development grants.

YEAR PROGRAM STARTED: 1994

PURPOSE:
To assist native communities to control their assets and to build capacity so that they can direct their economic futures.

LEGAL BASIS:
Nonprofit organization.

ELIGIBILITY:
Eligible organizations include:
(1) tribal or Native government programs, entities, and enterprises;
(2) tribally or community-controlled development organizations;
(3) tribally or Native-controlled health, education, or other social programs or institutions;
(4) Native arts and crafts associations, co-ops and guilds;
(5) intertribal and regional tribal or Native groups;
(6) Native grassroots efforts and community programs and;
(7) Native nonprofit on or near Reservation.

Grants are not made to individuals for for-profit businesses, programs serving exclusively urban Native communities, programs serving Natives but not controlled by a majority of Natives, for-profit Native consulting firms, for-profit Native businesses except those associated with a nonprofit Native enterprise, or religious organizations (except for traditional Native American spiritual programs).

GEOGRAPHIC RESTRICTIONS:
United States and its territories.

FINANCIAL DATA:
Amount of support per award: Varies.
Total amount of support: Varies.

NUMBER OF AWARDS: 26.

APPLICATION INFORMATION:
Application must be made online. Complete information is available on the web site.
Duration: Typically one year.

PUBLICATIONS:
Publications list; annual report.

IRS IDENTIFICATION NUMBER: 54-1254491

ADDRESS INQUIRIES TO:
Marsha Whiting, Senior Program Officer
(See address above.)

HOLLAND & KNIGHT CHARITABLE FOUNDATION, INC.   [1050]
P.O. Box 2877
Tampa, FL 33601-2877
(813) 227-8500

E-MAIL ADDRESS:
nativewriters@hklaw.com

WEB SITE ADDRESS:
foundation.hklaw.com

AREAS OF INTEREST:
The development of Native American youth.

NAME(S) OF PROGRAMS:
● **Young Native Writers Essay Contest**

TYPE:
Awards/prizes; Scholarships. Young Native Writers Essay Contest is a writing contest for Native American high school students.

PURPOSE:
To encourage young Native Americans to think about the critical issues impacting their tribal communities today.

ELIGIBILITY:
Contest is open to Native American high school students currently enrolled in grades nine to 12 only. All students participating in Young Native Writers Essay Contest should have a significant and current relationship with a Native American tribal community.

FINANCIAL DATA:
The five First-Place Winners will each receive an all-expense-paid trip to Washington, DC, to visit the National Museum of the American Indian and other prominent sites. The winners will be accompanied by the teachers who inspired their entries into the contest. First-Place Winners will receive a special award for display at home or school.
Amount of support per award: Each First-Place Winner will receive a scholarship of $2,500 to be paid directly to the college or university of his or her choice.

APPLICATION INFORMATION:
All essays must be uploaded to the contest web. Essays sent by mail, faxed or e-mailed will be disqualified. The body of contestant's essay may be no more than 1,200 words. The essays must be written in English. Every student must also submit an entry form which he or she will be prompted to complete before he or she uploads his/her essay. Every essay must include a Bibliography, Works Cited or Reference Page (which are not to be included in the word count).

The Foundation will identify contestant's essay electronically through the entry form completed when entering the contest. Contestant must not include his/her name anywhere on any page of his/her essay.

Those entering this contest must read carefully the entire body of instructions on the contest web site.
Deadline: April 30.

*SPECIAL STIPULATIONS:
The winners of the essay contest must agree to participate in the entire trip to Washington, DC, in order to receive a scholarship. In the event that a winner is unable or unwilling to participate in the trip to Washington, DC, in its entirety, no substitution prize will be awarded.

INSTITUTE OF AMERICAN INDIAN ARTS (IAIA)   [1051]
83 Avan Nu Po Road
Santa Fe, NM 87508
(505) 424-5724
(800) 804-6422
Fax: (505) 424-0909

E-MAIL ADDRESS:
lbarela@iaia.edu

WEB SITE ADDRESS:
www.iaia.edu

FOUNDED: 1962

AREAS OF INTEREST:
Education of Native American and Alaska Native Corporation students through a four-year program leading to a Bachelor of Fine Arts or Bachelor of Arts degree.

CONSULTING OR VOLUNTEER SERVICES:
Serve as a resource to Indian tribes seeking to develop arts educational programs or tribal museums and cultural centers.

NAME(S) OF PROGRAMS:
● **IAIA Merit Scholarship**
● **IAIA Tuition Scholarship**

TYPE:
Awards/prizes; Scholarships.

YEAR PROGRAM STARTED: 1962

PURPOSE:
To provide a four-year postsecondary education to American Indian and Alaska natives.

LEGAL BASIS:
Congressionally chartered, fully accredited institute.

ELIGIBILITY:
Applicants for scholarships must be members of federally recognized tribes and must be enrolled at IAIA.

IAIA Tuition Scholarship is awarded, based on need, to full- or part-time degree-seeking students who are from a federally recognized Indian tribe or are Alaskan natives.

Any student, regardless of nationality, with academic performance of 3.0 or above may apply for the IAIA Merit Scholarship.

American Indian College Fund is awarded based on need and merit.

FINANCIAL DATA:
Amount of support per award: IAIA Merit Scholarship: $500 to $1,000; IAIA Tuition Scholarship: $200 to $500.
Total amount of support: Varies.

COOPERATIVE FUNDING PROGRAMS: Federal Pell Grant; Federal College Work-Study; Bureau of Indian Affairs fund programs (home agency): awarded for personal/miscellaneous, books, supplies and transportation.

NUMBER OF APPLICANTS MOST RECENT YEAR:
Approximately 300.

APPLICATION INFORMATION:
Contact IAIA Financial Aid Manager for information. Submit FAFSA and tax information, as well as tribal enrollment documentation.
Duration: One year.
Deadline: Mid-August and mid-January.

PUBLICATIONS:
Academic catalog; academic brochures; admissions application; financial aid applications.

IRS IDENTIFICATION NUMBER: 85-0365964

OFFICERS:
Dr. Robert Martin, President
Lawrence Mirabal, Chief Financial Officer
Nena Anaya, Director of Students Success Center and Enrollment Management Director
Dr. Ann Filemyr, Academic Dean
Carmen Henan, Dean of Students

ADDRESS INQUIRIES TO:
Lara Barela, Financial Aid Director
(See address above.)

*PLEASE NOTE:
Non-Indian and/or foreign students accepted.

NATIONAL SOCIETY DAUGHTERS OF THE AMERICAN REVOLUTION

1776 D Street, N.W.
Washington, DC 20006-5303
(202) 879-3292
Fax: (202) 879-3348

WEB SITE ADDRESS:
www.dar.org

TYPE:
Scholarships. Intended to help Native American college/university and technical school students at the undergraduate or graduate level.

See entry 1722 for full listing.

NATIONAL SOCIETY DAUGHTERS OF THE AMERICAN REVOLUTION

1776 D Street, N.W.
Washington, DC 20006-5303
(202) 879-3292
Fax: (202) 879-3348

WEB SITE ADDRESS:
www.dar.org

TYPE:
Scholarships. Intended to help Native American students enrolled full-time at a two- or four-year college or university.

See entry 1723 for full listing.

NATIVE AMERICAN COMMUNITY BOARD (NACB)   [1052]

P.O. Box 572
Lake Andes, SD 57356-0572
(605) 487-7072
Fax: (605) 487-7964

E-MAIL ADDRESS:
charon@charles-mix.com

WEB SITE ADDRESS:
www.nativeshop.org

FOUNDED: 1986

AREAS OF INTEREST:
Civil rights, women's rights, reproductive justice, and a healthy environment.

NAME(S) OF PROGRAMS:
● **College Intern Program**

TYPE:
Internships.

PURPOSE:
To address pertinent issues of health, education, land and water rights, and economic development of Native American people.

ELIGIBILITY:
College juniors, seniors or graduate students interested in Native American rights and health issues. Priority will be given to those wishing to stay long-term (six months or longer).

FINANCIAL DATA:
Amount of support per award: $250 biweekly.
Total amount of support: Varies.

NUMBER OF AWARDS: 8.

APPLICATION INFORMATION:
Contact the NACB for application procedures.

Duration: Three months to one year, with three months being the preferred minimum stay.
Deadline: Contact the NACB for openings.

ADDRESS INQUIRIES TO:
Charon Asetoyer, Executive Director
(See address above.)

THE NEWBERRY LIBRARY   [1053]

Committee on Awards
60 West Walton Street
Chicago, IL 60610-7324
(312) 255-3666

E-MAIL ADDRESS:
research@newberry.org

WEB SITE ADDRESS:
www.newberry.org/fellowships

AREAS OF INTEREST:
Native American women, humanities and social sciences.

NAME(S) OF PROGRAMS:
● **Frances C. Allen Fellowships**

TYPE:
Fellowships; Visiting scholars. Allen fellows are expected to spend a significant part of their tenure in residence at Newberry's D'Arcy McNickle Center for American Indian History.

PURPOSE:
To encourage study by Native American women of the humanities and social sciences.

LEGAL BASIS:
Private research library.

ELIGIBILITY:
Applicants must be women of Native American heritage. While candidates for this award may be working on any graduate or pre-professional field related to the Newberry's collection, the particular goal of the Fellowship is to encourage Native American women in their studies of the humanities and social sciences.

FINANCIAL DATA:
Amount of support per award: $2,500 per month stipend; supplemental funding may be available.

NUMBER OF APPLICANTS MOST RECENT YEAR:
4.

NUMBER OF AWARDS: 1.

APPLICATION INFORMATION:
Applications must be submitted through the online webform.
Duration: One to 12 months.
Deadline: January 15.

STAFF:
Diane Dillon, Director of Scholarly and Undergraduate Programs

ADDRESS INQUIRIES TO:
See e-mail address above.

*SPECIAL STIPULATIONS:
Allen Fellows are expected to spend a significant part of their tenure in residence at the D'Arcy McNickle Center for American Indian History.

NORTH DAKOTA STATE BOARD FOR INDIAN SCHOLARSHIPS   [1054]

1815 Schafer Street
Suite 202
Bismarck, ND 58501-1217
(701) 224-2647
Fax: (701) 224-5707

E-MAIL ADDRESS:
ndfinaid@ndus.edu

WEB SITE ADDRESS:
www.ndus.edu

FOUNDED: 1963

AREAS OF INTEREST:
Native Americans interested in pursuing a higher education degree.

NAME(S) OF PROGRAMS:
● **North Dakota Indian Scholarship Program**

TYPE:
Scholarships. Grants to undergraduate and graduate Native American students in North Dakota colleges.

YEAR PROGRAM STARTED: 1963

PURPOSE:
To provide assistance for Native Americans to attend college.

LEGAL BASIS:
N.D.C.C. 15-63-02.

ELIGIBILITY:
An applicant must be an enrolled member of a federally recognized Indian tribe and a resident of North Dakota. Students must be enrolled on a full-time basis to qualify for the scholarship. An annual application, needs analysis and a current high school or college transcript are required. Additionally, applicants must submit certification of tribal enrollment to the program administrator. Awards are based on merit or need, depending on grade point average. A minimum grade point average of 2.0 is required. All completed applications received by the deadline of July 15 will be given equal consideration.

GEOGRAPHIC RESTRICTIONS:
North Dakota.

FINANCIAL DATA:
Amount of support per award: $1,250 per academic year for undergraduate students and $1,870 per academic year for graduate students. Annual sum is divided into semester or quarter amounts and payment is dependent upon maintenance of C average.

COOPERATIVE FUNDING PROGRAMS: College financial aid directors work out students' aid packages using BIA, Pell, GI Bill, etc.

NUMBER OF APPLICANTS MOST RECENT YEAR:
473.

NUMBER OF AWARDS: 253.

APPLICATION INFORMATION:
Submit application form, budget form, certificate of Indian blood and residence or tribal enrollment, high school credit record and college transcript if previously enrolled.
Deadline: July 15.

OFFICERS:
Sonia Cowen, Interim Vice Chancellor for Academic and Student Affairs, North Dakota University System
Scott Davis, Secretary
Cornelius P. Grant, Appointee

ADDRESS INQUIRIES TO:
Financial Aid Director
(See address above.)

OFFICE OF INDIAN ENERGY AND ECONOMIC DEVELOPMENT [1055]

Division of Workforce Development
MS-SIB-20
1951 Constitution Avenue, N.W.
Washington, DC 20245
(202) 219-0740
Fax: (202) 208-4564

E-MAIL ADDRESS:
jack.stevens@bia.gov

WEB SITE ADDRESS:
www.doi.gov
www.bia.gov

FOUNDED: 1824

AREAS OF INTEREST:
Vocational training, job placement, education, childcare and related services.

NAME(S) OF PROGRAMS:
● **Indian Employment Assistance**
● **Public Law 102-477**

TYPE:
Project/program grants; Training grants. Vocational training and job placement, advisory services and counseling, education, childcare and youth development programs.

YEAR PROGRAM STARTED: 1956

PURPOSE:
To provide individual grants for adult vocational training and job placement services for Indians.

LEGAL BASIS:
Public Law 67-85, The Snyder Act of November 2, 1921; Public Law 84-959, Indian Adult Vocational Training Act of August 3, 1956; Public Law 102-477.

ELIGIBILITY:
Applicant must be a member of a federally recognized tribe, band or group of Indians, whose residence is on or near an Indian reservation under the jurisdiction of BIA.

GEOGRAPHIC RESTRICTIONS:
United States.

FINANCIAL DATA:
Amount of support per award: $800 to $6,500 per year. $5,000 average.
Total amount of support: Over $100,000,000 annually.

COOPERATIVE FUNDING PROGRAMS: Indian Education, Training and Employment.

APPLICATION INFORMATION:
Applicants should make application to the nearest Agency or Tribal Employment Assistance. Contact tribal office nearest to place of residence.
Duration: One year. Renewal possible if continuing training.

STAFF:
Jack Stevens, Acting Chief
Jody Garrison, Workforce Development Specialist

ADDRESS INQUIRIES TO:
Jack Stevens, Acting Chief
(See address above.)

RUNNING STRONG FOR AMERICAN INDIAN YOUTH [1056]

8301 Richmond Highway
Alexandria, VA 22309
(703) 317-9881
(888) 491-9859
Fax: (703) 317-9690

E-MAIL ADDRESS:
info@indianyouth.org

WEB SITE ADDRESS:
www.indianyouth.org

FOUNDED: 1986

AREAS OF INTEREST:
Native Americans.

TYPE:
Capital grants; Challenge/matching grants; General operating grants; Project/program grants; Seed money grants.

YEAR PROGRAM STARTED: 1986

PURPOSE:
To help American Indian people meet their immediate survival needs - food, water and shelter - while implementing and supporting programs designed to create opportunities for self-sufficiency and self-esteem, particularly for tribal youth.

ELIGIBILITY:
No grants are made to individuals or fund-raising events. Grants made only to programs that support Native Americans.

GEOGRAPHIC RESTRICTIONS:
United States.

FINANCIAL DATA:
Amount of support per award: Up to $5,000 for new applicants.

NUMBER OF AWARDS: Varies.

APPLICATION INFORMATION:
E-mail or call for grant guidelines.
Duration: Up to five years. Must reapply each year.

PUBLICATIONS:
Annual report; application guidelines.

IRS IDENTIFICATION NUMBER: 54-1594578

ADDRESS INQUIRIES TO:
Lauren Haas Finkelstein
Executive Director
(See address above.)

U.S. DEPARTMENT OF EDUCATION [1057]

Office of Indian Education
400 Maryland Avenue, S.W.
LBJ Building, 3E205
Washington, DC 20202-6335
(202) 260-3774
(202) 260-1454
Fax: (202) 260-7779

E-MAIL ADDRESS:
indian.education@ed.gov

WEB SITE ADDRESS:
www.ed.gov

NAME(S) OF PROGRAMS:
● **Indian Education-Formula Grants to Local Education Agencies (LEAs)**

TYPE:
Formula grants. Grants to provide financial assistance to LEAs and tribal schools to develop and carry out elementary and secondary school programs specially

designed to meet the special educational and culturally related educational needs of Indian children.

LEGAL BASIS:
Public Law 92-318, Title IV, Part A, as amended (25 U.S.C. 2601-2606, 2651).

ELIGIBILITY:
Local educational agencies which have at least 10 Indian children or in which Indians constitute at least 25% of the total enrollment may apply. However, these enrollment requirements do not apply to an LEA in Alaska, California or Oklahoma that serves Indian children or an LEA on, or in proximity to, an Indian reservation. An Indian tribe or an organization controlled or sanctioned by an Indian tribal government and that operates a school for children of that tribe is eligible if that school provides its students an educational program that meets the standards established by the Bureau of Indian Affairs (BIA) or is operated by that tribe or organization under a contract with the BIA.

FINANCIAL DATA:
Amount of support per award: Varies.
Total amount of support: Varies.

APPLICATION INFORMATION:
Application instructions and forms are available upon request.
Duration: 12 to 36 months, with budget periods of one year's duration.

ADDRESS INQUIRIES TO:
Indian Education Programs
(See address above.)

U.S. DEPARTMENT OF HEALTH AND HUMAN SERVICES [1058]

HHS/ACF/ANA Aerospace Center
901 D Street, S.W., 2nd Floor West
Washington, DC 20447
(202) 690-7776
(877) 922-9262 (Help Desk)
Fax: (202) 690-8145; (202) 690-7441

E-MAIL ADDRESS:
anacomments@acf.hhs.gov

WEB SITE ADDRESS:
www.acf.hhs.gov

FOUNDED: 1974

AREAS OF INTEREST:
General community programming, training and technical assistance and research, demonstration and evaluation.

NAME(S) OF PROGRAMS:
● **Native American Programs**

TYPE:
Demonstration grants; Development grants; Project/program grants; Research grants; Seed money grants; Technical assistance; Training grants. Financial Assistance grants may be used for such purposes as, but not limited to, Governance Projects, development of codes and ordinances and status clarification activities; Economic Development Projects, to promote business starts for Native-owned businesses and improve Native American housing management; and Social Development Projects, to assume local control of planning and delivering social services in Native American communities, developing local models related to comprehensive planning and delivery of social services and developing or coordinating activities with

state-funded projects in decreasing the incidence of child abuse, neglect and fetal alcohol syndrome.

YEAR PROGRAM STARTED: 1973

PURPOSE:
To support projects that improve social and economic conditions of Native Americans within their communities and increase the effectiveness of Indian Tribes and Native American organizations in meeting their economic and social goals.

LEGAL BASIS:
Native American Programs Act of 1974, as amended, Public Law 93-644; Older Americans Act Amendments of 1987, Title V, Public Law 100-175; Indian Reorganization Act Amendments, Section 215, Public Law 100-581; Older Americans Act Amendments of 1992, Title VIII, Public Law 102-375; 42 U.S.C. 2991 et. seq.

ELIGIBILITY:
Governing bodies of Indian tribes, Alaskan Native villages and regional associations established by the Alaska Native Claims Settlement Act, Indian and Alaska Native Organizations in urban or rural nonreservation areas, public and nonprofit agencies serving Native Hawaiians and other Native American Pacific Islanders which include the Native peoples from Guam, American Samoa, Palau or the Commonwealth of the Northern Mariana Islands. The populations served may be located on those islands or in the U.S.

GEOGRAPHIC RESTRICTIONS:
United States.

FINANCIAL DATA:
Amount of support per award: Approximately $125,000 average.

Total amount of support: Approximately $38,500,000 annually.

Matching fund requirements: A matching share of 20% is required unless waived in accordance with criteria which is published in 45 CFR, Part 1336.50. This program has maintenance of effort requirements.

APPLICATION INFORMATION:
Nonprofit organizations which have not previously received ACF program support must submit proof of nonprofit status. The Administration for Native Americans will provide each applicant agency with the appropriate forms for applying for Federal Assistance and instructions for preparation of application for grants from Human Development Services programs.

Applications should be submitted to ACF Division of Grants Management Administration for Children and Families, Mail Stop AERO-6, OPS/ODG, 370 L'Enfant Promenade, S.W., Washington, DC 20447.

Duration: One year with possibility of multiyear funding.

Deadline: Varies.

STAFF:
Lillian Sparks, Commissioner

ADDRESS INQUIRIES TO:
Administration for Native Americans
(See address above.)

THE MORRIS K. UDALL AND STEWART L. UDALL FOUNDATION   [1059]
130 South Scott Avenue
Tucson, AZ 85701
(520) 901-8561
Fax: (520) 901-8570

E-MAIL ADDRESS:
bravo@udall.gov

WEB SITE ADDRESS:
www.udall.gov

FOUNDED: 1992

AREAS OF INTEREST:
Educating young Americans in our nation's heritage, environmental studies, Native American affairs and public policy conflict resolution.

NAME(S) OF PROGRAMS:
● **Congressional Internships**

TYPE:
Internships. Congressional Internships: Native American college students work in congressional offices and the White House to gain a firsthand understanding of the federal government. They also take field trips and meet with congressional members, agency heads and cabinet secretaries.

YEAR PROGRAM STARTED: 1996

PURPOSE:
To educate a new generation of Americans to preserve and protect their national heritage through studies in the environment, Native American health and tribal policy and effective public policy conflict resolution.

LEGAL BASIS:
The Foundation is an executive branch agency. The President of the U.S. appoints its board of trustees with the advice and consent of the U.S. Senate.

ELIGIBILITY:
Interns will be selected by an independent committee. Applicants must demonstrate a commitment to learning about the federal government. They must be self-motivated and interested in taking advantage of the rich and diverse resources available to them in Washington, DC. Additionally, candidates for the internship program must:
(1) be an enrolled member of a recognized tribe or state-recognized tribe;
(2) be a college junior, senior, graduate student, law student or graduating from a tribal college;
(3) have a minimum 3.0 grade point average or a "B" average and;
(4) have an interest in tribal government and policy.

FINANCIAL DATA:
Interns are provided with airfare to and from Washington, DC, lodging convenient to Capitol Hill, and a daily allowance sufficient for meals, transportation and incidentals.

Amount of support per award: $1,200 educational stipend to be paid at the conclusion of the internship.

NUMBER OF APPLICANTS MOST RECENT YEAR:
50.

NUMBER OF AWARDS: 12.

APPLICATION INFORMATION:
Application packet must be sent to The Morris K. Udall and Stewart L. Udall Foundation, Internship Program, at the address above.
Duration: 10 weeks.

Deadline: January 31.

STAFF:
Teresa Bravo, Program Manager

ADDRESS INQUIRIES TO:
Teresa Bravo, Program Manager
(See address above.)

UNITED SOUTH AND EASTERN TRIBES, INC.   [1060]
711 Stewarts Ferry Pike
Suite 100
Nashville, TN 37214
(615) 872-7900
Fax: (615) 872-7417

E-MAIL ADDRESS:
cleasure@usetinc.org

WEB SITE ADDRESS:
www.usetinc.org

FOUNDED: 1969

AREAS OF INTEREST:
Indian tribes.

TYPE:
Scholarships.

PURPOSE:
To enhance the development of Indian Tribes; to improve the capabilities of Tribal governments; to assist the member Tribes and their governments in dealing effectively with public policy issues and in serving the broad needs of Indian people.

ELIGIBILITY:
Supplemental monies are awarded to USET area Indian students who are enrolled members of USET member tribes.

Must be an Indian student that meets the following criteria:
(1) a demonstrated need for additional funding;
(2) satisfactory scholastic standing and;
(3) current enrollment or acceptance in a postsecondary educational institution.

FINANCIAL DATA:
Amount of support per award: Supplemental scholarships: $500.

APPLICATION INFORMATION:
Contact the Organization for application procedures.
Duration: Annual supplemental scholarship. Must reapply for additional term.
Deadline: Postmark or delivery of applications: April 30.

ADDRESS INQUIRIES TO:
USET Scholarship Fund
(See address above.)

UNIVERSITY OF CALIFORNIA, LOS ANGELES   [1061]
American Indian Studies Center
UCLA - 3220 Campbell Hall, Box 951548
Los Angeles, CA 90095-1548
(310) 825-7315
Fax: (310) 206-7060

E-MAIL ADDRESS:
info@aisc.ucla.edu

WEB SITE ADDRESS:
www.aisc.ucla.edu

FOUNDED: 1970

AREAS OF INTEREST:
American Indian studies and related topics in policy, education, economics, culture and community.

NAME(S) OF PROGRAMS:
● **Institute of American Cultures Grant**

TYPE:
Fellowships; Research grants; Visiting scholars.

YEAR PROGRAM STARTED: 1969

PURPOSE:
To conduct research in Native American Studies.

LEGAL BASIS:
University research organization; nonprofit organization.

ELIGIBILITY:
Applicants must hold the Ph.D. Faculty members at U.C.L.A. are eligible for support. Visiting scholars must be affiliated with another university.

FINANCIAL DATA:
Senior scholars receive a supplement to the sabbatical salaries provided by their own institutions. Additional support, including office space and computer support, may be available for specific research upon application to the center.
Amount of support per award: Institute of American Cultures Grant: $35,000; Visiting Scholars: $27,000 to $32,000, depending upon rank and experience.
Total amount of support: Varies.

APPLICATION INFORMATION:
Application information is available on the web site.
Duration: Nine to 12 months. Nonrenewable.
Deadline: Varies.

PUBLICATIONS:
American Indian Culture and Research Journal; brochures; books.

IRS IDENTIFICATION NUMBER: 195006143-AI

STAFF:
Angela Riley, Director
Rebecca Rosser, Assistant Director
Pam Grieman, Managing Editor
Ken Wade, Librarian

ADDRESS INQUIRIES TO:
Rebecca Rosser, Assistant Director
(See address above.)

WASHINGTON HIGHER EDUCATION COORDINATING BOARD   [1062]
American Indian Endowed Scholarship
917 Lakeridge Way
Olympia, WA 98502
(360) 753-7843
Fax: (360) 704-6243; (360) 753-7808

E-MAIL ADDRESS:
aies@hecb.wa.gov
annv@wsac.wa.gov

WEB SITE ADDRESS:
www.hecb.wa.gov

AREAS OF INTEREST:
Student financial aid.

NAME(S) OF PROGRAMS:
● **American Indian Endowed Scholarship Program**

TYPE:
Scholarships.

YEAR PROGRAM STARTED: 1993

PURPOSE:
To create an educational opportunity for students with close social and cultural ties to

the American Indian community to pursue undergraduate and graduate studies who might not be able otherwise to attend and graduate from higher education institutions in Washington state.

LEGAL BASIS:
Government agency.

ELIGIBILITY:
Applicants must be financially needy residents and students of Washington state with close social and cultural ties to the American Indian community in the state. Must have applied for financial aid via FAFSA. Applicant must commit to return service to the state Native American community. Academic merit is also a consideration.

FINANCIAL DATA:
Amount of support per award: $500 to $2,000.
Total amount of support: Varies.

APPLICATION INFORMATION:
Application includes statement of commitment to return service to Washington American Indian communities, statement of close social and cultural ties, three letters of recommendation, completed application and release of information form and transcripts.
Duration: One year. Renewable for a maximum of four additional years.
Deadline: February 1. Announcement will be made by April.

ADDRESS INQUIRIES TO:
Ann M. Voyles, Program Manager
American Indian Endowed Scholarship
P.O. Box 43430
Olympia, WA 98504-3430

Spanish-speaking

BNSF RAILWAY FOUNDATION   [1063]
2650 Lou Menk Drive
Fort Worth, TX 76131-2830
(817) 867-6458
Fax: (817) 352-7925

E-MAIL ADDRESS:
bnsffoundation@bnsf.com

WEB SITE ADDRESS:
www.bnsffoundation.org

NAME(S) OF PROGRAMS:
● **Hispanic American Scholarship Program**

TYPE:
Scholarships. Scholarships awarded to high school graduates of Hispanic origin through the Hispanic College Fund (HCF).

LEGAL BASIS:
Corporate foundation.

ELIGIBILITY:
Scholarships are awarded to high school graduates of Hispanic origin. All applicants must be U.S. citizens or legal residents and have already been accepted or enrolled in a college (two-year leading to a four-year degree) or university. Winners are selected by Hispanic Scholarship Fund (HSF) with scholarships to be awarded in each of the following Burlington Northern Santa

Fe-served states: Arizona, California, Colorado, Illinois, Kansas, Missouri, New Mexico and Texas.

GEOGRAPHIC RESTRICTIONS:
Arizona, California, Colorado, Illinois, Kansas, Missouri, New Mexico and Texas.

FINANCIAL DATA:
Each Scholarship stipend is determined by HSF and funds are allocated from an annual $25,000 grant provided by the Foundation.
Amount of support per award: $500 to $2,500.
Total amount of support: $25,000 per academic year.

APPLICATION INFORMATION:
Applications are available from Hispanic College Fund, Inc., 1301 K Street, N.W., Suite 450-A West, Washington, DC 20005.
Deadline: April 1.

ADDRESS INQUIRIES TO:
Hispanic College Fund, Inc.
1301 K Street, N.W.
Suite 450-A West
Washington, DC 20005

CONGRESSIONAL HISPANIC CAUCUS INSTITUTE   [1064]
911 2nd Street, N.E.
Washington, DC 20002
(202) 543-1771
(800) 392-3532
Fax: (202) 546-2143

WEB SITE ADDRESS:
www.chci.org

FOUNDED: 1978

AREAS OF INTEREST:
Leadership training in the legislative process for promising Latino undergraduates.

NAME(S) OF PROGRAMS:
● **CHCI Congressional Internship**

TYPE:
Internships. Internships provide college students with a paid work placement in a congressional office or federal agency for a period of 12 weeks (Spring and Fall Programs) or eight weeks (Summer Program).

PURPOSE:
To expose young Latinos to the legislative process and to strengthen their professional leadership skills, ultimately promoting the presence of Latinos on Capitol Hill and in federal agencies.

ELIGIBILITY:
Students must currently be enrolled full-time and working towards their undergraduate degree. Students must also be U.S. citizens or residents.

GEOGRAPHIC RESTRICTIONS:
United States.

FINANCIAL DATA:
Internship includes stipend, domestic round-trip transportation to Washington, DC, housing (all expenses covered) and academic credit if eligible.
Amount of support per award: Spring and Fall Programs: $3,750 stipend (12 weeks); Summer Program: $2,500 (eight weeks).

APPLICATION INFORMATION:
Application must be made online. See web site for complete information.
Duration: Spring and Fall Programs: 12 weeks; Summer Program: Eight weeks. Internships are not renewable.

Deadline: Spring Program: Early November. Fall Program: End of April. Summer Program: End of January.

CONGRESSIONAL HISPANIC CAUCUS INSTITUTE [1065]

911 2nd Street, N.E.
Washington, DC 20002
(202) 543-1771
(800) 392-3532
Fax: (202) 546-2143

WEB SITE ADDRESS:
www.chci.org

FOUNDED: 1978

AREAS OF INTEREST:
Postsecondary education for Latino students.

NAME(S) OF PROGRAMS:
● **CHCI Scholarship Fund**

TYPE:
Scholarships. The Institute's scholarship opportunities are afforded to Latino students in the U.S. who have a history of performing public service-oriented activities in their communities and who demonstrate a desire to continue their civic engagement in the future. There is no grade point average or academic major requirement. Students with excellent leadership potential are encouraged to apply.

PURPOSE:
To ensure the benefits of a postsecondary education are available to Latino students for whom the cost of community college, a four-year college or graduate school would otherwise be out of reach.

ELIGIBILITY:
The following requirements apply:
(1) full-time enrollment in a U.S. Department of Education-accredited community college, four-year university, or graduate/professional program during the period for which scholarship is requested;
(2) demonstrated financial need;
(3) consistent, active participation in public and/or community service activities;
(4) strong writing skills and;
(5) applicants must be U.S. citizens, lawful permanent residents, asylees, or individuals who are lawfully authorized to work full-time without restriction for any U.S. employer and who, at the time of application, possess lawful evidence of employment authorization.

GEOGRAPHIC RESTRICTIONS:
United States.

FINANCIAL DATA:
Scholarship awards are intended to provide assistance with tuition, room and board, textbooks and other educational expenses associated with college enrollment.
Amount of support per award: $1,000 to pursue an associate degree; $2,500 to pursue an undergraduate degree; $5,000 to pursue graduate-level study.

APPLICATION INFORMATION:
See the web site for complete information. Application process opens in September. An application form is required.
Duration: Up to four years; nonrenewable.
Deadline: April 16.

*SPECIAL STIPULATIONS:
Associate- and undergraduate-level scholarship awards are divided over the number of years required for graduation. Students continue to receive annual disbursements as long as they maintain good academic standing.

CONGRESSIONAL HISPANIC CAUCUS INSTITUTE [1066]

911 2nd Street, N.E.
Washington, DC 20002
(202) 543-1771
(800) 392-3532
Fax: (202) 546-2143

WEB SITE ADDRESS:
www.chci.org

FOUNDED: 1978

AREAS OF INTEREST:
Graduate Fellowship Program: Higher education, secondary education, health, housing, and law. Public Policy Fellowship: Varies.

NAME(S) OF PROGRAMS:
● **CHCI Graduate Fellowship Program**
● **CHCI Public Policy Fellowship**

TYPE:
Fellowships. Graduate Fellowship Program offers exceptional Latinos who have earned a graduate degree or higher related to a chosen policy issue area within three years of program start date unparalleled exposure to hands-on experience in public policy.

Public Policy Fellowship offers talented Latinos who have earned a Bachelor's degree within two years of the program start date the opportunity to gain hands-on experience at the national level in public policy.

PURPOSE:
To help increase opportunities for Hispanics to participate in and contribute to the American policymaking process.

GEOGRAPHIC RESTRICTIONS:
United States.

FINANCIAL DATA:
Amount of support per award: CHCI Graduate Fellowship Program: Initial stipend of approximately $2,900; biweekly stipend of approximately $1,160. CHCI Public Policy Fellowship: Initial stipend of approximately $2,700; biweekly stipend of approximately $960.

APPLICATION INFORMATION:
See web site for complete information. Application process opens in September.
Duration: Nine months: Mid-August to mid-May.
Deadline: Early February.

FLORIDA DEPARTMENT OF EDUCATION [1067]

Office of Student Financial Assistance
325 West Gaines Street, Suite 1314
Tallahassee, FL 32399-0400
(888) 827-2004
Fax: (850) 487-1809

E-MAIL ADDRESS:
osfa@fldoe.org

WEB SITE ADDRESS:
www.FloridaStudentFinancialAid.org

NAME(S) OF PROGRAMS:
● **Jose Marti Scholarship Challenge Grant Fund**

TYPE:
Challenge/matching grants; Grants-in-aid. Jose Marti Scholarship Challenge Grant Fund is a need-based merit scholarship that provides financial assistance to eligible students of Hispanic origin who will attend Florida public or eligible private institutions.

YEAR PROGRAM STARTED: 1986

PURPOSE:
To provide financial assistance to Hispanic-American high school seniors and graduate students in Florida.

LEGAL BASIS:
Florida Department of Education.

ELIGIBILITY:
Applicants for undergraduate study must apply during their senior year of high school. Graduate students may apply; however, priority for the scholarship is given to graduating high school seniors.

For the applying student, initial eligibility requirements to receive funding are as follows:
(1) be a Florida resident and a U.S. citizen or eligible noncitizen; a student's residency and citizenship status are determined by the postsecondary institution; consult the financial aid office or admissions office of the institution the student plans to attend for questions;
(2) not owe a repayment or be in default under any state or federal grant, loan or scholarship program unless satisfactory arrangements to repay have been made;
(3) be of Spanish culture, born in or having a natural parent who was born in either Mexico, or a Hispanic country of the Caribbean, Central or South America, regardless of race;
(4) have earned, by the end of the seventh semester, a minimum unweighted cumulative grade point average of 3.0 on a 4.0 scale in high school for an undergraduate scholarship, or a 3.0 institutional cumulative grade point average for undergraduate college work if applying for a graduate-level scholarship and;
(5) enroll as a degree-seeking student at an eligible postsecondary institution and enroll each academic term for a minimum of 12 credit hours for undergraduate study or nine credit hours for graduate study.

GEOGRAPHIC RESTRICTIONS:
Florida.

NUMBER OF AWARDS: Varies.

APPLICATION INFORMATION:
Detailed program information can be found on the web site.
Deadline: For undergraduate study, submit a fully completed error-free Initial Student Florida Financial Aid Application during the student's last year in high school by April 1. For graduate study, submit a fully completed error-free Initial Student Florida Financial Aid Application by April 1 prior to the year of graduate study. Demonstrate sufficient financial need to receive a full $2,000 scholarship by completing and submitting the Free Application for Federal Student Aid (FAFSA) in time to be processed error free by the U.S. Department of Education on or before May 15.

ADDRESS INQUIRIES TO:
State Scholarship and Grant Programs
(See address above.)

HISPANIC NATIONAL BAR FOUNDATION

1900 K Street, N.W.
Suite 100
Washington, DC 20006
(202) 496-7206
Fax: (202) 496-7756

E-MAIL ADDRESS:
mprego@hnbf.org

WEB SITE ADDRESS:
www.hnbf.org

TYPE:
Scholarships. Winners of the HNBF
Princeton Review Duard Bradshaw
Scholarship will receive a Princeton Review
LSAT preparation course. The winner will
enroll in the Accelerated LSAT course in
their hometown. This course consists of 30
classroom hours and four full-length practice
tests. It takes about four to five weeks to
complete. Students will then take the July or
September LSAT examination upon
completion of the Accelerated LSAT course.
Students must request special permission to
apply this scholarship to the December test.

See entry 1981 for full listing.

HISPANIC NATIONAL BAR FOUNDATION

1900 K Street, N.W.
Suite 100
Washington, DC 20006
(202) 496-7206
Fax: (202) 496-7756

E-MAIL ADDRESS:
mprego@hnbf.org

WEB SITE ADDRESS:
www.hnbf.org

TYPE:
Conferences/seminars; Training grants.
Week-long program held by the Foundation
in Washington, DC which provides 25 to 30
Latino high school students with the
opportunity to learn more about the legal
profession. The Law Camp offers students
the chance to come to the nation's capital
and learn more about the college application
process, meet influential Latino leaders, and
tour national monuments and various
government agencies.

See entry 1982 for full listing.

HISPANIC SCHOLARSHIP FUND   [1068]

1411 West 190th Street
Suite 325
Gardena, CA 90248
(877) 473-4636

E-MAIL ADDRESS:
info@hsf.net
gmsinfo@hsf.net

WEB SITE ADDRESS:
www.hsf.net
www.gmsp.org

FOUNDED: 1975

AREAS OF INTEREST:
College scholarships for Hispanic American
students.

NAME(S) OF PROGRAMS:
● **Gates Millennium Scholars Program**
● **General College Scholarship Program**

TYPE:
Scholarships. Awarded to Hispanic
community college, undergraduate and
graduate students.

YEAR PROGRAM STARTED: 1975

PURPOSE:
To strengthen America by generating support
for the educational advancement of Hispanics
by increasing the rate of Hispanics earning a
college degree.

LEGAL BASIS:
Nonprofit 501(c)(3) organization.

ELIGIBILITY:
For the Gates Millennium Scholars Program,
the applicant must:
(1) be African American, American
Indian/Alaska Native, Asian Pacific Islander
American or Hispanic American;
(2) be a citizen, national or legal permanent
resident of the U.S.;
(3) have attained a cumulative high school
grade point average of 3.3 on a 4.0 scale
(unweighted) or have earned a GED;
(4) be enrolling for the first time at a
U.S.-accredited college or university as a
full-time, degree-seeking, first-year student in
the coming fall;
(5) have demonstrated leadership abilities
through participation in community service,
extracurricular or other activities;
(6) meet the federal Pell Grant eligibility
criteria and;
(7) have completed and submitted all three
required forms (Nominee Personal
Information Form, Nominator Form and
Recommender Form) by the deadline.

For the General College Scholarship
Program, the applicant must:
(1) be of Hispanic heritage;
(2) be a U.S. citizen or legal permanent
resident;
(3) have a minimum 3.0 cumulative grade
point average (on a 4.0 scale) and;
(4) apply for federal financial aid using
FAFSA.

FINANCIAL DATA:
Amount of support per award: Gates
Millennium Scholars Program: Varies
depending on unmet need; General College
Scholarship Program: $1,000 to $15,000.
Total amount of support: Approximately
$28,000,000 for the year 2012.

NUMBER OF AWARDS: 4,650 for the year 2011.

APPLICATION INFORMATION:
Electronic application only; forms available
at the web site.
Duration: Students may reapply until they
obtain a degree, providing they satisfy
full-time enrollment.
Deadline: Gates Millenium Scholars
Program: Applications become available
August 1, deadline in mid-January; General
College Scholarship Program: Early to
mid-December.

PUBLICATIONS:
Annual report; newsletter.

IRS IDENTIFICATION NUMBER: 52-1051044

BOARD OF DIRECTORS:
James McNamara, Chairperson
Fidel A. Vargas, President and Chief
Executive Officer
Anthony Salcido, Treasurer
Gene Camarena
Kimberly Casiano
Margarita Flores
Nely Galan
Juan Galarraga
Lisa M. Garcia
Tim Hanlon
Cheech Marin
Angel Luis Morales

Elizabeth Oliver-Farrow
Adam Rodriguez
Frank Ros
Thomas A. Roupe
Maria Elena Salinas
Edgar A. Sandoval
Violeta Vera Seidell

UCLA CHICANO STUDIES RESEARCH CENTER   [1069]

193 Haines Hall
Box 951544
Los Angeles, CA 90095
(310) 794-9646
Fax: (310) 206-1784

E-MAIL ADDRESS:
csrcinfo@chicano.ucla.edu

WEB SITE ADDRESS:
www.chicano.ucla.edu

FOUNDED: 1969

AREAS OF INTEREST:
Chicano Studies and relevant fields.

NAME(S) OF PROGRAMS:
● **Institute of American Cultures Fellowship Program**

TYPE:
Fellowships; Visiting scholars.

YEAR PROGRAM STARTED: 1976

PURPOSE:
To advance scholarship in the Chicano
community in the U.S.

LEGAL BASIS:
University program.

ELIGIBILITY:
Applicants must possess a Ph.D. and a
project proposal.

FINANCIAL DATA:
Amount of support per award: $32,000 to
$35,000, health insurance, and $4,000
research grant, of which $1,000 can be used
for relocation expenses.
Total amount of support: Up to $39,000
annually.

NUMBER OF APPLICANTS MOST RECENT YEAR:
16.

NUMBER OF AWARDS: 1.

APPLICATION INFORMATION:
Application information available upon
request.
Duration: One fiscal year, July 1 to June 30.
Deadline: January.

OFFICERS:
Chon Noriega, Director
Belinda Tucker, Vice Provost of the Institute
of American Cultures

ADDRESS INQUIRIES TO:
Javier Iribarren
Assistant Director/IAC Coordinator
(See address above.)

Women

THE ISABEL ALLENDE FOUNDATION   [1070]

116 Caledonia Street
Sausalito, CA 94965
(415) 289-0992
Fax: (415) 332-4149

E-MAIL ADDRESS:
lori@isabelallendefoundation.org

WEB SITE ADDRESS:
www.isabelallendefoundation.org

FOUNDED: 1996

AREAS OF INTEREST:
Women's social and economic justice,
empowerment of women and girls, and
protection of women and children.

NAME(S) OF PROGRAMS:
• **Esperanza Grants**

TYPE:
Project/program grants. Promotes and
preserves the fundamental rights of women
and children to be empowered and protected.

PURPOSE:
To promote reproductive self-determination
and health care, economic independence and
social justice for women and girls, and the
protection of women and children.

ELIGIBILITY:
Nonprofit 501(c)(3) grassroots organizations
and equivalent international organizations that
benefit the San Francisco Bay area and/or
Chile are eligible to apply. No grants to
individuals.

The Foundation does not fund capital
campaigns, individual trips or tours,
conferences or events, and projects that
benefit political, religious, and/or military
organizations.

Unsolicited requests are not accepted.

GEOGRAPHIC RESTRICTIONS:
San Francisco Bay area, California and Chile.

FINANCIAL DATA:
Amount of support per award: $3,000 to
$8,000.
Total amount of support: Approximately
$400,000.

APPLICATION INFORMATION:
New organization proposals are not being
accepted at this time. Current grantees may
apply for renewal and will receive
instructions from the Foundation on how to
apply.
Duration: One year. Must submit report for
renewal.
Deadline: January 1, April 1, July 1 and
October 1.

ADDRESS INQUIRIES TO:
Lori Barra, Executive Director
(See address above.)

AMERICAN ASSOCIATION OF UNIVERSITY WOMEN [1071]
P.O. Box 4030
Iowa City, IA 52243-4030
(319) 337-1716
(800) 326-2289
Fax: (319) 337-1204

E-MAIL ADDRESS:
aauw@act.org

WEB SITE ADDRESS:
www.aauw.org

FOUNDED: 1888

AREAS OF INTEREST:
Advancement of educational and professional
opportunities for women in the U.S.

NAME(S) OF PROGRAMS:
• **Selected Professions Fellowships**

TYPE:
Fellowships. Awarded to women who are
U.S. citizens or permanent residents and who

intend to pursue a full-time course of study
(during the fellowship year) in designated
degree programs where women's
participation has been traditionally low.

PURPOSE:
To encourage women's participation in fields
where they have been traditionally
underrepresented.

ELIGIBILITY:
Selected Professions Fellowships are awarded
for the following Master's programs:
(1) Architecture;
(2) Computer/information sciences;
(3) Engineering and;
(4) Mathematics/statistics.

Fellowships in the following degree programs
are restricted to women of color, who have
been underrepresented in these fields:
(1) Master's in business administration -
applicants may apply for second year of
study only;
(2) Law - applicants may apply for third year
of study only and;
(3) Doctorate in medicine - applicants may
apply for third or fourth year of study only.

GEOGRAPHIC RESTRICTIONS:
United States.

FINANCIAL DATA:
Amount of support per award: $5,000 to
$18,000.

APPLICATION INFORMATION:
Applications are available August 1.

AMERICAN ASSOCIATION OF UNIVERSITY WOMEN EDUCATIONAL FOUNDATION [1072]
327 Second Street, Suite 103
Coralville, IA 52241
(319) 688-4334

E-MAIL ADDRESS:
aauw@scholarshipamerica.org

WEB SITE ADDRESS:
www.aauw.org

FOUNDED: 1958

AREAS OF INTEREST:
Advancement of educational and professional
opportunities for women in the U.S. and
around the globe.

NAME(S) OF PROGRAMS:
• **American Fellowships**

TYPE:
Fellowships; Visiting scholars. Dissertation,
postdoctoral and summer/short-term research
publication grants for women, for the support
of scholarly research. Open to all fields of
study.

YEAR PROGRAM STARTED: 1888

PURPOSE:
To encourage and support American women
who show distinction or promise of
distinction in their fields of scholarly work
and who plan to pursue professional careers
in the U.S.

ELIGIBILITY:
Applicants must be citizens of the U.S. There
are no restrictions as to place of study or
age. Fellowship is open to women who will
have completed all requirements for the
Doctorate, except the writing of the
dissertation, by November 15 preceding the
fellowship year, July 1 to June 30, or who
hold the Ph.D. at the time of application.

Applicants are evaluated by academic
professionals on the scholarly excellence of
their proposals, experience teaching or
mentoring female students. In addition,
applicants will be asked to outline their
commitment to helping women and girls
through community service, service in their
profession and/or service in their field of
research.

FINANCIAL DATA:
Amount of support per award: Stipend for
dissertation: $20,000; Postdoctoral award
stipend: $30,000; Summer/Short-term award
stipend: $6,000.
Total amount of support: Approximately
$1,550,000 for the year 2012-13.

NUMBER OF APPLICANTS MOST RECENT YEAR:
Approximately 1,000.

NUMBER OF AWARDS: 88.

APPLICATION INFORMATION:
Application form is available online.
Duration: Fellowships are tenable for a year
of full-time project research beginning July
1.
Deadline: Completed applications must be
submitted by November 15.

ADDRESS INQUIRIES TO:
See e-mail address above.

AMERICAN ASSOCIATION OF UNIVERSITY WOMEN EDUCATIONAL FOUNDATION [1073]
327 Second Street, Suite 103
Coralville, IA 52241
(319) 688-4334

E-MAIL ADDRESS:
aauw@scholarshipamerica.org

WEB SITE ADDRESS:
www.aauw.org

FOUNDED: 1888

AREAS OF INTEREST:
Nontraditional fields.

NAME(S) OF PROGRAMS:
• **Career Development Grants**

TYPE:
Grants-in-aid. Support women currently
holding a Bachelor's degree who are
preparing to advance their careers, change
careers or re-enter the workforce.

YEAR PROGRAM STARTED: 1972

PURPOSE:
To assist women who are continuing their
self-development through higher education.

ELIGIBILITY:
Funding is provided to women who are
preparing to re-enter the workforce, change
careers or advance their current careers.
Candidates must be in the early stages of
their programs. Special consideration is given
to qualified AAUW members, minority
women and applicants who are not pursuing
a second Master's or terminal degree.
Preference is also given to women pursuing
degrees in nontraditional fields.

Grants are open to women who are U.S.
citizens or permanent residents, hold a
Baccalaureate degree, plan to pursue course
work at a fully accredited two- or four-year
college or university or at a technical school
that is licensed, accredited or approved by
the Department of Education and enroll in

courses that are prerequisites for professional employment plans and are not in the final year of a degree program at the time of application. Funds are provided for study at professional development institutes.

Funds are not available for the final year of terminal degree professional programs (i.e., MBA, J.D., M.D., etc.). Funds are not provided for doctoral study. Candidates who fulfill eligibility requirements of other fellowship programs offered by the AAUW Educational Foundation will not be considered for funding from this grant and therefore must apply to the appropriate program.

GEOGRAPHIC RESTRICTIONS:
United States.

FINANCIAL DATA:
Funds are provided for tuition, fees, books, transportation (to, from and at school) and dependent care.
Amount of support per award: $2,000 to $12,000.
Total amount of support: Varies.

NUMBER OF APPLICANTS MOST RECENT YEAR:
628 for the year 2011-12.

NUMBER OF AWARDS: 47 for the year 2011-12.

APPLICATION INFORMATION:
Official application materials are available August 1 to December 15. Application and recommendations must be submitted online.
Duration: One academic year, beginning July 1.
Deadline: December 15.

PUBLICATIONS:
Application guidelines.

ADDRESS INQUIRIES TO:
American Association of University Women Educational Foundation Career Development Academic Grants (See address above.)

*SPECIAL STIPULATIONS:
Previous and current recipients of an AAUW Educational Foundation Career Development Grant are not eligible to apply.

AMERICAN ASSOCIATION OF UNIVERSITY WOMEN EDUCATIONAL FOUNDATION   [1074]

327 Second Street, Suite 103
Coralville, IA 52241
(319) 688-4334

E-MAIL ADDRESS:
aauw@scholarshipamerica.org

WEB SITE ADDRESS:
www.aauw.org

FOUNDED: 1888

AREAS OF INTEREST:
Equity and education for women and girls.

NAME(S) OF PROGRAMS:
● **Community Action Grants**

TYPE:
Project/program grants; Seed money grants.

YEAR PROGRAM STARTED: 1972

PURPOSE:
To provide seed money to AAUW branches, AAUW state organizations, community-based nonprofit organizations, and individual women for projects that promote education and equity for women and girls.

ELIGIBILITY:
Project directors must be U.S. citizens or permanent residents. The proposed activity must demonstrate direct community or public impact. Proposals from AAUW branches and AAUW state organizations must be approved and signed by the branch or state president. Men, as leaders of AAUW branches and organizations, are eligible to apply.

Grant projects may not seek to influence new or pending legislation or favor a particular political candidate or party. Nonpartisan study analysis and research must present findings based on facts.

GEOGRAPHIC RESTRICTIONS:
United States and its territories.

FINANCIAL DATA:
Funds are available for such project-related costs as office and mailing expenses, promotional materials, honoraria and transportation costs. Funds cannot cover salaries for project directors.
Amount of support per award: $2,000 to $7,000 for one-year grants; $5,000 to $10,000 for two-year grants.
Total amount of support: Varies.

REPRESENTATIVE AWARDS:
Projects funded in the past include math/science camps for girls, mentoring programs for girls and women, parenting/family education programs, adolescent pregnancy prevention campaigns, and women's history projects.

APPLICATION INFORMATION:
Complete application details are available online August 1 to January 15. All applications must be submitted online.
Deadline: January 15.

PUBLICATIONS:
Application guidelines.

ADDRESS INQUIRIES TO:
Program Officer
(See address above.)

AMERICAN ASSOCIATION OF UNIVERSITY WOMEN EDUCATIONAL FOUNDATION

327 Second Street, Suite 103
Coralville, IA 52241
(319) 688-4334

E-MAIL ADDRESS:
aauw@scholarshipamerica.org

WEB SITE ADDRESS:
www.aauw.org

TYPE:
Fellowships. Awards for women who are not citizens or permanent residents of the U.S. for full-time graduate or postgraduate study or research in the U.S.

A limited number of project grants are available to successful applicants who wish to implement a community-based project in the year immediately following the fellowship. Eligible project proposals must demonstrate that they will be implemented in the applicant's home country and will have a direct impact on women and girls. Only applicants who are selected to receive an International Fellowship will be considered for project grant funding.

See entry 957 for full listing.

AMERICAN NUCLEAR SOCIETY (ANS)

555 North Kensington Avenue
LaGrange Park, IL 60526
(708) 352-6611
Fax: (708) 352-0499

E-MAIL ADDRESS:
outreach@ans.org

WEB SITE ADDRESS:
www.ans.org

TYPE:
Scholarships. Delayed Education for Women Scholarship is designed for women in a nuclear-related field whose formal studies have been delayed or interrupted for at least one year.

Landis Scholarships are administered by the ANS NEED Committee, and are awarded to undergraduate and graduate students who have greater-than-average financial need.

See entry 2634 for full listing.

BERKSHIRE CONFERENCE OF WOMEN HISTORIANS

11 Granite Street
Portland, ME 04101
(207) 780-4921

E-MAIL ADDRESS:
acameron@usm.maine.edu

WEB SITE ADDRESS:
www.berksconference.org

TYPE:
Awards/prizes. One prize awarded annually for the best first book and one for the best article of historical scholarship published by a woman historian in any field of history during the preceding year.

See entry 583 for full listing.

BOSTON WOMEN'S FUND   [1075]

14 Beacon Street
Suite 805
Boston, MA 02108
(617) 725-0035
Fax: (617) 725-0277

E-MAIL ADDRESS:
josefina@bostonwomensfund.org
amy@bostonwomensfund.org

WEB SITE ADDRESS:
www.bostonwomensfund.org

FOUNDED: 1984

AREAS OF INTEREST:
Women organized for social and economic change.

TYPE:
General operating grants; Grants-in-aid; Internships; Project/program grants; Seed money grants.

PURPOSE:
To pool funds from individuals; to channel money to support women's and girls' organizations for economic and social justice.

LEGAL BASIS:
Public foundation.

ELIGIBILITY:
Applicants or their fiscal agents must be 501(c)(3) organizations. Also funded are direct-service projects which have an organizing component. Groups just getting started are encouraged to apply, particularly those women who are most vulnerable and

have the least access to other resources including women of color, low-income women, disabled women, lesbians, girls, older women, transgender people, immigrant and refugee women. Applicants with organizational budgets of less than $350,000 per year are preferred. No grants to individuals.

GEOGRAPHIC RESTRICTIONS:
Preference given to the Boston metropolitan area, and to selected outlying areas such as Brockton, Lawrence, Lowell and Worcester, Massachusetts.

FINANCIAL DATA:
Amount of support per award: Up to $20,000.

NUMBER OF APPLICANTS MOST RECENT YEAR:
Varies.

NUMBER OF AWARDS: Varies.

APPLICATION INFORMATION:
Download a Letter of Intent form at the web site, complete and submit to the Fund. Selected letters will be invited to submit a proposal.
Duration: One year.

PUBLICATIONS:
Application guidelines; donor contribution information in annual report.

ADDRESS INQUIRIES TO:
Amy Leung, Program Officer
(See address above.)

BROOKHAVEN WOMEN IN SCIENCE   [1076]
P.O. Box 183
Upton, NY 11973
(631) 344-2425
Fax: (631) 344-5676

E-MAIL ADDRESS:
bwisawards@bnl.gov

WEB SITE ADDRESS:
www.bnl.gov/bwis/scholarships.php

FOUNDED: 1979

AREAS OF INTEREST:
Advancement of women in the natural sciences, engineering or mathematics fields.

NAME(S) OF PROGRAMS:
● **Renate W. Chasman Scholarship for Women**

TYPE:
Awards/prizes; Scholarships. These scholarships are offered to encourage women to resume their formal education in the natural sciences, engineering or mathematics.

YEAR PROGRAM STARTED: 1986

PURPOSE:
To encourage women to resume their formal education in a technical field.

LEGAL BASIS:
Tax-exempt, incorporated under the Educational Laws of New York state.

ELIGIBILITY:
Applicants must be:
(1) women;
(2) undergraduate seniors or graduate students at an accredited educational institution;
(3) performing research at Brookhaven National Laboratory in the STEM disciplines (science, technology, engineering or

mathematics) and;
(4) receiving their degree not prior to May of the year of the award.

FINANCIAL DATA:
Amount of support per award: $1,000.

NUMBER OF AWARDS: 1 per year.

APPLICATION INFORMATION:
Requests for application via mail must include a self-addressed, stamped envelope.
Duration: One-time award.
Deadline: All application materials - forms, transcripts, reference letters and goal statement - are due by November 30 for the following year's competition. The award will be presented in May.

ADDRESS INQUIRIES TO:
Chasman Scholarship Fund
Brookhaven Women in Science
(See street or e-mail address above.)

CANADIAN FEDERATION OF UNIVERSITY WOMEN   [1077]
331 Cooper Street, Suite 502
Ottawa ON K2P 0G5 Canada
(613) 234-8252
Fax: (613) 234-8221

E-MAIL ADDRESS:
fellowships@cfuw.org

WEB SITE ADDRESS:
www.cfuw.org

FOUNDED: 1919

AREAS OF INTEREST:
Graduate education for women.

NAME(S) OF PROGRAMS:
● **Ruth Binnie Fellowship**
● **Canadian Home Economics Association (CHEA) Fellowship**
● **CFUW Beverly Jackson Fellowship**
● **CFUW Bourse Georgette Lemoyne**
● **CFUW Dr. Alice E. Wilson Awards**
● **CFUW Dr. Margaret McWilliams Pre-Doctoral Fellowship**
● **CFUW Elizabeth Massey Award**
● **CFUW Margaret Dale Philp Award**
● **CFUW Memorial Fellowship**
● **CFUW 1989 Ecole Polytechnique Commemorative Awards**

TYPE:
Fellowships. The Ruth Binnie Fellowship is for Master's studies with a focus on one or more aspects of the field of home economics. The candidate may be studying abroad.

Canadian Home Economics Association Fellowship candidate must be studying one or more aspects in the field of home economics at the Master's or doctoral level in Canada.

CFUW Bourse Georgette Lemoyne Fellowship is for graduate study at a Canadian university. The candidate must be studying in French.

CFUW Beverley Jackson Fellowship, funded by UWC North York, is awarded to a candidate over the age of 35 enrolled in graduate work at an Ontario university.

CFUW Elizabeth Massey Award is for postgraduate studies in the visual arts such as painting, sculpture or in music in Canada or abroad.

CFUW Margaret McWilliams Pre-Doctoral Fellowship candidate must have completed at least one full calendar year as a full-time

student in doctoral-level studies and be a full-time student in Canada or abroad at the time of application.

CFUW Memorial Fellowship candidate must be enrolled in a Master's degree program in science, mathematics, or engineering in Canada or abroad.

CFUW 1989 Ecole Polytechnique Commemorative Award is for graduate studies in any field. The candidate must justify the relevance of her work to women.

CFUW Margaret Dale Philp Award, funded by CFUW Kitchener-Waterloo, is for graduate studies in the humanities or social sciences, with special consideration given to study in Canadian history. The candidate must reside in Canada.

CFUW Dr. Alice E. Wilson Award is for graduate studies in any field, with special consideration given to candidates returning to study after at least three years.

YEAR PROGRAM STARTED: 1921

PURPOSE:
To support the education of women at the postgraduate level in Canada and abroad.

LEGAL BASIS:
Foundation of a nonprofit organization.

ELIGIBILITY:
Candidates must hold at least a Bachelor's degree or equivalent from a recognized university, have been accepted into the proposed program and place of study, and be a Canadian citizen or permanent resident.

GEOGRAPHIC RESTRICTIONS:
Canada.

FINANCIAL DATA:
Amount of support per award: $2,000 to $11,000 (CAN).
Total amount of support: Approximately $78,500 for the year 2014-15.

NUMBER OF AWARDS: 10 different categories, with 15 awards.

APPLICATION INFORMATION:
Application form and guidelines are posted in May on the Federation's web site.
Duration: One year. Grants not renewable.
Deadline: November 1 (postmark). Announcement May 31.

PUBLICATIONS:
The Communicator; CFUW Education and Outreach; The Chronicle; CFUW Charitable Trust; CFUW Fellowships and Awards; CFUW External Annual Report; Action and Advocacy; Women in Action.

ADDRESS INQUIRIES TO:
Betty Dunlop
Fellowships Program Manager
(See address above.)

THE COORDINATING COUNCIL FOR WOMEN IN HISTORY, INC.   [1078]
Department of History and Women's Studies
715 Zulauf Hall
Northern Illinois University
DeKalb, IL 60115
(815) 895-2624

E-MAIL ADDRESS:
execdir@theccwh.org

WEB SITE ADDRESS:
www.theccwh.org

FOUNDED: 1969

AREAS OF INTEREST:
Women's history.

NAME(S) OF PROGRAMS:
● **Catherine Prelinger Award**

TYPE:
Scholarships. The Catherine Prelinger Award is given to a scholar, with a Ph.D. or A.B.D., whose career has not followed a traditional academic path through secondary and higher education and whose work has contributed to women in the historical profession.

YEAR PROGRAM STARTED: 1998

PURPOSE:
To explore the diverse experiences and histories of all women; to honor scholars that have not followed a traditional academic path of uninterrupted and completed secondary, undergraduate, and graduate degrees leading into a tenured faculty position and whose work has contributed to women in the historical profession; to promote research and interpretation in areas of women's history; to recognize or to enhance the ability of the recipient to contribute significantly to women in history, whether in the profession in the present or in the study of women in the past.

ELIGIBILITY:
The applicant:
(1) must be a member in good standing of the Coordinating Council for Women in History;
(2) must hold either A.B.D. status or the Ph.D. at the time of application;
(3) shall be actively engaged in scholarship that is historical in nature, although the degree may be in related fields;
(4) shall have already contributed or shown potential for contributing significantly to women in history, whether in the profession in the present or in the study of women in the past and;
(5) has not followed a traditional academic path of uninterrupted and completed secondary, undergraduate and graduate degrees leading to a tenure-track faculty position.

FINANCIAL DATA:
Funds issued in U.S. dollars only.
Amount of support per award: $20,000.

NUMBER OF APPLICANTS MOST RECENT YEAR: 18.

NUMBER OF AWARDS: 1.

APPLICATION INFORMATION:
Contact the organization.
Deadline: September 15.

ADDRESS INQUIRIES TO:
Sandra Trudgen Dawson, Executive Director
(See e-mail address above.)

*SPECIAL STIPULATIONS:
All recipients will be required to submit a final paper to CCWH on how the award was expended and summarizing the scholarly work completed.

THE COORDINATING COUNCIL FOR WOMEN IN HISTORY, INC.
Department of History and Women's Studies
715 Zulauf Hall
Northern Illinois University
DeKalb, IL 60115
(815) 895-2624

E-MAIL ADDRESS:
execdir@theccwh.org

WEB SITE ADDRESS:
www.theccwh.org

TYPE:
Awards/prizes; Fellowships.
See entry 588 for full listing.

DALLAS WOMEN'S FOUNDATION [1079]
Campbell Centre II
8150 North Central Expressway, Suite 110
Dallas, TX 75206
(214) 965-9977
Fax: (214) 526-3633

E-MAIL ADDRESS:
dwf@dallaswomensfdn.org

WEB SITE ADDRESS:
www.dallaswomensfdn.org

FOUNDED: 1985

AREAS OF INTEREST:
Economic independence of women and girls.

TYPE:
General operating grants; Project/program grants.

YEAR PROGRAM STARTED: 1985

PURPOSE:
To promote women's philanthropy and raise money to support community programs that help women and girls realize their full potential.

LEGAL BASIS:
Community organization.

ELIGIBILITY:
Applicants must be 501(c)(3) organizations with 75% of the recipients residing in Dallas, Denton or Collin counties, TX. The applying program must serve at least 75% women and/or girls.

GEOGRAPHIC RESTRICTIONS:
Collin, Dallas and Denton counties, Texas.

FINANCIAL DATA:
Amount of support per award: Up to $30,000.
Total amount of support: $2,500,000 for fiscal year 2013.

APPLICATION INFORMATION:
The guidelines and application form are available online.
Duration: One year.
Deadline: January and August.

IRS IDENTIFICATION NUMBER: 75-2048261

STAFF:
Roslyn Dawson Thompson, President and Chief Executive Officer
Lesly Annen, Vice President-Development and External Affairs
Becky R. Sykes, Executive Director
Mary Valadez, Grants Director
Chayse Hood, Assistant Philanthropy Director
Twyla Allison, Controller

ADDRESS INQUIRIES TO:
Mary Valadez, Grants Director
E-mail: mvaladez@dallaswomensfdn.org

DAUGHTERS OF PENELOPE FOUNDATION, INC. [1080]
Supreme Headquarters
1909 Q Street, N.W., Suite 500
Washington, DC 20009
(202) 234-9741
Fax: (202) 483-6983

E-MAIL ADDRESS:
dophq@ahepa.org

WEB SITE ADDRESS:
www.dopfoundationinc.com

FOUNDED: 1983

AREAS OF INTEREST:
Education, health and philanthropy.

NAME(S) OF PROGRAMS:
● **Paula J. Alexander Memorial Scholarship (Undergraduate)**
● **Helen J. Beldecos, Past Grand President, Scholarship (Undergraduate)**
● **The Big Five Graduate Scholarship**
● **Daughters of Penelope Past Grand Presidents Memorial Scholarship (Undergraduate)**
● **Daughters of Penelope Past Grand Presidents Undergraduate Scholarship**
● **Daughters of Penelope - St. Basil's Academy**
● **Eos #1 Mother Lodge Chapter Scholarship (Undergraduate)**
● **Joanne V. Hologgitas, Ph.D., Past Grand President, Scholarship (Undergraduate)**
● **Hopewell Agave Chapter #224 Scholarship (Undergraduate)**
● **Kottis Family Scholarship (Undergraduate)**
● **Dorothy Lillian Quincey Memorial Graduate Scholarship**
● **Alexandra Apostolides Sonenfeld Memorial Undergraduate Scholarship**
● **Sonja B. Stefanadis Graduate Student Scholarship**
● **Barbara Edith Quincey Thorndyke Memorial Undergraduate Scholarship**
● **Mary M. Verges, Past Grand President, Scholarship (Undergraduate)**
● **The Sotiri Zervoulias & Lea Soupata Scholarship (St. Basil's Academy)**

TYPE:
Scholarships.

YEAR PROGRAM STARTED: 1983

PURPOSE:
To support education for women of Greek descent.

LEGAL BASIS:
The Foundation is a recognized 501(c)(3) organization; tax-exempt.

ELIGIBILITY:
Scholarships are based on financial need or academic merit (or both). Contact the organization for full details.

GEOGRAPHIC RESTRICTIONS:
Canada, Greece and United States.

FINANCIAL DATA:
Amount of support per award: $500 to $2,500.

NUMBER OF AWARDS: 23 for the year 2012.

APPLICATION INFORMATION:
Information and guidelines available online.
Deadline: Postmarked by May 15.

PUBLICATIONS:
President's Bulletin, monthly publication.

IRS IDENTIFICATION NUMBER: 52-1346043

ADDRESS INQUIRIES TO:
Elena Skardis Saviolakis
Executive Director
Daughters of Penelope Foundation, Inc.
(See address above.)

*SPECIAL STIPULATIONS:
Scholarship may not be deferred to be used at a later date. These awards are not renewable and must be used strictly for tuition and/or books. Application must be typewritten. All requirements must be met and all questions answered or applicant will be disqualified.

DAUGHTERS OF THE CINCINNATI
20 West 44th Street, Room 508
New York, NY 10036
(212) 991-9945

E-MAIL ADDRESS:
scholarships@daughters1894.org

WEB SITE ADDRESS:
www.daughters1894.org

TYPE:
Scholarships. Undergraduate scholarships.

See entry 1682 for full listing.

DREXEL UNIVERSITY COLLEGE OF MEDICINE   [1081]
The Legacy Center:
Archives and Special Collections
2900 West Queen Lane
Philadelphia, PA 19129
(215) 991-8340
Fax: (215) 991-8172

E-MAIL ADDRESS:
archives@drexelmed.edu

WEB SITE ADDRESS:
archives.drexelmed.edu

FOUNDED: 1977

AREAS OF INTEREST:
Medicine as it relates to women in professional practice.

NAME(S) OF PROGRAMS:
● **M. Louise Gloeckner, M.D., Summer Research Fellowship**

TYPE:
Fellowships. For four to six weeks of research at The Legacy Center. Collections house the business and academic records of the Woman's Medical College of Pennsylvania, the Medical College of Pennsylvania, and Drexel University College of Medicine, the personal papers of women physicians, records of national and international women's medical organizations, schools, associations, hospitals and a historic photograph collection.

YEAR PROGRAM STARTED: 1985

PURPOSE:
To encourage the use of the institution's archival collections in the study of women in medicine, and history generally.

LEGAL BASIS:
University.

ELIGIBILITY:
Applicants must be either undergraduate or graduate students, medical students, faculty members or independent researchers. Preference is given to researchers with well-defined projects to be completed in one summer.

FINANCIAL DATA:
Total amount of support: $4,000.

NUMBER OF AWARDS: 1.

APPLICATION INFORMATION:
Guidelines and application form are available on the web site.
Duration: Four to six weeks depending on project.
Deadline: March 1.

PUBLICATIONS:
Program announcement.

STAFF:
Joanne Murray, Historian and Director

ADDRESS INQUIRIES TO:
Joanne Murray, Historian and Director
(See address above.)

THE EDUCATIONAL FOUNDATION FOR WOMEN IN ACCOUNTING
136 South Keowee Street
Dayton, OH 45402-2241
(937) 424-3391
Fax: (937) 222-5794

E-MAIL ADDRESS:
info@efwa.org

WEB SITE ADDRESS:
www.efwa.org

TYPE:
Scholarships. Laurels Fund provides a one-year academic scholarship for women pursuing a Ph.D. in accounting.

Women in Need Scholarship is available to women in their third, fourth or fifth year of academic pursuit who need the financial support to complete their degrees. It is renewable annually upon satisfactory completion of course requirements.

Women in Transition Scholarship is intended for women returning to school as freshmen to earn a Bachelor's degree in accounting. It is renewable annually upon satisfactory completion of course requirements.

See entry 1896 for full listing.

GENERAL BOARD OF HIGHER EDUCATION AND MINISTRY, THE UNITED METHODIST CHURCH
1001 19th Avenue South
Nashville, TN 37212
(615) 340-7338
Fax: (615) 340-7529

E-MAIL ADDRESS:
mbigord@gbhem.org

WEB SITE ADDRESS:
www.gbhem.org

TYPE:
Awards/prizes; Scholarships. Awards to encourage women over age 35 to prepare for ordained ministry as an Elder in the United Methodist Church as a second career. The scholarship is to be used for study toward the basic seminary degree in an accredited school of theology.

See entry 812 for full listing.

GLOBAL FUND FOR WOMEN   [1082]
222 Sutter Street, Suite 500
San Francisco, CA 94108
(415) 248-4800
Fax: (415) 248-4801

WEB SITE ADDRESS:
www.globalfundforwomen.org

FOUNDED: 1987

AREAS OF INTEREST:
Female human rights, women's access to communications, economic autonomy of women, and girls' education.

NAME(S) OF PROGRAMS:
● **Assisting Women's Groups Globally**

TYPE:
Conferences/seminars; General operating grants; Seed money grants; Technical assistance; Training grants. The Global Fund for Women is a grantmaking foundation that brings together a worldwide network of women and men to strengthen women's rights around the world. Initiatives include promoting women's economic independence, girls' education, women's rights within religious and cultural tradition, and women's health and safety. The Fund also provides assistance to groups overseas that wish to establish philanthropic organizations designed to benefit women.

YEAR PROGRAM STARTED: 1987

PURPOSE:
To promote a world of equality and social justice; to provide the financial means to enable women to attain this vision.

LEGAL BASIS:
Nonprofit corporation, 501(c)(3) tax-exempt.

ELIGIBILITY:
The Global Fund does not make grants to individuals, groups based and working primarily or solely in the U.S., groups whose main or only purpose is to generate income for its members or the community or groups headed and managed by men and without women in important management functions.

The Global Fund considers support to groups which demonstrate a clear commitment to women's equality and female human rights, are governed and directed primarily by women, have defined plans to strengthen the work of the group over time and may be unlikely to obtain funding from other sources.

APPLICATION INFORMATION:
Applicants may request and respond to grant request guidelines or send a letter describing the group and including contact information, organizational information and grant request information.
Duration: Varies depending on needs and nature of the request.

PUBLICATIONS:
Annual report; brochure; *Raising Our Voices*, newsletter.

IRS IDENTIFICATION NUMBER: 77-0155782

STAFF:
Deborah Holmes, Vice President of Communications
Jane Sloane, Vice President Programs
Elizabeth Schaffer, Chief Financial Officer

THE HAFIF FAMILY FOUNDATION   [1083]
Claremont Professional Building
265 West Bonita Avenue
Claremont, CA 91711
(909) 625-7971
Fax: (909) 621-4851

E-MAIL ADDRESS:
hffconcerts@yahoo.com

WEB SITE ADDRESS:
www.hafiffamilyfoundation.com

FOUNDED: 1987

AREAS OF INTEREST:
Drugs, gangs, battered women, poverty and education.

TYPE:
Scholarships.

PURPOSE:
To serve the poorest of the poor.

LEGAL BASIS:
Private foundation.

ELIGIBILITY:
No capital projects; no large staffs; more volunteer work.

GEOGRAPHIC RESTRICTIONS:
The inland empire, California.

FINANCIAL DATA:
Amount of support per award: Varies.
Total amount of support: $200,000 for the year 2012.

NUMBER OF AWARDS: Over 100.

APPLICATION INFORMATION:
Contact the Foundation for guidelines.
Duration: One year.

ADDRESS INQUIRIES TO:
Burnis Simon, Executive Director
(See address above.)

HORIZONS FOUNDATION [1084]
WID HORIZONS
2111 Wilson Boulevard, Suite 400
Arlington, VA 22201
(703) 522-1820
Fax: (703) 522-1885

E-MAIL ADDRESS:
jcasey@ndia.org

WEB SITE ADDRESS:
wid.ndia.org

AREAS OF INTEREST:
Increasing women's participation in national security fields.

NAME(S) OF PROGRAMS:
● **Horizons Foundation Scholarship Program**

TYPE:
Scholarships. The Horizons Foundation Scholarship Program is supported by accredited colleges and universities. Awards are made on an annual basis. The Foundation selects all scholarship recipients based on criteria it sets. Scholarships are awarded to applicants who require financial assistance, demonstrate strong academic credentials and a commitment to a career in national security.

PURPOSE:
To encourage women to pursue careers related to the national security interests of the U.S.; to provide development opportunities to women who are already working in national security fields.

ELIGIBILITY:
Scholarship Program applicants should be pursuing studies in engineering, computer science, physics, mathematics, business, law, international relations, political science, operations research or economics. Other disciplines will be considered if the applicant can successfully demonstrate relevance to a career in the areas of national security or defense.

Scholarship Program applicants also must meet the following criteria (no exceptions will be considered):
(1) be currently enrolled at an accredited university or college, either full-time or part-time;
(2) undergraduate and graduate students are eligible; undergraduates must have attained at least junior-level status (60 credits);
(3) demonstrate interest in pursuing a career related to national security/national defense;
(4) demonstrate financial need;
(5) have a minimum grade point average of 3.25 and;
(6) be a citizen of the U.S.

Recipients of past awards may apply for future financial assistance.

NUMBER OF AWARDS: 6 for academic year 2012-13.

APPLICATION INFORMATION:
Applications must be completed in full and include only the requested items (essays, recommendations and transcripts). Do not include copies of awards, certificates or photographs. Only students meeting eligibility requirements will be considered.
Deadline: July 1.

INTERNATIONAL FEDERATION OF UNIVERSITY WOMEN [1085]
10, rue du Lac
CH 1207 Geneva Switzerland
+4122 731 23 80

E-MAIL ADDRESS:
fellowships@ifuw.org

WEB SITE ADDRESS:
www.ifuw.org

FOUNDED: 1919

AREAS OF INTEREST:
Secondary, tertiary, continuing and nontraditional education for girls and women, human rights, status of women.

CONSULTING OR VOLUNTEER SERVICES:
At the international level, IFUW has working relationships with a number of nongovernmental organizations, consultative status with ECOSOC, ILO and UNESCO, as well as periodic cooperation with other UN bodies. At the national level, affiliates in 61 countries work to accomplish IFUW's goals and to address issues of global concern, both through project work and interaction with their governments and other interested groups.

NAME(S) OF PROGRAMS:
● **British Federation Crosby Hall Fellowship**
● **CFUW/A. Vibert Douglas Fellowship**
● **Winifred Cullis Grant**
● **IFUW Recognition Award**
● **Dorothy Leet Grant**
● **Ida Smedley MacLean Fellowship**
● **NZFGW Daphne Purves Grant**

TYPE:
Awards/prizes; Capital grants; Fellowships; Research grants; Training grants. IFUW fellowships and grants are awarded biennially to encourage and enable women graduates to undertake original research or obtain further training in the humanities, social sciences and natural sciences.

YEAR PROGRAM STARTED: 1919

PURPOSE:
To promote understanding and friendship among the university women of the world,

irrespective of their race, nationality, religion or political opinions; to encourage international cooperation; to further the development of education; to represent university women in international organizations; to encourage the full application of members' skills to the problems which arise at all levels of public life, whether local, national, regional or worldwide; to encourage their participation in the solving of these problems.

LEGAL BASIS:
International nongovernmental organization, based in Geneva, Switzerland.

ELIGIBILITY:
Open to women graduates:
(1) who are members of IFUW enrolled in a Ph.D. programme of which they have completed the first year and;
(2) who are nonmembers and independent members of less than the nominated period of membership; these may apply subject to payment of an administrative fee.

Winifred Cullis Grants are open to women graduates who seek to obtain specialized training essential to their research, train in new techniques or carry out independent research, including completion of a piece of research well-advanced.

Dorothy Leet Grants are open to women graduates of countries with a comparatively low per capita income and to other women graduates who either wish to work as experts in these countries or whose research is of value to such countries. They are available for obtaining special training essential to research and survey work, training in new techniques in group research and further study and carrying out independent research or surveys, including completion of a project well-advanced at the time of the application. Special consideration will be given to applicants whose research or training will have a multiplier effect in their home country.

In the case of both Winifred Cullis and Dorothy Leet Grants, preference is given for work in a country other than that in which the candidate has received her education or habitually resides.

Applications are welcomed from the humanities, social sciences and natural sciences. Membership in a national association is also an eligibility factor.

FINANCIAL DATA:
Candidates must provide evidence of adequate budgetary provision to meet the costs of their studies over and above the amount requested for the IFUW award.
Amount of support per award: Fellowships: CHF 3,000 to 10,000; Grants: CHF 1,000 to 6,000.

NUMBER OF APPLICANTS MOST RECENT YEAR: 70.

NUMBER OF AWARDS: 6 to 12 fellowships and grants.

APPLICATION INFORMATION:
All applications must be submitted electronically. Application forms are available on the web site. Members of one of IFUW's national affiliates must submit applications when completed with required supporting documentation to their NFA. Independent members and nonmembers must submit their

completed applications directly to the IFUW Office in Geneva with any administrative fee that is required.

Duration: Fellowships are intended to cover at least eight months of work. Grants are awarded for a few months.

Deadline: The final deadline for all applications to reach the IFUW Office in Geneva is 30 June.

ADDRESS INQUIRIES TO:
See e-mail address above.

*SPECIAL STIPULATIONS:
Women graduates only.

KENTUCKY FOUNDATION FOR WOMEN [1086]
1215 Heyburn Building
332 West Broadway
Louisville, KY 40202-2184
(502) 562-0045
Fax: (502) 561-0420

E-MAIL ADDRESS:
team@kfw.org

WEB SITE ADDRESS:
www.kfw.org

FOUNDED: 1985

AREAS OF INTEREST:
Arts, social change and feminism.

NAME(S) OF PROGRAMS:
- **Art Meets Activism**
- **Artist Enrichment**
- **Hopscotch House Artist Retreat Center**

TYPE:
Project/program grants; Residencies.

PURPOSE:
To promote positive social change through feminist expression in the arts.

ELIGIBILITY:
Individuals must be doing work focusing exclusively in Kentucky.

GEOGRAPHIC RESTRICTIONS:
Kentucky.

FINANCIAL DATA:
Amount of support per award: $1,000 to $7,500.
Total amount of support: $200,000 annually.

NUMBER OF APPLICANTS MOST RECENT YEAR:
Varies.

NUMBER OF AWARDS: Varies.

APPLICATION INFORMATION:
Contact the Foundation for guidelines and application form.
Duration: One year.
Deadline: Art Meets Activism: first Friday of March; Artist Enrichment: first Friday of September.

STAFF:
Rae Strobel, Grant Programs Administrator

ADDRESS INQUIRIES TO:
Executive Director
(See address above.)

THE LEEWAY FOUNDATION [1087]
1315 Walnut Street
Suite 832
Philadelphia, PA 19107
(215) 545-4078
Fax: (215) 545-4021

E-MAIL ADDRESS:
info@leeway.org

WEB SITE ADDRESS:
www.leeway.org

FOUNDED: 1993

AREAS OF INTEREST:
Women and trans artists and art for social change.

NAME(S) OF PROGRAMS:
- **Art and Change Grant**
- **Leeway Transformation Award**

TYPE:
Project/program grants. Art and Change Grants provide project-based grants to fund art for social change projects.

Leeway Transformation Award is an unrestricted award (not project-based) for women and trans people demonstrating a commitment to art for social change work.

YEAR PROGRAM STARTED: 1998

PURPOSE:
To support women and trans artists who create art for social change.

ELIGIBILITY:
Women and trans artists living in the Delaware Valley region may apply. The Transformation Award is open to women and trans people working in any art form who create art and social change and have done so for the past five years or more, demonstrating a commitment to art for social change work.

GEOGRAPHIC RESTRICTIONS:
Camden County, New Jersey; Bucks, Chester, Delaware, Montgomery and Philadelphia counties, Pennsylvania.

FINANCIAL DATA:
Amount of support per award: Art and Change Grant: $2,500; Leeway Transformation Award: $15,000.

NUMBER OF APPLICANTS MOST RECENT YEAR:
Varies.

NUMBER OF AWARDS: Varies.

APPLICATION INFORMATION:
Contact the Foundation for application or download a copy of the current application and guideline procedures from the web site.
Deadline: Art and Change Grant: March 1 and September 1; Leeway Transformation Award: May 15.

STAFF:
Denise Brown, Executive Director

ADDRESS INQUIRIES TO:
Sham-e-Ali Nayeem, Program Director
(See address above.)

MICHIGAN WOMEN'S FOUNDATION [1088]
333 W. Fort Street
Suite 1920
Detroit, MI 48226
(313) 962-1920
Fax: (313) 962-1926

E-MAIL ADDRESS:
grants@miwf.org

WEB SITE ADDRESS:
www.miwf.org

FOUNDED: 1986

AREAS OF INTEREST:
Needs of women and girls.

NAME(S) OF PROGRAMS:
- **Young Women for Change**

TYPE:
General operating grants; Project/program grants; Seed money grants. Specific focus changes yearly and is determined by each of seven chapters.

YEAR PROGRAM STARTED: 1986

PURPOSE:
To develop young women through the process of philanthropy and grantmaking into successful, fiscally responsible and socially responsive women.

LEGAL BASIS:
Nonprofit 501(c)(3) organization.

ELIGIBILITY:
Eligible organizations must be IRS 501(c)(3) tax-exempt.

GEOGRAPHIC RESTRICTIONS:
Michigan.

FINANCIAL DATA:
Amount of support per award: $500 to $5,000.
Total amount of support: Varies.

APPLICATION INFORMATION:
Guidelines and application form are available on the web site.
Duration: One year.
Deadline: Mid-February.

PUBLICATIONS:
Trillium, newsletter.

IRS IDENTIFICATION NUMBER: 38-2689979

STAFF:
Carolyn J. Cassin, President and Chief Executive Officer
Kate Spratt, Senior Financial Consultant

ADDRESS INQUIRIES TO:
E-mail: grants@miwf.org

MONEY FOR WOMEN/BARBARA DEMING MEMORIAL FUND, INC. [1089]
P.O. Box 309
Wilton, NH 03086

E-MAIL ADDRESS:
demingfund@gmail.com

WEB SITE ADDRESS:
demingfund.org

FOUNDED: 1975

AREAS OF INTEREST:
Visual art, fiction, nonfiction and poetry.

NAME(S) OF PROGRAMS:
- **Individual Artist Support Grants**

TYPE:
Awards/prizes. Small grants awarded biannually to individual feminists in the arts.

PURPOSE:
To support feminists in the arts.

LEGAL BASIS:
Private foundation.

ELIGIBILITY:
Open to individual feminist women in the arts, in visual art, fiction (prose), nonfiction (prose) and poetry whose work addresses women's concerns and/or speaks for peace and justice from a feminist perspective. Applicants must be citizens of the U.S. or Canada. No educational or study scholarships.

GEOGRAPHIC RESTRICTIONS:
United States and Canada.

FINANCIAL DATA:
Amount of support per award: $500 to
$1,500.

Total amount of support: Varies.

NUMBER OF APPLICANTS MOST RECENT YEAR:
550.

NUMBER OF AWARDS: 20.

REPRESENTATIVE AWARDS:
Ana-Maurine Lara (poetry), Austin, TX,
Kohnjehr Woman; Sarah Levine (nonfiction),
Cambridge, MA, *What Hands Can Do*;
Robin Parks (nonfiction), Bryn Mawr, PA,
Famished.

APPLICATION INFORMATION:
Visit the Fund web site to download
application form (required) and guidelines. A
new application is required for each round.
Completed applications require an
application/processing fee of $25.

Deadline: June 30 for nonfiction and poetry.
December 31 for fiction, visual art and mixed
genre. Announcement by May and October.

PUBLICATIONS:
Newsletter.

IRS IDENTIFICATION NUMBER: 51-0176956

BOARD OF DIRECTORS:
Maureen Brady
Julie R. Enszer
Martha Hughes
Lise Weil

ADDRESS INQUIRIES TO:
Susan Pliner, Executive Director
(See e-mail address above.)

MS. FOUNDATION FOR WOMEN   [1090]
12 Metro Tech Center
26th Floor
Brooklyn, NY 11201
(212) 742-2300
Fax: (212) 742-1653

E-MAIL ADDRESS:
info@ms.foundation.org

WEB SITE ADDRESS:
www.ms.foundation.org

FOUNDED: 1972

AREAS OF INTEREST:
Economic justice, women's health, and
safety.

NAME(S) OF PROGRAMS:
● **Economic Justice**
● **Ending Violence**
● **Women's Health**

TYPE:
Fellowships; Internships; Project/program
grants; Technical assistance; Training grants.
General support.

YEAR PROGRAM STARTED: 1976

PURPOSE:
To support the efforts of women and girls to
govern their own lives and influence the
world around them; to champion an equitable
society by effecting change in public
consciousness, law, philanthropy and social
policy through its leadership, expertise and
financial support.

LEGAL BASIS:
Public foundation.

ELIGIBILITY:
Funding is by invitation only. Within its
funding priorities, the Foundation gives
priority to:
(1) efforts that engage women and girls in
crafting activist solutions to the particular
challenges they face in their communities
based on gender, race, ethnicity, class, age,
disability, sexual orientation and culture and;
(2) national-, regional- or state-level public
policy advocacy informed by local organizing
work and undertaken by organizations with
strong linkages to a grassroots constituency.

Special consideration is given to the
organizations that:
(1) are pro-women's empowerment,
proactively antiracist and working to
dismantle heterosexism, class oppression and
discrimination based on disability;
(2) address the particular challenges faced by
low-income women and girls;
(3) clearly articulate and respond to issues of
gender as related to class and race/ethnicity;
(4) are multi-issue and involved in a form of
cross-constituency organizing and coalition
work;
(5) encourage intergenerational work that
empowers younger as well as older women;
(6) include in leadership positions those who
are affected most directly by the issues
addressed and;
(7) have limited access to other funding
sources.

The Foundation does not fund direct-service
projects, stand-alone cultural or media
projects, publications, individuals,
scholarships, religious institutions,
conferences, university-based research or
government agencies.

GEOGRAPHIC RESTRICTIONS:
United States.

FINANCIAL DATA:
Amount of support per award: Varies.

Total amount of support: Varies.

NUMBER OF APPLICANTS MOST RECENT YEAR:
1,000.

NUMBER OF AWARDS: 100.

APPLICATION INFORMATION:
Contact the Foundation.

Duration: Generally one-time grants. Some
renewal funding.

Deadline: Varies per program.

PUBLICATIONS:
Annual report; application guidelines; most
recent grants list.

BOARD OF DIRECTORS:
Cathy Raphael, Chairperson
Ashley Blanchard, Vice Chairperson
Eve Ellis, Treasurer
Kathleen Stephansen, Treasurer
Verna L. Williams, Secretary
Heather Arnet
Elizabeth Bremner
Michael Campbell
Jeannie Diefenderfer
Lauren Embrey
Phoebe Eng
Gara LaMarche
Alicia Lara
Rene Redwood
Dorothy Q. Thomas

NATIONAL FEDERATION OF REPUBLICAN WOMEN   [1091]
124 North Alfred Street
Alexandria, VA 22314
(703) 548-9688
Fax: (703) 548-9836

E-MAIL ADDRESS:
mail@nfrw.org

WEB SITE ADDRESS:
www.nfrw.org

FOUNDED: 1938

AREAS OF INTEREST:
The political process.

NAME(S) OF PROGRAMS:
● **Dorothy Kabis Internship**
● **National Pathfinder's Scholarship**
● **Betty Rendel Scholarship**

TYPE:
Internships; Scholarships. Dorothy Kabis
Internship includes a six-week internship in
Washington, DC, housing, travel and stipend.

National Pathfinder's Scholarships are given
to the best nominated candidates.

Betty Rendel Scholarships are given to
undergraduate women who are majoring in
political science, government or economics.

PURPOSE:
To involve more women in the political
process and provide educational
opportunities.

ELIGIBILITY:
National Pathfinder's Scholarship is open to
young women seeking undergraduate or
postgraduate degrees, college sophomores,
juniors, seniors and students enrolled in a
Master's program. Recent high school
graduates and first-year college women are
not eligible.

Betty Rendel Scholarship applicants must be
undergraduate women who are majoring in
political science, government or economics.
Open only to women who have successfully
completed two years of college work.

GEOGRAPHIC RESTRICTIONS:
United States.

FINANCIAL DATA:
Dorothy Kabis Internship includes a small
stipend, housing and airfare.

Amount of support per award: National
Pathfinder's Scholarship: $2,500; Betty
Rendel Scholarship: $1,000.

NUMBER OF AWARDS: 3 for each program.

APPLICATION INFORMATION:
All grant information, including a printable
version of the application, can be found
online.

Duration: One-time award.

Deadline: June 1 for the National
Pathfinder's Scholarship and Betty Rendel
Scholarship. February 20 for Dorothy Kabis
Internship.

ADDRESS INQUIRIES TO:
Scholarship Coordinator
(See address above.)

*SPECIAL STIPULATIONS:
Applicants must be U.S. citizens and may
only apply to one program in a given year.
Winners may not reapply.

NATIVE AMERICAN COMMUNITY BOARD (NACB)

P.O. Box 572
Lake Andes, SD 57356-0572
(605) 487-7072
Fax: (605) 487-7964

E-MAIL ADDRESS:
charon@charles-mix.com

WEB SITE ADDRESS:
www.nativeshop.org

TYPE:
Internships.

See entry 1052 for full listing.

THE NEWBERRY LIBRARY

Committee on Awards
60 West Walton Street
Chicago, IL 60610-7324
(312) 255-3666

E-MAIL ADDRESS:
research@newberry.org

WEB SITE ADDRESS:
www.newberry.org/fellowships

TYPE:
Fellowships; Visiting scholars. Allen fellows are expected to spend a significant part of their tenure in residence at Newberry's D'Arcy McNickle Center for American Indian History.

See entry 1053 for full listing.

OPEN MEADOWS FOUNDATION   [1092]

P.O. Box 1363
Bronx, NY 10475
(718) 885-0969

E-MAIL ADDRESS:
openmeadows@igc.org

WEB SITE ADDRESS:
www.openmeadows.org

FOUNDED: 1986

AREAS OF INTEREST:
Projects led by and benefiting women and girls, reflecting community diversity, building community power, and promoting racial, social, economic and environmental justice.

TYPE:
Development grants; Project/program grants; Training grants. International program for women and girls.

PURPOSE:
To fund projects that are led by and benefit women and girls.

ELIGIBILITY:
Applicant organization must be nonprofit 501(c)(3) or have a fiscal sponsor that is tax-exempt 501(c)(3). Small and start-up organizations are strongly encouraged to apply. Proposals not previously funded have priority. Proposals for projects that have limited financial access or have encountered obstacles in their search for funding are eligible to apply. Applicant's organizational budget should not exceed $150,000. Projects must be led by and benefit women and girls. No grants are made to individuals.

FINANCIAL DATA:
Amount of support per award: Up to $2,000.
Total amount of support: $60,000 per year.

NUMBER OF APPLICANTS MOST RECENT YEAR:
500.

NUMBER OF AWARDS: 40 per year.

APPLICATION INFORMATION:
Only mailed applications are accepted. Must include copy of tax-exempt letter from the IRS giving 501(c)(3) status.
Duration: One year. Must reapply.
Deadline: February 15 and August 15.

ADDRESS INQUIRIES TO:
Di Eckerle, Director
(See address above.)

P.E.O. SISTERHOOD

P.E.O. Executive Office
3700 Grand Avenue
Des Moines, IA 50312
(515) 255-3153
Fax: (515) 255-3820

E-MAIL ADDRESS:
ips@peodsm.org

WEB SITE ADDRESS:
www.peointernational.org

TYPE:
Grants-in-aid; Scholarships. Awards for selected women from countries other than the U.S. and Canada to pursue graduate study in the U.S. or Canada. Support is available for advanced study in any field except for research. No new applications at the dissertation level.

See entry 964 for full listing.

THE PHI BETA KAPPA SOCIETY   [1093]

1606 New Hampshire Avenue, N.W.
Washington, DC 20009
(202) 745-3287
Fax: (202) 986-1601

E-MAIL ADDRESS:
awards@pbk.org

WEB SITE ADDRESS:
www.pbk.org

FOUNDED: 1776

AREAS OF INTEREST:
French language, literature and culture; Greek language, literature and history.

NAME(S) OF PROGRAMS:
• **Mary Isabel Sibley Fellowship**

TYPE:
Fellowships. Grant to women scholars made in alternate years for advanced research dealing with Greek language, literature, history or archaeology (odd-numbered years) or with French language or literature (even-numbered years).

YEAR PROGRAM STARTED: 1939

PURPOSE:
To assist women scholars conducting original research.

LEGAL BASIS:
National scholarly honorary society.

ELIGIBILITY:
Unmarried women between 25 and 35 years of age (inclusive) are eligible to apply. They must hold the Doctorate or have fulfilled all requirements for the Doctorate except the dissertation. Applicants must have demonstrated ability to carry on original research and must plan to devote full-time work to research during the fellowship year. Eligibility is not restricted to members of the Society or to U.S. citizens.

FINANCIAL DATA:
The Fellowship carries a $20,000 stipend with one-half of the amount payable after July following announcement of the Fellowship and the balance after another six months have elapsed.
Amount of support per award: $20,000.
Total amount of support: $20,000.

NUMBER OF APPLICANTS MOST RECENT YEAR:
40.

NUMBER OF AWARDS: 1 each year.

APPLICATION INFORMATION:
Official application materials are available upon request to the Awards Coordinator or on the web site. Fellowships are awarded alternately in the fields of Greek language, literature, history or archaeology (odd-numbered years) and French language or literature (even-numbered years). Send brief description of intended research project when requesting an application.
Duration: The Fellowship is tenable for one year.
Deadline: Applications must be filed in January for the Fellowship to be announced by the following May. Contact Society for exact date.

OFFICERS:
Kate Soule, President
John Churchill, Secretary

ADDRESS INQUIRIES TO:
Mary Isabel Sibley Fellowship Committee
(See address above.)

ROCHESTER AREA COMMUNITY FOUNDATION   [1094]

500 East Avenue
Rochester, NY 14607-1912
(585) 271-4100
Fax: (585) 271-4292

E-MAIL ADDRESS:
mhartstein@racf.org

WEB SITE ADDRESS:
www.racf.org

FOUNDED: 1972

AREAS OF INTEREST:
Women and girls, organizational capacity building, aging, arts, the environment, civic engagement, youth and families, historical preservation and health.

TYPE:
Project/program grants; Scholarships.

PURPOSE:
To support community responsibility and leadership, healthy options for young people and their families, early childhood development and quality of life.

LEGAL BASIS:
Tax-exempt public charity.

GEOGRAPHIC RESTRICTIONS:
Genesee, Livingston, Monroe, Ontario, Orleans, Seneca, Wayne and Yates counties, New York.

FINANCIAL DATA:
$312,000,000 in grants since 1972.
Amount of support per award: Varies.
Total amount of support: $21,100,000 in grants for fiscal year 2012-13.

IRS IDENTIFICATION NUMBER: 23-7250641

ADDRESS INQUIRIES TO:
Grant inquiries to: Mary Hartstein
Program Administrator
All other inquiries to: Jennifer Leonard
President and Executive Director

SIGMA DELTA EPSILON/GRADUATE WOMEN IN SCIENCE
P.O. Box 240607
St. Paul, MN 55124-0607
(952) 236-9112

E-MAIL ADDRESS:
gwised@mac.com

WEB SITE ADDRESS:
www.gwis.org

TYPE:
Awards/prizes; Fellowships; Travel grants.
Leadership Awards are given to Graduate
Women in Science officers.

See entry 1837 for full listing.

SKILLBUILDERS FUND   [1095]
4701 College Boulevard, Suite 214
Leawood, KS 66211
(913) 608-7545

E-MAIL ADDRESS:
info@skillbuildersfund.org

WEB SITE ADDRESS:
www.skillbuildersfund.org

FOUNDED: 1983

AREAS OF INTEREST:
Programs benefiting low-income women and
girls.

TYPE:
Project/program grants. Programs that help
women and girls with economic
self-sufficiency. Matching gifts are for
directors only. Scholarships are only given to
organizations, not to individuals.

YEAR PROGRAM STARTED: 1984

PURPOSE:
To enhance the capabilities of women and
girls of all ages in the Kansas City
metropolitan area and to realize their full
potential.

LEGAL BASIS:
Private foundation.

ELIGIBILITY:
Organizations must be IRS 501(c)(3)
not-for-profit. Funding primarily is directed
to 501(c)(3) organizations that specifically
benefit women and girls. Individuals,
businesses and other for-profit organizations
do not qualify.

GEOGRAPHIC RESTRICTIONS:
Kansas City metropolitan area, including
Cass, Clay, Jackson, Johnson, Leavenworth,
Platte, Ray and Wyandotte counties.

FINANCIAL DATA:
Amount of support per award: $20,000 to
$50,000.
Total amount of support: Varies.

NUMBER OF AWARDS: 3 to 9 annually.

APPLICATION INFORMATION:
Application information is available on the
web site. Applicants must include a copy of
their IRS tax determination letter with the
application.
Duration: One year.

Deadline: Varies from year to year.

PUBLICATIONS:
Information brochure with application
procedures.

IRS IDENTIFICATION NUMBER: 48-0984713

STAFF:
Jennifer Sullivan, Administrative Coordinator

ADDRESS INQUIRIES TO:
Jennifer Sullivan
Administrative Coordinator
(See address above.)

SOCIETY OF DAUGHTERS OF THE U.S. ARMY
11804 Grey Birch Place
Reston, VA 20191-4223

TYPE:
Scholarships.

See entry 1756 for full listing.

SOCIETY OF WOMEN ENGINEERS   [1096]
203 North La Salle Street
Suite 1675
Chicago, IL 60601
(312) 596-5223
Fax: (312) 596-5252

E-MAIL ADDRESS:
scholarships@swe.org

WEB SITE ADDRESS:
www.swe.org/scholarships

FOUNDED: 1950

AREAS OF INTEREST:
Engineering.

NAME(S) OF PROGRAMS:
● **Society of Women Engineers
Scholarship Program**

TYPE:
Awards/prizes; Conferences/seminars;
Scholarships. Support for undergraduate and
graduate engineering studies including
women who have been out of the engineering
job market for a minimum of two years and
who will return to school for an engineering
program.

PURPOSE:
To encourage women to achieve their utmost
in careers as professional engineers and as
the leaders of tomorrow and to attain high
levels of education.

LEGAL BASIS:
Nonprofit educational organization under IRS
501(c)(3) classification.

ELIGIBILITY:
Scholarships are open only to women
studying an accredited engineering program
in a school, college, or university. Candidate
is evaluated on the basis of scholastic
standing in high school and/or college and
extracurricular activity. Students must be
studying in the U.S. (or Mexico) in the
upcoming year.

Some scholarships require applicant to be a
U.S. citizen.

Additional criteria can be found on the
Society web site.

FINANCIAL DATA:
Scholarship payments are made directly to
academic institutions on the recipient's
behalf.

Amount of support per award: $1,000 to
$20,000.

Total amount of support: $500,000 awarded
for the year 2013.

NUMBER OF APPLICANTS MOST RECENT YEAR:
Over 3,000.

NUMBER OF AWARDS: 200 for the year 2013.

APPLICATION INFORMATION:
Completed application form and letters of
reference are required.
Duration: One year. Possible renewal.
Deadline: May 15 for freshmen. February 15
for sophomore, junior, senior and graduate.
Announcement in late spring and summer,
respectively, for use during the following
academic year.

PUBLICATIONS:
Applications; *SWE* magazine.

IRS IDENTIFICATION NUMBER: 13-1947735

ADDRESS INQUIRIES TO:
See e-mail address above.

WASHINGTON UNIVERSITY
Graduate School of Arts and Sciences
Campus Box 1187
One Brookings Drive
St. Louis, MO 63130
(314) 935-6818
Fax: (314) 935-4887

E-MAIL ADDRESS:
cecilyhawksworth@wustl.edu

WEB SITE ADDRESS:
pages.wustl.edu/olinfellowship

TYPE:
Fellowships. The Olin Fellowships are open
to candidates for any of the following
graduate and professional schools at
Washington University: architecture, art, arts
and sciences, business, engineering,
medicine, and social work.

See entry 1802 for full listing.

WELLESLEY COLLEGE   [1097]
Center for Work and Service
Green Hall 439A, 106 Central Street
Wellesley, MA 02481-8203
(781) 283-2347
Fax: (781) 283-3674

E-MAIL ADDRESS:
cws-fellowships@wellesley.edu

WEB SITE ADDRESS:
www.wellesley.edu/CWS

AREAS OF INTEREST:
Graduate education.

NAME(S) OF PROGRAMS:
● **Anne Louise Barrett Fellowship**
● **Margaret Freeman Bowers Fellowship**
● **The Eugene L. Cox Fellowship**
● **Professor Elizabeth F. Fisher
Fellowship**
● **Ruth Ingersoll Goldmark Fellowship**
● **Horton-Hallowell Fellowship**
● **Peggy Howard Fellowship in
Economics**
● **Edna V. Moffett Fellowship**
● **Alice Freeman Palmer Fellowship**
● **Kathryn Conway Preyer Fellowship**
● **Vida Dutton Scudder Fellowship**
● **Harriet A. Shaw Fellowship**
● **Mary Elvira Stevens Traveling
Fellowship**
● **Maria Opasnov Tyler '52 Scholarship**

- **Sarah Perry Wood Medical Fellowship**
- **Fanny Bullock Workman Fellowship**

TYPE:
Fellowships; Research grants. The Anne Louise Barrett Fellowship is given preferably in music and primarily for study or research in musical theory, composition, or in the history of music, abroad or in the U.S.

The Margaret Freeman Bowers Fellowship is given for first year of study in the fields of social work, law, or policy/public administration, including MBA candidates with plans for a career in the field of social services.

The Eugene L. Cox Fellowship is for graduate study in medieval or renaissance history and culture abroad or in the U.S.

The Professor Elizabeth F. Fisher Fellowship is given for research or further study in geology or geography, including urban, environmental or ecological studies.

The Ruth Ingersoll Goldmark Fellowship is awarded for graduate study in English literature, English composition or in the classics.

The Horton-Hallowell Fellowship is awarded for graduate study in any field, preferably in the last two years of candidacy for the Ph.D. degree, or its equivalent, or for private research of equivalent standard.

The Peggy Howard Fellowship in Economics is given to provide financial aid for Wellesley students or alumnae continuing their study of economics. Administered by the economics faculty who may name one or two recipients depending on the income available.

The Edna V. Moffett Fellowship is given to a young alumna, preferably for a first year of graduate study in history.

The Alice Freeman Palmer Fellowship is awarded for study or research abroad or in the U.S.

The Kathryn Conway Preyer Fellowship is for advanced study in history.

The Vida Dutton Scudder Fellowship is given for study in the field of social science, political science or literature.

The Harriet A. Shaw Fellowship is given for study or research in music and the allied arts, in the U.S. or abroad.

Mary Elvira Stevens Traveling Fellowship is awarded for travel or study outside the U.S.

The Maria Opasnov Tyler '52 Scholarship is for graduate study in Russian studies.

The Sarah Perry Wood Medical Fellowship is awarded for the study of medicine at an accredited medical school approved by the American Medical Association.

The Fanny Bullock Workman Fellowship is given for graduate study in any field.

ELIGIBILITY:
Awards will be based on merit and financial need. Awards are usually made to applicants who plan full-time graduate study for the coming year. Preference in all cases, except for the Peggy Howard Fellowship, will be given to applicants who have not held one of these awards.

Alice Freeman Palmer Fellows must be no more than 26 years of age at the time of their appointment and unmarried throughout the whole of their tenure.

Preference for the Harriet A. Shaw Fellowship is given to music candidates; undergraduate work in history of art is required of other candidates.

Candidates for the Mary Elvira Stevens Traveling Fellowship must be at least 25 years of age in the year of application. Any scholarly, artistic, or cultural purpose may be considered.

FINANCIAL DATA:
Amount of support per award: $3,000 to $76,000.

Total amount of support: Varies.

NUMBER OF APPLICANTS MOST RECENT YEAR: 207.

APPLICATION INFORMATION:
Application forms for the Peggy Howard Fellowship may be obtained from the Economics Department at the College.

Deadline: Peggy Howard Fellowship: Early April. Mary Elvira Stevens Fellowship: Early December. All other awards: Early January.

PUBLICATIONS:
Program announcement.

*SPECIAL STIPULATIONS:
These fellowships are for study at institutions other than Wellesley College. Applicants must be graduating seniors or alumnae of Wellesley College for all fellowships.

WELLESLEY COLLEGE [1098]
Center for Work and Service
Green Hall 439A, 106 Central Street
Wellesley, MA 02481-8203
(781) 283-2347
Fax: (781) 283-3674

E-MAIL ADDRESS:
cws-fellowships@wellesley.edu

WEB SITE ADDRESS:
www.wellesley.edu/CWS

AREAS OF INTEREST:
Graduate study for women.

NAME(S) OF PROGRAMS:
- **Mary McEwen Schimke Scholarship**
- **M.A. Cartland Shackford Medical Fellowship**

TYPE:
Fellowships; Scholarships. Awards are made to female applicants who plan for full-time graduate study for the coming year.

The Mary McEwen Schimke Scholarship is a supplemental award given to afford relief from household and child care expenses while pursuing graduate study.

The M.A. Cartland Shackford Medical Fellowship is given for study of medicine with a view to general practice, not psychiatry.

ELIGIBILITY:
Applicant must be graduate woman of any American university.

The Mary McEwen Schimke Scholarship is made on the basis of scholarly expectation and identified need. The candidate must be over 30 years of age, have household and child care responsibilities, and be currently engaged in graduate study in literature and/or history. Preference is given to American Studies.

FINANCIAL DATA:
Amount of support per award: McEwen Scholarship: Up to $1,500; Shackford Medical Fellowship: Up to $10,000.

Total amount of support: Varies.

APPLICATION INFORMATION:
Application information is available on the web site.

Duration: One year.
Deadline: Early January.

PUBLICATIONS:
Announcement.

THE WHO (WOMEN HELPING OTHERS) FOUNDATION [1099]
2121 Midway Road
Carrollton, TX 75006
(972) 458-0601
(800) 946-4663
Fax: (972) 341-3080

E-MAIL ADDRESS:
who@beauticontrol.com

WEB SITE ADDRESS:
www.whofoundation.org

FOUNDED: 1993

AREAS OF INTEREST:
Women's and children's health, education and social services issues.

TYPE:
Development grants; Product donations; Project/program grants.

YEAR PROGRAM STARTED: 1993

PURPOSE:
To support community-focused charities that serve the overlooked needs of women, children and families.

LEGAL BASIS:
Tax-exempt, nonprofit foundation.

ELIGIBILITY:
Applicants must be nonpolitical charities and organizations that have been incorporated with 501(c)(3) status for a minimum of three years prior to application. No grants to individuals. Prefer requests dealing with projects and programs.

Volunteer service grant available for BeautiControl consultants only.

GEOGRAPHIC RESTRICTIONS:
United States and Puerto Rico.

FINANCIAL DATA:
Amount of support per award: Varies depending on needs and nature of the request.

NUMBER OF AWARDS: 8 for the year 2013.

APPLICATION INFORMATION:
Application form required. Required attachments include a copy of the organization's most recent audit, board list, budget outline and most recent annual report, if available, and 501(c)(3) document.

Duration: Varies.
Deadline: May.

PUBLICATIONS:
Application; newsletters; cancer booklet for women.

IRS IDENTIFICATION NUMBER: 75-2504646

BOARD OF DIRECTORS:
Jasmine B. Harris, Ed.D., Chairman
Gary Jones, Chairperson-Elect
Judy Mynett Ward, Treasurer
Shay Wyrick Cathey, Secretary
Tonya Johannsen
Madeline Otero
Karissa Schuler
Tracey Wallace

ADDRESS INQUIRIES TO:
Grants Manager
(See address above.)

WOMEN IN FILM [1100]
6100 Wilshire Boulevard
Suite 710
Los Angeles, CA 90048
(323) 935-2211
Fax: (323) 935-2212

E-MAIL ADDRESS:
foundation@wif.org

WEB SITE ADDRESS:
www.wif.org/fff

FOUNDED: 1985

AREAS OF INTEREST:
Filmmaking.

NAME(S) OF PROGRAMS:
● Women in Film Foundation Film
Finishing Fund

TYPE:
Project/program grants. Awards for
completion of films or videotapes on subjects
that meet the stated guidelines of WIF on an
annual basis.

YEAR PROGRAM STARTED: 1985

PURPOSE:
To increase employment and promote equal
opportunities for women; to encourage
individual creative projects by women; to
enhance media images of women; to further
the professional development of women; to
influence prevailing attitudes and practices
regarding and on behalf of women.

LEGAL BASIS:
Nonprofit organization.

ELIGIBILITY:
All independent producers and nonprofit
corporations are eligible to submit proposals
for completion funding on an existing film or
video. Projects in development or
pre-production will not be considered. No
student projects, graduate or undergraduate,
will be considered. Applicants do not need to
be members of Women In Film.

FINANCIAL DATA:
Amount of support per award: Up to $15,000
in cash and/or in-kind services.
Total amount of support: Varies.

NUMBER OF APPLICANTS MOST RECENT YEAR:
Over 100.

NUMBER OF AWARDS: Approximately 7.

APPLICATION INFORMATION:
Detailed guidelines and application form may
be obtained from the Foundation's web site.
Duration: Varies.
Deadline: April 29.

ADDRESS INQUIRIES TO:
April Wright
Foundation Manager
(See address above.)

*SPECIAL STIPULATIONS:
Projects must be in post-production by the
deadline. Filmmakers must submit a rough
cut of their films to be considered.

WOMEN'S FOUNDATION OF
MINNESOTA [1101]
155 Fifth Avenue South
Suite 500
Minneapolis, MN 55401-2549
(612) 337-5010
Fax: (612) 337-0404

E-MAIL ADDRESS:
contactus@wfmn.org

WEB SITE ADDRESS:
www.wfmn.org

FOUNDED: 1983

AREAS OF INTEREST:
Women and girls in Minnesota.

NAME(S) OF PROGRAMS:
● Social Change Fund

TYPE:
Development grants; General operating
grants; Project/program grants; Technical
assistance. Start-up grants.

YEAR PROGRAM STARTED: 1986

PURPOSE:
To increase financial resources available to
programs and organizations by and for
women and girls creating change on their
own behalf.

LEGAL BASIS:
Public foundation.

ELIGIBILITY:
Must primarily benefit women and girls and
be not-for-profit or informal not-for-profit.

GEOGRAPHIC RESTRICTIONS:
Minnesota.

FINANCIAL DATA:
Amount of support per award: $15,000 to
$20,000.
Total amount of support: Approximately
$2,000,000 total funding in all programs.

NUMBER OF APPLICANTS MOST RECENT YEAR:
200.

APPLICATION INFORMATION:
Detailed instructions and guidelines are
available from the Foundation.
Duration: Three years.
Deadline: Varies.

PUBLICATIONS:
Annual report; equality report; brochure;
grant guidelines; research/issue reports.

IRS IDENTIFICATION NUMBER: 41-1635761

BOARD OF TRUSTEES:
Julia Classen, Chairperson
Jean Adams
Julie Corty
Wilhelmina Holder
Catherine McBride
Elizabeth Olson
Ashley Rajaratnam
Lucy Rogers
Sudha Shetty
Valerie Spencer
April Sutor
Rosa Tock
Victoria White

ADDRESS INQUIRIES TO:
Saanii Hernandez-Mohr
(See address above.)

*SPECIAL STIPULATIONS:
Funds only in Minnesota. Does not fund
individuals.

WOMEN'S FOUNDATION OF
MINNESOTA [1102]
105 Fifth Avenue South
Suite 300
Minneapolis, MN 55401
(612) 337-5010
Fax: (612) 337-0404

E-MAIL ADDRESS:
contactus@wfmn.org

WEB SITE ADDRESS:
www.wfmn.org

FOUNDED: 1983

AREAS OF INTEREST:
Women and girls in Minnesota.

NAME(S) OF PROGRAMS:
● girlsBEST

TYPE:
Project/program grants. The girlsBEST
program has four program tracks: Academic;
Entrepreneurial; Employment Development
and High-Paying/High-Skill Careers; Public
Education and Advocacy.

PURPOSE:
To increase financial resources available to
programs and organizations by and for
women and girls creating change on their
own behalf; to increase future economic
success for women and girls.

LEGAL BASIS:
Public foundation.

ELIGIBILITY:
Must primarily benefit women and girls and
be not-for-profit or informal not-for-profit.

GEOGRAPHIC RESTRICTIONS:
Minnesota.

FINANCIAL DATA:
Amount of support per award: $10,000 to
$15,000.
Total amount of support: Approximately
$200,000 for the year 2012.

NUMBER OF APPLICANTS MOST RECENT YEAR:
54.

NUMBER OF AWARDS: 13.

REPRESENTATIVE AWARDS:
Entrepreneurial: $10,000 to Centro, Inc.;
Academic: $12,000 to Laura Jeffrey
Academy; Public Education and Advocacy:
$11,000 to Crisis Center for Teens Against
Dating Abuse.

APPLICATION INFORMATION:
Application information is available on the
web site.
Duration: Three years.
Deadline: May 1.

ADDRESS INQUIRIES TO:
Saanii Hernandez-Mohr
Senior Program Officer
(See address above.)

*SPECIAL STIPULATIONS:
Funds only in Minnesota. Does not fund
individuals.

WOMEN'S POLICY, INC.
(WPI) [1103]
409 12th Street, S.W.
Suite 310
Washington, DC 20024
(202) 554-2323

E-MAIL ADDRESS:
webmaster@womenspolicy.org

WEB SITE ADDRESS:
www.womenspolicy.org

FOUNDED: 1995

AREAS OF INTEREST:
Women's public policy issues.

NAME(S) OF PROGRAMS:
- **Congressional Fellowships on Women and Public Policy**

TYPE:
Fellowships.

YEAR PROGRAM STARTED: 1980

PURPOSE:
To encourage more effective participation by women in the formulation of policy options that recognize the needs of all people; to promote activities that encourage the translation of research into policy; to raise awareness that national and international issues concerning women are interdependent; to increase understanding that those issues often defined as women's issues are, in fact, human issues of equal importance to both women and men.

LEGAL BASIS:
501(c)(3) nonprofit organization.

ELIGIBILITY:
Applicants must be currently enrolled in, or have graduated within the last 18 months from, a graduate or professional degree program in the U.S. Preliminary selection is based on academic performance, writing skills, experience with community groups and interest in the analysis of gender differences as they affect federal laws and legislating. Candidates from all academic disciplines are considered. Final selection follows an interview by WPI.

FINANCIAL DATA:
Amount of support per award: Monthly stipends of $1,500, plus $1,500 for tuition and $500 health care allowance.
Total amount of support: $12,000 per awardee for academic year 2015.

NUMBER OF APPLICANTS MOST RECENT YEAR:
Approximately 100.

NUMBER OF AWARDS: Approximately 5 to 7 each year.

APPLICATION INFORMATION:
Applications are available in early May. Applicants must submit all academic transcripts, three letters of recommendation, completed application form and an essay.
Duration: January to August. No renewals.
Deadline: June 20. Regional interviews of semi-finalists are held in July and awards made by August 30.

IRS IDENTIFICATION NUMBER: 52-1914894

STAFF:
Cindy Hall, President
Cheryl Williams, Vice President

ADDRESS INQUIRIES TO:
Cindy Hall, President
(See address above.)

*SPECIAL STIPULATIONS:
Foreign students at international universities are not eligible. Must come to Washington to work full-time in a congressional office from January until July/August.

WOMEN'S SPORTS FOUNDATION [1104]

Eisenhower Park
1899 Hempstead Turnpike, Suite 400
East Meadow, NY 11554
(516) 542-4700
(800) 227-3988
Fax: (516) 542-0095

E-MAIL ADDRESS:
info@womenssportsfoundation.org

WEB SITE ADDRESS:
www.womenssportsfoundation.org

FOUNDED: 1974

AREAS OF INTEREST:
The Foundation - the leading authority on the participation of women and girls in sports - advocates for equality, educates the public, conducts research and offers grants to promote sports and physical activity for girls and women.

NAME(S) OF PROGRAMS:
- **Travel & Training Fund**

TYPE:
Travel grants. Founded by Billie Jean King in 1974, the Women's Sports Foundation builds on her legacy as a champion athlete, advocate of social justice and agent of change. The Foundation strives for gender equity and fights discrimination in sports. Its work shapes public attitude about women's sports and athletes, builds capacities for organizations that get girls active, provides equal opportunities for girls and women, and supports physically and emotionally healthy lifestyles. The Foundation is recognized worldwide for its leadership, vision, strength, expertise and influence.

The goal of the fund is to provide direct financial assistance to aspiring female athletes with successful competitive records who have the potential to achieve even higher performance levels and rankings.

YEAR PROGRAM STARTED: 1984

PURPOSE:
To provide financial assistance in the training of women as sports leaders, coaches, officials and administrators of girls and women in sports; to advance the lives of girls and women through sports and physical activity.

LEGAL BASIS:
501(c)(3) nonprofit organization.

ELIGIBILITY:
Individual applicants and all members of a team must be female U.S. citizens or legal residents and be eligible to compete for a U.S. national team. Applicants must have amateur status.

GEOGRAPHIC RESTRICTIONS:
United States.

FINANCIAL DATA:
Amount of support per award: $2,500 to $10,000.
Total amount of support: Minimum $100,000 annually.

NUMBER OF AWARDS: Varies.

APPLICATION INFORMATION:
Contact the Foundation for guidelines.
Duration: One year.
Deadline: Online applications must be submitted by 5 P.M. May 2. Grants will be disbursed during the fourth quarter of the year.

PUBLICATIONS:
Annual report; research reports; educational guides; educational curriculum.

IRS IDENTIFICATION NUMBER: 23-7380557

OFFICERS:
Kathryn Olson, Chief Executive Officer
Angela Ruggiero, President

ADDRESS INQUIRIES TO:
Elizabeth Flores, Program Officer
(See address above.)

*SPECIAL STIPULATIONS:
Applicants must demonstrate accomplishments and potential to be considered. No travel grants outside the U.S. An individual or team may be awarded only one grant per calendar year and a maximum of three grants in a lifetime.

ZONTA INTERNATIONAL FOUNDATION

1211 West 22nd Street, Suite 900
Oak Brook, IL 60523-3384
(630) 928-1400
Fax: (630) 928-1559

E-MAIL ADDRESS:
programs@zonta.org

WEB SITE ADDRESS:
www.zonta.org

TYPE:
Fellowships. Awarded annually to women for graduate study in aerospace-related sciences or aerospace-related engineering at any university or college offering accredited graduate courses and degrees.

See entry 2059 for full listing.

ZONTA INTERNATIONAL FOUNDATION

1211 West 22nd Street, Suite 900
Oak Brook, IL 60523-3384
(630) 928-1400
Fax: (630) 928-1559

E-MAIL ADDRESS:
programs@zonta.org

WEB SITE ADDRESS:
www.zonta.org

TYPE:
Awards/prizes; Scholarships. For women of any nationality pursuing degrees in business who demonstrate outstanding potential in the field of business.

See entry 1919 for full listing.

ZONTA INTERNATIONAL FOUNDATION [1105]

1211 West 22nd Street, Suite 900
Oak Brook, IL 60523-3384
(630) 928-1400
Fax: (630) 928-1559

E-MAIL ADDRESS:
programs@zonta.org

WEB SITE ADDRESS:
www.zonta.org

FOUNDED: 1919

AREAS OF INTEREST:
Encouraging women's involvement in public affairs.

NAME(S) OF PROGRAMS:
- **Young Women in Public Affairs Awards**

TYPE:
Awards/prizes.

YEAR PROGRAM STARTED: 1990

PURPOSE:
To encourage young women's involvement and interest in public affairs.

LEGAL BASIS:
Incorporated in the state of Illinois as a nonprofit organization.

ELIGIBILITY:
Women of ages 16 to 19 on April 1 of each year, living in a Zonta district/region, or a citizen of a Zonta country, who demonstrate evidence of the following, are eligible to apply:
(1) active commitment to volunteerism;
(2) experience in local government, student government or workplace leadership (paid or unpaid);
(3) volunteer leadership achievements;
(4) knowledge of Zonta International and its programs and;
(5) advocating for Zonta International's mission of advancing the status of women worldwide.

GEOGRAPHIC RESTRICTIONS:
Applicants from geographic areas within a Zonta district/region where no clubs are located will be considered and also eligible to apply for the district/region award.

FINANCIAL DATA:
Amount of support per award: District award recipients receive $1,000 (U.S.) from the Zonta International Foundation YWPA Fund. Districts may choose to add to this award amount. Also, 10 international award recipients are selected from district recipients and receive an additional $4,000 (U.S.)

Total amount of support: Varies.

NUMBER OF APPLICANTS MOST RECENT YEAR: 32.

NUMBER OF AWARDS: 10.

APPLICATION INFORMATION:
The YWPA Awards program operates at the club, district and international levels of Zonta International and is managed by Zonta members. To apply, contact the Zonta Club within the applicant's district/region for deadlines and an address to which to mail application. (Such contact information is available on the web site.) Alternatively, one can e-mail one's name and contact information to the Young Women in Public Affairs Committee Chairman at ywpachairman@zonta.org.

Deadline: Must contact Zonta Club directly for deadline.

ADDRESS INQUIRIES TO:
Martina Gamboa
Programs Coordinator
(See e-mail address above.)

URBAN AND REGIONAL AFFAIRS

Children and youth

THE JOHN W. ALDEN TRUST [1106]

c/o Rackemann, Sawyer & Brewster
160 Federal Street, 15th Floor
Boston, MA 02110-1700
(617) 951-1108
Fax: (617) 542-7437

E-MAIL ADDRESS:
smonahan@rackemann.com

WEB SITE ADDRESS:
www.cybergrants.com/alden

AREAS OF INTEREST:
Education and therapy for children who are
blind, retarded, disabled, mentally or
physically ill; medical and scientific research
for the prevention and/or cure of the
conditions.

TYPE:
Capital grants; Challenge/matching grants;
Conferences/seminars; Demonstration grants;
Development grants; Matching gifts;
Project/program grants; Research grants;
Scholarships; Seed money grants; Technical
assistance; Training grants. Grants will
normally be made for specific projects rather
than general operating expenses.

LEGAL BASIS:
Private foundation.

ELIGIBILITY:
Organizations must be IRS 501(c)(3)
tax-exempt and be located in eastern
Massachusetts.

GEOGRAPHIC RESTRICTIONS:
Eastern Massachusetts.

FINANCIAL DATA:
Amount of support per award: $5,000 to
$15,000.
Total amount of support: $314,650 for fiscal
year 2012.
Matching fund requirements: Determined on
a case-by-case basis.

NUMBER OF AWARDS: 27 grants for the year
2012.

REPRESENTATIVE AWARDS:
Massachusetts General Hospital; New
England Home for Little Wanderers; Cotting
School; Adolescent Consultation Services;
Perkins School for the Blind.

APPLICATION INFORMATION:
All applications must be submitted online.
Duration: Varies.
Deadline: January 5, April 5, July 5 and
October 5; dates may vary.

PUBLICATIONS:
Guidelines.

TRUSTEES:
Miki Akimoto
Susan T. Monahan, Grants Coordinator
William B. Tyler, Esq.

ADDRESS INQUIRIES TO:
Susan T. Monahan, Grants Coordinator
(See e-mail address above.)

THE ISABEL ALLENDE FOUNDATION

116 Caledonia Street
Sausalito, CA 94965
(415) 289-0992
Fax: (415) 332-4149

E-MAIL ADDRESS:
lori@isabelallendefoundation.org

WEB SITE ADDRESS:
www.isabelallendefoundation.org

TYPE:
Project/program grants. Promotes and
preserves the fundamental rights of women
and children to be empowered and protected.

See entry 1070 for full listing.

AMERICAN ACADEMY OF CHILD AND ADOLESCENT PSYCHIATRY

3615 Wisconsin Avenue, N.W.
Washington, DC 20016-3007
(202) 966-7300 ext. 117
Fax: (202) 966-5894

E-MAIL ADDRESS:
arutter@aacap.org

WEB SITE ADDRESS:
www.aacap.org

TYPE:
Awards/prizes; Conferences/seminars;
Fellowships; Research grants; Travel grants.
The Robinson-Cunningham Award recognizes
a paper on some aspect of child and
adolescent psychiatry started during residency
and completed within three years of
graduation. Preference will be given to
independent work. If the research is done as
part of a collaborative team, the resident or
recently trained child and adolescent
psychiatrist should be the first author or
principal investigator. The selected author
will be invited to attend the AACAP Annual
Meeting.

Jeanne Spurlock Research Fellowship in
Substance Abuse and Addiction for Minority
Medical Students Program, supported by the
National Institute on Drug Abuse (NIDA),
includes a fellowship for work during the
summer with a child and adolescent
psychiatrist research-mentor, plus four days
at the AACAP Annual Meeting.

See entry 2562 for full listing.

ANDRUS FAMILY FUND

330 Madison Avenue
Suite 30
New York, NY 10017
(212) 687-6975
Fax: (212) 687-6978

E-MAIL ADDRESS:
info@affund.org

WEB SITE ADDRESS:
www.affund.org

TYPE:
Project/program grants; Research grants.

See entry 1169 for full listing.

BASEBALL TOMORROW FUND [1107]

245 Park Avenue
New York, NY 10167
(212) 931-7991
Fax: (212) 949-5405

E-MAIL ADDRESS:
btf@mlb.com

WEB SITE ADDRESS:
www.baseballtomorrowfund.com

FOUNDED: 1999

AREAS OF INTEREST:
Youth baseball and softball.

TYPE:
Capital grants; Challenge/matching grants;
Project/program grants. These grants are
offered to promote and enhance the growth
of youth baseball and softball in the U.S.,
Canada and throughout the world.

YEAR PROGRAM STARTED: 2000

PURPOSE:
To promote and enhance the growth of
baseball in the U.S., Canada and throughout
the world by funding programs, fields,
equipment purchases, designed to encourage
and maintain youth participation in the game.

ELIGIBILITY:
Grants are made to incremental programs
and/or for facilities for youth baseball and
softball. Organizations must be nonprofit or
tax-exempt.

FINANCIAL DATA:
Amount of support per award:
Approximately $40,000.
Total amount of support: $2,000,000
annually.
Matching fund requirements: 50% match
required.

NUMBER OF APPLICANTS MOST RECENT YEAR:
500.

NUMBER OF AWARDS: Over 650 since inception.

APPLICATION INFORMATION:
Initially, a Letter of Inquiry (no more than
two pages) on organization letterhead must
be submitted to determine whether the
project meets the basic criteria of the Fund.
If invited to submit a formal grant
application, include only information that
creates a better understanding of the project
and how it corresponds to the Fund's grant
evaluation criteria. Applications will not be
accepted via fax.
Deadline: January 1, April 1, July 1 and
October 1.

ADDRESS INQUIRIES TO:
Executive Director
(See address above.)

THE BOY SCOUTS OF AMERICA, NATIONAL EAGLE SCOUT ASSOCIATION [1108]

1325 West Walnut Hill Lane
P.O. Box 152079
Irving, TX 75015-2079
(972) 580-2000

E-MAIL ADDRESS:
nesa@scouting.org

WEB SITE ADDRESS:
www.nesa.org

AREAS OF INTEREST:
Scouting and youth.

NAME(S) OF PROGRAMS:
● **Hall/McElwain Merit Scholarships**

TYPE:
Scholarships.

PURPOSE:
To serve Eagle Scouts and through them, the
entire movement of Scouting.

ELIGIBILITY:
Must be graduating high school seniors or an
undergraduate college student no later than
completion of their junior year. Applicant

must have demonstrated leadership ability in scouting and a strong record of participation in activities outside of scouting.

Must supply Scout history and participation. Award is not based on financial need or grades.

FINANCIAL DATA:
Scholarships are for tuition, room, board and books.
Amount of support per award: $1,000 to $2,500.
Total amount of support: Varies.

NUMBER OF AWARDS: Varies, depending on funds available.

APPLICATION INFORMATION:
Contact the Association for application procedures.
Duration: One-time award.
Deadline: Applications must be postmarked after October 1, but no later than midnight on the following December 31.

ADDRESS INQUIRIES TO:
Jeff Laughlin, Manager
(See address above.)

*PLEASE NOTE:
This scholarship is not available to students attending any of the U.S. military academies.

*SPECIAL STIPULATIONS:
Applicant must fill out new application each year.

THE BOY SCOUTS OF AMERICA, NATIONAL EAGLE SCOUT ASSOCIATION [1109]
1325 West Walnut Hill Lane
P.O. Box 152079
Irving, TX 75015-2079
(972) 580-2000

E-MAIL ADDRESS:
nesa@scouting.org

WEB SITE ADDRESS:
www.nesa.org

AREAS OF INTEREST:
Scouting and youth.

NAME(S) OF PROGRAMS:
- **Mabel and Lawrence S. Cooke Scholarship**
- **National Eagle Scout Scholarship Fund**
- **STEM Scholarship**
- **United Health Foundation Scholarship**

TYPE:
Scholarships.

PURPOSE:
To serve Eagle Scouts and through them, the entire movement of Scouting.

ELIGIBILITY:
For the Mabel and Lawrence S. Cooke Scholarship, applicant must register and maintain status as a full-time student at a college/university. The scholarship is not available to students attending any of the U.S. military academies, because the U.S. government pays expenses that are covered by NESA scholarships at these academies.

National Eagle Scout Scholarship Fund applicants must register and maintain status as a full-time student at a college/university.

FINANCIAL DATA:
Funds are for tuition, room, board, and books.

Amount of support per award: Mabel and Lawrence S. Cooke Scholarship: One scholarship of up to $48,000 (up to $12,000 per year for four years) and four $20,000 scholarships ($5,000 per year for four years) are given annually; National Eagle Scout Scholarship Fund: Varies each year, depending on the funds available; STEM Scholarship: Up to $50,000 for four years ($12,500 per year); United Health Foundation Scholarship: Up to $25,000 for four years ($6,250 per year).
Total amount of support: Varies.

NUMBER OF AWARDS: Varies.

APPLICATION INFORMATION:
Application information is available on the web site.
Duration: Up to four years.
Deadline: Applications must be postmarked after October 1, but no later than midnight on the following December 31. Use sufficient postage.

ADDRESS INQUIRIES TO:
Jeff Laughlin, Manager
(See address above.)

THE LOUIS CALDER FOUNDATION [1110]
125 Elm Street
New Canaan, CT 06840
(203) 966-8925
Fax: (203) 966-5785

E-MAIL ADDRESS:
proposals@calderfdn.org

WEB SITE ADDRESS:
www.louiscalderfoundation.org

FOUNDED: 1951

AREAS OF INTEREST:
Education.

TYPE:
Capital grants; Project/program grants. Curriculum development.

YEAR PROGRAM STARTED: 1951

PURPOSE:
To promote scholastic development of children and youth by improving elementary and secondary education through its support of charter and parochial schools.

LEGAL BASIS:
Private foundation.

ELIGIBILITY:
Nonprofit 501(c)(3) organizations.

GEOGRAPHIC RESTRICTIONS:
Continental United States.

FINANCIAL DATA:
Amount of support per award: $2,000 to $500,000.
Total amount of support: $6,531,515 for the year 2012.

REPRESENTATIVE AWARDS:
$300,000 to Teach for America for expansion in the Mississippi Delta, South Carolina and Appalachia; $200,000 to Seton Education Partners for founding year of New York City charter school; $50,000 to Diocese of Bridgeport for STEM programming.

APPLICATION INFORMATION:
The Foundation does not accept unsolicited proposals. Charter management organizations, new and existing charter schools, parochial schools and not-for-profit organizations providing content-rich curricula are encouraged to submit a letter of inquiry via the web site. If the project is of interest to the Foundation, a proposal will be requested.
Duration: Varies.

PUBLICATIONS:
Annual report.

IRS IDENTIFICATION NUMBER: 13-6015562

TRUSTEES:
Peter D. Calder
Frank E. Shanley

ADDRESS INQUIRIES TO:
Holly Nuechterlein
Grant Program Director
(See address and e-mail above.)

CAMPBELL FOUNDATION, INC. [1111]
705 York Road
Towson, MD 21204
(410) 828-1961
Fax: (410) 821-8814

E-MAIL ADDRESS:
lsperato@stoycpa.com

AREAS OF INTEREST:
Social services, education, arts and cultural programs.

TYPE:
Capital grants; General operating grants; Project/program grants.

PURPOSE:
To provide support for cultural, educational and social services and institutions.

LEGAL BASIS:
Nonprofit foundation.

GEOGRAPHIC RESTRICTIONS:
Maryland, primarily Baltimore.

FINANCIAL DATA:
Amount of support per award: Up to $1,500 general operating grant; $20,000 capital grant.
Total amount of support: Average $150,000 per year.

APPLICATION INFORMATION:
Organizations must submit a written proposal, up to two pages in length.
Duration: One year. Renewal by reapplication.
Deadline: November 15.

ADDRESS INQUIRIES TO:
Virginia T. Campbell, President
(See address above.)

THE CARSON SCHOLARS FUND, INC.
305 West Chesapeake Avenue
Suite 310
Towson, MD 21204
(410) 828-1005
Fax: (410) 828-1007

E-MAIL ADDRESS:
katie@carsonscholars.org

WEB SITE ADDRESS:
carsonscholars.org

TYPE:
Scholarships. The Carson Scholars Fund awards $1,000 college scholarships to students in grades 4-11 who excel academically and are dedicated to serving their communities.

See entry 1675 for full listing.

THOMAS AND AGNES CARVEL FOUNDATION   [1112]
35 East Grassy Sprain Road
Yonkers, NY 10710
(914) 793-7300
Fax: (914) 793-7381

AREAS OF INTEREST:
Children, youth, health and religion.

TYPE:
General operating grants; Grants-in-aid;
Matching gifts; Project/program grants;
Research grants.

ELIGIBILITY:
Applicants must be 501(c)(3) tax-exempt
organizations. Grants may be given to
religious organizations that meet geographic
requirements. No grants to individuals.

GEOGRAPHIC RESTRICTIONS:
Connecticut, New Jersey and New York.

FINANCIAL DATA:
Amount of support per award: Varies,
depending on needs and nature of the
request.

APPLICATION INFORMATION:
No application form required. Applicants
must provide IRS tax-exempt documentation.
Duration: One year. Nonrenewable.

ADDRESS INQUIRIES TO:
Peter A. Smith, President
(See address above.)

CHILDREN'S BRAIN TUMOR FOUNDATION   [1113]
274 Madison Avenue
Suite 1004
New York, NY 10016
(212) 448-9494
Fax: (212) 448-1022

E-MAIL ADDRESS:
info@cbtf.org

WEB SITE ADDRESS:
www.cbtf.org

FOUNDED: 1988

AREAS OF INTEREST:
Children with brain and spinal cord tumors.

NAME(S) OF PROGRAMS:
• Brain Research Tumor Grant

TYPE:
Research grants. Basic science research
grants for pediatric brain and spinal cord
tumors.

YEAR PROGRAM STARTED: 1988

PURPOSE:
To improve the treatment, quality of life and
the long-term outlook for children with brain
and spinal cord tumors through research,
support, education, and advocacy to families
and survivors.

ELIGIBILITY:
No grants are made to individuals.

GEOGRAPHIC RESTRICTIONS:
United States and Canada.

FINANCIAL DATA:
Amount of support per award: $75,000 per
year.
Total amount of support: Up to $150,000,
depending on positive review after first year.

NUMBER OF AWARDS: 4.

APPLICATION INFORMATION:
Contact the Foundation for application
procedures.

Duration: Up to two years.
Deadline: July.

IRS IDENTIFICATION NUMBER: 13-3512123

ADDRESS INQUIRIES TO:
Joseph Fay, Executive Director
(See address above.)

CHILDREN'S BUREAU   [1114]
Administration on Children, Youth and Families
1250 Maryland Avenue, S.W., Eighth Floor
Washington, DC 20024
(202) 205-8172
Fax: (202) 260-9345

E-MAIL ADDRESS:
jan.shafer@acf.hhs.gov

WEB SITE ADDRESS:
www.acf.hhs.gov/programs/cb

FOUNDED: 1974

AREAS OF INTEREST:
Prevention, identification, assessment and
treatment of child abuse and neglect, sexual
abuse, incidence of abuse and neglect.

NAME(S) OF PROGRAMS:
• Child Abuse Prevention and Treatment
Act (CAPTA) Research and
Demonstration Grants

TYPE:
Demonstration grants; Project/program
grants; Research grants; Technical assistance;
Training grants.

YEAR PROGRAM STARTED: 1974

PURPOSE:
To assist state, local and voluntary agencies
and organizations to strengthen their
capacities to prevent child abuse and neglect,
identify and assess abused and neglected
children and provide necessary ameliorative
services to them and their families.

LEGAL BASIS:
Public Law 102-295, 45 CFR Subtitle B, part
1340.

ELIGIBILITY:
Grants for demonstration programs or
projects and research projects may be made
to states, public agencies, community-based
organizations or nonprofit private
organizations.

FINANCIAL DATA:
Amount of support per award: Average
$400,000.

APPLICATION INFORMATION:
Standard grant application forms provided by
the agency must be used. Complete
instructions and necessary forms are issued
with each announcement or solicitation.
Duration: Normally 36 to 60 months.
Deadline: Varies.

ADDRESS INQUIRIES TO:
Jan Shafer, Director
Division of Program Innovation
(See address above.)

*SPECIAL STIPULATIONS:
Financial and program progress reports are
required semiannually; a final report and an
expenditure report are required no later than
90 days after the completion of the project.
Audits conducted. Records must be
maintained for three years.

COMMONWEAL FOUNDATION, INC.   [1115]
10770 Columbia Pike, Suite 150
Silver Spring, MD 20901
(240) 450-0000
Fax: (240) 450-4115

E-MAIL ADDRESS:
vgentilcore@cweal.org

WEB SITE ADDRESS:
www.cweal.org

FOUNDED: 1968

AREAS OF INTEREST:
Underserved youth.

TYPE:
General operating grants; Project/program
grants.

YEAR PROGRAM STARTED: 1968

PURPOSE:
To support educational programs assisting
disadvantaged youth.

LEGAL BASIS:
Private foundation.

ELIGIBILITY:
Eligible organizations must be IRS 501(c)(3)
tax-exempt.

GEOGRAPHIC RESTRICTIONS:
Baltimore, Montgomery and Prince Georges
counties, Maryland; and Washington, DC.

FINANCIAL DATA:
Amount of support per award: $5,000 to
$50,000.
Total amount of support: Approximately
$1,300,000 for the year 2012.

APPLICATION INFORMATION:
Applications must include IRS tax
determination letter, audited financial reports
and most recent 990.
Duration: One year.
Deadline: February 1 and August 1.

ADDRESS INQUIRIES TO:
Jennifer Schauffler, Grants Manager
(See address above.)

ADOLPH COORS FOUNDATION   [1116]
4100 East Mississippi Avenue, Suite 1850
Denver, CO 80246
(303) 388-1636
Fax: (303) 388-1684

E-MAIL ADDRESS:
info@acoorsfdn.org

WEB SITE ADDRESS:
www.coorsfoundation.org

FOUNDED: 1975

AREAS OF INTEREST:
Primarily youth, job training, and
self-sufficiency.

TYPE:
Capital grants; General operating grants;
Project/program grants.

PURPOSE:
To build a stronger, healthier society.

ELIGIBILITY:
Organizations must be classified as 501(c)(3)
and operate within the U.S. The Foundation
does not consider grants to organizations that
in policy or practice discriminate on the basis
of race, creed or gender. No grants to
religious organizations or individuals.

GEOGRAPHIC RESTRICTIONS:
Colorado.

FINANCIAL DATA:
Amount of support per award: Average:
$10,000.
Total amount of support: $6,200,000.

APPLICATION INFORMATION:
Applications may only be submitted online.
Duration: One year.
Deadline: March 1, July 1 and November 1.

ADDRESS INQUIRIES TO:
John Jackson, Executive Director
(See address above.)

THE CRAIL-JOHNSON FOUNDATION   [1117]
461 West 6th Street
Suite 300
San Pedro, CA 90731
(310) 519-7413
Fax: (310) 519-7221

E-MAIL ADDRESS:
rachelr@crail-johnson.org

WEB SITE ADDRESS:
www.crail-johnson.org

FOUNDED: 1987

AREAS OF INTEREST:
Underserved children, youth and families in
the areas of health, education and human
services.

TYPE:
Capital grants; Challenge/matching grants;
Development grants; General operating
grants; Matching gifts; Project/program
grants; Seed money grants; Technical
assistance.

YEAR PROGRAM STARTED: 1987

PURPOSE:
To promote the well-being of children in
need through effective application of human
and financial resources.

LEGAL BASIS:
Private foundation.

ELIGIBILITY:
Applicants must be tax-exempt 501(c)(3)
organizations. No grants to individuals.

GEOGRAPHIC RESTRICTIONS:
Los Angeles, California.

FINANCIAL DATA:
Amount of support per award: $5,000 to
$30,000.
Total amount of support: Approximately
$893,135 for the year 2013.

NUMBER OF APPLICANTS MOST RECENT YEAR:
75 to 80.

REPRESENTATIVE AWARDS:
$30,000 to Boys & Girls Clubs of the South
Bay; $20,000 to Pediatric Therapy Network;
$30,000 to Harbor Interfaith Services.

APPLICATION INFORMATION:
Consult applications procedure page of web
site.
Duration: Typically one year.
Deadline: Varies.

PUBLICATIONS:
Guidelines.

OFFICERS:
Craig C. Johnson, Chairman
Alan C. Johnson, President
Eric C. Johnson, Vice President
Byung Kim, Chief Financial Officer

John S. Peterson, General Counsel
Rachel Roth, Program Officer

ADDRESS INQUIRIES TO:
Rachel Roth, Program Officer
(See address above.)

MICHAEL AND SUSAN DELL FOUNDATION   [1118]
P.O. Box 163867
Austin, TX 78716
Fax: (512) 600-5501

E-MAIL ADDRESS:
info@msdf.org

WEB SITE ADDRESS:
www.msdf.org

AREAS OF INTEREST:
Needs of children, health, education, safety,
youth development and early childhood care.

TYPE:
Project/program grants. Grants to support and
initiate programs that directly serve the needs
of children living in urban poverty.

PURPOSE:
To improve outcomes for children, living in
urban poverty around the world, in a
measurable way.

ELIGIBILITY:
Eligible organizations must be 501(c)(3) or
have a fiscal sponsor which is 501(c)(3).

GEOGRAPHIC RESTRICTIONS:
United States, India and South Africa.

FINANCIAL DATA:
Foundation will not fund more than 25% of a
project's budget or more than 10% of an
organization's total annual operating
expenses.
Amount of support per award: Varies.
Total amount of support: Varies.

APPLICATION INFORMATION:
All grant requests should be submitted via
online form.
Duration: Varies.

THE CLEVELAND H. DODGE FOUNDATION, INC.   [1119]
420 Lexington Avenue, Suite 2331
New York, NY 10170
(212) 972-2800
Fax: (212) 972-1049

E-MAIL ADDRESS:
chdodgefdn@aol.com

WEB SITE ADDRESS:
www.chdodgefoundation.org

FOUNDED: 1917

AREAS OF INTEREST:
Educational institutions and welfare agencies
serving the needs and training of young
people.

TYPE:
Project/program grants.

YEAR PROGRAM STARTED: 1917

PURPOSE:
To help better mankind by providing funds
for education and social welfare
organizations.

LEGAL BASIS:
Private foundation.

ELIGIBILITY:
Grants are made to nonprofit, 501(c)(3)
organizations in the Foundation's areas of
interest. No grants are made to individuals.

GEOGRAPHIC RESTRICTIONS:
United States.

FINANCIAL DATA:
Amount of support per award: $5,000 to
$500,000; average grant: $25,000.
Total amount of support: $1,817,637 for the
year 2013.

NUMBER OF APPLICANTS MOST RECENT YEAR:
150.

NUMBER OF AWARDS: 75.

APPLICATION INFORMATION:
Applicants must provide:
(1) a letter describing the organization and
grant request, including budget;
(2) annual report and;
(3) proof of 501(c)(3) status.
Duration: One year. Some renewable.
Deadline: January 15, April 15 and
September 15.

ADDRESS INQUIRIES TO:
Phyllis M. Criscuoli, Executive Director
(See address above.)

DUPONT PIONEER   [1120]
7100 N.W. 62nd Avenue
Johnston, IA 50131
(515) 535-6677
(800) 247-6803 ext. 56867
Fax: (515) 535-4842

E-MAIL ADDRESS:
community.investment@pioneer.com

WEB SITE ADDRESS:
www.pioneer.com

AREAS OF INTEREST:
Education, food security and community
betterment.

NAME(S) OF PROGRAMS:
● **Community Betterment**
● **Food Security**
● **Science Education**

TYPE:
Capital grants; Fellowships; General
operating grants; Matching gifts; Research
grants; Scholarships. Community outreach
programs.

PURPOSE:
To help improve the quality of life in the
communities in which customers and
employees live and work.

LEGAL BASIS:
Corporation giving program.

ELIGIBILITY:
Must be an IRS tax-exempt 501(c)(3)
organization. No grants to individuals or
religious organizations that promote a
particular doctrine.

GEOGRAPHIC RESTRICTIONS:
Canada, Latin America and the United States.

FINANCIAL DATA:
Amount of support per award: Varies.
Total amount of support: $5,000,000 for the
year 2012.

NUMBER OF AWARDS: Approximately 1,000 per
year.

APPLICATION INFORMATION:
Guidelines and application forms are
available on the web site.
Duration: One year.

EAST TENNESSEE FOUNDATION [1121]

625 Market Street
Suite 1400
Knoxville, TN 37902
(865) 524-1223
(877) 524-1223
Fax: (865) 637-6039

E-MAIL ADDRESS:
etf@etf.org

WEB SITE ADDRESS:
www.easttennesseefoundation.org

FOUNDED: 1986

AREAS OF INTEREST:
Arts and culture, youth-at-risk, community development, affordable housing construction, and scholarships.

CONSULTING OR VOLUNTEER SERVICES:
A variety of technical assistance to applicants and grantees.

TYPE:
Project/program grants; Scholarships; Seed money grants; Technical assistance. The Foundation administers 12 affiliate funds.

LEGAL BASIS:
Community foundation; 501(c)(3) organization.

ELIGIBILITY:
The Foundation does not make grants or loans to individuals.

GEOGRAPHIC RESTRICTIONS:
Counties in East Tennessee.

FINANCIAL DATA:
Amount of support per award: Funding support generally $500 to $10,000 per year for competitive grants and scholarships; $15,000 to $140,000 in Affordable Housing Trust Fund (AHTF) grants.
Total amount of support: $8,800,000.

APPLICATION INFORMATION:
Contact the Foundation for procedures.
Duration: Varies.
Deadline: Varies.

PUBLICATIONS:
Connections, Funding Focus, quarterly newsletter; annual reports; documents; brochures.

IRS IDENTIFICATION NUMBER: 62-0807696

STAFF:
Michael McClamroch, President and Chief Executive Officer
Carolyn Schwenn, Senior Vice President for Finance and Administration
Terry L. Holley, Senior Vice President for Programs and Regional Development
Sherri Alley, Vice President for Advancement
Jackie Lane, Vice President for Communications
Leanna Brackett, Director of Finance and Administration
Jeanette Kelleher, Housing and Financial Officer
Jan Elston, Senior Program Officer
Beth Heller, Program Officer and Scholarships
Dan Foltz-Gray, Coordinator, Coffey Memorial Scholarship Fund
Mary Amber Dunn, Advancement Associate
Precy Sturgeon, Financial Administrator

ADDRESS INQUIRIES TO:
Terry L. Holley, Senior Vice President for Programs and Regional Development
(See address above.)

*PLEASE NOTE:
Organizations located outside of the Foundation's service area are not eligible for funding.

THE EISNER FOUNDATION [1122]

9401 Wilshire Boulevard
Suite 735
Beverly Hills, CA 90212
(310) 228-6808

E-MAIL ADDRESS:
info@eisnerfoundation.org

WEB SITE ADDRESS:
www.eisnerfoundation.org

FOUNDED: 1996

AREAS OF INTEREST:
After-school programs, learning differences, K-12 public education, and prevention and treatment of abused children.

TYPE:
Grants-in-aid.

PURPOSE:
To provide financial support to organizations working to create lasting positive changes in the lives of at-risk and disadvantaged seniors and children in the community; to fund programs that will make permanent changes in a child's life and give them tools to enable them to achieve their dreams and become productive adults.

LEGAL BASIS:
501(c)(3) organization.

ELIGIBILITY:
Grants are made to 501(c)(3) nonprofit organizations that serve Los Angeles County, California. Grants are not made to individuals.

GEOGRAPHIC RESTRICTIONS:
Los Angeles County, California.

FINANCIAL DATA:
Total amount of support: Approximately $7,500,000 per year.

APPLICATION INFORMATION:
Applicants must submit a letter of inquiry (no more than two pages) to the Executive Director via regular mail. If deemed eligible, the applicant will be sent full application and guideline information.

IRS IDENTIFICATION NUMBER: 95-4607191

ADDRESS INQUIRIES TO:
Trent Stamp, Executive Director
(See address above.)

LOIS & RICHARD ENGLAND FAMILY FOUNDATION [1123]

P.O. Box 341077
Bethesda, MD 20827
(301) 657-7737
Fax: (301) 657-7738

E-MAIL ADDRESS:
englandfamilyfdn@verizon.net

WEB SITE ADDRESS:
fdncenter.org/grantmaker/england

FOUNDED: 1990

AREAS OF INTEREST:
Human services, education, Jewish life and causes, and after-school programs in Washington, DC.

TYPE:
Capital grants; Challenge/matching grants; Development grants; General operating grants; Matching gifts; Project/program grants; Seed money grants; Technical assistance; Training grants.

YEAR PROGRAM STARTED: 1994

PURPOSE:
To improve the lives of those in need in the Washington, DC metropolitan area; to strengthen Jewish life and institutions locally, nationally and in Israel.

LEGAL BASIS:
Private family foundation.

ELIGIBILITY:
Organizations must be classified by the Internal Revenue Service as public charities and tax-exempt under Section 501(c)(3) of the IRS Code of 1986. Unsolicited proposals are not considered. No grants to individuals.

GEOGRAPHIC RESTRICTIONS:
Washington, DC and Israel.

FINANCIAL DATA:
Amount of support per award: $5,000 to $50,000; average $15,000 to $25,000.
Total amount of support: $920,000 for the year 2012.

NUMBER OF APPLICANTS MOST RECENT YEAR: 80.

NUMBER OF AWARDS: Approximately 50.

REPRESENTATIVE AWARDS:
Jewish Giving: $15,000 to American Jewish Committee. Washington, DC Giving: $25,000 to Heads Up. Discretionary Grants: $30,000 to Lymphoma Research Foundation.

APPLICATION INFORMATION:
Detailed instructions are available online.
Duration: Annual grants.

BOARD OF DIRECTORS:
Cathy England, Chairperson
Rick England, President and Treasurer
Lois England, Vice President
Larry Akman
Nonie Akman
Diana England

ADDRESS INQUIRIES TO:
Monica Smith, Program Assistant
(See address above.)

FOSTER CARE TO SUCCESS

21351 Gentry Drive, Suite 130
Sterling, VA 20166
(571) 203-0270
Fax: (571) 203-0273

E-MAIL ADDRESS:
scholarships@fc2success.org
office@fc2success.org

WEB SITE ADDRESS:
www.fc2success.org

TYPE:
Scholarships.

See entry 1544 for full listing.

H.B. FULLER COMPANY FOUNDATION [1124]

1200 Willow Lake Boulevard
St. Paul, MN 55164
Fax: (651) 236-5056

E-MAIL ADDRESS:
hbfullerfoundation@hbfuller.com

WEB SITE ADDRESS:
www.hbfuller.com/community

FOUNDED: 1974

AREAS OF INTEREST:
STEM education for youth (science, technology, engineering and math) and youth leadership development.

TYPE:
Matching gifts; Project/program grants.

PURPOSE:
To support charitable activities of the company.

ELIGIBILITY:
Must be an eligible 501(c)(3) organization.

GEOGRAPHIC RESTRICTIONS:
Twin Cities metropolitan area, Minnesota; Roseville, California; Covington, Georgia; Aurora, Illinois; Paducah, Kentucky; and Vancouver, Washington.

FINANCIAL DATA:
Amount of support per award: Varies.
Total amount of support: Varies.

APPLICATION INFORMATION:
Online application process.
Duration: Typically one year.
Deadline: March 31 and August 31.

ADDRESS INQUIRIES TO:
H.B. Fuller Community Affairs
(See address above.)

THE GERBER FOUNDATION   [1125]
4747 West 48th Street
Suite 153
Fremont, MI 49412
(231) 924-3175
Fax: (231) 924-7906

E-MAIL ADDRESS:
tgf@ncresa.org

WEB SITE ADDRESS:
www.gerberfoundation.org

FOUNDED: 1952

AREAS OF INTEREST:
Enhancing the quality of life of infants and young children in nutrition, care and development.

TYPE:
Research grants. Grants to ensure the continuity of scientific and educational research in infant nutrition and child health. Matching gifts to 501(c)(3) educational, health and human services institutions within the U.S.

YEAR PROGRAM STARTED: 1952

PURPOSE:
To enhance the quality of life of infants and young children.

LEGAL BASIS:
Private foundation.

ELIGIBILITY:
Must be 501(c)(3).

GEOGRAPHIC RESTRICTIONS:
United States.

FINANCIAL DATA:
Amount of support per award: $20,000 to $300,000.
Total amount of support: $3,525,800 for the year 2013.

NUMBER OF APPLICANTS MOST RECENT YEAR:
286 for the year 2013.

NUMBER OF AWARDS: 78 for the year 2013.

APPLICATION INFORMATION:
Applicants should submit a two- to three-page letter of inquiry initially. If accepted, an application form will be provided.
Duration: One-time award with annual review.
Deadline: Letters of inquiry due June 1 and December 1. Grants made in May and November.

PUBLICATIONS:
Guidelines; application.

IRS IDENTIFICATION NUMBER: 38-6068090

OFFICERS:
Barbara J. Ivens, President
Fernando Flores-New, Vice President
Stan VanderRoest, Treasurer
Tracy Baker, Secretary

ADDRESS INQUIRIES TO:
Catherine Obits, Program Manager
(See address above.)

THE GRABLE FOUNDATION   [1126]
650 Smithfield Street
Suite 240
Pittsburgh, PA 15222
(412) 471-4550
Fax: (412) 471-2267

E-MAIL ADDRESS:
grable@grable.org

WEB SITE ADDRESS:
www.grable.org

FOUNDED: 1976

AREAS OF INTEREST:
Education, youth, leadership and families.

TYPE:
Project/program grants. This grant is offered to support community efforts that create an environment in which children can achieve and succeed.

YEAR PROGRAM STARTED: 1976

PURPOSE:
To improve educational opportunities so that children can achieve their potential; to strengthen families so they can serve as the core support of children and society; to support community efforts that create an environment in which children can succeed.

LEGAL BASIS:
Private foundation.

ELIGIBILITY:
Organizations must be classified as 501(c)(3) and include copy of IRS letter of determination. Grants are not awarded to individuals. Focus of grant must be southwestern Pennsylvania.

GEOGRAPHIC RESTRICTIONS:
Southwestern Pennsylvania.

FINANCIAL DATA:
Amount of support per award: Varies.
Total amount of support: $12,117,004 for the year 2013.

NUMBER OF APPLICANTS MOST RECENT YEAR:
277 for the year 2013.

NUMBER OF AWARDS: 171 for the year 2013.

REPRESENTATIVE AWARDS:
For the year 2012: $225,000 to the Allegheny Intermediate Unit to support grantmaking to local school districts for curricula, professional development, and/or projects that advance interdisciplinary learning, combining the arts and sciences through digital and/or maker practices for students and teachers in grades pre-K to 12; $150,000 to The Pittsburgh Cultural Trust to support regional cultural festivals and programming for children and families; $75,000 to the United Way of Allegheny County to support a campaign focusing on out-of-school time systems building; $65,000 to Carnegie Library of Pittsburgh to support a digital learning librarian for teen services at the library and an online program that allows children to create and share their own stories.

APPLICATION INFORMATION:
All organizations applying to the Foundation should submit a one- to two-page letter of inquiry describing the project prior to submitting a full proposal.

Proposals must include:
(1) Grable inquiry sheet;
(2) one-page summary of the proposal;
(3) description of the applicant organization;
(4) statement of need for the project;
(5) project description, including a detailed listing of project activities;
(6) anticipated project outcomes and how they will be measured;
(7) project budget, detailing expenses, committed and anticipated revenues, and including a narrative;
(8) organization's current operating budget;
(9) explanation of how the project will be sustained after the grant has ended;
(10) list of board members;
(11) copy of IRS tax-exempt certification;
(12) current audited financial statements and;
(13) letters of support when appropriate, e.g., from collaborating organizations.
Duration: Funding for up to three years.
Deadline: Letters of inquiry: January 1, May 1 and September 1 of each year. Full proposals: February 1, June 1 and October 1 of each year.

PUBLICATIONS:
Program announcement; guidelines.

IRS IDENTIFICATION NUMBER: 25-1309888

STAFF:
Gregg S. Behr, Executive Director
Steven E. Burke, Treasurer
Dana M. Lamenza, Financial Administrator
Mary Anne Mistick, Grants Administrator
D'Ann Swanson, Senior Program Officer
Kristen Burns, Program Officer

BOARD OF TRUSTEES:
Charles R. Burke, Jr., Chairman
Jan Nicholson, President
Susan H. Brownlee
Patricia Grable Burke
Steven E. Burke
William H. Isler
Barbara Nicholson McFayden

ADDRESS INQUIRIES TO:
Mary Anne Mistick, Grants Administrator
(See address above.)

THE WILLIAM T. GRANT FOUNDATION   [1127]
570 Lexington Avenue
18th Floor
New York, NY 10022-6837
(212) 752-0071
Fax: (212) 752-1398

E-MAIL ADDRESS:
info@wtgrantfdn.org

WEB SITE ADDRESS:
www.wtgrantfoundation.org

FOUNDED: 1936

AREAS OF INTEREST:
Supporting research to improve the lives of young people in the U.S.

NAME(S) OF PROGRAMS:
- **William T. Grant Distinguished Fellows**
- **William T. Grant Scholars Program**
- **Investigator Initiated Grants**
- **Youth Service Improvement Grants Program**

TYPE:
Fellowships; Project/program grants; Research grants. William T. Grant Distinguished Fellows program gives influential midcareer researchers the opportunity to immerse themselves in practice or policy settings and conversely influential practitioners and policymakers the opportunity to work in research settings.

William T. Grant Scholars Program supports promising early career researchers from diverse disciplines. The award is intended to facilitate the professional development of early career scholars who have demonstrated success in conducting high-quality research and are seeking to further develop their skills and research program.

Investigator Initiated Grants support high-quality research that addresses the Foundation's current research interests: enhancing our understanding of how youth settings work, how they affect youth development, and how they can be improved; and when, how, and under what conditions research evidence is used in policy and practice that affect youth, and how its use can be improved.

The Youth Service Improvement Grants Program supports activities conducted by community-based organizations in the five boroughs of New York City to improve the quality of services for young people ages 8 to 25.

YEAR PROGRAM STARTED: 1936

PURPOSE:
To help create a society that values young people and enables them to reach their full potential. In pursuit of this goal, the Foundation invests in research and in people and projects that use evidence-based approaches.

LEGAL BASIS:
Private foundation.

ELIGIBILITY:
Organization must have 501(c)(3) status. No grants to individuals.

GEOGRAPHIC RESTRICTIONS:
United States.

FINANCIAL DATA:
Amount of support per award: William T. Grant Distinguished Fellows: Up to $175,000, with up to $25,000 to fellowship site(s) to defray hosting costs; William T. Grant Scholars Program: $350,000; Investigator Initiated Grants: $100,000 to $600,000; Youth Service Improvement Grants Program: $25,000.
Total amount of support: Varies.

NUMBER OF AWARDS: William T. Grant Scholars Program: 4 to 6 annually; Youth Service Improvement Grants Program: Varies.

APPLICATION INFORMATION:
Application, requirements and procedures are available online.
Duration: William T. Grant Distinguished Fellows and Youth Service Improvement Grants: Six months to two years; William T. Grant Scholars Program: Five years; Investigator Initiated Grants: Two to three years.
Deadline: Varies.

PUBLICATIONS:
Annual report; guidelines; *William T. Grant Scholars,* brochure.

TRUSTEES:
Margaret R. Burchinal
Prudence L. Carter
Scott Evans
Adam Gamoran
Olivia Golden
Nancy Gonzales
Henry Gooss
Christine James-Brown
Russell P. Pennoyer
Andrew Porter
Kenneth Prewitt
Judson Reis

STAFF:
Adam Gamoran, President
Deborah McGinn, Vice President, Finance and Administration
Vivian Tseng, Vice President, Programs
Julie Wong, Manager, Grantmaking Operations
Nancy Rivera-Torres, Major Grants Coordinator, Research
Sharon Brewster, Grants Coordinator, Discretionary Grants
Irene Williams, Grants Coordinator, Scholars Program

ADDRESS INQUIRIES TO:
Mary Heglar, Communications Specialist (See address above.)

HASBRO CHILDREN'S FUND [1128]
1027 Newport Avenue
Pawtucket, RI 02862
(401) 727-5091
Fax: (401) 721-7275

WEB SITE ADDRESS:
www.hasbro.org

FOUNDED: 2006

AREAS OF INTEREST:
The welfare and development of children.

NAME(S) OF PROGRAMS:
- **Community Grants**

TYPE:
Product donations; Project/program grants. The Fund supports programs which provide terminal and seriously ill children respite and access to play, educational programs for children at risk, and basics for children in need.

YEAR PROGRAM STARTED: 1985

PURPOSE:
To assist children in triumphing over critical life obstacles as well as bringing the joy of play into their lives.

ELIGIBILITY:
U.S.-based 501(c)(3) organizations who deliver programs to children in Springfield, MA; Rhode Island; Renton/Seattle, WA; or Los Angeles, CA.

FINANCIAL DATA:
Amount of support per award: Varies.
Total amount of support: Varies.

APPLICATION INFORMATION:
All interested organizations are asked to apply through the Fund's online application system.

CHARLES HAYDEN FOUNDATION [1129]
140 Broadway, 51st Floor
New York, NY 10005
(212) 785-3677
Fax: (212) 785-3689

E-MAIL ADDRESS:
fdn@chf.org

WEB SITE ADDRESS:
www.charleshaydenfoundation.org

FOUNDED: 1937

AREAS OF INTEREST:
Education and youth agencies.

TYPE:
Capital grants; Challenge/matching grants; Project/program grants. Grant priorities focus on institutions and programs primarily serving youth at risk of not reaching their full potential, especially youth in low-income communities. Support is provided for youth development programs, charter schools, independent and parochial schools, and informal educational enrichment programs in institutions such as zoos, museums or libraries.

YEAR PROGRAM STARTED: 1937

PURPOSE:
To promote the mental, moral and physical development of children and youth five to 18 years of age in the New York and Boston metropolitan areas.

LEGAL BASIS:
Private foundation.

ELIGIBILITY:
Grants are restricted to institutions and organizations in the New York and Boston metropolitan areas, as defined by the Foundation. The Foundation focuses on those grants primarily serving youth, five to 18 years of age, that are most at-risk of not reaching their full potential, especially youth in low-income communities. Grants are available for capital and program support. Program grants must have clear goals to be met within the specified time frame. Program support goes mainly for new and expanded programs. No grants are awarded to individuals.

GEOGRAPHIC RESTRICTIONS:
New York and Boston, Massachusetts metropolitan areas.

FINANCIAL DATA:
Amount of support per award: Average $50,000.
Total amount of support: $13,861,307 in grants paid and $14,500,207 in new authorizations for the fiscal year ended June 30, 2013.

NUMBER OF APPLICANTS MOST RECENT YEAR: 293.

NUMBER OF AWARDS: 167.

APPLICATION INFORMATION:
Applicants are required to use the New York Area or AGM (Boston Area) Common Application Forms. All applications should note number and ages of youth to be served.

Interviews, if required or requested, are not arranged until the written grant application has been submitted and the preliminary review is completed.

Duration: Most grants are for one year. Grant renewals are sometimes considered.

IRS IDENTIFICATION NUMBER: 13-5562237

OFFICERS:
Dean H. Steeger, Chairman of the Board
Kenneth D. Merin, President and Chief Executive Officer
Robert Howitt, Treasurer
Robert Andrews, Secretary
Maureen T. Fletcher, Assistant Secretary
Carol Van Atten, Assistant Secretary

BOARD OF TRUSTEES:
Robert Andrews
Robert Howitt
Kristen J. McCormack
Kenneth D. Merin
Dean H. Steeger

ADDRESS INQUIRIES TO:
Kenneth D. Merin
President and Chief Executive Officer
(See address above.)

*SPECIAL STIPULATIONS:
Institutions receiving capital support must wait two years before seeking additional assistance.

EDWARD W. HAZEN FOUNDATION   [1130]
333 Seventh Avenue, 14th Floor
New York, NY 10001
(212) 889-3034
Fax: (212) 889-3039

E-MAIL ADDRESS:
hazen@hazenfoundation.org

WEB SITE ADDRESS:
www.hazenfoundation.org

FOUNDED: 1925

AREAS OF INTEREST:
Public education and youth organizing, school reform, community organizations, and racial justice.

NAME(S) OF PROGRAMS:
● **Public Education Grants**
● **Youth Organizing Grants**

TYPE:
Grants-in-aid; Project/program grants. In the area of Public Education, current programs support the strengthening of the connection between schools and community organizations, including school reform. The Foundation is primarily interested in parent organizing and training initiatives.

In the area of Youth Organizing, there is support for youth organizing around concrete social issues or issues of concern to youth.

For both Public Education and Youth Organizing, community-based projects directed toward middle and high school-age minority and low-income youth are given priority consideration.

There is limited support for Philanthropy and Special Projects including support for collaborative projects that encourage the growth of grantmaking.

PURPOSE:
To increase opportunities for middle and high school-age minority and low-income youth by strengthening those community-based

organizations that focus on the needs of the young and the institutions that most directly and profoundly influence them.

LEGAL BASIS:
Nonprofit, tax-exempt organization.

ELIGIBILITY:
Grants are made only to federally tax-exempt, nonprofit organizations. The Foundation does not consider requests for endowments or buildings, deficits or individual scholarships or fellowships. No support for schools, school districts or public agencies.

GEOGRAPHIC RESTRICTIONS:
United States.

APPLICATION INFORMATION:
The Board does not accept unsolicited requests. There is a two-step process. Applicants should first send a two-page letter of inquiry, highlighting the goals, objectives, approach, target population, duration and total cost of the project for which funding is sought. Additional materials such as video, audio cassettes, books, etc. and articles should not be sent unless specifically requested by the Foundation staff. Grant applications will be sent if the staff decides the goals of the project address the Foundation's mission and program interest. The board has the ultimate responsibility for setting Foundation policy and making grants at meetings held twice a year. Neither a request for a formal application nor recommendation to the board guarantees funding.

The Foundation does not accept faxed or electronic requests.

Duration: One year.

PUBLICATIONS:
Hazen Highlights, newsletter; guidelines.

ADMINISTRATION:
Lori Bezahler, President
Phillip Giles, Program Officer

TRUSTEES AND OFFICERS:
Sonia Jarvis, Chairperson
Beverly Cross, Vice Chairperson
Lori Bezahler, Secretary
Jennifer Arwade
Charles Fields
Michael Lent
Angela Sanbrano
Rachel Tompkins
Lori Villarosa

ADDRESS INQUIRIES TO:
Lori Bezahler, President
(See address above.)

THE JACK AND JILL OF AMERICA FOUNDATION
1930 17th Street, N.W.
Washington, DC 20009-6207
(202) 232-5290
Fax: (202) 232-1747

E-MAIL ADDRESS:
administration@jackandjillfoundation.org

WEB SITE ADDRESS:
www.jackandjillfoundation.org

TYPE:
Project/program grants; Scholarships. Volunteer opportunities.

See entry 1029 for full listing.

KANSAS HEALTH FOUNDATION
309 East Douglas
Wichita, KS 67202
(316) 262-7676
(800) 373-7681
Fax: (316) 262-2044

E-MAIL ADDRESS:
ghess@khf.org

WEB SITE ADDRESS:
kansashealth.org

TYPE:
Project/program grants.

See entry 1446 for full listing.

THE KLINGENSTEIN THIRD GENERATION FOUNDATION
125 Park Avenue
Suite 1700
New York, NY 10017-5529
(212) 492-6179
Fax: (212) 492-7007

E-MAIL ADDRESS:
sally@ktgf.org
info@ktgf.org

WEB SITE ADDRESS:
www.ktgf.org

TYPE:
Fellowships; Research grants. The Foundation funds research and other programs related to childhood and adolescent ADHD and depression. All funding is directed towards two research fellowship programs and the medical student training program. The Foundation does not accept general applications for project or research funding.

See entry 2580 for full listing.

THE AGNES M. LINDSAY TRUST   [1131]
660 Chestnut Street
Manchester, NH 03104
(603) 669-1366
(866) 669-1366
Fax: (603) 665-8114

E-MAIL ADDRESS:
admin@lindsaytrust.org
proposals@lindsaytrust.org (for grants)

WEB SITE ADDRESS:
www.lindsaytrust.org

FOUNDED: 1939

AREAS OF INTEREST:
Health and welfare, children, and the elderly.

TYPE:
Capital grants; Scholarships. Awards grants for capital campaigns, capital items and renovation needs. Also, supports a number of health and welfare organizations, health projects, dental projects, special needs including blind, deaf and learning-disabled, elderly, children's hospitals, children's homes, youth organizations, youth and family services and summer camperships (summer enrichment programs). In addition, Trust supports colleges and universities and private secondary schools through scholarship aid.

PURPOSE:
To support the education of poor and deserving students from rural communities; to relieve suffering through child welfare.

ELIGIBILITY:
Eligible organizations must be IRS 501(c)(3) tax-exempt and be located in the New

England states of Maine, Massachusetts, New Hampshire and Vermont. The Trust does not fund in Connecticut or Rhode Island.

The Trust does not make grants to operating funds or to individuals.

The Trust rarely, if ever, approves grants for general operating funds, nor does it fund grant requests from public entities, municipalities, sectarian organizations, or individuals.

GEOGRAPHIC RESTRICTIONS:
Maine, Massachusetts, New Hampshire and Vermont.

FINANCIAL DATA:
$25,000,000 in assets for the year ended 2013.
Amount of support per award: $500 to $2,500 (for capital and camperships).
Total amount of support: Varies.

NUMBER OF APPLICANTS MOST RECENT YEAR:
597.

NUMBER OF AWARDS: 188.

APPLICATION INFORMATION:
Guidelines are available online. Proposals can be submitted electronically at proposals@lindsaytrust.org.
Duration: One year.
Deadline: Trustees meet monthly. It generally takes two months from time of submission of application to receipt of letter of decision.

IRS IDENTIFICATION NUMBER: 02-6004971

TRUSTEES:
Michael S. DeLucia
Ernest E. Dion
Alan G. Lampert

ADDRESS INQUIRIES TO:
Susan Bouchard, Administrative Director
(See address above.)

*PLEASE NOTE:
It is highly recommended that applicants review the information available online prior to submission of a grant proposal.

*SPECIAL STIPULATIONS:
If your organization is awarded a grant, the Trust requests that your organization wait one year before reapplying.

THE DR. JOHN T. MACDONALD FOUNDATION, INC. [1132]
1550 Madruga Avenue, Suite 215
Coral Gables, FL 33146
(305) 667-6017
Fax: (305) 667-9135

E-MAIL ADDRESS:
info@jtmacdonaldfdn.org

WEB SITE ADDRESS:
www.jtmacdonaldfdn.org

FOUNDED: 1992

AREAS OF INTEREST:
Health education, prevention and early detection of disease, children, economically disadvantaged, and medical rehabilitation.

TYPE:
Challenge/matching grants; Demonstration grants; General operating grants; Matching gifts; Project/program grants; Scholarships; Seed money grants.

YEAR PROGRAM STARTED: 1992

PURPOSE:
To provide funding for programs and projects designed to improve, preserve or restore the health and health care of people in Miami-Dade County, FL.

LEGAL BASIS:
Private.

ELIGIBILITY:
Tax-exempt organizations that are registered to solicit funds under Florida law. The Foundation funds projects for medical and health-related programs. The Foundation does not fund national projects, multiyear funding requests, for-profit organizations, political candidates or campaigns, religious projects, support for individuals, or other grantmaking foundations.

GEOGRAPHIC RESTRICTIONS:
Miami-Dade County, Florida.

FINANCIAL DATA:
Amount of support per award: $5,000 to $65,000.
Total amount of support: $2,600,000 per year.

NUMBER OF APPLICANTS MOST RECENT YEAR:
53 letters of inquiry in 2013.

NUMBER OF AWARDS: 18, plus 4 scholarships and awards; 2 major multimillion-dollar awards.

REPRESENTATIVE AWARDS:
Small Grants 2012: Lotus House Women's Shelter to support two counselor/resource coordinators for one year; Hearing Research Institute to support the purchase of more hearing testing equipment and hearing aids for needy children and adults.

Scholarships 2012: Florida International University College of Nursing and Health Sciences for the Dr. Frederick Poppe Scholarship.

Multi-year Million+ Signature Programs: Dr. John T. Macdonald Foundation School Health Initiative; Dr. John T. Macdonald Foundation Biomedical Nanotechnology Institute.

APPLICATION INFORMATION:
All qualified, tax-exempt organizations which propose to conduct projects or programs related to the health needs of the citizens of Miami-Dade County and are seeking funding support from the Foundation should first submit a letter of inquiry on the Foundation web site. The Foundation will make an initial review. If the request is felt to be of interest, an organization will then be asked to submit a complete grant proposal for consideration by the Board of Directors.

General Online Instructions: When clicking on the "Apply Now" button for the first time, applicant will be asked to create an account. Once an account and a password are created, applicant will be able to log in using his or her e-mail address as well as the password he or she created. Questions during the application process should be directed through the Foundation e-mail address.
Deadline: Letters of inquiry: Accepted from February 1 to April 16.

PUBLICATIONS:
Program announcement; guidelines; application packet.

IRS IDENTIFICATION NUMBER: 59-0818918

ADDRESS INQUIRIES TO:
Kim Greene, Executive Director
(See address above.)

MAURICE J. MASSERINI CHARITABLE TRUST
c/o Wells Fargo Private Bank
4475 Executive Drive, Suite 100
San Diego, CA 92121
(888) 234-1999
Fax: (877) 746-5889

E-MAIL ADDRESS:
grantadministration@wellsfargo.com

WEB SITE ADDRESS:
www.wellsfargo.com/privatefoundationgrants/masserini

TYPE:
Project/program grants.
See entry 998 for full listing.

RONALD MCDONALD HOUSE CHARITIES [1133]
2915 Jorie Boulevard
Oak Brook, IL 60523
(630) 623-6753
Fax: (630) 623-7488

E-MAIL ADDRESS:
vicky.laws@us.mcd.com

WEB SITE ADDRESS:
www.rmhc.org

FOUNDED: 1984

AREAS OF INTEREST:
Primarily, the health and well-being of children.

TYPE:
Challenge/matching grants; Grants-in-aid; Project/program grants; Training grants.

YEAR PROGRAM STARTED: 1984

PURPOSE:
To directly improve the health and well-being of children.

LEGAL BASIS:
Nonprofit, 501(c)(3) tax-exempt organization.

ELIGIBILITY:
Not-for-profit tax-exempt organizations, based in the U.S. but operating either domestically or internationally. Projects must be sustainable and measurable. Proposed projects must directly benefit children. No grants to individuals, political campaigns, secular religious activities, for salaries, travel or ongoing expenses, or capital expenses. Projects must include a "Train-the-Trainer" component in the methodology.

Grant requests from organizations more regional in nature will be referred to the closest local chapter.

FINANCIAL DATA:
Amount of support per award: $30,000 and up.
Total amount of support: Approximately $4,000,000 for the year 2014.

NUMBER OF APPLICANTS MOST RECENT YEAR:
150.

NUMBER OF AWARDS: 11.

REPRESENTATIVE AWARDS:
$169,043 over two years to Curamericas, Liberia; $179,800 to Lwala Community Alliance, Kenya; $627,637 to Resurge, Nepal and India; $50,000 to Wyman Center, U.S.

APPLICATION INFORMATION:
Application information is available on the web site.
Duration: One-year to multiyear funding.

Deadline: Applications should be submitted between July 1 and the end of August. Board decisions are made in December.

PUBLICATIONS:
Application form; annual report; application guidelines.

BOARD OF TRUSTEES:
Linda Dunham, Chairman of the Board
J.C. Gonzalez-Mendez, President and Chief Executive Officer

ADDRESS INQUIRIES TO:
Vicky Laws, Administrative Assistant
Public Relations and Marketing
(See address above.)

*SPECIAL STIPULATIONS:
Applications only accepted online.

R.J. MCELROY TRUST   [1134]
425 Cedar Street, Suite 312
Waterloo, IA 50701-1351
(319) 287-9102
Fax: (319) 287-9105

E-MAIL ADDRESS:
vangorp@mcelroytrust.org

WEB SITE ADDRESS:
www.mcelroytrust.org

FOUNDED: 1965

AREAS OF INTEREST:
Education, children and youth.

TYPE:
Capital grants; Challenge/matching grants; General operating grants; Internships; Project/program grants; Scholarships; Seed money grants; Technical assistance.

PURPOSE:
To invest in nonprofit and public organizations that inspire and transform youth.

LEGAL BASIS:
Private.

ELIGIBILITY:
The Trust only supports programs, projects or endeavors that help young people. Applicant must be nonprofit or tax-exempt.

The Trust does not make grants to religious organizations for religious programming or to schools or school districts for one-to-one technology/computers for students.

GEOGRAPHIC RESTRICTIONS:
Allamakee, Black Hawk, Bremer, Buchanan, Butler, Chickasaw, Clayton, Delaware, Dubuque, Fayette, Floyd, Grundy, Howard, Tama and Winneshiek counties, Iowa.

FINANCIAL DATA:
Amount of support per award: Varies per project.
Total amount of support: Approximately $1,800,000 for the year 2013.
Matching fund requirements: The Trust seldom funds 100% of a project.

NUMBER OF AWARDS: 63 for the year 2012.

APPLICATION INFORMATION:
Applicants must submit a one-page letter to the Trust describing the need for funding, which includes:
(1) contact information (address, phone and e-mail);
(2) organization's federal tax identification number;
(3) description of the project, program or

endeavor and;
(4) funding request and total cost of the project.
Duration: One year. Renewal possible.
Deadline: March 1, June 1, September 1 and December 1. Announcement by February 1, May 1, August 1 and November 1, respectively.

IRS IDENTIFICATION NUMBER: 42-6173496

TRUSTEES:
Dr. Raleigh D. Buckmaster
Kathy Flynn
Robert Smith, Jr.
James B. Waterbury
Rick Young

STAFF:
Dr. Stacy Van Gorp, Executive Director

ADDRESS INQUIRIES TO:
Dr. Stacy Van Gorp, Executive Director
(See address above.)

*PLEASE NOTE:
Contact the Executive Director before applying.

THE MCJ AMELIOR FOUNDATION   [1135]
310 South Street
Morristown, NJ 07960
(973) 540-1946
Fax: (973) 538-8175

AREAS OF INTEREST:
Youths at risk, children, community empowerment and mentoring.

TYPE:
Challenge/matching grants; General operating grants; Project/program grants; Seed money grants; Technical assistance.

LEGAL BASIS:
Private foundation.

ELIGIBILITY:
Applicants must be 501(c)(3) organizations.

GEOGRAPHIC RESTRICTIONS:
Newark, New Jersey.

FINANCIAL DATA:
Amount of support per award: Varies.
Total amount of support: Varies.

APPLICATION INFORMATION:
The Foundation does not accept unsolicited proposals.
Duration: Varies.

STAFF:
Suzanne Spero, Executive Director
Christine C. Gilfillan, President

ADDRESS INQUIRIES TO:
Suzanne Spero, Executive Director
(See address above.)

MEBANE CHARITABLE FOUNDATION, INC.   [1136]
232 South Main Street
Mocksville, NC 27028
(336) 936-0041
Fax: (336) 936-0038

E-MAIL ADDRESS:
lcolbourne@mebanefoundation.com

WEB SITE ADDRESS:
www.mebanefoundation.com

FOUNDED: 1992

AREAS OF INTEREST:
Children's education.

NAME(S) OF PROGRAMS:
● **The Davie & Yadkin County Program**
● **The Early Childhood Development Program**
● **The Teacher Training and Professional Development Program**

TYPE:
Project/program grants.

PURPOSE:
To teach children first to read and to further their education at all levels of learning, thereby attempting to break the cycle of poverty.

ELIGIBILITY:
Organizations qualified for exemption under Section 501(c)(3) of the IRS code and not private foundations as defined by Section 509(a).

GEOGRAPHIC RESTRICTIONS:
North Carolina.

FINANCIAL DATA:
Amount of support per award: Varies.
Total amount of support: $1,900,000 for the year 2012.

APPLICATION INFORMATION:
Organization must first complete a phone interview with the President to determine if their proposal is within the objectives and interest of the Foundation.
Duration: Varies.
Deadline: Application must be postmarked by July 1 for fall meeting of the board of directors, or by January 1 for spring meeting.

ADDRESS INQUIRIES TO:
Larry Colbourne, President
(See address above.)

THE MOYER FOUNDATION   [1137]
One Penn Center
1617 JFK Boulevard, No. 580
Philadelphia, PA 19103
(267) 687-7724
(206) 298-1217
Fax: (267) 687-7705; (206) 298-1207

E-MAIL ADDRESS:
info@moyerfoundation.org

WEB SITE ADDRESS:
www.moyerfoundation.org

FOUNDED: 2000

AREAS OF INTEREST:
Children suffering and enduring severe physical or emotional distress.

NAME(S) OF PROGRAMS:
● **Camp Erin**
● **Camp Mariposa**

TYPE:
Grants-in-aid; Internships; Matching gifts.

YEAR PROGRAM STARTED: 2000

PURPOSE:
To empower children in distress by providing education and support, thereby helping them to live a healthy and inspired life.

LEGAL BASIS:
Public, 501(c)(3) nonprofit organization.

ELIGIBILITY:
501(c)(3) nonprofit organizations. Grants are not made to individuals.

GEOGRAPHIC RESTRICTIONS:
Pacific Northwest.

FINANCIAL DATA:
Total amount of support: $50,000 in grants awarded in Pennsylvania in the past year.

NUMBER OF APPLICANTS MOST RECENT YEAR: 100.

NUMBER OF AWARDS: 15.

APPLICATION INFORMATION:
Application information is available on the web site.
Duration: Nonrenewable.
Deadline: August 15.

IRS IDENTIFICATION NUMBER: 91-2065051

ADDRESS INQUIRIES TO:
Karen Gallagher
Director of Development and Communications
(See address above.)

NATIONAL FOOTBALL LEAGUE FOUNDATION
345 Park Avenue
New York, NY 10154
(212) 450-2000
Fax: (212) 847-1812

E-MAIL ADDRESS:
alexia.gallagher@nfl.com

WEB SITE ADDRESS:
www.nflfoundation.org

TYPE:
Awards/prizes; Challenge/matching grants; General operating grants; Project/program grants; Research grants; Seed money grants; Training grants.

See entry 1336 for full listing.

NATIONAL FOSTER PARENT ASSOCIATION [1138]
2021 East Hennepin Avenue
Suite 320
Minneapolis, MN 55413-1769
(512) 775-9781
(800) 557-5238
Fax: (253) 238-4252

E-MAIL ADDRESS:
info@nfpaonline.org

WEB SITE ADDRESS:
www.nfpaonline.org

FOUNDED: 1972

AREAS OF INTEREST:
Foster parents and children in foster care.

NAME(S) OF PROGRAMS:
• **NFPA Scholarship**

TYPE:
Scholarships.

PURPOSE:
To support foster youth and children of foster parents that wish to further their education beyond high school, including college or university studies, vocational and job training, and correspondence courses, including the GED.

LEGAL BASIS:
Nonprofit, volunteer organization established in 1972, with tax-exempt status under Section 501(c)(3) of the Internal Revenue Code.

ELIGIBILITY:
Must be a foster youth or an adoptive or birth child of foster parent members who is a college- or university-bound senior or is 17 years of age (either in school or out) in

pursuit of vocational/job training/correspondence GED/other educational advancement.

GEOGRAPHIC RESTRICTIONS:
United States and territories.

FINANCIAL DATA:
Amount of support per award: $500.
Total amount of support: $2,500.

NUMBER OF APPLICANTS MOST RECENT YEAR: 23.

NUMBER OF AWARDS: 5; 3 to foster children and 2 to adoptive or birth children of foster parents.

APPLICATION INFORMATION:
Application is available from the Association at the address above. A minimum of two letters of recommendation and a typewritten statement of 300 to 500 words on "Why I want to further my education and why I should be considered for a National Foster Parent Association Scholarship" is also required.
Duration: Possible renewal.
Deadline: Applications must be postmarked on or before March 15.

IRS IDENTIFICATION NUMBER: 06-0894870

ADDRESS INQUIRIES TO:
Irene Clements, President
(See address above.)

NATIONAL JEWISH COMMITTEE ON SCOUTING
1325 West Walnut Hill Lane
Irving, TX 75015
(972) 580-2097
Fax: (972) 580-2535

E-MAIL ADDRESS:
lee.shaw@scouting.org

WEB SITE ADDRESS:
www.jewishscouting.org

TYPE:
Scholarships.

See entry 1721 for full listing.

ORLANDO MAGIC YOUTH FUND [1139]
8701 Maitland Summit Boulevard
Orlando, FL 32810
(407) 916-2400
Fax: (407) 916-2985

E-MAIL ADDRESS:
omyf@orlandomagic.com

WEB SITE ADDRESS:
www.omyf.org

FOUNDED: 1988

AREAS OF INTEREST:
Children and families at-risk in central Florida in the areas of education, health and wellness, the arts, and housing.

NAME(S) OF PROGRAMS:
• **Orlando Magic Youth Fund, a McCormick Foundation Fund**

TYPE:
Challenge/matching grants.

PURPOSE:
To nourish the minds and bodies of children who need it most in central Florida.

ELIGIBILITY:
Organizations must be classified as 501(c)(3) or 170(c)(3) by the IRS and have a

constituency open to all segments of the community with a focus on low income. The Fund does not typically provide funding for private schools, legal aid societies, political, lobbying or advocacy groups, or capital requests for building and/or major improvements, except those for equipment/supplies that are critical to the delivery of a program or service.

GEOGRAPHIC RESTRICTIONS:
Orange, Osceola and Seminole counties, Florida.

FINANCIAL DATA:
Amount of support per award: $10,000 to $100,000.
Total amount of support: $1,050,000.
Matching fund requirements: The McCormick Foundation contributes $.50 for every dollar that the OMYF generates to supplement contributions in the partners' local communities. In addition to the matching monies, they assist in the administration of the funds and share expenses.

NUMBER OF APPLICANTS MOST RECENT YEAR: 75.

NUMBER OF AWARDS: 25.

APPLICATION INFORMATION:
Applicants are invited to submit Letter of Inquiry.
Duration: One year. May reapply.
Deadline: Letter of Inquiry: Early April.

LUCILE PACKARD FOUNDATION FOR CHILDREN'S HEALTH [1140]
400 Hamilton Avenue, Suite 340
Palo Alto, CA 94301
(650) 736-0675
(650) 497-8365

E-MAIL ADDRESS:
grants@lpfch.org

WEB SITE ADDRESS:
www.lpfch-cshcn.org/grants

FOUNDED: 1997

AREAS OF INTEREST:
Children's health.

TYPE:
Project/program grants.

YEAR PROGRAM STARTED: 2000

PURPOSE:
To promote the health and well-being of children through statewide and local partnerships.

ELIGIBILITY:
Organizations must be 501(c)(3) nonprofit.

GEOGRAPHIC RESTRICTIONS:
California.

FINANCIAL DATA:
Amount of support per award: Varies.

NUMBER OF APPLICANTS MOST RECENT YEAR: 4.

NUMBER OF AWARDS: Varies.

APPLICATION INFORMATION:
Application information is available on the web site.
Duration: Varies.

ADDRESS INQUIRIES TO:
Stacey Angeles
Grants Management Associate
(See address above.)

PARENTS WITHOUT PARTNERS

1100-H Brandywine Boulevard
Zanesville, OH 43701
(740) 450-1332
Fax: (740) 452-2552

E-MAIL ADDRESS:
intl.hq@parentswithoutpartners.org

WEB SITE ADDRESS:
www.parentswithoutpartners.org

TYPE:
Scholarships.

See entry 1584 for full listing.

THE PINKERTON FOUNDATION   [1141]

610 Fifth Avenue
Suite 316
New York, NY 10020
(212) 332-3385
Fax: (212) 332-3399

E-MAIL ADDRESS:
pinkfdn@pinkertonfdn.org

WEB SITE ADDRESS:
www.thepinkertonfoundation.org

FOUNDED: 1966

AREAS OF INTEREST:
Economically disadvantaged children, youth
and families.

TYPE:
General operating grants; Internships;
Project/program grants. Support for programs
that develop individual competencies, instill
values and increase opportunities to
participate in society.

Support for community-based programs with
preference given to projects for children,
youth and families that intervene before a
pattern of failure has been established.

YEAR PROGRAM STARTED: 1968

LEGAL BASIS:
Not-for-profit corporation organized in the
state of Delaware in 1966.

ELIGIBILITY:
Grant applicants must be nonprofit public
charitable organizations which are tax-exempt
under Section 501(c)(3) of the Internal
Revenue Code. The Foundation does not
make grants to individuals or give loans or
emergency assistance, nor does it support
medical research or the direct provision of
health care or religious education. It
generally does not make grants to support
conferences, publications, media or to
building renovations or other capital projects,
unless they are integrally related to the
Foundation's program objectives or are an
outgrowth of one of its grantee's programs.

GEOGRAPHIC RESTRICTIONS:
New York, New York.

FINANCIAL DATA:
Amount of support per award: $25,000 to
$150,000; average $75,000.
Total amount of support: $18,000,000
annually.

NUMBER OF APPLICANTS MOST RECENT YEAR:
300.

NUMBER OF AWARDS: 180 for the year 2012.

APPLICATION INFORMATION:
Applicants should write a brief letter of
inquiry, not exceeding two pages, before
submitting a formal proposal or applying for
a grant. The proposal should describe the
grantee organization and the proposed project
and its goals and include an estimated budget
and the name and qualifications of the person
directing the project. For other than direct
service projects, the program description
should also include the possibilities for
practical application of the efforts and
findings of the project or program.

The Foundation's program staff will
determine whether or not a proposal will be
considered. They will request other materials
or arrange meetings as appropriate after
reviewing the initial letter.

Duration: Usually up to three years.
Deadline: February 1 and September 1.

OFFICERS:
George J. Gillespie, III, Chairman
Richard Smith, President
Daniel Mosley, Treasurer
Joan Colello, Secretary and Executive
Director

STAFF:
Laurie Dien, Senior Program Officer
Julie Peterson, Senior Program Officer
Jennifer Correa, Program Officer

ADDRESS INQUIRIES TO:
Laurie Dien or Julie Peterson
Senior Program Officers
(See address above.)

PRITCHETT TRUST   [1142]

BMO Harris Bank
417 North Broadway
Pittsburg, KS 66762
(414) 287-7317
Fax: (414) 287-8580

AREAS OF INTEREST:
Children, families and youth.

TYPE:
Project/program grants; Seed money grants.

PURPOSE:
To promote projects that support children,
youth and families.

LEGAL BASIS:
Private trust.

ELIGIBILITY:
Grants are made to organizations that have
tax-exempt status under Section 501(c)(3) of
the Internal Revenue Code. No grants are
made to individuals.

GEOGRAPHIC RESTRICTIONS:
Southeast Kansas, with an emphasis on
Crawford County.

FINANCIAL DATA:
Amount of support per award: Varies.
Total amount of support: $300,000 to
$400,000.

APPLICATION INFORMATION:
Applicants must submit a brief letter
outlining the purpose of the grant.
Duration: One year. Renewal possible.
Deadline: May 31.

ADDRESS INQUIRIES TO:
Joseph Brzycki
Account Administrator
(See address above.)

HENRY AND RUTH BLAUSTEIN ROSENBERG FOUNDATION

10 East Baltimore Street, Suite 1111
Baltimore, MD 21202
(410) 347-7201
Fax: (410) 347-7210

E-MAIL ADDRESS:
info@blaufund.org

WEB SITE ADDRESS:
www.blaufund.org

TYPE:
Capital grants; General operating grants;
Project/program grants. Programs of benefit
to the underserved community in the
Baltimore, MD area.

See entry 1361 for full listing.

THE SAIGH FOUNDATION   [1143]

7777 Bonhomme Avenue
Suite 2007
St. Louis, MO 63105
(314) 862-3055
Fax: (314) 862-9288

E-MAIL ADDRESS:
joann@thesaighfoundation.org

WEB SITE ADDRESS:
www.thesaighfoundation.org

FOUNDED: 2000

AREAS OF INTEREST:
Children and youth in the field of education
and health care in the St. Louis metropolitan
area.

TYPE:
Endowments; General operating grants.

PURPOSE:
To enhance the quality of life in St. Louis
metropolitan region through support for
charitable projects and initiatives which
primarily benefit children and youth through
education and health care.

LEGAL BASIS:
501(c)(3).

GEOGRAPHIC RESTRICTIONS:
St. Louis, Missouri metropolitan area.

FINANCIAL DATA:
Amount of support per award: Varies.
Total amount of support: Varies.

APPLICATION INFORMATION:
Guidelines for submitting the application and
application forms are available on the
Foundation web site.
Deadline: January 15, April 15, July 15 and
October 15.

STAFF:
JoAnn Hejna, Executive Director
Mary Kemp, Assistant Director

ADDRESS INQUIRIES TO:
JoAnn Hejna, Executive Director
(See address above.)

ST. LOUIS RAMS FOUNDATION   [1144]

Community Outreach
One Rams Way
St. Louis, MO 63045
(314) 982-7267
Fax: (314) 770-9261; (314) 516-8888

E-MAIL ADDRESS:
mmccarthy@rams.nfl.com

WEB SITE ADDRESS:
www.stlouisrams.com

FOUNDED: 1997

AREAS OF INTEREST:
Youth health, fitness and character education.

TYPE:
General operating grants; Project/program grants.

YEAR PROGRAM STARTED: 1997

PURPOSE:
To support programs designed to engage youth in activities that promote health, fitness and character development.

ELIGIBILITY:
Grants are made to organizations that have tax-exempt status under Section 501(c)(3) of the Internal Revenue Code. No unsolicited grants are accepted.

GEOGRAPHIC RESTRICTIONS:
The Greater St. Louis area, Missouri.

FINANCIAL DATA:
Since 1997, the Foundation has donated more than $6,000,000 in cash, grants, merchandise and tickets to area charities.
Amount of support per award: Varies based on program or project scope.
Total amount of support: Up to $250,000 annually.

NUMBER OF AWARDS: 30 to 50.

REPRESENTATIVE AWARDS:
St. Louis Public Schools Foundation; Cooperating School Districts.

APPLICATION INFORMATION:
Proposals are accepted by invitation only; however, letters and collateral material from potential grant recipients are welcome.

ADDRESS INQUIRIES TO:
Michael Yarbrough
Director of Community Outreach
(See address above.)

THE SCHUMANN FUND FOR NEW JERSEY [1145]
21 Van Vleck Street
Montclair, NJ 07042
(973) 509-9883

FOUNDED: 1988

AREAS OF INTEREST:
Children and youth, education, environment and public policy (statewide) as well as social services in Essex County, NJ.

TYPE:
Demonstration grants; General operating grants; Project/program grants. Priorities include early childhood development, supporting efforts to heighten the chances of academic and social success for young children, especially the urban poor. Other focus areas include environmental protection, public policy and local activities directed at solving community problems, with particular concern for families with young children and education.

YEAR PROGRAM STARTED: 1988

LEGAL BASIS:
Tax-exempt, private foundation.

ELIGIBILITY:
Organizations seeking grants must be designated 501(c)(3) by the IRS. No applications for capital campaigns, annual giving, endowment, direct support of individuals and local programs in counties other than Essex. Projects in the arts, health care and housing development normally fall outside the Schumann Fund priority areas.

GEOGRAPHIC RESTRICTIONS:
New Jersey, with special emphasis on Essex County.

FINANCIAL DATA:
Amount of support per award: $15,000 to $50,000.
Total amount of support: Approximately $1,000,000 to $1,500,000.

APPLICATION INFORMATION:
There is no standard application form to be used in presenting a request to the Schumann Fund. The Fund, however, encourages the use of the New York/New Jersey Common Application Form. A written proposal should be submitted which includes a detailed description of the purpose for which assistance is desired and the plan for accomplishment. The proposal should be accompanied by a copy of the organization's latest financial statement, an expense budget which identifies all sources of income, the project's time frame and future funding plans, a list of the organization's Board of Directors, IRS documents confirming the organization's status as a 501(c)(3) tax-exempt organization and not a private foundation, and the most recent audit.
Duration: Usually one year. Multiyear grants possible.
Deadline: January 15, April 15, July 15 and October 15.

PUBLICATIONS:
Annual report.

IRS IDENTIFICATION NUMBER: 52-1556076

TRUSTEES:
Aubin Z. Ames
Anthony Cicatello
Leonard S. Coleman, Jr.
Christopher J. Daggett
Martha Day
Roger Pratt

STAFF:
Barbara Reisman, Executive Director
Annette B. Strickland, Program and Administrative Officer

ADDRESS INQUIRIES TO:
Barbara Reisman, Executive Director
(See address above.)

*PLEASE NOTE:
Grants are restricted to projects in New Jersey.

THE SEYBERT FOUNDATION [1146]
P.O. Box 1286
Doylestown, PA 18901
(215) 696-9336

E-MAIL ADDRESS:
admin@seybertfoundation.org

WEB SITE ADDRESS:
www.seybertfoundation.org

FOUNDED: 1914

AREAS OF INTEREST:
Operating support for nonprofit organizations serving disadvantaged children and youth who are residents of the city of Philadelphia. The Institution is limited under the terms of the will setting up the fund to disadvantaged boys and girls of the city of Philadelphia only.

TYPE:
General operating grants.

LEGAL BASIS:
501(c)(3) charitable foundation.

ELIGIBILITY:
Grants are limited to nonprofit organizations serving disadvantaged young people through the high school ages who are residents of the city of Philadelphia. Grants are made to qualifying tax-exempt organizations under Sections 501(c)(3) and 509(a) of the Internal Revenue Code. Priority is given to organizations with operating budgets of less than $1,500,000.

GEOGRAPHIC RESTRICTIONS:
Philadelphia, Pennsylvania.

FINANCIAL DATA:
Amount of support per award: Average: $3,500.
Total amount of support: $330,000 for the year 2013.

NUMBER OF APPLICANTS MOST RECENT YEAR: 180.

NUMBER OF AWARDS: 89.

REPRESENTATIVE AWARDS:
Anti-Violence Partnership, Juvenile Law Center, Taller Puertorriqueno, Al-Bustan Seeds of Culture.

APPLICATION INFORMATION:
Guidelines are available on the Foundation web site.
Duration: One year. Renewal possible.
Deadline: March 15 and September 15. No more than one request will be considered per calendar year except under special circumstances.

PUBLICATIONS:
Application guidelines.

IRS IDENTIFICATION NUMBER: 23-6260105

OFFICERS AND BOARD OF DIRECTORS:
Dwayne Wharton, President
Aishah Miller, Vice President
Dario Bellot, Treasurer
Julie Cousler-Emig, Secretary
Obinna I. Abara, Esq.
C. Richard Cox
Dee Hillas
Sara S. Moran
Deepa Vasudevan

ADDRESS INQUIRIES TO:
Diana Loukedis Doherty, Manager
(See address above.)

*PLEASE NOTE:
Grants must benefit poor boys and girls of the city of Philadelphia.

SIERRA HEALTH FOUNDATION
1321 Garden Highway
Sacramento, CA 95833
(916) 922-4755
Fax: (916) 922-4024

E-MAIL ADDRESS:
info@sierrahealth.org

WEB SITE ADDRESS:
www.sierrahealth.org

TYPE:
Matching gifts; Project/program grants. Specific to funding opportunities - solicited.

See entry 1509 for full listing.

SILICON VALLEY COMMUNITY FOUNDATION

2440 West El Camino Real
Suite 300
Mountain View, CA 94040-1498
(650) 450-5400
Fax: (650) 450-5401

E-MAIL ADDRESS:
info@siliconvalleycf.org

WEB SITE ADDRESS:
www.siliconvalleycf.org

TYPE:
General operating grants; Project/program grants; Scholarships; Seed money grants. Nonprofit organizations that provide services or programs related to the specific five grantmaking strategies in San Mateo and Santa Clara counties may be eligible to apply for funding from the Foundation's endowment. Scholarships for college-bound students are also open to application.

See entry 1376 for full listing.

STUART FOUNDATION   [1147]

500 Washington Street
Eighth Floor
San Francisco, CA 94111
(415) 393-1551
Fax: (415) 568-9815

E-MAIL ADDRESS:
info@stuartfoundation.org

WEB SITE ADDRESS:
www.stuartfoundation.org

FOUNDED: 1985

NAME(S) OF PROGRAMS:
* **Child Welfare**
* **Public Education**

TYPE:
Conferences/seminars; Demonstration grants; Development grants; General operating grants; Project/program grants; Research grants; Technical assistance; Training grants. Systematic change and collaborative service delivery.

YEAR PROGRAM STARTED: 1985

PURPOSE:
To provide a coordinated set of programs, activities, research, and policy analysis that improve opportunities for children and youth in California and Washington to become self-reliant, responsible and contributing members of their communities.

LEGAL BASIS:
Private foundation.

ELIGIBILITY:
No grants to individuals.

GEOGRAPHIC RESTRICTIONS:
California and Washington.

FINANCIAL DATA:
Amount of support per award: $114,878.94 average grant for the year 2012.
Total amount of support: $14,600,000 in total grants for the year 2012.

NUMBER OF AWARDS: 128.

APPLICATION INFORMATION:
Application information is available on the web site.
Duration: Grants are approved for one year at a time, although projects can be funded for several years.

IRS IDENTIFICATION NUMBER: 20-0882784

STAFF:
Christy Pichel, President
David Barlow, Chief Financial Officer
Teri Kook, Director of Child Welfare
Michelle Francois, Associate Director, Child Welfare

BOARD MEMBERS:
Dwight L. Stuart, Jr., Chairman
Stuart Lucas, Vice Chairman
Elbridge H. Stuart, III, Vice Chairman and Treasurer
Davis Campbell, Director

ADDRESS INQUIRIES TO:
Grants Manager
(See address above.)

SUBARU OF AMERICA FOUNDATION, INC.

2235 Route 70 West
Cherry Hill, NJ 08002
(856) 488-5099
Fax: (856) 488-3255

E-MAIL ADDRESS:
foundation@subaru.com

WEB SITE ADDRESS:
www.subaru.com/csr/soa-foundation.html

TYPE:
General operating grants; Project/program grants; Scholarships. Special programs; Employee matching gift program.

See entry 1589 for full listing.

THE FRANK M. TAIT FOUNDATION   [1148]

1530 Kettering Tower
40 North Main Street
Dayton, OH 45423
(937) 222-2401
Fax: (937) 224-6015

E-MAIL ADDRESS:
taitfoundation@gmail.com

FOUNDED: 1955

AREAS OF INTEREST:
Early childhood development, youth development and cultural activities for underserved youth.

TYPE:
Project/program grants. Focus on youth development, particularly early childhood development.

YEAR PROGRAM STARTED: 1956

PURPOSE:
To provide programs that develop youth (particularly early childhood development programs); to provide cultural enrichment experiences for underserved youth.

LEGAL BASIS:
Ohio corporation, not for profit.

ELIGIBILITY:
Organizations must be exempt under 501(c)(3). No private foundations.

The Foundation does not fund:
(1) medical research or equipment;
(2) operating budgets or annual fund drives;
(3) emergency requests for crash programs;
(4) endowment funds;
(5) religious programs or activities or;
(6) lobbying or propaganda activities.

GEOGRAPHIC RESTRICTIONS:
Montgomery County, Ohio.

FINANCIAL DATA:
Amount of support per award: Typically $5,000 to $50,000.
Total amount of support: $323,500 for the year 2013.

APPLICATION INFORMATION:
Must contact the Executive Director at the phone number above to discuss the prospective grant proposal and to obtain approval for its subsequent submission.
Duration: Usually one year. Reapply for renewal.

PUBLICATIONS:
Guidelines.

IRS IDENTIFICATION NUMBER: 31-6037499

ADDRESS INQUIRIES TO:
Jenni Roer, Executive Director
(See address above.)

TEAMMATES FOR KIDS FOUNDATION   [1149]

1900 Wazee Street, Suite 205
Denver, CO 80202
(303) 759-9777

E-MAIL ADDRESS:
jason@tfkf.com

WEB SITE ADDRESS:
www.teammates4kids.com

FOUNDED: 1999

AREAS OF INTEREST:
Serving children's needs in the areas of health, education or providing inner-city services.

TYPE:
Grants-in-aid. Foundation grants are directed to nonprofit organizations that specialize in working with children.

PURPOSE:
To develop and implement innovative concepts that generate funds for the benefit of children's charities.

ELIGIBILITY:
To qualify for a grant from the Foundation, an organization must:
(1) be a 501(c)(3) tax-exempt nonprofit organization in good standing with the IRS;
(2) have a record of outstanding service in effectively and efficiently delivering programs and services that improve the lives of needy children;
(3) serve children's needs in the areas of health, education or providing inner-city services;
(4) deliver services which impact the lives of children, both short- and long-term and;
(5) ensure that 100% of grant monies received from the Foundation are used for the exclusive benefit of children.

FINANCIAL DATA:
Amount of support per award: Most grants are from $5,000 to $50,000. Average grant $10,000.
Total amount of support: Varies.

APPLICATION INFORMATION:
By invitation only.

ADDRESS INQUIRIES TO:
Jason Graham
Director of Charitable Giving
(See address above.)

## TURRELL FUND				[1150]

21 Van Vleck Street
Montclair, NJ 07042-2358
(973) 783-9358
Fax: (973) 783-9283

E-MAIL ADDRESS:
 turrell@turrellfund.org

WEB SITE ADDRESS:
 www.turrellfund.org

FOUNDED: 1935

AREAS OF INTEREST:
 Agencies rendering direct services to at-risk
 children in the state of Vermont, and,
 primarily, in the New Jersey counties of
 Essex, Hudson, Passaic and Union; policy
 initiatives for the very young child. While
 there are exceptions, the Fund's emphasis is
 on programs serving children, from birth to
 five years of age, and advocacy programs
 which support children in the same age
 range.

TYPE:
 General operating grants; Project/program
 grants.

YEAR PROGRAM STARTED: 1935

PURPOSE:
 To financially and strategically support
 organizations which directly provide or foster
 the creation and delivery of high-quality,
 developmental and educational services to
 at-risk children, especially the youngest and
 their families in Vermont and designated
 areas of New Jersey.

LEGAL BASIS:
 Tax-exempt private foundation.

ELIGIBILITY:
 Tax-exempt 501(c)(3) organizations in New
 Jersey and Vermont only may apply. In New
 Jersey, emphasis is on northern urban areas
 centered in Essex, Hudson, Passaic and
 Union counties only. No grants are awarded
 for lobbying, endowments or research. No
 grants to individuals and most hospital work
 and health delivery services. Only
 organizations providing direct services and
 advocacy for children and youth are eligible.

GEOGRAPHIC RESTRICTIONS:
 Essex, Hudson, Passaic and Union counties,
 New Jersey and Vermont.

FINANCIAL DATA:
 Amount of support per award: $1,000 to
 $100,000. $17,000 average grant.
 Total amount of support: $3,833,993 for the
 year 2013.

NUMBER OF APPLICANTS MOST RECENT YEAR:
 370 for the year 2012.

NUMBER OF AWARDS: 270 for the year 2012.

REPRESENTATIVE AWARDS:
 Vermont Community Preschool
 Collaborative; St. Benedict's Preparatory
 School; Team Academy.

APPLICATION INFORMATION:
 Applications are accepted online only.
 Scanned into the proposal should be the
 following:
 (1) a brief letter describing the project;
 (2) a copy of the IRS letter granting tax
 exemption;
 (3) operating and project budgets and;
 (4) either a 990 form and audited statement
 from most recent year available.

 The proposal should include:
 (1) background information about the
 organization;

(2) identification of board members;
 (3) staff qualifications;
 (4) a financial report;
 (5) current budget and;
 (6) project costs.
 Duration: One year.
 Deadline: August 1 and February 1.
 Announcement in late June and late
 December.

PUBLICATIONS:
 Annual report.

IRS IDENTIFICATION NUMBER: 22-1551936

OFFICERS:
 S. Lawrence Prendergast, Chairman of the
 Board
 Sonyia Woloshyn, Treasurer
 Curtland E. Fields, Secretary

TRUSTEES:
 Robert E. Angelica
 Elizabeth W. Christie
 Curtland E. Fields
 Rev. William S. Gannon
 Matthew E. Melmed
 Dr. Julia A. Miller
 Rev. Dr. John P. Mitchell
 John Morning
 S. Lawrence Prendergast
 Mark Sustic

ADDRESS INQUIRIES TO:
 Curtland E. Fields, President
 and Chief Executive Officer
 (See address above.)

U.S. DEPARTMENT OF HEALTH
## AND HUMAN SERVICES		[1151]

Administration for Children and Families
Office of Head Start
1250 Maryland Avenue, S.W., Suite 8000
Washington, DC 20024
(866) 763-6481
(202) 205-8573
(202) 205-8396
Fax: (202) 401-9721; (202) 205-9721

WEB SITE ADDRESS:
 www.acf.hhs.gov/programs/ohs/
 www.eclkc.ohs.acf.hhs.gov

NAME(S) OF PROGRAMS:
 ● **Head Start**

TYPE:
 Project/program grants. Grants for
 comprehensive programs focused primarily
 upon children from low-income families who
 have not reached the age of compulsory
 school attendance. Supported projects should
 involve:
 (1) comprehensive health (including medical
 and dental examinations), nutritional, social,
 psychological, educational and mental health
 services;
 (2) appropriate activities to encourage and
 provide opportunities for participation of
 parents and effective use of provided services
 and;
 (3) other pertinent training, technical
 assistance, evaluation and follow-through
 activities.

YEAR PROGRAM STARTED: 1965

PURPOSE:
 To provide children from low-income
 families with comprehensive health, nutrition,
 educational, social and other services; to aid
 children to attain their full potential.

LEGAL BASIS:
 Omnibus Budget and Reconciliation Act of
 1981 (Public Law 97-35).

ELIGIBILITY:
 Local public and private nonprofit and
 for-profit organizations are eligible to apply.
 However, the actual operation of a Head Start
 program may be delegated to an organization
 qualified to and capable of operating such a
 program.

FINANCIAL DATA:
 Federal funds may not exceed 80% except in
 certain limited situations where grantees may
 be relieved of all or part of the nonfederal
 share.
 Amount of support per award: Varies.
 Total amount of support: $7,559,634,000
 (federal appropriation) for fiscal year 2011.
 Matching fund requirements: Grantees are
 required to provide 20% of the total cost of
 the project.

NUMBER OF APPLICANTS MOST RECENT YEAR:
 1,305.

APPLICATION INFORMATION:
 Applications from organizations which are
 not current grantees are accepted only in
 response to announcements in the *Federal
 Register.* Applicants for a Head Start grant
 should contact the Health and Human
 Services regional office in their area. Parents
 wishing to enroll their children should
 consult the local Head Start Program in their
 Community.

U.S. DEPARTMENT OF HEALTH
## AND HUMAN SERVICES		[1152]

Administration for Children and Families
Family and Youth Services Bureau
Portals Building, Suite 800
1250 Maryland Avenue, S.W.
Washington, DC 20024
(301) 608-8098
Fax: (301) 587-4352

E-MAIL ADDRESS:
 ncfy@acf.hhs.gov

WEB SITE ADDRESS:
 www.acf.hhs.gov/programs/fysb

FOUNDED: 1974

AREAS OF INTEREST:
 Crisis and referral services for runaway and
 homeless youth.

NAME(S) OF PROGRAMS:
 ● **Runaway and Homeless Youth (RHY)**
 Programs

TYPE:
 Development grants; General operating
 grants; Project/program grants; Technical
 assistance. Title III of the Juvenile Justice
 and Delinquency Prevention Act of 1974, et
 seq., to authorize the Runaway and Homeless
 Youth Program.

 Basic Center, Street Outreach, and
 Transitional Living are components of this
 Program.

 Through Basic Center, the Bureau provides
 financial assistance to establish or strengthen
 community-based programs that address the
 immediate needs of runaway and homeless
 youth and their families. These programs are
 designed to provide youth with emergency
 shelter, food, clothing, counseling and
 referrals for health care.

 Through Street Outreach, the Bureau awards
 grants to private, nonprofit agencies to
 conduct outreach designed to build

relationships between grantee staff and street youth. These efforts are intended to help young people leave the streets.

Through Transitional Living, the Bureau supports projects that provide longer-term residential services to homeless youth, 16 to 21 years of age, for up to 18 months. Services are intended to help homeless youth make a successful transition to self-sufficient living. Transitional Living also supports youth maternity group home.

YEAR PROGRAM STARTED: 1974

PURPOSE:
To establish or strengthen locally controlled community programs that address the immediate needs of runaway and homeless youth and their families. Services must be provided outside of the law enforcement, juvenile justice system, child welfare or mental health. The program is designed to alleviate problems of RHY youth, reunite youth with their families, and encourage the resolution of intrafamily problems through counseling and other services, strengthen family relationships and encourage stable living conditions for youth and help youth decide upon constructive courses of action.

ELIGIBILITY:
Grants are available to states, localities, nonprofit private agencies, coordinated networks and Indian Tribes.

GEOGRAPHIC RESTRICTIONS:
United States and its territories.

FINANCIAL DATA:
Amount of support per award: Maximum of $200,000 per year.
Total amount of support: Approximately $113,000,000 annually.

NUMBER OF APPLICANTS MOST RECENT YEAR:
182 Basic Center, 144 Street Outreach, 163 Transitional Living.

APPLICATION INFORMATION:
Guidelines available on the web site.
Duration: Three years for Basic Center and Street Outreach. Five years for Transitional Living.
Deadline: Varies.

ADDRESS INQUIRIES TO:
National Clearinghouse on Families and Youth
5515 Security Lane, Suite 800
North Bethesda, MD 20852

U.S. DEPARTMENT OF HEALTH AND HUMAN SERVICES   [1153]
Administration for Children and Families
Children's Bureau
1250 Maryland Avenue, S.W.
Washington, DC 20024
(202) 205-8618
Fax: (202) 260-9345

WEB SITE ADDRESS:
www.acf.hhs.gov/programs/cb

NAME(S) OF PROGRAMS:
- **Discretionary Grant Programs**
- **Promoting Safe and Stable Families**
- **State & Tribal Grant Programs**
- **State Formula Grants**

TYPE:
Formula grants; Project/program grants. Discretionary Grants are awarded for research and program development, through a competitive peer-review process, to State,

Tribal and local agencies, faith-based and community-based organizations, and other nonprofit and for-profit groups.

Promoting Safe and Stable Families (PSSF) primarily aims to prevent the unnecessary separation of children from their families, improve the quality of care and services to children and their families, and ensure permanency for children by reuniting them with their parents, by adoption or by another permanent living arrangement.

State & Tribal Grant Programs provide matching funds to States and Tribes to help them operate every aspect of their child welfare systems–from prevention of child abuse and neglect to adoption–and the information systems necessary to support these programs.

State Formula Grants assist States and Territories in establishing, maintaining and expanding programs and projects to prevent family violence and to provide immediate shelter and related assistance for victims of family violence and their dependents.

PURPOSE:
To fund projects, programs and research that serve children, families or the community to states, territories and tribes.

ELIGIBILITY:
Discretionary Grants: States, local governments, tribes, public agencies or private agencies or organizations with expertise in providing technical assistance related to family preservation, family support, time-limited family reunification and adoption promotion and support.

Promoting Safe and Stable Families: Families and children who need services to assist them to stabilize their lives, strengthen family functioning, prevent out-of-home placement of children, enhance child development and increase competence in parenting abilities, facilitate timely reunification of the child and promote appropriate adoptions.

State & Tribal Grant Programs and State Formula Grants: States, territories and certain Indian Tribes are eligible.

FINANCIAL DATA:
Amount of support per award: Varies.

APPLICATION INFORMATION:
ACF requires electronic submission of applications. Information on applying electronically is available at Grants.gov. Applicants who do not have an Internet connection or sufficient capacity to upload large files to the Internet may contact ACF for an exception that will allow these applicants to submit an application in paper format.

Duration: Discretionary Grants are generally for a 12-, 24- or 36-month period; some may be renewed for up to five years. Formula Grants: Awards will be made quarterly on a fiscal year basis through a letter of credit.

Deadline: Formula Grants: June 30. Contact the headquarters or regional office, as appropriate, for other application deadlines.

ADDRESS INQUIRIES TO:
Catherine Heath, Program Specialist
(See address above.)

U.S. DEPARTMENT OF JUSTICE
Office of Juvenile Justice and Delinquency Prevention
810 Seventh Street, N.W., 5th Floor
Washington, DC 20531
(202) 307-5911
Fax: (202) 307-2093

WEB SITE ADDRESS:
www.ojjdp.ncjrs.gov/

TYPE:
Block grants; Challenge/matching grants; Demonstration grants; Formula grants; Internships; Project/program grants; Research grants; Technical assistance; Training grants. Grants to increase the capacity of state and local governments to conduct effective juvenile justice and delinquency prevention programs as developed in the state comprehensive action plan.

See entry 1413 for full listing.

USDA FOOD AND NUTRITION SERVICE   [1154]
Child Nutrition Division
3101 Park Center Drive, Room 640
Alexandria, VA 22302
(703) 305-2590
Fax: (703) 305-2879

WEB SITE ADDRESS:
www.fns.usda.gov/cnd

FOUNDED: 1969

AREAS OF INTEREST:
Child nutrition.

NAME(S) OF PROGRAMS:
- **The Child and Adult Care Food Program**
- **The National School Lunch Program**
- **The School Breakfast Program**
- **The Special Milk Program for Children**
- **The Summer Food Service Program for Children**

TYPE:
Formula grants; Grants-in-aid; Project/program grants. Reimbursement for the support of food service in schools, child and adult care institutions to improve nutrition.

The Child and Adult Care Food Program helps child care facilities and institutions serve nutritious meals and snacks to preschool and school-age children. To participate, facilities and institutions must be licensed or approved to provide child care services. They must also meet certain other eligibility requirements. The program operates in nonresidential day care centers, settlement houses, outside-school-hours care centers, family day care homes, institutions providing day care for handicapped children and others. Participating facilities and institutions get cash assistance, USDA-donated foods and technical guidance. In child care centers, the amount of cash assistance varies according to the family size and income of children served. In day care homes, the amount of cash assistance is based on a food service payment rate. Similar benefits are also now available to adult day care centers which serve functionally impaired adults or persons 60 years of age or older.

The National School Lunch Program makes well-planned nutritious meals available to school children. Any public or nonprofit private schools of high school grade or under and licensed public or nonprofit private residential child care institutions are eligible to participate in the National School Lunch and School Breakfast Programs. Schools that participate are required to provide free and reduced-price meals to children unable to pay the full price. Eligibility is based on application information submitted by a parent or guardian. The household income limit for free lunches is set at or below 130% of the federal poverty level and for reduced price lunches household income must be above 130% or at or below 185% of the federal poverty level. Children from households not eligible for free or reduced-price meals must pay the school's full price charge for lunch. Cash and donated commodities are provided to participating schools and institutions according to the number of meals served.

The School Breakfast Program makes nutritious breakfasts available to school children under the same eligibility guidelines and general requirements as the National School Lunch Program.

The Special Milk Program for Children makes it possible for all children attending a participating school or institution to purchase milk at a reduced price or receive it free, if they are eligible. Reimbursement is provided for each half-pint of milk served under the program. Schools and institutions that participate in other federal child nutrition programs authorized under the National School Lunch Act or the Child Nutrition Act of 1966 may not participate in the Special Milk Program for Children, except for split-session kindergarten programs conducted in schools in which the children do not have access to the other meal program.

The Summer Food Service Program for Children helps communities serve meals to needy children when school is not in session. The program is sponsored by public or private nonprofit school food authorities or local, municipal, county or state governments. Public or private nonprofit residential camps, other private nonprofit organizations, colleges and universities which participate in the National Youth Sports Program also may be sponsors. The program operates in areas in which at least 50% of the children meet the income criteria for free and reduced-price school meals. USDA reimburses sponsors for operating costs of food services up to a specified maximum rate for each meal served. In addition, sponsors receive some reimbursement for planning, operating and supervising expenses.

YEAR PROGRAM STARTED: 1946

PURPOSE:
To help safeguard the health and well-being of the nation's children and to encourage the domestic consumption of nutritious agricultural commodities and other foods.

LEGAL BASIS:
The National School Lunch Act as amended and the Child Nutrition Act of 1966, as amended.

ELIGIBILITY:
Family size and number of children based on income poverty levels.

GEOGRAPHIC RESTRICTIONS:
United States and its territories.

FINANCIAL DATA:
Amount of support per award: Varies.
Total amount of support: Varies.

Matching fund requirements: Varies.

APPLICATION INFORMATION:
Official application materials are available upon request to state educational agencies or other state-designated agency. In states where education agencies do not administer the programs for nonprofit private schools, contact the appropriate Food and Nutrition Service Regional Office of the Department of Agriculture for more information.
Deadline: Applications are accepted throughout the year.

FRANKLIN H. AND RUTH L. WELLS FOUNDATION [1155]
3607 Rosemont Avenue, Suite 404
Camp Hill, PA 17011
(717) 763-1157

E-MAIL ADDRESS:
mgibbons989@verizon.net

FOUNDED: 1981

AREAS OF INTEREST:
Health care, youth, human services and education.

TYPE:
Project/program grants; Seed money grants. Seed money grants are primarily for new programs.

PURPOSE:
To improve the quality of life in central Pennsylvania.

LEGAL BASIS:
Private foundation.

ELIGIBILITY:
Grants are made to organizations that have tax-exempt status under Section 501(c)(3) of the Internal Revenue Code. No grants are made to individuals. Nonsectarian religious programs may apply.

GEOGRAPHIC RESTRICTIONS:
Cumberland, Dauphin and Perry counties, Pennsylvania.

FINANCIAL DATA:
Amount of support per award: $500 to $20,000.
Total amount of support: Approximately $300,000 annually.

NUMBER OF AWARDS: Approximately 40 annually.

APPLICATION INFORMATION:
Send proposal to the address listed above.
Duration: One or two years. Renewal possible for third year.
Deadline: April 1 and October 1.

ADDRESS INQUIRIES TO:
Miles J. Gibbons, Jr., Executive Director
(See address above.)

*PLEASE NOTE:
Applications should be submitted by mail.

JOSEPH B. WHITEHEAD FOUNDATION [1156]
191 Peachtree Street, Suite 3540
Atlanta, GA 30303
(404) 522-6755
Fax: (404) 522-7026

E-MAIL ADDRESS:
fdns@woodruff.org

WEB SITE ADDRESS:
www.jbwhitehead.org

FOUNDED: 1937

AREAS OF INTEREST:
Human services, public education, children and youth services.

TYPE:
Capital grants; Project/program grants.

LEGAL BASIS:
Supporting organization.

ELIGIBILITY:
Limited to a selected list of beneficiaries.

GEOGRAPHIC RESTRICTIONS:
Metropolitan Atlanta, Georgia.

FINANCIAL DATA:
Amount of support per award: $100,000 to $1,000,000.
Total amount of support: $35,675,000 for the year 2012.

NUMBER OF AWARDS: 24.

APPLICATION INFORMATION:
An application form is not required. Proposals should be made in letter form and should include the following information:
(1) a description of the organization, its purposes, programs, staffing and governing board;
(2) organization's latest financial statements, including the most recent report;
(3) a description of the proposed project and full justification for its funding;
(4) an itemized project budget, including other sources of support in hand anticipated and;
(5) evidence from the IRS of the organization's tax-exempt status and the applying organization itself is not a private foundation.
Deadline: February 1 and September 1.

TRUSTEES:
James B. Williams, Chairman
James M. Sibley, Vice Chairman
Charles H. McTier

OFFICERS:
P. Russell Hardin, President
J. Lee Tribble, Treasurer
Erik S. Johnson, Secretary

ADDRESS INQUIRIES TO:
P. Russell Hardin, President
(See address above.)

THE WHO (WOMEN HELPING OTHERS) FOUNDATION
2121 Midway Road
Carrollton, TX 75006
(972) 458-0601
(800) 946-4663
Fax: (972) 341-3080

E-MAIL ADDRESS:
who@beauticontrol.com

WEB SITE ADDRESS:
www.whofoundation.org

TYPE:
Development grants; Product donations; Project/program grants.

See entry 1099 for full listing.

WIDENER MEMORIAL FOUNDATION IN AID OF HANDICAPPED CHILDREN
4060 Butler Pike
Suite 225
Plymouth Meeting, PA 19462
(610) 825-8900
Fax: (610) 825-8904

E-MAIL ADDRESS:
    jhagerty@erdixon.com

TYPE:
    Capital grants; Project/program grants.

See entry 1023 for full listing.

Community development and services

ABEL FOUNDATION   [1157]
1815 Y Street
Lincoln, NE 68508
(402) 434-1212
Fax: (402) 434-1799

WEB SITE ADDRESS:
    www.abelfoundation.org

AREAS OF INTEREST:
    Health and human services, higher education
    and community development programs.

TYPE:
    Capital grants; Matching gifts;
    Project/program grants.

PURPOSE:
    To improve the quality of life, particularly in
    communities where the company has
    facilities.

ELIGIBILITY:
    Grants are made to organizations that have
    tax-exempt status under Section 501(c)(3) of
    the Internal Revenue Code. No grants are
    made to individuals.

GEOGRAPHIC RESTRICTIONS:
    Nebraska, particularly Lincoln.

FINANCIAL DATA:
    Amount of support per award: Varies.
    Total amount of support: $532,000 for the
    year 2013.

APPLICATION INFORMATION:
    Applicants are requested to use the
    Lincoln/Lancaster County Grant Maker
    Common Application Form.
    Duration: One year. Renewal possible.
    Deadline: March 15, July 15 and October 31.
    Foundation meets in May, September and
    December, respectively, to review funding
    requests.

ADDRESS INQUIRIES TO:
    J. Ross McCown, Vice President
    (See address above.)

ADCO FOUNDATION
c/o AA Shareholders Service Company, LLC
1060 First Avenue, Suite 400
King of Prussia, PA 19406
(610) 768-8020

TYPE:
    General operating grants; Project/program
    grants; Seed money grants.

See entry 1613 for full listing.

AKRON COMMUNITY FOUNDATION   [1158]
345 West Cedar Street
Akron, OH 44307-2407
(330) 376-8522
Fax: (330) 376-0202

E-MAIL ADDRESS:
    jgarofalo@akroncf.org

WEB SITE ADDRESS:
    www.akroncf.org

FOUNDED: 1955

AREAS OF INTEREST:
    Arts and culture, civic affairs, health and
    human services, and education.

TYPE:
    Capital grants; General operating grants;
    Project/program grants; Scholarships; Seed
    money grants.

YEAR PROGRAM STARTED: 1955

LEGAL BASIS:
    Community foundation.

ELIGIBILITY:
    Organizations must be tax-exempt.

GEOGRAPHIC RESTRICTIONS:
    Summit County, Ohio.

FINANCIAL DATA:
    Assets of $182,000,000 for the year ended
    December 31, 2013.
    Amount of support per award: Average
    $14,000 to $18,000.
    Total amount of support: $7,350,900 for the
    year 2013.

COOPERATIVE FUNDING PROGRAMS: City of
    Akron Neighborhood Partnership.

NUMBER OF APPLICANTS MOST RECENT YEAR:
    1,086.

NUMBER OF AWARDS: 1,004.

APPLICATION INFORMATION:
    Applicants must contact the Foundation
    before submitting an application.
    Deadline: Arts and Culture: April 1; Civic
    Affairs: July 1; Health and Human Services:
    October 1; Education: December 13.

PUBLICATIONS:
    Guidelines.

IRS IDENTIFICATION NUMBER: 34-1087615

ADDRESS INQUIRIES TO:
    John F. Garofalo
    Vice President of Community Investment
    (See address above.)

ALBION COMMUNITY FOUNDATION   [1159]
P.O. Box 156
Albion, MI 49224-0156
(517) 629-3349
Fax: (517) 629-8027

E-MAIL ADDRESS:
    foundation@albionfoundation.org

WEB SITE ADDRESS:
    www.albionfoundation.org

FOUNDED: 1969

AREAS OF INTEREST:
    Promoting philanthropy addressing
    community needs through grantmaking, and
    providing leadership on key community
    issues.

TYPE:
    Capital grants; Challenge/matching grants;
    Development grants; Project/program grants.

PURPOSE:
    To provide a favorable ratio between the
    amount of money requested and the number
    of people served, show innovation and
    creativity in addressing a community need
    that demonstrates careful planning that
    provides for successful completion of the
    project.

LEGAL BASIS:
    501(c)(3).

GEOGRAPHIC RESTRICTIONS:
    Greater Albion, Michigan area.

FINANCIAL DATA:
    Amount of support per award: $250 to
    $5,000.
    Total amount of support: Approximately
    $80,000 to $100,000 each year.

APPLICATION INFORMATION:
    One complete, hard copy of the application
    and attachments, with original signatures,
    must be sent to the Foundation at the address
    above. Complete details and application
    forms are available on the Foundation web
    site.
    Deadline: Varies annually.

ALBUQUERQUE COMMUNITY FOUNDATION   [1160]
624 Tijeras, N.W.
Albuquerque, NM 87102
(505) 883-6240
Fax: (505) 883-3629

E-MAIL ADDRESS:
    nancy@albuquerquefoundation.org

WEB SITE ADDRESS:
    www.albuquerquefoundation.org

FOUNDED: 1981

AREAS OF INTEREST:
    Arts and culture, education, environmental
    and historic preservation, health and human
    services.

TYPE:
    Challenge/matching grants; General operating
    grants; Project/program grants; Scholarships;
    Seed money grants; Technical assistance.

YEAR PROGRAM STARTED: 1983

PURPOSE:
    To improve the quality of life in the greater
    Albuquerque area by providing support for
    projects and organizations that serve the
    community.

LEGAL BASIS:
    Community foundation.

ELIGIBILITY:
    Grants are made to nonprofit organizations.
    Foundation grants are generally not made to
    individuals, for political or religious
    purposes, to retire indebtedness, for the
    payment of interest or taxes, annual
    campaigns, endowments, emergency funding,
    to influence legislation or elections, to private
    foundations and other grantmaking
    organizations, or to organizations that
    discriminate on the basis of race, creed or
    sex.

GEOGRAPHIC RESTRICTIONS:
    Albuquerque, New Mexico.

FINANCIAL DATA:
    $63,000,000 in assets for fiscal year ended
    December 31, 2013.
    Amount of support per award: Varies.
    Total amount of support: $2,325,710 in
    grants and scholarships for fiscal year ended
    December 31, 2013.

APPLICATION INFORMATION:
    Current guidelines and criteria are available
    on the web site.
    Duration: One year.

PUBLICATIONS:
Report to the Community.

IRS IDENTIFICATION NUMBER: 85-0295444

STAFF:
Randy Royster, President and Chief
Executive Officer
Kelli Cooper, Communications Director
John Maes, Finance Director
Nancy Johnson, Program Director
Andy Williams, Communications Associate

BOARD OF TRUSTEES:
Kevin Yearout, Chair
Jennifer S. Thomas, Chair-Elect
Carl M. Alongi, Treasurer
Chester French Stewart, Secretary
Karen Bard
Julia B. Bowdich
William E. Ebel
Glenn Fellows
Teri Giron-Gordon
Mark L. Gorham
Albert T. Jorgensen
Steve Keene
Bill Lang
Steve Maestas
Bev McMillan
Marcus Mims, C.P.A.
Diane Harrison Ogawa
Deborah Peacock
Kathleen Raskob
Ron J. Rivera, C.P.A.
Jerrald J. Roehl
Peter Touche
Julie Weaks-Gutierrez

ADDRESS INQUIRIES TO:
Nancy Johnson, Program Director
(See address above.)

ALGER REGIONAL COMMUNITY FOUNDATION [1161]

100 West Munising Avenue
Munising, MI 49862
(906) 387-3900
Fax: (906) 387-2988

E-MAIL ADDRESS:
algercf@jamadots.com

WEB SITE ADDRESS:
www.cfup.org

AREAS OF INTEREST:
Cultural arts, community service, education,
the environment and conservation, health and
human services, and youth.

TYPE:
Project/program grants; Scholarships.

YEAR PROGRAM STARTED: 1995

PURPOSE:
To provide support to organizations that
enhance the quality of life in Alger County.

ELIGIBILITY:
Grants are made to organizations that have
tax-exempt status under Section 501(c)(3) of
the Internal Revenue Code. Non-sectarian
religious programs may apply. Organizations
must serve or be located in Alger County,
MI. No grants are made to individuals.

GEOGRAPHIC RESTRICTIONS:
Alger County, Michigan.

FINANCIAL DATA:
Amount of support per award: Varies.

APPLICATION INFORMATION:
Foundation staff members are available to
talk with potential applicants who are
interested in learning about opportunities and
needs in the community.

ADDRESS INQUIRIES TO:
Nancy Micallef
P.O. Box 39
Munising, MI 49862

ALLEGAN COUNTY COMMUNITY FOUNDATION [1162]

524 Marshall Street
Allegan, MI 49010-1632
(269) 673-8344
Fax: (269) 673-8745

E-MAIL ADDRESS:
theresa.accf@gmail.com

WEB SITE ADDRESS:
www.alleganfoundation.org

FOUNDED: 1965

AREAS OF INTEREST:
Education, health and human services,
culture, community development,
environmental issues and art.

TYPE:
General operating grants; Project/program
grants; Scholarships; Technical assistance.
Grants fall into the following categories:
youth and general.

PURPOSE:
To positively impact the Allegan County
community through the establishment of
permanently endowed funds.

LEGAL BASIS:
Community foundation.

ELIGIBILITY:
Applications accepted from charitable
organizations serving Allegan County, MI
residents. No funding for individuals except
for scholarships.

GEOGRAPHIC RESTRICTIONS:
Allegan County, Michigan.

FINANCIAL DATA:
Amount of support per award: $100 to
$25,000.
Total amount of support: Varies.

NUMBER OF APPLICANTS MOST RECENT YEAR:
53 for the year 2011.

NUMBER OF AWARDS: 43 for the year 2011.

APPLICATION INFORMATION:
Applications must include a copy of the IRS
501(c)(3) tax determination letter.
Duration: One year.
Deadline: TAG Grants: First Friday in
November; Legacy Grants: Second Friday in
December.

PUBLICATIONS:
Annual report.

IRS IDENTIFICATION NUMBER: 38-6189947

ADDRESS INQUIRIES TO:
Theresa Bray, Executive Director
(See address above.)

*SPECIAL STIPULATIONS:
Potential applicants must meet with the
Executive Director before receiving the grant
application(s).

ALTMAN FOUNDATION [1163]

521 Fifth Avenue
35th Floor
New York, NY 10175
(212) 682-0970

E-MAIL ADDRESS:
info@altman.org

WEB SITE ADDRESS:
www.altmanfoundation.org

FOUNDED: 1913

AREAS OF INTEREST:
Strengthening communities, health, education
(independent and non-public schools), arts
and culture.

TYPE:
Project/program grants.

YEAR PROGRAM STARTED: 1913

PURPOSE:
To provide direct services grants to New
York City-based organizations working in the
Foundation's four program areas.

LEGAL BASIS:
Private foundation.

ELIGIBILITY:
Must have a current IRS 501(c)(3)
tax-exemption letter. No grants to individuals.
No grants for bricks and mortar or capital
equipment.

GEOGRAPHIC RESTRICTIONS:
New York.

FINANCIAL DATA:
Amount of support per award: Varies.
Total amount of support: $10,952,850 in
grants authorized for the year 2013.

NUMBER OF APPLICANTS MOST RECENT YEAR:
326.

NUMBER OF AWARDS: 137 for the year 2013.

APPLICATION INFORMATION:
Applicants should review material on the
Foundation's web site regarding funding
approach, guidelines, limitations and
procedures.
Duration: One year. Renewal possible.

PUBLICATIONS:
Annual report.

IRS IDENTIFICATION NUMBER: 13-1623879

STAFF:
Karen L. Rosa, Vice President and Executive
Director
Deborah Thompson Velazquez, Senior
Program Officer
Megan McAllister, Program Officer
Rachael Pine, Program Officer

ADDRESS INQUIRIES TO:
Karen L. Rosa
Vice President and Executive Director
(See address above.)

AMARILLO AREA FOUNDATION [1164]

801 South Fillmore
Suite 700
Amarillo, TX 79101
(806) 376-4521
Fax: (806) 373-3656

E-MAIL ADDRESS:
kathie@aaf-hf.org

WEB SITE ADDRESS:
www.amarilloareafoundation.org

FOUNDED: 1957

AREAS OF INTEREST:
Community, arts and culture, education,
health and human services, teen pregnancy
prevention, youth-oriented programs and
elderly services.

TYPE:
Project/program grants; Scholarships. Also discretionary grants.

PURPOSE:
To exercise leadership on charitable issues, advance the cause of philanthropy throughout the region and promote efficient and effective delivery of services from nonprofit organizations.

LEGAL BASIS:
501(c)(3).

ELIGIBILITY:
No grants to individuals. Scholarships go to educational institutions.

GEOGRAPHIC RESTRICTIONS:
26 northernmost counties in the Texas panhandle.

APPLICATION INFORMATION:
Contact Grants Coordinator for counseling prior to submitting application. Application is available online for download as a Word document.
Duration: Typically one year.

ADDRESS INQUIRIES TO:
Kathie Grant, Grants Coordinator
(See address above.)

AMERICAN PLANNING ASSOCIATION
205 North Michigan Avenue
Suite 1200
Chicago, IL 60601
(202) 349-1027

E-MAIL ADDRESS:
mgroh@planning.org

WEB SITE ADDRESS:
www.planning.org

TYPE:
Fellowships; Scholarships.
See entry 973 for full listing.

AMERICAN PLANNING ASSOCIATION   [1165]
205 North Michigan Avenue
Suite 1200
Chicago, IL 60601
(202) 349-1027

E-MAIL ADDRESS:
mgroh@planning.org

WEB SITE ADDRESS:
www.planning.org

FOUNDED: 1909

AREAS OF INTEREST:
Urban and regional planning and promotion of the art and science of planning.

NAME(S) OF PROGRAMS:
• **Charles Abrams Scholarship Program**

TYPE:
Scholarships. For a student enrolled in a graduate planning program, leading to a Master's degree, who attends one of the following schools:
(1) Columbia University, Division of Urban Planning;
(2) Harvard University, City & Regional Planning Program of the Graduate School of Architecture and Design;
(3) Massachusetts Institute of Technology, Department of Urban Studies and Planning;
(4) The New School for Social Research, New York Department for Urban Affairs and

Policy Analysis or;
(5) University of Pennsylvania, Department of City and Regional Planning.

PURPOSE:
To aid students who will pursue careers as practicing planners.

LEGAL BASIS:
Private, nonprofit educational association.

ELIGIBILITY:
An applicant must be a U.S. citizen and have been accepted into the graduate planning program of one of the five eligible schools. Incoming students are eligible. An applicant must be in need of financial assistance, as determined by a review of the applicant's financial needs. A nomination by the department chair is required.

FINANCIAL DATA:
Student also receives one-year membership in the American Planning Association.
Amount of support per award: $2,000 paid directly to the student's school to defray tuition costs.
Total amount of support: $2,000 each year.

NUMBER OF APPLICANTS MOST RECENT YEAR: 4.

NUMBER OF AWARDS: 1 each year.

APPLICATION INFORMATION:
An eligible applicant should apply through one of the five designated schools on forms supplied to the participating university by APA. Applicant needs to be nominated by Department Chair.
Duration: One academic year.
Deadline: April 30.

OFFICERS:
William Anderson, FAICP, President
W. Paul Farmer, FAICP, Executive Director

ADDRESS INQUIRIES TO:
Monica Groh, Director of Early Career Programs
(See address above.)

THE ANDERSEN CORPORATE FOUNDATION   [1166]
White Pine Building
342 Fifth Avenue North, Suite 200
Bayport, MN 55003
(651) 275-4450
Fax: (651) 439-9480

E-MAIL ADDRESS:
andersencorpfdn@srinc.biz

WEB SITE ADDRESS:
www.srinc.biz/foundations/andersen-corporate-foundation/

FOUNDED: 1941

AREAS OF INTEREST:
Education and youth development, health and safety, human services, civic support and affordable housing.

TYPE:
Capital grants; General operating grants; Project/program grants.

YEAR PROGRAM STARTED: 1941

PURPOSE:
To better people's lives and strengthen communities, focusing primarily where Andersen employees live and work.

LEGAL BASIS:
Private foundation.

ELIGIBILITY:
Qualified tax-exempt organizations. Primary focus on Washington County, MN and portions of western Wisconsin.

GEOGRAPHIC RESTRICTIONS:
Des Moines and Dubuque, Iowa; east metro area of St. Paul and Washington County, Minnesota; North Brunswick, New Jersey; Marion, Ohio; Page County, Virginia; and Menomonie and portions of western Wisconsin.

FINANCIAL DATA:
$47,962,474 in assets as of November 30, 2013.
Amount of support per award: $1,500 to $100,000.
Total amount of support: $2,200,600 for the year 2012-13.

APPLICATION INFORMATION:
Cover form and checklist are available online.
Duration: One year. Renewal by reapplication.
Deadline: October 15, December 15, April 15 and July 15 for board meetings in February, May, July and November, respectively.

PUBLICATIONS:
Application guidelines and Form 990PF.

IRS IDENTIFICATION NUMBER: 41-6020912

OFFICERS AND BOARD OF DIRECTORS:
Keith Olson, President
Susan Roeder, Vice President
Phil Donaldson, Treasurer
Laurie Bauer
Jay Lund
Jerry Redmond

ADDRESS INQUIRIES TO:
Chloette Haley, Program Officer
(See address above.)

*PLEASE NOTE:
Foundation prefers that the proposal be sent to the address above.

FRED C. AND KATHERINE B. ANDERSEN FOUNDATION [1167]
P.O. Box 80
Bayport, MN 55003
(651) 264-7355
Fax: (651) 264-5537

E-MAIL ADDRESS:
marygillstrom@sbcglobal.net

FOUNDED: 1959

AREAS OF INTEREST:
Education, youth, elderly and health programs.

TYPE:
Capital grants; General operating grants; Project/program grants. The Foundation supports four-year accredited colleges and universities that do not accept state or federal funding.

YEAR PROGRAM STARTED: 1959

PURPOSE:
To support organizations of higher learning that are four-year institutions that do not accept state or federal funding.

LEGAL BASIS:
Private foundation.

ELIGIBILITY:
Grants are made to organizations that have tax-exempt status under Section 501(c)(3) of the Internal Revenue Code. No grants are made to individuals.

GEOGRAPHIC RESTRICTIONS:
Washington County, Minnesota; Pierce, Polk and St. Croix counties, Wisconsin.

FINANCIAL DATA:
Amount of support per award: Varies by need.

Total amount of support: $20,432,713 for the year 2013.

APPLICATION INFORMATION:
Organizations should submit a letter of intent to the Foundation.

Duration: One year. Must reapply for future grants.

Deadline: March 11, July 15 and October 14.

ADDRESS INQUIRIES TO:
Mary Gillstrom, Vice President/Secretary
(See address above.)

HUGH J. ANDERSEN FOUNDATION   [1168]
342 Fifth Avenue North, Suite 200
Bayport, MN 55003-1201
(651) 439-1557
Fax: (651) 439-9480

E-MAIL ADDRESS:
hjafdn@srinc.biz

WEB SITE ADDRESS:
www.srinc.biz/foundations/hugh-j-andersen-foundation

FOUNDED: 1962

AREAS OF INTEREST:
Humanities, arts/culture, elementary and secondary education, health care, human services, women and homelessness.

TYPE:
Capital grants; General operating grants; Project/program grants. Supports focused efforts that foster inclusivity, promotes equality, and lends to increased human independence, self-sufficiency and dignity.

PURPOSE:
To improve the quality of life in the St. Croix Valley.

LEGAL BASIS:
Private organization.

ELIGIBILITY:
Eligible organizations must be IRS 501(c)(3) tax-exempt.

GEOGRAPHIC RESTRICTIONS:
Primarily Washington County, Minnesota and Pierce, Polk, and St. Croix counties in Wisconsin, with secondary focus in St. Paul, Minnesota.

FINANCIAL DATA:
Amount of support per award: $500 to $85,000.

Total amount of support: $2,517,351 for fiscal year ended February 2012.

NUMBER OF AWARDS: 262.

REPRESENTATIVE AWARDS:
$9,000 to Human Services, Inc. in Washington County for general operating support; $20,000 to The Phipps Center for the Arts for general operating support; $18,000 to Store to Door for general operating support; $12,000 to The Raptor Center, University of Minnesota Foundation for education programs; $10,000 to Kinship of Polk County for general operating support.

APPLICATION INFORMATION:
Applicant organizations must use the Foundation's application form and include a copy of the IRS tax-exempt determination letter.

Duration: One year. Renewal by reapplication.

Deadline: March 15, June 15, August 15 and November 15.

PUBLICATIONS:
Annual report; application guidelines.

ADDRESS INQUIRIES TO:
Brad Kruse, Program Director
(See address above.)

ANDRUS FAMILY FUND   [1169]
330 Madison Avenue
Suite 30
New York, NY 10017
(212) 687-6975
Fax: (212) 687-6978

E-MAIL ADDRESS:
info@affund.org

WEB SITE ADDRESS:
www.affund.org

FOUNDED: 2000

AREAS OF INTEREST:
Community reconciliation and foster care.

NAME(S) OF PROGRAMS:
● **Community Reconciliation**
● **Foster Care to Independence**

TYPE:
Project/program grants; Research grants.

YEAR PROGRAM STARTED: 2000

PURPOSE:
To contribute to the body of knowledge and experience about what is necessary to create and sustain effective social change.

LEGAL BASIS:
501(c)(3).

ELIGIBILITY:
AFF does not fund endowments, capital improvements, fund-raising events/sponsorships, scholarships, or loans. Nor does AFF make grants to individuals. Presently, AFF does not fund international projects.

GEOGRAPHIC RESTRICTIONS:
United States.

FINANCIAL DATA:
Amount of support per award: $20,000 to $200,000.

Total amount of support: $3,500,000 to $4,000,000.

NUMBER OF AWARDS: 40.

APPLICATION INFORMATION:
Applications may be submitted at any time. The first step in applying for a grant is to submit an Online AFF Application, which includes a two- or three-page letter of inquiry explaining the project for which funds are sought. The letter should include:
(1) a succinct description of the application organization;
(2) a brief description of the project and how it accomplishes AFF's program strategies;
(3) information about the key participants, including staff members and beneficiaries and;
(4) a section on how you envision the transition framework will be intentionally and consistently incorporated into your work.

Deadline: Grants are awarded by the trustees, who meet in September, January, April and June.

ADDRESS INQUIRIES TO:
Leticia Peguero, Executive Director
(See address above.)

ANN ARBOR AREA COMMUNITY FOUNDATION   [1170]
301 North Main Street
Suite 300
Ann Arbor, MI 48104-1133
(734) 663-0401
Fax: (734) 663-3514

E-MAIL ADDRESS:
info@aaacf.org

WEB SITE ADDRESS:
www.aaacf.org

FOUNDED: 1963

AREAS OF INTEREST:
Environment, arts, health and human services, youth and seniors.

NAME(S) OF PROGRAMS:
● **The African American Endowment Fund**
● **The Anna Botsford Bach Fund**
● **Community Foundation of Plymouth**
● **General Grantmaking**
● **Youth Council**
● **The Ypsilanti Area Community Fund**

TYPE:
Challenge/matching grants; Demonstration grants; Development grants; Project/program grants; Scholarships; Seed money grants; Technical assistance.

YEAR PROGRAM STARTED: 1963

PURPOSE:
To improve the quality of life in the Foundation's region.

ELIGIBILITY:
Eligible organizations must be nonprofit and located in the Ann Arbor, MI region.

GEOGRAPHIC RESTRICTIONS:
Plymouth and Washtenaw County, Michigan.

FINANCIAL DATA:
Amount of support per award: $500 to $20,000.

Total amount of support: $3,400,000 for the year 2013.

APPLICATION INFORMATION:
A guideline on how to apply and application form are available on the Foundation web site.

Duration: One year.

Deadline: March and September. Contact the Foundation for exact dates.

ADDRESS INQUIRIES TO:
Neel Hajra, Chief Operating Officer and Vice President for Community Investment
(See address above.)

THE ANNENBERG FOUNDATION
2000 Avenue of the Stars
Suite 1000 S
Los Angeles, CA 90067
(310) 209-4560
Fax: (310) 209-1631

E-MAIL ADDRESS:
requests@annenbergfoundation.org

WEB SITE ADDRESS:
www.annenbergfoundation.org

TYPE:
General operating grants; Grants-in-aid;
Project/program grants; Technical assistance.

See entry 18 for full listing.

ARIZONA COMMUNITY FOUNDATION [1171]
2201 East Camelback Road
Suite 405-B
Phoenix, AZ 85016
(602) 381-1400
(800) 222-8221
Fax: (602) 381-1575

WEB SITE ADDRESS:
www.azfoundation.org

FOUNDED: 1978

AREAS OF INTEREST:
Children's mental health and prevention
programs, economic development, arts and
culture, youth agencies and health agencies.

NAME(S) OF PROGRAMS:
• **Arizona Economic Success**
• **Communities for All Ages**

TYPE:
Project/program grants.

YEAR PROGRAM STARTED: 1978

PURPOSE:
To benefit the quality of life in the Phoenix,
AZ community and the surrounding area.

LEGAL BASIS:
Community foundation.

ELIGIBILITY:
Tax-exempt, nonprofit organizations. No
grants are made to individuals.

GEOGRAPHIC RESTRICTIONS:
Arizona.

FINANCIAL DATA:
Amount of support per award: $10,000
average.

APPLICATION INFORMATION:
Application information is available on the
web site.
Duration: Typically, one year.

PUBLICATIONS:
Annual report.

OFFICERS:
Bill Hodges, Chairman

ADDRESS INQUIRIES TO:
Keva Womble, Philanthropic Advisor
(See address above.)

ARKANSAS COMMUNITY FOUNDATION [1172]
1400 West Markham St
Suite 206
Little Rock, AR 72201
(501) 372-1116
Fax: (501) 372-1166

E-MAIL ADDRESS:
arcf@arcf.org

WEB SITE ADDRESS:
www.arcf.org

FOUNDED: 1976

AREAS OF INTEREST:
Grants are made in all fields.

TYPE:
Project/program grants; Scholarships; Seed
money grants.

PURPOSE:
To serve as a vehicle for Arkansans in
carrying out their long-term philanthropic
plans; to exercise stewardship in the
investment of and grantmaking from both
permanent and short-term charitable funds; to
provide leadership to increase public
understanding of emerging problems, issues
and the importance of philanthropy to the
future of the state.

LEGAL BASIS:
Community foundation.

ELIGIBILITY:
Applicants must be nonprofit organizations
with projects to benefit Arkansans. Few
unrestricted grants are made. Only Arkansas
organizations need apply.

Most funds are restricted or designated for
specific organizations. Very few unrestricted
grants are made.

GEOGRAPHIC RESTRICTIONS:
Arkansas.

FINANCIAL DATA:
Total amount of support: $9,600,000 for
fiscal year 2012.

APPLICATION INFORMATION:
Application information is available on the
web site.
Duration: One year.

PUBLICATIONS:
Annual report; newsletter.

IRS IDENTIFICATION NUMBER: 52-1055743

BOARD OF DIRECTORS:
Jerry Adams, Chairperson
Jim Williamson, Vice Chairperson and
Finance Chairperson
Heather Larkin, President and Chief
Executive Officer
Ted Belden
Carolyn Blakely
Charlotte Brown
Mary Elizabeth Eldridge
Jackson Farrow
Glenn Freeman
Tina Green
Dennis Hunt
Mahlon Maris
George E. McLeod
Sam Scruggs
Philip Tappan
Robert Thompson
Estella Tullgren
Robert Zunick

ADDRESS INQUIRIES TO:
Grants Coordinator
(See address above.)

THE AUSTIN COMMUNITY FOUNDATION FOR THE CAPITAL AREA [1173]
4315 Guadalupe, Suite 300
Austin, TX 78751
(512) 472-4483
Fax: (512) 472-4486

E-MAIL ADDRESS:
info@austincf.org

WEB SITE ADDRESS:
www.austincf.org

FOUNDED: 1977

AREAS OF INTEREST:
Arts and culture, community development,
community service, education and training,
environment, health and human services,
recreation and animal-related services.

TYPE:
Project/program grants; Scholarships.

YEAR PROGRAM STARTED: 1977

PURPOSE:
To promote philanthropy in central Texas; to
improve the quality of life now and in the
future.

ELIGIBILITY:
Organizations must be 501(c)(3) or
170(b)(1)(a)(vi) and located in the central
Texas area, including Travis and contiguous
counties. Funds are not given to individuals.

GEOGRAPHIC RESTRICTIONS:
Central Texas.

FINANCIAL DATA:
Amount of support per award: Varies;
average competitive grant is $17,500.

APPLICATION INFORMATION:
Applications must include the IRS letter
ruling 501(c)(3) status.
Duration: One year. Must reapply.
Deadline: Proposals are reviewed on an
ongoing basis; four- to six-month process.

IRS IDENTIFICATION NUMBER: 74-1934031

ADDRESS INQUIRIES TO:
Meagan A. Longley
Director of Grants and Scholarships
(See address above.)

AUTRY FOUNDATION [1174]
4383 Colfax Avenue
Studio City, CA 91604
(818) 752-7770
Fax: (818) 752-7779

AREAS OF INTEREST:
Culture, education, children's and seniors'
groups, hunger and health.

TYPE:
Project/program grants.

PURPOSE:
To offer assistance to communities in
southern California.

LEGAL BASIS:
Private foundation.

ELIGIBILITY:
Eligible organizations must be IRS 501(c)(3)
tax-exempt.

GEOGRAPHIC RESTRICTIONS:
Southern California.

FINANCIAL DATA:
Amount of support per award: Varies.
Total amount of support: Varies.

APPLICATION INFORMATION:
Applicants should submit a letter and include
a copy of the IRS tax determination letter.
Duration: Depends on project. Renewable.

ADDRESS INQUIRIES TO:
Maxine Hansen, Secretary
(See address above.)

BADGER METER FOUNDATION, INC. [1175]
4545 West Brown Deer Road
Milwaukee, WI 53223-2479
(414) 355-0400
Fax: (414) 371-5950

AREAS OF INTEREST:
Social services, education, conservation and community funds.

TYPE:
General operating grants; Research grants; Seed money grants.

PURPOSE:
To support education and community service organizations, health associations, the handicapped, the arts and conservation.

ELIGIBILITY:
Organizations classified as 501(c)(3) by the IRS can apply. No grants to individuals and religious organizations.

GEOGRAPHIC RESTRICTIONS:
Milwaukee area, Wisconsin.

FINANCIAL DATA:
Amount of support per award: Varies.
Total amount of support: Varies.

NUMBER OF AWARDS: 50.

APPLICATION INFORMATION:
Request must be submitted on organization's letterhead paper.
Duration: One year. Grants are renewable.

ADDRESS INQUIRIES TO:
John Biever, Treasurer and Secretary
(See address above.)

BALTIMORE COMMUNITY FOUNDATION

2 East Read Street, 9th Floor
Baltimore, MD 21202
(410) 332-4171
Fax: (410) 837-4701

E-MAIL ADDRESS:
info@bcf.org

WEB SITE ADDRESS:
www.bcf.org

TYPE:
Scholarships. Neighborhood grants. Education grants.

See entry 31 for full listing.

BARAGA COUNTY COMMUNITY FOUNDATION [1176]

100 Hemlock Street
Baraga, MI 49908
(906) 353-7898
Fax: (906) 353-7896

E-MAIL ADDRESS:
baragacf@up.net

WEB SITE ADDRESS:
www.baragacountyfoundation.org

FOUNDED: 1994

AREAS OF INTEREST:
Arts and culture, community development, education, senior well-being, and youth development.

TYPE:
Capital grants; Challenge/matching grants; Endowments; Project/program grants; Scholarships; Seed money grants; Technical assistance. Community convening.

YEAR PROGRAM STARTED: 1994

PURPOSE:
To enhance the quality of life for the citizens of the community.

LEGAL BASIS:
501(c)(3).

ELIGIBILITY:
Grants are made to organizations that have tax-exempt status under Section 501(c)(3) of the Internal Revenue Code. Grants are made to individuals. Nonsectarian religious programs may apply.

GEOGRAPHIC RESTRICTIONS:
Baraga County, Michigan.

FINANCIAL DATA:
Amount of support per award: $200 is a common grant amount. However, grants vary in amount depending upon the needs and nature of the request.
Total amount of support: $2,000.

NUMBER OF AWARDS: Varies.

APPLICATION INFORMATION:
Application information is available on the web site.
Duration: One year. Renewal possible.
Deadline: Varies.

IRS IDENTIFICATION NUMBER: 38-3198122

ADDRESS INQUIRIES TO:
Gordette Marie Leutz, Executive Director
(See address above.)

BARNES GROUP FOUNDATION [1177]

123 Main Street
Bristol, CT 06010
(860) 583-7070
Fax: (860) 589-7466

WEB SITE ADDRESS:
www.bginc.com

AREAS OF INTEREST:
Cultural arts, education, and health and welfare.

TYPE:
General operating grants; Scholarships. Employee scholarship program.

PURPOSE:
To support higher education, cultural arts, and health and welfare.

ELIGIBILITY:
Organizations classified as 501(c)(3) by the IRS can apply. Individuals and religious organizations are ineligible.

GEOGRAPHIC RESTRICTIONS:
United States, with emphasis on Connecticut and New England.

FINANCIAL DATA:
Amount of support per award: Varies.
Total amount of support: Varies.

APPLICATION INFORMATION:
Applicants must write to the Foundation for an application form.
Duration: One year. Grants are renewable.

ADDRESS INQUIRIES TO:
Tom Barnes, Secretary
(See address above.)

BARR FOUNDATION [1178]

The Pilot House, Lewis Wharf
Fourth Floor
Boston, MA 02110
(617) 854-3500
Fax: (617) 854-3501

E-MAIL ADDRESS:
info@barrfoundation.org

WEB SITE ADDRESS:
www.barrfoundation.org

FOUNDED: 1987

AREAS OF INTEREST:
Education, the environment, arts and cultural activities with a focus on Boston, MA.

TYPE:
Capital grants; Challenge/matching grants; Conferences/seminars; Demonstration grants; Development grants; Endowments; Fellowships; General operating grants; Matching gifts; Project/program grants; Technical assistance. The work of the Foundation focuses on three critical areas with a focus on Boston, MA:
(1) closing education opportunity gaps;
(2) mitigating climate change and;
(3) enhancing cultural vitality.

PURPOSE:
To enhance the quality of life for all of Boston's citizens.

ELIGIBILITY:
No unsolicited proposals.

GEOGRAPHIC RESTRICTIONS:
Boston, Massachusetts.

FINANCIAL DATA:
Amount of support per award: Varies.

APPLICATION INFORMATION:
By invitation only.
Deadline: Quarterly, in conjunction with quarterly meeting.

IRS IDENTIFICATION NUMBER: 04-6579815

ADDRESS INQUIRIES TO:
Kerri Ann Hurley, Grants Manager
(See address above.)

NORWIN S. AND ELIZABETH N. BEAN FOUNDATION [1179]

40 Stark Street
Manchester, NH 03101
(603) 493-7257

E-MAIL ADDRESS:
kcook@beanfoundation.org

WEB SITE ADDRESS:
www.beanfoundation.org

FOUNDED: 1967

AREAS OF INTEREST:
Arts and humanities, education, environment, health, social and community services and development of the voluntary sector.

TYPE:
Capital grants; Challenge/matching grants. Grants to tax-exempt charitable organizations operating in Amherst or Manchester, NH, for broad charitable purposes. Generally, at least two-thirds of available funds are awarded as grants for programs undertaken by nonprofit organizations and public agencies. The remaining one-third is allocated for capital needs, including acquisition of equipment, renovation or construction of facilities and additions to endowment.

General operating support grants are not made to ongoing programs, nor are grants made to eliminate previously incurred deficits. Short-term operating support may be provided to new organizations or for new program initiatives of established organizations. Generally, grants are provided for expenditure over a period of one year.

YEAR PROGRAM STARTED: 1967

PURPOSE:
To promote the general welfare.

LEGAL BASIS:
Private foundation.

ELIGIBILITY:
Applications are accepted from nonprofit
501(c)(3) organizations, municipal and public
agencies serving the communities of Amherst
or Manchester, NH. Priority consideration is
given to organizations operating primarily in
those two communities. However, the
Foundation will consider applications from
statewide or regional organizations which
provide a substantial and documented level of
service to Manchester and Amherst. The
Foundation does not make grants to
individuals or provide scholarship aid.

GEOGRAPHIC RESTRICTIONS:
Amherst or Manchester, New Hampshire.

FINANCIAL DATA:
Amount of support per award: $1,000 to
$50,000.
Total amount of support: $480,000 for fiscal
year 2013.

NUMBER OF AWARDS: 37 for the year 2013.

REPRESENTATIVE AWARDS:
$30,000 to the capital campaign for a
wildlife sanctuary and educational facility to
be built by the Audubon Society of New
Hampshire; $7,000 to Child and Family
Services of New Hampshire to establish a
volunteer management position; $3,000 to the
Franco-American Centre for the preservation
and cataloging of historic documents;
$15,000 for the Manchester Families in
Transition program; $2,000 to The
Caregivers, Inc. for an improved development
tracking system.

APPLICATION INFORMATION:
Applications should include a completed
cover letter sheet and proposal with
appropriate enclosures explaining the purpose
of the project, describing how the project will
be accomplished, and indicating the amount
of grant support sought.
Duration: Grants are usually awarded for a
one-year period only. The Foundation does
not consider multiyear grants except in very
rare circumstances.
Deadline: April 1, September 1 and
December 1 for decisions made in February,
June and November, respectively.

PUBLICATIONS:
Guidelines.

TRUSTEES:
John F. Dinkel, Jr.
Thomas J. Donovan
William Dunlap
Cathryn E. Vaughn
Michael Whitney

STAFF:
Kathleen D. Cook, Grant Manager

ADDRESS INQUIRIES TO:
Kathleen D. Cook, Grant Manager
(See address above.)

BENTON FOUNDATION
1250 Connecticut Avenue, N.W.
Suite 200
Washington, DC 20036
(202) 638-5770
Fax: (240) 235-5024

E-MAIL ADDRESS:
cgarcia@benton.org

WEB SITE ADDRESS:
www.benton.org

TYPE:
Technical assistance. Program is funded for
preserving, protecting and strengthening the
public benefits in America's media
environment.

See entry 1923 for full listing.

BERKS COUNTY COMMUNITY FOUNDATION   [1180]
237 Court Street
Reading, PA 19601
(610) 685-2223
Fax: (610) 685-2240

E-MAIL ADDRESS:
info@bccf.org

WEB SITE ADDRESS:
www.bccf.org

FOUNDED: 1994

AREAS OF INTEREST:
Community, health, energy, smart growth and
public policy.

NAME(S) OF PROGRAMS:
● **Boyertown Area Grantmaking**
● **Governor Mifflin Area Grantmaking**
● **Metropolitan Edison Energy Fund**

TYPE:
Project/program grants; Scholarships.

PURPOSE:
To promote philanthropy and improve the
quality of life in Berks County; to encourage
and nurture performing artists at critical
points in their careers.

LEGAL BASIS:
501(c)(3).

GEOGRAPHIC RESTRICTIONS:
Berks County, Pennsylvania.

FINANCIAL DATA:
$50,000,000 in assets.
Amount of support per award: Varies,
depending on fund.
Total amount of support: Varies.

APPLICATION INFORMATION:
Applicants must submit a letter of inquiry.
Duration: Varies.

PUBLICATIONS:
Annual report.

ADDRESS INQUIRIES TO:
See e-mail address above.

WILLIAM BLAIR AND COMPANY FOUNDATION   [1181]
222 West Adams
Chicago, IL 60606
(312) 236-1600
Fax: (312) 236-3612

AREAS OF INTEREST:
Cultural programs, hospitals, education,
social services, Jewish giving and Catholic
giving.

TYPE:
Capital grants; Endowments; Fellowships;
General operating grants.

ELIGIBILITY:
Organizations, including religious, must be
classified as 501(c)(3) by the IRS. No grants
to individuals. Limited to employees or
clients of William Blair. Not open to the
public.

FINANCIAL DATA:
Amount of support per award: $500 to
$5,000.
Total amount of support: Varies.

APPLICATION INFORMATION:
Contact the Foundation.
Duration: One year.

ADDRESS INQUIRIES TO:
E. David Coolidge, III, Vice Chairman
(See address above.)

BLOWITZ-RIDGEWAY FOUNDATION   [1182]
1701 East Woodfield Road
Suite 201
Schaumburg, IL 60173-5127
(847) 330-1020
Fax: (847) 330-1028

E-MAIL ADDRESS:
serena@blowitzridgeway.org

WEB SITE ADDRESS:
www.blowitzridgeway.org

FOUNDED: 1984

AREAS OF INTEREST:
Health and human services.

TYPE:
Capital grants; General operating grants;
Project/program grants; Research grants;
Scholarships. Scholarships are given through
schools.

YEAR PROGRAM STARTED: 1984

PURPOSE:
To support advances in medical, psychiatric,
psychological and/or residential care, and
research programs in medicine, psychology,
social science and education.

LEGAL BASIS:
Private independent foundation.

ELIGIBILITY:
Organizations classified as 501(c)(3) by the
IRS can apply. Preference will be given to
organizations in Illinois and to programs or
services which benefit youth, seniors or
individuals lacking sufficient resources to
care for themselves. No grants to individuals,
religious or political organizations,
government agencies, organizations that
subsist mainly on third-party funding nor for
the production or writing of audio-visual
materials.

GEOGRAPHIC RESTRICTIONS:
Illinois.

FINANCIAL DATA:
Assets of $23,400,000 for the year ended
September 30, 2013.
Amount of support per award: Generally,
$1,000 to $15,000; some larger grants.
Total amount of support: Approximately
$1,100,000 for fiscal year 2013.

NUMBER OF APPLICANTS MOST RECENT YEAR:
231 for the year 2011.

NUMBER OF AWARDS: 105 grants for the year
2011.

APPLICATION INFORMATION:
The Blowitz-Ridgeway application form must
accompany all grant requests. If declined,
applicants may reapply the next year.
Duration: One year. Grants are renewable.

PUBLICATIONS:
Annual report; application guidelines.

IRS IDENTIFICATION NUMBER: 36-2488355

ADDRESS INQUIRIES TO:
Serena Moy, Administrator
(See address above.)

BLUE MOUNTAIN COMMUNITY FOUNDATION [1183]

22 East Poplar Street
Suite 206
Walla Walla, WA 99362
(509) 529-4371
Fax: (509) 529-5284

E-MAIL ADDRESS:
bmcf@bluemountainfoundation.org

WEB SITE ADDRESS:
www.bluemountainfoundation.org

FOUNDED: 1984

AREAS OF INTEREST:
Social and community services, education, health, and the arts and humanities.

TYPE:
Grants-in-aid; Scholarships. The Foundation administers and awards scholarships to local area students to enable them to attend college, graduate school or trade school.

PURPOSE:
To seek, steward and share charitable gifts in the Blue Mountain area.

ELIGIBILITY:
The Foundation awards grants to nonprofit, tax-exempt organizations in the Foundation's service area which includes the counties of Columbia, Garfield and Walla Walla in the state of Washington and the communities of Athena, Milton-Freewater and Weston in Umatilla County, OR. It strives to make awards to agencies and programs that meet community needs and bring the most benefit to people in the Blue Mountain area.

GEOGRAPHIC RESTRICTIONS:
Columbia, Garfield and Walla Walla counties in Washington, and the northern parts of Umatilla County in Oregon.

FINANCIAL DATA:
Amount of support per award: Varies.
Total amount of support: $1,500,000.

APPLICATION INFORMATION:
Grant guidelines and application forms can be obtained through the Foundation's web site. Grant applicants should submit an original and nine copies each of the completed Summary of Applicant Organization form and a one-page description of the program/project or idea on the organization's letterhead. Upon review, the Foundation may request additional information, including but not limited to financial statements, project budgets, 501(c)(3) verification and a list of members of the governing board.
Duration: Typically one year.
Deadline: Grants: July 1; Scholarships: March 1.

THE BNY MELLON FOUNDATION OF SOUTHWESTERN PENNSYLVANIA [1184]

BNY Mellon Center, Room 1830
Pittsburgh, PA 15258-0001
(412) 234-2732
Fax: (412) 234-0831

E-MAIL ADDRESS:
doreen.tumminello@bnymellon.com

WEB SITE ADDRESS:
www.bnymellon.com

FOUNDED: 1974

AREAS OF INTEREST:
Basic needs provisions: food, clothing, and housing assistance; Workforce development: access to employment through job training, education, mentoring and skills development.

TYPE:
Capital grants; Challenge/matching grants; General operating grants; Project/program grants; Technical assistance.

YEAR PROGRAM STARTED: 1974

PURPOSE:
To identify and support initiatives that improve the social and economic conditions of residents where the company does business and where employees live and work. Through powering potential, the company's strategic philanthropic investments will emphasize basic needs, provisions, and workforce development.

LEGAL BASIS:
Corporate foundation, part of BNY Mellon's Charitable Giving Program.

ELIGIBILITY:
Organizations requesting support must have 501(c)(3) tax-exempt charitable status and must be public charities as defined under Section 509(a)(1) of the Internal Revenue Code.

No support is available for loans or direct grants to individuals, religious programs of churches or other sectarian organizations and political parties, campaigns or candidates. As a general rule, support is not available for fraternal organizations, such as police or fire associations, scholarships, fellowships and travel grants, conference or seminar attendance, specialized health campaigns, endowment campaigns, individual United Way agencies which already benefit from the Corporation's gift to the United Way appeal, national organizations, projects or programs or those which operate outside the U.S. and multiyear commitments.

GEOGRAPHIC RESTRICTIONS:
Southwestern Pennsylvania.

FINANCIAL DATA:
Amount of support per award: $2,500 to $10,000 average.
Total amount of support: $3,700,000 for the year 2013.

NUMBER OF APPLICANTS MOST RECENT YEAR: 500.

NUMBER OF AWARDS: Approximately 125.

APPLICATION INFORMATION:
Contact the Foundation.
Duration: One year.
Deadline: Requests are considered upon receipt.

PUBLICATIONS:
Annual report which contains contributions policy and application guidelines; *Discover Total Resources: A Guide for Nonprofits.*

STAFF:
James P. McDonald, President
Kenya Boswell, Vice President and Secretary
Doreen Tumminello, Administrator

ADDRESS INQUIRIES TO:
James P. McDonald, President
(See address above.)

BOSTON FOUNDATION [1185]

75 Arlington Street, 10th Floor
Boston, MA 02116-3936
(617) 338-1700
Fax: (617) 338-1604

E-MAIL ADDRESS:
grantsinfo@tbf.org

WEB SITE ADDRESS:
www.tbf.org

FOUNDED: 1915

AREAS OF INTEREST:
Health, welfare, educational, cultural, planning and housing needs of the Boston metropolitan area community.

TYPE:
General operating grants; Project/program grants; Technical assistance. Capacity building. Grants for new or experimental programs of both new and established institutions.

LEGAL BASIS:
Community foundation established in 1915 in Massachusetts by agreement and declaration of trust. Incorporated in 1917.

ELIGIBILITY:
Grants are made to organizations or for programs in the Boston standard metropolitan statistical area only. Organizations must have federal tax-exempt status or a fiscal nonprofit agent. No grants are made to individuals. Grants are not made for scholarship, travel, medical or scientific research, religious purposes, publications or films or for national/international organizations.

GEOGRAPHIC RESTRICTIONS:
Greater Boston, Massachusetts.

FINANCIAL DATA:
Amount of support per award: Averages approximately $50,000 to $75,000.
Total amount of support: Approximately $16,500,000 annually.
Matching fund requirements: Varies.

NUMBER OF APPLICANTS MOST RECENT YEAR:
Approximately 300.

APPLICATION INFORMATION:
The Foundation requires submission of a Letter of Inquiry. It will review only proposals that have been invited based on its review.
Duration: Up to five years.

PUBLICATIONS:
Annual report; application guidelines; quarterly newsletters.

OFFICERS:
Michael Keating, Chairman
Catherine D'Amato, Vice Chairperson
Alfred F. Van Ranst, Jr., Treasurer and Chief Financial Officer
Timothy Gassert, Secretary

BOARD MEMBERS:
Sandra M. Edgerley
Michael R. Eisenson
Grace Fey
Paul C. Gannon
Paul S. Grogan
Rev. Dr. Gregory G. Groover, Sr.
Jackie Jenkins-Scott
Paul LaCamera
Paul W. Lee
Claudio Martinez
Jane Mendillo
Jack Meyer
Dr. Myechia Minter-Jordan

Herbert Morse
Ron O'Hanley
Greg Shell
Binkley C. Shorts
Micho Spring

ADDRESS INQUIRIES TO:
Grants Manager or Program Officer
(See address above.)

OTTO BREMER FOUNDATION [1186]

445 Minnesota Street, Suite 2250
St. Paul, MN 55101
(651) 227-8036
(888) 291-1123
Fax: (651) 312-3665

E-MAIL ADDRESS:
obf@ottobremer.org

WEB SITE ADDRESS:
www.ottobremer.org

AREAS OF INTEREST:
Community economic, civic, and social betterment.

TYPE:
Capital grants; Challenge/matching grants; General operating grants; Project/program grants.

PURPOSE:
To assist people in achieving full economic, civic and social participation in and for the betterment of their communities.

ELIGIBILITY:
Grants are restricted to private nonprofit or public tax-exempt organizations for purposes defined under Section 501(c)(3) of the Internal Revenue Code. Grants are only made to organizations whose beneficiaries are residents of Minnesota, North Dakota or Wisconsin. Grants are not made to individuals.

GEOGRAPHIC RESTRICTIONS:
Minnesota, North Dakota and Wisconsin.

FINANCIAL DATA:
Amount of support per award: $1,000 to $500,000; average $35,000.
Total amount of support: $24,000,000 for the year 2012.

APPLICATION INFORMATION:
Must include copy of IRS 501(c)(3) letter of determination.
Duration: One year. Must reapply.
Deadline: Varies.

THE HARRY B. AND JANE H. BROCK FOUNDATION [1187]

2101 Highland Avenue South, Suite 250
Birmingham, AL 35205
(205) 939-0236
Fax: (205) 939-0806

FOUNDED: 1987

AREAS OF INTEREST:
Higher education, community development and early education.

TYPE:
Project/program grants.

YEAR PROGRAM STARTED: 1985

PURPOSE:
To support higher education and community development in Alabama.

LEGAL BASIS:
Private family foundation.

ELIGIBILITY:
Organizations must be IRS 501(c)(3) tax-exempt.

GEOGRAPHIC RESTRICTIONS:
Alabama, mainly Jefferson County.

FINANCIAL DATA:
Amount of support per award: $5,000 average.
Total amount of support: $507,222 for the year 2013.

NUMBER OF APPLICANTS MOST RECENT YEAR: 49.

NUMBER OF AWARDS: 37.

REPRESENTATIVE AWARDS:
Samford University; University of Alabama; Cahaba River.

APPLICATION INFORMATION:
Applicants may submit a written proposal and must include a copy of the IRS tax determination letter.
Duration: One year. Renewable by reapplication.
Deadline: November 1.

ADDRESS INQUIRIES TO:
Harry B. Brock, Jr., President
(See address above.)

GLADYS BROOKS FOUNDATION [1188]

1055 Franklin Avenue
Suite 208
Garden City, NY 11530-2903
(516) 746-6103

WEB SITE ADDRESS:
www.gladysbrooksfoundation.org

FOUNDED: 1981

AREAS OF INTEREST:
Libraries, education, hospitals and clinics.

TYPE:
Capital grants; Challenge/matching grants; Demonstration grants; Development grants; Endowments; Matching gifts; Project/program grants; Scholarships. Grants to private, not-for-profit publicly supported libraries, educational institutions, hospitals and clinics in the eastern U.S.

YEAR PROGRAM STARTED: 1981

PURPOSE:
To provide for the intellectual, moral and physical welfare of the people of this country by establishing and supporting nonprofit libraries, educational institutions, hospitals and clinics.

ELIGIBILITY:
Applicants must be publicly supported, not-for-profit tax-exempt organizations. Generally speaking, grant applications will only be considered where outside funding, including governmental, is not available. The project will be largely funded by the grant unless the grant request covers a discrete component of a larger project. The funds will be used for capital projects including equipment or endowments. Applications for direct salary support will not be accepted.

Grant applications will be considered only for major expenditures generally between $50,000 and $100,000 and greater or lesser amounts in certain circumstances.

GEOGRAPHIC RESTRICTIONS:
Connecticut, Delaware, District of Columbia, Florida, Indiana, Louisiana, Maine,

Maryland, Massachusetts, New Hampshire, New Jersey, New York, Ohio, Pennsylvania, Rhode Island, Tennessee and Vermont.

FINANCIAL DATA:
Amount of support per award: $50,000 to $100,000.

APPLICATION INFORMATION:
Foundation application form must be used and is available by contacting Ms. Kathleen Petry. Applications must be completed and postmarked and sent with all supporting documents to the Foundation within 45 days from the date of the letter from the Foundation furnishing the application materials. The only exception to this is if the letter is dated after April 18, in which case application materials must be postmarked with all supporting materials before June 1. Applicants must furnish audited financial statements and include a specific budget for the project; also an annual report or a brief description of applicant organization.

Electronic submissions are not acceptable.
Duration: One year.
Deadline: June 1.

PUBLICATIONS:
Annual report.

GOVERNING BOARD:
James J. Daly, Chairman
Christopher R. Hawkins
Thomas Q. Morris, M.D.

ADDRESS INQUIRIES TO:
Kathleen Petry
(See web site above.)

*PLEASE NOTE:
All grant awards are made on the condition that the entirety of the funds advanced shall be utilized in direct furtherance of the project and that no portion thereof shall be appropriated by the grantee as an administrative or processing fee, for overseeing the project or for its general overhead.

BRUNSWICK FOUNDATION, INC. [1189]

One Northfield Court
Lake Forest, IL 60045
(847) 735-4344
Fax: (847) 735-4330

E-MAIL ADDRESS:
lisa.debartolo@brunswick.com

FOUNDED: 1957

AREAS OF INTEREST:
Organizations that support the company's products.

NAME(S) OF PROGRAMS:
● **Brunswick Employee Sons and Daughters Scholarship**
● **Dollars for Doers Volunteer Program**

TYPE:
General operating grants. Scholarships to employee's children.

PURPOSE:
To support causes and/or projects that are related to boating and outdoor/indoor recreation activities.

LEGAL BASIS:
Private foundation.

ELIGIBILITY:
Organizations in areas of company operation classified as 501(c)(3) by the IRS will be

considered. The Foundation does not have and is not able to donate equipment or products.

FINANCIAL DATA:
Amount of support per award: Dollars for Doers: $75 to $1,000.
Total amount of support: $275,000 for the year 2013.

NUMBER OF APPLICANTS MOST RECENT YEAR: 250.

NUMBER OF AWARDS: Varies.

APPLICATION INFORMATION:
Applications are sent out by invitation only.
Duration: One year.
Deadline: Varies.

IRS IDENTIFICATION NUMBER: 36-6033576

STAFF:
Lisa DeBartolo, Coordinator

DIRECTORS:
Judith Zelisko, President
B. Russell Lockridge, Vice President
William L. Metzger, Treasurer
Marsha Vaughn, Secretary

ADDRESS INQUIRIES TO:
Lisa DeBartolo, Coordinator
(See address above.)

THE BUHL FOUNDATION [1190]
650 Smithfield Street
Suite 2300
Pittsburgh, PA 15222
(412) 566-2711
Fax: (412) 566-2714

E-MAIL ADDRESS:
buhl@buhlfoundation.org

WEB SITE ADDRESS:
www.buhlfoundation.org

FOUNDED: 1927

AREAS OF INTEREST:
Education, youth development, human services and economic and community development.

CONSULTING OR VOLUNTEER SERVICES:
Wide variety of community initiatives to improve quality of life in greater Pittsburgh area.

TYPE:
Demonstration grants; Development grants; Grants-in-aid; Project/program grants; Seed money grants; Training grants. Capacity building. Grants-in-aid, primarily to institutions in the Pittsburgh metropolitan area, Allegheny County and western Pennsylvania for developmental and innovative projects in education, children and youth, and community services.

YEAR PROGRAM STARTED: 1928

PURPOSE:
To support efforts that contribute to the vibrancy and well-being of the North Side and the Pittsburgh region, create learning environments so that young people will thrive and be prepared for adulthood, encourage innovation and entrepreneurial solutions to improve quality of life, and make a definitive difference in addressing persistent community challenges or unmet needs of at-risk neighborhoods.

LEGAL BASIS:
Independent private foundation established by will probated on June 20, 1927.

ELIGIBILITY:
Tax-exempt, nonprofit institutions with appropriate interests in southwestern Pennsylvania are eligible to apply. Emphasis is on grants to institutions in the Pittsburgh metropolitan area. Programs and projects which combine different professional interests and relate agencies in cooperative endeavors are often recognized as worthy of a grant. Grants are not made to individuals.

GEOGRAPHIC RESTRICTIONS:
Southwestern Pennsylvania, including Pittsburgh and Allegheny counties.

FINANCIAL DATA:
Total amount of support: $2,620,450 for the year ended June 30, 2013.

NUMBER OF APPLICANTS MOST RECENT YEAR: 202.

NUMBER OF AWARDS: 118.

REPRESENTATIVE AWARDS:
$100,000 to The Pittsburgh Foundation for continued support of the Fund for Excellence with a mission to improve the success of Pittsburgh Public School students; $50,000 to Bike Pittsburgh to support a public bicycle network that will bring safer streets and more biking infrastructure and tourism to Pittsburgh's North Side; $25,000 to Homeless Children's Education Fund for support of an innovative and collaborative strategy to improve school transportation for children experiencing homelessness in Allegheny County; $30,000 (over three years) to Saltworks Theatre Company to support educational plays and related materials on bullying and drug and alcohol abuse prevention presented to Pittsburgh Public School students.

APPLICATION INFORMATION:
Applicants must write a letter of inquiry to the President at the address above, followed, if requested, by a formal proposal. Interviews and other follow-up procedures are then initiated by staff. Applications must contain a statement of objectives and the proposed means of attaining these, a description of the program and budget as well as information regarding the applicant agency, its organization and structure, its tax status and its capacity to implement the project.
Duration: Usually one year. Some grants cover two or three years.

PUBLICATIONS:
Annual report; application procedures.

IRS IDENTIFICATION NUMBER: 25-0378910

OFFICERS:
Frederick W. Thieman, President
Diana A. Bucco, Vice President

TRUSTEES:
Jean A. Robinson, Chairman
Peter F. Mathieson, Vice Chairman
Saleem H. Ghubril, Treasurer
Kim Tillotson Fleming
Lara E. Washington

ADDRESS INQUIRIES TO:
Frederick W. Thieman, President
(See address above.)

PATRICK AND AIMEE BUTLER FAMILY FOUNDATION [1191]
2356 University Avenue West
Suite 420
St. Paul, MN 55114
(651) 222-2565

E-MAIL ADDRESS:
bffinfo@visi.com

WEB SITE ADDRESS:
www.butlerfamilyfoundation.org

FOUNDED: 1951

AREAS OF INTEREST:
Arts and culture, environment, and human services.

TYPE:
General operating grants; Project/program grants.

YEAR PROGRAM STARTED: 1951

PURPOSE:
To support solid progressive ideas in art and culture, the environment, social service and social change.

LEGAL BASIS:
Private foundation.

ELIGIBILITY:
Eligible organizations must be IRS 501(c)(3) tax-exempt. The Foundation does not fund criminal justice, economic development or education, employment or vocational programs, films or videos, health, hospitals or medical research, loans or grants to individuals, secondary or elementary education, theater or dance, or projects outside the U.S.

GEOGRAPHIC RESTRICTIONS:
Twin Cities Metropolitan area, Minnesota.

FINANCIAL DATA:
Amount of support per award: Average $20,000.
Total amount of support: $4,068,500 for the year 2013.

NUMBER OF APPLICANTS MOST RECENT YEAR: 96 for the year 2012.

NUMBER OF AWARDS: 118 for the year 2013.

APPLICATION INFORMATION:
Application must include a copy of the IRS tax determination letter. Must apply online through web site link.
Duration: Two years.
Deadline: May 1.

PUBLICATIONS:
Guidelines.

TRUSTEES:
John K. Butler, President
Patrick Butler, Vice President
Peter M. Butler, Treasurer
Brigid M. Butler
Katherine Butler
Patricia M. Butler
Paul S. Butler
Sandra K. Butler
Suzanne A. LeFevour
Melanie Martinez
Temple Peterson

STAFF:
Kerrie Blevins, Foundation Director
Nora McKinnon, Grants Administrator
Connie O'Brien, Controller
JoAnne Peters, Program Associate

ADDRESS INQUIRIES TO:
Kerrie Blevins, Foundation Director
(See address above.)

CALIFORNIA COMMUNITY FOUNDATION [1192]
221 South Figueroa Street, Suite 400
Los Angeles, CA 90012
(213) 413-4130
Fax: (213) 383-2046

E-MAIL ADDRESS:
info@calfund.org

WEB SITE ADDRESS:
www.calfund.org

FOUNDED: 1915

AREAS OF INTEREST:
Education, arts and culture, health prevention
and treatment services, health care coverage
expansion, and affordable housing.

NAME(S) OF PROGRAMS:
- Arts
- Civic Engagement
- Education
- Health Care
- Housing and Economic Development
- Human Development
- Scholarships

TYPE:
Fellowships; General operating grants;
Project/program grants; Scholarships.
Program-related investments. Policy analysis
and advocacy.

YEAR PROGRAM STARTED: 1915

PURPOSE:
To strengthen Los Angeles communities
through effective philanthropy and civic
engagement.

LEGAL BASIS:
Community foundation, designated a public
charity by the IRS.

ELIGIBILITY:
The Foundation will consider applications
that are consistent with current program
priorities and goals. Eligible organizations
are:
(1) nonprofit agencies with evidence of
tax-exempt status under Section 501(c)(3) of
the Internal Revenue Code and not classified
as a private foundation;
(2) located within and primarily serving
residents of Los Angeles County, with the
exception of regional, statewide or national
public policy efforts that may benefit a
substantial portion of the local population
and;
(3) operated and organized so that they do
not discriminate in the hiring of staff or the
provision of services on the basis of race,
religion, gender, sexual orientation, age,
national origin or disability.

GEOGRAPHIC RESTRICTIONS:
Los Angeles County, California.

FINANCIAL DATA:
Amount of support per award: Nonprofit
Organization Grants: Generally $75,000 to
$100,000; Scholarships: Generally $250 to
$15,000; Fellowship for Visual Artists
Awards: $15,000 to $20,000.

Total amount of support: $164,000,000 for
the year 2013.

COOPERATIVE FUNDING PROGRAMS: Building a
Lifetime of Options and Opportunities for
Men - BLOOM; Ford Extended Learning
Time Partnership; Los Angeles Preschool
Advocacy Initiative; One Los Angeles, One
Nation Initiative.

NUMBER OF APPLICANTS MOST RECENT YEAR:
584.

NUMBER OF AWARDS: 224.

APPLICATION INFORMATION:
Organizations seeking support from the
Foundation must submit a letter of intent
(LOI) to apply for a grant. Information about
how to apply can be found on the web site.

Duration: Generally two years.
Deadline: Varies.

PUBLICATIONS:
Annual report; biannual newsletter;
application form; application guidelines;
philanthropic white papers; fund brochures.

IRS IDENTIFICATION NUMBER: 95-3510055

STAFF:
Antonia Hernandez, President and Chief
Executive Officer
William C. Choi, General Counsel

BOARD OF DIRECTORS:
Cynthia Ann Telles, Ph.D., Chairperson
Tom Unterman, Chairperson-elect
James Berliner
Louise Henry Bryson
Dr. Patrick Dowling
David W. Fleming
Meloni M. Hallock
Preston L.C. Johnson
Joanne Corday Kozberg
Melvin D. Lindsey
Todd Quinn
Paul Schulz
Jean Bixby Smith
Melanie Staggs
Catherine L. Unger
Fidel Vargas
Sonia Marie De Leon de Vega
Ronald T. Vera
Marie Brooks Washington

*PLEASE NOTE:
Online applications are preferred, though
hard copies are accepted.

CALLAWAY FOUNDATION, INC. [1193]
209 Broome Street
LaGrange, GA 30240
(706) 884-7348
Fax: (706) 884-0201

E-MAIL ADDRESS:
hsburdette@callawayfoundation.org

WEB SITE ADDRESS:
www.callawayfoundation.org

FOUNDED: 1943

AREAS OF INTEREST:
Charitable, religious and educational
interests.

TYPE:
Capital grants; Challenge/matching grants;
Matching gifts. Matching grants focus on
construction.

YEAR PROGRAM STARTED: 1943

PURPOSE:
To improve the quality of life in the city of
LaGrange and Troup County, Georgia.

LEGAL BASIS:
Private foundation.

ELIGIBILITY:
Eligible organizations must be IRS 501(c)(3).
Each application is considered on its merits.

GEOGRAPHIC RESTRICTIONS:
City of LaGrange and Troup County,
Georgia.

FINANCIAL DATA:
Amount of support per award: Varies.
Total amount of support: Varies.

NUMBER OF APPLICANTS MOST RECENT YEAR:
500.

NUMBER OF AWARDS: Varies.

REPRESENTATIVE AWARDS:
$3,000,000 to LaGrange College; $450,000
to Downtown LaGrange Development
Authority; $155,000 to Lafayette Society for
Performing Arts.

APPLICATION INFORMATION:
Applicants may submit a written proposal
and must include a copy of the IRS tax
determination letter.
Duration: Varies.
Deadline: March 31, June 30, September 30
and December 31.

PUBLICATIONS:
Annual report.

IRS IDENTIFICATION NUMBER: 58-0566147

ADDRESS INQUIRIES TO:
H. Speer Burdette, III
President and General Manager
(See address above.)

CAPITAL REGION COMMUNITY FOUNDATION [1194]
330 Marshall Street
Suite 300
Lansing, MI 48912
(517) 272-2870
Fax: (517) 272-2871

E-MAIL ADDRESS:
ppasch@crcfoundation.org

WEB SITE ADDRESS:
crcfoundation.org

FOUNDED: 1987

AREAS OF INTEREST:
Education, environment, health care, human
services, humanities and youth.

TYPE:
Capital grants; Challenge/matching grants;
Development grants; General operating
grants; Project/program grants; Scholarships;
Seed money grants.

YEAR PROGRAM STARTED: 1989

PURPOSE:
To build a permanent endowment; to meet
charitable needs in the tri-county area.

LEGAL BASIS:
Community foundation.

ELIGIBILITY:
Eligible organizations must be IRS 501(c)(3)
tax-exempt and be located in the tri-county
area.

GEOGRAPHIC RESTRICTIONS:
Clinton, Eaton and Ingham counties,
Michigan.

FINANCIAL DATA:
Amount of support per award: $2,000 to
$15,000.
Total amount of support: Varies.

APPLICATION INFORMATION:
Application information is available on the
web site.
Duration: One year. No renewals.
Deadline: March 1.

PUBLICATIONS:
Annual report; grant guidelines.

IRS IDENTIFICATION NUMBER: 38-2776652

ADDRESS INQUIRIES TO:
Pauline Pasch, Senior Program Officer
(See address above.)

CAPITOL FEDERAL FOUNDATION [1195]

700 South Kansas Avenue, Suite 606
Topeka, KS 66603-3809
(785) 270-6040
(785) 270-6041

WEB SITE ADDRESS:
www.capfed.com/content/site/en/home/community/foundation.html

AREAS OF INTEREST:
Education, community development, the United Way and other charitable purposes.

TYPE:
Project/program grants.

PURPOSE:
To benefit the communities in which Capitol Federal operates; to improve the quality of life in these communities by investing in the citizens of today and tomorrow; to serve as "A Community Cornerstone" within the Bank's marketing areas.

ELIGIBILITY:
Organizations recognized as tax-exempt under Section 501(c)(3) of the Internal Revenue Code. Foundation does not give grants to individuals.

GEOGRAPHIC RESTRICTIONS:
Communities of Emporia, Kansas City, Lawrence, Manhattan, Salina, Topeka and Wichita, Kansas.

FINANCIAL DATA:
Total assets of $94,700,000 for year ended December 31, 2012.
Amount of support per award: Varies.
Total amount of support: $3,200,000 for year ended December 31, 2012.

APPLICATION INFORMATION:
Contact the Foundation for guidelines.
Duration: One year to multiyear.

THE CARPENTER FOUNDATION [1196]

824 East Main Street
Suite 102
Medford, OR 97504
(541) 772-5851
(541) 772-5732
Fax: (541) 773-3970

E-MAIL ADDRESS:
pwilliams@carpenter-foundation.org

WEB SITE ADDRESS:
www.carpenter-foundation.org

FOUNDED: 1958

AREAS OF INTEREST:
Arts, education, human services and public interest issues.

TYPE:
Capital grants; Challenge/matching grants; Demonstration grants; Development grants; General operating grants; Matching gifts; Project/program grants; Scholarships; Technical assistance; Training grants.

YEAR PROGRAM STARTED: 1958

PURPOSE:
To add opportunity, choice, inclusiveness, enrichment and a climate for change for those living in the Rogue Valley. The Foundation works in partnership with other agencies, organizations and public entities.

LEGAL BASIS:
Private family foundation.

ELIGIBILITY:
Grant applications will be accepted only from tax-exempt agencies. No grants are made to individuals. Only one grant per year to any agency is usually considered. The Foundation makes grants only within Jackson and Josephine counties with the exception of a few statewide public interest issues directly affecting persons living in these counties. The Foundation rarely makes multiyear grants, grants for historical applications, hospital construction or equipment, group or individual trips, or activities for religious purposes.

GEOGRAPHIC RESTRICTIONS:
Jackson and Josephine counties, Oregon.

FINANCIAL DATA:
Total assets as of June 30, 2013: $17,811,845.
Amount of support per award: Varies.
Total amount of support: $588,115 in grants for fiscal year ended June 30, 2013.

NUMBER OF APPLICANTS MOST RECENT YEAR: 100.

NUMBER OF AWARDS: 90.

REPRESENTATIVE AWARDS:
Human Services: $15,000 to Boys & Girls Clubs of the Rogue Valley, Grants Pass, OR, in support of a program that provides free dinners and nutrition education to children; Education: $6,000 to Ashland Family YMCA, for support staff to help children in YMCA after-school programs with their homework; Arts: $20,000 to Britt Festivals, Medford, OR, for support for 2010 classical music season; Public Interest: $6,000 to Cascade Community Pool, White City, OR, for staff time to focus on various membership and fund development activities.

APPLICATION INFORMATION:
Cover letter (no more than one page) from the applicant organization summarizing the scope of the project, the amount of the request, and the name, address, telephone number and e-mail address of the person to contact regarding the request is required.

Proposal information (no more than four pages) including:
(1) description of proposal or project, and the community needs or strengths that it addresses;
(2) review of the applicant agency, its purpose and services to the community, its staffing and use of volunteers;
(3) the project budget, showing specifically how the grant funds will be used, as well as other possible funding sources for this project;
(4) description of how the project will be funded in the future (if applicable);
(5) the planning process, staffing and timeline for the project;
(6) result expected and proposed evaluation method and;
(7) any recent independent board fund-raising efforts.

Required attachments (do not staple or clip):
(1) detailed budget for the agency's current year and the year for which the project is proposed (if different);
(2) income statement and balance sheet from the most recently completed fiscal year (or audit, if available); no 990s please;
(3) list of board of directors, occupations and addresses;
(4) approval of the application by the agency's board of directors and;
(5) copy of the IRS exemption letter under Section 501(c)(3).
Duration: One year.
Deadline: Applications are reviewed on a quarterly basis.

ADDRESS INQUIRIES TO:
Polly Williams, Program Officer
Tel: (541) 772-5732 or
(See e-mail address above.)

CATERPILLAR CORPORATE GIVING PROGRAM [1197]

100 N.E. Adams Street
Peoria, IL 61629-1480
(309) 675-1000
Fax: (309) 675-5815

WEB SITE ADDRESS:
www.caterpillar.com/foundation

AREAS OF INTEREST:
Basic human needs, education and environment.

TYPE:
General operating grants; Project/program grants.

PURPOSE:
To support local and community activities where the company has a major manufacturing presence, as well as national organizations.

ELIGIBILITY:
Organizations in areas of company manufacturing operations and classified as 501(c)(3) by the IRS can apply. No grants to individuals and religious organizations.

FINANCIAL DATA:
Amount of support per award: Varies.

APPLICATION INFORMATION:
Applications must be submitted online.
Duration: One year. Grants are renewable.

CATHOLIC CAMPAIGN FOR HUMAN DEVELOPMENT [1198]

3211 4th Street, N.E.
Washington, DC 20017
(202) 541-3210
Fax: (202) 541-3399

E-MAIL ADDRESS:
cchdgrants@usccb.org

WEB SITE ADDRESS:
www.usccb.org/cchd

FOUNDED: 1970

AREAS OF INTEREST:
Humanitarianism.

NAME(S) OF PROGRAMS:
- **Community Development Grant**
- **Economic Development Grant**
- **Strategic National Grant**

TYPE:
Project/program grants.

YEAR PROGRAM STARTED: 1970

PURPOSE:
To address the root causes of poverty by nurturing solidarity between the poor and non-poor and facilitating the participation of people living in poverty.

LEGAL BASIS:
Roman Catholic Church-sponsored funding agency.

ELIGIBILITY:
To qualify for CCHD funds, applicant organizations must not promote, in any way, activities that work against Catholic values. CCHD's grants to local anti-poverty efforts are screened, awarded and monitored in close partnership with local Catholic dioceses. CCHD grants to groups in a local community require the explicit approval of the Bishop of that diocese.

GEOGRAPHIC RESTRICTIONS:
United States and territories.

FINANCIAL DATA:
Amount of support per award: $25,000 to $75,000.
Total amount of support: Up to $9,000,000 for the year 2013-14.

NUMBER OF APPLICANTS MOST RECENT YEAR: 650.

NUMBER OF AWARDS: 300.

APPLICATION INFORMATION:
Contact CCHD for guidelines.
Duration: Up to six years.
Deadline: Proposals accepted on a rolling basis.

ADDRESS INQUIRIES TO:
Grants Administrator
(See address above.)

CENTRAL INDIANA COMMUNITY FOUNDATION [1199]
615 North Alabama Street
Suite 119
Indianapolis, IN 46204
(317) 634-2423
Fax: (317) 684-0943

E-MAIL ADDRESS:
info@cicf.org

WEB SITE ADDRESS:
www.cicf.org

FOUNDED: 1997

AREAS OF INTEREST:
Arts, culture, civic affairs, education, environment, parks, and health and human services.

TYPE:
Capital grants; Endowments; General operating grants; Project/program grants; Research grants; Scholarships; Technical assistance; Training grants.

PURPOSE:
To strengthen Marion and Hamilton counties by attracting charitable endowments; to maximize benefits to donors; to make effective grants; to provide leadership to address community needs by developing productive citizens, building strong neighborhoods, embracing inclusiveness, and promoting community amenities.

LEGAL BASIS:
Community foundation.

ELIGIBILITY:
Grants are made to nonprofit charitable organizations exempt from federal taxation under Section 501(c)(3) of the Internal Revenue Code. Priority is given to programs and projects which expect to have a positive effect on Marion and Hamilton counties.

FINANCIAL DATA:
Amount of support per award: $250 to $1,000,000.
Total amount of support: Varies.

APPLICATION INFORMATION:
Contact the program officer prior to submitting a proposal.
Duration: One year.
Deadline: Varies.

PUBLICATIONS:
Annual report; newsletter.

IRS IDENTIFICATION NUMBER: 35-1793630

ADDRESS INQUIRIES TO:
Julie Wright
Grants and Scholarship Coordinator
(See address above.)

CENTRAL MINNESOTA COMMUNITY FOUNDATION [1200]
101 7th Avenue South, No. 100
St. Cloud, MN 56301
(320) 253-4380
(877) 253-4380
Fax: (320) 240-9215

E-MAIL ADDRESS:
slorenz@communitygiving.org

WEB SITE ADDRESS:
www.communitygiving.org

FOUNDED: 1985

AREAS OF INTEREST:
Philanthropy to support arts and culture, education, environment, youth and families, and human services.

TYPE:
Challenge/matching grants; Conferences/seminars; General operating grants; Project/program grants; Scholarships; Seed money grants; Technical assistance. Assistance to organizations working to strengthen youth and families through recognition and appreciation of diversity.

PURPOSE:
To attract and administer funds to improve the quality of life for citizens of central Minnesota.

LEGAL BASIS:
Community foundation.

ELIGIBILITY:
Eligible organizations must be IRS 501(c)(3) tax-exempt and located within Benton, Sherburne and Stearns counties, Minnesota. Funding to religious organizations of a nonsectarian nature, which benefits the entire community. No grants to individuals.

GEOGRAPHIC RESTRICTIONS:
Benton, Sherburne and Stearns counties, Minnesota.

FINANCIAL DATA:
$85,000,000 in assets as of December 30, 2012.
Amount of support per award: Average: $5,000.

Total amount of support: $4,218,863 in grants paid as of June 30, 2012.

APPLICATION INFORMATION:
Applicants may use the Minnesota Common Grant application (online form only) and must include a copy of the IRS 501(c)(3) tax determination letter.
Duration: One year.
Deadline: Varies; contact the Foundation for program deadlines.

PUBLICATIONS:
Annual report; application guidelines.

IRS IDENTIFICATION NUMBER: 36-3412544

ADDRESS INQUIRIES TO:
Susan Lorenz, Director of Programs
(See address above.)

CENTRAL NEW YORK COMMUNITY FOUNDATION [1201]
431 East Fayette Street
Suite 100
Syracuse, NY 13202-3314
(315) 422-9538
Fax: (315) 471-6031

E-MAIL ADDRESS:
jeberle@cnycf.org
info@cnycf.org

WEB SITE ADDRESS:
www.cnycf.org

FOUNDED: 1927

AREAS OF INTEREST:
Literacy, capacity building, sabbaticals for nonprofit executives, and classroom leadership.

TYPE:
Capital grants; Project/program grants; Seed money grants; Training grants. Grants to help provide training to develop leadership and grantwriting skills and to help build neighborhood stability. Grants also help participants learn from each other and become keenly aware of the level of need in the community.

PURPOSE:
To identify and initiate effective, creative actions which enrich the community by receiving, managing and disbursing charitable funds.

LEGAL BASIS:
Community foundation.

ELIGIBILITY:
Applicants must be tax-exempt, 501(c)(3) not-for-profit organizations in Madison and Onondaga counties which will fund innovative programs that address unmet community needs.

The Foundation encourages proposals that:
(1) suggest practical solutions to community problems;
(2) promote cooperation among not-for-profits without duplicating existing services;
(3) generate community support, both professional and volunteer;
(4) strengthen the organization's effectiveness or stability;
(5) demonstrate the organization's ability to secure realistic funding and;
(6) address prevention as well as remediation.

The Foundation does not make grants for annual operating budgets, endowments, sectarian purposes, loans or assistance to individuals, medical or academic research except when directed by donor, or activities that occurred before the Community Foundation's decision date.

GEOGRAPHIC RESTRICTIONS:
Madison and Onondaga counties, New York.

FINANCIAL DATA:
Amount of support per award: Varies.

APPLICATION INFORMATION:
Standard application forms are available. Foundation staff is available to answer questions or discuss with any prospective applicant the appropriateness of a request.
Duration: Varies.
Deadline: July, September and April.

PUBLICATIONS:
Annual report.

OFFICERS:
Peter A. Dunn, President and Chief Executive Officer
Mary Meyer, Esq., Senior Vice President, Finance and Operations
John G. Eberle, Vice President, Grants and Community Initiatives
Gay M. Pomeroy, Esq., Counsel

ADDRESS INQUIRIES TO:
John G. Eberle
Vice President, Grants and Community Initiatives
(See address above.)

THE CH FOUNDATION

P.O. Box 94038
Lubbock, TX 79493-4038
(806) 792-0448
Fax: (806) 792-7824

E-MAIL ADDRESS:
ksanford@chfoundation.com

WEB SITE ADDRESS:
www.chfoundationlubbock.com

TYPE:
Capital grants; Project/program grants.

See entry 2117 for full listing.

HARRY CHAPIN FOUNDATION [1202]

16 Gerard Street
Huntington, NY 11743
(631) 423-7558
Fax: (631) 423-7596

E-MAIL ADDRESS:
harrychapinfound@aol.com

WEB SITE ADDRESS:
www.harrychapinfoundation.org

FOUNDED: 1981

AREAS OF INTEREST:
Community education, arts-in-education, agriculture and environment.

TYPE:
Challenge/matching grants; General operating grants.

YEAR PROGRAM STARTED: 1981

PURPOSE:
To address the problems of the disadvantaged and promote educational programs that lead to a greater understanding of human suffering.

ELIGIBILITY:
Only programs operating in the U.S. will be funded. Applicants must be 501(c)(3)

nonprofit. Complete description of focus areas is available on the Foundation web site. No grants to individuals.

GEOGRAPHIC RESTRICTIONS:
United States.

FINANCIAL DATA:
Amount of support per award: Up to $10,000.

NUMBER OF APPLICANTS MOST RECENT YEAR:
More than 200.

NUMBER OF AWARDS: 20 for the year 2011.

APPLICATION INFORMATION:
Application should be made in a brief written proposal to Ms. Leslie Ramme, Executive Director, at the HCF Office. HCF also accepts the New York/New Jersey Area Common Grant Application Form.
Duration: One year. Must reapply.
Deadline: Applications are accepted on an ongoing basis.

EXECUTIVE DIRECTOR:
Leslie Ramme

ADDRESS INQUIRIES TO:
Leslie Ramme, Executive Director
(See address above.)

CHARLESTON AREA CHARITABLE FOUNDATION [1203]

c/o Gilbert, Metzger & Madigan
P.O. Box 677
Charleston, IL 61920
(217) 345-2128
Fax: (217) 345-2315

AREAS OF INTEREST:
Community and education.

TYPE:
Grants-in-aid; Project/program grants.

PURPOSE:
To enhance and support the quality of life in Charleston, IL area.

ELIGIBILITY:
Grants are made to organizations that have tax-exempt status under Section 501(c)(3) of the Internal Revenue Code. No grants are made to individuals.

GEOGRAPHIC RESTRICTIONS:
Charleston, Illinois and surrounding area.

FINANCIAL DATA:
Amount of support per award: Grants vary in amount, depending upon the needs and nature of the request.
Total amount of support: Varies.

APPLICATION INFORMATION:
Applicants must submit a brief letter outlining the purpose of the grant.
Duration: One-time grants.
Deadline: Quarterly; two weeks prior to Board meetings to be held in February, May, August and November.

ADDRESS INQUIRIES TO:
Michael Metzger, President
(See address above.)

THE CHAUTAUQUA REGION COMMUNITY FOUNDATION [1204]

418 Spring Street
Jamestown, NY 14701
(716) 661-3390
Fax: (716) 488-0387

E-MAIL ADDRESS:
rsweeney@crcfonline.org

WEB SITE ADDRESS:
www.crcfonline.org

FOUNDED: 1978

AREAS OF INTEREST:
Community.

NAME(S) OF PROGRAMS:
● Axel W. Carlson Award
● John D. Hamilton Community Service Award

TYPE:
Awards/prizes; Capital grants; Challenge/matching grants; Matching gifts; Project/program grants; Scholarships; Seed money grants; Technical assistance; Training grants. Axel W. Carlson Award has been a tribute to the unsung heroes of our community. These individuals have made significant contributions through their efforts while neither receiving nor expecting reward or recognition.

The John D. Hamilton Community Service Award recognizes an individual's dedication, leadership and support in furthering community spirit and enhancing the quality of life in the Chautauqua Community.

YEAR PROGRAM STARTED: 1978

PURPOSE:
To enrich the quality of life in the Chautauqua region.

LEGAL BASIS:
501(c)(3).

GEOGRAPHIC RESTRICTIONS:
Chautauqua region, New York.

FINANCIAL DATA:
Amount of support per award: Varies.
Total amount of support: $2,500,000.
Matching fund requirements: Varies depending on the request.

NUMBER OF APPLICANTS MOST RECENT YEAR:
1,752.

NUMBER OF AWARDS: 1,649.

APPLICATION INFORMATION:
Nominations are to be submitted by letter or e-mail, with the full name, address and detailed explanation of that person's contributions and accomplishments, along with an explanation of why the nominee is deserving of the award. If the nominator is uncertain if they should submit the nomination or has additional questions, please contact the office via telephone for clarification.
Duration: One calendar year.
Deadline: Carlson Award: March 1; Hamilton Award: April.

PUBLICATIONS:
Annual report; newsletters; scholarship booklet.

IRS IDENTIFICATION NUMBER: 16-1116837

STAFF:
Randall J. Sweeney, Executive Director
Sarah M. Marciniak, Communications Officer
Jacob S. Schrantz, Fiscal Officer
Bev Lubi, Fund Development Officer
June C. Diethrick, Operations Officer
Lisa W. Lynde, Program Officer
Kase Kinney, Program Associate

ADDRESS INQUIRIES TO:
Randall J. Sweeney, Executive Director
(See address above.)

CHESTER COUNTY COMMUNITY FOUNDATION [1205]

28 West Market Street
West Chester, PA 19382
(610) 696-8211
Fax: (610) 696-8213

E-MAIL ADDRESS:
info@chescocf.org

WEB SITE ADDRESS:
www.chescocf.org

FOUNDED: 1994

AREAS OF INTEREST:
Quality of life in the Chester County, Pennsylvania area.

TYPE:
Capital grants; Challenge/matching grants; General operating grants; Grants-in-aid; Project/program grants; Scholarships.

YEAR PROGRAM STARTED: 1994

PURPOSE:
To improve the quality of life in communities within Chester County, Pennsylvania.

LEGAL BASIS:
501(c)(3) public charity.

GEOGRAPHIC RESTRICTIONS:
Primarily Chester County, Pennsylvania.

FINANCIAL DATA:
$30,000,000 in assets.
Amount of support per award: $1,000 to $15,000.
Total amount of support: $1,800,000 for the year 2012.

NUMBER OF APPLICANTS MOST RECENT YEAR:
150 for the year 2012.

NUMBER OF AWARDS: 500 for the year 2012.

APPLICATION INFORMATION:
Information may be obtained from the Foundation web site.
Duration: One year. Renewal by reapplication.
Deadline: Proposals are accepted year-round.

ADDRESS INQUIRIES TO:
Beth Harper Briglia, Vice President of Donor Services and Grantmaking
(See address above.)

THE CHICAGO COMMUNITY TRUST [1206]

225 North Michigan Avenue
Suite 2200
Chicago, IL 60601
(312) 616-8000
Fax: (312) 616-7955

E-MAIL ADDRESS:
sandy@cct.org

WEB SITE ADDRESS:
www.cct.org

FOUNDED: 1915

AREAS OF INTEREST:
The well-being of the residents of Cook County, IL in the fields of health, basic human needs, community development, education, cultural arts, sustainability and the environment.

TYPE:
General operating grants; Project/program grants; Technical assistance. Grants to tax-exempt institutions and organizations for charitable purposes. Special initiatives are developed periodically.

YEAR PROGRAM STARTED: 1915

PURPOSE:
To provide for the broad charitable needs of the community in a manner which will assure response to the most pressing problems of the day.

LEGAL BASIS:
Community foundation.

ELIGIBILITY:
Applicants must be tax-exempt, 501(c)(3) organizations. Funded projects must benefit the residents of Cook County, IL. Some grants are made for the region.

GEOGRAPHIC RESTRICTIONS:
Cook County, Illinois.

FINANCIAL DATA:
Amount of support per award: Varies.
Total amount of support: $177,331,001 for the year 2012.

NUMBER OF APPLICANTS MOST RECENT YEAR:
700 to 800.

APPLICATION INFORMATION:
Applicants must register through the online grant system. Paper letters of inquiry will not be accepted.
Duration: One year.
Deadline: Requests for proposals accepted in March, July and November.

PUBLICATIONS:
Guidelines; annual report.

STAFF:
Terry Mazany, President and Chief Executive Officer

ADDRESS INQUIRIES TO:
Sandy Phelps, Director of Grants Management
(See address above.)

ROBERT STERLING CLARK FOUNDATION [1207]

135 East 64th Street
New York, NY 10065
(212) 288-8900
Fax: (212) 288-1033

E-MAIL ADDRESS:
rscf@rsclark.org

WEB SITE ADDRESS:
www.rsclark.org

FOUNDED: 1952

AREAS OF INTEREST:
Promoting international arts engagement nationally, improving the performance of government agencies in New York City and the state of New York, and protecting reproductive freedom and access to family planning services nationally.

TYPE:
Project/program grants; Research grants.

YEAR PROGRAM STARTED: 1976

PURPOSE:
For cultural institutions and improving performance of government programs.

LEGAL BASIS:
501(c)(3).

ELIGIBILITY:
Applicants must be nonprofit organizations in the U.S.

GEOGRAPHIC RESTRICTIONS:
New York City.

FINANCIAL DATA:
Amount of support per award:
Approximately $15,000 to $120,000.
Total amount of support: Approximately $4,787,000 appropriated for the year 2012.

NUMBER OF APPLICANTS MOST RECENT YEAR:
700.

REPRESENTATIVE AWARDS:
$50,000 to Citizens Committee for Children; $100,000 to National Abortion Federation.

APPLICATION INFORMATION:
Applicant organization must submit budgets (past, current and projected), audited financial statements, IRS letter documenting tax status, names and occupations of trustees, project budget, expectations, plans for evaluations and plans for future support, as well as resumes of key personnel.
Duration: Usually one year.
Deadline: Proposals are accepted throughout the year.

PUBLICATIONS:
Annual report; guidelines.

STAFF:
Laura Wolff, Acting Executive Director and Senior Program Officer
Roslyn Black, Program Officer

BOARD OF DIRECTORS:
James Allen Smith, Chairman
Clara Miller, Treasurer
Paul Dolan
Philip Li
Julie Muraco
John Hoyt Stookey

ADDRESS INQUIRIES TO:
Laura Wolff, Senior Program Officer
(See address above.)

THE CLEVELAND FOUNDATION [1208]

1422 Euclid Avenue
Suite 1300
Cleveland, OH 44115-2001
(216) 861-3810
Fax: (216) 861-1729

E-MAIL ADDRESS:
grantsmgmt@clevefdn.org

WEB SITE ADDRESS:
www.clevelandfoundation.org

FOUNDED: 1914

AREAS OF INTEREST:
Economic development in advanced energy and international relations, public education reform, neighborhood and housing, human services and youth development strengthening the quality of life in early childhood, strengthening the arts and cultural community and greater university circle.

TYPE:
Awards/prizes; Project/program grants; Research grants; Scholarships.

YEAR PROGRAM STARTED: 1914

PURPOSE:
To enhance the quality of life for all citizens of greater Cleveland, now and for generations to come, by building endowment, addressing needs through grantmaking and providing leadership on key community issues.

LEGAL BASIS:
Community foundation.

ELIGIBILITY:
Grantmaking is restricted to programs and services in the Greater Cleveland community, Cuyahoga, Geauga and Lake counties. Requests are considered from tax-exempt agencies in the following areas: civic affairs, economic development, education, health, social services, arts and culture, and environment. Careful consideration is given to such criteria as benefit the entire community and applicant's ability to successfully carry out the proposed activity. Applicant must be a nonprofit organization.

Giving is limited to the Greater Cleveland area unless specified by the donor. No grants to individuals or religious institutions for religious purposes. No support for community services such as fire and police protection, fund-raising campaigns, memberships and travel. No support for publications or audiovisual materials unless they are an integral part of a key program. Capital support for buildings, major equipment, land or renovation is only provided when there is strong evidence that the project has high priority for the community.

GEOGRAPHIC RESTRICTIONS:
Greater Cleveland, Cuyahoga, Geauga and Lake counties, Ohio.

FINANCIAL DATA:
Amount of support per award: $200 to $4,000,000; average $50,000.
Total amount of support: $85,000,000 annually.
Matching fund requirements: Depending upon proposal, grants may be authorized contingent upon receipt of matching funds from agency's own or other sources.

COOPERATIVE FUNDING PROGRAMS: Fund for Our Economic Future; Literacy Cooperative of Greater Cleveland.

APPLICATION INFORMATION:
The Foundation requires organizations to submit inquiries and applications electronically. Guidelines can be found on the web site.
Duration: Usually one year.

PUBLICATIONS:
Annual report; *Giving Voice*, quarterly; Grantee e-newsletter.

IRS IDENTIFICATION NUMBER: 34-0714588

COASTAL COMMUNITY FOUNDATION OF SOUTH CAROLINA [1209]
635 Rutledge Avenue
Suite 201
Charleston, SC 29403
(843) 723-3635
Fax: (843) 577-3671

E-MAIL ADDRESS:
info@coastalcommunityfoundation.org

WEB SITE ADDRESS:
www.coastalcommunityfoundation.org

FOUNDED: 1974

AREAS OF INTEREST:
Community development, health, education, human needs, environment and arts.

TYPE:
Awards/prizes; Challenge/matching grants; Endowments; Project/program grants; Scholarships; Technical assistance; Training grants.

ELIGIBILITY:
Generally, applicants must be charitable 501(c)(3) organizations in Beaufort, Berkeley, Charleston, Colleton, Dorchester, Georgetown, Hampton and Jasper counties, South Carolina.

GEOGRAPHIC RESTRICTIONS:
Coastal South Carolina.

FINANCIAL DATA:
Amount of support per award: Generally $10,000 maximum.
Total amount of support: Varies.

APPLICATION INFORMATION:
Application and instructions are available online.
Duration: Varies.
Deadline: Varies.

THE COLUMBUS FOUNDATION [1210]
1234 East Broad Street
Columbus, OH 43205
(614) 251-4000
Fax: (614) 251-4009

E-MAIL ADDRESS:
info@columbusfoundation.org

WEB SITE ADDRESS:
www.columbusfoundation.org

FOUNDED: 1943

AREAS OF INTEREST:
Advancing philanthropy, arts and humanities, urban affairs, conservation, education, health and social services.

NAME(S) OF PROGRAMS:
- **Community Improvement Project**
- **Fund for Financial Innovation**
- **Fund for Innovative Operations**
- **Fund for Targeted Needs**

TYPE:
Grants-in-aid; Project/program grants. The Foundation awards competitive grants from the unrestricted and field-of-interest funds created by donors.

The Community Improvement Project supports a concentrated initiative to advance progress over a longer term in an identified area of community need.

The Fund for Financial Innovation will support nonprofit leaders and their organizations to adapt to the new economic reality.

The Fund for Innovative Operations addresses significant needs of local organizations through grants supporting continuous improvement, capacity-building, and arts and cultural efforts.

The Fund for Targeted Needs addresses basic needs, disadvantaged children, developmental disabilities (traditional grants program), as well as more narrow and specific grant programs.

YEAR PROGRAM STARTED: 1943

PURPOSE:
To provide a pool of charitable funds for the development of community programs and services and to offer various ways of giving for citizens who wish to benefit the community.

LEGAL BASIS:
Community foundation, exempt under Section 501(c)(3) of the Internal Revenue Code.

ELIGIBILITY:
Organizations in the central Ohio region having recognition under Section 501(c)(3) of the Internal Revenue Code. No grants are made to individuals.

GEOGRAPHIC RESTRICTIONS:
Primarily Franklin County and surrounding area.

FINANCIAL DATA:
Amount of support per award: $250 to $1,250,000.
Total amount of support: Varies.

REPRESENTATIVE AWARDS:
Capacity Building and Leadership Grants: $6,000 to Jeanne B. McCoy Community Center for the Arts Corporation to support the fund-raising planning component of the business plan; Innovative Operations-Continuous Improvement: $273,500 to Ohio Association of Second Harvest Foodbanks to support overall operations; Basic Needs: $95,000 to Community Shelter Board to support general operating expenses to address homelessness.

APPLICATION INFORMATION:
Those seeking grants may submit a Letter of Intent or a Full Proposal to the Foundation by accessing its online grant application system through its web site.
Duration: Typically one year.
Deadline: Varies.

PUBLICATIONS:
Annual yearbook; application guidelines.

IRS IDENTIFICATION NUMBER: 31-6044264

STAFF:
Douglas F. Kridler, President and Chief Executive Officer
Lisa S. Courtice, Ph.D., Executive Vice President, Community Research and Grants Management
Raymond J. Biddiscombe, Senior Vice President, Finance and Administration

ADDRESS INQUIRIES TO:
Melissa Neely
Grants Management Administrator
(See address above.)

COLUMBUS JEWISH FOUNDATION [1211]
Robins Center for Philanthropy
1175 College Avenue
Columbus, OH 43209
(614) 338-2365
Fax: (614) 338-2361

E-MAIL ADDRESS:
jjacobs@tcjf.org

WEB SITE ADDRESS:
www.columbusjewishfoundation.org

FOUNDED: 1955

AREAS OF INTEREST:
Jewish education, Jewish leadership development and the preservation of the integrity of the Jewish family.

TYPE:
Challenge/matching grants; Demonstration grants; Seed money grants.

YEAR PROGRAM STARTED: 1955

PURPOSE:
To develop sustainable financial resources to fulfill the Foundation's mission to ensure

continuity of Jewish life and to meet changing needs locally, in Israel, and in our worldwide community.

LEGAL BASIS:
Public charity.

ELIGIBILITY:
Applicants must be 501(c)(3) organizations. Money will be designated for pilot projects or as seed money only. Particular emphasis on central Ohio Jewish organizations.

No grants to individuals. No operating support.

FINANCIAL DATA:
Amount of support per award: Varies depending on needs and nature of the request.

Total amount of support: $386,000.

COOPERATIVE FUNDING PROGRAMS: The Foundation prefers to set up networks for funding with other organizations.

NUMBER OF APPLICANTS MOST RECENT YEAR: 27.

NUMBER OF AWARDS: 22.

REPRESENTATIVE AWARDS:
$60,000 to Columbus Jewish Federation for 2013 Community Population Study; $5,000 to Mental Health America of Franklin County for pro bono counseling.

APPLICATION INFORMATION:
Formal request forms are available from the Foundation.

PUBLICATIONS:
Annual report; guidelines.

IRS IDENTIFICATION NUMBER: 31-1384772

OFFICERS:
Steven Schottenstein, President
Jeff Meyer, Vice President and President-Elect
Randall Arndt, Vice President
Denise Glimcher, Vice President
Harlan Robins, Treasurer
William Byers, Assistant Treasurer
Nevada Smith, Secretary
Michael Schlonsky, Assistant Secretary

ADDRESS INQUIRIES TO:
Susan Tanur, Director of Grants
E-mail: stanur@tcjf.org
(See address above.)

COMMON COUNSEL FOUNDATION [1212]

405 14th Street, Suite 809
Oakland, CA 94612
(510) 834-2995
Fax: (510) 834-2998

E-MAIL ADDRESS:
info@commoncounsel.org

WEB SITE ADDRESS:
www.commoncounsel.org

FOUNDED: 1988

AREAS OF INTEREST:
Economic, environmental and social justice.

TYPE:
General operating grants; Training grants; Travel grants.

PURPOSE:
To offer strategic philanthropic advisory services to donors and family foundations while serving the community at large.

ELIGIBILITY:
501(c)(3) nonprofit organizations. Religious organizations must be working in interfaith coalitions. Grants are not made to individuals. Also, must involve low- and moderate-income members in grassroots community organizing to bring about long-term policy change. Organizational budget must be $400,000 or less except for the small Grassroots Exchange Fund (travel grants), which considers requests from organizations with budgets up to $1,000,000 (higher priority is given to those with budgets less than $750,000).

FINANCIAL DATA:
Amount of support per award: Travel and training grants: $500 to $1,000 with an average of approximately $800; General operating grants: $5,000 to $15,000.

COOPERATIVE FUNDING PROGRAMS: Abelard Foundation West; Acorn Foundation; Penney Family Fund; Victor and Lorraine Honig Fund; Grassroots Exchange Fund; Social and Economic Justice Fund.

NUMBER OF APPLICANTS MOST RECENT YEAR: 280.

APPLICATION INFORMATION:
Applicant should submit a letter of inquiry. Full proposals for most of the Funds are by invitation only.

Deadline: January 15 and June 15 (or February through November for Grassroots Exchange Fund).

THE COMMUNITY FOUNDATION [1213]

7501 Boulders View Drive, Suite 110
Richmond, VA 23225-4047
(804) 330-7400
Fax: (804) 330-5992

E-MAIL ADDRESS:
info@tcfrichmond.org

WEB SITE ADDRESS:
www.tcfrichmond.org

FOUNDED: 1968

AREAS OF INTEREST:
Children, families, communities, health care, education and arts.

NAME(S) OF PROGRAMS:
● **Garland and Agnes Taylor Gray Foundation**
● **The Jenkins Foundation: Improving the Health of Greater Richmond**
● **Medarva Foundation Fund**
● **R.E.B. Awards for Teaching Excellence**
● **Sheltering Arms Fund**

TYPE:
Project/program grants; Scholarships. Competitive grants.

YEAR PROGRAM STARTED: 1968

PURPOSE:
To improve life for generations of children; to improve public education; to support innovative health care projects.

LEGAL BASIS:
Charitable trust.

ELIGIBILITY:
Proposals are accepted from charitable 501(c)(3) organizations serving residents of Greater Richmond and/or the Tri-Cities.

GEOGRAPHIC RESTRICTIONS:
Richmond and central Virginia.

FINANCIAL DATA:
Amount of support per award: Varies.
Total amount of support: Varies.

APPLICATION INFORMATION:
Guidelines and application forms are available on the web site.
Duration: Typically one year.
Deadline: Varies per program.

PUBLICATIONS:
Annual report.

OFFICERS:
Farhad Aghdami, Chairman

ADDRESS INQUIRIES TO:
Susan Hallett, Vice President, Programs
(See address above.)

COMMUNITY FOUNDATION FOR GREATER ATLANTA, INC. [1214]

50 Hurt Plaza, Suite 449
Atlanta, GA 30303
(404) 688-5525
Fax: (404) 688-3060

E-MAIL ADDRESS:
nbattle@cfgreateratlanta.org

WEB SITE ADDRESS:
www.cfgreateratlanta.org

FOUNDED: 1951

AREAS OF INTEREST:
Operational grants to nonprofits serving a 23-county region in Georgia.

NAME(S) OF PROGRAMS:
● **Arts Fund**
● **Common Good**
● **Grants to Green**
● **Neighborhood Fund**

TYPE:
General operating grants; Project/program grants; Scholarships; Technical assistance; Training grants. Project/program grants are for community development only.

YEAR PROGRAM STARTED: 1951

PURPOSE:
To strengthen private philanthropy and promote the well-being of the people of the metropolitan Atlanta community.

LEGAL BASIS:
501(c)(3) community foundation.

ELIGIBILITY:
Applicant organizations must have 501(c)(3) status. Project must be within the metropolitan Atlanta area. Request for funding may not exceed 10% of organization's operational budget. For general operation grants, organization must have an operating budget of $100,000.

No grants to individuals.

GEOGRAPHIC RESTRICTIONS:
23 counties in the metropolitan Atlanta area.

FINANCIAL DATA:
Amount of support per award: Maximum $75,000.
Total amount of support: $6,429,107.13 in competitive grants for 2013.

NUMBER OF APPLICANTS MOST RECENT YEAR: 300 for discretionary monies.

NUMBER OF AWARDS: 75 discretionary grants.

APPLICATION INFORMATION:
Grant application guidelines available from the Foundation. Initial approach by letter or phone.

Duration: No grants are awarded on a continuing basis. Generally, grants are one year. Common Good grants can be up to two years.

Deadline: Arts Fund and Common Good: May; Grants: February and October.

PUBLICATIONS:
Annual report; policy and application guidelines.

OFFICERS:
Christie Brown, Chief Operating Officer
Alicia Philipp, President
Benjamin T. White, Assistant Secretary and Legal Counsel

BOARD MEMBERS:
Suzanne E. Boas, Chairperson
Kenneth L. Bernhardt
Becky Blalock
Kenneth F. Britt
Robert L. Brown
Ann W. Cramer
Edward S. Croft, III
Brian C. Friedman
Carol W. Hatfield
Dr. Sivan Hines
Ms. Lynn Huntley
Tad Hutcheson
Donata Russell Major
Michael A. Nadal
Roger Chip Patterson, Jr.
Katy Pattillo
Prof. Jagdish N. Sheth, Ph.D.
Benjamin T. White, Legal Counsel

ADDRESS INQUIRIES TO:
Natasha Battle-Edwards, Grants Manager
(See address above.)

COMMUNITY FOUNDATION FOR GREATER BUFFALO [1215]

726 Exchange Street
Suite 525
Buffalo, NY 14210
(716) 852-2857
Fax: (716) 852-2861

E-MAIL ADDRESS:
mail@cfgb.org

WEB SITE ADDRESS:
www.cfgb.org

FOUNDED: 1919

TYPE:
Grants-in-aid; Scholarships. Grants to organizations in the eight counties of western New York state.

YEAR PROGRAM STARTED: 1919

PURPOSE:
To connect people, ideas and resources to improve lives in western New York state. The four focus areas of the Foundation are:
(1) to improve educational achievement for low-income students;
(2) to increase racial/ethnic equity;
(3) to enhance and leverage significant natural resources and;
(4) to strengthen the region as a center for architecture, arts and culture.

LEGAL BASIS:
Community trust; 501(c)(3) tax determination; public charity under Section 170(b)(1)(a)(vi).

ELIGIBILITY:
Programs and agencies must benefit residents of the eight counties of western New York state.

GEOGRAPHIC RESTRICTIONS:
8 counties of western New York state.

FINANCIAL DATA:
Amount of support per award: $3,000 to $50,000 in 2013.

Total amount of support: $426,958.

NUMBER OF APPLICANTS MOST RECENT YEAR:
143 for the year 2013.

NUMBER OF AWARDS: 22.

REPRESENTATIVE AWARDS:
Boys and Girls Club of Buffalo; Buffalo Museum of Science; Buffalo Niagara Riverkeeper; Dale Association; Forest Lawn Heritage Foundation; Genesee-Orleans Regional Arts Council.

APPLICATION INFORMATION:
Application information is available on the web site.

Deadline: Letters of Intent accepted from January 1 to February 3. Selected Letters of Intent invited to submit a full proposal by April 18. Applicants notified in mid-June.

STAFF:
Clotilde Perez-Bode Dedecker, President/Chief Executive Officer
Gerald Reger, Chief Financial Officer/Chief Administrative Officer
Cara Matteliano, Vice President, Community Impact
Jean McKeown, Vice President, Community Impact
Myra Lawrence, Vice President, Finance
Betsy Constantine, Vice President, Giving Strategies
Meg Auerbach, Esq., Foundation Counsel
Colleen Becht, Controller
Kristin Cipollone, Ph.D., Knowledge Management Officer
Justine David, Program Associate
Jillian Fiorella, Director, Communications and Branding
Linda Gallagher, Accountant
Erin Gorton, Client Relations Associate
Kristen Kaszubowski, Environmental Communications Coordinator
Roxanne Linton, Accountant
Kate Masiello, Director, Client Relations
Alaska McInnis, Scholarship Officer
Holly Mergenhagen, Esq., Giving Strategies Analyst
Jane Mogavero, Esq., Director, Client Relations
Darren Penoyer, Program Officer
Elaine Rowland, Client Relations Associate

BOARD OF DIRECTORS:
Melissa Baumgart
James Biltekoff
Gary Brost
Valerie DeBerry
Elizabeth Diachun
Ross Eckert
Larry Franco
Scott Gardner
Danis J. Gehl, Ph.D.
William Joyce
Gerard Mazurkiewicz, C.P.A.
John Mitchell
Alex Montante
Gary L. Mucci
Alphonso O'Neil-White
Jennifer J. Parker, J.D.
Anne Saldanha, M.D.
Katie Schneider
Richard Stockton, Ph.D.
Marsha Joy Sullivan
Francisco Vasquez, Ph.D.
John Walsh, III

ADDRESS INQUIRIES TO:
Darren Penoyer, Program Officer
(See address above.)

THE COMMUNITY FOUNDATION FOR GREATER NEW HAVEN [1216]

70 Audubon Street
New Haven, CT 06510
(203) 777-2386
Fax: (203) 787-6584

E-MAIL ADDRESS:
contactus@cfgnh.org

WEB SITE ADDRESS:
www.cfgnh.org

FOUNDED: 1928

AREAS OF INTEREST:
Health, education, community development, regional and economic development, arts and culture, youth, environment, and food and shelter.

TYPE:
Capital grants; General operating grants; Matching gifts; Project/program grants; Scholarships. Capacity building grants. Support for youth and welfare agencies, social services, hospitals and health agencies, educational institutions, community funds and the humanities, including music and art, to organizations serving the residents of greater New Haven.

LEGAL BASIS:
Community foundation established in Connecticut by Resolution and Declaration of Trust.

ELIGIBILITY:
The Foundation welcomes grant requests from greater New Haven area organizations that are defined as tax-exempt under Section 501(c)(3) or any applicable statute of the Internal Revenue Code. While grants are occasionally made to governmental agencies, local nonprofits receive priority.

GEOGRAPHIC RESTRICTIONS:
Greater New Haven, Connecticut: Ansonia, Bethany, Branford, Cheshire, Derby, East Haven, Guilford, Hamden, Madison, Milford, New Haven, North Branford, North Haven, Orange, Oxford, Seymour, Shelton, Wallingford, West Haven, and Woodbridge.

FINANCIAL DATA:
Amount of support per award: $250 to $100,000.

Total amount of support: Varies.

NUMBER OF APPLICANTS MOST RECENT YEAR:
1,188.

NUMBER OF AWARDS: 1,098.

REPRESENTATIVE AWARDS:
$35,000 to Housatonic Valley Association to support the stewardship manager position and to support the stream teams; $32,000 to Literacy Volunteers of Greater New Haven to support increasing the level of outreach to parents of school-age children in New Haven public schools and to provide literacy tutoring to at least 80 parents so they will participate more fully in their child's education; $18,000 to Downtown Evening Soup Kitchen to provide 28,000 free, nutritious meals to the homeless, unemployed, and working poor seven days a week, as well as to provide 4,000 bags of groceries to families on an emergency basis.

APPLICATION INFORMATION:
Nonprofit organizations that have been certified by the IRS as charitable organizations are encouraged to contact the Foundation staff to discuss a program and its funding requirements. If a strong need is shown in an area of concern to the region served by the Foundation, the applicant is encouraged to apply. Additional information is available on the Foundation web site.
Duration: One year with multiyears considered annually.
Deadline: Varies from year to year.

PUBLICATIONS:
Annual report; grant guidelines; newsletters.

IRS IDENTIFICATION NUMBER: 06-6032106

STAFF:
William W. Ginsberg, President and Chief Executive Officer
A.F. Drew Alden, Senior Vice President for Investments, Chief Financial Officer and Chief Compliance Officer

ADDRESS INQUIRIES TO:
Denise Canning, Grants Manager
(See address above.)

THE COMMUNITY FOUNDATION FOR MONTEREY COUNTY   [1217]
2354 Garden Road
Monterey, CA 93940
(831) 375-9712
Fax: (831) 375-4731

E-MAIL ADDRESS:
info@cfmco.org

WEB SITE ADDRESS:
www.cfmco.org/grantsandsupport

AREAS OF INTEREST:
Animal welfare, arts and culture, community services, education, environment, health, historic preservation, social services and technical assistance.

NAME(S) OF PROGRAMS:
• **Community Impact Program**
• **Neighborhood Grants Program**

TYPE:
Capital grants; Challenge/matching grants; Project/program grants; Seed money grants.

PURPOSE:
To increase charitable giving to improve the quality of life for all residents of Monterey County and to strengthen the institutions which help build healthy communities.

LEGAL BASIS:
Community foundation.

ELIGIBILITY:
Community-based, nonprofit organizations whose programs benefit the residents of Monterey County, CA.

The Foundation does not make Community Impact Grants to support individuals, for normal operating costs usually covered by operating income, for endowment funds, to support sectarian religious programs, for annual campaigns, dinners, or special events, to pay off past debts or existing obligations, for scholarships, fellowships or travel grants, or for technical or specialized research.

GEOGRAPHIC RESTRICTIONS:
Monterey County, California.

FINANCIAL DATA:
Amount of support per award: Varies.

Total amount of support: Varies.

APPLICATION INFORMATION:
Detailed guidelines and application form can be obtained at the Foundation web site.
Duration: One year. Reapplication annually.
Deadline: Varies.

ADDRESS INQUIRIES TO:
Senior Program Officer
(See address above.)

THE COMMUNITY FOUNDATION FOR NORTHEAST FLORIDA   [1218]
245 Riverside Avenue
Suite 310
Jacksonville, FL 32202
(904) 356-4483
Fax: (904) 356-7910

E-MAIL ADDRESS:
kshaw@jaxcf.org

WEB SITE ADDRESS:
www.jaxcf.org

AREAS OF INTEREST:
Early childhood, seniors, and the arts.

TYPE:
Project/program grants.

PURPOSE:
To stimulate philanthropy to build a better community.

ELIGIBILITY:
Eligible organizations must be IRS 501(c)(3) tax-exempt.

GEOGRAPHIC RESTRICTIONS:
Baker, Clay, Duval, Nassau and St. Johns counties in northern Florida.

FINANCIAL DATA:
Amount of support per award: Varies.
Total amount of support: Varies.

APPLICATION INFORMATION:
Application information is available on the web site.
Duration: Up to 24 months.
Deadline: Varies.

PUBLICATIONS:
Newsletter; annual report.

STAFF:
John Zell, Vice President, Development
Kathleen Shaw, Vice President, Programs

ADDRESS INQUIRIES TO:
Kathleen Shaw
Vice President of Programs
(See address above.)

COMMUNITY FOUNDATION FOR NORTHEAST GEORGIA   [1219]
6500 Sugarloaf Parkway, Suite 220
Duluth, GA 30097
(770) 813-3380
Fax: (770) 813-3375

E-MAIL ADDRESS:
jwaters@cfneg.org

WEB SITE ADDRESS:
www.cfneg.org

FOUNDED: 1985

AREAS OF INTEREST:
The quality of life in northeast Georgia.

TYPE:
Grants-in-aid.

PURPOSE:
To improve the quality of life throughout northeast Georgia.

ELIGIBILITY:
Grants can be made to tax-exempt private agencies that the IRS classifies as 501(c)(3) organizations, public charities and government agencies. The Foundation will consider organizations that serve people in the areas of education, health and human services, community service and the arts.

GEOGRAPHIC RESTRICTIONS:
Northeast Georgia.

FINANCIAL DATA:
Over $50,000,000 has been granted since inception.
Amount of support per award: Varies.
Total amount of support: More than $3,700,000 in grants for the year 2011.

APPLICATION INFORMATION:
The grant request must be completed according to the standard Grant Proposal Guidelines issued by the Foundation. Application can be downloaded from the web site.
Duration: Typically one year.
Deadline: March 1.

ADDRESS INQUIRIES TO:
Margaret Bugbee, Director of Finance
(See address above.)

COMMUNITY FOUNDATION FOR NORTHEAST MICHIGAN   [1220]
100 North Ripley
Suite F
Alpena, MI 49707
(989) 354-6881
Fax: (989) 356-3319

E-MAIL ADDRESS:
bfrantz@cfnem.org

WEB SITE ADDRESS:
www.cfnem.org

FOUNDED: 1974

AREAS OF INTEREST:
Education, health, youth services, arts and community needs.

TYPE:
Project/program grants. Tobacco-related programs/projects. Women's Giving Circle for issues important to women. Youth-related programs/projects.

YEAR PROGRAM STARTED: 1974

PURPOSE:
To provide resources for community projects.

LEGAL BASIS:
Community foundation.

ELIGIBILITY:
Eligible organizations must be IRS 501(c)(3) tax-exempt, government schools or churches, providing the project is nonsectarian. No grants to individuals.

GEOGRAPHIC RESTRICTIONS:
Alcona, Alpena, Montmorency and Presque Isle counties, Michigan.

FINANCIAL DATA:
Amount of support per award: General Community Common Grant: $3,000; Youth-related programs/projects: $2,500.
Total amount of support: Over $262,000 in grants for fiscal year 2013.

COOPERATIVE FUNDING PROGRAMS:
Collaboration between organizations is encouraged.

NUMBER OF APPLICANTS MOST RECENT YEAR: 174.

NUMBER OF AWARDS: 156.

REPRESENTATIVE AWARDS:
Sunrise Mission, for computer equipment; Northeast Michigan Rehab and Opportunity Center, for renovations; Thunder Bay Arts Council, for programs; Child Abuse and Neglect Team, for baby pantry items; United Way; Schools; etc.

APPLICATION INFORMATION:
Applications must include a copy of the IRS 501(c)(3) determination documentation letter, except for schools, churches and government agencies.
Duration: One year, with the possibility of a six-month extension.
Deadline: Varies. Details are available online.

PUBLICATIONS:
Annual report; biannual newsletter; brochures; application guidelines.

IRS IDENTIFICATION NUMBER: 23-7384822

EXECUTIVE DIRECTOR:
Barbara Frantz

ADDRESS INQUIRIES TO:
For common general applications:
Julie Wiesen, Program Director

For youth-related grants:
Jennifer LaGrow
Youth Advisory Council Coordinator
(See address above.)

COMMUNITY FOUNDATION FOR PALM BEACH AND MARTIN COUNTIES [1221]

700 South Dixie Hwy
Suite 200
West Palm Beach, FL 33401-5854
(561) 659-6800
(888) 853-4438 (Florida only)
Fax: (561) 832-6542

E-MAIL ADDRESS:
info@cfpbmc.org

WEB SITE ADDRESS:
www.yourcommunityfoundation.org

FOUNDED: 1972

AREAS OF INTEREST:
Community development, arts and culture, hunger and capacity building, and environment.

TYPE:
Challenge/matching grants; Conferences/seminars; Development grants; Project/program grants; Scholarships; Technical assistance; Training grants.

PURPOSE:
To develop a shared vision of building a sense of community.

ELIGIBILITY:
501(c)(3) organizations are eligible to apply for grants.

GEOGRAPHIC RESTRICTIONS:
Martin and Palm Beach counties, Florida.

FINANCIAL DATA:
Amount of support per award: Varies.
Total amount of support: $6,400,000 for the year ended June 30, 2013.

Matching fund requirements: Varies.

NUMBER OF APPLICANTS MOST RECENT YEAR:
618 grant applicants and 600 scholarship applicants for the year ended June 30, 2011.

NUMBER OF AWARDS: 518 grants and scholarships for the year ended June 30, 2013.

APPLICATION INFORMATION:
Applicants must complete a proposal summary and budget form. Check online for application and submission information.
Duration: Scholarships: Up to four years. Grants: Varies.
Deadline: Scholarships: February 1. Grants: Varies.

PUBLICATIONS:
Annual report; newsletter.

OFFICERS:
Bradley Herbert, President and Chief Executive Officer
Gloria O. Rex, Vice President for Finance and Administration

ADDRESS INQUIRIES TO:
Daryl Houston, Community Investment Officer
(See address above.)

THE COMMUNITY FOUNDATION FOR THE GREATER CAPITAL REGION [1222]

6 Tower Place
Albany, NY 12203
(518) 446-9638
Fax: (518) 446-9708

E-MAIL ADDRESS:
jmahoney@cfgcr.org

WEB SITE ADDRESS:
www.cfgcr.org

FOUNDED: 1968

AREAS OF INTEREST:
Health, science, education, youth and environment.

NAME(S) OF PROGRAMS:
• **Capacity-Building Grant Initiative**
• **Regular Competitive Grants**

TYPE:
Capital grants; Challenge/matching grants; General operating grants; Matching gifts; Project/program grants; Research grants; Scholarships; Technical assistance. Small, flexible grants to support some of the costs associated with organizational capacity-building.

The Foundation creates networks of opportunity - opportunities to bring together interested donors and community service providers to address a particular problem or need in the local community served. It serves the Capital Region of New York state by funding creative, visionary and sensitive projects - often seed money for innovative programs - that address the evolving needs of the community. The Foundation also serves as a vehicle for individuals, families, corporations, private foundations and nonprofit organizations to use in carrying out their long-term philanthropic plans.

Homelessness: Grants are designed to eliminate homelessness in the Capital Region.

Disabilities: The purpose of these grants is to serve the needs of the mentally and/or physically disabled, including the hearing- and sight-impaired.

Health: Program and capital grants are available for health care organizations working to improve the health of residents of the four-county region around Albany, NY.

Science: This program makes grants to support and promote discovery and development in medicine, science and technology in the Capital District.

PURPOSE:
To support capacity-building efforts of organizations including projects that are designed to generate new thinking about ways to improve an organization's ability to serve the community, more effectively carry out its mission, and plan for the future.

LEGAL BASIS:
Classified by the Internal Revenue Code as a public charity.

ELIGIBILITY:
Grants are made to applicants that qualify under Section 501(c)(3) of the Internal Revenue Code as a nonprofit organization, or operate under the fiscal sponsorship of an organization that does, and serve residents and be located in Albany, Rensselaer, Saratoga and/or Schenectady counties. No grants are made to individuals. Nonsectarian religious programs may apply.

The Foundation's competitive grants support organizations that do not discriminate in their employment practices, volunteer opportunities, or delivery of programs or services on the basis of race, color, religion, gender, national origin, ancestry, age, medical condition, disability, veteran status, marital status, sexual orientation, or any other characteristic protected by law.

GEOGRAPHIC RESTRICTIONS:
Albany, Rensselaer, Saratoga or Schenectady counties, New York.

FINANCIAL DATA:
Assets of over $40,000,000.
Amount of support per award: Homelessness Grants: Usually $5,000 to $10,000; Disabilities Grants: Usually $2,500 to $20,000; Health Care Grants: Up to $30,000; Science Grants: Up to $10,000; Youth Grants: Up to $30,000.
Total amount of support: More than $3,000,000 in grant distributions annually.

NUMBER OF APPLICANTS MOST RECENT YEAR:
Over 800.

NUMBER OF AWARDS: 700 grants awarded.

APPLICATION INFORMATION:
An application form is required and may be obtained by e-mailing the Community Foundation. Prospective applicants are encouraged to discuss their plans with the Foundation's program staff prior to submitting an application. Applicants may submit only one application to the Foundation's regular competitive grantmaking program per year.
Duration: With the exception of operating grants, grant periods do not exceed one year in duration. Organizations that have been funded by the Foundation must wait one year from denial date until they can reapply.

PUBLICATIONS:
Grantmaking Guidelines.

ADDRESS INQUIRIES TO:
Jackie Mahoney, Director of Grantmaking
(See address above.)

COMMUNITY FOUNDATION OF ABILENE   [1223]

500 Chestnut, Suite 1634
Abilene, TX 79604
(325) 676-3883
Fax: (325) 676-4206

E-MAIL ADDRESS:
cfainfo@abilene.org

WEB SITE ADDRESS:
www.cfabilene.org

FOUNDED: 1986

AREAS OF INTEREST:
Human services, arts and culture, education, health, community development and civic affairs.

TYPE:
Capital grants; Challenge/matching grants; Project/program grants; Technical assistance.

PURPOSE:
To increase the quality of life in Abilene, TX; to increase the awareness of philanthropy in the area.

ELIGIBILITY:
Eligible organizations must be IRS 501(c)(3) tax-exempt and be located in the immediate Abilene, TX area.

GEOGRAPHIC RESTRICTIONS:
Abilene, Texas.

FINANCIAL DATA:
Amount of support per award: $1,000 to $50,000.
Total amount of support: $5,400,000.

NUMBER OF APPLICANTS MOST RECENT YEAR:
70.

NUMBER OF AWARDS: 50.

APPLICATION INFORMATION:
Applicants may submit a letter of intent and include a copy of the IRS tax determination letter.
Duration: One year.

ADDRESS INQUIRIES TO:
Courtney Vletas, Grants Director
(See address above.)

COMMUNITY FOUNDATION OF COLLIER COUNTY   [1224]

2400 Tamiami Trail North, Suite 300
Naples, FL 34103
(239) 649-5000
Fax: (239) 649-5337

E-MAIL ADDRESS:
akirk@cfcollier.org

WEB SITE ADDRESS:
cfcollier.org

FOUNDED: 1987

AREAS OF INTEREST:
Health, human services, education, civic affairs, environment, arts and humanities.

NAME(S) OF PROGRAMS:
- **The Daphne Vocational Fund**
- **Joel A. Deifik Memorial Scholarship Fund**
- **Diano-Tougas Memorial Scholarship Fund**
- **Dorothy Edwards Vocational Scholarship Fund**

- **Judy B. and David M. Jones Scholarship Fund**
- **Ashley Kelly Memorial Scholarship Fund**
- **John and Edith Meli Scholarship Fund**
- **Louise Prothero Leadership Fund - Women's Club**
- **Jimmy Schneeberger Scholarship Fund**
- **Raymond D. and Sara Thomas Fund**

TYPE:
Conferences/seminars; Matching gifts; Project/program grants; Scholarships. Community Grant Programs in the area of professional development.

YEAR PROGRAM STARTED: 1987

PURPOSE:
To establish a perpetual endowment and to improve the quality of life in Collier County.

LEGAL BASIS:
Public foundation.

ELIGIBILITY:
Eligible organizations must be IRS 501(c)(3) tax-exempt.

GEOGRAPHIC RESTRICTIONS:
Collier County, Florida.

FINANCIAL DATA:
Amount of support per award: Varies.
Total amount of support: Varies.

APPLICATION INFORMATION:
Request guidelines two to three months prior to deadlines.
Duration: Renewal applications may be considered.
Deadline: Scholarships: Postmarked March 1.

PUBLICATIONS:
Guidelines.

STAFF:
Eileen Connolly-Keesler, President and Chief Executive Officer
Mary George, Vice President of Community Impact
Karen Warnken, Chief Operating Officer

ADDRESS INQUIRIES TO:
Annette Kirk
Financial Services Representative
(See address above.)

COMMUNITY FOUNDATION OF EASTERN CONNECTICUT   [1225]

147 State Street
New London, CT 06320
(860) 442-3572
Fax: (860) 442-0584

E-MAIL ADDRESS:
jennob@cfect.org

WEB SITE ADDRESS:
www.cfect.org

FOUNDED: 1982

AREAS OF INTEREST:
Arts, charity, civic affairs, community needs and development, culture, education, environment, health and human services.

NAME(S) OF PROGRAMS:
- **Community Foundation Grants**
- **Community Foundation Scholarship Awards**
- **Norwich Women and Girls Fund**
- **Norwich Youth Fund**
- **Windham Women and Girls Fund**
- **Women and Girls Fund**

TYPE:
General operating grants; Project/program grants; Scholarships.

YEAR PROGRAM STARTED: 1982

PURPOSE:
To connect the generosity of private donors with the changing needs of the residents of eastern Connecticut by promoting local philanthropy and funding local projects.

ELIGIBILITY:
Federally recognized 501(c)(3) organizations and most charitable, educational and civic institution organizations that serve the towns listed below.

GEOGRAPHIC RESTRICTIONS:
Towns of East Lyme, Groton, Ledyard, Lyme, Montville, New London, North Stonington, Old Lyme, Salem, Stonington, and Waterford, Connecticut.

FINANCIAL DATA:
Amount of support per award: Grants: $1,000 to $10,000; Scholarships: $500 to $5,000.
Total amount of support: Varies.

NUMBER OF APPLICANTS MOST RECENT YEAR:
170.

NUMBER OF AWARDS: 100.

APPLICATION INFORMATION:
Contact the Foundation for specific details on the various grant programs.
Duration: Typically one year.
Deadline: Women and Girls Fund: August 15; General grants: November 15; Scholarships: April 1.

ADDRESS INQUIRIES TO:
Jennifer O'Brien, Program Director
(See address above.)

THE COMMUNITY FOUNDATION OF FREDERICK COUNTY, MD, INC.   [1226]

312 East Church Street
Frederick, MD 21701
(301) 695-7660
Fax: (301) 695-7775

E-MAIL ADDRESS:
info@cffredco.org

WEB SITE ADDRESS:
www.cffredco.org

FOUNDED: 1986

AREAS OF INTEREST:
Community development.

TYPE:
Project/program grants; Scholarships.

YEAR PROGRAM STARTED: 1986

PURPOSE:
To make charitable dreams come true by working with donors to establish funds that award grants and scholarships.

ELIGIBILITY:
For grants, applicant organizations must have 501(c)(3) not-for-profit status.

GEOGRAPHIC RESTRICTIONS:
Frederick County, Maryland.

FINANCIAL DATA:
Amount of support per award: Varies depending on need.
Total amount of support: Scholarships: Varies; Grants: Over $1,900,000 for fiscal year ended June 30, 2012.

NUMBER OF AWARDS: More than 300 scholarships for the academic year 2012-13.

APPLICATION INFORMATION:
Grant period opens September 1 annually. Additional information may be found on the Foundation web site.
Duration: Varies.
Deadline: Varies.

PUBLICATIONS:
Annual report; newsletters; grant applications.

IRS IDENTIFICATION NUMBER: 52-2028247

ADDRESS INQUIRIES TO:
Gayle Sutch, Director of Donor Services
(See address above.)

THE COMMUNITY FOUNDATION OF GREATER CHATTANOOGA, INC. [1227]
1270 Market Street
Chattanooga, TN 37402
(423) 265-0586
Fax: (423) 265-0587

E-MAIL ADDRESS:
info@cfgc.org

WEB SITE ADDRESS:
www.cfgc.org

FOUNDED: 1963

AREAS OF INTEREST:
Nonprofit organizations.

NAME(S) OF PROGRAMS:
- **Coca-Cola Centennial Scholarship Fund**
- **Together We Can Scholarship Fund**

TYPE:
Scholarships.

YEAR PROGRAM STARTED: 1963

PURPOSE:
To encourage giving and inspire action to improve lives in the Chattanooga area.

LEGAL BASIS:
501(c)(3).

ELIGIBILITY:
Must be a nonprofit corporation with 501(c)(3) tax-exempt status based in or primarily serving Hamilton County, TN.

Students for Together We Can Scholarship Fund must live in Chattanooga and attend a public high school.

GEOGRAPHIC RESTRICTIONS:
Hamilton County, Tennessee.

FINANCIAL DATA:
Amount of support per award: Varies.

APPLICATION INFORMATION:
Prior to submitting an application, potential applicants are required to submit a letter of intent form and receive written approval from the Foundation to continue the application process. A completed application can then be submitted along with required documentation.
Duration: Coca-Cola Centennial Scholarship Fund: Renewable up to four academic years; Together We Can Scholarship Fund: Up to five years.
Deadline: Varies.

IRS IDENTIFICATION NUMBER: 62-6045999

STAFF:
Peter T. Cooper, President
Marty Robinson, Vice President
Rebecca Smith, Director of Scholarships

BOARD OF DIRECTORS:
Mike Berry
Charlie Brock
Paul Campbell, III
Lakweshia Ewing
Tom Glenn
Patsy Hazlewood
Wade Hinton
Tim Kelly
James McKissic
Hugh Moore
Linda Mosley
Ward Nelson
Rachel Schulson
Alfred Smith
Chris Smith
Lacie Stone
Niti Tejani
Edna Varner

EXECUTIVE COMMITTEE:
Patsy Hazlewood, Chairperson
Charlie Brock, Vice Chairperson
Paul Campbell, III, Vice Chairperson
Linda Mosley, Treasurer
Ansley Moses, Corporate Secretary

ADDRESS INQUIRIES TO:
Rebecca Smith
Director of Scholarships
(See address above.)

*SPECIAL STIPULATIONS:
All grants limited to students from or programs in Hamilton County, TN.

COMMUNITY FOUNDATION OF GREATER GREENSBORO [1228]
330 South Greene Street
Suite 100
Greensboro, NC 27401
(336) 379-9100
Fax: (336) 378-0725

E-MAIL ADDRESS:
info@cfgg.org

WEB SITE ADDRESS:
www.cfgg.org

FOUNDED: 1983

AREAS OF INTEREST:
Serving the Greater Greensboro, NC area.

NAME(S) OF PROGRAMS:
- **Thornton H. Brooks Award**
- **Community Service Award**
- **Hugh Humphrey Award**

TYPE:
Challenge/matching grants; Conferences/seminars; Demonstration grants; Development grants; Endowments; General operating grants; Project/program grants; Scholarships. Recognition Awards.

Brooks Award recognizes individuals for outstanding leadership to the Foundation and its mission.

Community Service Award recognizes individuals who have exhibited outstanding community service.

Hugh Humphrey Award recognizes the most improved high school in Guilford County, NC.

GEOGRAPHIC RESTRICTIONS:
Alamance and Randolph counties and the greater Greensboro, North Carolina area.

FINANCIAL DATA:
Amount of support per award: Varies.
Total amount of support: Varies.

APPLICATION INFORMATION:
Nomination only.
Duration: Varies.
Deadline: Varies.

IRS IDENTIFICATION NUMBER: 56-1380249

ADDRESS INQUIRIES TO:
H. Walker Sanders, President
(See address above.)

COMMUNITY FOUNDATION OF GREATER ROCHESTER [1229]
P.O. Box 80431
Rochester, MI 48308-0431
(248) 608-2804
Fax: (248) 608-2826

E-MAIL ADDRESS:
director@cfound.org

WEB SITE ADDRESS:
www.cfound.org

FOUNDED: 1983

AREAS OF INTEREST:
Arts, conservation of natural resources, community needs and development, culture, education, environment, health, historic preservation and human services.

TYPE:
Endowments; Project/program grants; Scholarships; Travel grants. Community grants.

PURPOSE:
To enhance the quality of life for the citizens of Greater Rochester area by serving as a community endowment builder, grantmaker and leader.

ELIGIBILITY:
Grants are made to organizations that have tax-exempt status under Section 501(c)(3) of the Internal Revenue Code. Nonsectarian religious programs may apply.

GEOGRAPHIC RESTRICTIONS:
Greater Rochester, Michigan and surrounding area.

FINANCIAL DATA:
Amount of support per award: Varies.
Total amount of support: Varies.

APPLICATION INFORMATION:
Contact the Foundation for application procedures.
Duration: Varies.
Deadline: Varies.

ADDRESS INQUIRIES TO:
Peggy Hamilton, Executive Director
(See address above.)

THE COMMUNITY FOUNDATION OF HERKIMER & ONEIDA COUNTIES, INC. [1230]
1222 State Street
Utica, NY 13502
(315) 735-8212
Fax: (315) 735-9363

E-MAIL ADDRESS:
info@foundationhoc.org

WEB SITE ADDRESS:
foundationhoc.org

FOUNDED: 1952

AREAS OF INTEREST:
Economic development, education, health, arts and culture.

TYPE:
Capital grants; Challenge/matching grants; Fellowships; Project/program grants; Scholarships; Seed money grants; Technical assistance; Training grants.

PURPOSE:
To improve the quality of life of the residents of Herkimer and Oneida counties in New York.

LEGAL BASIS:
Community foundation.

ELIGIBILITY:
Applications are entertained from organizations that are tax-exempt under Section 501(c)(3) of the Internal Revenue Code. Grants may be made for program or capital expenses. Operating funds will receive consideration on a short-term or emergency basis, with the understanding that applicants must submit a clear, realistic plan to secure alternative funding at the end of a specific time.

The Community Foundation does not make grants for religious purposes, nor does it provide financial assistance or scholarships directly to individuals, support for nonemergency expenses already incurred, requests over $100,000, or ongoing operating support.

GEOGRAPHIC RESTRICTIONS:
Herkimer and Oneida counties, New York.

FINANCIAL DATA:
Amount of support per award: $1,000 to $100,000; average $3,000 to $30,000.
Total amount of support: $1,500,000 for the year 2013.

APPLICATION INFORMATION:
Applicants should call the Senior Program Officer prior to submitting a written request.
Duration: One year.
Deadline: Grant requests are accepted on an ongoing basis.

PUBLICATIONS:
Annual report; newsletter for applicants/grantees; application guidelines; foundation brochure; history book.

ADDRESS INQUIRIES TO:
Jan Squadrito, Senior Program Officer
(See address above.)

COMMUNITY FOUNDATION OF JACKSON HOLE   [1231]
245 East Simpson Street
Jackson, WY 83001
(307) 739-1026
Fax: (307) 734-2841

E-MAIL ADDRESS:
info@cfjacksonhole.org

WEB SITE ADDRESS:
www.cfjacksonhole.org

FOUNDED: 1989

AREAS OF INTEREST:
Art, education, environment, health and social services.

TYPE:
Development grants; General operating grants; Grants-in-aid; Project/program grants; Research grants.

PURPOSE:
To improve lives through philanthropic leadership.

LEGAL BASIS:
501(c)(3).

ELIGIBILITY:
Must be a 501(c)(3) corporation.

GEOGRAPHIC RESTRICTIONS:
Teton County, Wyoming.

APPLICATION INFORMATION:
Application information is available on the web site.

IRS IDENTIFICATION NUMBER: 83-0308856

ADDRESS INQUIRIES TO:
Katharine Conover, President
(See address above.)

THE COMMUNITY FOUNDATION OF LORAIN COUNTY   [1232]
9080 Leavitt Road
Elyria, OH 44035
(440) 984-7390
Fax: (440) 984-7399

E-MAIL ADDRESS:
foundation@peoplewhocare.org

WEB SITE ADDRESS:
www.peoplewhocare.org

FOUNDED: 1980

AREAS OF INTEREST:
Community of Lorain County, OH.

TYPE:
General operating grants; Project/program grants. Grants are given to improve the quality of life in Lorain County.

YEAR PROGRAM STARTED: 1980

PURPOSE:
To connect people who care with causes that matter.

ELIGIBILITY:
Organization or sponsor must be 501(c)(3). Funding must serve the people of Lorain County.

GEOGRAPHIC RESTRICTIONS:
Lorain County, Ohio.

FINANCIAL DATA:
Amount of support per award: Varies.
Total amount of support: Varies.

APPLICATION INFORMATION:
Application can be downloaded at the web site.
Deadline: February 1 and July 1.

ADDRESS INQUIRIES TO:
Linda Styer, Senior Program Officer
E-mail: lstyer@peoplewhocare.org

THE COMMUNITY FOUNDATION OF MUNCIE AND DELAWARE COUNTY, INC. [1233]
201 East Jackson Street
Muncie, IN 47305
(765) 747-7181
Fax: (765) 289-7770

E-MAIL ADDRESS:
commfound@cfmdin.org

WEB SITE ADDRESS:
www.cfmdin.org

FOUNDED: 1985

AREAS OF INTEREST:
Arts and culture, education, human services, economic development and community betterment.

TYPE:
Capital grants; General operating grants; Project/program grants; Scholarships; Seed money grants; Training grants.

PURPOSE:
To improve the quality of life in the city of Muncie and Delaware County, IN.

ELIGIBILITY:
Organizations must be IRS 501(c)(3) tax-exempt. The Foundation does not make grants to individuals, for religious purposes, for covering budget deficits, for endowments or for projects normally the responsibility of a government agency.

GEOGRAPHIC RESTRICTIONS:
The city of Muncie and Delaware County, Indiana.

FINANCIAL DATA:
Total amount of support: $1,800,000.

NUMBER OF APPLICANTS MOST RECENT YEAR: 400.

NUMBER OF AWARDS: 360.

APPLICATION INFORMATION:
Applicant organizations should secure an application from the address above. Applicants should submit 17 copies of the application and also include supporting material, goals and objectives, method of evaluation, how the proposal benefits the community, a list of officers and board of directors, the most recent financial report, and a copy of the IRS tax-exempt determination letter.
Deadline: Mid-January, April, July and October.

PUBLICATIONS:
Guidelines.

IRS IDENTIFICATION NUMBER: 35-1640051

STAFF:
Suzanne Kadinger, Program Officer

ADDRESS INQUIRIES TO:
Suzanne Kadinger, Program Officer
P.O. Box 807
Muncie, IN 47308

*SPECIAL STIPULATIONS:
The Foundation will periodically review each grant awarded and will request a final postgrant report from each grantee.

COMMUNITY FOUNDATION OF NORTH CENTRAL WISCONSIN   [1234]
500 First Street
Suite 2600
Wausau, WI 54403
(715) 845-9555
Fax: (715) 845-5423

E-MAIL ADDRESS:
info@cfoncw.org

WEB SITE ADDRESS:
www.cfoncw.org

FOUNDED: 1987

AREAS OF INTEREST:
Arts, education, health and human services, and resource preservation.

TYPE:
Awards/prizes; Capital grants; Development grants; Project/program grants; Scholarships; Seed money grants; Technical assistance.

YEAR PROGRAM STARTED: 1987

PURPOSE:
To enhance the quality of the greater Wausau (WI) area.

ELIGIBILITY:
Consideration is given primarily to those organizations that are tax-exempt under Section 501(c)(3) of the Internal Revenue Code.

GEOGRAPHIC RESTRICTIONS:
Greater Wausau area, Marathon County, Wisconsin.

FINANCIAL DATA:
Amount of support per award: $2,500 to $10,000.
Total amount of support: Varies.

COOPERATIVE FUNDING PROGRAMS: Community Arts Grants are funded through the Wisconsin Arts Board; B.A. and Esther Greenheck Foundation and Community Foundation.

NUMBER OF APPLICANTS MOST RECENT YEAR: 39.

NUMBER OF AWARDS: 18.

REPRESENTATIVE AWARDS:
Performing Arts Foundation; Wausau Community Theatre; Wisconsin Institute for Public Policy and Service; Marathon County Historical Society; Stable Hands.

APPLICATION INFORMATION:
Application information is available on the web site.
Duration: One year.
Deadline: Applications are due the first business day of March, June, September and December.

STAFF:
Jean Tehan, Executive Director
Tammy Szekress, Operations Director
Sue Nelson, Program Manager
Pauline Zweck, Accountant

ADDRESS INQUIRIES TO:
Jean Tehan, Executive Director
(See address above.)

COMMUNITY FOUNDATION OF NORTHEAST ALABAMA [1235]

1130 Quintard Avenue
Suite 100
Anniston, AL 36201
(256) 231-5160
Fax: (256) 231-5161

E-MAIL ADDRESS:
etatman@yourcommunityfirst.org

WEB SITE ADDRESS:
www.yourcommunityfirst.org

AREAS OF INTEREST:
Arts, community needs, culture, education, health and human services.

TYPE:
Project/program grants; Scholarships; Technical assistance.

PURPOSE:
To support the most discernible needs and most promising opportunities within Calhoun County and northeast Alabama.

ELIGIBILITY:
Grants are made to organizations that have tax-exempt status under Section 501(c)(3) of the Internal Revenue Code. No grants are made to individuals. Nonsectarian religious programs may apply.

GEOGRAPHIC RESTRICTIONS:
Calhoun County, Alabama.

FINANCIAL DATA:
Amount of support per award: $100 to $10,000.
Total amount of support: Over $1,000,000 in grants and scholarships each year.

NUMBER OF AWARDS: Varies.

APPLICATION INFORMATION:
Grant request must be completed online.
Duration: One year. Renewal possible.
Deadline: Grants: March 1 and September 1; Scholarships: March 1.

ADDRESS INQUIRIES TO:
Eula Tatman, Vice President
(See address above.)

COMMUNITY FOUNDATION OF SAINT JOSEPH COUNTY [1236]

P.O. Box 837
South Bend, IN 46624
(574) 232-0041
Fax: (574) 233-1906

E-MAIL ADDRESS:
info@cfsjc.org

WEB SITE ADDRESS:
www.cfsjc.org

AREAS OF INTEREST:
Arts and culture; community development and urban affairs; health and human services; parks, recreation, and environment; youth and education.

NAME(S) OF PROGRAMS:
- **African American Community Fund**
- **ArtsEverywhere Fund**
- **Leighton Award for Nonprofit Excellence**
- **Robert P. and Clara I. Milton Fund for Senior Housing**
- **Special Project Challenge Grant**

TYPE:
Capital grants; Challenge/matching grants; Project/program grants; Scholarships. Donor-advised grants.

PURPOSE:
To promote organizations whose programs benefit the residents of St. Joseph County; to assist existing agencies to better respond to the needs of the community.

ELIGIBILITY:
Grants are made to organizations that have tax-exempt status under Section 501(c)(3) of the Internal Revenue Code. No grants are made to individuals. Nonsectarian religious programs may apply. Funded projects should benefit a significant constituency within the community and the organization must exhibit the ability to raise the required matching funds, if applicable.

GEOGRAPHIC RESTRICTIONS:
Saint Joseph County, Indiana.

FINANCIAL DATA:
Amount of support per award: Varies per award.
Matching fund requirements: Some programs require matching funds.

APPLICATION INFORMATION:
Application information is available on the web site.
Duration: Varies.
Deadline: Special Project Challenge Grant and African American Community Fund: March 1 and October 1; Robert P. and Clara I. Milton Fund and ArtsEverywhere Fund:

May 1 and November 1; Leighton Award for Nonprofit Excellence: July 1 of odd-numbered years.

STAFF:
Rose Meissner, President

ADDRESS INQUIRIES TO:
Angela Butiste, Senior Program Officer
(See address above.)

THE COMMUNITY FOUNDATION OF SHELBY COUNTY [1237]

Courtview Center, Suite 202
100 South Main Avenue
Sidney, OH 45365-2771
(937) 497-7800
Fax: (937) 497-7799

E-MAIL ADDRESS:
info@commfoun.com

WEB SITE ADDRESS:
www.commfoun.com

FOUNDED: 1952

AREAS OF INTEREST:
Arts and culture, family and community, education, environment, and health.

TYPE:
Capital grants; Scholarships; Seed money grants.

PURPOSE:
To improve the quality of life and to cultivate, administer and distribute legacy gifts for the benefit of its local community.

ELIGIBILITY:
Organizations must have 501(c)(3) status.

GEOGRAPHIC RESTRICTIONS:
Shelby County, Ohio.

FINANCIAL DATA:
Amount of support per award: Discretionary grants: $500 to $2,000.
Total amount of support: $12,000 in discretionary grants for the year 2012; approximately $800,000 in total grantmaking for fiscal year 2012.

NUMBER OF APPLICANTS MOST RECENT YEAR: 23.

NUMBER OF AWARDS: 10.

APPLICATION INFORMATION:
Applicants must call the Executive Director of the Foundation to discuss the grant request idea and whether the project appears to fit within the Foundation's guidelines. Preliminary Grant Proposals and Full Proposals will not be accepted if they have not been requested by the Executive Director.
Applications for most of the scholarships are available online.
Deadline: Discretionary grants: March 15. Designated purpose grants: Varies.

ADDRESS INQUIRIES TO:
Marian Spicer, Executive Director
(See address above.)

THE COMMUNITY FOUNDATION OF SOUTH ALABAMA [1238]

212 St. Joseph Street
Mobile, AL 36602
(251) 438-5591
Fax: (251) 438-5592

E-MAIL ADDRESS:
info@communityendowment.org

WEB SITE ADDRESS:
www.communityendowment.org

FOUNDED: 1976

AREAS OF INTEREST:
Community, health, social services, arts and education.

TYPE:
Challenge/matching grants; Development grants; General operating grants; Project/program grants; Scholarships; Seed money grants.

PURPOSE:
To strengthen the future of nonprofit organizations in southwest Alabama by encouraging gifts, large and small, from all segments of the community.

LEGAL BASIS:
Alabama not-for-profit corporation/community foundation.

ELIGIBILITY:
Eligible organizations must be IRS 501(c)(3) tax-exempt and located in southwest Alabama.

GEOGRAPHIC RESTRICTIONS:
Southwestern Alabama (Baldwin, Choctaw, Clarke, Conecah, Escambia, Mobile, Monroe and Washington counties).

FINANCIAL DATA:
Amount of support per award: Varies.
Total amount of support: Varies.

APPLICATION INFORMATION:
Request for Proposals will be issued by the Foundation to announce when funding is available. Applications are to be submitted electronically using the Common Grant Application form. Applicants must include a copy of the IRS tax determination letter.
Duration: One year. Renewal by reapplication.

PUBLICATIONS:
Annual report; newsletter; application guidelines; *Charitable Gift Annuity*; *Real Estate Gifts*.

IRS IDENTIFICATION NUMBER: 63-0695166

STAFF:
Alvertha Penny, President and Chief Executive Officer
Linette Clausman, Director of Finance and Administration
Simone Washington, Director of Programs

ADDRESS INQUIRIES TO:
Simone Washington, Director of Programs (See address above.)

COMMUNITY FOUNDATION OF THE EASTERN SHORE   [1239]
1324 Belmont Avenue, Suite 401
Salisbury, MD 21804
(410) 742-9911
Fax: (410) 742-6638

E-MAIL ADDRESS:
cfes@cfes.org

WEB SITE ADDRESS:
www.cfes.org

FOUNDED: 1984

AREAS OF INTEREST:
Arts, civic affairs, community needs, conservation, culture, education, health and historic preservation.

CONSULTING OR VOLUNTEER SERVICES:
ShoreCAN Regional Volunteer Center.

NAME(S) OF PROGRAMS:
● **Community Needs Grants**
● **Excellence in Education Program**
● **Richard A. Henson Award of Excellence**
● **Frank H. Morris Humanitarian Award**
● **Nonprofit Support Program**
● **Small Grants Program**

TYPE:
Awards/prizes; Challenge/matching grants; Demonstration grants; Project/program grants; Scholarships; Seed money grants; Technical assistance; Training grants.

YEAR PROGRAM STARTED: 1984

PURPOSE:
To improve the quality of life in the area by acting as a funding source for present and future generations.

ELIGIBILITY:
Grants are made to organizations that have tax-exempt status under Section 501(c)(3) of the Internal Revenue Code and not classified as a private foundation that is located or serves the residents of the counties. No grants are made to individuals. Nonsectarian religious programs may apply. Agencies must be operated and organized so that they do not discriminate in the hiring of staff on the basis of race, religion, gender, sexual orientation, age, national origin or disability.

GEOGRAPHIC RESTRICTIONS:
Somerset, Wicomico and Worcester counties, Maryland.

FINANCIAL DATA:
Amount of support per award: Community Needs: $2,000 to $7,500; Excellence in Education Program: $1,500 to $5,000; Henson and Morris Awards: Approximately $1,000; Small Grants Program: $200 to $2,000.
Total amount of support: $4,400,000 for the year 2012.

APPLICATION INFORMATION:
Application information is available on the web site.
Duration: One year.
Deadline: Community Needs: February and August; Excellence in Education: August; Henson and Morris Awards: Late September.

STAFF:
Erica Joseph, Program Director

ADDRESS INQUIRIES TO:
Erica Joseph, Program Director (See address above.)

COMMUNITY FOUNDATION OF THE FOX RIVER VALLEY [1240]
111 West Downer Place
Suite 312
Aurora, IL 60506
(630) 896-7800
Fax: (630) 896-7811

E-MAIL ADDRESS:
info@communityfoundationfrv.org

WEB SITE ADDRESS:
www.communityfoundationfrv.org

AREAS OF INTEREST:
Education, health care, social services, the arts, and other charitable fields.

TYPE:
Capital grants; Scholarships.

PURPOSE:
To support worthwhile projects in the served communities.

ELIGIBILITY:
Grants are made to organizations that have tax-exempt status under Section 501(c)(3) of the Internal Revenue Code. No grants are made to individuals.

GEOGRAPHIC RESTRICTIONS:
Aurora, southern Kane County, and Kendall County, Illinois.

FINANCIAL DATA:
Amount of support per award: $1,000 to $10,000.
Total amount of support: Varies.

NUMBER OF APPLICANTS MOST RECENT YEAR:
Scholarships: 462.

NUMBER OF AWARDS: Scholarships: 219.

APPLICATION INFORMATION:
Applications may be obtained from the Foundation web site.
Duration: Varies.
Deadline: Grant proposals: First business day in June and December. Scholarships: January.

COMMUNITY FOUNDATION OF THE OZARKS   [1241]
425 East Trafficway
Springfield, MO 65806
(417) 864-6199
Fax: (417) 864-8344

E-MAIL ADDRESS:
jleeth@cfozarks.org

WEB SITE ADDRESS:
www.cfozarks.org

AREAS OF INTEREST:
Health and social services; arts, culture and environment; education and community development.

TYPE:
Challenge/matching grants; Demonstration grants; Development grants; Endowments; Project/program grants; Scholarships. Initiative grants and Technical/Capacity-building grants.

PURPOSE:
To build a community endowment; to provide leadership; to prompt collaboration on community issues; to improve the quality of life for citizens in Greene County, MO and the surrounding region.

LEGAL BASIS:
Community foundation.

ELIGIBILITY:
Eligible organizations must be IRS 501(c)(3) tax-exempt and located in Greene County, MO or counties represented by our affiliate organizations which are located throughout the central and southern half of Missouri.

GEOGRAPHIC RESTRICTIONS:
Central and southern Missouri.

FINANCIAL DATA:
Amount of support per award: Grants: $1,500 to $25,000; Initiative Awards: $100,000 to $1,000,000.
Total amount of support: Discretionary Grants and Scholarships Programs: $2,000,000.

APPLICATION INFORMATION:
Complete application information is available online.
Duration: Typically one year.
Deadline: Varies.

ADDRESS INQUIRIES TO:
Randy Russell, Senior Program Officer
(See address above.)

COMMUNITY FOUNDATION OF THE TEXAS HILL COUNTRY [1242]
301 Junction Highway, Suite 346-B
Kerrville, TX 78028
(830) 896-8811
Fax: (830) 792-5956

E-MAIL ADDRESS:
paul@communityfoundation.net

WEB SITE ADDRESS:
www.communityfoundation.net

FOUNDED: 1982

AREAS OF INTEREST:
Community development.

NAME(S) OF PROGRAMS:
- **Arts**
- **Children and Education**
- **Community**
- **Designated and Donor Advised Funds**
- **Healers**
- **Pass Through Grants**

TYPE:
Capital grants; Challenge/matching grants; Development grants; Grants-in-aid; Matching gifts; Project/program grants; Scholarships; Technical assistance.

PURPOSE:
To improve the quality of life in the Texas Hill Country of Texas.

LEGAL BASIS:
Corporation.

ELIGIBILITY:
Grants are generally not awarded to individuals or to religious organizations.

GEOGRAPHIC RESTRICTIONS:
Bandera, Gillespie, Kendell and Kerr counties, Texas.

FINANCIAL DATA:
More than $11,500,000 in assets.
Amount of support per award: Varies.
Total amount of support: Varies.

NUMBER OF APPLICANTS MOST RECENT YEAR:
96.

NUMBER OF AWARDS: 32.

APPLICATION INFORMATION:
Applicants must submit a cover letter, signed by the Board Chairman and the Executive Director, describing the proposal and need for the project in the community. Grant application must also include:
(1) completed application form including project description;
(2) detailed project budget along with indication of what portion of the project is funded or expected to be funded by other sources;
(3) organizational budget for the current fiscal year;
(4) financial statements, including balance sheet and statement of activity for the organization for the fiscal year most recently completed, or certified audit for the fiscal year most recently completed;
(5) most recent 990 tax return filed by the organization;
(6) copy of IRS 501(c)(3) letter of determination;
(7) list of board of directors and executive staff;
(8) board and staff training for previous 12-month period and;
(9) letters of support for cooperative projects between organizations (if applicable).

First-time applicants should include a one- to two-page history of their organization. A plan for the evaluation of the project's results and dissemination of its findings must be included. Provide one original and two copies of the grant proposal and all attachments.

IRS IDENTIFICATION NUMBER: 74-2225369

STAFF:
Paul Urban, Executive Director
Amy Rector, Business Manager
Jayne Zirkel, Public Relations and Event Coordinator

ADDRESS INQUIRIES TO:
Paul Urban, Executive Director
(See address above.)

COMMUNITY FOUNDATION OF WESTERN MASSACHUSETTS (CFWM) [1243]
1500 Main Street
Springfield, MA 01115
(413) 732-2858
Fax: (413) 733-8565

E-MAIL ADDRESS:
wmass@communityfoundation.org

WEB SITE ADDRESS:
www.communityfoundation.org

FOUNDED: 1990

AREAS OF INTEREST:
Human services, education, arts and culture, health, housing and environment.

TYPE:
Capital grants; Challenge/matching grants; Demonstration grants; Development grants; Project/program grants; Scholarships; Seed money grants; Technical assistance; Training grants. Arts and equipment.

YEAR PROGRAM STARTED: 1990

PURPOSE:
To support charitable programs in developing and expanding their services.

ELIGIBILITY:
Grants are restricted to worthy public charities serving residents of Franklin, Hampden and Hampshire counties in Massachusetts.

GEOGRAPHIC RESTRICTIONS:
Franklin, Hampden and Hampshire counties, Massachusetts.

FINANCIAL DATA:
Amount of support per award: $10,000 average award for the year 2013.
Total amount of support: $9,900,000 for fiscal year 2013.

COOPERATIVE FUNDING PROGRAMS: Informal linkages as well as funds established by family foundations within the community foundation.

NUMBER OF APPLICANTS MOST RECENT YEAR:
178 for the year 2013.

NUMBER OF AWARDS: 119 for the year 2013.

APPLICATION INFORMATION:
Contact the Foundation for application procedures.
Duration: One year. Nonrenewable.
Deadline: To be determined for 2015.

PUBLICATIONS:
Annual report; newsletter; application with guidelines; brochures for donors and applicants.

STAFF:
Katie Allan Zobel, President and Chief Executive Officer
Nancy Reiche, Vice President for Programs

ADDRESS INQUIRIES TO:
Nancy Reiche
Vice President for Programs
(See address above.)

COMMUNITY FOUNDATIONS OF THE HUDSON VALLEY [1244]
80 Washington Street, Suite 201
Poughkeepsie, NY 12601
(845) 452-3077
Fax: (845) 452-3083

E-MAIL ADDRESS:
areynolds@cfhvny.org

WEB SITE ADDRESS:
www.cfhvny.org

FOUNDED: 1969

AREAS OF INTEREST:
Health, education and social services.

NAME(S) OF PROGRAMS:
- **Community Response Grants of Dutchess County**
- **Community Response Grants of Ulster County**
- **Fund for Excellence in Education Grants**

TYPE:
Project/program grants; Scholarships; Training grants. Equipment to improve office operations.

PURPOSE:
To improve the quality of life in Dutchess, Putnam and Ulster counties, New York.

ELIGIBILITY:
Eligible organizations must be IRS 501(c)(3) tax-exempt or have a fiscal sponsor.

GEOGRAPHIC RESTRICTIONS:
Primarily Dutchess, Putnam and Ulster counties, New York.

FINANCIAL DATA:
Amount of support per award: Varies.
Total amount of support: $2,500,000 for fiscal year ended June 30, 2013.

NUMBER OF APPLICANTS MOST RECENT YEAR:
150.

NUMBER OF AWARDS: 50.

APPLICATION INFORMATION:
Applications are submitted through the online application system.

PUBLICATIONS:
Annual report; newsletters.

IRS IDENTIFICATION NUMBER: 23-7026859

ADDRESS INQUIRIES TO:
Andrea L. Reynolds
President and Chief Executive Officer
(See address above.)

CONNECTICUT COMMUNITY FOUNDATION [1245]
43 Field Street
Waterbury, CT 06702
(203) 753-1315
Fax: (203) 756-3054

E-MAIL ADDRESS:
info@conncf.org

WEB SITE ADDRESS:
www.conncf.org

FOUNDED: 1923

AREAS OF INTEREST:
The arts, education, environment, leadership, health care and human services.

CONSULTING OR VOLUNTEER SERVICES:
Nonprofit advisor services available.

NAME(S) OF PROGRAMS:
- **Capacity Building Grants**
- **Nonprofit Assistance Initiative**
- **Program Grants**
- **Training Programs**

TYPE:
Capital grants; Challenge/matching grants; Project/program grants; Scholarships; Seed money grants; Technical assistance. Sponsorships. Organizational development.

YEAR PROGRAM STARTED: 1923

PURPOSE:
To serve the people of the Greater Waterbury and Litchfield Hills to improve the quality of life.

LEGAL BASIS:
Community foundation.

ELIGIBILITY:
The following requirements apply:
(1) Applicant is a public institution or private tax-exempt organization under Section 501(c)(3) of the Internal Revenue Code. Individuals may apply for scholarships or awards only;
(2) Political, lobbying or religious activities are ineligible. Religiously affiliated organizations may propose nonsectarian projects;
(3) Organization must have a board, representative of the community, of which a majority are neither employees nor relatives of employees and;
(4) Organization or proposed program must be located in Beacon Falls, Bethlehem, Bridgewater, Cheshire, Goshen, Litchfield, Middlebury, Morris, Naugatuck, New Milford, Oxford, Prospect, Roxbury, Southbury, Thomaston, Warren, Washington, Waterbury, Watertown, Wolcott or Woodbury.

GEOGRAPHIC RESTRICTIONS:
Greater Waterbury and Litchfield Hills, Connecticut.

FINANCIAL DATA:
Amount of support per award: Varies.

Total amount of support: Approximately $3,000,000 in grants and scholarships for the year 2013.

APPLICATION INFORMATION:
Guidelines and application form may be obtained online.

Duration: One year. Multiyear funding should be applied for at the outset and is subject to review.

PUBLICATIONS:
Annual report.

ADDRESS INQUIRIES TO:
Josh Carey, Director of Grants Management
(See address above.)

COOK FAMILY FOUNDATION [1246]
P.O. Box 278
Owosso, MI 48867-0278
(989) 725-1621
Fax: (989) 936-5910

E-MAIL ADDRESS:
tom@cookfamilyfoundation.org

WEB SITE ADDRESS:
www.cookfamilyfoundation.org

FOUNDED: 1978

AREAS OF INTEREST:
Education and community development.

TYPE:
Capital grants; Challenge/matching grants; Demonstration grants; Development grants; Matching gifts; Project/program grants; Scholarships; Seed money grants; Technical assistance. Educational support.

YEAR PROGRAM STARTED: 1978

PURPOSE:
To strengthen community institutions in Shiawassee County; to support the University of Michigan.

LEGAL BASIS:
Family (private) foundation.

ELIGIBILITY:
Eligible organizations must be IRS 501(c)(3) tax-exempt.

GEOGRAPHIC RESTRICTIONS:
Shiawassee County, Michigan.

FINANCIAL DATA:
Amount of support per award: $500 to $50,000.

Total amount of support: $500,000.

Matching fund requirements: Varies based on grant; average 20% cash/in-kind.

APPLICATION INFORMATION:
Applicants should submit a short letter of inquiry.

STAFF:
Yvette Collard, Business Manager

ADDRESS INQUIRIES TO:
Thomas Cook, Executive Director
(See address above.)

COOPERATIVE DEVELOPMENT FOUNDATION [1247]
1401 New York Avenue, N.W.
Suite 1100
Washington, DC 20005
(202) 442-2331

E-MAIL ADDRESS:
equinn@cdf.coop

WEB SITE ADDRESS:
www.cdf.coop
www.heroes.coop
seniors.coop

FOUNDED: 1944

AREAS OF INTEREST:
Community, economic and social development through cooperative enterprise.

TYPE:
Grants-in-aid. The Foundation makes grants and loans for cooperative development through its various funds.

PURPOSE:
To promote self-help and mutual aid in community, economic and social development through cooperative enterprise.

LEGAL BASIS:
501(c)(3) organization.

ELIGIBILITY:
The Foundation does not award grants for purely personal needs. It works only in the cooperative sector.

GEOGRAPHIC RESTRICTIONS:
Primarily the United States.

FINANCIAL DATA:
Amount of support per award: Varies.
Total amount of support: Varies.

NUMBER OF APPLICANTS MOST RECENT YEAR:
Approximately 35.

NUMBER OF AWARDS: 27.

APPLICATION INFORMATION:
Contact the Foundation after reviewing the various fund descriptions to determine if the proposed project fits within the Foundation's funding priorities. The Foundation supports cooperative development only.

PUBLICATIONS:
Annual report.

STAFF:
Leslie Mead, Executive Director
Ellen Quinn, Funds Manager
Cassandra Durand, Events Coordinator

ADDRESS INQUIRIES TO:
See e-mail address above.

*SPECIAL STIPULATIONS:
The Foundation supports cooperative development only.

ADOLPH COORS FOUNDATION
4100 East Mississippi Avenue, Suite 1850
Denver, CO 80246
(303) 388-1636
Fax: (303) 388-1684

E-MAIL ADDRESS:
info@acoorsfdn.org

WEB SITE ADDRESS:
www.coorsfoundation.org

TYPE:
Capital grants; General operating grants; Project/program grants.

See entry 1116 for full listing.

CORPORATION FOR NATIONAL AND COMMUNITY SERVICE [1248]
1201 New York Avenue, N.W.
Washington, DC 20525
(202) 606-5000
(202) 606-6608

E-MAIL ADDRESS:
vista@cns.gov

WEB SITE ADDRESS:
www.nationalservice.gov

FOUNDED: 1964

AREAS OF INTEREST:
Anti-poverty or poverty-related activities.

NAME(S) OF PROGRAMS:
- **AmeriCorps VISTA**

TYPE:
Project/program grants. Provides full-time, full-year volunteers at the request of community groups to work on clearly defined tasks that lead to mobilization of the community's resources. The volunteers live among the people they serve at subsistence levels of support.

YEAR PROGRAM STARTED: 1965

PURPOSE:
To supplement efforts to eliminate poverty and poverty-related problems.

LEGAL BASIS:
Domestic Volunteer Service Act of 1973, as amended (P.L. 93-113).

ELIGIBILITY:
Sponsors applying for AmeriCorps VISTA must be nonprofit organizations. They may be public or private and include state and local governments.

GEOGRAPHIC RESTRICTIONS:
United States and its territories.

FINANCIAL DATA:
Volunteers receive a basic monthly subsistence allowance. An additional stipend is paid upon completion of service or the Americorps educational award.
Amount of support per award: Approximately $22,000 per volunteer service year.
Total amount of support: Varies.

NUMBER OF APPLICANTS MOST RECENT YEAR:
Organizations: Approximately 6,000; Individuals: Approximately 70,000.

NUMBER OF AWARDS: Organizations: 350.

APPLICATION INFORMATION:
Application information is available on the web site.
Duration: One to five years.
Deadline: Applications accepted on an ongoing basis.

ADDRESS INQUIRIES TO:
See e-mail address above.

THE DALLAS FOUNDATION [1249]
3963 Maple Avenue
Suite 390
Dallas, TX 75219
(214) 741-9898
Fax: (214) 741-9848

E-MAIL ADDRESS:
mjalonick@dallasfoundation.org

WEB SITE ADDRESS:
www.dallasfoundation.org

FOUNDED: 1929

AREAS OF INTEREST:
Arts, education, health and human services, and social services.

TYPE:
Capital grants; Project/program grants; Scholarships.

YEAR PROGRAM STARTED: 1929

PURPOSE:
To improve the quality of life for residents of the city and county of Dallas.

LEGAL BASIS:
Community foundation.

ELIGIBILITY:
Applicant organizations must be tax-exempt nonprofit focused on needs within Dallas County. Grants from the field of interest funds require a match between the purpose of the grant and the purpose of the available funds. Grants from the unrestricted funds may be given to any type of need within Dallas County.

Funds are not available from discretionary funds for individuals, endowments, research, debt retirement, annual campaigns,

underwriting of fund-raising events, or for organizations that have received support within the preceding three to five years.

GEOGRAPHIC RESTRICTIONS:
City and county of Dallas, Texas.

APPLICATION INFORMATION:
The application form is available on the Foundation web site, or by request. Unrestricted funds must have a letter of inquiry submitted by August 1.
Deadline: Interest funds: April 1 with announcement in June. Unrestricted funds: October 1 with announcement in December.

PUBLICATIONS:
Annual report; application guidelines.

ADDRESS INQUIRIES TO:
Laura Ward
Director of Community Philanthropy
(See address above.)

DANIELS FUND
101 Monroe Street
Denver, CO 80206-4467
(303) 393-7220
Fax: (720) 941-4110

E-MAIL ADDRESS:
info@danielsfund.org
grantsinfo@danielsfund.org
scholarrelations@danielsfund.org

WEB SITE ADDRESS:
www.danielsfund.org

TYPE:
Capital grants; General operating grants; Project/program grants; Scholarships. Daniels Fund Grants Program supports nonprofit organizations in the four-state region as well as national programs.

Daniels Fund Scholarship Program consists of the Daniels Scholarship and the Daniels Boundless Opportunity Scholarship. The Daniels Scholarship is a four-year scholarship that applies toward the expenses of attaining a Bachelor's degree at any nonprofit, accredited college or university in the U.S. The Daniels Boundless Opportunity Scholarships are distributed to select two- and four-year colleges and universities in Colorado, New Mexico, Utah and Wyoming, which then provide scholarships to support nontraditional students.

See entry 92 for full listing.

IRENE E. AND GEORGE A. DAVIS FOUNDATION [1250]
One Monarch Place
Suite 1300
Springfield, MA 01144-1300
(413) 734-8336
Fax: (413) 734-7845

E-MAIL ADDRESS:
info@davisfdn.org

WEB SITE ADDRESS:
www.davisfdn.org

FOUNDED: 1970

AREAS OF INTEREST:
Community, social services and early education.

TYPE:
Capital grants; Challenge/matching grants; General operating grants; Project/program grants.

PURPOSE:
To make strategically significant investments in organizations and projects that promise demonstrable long-range benefits improving the quality of life of citizens residing in Hampden County, MA.

LEGAL BASIS:
Private foundation.

ELIGIBILITY:
Grants are made to organizations that have tax-exempt status under Section 501(c)(3) of the Internal Revenue Code. Catholic organizations may apply. No grants are made to individuals.

GEOGRAPHIC RESTRICTIONS:
Hampden County, Massachusetts.

FINANCIAL DATA:
Amount of support per award: Varies.

APPLICATION INFORMATION:
Guidelines and application form are available on the Foundation web site.
Duration: One year.
Deadline: February 1, May 1, August 1 and November 1.

ADDRESS INQUIRIES TO:
Mary E. Walachy, Executive Director
(See address above.)

DEARBORN COMMUNITY FOUNDATION, INC. [1251]
322 Walnut Street
Lawrenceburg, IN 47025
(812) 539-4115
Fax: (812) 539-4119

WEB SITE ADDRESS:
www.dearborncf.org

FOUNDED: 1997

AREAS OF INTEREST:
Art, culture and humanities, community and public benefit, education, environmental and animal protection, and human services and youth.

TYPE:
Capital grants; Challenge/matching grants; Development grants; General operating grants; Project/program grants; Scholarships; Seed money grants; Technical assistance; Training grants.

YEAR PROGRAM STARTED: 1997

PURPOSE:
To connect people who care with causes that improve the quality of life in the community by advancing cultural, educational and social opportunities, while preserving the community's heritage and helping donors create a permanent legacy in Dearborn County, IN.

ELIGIBILITY:
Grants are made to organizations that are tax-exempt under Section 501(c)(3) of the Internal Revenue Code and recognized by the state of Indiana as current and active not-for-profit organizations. No grants are made to individuals outside of scholarships and/or educational grants. Nonsectarian religious programs may apply.

GEOGRAPHIC RESTRICTIONS:
Dearborn County, Indiana.

FINANCIAL DATA:
Amount of support per award: Varies.
Total amount of support: Maximum $100,000.

APPLICATION INFORMATION:
Application information is available on the web site.
Duration: One year.
Deadline: Varies.

STAFF:
Fred McCarter, Executive Director
Denise Sedler, Program Director

ADDRESS INQUIRIES TO:
Denise Sedler, Program Director
(See address above.)

DELAWARE COUNTY FOUNDATION   [1252]
3954 North Hampton Drive
Powell, OH 43065
(614) 764-2332
Fax: (614) 764-2333

E-MAIL ADDRESS:
foundation@delawarecf.org

WEB SITE ADDRESS:
www.delawarecf.org

FOUNDED: 1995

AREAS OF INTEREST:
Arts, civic affairs, community needs, culture, education, environment, health and human services.

NAME(S) OF PROGRAMS:
• **Designated Funds**
• **Donor Advised Funds**
• **Field of Interest Funds**
• **Organizational Endowment Funds**
• **Scholarship Funds**
• **Special Project Funds**
• **Unrestricted Funds**

TYPE:
Scholarships.

PURPOSE:
To enhance the quality of life for Delaware County residents.

ELIGIBILITY:
Grants are made to organizations that have tax-exempt status under Section 501(c)(3) of the Internal Revenue Code that serve Delaware County. No grants are made to individuals, religious programs, political groups or for deficit reduction.

GEOGRAPHIC RESTRICTIONS:
Delaware County, Ohio.

FINANCIAL DATA:
Amount of support per award: $500 to $100,000. Gooding Memorial Scholarships do not exceed $15,000.
Total amount of support: $677,740 in grants and scholarships for the year 2012.

APPLICATION INFORMATION:
Information may be obtained from the Foundation web site.
Duration: Typically one year.
Deadline: Scholarships: Mid-April and mid-June.

STAFF:
Marlene A. Casini, President and Chief Executive Officer

ROGER L. AND AGNES C. DELL CHARITABLE TRUST   [1253]
800 Nicollet Mall, BC-MN-H16A
Minneapolis, MN 55402
(612) 303-4414
Fax: (612) 303-3219

E-MAIL ADDRESS:
charitableservicesgroupmpls@usbank.com

AREAS OF INTEREST:
Arts and culture, education and youth in the Fergus Falls, MN region.

TYPE:
Capital grants; General operating grants; Project/program grants.

PURPOSE:
To improve the quality of life in Fergus Falls, MN and the surrounding area.

ELIGIBILITY:
Eligible organizations must be IRS 501(c)(3) tax-exempt.

GEOGRAPHIC RESTRICTIONS:
Fergus Falls, Minnesota and the surrounding area.

FINANCIAL DATA:
Amount of support per award: Varies.
Total amount of support: Varies.

APPLICATION INFORMATION:
Application should be submitted in writing outlining the nature of the request.

ADDRESS INQUIRIES TO:
Matt McGovern
Pemberton Sorlie Rufer Kershner PLLP
110 North Mill Street
P.O. Box 866
Fergus Falls, MN 56538-0866

*SPECIAL STIPULATIONS:
Unsolicited proposals not accepted.

DEPAUW UNIVERSITY KEY CLUB INTERNATIONAL BONNER/WRIGHT SCHOLARSHIP   [1254]
204 East Seminary Street
Greencastle, IN 46135
(765) 658-4030
(800) 447-2495
Fax: (765) 658-4137

E-MAIL ADDRESS:
jenniecoy@depauw.edu

WEB SITE ADDRESS:
www.keyclub.org

AREAS OF INTEREST:
Leadership and community service.

NAME(S) OF PROGRAMS:
• **Bonner Scholarship**
• **John Ellis Wright Award**

TYPE:
Scholarships.

PURPOSE:
To encourage youth to become actively involved in the community around them.

ELIGIBILITY:
Applicant must be a college-bound graduating high school senior with a grade point average of B or higher and have been an active Key Club member for two years, not serving as International Board member or governor.

Selection is based on academic achievement, commitment to community service, and leadership.

Women, ethnic minorities, and high-need students are encouraged to apply.

GEOGRAPHIC RESTRICTIONS:
United States.

FINANCIAL DATA:
Amount of support per award: Recipient receives $10,000 annual John Ellis Wright award and $2,500 Bonner Scholarship.

COOPERATIVE FUNDING PROGRAMS: Corella and Bertram F. Bonner Foundation.

APPLICATION INFORMATION:
No special application is required. Applicants involved in Key Club will be identified via their admissions application.
Duration: Four years.
Deadline: March 1 for early consideration; however, applications will be received until all selections are made.

ADDRESS INQUIRIES TO:
DePauw University Office of Admission
Bonner/Wright Scholarship Program
Greencastle, IN 46135-1778

*SPECIAL STIPULATIONS:
Bonner scholars are expected to maintain good academic standing at DePauw (2.5 grade point average or better), participate in educational and enrichment activities, successfully complete the Bonner Program First-Year Student Seminar, as well as participate in community-service programs for an average of 10 hours per week during the school year, and complete two summer internships consisting of 280 hours each.

RICHARD AND HELEN DEVOS FOUNDATION   [1255]
P.O. Box 230257
Grand Rapids, MI 49523-0257
(616) 643-4700
Fax: (616) 774-0116

E-MAIL ADDRESS:
michaelenem@rdvcorp.com

AREAS OF INTEREST:
Christian ministry and outreach and local community support.

TYPE:
General operating grants; Project/program grants.

PURPOSE:
To improve the quality of people's lives and to build a stronger community.

LEGAL BASIS:
Private foundation.

ELIGIBILITY:
Primarily, organizations that have prior affiliation with the family of DeVos and are located in western Michigan. Also, they must have evidence of tax-exempt status as an IRS 501(c)(3) public charity.

GEOGRAPHIC RESTRICTIONS:
Western Michigan.

FINANCIAL DATA:
Amount of support per award: Varies as to need and project.
Total amount of support: Varies.

APPLICATION INFORMATION:
Organizations should submit a statement of purpose and history of organization, budget, sources of support, goals and specifics regarding the program to be funded, annual report (if available) and copy of the organization's tax-exempt letter.
Duration: One year. Renewal possible.
Deadline: Proposals are reviewed quarterly.

ADDRESS INQUIRIES TO:
Sue Volkers, Grants Manager
(See address above.)

DICKINSON AREA COMMUNITY FOUNDATION [1256]

333 South Stephenson Avenue
Suite 204
Iron Mountain, MI 49801
(906) 774-3131
Fax: (906) 774-7640

E-MAIL ADDRESS:
dacf@uplogon.com

WEB SITE ADDRESS:
www.dickinsonareacommunityfoundation.org

AREAS OF INTEREST:
Arts, community needs and development, culture, education, environment, health and human services.

TYPE:
Grants-in-aid; Scholarships.

PURPOSE:
To encourage philanthropic investment in Dickinson County and surrounding Wisconsin communities.

ELIGIBILITY:
Grants are made to organizations that have tax-exempt status under Section 501(c)(3) of the Internal Revenue Code. No grants are made to individuals. Nonsectarian religious programs may apply.

GEOGRAPHIC RESTRICTIONS:
Dickinson County, Michigan and surrounding Wisconsin and Michigan communities.

FINANCIAL DATA:
Amount of support per award: $200 to $5,000.
Total amount of support: Varies.

APPLICATION INFORMATION:
When grants are available, application information is available on the web site.

Scholarship applicants can apply at their local schools.
Duration: One year.
Deadline: March 15.

PUBLICATIONS:
Brochures.

ADDRESS INQUIRIES TO:
Tamara Juul, Executive Director
(See address above.)

THE DIXON FOUNDATION [1257]

One Chase Corporate Drive
Suite 400
Birmingham, AL 35244-7001
(205) 313-6501
Fax: (205) 313-6502

E-MAIL ADDRESS:
diane@dixon-group.com

FOUNDED: 1986

AREAS OF INTEREST:
Local community.

TYPE:
General operating grants.

PURPOSE:
To support social services in northern Alabama and northern Georgia.

ELIGIBILITY:
Eligible organizations must be IRS 501(c)(3) tax-exempt. No funding to individuals.

GEOGRAPHIC RESTRICTIONS:
Central Alabama and northern Georgia.

FINANCIAL DATA:
Amount of support per award: Varies.
Total amount of support: Up to $400,000.

APPLICATION INFORMATION:
Applicants should send in a brief summary, budget, and copy of IRS 501(c)(3) tax determination letter.
Duration: One year. Grants renewable by reapplication.

ADDRESS INQUIRIES TO:
Diane Gentry, Operations Manager
(See address above.)

THE JEAN AND LOUIS DREYFUS FOUNDATION, INC. [1258]

315 Madison Avenue, Suite 900
New York, NY 10017
(212) 599-1931
Fax: (212) 599-2956

E-MAIL ADDRESS:
info@jldreyfus.org

WEB SITE ADDRESS:
www.foundationcenter.org/grantmaker/dreyfus

FOUNDED: 1979

AREAS OF INTEREST:
Aging and disadvantaged, arts-in-education, education and literacy, and social services.

TYPE:
Challenge/matching grants; General operating grants; Project/program grants. Funding to direct-service organizations and those projects which will produce systemic change.

PURPOSE:
To enhance the quality of life of New Yorkers, particularly the aging and disadvantaged.

ELIGIBILITY:
Nonprofit 501(c)(3) direct-service organizations focusing on enhancing the quality of life of New Yorkers.

GEOGRAPHIC RESTRICTIONS:
New York City (five boroughs), New York.

FINANCIAL DATA:
Amount of support per award: $5,000 to $20,000.
Total amount of support: $649,500.

APPLICATION INFORMATION:
Initially, a one- to two-page letter of inquiry describing the grantee organization and outlining the project in question. Letters should be sent by mail to the attention of Ms. Edmee de M. Firth, Executive Director.

Letters of inquiry from organizations not previously funded are not being accepted at this time.
Duration: One year. Must reapply.
Deadline: Letter of inquiry: January 15 and July 15.

ADDRESS INQUIRIES TO:
Edmee de M. Firth, Executive Director
(See address above.)

*PLEASE NOTE:
Letters of inquiry from organizations not previously funded are not being accepted at this time.

DULUTH SUPERIOR AREA COMMUNITY FOUNDATION [1259]

222 East Superior Street
Suite 302
Duluth, MN 55802
(218) 726-0232
Fax: (218) 726-0257

E-MAIL ADDRESS:
grantsinfo@dsacommunityfoundation.com

WEB SITE ADDRESS:
www.dsacommunityfoundation.com

FOUNDED: 1982

AREAS OF INTEREST:
Arts, community and economic development, education, environment and human services.

TYPE:
Challenge/matching grants; Development grants; Project/program grants; Seed money grants.

YEAR PROGRAM STARTED: 1983

PURPOSE:
To improve the quality of life in Duluth, Superior and surrounding counties.

LEGAL BASIS:
Community foundation.

ELIGIBILITY:
Eligible organizations must be IRS 501(c)(3) tax-exempt.

GEOGRAPHIC RESTRICTIONS:
Aitkin, Carlton, Cook, Itasca, Koochiching, Lake and St. Louis counties, Minnesota; Ashland, Bayfield and Douglas counties, Wisconsin.

FINANCIAL DATA:
Amount of support per award: $200 to $50,000.
Total amount of support: Varies.

APPLICATION INFORMATION:
Information regarding the inquiry process is available online.
Duration: Usually one year.
Deadline: Varies according to program.

PUBLICATIONS:
Elements, newsletter; annual report.

THE JOHN G. DUNCAN TRUST [1260]

c/o Wells Fargo Bank, N.A.
1740 Broadway
MAC C7300-493
Denver, CO 80274
(720) 947-6766
Fax: (720) 947-6832

E-MAIL ADDRESS:
kathy.cordova@wellsfargo.com

WEB SITE ADDRESS:
www.wellsfargo.com/privatefoundationgrants/duncan

FOUNDED: 1955

AREAS OF INTEREST:
Human services, health, education, religion and arts.

TYPE:
Project/program grants.

YEAR PROGRAM STARTED: 1956

PURPOSE:
To support education and health care, including dental care, food, children and youth, social, blind and aging services.

LEGAL BASIS:
Private foundation.

ELIGIBILITY:
501(c)(3) tax-exempt organizations in Colorado only may apply. Grants are not made for individuals, general operating expenses, endowments, organizations outside of Colorado, or other grantmaking organizations.

Organizations receiving a grant are not eligible to apply for a grant in the following calendar year.

GEOGRAPHIC RESTRICTIONS:
Colorado.

FINANCIAL DATA:
Amount of support per award: Typically $1,000 to $10,000.
Total amount of support: Approximately $300,000 per year.

APPLICATION INFORMATION:
Proposals should include standard summary and budget information, evidence of tax-exempt status, and written information deemed appropriate by the applicant organizations to be helpful in evaluating their proposal. Mission statement is required. Do not include audio or video materials.

Guidelines for reference are found on the web site.
Duration: No grants are made on a continuing basis.
Deadline: The last day of January, April, July and October.

ADDRESS INQUIRIES TO:
Kathy Cordova
(See e-mail address or phone number above.)

*PLEASE NOTE:
The Trust strongly discourages paper applications. If unable to apply online, contact Kathy Cordova at the telephone or e-mail address above.

THE EAST BAY COMMUNITY FOUNDATION   [1261]

DeDomenico Building
200 Frank H. Ogawa Plaza
Oakland, CA 94612
(510) 836-3223
Fax: (510) 836-7418

E-MAIL ADDRESS:
communityinvestment@eastbaycf.org

WEB SITE ADDRESS:
www.ebcf.org

FOUNDED: 1928

AREAS OF INTEREST:
Preparing young people for success in the educational system and providing economic opportunities for the underprivileged and families.

TYPE:
Project/program grants. Building leadership capacity grants.

YEAR PROGRAM STARTED: 1928

PURPOSE:
To transform the lives of people in the East Bay with pressing needs.

LEGAL BASIS:
Public foundation.

ELIGIBILITY:
Eligible organizations must be IRS 501(c)(3) tax-exempt.

GEOGRAPHIC RESTRICTIONS:
Alameda and Contra Costa counties, California.

FINANCIAL DATA:
Amount of support per award: Varies.
Total amount of support: $1,000,000 annually.

APPLICATION INFORMATION:
Guidelines and application are available online.

PUBLICATIONS:
Guidelines.

EAST TEXAS COMMUNITIES FOUNDATION   [1262]

315 North Broadway Avenue
Tyler, TX 75702-5712
(903) 533-0208
Fax: (903) 533-0258

E-MAIL ADDRESS:
info@etcf.org

WEB SITE ADDRESS:
www.etcf.org

FOUNDED: 1989

AREAS OF INTEREST:
Community development.

TYPE:
Grants-in-aid; Scholarships. The Foundation administers scholarship funds for donors, nonprofit organizations, civic clubs, service groups and businesses.

PURPOSE:
To promote charitable giving which enhances the quality of life for the people of east Texas.

ELIGIBILITY:
Grants are made to 501(c)(3) organizations. Scholarship applicants must be citizens or permanent residents of the U.S.

GEOGRAPHIC RESTRICTIONS:
East Texas.

FINANCIAL DATA:
Amount of support per award: Varies.
Total amount of support: Varies.

APPLICATION INFORMATION:
Application information is available on the web site. Scholarship applications must be submitted electronically.
Duration: Varies.
Deadline: Varies.

ADDRESS INQUIRIES TO:
Mary Lynn Smith, Program Officer
(See address above.)

EAU CLAIRE COMMUNITY FOUNDATION   [1263]

306 South Barstow Street, Suite 104
Eau Claire, WI 54701
(715) 552-3801
Fax: (715) 552-3802

E-MAIL ADDRESS:
suebornick@eccommunityfoundation.org

WEB SITE ADDRESS:
www.eccommunityfoundation.org

FOUNDED: 1997

AREAS OF INTEREST:
Serving the charitable needs of the Eau Claire, WI area.

TYPE:
Project/program grants.

YEAR PROGRAM STARTED: 1997

PURPOSE:
To strengthen our community by offering donors opportunities to establish charitable legacies, by making grants, and by serving as a catalyst to address community needs.

LEGAL BASIS:
Nonprofit community foundation.

ELIGIBILITY:
Eligible organizations must have 501(c)(3) status. Grants are available to religious organizations when recipients of services are not required to profess membership or belief in the religious organization.

GEOGRAPHIC RESTRICTIONS:
Eau Claire County, Wisconsin.

FINANCIAL DATA:
Amount of support per award: Varies.

NUMBER OF APPLICANTS MOST RECENT YEAR:
48 for the year 2012.

NUMBER OF AWARDS: 75.

REPRESENTATIVE AWARDS:
$1,500 to Literacy Volunteers-Chippewa Valley.

APPLICATION INFORMATION:
Submit original application and cover letter, plus 12 copies (three-hole punched). Include one copy of each of the following:
(1) most recent audited financial statement or Form 990 tax return;
(2) list of Board of Directors and;
(3) copy of current IRS determination letter indicating 501(c)(3) or 509(a) tax-exempt status, or evidence the organization is not a private foundation as defined in Section 509(a). If not available, explain status.

Applications must be delivered or mailed. Applications sent by fax or e-mail are not accepted.
Duration: One year.
Deadline: February 1.

STAFF:
Sue Bornick, Executive Director

ADDRESS INQUIRIES TO:
Sue Bornick, Executive Director
(See address above.)

ECOLAB FOUNDATION   [1264]

370 North Wabasha Street, EUC/12
St. Paul, MN 55102
(651) 293-2923
Fax: (651) 225-3191

E-MAIL ADDRESS:
ecolabfoundation@ecolab.com

WEB SITE ADDRESS:
www.ecolab.com

FOUNDED: 1986

AREAS OF INTEREST:
Arts and culture, education, environment and community development.

CONSULTING OR VOLUNTEER SERVICES:
501(c)(3) organizations.

TYPE:
General operating grants; Project/program grants. Employee matching gifts.

YEAR PROGRAM STARTED: 1986

PURPOSE:
To enrich the quality of life in communities where Ecolab operates.

LEGAL BASIS:
Corporate foundation.

ELIGIBILITY:
Eligible organizations must be IRS 501(c)(3) tax-exempt.

GEOGRAPHIC RESTRICTIONS:
City of Industry, California; McDonough, Georgia; Elk Grove Village, Joliet and Naperville, Illinois; Huntington, Indiana; Garyville, Louisiana; St. Paul, Minnesota; Columbus, Mississippi; Greensboro, North Carolina; Ellwood City, Pennsylvania; Fort Worth, Garland and Sugar Land, Texas; Martinsburg, West Virginia; and Beloit, Wisconsin.

FINANCIAL DATA:
Amount of support per award: $5,000 to $60,000.

Total amount of support: $4,900,000 in grants as of fiscal year 2013.

Matching fund requirements: Must be an Ecolab employee.

NUMBER OF APPLICANTS MOST RECENT YEAR: 300.

NUMBER OF AWARDS: 200.

APPLICATION INFORMATION:
Application form is available online.
Duration: One year.
Deadline: December 1.

PUBLICATIONS:
Guidelines (on web site).

ADDRESS INQUIRIES TO:
Lisa Maloney-Vinz
Community Relations Program Manager
(See address above.)

EL PASO COMMUNITY FOUNDATION   [1265]

333 North Oregon Street
2nd Floor
El Paso, TX 79901
(915) 533-4020
Fax: (915) 532-0716

E-MAIL ADDRESS:
info@epcf.org

WEB SITE ADDRESS:
www.epcf.org

FOUNDED: 1977

AREAS OF INTEREST:
Arts and humanities, education, public benefit, health and disabilities, environment and animals, and human services.

TYPE:
General operating grants; Scholarships. A charitable fund established at the Foundation by individuals, corporations or organizations.

YEAR PROGRAM STARTED: 1972

PURPOSE:
To improve the quality of life in the El Paso region, TX.

LEGAL BASIS:
501(c)(3) agencies.

ELIGIBILITY:
Grant request will be considered only from 501(c)(3) agencies located within or offering services to the community which includes far west Texas, southern New Mexico and northern Chihuahua, Mexico. Grants are not made to individuals or religious organizations.

GEOGRAPHIC RESTRICTIONS:
Far west Texas, southern New Mexico and northern Chihuahua, Mexico.

FINANCIAL DATA:
Amount of support per award: $4,000 to $40,000.

Total amount of support: Varies.

APPLICATION INFORMATION:
The Foundation utilizes an online application process.
Duration: One year.
Deadline: Grants: February 1 and August 1.

ADDRESS INQUIRIES TO:
Bonita Johnson, Grants Administrator
(See address above.)

FRED L. EMERSON FOUNDATION, INC.   [1266]

5654 South Street Road
Auburn, NY 13021
(315) 253-9621 ext. 222
Fax: (315) 253-5235

E-MAIL ADDRESS:
info@emersonfoundation.com

WEB SITE ADDRESS:
www.emersonfoundation.com

AREAS OF INTEREST:
Education (primarily private higher education), hospital and health programs, community agencies, cultural institutions, youth and community service programs, and social welfare agencies.

TYPE:
Capital grants; Challenge/matching grants; Endowments; Project/program grants; Research grants.

PURPOSE:
To improve the quality of life in Auburn, Cayuga County and upstate New York.

ELIGIBILITY:
Organizations must be tax-exempt. No grants are made to individuals; no loans or funding of operating expenses.

GEOGRAPHIC RESTRICTIONS:
Community of Auburn, Cayuga County and upstate New York.

FINANCIAL DATA:
Amount of support per award: Varies.
Total amount of support: Varies.

APPLICATION INFORMATION:
Proposals may be submitted in letter form, detailing the project for which support is being sought, along with a copy of the 501(c)(3) IRS tax-exempt determination letter, project budget and fund-raising plan, list of board of directors, and most recent copy of financial statement.
Duration: Varies.
Deadline: Proposals are accepted on an ongoing basis.

PUBLICATIONS:
Guidelines.

ADDRESS INQUIRIES TO:
Daniel Fessenden
Executive Director and Secretary
(See address above.)

ENTERPRISE COMMUNITY PARTNERS

11000 Broken Land Parkway
Columbia, MD 21044
(781) 235-2006
Fax: (781) 235-4011

WEB SITE ADDRESS:
www.enterprisecommunity.org

TYPE:
Fellowships.

See entry 415 for full listing.

ESSEX COUNTY COMMUNITY FOUNDATION   [1267]

175 Andover Street
Suite 101
Danvers, MA 01923
(978) 777-8876 ext. 28
Fax: (978) 777-9454

E-MAIL ADDRESS:
j.bishop@eccf.org

WEB SITE ADDRESS:
www.eccf.org

FOUNDED: 1999

AREAS OF INTEREST:
Arts and culture, education, environment, health, social and community services and youth services.

CONSULTING OR VOLUNTEER SERVICES:
Nonprofit organizations in Essex County, MA.

NAME(S) OF PROGRAMS:
• **Center for Nonprofit Excellence**
• **Essex County Youth-at-Risk**
• **First Jobs**
• **Greater Lawrence Summer Fund**
• **The Hunger Project**
• **Institute for Trustees**
• **The Women's Fund of Essex County**

TYPE:
Capital grants; Conferences/seminars; Endowments; General operating grants; Project/program grants; Scholarships; Technical assistance. Capacity-building grants. Various grantmaking funds. Mostly project/program grants. Agencies can establish endowment funds.

The Foundation has eight competitive grant funds and 22 scholarship programs. There are 120 donor-advised funds.

YEAR PROGRAM STARTED: 1999

PURPOSE:
To promote local philanthropy and to strengthen the nonprofit organizations of Essex County.

LEGAL BASIS:
Public 501(c)(3) charity.

ELIGIBILITY:
Organizations offering programs and services in Essex County (MA) communities, recognized as tax-exempt under Section 501(c)(3) of the Internal Revenue Code and, in some cases, to agencies of local or state government. Organizations with a qualified fiscal sponsor are also considered.

GEOGRAPHIC RESTRICTIONS:
Primarily Essex County, Massachusetts.

FINANCIAL DATA:
Approximately $25,000,000 in assets under management.

Amount of support per award: $1,000 to $20,000 for competitive grants; donor-advised funds may award larger grants.

Total amount of support: $4,500,000 for fiscal year 2013.

NUMBER OF AWARDS: 571 for fiscal year 2013.

REPRESENTATIVE AWARDS:
$9,000 to Elder Services of the Merrimack Valley, Inc., to support the financial literacy education program for elderly Spanish-speaking women; $15,000 to Pingree School, to support Prep@Pingree, an academic summer enrichment program for inner-city middle school students, to help sharpen their analytical, verbal and written skills.

APPLICATION INFORMATION:
Application information for grants is available on the web site. Scholarship applicants should enquire at their local school.
Duration: Up to three years, depending on fund.
Deadline: Varies.

PUBLICATIONS:
Annual report; newsletter; brochure.

IRS IDENTIFICATION NUMBER: 04-3407816

STAFF:
David Welbourn, President and Chief Executive Officer

ADDRESS INQUIRIES TO:
Julie Bishop, Vice President
Grants and Services
(See address above.)

FAIR OAKS FOUNDATION [1268]
600 Grant Street, Suite 4600
Pittsburgh, PA 15219
(412) 456-4418
(412) 456-4400
Fax: (412) 456-4404

E-MAIL ADDRESS:
rhoover@ampcopgh.com

AREAS OF INTEREST:
United Way, universities and community funds.

TYPE:
Cash contributions.

PURPOSE:
To provide support for community funds and higher education.

ELIGIBILITY:
Organizations classified as 501(c)(3) by the IRS can apply. No grants to individuals.

GEOGRAPHIC RESTRICTIONS:
United States.

FINANCIAL DATA:
Amount of support per award: $250 to $1,000.
Total amount of support: $400,000 per year.

APPLICATION INFORMATION:
Request should be in letter format.
Deadline: November 1.

ADDRESS INQUIRIES TO:
Rose Hoover, Secretary, Vice President and Trustee
(See address above.)

FAIRFIELD COUNTY COMMUNITY FOUNDATION [1269]
383 Main Avenue
Norwalk, CT 06851
(203) 750-3200
Fax: (203) 750-3232

E-MAIL ADDRESS:
info@fccfoundation.org

WEB SITE ADDRESS:
www.fccfoundation.org

FOUNDED: 1992

AREAS OF INTEREST:
Community development, housing, education, youth development, health and human services, arts and culture, and the environment.

NAME(S) OF PROGRAMS:
● **Center for Nonprofit Excellence (CNE)**

TYPE:
Challenge/matching grants; Demonstration grants; Development grants; General operating grants; Project/program grants; Scholarships; Seed money grants; Technical assistance. Scholarships are for high school students pursuing college or postsecondary training.

The Center for Nonprofit Excellence (CNE) was created to enhance the effectiveness of Fairfield County nonprofit organizations. The CNE offers nonprofit executive directors, senior staff and board members high-quality and affordable professional development workshops taught at Essential, Intermediate and Advanced levels.

YEAR PROGRAM STARTED: 1992

PURPOSE:
To promote the growth of philanthropy in order to strengthen the communities of Fairfield County, CT.

ELIGIBILITY:
Grants are made to organizations that have tax-exempt status under Section 501(c)(3) of the Internal Revenue Code. No grants are made to individuals.

Discretionary grants are only made to organizations serving Fairfield County, CT.

Donor-advised grants can be awarded to nonprofits throughout the U.S. and also abroad.

FINANCIAL DATA:
Assets over $160,000,000 for the year ended December 31, 2013.
Amount of support per award: Grants vary in amount, depending upon the needs and nature of the request.
Total amount of support: $18,000,000 in grants per year.

APPLICATION INFORMATION:
Application information is available on the web site.
Duration: One year. Renewal possible.

ADDRESS INQUIRIES TO:
Sharon Jones, Program Assistant
E-mail: sjones@fccfoundation.org
(See address above.)

THE FEINSTEIN FOUNDATION
37 Alhambra Circle
Cranston, RI 02905
(401) 467-5155
(401) 941-5913
Fax: (401) 941-0988

E-MAIL ADDRESS:
asf@feinsteinfoundation.org

WEB SITE ADDRESS:
www.feinsteinfoundation.org

TYPE:
Challenge/matching grants. Each participating agency receives a share of $1,000,000 that represents their portion of the total amount

reported to the Foundation that was raised by anti-hunger agencies using the Foundation's challenge in their fight to end hunger fund-raising.

See entry 1482 for full listing.

SAMUEL S. FELS FUND [1270]
1528 Walnut Street
Suite 1002
Philadelphia, PA 19102
(215) 731-9455
Fax: (215) 731-9457

E-MAIL ADDRESS:
helenc@samfels.org

WEB SITE ADDRESS:
www.samfels.org

FOUNDED: 1936

AREAS OF INTEREST:
Public education, community services and arts.

NAME(S) OF PROGRAMS:
● **Arts and Culture**
● **Community Concerns**
● **Public Education**

TYPE:
Challenge/matching grants; Demonstration grants; Development grants; General operating grants; Project/program grants; Seed money grants; Technical assistance.

YEAR PROGRAM STARTED: 1936

PURPOSE:
To improve the quality of life for the citizens of Philadelphia, especially the least fortunate.

LEGAL BASIS:
Private foundation.

ELIGIBILITY:
Applicants must be agencies located in the city of Philadelphia. Excluded from the Fund's program of grants are contributions to national organizations, capital campaigns, general support, scholarships, fellowships and grants-in-aid for travel, research and publication; grants to individual day care or afterschool programs. No grants are made to individuals.

GEOGRAPHIC RESTRICTIONS:
Philadelphia, Pennsylvania.

FINANCIAL DATA:
Amount of support per award: $3,000 to $30,000.
Total amount of support: $2,000,000 for the year 2014.

NUMBER OF APPLICANTS MOST RECENT YEAR:
Approximately 500.

NUMBER OF AWARDS: Approximately 200.

APPLICATION INFORMATION:
Guidelines are available on the web site.
Duration: Primarily one year.
Deadline: Arts: January 15 and May 15.

PUBLICATIONS:
Annual report; guidelines for applicants.

TRUSTEES:
Valerie Clayton, President
Beverly Coleman, Vice President
John H. Rice, Treasurer
Helen Cunningham, Secretary
Phoebe Haddon, Member Director
Ida Chen
Sandra Featherman
Gabriel Mandujano

Len Rieser
David Wice

ADDRESS INQUIRIES TO:
Helen Cunningham, Executive Director
(See telephone number above.)

FIREMAN'S FUND INSURANCE COMPANY [1271]

777 San Marin Drive
Novato, CA 94998
(415) 899-2000

E-MAIL ADDRESS:
heritage@ffic.com

WEB SITE ADDRESS:
www.firemansfund.com/heritage

FOUNDED: 1863

AREAS OF INTEREST:
Fire service organizations and fire and burn prevention programs.

NAME(S) OF PROGRAMS:
● **Heritage Program**

TYPE:
Project/program grants.

YEAR PROGRAM STARTED: 2004

PURPOSE:
To support firefighters for safer communities; to provide awards to fire departments for needed equipment, training and community education programs.

LEGAL BASIS:
Company corporate giving program.

ELIGIBILITY:
Must be a nonprofit, tax-exempt 501(c)(3) organization. No grants to individuals, fraternal, veteran, sectarian, religious or political organizations.

GEOGRAPHIC RESTRICTIONS:
United States.

FINANCIAL DATA:
Amount of support per award: Varies.
Total amount of support: Varies.

NUMBER OF AWARDS: 200.

REPRESENTATIVE AWARDS:
$12,330 to Berea Fire Department, Berea, OH, for critical protective gear and clothing; $7,500 to Fort Washington Fire Company, Fort Washington, PA, for extrication equipment.

APPLICATION INFORMATION:
Employees and independent agencies nominate fire departments for grants.
Duration: Varies.

ADDRESS INQUIRIES TO:
See e-mail address above.

*PLEASE NOTE:
No request considered by phone call.

FIRST HORIZON NATIONAL CORPORATION [1272]

P.O. Box 84
Memphis, TN 38101-0084
(901) 523-4444
(901) 523-4207
Fax: (901) 523-4354

E-MAIL ADDRESS:
foundation@firsttennessee.com

WEB SITE ADDRESS:
www.firsttennesseefoundation.com

FOUNDED: 1864

AREAS OF INTEREST:
Financial literacy and economic development, education and helping youth, health and human services, and arts and culture.

TYPE:
Capital grants; Challenge/matching grants; Development grants; General operating grants; Matching gifts; Project/program grants; Research grants; Scholarships.

PURPOSE:
To generate economic development in core market; to preserve and enhance what is special about core market and its communities; to leverage additional resources for the community.

LEGAL BASIS:
Corporate contributions program.

ELIGIBILITY:
Grants are made to tax-exempt organizations whose activities meet the objectives outlined above. First Horizon National Corp. does not use corporate contributions to support individuals, charities sponsored solely by a single civic organization, charities which redistribute funds to other charitable organizations, except in the case of recognized united fund-type organizations, bank "clearing-house" organizations, agencies supported by United Way or united arts funds, religious, veteran, social, athletic or fraternal organizations, political organizations or those having the primary purpose of influencing legislation or promoting a particular ideological point of view, trips and tours, operating budget deficits, multiyear commitments of four years or more and/or endowments.

Grants are limited to North Carolina and Tennessee communities where First Horizon National Corp. has a presence.

FINANCIAL DATA:
Amount of support per award: $1,000 and up.
Total amount of support: Approximately $5,000,000 annually.

APPLICATION INFORMATION:
Details available on the web site.
Duration: Typically one year. Funding is not automatically renewed. Recipients desiring continued support should submit a request for review in the fall.
Deadline: November 1 prior to the year for which funds are being requested.

PUBLICATIONS:
Program guidelines and application procedures.

STAFF:
Melissa Duong, Community Investment Manager, First Tennessee Foundation

ADDRESS INQUIRIES TO:
Melissa Duong, Community Investment Manager
First Tennessee Foundation
(See address above.)

*SPECIAL STIPULATIONS:
Grants are limited to communities served by First Horizon National Corp.

THE FLINN FOUNDATION

1802 North Central Avenue
Phoenix, AZ 85004
(602) 744-6800
Fax: (602) 744-6815

E-MAIL ADDRESS:
info@flinn.org

WEB SITE ADDRESS:
www.flinn.org

TYPE:
Demonstration grants; Fellowships; Project/program grants; Scholarships; Seed money grants. The arts and culture grants program assists Arizona's large arts and culture organizations in generating capital through creative programming and fiscal planning.

The Foundation's biosciences grant projects aim to strengthen Arizona's biosciences infrastructure and thereby improve the state's capacity to compete nationally and internationally in the biosciences economy.

The Arizona Center for Civic Leadership seeks to strengthen civic leadership in Arizona.

The Flinn Scholars Program annually awards top Arizona high school graduates full scholarship support.

See entry 128 for full listing.

THE FOUNDATION FOR ENHANCING COMMUNITIES [1273]

200 North Third Street, 8th Floor
Harrisburg, PA 17108
(717) 236-5040
Fax: (717) 231-4463

E-MAIL ADDRESS:
info@tfec.org

WEB SITE ADDRESS:
www.tfec.org

FOUNDED: 1920

AREAS OF INTEREST:
Education, human services, arts and culture, children and youth.

CONSULTING OR VOLUNTEER SERVICES:
Consulting services available.

NAME(S) OF PROGRAMS:
● **Capital Beginnings**
● **Women's Fund**

TYPE:
Challenge/matching grants; Conferences/seminars; Endowments; Internships; Matching gifts; Project/program grants; Scholarships; Seed money grants; Technical assistance. Management services.

YEAR PROGRAM STARTED: 1920

PURPOSE:
To stimulate philanthropy and enhance the quality of life in the community through accumulating, managing and disbursing financial assets and by serving as a catalyst and neutral convener to meet a wide range of community needs in south central Pennsylvania counties of Cumberland, Dauphin, Franklin, Lebanon and Perry.

LEGAL BASIS:
Community foundation.

ELIGIBILITY:
Eligible organizations must have 501(c)(3) status. No grants are made to individuals or religious organizations for religious purposes.

GEOGRAPHIC RESTRICTIONS:
Cumberland, Dauphin, Franklin, Lebanon and Perry counties, Pennsylvania.

FINANCIAL DATA:
Assets of $72,759,531 for the year ended December 31, 2013.
Amount of support per award: $2,000 average.

NUMBER OF AWARDS: 1,760.

APPLICATION INFORMATION:
Applicants should:
(1) review the grantmaking guidelines for each regional foundation;
(2) contact the Program Officer to determine eligibility to apply and discuss the proposal and;
(3) submit a grant application according to the guidelines provided on the Foundation's web site.
Duration: One year. Nonrenewable.

PUBLICATIONS:
Annual report.

IRS IDENTIFICATION NUMBER: 01-0564355

STAFF:
Janice R. Black, President and Chief Executive Officer
Kirk C. Demyan, Chief Financial Officer
Jeanne Predmore, Capital Beginnings Project Director
Jennifer Doyle, Director of Development and Community Investment
Jennifer Kuntch, Program Officer for Community Investment
Allison Moesta, Program Officer for Educational Enhancement
James Lloyd, Communications Officer
Jim Martin, Senior Financial Services Associate
Brandon Tressler, Financial Services Associate
Deborah Fulham-Winston, Asset Development Associate

ADDRESS INQUIRIES TO:
Director of Development and Community Investment
(See address above.)

***SPECIAL STIPULATIONS:**
All discretionary grants must be awarded in the five-county region of Cumberland, Dauphin, Franklin, Lebanon and Perry counties.

FOUNDATION FOR THE CAROLINAS [1274]
220 North Tryon Street
Charlotte, NC 28202
(704) 973-4500
(704) 973-4556
Fax: (704) 973-4956
(800) 973-7244

E-MAIL ADDRESS:
bcollier@fftc.org

WEB SITE ADDRESS:
www.fftc.org

FOUNDED: 1958

AREAS OF INTEREST:
Education, human services, health and medical research, arts, environment and historical preservation, youth, senior programs and social capital.

TYPE:
Demonstration grants; General operating grants; Project/program grants; Scholarships; Seed money grants.

YEAR PROGRAM STARTED: 1958

PURPOSE:
To advance philanthropy by serving donors, increasing charitable giving and improving communities in its area of service.

LEGAL BASIS:
Community foundation.

ELIGIBILITY:
Grants will be made only to organizations recognized by the IRS as 501(c)(3) in the greater Charlotte area.

The Foundation generally does not fund capital campaigns and buildings, computers, vehicles and similar equipment, publication of books and production of videos, conferences and travel, grants to individuals or endowment funds.

GEOGRAPHIC RESTRICTIONS:
Greater Charlotte, North Carolina.

FINANCIAL DATA:
Amount of support per award: $2,500 to $100,000.
Total amount of support: $50,000,000 for the year 2013.

APPLICATION INFORMATION:
Contact the Foundation.
Duration: One year.
Deadline: Varies.

BOARD OF DIRECTORS:
Catherine P. Bessant, Chairperson
Angela Bower
Ron Carter, Ph.D.
Eugene Flood
Harvey Gantt
W. Barnes Hauptfuhrer
James Johnson
Chris Kearney
Todd Mansfield
Pat Rodgers
Art Rogers
James E. Rogers
Geri Rucker
Laura Schulte
Ruth Shaw, Ph.D.
Lori Levine Sklut
Tom E. Smith

ADDRESS INQUIRIES TO:
Brian Collier, Senior Vice President
(See address above.)

FOUNDATION FOR THE MID SOUTH [1275]
134 East Amite Street
Jackson, MS 39201
(601) 355-8167
Fax: (601) 355-6499

E-MAIL ADDRESS:
iallen@fndmidsouth.org

WEB SITE ADDRESS:
www.fndmidsouth.org

FOUNDED: 1989

AREAS OF INTEREST:
Improving the quality of life for residents in the states of Arkansas, Louisiana and Mississippi, with a primary focus on education, community development, health and wellness, and wealth building.

NAME(S) OF PROGRAMS:
• **Community Development**
• **Education**
• **Health & Wellness**
• **Wealth Building**

TYPE:
Conferences/seminars; Fellowships; General operating grants; Internships; Training grants.

PURPOSE:
To nurture families and children; to improve schools; to build the economy for all people in the region.

ELIGIBILITY:
Applicants must be tax-exempt organizations under Section 501(c)(3) of the Internal Revenue Code.

GEOGRAPHIC RESTRICTIONS:
Arkansas, Louisiana and Mississippi.

FINANCIAL DATA:
Amount of support per award: Varies.
Total amount of support: Varies.

APPLICATION INFORMATION:
The Foundation awards most grants by issuing Requests for Proposals (RFPs). If an RFP is not available and a project is within the scope and strategy of the Foundation's priorities, an eligible organization may submit an initial inquiry using the Grant Inquiry Form. The form seeks basic information about the organization and a brief overview of the concept and request. If the inquiry is deemed favorable after review, applicants will be contacted by the appropriate program officer to discuss the request in greater detail.
Duration: One to three years.
Deadline: Varies.

ADDRESS INQUIRIES TO:
E-mail: concept@fndmidsouth.org

FOUNDATION FOR THE TRI-STATE COMMUNITY, INC. [1276]
855 Central Avenue
Suite 300
Ashland, KY 41101
(606) 324-3888
Fax: (606) 324-5961

E-MAIL ADDRESS:
ftsc_mwwiseman@yahoo.com

WEB SITE ADDRESS:
www.tristatefoundation.org

FOUNDED: 1972

AREAS OF INTEREST:
Arts and cultural programs, education, science and charity.

NAME(S) OF PROGRAMS:
• **21st Century Endowment Fund**

TYPE:
Challenge/matching grants; Project/program grants; Scholarships; Seed money grants; Technical assistance.

YEAR PROGRAM STARTED: 1980

PURPOSE:
To improve the quality of life in the tri-state area by encouraging, raising, administering and distributing gifts for charitable, cultural, educational and scientific purposes.

LEGAL BASIS:
Community foundation.

ELIGIBILITY:
Priority will be given to organizations who are 501(c)(3) and other organizations that meet the Foundation's special charitable grant guidelines. The Foundation does not fund sectarian activities or individuals.

GEOGRAPHIC RESTRICTIONS:
Boyd and Greenup counties, Kentucky; Lawrence County, Ohio; Cabell and Wayne counties, West Virginia.

FINANCIAL DATA:
Amount of support per award: $500 to $5,000.
Total amount of support: Typically, around $15,000 per quarter.

NUMBER OF APPLICANTS MOST RECENT YEAR: 25.

NUMBER OF AWARDS: 21 for the year 2013.

REPRESENTATIVE AWARDS:
$2,500 to Huntington Area Food Bank; $2,500 to Greenup County Health Department; $4,000 to Habitat for Humanity; $2,500 to Lawrence County Horseman's Association.

APPLICATION INFORMATION:
Applicants must submit the application form and IRS tax determination letter.
Duration: One-time award. Applicants may reapply after a one-year period.
Deadline: Applications are accepted at any time and are currently reviewed on a quarterly basis.

PUBLICATIONS:
Annual report; *How We've Grown*; grant guidelines; 35th anniversary report.

IRS IDENTIFICATION NUMBER: 61-0729266

STAFF:
Mary Witten Wiseman, President

ADDRESS INQUIRIES TO:
Mary Witten Wiseman, President
(See address above.)

THE FREMONT AREA COMMUNITY FOUNDATION   [1277]
4424 West 48th Street
Fremont, MI 49412
(231) 924-5350
Fax: (231) 924-5391

E-MAIL ADDRESS:
info@tfacf.org

WEB SITE ADDRESS:
www.tfacf.org

AREAS OF INTEREST:
Arts and culture, children, community development, community health, education, environment and natural resources, family and youth.

TYPE:
Challenge/matching grants; Project/program grants.

YEAR PROGRAM STARTED: 1951

PURPOSE:
To bring community development to life in Newaygo County.

LEGAL BASIS:
Public community foundation.

ELIGIBILITY:
Eligible organizations must be IRS 501(c)(3) tax-exempt.

GEOGRAPHIC RESTRICTIONS:
Newaygo County, Michigan.

FINANCIAL DATA:
Total value of assets: $203,000,000 as of December 2012.
Amount of support per award: Varies.

Total amount of support: $9,100,000 for the year 2012.

APPLICATION INFORMATION:
Applications are available from the Foundation and must include a copy of the IRS tax determination letter.
Duration: One year. Renewal by reapplication.
Deadline: February 15 and September 15.

STAFF:
Carla A. Roberts, President and Chief Executive Officer

ADDRESS INQUIRIES TO:
Carla A. Roberts
President and Chief Executive Officer
(See address above.)

THE FRIST FOUNDATION   [1278]
3100 West End Avenue, Suite 1200
Nashville, TN 37203
(615) 292-3868
Fax: (615) 292-5843

E-MAIL ADDRESS:
askfrist@fristfoundation.org

WEB SITE ADDRESS:
www.fristfoundation.org

FOUNDED: 1982

AREAS OF INTEREST:
Health, human services, education, technology, civic affairs and the arts.

NAME(S) OF PROGRAMS:
- **The Frist Foundation Awards of Achievement**
- **The Frist Foundation Technology Grants Program**

TYPE:
Capital grants; General operating grants; Project/program grants; Technical assistance. The Foundation makes direct grants to tax-exempt organizations in the greater Nashville area in the fields of health, human services, education, civic affairs and the arts, with a special emphasis on vulnerable populations.

In addition to conducting a grantmaking program responsive to external requests, the Frist Foundation actively seeks out and initiates programs addressing particular needs. Among these programs are the Center for Nonprofit Management, a community-wide effort to provide specialized management training and consulting to nonprofit community organizations.

Operating grants are given to organizations that offer management assistance, training, volunteers, goods or services to large numbers of Nashville agencies.

YEAR PROGRAM STARTED: 1983

PURPOSE:
To invest its resources in selected not-for-profit organizations in the greater Nashville area in ways that strengthen their ability to provide services; to enhance unique community assets in Nashville; to develop new sources of revenue through social enterprise.

LEGAL BASIS:
509(a) private foundation.

ELIGIBILITY:
Grantees must be tax-exempt under Section 501(c)(3) of the Internal Revenue Code and not private foundations as described in Section 509(a). The Foundation ordinarily

does not make grants or provide support to:
(1) international, regional or local organizations outside the Nashville area;
(2) projects, programs or organizations that serve a limited audience or a relatively small number of people;
(3) hospitals, biomedical or clinical research, or disease-specific organizations seeking support for national projects and programs;
(4) organizations during their first three years of operation;
(5) endowments;
(6) social events, fund-raising activities or telethons;
(7) individuals or their projects;
(8) political activities;
(9) religious organizations for religious purposes;
(10) private foundations;
(11) advertising sponsorships or;
(12) schools below the college level, except for projects intended to serve the broader community.

Special emphasis is placed on organizations that provide services to vulnerable populations.

GEOGRAPHIC RESTRICTIONS:
Nashville, Tennessee area.

FINANCIAL DATA:
Amount of support per award: $500 to $100,000. Average $3,500.
Total amount of support: $8,435,974 for the year 2013.

NUMBER OF APPLICANTS MOST RECENT YEAR: 333 for the year 2013.

NUMBER OF AWARDS: 213 for the year 2013.

APPLICATION INFORMATION:
If an organization wishes to apply for support, it should make contact by phone, by letter of inquiry, or by completing an application through the web site. If applying by mail, the letter should describe in no more than two pages:
(1) the organization and its record of accomplishment;
(2) the objectives of the program to be funded and whom it would benefit;
(3) the amount sought from the Foundation in relation to the total need;
(4) exactly how Foundation funds would be used and;
(5) the proposed method to evaluate the program's success.

The initial inquiry should also include an annual report, if available, and a copy of the IRS letter confirming that the organization is tax-exempt under Section 501(c)(3) of the Internal Revenue Code and not a private foundation as described in Section 509(a).
Duration: Up to three years. Renewals are not automatic, and applications from organizations supported in the past will be considered new requests.

IRS IDENTIFICATION NUMBER: 62-1134070

STAFF:
Peter F. Bird, Jr., President and Chief Executive Officer
Colette R. Easter, Treasurer
Barbara W. Baker, Program Assistant and Corporate Secretary

DIRECTORS:
Thomas F. Frist, Jr., Chairman
Peter F. Bird, Jr.
Frank F. Drowota, III
Patricia Frist Elcan
Patricia C. Frist

Thomas F. Frist, III
William R. Frist
Kenneth L. Roberts

ADDRESS INQUIRIES TO:
Peter F. Bird, Jr., President
and Chief Executive Officer
(See address above.)

THE ROSAMOND GIFFORD CHARITABLE CORPORATION   [1279]

100 Clinton Square
126 North Salina Street, 3rd Floor
Syracuse, NY 13202
(315) 474-2489
Fax: (315) 475-4983

WEB SITE ADDRESS:
www.giffordfoundation.org

FOUNDED: 1954

AREAS OF INTEREST:
Youth development, education and job
readiness, and capacity building.

TYPE:
Capital grants; Challenge/matching grants;
Conferences/seminars; Demonstration grants;
Development grants; General operating
grants; Project/program grants; Research
grants; Seed money grants; Training grants.
Grants to support educational, scientific,
religious and general charitable organizations
and programs in Syracuse and Onondaga
County, NY. Emphasis is on grants which
deal with capacity building in Onondaga
County, and neighborhood-based grants near
West and Southside of Syracuse.

YEAR PROGRAM STARTED: 1954

PURPOSE:
To provide funds for education, scientific,
religious and general charitable purposes.

LEGAL BASIS:
Private.

ELIGIBILITY:
Only tax-exempt organizations may apply.
Organizations must show evidence of
problems to be solved and how proposed
solution will benefit constituency and the
community. No grants to individuals.

GEOGRAPHIC RESTRICTIONS:
Madison, Onondaga and Oswego counties,
New York.

FINANCIAL DATA:
Amount of support per award: Up to
$15,000.
Total amount of support: Varies.

APPLICATION INFORMATION:
Application information is available on the
web site.
Duration: One year.

PUBLICATIONS:
Application guidelines; statement of policies;
mission statement.

STAFF:
Dirk E. Sonneborn, Executive Director
Sheena Solomon, Director of Community
Grantmaking
Lindsay McClung, Director of Neighborhood
Programs
Heidi Holtz, Director of Projects and
Research

ADDRESS INQUIRIES TO:
Lindsay McClung
Director of Neighborhood Programs
(See address above.)

LISA AND DOUGLAS GOLDMAN FUND   [1280]

One Montgomery Street, Suite 3440
San Francisco, CA 94104
(415) 771-1717

WEB SITE ADDRESS:
www.ldgfund.org

FOUNDED: 1992

AREAS OF INTEREST:
Jewish affairs, environment, democracy and
civil liberties, health and recreation, literacy
and education, and reproductive health and
rights.

TYPE:
Capital grants; Project/program grants.

YEAR PROGRAM STARTED: 1992

PURPOSE:
To improve the quality of life, primarily in
San Francisco.

LEGAL BASIS:
Private foundation.

ELIGIBILITY:
Eligible organizations must be IRS 501(c)(3)
tax-exempt.

GEOGRAPHIC RESTRICTIONS:
Primarily San Francisco area, California.

FINANCIAL DATA:
Amount of support per award: $10,000 to
$150,000.
Total amount of support: Generally
$8,000,000.

APPLICATION INFORMATION:
Online application process. Applicants must
include a copy of the IRS tax determination
letter. Letter of inquiry must be submitted
before proposal.
Duration: Varies.

PUBLICATIONS:
Annual report; application guidelines.

ADDRESS INQUIRIES TO:
E-mail: grantsmanager@ldgfund.org

GOLDSEKER FOUNDATION   [1281]

1040 Park Avenue
Suite 310
Baltimore, MD 21201
(410) 837-5100
Fax: (410) 837-7927

E-MAIL ADDRESS:
terri@goldsekerfoundation.org

WEB SITE ADDRESS:
www.goldsekerfoundation.org

FOUNDED: 1973

AREAS OF INTEREST:
Community development and the nonprofit
sector.

TYPE:
Challenge/matching grants; General operating
grants; Matching gifts; Project/program
grants; Technical assistance. Project grants
and ongoing operating support.

The Foundation maintains a two-track
grantmaking program that designates two
priority areas, but retains the ability to
initiate and respond to new ideas and
opportunities within our established program
areas. In each of the priority grant areas -
community development and the nonprofit
sector - the Foundation is a directly engaged

and active partner. Grants include a mix of
Foundation initiatives and projects submitted
independently by potential grantees. The
Foundation's established program areas are
community affairs, education, and human
services.

YEAR PROGRAM STARTED: 1976

PURPOSE:
To support programs which directly benefit
the people of the Baltimore metropolitan
area.

LEGAL BASIS:
Private, nonprofit.

ELIGIBILITY:
Qualified nonprofit, charitable and
educational organizations as defined under
federal and state laws as permissible grantees
of private foundations. Support is limited to
institutions in the Baltimore metropolitan
area with special emphasis on disadvantaged
persons, giving priority to programs intended
to assist children and families and to
strengthen neighborhoods.

No support for endowment, capital, deficits,
annual giving, publications, religious
purposes, arts and culture, specific diseases
or disabilities or projects typically supported
with public funds.

GEOGRAPHIC RESTRICTIONS:
Metropolitan Baltimore, Maryland.

FINANCIAL DATA:
No distribution in any calendar year to any
single institution is to exceed five percent of
the Foundation's net income for that year.
Amount of support per award: $1,500 to
$165,000 for the year 2013.
Total amount of support: Approximately
$3,200,000 for the year 2013.
Matching fund requirements: Varies with
specific request.

NUMBER OF APPLICANTS MOST RECENT YEAR:
135 requests received.

NUMBER OF AWARDS: 92.

REPRESENTATIVE AWARDS:
$75,000 to Baltimore Neighborhood
Collaborative; $25,000 to
Hamilton-Lauraville Main Street, Inc.;
$15,000 to Maryland Association of
Nonprofit Organizations.

APPLICATION INFORMATION:
Preliminary proposals submitted should
include details as outlined in the Annual
Report, available upon request. Program
guidelines also available, and phone calls are
welcomed.
Duration: Typically one year. Occasional
multiyear grants.
Deadline: February 1, May 1 and September
1.

PUBLICATIONS:
Annual report; program guidelines.

IRS IDENTIFICATION NUMBER: 52-0983502

OFFICERS:
Sheldon Goldseker, Chairman
Simon Goldseker, Vice Chairman
Matthew D. Gallagher, President and Chief
Executive Officer
Sheila L. Purkey, Vice President, Secretary,
Treasurer, Controller

STAFF:
Laurie Latuda Kinkel, Program Officer

BOARD OF DIRECTORS:
Ana Goldseker
Deby Goldseker
Sharna Goldseker
Sheldon Goldseker
Simon Goldseker
Susan B. Katzenberg
Howard M. Weiss

ADDRESS INQUIRIES TO:
Program Officer
(See address above.)

*SPECIAL STIPULATIONS:
Grantmaking is limited to the metropolitan area of Baltimore, Maryland.

THE GRACO FOUNDATION   [1282]
3501 North 4th Avenue
Sioux Falls, SD 57104
(605) 333-6767
Fax: (605) 333-4979

E-MAIL ADDRESS:
kklee@graco.com

WEB SITE ADDRESS:
www.graco.com

FOUNDED: 1956

AREAS OF INTEREST:
Education, workforce development, youth development and civic projects.

CONSULTING OR VOLUNTEER SERVICES:
Through established community programs.

NAME(S) OF PROGRAMS:
• **Financial Grants of Support**

TYPE:
Capital grants; Development grants; Scholarships. Grants for a variety of local programs concerning education and social problems. Emphasis is on support of local community programs.

YEAR PROGRAM STARTED: 1956

PURPOSE:
To provide financial support to well-screened and -evaluated community programs for making the community a better place in which to live.

LEGAL BASIS:
Established under the Minnesota Nonprofit Corporation Act as a nonprofit corporation under the provisions of Chapter 317, Minnesota Statutes 1953 and Acts amendatory thereof.

ELIGIBILITY:
Accredited institutions of higher education and other nonprofit organizations which have been validated by the IRS as charitable organizations under 501(c)(3) and not a private foundation as defined in 509(a) are eligible to apply. Must be located near Graco facilities. No grants are awarded to individuals or to churches and schools of religion.

FINANCIAL DATA:
Amount of support per award: Varies.
Total amount of support: $633,977 for the year 2012.
Matching fund requirements: Limited to educational institutions.

REPRESENTATIVE AWARDS:
$5,000 to Minneapolis Riverfront Corporation; $10,000 to Dunwoody College of Technology; $6,000 to FIRST Robotics.

APPLICATION INFORMATION:
New applications by invitation only.

PUBLICATIONS:
Annual report/guidelines available on web site.

IRS IDENTIFICATION NUMBER: 41-6023537

BOARD OF DIRECTORS:
Patrick J. McHale, President
Karen P. Gallivan, Director
Janel W. French, Treasurer
Kristi K. Lee, Secretary

ADDRESS INQUIRIES TO:
Kristi Lee
Manager, Community Relations
(See address above.)

*PLEASE NOTE:
Unsolicited requests are not accepted.

GRAND HAVEN AREA COMMUNITY FOUNDATION   [1283]
One South Harbor Drive
Grand Haven, MI 49417
(616) 842-6378
Fax: (616) 842-9518

E-MAIL ADDRESS:
lgrevel@ghacf.org

WEB SITE ADDRESS:
www.ghacf.org

FOUNDED: 1971

AREAS OF INTEREST:
Arts, environment, social services, education and support of local nonprofit organizations.

TYPE:
Project/program grants; Scholarships; Seed money grants. Pool of funds contributed by donors for the benefit of the Tri-Cities area.

YEAR PROGRAM STARTED: 1971

PURPOSE:
To enrich and enhance the quality of life in the Tri-Cities area; to link donors' interests with the needs of the community.

LEGAL BASIS:
Community foundation.

ELIGIBILITY:
Grant applicants must have a charitable 501(c)(3) classification by the IRS. The Foundation will consider grant requests submitted by religious organizations if the proposed project meets a general need in the community. Grants are generally given one time only for specific purposes. The Foundation has no obligation or commitment to provide ongoing or additional support to the grantee. No grants to individuals, except in the form of scholarships. Grants are not given to fund an organization's continued operating support or expenses, including salaries.

GEOGRAPHIC RESTRICTIONS:
Ferrysburg, Grand Haven and Spring Lake areas of western Michigan.

FINANCIAL DATA:
Amount of support per award: Varies depending on needs and nature of the request.
Total amount of support: $3,711,500 for the year 2012.

NUMBER OF APPLICANTS MOST RECENT YEAR:
1,190.

NUMBER OF AWARDS: 1,100.

REPRESENTATIVE AWARDS:
$4,000 to Bluebird Cancer Retreats to assist in offering a weekend retreat; $25,000 to Greater Ottawa County United Way to provide a comprehensive community needs analysis; $15,000 to OAR to initiate a Family Education/Outreach Program for those with a loved one with a substance abuse problem; $23,000 to provide enhancements to Robinson Township Park; $2,500 to YMCA to support Healthy Kids Day.

APPLICATION INFORMATION:
Application form required. Contact Foundation for specific requirements.
Duration: Varies.

PUBLICATIONS:
Annual report; application.

STAFF:
Holly Johnson, President
Barbara Post, Donor Services and Scholarship Director
Patty McDonald, Finance Director

BOARD OF TRUSTEES:
Tom Creswell, Chairperson
Cal Bosman, Vice Chairperson
Tim Parker, Treasurer
Lana Jacobson, Secretary
Tammy Bailey
Kennard Creason
Edward Hanenburg
Steven Moreland
Sheila Steffel
Bonnie Suchecki
Monica Verplank

ADDRESS INQUIRIES TO:
Beth Larson
(See address above.)

THE GREATER CEDAR RAPIDS COMMUNITY FOUNDATION   [1284]
324 Third Street, S.E.
Cedar Rapids, IA 52401
(319) 366-2862
Fax: (319) 366-2912

E-MAIL ADDRESS:
grants@gcrcf.org

WEB SITE ADDRESS:
www.gcrcf.org

FOUNDED: 1948

AREAS OF INTEREST:
Arts and culture, community development, education, environment, health and human services.

NAME(S) OF PROGRAMS:
• **Nonprofit Network**
• **Youth Power**

TYPE:
Demonstration grants; Project/program grants; Scholarships; Seed money grants; Technical assistance; Training grants.

YEAR PROGRAM STARTED: 1989

PURPOSE:
To enrich the quality of life in Linn County, IA.

LEGAL BASIS:
Community foundation.

ELIGIBILITY:
Eligible organizations must be IRS 501(c)(3) tax-exempt, public agencies/units of government or have a fiscal sponsor.

GEOGRAPHIC RESTRICTIONS:
Cedar Rapids and surrounding Linn County, Iowa.

FINANCIAL DATA:
  Amount of support per award: $700 to $50,000. Average: $6,500.
  Total amount of support: $5,900,000 for the year 2011.

COOPERATIVE FUNDING PROGRAMS: A variety of donor advisors operate competitive funds.

NUMBER OF APPLICANTS MOST RECENT YEAR: 670 competitive applications received.

NUMBER OF AWARDS: 1,054 grants awarded: 484 competitive awards, 72 scholarships and 498 other grants.

APPLICATION INFORMATION:
  Applications must include a copy of the IRS tax determination letter.
  Duration: One year for most funds. Renewal by reapplication.
  Deadline: Approximately February 15, June 15 and October 15.

PUBLICATIONS:
  Annual report; "Community" newsletter; guidelines.

ADDRESS INQUIRIES TO:
  Vice President of Programs
  (See address above.)

*SPECIAL STIPULATIONS:
  The Foundation makes competitive grant awards only within Linn County, Iowa and its immediate vicinity.

THE GREATER CINCINNATI FOUNDATION   [1285]
200 West 4th Street
Cincinnati, OH 45202-2602
(513) 241-2880
Fax: (513) 768-6122

WEB SITE ADDRESS:
  www.gcfdn.org

FOUNDED: 1963

AREAS OF INTEREST:
  Addressing racial disparities and improving race relations, comprehensive community development, public education, economic development and strengthening the region's arts and cultural assets.

CONSULTING OR VOLUNTEER SERVICES:
  General staff support provided by volunteers.

TYPE:
  Capital grants; Development grants. Funds for capital improvements, one-time needs, demonstration projects, demands normally outside the reach of philanthropic budgets. Funds may not be used for operating budgets.

LEGAL BASIS:
  Tax-exempt under Section 501(c)(3) of IRS code.

ELIGIBILITY:
  Recipient must be a local agency in the Greater Cincinnati area and must be tax-exempt under Section 501(c)(3) of the IRS code.
  No unsolicited proposals accepted.

GEOGRAPHIC RESTRICTIONS:
  Greater Cincinnati, Ohio, northern Kentucky and southeast Indiana.

FINANCIAL DATA:
  Amount of support per award: $5,000 to $100,000.
  Total amount of support: $60,407,812 for the year 2011.

NUMBER OF APPLICANTS MOST RECENT YEAR: 141.

NUMBER OF AWARDS: 108 to agencies from unrestricted funds.

REPRESENTATIVE AWARDS:
  Dan Beard Council, Boy Scouts of America; Children's Protective Service, Cincinnati Association for the Blind.

APPLICATION INFORMATION:
  Application information is available on the web site.
  Duration: Typically one year.
  Deadline: Letter of Inquiry: January 15 and July 15. Proposals: March 1 and September 1.

IRS IDENTIFICATION NUMBER: 31-0669700

STAFF:
  Kathryn E. Merchant, President and Chief Executive Officer
  Elizabeth Reiter Benson, Vice President for Communications and Marketing
  Shiloh Turner, Vice President for Community Investment
  Scott McReynolds, Vice President for Finance and Administration
  Amy Cheney, Vice President for Giving Strategies
  Ronald C. Christian, Esq., Legal Counsel

GOVERNING BOARD:
  Peter S. Strange, Chairperson
  Dianne M. Rosenberg, Vice Chairperson
  Calvin D. Buford
  Neil Comber
  Alva Jean Crawford
  Thomas D. Croft
  David W. Ellis, III
  Linda C. Fath
  Christopher L. Fister
  Wijdan Jreisat, Esq.
  Molly A. Katz, M.D.
  Janet B. Reid, Ph.D.
  Ryan M. Rybolt
  Charles R. Scheper
  Ann M. Schwister
  Patricia Mann Smitson, Esq.

ADDRESS INQUIRIES TO:
  Kay Pennington
  Community Investment Coordinator
  (See address above.)

GREATER GREEN BAY COMMUNITY FOUNDATION   [1286]
310 West Walnut Street
Suite 350
Green Bay, WI 54303-2734
(920) 432-0800
Fax: (920) 432-5577

E-MAIL ADDRESS:
  martha@ggbcf.org

WEB SITE ADDRESS:
  www.ggbcf.org

FOUNDED: 1991

AREAS OF INTEREST:
  Improving the quality of life for the residents of the Greater Green Bay, WI area.

TYPE:
  Project/program grants; Scholarships. Donor-advised funds.

PURPOSE:
  To improve the quality of life in the local area.

ELIGIBILITY:
  Eligible organizations must have 501(c)(3) not-for-profit status. No grants are made to individuals.

GEOGRAPHIC RESTRICTIONS:
  Brown, Kewaunee and Oconto counties, Wisconsin.

FINANCIAL DATA:
  Net assets of $66,000,000 for fiscal year ended June 30, 2012.
  Amount of support per award: Varies by need.
  Total amount of support: $4,000,000 per year.

APPLICATION INFORMATION:
  All applicants should share their ideas with the Foundation prior to the submission of a formal application.
  Duration: Varies by grant program; usually one year.
  Deadline: Varies by grant program.

ADDRESS INQUIRIES TO:
  Martha Ahrendt, Vice President, Programs
  (See address above.)

THE GREATER KANAWHA VALLEY FOUNDATION   [1287]
Huntington Square, Suite 1600
900 Lee Street East
Charleston, WV 25301
(304) 346-3620
Fax: (304) 346-3640

E-MAIL ADDRESS:
  sryder@tgkvf.org

WEB SITE ADDRESS:
  www.tgkvf.org

FOUNDED: 1962

AREAS OF INTEREST:
  Improving the lives within the greater Kanawha Valley area.

TYPE:
  Project/program grants; Scholarships.

YEAR PROGRAM STARTED: 1964

PURPOSE:
  To serve the greater Kanawha Valley and surrounding areas.

LEGAL BASIS:
  501(c)(3).

ELIGIBILITY:
  Applicant must be a charitable organization located in or directly benefiting residents of the Greater Kanawha Valley.

GEOGRAPHIC RESTRICTIONS:
  Boone, Clay, Fayette, Kanawha, Lincoln and Putnam, West Virginia.

FINANCIAL DATA:
  Amount of support per award: Grants: Varies; Scholarships: Usually $1,000.
  Total amount of support: $1,385,992 in grants and $459,100 in scholarships for the year ended December 31, 2013.
  Matching fund requirements: Must have a match, not a specific percent.

NUMBER OF APPLICANTS MOST RECENT YEAR: 101 grant applicants for the year 2011; 548 scholarship applicants for the academic year 2011-12.

NUMBER OF AWARDS: 93 grants for the year 2011; 369 scholarships for the academic year 2011-12.

APPLICATION INFORMATION:
  Applications are accepted online only.

Duration: Varies.

Deadline: Scholarships: January 15.

PUBLICATIONS:
Annual report.

IRS IDENTIFICATION NUMBER: 55-6024430

STAFF:
Sheri Ryder, Senior Program Officer
Susan Hoover, Scholarship Program Officer
Stephanie Hyre, Program Officer

ADDRESS INQUIRIES TO:
For grants:
Stephanie Hyre, Program Officer
(See address above.)
E-mail: shyre@tgkvf.org
For scholarships:
Susan Hoover, Scholarship Program Officer
(See address above.)
E-mail: shoover@tgkvf.org

THE GREATER KANSAS CITY COMMUNITY FOUNDATION AND AFFILIATED TRUSTS [1288]

1055 Broadway, Suite 130
Kansas City, MO 64105
(816) 842-0944
(866) 719-7886
Fax: (816) 842-8079; (816) 842-0318

E-MAIL ADDRESS:
info@gkccf.org

WEB SITE ADDRESS:
www.gkccf.org

FOUNDED: 1978

AREAS OF INTEREST:
Public education and life sciences.

CONSULTING OR VOLUNTEER SERVICES:
Grantmaking services.

TYPE:
Project/program grants; Scholarships. Grants in the areas of public education and life sciences and scholarships are given to make a positive support of the nonprofit sector and to promote philanthropy for the benefit of the community.

PURPOSE:
To improve the quality of life in greater Kansas City by increasing charitable giving, connecting donors to community needs they care about, and providing leadership on critical community issues.

LEGAL BASIS:
Public foundation.

ELIGIBILITY:
Unsolicited applications will not be accepted.

The Community Foundation does not ordinarily fund endowment campaigns, debt reduction, annual appeals and membership contributions, operating expenses and fund-raising projects of religious organizations, capital fund drives, including brick and mortar, land acquisition, equipment purchases, renovation or purchase of buildings, construction or the improvement of public spaces or financial assistance for individuals.

FINANCIAL DATA:
Amount of support per award: Varies.
Total amount of support: Approximately $212,000,000 annually.

NUMBER OF AWARDS: 20,000.

REPRESENTATIVE AWARDS:
$100,000 over three years to the University of Missouri-Kansas City Institute for Urban Education.

APPLICATION INFORMATION:
Application information is available on the web site.

Duration: Typically one year.

Deadline: Varies.

IRS IDENTIFICATION NUMBER: 43-1152398

OFFICERS:
Deborah L. Wilkerson, President and Chief Executive Officer
Brenda Chumley, Senior Vice President of Development and Donor Services
Janeen Kammerer, Senior Vice President of Finance and Foundation Services

ADDRESS INQUIRIES TO:
E-mail: grants@gkccf.org

*PLEASE NOTE:
Unsolicited requests will not be accepted.

THE GREATER LANSING FOUNDATION [1289]

120 North Washington Square
Suite 650
Lansing, MI 48933
(517) 334-5299
Fax: (517) 334-5445

FOUNDED: 1947

AREAS OF INTEREST:
Arts, education, general charitable giving, handicapped and health.

NAME(S) OF PROGRAMS:
* **The Greater Lansing Foundation General Fund**

TYPE:
Capital grants; Development grants; Project/program grants; Scholarships; Seed money grants; Training grants; Work-study programs. General support for seed money and capital funds.

YEAR PROGRAM STARTED: 1947

PURPOSE:
To promote the well-being of the inhabitants of Clinton, Eaton and Ingham counties by distributing income to local charitable, public or educational institutions.

LEGAL BASIS:
Private foundation.

ELIGIBILITY:
Applicants must have a 501(c)(3) IRS exemption and be a public charity.

GEOGRAPHIC RESTRICTIONS:
Greater Lansing, Michigan counties.

FINANCIAL DATA:
Amount of support per award: Up to $10,000.
Total amount of support: Approximately $50,000 annually.

APPLICATION INFORMATION:
Grant application requests should be made to:
Capital Region Community Foundation
c/o The Greater Lansing Foundation Fund
330 Marshall Street, Suite 300
Lansing, MI 48912
E-mail: info@crcfoundation.org
Tel: (517) 272-2870.

Duration: One year.

Deadline: April 1.

IRS IDENTIFICATION NUMBER: 38-6057513

ADDRESS INQUIRIES TO:
Steven J. Peters, Secretary
(See address above.)

*PLEASE NOTE:
The Foundation does not usually make grants to fund normal operating costs. The Committee prefers to consider grants in the nature of capital expenditures, expansion or improvement of existing programs or grants of a nonrecurring nature.

GREATER LOWELL COMMUNITY FOUNDATION [1290]

100 Merrimack Street
Suite 202
Lowell, MA 01852-1707
(978) 970-1600
Fax: (978) 970-2444

E-MAIL ADDRESS:
info@glcfoundation.org

WEB SITE ADDRESS:
www.glcfoundation.org

FOUNDED: 1997

AREAS OF INTEREST:
The quality of life in the Greater Lowell, Massachusetts area.

TYPE:
The usual type of grant is a capacity grant: It has to benefit the capacity or structure of the applicant organization (e.g., installing a new phone or e-mail system, purchasing a new computer, hiring a consultant to strengthen a short-term project in an organizational capacity, etc.).

PURPOSE:
To improve the quality of life in the Greater Lowell, Massachusetts area.

LEGAL BASIS:
501(c)(3) organization.

ELIGIBILITY:
Grants are not given to individuals. Eligible organizations must have 501(c)(3) status.

GEOGRAPHIC RESTRICTIONS:
Western Merrimack Valley/Northern Middlesex County, Massachusetts area.

FINANCIAL DATA:
Total assets of $22,000,000.
Amount of support per award: $1,000 to $10,000.
Total amount of support: Over $1,000,000 for the year 2012.

APPLICATION INFORMATION:
Applications are posted on the web site and can be accessed from June 30 until early August.

Duration: One year. Nonrenewable.

Deadline: Mid-August for receiving grant application. Grants are distributed late September to early October.

ADDRESS INQUIRIES TO:
Raymond Riddick, Jr., Executive Director
(See address above.)

GREATER MILWAUKEE FOUNDATION [1291]

101 West Pleasant Street
Suite 210
Milwaukee, WI 53212
(414) 272-5805
Fax: (414) 272-6235

E-MAIL ADDRESS:
info@greatermilwaukeefoundation.org

WEB SITE ADDRESS:
www.greatermilwaukeefoundation.org

FOUNDED: 1915

AREAS OF INTEREST:
Unrestricted grantmaking in the areas of
strengthening neighborhoods, strengthening
education, increasing economic opportunities,
and promoting equity and inclusion.

TYPE:
Awards/prizes; Capital grants;
Challenge/matching grants; Demonstration
grants; Development grants; Matching gifts;
Professorships; Project/program grants;
Research grants; Scholarships; Seed money
grants; Technical assistance; Training grants.
The Foundation's unrestricted grantmaking
does not support general operations.

The Foundation operates as a community
trust, a public nonprofit organization
established to administer charitable funds for
the benefit of the people of the community. It
is composed of more than 1,100 funds, each
created by donors to serve the charitable
causes of their choice. Donors can make
grants locally, nationally or around the world.

The component funds are of several types,
depending upon the wishes of the donor
expressed at the time the originating gift or
bequest was made:
(1) Unrestricted funds are those in which the
Foundation's Board is given full discretion in
determining how income can best be
disbursed each year for charitable purposes;
(2) Field of interest funds are administered
with a particular charitable purpose in mind,
such as support of the arts, child welfare or
education;
(3) Designated funds have been established
to favor specific charitable agencies and
institutions; the income earned by this type
of fund is paid annually to a particular
agency or agencies named by the donor;
grants are usually intended to provide general
sustaining support for current agency
operations and;
(4) Donor-advised funds are those established
by gifts from individuals, foundations or
corporations in which the original
contributors make suggestions to the
Foundation Board about grant distributions.

YEAR PROGRAM STARTED: 1915

PURPOSE:
To inspire philanthropy, serve donors, and
strengthen communities now and for future
generations.

LEGAL BASIS:
Public nonprofit organization exempt from
federal taxation under Section 501(c)(3) of
the Internal Revenue Code.

ELIGIBILITY:
The Greater Milwaukee Foundation Board
welcomes grant applications from agencies
serving the people of the greater Milwaukee
community. Details regarding grantmaking
criteria are available online.

The Foundation is committed to promoting
equity and inclusion with a focus on racial
equity in its community. This commitment
applies to its grantmaking. Nonprofit board
diversity is the first of many things it
considers. Eligible nonprofits must have
board membership that is at least 10% people
of color (African Americans, Asian
Americans, Hispanic/Latino Americans and
all other persons not categorized as white by
the U.S. Census).

GEOGRAPHIC RESTRICTIONS:
Greater Milwaukee, Wisconsin, including
Milwaukee, Ozaukee, Washington and
Waukesha counties.

FINANCIAL DATA:
The funds vary in size from $25,000 to
$27,400,000.
Amount of support per award: $10,300
average.
Total amount of support: $38,973,353 for the
year 2013.

COOPERATIVE FUNDING PROGRAMS: Nonprofit
Management Fund and Milwaukee Teen
Pregnancy Prevention Initiative Collaborative
Fund.

NUMBER OF AWARDS: 3,806 grants for the year
2013.

APPLICATION INFORMATION:
To facilitate fair and equitable consideration,
grant applicants are expected to use a
prescribed proposal format. The application
process is as follows:
(1) applicant organization should update (or
add) its information on the Philanthropy
Online database (see Grantseekers section of
Foundation web site);
(2) organization must then submit a Letter of
Inquiry to the Foundation (again, see
Foundation web site);
(3) Foundation staff will then review
applicant's proposal for merit;
(4) if encouraged by staff to apply, the
applicant must complete a detailed online
proposal;
(5) Foundation staff will thoroughly review
the proposal;
(6) the Foundation Board's Community
Investment Committee will review the
proposal and make recommendations to the
full Board, which must approve all grant
awards and;
(7) each applicant will receive written
notification of the Board's action; those
selected for grants must adhere to the
stipulated terms.

Grant seekers are strongly encouraged to
consult with a program officer at the
Foundation prior to submitting a Letter of
Inquiry. Details for grant seekers are
available online.

Duration: Generally, one year.

Deadline: Letters of Inquiry are accepted and
reviewed quarterly. Funding decisions are
made quarterly.

PUBLICATIONS:
Newsletters; annual report.

IRS IDENTIFICATION NUMBER: 39-6036407

STAFF:
Patti Dew, Vice President and Chief Financial
Officer
Kathryn Dunn, Vice President, Community
Investment
Marcus White, Vice President, Community
Partnerships
Tim Larson, Vice President, Development
and Donor Services
Sue Smith, Vice President, Marketing and
Communications

BOARD OF DIRECTORS:
Peter W. Bruce, Chairperson
Thomas L. Spero, Vice Chairperson
Wendy Reed Bosworth
John W. Daniels, Jr.
Ness Flores
Janine P. Geske
Jacqueline Herd-Barber

Judy Jorgensen
David Kundert
David Lubar
Cory Nettles
Mary B. Read

OFFICER:
Ellen M. Gilligan, President and Chief
Executive Officer

ADDRESS INQUIRIES TO:
Sue Smith
Vice President, Marketing and
Communications
(See address above.)

THE GREATER NEW ORLEANS FOUNDATION   [1292]
K & B Plaza, Suite 100
1055 St. Charles Street
New Orleans, LA 70130
(504) 598-4663
Fax: (504) 598-4676

E-MAIL ADDRESS:
richard@gnof.org

WEB SITE ADDRESS:
www.gnof.org

AREAS OF INTEREST:
Housing, environment, workforce
development, and children and youth.

TYPE:
Project/program grants. The Foundation
provides start-up funds for promising new
organizations or programs. It also funds
demonstration grants to new or established
organizations with innovative program
models and offers transition grants to
nonprofit organizations moving into a new
state of organizational development.

PURPOSE:
To create a thriving community for all in the
greater New Orleans region.

ELIGIBILITY:
The Foundation makes grants only to
nonprofit, tax-exempt organizations that serve
the greater New Orleans area.

GEOGRAPHIC RESTRICTIONS:
Southeastern Louisiana and greater New
Orleans region.

FINANCIAL DATA:
Amount of support per award: Varies.

APPLICATION INFORMATION:
Guidelines are available online.
Duration: Renewal by reapplication.
Deadline: Varies.

PUBLICATIONS:
Guidelines.

*SPECIAL STIPULATIONS:
Upon completion of the funded project, or
within one year, grant recipients must
provide an end-of-grant report based on their
proposed program evaluation.

THE GRUNDY FOUNDATION   [1293]
680 Radcliffe Street
Bristol, PA 19007
(215) 788-5460
Fax: (215) 788-0915

E-MAIL ADDRESS:
ejw@grundyfoundation.com

WEB SITE ADDRESS:
www.grundyfoundation.com

FOUNDED: 1961

AREAS OF INTEREST:
Arts and culture, education and human services.

TYPE:
Capital grants. Capital grants for 501(c)(3) organizations throughout Bucks County, PA, primarily Lower Bucks County. Operating/programmatic support only for pre-selected organizations primarily in Bristol, PA and other parts of Lower Bucks County.

YEAR PROGRAM STARTED: 1961

PURPOSE:
To promote the well-being of the Commonwealth of Pennsylvania, with a particular emphasis in Bucks County.

LEGAL BASIS:
501(c)(3) private foundation.

ELIGIBILITY:
Applicants must be nonprofit organizations that have public charity status. No grants to individuals or for fellowships or loans.

GEOGRAPHIC RESTRICTIONS:
Primarily Lower Bucks County, Pennsylvania.

FINANCIAL DATA:
Amount of support per award: Excluding two impact grants each year, average grant $2,941 for the year 2012; $11,167 for the year 2013.
Total amount of support: $220,545 for the year 2012; $143,500 for the year 2013.
Matching fund requirements: Stipulated with specific programs.

NUMBER OF APPLICANTS MOST RECENT YEAR: 15.

NUMBER OF AWARDS: 20 for the year 2012; 5 for the year 2013.

APPLICATION INFORMATION:
Letter of request and related documentation should be submitted to Eugene J. Williams, Executive Director.
Duration: No grants are awarded on a continuing basis.

PUBLICATIONS:
Application guidelines.

ADDRESS INQUIRIES TO:
Eugene J. Williams, Executive Director (See address above.)

GULF COAST COMMUNITY FOUNDATION [1294]
601 Tamiami Trail South
Venice, FL 34285
(941) 486-4600
Fax: (941) 486-4699

E-MAIL ADDRESS:
info@gulfcoastcf.org

WEB SITE ADDRESS:
www.gulfcoastcf.org

FOUNDED: 1995

AREAS OF INTEREST:
Arts and culture, civic affairs, the environment, education, health and human services, and economic development.

TYPE:
Project/program grants.

YEAR PROGRAM STARTED: 1995

PURPOSE:
To improve the quality of life in communities the Foundation serves.

LEGAL BASIS:
Community foundation.

ELIGIBILITY:
Nonprofit organizations, 501(c)(3) tax-exempt, are eligible to apply.

GEOGRAPHIC RESTRICTIONS:
Charlotte, DeSoto, Lee, Manatee and Sarasota counties, Florida.

FINANCIAL DATA:
Amount of support per award: Varies.
Total amount of support: Varies.
Matching fund requirements: Varies.

REPRESENTATIVE AWARDS:
Charlotte County Homeless Coalition to provide first-year operating support for Safe House Shelter; Legal Aid of Manasota to provide free legal representation for southern Sarasota County homeowners facing foreclosure on their homes; United Way of Sarasota County to fund site coordinators who will facilitate the new Volunteer Income Tax Assistance Program.

APPLICATION INFORMATION:
Application information is available on the web site.
Duration: Varies.
Deadline: Varies.

PUBLICATIONS:
Annual report; application guidelines.

ADDRESS INQUIRIES TO:
See e-mail address above.

HALL FAMILY FOUNDATION
P.O. Box 419580
Maildrop 323
Kansas City, MO 64141-6580
(816) 274-8516
Fax: (816) 274-8547

WEB SITE ADDRESS:
www.hallfamilyfoundation.org

TYPE:
Capital grants; Project/program grants; Technical assistance; Training grants.

See entry 153 for full listing.

HAMILTON COMMUNITY FOUNDATION [1295]
120 King Street West, Suite 700
Hamilton ON L8P 4V2 Canada
(905) 523-5600
Fax: (905) 523-0741

E-MAIL ADDRESS:
information@hcf.on.ca

WEB SITE ADDRESS:
www.hcf.on.ca

FOUNDED: 1954

AREAS OF INTEREST:
Community development and services for Hamilton, ON.

TYPE:
Project/program grants.

YEAR PROGRAM STARTED: 1954

PURPOSE:
To foster the growth of community philanthropy; to build and prudently manage community endowments; to provide exceptional services to donors; to address needs through strategic grantmaking and organizational support; to provide leadership on key community issues.

LEGAL BASIS:
Community foundation.

GEOGRAPHIC RESTRICTIONS:
Community of Hamilton, Ontario, Canada.

FINANCIAL DATA:
Total amount of support: $5,200,000 for the year 2011-12.

APPLICATION INFORMATION:
Application information is available on the web site.
Duration: One year or multiyear grants.

STAFF:
Terry Cooke, President and Chief Executive Officer

ADDRESS INQUIRIES TO:
Grace Diffey
Vice-President Community Relations
(See address above.)

THE HAMPTON ROADS COMMUNITY FOUNDATION [1296]
101 West Main Street
Suite 4500
Norfolk, VA 23510
(757) 622-7951
Fax: (757) 622-1751

E-MAIL ADDRESS:
info@hamptonroadscf.org

WEB SITE ADDRESS:
www.hamptonroadscf.org

FOUNDED: 1950

AREAS OF INTEREST:
Community development, education and social welfare.

TYPE:
Capital grants; Challenge/matching grants; Project/program grants; Seed money grants. Grants for educational institutions, family, child and social welfare, cultural and civic affairs.

YEAR PROGRAM STARTED: 1950

PURPOSE:
To make grants that transform the quality of life and inspire philanthropy in southeastern Virginia.

LEGAL BASIS:
Nonprofit corporation.

ELIGIBILITY:
501(c)(3) nonprofit organizations that provide benefits to the residents.

GEOGRAPHIC RESTRICTIONS:
Southeastern Virginia.

FINANCIAL DATA:
Amount of support per award: $15,000 to $1,000,000.
Total amount of support: $14,700,000.

APPLICATION INFORMATION:
Application information is available on the web site.
Duration: Grants: One year to multiyear; Scholarships: One to four years.
Deadline: Varies depending upon program.

PUBLICATIONS:
Annual report; application guidelines; quarterly newsletter.

IRS IDENTIFICATION NUMBER: 54-2035996

STAFF:
Deborah M. DiCroce, President and Chief Executive Officer

Linda Rice, Vice President of Initiatives
Leigh Evans Davis, Director of Programs and
Donor Services
Robin Foreman, Director of Scholarships and
Administration
Vivian Oden, Program and Donor Services
Manager

ADDRESS INQUIRIES TO:
E-mail: grants@hamptonroadscf.org

*SPECIAL STIPULATIONS:
All discretionary grants are to charitable
organizations for special purposes only.

HANCOCK COUNTY COMMUNITY FOUNDATION [1297]

312 East Main Street
Greenfield, IN 46140
(317) 462-8870
Fax: (317) 467-3330

E-MAIL ADDRESS:
mgibble@hccf.cc

WEB SITE ADDRESS:
www.hccf.cc

FOUNDED: 1992

AREAS OF INTEREST:
Arts, civic affairs, culture, education, youth,
and health and human services.

TYPE:
Project/program grants; Scholarships.

PURPOSE:
To build and improve the quality of life
within the community.

ELIGIBILITY:
Grants are made to organizations that have
tax-exempt status under Section 501(c)(3) of
the Internal Revenue Code. No grants are
made to individuals. Nonsectarian religious
programs may apply.

GEOGRAPHIC RESTRICTIONS:
Hancock County, Indiana.

FINANCIAL DATA:
Amount of support per award: $500 to
$7,500.
Total amount of support: Approximately
$945,000 for the year 2012.

APPLICATION INFORMATION:
Send a Letter of Intent, which outlines the
request and projected request amount. Upon
receiving the Letter of Intent, the Program
Officer will follow up with the applicant
organization to discuss the submission of a
formal grant application.
Duration: One year. Extension possible.

ADDRESS INQUIRIES TO:
Alyse Vail, Program Officer
(See address above.)

HAWAII COMMUNITY FOUNDATION [1298]

827 Fort Street Mall
Honolulu, HI 96813
(808) 537-6333
(888) 731-3863 (Hawaii)
Fax: (808) 521-6286

E-MAIL ADDRESS:
info@hcf-hawaii.org

WEB SITE ADDRESS:
www.hawaiicommunityfoundation.org

FOUNDED: 1916

AREAS OF INTEREST:
Culture and art, natural resources
conservation, education, health and medical
research, human services, disability,
mentoring and media, scholarships, neighbor
island assistance, persons in need and the
FLEX Program.

TYPE:
Development grants; Project/program grants;
Scholarships; Seed money grants; Technical
assistance; Training grants; Travel grants.

PURPOSE:
To build community among the people of
Hawaii.

LEGAL BASIS:
Community foundation.

ELIGIBILITY:
Grantseeker must be a tax-exempt
organization, either a unit of government or
one classified by the IRS as a 501(c)(3)
charity which is not a private foundation. The
organization must serve Hawaii's people and
environment and have leadership which
represents the community served. It must
make a request that is time-limited or has
other source of future funding.

The Foundation supports innovative and
creative programs that fit within specific
areas. It also provides scholarships for
college studies.

GEOGRAPHIC RESTRICTIONS:
Hawaii.

FINANCIAL DATA:
Foundation has more than $284,000,000 in
charitable assets.
Amount of support per award: Varies.
Total amount of support: Varies.

APPLICATION INFORMATION:
Applicant must submit a written proposal
describing the proposed project.
Duration: Varies.
Deadline: Varies by program.

PUBLICATIONS:
Annual report.

ADDRESS INQUIRIES TO:
Lynelle Marble
Associate Director of Communications
(See address above.)

THE HEALTH FOUNDATION OF GREATER INDIANAPOLIS

429 East Vermont Street, Suite 300
Indianapolis, IN 46202-3698
(317) 630-1805
Fax: (317) 630-1806

E-MAIL ADDRESS:
bwilson@thfgi.org

WEB SITE ADDRESS:
www.thfgi.org

TYPE:
Project/program grants.

See entry 1484 for full listing.

THE HEALTHCARE FOUNDATION FOR ORANGE COUNTY

1450 North Tustin Avenue
Suite 209
Santa Ana, CA 92705-8641
(714) 245-1650
Fax: (714) 245-1653

E-MAIL ADDRESS:
ckoenig@hfoc.org

WEB SITE ADDRESS:
www.hfoc.org

TYPE:
Awards/prizes; Demonstration grants;
Development grants; General operating
grants; Project/program grants; Technical
assistance; Training grants.

See entry 1440 for full listing.

HILLSDALE COUNTY COMMUNITY FOUNDATION [1299]

2 South Howell
Hillsdale, MI 49242-1634
(517) 439-5101
Fax: (517) 439-5109

E-MAIL ADDRESS:
s.bisher@abouthccf.org

WEB SITE ADDRESS:
www.abouthccf.org

FOUNDED: 1991

AREAS OF INTEREST:
Arts, education, community needs,
scholarships and philanthropy.

TYPE:
Project/program grants; Scholarships.

YEAR PROGRAM STARTED: 1991

PURPOSE:
To improve the quality of life in Hillsdale
County. ·

LEGAL BASIS:
Community foundation.

ELIGIBILITY:
For grants, organizations must be in and
benefit Hillsdale County and be IRS
501(c)(3) tax-exempt. For scholarships,
students must be graduates of Hillsdale
County High School, residents of Hillsdale
County and citizens of the U.S.

GEOGRAPHIC RESTRICTIONS:
Hillsdale County, Michigan.

FINANCIAL DATA:
Amount of support per award: $300 to
$25,000.

APPLICATION INFORMATION:
Applications are available at the address
above and must include all required
documentation, completed application
according to requirements, and a copy of the
IRS 501(c)(3) tax determination letter.
Duration: One year.
Deadline: Foundation Grants: May 1 and
November 1.

ADDRESS INQUIRIES TO:
Sharon Bisher, Executive Director
(See address above.)

THE HOME DEPOT FOUNDATION [1300]

2455 Paces Ferry Road, C-17
Atlanta, GA 30339
(770) 384-3889
(866) 593-7019
Fax: (770) 384-3908; (866) 593-7027

E-MAIL ADDRESS:
hd_foundation@homedepot.com

WEB SITE ADDRESS:
www.homedepotfoundation.org

FOUNDED: 1978

AREAS OF INTEREST:
Affordable housing, sustainable community development and community affairs.

CONSULTING OR VOLUNTEER SERVICES:
Team Depot volunteer program.

NAME(S) OF PROGRAMS:
- **Community Impact Grants Program**
- **Framing Hope Program**
- **Sustainable Community Development Program**
- **Team Depot**

TYPE:
Challenge/matching grants; Development grants; Product donations; Project/program grants. Environmental research grants.

YEAR PROGRAM STARTED: 2002

PURPOSE:
To contribute to the development of affordable housing in communities where The Home Depot does business; to support employee participation in the community; to promote economic development in The Home Depot communities.

LEGAL BASIS:
Corporate giving program.

ELIGIBILITY:
Most grants are made in communities where The Home Depot operates stores. No grants to individuals, religious, fraternal, political, labor, athletic, social or veterans groups, fund-raising benefits, dinners, exhibits, conferences and sports events, charities sponsored solely by a single civic organization, courtesy or journal advertising campaigns, multiyear commitments, or organizations that are not 501(c)(3) or Revenue Canada-designated charities.

GEOGRAPHIC RESTRICTIONS:
United States, Canada and Mexico.

FINANCIAL DATA:
Amount of support per award: Varies depending on needs and nature of the request.
Matching fund requirements: Employees making contributions to recognized nonprofits may apply for matching gifts up to $500 through The Home Depot Matching Gift Program.

APPLICATION INFORMATION:
Contact the Foundation for application guidelines.
Duration: Varies.
Deadline: Varies according to program.

PUBLICATIONS:
Brochure; *Social Responsibility Report.*

ADDRESS INQUIRIES TO:
See e-mail address above.

HOUSING EDUCATION AND RESEARCH ASSOCIATION (HERA) [1301]
Montana State University, 102 Taylor Hall
P.O. Box 173580
Bozeman, MT 59717-3580
(406) 994-3451
Fax: (406) 994-5417

E-MAIL ADDRESS:
mvogel@montana.edu

WEB SITE ADDRESS:
www.housingeducators.org

AREAS OF INTEREST:
Housing education.

NAME(S) OF PROGRAMS:
- **Tessie Agan Award Competition**

TYPE:
Awards/prizes.

ELIGIBILITY:
Open to graduate and undergraduate students.

FINANCIAL DATA:
Amount of support per award: Graduate Award: $750 presented at the HERA Annual Meeting; Undergraduate Award: $250 and opportunity to present paper at the HERA Annual Conference.

APPLICATION INFORMATION:
Information and specific guidelines pertaining to all grants can be found online.
Duration: One-time award.

ADDRESS INQUIRIES TO:
Michael P. Vogel, Executive Director
(See address above.)

*SPECIAL STIPULATIONS:
Award is contingent upon attending the meeting and presenting the paper. Conference registration fees are waived.

HUDSON-WEBBER FOUNDATION [1302]
333 West Fort Street
Suite 1310
Detroit, MI 48226-3134
(313) 963-7777
Fax: (313) 963-2818

WEB SITE ADDRESS:
www.hudson-webber.org

FOUNDED: 1943

AREAS OF INTEREST:
The primary concern of the Foundation is the vitality of the metropolitan Detroit community. The Foundation's Trustees have defined four specific program missions in which they will concentrate their efforts and resources: the physical revitalization of downtown Detroit, the enhancement of major art and cultural resources in Detroit, the reduction of crime in Detroit and the economic development of Detroit, with emphasis on the creation of additional employment opportunities.

TYPE:
General operating grants; Matching gifts.

YEAR PROGRAM STARTED: 1943

PURPOSE:
To improve the vitality and quality of life of the metropolitan Detroit community.

LEGAL BASIS:
Private foundation.

ELIGIBILITY:
The Foundation assigns highest priority of support to programs in the city of Detroit. Programs outside of Detroit generally are not supported.

The Foundation does not make grants for endowments, fund-raising social events, conferences or exhibits. With the exception of the Foundation's program for Hudsonians, the Foundation does not make grants to individuals.

GEOGRAPHIC RESTRICTIONS:
Southeastern Michigan, specifically the city of Detroit.

FINANCIAL DATA:
Amount of support per award: $5,000 to $500,000.
Total amount of support: $7,717,403 for the year 2013.

APPLICATION INFORMATION:
Information may be obtained from the Foundation's web site.
Duration: One year.

BOARD OF TRUSTEES:
Jennifer Hudson Parke, Chairperson
David O. Egner, President and Chief Executive Officer
David E. Meador, Treasurer
Amanda Van Dusen, Secretary
Toby Barlow
Matthew P. Cullen
Stephen R. D'Arcy
W. Frank Fountain
Gilbert Hudson
Joseph L. Hudson, IV
Joseph L. Hudson, Jr.
Reginald M. Turner
Jean Hudson Witmer

ADDRESS INQUIRIES TO:
Stephanie Armes, Grants Manager
(See address above.)

HUMBOLDT AREA FOUNDATION [1303]
363 Indianola Road
Bayside, CA 95524
(707) 442-2993
Fax: (707) 442-3811

E-MAIL ADDRESS:
jenr@hafoundation.org

WEB SITE ADDRESS:
www.hafoundation.org

FOUNDED: 1972

AREAS OF INTEREST:
Children, youth and families; community, economy and the environment; health and well-being; arts and humanities; native cultures.

NAME(S) OF PROGRAMS:
- **Community Building Grants**
- **Community Response Grants**
- **Field of Interest Grant Program**
- **Summer Youth Program**

TYPE:
Capital grants; Project/program grants; Scholarships; Seed money grants; Technical assistance.

YEAR PROGRAM STARTED: 1972

PURPOSE:
To improve the quality of life on the north coast of California.

ELIGIBILITY:
Eligible organizations must be IRS 501(c)(3) tax-exempt. Applications will be evaluated using the following criteria: need, planning and management, leadership and collaboration.

The Foundation will not fund projects outside of its service area, projects without sound planning and development, deferred maintenance, annual operating costs, travel, scholarships and fellowships, or projects which violate the nonprofit public laws.

GEOGRAPHIC RESTRICTIONS:
Del Norte, Humboldt and Trinity counties, California.

FINANCIAL DATA:
Amount of support per award: Varies.

APPLICATION INFORMATION:
Information, guidelines and applications are available online.

PUBLICATIONS:
Guidelines.

ADDRESS INQUIRIES TO:
Chris Witt, Director of Grantmaking and Donor Services
(See address above.)

INTERNATIONAL DEVELOPMENT RESEARCH CENTRE (IDRC)   [1304]
150 Kent Street
Ottawa ON K1P 0B2 Canada
(613) 696-2098
Fax: (613) 236-4026

E-MAIL ADDRESS:
awards@idrc.ca

WEB SITE ADDRESS:
www.idrc.ca/awards

FOUNDED: 1970

NAME(S) OF PROGRAMS:
● **IDRC Doctoral Research Awards (IDRA)**

TYPE:
Awards/prizes. These awards are offered once a year and are intended for field research in one or more developing countries. Candidates must conduct their research in areas corresponding to IDRC's research priorities.

PURPOSE:
To support the field research of Canadian graduate students and developing country nationals enrolled in a Canadian university for doctoral research on a topic of relevance to sustainable and equitable development.

ELIGIBILITY:
Applicants must meet the following conditions for eligibility:
(1) hold Canadian citizenship (or permanent residency status), or hold citizenship of a developing country;
(2) be enrolled at a Canadian university at the doctoral level;
(3) research proposal is for a doctoral thesis and has been approved by the thesis supervisor;
(4) proposed field research must take place in one or more developing countries and be conducted for a doctoral dissertation;
(5) provide evidence of affiliation with an institution or organization in the developing-country region(s) in which the research will take place and;
(6) have completed course work and passed comprehensive examinations before taking up the award.

Program can involve research in any developing region of the world, excluding Central Asia, Cuba, Eastern Europe, Iran, Iraq, Korea (Democratic People's Republic of) and Somalia.

FINANCIAL DATA:
Total amount of support: Up to $20,000 (CAN).

NUMBER OF AWARDS: 35 to 45 per year.

APPLICATION INFORMATION:
Applications are to be submitted online from the IDRC's competitions page. Paper applications are not accepted.
Duration: Up to 12 months.

ADDRESS INQUIRIES TO:
Fellowships and Awards
(See e-mail address above.)

INTERNATIONAL DEVELOPMENT RESEARCH CENTRE (IDRC)   [1305]
150 Kent Street
Ottawa ON K1P 0B2 Canada
(613) 696-2098
Fax: (613) 236-4026

E-MAIL ADDRESS:
awards@idrc.ca

WEB SITE ADDRESS:
www.idrc.ca/awards

FOUNDED: 1970

AREAS OF INTEREST:
Research for international development.

NAME(S) OF PROGRAMS:
● **IDRC Research Awards**

TYPE:
Awards/prizes. Program provides training in research management and grant administration under the guidance of Centre program staff. Approximately 50% of the time spent on own research project.

PURPOSE:
To provide exposure to research for international development through a program of training in research management and grant administration.

ELIGIBILITY:
Canadian citizens, permanent residents of Canada, and citizens of developing countries are eligible. Applicant must be registered in a Master's or Ph.D. program or have completed a Master's or Ph.D. degree in a recognized university.

Program can involve research in any developing region of the world, excluding Central Asia, Cuba, Eastern Europe, Iran, Iraq, Korea (Democratic People's Republic of) and Somalia.

NUMBER OF AWARDS: 10 to 19.

APPLICATION INFORMATION:
Applications must be submitted online from the IDRC's competitions page.
Duration: One year.

ADDRESS INQUIRIES TO:
Fellowships and Awards
(See e-mail address above.)

AUDREY AND SYDNEY IRMAS CHARITABLE FOUNDATION   [1306]
15910 Ventura Boulevard, Suite 1019
Encino, CA 91436
(818) 382-3313
Fax: (818) 382-3315

E-MAIL ADDRESS:
robirm@gmail.com

AREAS OF INTEREST:
Arts, religious organizations, homeless and urban issues.

TYPE:
Challenge/matching grants; Matching gifts. Long-term pledges.

LEGAL BASIS:
501(c)(3).

ELIGIBILITY:
Organizations classified as 501(c)(3) by the IRS can apply.

GEOGRAPHIC RESTRICTIONS:
Los Angeles County, California.

FINANCIAL DATA:
Amount of support per award: Varies.
Total amount of support: Varies.

APPLICATION INFORMATION:
Contact the Foundation by mail for application procedures.
Duration: Varies.

ADDRESS INQUIRIES TO:
Robert Irmas, Trustee and Administrator
(See address above.)

JEWEL-OSCO   [1307]
150 Pearce Road
Suite 200
Itasca, IL 60143
(630) 948-6000

WEB SITE ADDRESS:
www.jewelosco.com

FOUNDED: 1899

AREAS OF INTEREST:
Hunger relief, environmental stewardship and nutrition education.

TYPE:
Project/program grants.

YEAR PROGRAM STARTED: 1943

PURPOSE:
To support programs that meet the needs of society and improve the quality of life, particularly in communities where the company has facilities.

LEGAL BASIS:
Corporate giving program.

ELIGIBILITY:
Grants are made to organizations that have tax-exempt status under Section 501(c)(3) of the Internal Revenue Code. No grants are made to individuals.

GEOGRAPHIC RESTRICTIONS:
Illinois, Indiana and Iowa (in communities where the company has facilities).

FINANCIAL DATA:
Amount of support per award: Grants vary in amount, depending upon the needs and nature of the request.
Total amount of support: Varies.

APPLICATION INFORMATION:
Guidelines are available on the web site.
Duration: One year. Renewal possible.

ADDRESS INQUIRIES TO:
See web site above.

JEWISH COMMUNITY FOUNDATION OF LOS ANGELES   [1308]
6505 Wilshire Boulevard
Suite 1200
Los Angeles, CA 90048
(323) 761-8700
Fax: (323) 761-8666

E-MAIL ADDRESS:
thecenter@jewishfoundationla.org

WEB SITE ADDRESS:
www.jewishfoundationla.org

FOUNDED: 1954

AREAS OF INTEREST:
Jewish life, community and health services, education, social services, arts and culture, and civic life.

CONSULTING OR VOLUNTEER SERVICES:
Center for Designed Philanthropy - consultation with family foundations and individual funders regarding the effectiveness of their grantmaking.

NAME(S) OF PROGRAMS:
● **Capital Grants**
● **Cutting Edge Grants**
● **General Community Grants**
● **Israel Grants**

TYPE:
Awards/prizes; Capital grants; Project/program grants; Seed money grants.

YEAR PROGRAM STARTED: 1976

PURPOSE:
To provide endowment resources to enable the community to initiate model programs, assist agencies to address the diverse and demanding challenges to face emergencies and the needs of the Jewish community and the Los Angeles community at large.

LEGAL BASIS:
Jewish community foundation.

ELIGIBILITY:
Grants are made to nonprofit 501(c)(3) organizations.

GEOGRAPHIC RESTRICTIONS:
Primarily Los Angeles and Israel.

FINANCIAL DATA:
Amount of support per award: Varies.
Total amount of support: $53,000,000 for the year 2012.

REPRESENTATIVE AWARDS:
$50,000 to Beit T'Shuvah for expanded treatment center; $50,000 to Shalom Institute for boy's side renovation; $30,000 to Temple Akiba for Campaign of Light.

APPLICATION INFORMATION:
Application information is available on the web site.
Duration: One to three years. No renewals.
Deadline: Varies.

PUBLICATIONS:
Annual report.

OFFICERS:
Lawrence Rauch, Chairperson
Leah M. Bishop, Vice President
Anthony Chanin, Vice President
William R. Feiler, Vice President
Abby L.T. Feinman, Vice President
Harold J. Masor, Vice President
Eugene Stein, Vice President
Alan Stern, Vice President
Adlai W. Wertman, Vice President
Scott H. Richland, Treasurer
Selwyn Gerber, Secretary

EXECUTIVE STAFF:
Marvin I. Schotland, President and Chief Executive Officer
Michael J. Januzik, Senior Vice President, Finance and Administration/Chief Financial Officer
Daniel M. Rothblatt, Senior Vice President, Philanthropic Services
Amelia Xann, Vice President, Center for Designed Philanthropy
Elliot B. Kristal, Vice President, Charitable Gift Planning
Baruch S. Littman, Vice President, Development

ADDRESS INQUIRIES TO:
Amelia Xann, Vice President
Center for Designed Philanthropy
(See address above.)

KALAMAZOO COMMUNITY FOUNDATION   [1309]
151 South Rose Street
Suite 332
Kalamazoo, MI 49007-4775
(269) 381-4416
Fax: (269) 381-3146

E-MAIL ADDRESS:
info@kalfound.org

WEB SITE ADDRESS:
www.kalfound.org

FOUNDED: 1925

AREAS OF INTEREST:
Community investment and leadership priorities in Kalamazoo County: individuals and families, community engagement and youth development, education and learning, and economic development.

TYPE:
Capital grants; Development grants; Endowments; General operating grants; Matching gifts; Project/program grants; Seed money grants. Economic development.

LEGAL BASIS:
Community foundation established in 1925. Incorporated in 1930.

ELIGIBILITY:
Grants are available to institutions with 501(c)(3) status and charitable activities operating in Kalamazoo County, MI.

GEOGRAPHIC RESTRICTIONS:
Kalamazoo County, Michigan.

FINANCIAL DATA:
Amount of support per award: $9,000 to $300,000. Average $64,708.68.
Total amount of support: Responsive grants: $2,588,347; $20,885,541.95 for all grants for the year 2013.

NUMBER OF APPLICANTS MOST RECENT YEAR:
Competitive Grants: 45; Responsive Grants: 40; All others: 178.

NUMBER OF AWARDS: 258.

APPLICATION INFORMATION:
Electronic grant application is available at the Foundation web site.
Duration: One year.
Deadline: First working day of each quarter: January, April, July and October.

IRS IDENTIFICATION NUMBER: 38-3333202

OFFICERS:
Carrie Pickett-Erway, President and Chief Executive Officer

TRUSTEES:
Barbara L. James, Chairperson
Ronda E. Stryker, Vice Chairperson
James Escamilla
Si Johnson
Frank J. Sardone
Hon. Carolyn H. Williams
Dr. Eileen Wilson-Oyelaran

ADDRESS INQUIRIES TO:
Vice President, Community Investment
(See address above.)

THE KANTZLER FOUNDATION   [1310]
Pere Marquette Depot
1000 Adams Street, Suite 200
Bay City, MI 48708
(989) 893-4438
Fax: (989) 893-4448

E-MAIL ADDRESS:
peremarquettedepot@bayfoundation.org

FOUNDED: 1974

AREAS OF INTEREST:
Initial funding for educational, recreational and charitable projects in the Bay City area.

TYPE:
Capital grants; Development grants; Project/program grants.

YEAR PROGRAM STARTED: 1974

PURPOSE:
To increase the quality of life in the Bay City area.

LEGAL BASIS:
Michigan nonprofit corporation.

ELIGIBILITY:
Organizations must be IRS 501(c)(3) tax-exempt. Priority is given to projects that will have a multiplier effect upon the community. The grants must be used to finance the cost of special projects and capital improvements and not to defray current operating expenses. The Foundation will not provide the entire support for a project and will expect that others will share the costs.

GEOGRAPHIC RESTRICTIONS:
Bay City area, Michigan.

FINANCIAL DATA:
Amount of support per award: $1,000 to $250,000.
Total amount of support: Varies.

APPLICATION INFORMATION:
Grant requests must include 10 copies of the following:
(1) cover letter, including the amount being requested;
(2) organizational mission;
(3) executive summary, which includes the benefits to the community and anticipated outcomes;
(4) project description, funding goal with names of all sources and dollar amounts, benefit to organization/community and segment of community served;
(5) financial data including program budget with all sources of revenue, current balance sheet, current income statement, copy of federal tax-exempt ruling from the IRS, copy of form 990, and primary sources of revenue for the organization;
(6) board of directors/trustees names and occupations and;
(7) letters of support.

Also include additional information or documentation deemed pertinent to the grant request. If the information requested is not available, please explain.
Duration: Usually one year. In appropriate circumstances, however, a commitment may be made on an extended basis.
Deadline: Two weeks prior to trustees meetings in mid-April, mid-July and mid-November.

PUBLICATIONS:
Brochure.

ADDRESS INQUIRIES TO:
Administrator for the Board of Trustees
(See address above.)

EDWARD BANGS KELLEY & ELZA KELLEY FOUNDATION, INC. [1311]

20 North Main Street
South Yarmouth, MA 02664
(508) 775-3117
Fax: (508) 775-3720

E-MAIL ADDRESS:
contact@kelleyfoundation.org

WEB SITE ADDRESS:
www.kelleyfoundation.org

FOUNDED: 1954

AREAS OF INTEREST:
Health, psychology, sociology, education, culture, and environment.

TYPE:
Capital grants; Challenge/matching grants; Development grants; Matching gifts; Project/program grants.

YEAR PROGRAM STARTED: 1954

PURPOSE:
To promote the health and welfare of the residents of Barnstable County.

LEGAL BASIS:
Private foundation.

ELIGIBILITY:
Applicants must be U.S. citizens, residents of Barnstable County, or organizations who serve Barnstable County. Grants must benefit health and welfare of Barnstable County (MA) residents.

GEOGRAPHIC RESTRICTIONS:
Barnstable County, Massachusetts.

FINANCIAL DATA:
Amount of support per award: Varies.
Total amount of support: $250,000.

COOPERATIVE FUNDING PROGRAMS: Cape Cod Grantmakers Collaborative, other foundations.

APPLICATION INFORMATION:
Grant applicants should contact Joel Crowell, President of the Foundation, for information and application forms. Additional information is available on the web site.
Duration: One year. Renewals by reapplication.

IRS IDENTIFICATION NUMBER: 04-6039660

ADDRESS INQUIRIES TO:
Joel Crowell, President
(See address above.)

KEWEENAW COMMUNITY FOUNDATION [1312]

236 Quincy Street
Hancock, MI 49930
(906) 482-9673
Fax: (906) 482-9679

E-MAIL ADDRESS:
mail@k-c-f.org

WEB SITE ADDRESS:
www.k-c-f.org

FOUNDED: 1994

AREAS OF INTEREST:
Environment, health and youth.

TYPE:
Awards/prizes; Challenge/matching grants; Development grants; Endowments; Project/program grants; Scholarships.

YEAR PROGRAM STARTED: 1994

PURPOSE:
To enhance and support the quality of life in the Keweenaw area.

ELIGIBILITY:
Grants are made to organizations that have tax-exempt status under Section 501(c)(3) of the Internal Revenue Code. No grants are made to individuals. Religious programs may apply. Grants can also be given to governmental units or eligible educational institutions.

GEOGRAPHIC RESTRICTIONS:
Houghton and Keweenaw counties, Michigan.

FINANCIAL DATA:
Amount of support per award: Grants vary in amount, depending upon the needs and nature of the request.
Total amount of support: Varies.

APPLICATION INFORMATION:
Information is available on the web site.
Duration: One year. Renewal possible.

ADDRESS INQUIRIES TO:
Heather McCloskey, Office Manager
(See address above.)

KITSAP COMMUNITY FOUNDATION [1313]

9657 Levin Road, N.W.
Suite L0-8
Silverdale, WA 98383
(360) 698-3622
Fax: (360) 698-6043

E-MAIL ADDRESS:
kcf@kitsapfoundation.org

WEB SITE ADDRESS:
www.kitsapfoundation.org

FOUNDED: 1993

TYPE:
General operating grants; Project/program grants; Scholarships.

YEAR PROGRAM STARTED: 1999

PURPOSE:
To improve the quality of life in the community.

LEGAL BASIS:
501(c)(3).

ELIGIBILITY:
Grant support mostly for nonprofit organizations serving Kitsap County, Washington and surrounding areas.

GEOGRAPHIC RESTRICTIONS:
Kitsap County, Washington and its surrounding areas.

FINANCIAL DATA:
$2,000,000 in assets for the year 2012.
Amount of support per award: $500 to $5,000.
Total amount of support: $130,000 in grants and $5,000 in scholarships for the year 2012.

NUMBER OF APPLICANTS MOST RECENT YEAR: 106.

NUMBER OF AWARDS: 24.

REPRESENTATIVE AWARDS:
Boys & Girls Clubs; Great Peninsula Conservancy; Joy of Freedom; Kitsap Community Resources; Washington CASH.

APPLICATION INFORMATION:
Applications are to be submitted online at commongrantapplication.com
Duration: One year.

PUBLICATIONS:
Newsletter; annual report.

IRS IDENTIFICATION NUMBER: 94-3205217

STAFF:
Kol Medina, Executive Director

ADDRESS INQUIRIES TO:
Kol Medina, Executive Director
(See address above.)

KOHL'S CORPORATION

N56 W17000 Ridgewood Drive
Menomonee Falls, WI 53051
(262) 703-7000
Fax: (262) 703-6305

E-MAIL ADDRESS:
kohls@scholarshipamerica.org

WEB SITE ADDRESS:
www.kohls.scholarshipamerica.org

TYPE:
Awards/prizes; Scholarships.

See entry 1709 for full listing.

THE KROGER COMPANY FOUNDATION [1314]

1014 Vine Street
Cincinnati, OH 45202-1100
(513) 762-4000
Fax: (513) 762-1100

WEB SITE ADDRESS:
www.thekrogerco.com

FOUNDED: 1987

AREAS OF INTEREST:
Education, human services, hunger relief and women's health.

TYPE:
General operating grants.

YEAR PROGRAM STARTED: 1987

PURPOSE:
To feed the hungry, support breast cancer initiatives, provide disaster relief and assist local grassroots organizations.

LEGAL BASIS:
Corporate giving program.

ELIGIBILITY:
Only proposals from 501(c)(3) organizations located in communities where the Kroger Company has operations are considered.

The Foundation does not support international projects or national organizations, except when local chapter is active in a community served by the Kroger Company.

FINANCIAL DATA:
Amount of support per award: Typically $1,000 to $5,000.
Total amount of support: Approximately $8,000,000 for the year 2011.

APPLICATION INFORMATION:
Eligible organizations may submit proposals at any time through the community relations department of the local retail division office. Proposals must include an IRS tax-exempt determination letter and should include a statement of the reason for the request.

PUBLICATIONS:
Program announcement; application guidelines.

ADDRESS INQUIRIES TO:
Foundation Administrator
(See address above.)

*SPECIAL STIPULATIONS:
Funding limited to organizations serving communities where Kroger operates.

LAWRENCE COUNTY COMMUNITY FOUNDATION [1315]

1324 K Street, Suite 150
Bedford, IN 47421
(812) 279-2215
Fax: (812) 279-1984

E-MAIL ADDRESS:
lccf@cfpartner.org

WEB SITE ADDRESS:
www.cfpartner.org

AREAS OF INTEREST:
Community improvement.

TYPE:
Endowments; Project/program grants; Scholarships. Collaborative projects. Classroom grants.

PURPOSE:
To be proactive in creating and growing an enduring source of charitable assets that will help to identify and respond to the emerging and changing needs of the community.

ELIGIBILITY:
Organizations and agencies who may or may not be tax-exempt according to Section 501(c)(3) of the Internal Revenue Code or for-profit entities interested in funding a charitable, not-for profit program are eligible. Population served by the program must be within Lawrence County, IN.

GEOGRAPHIC RESTRICTIONS:
Lawrence County, Indiana.

FINANCIAL DATA:
Amount of support per award: Varies.
Total amount of support: Varies.

APPLICATION INFORMATION:
Application form can be requested from the Foundation or downloaded from the web site. Applicants must submit the following documents with the application form:
(1) concise summary of the proposed project, two or three paragraphs in length, stating the community need to be addressed by the project and why the organization is qualified to address the need, the target population and estimated number to be served, the organization's experience with similar projects, and a description of how the project will fit into and further the organization's overall mission;
(2) description of the activities or steps that will be taken to carry out the project, including project timeline;
(3) summary of funding details, including how the funds will be used, as well as other funding sources. Attach a detailed budget sheet showing projected income and expenses for the project;
(4) an explanation of how the success of this project will be evaluated. If the organization plans to continue the project, explain how will it be sustained after grant funding is expended and;
(5) list of names and amounts from sources

contributing 10% or more of the organization's budget in the past two years. Also list affiliations with religious groups.

Application must be signed by the organization President or another non-paid board officer. Staple or clip each grant application copy.

Duration: Funding for a multiyear project will usually be considered on an annual basis and not extend beyond three years.

ADDRESS INQUIRIES TO:
Hope Flores, Executive Director
(See address above.)

THE LEARY FIREFIGHTERS FOUNDATION [1316]

594 Broadway, Suite 409
New York, NY 10012-3234
(212) 343-0240
Fax: (212) 343-1762

E-MAIL ADDRESS:
info@learyfirefighters.org

WEB SITE ADDRESS:
www.learyfirefighters.org

FOUNDED: 2000

AREAS OF INTEREST:
Firefighting.

NAME(S) OF PROGRAMS:
● The Jeremiah Lucey Grant Program

TYPE:
Grants-in-aid; Project/program grants; Training grants. Grant program to assist professional fire departments.

YEAR PROGRAM STARTED: 2000

PURPOSE:
To provide funding and resources for fire departments to obtain the highest level of equipment, training and technology.

LEGAL BASIS:
Publicly funded tax-exempt organization under Section 501(c)(3) of the Internal Revenue Code.

ELIGIBILITY:
Fire departments with a financial need not covered by a municipal budget in order to maintain the highest level of public safety. Grants only to union-affiliated uniformed fire departments. No grants to individuals.

GEOGRAPHIC RESTRICTIONS:
Massachusetts and New York.

FINANCIAL DATA:
Amount of support per award: $25,000 to $50,000.
Total amount of support: Varies.

APPLICATION INFORMATION:
Initial letter of inquiry, up to two pages, and project budget. Full details are available on the Foundation web site.
Duration: Varies.

IRS IDENTIFICATION NUMBER: 13-4125074

STAFF:
Sharon Badal, Associate, Grant Program

ADDRESS INQUIRIES TO:
Mardi Grant, Executive Director
(See address above.)

THE JOHN J. LEIDY FOUNDATION [1317]

c/o Pierson & Pierson
305 West Chesapeake Avenue, Suite 308
Towson, MD 21204
(410) 821-3006
Fax: (410) 821-3007

E-MAIL ADDRESS:
info@leidyfoundation.org

WEB SITE ADDRESS:
www.leidyfoundation.org

FOUNDED: 1957

AREAS OF INTEREST:
Education, health care, arts/culture, food services, human services, children and youth.

TYPE:
General operating grants; Scholarships.

PURPOSE:
To improve the quality of life in the Baltimore area.

LEGAL BASIS:
Private foundation.

ELIGIBILITY:
Organizations must be IRS 501(c)(3) tax-exempt and be located in Maryland. The Foundation does not fund individuals.

GEOGRAPHIC RESTRICTIONS:
Baltimore metropolitan area.

FINANCIAL DATA:
Amount of support per award: $350 to $20,000.
Total amount of support: $427,790 for the year 2012.

NUMBER OF APPLICANTS MOST RECENT YEAR:
120.

NUMBER OF AWARDS: 97.

APPLICATION INFORMATION:
Applications must include the proposed budget and a copy of the IRS tax-exempt letter. Please submit an original and four copies.
Duration: Typically one year.

PUBLICATIONS:
Application guidelines.

OFFICER:
Robert L. Pierson, President

ADDRESS INQUIRIES TO:
Lu Pierson, Grants Administrator
(See address above.)

THE LES CHENEAUX COMMUNITY FOUNDATION [1318]

P.O. Box 249
Cedarville, MI 49719
(906) 484-2484
Fax: (906) 484-2072

E-MAIL ADDRESS:
lccommunityfoundation@gmail.com

WEB SITE ADDRESS:
www.lescheneauxcommunityfoundation.org

AREAS OF INTEREST:
Education, culture and recreation, environment and youth.

TYPE:
Grants-in-aid; Project/program grants; Scholarships.

PURPOSE:
To support programs that improve the quality of life in the community.

LEGAL BASIS:
Community foundation.

ELIGIBILITY:
Grants are made to organizations that have tax-exempt status under Section 501(c)(3) of the Internal Revenue Code. Nonsectarian religious programs may apply. No grants are made to individuals.

GEOGRAPHIC RESTRICTIONS:
Les Cheneaux, Michigan.

FINANCIAL DATA:
Amount of support per award: Grants vary in amount, depending upon the needs and nature of the request.
Total amount of support: Varies.

NUMBER OF APPLICANTS MOST RECENT YEAR:
Approximately 30.

NUMBER OF AWARDS: Approximately 24.

APPLICATION INFORMATION:
Information is available on the web site.
Duration: Varies.

LOCAL INITIATIVES SUPPORT CORPORATION   [1319]
501 Seventh Avenue, 7th Floor
New York, NY 10018
(212) 455-9800
Fax: (212) 682-5929

E-MAIL ADDRESS:
info@lisc.org

WEB SITE ADDRESS:
www.lisc.org

FOUNDED: 1980

AREAS OF INTEREST:
Urban and rural community revitalization.

TYPE:
Project/program grants; Technical assistance.

YEAR PROGRAM STARTED: 1980

PURPOSE:
To build sustainable communities, which are good places to work, do business and raise children.

ELIGIBILITY:
Nonprofit 501(c)(3) IRS status.

GEOGRAPHIC RESTRICTIONS:
United States.

FINANCIAL DATA:
Amount of support per award: Varies.
Total amount of support: Varies.
Matching fund requirements: A strict matching requirement, dollar-for-dollar of new money from local private sources.

APPLICATION INFORMATION:
Contact the Corporation.
Duration: Varies.

IRS IDENTIFICATION NUMBER: 13-3030229

BOARD OF DIRECTORS:
Robert E. Rubin, Chairman
Michael Rubinger, President and Chief Executive Officer

LONG ISLAND COMMUNITY FOUNDATION   [1320]
Nassau Hall
1864 Muttontown Road
Syosset, NY 11791
(516) 348-0575 ext. 233
Fax: (516) 348-0570

E-MAIL ADDRESS:
narnold@licf.org

WEB SITE ADDRESS:
www.licf.org

FOUNDED: 1978

AREAS OF INTEREST:
Environment, arts, education, health and the community.

NAME(S) OF PROGRAMS:
- **Henry Phillip Kraft Memorial Fund-Environmental Grants**
- **LIUU Fund-Progressive Social Change Grants**

TYPE:
Challenge/matching grants; Demonstration grants; Development grants; General operating grants; Project/program grants; Seed money grants; Technical assistance; Research contracts.

YEAR PROGRAM STARTED: 1978

PURPOSE:
To provide leadership in identifying current and future community needs, and building a permanent endowment to address these needs.

LEGAL BASIS:
501(c)(3) or fiscal agent.

ELIGIBILITY:
Programs and projects benefiting Nassau and Suffolk counties, NY.

GEOGRAPHIC RESTRICTIONS:
Nassau and Suffolk counties, New York.

FINANCIAL DATA:
Amount of support per award: Varies.
Total amount of support: Varies.

NUMBER OF AWARDS: Over 60.

APPLICATION INFORMATION:
The Foundation has three grant cycles throughout the year. Detailed instructions are provided on the Foundation's web site. Applicants should review the instructions carefully before submitting an application.

STAFF:
Sol Marie Alfonso-Jones, Program Officer
Nancy Arnold, Grants Administrator

EXECUTIVE DIRECTOR:
David Okorn

ADDRESS INQUIRIES TO:
Nancy Arnold, Grants Administrator
(See address above.)

LUBBOCK AREA FOUNDATION, INC.   [1321]
2509 80th Street
Lubbock, TX 79423
(806) 762-8061
Fax: (806) 762-8551

E-MAIL ADDRESS:
michelle@lubbockareafoundation.org

WEB SITE ADDRESS:
www.lubbockareafoundation.org

FOUNDED: 1981

AREAS OF INTEREST:
Charitable organizations and community development.

NAME(S) OF PROGRAMS:
- **Mini Grant for Teachers Program**

TYPE:
Grants-in-aid; Scholarships. Responsiveness to changing or emerging community needs approach for solving community problems in South Plains area.

YEAR PROGRAM STARTED: 1981

PURPOSE:
To improve the quality of life in the South Plains area of Texas.

ELIGIBILITY:
Organizations must be 501(c)(3) not-for-profit.

GEOGRAPHIC RESTRICTIONS:
South Plains area of Texas.

FINANCIAL DATA:
Amount of support per award: Grant awards: Up to $1,000.
Total amount of support: Varies.

COOPERATIVE FUNDING PROGRAMS: Community Endowment Challenge, Mini Grants for Teachers.

APPLICATION INFORMATION:
Application information is available on the web site.
Duration: One year. Must reapply.
Deadline: June 15.

ADDRESS INQUIRIES TO:
Michelle Stephens
Director, Educational Initiatives
(See address above.)

M & M AREA COMMUNITY FOUNDATION   [1322]
1101 11th Avenue, Suite One
Menominee, MI 49858-3018
(906) 864-3599
Fax: (906) 864-3657

E-MAIL ADDRESS:
info@mmcommunityfoundation.org

WEB SITE ADDRESS:
www.mmcommunityfoundation.org

FOUNDED: 1994

AREAS OF INTEREST:
Arts, charity, civic affairs, community development, culture, education, health, historic preservation and human services.

TYPE:
Project/program grants; Scholarships; Training grants.

YEAR PROGRAM STARTED: 1997

PURPOSE:
To make people's lives better: more meaningful, secure, and safe.

ELIGIBILITY:
Grants are made to organizations that have tax-exempt status under Section 501(c)(3) of the Internal Revenue Code. No grants are made to individuals. Nonsectarian religious programs may apply.

GEOGRAPHIC RESTRICTIONS:
Menominee County, Michigan and Marinette County, Wisconsin.

FINANCIAL DATA:
Amount of support per award: Up to $10,000.
Total amount of support: $330,000 for the year 2011.

NUMBER OF APPLICANTS MOST RECENT YEAR:
75.

NUMBER OF AWARDS: 47.

APPLICATION INFORMATION:
Applications must be submitted online.
Duration: One year. Renewal possible.
Deadline: March 31.

ADDRESS INQUIRIES TO:
Richard O'Farrell, Executive Director
P.O. Box 846
Menominee, MI 49858-0846
(See e-mail address above.)

MADISON COMMUNITY FOUNDATION　　[1323]
2 Science Court
Madison, WI 53711
(608) 232-1763
Fax: (608) 232-1772

E-MAIL ADDRESS:
tlinfield@madisoncommunityfoundation.org

WEB SITE ADDRESS:
www.madisoncommunityfoundation.org

FOUNDED: 1942

AREAS OF INTEREST:
Children, arts and culture, community development, environment, elderly, learning and youth.

TYPE:
Capital grants; Project/program grants. Program grants support new programs or expansion of existing programs. Capital grants support the construction, acquisition and renovation of facilities and the purchase of equipment. Investments in technology are given to significantly enhance the organization's ability to operate or to improve services.

PURPOSE:
To enhance the quality of life for residents in Dane County.

LEGAL BASIS:
Community foundation.

ELIGIBILITY:
Organizations must be nonprofit IRS 501(c)(3) tax-exempt, serve the people of Dane County, employ a staff, elect a governing board, and conduct business without discrimination on the basis of race, religion, gender, sexual preference, age, marital status, disability or national origin.

Generally grants are not made for operating expenses, individuals, endowments, debt retirement, lobbying, annual campaigns, scholarships, religious organizations for religious purposes, conferences, fund-raising, celebrations or substance abuse treatment.

GEOGRAPHIC RESTRICTIONS:
Dane County, Wisconsin.

FINANCIAL DATA:
Approximately 30% of grant applications are funded at some level. The Foundation is rarely the sole funder of projects; other sources will be sought to accomplish project goals.
Amount of support per award: Program average: $35,000; Capital average: $55,000.
Total amount of support: Approximately $2,000,000 in unrestricted and field-of-interest grants for the year 2013.

NUMBER OF APPLICANTS MOST RECENT YEAR:
56 for the year 2013.

NUMBER OF AWARDS: 23 for the year 2013.

REPRESENTATIVE AWARDS:
Neighborhood Center STEM Project; Madison Public Library Capital Campaign; Madison Parks Foundation; Boys and Girls Club; Madison Opera.

APPLICATION INFORMATION:
Guidelines and applications are available from the Foundation. Proposals must be submitted in both paper and electronic form. Proposals by fax are not accepted. An online letter of inquiry (LOI) is required.
Duration: One to two years.
Deadline: Letter of Inquiry: January 15 and July 15. Those asked to submit a full proposal: March 1 and September 1.

PUBLICATIONS:
Grantmaking Guidelines.

ADDRESS INQUIRIES TO:
Tom Linfield
Vice President, Grantmaking
(See address above.)

MARIETTA COMMUNITY FOUNDATION　　[1324]
100 Putnam Street
Marietta, OH 45750
(740) 373-3286
Fax: (740) 373-3937

E-MAIL ADDRESS:
carol@mcfohio.org

WEB SITE ADDRESS:
www.mcfohio.org

FOUNDED: 1974

AREAS OF INTEREST:
Civic affairs, the elderly, community needs and education.

TYPE:
Challenge/matching grants; Conferences/seminars; Development grants; Endowments; Grants-in-aid; Matching gifts; Scholarships; Seed money grants; Technical assistance; Training grants.

YEAR PROGRAM STARTED: 1974

PURPOSE:
To support philanthropy and the efforts of citizens to improve natural, human and civic resources.

LEGAL BASIS:
Community foundation.

ELIGIBILITY:
Must be a 501(c)(3) organization in or serving Washington County, OH.

GEOGRAPHIC RESTRICTIONS:
Greater Washington County, Ohio, and surrounding area.

FINANCIAL DATA:
Amount of support per award: $200 to $20,000.
Total amount of support: $110,000 unrestricted for the year 2013.

NUMBER OF APPLICANTS MOST RECENT YEAR:
60.

NUMBER OF AWARDS: 35.

APPLICATION INFORMATION:
Organizations may either send a one-page letter of inquiry or submit a formal application form.
Duration: Varies.
Deadline: Proposals are accepted at any time during the year. To be considered in a particular quarter, the in-hand deadlines are February 7, June 7 and October 7. Applicants should allow 45 to 75 days for processing and response.

PUBLICATIONS:
Annual report; grant guidelines; memorial brochure.

FREDA MAYTAG-GRACE CRAWFORD TRUST
c/o JPMorgan Private Client Services
402 North Tejon Street, Suite 200
Colorado Springs, CO 80903
(719) 227-6445
Fax: (719) 227-6448

E-MAIL ADDRESS:
julie.golden@jpmorgan.com

WEB SITE ADDRESS:
www.jpmorgan.com/onlinegrants

TYPE:
Project/program grants.

See entry 1449 for full listing.

LUTHER T. MCCAULEY CHARITABLE TRUST　　[1325]
c/o JPMorgan
370 17th Street, Suite 3200
Denver, CO 80202
(303) 607-7810
Fax: (303) 607-7761

E-MAIL ADDRESS:
julie.golden@jpmorgan.com

WEB SITE ADDRESS:
www.jpmorgan.com/onlinegrants

AREAS OF INTEREST:
Economically deprived, the socially disadvantaged, mentally and physically handicapped citizens, with preference made toward the youth of the community for their educational, social, recreational and medical needs.

TYPE:
Project/program grants.

ELIGIBILITY:
Qualifying charities, agencies and institutions which direct their attention to the economically deprived, the socially disadvantaged and the mentally and physically handicapped citizens of El Paso County, CO. No grants to individuals.

Organization must provide copy of current IRS determination letter showing tax-exempt status under Section 501(c)(3) and public charity status under Section 509(a).

GEOGRAPHIC RESTRICTIONS:
El Paso County, Colorado.

FINANCIAL DATA:
Total amount of support: Average: $3,000 to $5,000.

APPLICATION INFORMATION:
Applications must be submitted online. No physical applications will be accepted.
Duration: One year. No renewals.
Deadline: March 31, June 30 and October 31.

ADDRESS INQUIRIES TO:
Julie Golden, Trust Advisor
(See address above.)

RICHARD KING MELLON FOUNDATION [1326]

BNY/Mellon Center
500 Grant Street, Suite 4106
Pittsburgh, PA 15219-2502
(412) 392-2800
Fax: (412) 392-2837

E-MAIL ADDRESS:
lreed@rkmf.org

WEB SITE ADDRESS:
www.fdncenter.org/grantmaker/rkmellon

FOUNDED: 1947

AREAS OF INTEREST:
Conservation; regional economic
development; children, youth and young
adults; education; human services and
nonprofit capacity building.

TYPE:
Capital grants; Challenge/matching grants;
Grants-in-aid; Project/program grants. Grant
program for improving the quality of life in
southwestern Pennsylvania.

PURPOSE:
To promote conservation, economic
development, education, human services and
programs in the public interest.

ELIGIBILITY:
Must be 501(c)(3) nonprofit organizations.
Priority is given to projects and programs
that have clearly defined outcomes and an
evaluation component. Funding is almost
exclusively committed to southwestern
Pennsylvania. Preference is given for support
of established organizations with specific
objectives, and for partnering with other
donors rather than solely underwriting the
entire cost of projects.

GEOGRAPHIC RESTRICTIONS:
Southwestern Pennsylvania.

FINANCIAL DATA:
Total amount of support: Varies.

APPLICATION INFORMATION:
Applications must be mailed; faxes are not
accepted. Current IRS determination letter
indicating 501(c)(3) tax-exempt status
required.

ADDRESS INQUIRIES TO:
Lisa Reed, Grant Manager
(See address above.)

EUGENE AND AGNES E. MEYER FOUNDATION [1327]

1250 Connecticut Avenue, N.W.
Suite 800
Washington, DC 20036
(202) 483-8294
Fax: (202) 328-6850

E-MAIL ADDRESS:
meyer@meyerfdn.org

WEB SITE ADDRESS:
www.meyerfoundation.org

FOUNDED: 1944

AREAS OF INTEREST:
Education, healthy communities, economic
security, and a strong nonprofit sector.

TYPE:
Capital grants; Challenge/matching grants;
General operating grants; Project/program
grants; Technical assistance. Grants for a
wide variety of projects in the above areas of
interest in the Washington, DC metropolitan
area.

YEAR PROGRAM STARTED: 1944

PURPOSE:
To identify and invest in visionary leaders
and effective community-based nonprofit
organizations that are working to create
lasting improvements in the lives of
low-income people in the Washington, DC
metropolitan region; to work to strengthen
the region's nonprofit sector as a vital and
respected partner in meeting community
needs.

LEGAL BASIS:
Private foundation.

ELIGIBILITY:
The Foundation distributes its funds to and
through tax-exempt nonprofit organizations. It
does not make grants for projects that are
primarily sectarian in character. Grants are
seldom made for projects outside the
geographical boundaries of Greater
Washington and are never made to
individuals. The Foundation does not support
endowment drives, scientific or medical
research, scholarship programs, seasonal
programs, special or annual events or
conferences.

GEOGRAPHIC RESTRICTIONS:
Montgomery and Prince George's counties,
Maryland; Arlington, Fairfax and Prince
William counties and the cities of
Alexandria, Falls Church, Manassas and
Manassas Park, Virginia; Washington, DC.

FINANCIAL DATA:
Amount of support per award: $1,000 to
$500,000; $25,000 average.
Total amount of support: $6,280,470 in
grants authorized for the year 2012.

COOPERATIVE FUNDING PROGRAMS: Occasional
joint funding.

NUMBER OF APPLICANTS MOST RECENT YEAR:
Approximately 500.

NUMBER OF AWARDS: 211 grants for the year
ended December 31, 2013.

APPLICATION INFORMATION:
Applications must be submitted online via
link on the Foundation's web site.
Duration: Generally one-year support from
date of award.

PUBLICATIONS:
E-newsletter.

IRS IDENTIFICATION NUMBER: 53-0241716

STAFF:
Julie L. Rogers, President and Chief
Executive Officer
Janice Thomas, Vice President of Finance
and Administration
Richard L. Moyers, Vice President, Programs
and Communications
Karen FitzGerald, Senior Program Officer
Danielle Reyes, Senior Program Officer
Maegan Scott, Communications and Program
Officer
Jane Ward, Grants Manager
Andrew Brown, Program Assistant
Melody Fitzgerald, Program Assistant
Jennifer Burke, Business Operations
Assistant

OFFICERS AND BOARD OF DIRECTORS:
Joshua Bernstein, Chairperson
Deborah Ratner Salzberg, Vice Chairperson
Julie L. Rogers, President and Chief
Executive Officer
Barbara Lang, Secretary-Treasurer
Newman T. Halvorson, Jr., Assistant
Secretary-Treasurer

William Dunbar
Ginger Lew
James Sandman
Lidia Soto-Harmon
Dr. Robert G. Templin, Jr.
Kerrie B. Wilson

ADDRESS INQUIRIES TO:
Julie L. Rogers, President and
Chief Executive Officer
(See address above.)

MICHIGAN GATEWAY COMMUNITY FOUNDATION [1328]

111 Days Avenue
Buchanan, MI 49107-1609
(269) 695-3521
Fax: (269) 695-4250

E-MAIL ADDRESS:
info@mgcf.org

WEB SITE ADDRESS:
www.mgcf.org

FOUNDED: 1978

AREAS OF INTEREST:
Health, culture, education and community
development.

TYPE:
Challenge/matching grants; Development
grants; Project/program grants; Scholarships;
Seed money grants.

YEAR PROGRAM STARTED: 1978

PURPOSE:
To address the changing needs of the
community in Cass and South Berrien
counties.

LEGAL BASIS:
501(c)(3) nonprofit foundation.

ELIGIBILITY:
Eligible organizations must be IRS 501(c)(3)
tax-exempt.

GEOGRAPHIC RESTRICTIONS:
Cass and South Berrien counties, Michigan.

FINANCIAL DATA:
Amount of support per award: Varies.
Total amount of support: Varies.

REPRESENTATIVE AWARDS:
$2,500 over six weeks for Group Counseling
"Life on a Tightrope" for High School Girls
at risk for low self-esteem and peer pressure.

APPLICATION INFORMATION:
Applicants may use the Common Grant
Application Form of the Council of Michigan
Foundations. Applications must include a
copy of the IRS tax determination letter.
Duration: One year. Most grants not
renewable.
Deadline: February 1, May 1, August 1 and
November 1.

PUBLICATIONS:
Annual report; scholarship programs.

IRS IDENTIFICATION NUMBER: 38-2180730

ADDRESS INQUIRIES TO:
Rob Habicht
President and Chief Executive Officer
(See address above.)

THE MINNEAPOLIS FOUNDATION [1329]

800 IDS Center
80 South Eighth Street
Minneapolis, MN 55402
(612) 672-3878
Fax: (612) 672-3846

E-MAIL ADDRESS:
grants@mplsfoundation.org

WEB SITE ADDRESS:
www.minneapolisfoundation.org

FOUNDED: 1915

AREAS OF INTEREST:
Education, homelessness, racial and economic equity, immigration, economic development, jobs, small business, and civic engagement.

CONSULTING OR VOLUNTEER SERVICES:
Philanthropic services for other foundations.

NAME(S) OF PROGRAMS:
- **Community Action Funds**
- **Designated Beneficiary Funds**
- **Donor-Advised Funds**
- **Field of Interest Funds**
- **Investment Management Services**
- **Nonprofit Assistance Fund**
- **Robins, Kaplan, Miller and Ciresi Foundation for Children**

TYPE:
General operating grants; Project/program grants.

PURPOSE:
To invest the Foundation's unrestricted resources towards specific results in order to achieve social, economic and racial equity for Minneapolis residents.

LEGAL BASIS:
Community foundation incorporated in Minnesota.

ELIGIBILITY:
Organizations must advance social, economic, and/or racial equity to be eligible for funding. The Foundation grants to 501(c)(3) organizations, some 501(c)(4) nonprofits, governmental or tribal organizations, and groups organized for nonprofit purposes (informal, emerging or collaborative groups).

The Foundation does not fund individuals, organizations/activities outside of Minnesota, conference registration fees, memberships, direct religious activities, political organizations or candidates' fund-raising efforts, conferences, events or sponsorships, financial deficits, replacement of public sector funds, emergency/safety net services, regranting/loans, production of housing units, or purchase or repair of vehicles.

GEOGRAPHIC RESTRICTIONS:
Primarily Minneapolis, Minnesota.

FINANCIAL DATA:
Amount of support per award: Competitive grants: $30,000 to $100,000; average approximately $50,000.

Total amount of support: $4,135,024 in competitive grants for fiscal year 2013-14.

NUMBER OF APPLICANTS MOST RECENT YEAR:
Competitive Community Grants: 177 for fiscal year 2013-14.

NUMBER OF AWARDS: Competitive Community Grants: 64 for fiscal year 2013-14.

REPRESENTATIVE AWARDS:
$35,000 to African Development Center of Minnesota to produce affordable housing opportunities and support a more competitive workforce; $40,000 to State Voices to increase voter participation in communities of color; $50,000 to EMPOWER to recruit, prepare, train and mobilize a cohort of underserved and underrepresented low-income and communities of color across Minneapolis to advocate for high-quality educational options for all children.

APPLICATION INFORMATION:
Application information and updates on the Foundation grantmaking cycle are available on the web site.

Duration: Annual. Must reapply for additional funding. No multiyear grants.

IRS IDENTIFICATION NUMBER: 41-6029402

OFFICERS:
Sandra Vargas, President and Chief Executive Officer
Jean Adams, Chief Operating Officer/Chief Financial Operator

ADDRESS INQUIRIES TO:
Community Grantmaking
(See address above.)

MIZUHO USA FOUNDATION, INC. [1330]

Mizuho Corporate Bank, Ltd.
1251 Avenue of the Americas
31st Floor
New York, NY 10020-1104
(212) 282-4192

E-MAIL ADDRESS:
mizuho.usa.foundation@mizuhocbus.com

WEB SITE ADDRESS:
www.mizuhocbk.com/americas/community/foundation/index.html

FOUNDED: 2003

AREAS OF INTEREST:
Community development, with a focus on affordable housing, economic development and workforce development.

NAME(S) OF PROGRAMS:
- **Fostering Economic Self-Sufficiency**
- **Mizuho Community Involvement Grants Program**
- **Mizuho Matching Gifts Program**
- **Promoting Economic Development**
- **Strengthening Affordable Housing**

TYPE:
Demonstration grants; Matching gifts; Project/program grants; Seed money grants. The Foundation awards grants to not-for-profit charitable organizations for community development programs that help sustain and revitalize economically distressed urban communities, and assist individuals who live in these neighborhoods.

Fostering Economic Self-Sufficiency funds programs that strengthen the workforce development field through the provision of technical assistance and/or training to not-for-profit organizations.

Mizuho Community Involvement Grants Program makes small grants available to the not-for-profit charitable organizations with which Mizuho Corporate Bank volunteer activities take place.

Mizuho Matching Gifts Program is for qualifying contributions made by eligible Mizuho Financial Group U.S. employees to qualifying not-for-profit charitable organizations in the areas of education, arts and culture, health and community affairs.

Promoting Economic Development supports programs that promote economic and commercial revitalization of communities by fostering small business development, entrepreneurship, job creation and job retention.

Strengthening Affordable Housing provides funding for programs that facilitate access to affordable housing for low- and moderate-income individuals and families.

YEAR PROGRAM STARTED: 2003

PURPOSE:
To provide grants to not-for-profit charitable organizations to support community development programs that contribute to the strength and vitality of urban neighborhoods; to serve as a catalyst for innovative programs in the U.S. that strengthen urban communities.

LEGAL BASIS:
Corporate foundation.

ELIGIBILITY:
Organizations applying to the Foundation must:
(1) be recognized as tax-exempt under Section 501(c)(3) of the Internal Revenue Code and classified as a public charity under Section 509(a)(1) or (2) of the Internal Revenue Code and not a supporting organization under Section 509(a)(3);
(2) present a proposal that satisfies the Foundation's guidelines;
(3) not discriminate against a person or group on the basis of age, race, national origin, ethnicity, gender, disability, sexual orientation, political affiliation or religious belief and;
(4) be in full compliance with U.S. anti-terrorism laws and regulations, including the USA Patriot Act and Executive Order 13224, pertaining to U.S.-based, not-for-profit charitable organizations conducting activities outside of the U.S.

The Foundation does not fund:
(1) general operating support;
(2) individuals;
(3) religious, sectarian, fraternal, veteran, athletic or labor groups;
(4) organizations or programs outside the U.S.;
(5) political organizations, political candidates or political activity;
(6) organizations whose primary purpose is to influence legislation;
(7) fund-raising activities such as charitable dinners, benefits, courtesy advertising, telethons, races or other sporting events;
(8) advertising and;
(9) endowment or capital campaigns.

GEOGRAPHIC RESTRICTIONS:
New York City, New York.

FINANCIAL DATA:
Foundation's endowment is approximately $14,300,000.

Amount of support per award: $10,000 to $100,000; average $50,000.

Total amount of support: $677,891 in grants for the year 2013.

Matching fund requirements: Mizuho Matching Gifts Program: 1:1 match for qualifying contributions. Requests for matching gifts must come from eligible employees of the Mizuho Financial Group in the U.S.

COOPERATIVE FUNDING PROGRAMS:
Neighborhood Opportunities Fund (New York City, NY) and New York City Workforce Development Fund.

NUMBER OF APPLICANTS MOST RECENT YEAR:
50.

NUMBER OF AWARDS: 22 for the year 2011, in addition to matching gifts.

REPRESENTATIVE AWARDS:
$75,000 to WHEDco, New York, NY, for Childcare Improvement Project to expand the training component of a state-funded initiative to register unlicensed family day care providers in New York City; $10,000 to Los Angeles Neighborhood Housing Services for homeownership preservation and foreclosure prevention; $25,000 to Japan Center for International Exchange - USA for a new fund to support Japanese nongovernmental organizations and community associations working to rebuild communities in the aftermath of the Great East Japan Earthquake and tsunami.

APPLICATION INFORMATION:
Qualifying organizations must submit a short concept paper of up to three pages for preliminary review. The concept paper should include:
(1) a brief description of the organization including its legal name, history, mission/goals, activities and, if applicable, web address;
(2) copy of the IRS determination letter indicating 501(c)(3) tax-exempt status and 509(a) public charity classification and;
(3) a description of the program for which funding is sought, including statement of need, goals and activities of the program, expected outcomes and evaluation methods, projected time frame, population(s)/geographies served, grant amount requested, and a preliminary program budget, with projected expenses and revenues, including funding commitments received to date for the program as well as pending requests (may be provided in attachment form).

The Foundation staff will review all initial submissions and invite organizations on a selective basis to submit more detailed proposals. Each applicant will be notified of the Foundation's interest within eight weeks of the annual deadline. Selected proposals are presented to the Foundation's Board of Directors, which makes funding decisions each fall.
Duration: Usually one year; some multiyear grants may be awarded.
Deadline: First weekday in July, to be considered for funding in the same year.

PUBLICATIONS:
Brochure; application guidelines.

IRS IDENTIFICATION NUMBER: 13-3550008

OFFICERS:
John H. Higgs, Chairman
Kenji Yoshioka, President
Paul Dankers, Treasurer
Koji Nishiwaki, Secretary
Lesley H. Palmer, Executive Director
Albert Scarola, Assistant Treasurer
Leah Markham, Program Officer

BOARD OF DIRECTORS:
Nancy Bercovici
John H. Higgs
Koji Nishiwaki
Hiroshi Suehiro
Kenji Yoshioka

ADDRESS INQUIRIES TO:
Lesley H. Palmer, Executive Director
(See address above.)

MONTANA COMMUNITY FOUNDATION [1331]
One North Last Chance Gulch
Suite 1
Helena, MT 59601
(406) 443-8313
Fax: (406) 442-0482

E-MAIL ADDRESS:
info@mtcf.org

WEB SITE ADDRESS:
www.mtcf.org

FOUNDED: 1988

AREAS OF INTEREST:
General charitable purposes.

NAME(S) OF PROGRAMS:
● **Social Justice Montana**
● **Women's Foundation of Montana**

TYPE:
Grants-in-aid. The Foundation does almost no competitive grantmaking. Although it provides $2,000,000 yearly in grants and scholarships, almost all of that money is designated. It also has a large number of donor-advised and scholarship funds. The only competitive granting programs are the following:
Social Justice Montana: The mission of this Fund is to promote tolerance and combat bigotry and discrimination, with a focus on youth, ages elementary through high school and;
Women's Foundation of Montana: Its mission is to promote economic self-sufficiency and a brighter future for girls.

All of the Foundation's other unrestricted grant funds are devoted to matching programs, technical assistance programs and other supportive services for building local community foundations.

PURPOSE:
To cultivate a culture of giving so Montana communities can flourish.

LEGAL BASIS:
501(c)(3) organization.

GEOGRAPHIC RESTRICTIONS:
Montana.

FINANCIAL DATA:
Amount of support per award: Women's Foundation of Montana: Up to $10,000.
Total amount of support: $2,000,000 per year in grants and scholarships; almost all of this money is designated funding.
Women's Foundation of Montana: Up to $55,000 per year.

ADDRESS INQUIRIES TO:
Emily Kovarik, Controller
(See address above.)

THE MORTON-KELLY CHARITABLE TRUST [1332]
c/o Jensen Baird Gardner & Henry
10 Free Street
Portland, ME 04101
(207) 775-7271
Fax: (207) 775-7935

E-MAIL ADDRESS:
mquinlan@jbgh.com

FOUNDED: 1988

AREAS OF INTEREST:
The arts, education, environment and history.

TYPE:
Capital grants; Challenge/matching grants; Development grants; Project/program grants; Seed money grants. One-time cash award.

YEAR PROGRAM STARTED: 1988

PURPOSE:
To support organizations in the arts, education, environment and history.

LEGAL BASIS:
Private foundation.

ELIGIBILITY:
Organizations must be IRS 501(c)(3) tax-exempt and be located in Maine.

GEOGRAPHIC RESTRICTIONS:
Maine.

FINANCIAL DATA:
Amount of support per award: Varies.
Total amount of support: $645,750 for the year 2013.

NUMBER OF APPLICANTS MOST RECENT YEAR:
128 for the year 2013.

NUMBER OF AWARDS: 74 for the year 2013.

REPRESENTATIVE AWARDS:
$7,000 to Appalachian Mountain Club; $5,000 to Bethel Historical Society; $10,000 to Children's Museum and Theatre of Maine; $2,500 to Midcoast Symphony Orchestra.

APPLICATION INFORMATION:
Applicants may submit a written proposal and must include a copy of the IRS tax determination letter.
Duration: One year.
Deadline: October 1.

IRS IDENTIFICATION NUMBER: 01-0442078

ADDRESS INQUIRIES TO:
Michael J. Quinlan, Secretary
(See address above.)

*PLEASE NOTE:
Applications not accepted before July 1 each year.

CHARLES STEWART MOTT FOUNDATION [1333]
Mott Foundation Building
503 South Saginaw Street, Suite 1200
Flint, MI 48502-1851
(810) 238-5651
Fax: (810) 766-1753

E-MAIL ADDRESS:
info@mott.org

WEB SITE ADDRESS:
www.mott.org

FOUNDED: 1926

AREAS OF INTEREST:
Civil society, environment, pathways out of poverty and Flint, MI area, besides exploratory interests.

TYPE:
Challenge/matching grants; Demonstration grants; General operating grants; Project/program grants; Seed money grants; Technical assistance; Training grants. Grants for improvement of the quality of living in the community through pilot ventures in a number of human service areas. Emphasis is

on improving opportunity for the individual, partnership with the community, effectiveness of community systems and leadership.

PURPOSE:
To support efforts that promote a just, equitable and sustainable society.

LEGAL BASIS:
Private foundation.

ELIGIBILITY:
Applicants must be organizations and institutions with appropriate interests. No grants to individuals. Tax-exempt status is required.

FINANCIAL DATA:
Amount of support per award: $15,000 to $250,000.
Total amount of support: $101,000,000 for the year 2013.

NUMBER OF AWARDS: 400 grants for the year 2013.

APPLICATION INFORMATION:
Information on application procedures is available online.
Duration: One year; occasionally multiyear.

PUBLICATIONS:
Annual report.

TRUSTEES:
William S. White, Chairman, President and Chief Executive Officer
A. Marshall Acuff, Jr.
Lizabeth Ardisana
Frederick S. Kirkpatrick
Tiffany W. Lovett
Webb F. Martin
Olivia P. Maynard
John Morning
Maryanne Mott
Charlie Nelms
Douglas X. Patino
William H. Piper
Marise M.M. Stewart

ADDRESS INQUIRIES TO:
Office of Proposal Entry
(See address above.)

MUSKINGUM COUNTY COMMUNITY FOUNDATION [1334]
534 Putnam Avenue
Zanesville, OH 43701
(740) 453-5192
Fax: (740) 453-5734

E-MAIL ADDRESS:
giving@mccf.org

WEB SITE ADDRESS:
www.mccf.org
zanesvilleprize.org

FOUNDED: 1985

AREAS OF INTEREST:
Improving the quality of life in Muskingum County, OH.

CONSULTING OR VOLUNTEER SERVICES:
Assistance to college-bound students, grantseekers and grantmakers in the Muskingum County, OH area.

NAME(S) OF PROGRAMS:
● **Scholarship Central**
● **Zanesville Prize for Contemporary Ceramics**

TYPE:
Awards/prizes; Challenge/matching grants; Conferences/seminars; Development grants;

Endowments; Project/program grants; Scholarships; Seed money grants; Technical assistance; Visiting scholars. Scholarships for Muskingum County, OH residents and others designated in fund agreements. Support for contemporary ceramics through largest prize in the Western Hemisphere.

YEAR PROGRAM STARTED: 1985

PURPOSE:
To improve the quality of life and to serve the charitable needs of the community by attracting and administering charitable funds.

LEGAL BASIS:
Ohio nonprofit corporation classified by the IRS as a 501(c)(3) entity.

ELIGIBILITY:
Organization with primary or sole impact on Muskingum County, OH.

GEOGRAPHIC RESTRICTIONS:
Muskingum and contiguous counties, Ohio.

FINANCIAL DATA:
Assets of $20,000,000.
Amount of support per award: Zanesville Prize: Top prize of $20,000; All others: Varies.
Total amount of support: $1,000,000 annually; Zanesville Prize: $30,000.

APPLICATION INFORMATION:
Application information is available on the web site.
Deadline: Varies.

ADDRESS INQUIRIES TO:
David P. Mitzel, Executive Director
(See address above.)

NATIONAL BLACK MBA ASSOCIATION [1335]
One East Wacker Drive
Suite 3500
Chicago, IL 60601
(312) 236-2622
Fax: (312) 236-0390

E-MAIL ADDRESS:
scholarship@nbmbaa.org

WEB SITE ADDRESS:
www.nbmbaa.org

AREAS OF INTEREST:
The economic and intellectual wealth of the black community.

NAME(S) OF PROGRAMS:
● **NBMBAA Graduate Scholarship Program**

TYPE:
Scholarships.

PURPOSE:
To help create economic and intellectual wealth for the black community; to identify and increase the pool of Black talent for business, public, private and nonprofit sectors.

ELIGIBILITY:
Open to qualified business students enrolled full-time in an accredited Association to Advance Collegiate Schools of Business (AACSB) graduate business program in the U.S. This Program identifies students who have demonstrated potential to make significant contributions in the field of business in the public and private sectors. Applicants must demonstrate academic excellence, exceptional leadership potential and be actively involved in their local communities through service to others.

GEOGRAPHIC RESTRICTIONS:
United States and Canada.

FINANCIAL DATA:
Amount of support per award: Up to $15,000.
Total amount of support: Over $500,000.

NUMBER OF APPLICANTS MOST RECENT YEAR: 550.

NUMBER OF AWARDS: Minimum of 25.

APPLICATION INFORMATION:
Applicants must submit a two-page essay (with applicant's name omitted entirely from document), resume (not to exceed two pages), and official transcripts for all college coursework or the current graduate program. Essay and resume must be submitted through Association's online process only.
Deadline: May 15.

NATIONAL FOOTBALL LEAGUE FOUNDATION [1336]
345 Park Avenue
New York, NY 10154
(212) 450-2000
Fax: (212) 847-1812

E-MAIL ADDRESS:
alexia.gallagher@nfl.com

WEB SITE ADDRESS:
www.nflfoundation.org

FOUNDED: 1973

AREAS OF INTEREST:
Health and safety, youth football, and community.

NAME(S) OF PROGRAMS:
● **Field Grants**
● **Player Foundation Grants**
● **Pro Bowl Grants**
● **Youth Football Grants**

TYPE:
Awards/prizes; Challenge/matching grants; General operating grants; Project/program grants; Research grants; Seed money grants; Training grants.

YEAR PROGRAM STARTED: 1973

PURPOSE:
To support youth-oriented programs that promote education, physical fitness and the value of a healthy lifestyle.

LEGAL BASIS:
Private foundation.

ELIGIBILITY:
Grants will be awarded to organizations that focus on youth-centered educational and recreational programming on a national scale.

GEOGRAPHIC RESTRICTIONS:
United States.

FINANCIAL DATA:
Amount of support per award: Varies.
Total amount of support: Varies.

NUMBER OF APPLICANTS MOST RECENT YEAR:
Approximately 1,200.

NUMBER OF AWARDS: Varies.

APPLICATION INFORMATION:
Application information is available on the web site.

IRS IDENTIFICATION NUMBER: 23-7315236

ADDRESS INQUIRIES TO:
Alexia Gallagher
Director
(See address above.)

NATIONAL TRUST FOR HISTORIC PRESERVATION

2600 Virginia Avenue, Suite 1000
Washington, DC 20037
(202) 588-6277
Fax: (202) 588-6223

E-MAIL ADDRESS:
grants@savingplaces.org

WEB SITE ADDRESS:
www.preservationnation.org/funding

TYPE:
Challenge/matching grants; Project/program grants; Seed money grants; Technical assistance; Training grants. Education program curricula. Project grants to support consultants with professional expertise in areas such as architecture, law, planning, economics, archeology and graphic design. Conferences that address subjects of particular importance to historic preservation also are funded. In addition, grants are made for curriculum development in preservation education directed at select audiences.

See entry 615 for full listing.

NBCC FOUNDATION, INC.

3 Terrace Way
Greensboro, NC 27403
(336) 232-0376
Fax: (336) 232-0010

E-MAIL ADDRESS:
foundation@nbcc.org

WEB SITE ADDRESS:
www.nbccf.org

TYPE:
Fellowships; Scholarships. Academic scholarships for individuals pursuing a graduate-level degree in professional counseling.

See entry 1727 for full listing.

NEW MEXICO COMMUNITY FOUNDATION   [1337]

502 West Cordova Road, Suite 1
Santa Fe, NM 87505
(505) 820-6860
Fax: (505) 820-7860

E-MAIL ADDRESS:
nmcf@nmcf.org

WEB SITE ADDRESS:
www.nmcf.org

FOUNDED: 1983

AREAS OF INTEREST:
New Mexico's communities and their people.

NAME(S) OF PROGRAMS:
● **New Mexico Community AIDS Partnership Initiative (NMCAP)**

TYPE:
Endowments; Grants-in-aid. Supports community-based projects and organizations around the state that provide HIV/AIDS prevention, education, harm reduction and direct services.

GEOGRAPHIC RESTRICTIONS:
New Mexico.

FINANCIAL DATA:
Amount of support per award: $100 to $300,000.

APPLICATION INFORMATION:
Applicants must first submit the online Letter of Inquiry. This letter must provide brief, but

basic, information about the project, its mission, planned activity or delivery of services, its current stage of development, and the proposed budget/funding. If the project meets the necessary preliminary criteria, the Foundation will then invite a detailed application.

ADDRESS INQUIRIES TO:
Denise Gonzales
Director, Community Philanthropy
(See address above.)

THE NORCLIFFE FOUNDATION

Wells Fargo Center
999 Third Avenue, Suite 1006
Seattle, WA 98104
(206) 682-4820
Fax: (206) 682-4821

E-MAIL ADDRESS:
arline@thenorcliffefoundation.com

WEB SITE ADDRESS:
www.thenorcliffefoundation.com

TYPE:
Capital grants; Endowments; General operating grants; Project/program grants; Research grants; Seed money grants. Social service grants.

See entry 245 for full listing.

NORTHEAST AGRICULTURAL EDUCATION FOUNDATION

101 South Salina Street
Suite 400
Syracuse, NY 13202
(315) 671-0588
Fax: (315) 671-0589

E-MAIL ADDRESS:
info@northeastagriculture.org

WEB SITE ADDRESS:
www.northeastagriculture.org

TYPE:
Project/program grants.

See entry 2126 for full listing.

NORTHERN TRUST CORPORATION   [1338]

50 South LaSalle Street, L7
Chicago, IL 60603
(312) 444-4059
Fax: (312) 630-1809

E-MAIL ADDRESS:
communityaffairs@northerntrust.com

WEB SITE ADDRESS:
www.northerntrust.com

FOUNDED: 1889

AREAS OF INTEREST:
Education, social welfare, and culture and the arts.

NAME(S) OF PROGRAMS:
● **The Northern Trust Company Charitable Trust**
● **The Northern Trust Matching Gift Program**
● **Volunteer Grants Program**

TYPE:
Capital grants; Endowments; General operating grants; Matching gifts; Project/program grants; Technical assistance; Training grants. Grants within the Bank's

areas of interest, including matching gifts to hospitals, educational institutions, cultural institutions and social welfare organizations.

YEAR PROGRAM STARTED: 1966

PURPOSE:
To reach out to people in the Chicago area who are in need or face obstacles that impede their full participation in society.

LEGAL BASIS:
Northern Trust Company is a multi-bank holding company.

ELIGIBILITY:
Applicant must be a not-for-profit organization, tax-exempt under IRS requirements and located in the U.S., Chicago metropolitan area.

Normally, contributions will not be made to support individuals, fraternal groups, individual churches or sectarian organizations, political activity, research, tickets or advertising for fund-raising benefits and agencies receiving more than 5% of their funding from the United Way.

GEOGRAPHIC RESTRICTIONS:
Chicago, Illinois.

FINANCIAL DATA:
Amount of support per award: Typical grant is $10,000 to $15,000.
Total amount of support: $13,800,000 for the year 2013.
Matching fund requirements: Will match 100% of any gifts at least $25 to a maximum of $2,000 per person per year.

NUMBER OF APPLICANTS MOST RECENT YEAR:
500.

NUMBER OF AWARDS: 300.

APPLICATION INFORMATION:
New applicants must submit an online letter of inquiry eight weeks before application deadline. If proposal is approved, then applicant must submit:
(1) a completed application form;
(2) a copy of organization's IRS 501(c)(3) notification letter;
(3) a copy of organization's operating budget and specific project budget, if applicable;
(4) financial information for previous two years;
(5) a list of Chicago-area corporate and foundation contributors and amounts given in the last and the current year;
(6) a list of board members, with affiliations and;
(7) a list of organization's management staff and their qualifications.

Prior successful applicants are not required to submit the letter of inquiry.
Duration: Grants are annual. Multiyear pledges for capital or endowments. Requests for renewals are considered annually.
Deadline: Varies.

PUBLICATIONS:
Annual report.

IRS IDENTIFICATION NUMBER: 36-6147253

STAFF:
K. Kelly Mannard, Executive Vice President
Deborah Liverett, Senior Vice President
Alexis Geocaris, Vice President
Chastity Davis, Officer
Edrea Jones, Coordinator
Dawn McGovern, Coordinator

ADDRESS INQUIRIES TO:
Deborah Liverett, Senior Vice President and Director of Community Affairs
(See address above.)

THE NORTHWEST MINNESOTA FOUNDATION [1339]

201 Third Street, N.W.
Bemidji, MN 56601
(218) 759-2057
Fax: (218) 759-2328

E-MAIL ADDRESS:
nwmf@nwmf.org

WEB SITE ADDRESS:
www.nwmf.org

FOUNDED: 1986

TYPE:
Development grants; Endowments;
Project/program grants; Training grants.

PURPOSE:
To improve the quality of life for the people
of the region.

ELIGIBILITY:
Applicants must be a public agency or
private nonprofit organization with a
501(c)(3) federal tax-exempt status. If an
organization does not meet these criteria, it
may work with an affiliated tax-exempt
organization that may be the applicant and
fiscal agent for the project. The affiliate must
be a parent organization, provide similar
services and/or define in writing its
participation in project implementation. No
grants are made to individuals.

GEOGRAPHIC RESTRICTIONS:
Beltrami, Clearwater, Hubbard, Kittson, Lake
of the Woods, Mahnomen, Marshall,
Norman, Pennington, Polk, Red Lake and
Roseau counties, Minnesota.

FINANCIAL DATA:
Amount of support per award: Up to
$25,000, depending on the grant type.
Total amount of support: Varies.
Matching fund requirements: 50% typically
required.

APPLICATION INFORMATION:
A preproposal must be submitted on the
NMF preproposal application form.
Applicants are encouraged to contact NMF
staff to discuss projects prior to submission.
Once a project has been determined to be
eligible, a full application is invited and
NMF staff will explain the process for
submitting additional information.
Duration: Up to two years; multiyear
depending upon grant.
Deadline: Preproposals may be submitted at
any time.

ADDRESS INQUIRIES TO:
Nate Dorr, Program Officer-Grants
(See address above.)

THE NORTHWESTERN MUTUAL FOUNDATION [1340]

720 East Wisconsin Avenue
Milwaukee, WI 53202
(414) 665-2200
Fax: (414) 665-2199

E-MAIL ADDRESS:
foundationonline@northwesternmutual.com

WEB SITE ADDRESS:
www.nmfoundation.com

FOUNDED: 1992

AREAS OF INTEREST:
Education, childhood cancer, building
neighborhood capacity and volunteerism.

CONSULTING OR VOLUNTEER SERVICES:
MutualFriends is the name of the corporate
employee volunteer program.

TYPE:
Project, program and capacity-building
support, matching gifts, scholarships, disaster
relief, United Way and UPAF support.

PURPOSE:
To inspire human potential through lifelong
learning and community commitment.

GEOGRAPHIC RESTRICTIONS:
United States only.

FINANCIAL DATA:
Amount of support per award: Varies.
Total amount of support: Approximately
$17,000,000 for fiscal year 2013 (July 1,
2012 through June 30, 2013).

APPLICATION INFORMATION:
Guidelines and deadlines are communicated
annually in July on the Foundation web site.
Foundation accepts online applications only
through its web site.
Duration: One year. Must reapply.

OFFICER:
John Kordsmeier, President

ADDRESS INQUIRIES TO:
See e-mail address above.

OKLAHOMA CITY COMMUNITY FOUNDATION, INC. [1341]

P.O. Box 1146
Oklahoma City, OK 73101-1146
(405) 235-5603
Fax: (405) 235-5612

E-MAIL ADDRESS:
info@occf.org

WEB SITE ADDRESS:
www.occf.org

FOUNDED: 1969

AREAS OF INTEREST:
Beautification, education, the arts, social
services and civic organizations.

TYPE:
Project/program grants; Scholarships. Support
for philanthropic agencies designated by
donors. Discretionary grants by the
Foundation's trustees are relatively modest.

PURPOSE:
To serve the charitable purposes of its donors
and the charitable needs of the Oklahoma
City area through the development and
administration of endowment and other
charitable funds with the goal of preserving
capital and enhancing value.

LEGAL BASIS:
Public foundation.

ELIGIBILITY:
Applicants can be any IRS 501(c)(3)
organization.

GEOGRAPHIC RESTRICTIONS:
Oklahoma City, Oklahoma and surrounding
area.

FINANCIAL DATA:
Assets of $706,000,000 for the year ended
June 30, 2013.
Amount of support per award: Varies.
Total amount of support: $23,000,000 in
grant distributions for fiscal year ended June
30, 2013.

APPLICATION INFORMATION:
Application information is available on the
web site.
Duration: Varies.

IRS IDENTIFICATION NUMBER: 23-7024262

ADDRESS INQUIRIES TO:
Nancy Anthony, President
(See address above.)

OMAHA COMMUNITY FOUNDATION

302 South 36th Street
Suite 100
Omaha, NE 68131
(402) 342-3458
Fax: (402) 342-3582

E-MAIL ADDRESS:
betty@omahafoundation.org

WEB SITE ADDRESS:
www.omahafoundation.org

TYPE:
Capital grants; Project/program grants;
Scholarships. Donors can contribute through
the Omaha Community Foundation to any
nonprofit agency. The OCF also has five
discretionary grant programs.
See entry 252 for full listing.

OMNOVA SOLUTIONS FOUNDATION [1342]

175 Ghent Road
Fairlawn, OH 44333-3300
(330) 869-4289
Fax: (330) 869-4345

E-MAIL ADDRESS:
theresa.carter@omnova.com

WEB SITE ADDRESS:
www.omnova.com

FOUNDED: 1999

AREAS OF INTEREST:
Support of educational, cultural and 501(c)(3)
organizations in areas where OMNOVA
Solutions has large concentrations of
employment.

TYPE:
Capital grants; Development grants;
Endowments; General operating grants;
Matching gifts; Project/program grants;
Scholarships.

YEAR PROGRAM STARTED: 1999

PURPOSE:
To support education and other charitable
organizations in the communities where
OMNOVA Solutions has facilities.

LEGAL BASIS:
Nonprofit corporation, private foundation.

ELIGIBILITY:
Tax-exempt organizations are eligible.

GEOGRAPHIC RESTRICTIONS:
Georgia, Massachusetts, Mississippi, North
Carolina, Ohio, Pennsylvania, South Carolina
and Wisconsin.

FINANCIAL DATA:
Amount of support per award: $100 to
$25,000. Average $5,000.
Total amount of support: $1,550,000 for the
year 2013.

NUMBER OF AWARDS: 498 for the year 2013.

REPRESENTATIVE AWARDS:
American Red Cross; Akron Community
Service Center and Urban League; E.J.
Thomas Performing Arts Hall.

APPLICATION INFORMATION:
A brief letter is required.

Duration: One-time grants. Renewable.

Deadline: Applications are reviewed and grants awarded throughout the year.

PUBLICATIONS:
Application guidelines; annual report.

IRS IDENTIFICATION NUMBER: 34-1909350

TRUSTEES:
Michael E. Hicks, President
Frank Robers, Treasurer
Kristine Syrvalin, Secretary
Sandi Noah
Nick Triantafillopoulos

ADDRESS INQUIRIES TO:
Theresa Carter, President
(See address above.)

OPEN SOCIETY INSTITUTE - BALTIMORE   [1343]

201 North Charles Street
Suite 1300
Baltimore, MD 21201
(410) 234-1091
Fax: (410) 234-2816

E-MAIL ADDRESS:
kima.taylor@opensocietyfoundations.org

WEB SITE ADDRESS:
www.osi-baltimore.org

AREAS OF INTEREST:
Drug addiction.

NAME(S) OF PROGRAMS:
● **The Drug Addiction Treatment Program**

TYPE:
Project/program grants.

YEAR PROGRAM STARTED: 1998

PURPOSE:
To focus on critical national urban issues as they are expressed locally.

LEGAL BASIS:
Foundation.

ELIGIBILITY:
Grants are made to organizations that have tax-exempt status under Section 501(c)(3) of the Internal Revenue Code. No grants are made to individuals. Nonsectarian religious programs may apply.

GEOGRAPHIC RESTRICTIONS:
Baltimore City, Maryland.

FINANCIAL DATA:
Amount of support per award: Varies.
Total amount of support: Varies.

APPLICATION INFORMATION:
Applicants should submit a letter of inquiry of two to three pages which includes:
(1) a description of the program to be funded;
(2) the qualifications of the organization to carry out the program;
(3) the ways in which the program reflects the priorities of The Drug Addiction Treatment Program and;
(4) the amount requested.

Duration: Varies.

ADDRESS INQUIRIES TO:
Kima Taylor, Program Director
(See address above.)

THE ORDEAN FOUNDATION   [1344]

501 Ordean Building
424 West Superior Street
Duluth, MN 55802
(218) 726-4785
Fax: (218) 726-4848

E-MAIL ADDRESS:
smangan@ordean.org

FOUNDED: 1933

AREAS OF INTEREST:
Social services, education and health, services to low-income, mentally and physically handicapped, elderly, mentally ill, chemically dependent, prevention of delinquency, and scholarships for certain health-related majors at Duluth colleges.

TYPE:
Challenge/matching grants; Demonstration grants; General operating grants; Project/program grants; Scholarships.

YEAR PROGRAM STARTED: 1933

LEGAL BASIS:
Private foundation.

ELIGIBILITY:
Applicants must be nonprofit, tax-exempt IRS 501(c)(3) organizations located or providing services in Greater City of Duluth, MN.

GEOGRAPHIC RESTRICTIONS:
Greater City of Duluth, Minnesota.

FINANCIAL DATA:
Amount of support per award: $5,000 to $350,000.
Total amount of support: $2,000,000 for fiscal year 2013.

NUMBER OF AWARDS: Approximately 50.

REPRESENTATIVE AWARDS:
$350,000 to Lake Superior Community Health Center; $150,000 to Mentor Duluth to match caring adults with at-risk youths.

APPLICATION INFORMATION:
Guidelines are available from the Foundation office at the address above. Minnesota Common Council grant applications also accepted.

Duration: One year. Renewal possible up to three years.

Deadline: The 15th of every month, for the next month's meeting agenda.

STAFF:
Stephen Mangan, Executive Director
Joe Everett, Program Director

BOARD OF DIRECTORS:
Mary Beth Santori, Chairperson
Ann Niedringhaus, Vice Chairperson
Marge Bray, Treasurer
Ben Stromberg, Secretary
Carl Crawford
Jon Nelson
Dr. Tom Patnoe
Jim Vizanko
Chuck Walt

ADDRESS INQUIRIES TO:
Joe Everett, Program Director
(See address above.)

THE OREGON COMMUNITY FOUNDATION   [1345]

1221 S.W. Yamhill Street, Suite 100
Portland, OR 97205-2108
(503) 227-6846
Fax: (503) 274-7771

E-MAIL ADDRESS:
info@oregoncf.org

WEB SITE ADDRESS:
www.oregoncf.org

FOUNDED: 1973

AREAS OF INTEREST:
Children, families, culture, education, community involvement, jobs, the economy, and the environment.

NAME(S) OF PROGRAMS:
● **Community Grants Program**

TYPE:
Capital grants; Challenge/matching grants; Matching gifts; Project/program grants; Scholarships.

YEAR PROGRAM STARTED: 1974

PURPOSE:
To help communities achieve goals identified by a broad cross section of community members for which local support has been clearly demonstrated; to build a strong, inclusive spirit of community where all Oregonians are involved in community life.

LEGAL BASIS:
Community foundation.

ELIGIBILITY:
Applicants for programs must be nonprofit, tax-exempt organizations in Oregon.

Applicants must have received a community grant only once during the previous 12 months and must have completed evaluation reports for all prior grants. The Foundation gives preference to projects that demonstrate strong local support and promise tangible benefits or means of solving community problems or concerns.

GEOGRAPHIC RESTRICTIONS:
Oregon.

FINANCIAL DATA:
Amount of support per award: $5,000 to $50,000.
Total amount of support: $65,000,000 in grants, $6,000,000 in scholarships, and $5,000,000 to $6,000,000 for the Community Grants Program for the year 2013.
Matching fund requirements: Varies.

NUMBER OF APPLICANTS MOST RECENT YEAR: 587.

NUMBER OF AWARDS: 200 annually.

APPLICATION INFORMATION:
Application information is available on the web site.

Duration: Small grants: One year; Large grants: One to three years.

Deadline: Community Grants Program: Typically February 1 and August 1.

IRS IDENTIFICATION NUMBER: 23-7315673

STAFF:
Jeff Anderson, Chief Operating Officer

ADDRESS INQUIRIES TO:
Megan Schumaker, Senior Program Officer
(See address above.)

*SPECIAL STIPULATIONS:
Generally funds only in Oregon.

OUTER BANKS COMMUNITY FOUNDATION   [1346]

13 Skyline Road
Southern Shores, NC 27949
(252) 261-8839
Fax: (252) 261-0371

E-MAIL ADDRESS:
info@obcf.org

WEB SITE ADDRESS:
www.obcf.org

FOUNDED: 1982

AREAS OF INTEREST:
Outer Banks, from Corolla to Ocracoke Island.

TYPE:
Project/program grants; Scholarships. 40 different scholarship funds available to local students. Grants available for local nonprofit programs and projects.

YEAR PROGRAM STARTED: 1982

PURPOSE:
To help meet local needs in the Outer Banks of North Carolina, from Corolla to Ocracoke Island.

LEGAL BASIS:
501(c)(3).

GEOGRAPHIC RESTRICTIONS:
Corolla area of Currituck County, Dare County and Ocracoke Island in Hyde County, North Carolina.

FINANCIAL DATA:
Amount of support per award: Varies.
Total amount of support: Varies.

APPLICATION INFORMATION:
Application information is available on the web site.
Deadline: Varies.

IRS IDENTIFICATION NUMBER: 58-1516313

ADDRESS INQUIRIES TO:
Lorelei Costa, Executive Director
(See address above.)

PERMIAN BASIN AREA FOUNDATION [1347]

200 North Loraine, Suite 500
Midland, TX 79701
(432) 617-3213
Fax: (432) 617-0151

E-MAIL ADDRESS:
gmccrary@pbaf.org

WEB SITE ADDRESS:
www.pbaf.org

FOUNDED: 1989

AREAS OF INTEREST:
Community development.

TYPE:
Grants-in-aid; Scholarships.

PURPOSE:
To enrich the quality of life for the communities of the Permian Basin area of Texas.

LEGAL BASIS:
501(c)(3) organization.

GEOGRAPHIC RESTRICTIONS:
Communities of the Permian Basin region of Texas.

FINANCIAL DATA:
The Foundation has awarded nearly $40,500,000 in grants and scholarships since inception.
Amount of support per award: Grants: Average $15,000; Scholarships: $1,000 to $2,500.

APPLICATION INFORMATION:
Organizations wishing to apply for a grant must fully complete and submit one copy of

the Pre-Application Summary (SF-1). Organizations that have received funding during a previous grant cycle must also complete and submit the Grant Award Follow-up Form (SF-FW). Do not include a cover letter with the application.

A full application will be complete when one copy of the appropriate Standard Forms and additional documents indicated on the Standard Form Checklist are completed and submitted to the Foundation by the full application due date. (The list of required forms differs depending on the purpose of the grant request.) Upon receiving a full application, the Foundation will conduct a full application review which may include an applicant interview, a site visit, and/or a request for additional information.

All scholarship applications must contain the following:
(1) transcript with fall semester grades;
(2) college transcript if student is enrolled in concurrent college courses and;
(3) at least one letter of recommendation, but not more than three.

Some applications require an essay. Check the individual scholarship criteria to determine if an essay is required and the designated topic.
Duration: Grants: Typically one year. Can reapply every two years.
Deadline: Grant proposals: April 1 for Spring and October 1 for Fall.

ADDRESS INQUIRIES TO:
Lauren Young, Grants and Administration
(See address above.)

PETOSKEY-HARBOR SPRINGS AREA COMMUNITY FOUNDATION [1348]

616 Petoskey Street, Suite 203
Petoskey, MI 49770
(231) 348-5820
Fax: (231) 348-5883

E-MAIL ADDRESS:
info@phsacf.org

WEB SITE ADDRESS:
www.phsacf.org

FOUNDED: 1992

AREAS OF INTEREST:
Arts, education, environment, health, human service and community development.

TYPE:
Grants-in-aid; Scholarships. Grants are given for scholarships or for charitable needs.

YEAR PROGRAM STARTED: 1992

PURPOSE:
To build an endowment to serve community needs.

LEGAL BASIS:
Community foundation.

ELIGIBILITY:
Grants must be for charitable purposes, but not for individuals.

GEOGRAPHIC RESTRICTIONS:
Emmet County, Michigan.

FINANCIAL DATA:
Over $30,000,000 in assets.
Amount of support per award: $500 to $10,000.
Total amount of support: Varies.

APPLICATION INFORMATION:
Applications are available at the address above and must include a copy of the IRS tax determination letter. Call before you apply.
Duration: One year.
Deadline: March 1 and October 1.

PUBLICATIONS:
Annual report; application guidelines.

ADDRESS INQUIRIES TO:
Sara Ward, Program Officer
(See address above.)

THE PHILADELPHIA FOUNDATION [1349]

1234 Market Street
Suite 1800
Philadelphia, PA 19107
(215) 563-6417
Fax: (215) 563-6882

WEB SITE ADDRESS:
www.philafound.org

FOUNDED: 1918

AREAS OF INTEREST:
Arts, culture, humanities, education, environment, health, human services and public/community development.

TYPE:
General operating grants; Scholarships. Capacity building grants. The Philadelphia Foundation's grantmaking strategies are sensitive to the needs of diverse population groups in the community and reflect a commitment to stabilizing the infrastructure of nonprofit organizations.

YEAR PROGRAM STARTED: 1918

PURPOSE:
To serve as a vehicle and resource for philanthropy in Bucks, Chester, Delaware, Montgomery and Philadelphia counties, PA; to develop, manage and allocate community resources in partnership with donors and grantees to build on community assets, to respond to the needs of the entire community, and to promote empowerment, leadership, and civic participation among underserved groups; to practice and encourage diversity, equity, and inclusiveness as fundamental values of community life.

LEGAL BASIS:
Community foundation established in Pennsylvania by bank resolution.

ELIGIBILITY:
Organization must be IRS 501(c)(3), located in five-county area of southeastern Pennsylvania.

GEOGRAPHIC RESTRICTIONS:
Bucks, Chester, Delaware, Montgomery, and Philadelphia counties, Pennsylvania.

FINANCIAL DATA:
Amount of support per award: $3,000 to $50,000.
Total amount of support: $20,000,000 annually.

APPLICATION INFORMATION:
The Foundation encourages applicants to address:
(1) empowering people and groups;
(2) building community assets or;
(3) managing current issues or preparing for future trends when submitting grant requests.

Additional information is available from the Foundation.

Duration: One year.

PUBLICATIONS:
Newsletters; annual report.

OFFICERS:
R. Andrew Swinney, President
Beatriz Vieira, Vice President for Philanthropic Services
Patricia Meller, Vice President of Finance and Administration

ADDRESS INQUIRIES TO:
Grantmaking Services Department
(See address above.)

PIEDMONT HEALTH FOUNDATION

P.O. Box 9303
Greenville, SC 29604
(864) 370-0212
Fax: (864) 370-0212

E-MAIL ADDRESS:
katysmith@piedmonthealthfoundation.org

WEB SITE ADDRESS:
www.piedmonthealthfoundation.org

TYPE:
Demonstration grants; Project/program grants; Research grants; Seed money grants.

See entry 1457 for full listing.

THE PITTSBURGH FOUNDATION   [1350]

5 PPG Place
Suite 250
Pittsburgh, PA 15222
(412) 391-5122
Fax: (412) 391-7259

E-MAIL ADDRESS:
email@pghfdn.org

WEB SITE ADDRESS:
www.pittsburghfoundation.org

FOUNDED: 1945

AREAS OF INTEREST:
Education, family life, economic development, health care and the arts.

TYPE:
Capital grants; General operating grants; Project/program grants; Research grants; Scholarships. The Foundation promotes and champions the betterment of the greater Pittsburgh community and the quality of life for all its citizens by helping a wide variety of donors fulfill significant community needs and providing a vehicle to make giving easy, personally satisfying and effective. The Foundation awards grants through restricted and unrestricted funds. Purposes for which unrestricted grants are awarded include: organizational capacity building; systemic change; improved service delivery; planning and program development; capital and equipment (in limited and special circumstances) through one targeted fund; operating (in very limited and defined circumstances); research (in special circumstances).

Scholarships and medical research grants are awarded from specific funds established for this purpose.

PURPOSE:
To achieve educational excellence and equity; to support families; to foster economic development; to eliminate disparities in health outcomes; to advance the arts.

LEGAL BASIS:
Community foundation established in Pennsylvania by bank resolution and declaration of trust.

ELIGIBILITY:
Grant applicants must be tax-exempt, public charitable organizations and institutions located in Pittsburgh or Allegheny County. Generally, grants are nonrecurring and are not granted for operating budgets and not made to individuals.

GEOGRAPHIC RESTRICTIONS:
Pittsburgh and Allegheny County, Pennsylvania.

FINANCIAL DATA:
Amount of support per award: Varies.
Total amount of support: Approximately $9,000,000 in unrestricted funds; $9,000,000 in restricted funds.

NUMBER OF APPLICANTS MOST RECENT YEAR:
2,581.

NUMBER OF AWARDS: 2,255.

APPLICATION INFORMATION:
Applicants must submit grant application and IRS tax-exemption letter. Prior to sending a full proposal, applicants are encouraged to send a letter of inquiry that includes a brief statement about the organization, the proposed project, its intended results, and a general idea of costs.
Duration: Up to three years.

PUBLICATIONS:
Annual report; newsletter; donor information; application guidelines; scholarship brochure.

IRS IDENTIFICATION NUMBER: 25-0965466

STAFF:
Grant Oliphant, President and Chief Executive Officer
Jonathan Brelsford, Vice President of Investments
Marianne Cola, Executive Secretary

BOARD OF DIRECTORS:
Edith L. Shapira, M.D., Chairperson
John C. Harmon, Esq., Vice Chairperson
Kim Tillotson Fleming, Treasurer
Nancy L. Rackoff, Secretary
Morton Coleman
Edward J. Donnelly
Lee B. Foster, II
Evan Frazier
David McL. Hillman
William E. Hunt
Anne Lewis
Claudette R. Lewis
David Malone
Vincent J. Quatrini
James C. Roddey
Dr. Howard Slaughter, Jr.
Walter H. Smith, Jr., Ph.D.
William Strickland

ADDRESS INQUIRIES TO:
Grant Oliphant
President and Chief Executive Officer
(See address above.)

PRINCETON AREA COMMUNITY FOUNDATION   [1351]

15 Princess Road
Lawrenceville, NJ 08648
(609) 219-1800
Fax: (609) 219-1850

E-MAIL ADDRESS:
info@pacf.org

WEB SITE ADDRESS:
www.pacf.org

FOUNDED: 1991

AREAS OF INTEREST:
Connecting people who care with causes that matter across central New Jersey.

NAME(S) OF PROGRAMS:
- **The Fund for Women and Girls**
- **Greater Mercer Grants**

TYPE:
General operating grants; Project/program grants; Scholarships. The Fund for Women and Girls supports efforts that help girls and women develop special talents, build character and self-esteem, and expand their abilities.

Greater Mercer Grants focus support on current priorities with the greatest impact within Mercer County, NJ. There are two grant categories: one provides program and/or operating support for nonprofit organizations addressing the needs of low-income individuals and families; the other provides program support for building community within and among municipalities in Mercer County, NJ.

PURPOSE:
To connect people who care with causes that matter across central New Jersey.

LEGAL BASIS:
A public benefit (nonprofit) organization.

ELIGIBILITY:
Eligible organizations must have 501(c)(3) status.

GEOGRAPHIC RESTRICTIONS:
Trenton, the 12 other Mercer County (New Jersey) municipalities and surrounding communities in Burlington, Hunterdon, Middlesex, Monmouth and Somerset counties.

FINANCIAL DATA:
Since its founding, the Foundation has granted nearly $18,000,000 to its community area of service.
Amount of support per award: Varies.

APPLICATION INFORMATION:
Application information is available on the web site.
Duration: One year. Renewable.

STAFF:
Nancy W. Kieling, President and Executive Director
Justin Goldberg, Vice President of Communications
Elizabeth Wagner, Vice President of Development
Michelle Cash, Vice President of Grants and Programs
Maria Santisi, C.P.A., Chief Financial Officer
Trisha Volk, Director of Donor Services
Myriam Padro, Administrator
Ana Edmonds, Administrative Coordinator

ADDRESS INQUIRIES TO:
Michelle Cash
Vice President of Grants and Programs
(See address above.)

PROLITERACY WORLDWIDE   [1352]

104 Marcellus Street
Syracuse, NY 13204
(315) 422-9121
Fax: (315) 422-6369

COMMUNITY DEVELOPMENT AND SERVICES

E-MAIL ADDRESS:
mdiecuch@proliteracy.org

WEB SITE ADDRESS:
www.proliteracy.org

FOUNDED: 1955

AREAS OF INTEREST:
Literacy, adult basic education, English as a second language, and family literacy.

NAME(S) OF PROGRAMS:
● **National Book Fund (NBF)**

TYPE:
Project/program grants; Technical assistance.

YEAR PROGRAM STARTED: 1995

PURPOSE:
To provide grants for books and other materials local programs can use to expand their current volunteer literacy programs; to develop, promote and expand literacy programs in the U.S. that target the needs of women.

LEGAL BASIS:
Nonprofit organization.

ELIGIBILITY:
Adult literacy and adult basic education programs only.

GEOGRAPHIC RESTRICTIONS:
United States.

FINANCIAL DATA:
Amount of support per award: Typically $500 to $2,000.
Total amount of support: $106,000 for the year 2011.
Matching fund requirements: 10% to 20% match required.

NUMBER OF APPLICANTS MOST RECENT YEAR:
110 for the year 2011.

NUMBER OF AWARDS: 55 for the year 2011.

APPLICATION INFORMATION:
Application information is available on the web site.
Duration: One year. NBF grantee eligible again in three years.
Deadline: Mid-April to early May.

PUBLICATIONS:
Guidelines.

IRS IDENTIFICATION NUMBER: 16-1214734

ADDRESS INQUIRIES TO:
Michele Diecuch, Program Administrator
National Book Fund
(See address above.)

RANCHO SANTA FE FOUNDATION [1353]
6004-A Paseo Delicias
Rancho Santa Fe, CA 92067
(858) 756-6557
Fax: (858) 756-6561

E-MAIL ADDRESS:
christy@rsffoundation.org

WEB SITE ADDRESS:
www.rsffoundation.org

FOUNDED: 1981

AREAS OF INTEREST:
Charity, education, literature or science.

NAME(S) OF PROGRAMS:
● **Armed Forces Interest Group**
● **Rancho Santa Fe Women's Fund**

TYPE:
Challenge/matching grants; Development grants; Endowments; General operating grants; Project/program grants; Scholarships.

YEAR PROGRAM STARTED: 1981

PURPOSE:
To promote and sustain effective community philanthropy by assisting donors to build charitable endowments that strategically support worthy local and regional needs.

LEGAL BASIS:
Community foundation.

ELIGIBILITY:
San Diego County organizations who have been asked to submit a grant request are eligible for support.

Organizations must have tax-exempt status under Section 501(c)(3) of the Internal Revenue Code.

FINANCIAL DATA:
Amount of support per award: $500 to $1,000,000.
Total amount of support: $350,000 in grants from designated and discretionary funds. Nearly $5,000,000 from donor-advised funds.

APPLICATION INFORMATION:
The Foundation accepts the San Diego Grantmakers Common Grant Application, by invitation only. The Foundation does not accept unsolicited grant requests.
Duration: Typically one year.
Deadline: June 1.

PUBLICATIONS:
Annual report.

IRS IDENTIFICATION NUMBER: 95-3709639

STAFF:
Christina P. Wilson, Executive Director
Debbie Anderson, Programs Manager
Dan Beals, Finance Manager
Nancy Hashim, Administrative Manager
Susan Pyke, Donor Services Manager

ADDRESS INQUIRIES TO:
Christina P. Wilson, Executive Director
(See address above.)

RBC FOUNDATION - U.S.A. [1354]
RBC Plaza
60 South Sixth Street
Minneapolis, MN 55402-4422
(612) 371-2936
Fax: (612) 371-7933

E-MAIL ADDRESS:
fndapplication@rbc.com

WEB SITE ADDRESS:
www.rbcwm-usa.com/communityinvolvement

AREAS OF INTEREST:
Arts and culture, civic programs, education, health and human services.

NAME(S) OF PROGRAMS:
● **After School Grants**
● **Children's Mental Health**
● **Emerging Artists**

TYPE:
General operating grants; Project/program grants.

PURPOSE:
To improve the quality of life in communities where the company has facilities.

LEGAL BASIS:
Corporate foundation.

ELIGIBILITY:
Organizations must have tax-exempt status according to Internal Revenue Code 501(c)(3). Grants are made to organizations where RBC Wealth Management has employees actively involved.

FINANCIAL DATA:
Total amount of support: $2,200,000 for fiscal year 2012.

APPLICATION INFORMATION:
Guidelines and application forms are available on the web site.
Duration: One year.
Deadline: Varies.

ADDRESS INQUIRIES TO:
Liz Thatcher
E-mail: liz.thatcher@rbc.com

THE REINBERGER FOUNDATION [1355]
30000 Chagrin Boulevard, Suite 300
Cleveland, OH 44124
(216) 292-2790
Fax: (216) 292-4466

E-MAIL ADDRESS:
info@reinbergerfoundation.org

WEB SITE ADDRESS:
www.reinbergerfoundation.org

FOUNDED: 1968

AREAS OF INTEREST:
Arts, education, health care and social service.

NAME(S) OF PROGRAMS:
● **Arts, Culture and Humanities**
● **Education**
● **Human Service Health**
● **Human Service - Other**

TYPE:
Capital grants; Challenge/matching grants; General operating grants; Matching gifts; Project/program grants; Research grants; Scholarships.

PURPOSE:
To enhance quality of life for individuals from all walks of life.

LEGAL BASIS:
Private foundation.

ELIGIBILITY:
Eligible organizations must be IRS 501(c)(3) tax-exempt.

GEOGRAPHIC RESTRICTIONS:
Northeast Ohio or greater Columbus area.

FINANCIAL DATA:
Since its beginning, the Foundation has provided more than $100,000,000 in funding support to the community.
Amount of support per award: $5,000 to $500,000.
Total amount of support: $2,885,619 for the year 2013.

NUMBER OF APPLICANTS MOST RECENT YEAR:
241 for the year 2013.

NUMBER OF AWARDS: 103 for the year 2013.

APPLICATION INFORMATION:
Online application is available on the web site.
Duration: Up to seven years.
Deadline: March, June, September and December.

ADDRESS INQUIRIES TO:
Karen L. Hooser, President
(See address above.)

LUTHER I. REPLOGLE FOUNDATION [1356]
1720 N Street, N.W.
Washington, DC 20036-2907
(202) 679-0677
Fax: (202) 580-6579

E-MAIL ADDRESS:
gwenn@lirf.org

WEB SITE ADDRESS:
www.lirf.org

FOUNDED: 1966

AREAS OF INTEREST:
At-risk youth and children, educational
opportunities for inner-city children, and
affordable and supportive housing.

TYPE:
Challenge/matching grants; General operating
grants; Project/program grants; Seed money
grants. The Foundation supports programs
that:
(1) address the needs of youth and children
living in, or at risk of, long-term poverty,
especially children of inner-city residents. Of
particular interest are programs for teen
pregnancy prevention, counseling,
broad-spectrum social services, and other
programs that help young people improve
their own lives;
(2) improve educational opportunities for
inner-city children, including enrichment
programs in the arts and sciences, alternative
schools, after-school tutoring and mentoring,
and scholarship programs and;
(3) provide for affordable and supportive
housing that reaches people frequently left
out of traditional shelter programs, including
single mothers and families with children, the
elderly, ex-offenders, and youth. An emphasis
is placed on programs that enable individuals
to help themselves and become self-sufficient
over the long-term.

PURPOSE:
To address the needs of youth and children
living in, or at risk of, long-term poverty; to
improve educational opportunities for
inner-city children; to support programs for
affordable and supportive housing that reach
groups of people frequently left out of
traditional shelter programs.

ELIGIBILITY:
Organizations must be not-for-profit
501(c)(3). Grants are given to religious
organizations only for social services
programs, not for religious programs,
buildings or bibles. No grants to individuals.

GEOGRAPHIC RESTRICTIONS:
Washington, District of Columbia; Chicago,
Illinois; Minneapolis, Minnesota.

FINANCIAL DATA:
Amount of support per award: Usually
$5,000 to $10,000.

APPLICATION INFORMATION:
Applicants meeting the grant criteria through
the online eligibility quiz will be prompted to
complete the Letter of Inquiry form.
Duration: Renewable if grantee sends report.
Deadline: March 15 and September 15.

IRS IDENTIFICATION NUMBER: 36-6141697

ADDRESS INQUIRIES TO:
Gwenn H.S. Gebhard, Executive Director
(See address above.)

J.B. REYNOLDS FOUNDATION [1357]
3520 Broadway
Kansas City, MO 64111
(816) 753-7000
Fax: (816) 561-2415

AREAS OF INTEREST:
Education, research, civic affairs, youth
training and cultural organizations.

TYPE:
Grants-in-aid. Donations.

ELIGIBILITY:
Eligible organizations must be IRS 501(c)(3)
tax-exempt and be located within the local
Kansas City area. No grants to individuals.

GEOGRAPHIC RESTRICTIONS:
Kansas City, Missouri area.

FINANCIAL DATA:
Amount of support per award: Varies.
Total amount of support: Varies.

APPLICATION INFORMATION:
There is no application form. Applicants
should send a letter, two pages or less, to
smorehead@kclife.com.
Duration: One year. Renewal on a yearly
basis.
Deadline: July and November.

ADDRESS INQUIRIES TO:
Phillip Bixby, President and
Chief Executive Officer
(See address above.)

RGK FOUNDATION [1358]
1301 West 25th Street
Suite 300
Austin, TX 78705-4236
(512) 474-9298
Fax: (512) 474-7281

E-MAIL ADDRESS:
shaffey@rgkfoundation.org

WEB SITE ADDRESS:
www.rgkfoundation.org

FOUNDED: 1966

AREAS OF INTEREST:
Education, community and medicine/health.

TYPE:
Challenge/matching grants; Project/program
grants. The Foundation awards grants in the
broad areas of education, community and
medicine/health; its primary interests within
education include programs that focus on
formal K-12 education (particularly
mathematics, science and reading/literacy),
after-school tutoring and enrichment,
integrating technology into curriculum,
teacher development and higher education.
The Foundation is particularly interested in
programs that attract female and minority
students into the fields of mathematics,
science and technology. Within community,
the Foundation supports a broad range of
human services programs, youth development
programs, community improvement programs
and cultural arts programs. Its current
interests in the area of medicine/health are
programs that promote the health and
well-being of children and families, access to
health care and ALS.

LEGAL BASIS:
Private foundation.

ELIGIBILITY:
The Foundation prefers to provide
programmatic support for new programs or

expansion of ongoing successful programs.
While the Foundation occasionally awards
grants for operating expenses and capital
campaigns, such grants are infrequent and
usually initiated by the Foundation.

Grants are made only to nonprofit
organizations certified as tax-exempt under
Sections 501(c)(3) or 170(c) of the Internal
Revenue Code and are classified as "not a
private foundation" under Section 509(a).
Hospitals, educational institutions and
governmental institutions meeting these
requirements are eligible to apply.
Organizations that have completed and filed
Form 1023 but not yet received an IRS
determination letter are not eligible to apply.
The Foundation does not make grants or
loans to individuals.

GEOGRAPHIC RESTRICTIONS:
United States.

FINANCIAL DATA:
Amount of support per award: Average grant
to new organization: $25,000.
Total amount of support: Varies.

NUMBER OF APPLICANTS MOST RECENT YEAR:
2,437.

NUMBER OF AWARDS: 107.

APPLICATION INFORMATION:
Application is available online.
Duration: Most grants are awarded for a
one-year period; multiyear grants are
extremely rare.
Deadline: Proposals are reviewed on an
ongoing basis.

IRS IDENTIFICATION NUMBER: 74-6077587

STAFF:
Christina Collier, Executive Vice President
Jami Hampton, Senior Program Officer
Lindsey Aylierff, Program Officer
Beth Sexworth, Chief Investment Officer
Taddy Barnhill, Financial Analyst
Suzanne Haffey, Grants Associate
Traci Walker, Senior Accountant

OFFICERS AND DIRECTORS:
Gregory A. Kozmetsky, Chairman and
President
Nadya K. Scott, Vice Chairman
Cynthia H. Kozmetsky, Secretary
Caroline D. Avery
Douglas E. Bryant
Daniel A. Kozmetsky
Chris Miller
Sarah K. Miller
Laila P. Scott
Martha E. Smiley
F. Gary Valdez

ADDRESS INQUIRIES TO:
Suzanne Haffey, Grants Associate
(See address above.)

ROCHESTER AREA FOUNDATION [1359]
400 South Broadway
Suite 300
Rochester, MN 55904
(507) 282-0203
Fax: (507) 282-4938

E-MAIL ADDRESS:
raf-info@rochesterarea.org

WEB SITE ADDRESS:
www.rochesterarea.org

FOUNDED: 1944

AREAS OF INTEREST:
General grants to benefit residents of the Greater Rochester area.

TYPE:
Capital grants; Challenge/matching grants; Project/program grants; Seed money grants.

YEAR PROGRAM STARTED: 1944

PURPOSE:
To use its resources to improve the quality of life, promote greater equality of opportunities and to support development of effective methods to assist those in need in the Greater Rochester area.

LEGAL BASIS:
Community foundation.

ELIGIBILITY:
Applicants must be 501(c)(3) organizations or units of government agencies or government-created public agencies located in or serving the Greater Rochester area. Grants are not given to individuals.

GEOGRAPHIC RESTRICTIONS:
Greater Rochester, Minnesota.

FINANCIAL DATA:
Amount of support per award: Varies.
Total amount of support: $1,273,833 for the year 2012.

APPLICATION INFORMATION:
Pre-approved and approved application forms are required. Applicant organizations must include an IRS letter of tax determination.
Duration: One-time grants.
Deadline: Pre-approved: January 1 and September 1.
Approved: Last week of April, August and December.

ADDRESS INQUIRIES TO:
E-mail: max@rochesterarea.org

ROSE COMMUNITY FOUNDATION [1360]

600 South Cherry Street
Suite 1200
Denver, CO 80246-1712
(303) 398-7400
(303) 398-7446
Fax: (303) 398-7430

E-MAIL ADDRESS:
grantsmanager@rcfdenver.org

WEB SITE ADDRESS:
www.rcfdenver.org

FOUNDED: 1995

AREAS OF INTEREST:
Child and family development, education, the elderly, health of the community, Jewish life, human service, transportation (aging only), early childhood education, family self-sufficiency, health preventive, low-income health access and health policy leadership.

TYPE:
Capital grants; Challenge/matching grants; General operating grants; Project/program grants; Seed money grants; Technical assistance. Capacity-building grants.

YEAR PROGRAM STARTED: 1995

PURPOSE:
To enhance the quality of life of the greater Denver community through leadership, resources, traditions and values.

ELIGIBILITY:
Applicants must be charitable, nonprofit organizations classified as 501(c)(3) by the IRS or be a tax-supported institution, such as a school or government agency. New or emerging organizations are permitted to apply through a sponsoring tax-exempt organization. Applicants (including university departments) may have only one proposal pending at any given time.

The Foundation will not support grants to individuals or endowments, including academic chairs, grants to one organization to be passed to another, annual appeals or membership drives, fund-raising events, or political candidates.

GEOGRAPHIC RESTRICTIONS:
Denver metropolitan area, specifically Adams, Arapahoe, Boulder, Broomfield, Denver, Douglas and Jefferson counties, Colorado.

FINANCIAL DATA:
Amount of support per award: Varies depending on needs and nature of the request.
Total amount of support: $14,461,000 in grants for the year 2012.
Matching fund requirements: Varies by nature of award.

NUMBER OF AWARDS: 1,104 grants for the year 2012.

APPLICATION INFORMATION:
It is recommended to contact the Grants Manager prior to applying if the organization is new to the Foundation.
Duration: Varies.

IRS IDENTIFICATION NUMBER: 84-0920862

STAFF:
Sheila Bugdanowitz, President and Chief Executive Officer
Cheryl McDonald, Grants Manager

ADDRESS INQUIRIES TO:
Cheryl McDonald, Grants Manager
(See address above.)

HENRY AND RUTH BLAUSTEIN ROSENBERG FOUNDATION [1361]

10 East Baltimore Street, Suite 1111
Baltimore, MD 21202
(410) 347-7201
Fax: (410) 347-7210

E-MAIL ADDRESS:
info@blaufund.org

WEB SITE ADDRESS:
www.blaufund.org

AREAS OF INTEREST:
Arts and culture, youth development, adult self-sufficiency, and health.

TYPE:
Capital grants; General operating grants; Project/program grants. Programs of benefit to the underserved community in the Baltimore, MD area.

PURPOSE:
To promote arts and culture, youth development, and adult self-sufficiency within the underserved community.

ELIGIBILITY:
501(c)(3) nonprofit organizations. No grants to individuals.

GEOGRAPHIC RESTRICTIONS:
Baltimore, Maryland.

FINANCIAL DATA:
Amount of support per award: $5,000 to $25,000.
Total amount of support: Approximately $1,200,000.

APPLICATION INFORMATION:
Send two- to three-page letter of intent or application. IRS tax status determination letter is required. Faxed and e-mailed letters of intent are not accepted.
Duration: One to two years. Prior grantee organizations may be renewable.

ADDRESS INQUIRIES TO:
Betsy F. Ringel, Executive Director
(See address above.)

ROSS FOUNDATION [1362]

202 S. Fifth Street
Arkadelphia, AR 71923
(870) 246-9881
Fax: (870) 246-9674

E-MAIL ADDRESS:
info@rossfoundation.us

WEB SITE ADDRESS:
www.rossfoundation.us

FOUNDED: 1966

AREAS OF INTEREST:
Education, culture, conservation and community activities.

TYPE:
Project/program grants.

LEGAL BASIS:
Private foundation.

ELIGIBILITY:
Applicants must be IRS 501(c)(3) organizations located in Clark County or Arkadelphia, AR. No grants to individuals.

GEOGRAPHIC RESTRICTIONS:
Clark County or Arkadelphia, Arkansas.

FINANCIAL DATA:
Amount of support per award: Generally $1,000 to $25,000.
Total amount of support: $600,000 for the year 2013.

NUMBER OF APPLICANTS MOST RECENT YEAR:
Approximately 30 for the year 2013.

NUMBER OF AWARDS: 20 to 25.

APPLICATION INFORMATION:
Application form is available online.
Duration: Typically one year.
Deadline: Proposals are reviewed January 1, May 1 and September 1.

ADDRESS INQUIRIES TO:
Mary Elizabeth Eldridge
Director of Programs
(See address above.)

THE RUSSELL FAMILY FOUNDATION [1363]

3025 Harborview Drive
Gig Harbor, WA 98335
(253) 858-5050
Fax: (253) 851-0460

E-MAIL ADDRESS:
info@trff.org

WEB SITE ADDRESS:
www.trff.org

FOUNDED: 1999

AREAS OF INTEREST:
Elimination of poverty, healthy educational
and extracurricular activities for youth, and
social justice.

NAME(S) OF PROGRAMS:
● Jane's Fellowship Program

TYPE:
Fellowships. Fellowship program for
individuals who plan to work in the
Foundation's areas of interest.

YEAR PROGRAM STARTED: 2004

PURPOSE:
To support grassroots leaders in Pierce
County and Tacoma, WA.

ELIGIBILITY:
Must be a grassroots leader who has
demonstrated exceptional creativity, courage
and commitment in serving diverse needs in
Tacoma and countywide.

GEOGRAPHIC RESTRICTIONS:
Pierce County and Tacoma, Washington.

FINANCIAL DATA:
Amount of support per award: Varies.
Total amount of support: Varies.

APPLICATION INFORMATION:
Application information is available on the
web site.
Duration: Two years. Nonrenewable.
Deadline: Every two years.

SAGINAW COMMUNITY
FOUNDATION   [1364]
One Tuscola Street, Suite 100
Saginaw, MI 48607
(989) 755-0545
Fax: (989) 755-6524

E-MAIL ADDRESS:
brian@saginawfoundation.org

WEB SITE ADDRESS:
www.saginawfoundation.org

FOUNDED: 1984

AREAS OF INTEREST:
Arts, community development, culture,
education, health, youth and human services.

CONSULTING OR VOLUNTEER SERVICES:
Seminars, group presentations and
one-on-one consultation.

TYPE:
Grants-in-aid; Project/program grants;
Scholarships.

YEAR PROGRAM STARTED: 1984

PURPOSE:
To fulfill donor wishes and enable
community initiatives to come to life, now
and forever; to provide strategic leadership in
the community; to practice impactful
grantmaking in the areas of youth
development, early education, and
community improvement; to provide
stewardship of the Foundation's resources,
human and financial.

ELIGIBILITY:
Typically, grants are made to organizations
that have tax-exempt status under Section
501(c)(3) of the Internal Revenue Code.
Except for scholarships, no grants are made
to individuals. Nonsectarian religious
programs may apply.

GEOGRAPHIC RESTRICTIONS:
Saginaw County, Michigan.

FINANCIAL DATA:
Amount of support per award: Grants vary in
amount, depending upon the needs and
nature of the request.
Total amount of support: $1,670,000 for the
year 2013.
Matching fund requirements: Varies by
program.

NUMBER OF APPLICANTS MOST RECENT YEAR:
6,800.

NUMBER OF AWARDS: 627.

APPLICATION INFORMATION:
Application information is available on the
web site.

ADDRESS INQUIRIES TO:
Program Officer
(See address above.)

ST. CROIX VALLEY
FOUNDATION   [1365]
516 Second Street, Suite 214
Hudson, WI 54016
(715) 386-9490
Fax: (715) 386-1250

E-MAIL ADDRESS:
info@scvfoundation.org

WEB SITE ADDRESS:
www.scvfoundation.org

FOUNDED: 1995

AREAS OF INTEREST:
Arts, civic affairs, community needs and
development, environment, health and human
services, and education.

NAME(S) OF PROGRAMS:
● Health and Wellness Grant
● Music Education Grant
● Valley Arts Initiative Grant

TYPE:
Project/program grants; Scholarships.

YEAR PROGRAM STARTED: 1995

PURPOSE:
To advance the quality of life in the St. Croix
Valley of Wisconsin and Minnesota.

LEGAL BASIS:
501(c)(3).

ELIGIBILITY:
Grants are made to organizations that have
tax-exempt status under Section 501(c)(3) of
the Internal Revenue Code or serving the St.
Croix Valley of Wisconsin and Minnesota.
Nonsectarian religious programs may apply.

GEOGRAPHIC RESTRICTIONS:
Typically Pierce, Polk and St. Croix counties
in St. Croix Valley, Wisconsin; Chisago and
Washington counties in Minnesota.

FINANCIAL DATA:
Amount of support per award: Grants: $2,250
average; Scholarships: $1,000.
Total amount of support: $1,351,696 in
grants for fiscal year ended June 30, 2012.

APPLICATION INFORMATION:
Applicants must submit eight copies of the
following (original and seven copies, except
financial attachments which require only one
copy):
(1) cover sheet signed by board chair and/or
school principal/headmaster (and fiscal agent
if necessary);
(2) a one- to three-page proposal narrative;
(3) project budget;
(4) 501(c)(3) tax determination letter

(required for all organizations, except public
schools);
(5) for Nonprofit Management Assistance
Grants: If requesting funds for a consultant,
include the consultant's resume and their cost
estimate. If a consultant has not been
identified, include a description of the
intended process for selecting a consultant
and;
(6) organization financial statement for year
most recently completed and organization
budget and financial statement for year to
date (not required for Music Education grant
applications).
Applications without signatures will not be
considered.
Duration: Varies depending on the field of
interest. One year for the Valley Arts
Initiative Grant. Grants are renewable upon
review.
Deadline: Health and Wellness Grant:
Spring; Music Education Grant and Valley
Arts Initiative Grant: Fall.

IRS IDENTIFICATION NUMBER: 41-1817315

STAFF:
Jill Shannon, Director of Community
Partnerships

ADDRESS INQUIRIES TO:
Jane Hetland Stevenson, President
(See address above.)

SAINT-GOBAIN CORPORATION
FOUNDATION   [1366]
750 East Swedesford Road
Valley Forge, PA 19482
(610) 341-6937
Fax: (610) 341-7777

E-MAIL ADDRESS:
SGNorthAmericanInfo@saint-gobain.com

WEB SITE ADDRESS:
www.saint-gobain-northamerica.com

FOUNDED: 2001

AREAS OF INTEREST:
Education, energy conservation,
environmental concerns and
insulation/weatherization of homes.

NAME(S) OF PROGRAMS:
● Direct Grants Program

TYPE:
Project/program grants.

PURPOSE:
To play a vital role in the economic, social
and educational development of the
community.

LEGAL BASIS:
Corporation foundation.

ELIGIBILITY:
Eligible organizations must be IRS 501(c)(3)
tax-exempt and be located in areas where
Saint-Gobain Corporation has manufacturing
locations.

GEOGRAPHIC RESTRICTIONS:
Massachusetts and Pennsylvania.

FINANCIAL DATA:
Amount of support per award: Varies.
Total amount of support: Varies.

APPLICATION INFORMATION:
Applications are available from the
Foundation.
Duration: Typically one year.
Deadline: Applications must be submitted by
end of February for April Board Meeting and
by end of July for September Board Meeting.

ADDRESS INQUIRIES TO:
See e-mail address above.

SAN ANGELO AREA FOUNDATION [1367]

2201 Sherwood Way, Suite 205
San Angelo, TX 76901
(325) 947-7071
Fax: (325) 947-7322

E-MAIL ADDRESS:
infosaaf@saafound.org

WEB SITE ADDRESS:
www.saafound.org

FOUNDED: 2002

AREAS OF INTEREST:
Community development.

TYPE:
Grants-in-aid; Scholarships. To build a legacy of philanthropy by attracting and prudently managing endowed gifts in order to match donor interests with community needs of the area.

PURPOSE:
To improve the quality of life in the San Angelo, TX area.

LEGAL BASIS:
Community foundation.

ELIGIBILITY:
Must be a 501(c)(3) nonprofit organization. Grant funds must be used within and for the benefit of residents and communities of the 17 counties of the San Angelo area.

GEOGRAPHIC RESTRICTIONS:
San Angelo area, Texas.

FINANCIAL DATA:
Amount of support per award: Varies.
Total amount of support: Varies.

APPLICATION INFORMATION:
Application and proposal forms are available online.
Duration: Grants: Typically one year. Scholarships: One to eight semesters.
Deadline: Grants: September 1 for Executive Summary. Scholarships: March 1.

ADDRESS INQUIRIES TO:
Matt Lewis, President and Chief Executive Officer
(See address above.)

SAN ANTONIO AREA FOUNDATION [1368]

303 Pearl Parkway
Suite 114
San Antonio, TX 78215
(210) 225-2243
Fax: (210) 225-1980

E-MAIL ADDRESS:
gift@saafdn.org

WEB SITE ADDRESS:
www.saafdn.org

FOUNDED: 1964

AREAS OF INTEREST:
Animal services, arts and culture, biomedical research, community services, medical services, social services, high school completion, and strengthening nonprofits.

NAME(S) OF PROGRAMS:
• **Discretionary Grant Process**

TYPE:
Capital grants; Project/program grants; Research grants; Seed money grants; Technical assistance. Capital grants are only given after 75% of the goal has been met. Research grants are for biomedical research only.

YEAR PROGRAM STARTED: 1964

PURPOSE:
To help donors achieve their charitable goals for the greater benefit of the community.

LEGAL BASIS:
Community foundation.

ELIGIBILITY:
Eligible organizations must be IRS 501(c)(3) tax-exempt and located in Bexar County or surrounding counties. Endowments, scholarships, and debt reduction will not be funded. The Foundation does not provide grants to individuals.

GEOGRAPHIC RESTRICTIONS:
Bexar County and surrounding counties, Texas.

FINANCIAL DATA:
Amount of support per award: Varies.

NUMBER OF APPLICANTS MOST RECENT YEAR: 400.

NUMBER OF AWARDS: 108 for the year 2012.

APPLICATION INFORMATION:
Application and guidelines are available on the web site in September.
Duration: One year. Must reapply for additional funding.

PUBLICATIONS:
Newsletter; annual report.

IRS IDENTIFICATION NUMBER: 74-6065414

ADDRESS INQUIRIES TO:
Lydia Rodriguez
Program Officer, Community and Research Grants
(See address above.)

*SPECIAL STIPULATIONS:
The Foundation does not fund statewide; only in Bexar County and surrounding counties.

THE SAN DIEGO FOUNDATION [1369]

2508 Historic Decatur Road
Suite 200
San Diego, CA 92106-6138
(619) 235-2300
Fax: (619) 239-1710

E-MAIL ADDRESS:
info@sdfoundation.org

WEB SITE ADDRESS:
www.sdfoundation.org

FOUNDED: 1975

AREAS OF INTEREST:
Civil society, economic/employment development, education, health and human services, environment, arts and culture, capacity building, science and technology.

TYPE:
Awards/prizes; Capital grants; Challenge/matching grants; Demonstration grants; Development grants; Fellowships; General operating grants; Matching gifts; Project/program grants; Research grants; Scholarships; Seed money grants; Technical assistance; Training grants.

YEAR PROGRAM STARTED: 1975

PURPOSE:
To improve the quality of life for all San Diegans through effective responsible philanthropy.

LEGAL BASIS:
Community foundation.

ELIGIBILITY:
Applicant organizations must be IRS 501(c)(3).

GEOGRAPHIC RESTRICTIONS:
San Diego County, California.

FINANCIAL DATA:
Amount of support per award: Varies.
Total amount of support: Over $40,000,000 annually.
Matching fund requirements: On a case-by-case basis.

NUMBER OF AWARDS: 2,800.

APPLICATION INFORMATION:
Requests for proposals in the area of Community Partnerships must include a project budget, organization budget, and letter of qualification.
Duration: Generally, one year.
Deadline: Varies.

PUBLICATIONS:
Annual report; newsletters.

IRS IDENTIFICATION NUMBER: 95-2942582

OFFICERS:
Bob Kelly, President and Chief Executive Officer

*SPECIAL STIPULATIONS:
Most grants made only in San Diego region.

THE SAN FRANCISCO FOUNDATION [1370]

225 Bush Street
Suite 500
San Francisco, CA 94104
(415) 733-8500
Fax: (415) 477-2783

E-MAIL ADDRESS:
info@sff.org

WEB SITE ADDRESS:
www.sff.org

FOUNDED: 1948

AREAS OF INTEREST:
Societal and civic issues, health and environment, and arts and humanities.

NAME(S) OF PROGRAMS:
• **Community Leadership Awards**

TYPE:
Awards/prizes.

PURPOSE:
To recognize individuals and organizations whose leadership has made a significant impact in their particular Bay Area communities.

LEGAL BASIS:
Community foundation.

ELIGIBILITY:
Organizations must be 501(c)(3).

GEOGRAPHIC RESTRICTIONS:
Alameda, Contra Costa, Marin, San Francisco and San Mateo counties, California.

FINANCIAL DATA:
Amount of support per award: Individual leaders: $10,000; Organizations: $20,000.
Total amount of support: Varies.

NUMBER OF APPLICANTS MOST RECENT YEAR:
275.

NUMBER OF AWARDS: Varies.

APPLICATION INFORMATION:
Details are available online.
Deadline: Varies.

ADDRESS INQUIRIES TO:
Community Leadership Award Program
(See address above.)

SANTA BARBARA FOUNDATION   [1371]

1111 Chapala Street, Suite 200
Santa Barbara, CA 93101
(805) 963-1873
Fax: (805) 966-2345

E-MAIL ADDRESS:
info@sbfoundation.org

WEB SITE ADDRESS:
www.sbfoundation.org

FOUNDED: 1928

AREAS OF INTEREST:
Arts and culture expression, living and dying
with dignity, lifelong learning, safety, civic
engagement and sustainable protection of
environment/historic places.

NAME(S) OF PROGRAMS:
- **Express Grants**
- **Opportunity Grants**

TYPE:
Challenge/matching grants; Development
grants; General operating grants;
Project/program grants.

YEAR PROGRAM STARTED: 1928

PURPOSE:
To enrich the lives of the people of Santa
Barbara County, CA.

LEGAL BASIS:
Community foundation incorporated in
California.

ELIGIBILITY:
501(c)(3) organizations only. Funds must be
used to benefit the people of Santa Barbara
County, CA.

GEOGRAPHIC RESTRICTIONS:
Santa Barbara County, California.

FINANCIAL DATA:
Amount of support per award: Express
Grants: Up to $10,000; Opportunity Grants:
Up to $20,000.
Total amount of support: Approximately
$7,000,000 in discretionary grants for the
year ended December 31, 2011.
Matching fund requirements: Varies.

APPLICATION INFORMATION:
Contact the Foundation for guidelines.
Duration: One year. No guarantee for
continuation.
Deadline: Express Grants: Applications are
accepted on a rolling basis through
November 3, 2014. Opportunity Grants:
Applications are accepted on an ongoing
basis.

PUBLICATIONS:
Annual report; application guidelines;
quarterly newsletter.

IRS IDENTIFICATION NUMBER: 95-1866094

STAFF:
Ron Gallo, President and Chief Executive
Officer

Jan Campbell, Senior Vice President of
Philanthropic Services, Communications and
Marketing
Dee Jennings, Senior Vice President of
Finance and Administration/Chief Financial
Officer
Al Rodriguez, Vice President of Community
Investments

ADDRESS INQUIRIES TO:
Jack Azar, Grants Associate
(See address above.)

CHARLES AND LYNN SCHUSTERMAN FAMILY FOUNDATION   [1372]

110 West Seventh Street, Suite 2000
Tulsa, OK 74119
(918) 879-0290
Fax: (918) 392-9724

E-MAIL ADDRESS:
ahughes@schusterman.org

WEB SITE ADDRESS:
www.schusterman.org

FOUNDED: 1987

AREAS OF INTEREST:
Child advocacy, Jewish life, education, and
community service.

TYPE:
Capital grants; General operating grants;
Project/program grants.

PURPOSE:
To fund projects of interest to the Foundation
including, but not limited to, those working
with education, community life and Jewish
affairs.

LEGAL BASIS:
Family foundation.

ELIGIBILITY:
Tax-exempt U.S. and international
organizations that enhance Jewish life and
nonsectarian Oklahoma-based organizations
focused on child advocacy, education and
youth leadership through service are eligible.

FINANCIAL DATA:
Amount of support per award: Varies.
Total amount of support: Varies.

NUMBER OF APPLICANTS MOST RECENT YEAR:
582 requests received, January 1, 2013 to
December 31, 2013.

NUMBER OF AWARDS: 494 requests approved,
January 1, 2013 to December 31, 2013.

APPLICATION INFORMATION:
Grants are by invitation only.
Duration: One year; seldom more than three
years. Must reapply for renewal based on
performance.
Deadline: Applications are received on a
rolling basis.

ADDRESS INQUIRIES TO:
Alana Hughes, Chief Operating Officer
(See address above.)

SCRANTON AREA FOUNDATION   [1373]

321 Spruce Street, Suite 608
Scranton, PA 18503
(570) 347-6203
Fax: (570) 347-7587

E-MAIL ADDRESS:
safinfo@safdn.org

WEB SITE ADDRESS:
www.safdn.org

FOUNDED: 1954

AREAS OF INTEREST:
The people and community of the city of
Scranton and Lackawanna County, PA.

TYPE:
Challenge/matching grants; Demonstration
grants; Grants-in-aid; Project/program grants;
Scholarships; Seed money grants; Training
grants.

PURPOSE:
To strengthen the local community; to enrich
the lives of the people of Scranton and
Lackawanna County, PA.

ELIGIBILITY:
Grants to 501(c)(3) nonprofits serving
Lackawanna County, PA.

GEOGRAPHIC RESTRICTIONS:
The city of Scranton and Lackawanna
County, Pennsylvania.

FINANCIAL DATA:
Amount of support per award: Varies.
Total amount of support: Approximately
$569,000 for the year 2012.

APPLICATION INFORMATION:
Before a grant application is submitted to the
Foundation, it is strongly recommended that
the applicant submit a letter of intent (one to
two pages maximum).
Duration: Varies.
Deadline: Typically March, June, August and
November.

THE SELF FAMILY FOUNDATION   [1374]

120 Main Street
Greenwood, SC 29646
(864) 941-4011
Fax: (864) 941-4091

E-MAIL ADDRESS:
fwideman@selffoundation.org

WEB SITE ADDRESS:
www.selffoundation.org

FOUNDED: 1942

AREAS OF INTEREST:
Community wellness, education, with
emphasis on early childhood development
and youth, and health with emphasis on
prevention.

TYPE:
Challenge/matching grants; Project/program
grants. Project grants in areas of the
Foundation's interest.

YEAR PROGRAM STARTED: 1942

PURPOSE:
To help people to help themselves in South
Carolina.

LEGAL BASIS:
Tax-exempt, private foundation.

ELIGIBILITY:
Applicants must be tax-exempt organizations
in South Carolina only. No grants are
awarded directly to individuals.

GEOGRAPHIC RESTRICTIONS:
South Carolina, with preference to
Greenwood.

FINANCIAL DATA:
Amount of support per award: $1,000 to
$500,000. Typical grant: $25,000.
Total amount of support: $2,553,978 for the
year 2013.

Matching fund requirements: Stipulated with specific programs.

NUMBER OF APPLICANTS MOST RECENT YEAR: 65.

NUMBER OF AWARDS: 34.

REPRESENTATIVE AWARDS:
$50,000 to Greenwood Community Children's Center; $75,230 to Independent Colleges and Universities of South Carolina; $7,500 to Ed Venture Children's Museum; $15,000 to Greater Greenwood United Ministries.

APPLICATION INFORMATION:
There is no application form. Applicants are requested to submit a written proposal, leadership list, a description of the organization's activities and objectives and a description of the purpose for which funding is sought. Include copy of IRS tax determination letter, expense budget of the organization and copy of latest financial statement.

Duration: No grants on a continuing basis.

Deadline: March 1, June 1, September 1 and November 1. Announcements in April, July, October and December.

IRS IDENTIFICATION NUMBER: 57-0400594

OFFICERS:
W.M. Self, Chairman
Frank J. Wideman, III, President
J.C. Self, III, Treasurer
Dr. Sally E. Self, Secretary

TRUSTEES:
J. Welborn Adams
Jon Holloway
Cade Jackson
Furman C. Self
J.C. Self, III
Dr. Sally E. Self
W.M. Self
W.M. Self, Jr.

ADDRESS INQUIRIES TO:
Mamie Nicholson, Program Officer
(See address above.)

SHASTA REGIONAL COMMUNITY FOUNDATION [1375]
1335B Arboretum Drive
Redding, CA 96003
(530) 244-1219
Fax: (530) 244-0905

E-MAIL ADDRESS:
info@shastacf.org

WEB SITE ADDRESS:
www.shastacf.org

FOUNDED: 2000

AREAS OF INTEREST:
Arts and culture, community development, education, health and human services.

NAME(S) OF PROGRAMS:
● **The McConnell Foundation Fund**
● **Redding Rancheria Community Fund**

TYPE:
Project/program grants.

PURPOSE:
To enhance the quality of life of Shasta and Siskiyou communities through philanthropy, education and information.

ELIGIBILITY:
To be eligible for funding, the applicant must be a nonprofit 501(c)(3) organization or

public agency and provide specific and direct benefits to residents of Shasta and/or Siskiyou counties, primarily, or to Modoc, Tehema, or Trinity counties.

GEOGRAPHIC RESTRICTIONS:
Primarily Shasta and Siskiyou counties, California. Limited funding to Modoc, Tehema and Trinity counties, California.

FINANCIAL DATA:
Amount of support per award: Varies.
Total amount of support: $1,600,000 for fiscal year ended June 30, 2012.

APPLICATION INFORMATION:
Application is available on the Foundation web site.
Duration: Varies.
Deadline: Varies.

ADDRESS INQUIRIES TO:
Kerry Caranci, Program Officer
(See address above.)

SILICON VALLEY COMMUNITY FOUNDATION [1376]
2440 West El Camino Real
Suite 300
Mountain View, CA 94040-1498
(650) 450-5400
Fax: (650) 450-5401

E-MAIL ADDRESS:
info@siliconvalleycf.org

WEB SITE ADDRESS:
www.siliconvalleycf.org

FOUNDED: 2007

AREAS OF INTEREST:
This community foundation utilizes five grantmaking strategies: economic security; education (closing the middle school achievement gap in mathematics); immigrant integration; regional planning (land use and transportation planning); and a community opportunity fund currently focused on safety-net services of food and shelter.

TYPE:
General operating grants; Project/program grants; Scholarships; Seed money grants. Nonprofit organizations that provide services or programs related to the specific five grantmaking strategies in San Mateo and Santa Clara counties may be eligible to apply for funding from the Foundation's endowment. Scholarships for college-bound students are also open to application.

YEAR PROGRAM STARTED: 2008

PURPOSE:
To advance philanthropic solutions to challenging problems, engaging donors to make our region and world a better place for all.

LEGAL BASIS:
Community foundation.

ELIGIBILITY:
To be eligible for a grant, an organization should have current evidence of tax-exempt status under Section 501(c)(3) from the IRS, be a public entity or have a fiscal sponsor with tax-exempt status.

In general, the Foundation does not make grants from its endowment for or to:
(1) activities not directly benefiting the residents of San Mateo and Santa Clara counties;
(2) organizations that are discriminatory;
(3) individuals (contact the Foundation for

exceptions to this rule);
(4) costs already incurred;
(5) fraternal organizations, unless sponsoring a specific program open to the entire community;
(6) religious purposes; however, organizations with religious affiliations will be considered for grants if their programs seek to address the needs of the wider community without regard to religious beliefs;
(7) fund-raising events such as walk-a-thons, tournaments and fashion shows and general fund-raising solicitations;
(8) organizations and programs designed to elect candidates to public office or;
(9) out-of-area travel.

GEOGRAPHIC RESTRICTIONS:
San Mateo and Santa Clara counties only.

FINANCIAL DATA:
Amount of support per award: $10,000 to $250,000, with average grant size less than $100,000. Grant size varies according to the type of project, needs of the organization, and the Foundation's annual giving budget and program concentration.
Total amount of support: Dependent on the Foundation's annual giving budget.

NUMBER OF APPLICANTS MOST RECENT YEAR: 360.

APPLICATION INFORMATION:
The first step for any potential applicant is to learn the specific components of the grantmaking strategies. If the potential applicant's organization does work or plans to do work related to one of the grantmaking strategies and a Request for Proposal (RFP) regarding that strategy is open for application, then a representative should attend a grant information session. This will give the potential applicant an opportunity to learn more about the grantmaking strategy, the RFP process and talk with a program officer.

Step two would be to submit a proposal with all the required information outlined in the RFP application checklist. The Foundation encourages submission of proposals via e-mail and accepts proposals postmarked and submitted electronically by the respective deadline date.

Duration: Grants are usually for one year, and should not be considered a source of ongoing support.

Deadline: Contact the Foundation for the appropriate grantmaking strategy application.

PUBLICATIONS:
Annual report; RFP guidelines; research papers; *One Magazine.*

IRS IDENTIFICATION NUMBER: 20-5205488

BOARD OF DIRECTORS:
Thomas J. Friel, Chairperson
C.S. Park, Vice Chairperson
Jayne Battey
Gloria Brown
Emmett D. Carson, Ph.D.
Gregory M. Gallo
Nancy H. Handel
John F. Hopkins
Samuel Johnson, Jr.
Robert A. Keller
Daniel Lewin
David P. Lopez, Ed.D.
Anne F. Macdonald
Catherine A. Molnar
Ivonne Montes de Oca
Eduardo Rallo
Sanjay Vaswani

Thurman V. White, Jr.
Gordon Yamate

ADDRESS INQUIRIES TO:
Manuel J. Santamaria
Director of Grantmaking
(See address above.)

*SPECIAL STIPULATIONS:
Please note the geographical restriction
(above).

THE SOUTHFIELD COMMUNITY FOUNDATION [1377]

25630 Evergreen Road
Southfield, MI 48075
(248) 327-6125
Fax: (248) 327-6127

E-MAIL ADDRESS:
rrrobinson@scfmi.org

WEB SITE ADDRESS:
www.scfmi.org

AREAS OF INTEREST:
Community building, diversity, educational
programs and youth development.

TYPE:
Grants-in-aid; Project/program grants;
Scholarships.

PURPOSE:
To enhance the quality of life for those who
work or live in the community.

ELIGIBILITY:
Grants are made to organizations that have
tax-exempt status under Section 501(c)(3) of
the Internal Revenue Code. No grants are
made to individuals. Nonsectarian religious
programs may apply.

GEOGRAPHIC RESTRICTIONS:
Southfield or Lathrup Village, Michigan.

FINANCIAL DATA:
Amount of support per award: $500 to
$5,000.
Total amount of support: Approximately
$60,000 per year.

NUMBER OF APPLICANTS MOST RECENT YEAR:
Approximately 10 for the year 2012.

NUMBER OF AWARDS: Approximately 10 for the
year 2012.

APPLICATION INFORMATION:
Application information is available on the
web site.
Duration: One year.

ADDRESS INQUIRIES TO:
Raquel Robinson, Executive Director
(See address above.)

SOUTHWEST FLORIDA COMMUNITY FOUNDATION [1378]

8771 College Parkway
Building 2, Suite 201
Fort Myers, FL 33919
(239) 274-5900
Fax: (239) 274-5930

E-MAIL ADDRESS:
info@floridacommunity.com

WEB SITE ADDRESS:
www.floridacommunity.com

FOUNDED: 1977

AREAS OF INTEREST:
Arts, animal welfare and rights, community
needs and development, culture, education,
and health and human services.

TYPE:
Capital grants; Challenge/matching grants;
Demonstration grants; Project/program
grants; Scholarships; Seed money grants;
Technical assistance; Training grants.

PURPOSE:
To connect donors and their philanthropic
aspirations with evolving community needs.

LEGAL BASIS:
501(c)(3).

ELIGIBILITY:
Grants are made to organizations that have
tax-exempt status under Section 501(c)(3) of
the Internal Revenue Code. No grants are
made to individuals. Nonsectarian religious
programs may apply. Must serve the needs of
the communities listed below.

GEOGRAPHIC RESTRICTIONS:
Charlotte, Collier, Glades, Hendry and Lee
counties, Florida.

FINANCIAL DATA:
Amount of support per award: $5,000 to
$25,000; Initiative Grant Awards: Up to
$100,000.
Total amount of support: $2,274,100 for
fiscal year ended June 30, 2012.

NUMBER OF APPLICANTS MOST RECENT YEAR:
1,200.

NUMBER OF AWARDS: 300.

APPLICATION INFORMATION:
Contact the Foundation for application
procedures.
Duration: One year.
Deadline: Varies per program.

PUBLICATIONS:
Annual report; quarterly newsletter.

IRS IDENTIFICATION NUMBER: 59-6580974

ADMINISTRATORS:
Sarah Owen, President and Chief Executive
Officer

ADDRESS INQUIRIES TO:
Anne Douglas, Director of Programs
(See address above.)

STARK COMMUNITY FOUNDATION [1379]

400 Market Avenue North
Suite 200
Canton, OH 44702-2107
(330) 454-3426
Fax: (330) 454-5855

E-MAIL ADDRESS:
info@starkcf.org

WEB SITE ADDRESS:
www.starkcommunityfoundation.org

FOUNDED: 1963

AREAS OF INTEREST:
Advancement of the health, social welfare,
education, culture or civic improvement of
the community.

TYPE:
Capital grants; Challenge/matching grants;
Demonstration grants; Development grants;
General operating grants; Matching gifts;
Project/program grants; Research grants;

Scholarships; Seed money grants; Technical
assistance; Training grants; Loan forgiveness
programs.

YEAR PROGRAM STARTED: 1965

LEGAL BASIS:
Community foundation.

ELIGIBILITY:
Organizations with 501(c)(3) status serving
Stark County, OH, are eligible. The
Foundation will not support operating
expenses of well-established organizations,
deficit programs, or capital expenditures,
endowment funds, religious organizations or
religious purposes, annual appeal or
membership contributions, conferences or
recognition events.

GEOGRAPHIC RESTRICTIONS:
Stark County, Ohio.

FINANCIAL DATA:
Total assets $203,000,000 as of January 31,
2013.
Amount of support per award: $1,000 to
$225,000.
Total amount of support: Approximately
$110,000,000 annually.
Matching fund requirements: No general
requirements.

NUMBER OF APPLICANTS MOST RECENT YEAR:
Approximately 200.

NUMBER OF AWARDS: 130 Discretionary Field
of Interest and 60 Pro-Active Initiatives.

APPLICATION INFORMATION:
Application information is available on the
web site.
Duration: One year.
Deadline: January 5. August 1 for
discretionary funds.

PUBLICATIONS:
Annual report; guidelines and policies;
Community and Commitment, newsletter.

STAFF:
Mark Samolczyk, President

ADDRESS INQUIRIES TO:
Mark Samolczyk, President
(See address above.)

THE STEELE-REESE FOUNDATION [1380]

32 Washington Square West
New York, NY 10011
(212) 674-4039
Fax: (212) 286-8513

E-MAIL ADDRESS:
charles@steele-reese.org

WEB SITE ADDRESS:
www.steele-reese.org

FOUNDED: 1955

AREAS OF INTEREST:
Education, health, social welfare, the
humanities and the environment.

TYPE:
General operating grants; Project/program
grants. Funding is only provided for rural
projects of interest to the Foundation. The
projects must serve people in the geographic
area served by the Foundation.

YEAR PROGRAM STARTED: 1955

LEGAL BASIS:
Private foundation.

ELIGIBILITY:
Funding is provided to nonprofit organizations servicing communities in Appalachian Kentucky and the western states of Idaho and Montana.

All organizations seeking funds must demonstrate additional local community support for their programming.

GEOGRAPHIC RESTRICTIONS:
Appalachian Kentucky, Idaho and Montana.

FINANCIAL DATA:
Amount of support per award: Typically $5,000 to $50,000. Larger grants are typically for multiyear support.

Total amount of support: $1,984,000 for the year 2013.

Matching fund requirements: Some grants require that an organization raise a specific matching amount.

NUMBER OF APPLICANTS MOST RECENT YEAR:
200 to 250.

NUMBER OF AWARDS: Approximately 60.

APPLICATION INFORMATION:
The Foundation welcomes proposals that are accurately aimed. The Foundation's policies and guidelines in detail are available for review online. All applicants must submit proposal materials electronically through the Foundation's web site.

Duration: Grants payable over one to three years. Absolutely no renewals.

Deadline: March 1 for consideration during the current fiscal year.

PUBLICATIONS:
Annual report.

ADDRESS INQUIRIES TO:
For general inquiries about Foundation policies:
William T. Buice, Trustee
The Steele-Reese Foundation
(See address above.) or

Charles U. Buice, Trustee
The Steele-Reese Foundation
123 Fort Greene Place
Brooklyn, NY 11217
(See e-mail address above.)

For Kentucky:
Judy Owens, Appalachian Director
2613 Clubside Court
Lexington, KY 40513
Tel & Fax: (859) 313-5225
E-mail: jkowensjd@aol.com

For Idaho or Montana:
Linda Tracy, Western Program Director
P.O. Box 8311
Missoula, MT 59807-8311
Tel: (406) 207-7984
Fax: (207) 470-3872
E-mail: linda@steele-reese.org

THE ABBOT AND DOROTHY H. STEVENS FOUNDATION   [1381]
P.O. Box 111
North Andover, MA 01845
(978) 688-7211

E-MAIL ADDRESS:
grantprocess@stevensfoundation.com

AREAS OF INTEREST:
Education, community welfare, arts and youth programs.

TYPE:
Capital grants; General operating grants; Project/program grants.

PURPOSE:
To improve the quality of life in greater Lawrence and Merrimack Valley.

ELIGIBILITY:
Eligible organizations must be IRS 501(c)(3) tax-exempt.

GEOGRAPHIC RESTRICTIONS:
Greater Lawrence and Merrimack Valley, Massachusetts.

FINANCIAL DATA:
Amount of support per award: $8,000 average.

Total amount of support: Varies.

APPLICATION INFORMATION:
Applicants must include a copy of their IRS 501(c)(3) tax determination letter.

Duration: One year.

Deadline: Trustees meet monthly with the exception of July and August.

PUBLICATIONS:
Guidelines.

ADDRESS INQUIRIES TO:
Joshua Miner, Administrator
(See address above.)

THE NATHANIEL AND ELIZABETH P. STEVENS FOUNDATION   [1382]
P.O. Box 111
North Andover, MA 01845
(978) 688-7211

E-MAIL ADDRESS:
grantprocess@stevensfoundation.com

AREAS OF INTEREST:
Education, community welfare, arts and youth programs.

TYPE:
Capital grants; General operating grants; Project/program grants.

PURPOSE:
To improve the quality of life in the greater Lawrence and Merrimack Valley.

ELIGIBILITY:
Eligible organizations must be IRS 501(c)(3) tax-exempt.

GEOGRAPHIC RESTRICTIONS:
Greater Lawrence and Merrimack Valley, Massachusetts.

FINANCIAL DATA:
Amount of support per award: $8,000 average.

Total amount of support: Varies.

APPLICATION INFORMATION:
Applications must include a copy of the IRS 501(c)(3) tax determination letter.

Duration: One year.

Deadline: Trustees meet monthly with the exception of July and August.

PUBLICATIONS:
Guidelines.

ADDRESS INQUIRIES TO:
Joshua Miner, Administrator
(See address above.)

H. CHASE STONE TRUST
c/o JPMorgan
370 17th Street, Suite 3200
Denver, CO 80202
(303) 607-7810
Fax: (303) 607-7761

E-MAIL ADDRESS:
julie.golden@jpmorgan.com

WEB SITE ADDRESS:
www.jpmorgan.com/onlinegrants

TYPE:
Project/program grants.

See entry 502 for full listing.

SUDBURY FOUNDATION   [1383]
326 Concord Road
Sudbury, MA 01776
(978) 443-0849
Fax: (978) 579-9536

E-MAIL ADDRESS:
contact@sudburyfoundation.org

WEB SITE ADDRESS:
www.sudburyfoundation.org

FOUNDED: 1952

AREAS OF INTEREST:
Scholarships, environment, and charitable grants for communities in the Sudbury area.

NAME(S) OF PROGRAMS:
- **The Atkinson Scholarship Program**
- **Children, Youth and Families Program**
- **The Environmental Program**
- **The Sudbury Program**

TYPE:
Project/program grants; Scholarships.

YEAR PROGRAM STARTED: 1952

PURPOSE:
To improve the quality of life in Sudbury and the surrounding communities.

ELIGIBILITY:
Eligible organizations must be IRS 501(c)(3) tax-exempt. The Foundation funds projects in Sudbury and the 10 communities surrounding Sudbury that address the issues of Youth Development and Opportunity, Community Building, Preservation of Community Character and Assets, and/or Organizational Capacity and Effectiveness.

The Environmental Program focuses on Northern Forest of New York, Vermont, New Hampshire and Maine, and the fisheries and coastal communities of the Gulf of Maine.

The Atkinson Scholarship Program provides college financial aid to students connected to Sudbury, MA.

GEOGRAPHIC RESTRICTIONS:
Sudbury, Massachusetts and surrounding areas.

FINANCIAL DATA:
Scholarships are administered to the schools earmarked for specific students.

Amount of support per award: Scholarships: Up to $5,000; Grants: $5,000 to $50,000.

Total amount of support: Varies.

NUMBER OF AWARDS: Scholarships: 15 new awards per year; Grants to nonprofits: 50 per year.

APPLICATION INFORMATION:
Applicants should write to the Foundation at the address above. Must include a copy of the IRS tax determination letter.

ADDRESS INQUIRIES TO:
Marilyn Martino, Executive Director
(See address above.)

*SPECIAL STIPULATIONS:
Scholarship program open to local high school seniors only for undergraduate education.

THE SUMMERLEE FOUNDATION   [1384]
5556 Caruth Haven Lane
Dallas, TX 75225
(214) 363-9000
Fax: (214) 363-1941

E-MAIL ADDRESS:
info@summerlee.org

WEB SITE ADDRESS:
www.summerlee.org

FOUNDED: 1988

AREAS OF INTEREST:
Animal protection and Texas history.

NAME(S) OF PROGRAMS:
● **Animal Protection Program**
● **Texas History**

TYPE:
Project/program grants; Research grants; Technical assistance.

YEAR PROGRAM STARTED: 1988

PURPOSE:
To promote animal protection and the prevention of cruelty to animals; to research and document all facts of Texas history.

LEGAL BASIS:
Charitable foundation.

ELIGIBILITY:
No grants are made for religious purposes or to individuals. Must be 501(c)(3).

FINANCIAL DATA:
Amount of support per award: $5,000 to $10,000.

NUMBER OF APPLICANTS MOST RECENT YEAR: 219.

NUMBER OF AWARDS: 84.

APPLICATION INFORMATION:
Applicants should not apply until visiting with program officers. Applications should include:
(1) a brief history of the organization;
(2) a statement of organizational goals and purposes;
(3) a list of board of trustees and officers of the organization;
(4) the most recent audited financial statement;
(5) the most recent copy of the IRS determination letter which grants the organization 501(c)(3) status;
(6) the most recent copy of the 990 IRS information return;
(7) vitae of key personnel;
(8) the amount of time needed to complete the project;
(9) a budget forecast and;
(10) a plan of work to complete project.

Applications should be submitted in writing and signed by the chief executive officer of the applicant organization.
Duration: One year.
Deadline: The Foundation meets quarterly to review grant proposals.

IRS IDENTIFICATION NUMBER: 75-2252355

OFFICERS:
John W. Crain, President and Program Director-Texas History
Hon. David D. Jackson, Vice President

Melanie K. Anderson, Vice President and Program Director-Animal Protection
Martha L. Benson, Treasurer
Hon. Nikki DeShazo, Secretary

BOARD OF DIRECTORS:
Melanie K. Anderson
Martha L. Benson
Michael H. Collins
John W. Crain
Hon. Nikki DeShazo
Hon. David D. Jackson
Ron Tyler, Ph.D.

ADDRESS INQUIRIES TO:
Melanie K. Anderson
Program Director-Animal Protection or
John W. Crain
Program Director-Texas History
(See address above.)

THE SUMMIT FOUNDATION   [1385]
111 A Lincoln Street
Breckenridge, CO 80424
(970) 453-5970
Fax: (970) 453-1423

E-MAIL ADDRESS:
tsfdirector@summitfoundation.org

WEB SITE ADDRESS:
www.summitfoundation.org

FOUNDED: 1984

AREAS OF INTEREST:
Art and culture, health and human service, education, environment and sports.

TYPE:
Capital grants; Challenge/matching grants; Endowments; General operating grants; Project/program grants; Scholarships; Technical assistance. The Foundation supports scholarship programs at Summit High School and neighboring community high schools. Scholarships are available to graduating seniors each year.

YEAR PROGRAM STARTED: 1984

PURPOSE:
To improve the quality of life for residents and guests of Summit County and neighboring communities.

LEGAL BASIS:
Community foundation.

ELIGIBILITY:
Grants are made to organizations that have tax-exempt status under Section 501(c)(3) of the Internal Revenue Code. No grants are made to individuals.

GEOGRAPHIC RESTRICTIONS:
Summit County and neighboring communities of Alma, Fairplay, Kremmling and Leadville, Colorado.

FINANCIAL DATA:
Amount of support per award: Varies.
Total amount of support: Approximately $2,339,730 for the year 2013.

NUMBER OF APPLICANTS MOST RECENT YEAR: 97.

NUMBER OF AWARDS: 91.

APPLICATION INFORMATION:
Contact the Foundation for specific details on the various grant programs.
Deadline: Typically April and October.

IRS IDENTIFICATION NUMBER: 74-2341399

ADDRESS INQUIRIES TO:
Lee Zimmerman, Executive Director
(See address above.)

THOMAS THOMPSON TRUST   [1386]
c/o Rackemann, Sawyer & Brewster
160 Federal Street, 15th Floor
Boston, MA 02110-1700
(617) 951-1108
Fax: (617) 542-7437

E-MAIL ADDRESS:
smonahan@rackemann.com

WEB SITE ADDRESS:
www.thomasthompsontrust.org

AREAS OF INTEREST:
Education, health/mental health, social services and cultural.

TYPE:
Capital grants; Challenge/matching grants; Conferences/seminars; Demonstration grants; Development grants; Endowments; Professorships; Project/program grants; Seed money grants; Technical assistance; Training grants; Research contracts. Support for special programs, capital support, new construction, renovation and equipment.

PURPOSE:
To promote health, education, or general social and civic betterment.

LEGAL BASIS:
Private foundation.

ELIGIBILITY:
Eligible organizations must be in operation for three consecutive years prior to submitting an application.

GEOGRAPHIC RESTRICTIONS:
Dutchess County, New York, particularly in Rhinebeck; and Windham County, Vermont, particularly in Brattleboro.

FINANCIAL DATA:
Amount of support per award: $5,000 to $15,000.
Total amount of support: $523,975 for fiscal year 2012.
Matching fund requirements: Determined on case-by-case basis.

NUMBER OF AWARDS: 39 for fiscal year 2012.

REPRESENTATIVE AWARDS:
Brattleboro Boys and Girls Club; Windham Housing Trust; Young Rhinebeck.

APPLICATION INFORMATION:
Applications must be submitted online.
Duration: Varies.

PUBLICATIONS:
Application guidelines.

TRUSTEES:
Daniel W. Fawcett
Michael F. O'Connell
William B. Tyler, Esq.

ADDRESS INQUIRIES TO:
Susan T. Monahan, Grants Coordinator
(See address or e-mail above.)

TIDES FOUNDATION   [1387]
P.O. Box 29198
San Francisco, CA 94129
(415) 561-6400
Fax: (415) 561-6401

E-MAIL ADDRESS:
info@tides.org

WEB SITE ADDRESS:
www.tides.org

FOUNDED: 1976

AREAS OF INTEREST:
Civic participation, economic development, economic and racial justice, environment, environmental justice, LGBTIQ communities, HIV/AIDS, native communities, progressive media, arts and culture, violence prevention, women's empowerment and reproductive health, and youth organizing and development.

NAME(S) OF PROGRAMS:
- **Colin Higgins Youth Courage Awards**
- **Jane Bagley Lehman Awards for Excellence in Public Advocacy**
- **Antonio Pizzigati Prize for Software in the Public Interest**

TYPE:
General operating grants; Project/program grants.

YEAR PROGRAM STARTED: 1976

PURPOSE:
To partner with donors to increase and organize resources for social change.

LEGAL BASIS:
Public foundation.

FINANCIAL DATA:
Amount of support per award: Varies.

APPLICATION INFORMATION:
The Fund does not accept unsolicited grant requests.

IRS IDENTIFICATION NUMBER: 51-0198509

ADDRESS INQUIRIES TO:
Grants Manager
(See address above.)

TOLEDO COMMUNITY FOUNDATION [1388]
300 Madison Avenue, Suite 1300
Toledo, OH 43604
(419) 241-5049
Fax: (419) 242-5549

E-MAIL ADDRESS:
toledocf@toledocf.org

WEB SITE ADDRESS:
www.toledocf.org

FOUNDED: 1973

AREAS OF INTEREST:
Education, social services, physical and mental health, neighborhood and urban affairs, natural resources and the arts.

TYPE:
Challenge/matching grants; Project/program grants; Seed money grants. The Foundation has a particular interest in providing seed money for new programs designed to meet emerging community needs or to expand existing successful programs. Emphasis is placed on programs that will:
(a) create safe, positive living environments;
(b) enable families to develop the skills/resources needed to support and nurture each member and;
(c) foster the development of responsible young people who are capable of achieving their fullest potential.

PURPOSE:
To enrich the quality of life for individuals and families in the greater Toledo service area.

ELIGIBILITY:
Grants are awarded only to nonprofit, charitable organizations that are IRS 501(c)(3) tax-exempt. The Foundation usually will not make grants from its unrestricted funds to support general operating budgets (or budget deficits) of established organizations, annual campaigns, capital campaigns, purchase of equipment such as computer hardware/software or motor vehicles, production of films, videos, television programs, etc., or for sectarian activities of religious organizations.

GEOGRAPHIC RESTRICTIONS:
Northwest Ohio and southeast Michigan, with particular emphasis on the greater Toledo, Ohio area.

FINANCIAL DATA:
Amount of support per award: Varies.

APPLICATION INFORMATION:
Online grant application must be completed. No hard copies accepted.
Duration: Varies.
Deadline: January 15 and September 15.

PUBLICATIONS:
Guidelines.

ADDRESS INQUIRIES TO:
Anneliese Grytafey, Senior Program Officer
(See address above.)

THE TRULL FOUNDATION [1389]
404 Fourth Street
Palacios, TX 77465
(361) 972-5241
Fax: (361) 972-1109

E-MAIL ADDRESS:
info@trullfoundation.org

WEB SITE ADDRESS:
www.trullfoundation.org

FOUNDED: 1967

AREAS OF INTEREST:
Children and families, substance abuse problems, Texas coastal environment, and The Palacios, Matagorda County area.

CONSULTING OR VOLUNTEER SERVICES:
Assists local projects and to some extent, organizations in other geographical areas.

TYPE:
Challenge/matching grants; Development grants; General operating grants; Project/program grants; Scholarships.

YEAR PROGRAM STARTED: 1948

PURPOSE:
To support charitable and educational programs.

LEGAL BASIS:
Private (family) foundation.

ELIGIBILITY:
Applicants must have federal tax-exemption letter from IRS.

GEOGRAPHIC RESTRICTIONS:
Primarily in rural Texas.

FINANCIAL DATA:
Amount of support per award: $2,000 to $5,000 average.
Total amount of support: $2,221,295 for the year 2013.

NUMBER OF APPLICANTS MOST RECENT YEAR:
412 for the year 2012.

NUMBER OF AWARDS: 288 for the year 2013.

REPRESENTATIVE AWARDS:
$3,000 to Children's Discovery Museum, Victoria, TX; $5,000 to Central Texas Library System, Inc., Austin, TX; $4,000 to Pines and Prairies Land Trust, Bastrop, TX; $2,000 to Devereux Texas Treatment Network, Victoria, TX; $5,000 to Child Welfare Alliance of Calhoun County, Port Lavaca, TX.

APPLICATION INFORMATION:
Each applicant should submit the following:
(1) cover letter (two-page maximum);
(2) proposal fact sheet (two-page maximum);
(3) current agency budget (one to three pages), including sources of income;
(4) one-page project budget, if different from operating budget;
(5) documentation of IRS status 501(c)(3). If there is any matter which might affect the IRS status to cause the revocation of the exemption, include information about this matter and;
(6) selected additional material or information (limit five pages) (optional).

Proposals sent by fax or e-mail are not accepted.

The Foundation may request additional information if there is an interest in the proposal.
Duration: Usually no more than three years per project.
Deadline: Announcement within two months after receipt of proposal.

PUBLICATIONS:
Biennial report; application guidelines; proposal fact sheet.

IRS IDENTIFICATION NUMBER: 23-7423943

TRUSTEES:
R. Scott Trull, Chairman
Cara P. Herlin, Vice Chairman
Craig Wallis, Secretary/Treasurer
Colleen Claybourn, Trustee
Sarah H. Olfers, Trustee
Kristan Olfers, Associate Trustee
Marsha Baumann, Advisory Trustee
Susan Herlin, Advisory Trustee
Cathy Wakefield, Advisory Trustee
Bill Wigmore, Advisory Trustee

ADDRESS INQUIRIES TO:
E. Gail Purvis, Executive Director
(See address above.)

U.S. BANCORP FOUNDATION [1390]
BC-MN-H21B
800 Nicollet Mall
Minneapolis, MN 55402
(612) 303-4000

WEB SITE ADDRESS:
www.usbank.com/communityrelations

FOUNDED: 1979

AREAS OF INTEREST:
Arts and culture, education, affordable housing and economic opportunity.

TYPE:
Capital grants; Development grants; General operating grants; Matching gifts; Project/program grants.

PURPOSE:
To improve the quality of life in communities where U.S. Bancorp employees live and work.

LEGAL BASIS:
Corporate foundation.

ELIGIBILITY:
Organizations must be IRS 501(c)(3) tax-exempt and must be located in communities where U.S. Bank operates.

The Foundation charitable contributions program will not provide funding for:
(1) organizations not tax-exempt under Internal Revenue Code Section 501(c)(3);
(2) fraternal organizations, merchant associations, chamber memberships or programs, or 501(c)(4) or (6) organizations;
(3) fund-raising events or sponsorships, "pass through" organizations or private foundations;
(4) organizations outside U.S. Bancorp communities;
(5) programs operated by religious organizations for religious purposes;
(6) political organizations or organizations designed primarily to lobby;
(7) individuals;
(8) travel and related expenses;
(9) endowment campaigns;
(10) deficit reduction;
(11) organizations receiving primary funding from the United Way or;
(12) organizations whose practices are not in keeping with the Company's equal opportunity policy.

GEOGRAPHIC RESTRICTIONS:
Communities where U.S. Bank has operations.

FINANCIAL DATA:
Amount of support per award: Varies.
Total amount of support: Varies.

APPLICATION INFORMATION:
Application and guidelines are available online.
Duration: One year.
Deadline: Varies.

PUBLICATIONS:
Guidelines; Corporate Citizenship Report.

IRS IDENTIFICATION NUMBER: 41-1359579

ADDRESS INQUIRIES TO:
Grants Coordinator
(See address above.)

U.S. DEPARTMENT OF HEALTH AND HUMAN SERVICES   [1391]
Administration on Intellectual and Developmental Disabilities
One Massachusetts Avenue
Washington, DC 20201
(202) 401-4541
Fax: (202) 205-8037

WEB SITE ADDRESS:
www.acl.hhs.gov

AREAS OF INTEREST:
Developmental disabilities.

NAME(S) OF PROGRAMS:
- **Projects of National Significance for Persons with Developmental Disabilities**

TYPE:
Demonstration grants; Technical assistance; Training grants. Model demonstration grants. Support for persons with developmental disabilities.

YEAR PROGRAM STARTED: 1975

PURPOSE:
To provide grants and contracts for projects of national significance that increase and support the independence, productivity and integration of persons with developmental disabilities into the community.

LEGAL BASIS:
Government agency.

ELIGIBILITY:
Applicants must be nonprofit organizations, state agencies, or consortia.

GEOGRAPHIC RESTRICTIONS:
United States and its territories.

FINANCIAL DATA:
Amount of support per award: Varies.
Total amount of support: $8,300,000 for the year 2013.
Matching fund requirements: 25% local match.

NUMBER OF AWARDS: Approximately 20 for the year 2013.

APPLICATION INFORMATION:
Application information is available on the web site.
Duration: 12 to 60 months.
Deadline: Varies.

OFFICERS:
Aaron Bishop, Commissioner, Administration on Intellectual and Developmental Disabilities

ADDRESS INQUIRIES TO:
Ophelia McLain, Director
(See address above.)

U.S. DEPARTMENT OF HOUSING AND URBAN DEVELOPMENT   [1392]
451 7th Street, S.W.
Room 7286
Washington, DC 20410
(202) 708-3587 (Office of Block Grant Assistance)
(202) 708-1577 (Entitlement Division)
(202) 708-1322 (State/Small Cities Division)
Fax: (202) 401-2044

WEB SITE ADDRESS:
www.hud.
gov/offices/cpd/communitydevelopment

FOUNDED: 1974

AREAS OF INTEREST:
Community development.

NAME(S) OF PROGRAMS:
- **Community Development Block Grant Program: Entitlement Communities Program**
- **State Community Development Block Grant Program**

TYPE:
Block grants; Project/program grants. Acquisition, construction of certain public works, facilities and improvements, clearance, housing rehabilitation, relocation and demolition, public services (limited), activities relating to conservation and renewable energy resources, neighborhood revitalization and economic development projects, including assistance to micro enterprises.

YEAR PROGRAM STARTED: 1975

PURPOSE:
To develop viable urban communities, including decent housing and a suitable living environment and expand economic opportunities, principally for persons of low and moderate income.

LEGAL BASIS:
Units of general local government under Title I of the Housing and Community Development Act of 1974 (PL 93-383).

ELIGIBILITY:
The following units of general local government and states are all entitled to receive block grants from the CDBG Entitlement Communities Program and State and Small Cities Program. Grant amounts are determined by a statutory formula:
(1) principal cities of Metropolitan Statistical Areas (MSAs);
(2) other metropolitan cities with a population of at least 50,000 and;
(3) qualified urban counties, as defined in the Act, with populations of at least 200,000 (excluding the population of entitled cities).

Under the State CDBG Program, HUD provides grant assistance to 49 states and Puerto Rico that in turn award grants to units of general local government not eligible to receive grants from the Entitlement Communities Program. Grant amounts to states are determined by statutory formula.

Under the HUD Administered Small Cities Program, HUD directly awards grants to non-entitled units of general local government within the state of Hawaii by formula. The total value of grants awarded through this Program is determined by statutory formula.

FINANCIAL DATA:
Amount of support per award: Varies from city to city.
Total amount of support: Approximately $3.03 billion for fiscal year 2014.

APPLICATION INFORMATION:
For the CDBG Entitlement Communities Program, a grantee must develop and submit to HUD its consolidated plan, which is a jurisdiction's comprehensive planning document and application for funding under the Community Planning and Development formula grant programs: CDBG, HOME, Emergency Shelter Grants (ESG) and Housing Opportunities for Persons with AIDS (HOPWA). In its consolidated plan, the jurisdiction must identify its goals for these community planning and development programs, as well as for housing programs. These goals will serve as the criteria against which HUD will evaluate a jurisdiction's plan and its performance under the plan. In addition, the consolidated plan must include required certifications, including that not less than 70% of the CDBG funds expended over a one-, two- or three-year period specified by the grantee, will be used for activities that benefit low- and moderate-income persons. A consolidated plan submission will be approved by HUD unless the plan (or a portion of it) is inconsistent with the purposes of the National Affordable Housing Act or it is substantially incomplete.

Under the State CDBG Program, to receive a grant from HUD, a state must certify that it:
(1) is following a detailed citizen participation plan and that each funded unit of general local government is following a detailed citizen participation plan;
(2) has consulted with affected units of general local government in the nonentitled area in determining the method of distribution of funding; it engages or will engage in planning for community development activities; it will provide assistance to units of general local government; it will not refuse to distribute funds to any unit of general local government based on the particular eligible activity

chosen by the unit of general local government, except that a state is not prevented from establishing priorities based on the activities selected;
(3) has a consolidated plan that identifies community development and housing needs and short-term and long-term community development objectives;
(4) will conduct its program in accordance with the Civil Rights Act of 1964 and the Fair Housing Act of 1988 and will affirmatively further fair housing;
(5) will set forth a method of distribution that ensures that each of the funded activities will meet one or more of the program's three broad, national objectives (grant maximum feasible priority to activities which benefit low- and moderate-income families, aid in the prevention or elimination of slums or blight or, in unique circumstances, meet urgent community development needs) and at least 70% of the amount expended for activities over a period of one, two or three consecutive program years will benefit low- and moderate-income families, and that the state will not attempt to recover any capital costs of public improvements assisted with CDBG funds, except for certain exceptions found in 24 CFR 91.325(b)(4);
(6) will require units of general local government to certify that they are adapting and enforcing laws to prohibit the use of excessive force against nonviolent civil rights demonstrations, and they will enforce laws against barring entrance and exit from facilities that are the targets of nonviolent civil rights demonstrations in their jurisdiction and;
(7) will comply with Title I of the HCD Act and all other applicable laws.

Under the HUD Administered Small Cities Program, to receive a grant, the counties of Hawaii, Maui and Kauai in Hawaii must prepare and submit a consolidated plan to HUD.

ADDRESS INQUIRIES TO:
Office of Block Grant Assistance
(See address above.)

*SPECIAL STIPULATIONS:
Block grants made to states and local governments, not individuals.

THE UNITY FOUNDATION OF LAPORTE COUNTY   [1393]
115 East Fourth Street
Michigan City, IN 46360
(219) 879-0327
Fax: (219) 210-3881

E-MAIL ADDRESS:
unity@uflc.net

WEB SITE ADDRESS:
www.uflc.net

FOUNDED: 1992

AREAS OF INTEREST:
Community development in LaPorte County, IN.

CONSULTING OR VOLUNTEER SERVICES:
Technical assistance to nonprofits and donors.

NAME(S) OF PROGRAMS:
● Community Fund

TYPE:
Challenge/matching grants; Grants-in-aid; Project/program grants; Scholarships; Technical assistance. Community Fund makes grants to education, the arts, health

and human services, and the environment to the whole community. Grants are based on what the community needs at a given time.

YEAR PROGRAM STARTED: 1992

PURPOSE:
To improve the quality of life in LaPorte County, IN.

LEGAL BASIS:
Indiana corporation 501(c)(3).

ELIGIBILITY:
Nonprofits serving people of LaPorte County, IN.

GEOGRAPHIC RESTRICTIONS:
LaPorte County, Indiana.

FINANCIAL DATA:
Amount of support per award: $3,000.
Total amount of support: More than $700,000 in community grants and more than $130,000 in scholarships each year.

NUMBER OF APPLICANTS MOST RECENT YEAR:
Grants: 75.

NUMBER OF AWARDS: 53.

APPLICATION INFORMATION:
Applications should follow the format outlined in the online directions. The following information is required:
(1) narrative describing the program or specific need to be addressed, its significance to the community and its particular benefit to those living in the LaPorte County area, and the names and qualifications of those persons who will carry it out;
(2) complete budget for the project, including funding plan, amount of the request, and names of other funding sources the organization has applied to for assistance and;
(3) description of applicant organization(s) including the name, address, telephone and fax number of the contact person, a list of the officers and board members, a copy of the IRS letter designating the organization as 501(c)(3) federal tax-exempt, latest annual financial report, and any descriptive brochures or promotional literature.
Deadline: Mid-July.

PUBLICATIONS:
Report to Community.

STAFF:
Maggi Spartz, President

ADDRESS INQUIRIES TO:
Maggi Spartz, President
(See address above.)

VAN LOEBENSELS/REMBEROCK FOUNDATION   [1394]
131 Steuart Street
Suite 301
San Francisco, CA 94105
(415) 512-0500
Fax: (415) 371-0227

E-MAIL ADDRESS:
info@vlsrr.org

WEB SITE ADDRESS:
www.vlsrr.org

FOUNDED: 1964

AREAS OF INTEREST:
Legal services for rural underserved populations.

TYPE:
General operating grants; Project/program grants; Seed money grants.

YEAR PROGRAM STARTED: 1964

PURPOSE:
To support projects that will test potentially useful innovations in the areas of public interest law.

LEGAL BASIS:
Private independent foundation.

ELIGIBILITY:
Grants are restricted to northern California. Grants are not ordinarily made for projects requiring medical, scientific or other technical knowledge for evaluation, operating budgets of well-established organizations, capital expenditures, to national organizations unless for a specific local project, to individuals or for scholarships.

GEOGRAPHIC RESTRICTIONS:
Northern California.

FINANCIAL DATA:
Amount of support per award: Average grant: $10,000.
Total amount of support: $2,000,641 for the year 2013.

NUMBER OF AWARDS: 163 for the year 2012.

REPRESENTATIVE AWARDS:
$25,000 to East Bay Community Law Center; $32,000 to Immigrant Legal Resource Center.

APPLICATION INFORMATION:
Application information is available on the web site.
Duration: Most grants are awarded on a single-year basis, but may be renewed if warranted.
Deadline: Proposals are considered every two to three months. Announcement several days after Board meetings.

STAFF:
Dan Corsello, Interim Executive Director
Gail Shuster, Grants Manager

BOARD OF DIRECTORS:
Toni Rembe, President
Dan Corsello, Treasurer
Richard W. Odgers, Secretary
Julie Divola
Thomas C. Layton

ADDRESS INQUIRIES TO:
Toni Rembe, President
(See address above.)

VENTURA COUNTY COMMUNITY FOUNDATION   [1395]
4001 Mission Oaks Boulevard
Camarillo, CA 93012
(805) 988-0196
Fax: (805) 485-5537

E-MAIL ADDRESS:
vccf@vccf.org

WEB SITE ADDRESS:
www.vccf.org

FOUNDED: 1986

AREAS OF INTEREST:
Community needs and development, culture, education, health, human services, women's issues and Latino issues.

TYPE:
Project/program grants; Scholarships.

YEAR PROGRAM STARTED: 1987

PURPOSE:
To promote and enable philanthropy to improve our community, for good, forever.

ELIGIBILITY:
Must qualify under the Internal Revenue Code Section 501(c)(3) as a nonprofit organization, or operate under the fiscal sponsorship of an organization that does, and serve residents of Ventura County, CA.

GEOGRAPHIC RESTRICTIONS:
Ventura County, California.

FINANCIAL DATA:
Amount of support per award: Varies.
Total amount of support: Varies.

NUMBER OF AWARDS: 834.

APPLICATION INFORMATION:
Applications accepted only in response to an open request for proposals. See web site for details.
Duration: Varies per program.

ADDRESS INQUIRIES TO:
Appropriate program officer, as outlined in the Request for Proposals.

VICTORIA FOUNDATION, INC.   [1396]
31 Mulberry Street, Fifth Floor
Newark, NJ 07102
(973) 792-9200
Fax: (973) 792-1300

E-MAIL ADDRESS:
info@victoriafoundation.org

WEB SITE ADDRESS:
www.victoriafoundation.org

FOUNDED: 1924

AREAS OF INTEREST:
Education, neighborhood revitalization, youth and families in Newark, NJ, as well as statewide environmental issues.

TYPE:
Capital grants; Challenge/matching grants; Demonstration grants; Development grants; General operating grants; Project/program grants; Seed money grants; Technical assistance; Training grants. The focus in Education includes after-school programs, educational enrichment, teacher training and curriculum development.

Neighborhood Revitalization includes community development, employment training, housing programs and community organizing.

The focus in Youth and Families includes youth development programs and efforts to strengthen families.

The concentration in Environment includes open space preservation in New Jersey, particularly in the Highlands and Pinelands.

YEAR PROGRAM STARTED: 1924

PURPOSE:
To promote education, urban environment, neighborhood development and urban revitalization, and youth and families in the city of Newark; to preserve and conserve resources including land, water and energy in the state of New Jersey and within the city of Newark.

LEGAL BASIS:
Independent foundation.

ELIGIBILITY:
Organizations must be nonprofit per Internal Revenue Code 501(c)(3) and must address

the Foundation's interests. No grants are made to individuals or for programs dealing with specific diseases, afflictions or geriatric needs. Proposals from arts organizations will be considered only if they directly bear on education.

General programs are focused within Newark, NJ. Environmental programs encompass the state of New Jersey.

GEOGRAPHIC RESTRICTIONS:
New Jersey.

FINANCIAL DATA:
Amount of support per award: Varies.
Total amount of support: $9,500,000 in total grants paid for the year ended December 31, 2012.

NUMBER OF APPLICANTS MOST RECENT YEAR:
229.

NUMBER OF AWARDS: 161 for the year ended December 31, 2012.

REPRESENTATIVE AWARDS:
$75,000 to New Jersey Symphony Orchestra to support the Newark Early Strings Program, which provides Suzuki violin instruction to over 500 elementary school children; $130,000 to Ironbound Community Corporation towards general operating support.

APPLICATION INFORMATION:
Application information is available on the web site.
Duration: One year. Renewal based upon careful trustee and staff review of subsequent proposal submissions.
Deadline: Current grantees: January 15 and July 15; New applicants: February 1 and August 1; School applications: February 1; Summer camp: September 1. Announcements in late June and December.

PUBLICATIONS:
Annual report.

IRS IDENTIFICATION NUMBER: 22-1554541

ADDRESS INQUIRIES TO:
Irene Cooper-Basch, Executive Officer
(See address above.)

THE WACO FOUNDATION [1397]
Wells Fargo Building
1105 Wooded Acres Drive, Suite 701
Waco, TX 76710
(254) 754-3404
Fax: (254) 753-2887

E-MAIL ADDRESS:
info@wacofoundation.org

WEB SITE ADDRESS:
www.wacofoundation.org

FOUNDED: 1958

AREAS OF INTEREST:
Residents of McLennan County, TX.

NAME(S) OF PROGRAMS:
● **MAC Program Scholarship Fund**

TYPE:
Scholarships. Intended to promote postsecondary educational opportunities in the community, and thereby promote greater employment opportunities for those of working age.

YEAR PROGRAM STARTED: 1995

PURPOSE:
To make a positive difference in the lives and future of the people who live in Waco and McLennan County through grantmaking, promotion of community philanthropy, and support of the not-for-profit sector.

ELIGIBILITY:
Must have graduated from McLennan County high schools and have family income of less than $50,000.

GEOGRAPHIC RESTRICTIONS:
McLennan County, Texas.

FINANCIAL DATA:
Amount of support per award: Varies.
Total amount of support: $500,000 in contributions annually.

APPLICATION INFORMATION:
High school seniors must submit completed application form and FAFSA.
Duration: Two years. Renewable for two years.
Deadline: May 1.

ADDRESS INQUIRIES TO:
Robbie Stabeno, Director of Scholarships
(See address above.)

DENNIS & PHYLLIS WASHINGTON FOUNDATION   [1398]
P.O. Box 16630
Missoula, MT 59808
(406) 523-1300
Fax: (406) 523-1399

WEB SITE ADDRESS:
www.dpwfoundation.org

FOUNDED: 1987

AREAS OF INTEREST:
Youth-focused programs in arts and culture, community service, health and human services and education.

TYPE:
Project/program grants; Scholarships. Scholarship monies awarded to Montana's nine colleges and universities and seven Indian reservations.

YEAR PROGRAM STARTED: 1987

PURPOSE:
To invest in people to improve the quality of their lives.

LEGAL BASIS:
Private foundation.

ELIGIBILITY:
Eligible organizations must be IRS 501(c)(3) tax-exempt. Low administrative costs.

FINANCIAL DATA:
Amount of support per award: Average grant: $7,400.

APPLICATION INFORMATION:
Grant applicants must complete the online application process which includes reading grant guidelines, completion of a short eligibility review and submission of a preliminary application form. If qualified, the organization will be invited to submit a full application online.

Scholarship applicants can review application guidelines on the Foundation's web site.

Duration: One year. Renewals are rare but possible upon reapplication.

ADDRESS INQUIRIES TO:
Mike Halligan, Executive Director
(See address above.)

WASHINGTON FORREST FOUNDATION   [1399]

2407 Columbia Pike, Suite 200
Arlington, VA 22204
(703) 920-3688
Fax: (703) 920-0130

E-MAIL ADDRESS:
allison@washingtonforrest.org

FOUNDED: 1968

AREAS OF INTEREST:
Health and human services, education, religion and the arts.

TYPE:
Capital grants; Challenge/matching grants; General operating grants; Matching gifts; Project/program grants; Scholarships; Seed money grants.

PURPOSE:
To improve and enhance the quality of life in Arlington and especially South Arlington, VA.

LEGAL BASIS:
Public foundation.

ELIGIBILITY:
Eligible organizations must be IRS 501(c)(3) tax-exempt and be located in northern Virginia.

GEOGRAPHIC RESTRICTIONS:
Arlington and northern Virginia.

FINANCIAL DATA:
Amount of support per award: $500 to $25,000.

APPLICATION INFORMATION:
Applicants should first call the Foundation to discuss the proposal. Applications must include a copy of the IRS tax determination letter.

Duration: One year. Renewal by reapplication.

Deadline: August 1, November 1, February 1 and May 1.

ADDRESS INQUIRIES TO:
Allison A. Erdle, Executive Director
(See address above.)

WEGE FOUNDATION   [1400]

P.O. Box 6388
Grand Rapids, MI 49516-6388
(616) 957-0480
Fax: (616) 957-0616

E-MAIL ADDRESS:
tmccarthy@wegefoundation.org

WEB SITE ADDRESS:
www.wegefoundation.org

FOUNDED: 1968

AREAS OF INTEREST:
Education, environment, health care, human services and the arts in west Michigan.

TYPE:
Capital grants; Endowments; General operating grants; Project/program grants.

YEAR PROGRAM STARTED: 1968

PURPOSE:
To assist programs and projects in the areas of education, environment, health care, arts and culture, and human services.

ELIGIBILITY:
Grants are made to tax-exempt, nonprofit organizations which meet the Foundation's current program priorities and are located in the west Michigan area.

GEOGRAPHIC RESTRICTIONS:
Grand Rapids and west Michigan.

FINANCIAL DATA:
Amount of support per award: $500 to $40,000.

Total amount of support: Approximately $10,000,000 annually.

NUMBER OF APPLICANTS MOST RECENT YEAR: 175.

NUMBER OF AWARDS: 55.

APPLICATION INFORMATION:
Applications must be submitted through the Foundation's web site.

Duration: One year. Renewal possible.

Deadline: Proposals are accepted twice per year for Spring and Fall grant review.

BOARD OF DIRECTORS:
Peter M. Wege, Chairman
Peter M. Wege, II, President
Ellen Satterlee, Treasurer and Chief Executive Officer
W. Michael Van Haren, Secretary
Mary Goodwillie Nelson, Trustee
Christopher Wege, Trustee
Diana Wege, Trustee
Jonathan Wege, Trustee

ADDRESS INQUIRIES TO:
Terri McCarthy
Vice President of Programs
(See address above.)

THOMAS H. WHITE FOUNDATION   [1401]

1422 Euclid Avenue, Suite 966
Cleveland, OH 44115-1952
(216) 696-7273
Fax: (216) 621-8198

E-MAIL ADDRESS:
salthans@fmscleveland.com

WEB SITE ADDRESS:
www.fmscleveland.com/thomaswhite

FOUNDED: 1913

AREAS OF INTEREST:
Early childhood education, middle school to high school education, high school to higher education, and human services.

TYPE:
Project/program grants. The Foundation will focus its grantmaking in two major areas:

Education and Human Services. Specifically, the Foundation is interested in supporting programs that address four critical areas:
(1) Workforce readiness: programs that emphasize science and technology education, adequate employment preparation, support systems and the relationship to earning potential;
(2) School retention: programs that emphasize the critical transition issues that occur during early teenage years and affect family relationships and school attendance;
(3) Early childhood enrichment: programs which enhance the learning environment; provide support, training and ancillary services to parents; and/or enhance the recruitment and training of day care providers and;
(4) Programs that support education in science, technology, engineering and math.

Organizations and programs that contribute generally to the quality of life in Greater Cleveland may also be considered at the Foundation's discretion.

YEAR PROGRAM STARTED: 1913

PURPOSE:
To improve educational resources and support charitable purposes in the city of Cleveland, OH.

LEGAL BASIS:
Private foundation.

ELIGIBILITY:
Grants awarded to tax-exempt, nonprofit charitable and educational institutions located within Cuyahoga County, OH, if such organizations, and their services and facilities, primarily serve residents of the city of Cleveland.

Applicants are discouraged from submitting requests for endowment, general operating support, research, symposia or seminars. No grants are awarded to individuals. The Foundation does not respond to general solicitations or annual fund-raising campaigns.

GEOGRAPHIC RESTRICTIONS:
Cuyahoga County, Ohio; primarily the city of Cleveland.

FINANCIAL DATA:
Amount of support per award: $1,000 to $100,000.

Total amount of support: $1,082,548 in grants approved for the year 2013.

Matching fund requirements: Stipulated with individual programs.

NUMBER OF APPLICANTS MOST RECENT YEAR: 125 for the year 2012.

NUMBER OF AWARDS: 87.

REPRESENTATIVE AWARDS:
$5,000 to Cleveland Music School Settlement for the planning and development of an early childhood education classroom; $17,500 to Scranton Road Ministries Community Development Corporation for the Youth Jobs Partnership Program; $75,000 to Cleveland Metropolitan School District for upgrades to the fabrication laboratories at the MC2 STEM High School; $10,000 to Burten, Bell, Carr Development, Inc. for the Bridgeport Market and Community Kitchen.

APPLICATION INFORMATION:
Applications will only be accepted online and must contain the following:
(1) a brief history of the organization;
(2) explanation of request;

(3) evaluation plan and future funding plan;
(4) its total budget, other funding sources and its importance to the people of Cleveland;
(5) the amount requested;
(6) the organization's tax-exempt status;
(7) a list of the organization's trustees and;
(8) the proposal, plus one copy.

Foundation staff is available to assist applicants and/or to further clarify the Foundation's grantmaking policies and procedures.

Duration: Most grants are made for one year only. Two- to three-year grants are made occasionally.

Deadline: December 1, April 1 and August 1, respectively, for meetings which are held in February, May and September. Announcement is made within three weeks of meeting.

ADDRESS INQUIRIES TO:
Susan Althans, Consultant
(See address above.)

*SPECIAL STIPULATIONS:
Local giving only.

WICHITA COMMUNITY FOUNDATION   [1402]

301 North Main Street
Suite 100
Wichita, KS 67202
(316) 264-4880
Fax: (316) 264-7592

E-MAIL ADDRESS:
wcf@wichitacf.org

WEB SITE ADDRESS:
www.wichitacf.org

FOUNDED: 1986

AREAS OF INTEREST:
Arts, conservation, education, environmental health, humanities and social services.

TYPE:
Project/program grants; Scholarships; Seed money grants.

PURPOSE:
To provide a permanent resource for building community philanthropy.

LEGAL BASIS:
Community foundation.

ELIGIBILITY:
Grants are made to organizations that have tax-exempt status under Section 501(c)(3) of the Internal Revenue Code. No grants are made to individuals.

GEOGRAPHIC RESTRICTIONS:
Sedgwick County, Kansas.

FINANCIAL DATA:
Amount of support per award: $10,000 to $100,000.
Total amount of support: Approximately $3,600,000 for the year 2012.

APPLICATION INFORMATION:
Grant application information is available on the web site. High school students may apply for scholarships online.

Duration: Typically one year.

Deadline: Applications accepted throughout the year.

ADDRESS INQUIRIES TO:
Carol Nazar, Grants Administrator
(See address above.)

HARVEY RANDALL WICKES FOUNDATION   [1403]

4800 Fashion Square Boulevard
Suite 472
Saginaw, MI 48604
(989) 799-1850
Fax: (989) 799-3327

E-MAIL ADDRESS:
hrwickes@att.net

FOUNDED: 1945

AREAS OF INTEREST:
Arts, health, education, recreation, civic improvement and human services.

TYPE:
Matching gifts; Project/program grants.

YEAR PROGRAM STARTED: 1945

PURPOSE:
To improve the quality of life in Saginaw County.

ELIGIBILITY:
Eligible organizations must be IRS 501(c)(3) tax-exempt.

GEOGRAPHIC RESTRICTIONS:
Saginaw County, Michigan.

FINANCIAL DATA:
Amount of support per award: $10,000 average grant.
Total amount of support: $1,779,264 for the year 2013.

NUMBER OF AWARDS: 59 for the year 2013.

APPLICATION INFORMATION:
Applicants may send a written proposal and must include a copy of the IRS tax determination letter.

Duration: One year. Renewal possible by reapplication.

Deadline: Two weeks prior to board meetings, which are held on the second Tuesday in March, June and September and the first Tuesday in December.

PUBLICATIONS:
Annual report; grant guidelines.

IRS IDENTIFICATION NUMBER: 38-6061470

ADDRESS INQUIRIES TO:
Hugo E. Braun, Jr., President
(See address above.)

*SPECIAL STIPULATIONS:
No grants to individuals.

THE WINSTON-SALEM FOUNDATION   [1404]

860 West 5th Street
Winston-Salem, NC 27101
(336) 725-2382
Fax: (336) 727-0581

E-MAIL ADDRESS:
info@wsfoundation.org

WEB SITE ADDRESS:
www.wsfoundation.org

FOUNDED: 1919

AREAS OF INTEREST:
Human services, education, arts, culture, health, environment, animal welfare, community and economic development, public interest, and recreation.

NAME(S) OF PROGRAMS:
• **Black Philanthropy Grants**
• **Community Grants**
• **Elkin/Tri-County Grants**
• **Stokes County Grants**
• **Student Aid Grants, Scholarship, and Loans**
• **Teacher Grants**
• **Victim Assistance Grants**
• **Women's Fund Grants**
• **Youth Philanthropy Grants**

TYPE:
Capital grants; Challenge/matching grants; Development grants; Endowments; Project/program grants; Scholarships; Seed money grants; Training grants. Discretionary grants given to organizations providing benefit to citizens within the greater Forsyth County, NC area, subject to limitations on program areas expressed by the donor of the source fund. Student aid primarily for Forsyth County residents.

YEAR PROGRAM STARTED: 1919

PURPOSE:
To help agencies initiate, innovate and experiment, as well as to provide other types of support as appropriate.

LEGAL BASIS:
Community foundation.

ELIGIBILITY:
Applicants must be charitable organizations and publicly supported charities. No grants are made to individuals.

GEOGRAPHIC RESTRICTIONS:
Forsyth County, North Carolina and contiguous counties.

FINANCIAL DATA:
Amount of support per award: $500 to $200,000; average $25,000.
Total amount of support: $20,200,000 for the year 2012.

NUMBER OF APPLICANTS MOST RECENT YEAR: 173.

NUMBER OF AWARDS: 100.

APPLICATION INFORMATION:
Application information is available on the web site.

Duration: Generally, grants are for one year.

Deadline: Preliminary applications accepted on the first of each month.

PUBLICATIONS:
Annual report; guidelines for donors and grantseekers; newsletters.

IRS IDENTIFICATION NUMBER: 56-6037615

STAFF:
Scott F. Wierman, President
Lisa Purcell, Executive Vice President

ADDRESS INQUIRIES TO:
Robin DeVane, Grants Manager
(See address above.)

WOODS CHARITABLE FUND, INC.   [1405]

1248 O Street, Suite 1130
Lincoln, NE 68508
(402) 436-5971

E-MAIL ADDRESS:
twoods@woodscharitable.org

WEB SITE ADDRESS:
www.woodscharitable.org

FOUNDED: 1941

AREAS OF INTEREST:
Children, youth and families, education, community development and housing, arts and humanities.

TYPE:
Challenge/matching grants; Demonstration grants; General operating grants; Project/program grants; Seed money grants; Technical assistance. Grants to support organizations and projects located in and directly serving the residents of Lincoln, NE.

YEAR PROGRAM STARTED: 1941

PURPOSE:
To strengthen the community by improving opportunities and life outcomes for all people in Lincoln, NE.

LEGAL BASIS:
Private foundation.

ELIGIBILITY:
Grants are made only to tax-exempt organizations described in Section 501(c)(3) of the IRS Code and which have a written ruling from the IRS that they also qualify under 509(a)(1), (2) or (3) of the Code (publicly supported organizations and their affiliates).

Geographically, grants are limited to organizations in Lincoln. Occasionally, the Fund reviews proposals from outside the city if the proposed activities have statewide impact and a significant Lincoln component. While the Fund makes grants in very diverse fields, fund-raising benefits or program advertising, individual needs, endowments, scholarships or fellowships are not eligible for grant review.

GEOGRAPHIC RESTRICTIONS:
Lincoln, Nebraska.

FINANCIAL DATA:
Amount of support per award: Average payment: $22,324 for the year 2013.
Total amount of support: $1,205,500 grants paid for the year 2013.

NUMBER OF APPLICANTS MOST RECENT YEAR:
175 for the year 2013.

NUMBER OF AWARDS: 52 for the year 2013.

REPRESENTATIVE AWARDS:
$30,000 to Lincoln Public Schools for a family literacy program integrating literacy training for parents with their children's education; $75,000 to University of Nebraska-Lincoln Department of Community and Regional Planning for a collaborative project with NeighborWorks Lincoln and City Government departments to involve city neighborhoods in neighborhoodwide assessment to help set goals for neighborhood improvement; $50,000 to Family Violence Council for coordinated community response to handling child abuse investigations with co-occurring adult sexual assault, partnering with area agencies that work with victims and perpetrators of child abuse and domestic violence.

APPLICATION INFORMATION:
Guidelines are available on request. Before submitting a full proposal, applicants should contact the Fund with a two-page summary request and budget or a phone call. If the request appears suitable, a full proposal will be requested.
Deadline: March 1 to 15 for June Board Meeting. July 1 to 15 for November Board Meeting. November 1 to 15 for March Board Meeting. Proposals that arrive well before the deadline have a better chance for careful review.

PUBLICATIONS:
Grant payments for the year; 990 PF; Financial Review.

IRS IDENTIFICATION NUMBER: 47-6032847

STAFF:
Tom Woods, President and Secretary
Kathy Steinauer Smith, Community Investment Director
Angie Zmarzly, Community Investment Director
Joan Stolle, Operations Manager

DIRECTORS:
Donna W. Woods, Chairperson
Kathleen Rutledge, Vice Chairperson
Hank Woods, Treasurer
Michael J. Tavlin, Assistant Treasurer
Ernesto Castillo
Carl Eskridge
Nelle Jamison
Orville Jones

ADDRESS INQUIRIES TO:
Tom Woods, President
(See address above.)

WOODS FUND OF CHICAGO [1406]
35 East Wacker Drive
Suite 1760
Chicago, IL 60601
(312) 782-2698
Fax: (312) 782-4155

E-MAIL ADDRESS:
application@woodsfund.org

WEB SITE ADDRESS:
www.woodsfund.org

FOUNDED: 1941

AREAS OF INTEREST:
Arts and social justice, community organizing, intersection of community organizing and public policy, and public policy.

TYPE:
General operating grants; Project/program grants; Training grants. Small training grants. (Contact program officer prior to applying for grant.)

PURPOSE:
To increase opportunities for less advantaged people and communities in the metropolitan area, including the opportunity to contribute to decisions affecting them.

LEGAL BASIS:
Nonprofit.

ELIGIBILITY:
Grants are made to cultural organizations that have tax-exempt status under Section 501(c)(3) of the Internal Revenue Code. No grants are made to individuals.

GEOGRAPHIC RESTRICTIONS:
Metropolitan Chicago, Illinois.

FINANCIAL DATA:
Amount of support per award: $10,000 to $35,000.
Total amount of support: $2,281,550 for 2012.

APPLICATION INFORMATION:
The Woods Fund requires that prospective grantees first submit a completed Inquiry Form. If the Fund responds positively, applicants will be asked to submit a full application. Form and application instructions are available at the Fund web site.
Duration: One to three years.
Deadline: For March grants, letter of inquiry should be received by December 7. For September grants, letter of inquiry should be received by the last business day in May.

ADDRESS INQUIRIES TO:
Grant Processing
(See e-mail address above.)

WILLIAM C. WOOLF FOUNDATION [1407]
333 Texas Street, LASH30202T
Shreveport, LA 71101
(318) 429-1705
Fax: (318) 429-1021

FOUNDED: 1959

AREAS OF INTEREST:
Northwestern Louisiana.

TYPE:
Grants-in-aid.

PURPOSE:
To better the lives of citizens in Shreveport, LA.

ELIGIBILITY:
Eligible organizations must be IRS 501(c)(3) tax-exempt and be located in northwestern Louisiana.

GEOGRAPHIC RESTRICTIONS:
Northwestern Louisiana.

FINANCIAL DATA:
Amount of support per award: $150 to $50,000.

APPLICATION INFORMATION:
Applicants may send a written proposal and must include a copy of the IRS tax determination letter.
Duration: One year. Renewals by reapplication.
Deadline: February 1. Determination at board meeting end of February.

ADDRESS INQUIRIES TO:
Barbara R. York, Secretary
(See address above.)

WYOMING ARTS COUNCIL
2320 Capitol Avenue
Cheyenne, WY 82002
(307) 777-7742
Fax: (307) 777-5499

WEB SITE ADDRESS:
wyoarts.state.wy.us

TYPE:
General operating grants; Project/program grants. Individual Artist Professional Development Grants, Literary Arts Fellowships, Performing Arts Fellowships and Visual Arts Fellowships are for individual artists. General operating support grants and project/program grants are for 501(c)(3) nonprofit and government organizations.

See entry 523 for full listing.

Crime prevention

INTERNATIONAL CENTRE FOR COMPARATIVE CRIMINOLOGY [1408]
University of Montreal
C.P. 6128, Succursale Centre-Ville
Montreal QC H3C 3J7 Canada
(514) 343-7065
Fax: (514) 343-2269

E-MAIL ADDRESS:
cicc@umontreal.ca

WEB SITE ADDRESS:
www.cicc.umontreal.ca

FOUNDED: 1969

AREAS OF INTEREST:
Sociology of crime and deviance, comparative studies on criminal justice, police, courts, prisons, victims, national and international research, terrorism and counterterrorism.

CONSULTING OR VOLUNTEER SERVICES:
In all the fields of criminal justice.

NAME(S) OF PROGRAMS:
• **Research Fieldwork**

TYPE:
Conferences/seminars; Exchange programs; Fellowships. Postdoctoral scholarship. The Centre brings visiting professors and specialists to confer on projects and cooperate on research investigation and invites graduate and postgraduate students to do fieldwork at the Centre.

YEAR PROGRAM STARTED: 1969

PURPOSE:
To provide funding to encourage continued study in the field of crime and criminal justice.

LEGAL BASIS:
University.

ELIGIBILITY:
Applicants must have a Ph.D. from any country.

FINANCIAL DATA:
Amount of support per award: Postdoctoral scholarships: $35,000 (CAN) per year. Fixed sum for living expenses.

NUMBER OF APPLICANTS MOST RECENT YEAR:
6.

NUMBER OF AWARDS: Postdoctoral scholarships: 1 or 2 per year.

APPLICATION INFORMATION:
Submit research project, curriculum vitae, three letters from researchers who know the candidate and an abstract of the Ph.D. thesis.
Duration: One year.
Deadline: June 30.

PUBLICATIONS:
Annual report; Revue *Criminologie*.

OFFICERS:
Benoit Dupont, Director

ADDRESS INQUIRIES TO:
See e-mail address above.

NATIONAL INSTITUTE OF JUSTICE, U.S. DEPARTMENT OF JUSTICE [1409]
810 Seventh Street, N.W.
Washington, DC 20531
(202) 307-2942

WEB SITE ADDRESS:
www.nij.gov

FOUNDED: 1968

AREAS OF INTEREST:
Criminal justice research and evaluation, program development, dissemination of research-based criminal justice, and fellowships.

NAME(S) OF PROGRAMS:
• **Research Grants**

TYPE:
Research grants. Grants and contracts related to topics in criminal justice and social science, physical science, and forensic science, including those for evaluative research; research and development grants and contracts in science and technology for criminal justice applications.

The focus of NIJ research is on generating information that is useful to state and local public officials in developing policies related to crime reduction.

YEAR PROGRAM STARTED: 1968

PURPOSE:
To increase knowledge of the causes, prevention, and control of crime, the effectiveness and efficiency of the criminal justice system, and the responsiveness of the nation's law enforcement and justice administration systems; to disseminate this knowledge to the federal, state, and local policymakers.

LEGAL BASIS:
Omnibus Crime Control and Safe Streets Act of 1968; Homeland Security Act of 2002.

ELIGIBILITY:
NIJ awards grants to or enters into cooperative agreements with educational institutions, nonprofit organizations, public agencies, individuals, and profit-making organizations that are willing to waive their fees. Special eligibility criteria are indicated in NIJ's solicitations for proposals.

GEOGRAPHIC RESTRICTIONS:
United States.

FINANCIAL DATA:
All NIJ awards must be used to supplement existing funds, not to replace those already appropriated for the same purpose.
Amount of support per award: $10,000 to more than $1,000,000.
Total amount of support: Varies.
Matching fund requirements: Units of state and local governments are encouraged to contribute matching funds and other applicants are encouraged to seek matching contributions from government agencies or private organizations.

REPRESENTATIVE AWARDS:
Kenneth R. Freeman, Judge, Municipal Court Bench for Los Angeles, "A Study to Find More Effective Ways to Investigate and Prosecute Child Sexual Abuse Cases;" Lt. John Buchanan, II, Phoenix Police Department, "Assessing the Current Status of Police-Prosecutor Team Efforts;" Dr. Wesley G. Skogan, Professor, Northwestern University, "Crime and the Survival of Small Business."

APPLICATION INFORMATION:
Guidelines, applications, and information about specific solicitations for proposals are available on the web site.
Duration: Normally two years maximum. Renewal possible.
Deadline: Varies.

ADDRESS INQUIRIES TO:
National Criminal Justice Reference Service
P.O. Box 6000
Rockville, MD 20849-6000
Tel: (800) 851-3420

GARDINER HOWLAND SHAW FOUNDATION [1410]
355 Boylston Street
Boston, MA 02116
(617) 247-3500
Fax: (617) 247-3505

E-MAIL ADDRESS:
admin@shawfoundation.org

WEB SITE ADDRESS:
shawfoundation.org

FOUNDED: 1959

AREAS OF INTEREST:
Criminal justice, the study, prevention, correction and alleviation of crime and delinquency and the rehabilitation of juvenile and adult offenders.

CONSULTING OR VOLUNTEER SERVICES:
Technical assistance to grantees and other human service agencies on request.

NAME(S) OF PROGRAMS:
• **Grantee Workshops**
• **Shaw Foundation Grants**

TYPE:
Conferences/seminars; Demonstration grants; Development grants; General operating grants; Seed money grants; Technical assistance. Priorities for funding include programs which can effectively divert court-involved youth and juvenile offenders from escalating involvement in the criminal justice system, programs which promote the use and acceptance of alternatives to incarceration and intermediate criminal sanctions, innovative and effective approaches to rehabilitation for detained and incarcerated juvenile and adult offenders, methods which improve the administration of justice and the quality of services for individuals appearing before the criminal court, and initiatives which can impact current public policy in the field of criminal justice through education, training and effective advocacy. Added weight will be given to proposals which clearly demonstrate the ability to utilize Shaw Foundation support to attract new public and private resources to the field of criminal justice.

YEAR PROGRAM STARTED: 1959

PURPOSE:
To aid the study, prevention, correction and alleviation of crime and delinquency and the rehabilitation of adult and juvenile offenders.

LEGAL BASIS:
Private foundation.

ELIGIBILITY:
Applicant must have tax-exempt public charitable status from the IRS and must operate within Massachusetts. The Foundation does not support capital requests, the arts, endowments, grants to individuals or scholarships.

GEOGRAPHIC RESTRICTIONS:
Massachusetts.

FINANCIAL DATA:
Amount of support per award: Average $15,000 to $20,000.
Total amount of support: $629,200 for fiscal year ended April 30, 2013.

COOPERATIVE FUNDING PROGRAMS: The Shaw Foundation does, from time to time, work with other sources for the purpose of cooperative fundings.

NUMBER OF APPLICANTS MOST RECENT YEAR:
51.

REPRESENTATIVE AWARDS:
$30,000 to Criminal Justice Policy Coalition for public education; $10,000 to Advocacy City Mission Society for prison services program; $20,000 to Span Inc., service for ex-offenders in transition from prison to the community.

APPLICATION INFORMATION:
Potential applicants are encouraged to telephone the Foundation to discuss their ideas prior to submitting a proposal. All new applicants should also submit a concept paper describing their organization and the purposes for which funds are being sought, along with a budget and evidence of tax-exempt status. The applicant will be informed if the work being proposed fits with the current interests of the Foundation.
Duration: Typically, the Foundation will provide support up to three years, with renewal dependent upon grantee performance and program need.
Deadline: February 1. Decision by May.

PUBLICATIONS:
Annual report; guidelines.

TRUSTEES:
Peter P. Brown
Theodore E. Ober
Benjamin Williams, Jr.

ADDRESS INQUIRIES TO:
Thomas E. Coury, Executive Director
(See address above.)

U.S. DEPARTMENT OF JUSTICE [1411]
Bureau of Justice Statistics
810 7th Street, N.W.
Washington, DC 20531
(202) 307-0765
Fax: (202) 616-1351

E-MAIL ADDRESS:
devon.adams@usdoj.gov

WEB SITE ADDRESS:
bjs.ojp.usdoj.gov

FOUNDED: 1969

AREAS OF INTEREST:
Statistics on crime, victims of crime, criminal offenders and operations of justice systems at all levels of government throughout the U.S.

NAME(S) OF PROGRAMS:
● **State Justice Statistics for Statistical Analysis Centers**

TYPE:
Development grants; Research grants. Cooperative agreements for the development of statistical methods and techniques and the aggregation and analysis of statistical information on crime and criminal justice in the states.

YEAR PROGRAM STARTED: 1972

PURPOSE:
To develop and enhance the capabilities of the states in gathering, analyzing and using statistical information pertaining to crime and the criminal justice system and to obtain selected types of data for multistate aggregation.

LEGAL BASIS:
Government agency formed under the Justice System Improvement Act of 1979.

ELIGIBILITY:
Applicants must be state agencies whose activities include statistical analysis at the state level.

FINANCIAL DATA:
Amount of support per award: Usually $60,000.
Total amount of support: Varies.

NUMBER OF APPLICANTS MOST RECENT YEAR: 75.

APPLICATION INFORMATION:
Contact the U.S. Department of Justice.
Duration: 12 months.
Deadline: Varies.

ADDRESS INQUIRIES TO:
Devon Adams, Chief of Criminal History Improvement Program Section
(See address above.)

U.S. DEPARTMENT OF JUSTICE [1412]
Office of Juvenile Justice and Delinquency Prevention
810 7th Street, N.W., 5th Floor
Washington, DC 20531
(202) 307-5911
Fax: (202) 307-2093

WEB SITE ADDRESS:
www.ojjdp.ncjrs.gov

FOUNDED: 1975

AREAS OF INTEREST:
Delinquency prevention research, juvenile gangs, serious violent juvenile offenders and juvenile justice statistics.

NAME(S) OF PROGRAMS:
● **Juvenile Justice and Delinquency Prevention Program**

TYPE:
Conferences/seminars; Development grants; Fellowships; Internships; Project/program grants; Research grants; Residencies; Visiting scholars; Research contracts. Grants to conduct research, evaluation and development on juvenile justice and delinquency prevention activities, including the development of new or improved approaches, techniques, systems and program models to conduct behavioral research on the causes of juvenile crime, means of, intervention and prevention, and to evaluate juvenile programs and procedures.

YEAR PROGRAM STARTED: 1975

PURPOSE:
To encourage, coordinate and conduct research and evaluation of juvenile justice and delinquency prevention activities; to provide a clearinghouse and information center for collecting, publishing and distributing information on juvenile delinquency; to conduct a national training program; to establish standards for the administration on juvenile justice. Current emphasis is work in the area of serious and violent juvenile crime, drug involvement by youth and missing children.

LEGAL BASIS:
Juvenile Justice and Delinquency Prevention Act of 1974, Public Law 93-415, 42 U.S.C. 5601, as amended.

ELIGIBILITY:
Public or private agencies, organizations, including institutions of higher learning, or individuals.

GEOGRAPHIC RESTRICTIONS:
United States and its territories.

FINANCIAL DATA:
Amount of support per award: Varies.

Total amount of support: Varies.

NUMBER OF APPLICANTS MOST RECENT YEAR: 100.

NUMBER OF AWARDS: 80.

REPRESENTATIVE AWARDS:
Law Enforcement Agencies Policies Regarding Missing Children; School Crime and Discipline Research and Discipline; Causes and Correlates of Delinquency.

APPLICATION INFORMATION:
Contact the U.S. Department of Justice.
Duration: Generally one to three years.
Deadline: Varies.

PUBLICATIONS:
Annual report; annual program plan; various project reports.

ADDRESS INQUIRIES TO:
Juvenile Justice Clearinghouse
National Criminal Justice
Reference Service
P.O. Box 6000
Rockville, MD 20849-6000
Tel: (800) 851-3420
Fax: (301) 519-5600

U.S. DEPARTMENT OF JUSTICE [1413]
Office of Juvenile Justice and Delinquency Prevention
810 Seventh Street, N.W., 5th Floor
Washington, DC 20531
(202) 307-5911
Fax: (202) 307-2093

WEB SITE ADDRESS:
www.ojjdp.ncjrs.gov/

AREAS OF INTEREST:
Juvenile justice, delinquency prevention and child protection.

NAME(S) OF PROGRAMS:
● **Juvenile Justice and Delinquency Prevention Allocation to States**

TYPE:
Block grants; Challenge/matching grants; Demonstration grants; Formula grants; Internships; Project/program grants; Research grants; Technical assistance; Training grants. Grants to increase the capacity of state and local governments to conduct effective juvenile justice and delinquency prevention programs as developed in the state comprehensive action plan.

YEAR PROGRAM STARTED: 1974

LEGAL BASIS:
Juvenile Justice and Delinquency Prevention Act of 1974, Public Law 93-415, 42 U.S.C. 5601 as amended (JJDP Act).

ELIGIBILITY:
All states as defined by Section 103(7) of the JJDP Act and meeting the requirements of Section 223 of the Act.

GEOGRAPHIC RESTRICTIONS:
United States and its territories.

FINANCIAL DATA:
Amount of support per award: Varies.
Total amount of support: Varies.
Matching fund requirements: Formula is based upon population of people under age 18. No match is required except for construction programs, where the match is 50%. Seven and one half percent administrative funds are matched 100%.

NUMBER OF APPLICANTS MOST RECENT YEAR:
60.

NUMBER OF AWARDS: 60.

APPLICATION INFORMATION:
Contact the U.S. Department of Justice.
Duration: One to three years from the fiscal
year of awards.
Deadline: Varies.

ADDRESS INQUIRIES TO:
Juvenile Justice Clearinghouse
National Criminal Justice
Reference Service
P.O. Box 6000
Rockville, MD 20849-6000
Tel: (800) 851-3420
Fax: (301) 519-5600

U.S. DEPARTMENT OF
JUSTICE   [1414]
Office of Juvenile Justice and
Delinquency Prevention
810 Seventh Street, N.W.
Washington, DC 20531
(202) 307-5911
(202) 514-5655
Fax: (202) 307-2819

WEB SITE ADDRESS:
www.ojjdp.gov

FOUNDED: 1974

AREAS OF INTEREST:
Juvenile justice, delinquency prevention and
child protection.

NAME(S) OF PROGRAMS:
● **Enforcing the Underage Drinking Laws
Program**

TYPE:
Block grants; Demonstration grants.

YEAR PROGRAM STARTED: 1998

PURPOSE:
To support state and local efforts to prevent
juvenile delinquency, to improve the juvenile
system response to delinquency, and to
protect children from victimization.

LEGAL BASIS:
Government grant program.

ELIGIBILITY:
Applicants are limited to states (including
territories) units of local government as
determined by the Secretary of the Interior,
nonprofit and for-profit organizations and
institutions of higher education.

GEOGRAPHIC RESTRICTIONS:
United States and its territories.

FINANCIAL DATA:
Amount of support per award: $100,000 to
$500,000.

APPLICATION INFORMATION:
Applicants must register at Grants.gov prior
to submitting an application.
Deadline: June.

Public health

AAA FOUNDATION FOR
TRAFFIC SAFETY   [1415]
607 14th Street, N.W.
Suite 201
Washington, DC 20005
(202) 638-5944 ext. 7
Fax: (202) 638-5943

E-MAIL ADDRESS:
jgrabowski@aaafoundation.org

WEB SITE ADDRESS:
www.aaafoundation.org

FOUNDED: 1947

AREAS OF INTEREST:
Traffic safety.

TYPE:
Demonstration grants; Project/program
grants; Research grants; Research contracts.

YEAR PROGRAM STARTED: 1947

PURPOSE:
To save lives and reduce injuries by
preventing traffic crashes; to reduce injuries
when crashes do occur.

LEGAL BASIS:
Publicly supported not-for-profit 501(c)(3).

ELIGIBILITY:
Foundation grants to organizations only.

The Foundation does not fund research to
develop new devices, grants for community
action initiatives or other purely local traffic
safety programs, or projects outside the field
of traffic safety.

GEOGRAPHIC RESTRICTIONS:
Primarily United States and Canada.

FINANCIAL DATA:
Amount of support per award: $5,000 to
$1,000,000.

Total amount of support: Approximately
$5,000,000.

Matching fund requirements: Encourage
co-funding, but not required.

NUMBER OF APPLICANTS MOST RECENT YEAR:
100.

NUMBER OF AWARDS: 12.

APPLICATION INFORMATION:
Contact the Foundation for application
procedures.
Duration: Six months to five years.
Deadline: August 15.

PUBLICATIONS:
Annual report.

IRS IDENTIFICATION NUMBER: 52-0794368

ADDRESS INQUIRIES TO:
Jurek Grabowski, Director of Research
(See address above.)

ABMRF/THE FOUNDATION FOR
ALCOHOL RESEARCH   [1416]
1122 Kenilworth Drive
Suite 407
Baltimore, MD 21204-2189
(410) 821-7066
Fax: (410) 821-7065

E-MAIL ADDRESS:
grantinfo@abmrf.org

WEB SITE ADDRESS:
www.abmrf.org

FOUNDED: 1982

AREAS OF INTEREST:
Medical research on the effects of alcohol on
health and behavior.

TYPE:
Project/program grants; Research grants;
Seed money grants. Major research interests
include factors influencing transitions in
drinking patterns and behavior, the effects of
moderate use of alcohol on health and

well-being, mechanisms underlying the
behavioral and biomedical effects of alcohol
and biobehavioral/interdisciplinary research
on the etiology of alcohol misuse.

YEAR PROGRAM STARTED: 1982

PURPOSE:
To provide support for scientific studies on
the use, and prevention of misuse, of alcohol.

LEGAL BASIS:
Private foundation.

ELIGIBILITY:
Applicants must be U.S., Canadian or South
African institutions. Nonresearch activities
such as education projects, public awareness
efforts and treatment or referral services are
not eligible for support.

GEOGRAPHIC RESTRICTIONS:
United States, Canada and South Africa.

FINANCIAL DATA:
Approximately $2,000,000 (U.S.) is available
each year to fund newly approved
applications and continuation of previously
funded projects. Funds may be requested in
U.S. or Canadian currency for a period of up
to two years. Funding of the second year
depends on the availability of funds and
satisfactory research progress during the first
year.

Amount of support per award: Up to $50,000
(U.S.) per year.

NUMBER OF APPLICANTS MOST RECENT YEAR:
142.

NUMBER OF AWARDS: 23 new projects funded.

REPRESENTATIVE AWARDS:
$50,000 (for the second of two years) to M.
Scott Bowers, Ph.D., Virginia
Commonwealth University, "Role of rat
nucleus accumbens astrocytes in alcoholism;"
$50,000 (for the second of two years) to
Dingcai Cao, Ph.D., The University of
Chicago, "Alcohol effects on visual
processing in at-risk social-drinkers;"
$50,000 (for the second of two years) to Tara
Chaplin, Ph.D., Yale University, "Responses
during parent-child interactions and
alcohol-use behaviors in adolescents;"
$50,000 (for the second of two years) to
Cedrick D. Dotson, Ph.D., University of
Florida College of Medicine, "Hormonal
signaling by GLP-1 glucagon and leptin
modulates the taste of alcohol."

APPLICATION INFORMATION:
Application is available on the Foundation
web site.

Duration: One year. Two years if justified.

Deadline: February 15.

PUBLICATIONS:
Annual report; application guidelines.

IRS IDENTIFICATION NUMBER: 52-1234277

OFFICERS:
Mack C. Mitchell, Jr., M.D., President

ADDRESS INQUIRIES TO:
Grants Program Administrator
(See address above.)

AGENCY FOR HEALTHCARE RESEARCH AND QUALITY (AHRQ) [1417]

Office of Communications
and Knowledge Transfer
540 Gaither Road, 2nd Floor
Rockville, MD 20850
(301) 427-1104 (specify funding area)
(800) 518-4726

E-MAIL ADDRESS:
support@grants.gov

WEB SITE ADDRESS:
www.ahrq.gov

FOUNDED: 1968

AREAS OF INTEREST:
AHRQ is the primary source of federal support for research on problems related to the quality and delivery of health services.

NAME(S) OF PROGRAMS:
● **AHRQ Research Grants**

TYPE:
Conferences/seminars; Development grants; Fellowships; Project/program grants; Research grants; Training grants. Dissertation support highlighting primary care, market forces, cost containment, managed care, the cost of treating AIDS, the improvement of treatment for persons with HIV, rural health care, infant mortality, medical liability, malpractice reform, health care of the aged and disabled and policy studies.

YEAR PROGRAM STARTED: 1969

PURPOSE:
To develop knowledge concerning cost, quality, effectiveness, access and distribution of health services.

LEGAL BASIS:
AHCPR Research Grants: Section 304, 5, 7, 8, of the Public Health Service Act.

ELIGIBILITY:
Any academic institution, agency of a state or local government, nonprofit organization or individual is eligible to submit grant proposals under this program. For-profit entities are not eligible.

FINANCIAL DATA:
Amount of support per award: Varies according to the project type and nature of the individual research proposal.
Total amount of support: Varies.

APPLICATION INFORMATION:
Contact the Agency.
Duration: One to five years.
Deadline: Varies.

STAFF:
Kishna Wadhwani, Scientific Review Division

ADDRESS INQUIRIES TO:
Office of Communications
and Knowledge Transfer
(See address above.)

THE AMERICAN FOUNDATION FOR SUICIDE PREVENTION

120 Wall Street
29th Floor
New York, NY 10005
(212) 363-3500 ext. 2015
Fax: (212) 363-6237

E-MAIL ADDRESS:
grantsmanager@afsp.org

WEB SITE ADDRESS:
www.afsp.org

TYPE:
Research grants.

See entry 1515 for full listing.

THE AMERICAN FOUNDATION FOR SUICIDE PREVENTION

120 Wall Street
29th Floor
New York, NY 10005
(212) 363-3500 ext. 2015
Fax: (212) 363-6237

E-MAIL ADDRESS:
grantsmanager@afsp.org

WEB SITE ADDRESS:
www.afsp.org

TYPE:
Fellowships; Research grants.

See entry 1516 for full listing.

THE AMERICAN FOUNDATION FOR SUICIDE PREVENTION

120 Wall Street
29th Floor
New York, NY 10005
(212) 363-3500 ext. 2015
Fax: (212) 363-6237

E-MAIL ADDRESS:
grantsmanager@afsp.org

WEB SITE ADDRESS:
www.afsp.org

TYPE:
Research grants.

See entry 1517 for full listing.

THE AMERICAN FOUNDATION FOR SUICIDE PREVENTION

120 Wall Street
29th Floor
New York, NY 10005
(212) 363-3500 ext. 2015
Fax: (212) 363-6237

E-MAIL ADDRESS:
grantsmanager@afsp.org

WEB SITE ADDRESS:
www.afsp.org

TYPE:
Research grants. Standard Research Grants are awarded to individual investigators. An additional annual stipend is available for mentors on Young Investigator Awards in which the investigator is at the level of Assistant Professor or lower.

See entry 1518 for full listing.

AMERICAN MEDICAL WOMEN'S ASSOCIATION, INC.

12100 Sunset Hills Road
Suite 130
Reston, VA 20190
(703) 234-4069
Fax: (703) 435-4390

E-MAIL ADDRESS:
associatedirector@amwa-doc.org

WEB SITE ADDRESS:
www.amwa-doc.org

TYPE:
Awards/prizes; Conferences/seminars; General operating grants; Project/program grants; Training grants; Travel grants. Support for clinics serving the poor in medically underserved areas, scholarships and loans to qualifying women medical students, and continuing medical education for physicians in areas related to women's health.

See entry 2231 for full listing.

AMERICAN PSYCHOLOGICAL ASSOCIATION

Government Relations Office
Public Interest Directorate
750 First Street, N.E.
Washington, DC 20002-4242
(202) 336-5935
Fax: (202) 336-6063

E-MAIL ADDRESS:
mhaskell-hoehl@apa.org

WEB SITE ADDRESS:
www.apa.org/about/gr/fellows

TYPE:
Fellowships. Program provides trained scientists and practitioners an opportunity for enhanced understanding of and involvement in the federal policymaking process by serving as congressional staff in Washington, DC.

See entry 2566 for full listing.

AMERICAN SOCIETY FOR HEALTHCARE RISK MANAGEMENT [1418]

155 North Wacker Drive
Suite 400
Chicago, IL 60606
(312) 422-3980
Fax: (312) 422-4580

E-MAIL ADDRESS:
khoarle@aha.org

WEB SITE ADDRESS:
www.ashrm.org

FOUNDED: 2004

AREAS OF INTEREST:
Health care risk management.

TYPE:
Awards/prizes; Conferences/seminars; Development grants; Fellowships; Project/program grants; Research grants; Scholarships; Training grants. Education grants.

YEAR PROGRAM STARTED: 2004

PURPOSE:
To help facilitate the advancement of the health care risk management profession by funding education, research and scholarship programs; to promote professional development of hospital risk managers; to provide educational resources and programs on health care risk management; to address risk management issues affecting the health care industry; to foster research and innovation among professionals and graduate students; to identify and reward exemplary writing in the *Journal of Healthcare Risk Management* and encourage other members to write in it.

ELIGIBILITY:
Open to individual professionals in risk management or a related field, as well as

graduate students in health care risk management, health law, or health administration programs that wish to develop original research studies that enhance the profession of health care risk management. Must be original work related to health care risk management research and innovation for consideration.

FINANCIAL DATA:
Since inception, the Society has awarded more than $90,000.
Amount of support per award: Education Grants: Up to $1,500; Scholarship Grants: Up to $3,000; Research Grants: Up to $14,500.

APPLICATION INFORMATION:
Contact the Society.
Duration: One year. Must reapply.
Deadline: Early July.

ADDRESS INQUIRIES TO:
Kim Hoarle, Executive Director
(See address above.)

ARCHSTONE FOUNDATION   [1419]
401 East Ocean Boulevard
Suite 1000
Long Beach, CA 90802
(562) 590-8655
Fax: (562) 495-0317

E-MAIL ADDRESS:
archstone@archstone.org

WEB SITE ADDRESS:
www.archstone.org

FOUNDED: 1985

AREAS OF INTEREST:
Health and aging.

TYPE:
Challenge/matching grants; Conferences/seminars; Demonstration grants; Development grants; Project/program grants; Technical assistance.

YEAR PROGRAM STARTED: 1985

PURPOSE:
To contribute toward the preparation of the society in meeting the needs of an aging population.

ELIGIBILITY:
501(c)(3) organizations. Individuals may not apply. No funding available for capital expenditures, fundraisers, research or general operating funds.

GEOGRAPHIC RESTRICTIONS:
Southern California.

FINANCIAL DATA:
Limited indirect costs to 10%.
Amount of support per award: $15,000 to $400,000.
Total amount of support: $88,000,000.

NUMBER OF APPLICANTS MOST RECENT YEAR:
147.

NUMBER OF AWARDS: 33 for fiscal year ended June 30, 2013.

APPLICATION INFORMATION:
Application forms and reporting guidelines are available on the Foundation's web site.
Duration: One year. May be renewed for up to three years.

IRS IDENTIFICATION NUMBER: 33-0133359

BOARD OF DIRECTORS:
Robert C. Maxson, Ed.D., Chairman

Joseph F. Prevratil, President and Chief Executive Officer
Diana M. Bonta, Dr.P.H., R.N.
Lynn Daucher
Amye L. Leong, MBA
Renee B. Simon, M.S., M.L.S.
Mark D. Smith, M.D.
Rocky Suares, C.F.P.
Peter C. Szutu, M.P.H.

ADDRESS INQUIRIES TO:
Tanisha Davis, Grants Manager
(See address above.)

MAX BELL FOUNDATION   [1420]
1201 5th Street, S.W.
Suite 380
Calgary AB T2R 0Y6 Canada
(403) 215-7310
Fax: (403) 215-7319

E-MAIL ADDRESS:
white@maxbell.org

WEB SITE ADDRESS:
www.maxbell.org

FOUNDED: 1972

AREAS OF INTEREST:
Health, education and environment.

TYPE:
Challenge/matching grants; Development grants; Internships; Project/program grants.

YEAR PROGRAM STARTED: 1972

PURPOSE:
To develop innovative ideas that impact public policies and practices.

LEGAL BASIS:
Private foundation.

ELIGIBILITY:
Organizations must have a registered Canadian charitable number issued by Revenue Canada. Grants are not made for conferences and workshops, scholarships, individuals, sabbaticals, equipment purchases, capital campaigns, fund-raising drives or annual charitable appeals.

GEOGRAPHIC RESTRICTIONS:
Canada.

FINANCIAL DATA:
Amount of support per award: Varies.
Total amount of support: Approximately $1,800,000.
Matching fund requirements: Varies.

APPLICATION INFORMATION:
For Internship Grants: Interested applicants should initiate the process by outlining:
(1) tentative details, including objectives, intended output/deliverables, and summary work plan showing activities and outputs by month;
(2) process by which applicant would search for and hire an intern and;
(3) budget with line items for intern stipend, administration/overhead and mentoring/supervision.

This information should be forwarded by post or fax to Allan Northcott, Senior Program Officer.

Applicants for Project/Program Grants should submit a letter of intent to Alida White, Office Administrator.
Duration: One to three years. Nonrenewable.

OFFICERS:
Dr. David Elton, President
Alida White, Secretary and Treasurer

STAFF:
Alida White, Office Administrator
Allan Northcott, Senior Program Officer
Ralph Strother, Senior Program Officer

BOARD OF DIRECTORS:
Carolyn Hursh, Chairman
Ken Marra, Vice Chairman
Brenda Eaton
Jim Gray
Carol Hill
Prof. Tony Masi
Michael Wilson

ADDRESS INQUIRIES TO:
Allan Northcott, Senior Program Officer
(See address above.)

BRIGHAM AND WOMEN'S HOSPITAL   [1421]
75 Francis Street
Boston, MA 02115
(617) 732-8422
Fax: (617) 582-6112

E-MAIL ADDRESS:
bwhdeland@partners.org

WEB SITE ADDRESS:
www.brighamandwomens.org/delandfellowship

AREAS OF INTEREST:
Health care.

NAME(S) OF PROGRAMS:
● **Deland Fellowship Program in Health Care and Society**

TYPE:
Fellowships.

PURPOSE:
To train outstanding future leaders in health care.

ELIGIBILITY:
It is anticipated that candidates will come from a variety of careers and educational backgrounds including business, law, economics, public policy and medicine. Candidates are required to have an advanced degree from a U.S. accredited institution.

NUMBER OF APPLICANTS MOST RECENT YEAR:
106 for the year 2013.

NUMBER OF AWARDS: 2 annually.

APPLICATION INFORMATION:
Complete applications must be submitted to the e-mail address listed above by the deadline and must include the following items:
(1) completed application form;
(2) copy of curriculum vitae;
(3) list of three references and;
(4) candidates statement (application provides additional information).
Duration: One year.
Deadline: First Monday in October. Notification in November.

ADDRESS INQUIRIES TO:
Trishia Lichauco, Administrative Director
(See e-mail address above.)

BRIGHT FOCUS FOUNDATION   [1422]
22512 Gateway Center Drive
Clarksburg, MD 20871
(301) 948-3244
Fax: (301) 948-4403

E-MAIL ADDRESS:
researchgrants@brightfocus.org

WEB SITE ADDRESS:
www.brightfocus.org

FOUNDED: 1997

AREAS OF INTEREST:
Macular degeneration.

NAME(S) OF PROGRAMS:
• **Macular Degeneration Research Program**

TYPE:
Research grants.

YEAR PROGRAM STARTED: 1998

PURPOSE:
To fund research on and educate the public about macular degeneration.

LEGAL BASIS:
501(c)(3) nonprofit charitable organization.

ELIGIBILITY:
Grants are awarded on the basis of the proposal's scientific merit and its relevance to understanding the diseases studied. No funds for large equipment, institutional overhead cost, construction or building expenses.

The Foundation is particularly interested in receiving letters from new investigators and from established investigators seeking to explore new directions in macular degeneration research.

FINANCIAL DATA:
Amount of support per award: Up to $50,000 per year.
Total amount of support: Varies.

APPLICATION INFORMATION:
Must send initial letter of intent. Subsequent proposal by invitation.
Duration: Up to two years.

PUBLICATIONS:
Annual report; newsletters; clinical brochures.

ADDRESS INQUIRIES TO:
E-mail: researchgrants@brightfocus.org

THE CALIFORNIA ENDOWMENT [1423]
1000 North Alameda Street
Los Angeles, CA 90012
(213) 928-8645
(800) 449-4149
Fax: (213) 928-8818

E-MAIL ADDRESS:
destrada@calendow.org

WEB SITE ADDRESS:
www.calendow.org

FOUNDED: 1996

AREAS OF INTEREST:
Health care access, disparities in health, public health, multicultural health, health and well-being, cultural competency and work force diversity.

NAME(S) OF PROGRAMS:
• **Building Healthy Communities Initiative**

TYPE:
Challenge/matching grants; Conferences/seminars; General operating grants; Project/program grants; Technical assistance.

YEAR PROGRAM STARTED: 1998

PURPOSE:
To improve access to affordable, quality health care for underserved individuals and communities; to promote fundamental improvements in the health status of the people of California; to improve the health of Californians through community-based programs, collaborations and partnerships that strengthen leadership, stimulate policy development and contribute to systems change.

ELIGIBILITY:
Grants are awarded to tax-exempt organizations only. No grants to individuals.

GEOGRAPHIC RESTRICTIONS:
California.

FINANCIAL DATA:
Amount of support per award: Varies.

NUMBER OF APPLICANTS MOST RECENT YEAR:
844 for the year ended March 31, 2011.

NUMBER OF AWARDS: 1,246 for the year ended March 31, 2011.

APPLICATION INFORMATION:
The Grant Application Guide, located online, serves as the single-point-of-entry to all of the Endowment's funding. Innovative Ideas Challenge (IIC) is also available on the web site. The Endowment's focus is on place-based grantmaking. Funding opportunites are made on a commissioning basis.
Deadline: Innovative Ideas Challenge: May 1, September 1 and December 1.

IRS IDENTIFICATION NUMBER: 95-4523232

CALIFORNIA HEALTHCARE FOUNDATION [1424]
1438 Webster Street
Suite 400
Oakland, CA 94612
(510) 238-1040
Fax: (510) 238-1388

E-MAIL ADDRESS:
info@chcf.org

WEB SITE ADDRESS:
www.chcf.org

FOUNDED: 1996

AREAS OF INTEREST:
Better chronic disease care, market and policy monitor innovations for the underserved.

TYPE:
Project/program grants.

PURPOSE:
To commission research and analysis; to publish and disseminate information; to convene stakeholders and fund development of programs and models aimed at improving the health care delivery and financing systems.

GEOGRAPHIC RESTRICTIONS:
California.

FINANCIAL DATA:
Amount of support per award: Varies.
Total amount of support: Varies.

APPLICATION INFORMATION:
Letters of inquiry are preferred for unsolicited projects with description, timeline and estimated budget.
Duration: Varies.

ADDRESS INQUIRIES TO:
Lisa Kang
Director, Grants Administration
(See address above.)

THE CALIFORNIA WELLNESS FOUNDATION [1425]
6320 Canoga Avenue
Suite 1700
Woodland Hills, CA 91367-7111
(818) 702-1900
Fax: (818) 702-1999

WEB SITE ADDRESS:
www.calwellness.org

FOUNDED: 1991

AREAS OF INTEREST:
Diversity in the health professions, environmental health, healthy aging, mental health, teenage pregnancy prevention, violence prevention, women's health, and work and health.

TYPE:
Conferences/seminars; Demonstration grants; General operating grants; Project/program grants; Seed money grants. The Foundation makes grants within the scope of its eight health issues (above), plus in the category of special projects.

YEAR PROGRAM STARTED: 1992

PURPOSE:
To improve the health of the people of California by making grants for health promotion, wellness education and disease prevention.

LEGAL BASIS:
Private foundation.

ELIGIBILITY:
Applicants must be nonprofit organizations that are exempt under Section 501(c)(3) of the IRS and are defined as "not a private foundation" under Section 509(a)(1). The Foundation also funds government agencies.

The Foundation does not fund Section 509(a)(3) Type III non-functionally integrated supporting organizations and does not provide international funding or fund organizations located outside of the U.S. Grants are not made for annual fund drives, building campaigns, major equipment, biomedical research or to activities that exclusively benefit members of sectarian or religious organizations.

GEOGRAPHIC RESTRICTIONS:
California.

FINANCIAL DATA:
Amount of support per award: Varies depending on needs and nature of the request.
Total amount of support: Approximately $35,000,000 for the year 2013.

NUMBER OF APPLICANTS MOST RECENT YEAR:
More than 1,300 for the year 2013.

NUMBER OF AWARDS: 317 for the year 2013.

APPLICATION INFORMATION:
Application process begins with a succinct, two-page maximum letter of interest including a summary of the proposed program, its objectives and anticipated outcomes, its leadership, the organization(s) involved, region to be served, the project duration and the funds requested. Inquiries will be reviewed by the Foundation staff. Eligible organizations with programs that are

---

consistent with current priorities and most closely meet the Foundation's selection criteria will be invited to submit a proposal. Review of the initial materials may require additional information, a meeting or a site visit. Applicants will be notified of the results of the initial review normally within three months. Those encouraged to submit a proposal will receive guidance as to what information is required and how best to present it.

Duration: Varies.

PUBLICATIONS:
Annual report; brochure; quarterly newsletter.

IRS IDENTIFICATION NUMBER: 95-4292101

STAFF:
Cristina M. Regalado, Vice President of Programs
Fatima Angeles, Director of Evaluation and Organizational Learning
Amy B. Scop, Director of Grants Management
Frank A. Lalle, Director of Programs
Sandra J. Martinez, Director of Public Policy
Crystal D. Crawford, Program Director
Earl Lui, Program Director
Julio Marcial, Program Director

BOARD OF DIRECTORS:
Barbara C. Staggers, M.D., Chairperson
Eugene Washington, M.D., Vice Chairperson
David S. Barlow
M. Isabel Becerra
Elizabeth M. Gomez
Elisabeth Hallman, R.N.

ADMINISTRATIVE STAFF:
Margaret W. Minnich, Vice President of Administration and Finance
Magdalena Beltran-del Olmo, Vice President of Communications
Bruce Minnich, Director of Information Systems

EXECUTIVE STAFF:
Diana M. Bonta, Dr.P.H., R.N., President and Chief Executive Officer

ADDRESS INQUIRIES TO:
Amy B. Scop
Director of Grants Management
(See address above.)

CENTER FOR SCIENCE IN THE PUBLIC INTEREST
1220 L Street, N.W.
Suite 300
Washington, DC 20005
(202) 332-9110
Fax: (202) 265-4954

E-MAIL ADDRESS:
coday@cspinet.org

WEB SITE ADDRESS:
www.cspinet.org

TYPE:
Internships. Stipends allow interns to work on specific projects under the direction of a Project Director or the Executive Director.

See entry 2670 for full listing.

CHICAGO BOARD OF TRADE FOUNDATION [1426]
141 West Jackson Boulevard
Suite 1801
Chicago, IL 60604
(312) 789-8753
Fax: (312) 789-8256

E-MAIL ADDRESS:
cbotfoundation@henningcarey.com

WEB SITE ADDRESS:
www.cmegroup.com/company/corporate-citizenship/cbot-foundation.html

AREAS OF INTEREST:
Hospitals, handicapped, arts, education, youth and wildlife.

TYPE:
General operating grants; Project/program grants.

PURPOSE:
To support health care, education, arts and culture.

ELIGIBILITY:
Organizations classified as 501(c)(3) by the IRS can apply. Individuals and religious organizations are ineligible. Must be nondiscriminatory in its practices and may not give funds to ancillary organizations.

GEOGRAPHIC RESTRICTIONS:
Greater Chicago, Illinois metropolitan area.

FINANCIAL DATA:
Amount of support per award: $1,000 to $20,000.

APPLICATION INFORMATION:
Applicant must submit a copy of proposal, 501(c)(3), (4) or (10) documentation, and a recent financial statement.
Duration: One year. Grants are renewable.

ADDRESS INQUIRIES TO:
Diane Rhode, Foundation Administrator
(See address above.)

THE COLORADO TRUST [1427]
1600 Sherman Street
Denver, CO 80203-1604
(303) 837-1200
(888) 847-9140
Fax: (303) 839-9034

E-MAIL ADDRESS:
julian@coloradotrust.org

WEB SITE ADDRESS:
www.coloradotrust.org

FOUNDED: 1985

AREAS OF INTEREST:
Policies and information related to advancing health equity, as well as projects that address health equity in partnership with communities throughout Colorado.

NAME(S) OF PROGRAMS:
• **Community-based Participatory Grantmaking**
• **Health Equity Advocacy**
• **Health Equity Learning Series**

TYPE:
General operating grants; Project/program grants; Research grants; Technical assistance.

YEAR PROGRAM STARTED: 1985

PURPOSE:
To advance the health and well-being of the people of Colorado.

LEGAL BASIS:
Private foundation.

GEOGRAPHIC RESTRICTIONS:
Colorado.

FINANCIAL DATA:
Amount of support per award: Varies.
Total amount of support: $16,000,000 in total grantmaking for fiscal year 2012.

COOPERATIVE FUNDING PROGRAMS: Supporting the Colorado School of Public Health, along with Caring for Colorado, The Colorado Health Foundation, Kaiser Permanente and Rose Community Foundation; Supporting the Colorado Fresh Food Financing Fund, along with the Colorado Health Foundation and the Colorado Housing and Finance Authority.

APPLICATION INFORMATION:
Applications are accepted following the release of Requests for Proposals issued by The Colorado Trust. Application requirements are detailed specifically in Requests for Proposals.
Duration: Varies.

PUBLICATIONS:
Annual report; community connections blog; evaluation reports; program reports.

IRS IDENTIFICATION NUMBER: 84-0994055

BOARD OF TRUSTEES:
Ned Calonge, M.D., President and Chief Executive Officer
John P. Hopkins
Warren Johnson, M.D.
Donald Mares
Jennifer Paquette, C.F.A.
Rev. R. J. Ross
Gail Schoettler, Ph.D.
Colleen Schwarz, M.B.A.
Alan Synn, M.D.
William Wright, M.D.

ADDRESS INQUIRIES TO:
Julian Kesner, Director of Communications
(See address and e-mail above.)

CONGRESSIONAL BLACK CAUCUS FOUNDATION, INC.
1720 Massachusetts Avenue, N.W.
Washington, DC 20036
(202) 263-2800
Fax: (202) 263-0846

E-MAIL ADDRESS:
internships@cbcfinc.org

WEB SITE ADDRESS:
www.cbcfinc.org

TYPE:
Fellowships. The Louis Stokes Urban Health Policy Fellows Program is a 20-month policy training and leadership development program that targets early to mid-level policy professionals who are committed to eliminating health disparities nationally and globally. Fellows receive health policy training while working in a CBC Member's office as well as on a congressional committee. They spend 10 months working in a congressional Member's office and the remaining 10 months working on a congressional committee that focuses on health-related issues.

The program also includes educational enrichment opportunities through seminars on policy and politics.

See entry 1025 for full listing.

THE CULLEN TRUST FOR HEALTH CARE [1428]
601 Jefferson, Suite 4000
Houston, TX 77002
(713) 651-8860
Fax: (713) 651-8993

FOUNDED: 1978

AREAS OF INTEREST:
Health care.

TYPE:
Capital grants; Development grants; Endowments; General operating grants; Project/program grants. Clinical-based research grants.

YEAR PROGRAM STARTED: 1978

PURPOSE:
To provide financial assistance and to benefit institutions providing health care.

LEGAL BASIS:
Charitable trust.

ELIGIBILITY:
Applicants must be tax-exempt 501(c)(3).

GEOGRAPHIC RESTRICTIONS:
Primarily Houston, Texas area.

FINANCIAL DATA:
Amount of support per award: Average $50,000.
Total amount of support: Varies.

APPLICATION INFORMATION:
Applications are only accepted online through www.ghcf.org.
Duration: One to five years.
Deadline: February 1 and September 1.

RAY EDWARDS MEMORIAL TRUST [1429]
800 Nicollet Mall, BC-MN-H16A
Minneapolis, MN 55402
(612) 303-4414
Fax: (612) 303-3219

E-MAIL ADDRESS:
charitableservicesgroupmpls@usbank.com

FOUNDED: 1961

AREAS OF INTEREST:
Hospital-based health care delivery and direct health care services to indigent.

TYPE:
Capital grants; General operating grants; Project/program grants.

YEAR PROGRAM STARTED: 1961

PURPOSE:
To provide hospital-based health care services for those who are in greatest financial need and are enduring or experiencing serious illnesses.

LEGAL BASIS:
Private foundation.

ELIGIBILITY:
Eligible organizations must be IRS 501(c)(3) tax-exempt.

GEOGRAPHIC RESTRICTIONS:
Greater St. Paul, Minnesota and the metropolitan area to the east.

FINANCIAL DATA:
Amount of support per award: $5,000 to $150,000.
Total amount of support: Up to $845,000 annually.

NUMBER OF APPLICANTS MOST RECENT YEAR:
Approximately 200.

NUMBER OF AWARDS: 15 to 25.

REPRESENTATIVE AWARDS:
$30,000 ($15,000 per year for two years) to Children's Hospitals and Clinics.

APPLICATION INFORMATION:
Applications must include four copies of the following:

(1) one-page cover letter signed by Chief Executive Officer or Board Chair;
(2) Minnesota Common Grant Application (cover page only);
(3) audited financial statement from most recent fiscal year;
(4) IRS tax-exempt determination letter;
(5) Board of Directors listing and;
(6) report describing use and impact of any recent grants from the Trust.

The Foundation does not accept letters of inquiry.
Duration: Typically one year. Capital projects: Multiyear.
Deadline: May 1.

PUBLICATIONS:
Application guidelines.

ADDRESS INQUIRIES TO:
See e-mail address above.

*SPECIAL STIPULATIONS:
No inquiry letters. Submit proposals only.

FIRST CANDLE/SIDS ALLIANCE
2105 Laurel Bush Road
Suite 201
Bel Air, MD 21015
(443) 640-1049
Fax: (443) 640-1031

E-MAIL ADDRESS:
info@firstcandle.org

WEB SITE ADDRESS:
www.firstcandle.org

TYPE:
Conferences/seminars; Research grants. Professional medical research for SIDS, stillbirths and related issues.

See entry 2528 for full listing.

THE FOUNDATION FOR SPIRITUALITY AND MEDICINE [1430]
13500 Fork Road
Baldwin, MD 21013
(410) 592-3583
Fax: (410) 592-3583 (Call ahead)

E-MAIL ADDRESS:
smdcdaneker@comcast.net

WEB SITE ADDRESS:
www.foundationspiritmed.org

FOUNDED: 1981

AREAS OF INTEREST:
Health, health education and spirituality.

TYPE:
Challenge/matching grants; Conferences/seminars; Demonstration grants; Development grants; General operating grants; Project/program grants; Research grants; Seed money grants; Training grants.

YEAR PROGRAM STARTED: 1995

PURPOSE:
To promote the integration of spirituality into health care.

ELIGIBILITY:
Grants are given to any nonprofit organization whose mission is the training of professionals in the healing arts, the delivery of health care, or the provision of spiritual services. Preference may be given to applicants who demonstrate matching funds by their organization or from other sources.

GEOGRAPHIC RESTRICTIONS:
Primarily Maryland.

FINANCIAL DATA:
Net worth as of December 31, 2013: $2,024,000.
Amount of support per award: Maximum $25,000 per year.
Total amount of support: $110,000 for the year 2013.

NUMBER OF APPLICANTS MOST RECENT YEAR:
12 for the year 2013.

NUMBER OF AWARDS: 6 for the year 2013.

REPRESENTATIVE AWARDS:
Mobile medical clinic operations; Program for teens with development disabilities; Clinical pastoral education; Religious-oriented psych counseling program.

APPLICATION INFORMATION:
Applications must be no more than 10 pages in length (double-spaced) and should include the following:
(1) description and history of the project;
(2) description of organization and personnel;
(3) rationale for proposed project;
(4) goals and objectives of the project;
(5) short-term and long-term benefits expected from the project;
(6) plans for a continuation of the project;
(7) timetable and;
(8) budget.

Grantees must meet Foundation requirements for regular financial and project reporting, and submit an annual and final written report. An oral presentation to the board of directors of the Foundation may be requested as part of the application process and/or as part of the report.

Please send three copies of application if possible.
Duration: Two years.
Deadline: January 15 and July 15. Announcements April 1 and October 1.

PUBLICATIONS:
Form 990-PF; brochure.

IRS IDENTIFICATION NUMBER: 52-1238713

ADDRESS INQUIRIES TO:
David C. Daneker, Chairman
(See address above.)

THE FOUNDATION OF THE AMERICAN COLLEGE OF HEALTHCARE EXECUTIVES [1431]
One North Franklin Street
Suite 1700
Chicago, IL 60606-3529
(312) 424-9400
Fax: (312) 424-9405

E-MAIL ADDRESS:
contact@ache.org

WEB SITE ADDRESS:
www.ache.org/scholarships

FOUNDED: 1933

AREAS OF INTEREST:
Health care management.

NAME(S) OF PROGRAMS:
• **Albert W. Dent Graduate Student Scholarship**
• **Foster G. McGaw Graduate Student Scholarship**

TYPE:
Scholarships. Offered annually, the Albert W. Dent and the Foster G. McGaw Graduate Student Scholarships are designated for students enrolled in their final year of classroom work in a health care management graduate program.

Albert W. Dent Graduate Student Scholarship is only available to minority students.

YEAR PROGRAM STARTED: 1969

PURPOSE:
To provide financial aid, increase the enrollment in health care management graduate programs and to encourage students to obtain positions in the middle and upper levels of health care management.

ELIGIBILITY:
An applicant must:
(1) be a full-time student entering the final year of classroom work in a health care management graduate program;
(2) be able to demonstrate financial need;
(3) be a U.S. or Canadian citizen;
(4) have not been a previous recipient of the scholarship and;
(5) be a minority if applying for the Albert W. Dent Graduate Student Scholarship.

GEOGRAPHIC RESTRICTIONS:
United States and Canada.

FINANCIAL DATA:
Amount of support per award: $5,000.
Total amount of support: Varies.

COOPERATIVE FUNDING PROGRAMS: The initial gift for the McGaw Student Scholarship was from the Foster G. McGaw Charitable Fund. Additional gifts were made by Mr. McGaw from his personal funds before his death in 1986.

NUMBER OF APPLICANTS MOST RECENT YEAR: 75 to 100.

NUMBER OF AWARDS: 15 to 20 scholarships awarded per year.

APPLICATION INFORMATION:
Application is submitted online via the Foundation web site.
Duration: One year. Renewal by reapplication.
Deadline: March 31.

ADDRESS INQUIRIES TO:
Scholarship Committee
Division of Member Services
(See address above.)

THE DAVID GEFFEN FOUNDATION   [1432]
12011 San Vicente Boulevard
Suite 606
Los Angeles, CA 90049
(310) 581-5955
Fax: (310) 581-5949

E-MAIL ADDRESS:
ddishman@geffenco.com

FOUNDED: 1986

AREAS OF INTEREST:
AIDS/HIV, civil liberties, health and health care, the arts and issues of concern to the Jewish community.

TYPE:
Capital grants; General operating grants; Project/program grants.

PURPOSE:
To support the arts, health care, issues of concern to the Jewish community, HIV/AIDS and civil liberties.

LEGAL BASIS:
Private foundation.

ELIGIBILITY:
Applicants must be 501(c)(3) organizations. No grants for documentaries, audio-visual programming or publications. No grants to individuals.

GEOGRAPHIC RESTRICTIONS:
Primarily New York City and Los Angeles, California.

FINANCIAL DATA:
Amount of support per award: Varies depending on needs and nature of the request.

APPLICATION INFORMATION:
No application form. Proposals should include summary and description of the project or program, background information of the organization, description of key staff, list of Board of Directors, IRS letter confirming tax-exempt status and financial information including annual operating and project budgets. Applicants should not send videotapes or additional materials unless otherwise requested.
Duration: One-time grant and multiyear support. Renewal possible.
Deadline: Applications accepted throughout the year. Each request may take up to three months to evaluate.

PUBLICATIONS:
Application guidelines.

IRS IDENTIFICATION NUMBER: 95-4085811

STAFF:
J. Dallas Dishman, Ph.D., Executive Director

ADDRESS INQUIRIES TO:
J. Dallas Dishman, Ph.D., Executive Director
(See address above.)

GLAXOSMITHKLINE   [1433]
5 Moore Drive
Research Triangle Park, NC 27709
(215) 751-7074
Fax: (919) 483-8765

E-MAIL ADDRESS:
community.partnership@gsk.com

WEB SITE ADDRESS:
www.gsk.com

AREAS OF INTEREST:
Health care practice and education, mental health and welfare and science education.

TYPE:
Project/program grants.

PURPOSE:
To support health-related organizations working to improve health care practices and education; to promote the physical welfare of the disadvantaged, minorities, disabled persons, women and the aged; to promote interest and experience in science.

LEGAL BASIS:
Corporate foundation.

ELIGIBILITY:
Applicants must be nonprofit organizations with proposals consistent with guidelines and interest areas. No grants for capital projects, operating expenses, multiyear grants, conferences, symposia, publications,

fund-raising events, lobbying to influence legislation, religious organizations, sporting events, universities, free-standing research centers, scholar aid, expeditions or individuals.

GEOGRAPHIC RESTRICTIONS:
United States.

FINANCIAL DATA:
Amount of support per award: Varies depending on needs and nature of the request.

APPLICATION INFORMATION:
Applications must include a brief summary of the organization and the proposed project, amount requested, relevant interest area and reasoning for proposal and contact name, telephone number and fax number if available. If GlaxoSmithKline is interested in the project, the applicant will be contacted to request a formal proposal. All applications will be acknowledged. Additional application information is available on the website.
Duration: One year. Multiyear requests are not funded.
Deadline: Applications accepted throughout the year.

ADDRESS INQUIRIES TO:
Dawn Winters
Community Partnership
(See address above.)

HCR MANOR CARE FOUNDATION   [1434]
333 North Summit Street
Toledo, OH 43604
(419) 252-5989
Fax: (419) 252-5521

E-MAIL ADDRESS:
foundation@hcr-manorcare.com

WEB SITE ADDRESS:
www.hcr-manorcare.com

FOUNDED: 1997

AREAS OF INTEREST:
Community service and outreach, hospice-related programs, research and public education for diseases and disorders that affect the elderly, those requiring post-acute services and those requiring hospice or end-of-life care.

TYPE:
Challenge/matching grants; Project/program grants.

YEAR PROGRAM STARTED: 1997

PURPOSE:
To support organizations involved in research and public education about diseases and disorders affecting the elderly, and organizations which provide community service and outreach to such individuals; to provide support to programs addressing end-of-life care; to provide support for hospice.

LEGAL BASIS:
Corporate foundation.

ELIGIBILITY:
Preference is given to organizations in states where HCR Manor Care Corporation has strategic operations. Organizations must be IRS 501(c)(3) tax-exempt and have one other source of support.

HCR Manor Care will not fund advertising or fund-raising events, individuals, for-profit organizations, building or capital campaigns, endowments, organizations with primary service areas in non-HCR Manor Care states, multiyear commitments, research projects with overhead fees in excess of 10% or organizations that have applied for funding within the last 12 months.

GEOGRAPHIC RESTRICTIONS:
United States.

FINANCIAL DATA:
Amount of support per award: Varies.
Total amount of support: Varies.

NUMBER OF APPLICANTS MOST RECENT YEAR:
300.

NUMBER OF AWARDS: 150.

APPLICATION INFORMATION:
The Foundation does not accept unsolicited applications, and grants are only given through HCR Manor Care Corporation locations.
Duration: One year.

IRS IDENTIFICATION NUMBER: 52-2031975

ADDRESS INQUIRIES TO:
Bill White, Executive Director
(See address above.)

HEALTH EFFECTS INSTITUTE (HEI)   [1435]
101 Federal Street
Suite 500
Boston, MA 02110-1817
(617) 488-2338
Fax: (617) 488-2335

E-MAIL ADDRESS:
jrutledge@healtheffects.org

WEB SITE ADDRESS:
www.healtheffects.org

FOUNDED: 1980

AREAS OF INTEREST:
Health effects of air pollution.

NAME(S) OF PROGRAMS:
● **Health Effects of Air Pollution**
● **Walter A. Rosenblith New Investigator Award**

TYPE:
Research contracts.

YEAR PROGRAM STARTED: 1980

PURPOSE:
To provide high-quality, impartial, and relevant science on the health effects of air pollution.

LEGAL BASIS:
Public/Private partnership.

ELIGIBILITY:
Requirements vary according to program. Detailed information is available on the web site.

FINANCIAL DATA:
Amount of support per award: Varies.
Total amount of support: Varies.

APPLICATION INFORMATION:
Application information is available online.
Duration: Varies.
Deadline: Varies.

ADDRESS INQUIRIES TO:
For Health Effects:
Dr. Kate Adams
Tel: (617) 488-2330
For Walter A. Rosenblith New Investigator Award:

Geoff Sunshine
Tel: (617) 488-2303
(See address above.)

THE HEALTH FOUNDATION OF GREATER INDIANAPOLIS   [1436]
429 East Vermont Street, Suite 300
Indianapolis, IN 46202-3698
(317) 630-1805
Fax: (317) 630-1806

E-MAIL ADDRESS:
bwilson@thfgi.org

WEB SITE ADDRESS:
www.indianaaidsfund.org

AREAS OF INTEREST:
AIDS education and prevention.

NAME(S) OF PROGRAMS:
● **Indiana AIDS Fund**

TYPE:
Grants-in-aid.

PURPOSE:
To support HIV prevention and services programs throughout Indiana.

ELIGIBILITY:
Any Indiana-based nonprofit 501(c)(3) group, organization or agency that provides HIV/AIDS-related programs or services to local constituencies may apply for funding.

GEOGRAPHIC RESTRICTIONS:
Indiana.

FINANCIAL DATA:
Amount of support per award: Varies.
Total amount of support: $500,000 for the year 2012.

NUMBER OF AWARDS: Varies.

APPLICATION INFORMATION:
Submit one master copy of the proposal with all attachments and 10 copies of the proposal without attachments. Proposal must contain the following elements:
(1) the provided Proposal Cover Sheet;
(2) brief description of the organization and its qualifications for this project, no longer than two pages;
(3) proposal narrative which should describe need, target population, geographic area served by this project, project objectives and prospects for future funding, no longer than five pages;
(4) budget statement and justification, no longer than three pages, which should include form provided;
(5) evaluation component, no longer than two pages, which (a) describes the behavior change evaluation component; (b) explains what it will measure; (c) lists the expected outcomes and; (d) explains the rationale for choosing this component and;
(6) attachments.
Duration: One year.
Deadline: Varies.

ADDRESS INQUIRIES TO:
Betty Wilson, President and
Chief Executive Officer
(See address above.)

HEALTH FOUNDATION OF SOUTH FLORIDA   [1437]
One Biscayne Tower
2 South Biscayne Boulevard, Suite 1710
Miami, FL 33131
(305) 374-7200
Fax: (305) 374-7003

E-MAIL ADDRESS:
pwood@hfsf.org

WEB SITE ADDRESS:
www.hfsf.org

FOUNDED: 1993

AREAS OF INTEREST:
Primary care, healthy eating active communities, oral health, preventative health measures, and healthy aging.

TYPE:
Challenge/matching grants; General operating grants; Project/program grants; Technical assistance; Training grants.

PURPOSE:
For charitable, scientific and educational purposes to advance the health and well-being of the people of Broward, Miami-Dade and Monroe counties, FL; to facilitate and support efforts at the neighborhood, county and regional levels to improve the health status of underserved individuals and families.

ELIGIBILITY:
Eligible organizations must be IRS 501(c)(3) tax-exempt and be located in south Florida.

GEOGRAPHIC RESTRICTIONS:
South Florida counties of Broward, Miami-Dade and Monroe.

FINANCIAL DATA:
Amount of support per award: Typically $50,000 to $100,000.
Total amount of support: $5,000,000.

NUMBER OF APPLICANTS MOST RECENT YEAR:
320 for the year 2012.

NUMBER OF AWARDS: 105.

APPLICATION INFORMATION:
Preliminary proposal must be submitted electronically through the Foundation's web site.
Duration: One to two years.
Deadline: Preliminary proposals: August and December. Full proposals: September and January.

ADDRESS INQUIRIES TO:
Peter N. Wood
Vice President of Programs
and Community Investments
(See address above.)

THE HEALTH TRUST   [1438]
3180 Newberry Drive, Suite 200
San Jose, CA 95118
(408) 513-8700
Fax: (408) 448-4055

E-MAIL ADDRESS:
grants@healthtrust.org

WEB SITE ADDRESS:
www.healthtrust.org

FOUNDED: 1996

AREAS OF INTEREST:
Public health.

NAME(S) OF PROGRAMS:
● **Event Grants**

TYPE:
Project/program grants.

YEAR PROGRAM STARTED: 1996

PURPOSE:
To lead the Silicon Valley community to advance wellness.

LEGAL BASIS:
Nonprofit, public charity, qualifying as IRS 501(c)(3) organization.

ELIGIBILITY:
The organization must be tax-exempt and nonprofit. Health services must be provided within Santa Clara County and the following three zip codes of San Benito County: 95045, 95023 and 95024.

GEOGRAPHIC RESTRICTIONS:
Santa Clara and northern San Benito counties, California.

FINANCIAL DATA:
Amount of support per award: $250 to $5,000.
Total amount of support: Varies.

NUMBER OF APPLICANTS MOST RECENT YEAR:
Approximately 110.

APPLICATION INFORMATION:
Submit Event Grant application form written on organization's letterhead (not to exceed two pages) including:
(1) event name;
(2) requested amount;
(3) event purpose;
(4) one-page, line-item project budget and;
(5) IRS letter.

Additional guidelines are available on the Trust web site.
Duration: One year.

ADDRESS INQUIRIES TO:
Grants Administrator
(See address above.)

THE HEALTH TRUST   [1439]
3180 Newberry Drive
Suite 200
San Jose, CA 95118
(408) 513-8700
Fax: (408) 448-4055

E-MAIL ADDRESS:
grants@healthtrust.org

WEB SITE ADDRESS:
www.healthtrust.org

FOUNDED: 1996

AREAS OF INTEREST:
Public health.

NAME(S) OF PROGRAMS:
● **Health Partnership Grants**

TYPE:
Project/program grants.

PURPOSE:
To make grants to programs and projects that advance specific strategies under three initiatives: Healthy Living, Healthy Aging and Healthy Communities.

LEGAL BASIS:
Nonprofit, public charity.

ELIGIBILITY:
Organization must be tax-exempt and nonprofit. Health services must be provided within Santa Clara County and the following three zip codes of San Benito County: 95045, 95023 and 95024.

GEOGRAPHIC RESTRICTIONS:
Santa Clara and northern San Benito counties, California.

FINANCIAL DATA:
Amount of support per award: Varies.
Total amount of support: Varies.

NUMBER OF AWARDS: 29 for the year 2011.

APPLICATION INFORMATION:
Applicants should begin by submitting a two-page Letter of Intent. The Letter of Intent form and other details are available on the Trust web site.
Duration: Varies.

ADDRESS INQUIRIES TO:
Grants Administrator
(See address above.)

THE HEALTHCARE FOUNDATION FOR ORANGE COUNTY   [1440]
1450 North Tustin Avenue
Suite 209
Santa Ana, CA 92705-8641
(714) 245-1650
Fax: (714) 245-1653

E-MAIL ADDRESS:
ckoenig@hfoc.org

WEB SITE ADDRESS:
www.hfoc.org

FOUNDED: 1996

AREAS OF INTEREST:
Health care and community health.

CONSULTING OR VOLUNTEER SERVICES:
Some training and technical assistance.

NAME(S) OF PROGRAMS:
● **Gold Fund for Health**
● **Healthy Orange County**
● **Partners for Health**

TYPE:
Awards/prizes; Demonstration grants; Development grants; General operating grants; Project/program grants; Technical assistance; Training grants.

YEAR PROGRAM STARTED: 1999

PURPOSE:
To promote health and support health care for the benefit of the people of Orange County, CA; to improve the health of the neediest and most underserved residents of the county.

LEGAL BASIS:
Private 501(c)(3) foundation.

ELIGIBILITY:
Grants are made to nonprofit organizations that are exempt from taxation under Section 501(c)(3) of the Internal Revenue Code and that are defined as "not a private foundation" under Section 509(a). Government agencies may also be funded.

Grants are not generally awarded for annual fund drives, building campaigns, major equipment or biomedical research. Activities that exclusively benefit the members of a religious or fraternal organization are not funded.

GEOGRAPHIC RESTRICTIONS:
Primarily Anaheim, Orange, Santa Ana and Tustin, California.

FINANCIAL DATA:
Amount of support per award: Gold Fund for Health: $25,000; Healthy Orange County: $75,000; Partners for Health: $550,000.
Total amount of support: Under $650,000.

COOPERATIVE FUNDING PROGRAMS: Health Funders Partnership.

NUMBER OF APPLICANTS MOST RECENT YEAR:
Approximately 35.

NUMBER OF AWARDS: Approximately 10.

REPRESENTATIVE AWARDS:
$245,250 to Children's Hospital of Orange County to develop multidisciplinary treatment center for pediatric obesity; $75,000 to Hoag Memorial Hospital/MOMS Orange County for postpartum depression.

APPLICATION INFORMATION:
Requests for proposals may be obtained from the Foundation.
Duration: One year; multiyear funding at the Board's discretion.
Deadline: Gold Fund for Health: May; Healthy Orange County: December; Partners for Health: September.

IRS IDENTIFICATION NUMBER: 33-0644620

ADDRESS INQUIRIES TO:
Catherine Koenig, Foundation Coordinator
(See address above.)

HUGOTON FOUNDATION   [1441]
900 Park Avenue, Suite 17E
New York, NY 10075
(212) 734-5447
Fax: (212) 734-5447

AREAS OF INTEREST:
Patient care and health.

TYPE:
Project/program grants.

PURPOSE:
To improve patient care.

LEGAL BASIS:
Nonprofit organization.

ELIGIBILITY:
Eligible organizations must be IRS 501(c)(3) tax-exempt and be located in Miami, FL or the borough of Manhattan, NY.

GEOGRAPHIC RESTRICTIONS:
Miami, Florida and borough of Manhattan, New York.

FINANCIAL DATA:
Amount of support per award: $1,000 to $100,000.

APPLICATION INFORMATION:
Application should be made by letter and include a copy of the IRS tax determination letter.
Duration: One year. Nonrenewable.

ADDRESS INQUIRIES TO:
Joan K. Stout, President
(See address above.)

IRVINE HEALTH FOUNDATION   [1442]
18301 Von Karman Avenue
Suite 440
Irvine, CA 92612
(949) 253-2959

E-MAIL ADDRESS:
info@ihf.org

WEB SITE ADDRESS:
www.ihf.org

FOUNDED: 1986

AREAS OF INTEREST:
Prevention, services, research and policy.

TYPE:
Challenge/matching grants; General operating grants; Project/program grants. Focus grants by invitation only.

YEAR PROGRAM STARTED: 1987

PURPOSE:
To sponsor, promote and support activities related to health care and the health of the Orange County (CA) community.

LEGAL BASIS:
Independent, nonprofit foundation.

ELIGIBILITY:
Applicants must be qualified tax-exempt charitable organizations recognized as such by the IRS. To receive favorable consideration, a project or program must be economically viable, provide effective management and serve a legitimate purpose which avoids duplicating work performed by other organizations.

The Foundation emphasizes support of innovative projects, programs or endeavors designed to meet currently unmet health care needs of the Orange County (CA) community. It is also interested in supporting activities addressing needs of specific population groups, including youth, the elderly and various other segments of the population.

GEOGRAPHIC RESTRICTIONS:
Orange County, California.

FINANCIAL DATA:
Total amount of support: Varies.

APPLICATION INFORMATION:
Contact the Foundation.
Duration: Varies.

PUBLICATIONS:
Annual report.

STAFF:
Edward B. Kacic, President and Chief Executive Officer
Patricia A. Meredith, Vice President, Administration and Programs

BOARD OF DIRECTORS:
Timothy L. Strader, Chairman
Carol Mentor McDermott, Vice Chairman
Jeffrey E. Flocken, Treasurer
Thomas C. Cesario, M.D., Secretary
John C. Gaffney, Director
Gary H. Hunt, Director
Douglas M. Mancino, Esq., Director
Jack W. Peltason, Ph.D., Director
Margarita Pereyda, M.D., Director
Gerald B. Sinykin, M.D., Director

THE JENKINS FOUNDATION [1443]
7501 Boulders View Drive, Suite 110
Richmond, VA 23225
(804) 330-7400
Fax: (804) 330-5992

E-MAIL ADDRESS:
info@tcfrichmond.org

WEB SITE ADDRESS:
www.jenkinsfoundation-va.org

FOUNDED: 1995

AREAS OF INTEREST:
Health care services for the uninsured and underserved, violence prevention and substance abuse prevention in the greater Richmond, VA area.

TYPE:
General operating grants; Project/program grants.

YEAR PROGRAM STARTED: 1996

PURPOSE:
To expand access to community-based health care programs and improved health care in the greater Richmond area.

LEGAL BASIS:
Supporting organization of The Community Foundation Serving Richmond and Central Virginia.

ELIGIBILITY:
Eligible organizations must be IRS 501(c)(3) tax-exempt and serve the greater Richmond, VA area.

GEOGRAPHIC RESTRICTIONS:
Richmond and the counties of Chesterfield, Goochland, Hanover, Henrico and Powhatan, Virginia.

FINANCIAL DATA:
Amount of support per award: $20,000 to $100,000.
Total amount of support: $23,390,136 for the year 2011.

APPLICATION INFORMATION:
Application forms are available online.
Duration: Annually. May reapply.
Deadline: May 5 and November 5.

PUBLICATIONS:
Guidelines; annual report (online).

ADDRESS INQUIRIES TO:
Elaine Summerfield
Vice President of Programs
(See address above.)

THE JEWISH HEALTHCARE FOUNDATION OF PITTSBURGH [1444]
Centre City Tower, Suite 2400
650 Smithfield Street
Pittsburgh, PA 15222
(412) 594-2550
Fax: (412) 232-6240

E-MAIL ADDRESS:
feinstein@jhf.org

WEB SITE ADDRESS:
www.jhf.org

FOUNDED: 1990

AREAS OF INTEREST:
Health care.

CONSULTING OR VOLUNTEER SERVICES:
Research, planning, convening and technical assistance.

TYPE:
Challenge/matching grants; Demonstration grants; Fellowships; Project/program grants; Research grants; Seed money grants; Technical assistance; Training grants.

YEAR PROGRAM STARTED: 1991

PURPOSE:
To provide for the health care needs of the Jewish and general community in southwestern Pennsylvania.

LEGAL BASIS:
Public charity.

ELIGIBILITY:
Applicants must be 501(c)(3) organizations. No grants to programs without a health care component, general operations, endowments, capital campaigns, retirement of debt, scholarships, fellowships, travel or individual research grants.

GEOGRAPHIC RESTRICTIONS:
Southwestern Pennsylvania.

FINANCIAL DATA:
Assets of $122,000,000 for the year ended December 31, 2012.
Amount of support per award: Average $50,000.
Total amount of support: $6,504,925 for the year ended December 31, 2012.

NUMBER OF APPLICANTS MOST RECENT YEAR: 40.

NUMBER OF AWARDS: 50.

REPRESENTATIVE AWARDS:
Pittsburgh Regional Health Initiative; Brandeis University; University of Pittsburgh Graduate School of Public Health.

APPLICATION INFORMATION:
Send letter of intent (not to exceed six pages), including program objectives, timetable, long-term plans, board of directors list, budget, documentation of 501(c)(3) status and most recent financial statements.
Duration: Varies.
Deadline: Applications accepted on a continual basis.

PUBLICATIONS:
Annual report; Roots, reports; Branches, periodical.

IRS IDENTIFICATION NUMBER: 25-1624347

STAFF:
Karen Wolk Feinstein, Ph.D., President
Nancy Zionts, MBA, Chief Program Officer/Chief Operating Officer

ADDRESS INQUIRIES TO:
Nancy D. Zionts, Chief Operating Offcer
(See address above.)

THE JOHNS HOPKINS CENTER FOR ALTERNATIVES TO ANIMAL TESTING [1445]
Johns Hopkins University
615 North Wolfe Street, Room W7032
Baltimore, MD 21205
(410) 614-4983
Fax: (410) 614-2871

E-MAIL ADDRESS:
caat@jhsph.edu

WEB SITE ADDRESS:
altweb.jhsph.edu

FOUNDED: 1981

AREAS OF INTEREST:
Health and safety.

TYPE:
Development grants; Research grants.

YEAR PROGRAM STARTED: 1982

PURPOSE:
To develop innovative non-whole animal methods to evaluate fully commercial and/or therapeutic products to ensure the health and safety of the public. CAAT accomplishes this goal by funding research which will lead to the refinement, replacement or reduction of animals in toxicity testing and by disseminating scientifically correct information about these methods and their applications.

LEGAL BASIS:
University research program.

ELIGIBILITY:
Grants are made to institutions which have an established mechanism for handling private funding. Grant proposals should provide the fundamental knowledge base to develop alternative methods to whole animals for the safety evaluation of commercial

products. CAAT encourages the development of in vitro approaches to toxicity evaluation including, but not limited to, methods using human cells/cell lines and studies in the areas of skin hypersensitivity/toxicity, phototoxicity, target organ toxicity (e.g., neurotoxicity) and structure-activity relationships.

FINANCIAL DATA:
Amount of support per award: $25,000 maximum per year, including 15% overhead or actual costs, whichever is less.
Total amount of support: $25,000 maximum per year, per award.

APPLICATION INFORMATION:
Applicants must submit and receive approval of preproposal by deadline date using CAAT preproposal form.
Duration: One year. Renewal possible.
Deadline: March 10 for preproposal abstracts.

PUBLICATIONS:
CAAT Newsletter; technical reports; *Alternatives in Toxicology*, book series.

IRS IDENTIFICATION NUMBER: 52-0595110

STAFF:
Thomas Hartung, Director

ADDRESS INQUIRIES TO:
Ruth Brady, Grant Coordinator
(See address above.)

KANSAS HEALTH FOUNDATION   [1446]
309 East Douglas
Wichita, KS 67202
(316) 262-7676
(800) 373-7681
Fax: (316) 262-2044

E-MAIL ADDRESS:
ghess@khf.org

WEB SITE ADDRESS:
kansashealth.org

FOUNDED: 1985

AREAS OF INTEREST:
Improvement in the health of Kansans.

NAME(S) OF PROGRAMS:
● **Recognition Grants**

TYPE:
Project/program grants.

YEAR PROGRAM STARTED: 1994

PURPOSE:
To fund competitive grants to grassroots nonprofits and government entities doing innovative and meaningful work that fits within the Kansas Health Foundation's mission to improve the health of all Kansans. Recognition Grants expand the Foundation's support to a broad range of health-related organizations throughout the state.

ELIGIBILITY:
Applicants must be tax-exempt under Section 501(c)(3), a government entity, or a church (with certain exclusions), located within the state, and not a previous recipient of a Recognition Grant within the calendar year.

GEOGRAPHIC RESTRICTIONS:
Kansas.

FINANCIAL DATA:
Amount of support per award: Up to $25,000 per organization.

Total amount of support: Up to $2,000,000 annually in two cycles per year.

NUMBER OF AWARDS: Varies.

APPLICATION INFORMATION:
Applications are only accepted online. Projects are selected based on the following:
(1) focus on prevention;
(2) meeting a clear, identifiable need;
(3) creativity;
(4) operational strength of the applicant organization, including project leadership and;
(5) ranking when compared with other applications received during the funding cycle.
Duration: One year.
Deadline: September 15 and March 15. Announcement December 1 and June 1, respectively.

PUBLICATIONS:
Grant announcement press release.

IRS IDENTIFICATION NUMBER: 48-0873431

ADDRESS INQUIRIES TO:
Gina Hess, Grants Assistant
(See address above.)

LA84 FOUNDATION   [1447]
2141 West Adams Boulevard
Los Angeles, CA 90018
(323) 730-4600
Fax: (323) 730-9637

E-MAIL ADDRESS:
info@la84foundation.org

WEB SITE ADDRESS:
www.la84foundation.org

FOUNDED: 1984

AREAS OF INTEREST:
Youth sports.

TYPE:
Capital grants; Project/program grants. Field of play activities.

PURPOSE:
To promote and enhance youth sports opportunities in southern California.

LEGAL BASIS:
Private foundation.

ELIGIBILITY:
Grants are made only to organizations with nonrestrictive membership operating open to all, regardless of race, creed, sex, sexual orientation, religious affiliation, or nationality. No grants to individuals. Grants are discouraged for endowments, travel outside of southern California, general operating expenses, land purchases, or debt recovery and liability. Grants are need-based.

GEOGRAPHIC RESTRICTIONS:
Imperial, Los Angeles, Orange, Riverside, San Bernardino, San Diego, Santa Barbara and Ventura counties, California.

FINANCIAL DATA:
Amount of support per award: $5,000 to $500,000 for the year 2013.
Total amount of support: $4,038,153 for the year 2013.

NUMBER OF APPLICANTS MOST RECENT YEAR: 216 for the year 2013.

NUMBER OF AWARDS: 87 for the year 2013.

REPRESENTATIVE AWARDS:
Kids In Sports; LAUSD; LA's BEST; Students Run LA; Southern California Tennis Association.

APPLICATION INFORMATION:
Applicants are urged to carefully read the Grant Guidelines before completing the online grant application. Applicants will be asked to:
(1) state clearly the purpose for which funding is requested;
(2) briefly describe the organization, its history, status (nonprofit or for-profit, etc.), and connection to youth and sport;
(3) describe in detail how the program would work and whom it would serve. Include an estimate of the number of participants to be served by the grant;
(4) describe the personnel who would be carrying out the program, and include brief biographical statements of those who would be most centrally involved;
(5) describe efforts already made or underway to find matching grant funds and;
(6) provide a clear time schedule for the program.

Additionally, applicants may be asked to make available the following documents:
(1) the organization's most current annual operating budget;
(2) the most recent completed financial statement;
(3) the most recent IRS Form 990;
(4) IRS tax status determination letter;
(5) California tax status determination letter;
(6) a detailed program budget with justifications for each budget item and;
(7) list of board of directors.
Duration: One year.
Deadline: Applications are accepted year-round.

PUBLICATIONS:
Biannual report.

IRS IDENTIFICATION NUMBER: 95-3792725

OFFICERS:
Anita L. DeFrantz, President
Marcia Suzuki, Treasurer
Patrick Escobar, Vice President, Grants and Programs
Robert W. Wagner, Vice President, Partnerships
Wayne Wilson, Vice President, Communications and Education

ADDRESS INQUIRIES TO:
Patrick Escobar
Vice President, Grants and Programs
(See address above.)

LIVINGSTON MEMORIAL FOUNDATION   [1448]
c/o Musick, Peeler and Garrett
2801 Townsgate Road, Suite 200
Westlake Village, CA 91361-5842
(805) 418-3115
Fax: (805) 418-3101

E-MAIL ADDRESS:
l.mcavoy@mpglaw.com

WEB SITE ADDRESS:
www.livingstonmemorialfoundation.org

FOUNDED: 1974

AREAS OF INTEREST:
Medical and health care in Ventura County, CA.

NAME(S) OF PROGRAMS:
● **Operational Program Grants**
● **Special Project Grants**

TYPE:
Capital grants; General operating grants; Project/program grants. Capital grants are for medical and health care services.

Operational grants support well-established programs that continue to provide positive results.

Special project grants support those agencies and institutions that can demonstrate the need for assistance in funding a special project or with the cost of medical equipment that promises significant positive results.

YEAR PROGRAM STARTED: 1976

PURPOSE:
To promote medical and health-related services of benefit to the underserved and uninsured people of Ventura County, CA.

ELIGIBILITY:
Grant applications are assessed according to criteria that include giving preferential treatment to programs or projects that offer measurable medical benefits, are patient-specific or involve hands-on care.

Grants are not usually made to individuals, for projects or programs normally financed from government sources, conferences, seminars, workshops, exhibits, travel, or publishing activities.

GEOGRAPHIC RESTRICTIONS:
Ventura County, California.

FINANCIAL DATA:
Amount of support per award: $1,000 to $151,000 for the year 2012-13.
Total amount of support: $352,000 for the year 2013.

NUMBER OF APPLICANTS MOST RECENT YEAR: 37 for the 2012-13.

NUMBER OF AWARDS: 26.

APPLICATION INFORMATION:
Organizations should first submit a brief introductory letter, not to exceed three pages. The letter should include a concise statement of the need for the funds, the amount requested, pertinent factual information, and state the desired type of grant. Current verification of tax-exempt status should also be included. After review, eligible organizations may be invited to submit a formal grant application.
Duration: One year.
Deadline: Introductory letters may be submitted at any time. Formal applications are reviewed in mid-October. Awards announced after the first of the year.

PUBLICATIONS:
Brochure.

IRS IDENTIFICATION NUMBER: 23-7364623

DIRECTORS AND OFFICERS:
Charles M. Hair, M.D., President and Chairman
W. Cloyce Huff, M.D., Vice President and Vice Chairman
Richard M. Loft, M.D., Vice President and Vice Chairman
Marcia Donlon, Secretary
Laura K. McAvoy, Esq., Chief Financial Officer and Assistant Secretary
John R. Walters, M.D., Assistant Chief Financial Officer
Thomas P. Pecht, Director

ADDRESS INQUIRIES TO:
Laura K. McAvoy, Esq., Director
(See address above.)

THE DR. JOHN T. MACDONALD FOUNDATION, INC.
1550 Madruga Avenue, Suite 215
Coral Gables, FL 33146
(305) 667-6017
Fax: (305) 667-9135

E-MAIL ADDRESS:
info@jtmacdonaldfdn.org

WEB SITE ADDRESS:
www.jtmacdonaldfdn.org

TYPE:
Challenge/matching grants; Demonstration grants; General operating grants; Matching gifts; Project/program grants; Scholarships; Seed money grants.

See entry 1132 for full listing.

FREDA MAYTAG-GRACE CRAWFORD TRUST   [1449]
c/o JPMorgan Private Client Services
402 North Tejon Street, Suite 200
Colorado Springs, CO 80903
(719) 227-6445
Fax: (719) 227-6448

E-MAIL ADDRESS:
julie.golden@jpmorgan.com

WEB SITE ADDRESS:
www.jpmorgan.com/onlinegrants

AREAS OF INTEREST:
Tuberculosis and other respiratory diseases; preservation of a clean and healthy environment.

TYPE:
Project/program grants.

PURPOSE:
To provide medical and nursing care for individuals in the Colorado Springs community who are afflicted with tuberculosis or other respiratory diseases.

ELIGIBILITY:
Grants to 501(c)(3) nonprofit organizations. No grants to individuals.

GEOGRAPHIC RESTRICTIONS:
Colorado Springs, CO.

FINANCIAL DATA:
Amount of support per award: $3,000 to $5,000.

APPLICATION INFORMATION:
Application and guidelines are available online.
Duration: One year. No renewals.
Deadline: March 20, June 20, September 20 and December 20.

ADDRESS INQUIRIES TO:
Julie Golden, Trust Advisor
(See address above.)

MT. SINAI HEALTH CARE FOUNDATION   [1450]
11000 Euclid Avenue
Cleveland, OH 44106-1714
(216) 421-5500
Fax: (216) 421-5633

E-MAIL ADDRESS:
msb12@case.edu

WEB SITE ADDRESS:
www.mtsinaifoundation.org

FOUNDED: 1996

AREAS OF INTEREST:
Urban health, Jewish community, health policy, academic medicine and bioscience.

TYPE:
Challenge/matching grants; Demonstration grants; Development grants; Project/program grants; Seed money grants.

YEAR PROGRAM STARTED: 1997

PURPOSE:
To improve the health of the citizens in the greater Cleveland, OH area.

LEGAL BASIS:
Public charity.

ELIGIBILITY:
Eligible organizations must be IRS 501(c)(3) tax-exempt.

GEOGRAPHIC RESTRICTIONS:
Greater Cleveland, Ohio.

FINANCIAL DATA:
Total amount of support: $6,000,000 annually.

APPLICATION INFORMATION:
Contact the Foundation.
Deadline: January 1, April 1, July 1 and October 1.

PUBLICATIONS:
Guidelines; annual report; *Legacy*, newsletter.

IRS IDENTIFICATION NUMBER: 34-1777878

ADDRESS INQUIRIES TO:
Mitchell Balk, President
(See address above.)

NATIONAL HEALTH SERVICE CORPS (NHSC)   [1451]
U.S. Department of Health and Human Services
Health Resources and Services Administration
5600 Fishers Lane
Rockville, MD 20857
(877) 464-4772

E-MAIL ADDRESS:
CallCenter@hrsa.gov (grants information)

WEB SITE ADDRESS:
www.hrsa.gov

AREAS OF INTEREST:
Competitive scholarships for students enrolled in schools of osteopathic and allopathic medicine, family nurse practitioner, nurse midwifery and physician assistant training programs and dental school.

NAME(S) OF PROGRAMS:
● **National Health Service Corps Scholarship Program**

TYPE:
Scholarships. The scholarship award includes the payment of a monthly stipend, an amount for other reasonable educational expenses, tuition and required fees. Recipients owe one year of professional clinical service in a health professional shortage area (HPSA) for each year of support, with a two-year service minimum.

YEAR PROGRAM STARTED: 1973

PURPOSE:
To provide the National Health Service Corps with an adequate supply of trained health professionals to serve in health professional shortage areas.

ELIGIBILITY:
All applicants must be citizens or nationals of the U.S. at the time they apply, enrolled or accepted for enrollment in an accredited health professions education program.

FINANCIAL DATA:
Scholarship recipients receive a monthly stipend, one annual payment for other reasonable educational expenses, and payment to the school, on their behalf, of tuition and required fees. The stipend only is taxable.
Amount of support per award: Based on costs for every student in the program.
Total amount of support: Varies.

COOPERATIVE FUNDING PROGRAMS: Educational benefits from the Veterans Administration (G.I. Bill) may continue along with Scholarship Program funds since these benefits were earned by prior active duty in a uniformed service.

APPLICATION INFORMATION:
Application form is to be submitted online. Students must submit on paper, proof of U.S. citizenship, transcript, resume detailing volunteer and work experience (no more than five pages), verifications and evaluations from their school, and essays in response to prompts.

Applications submitted after the deadline are not reviewed.
Duration: The scholarship award is only for the year(s) that the contract is signed with a two-year minimum service obligation.
Deadline: Varies.

PUBLICATIONS:
Applicant information bulletin.

ADDRESS INQUIRIES TO:
See e-mail or telephone number above.

*SPECIAL STIPULATIONS:
Recipients must serve where needed in a designated Health Professional Shortage Area (HPSA).

NATIONAL INSTITUTE ON AGING   [1452]

Division of Extramural Activities
7201 Wisconsin Avenue, Room 2C218
Bethesda, MD 20892
(301) 496-9322
Fax: (301) 402-2945

E-MAIL ADDRESS:
barrr@mail.nih.gov

WEB SITE ADDRESS:
www.nia.nih.gov

FOUNDED: 1975

AREAS OF INTEREST:
Biology of aging research, geriatrics and gerontology research, neuroscience and neuropsychology of aging research, behavioral and social research on aging.

NAME(S) OF PROGRAMS:
● Aging Research

TYPE:
Conferences/seminars; Fellowships; Grants-in-aid; Project/program grants; Research grants; Technical assistance; Training grants; Research contracts. Loan repayment programs.

PURPOSE:
To support biomedical, clinical, social, neuroscience, neuropsychology and behavioral research and research training directed toward greater understanding of the aging process and the needs and problems of older people. The primary goal is to improve the health and well-being of older people through the development of new knowledge.

LEGAL BASIS:
Government agency.

ELIGIBILITY:
Grants and contracts are available to universities, colleges, medical, dental and nursing schools, schools of public health, laboratories, hospitals, state and local health departments and other public or private profit or nonprofit institutions.

NRSA awards are provided for individual postdoctoral and institutional pre-and postdoctoral research training in health and health-related areas which are periodically specified by the National Institutes of Health. Individuals with a professional or scientific degree are eligible. Applicants must be citizens of the U.S. or be admitted for permanent residency.

GEOGRAPHIC RESTRICTIONS:
United States.

FINANCIAL DATA:
Amount of support per award: Average: $392,500 for research project grants.
Total amount of support: Varies.

NUMBER OF APPLICANTS MOST RECENT YEAR:
2,000.

NUMBER OF AWARDS: 1,400.

APPLICATION INFORMATION:
Contact the Institute.
Duration: One year to multiyear.
Deadline: Varies.

OFFICERS:
Robin A. Barr, D.Phil., Director

ADDRESS INQUIRIES TO:
Division of Extramural Activities
(See address above.)

NATIONAL INSTITUTE ON ALCOHOL ABUSE AND ALCOHOLISM   [1453]

Office of Extramural Activities
5635 Fishers Lane
MSC 9304
Bethesda, MD 20892-9304
(301) 443-9737
Fax: (301) 443-6077

E-MAIL ADDRESS:
bautista@mail.nih.gov

WEB SITE ADDRESS:
www.niaaa.nih.gov

FOUNDED: 1971

NAME(S) OF PROGRAMS:
● **Academic Career Awards (K07)**
● **Career Enhancement Award for Stem Cell Research (K18)**
● **Independent Scientist Awards (K02)**
● **Mentored Patient-Oriented Research Career Development Award (K23)**
● **Mentored Quantitative Research Career Development Award (K25)**
● **Midcareer Investigator Award in Patient-Oriented Research (K24)**
● **NIH Pathway to Independence Award (K99/R00)**
● **Scientist Development Awards for Mentored Clinical (K08)**
● **Scientist Development Awards for Mentored Research (K01)**

TYPE:
Research grants. Support for full-time research on a long-term (five years) basis for research scientists.

Academic Career Awards (K07) support development of clinical faculty in clinical research and teaching related to alcohol problems. Developmental award only.

Career Enhancement Award for Stem Cell Research (K18) is to encourage investigators to obtain the training they need to appropriately use stem cells in their research.

Independent Scientist Awards (K02) support advanced research experience.

NIH Pathway to Independence (PI) Award (K99/R00) will provide up to five years of support consisting of two phases. The PI award is limited to postdoctoral trainees.

Scientist Development Awards for Mentored Research (K01) and Scientist Development Awards for Mentored Clinical (K08) support individuals with one to four years of postdoctoral training or experience, but no extensive research experience.

PURPOSE:
To provide salary support to talented investigators so that they can engage in full-time research on a long-term basis and develop their full research potential.

LEGAL BASIS:
PHS Act, Section 301 as amended (42 U.S.C. 241).

ELIGIBILITY:
Applicants can either be public or nonprofit private organizations and institutions located in the U.S. or its territories and possessions or U.S. citizens or permanent residents. Citizenship is mandatory for renewal beyond the initial five-year award.

FINANCIAL DATA:
Amount of support per award: Varies.
Total amount of support: Varies.

APPLICATION INFORMATION:
Application kits are available at most institutional offices of sponsored research and may be obtained from the Grants Information Office.
Duration: All awards five years. Renewal possible.
Deadline: February 12, June 12 and October 12.

PUBLICATIONS:
NIAAA additional information to the NIH Career Development Program Announcements (K Awards).

ADDRESS INQUIRIES TO:
Dr. Bob Huebner, Acting Director
Division of Treatment
and Recovery Research
Tel: (301) 443-4344 or

Dr. Ralph Hingson, Director
Division of Epidemiology
and Prevention Research
Tel: (301) 443-1274 or

Dr. Gary Murray
Division of Metabolism
and Health Effects
Tel: (301) 443-9940 or

Dr. Antonio Noronha
Division of Neuroscience and Behavior
Tel: (301) 443-7722
(See address above.)

NATIONAL INSTITUTE ON ALCOHOL ABUSE AND ALCOHOLISM [1454]

Division of Metabolism and Health Effect
5635 Fishers Lane, Room 2037
MSC 9304
Bethesda, MD 20892-9304
(301) 443-8744
Fax: (301) 594-0673

E-MAIL ADDRESS:
kathy.jung@nih.gov

WEB SITE ADDRESS:
www.niaaa.nih.gov

FOUNDED: 1971

AREAS OF INTEREST:
Pharmaceuticals, diagnostic instruments, and the prevention and treatment of alcoholism and alcohol abuse.

NAME(S) OF PROGRAMS:
● **Small Business Innovation Research Program**

TYPE:
Research grants; Research contracts. Separate grant applications are awarded for Phase I and Phase II of the program. Phase I is designed to establish the feasibility of the technological innovation and determine the quality of performance. The objective of Phase II is to further demonstrate the efficacy of the product for commercial exploitation. Only funded applicants from Phase I are eligible to apply for Phase II.

YEAR PROGRAM STARTED: 1983

PURPOSE:
To stimulate technological innovation in the alcohol field, increase private-sector commercialization of innovations derived from federal research and development and foster and encourage participation by minority and disadvantaged firms in technological innovation.

LEGAL BASIS:
The Small Business Innovation Development Act, P.L. 97-219.

ELIGIBILITY:
Each organization must qualify as a small business in accordance with the stipulations set forth in the Omnibus Solicitation of the PHS Small Business Innovation Research Program. In general, the organization must be independently owned and operated, must be located in the U.S. and at least 51% of the ownership must be by U.S. citizens or lawfully admitted permanent resident aliens. The primary employment of the principal investigator must be with the firm at the time of award and during the conduct of the proposed project. The performance site must be in the U.S.

GEOGRAPHIC RESTRICTIONS:
United States.

FINANCIAL DATA:
Amount of support per award: May not exceed $150,000 for both direct and indirect costs, for a maximum period of six months, for Phase I. May not exceed $1,000,000 for two years in total costs for Phase II. If costs exceed these amounts, contact the program officer named in the solicitation or the SBIR coordinator.

APPLICATION INFORMATION:
Applications may be obtained from grants.gov.
Duration: Six months for Phase I. Two years for Phase II.

Deadline: Contracts: Early November; Grants: April 5, August 5 and December 5.

PUBLICATIONS:
Omnibus solicitation for SBIR grant applications.

ADDRESS INQUIRIES TO:
Kathy Jung, SBIR Coordinator
Division of Metabolism and Health Effect
(See address above.)

NATIONAL INSTITUTES OF HEALTH [1455]

Division of International Services
31 Center Drive, B2BO7
MSC-2028
Bethesda, MD 20892-2028
(301) 496-6166
Fax: (301) 496-0847

E-MAIL ADDRESS:
dis@mail.nih.gov

WEB SITE ADDRESS:
www.training.nih.gov
dis.ors.od.nih.gov

FOUNDED: 1950

AREAS OF INTEREST:
Biomedical and behavioral sciences.

NAME(S) OF PROGRAMS:
● **The NIH Visiting Program**

TYPE:
Exchange programs; Fellowships.

YEAR PROGRAM STARTED: 1950

PURPOSE:
To provide talented scientists throughout the world an opportunity to participate in the varied research activities of the National Institutes of Health. Two categories of Visiting Program participants include Visiting Fellows for obtaining research training experience and Visiting Scientists for conducting health-related research.

LEGAL BASIS:
Government agency.

ELIGIBILITY:
Visiting Fellows must have a doctoral degree or its equivalent and not more than five years of relevant postdoctoral research experience when the fellowship begins. Visiting Fellows may be resident or nonresident aliens. U.S. citizens are not eligible for the Visiting Fellow award.

Visiting Scientists must have a doctoral degree or its equivalent and more than three years of postdoctoral research experience.

All Visiting Program participants must be proficient in the use and understanding of the English language, both written and spoken.

FINANCIAL DATA:
Visiting Fellows receive a monthly stipend during the award period to cover living expenses. The stipend level is determined by the number of years of relevant postdoctoral research experience. Visiting Scientists receive a salary based on the candidate's qualifications and several of the benefits available to employees of the U.S. Government.

Amount of support per award: Visiting Fellows: $41,200 to $78,700. Visiting Scientists start at $45,461. Funding may be increased annually by $1,500 to $2,000 per year.

NUMBER OF AWARDS: 1,700.

APPLICATION INFORMATION:
Individuals interested in a Visiting Program fellowship award or appointment should visit the NIH web site for application information.
Duration: Generally, two years. Renewable for a total of five years, based upon merit and depending on visa restrictions.
Deadline: Applications are accepted on a rolling basis.

PUBLICATIONS:
Program description.

ADDRESS INQUIRIES TO:
Candelario Zapata
(See address above.)

NATIONAL INSTITUTES OF HEALTH

Division of International Relations
Fogarty International Center
Building 31, Room B2C39
31 Center Drive, MSC 2220
Bethesda, MD 20892-2220
(301) 496-4784

E-MAIL ADDRESS:
chungt@mail.nih.gov
mili.ferreira@nih.gov

WEB SITE ADDRESS:
www.fic.nih.gov/programs/pages/japan-fellowships.aspx

TYPE:
Fellowships. A limited number of postdoctoral research fellowships are provided by the Japan Science and Technology Agency (JSTA) to U.S. scientists to conduct research in Japan. Types of activity supported include collaboration in basic or clinical research and familiarization with or utilization of special techniques and equipment not otherwise available to the applicant.

See entry 966 for full listing.

LUCILE PACKARD FOUNDATION FOR CHILDREN'S HEALTH

400 Hamilton Avenue, Suite 340
Palo Alto, CA 94301
(650) 736-0675
(650) 497-8365

E-MAIL ADDRESS:
grants@lpfch.org

WEB SITE ADDRESS:
www.lpfch-cshcn.org/grants

TYPE:
Project/program grants.

See entry 1140 for full listing.

THE PATRON SAINTS FOUNDATION [1456]

260 South Los Robles Avenue, No. 201
Pasadena, CA 91101
(626) 564-0444
Fax: (626) 564-0444

E-MAIL ADDRESS:
patronsaintsfdn@sbcglobal.net

WEB SITE ADDRESS:
www.patronsaintsfoundation.org

FOUNDED: 1986

AREAS OF INTEREST:
Health care.

TYPE:
Capital grants; Project/program grants; Research grants. Limited operating support will be awarded at the discretion of the Board of Directors.

YEAR PROGRAM STARTED: 1986

PURPOSE:
To improve the health of individuals residing in the West San Gabriel Valley through health care programs that are consistent with the moral and religious teachings of the Roman Catholic Church.

LEGAL BASIS:
Private foundation.

ELIGIBILITY:
Organizations must be IRS 501(c)(3) tax-exempt.

GEOGRAPHIC RESTRICTIONS:
West San Gabriel Valley, California.

FINANCIAL DATA:
Amount of support per award: $5,000 to $15,000.
Total amount of support: $450,856 for fiscal year ended June 30, 2013.

NUMBER OF APPLICANTS MOST RECENT YEAR: 46.

NUMBER OF AWARDS: 29 for fiscal year ended June 30, 2013.

APPLICATION INFORMATION:
Two copies of the application (not to exceed three pages, no less than 11-point type, one stapled and one paper-clipped) must be mailed to the Foundation, along with other required documents including financial statements, copy of the organization's 501(c)(3) determination letter and IRS Form 990.
Duration: One year. Renewal by reapplication.
Deadline: First Friday in March and first Friday in October.

PUBLICATIONS:
Grant guidelines; grant application form; brochure.

IRS IDENTIFICATION NUMBER: 95-3484257

EXECUTIVE DIRECTOR:
Kathleen T. Shannon

ADDRESS INQUIRIES TO:
Kathleen T. Shannon, Executive Director (See address above.)

PIEDMONT HEALTH FOUNDATION   [1457]
P.O. Box 9303
Greenville, SC 29604
(864) 370-0212
Fax: (864) 370-0212

E-MAIL ADDRESS:
katysmith@piedmonthealthfoundation.org

WEB SITE ADDRESS:
www.piedmonthealthfoundation.org

FOUNDED: 1985

AREAS OF INTEREST:
Health.

TYPE:
Demonstration grants; Project/program grants; Research grants; Seed money grants.

YEAR PROGRAM STARTED: 1986

PURPOSE:
To improve health in Greenville County, SC.

LEGAL BASIS:
Private foundation.

ELIGIBILITY:
Organizations must be nonprofit 501(c)(3). No grants to individuals.

GEOGRAPHIC RESTRICTIONS:
Greenville, South Carolina.

FINANCIAL DATA:
Amount of support per award: Grants typically $2,000 to $15,000.
Total amount of support: Approximately $100,000 for the year 2013.

NUMBER OF AWARDS: 6 for the year 2013.

REPRESENTATIVE AWARDS:
$75,000 over three years to LiveWell Greenville for operational support; $31,500 to Furman University for BMI study; $4,080 to Greenville Organic Foods Organization for Grow Healthy Kids program.

APPLICATION INFORMATION:
Application information is available on the web site.
Duration: One year.
Deadline: February 10, April 10, July 10 and October 10.

OFFICERS:
Jennifer Graf Smith, Chairman
Susan Cyr, Esq., Vice Chairman
Greg Taylor, Treasurer
Addy Matney, Secretary

ADDRESS INQUIRIES TO:
Katy Pugh Smith, Executive Director (See address above.)

THE DOROTHY RIDER POOL HEALTH CARE TRUST   [1458]
1050 South Cedar Crest Boulevard
Suite 202
Allentown, PA 18103
(610) 770-9346
Fax: (610) 770-9361

E-MAIL ADDRESS:
info@pooltrust.org

WEB SITE ADDRESS:
www.pooltrust.org

FOUNDED: 1975

AREAS OF INTEREST:
Community health, health services research, leadership development and medical education, recruitment and retention of outstanding health care providers, access to care, health studies, and clinical innovation.

TYPE:
Awards/prizes; Challenge/matching grants; Development grants; Endowments; Fellowships; Project/program grants. Grants addressing at least one of the key components of the Trust's Philanthropic Agenda: improved health status of the citizens of the region, recruitment and retention of outstanding health care providers, clinical innovation, access to care, medical education, community health and health service research.

PURPOSE:
To serve as a resource that enables Lehigh Valley Hospital to be a superior regional hospital and improve the health of the citizens of the region it serves.

ELIGIBILITY:
The Trust considers proposals from nonprofit organizations and institutions within the Trust's interest areas.

GEOGRAPHIC RESTRICTIONS:
Allentown, Pennsylvania and surrounding area.

FINANCIAL DATA:
Amount of support per award: Varies.
Total amount of support: $3,772,566 for the year 2013.

REPRESENTATIVE AWARDS:
$5,496,464 to Lehigh Valley Health Network for Continued Development of Population Health Management and Evaluation Infrastructure; $1,265,177 to Lehigh Valley Health Network for Future of Nursing: Leading Change, Advancing Health; $276,000 for Health Care Council of the Lehigh Valley - Hospital Collaborative 2013-2016 Health Improvement Plan and 2016 Community Health Needs Assessment.

APPLICATION INFORMATION:
Funding requests should be initiated with a letter of intent from the applicant. The letter should be two to four pages summarizing the need, objective, strategy, evaluation, budget and duration.

Electronic application process is available on the web site.
Duration: Varies.
Deadline: Submit letter of intent by August 1 and March 1. Funding notification by early March and October, respectively.

PUBLICATIONS:
Annual report.

IRS IDENTIFICATION NUMBER: 23-6627932

TRUSTEES:
Denise M. Gargan
John P. Jones, III
Peter M. Leibold, Esq.
Mary D. Naylor, Ph.D., R.N.
James O. Wolliscroft, M.D.

STAFF:
Edward F. Meehan, M.P.H., Executive Director
Ronald C. Dendas, M.S., Program Officer
Joseph J. Napolitano, Ph.D., M.P.H., Program Officer
Bridget I. Rassler, Manager, Finance and Administration
Regina M. Marks, Program Secretary
Brenda C. Schoenberger, Secretary

ADDRESS INQUIRIES TO:
Edward F. Meehan, M.P.H., Executive Director
(See address above.)

QUANTUM FOUNDATION   [1459]
2701 North Australian Avenue, Suite 200
West Palm Beach, FL 33407
(561) 832-7497
Fax: (561) 832-5794

E-MAIL ADDRESS:
randy@quantumfnd.org

WEB SITE ADDRESS:
www.quantumfnd.org

FOUNDED: 1995

AREAS OF INTEREST:
Health care access, health education, and health care workforce.

TYPE:
Capital grants; Challenge/matching grants; Demonstration grants; Matching gifts; Project/program grants; Seed money grants.

YEAR PROGRAM STARTED: 1997

PURPOSE:
To increase health care access, improve science and health education, and enhance the health care workforce.

LEGAL BASIS:
Private foundation.

ELIGIBILITY:
Eligible organizations must be IRS 501(c)(3) tax-exempt or state or local governments providing services in Palm Beach County.

GEOGRAPHIC RESTRICTIONS:
Palm Beach County, Florida.

FINANCIAL DATA:
Amount of support per award: Varies.
Total amount of support: Approximately $6,000,000 annually.

NUMBER OF APPLICANTS MOST RECENT YEAR:
199.

NUMBER OF AWARDS: 105 for the year 2011.

APPLICATION INFORMATION:
Submit a Letter of Inquiry at the Foundation's web site.

STAFF:
Randy Scheid, Program Officer

ADDRESS INQUIRIES TO:
Randy Scheid, Program Officer
(See e-mail address above.)

RESEARCH MANITOBA   [1460]
205 - 445 Ellice Avenue
Winnipeg MB R3B 3P5 Canada
(204) 775-1096
Fax: (204) 786-5401

E-MAIL ADDRESS:
info@researchmb.ca

WEB SITE ADDRESS:
researchmanitoba.ca

FOUNDED: 1980

AREAS OF INTEREST:
Health-related basic, clinical and applied scientific research in the Province of Manitoba.

CONSULTING OR VOLUNTEER SERVICES:
The Council advises the provincial Minister of Health on matters relating to health research, as the Minister may refer to the Council for its consideration.

TYPE:
Awards/prizes; Fellowships; General operating grants; Project/program grants; Research grants; Travel grants. Establishment grants. Postdoctoral Fellowships are meant to allow recent doctoral degree recipients, with considerable research training and accomplishments, to further their training to allow them to become independent investigators.

Graduate Studentships are offered to qualified graduate students who are undertaking full-time Master's or doctoral programs in the province of Manitoba.

Ph.D. Dissertation Awards are for graduate students in population and health-related social sciences fields.

Operating Grants are for investigators who have held an academic appointment at the rank of assistant professor or above (or equivalent) in Manitoba for a period of not more than five years. They are for new investigators only.

Establishment Grants are intended to allow recently recruited faculty members in the province of Manitoba to focus on research and to establish their research programs over a three-year period.

Bridge Funding awards are intended to allow investigators who have recently lost funding, after a sustained period of support from a major agency, to maintain their research program while attempting to regain their funding by reapplication.

Travel grants are for fellowship awards only.

Manitoba Partnership Program is intended to support operating grant applications that are judged to be of high scientific merit through peer review, but are below the funding capacity of CIHR's base budget, to increase their chances of success in their next submission.

YEAR PROGRAM STARTED: 1981

PURPOSE:
To provide support for health-related research in the Province of Manitoba.

LEGAL BASIS:
Established by an Act of the Provincial Legislature and provincially funded.

ELIGIBILITY:
Grants are awarded to individuals in the Province of Manitoba.

GEOGRAPHIC RESTRICTIONS:
Manitoba, Canada.

FINANCIAL DATA:
Amount of support per award: Dissertation Awards: Up to $5,000; Establishment Grants: $100,000; Fellowships: $36,750; Manitoba Partnership Program: $65,000 per year; Manitoba Research Chairs: $100,000 sponsorship awards; Operating Grants: Varies; Studentships: $17,850.
Total amount of support: Varies.
Matching fund requirements: For Bridge Funding, MMSF Awards, Partnered Chair and Regional Partnership Grants.

APPLICATION INFORMATION:
Applications must be made on the appropriate Research Manitoba forms online.
Duration: Establishment Grants: Three years. Operating Grants: Up to two years.
Deadline: Clinical Fellows, Fellowships and Studentships: February 1. Establishment Grants, Operating Grants and Research Chairs: March 1. Manitoba Partnership Fund: February 28.

PUBLICATIONS:
Annual report; awards guide; EGMS user guide.

STAFF:
Christina Weise, Executive Director
Liz Ford, Administrative Officer
Kristen Hooper, Communications Officer
Ted Catalla, Evaluation and Policy Analyst
Shannon Rogalski, Manager, Funding Programs

COUNCIL MEMBERS:
Dr. Brian Postl, Chairperson
Bob Brennan
Jan Currie
Hugh Eliasson
Karen Herd
Dr. Digvir Jayas
Kevin Kavanaugh
Dr. John Langstaff
Dr. Susan McClement
Dr. Peter Nickerson

Cathy Nieroda
Dr. Barbara Triggs-Raine
Arlene Wilgosh

ADDRESS INQUIRIES TO:
See e-mail address above.

JOSEPHINE G. RUSSELL TRUST   [1461]
9 Bartlet Street, Suite 343
Andover, MA 01810

E-MAIL ADDRESS:
russelltrust@yahoo.com

FOUNDED: 1933

AREAS OF INTEREST:
Education, health care, poverty and social services.

TYPE:
General operating grants; Project/program grants; Scholarships.

PURPOSE:
To provide care, healing and nursing of the sick and injured; to provide relief and aid to the poor; to provide training and education of the young; to assist in any other manner of social service in the City of Lawrence.

LEGAL BASIS:
Private charitable trust.

ELIGIBILITY:
Eligible organizations must be IRS 501(c)(3) tax-exempt and serve the Lawrence area. No grants to individuals. No grants are made for endowments, equipment, capital campaigns, construction or renovations of buildings and facilities. No matching gifts.

Organizations intending to submit applications for funds must be able to demonstrate that, if funds are awarded by the Trust, the program will confer a direct benefit to Lawrence residents who are sick, injured or poor; or for education or in any other manner of social services upon the people of the city of Lawrence, MA.

GEOGRAPHIC RESTRICTIONS:
Lawrence, Massachusetts.

FINANCIAL DATA:
Amount of support per award: Minimum $1,000.
Total amount of support: $410,000 for the year 2012.

NUMBER OF APPLICANTS MOST RECENT YEAR:
43.

NUMBER OF AWARDS: 38.

APPLICATION INFORMATION:
Guidelines are available upon request. Applicants may submit a written proposal and must include a copy of the IRS tax determination letter, budget and list of trustees in the organization.

Once application is completed, individual copies must be sent to all designated trustees.
Duration: One year. Renewal possible.
Deadline: January 31.

PUBLICATIONS:
Guidelines.

ADDRESS INQUIRIES TO:
See e-mail address above.

EUNICE KENNEDY SHRIVER NATIONAL INSTITUTE OF CHILD HEALTH AND HUMAN DEVELOPMENT [1462]

Division of Extramural Research
Executive Building, Room 4805
6100 Executive Boulevard, MSC 7510
Bethesda, MD 20852-7510
(800) 370-2943
Fax: (866) 760-5947

E-MAIL ADDRESS:
NICHDInformationResourceCenter@mail.nih.gov

WEB SITE ADDRESS:
www.nichd.nih.gov/about/org/der/branches/Pages/index.aspx

FOUNDED: 1963

AREAS OF INTEREST:
All health sciences pertaining to mothers and children.

NAME(S) OF PROGRAMS:
- **Child Development and Behavior Branch (CDBB)**
- **Obstetric and Pediatric Pharmacology and Therapeutics Branch (OPPTB)**
- **Pediatric Growth and Nutrition Branch (PGNB)**

TYPE:
Conferences/seminars; Development grants; Fellowships; General operating grants; Project/program grants; Training grants; Research contracts. Project grants and research contracts to expand the health and well-being of individuals from the moment of conception and extending through the later teenage years.

PURPOSE:
To discover new knowledge through research.

LEGAL BASIS:
Public Health Service Act, Sections 301(c), 444 and 472.

ELIGIBILITY:
Universities, colleges, medical, dental and nursing schools, schools of public health, laboratories, hospitals, state and local health departments, other public or private nonprofit institutions and commercial organizations are eligible. Individuals may apply for grants for academic and research training. They must have a professional or scientific degree and be citizens or permanent residents of the U.S.

FINANCIAL DATA:
Amount of support per award: Varies.

APPLICATION INFORMATION:
Contact the Institute.
Duration: One year to multiyear funding.

SICKKIDS FOUNDATION [1463]

525 University Avenue, 14th Floor
Toronto ON M5G 2L3 Canada
(416) 813-6166 ext. 2354
(800) 661-1083
Fax: (416) 813-4912

E-MAIL ADDRESS:
national.grants@sickkidsfoundation.com

WEB SITE ADDRESS:
www.sickkidsfoundation.com/about-us/grants

FOUNDED: 1973

AREAS OF INTEREST:
Healthier children; a better world.

NAME(S) OF PROGRAMS:
- **Community Conference Grants Program**
- **New Investigator Research Grants**

TYPE:
Awards/prizes; Conferences/seminars; Project/program grants; Research grants. Community Conference Grants program brings together families with researchers and clinicians for medical presentations and family-oriented discussions. It helps ensure knowledge exchange with families so that they are able to access the most up-to-date information about their children's health.

New Investigator Research Grants program focus is to ensure that there continues to be well-trained researchers across the country working to address the most pressing childhood diseases and conditions.

YEAR PROGRAM STARTED: 1974

PURPOSE:
To promote quality programs in child health, research and public health education in the field.

LEGAL BASIS:
Public foundation with charitable registration.

ELIGIBILITY:
Grants are paid to recognized Canadian charitable organizations. Institutions, agencies and other groups working in the field of child health in Canada may apply. Applications are subjected to peer assessment as to the merits of the project, feasibility, and significance for child health and study design criteria as appropriate.

GEOGRAPHIC RESTRICTIONS:
Canada.

FINANCIAL DATA:
Amount of support per award: $5,000 to $100,000 per year.
Total amount of support: Varies.

NUMBER OF APPLICANTS MOST RECENT YEAR:
100 for the year 2011-12.

NUMBER OF AWARDS: 15 for the year 2011-12.

APPLICATION INFORMATION:
Application guidelines are available online. To discuss eligibility, contact grants office directly.
Duration: Maximum of three years with annual review of progress. No renewals.
Deadline: Community Conference Grants: January 31, May 31 and September 30. New Investigator Research Grant: Fall.

ADDRESS INQUIRIES TO:
See e-mail address above.

SISTERS OF ST. JOSEPH HEALTHCARE FOUNDATION [1464]

440 South Batavia
Orange, CA 92868-3998
(714) 633-8121 ext. 7109
Fax: (714) 744-3135

E-MAIL ADDRESS:
rfox@csjorange.org

WEB SITE ADDRESS:
www.csjorange.org

FOUNDED: 1992

AREAS OF INTEREST:
Health care and health access.

TYPE:
General operating grants; Project/program grants. The Foundation sponsors or supports long-term efforts which are closely identified with the Sisters of St. Joseph of Orange and their mission of bringing unity and healing where divisiveness and oppression exist.

PURPOSE:
To fund programs which directly serve the needs of the underserved, especially families and children at risk.

LEGAL BASIS:
Public foundation.

ELIGIBILITY:
Applicants must be nonprofit organizations operating in Humbolt County, southern California and San Francisco Bay area which have programs that directly serve the needs of the underserved, especially families and children at risk, as well as programs of education and advocacy which are directed at improving health and access to health care. Religious organizations also receive support. A Sister of St. Joseph of Orange endorsement or Vice President for Mission Integration endorsement and/or involvement is required. Capital projects will not be considered.

The Foundation supports the concept of Healthy Communities, and desires to fund programs and organizations that:
(1) provide direct health-related services;
(2) support and transform the individual, social, economic, institutional, and cultural aspects of communities;
(3) provide change within larger societal systems to benefit low-income and at-risk populations and;
(4) develop the leadership and capacity for self-determination of those served by the Foundation's funding.

GEOGRAPHIC RESTRICTIONS:
Southern California, Humbolt County and San Francisco Bay area.

NUMBER OF APPLICANTS MOST RECENT YEAR:
106.

APPLICATION INFORMATION:
Contact the Foundation.
Duration: One year.
Deadline: Contact Foundation for exact dates.

ADDRESS INQUIRIES TO:
Sister Regina Fox, S.S.N.D.
Program Director
(See address above.)

GERTRUDE E. SKELLY CHARITABLE FOUNDATION

4600 North Ocean Boulevard
Suite 206
Boynton Beach, FL 33435
(561) 276-1008
Fax: (561) 272-2793

E-MAIL ADDRESS:
skelly@hhk.com

TYPE:
Challenge/matching grants; Conferences/seminars; Internships; Project/program grants; Research grants; Scholarships; Training grants. Emergency grants for continued education.

See entry 1641 for full listing.

THE CHRISTOPHER D. SMITHERS FOUNDATION, INC. [1465]

P.O. Box 67
Mill Neck, NY 11765
(516) 676-0067
Fax: (516) 676-0323

E-MAIL ADDRESS:
info@smithersfoundation.org

WEB SITE ADDRESS:
www.smithersfoundation.org

FOUNDED: 1952

AREAS OF INTEREST:
Education and prevention of alcoholism.

TYPE:
Conferences/seminars; Project/program grants; Research grants; Technical assistance; Training grants.

YEAR PROGRAM STARTED: 1952

PURPOSE:
To prevent alcoholism through education.

APPLICATION INFORMATION:
Grant proposal must include:
(1) brief description of the program and grant amount requested (budget);
(2) copy of 501(c)(3) nonprofit status and;
(3) copy of most recent annual report.

PUBLICATIONS:
Annual report.

OFFICERS:
Adele C. Smithers, President
Christopher B. Smithers, Vice President
Richard Esposito, Vice President/Treasurer
Nikki Smithers, Secretary

DIRECTORS:
Stacia Murphy
Nicholas A. Pace, M.D.
M. Elizabeth Brothers, Honorary Director

ARTEMAS W. STEARNS TRUST [1466]

9 Bartlet Street, Suite 343
Andover, MA 01810

E-MAIL ADDRESS:
stearnstrust@yahoo.com

FOUNDED: 1896

AREAS OF INTEREST:
The aged and poor, health care in the Lawrence area, social services and education.

TYPE:
General operating grants; Project/program grants; Scholarships. Elder and infirm support.

YEAR PROGRAM STARTED: 1896

PURPOSE:
To pay income to such nonprofit and charitable homes, nursing homes, convalescent homes, retirement homes, sanitaria, homes for the aged, hospitals, agencies and such other similar institutions, organizations and agencies as may provide for or care, in whole or in part, for the indigent aged people of both sexes; to provide relief of the deserving poor of the City of Lawrence, without distinction of nationality or religious belief.

LEGAL BASIS:
Private charitable trust.

ELIGIBILITY:
Eligible organizations must be IRS 501(c)(3) tax-exempt. No grants to individuals. No grants are made for endowments, equipment, capital campaigns, construction or renovations of buildings and facilities.

Organizations intending to submit applications for funds must be able to demonstrate that, if funds are awarded by the Trust, the program will confer a direct benefit upon the indigent aged people or to the deserving poor of the city of Lawrence, MA exclusively.

GEOGRAPHIC RESTRICTIONS:
Lawrence, Massachusetts.

FINANCIAL DATA:
Amount of support per award: Minimum $1,000.

Total amount of support: $194,000 for the year 2012.

NUMBER OF APPLICANTS MOST RECENT YEAR: 33.

NUMBER OF AWARDS: 28.

APPLICATION INFORMATION:
Guidelines are sent upon request. Applicants may submit a written proposal and must include a copy of the IRS tax determination letter, budget and list of trustees in the organization.

Once application is completed, individual copies must be sent to all designated trustees. Contact the Trust for complete guidelines.
Duration: One year. Renewal possible.
Deadline: January 31.

PUBLICATIONS:
Application guidelines.

ADDRESS INQUIRIES TO:
See e-mail address above.

U.S. DEPARTMENT OF HEALTH AND HUMAN SERVICES [1467]

Health Resources and Services Administration
Bureau of Primary Health Care
Parklawn Building, 5600 Fishers Lane
Room 17C26
Rockville, MD 20857
(301) 594-4300
(301) 594-4110
Fax: (301) 594-4997

WEB SITE ADDRESS:
www.hrsa.gov
www.bphc.hrsa.gov

FOUNDED: 1976

AREAS OF INTEREST:
Assisting communities located in medically underserved areas to develop needed primary health care services.

CONSULTING OR VOLUNTEER SERVICES:
Information and technical assistance is available from U.S. Public Health Service Regional Office staff.

NAME(S) OF PROGRAMS:
● **The Health Center Program**

TYPE:
Project/program grants. Grants may be made for planning and development of a community health center and for operations.

YEAR PROGRAM STARTED: 1975

PURPOSE:
To provide primary health care in ambulatory care settings located in severely medically underserved areas and to develop a network of services involving as many other health programs and facilities operating in the area as possible; to arrange for other federal programs not operating in the area to establish services within the federally funded primary care center whenever possible.

LEGAL BASIS:
Government agency.

ELIGIBILITY:
Grants may be made to public or private not-for-profit entities. Area to be served must be medically underserved. Priority will be given to areas of highest need.

GEOGRAPHIC RESTRICTIONS:
United States.

FINANCIAL DATA:
Amount of support per award: Approximately $650,000.

Matching fund requirements: The applicant must assume part of the project costs determined on a case-by-case basis.

COOPERATIVE FUNDING PROGRAMS: Cooperative funding with other federal programs, such as Migrant Health Centers, National Health Service Corps, MCH, or Mental Health Alcohol and Drug Abuse are encouraged, as well as cooperation with state and local programs.

APPLICATION INFORMATION:
Information available from HRSA Grant Application Center, 901 Russell Avenue, Suite 450, Gaithersburg, MD 20879, or call (877) 477-2123.

Duration: Project periods may be up to three years, with annual budget periods.

PUBLICATIONS:
Application guidelines.

STAFF:
Jim Macrae, Associate Administrator to Bureau of Primary Health Care Director

U.S. DEPARTMENT OF HEALTH AND HUMAN SERVICES [1468]

Centers for Medicare and Medicaid Services
7500 Security Boulevard
Baltimore, MD 21244-1850
(410) 786-3000
(877) 267-2323
Fax: (410) 786-1008

WEB SITE ADDRESS:
www.cms.gov

FOUNDED: 1967

NAME(S) OF PROGRAMS:
● **Medicaid**

TYPE:
Formula grants. Financial assistance to states for in- and outpatient hospital services, other laboratory services, home health care, family planning, physicians' services and early diagnosis and treatment for persons who are medically needy.

LEGAL BASIS:
Title XIX, Social Security Act as amended; Public Law 89-97; Public Law 90-248; Public Law 91-56; 42 U.S.C. 1396, et seq. Public Law 92-223; Public Law 92-603.

ELIGIBILITY:
State and local welfare agencies operating under an approved Medicaid plan are eligible for support.

GEOGRAPHIC RESTRICTIONS:
United States.

FINANCIAL DATA:
Amount of support per award: Varies.
Total amount of support: Varies.

APPLICATION INFORMATION:
Application forms are available from the address above or from regional or local offices of the Medical Services Administration to whom applications should be submitted.

Duration: Quarterly.

Deadline: States must submit quarterly estimates of funds no later than May 15, August 15, November 15 and February 15 in order to receive quarterly grant awards.

UNITED HOSPITAL FUND OF NEW YORK [1469]
1411 Broadway, 12th Floor
New York, NY 10018
(212) 494-0761
Fax: (212) 494-0801

E-MAIL ADDRESS:
hholmes@uhfnyc.org

WEB SITE ADDRESS:
www.uhfnyc.org

FOUNDED: 1879

AREAS OF INTEREST:
Strengthening health care finances, expanding health insurance coverage, improving quality of care, redesigning health care services and promoting health care volunteerism.

NAME(S) OF PROGRAMS:
● **Health Care Improvement Grant Program**

TYPE:
Project/program grants; Seed money grants.

YEAR PROGRAM STARTED: 1938

PURPOSE:
To provide support to innovative projects by nonprofit hospitals and health care and other organizations to improve the quality of health care for all New Yorkers.

LEGAL BASIS:
Public charity.

ELIGIBILITY:
Nonprofit 501(c)(3) tax-exempt organizations in New York City are eligible for support. No grants to individuals, capital or endowment campaigns or general operating grants..

GEOGRAPHIC RESTRICTIONS:
New York, New York, including the five boroughs.

FINANCIAL DATA:
Amount of support per award: $30,000 to $75,000.

Total amount of support: Approximately $1,000,000 for the year 2012-13.

NUMBER OF APPLICANTS MOST RECENT YEAR: 75.

NUMBER OF AWARDS: 30.

REPRESENTATIVE AWARDS:
$40,000 to Charles B. Wang Community Health Center; $75,000 to New Yorkers for Accessible Health Coverage; $50,000 to New York City Health and Hospitals Corporation.

APPLICATION INFORMATION:
Required documentation includes grant application form, budget, specifics regarding the particular project to be funded and sources of support.

Duration: One year. Nonrenewable.

Deadline: March 1, July 2 and November 1. Notification one week after board meets.

PUBLICATIONS:
Annual report; application guidelines.

OFFICERS:
J. Barclay Collins, II, Chairman
James R. Tallon, Jr., President
Sheila M. Abrams, Senior Vice President and Treasurer
Patricia S. Levinson, Vice Chairman
Frederick W. Telling, Ph.D., Vice Chairman
David A. Gould, Senior Vice President
Michael Birnbaum, Vice President
Deborah E. Halper, Vice President
Stephanie L. Davis, Corporate Secretary

BOARD OF DIRECTORS:
Richard A. Berman
Jo Ivey Boufford, M.D.
Rev. John E. Carrington
Philip Chapman
J. Barclay Collins, II
Richard Cotton
William M. Evarts, Jr.
Michael R. Golding, M.D.
Josh N. Kuriloff
Patricia S. Levinson
Howard P. Milstein
Susana R. Morales, M.D.
Robert C. Osborne
Peter J. Powers
Mary H. Schachne
John C. Simons
Michael A. Stocker, M.D.
Rev. Joseph M. Sullivan
James R. Tallon, Jr.
Frederick W. Telling, Ph.D.
Mary Beth C. Tully

ADDRESS INQUIRIES TO:
Hollis Holmes, Grants Manager
(See address above.)

THE WHITEHORSE FOUNDATION [1470]
1200 Fifth Avenue, Suite 1300
Seattle, WA 98101-3151
(206) 515-2131
Fax: (206) 622-7673

E-MAIL ADDRESS:
c.erickson@seattlefoundation.org

WEB SITE ADDRESS:
www.seattlefoundation.org

FOUNDED: 1989

AREAS OF INTEREST:
Preventative human services.

TYPE:
Capital grants; Development grants; Project/program grants; Training grants. Program development.

YEAR PROGRAM STARTED: 1990

PURPOSE:
To fund comprehensive preventive social service programs in Snohomish County, WA.

LEGAL BASIS:
Community foundation.

ELIGIBILITY:
Applicant organizations must be IRS 501(c)(3) tax-exempt. No grants to individuals.

GEOGRAPHIC RESTRICTIONS:
Snohomish County, Washington.

FINANCIAL DATA:
Amount of support per award: Average $50,000.

NUMBER OF APPLICANTS MOST RECENT YEAR: 10.

NUMBER OF AWARDS: 5.

APPLICATION INFORMATION:
Applications guidelines are available on the web site.

Duration: One year.

STAFF:
Ceil Erickson, Program Director

ADDRESS INQUIRIES TO:
Ceil Erickson, Program Director
(See address above.)

MR. AND MRS. P.A. WOODWARD'S FOUNDATION [1471]
1055 West Hastings Street, Suite 300
Vancouver BC V6E 2E9 Canada
(604) 682-8116

E-MAIL ADDRESS:
pawoodwardfoundation@gmail.com

WEB SITE ADDRESS:
www.woodwardfoundation.ca

FOUNDED: 1951

AREAS OF INTEREST:
Health care.

TYPE:
The Foundation supports those projects which affect the people of the Province of British Columbia where there is clear indication of the health benefit anticipated. The Foundation is charged with aiding in the purchase of the latest medical equipment of proven performance that provides direct benefit to the patient. A preference was expressed to fund items with direct patient benefit, as contrasted to that done in the laboratory with uncertain or delayed benefits.

PURPOSE:
To assist in projects which could contribute to better health care.

LEGAL BASIS:
Charitable foundation.

ELIGIBILITY:
Organizations applying for funding must be domiciled within the Province of British Columbia. All individuals and organizations applying must be in possession of a Charitable Gift Registration Number as issued by the Department of National Revenue of Canada.

The Foundation will consider applications in the following general areas:
(1) health care equipment of proven effectiveness and;
(2) special projects which will benefit the health of British Columbians.

The Foundation will not support routine operational budgets, fundamental research not directly related to patient care, conferences or annual meetings, endowments or capital building costs.

GEOGRAPHIC RESTRICTIONS:
British Columbia, Canada.

FINANCIAL DATA:
Amount of support per award: Grants vary in amount, depending upon the needs and nature of the request.

NUMBER OF AWARDS: Up to 30.

APPLICATION INFORMATION:
Letter of application, in duplicate, should contain the following:
(1) name and executive officer of applicant organization and membership of its board of

directors;
(2) the organization's charitable gift registration number from the Department of National Revenue of Canada;
(3) name, title, address and telephone number of person in charge of the project;
(4) description and budget of the project;
(5) dates project will be started and completed and;
(6) a copy of the applicant's latest year-end audited financial statements.

Deadline: Mid-January for April Board of Directors meeting and mid-July for October meeting.

OFFICERS:
Christopher C. Woodward, President
Jill Leversage, Treasurer
Leo P. Sauve, Secretary
Mark Cullen

MEMBERS AND DIRECTORS:
Robert J. Buchanan
E. Wallace Campbell
Mark Cullen
Jill Leversage
Gregory J.D. McKinstry
Hon. Madam Justice Mary V. Newbury
Leo P. Sauve
Christopher C. Woodward

ADDRESS INQUIRIES TO:
Dr. J. Wm. Ibbott, Medical Advisor
(See address above.)

Social welfare

THE ABELARD FOUNDATION-EAST [1472]
P.O. Box 148
Lincoln, MA 01773

E-MAIL ADDRESS:
eastabel@aol.com

WEB SITE ADDRESS:
foundationcenter.org/grantmaker/abelardeast/

AREAS OF INTEREST:
Progressive social change, community organizing, civil and human rights.

TYPE:
General operating grants; Project/program grants.

PURPOSE:
To support local progressive social change activities that expand and protect civil liberties and civil and human rights, and promote and strengthen community involvement in, and control over, the decisions that affect their lives.

ELIGIBILITY:
Applicants must represent or be associated with a nonprofit, 501(c)(3) tax-exempt organization. Priority is given to projects that are in their first years of development and have budgets less than $300,000.

GEOGRAPHIC RESTRICTIONS:
Eastern United States, east of the Mississippi River.

FINANCIAL DATA:
Amount of support per award: Average $10,000.
Total amount of support: Approximately $140,000 annually.

APPLICATION INFORMATION:
Applicants should submit one copy of a proposal (no more than seven to 10 pages)

which includes:
(1) background of the organization;
(2) description of the work for which funds are being sought;
(3) explanation of need and;
(4) impact the project will have.

Proposals prepared in a "common application" format will also be accepted.

Applying organizations must include IRS 501(c)(3) determination letter.

Duration: One year. Up to two renewals possible.

Deadline: Applications mailed by March 15 will be reviewed for the spring meeting, and applications mailed by September 15 will be reviewed for the fall meeting.

ADDRESS INQUIRIES TO:
Susan Collins, Trustee
The Abelard Foundation-East
(See address above.)

EMMA J. ADAMS MEMORIAL FUND, INC. [1473]
328 Eldert Lane
Brooklyn, NY 11208
(347) 789-6717
Fax: (347) 789-6717

FOUNDED: 1933

AREAS OF INTEREST:
Geriatric institutions, welfare, elderly, and needy, mostly through organizations.

TYPE:
Grants-in-aid. Financial support and organized aid to geriatric, needy and/or elderly institutional agencies and occasionally to referred respectable, aged indigent persons in financial difficulty through no fault of their own, in the greater New York City area.

YEAR PROGRAM STARTED: 1936

PURPOSE:
To aid elderly, needy and indigent people and geriatric institutions.

LEGAL BASIS:
Nonprofit corporation.

ELIGIBILITY:
Most grants are awarded to operating geriatric institutions.

No scholarships, program grants, administrative expenses, and no brick-and-mortar grants.

GEOGRAPHIC RESTRICTIONS:
Greater New York area.

FINANCIAL DATA:
Amount of support per award: $450 average.
Total amount of support: Average $60,000 per year.

NUMBER OF APPLICANTS MOST RECENT YEAR:
Over 200.

NUMBER OF AWARDS: Approximately 20.

REPRESENTATIVE AWARDS:
Stanley M. Isaacs Center; Episcopal Mission Society; St. Bartholomew's Outreach Service; Meals on Wheels, Inc.

APPLICATION INFORMATION:
Application forms available upon request. The letter must indicate the referral source. No telephone requests honored.

Duration: Varies.

Deadline: September 1.

IRS IDENTIFICATION NUMBER: 13-6116503

DIRECTORS:
Jill Arkwright
Dr. Mat D. Finch
Rev. Bruce Forbes
Rev. Elizabeth Jacks
Betsy Rowe
Sally Saran
Carolyn Swayze

ADDRESS INQUIRIES TO:
Sally Saran, President
(See address above.)

JUDD S. ALEXANDER FOUNDATION [1474]
500 First Street, Suite 10
Wausau, WI 54403
(715) 845-4556
Fax: (715) 843-9018

E-MAIL ADDRESS:
office@alexanderprop.org

WEB SITE ADDRESS:
juddsalexanderfoundation.org

FOUNDED: 1978

AREAS OF INTEREST:
Education, recreation, human services, children's services and economic development.

TYPE:
Capital grants; Challenge/matching grants; Project/program grants; Seed money grants. Support is provided for capital building and emergency funds.

YEAR PROGRAM STARTED: 1978

LEGAL BASIS:
Private foundation.

ELIGIBILITY:
Organizations classified as 501(c)(3) by the IRS can apply. The Foundation does not make grants to individuals or private businesses.

GEOGRAPHIC RESTRICTIONS:
Marathon County, Wisconsin.

FINANCIAL DATA:
Amount of support per award: Varies.
Total amount of support: Varies.

APPLICATION INFORMATION:
Five copies, unbound, of the proposal should be submitted. The Foundation has an application form available, should the applicant prefer to use a form. A fully reviewable proposal will include:
(1) a cover page with the exact name and location of the proposed grant recipient, along with the name, title, address and phone number of a contact at the organization;
(2) an application narrative, which includes a description of the organization's main activities and whether it is a public, private or not-for-profit entity, a description of the project or activity for which funding is requested, and the specific outcomes and goals of the project and;
(3) a project budget which includes revenue and expense pages and a budget narrative.

The following items must also be attached:
(1) the organization's current annual operating budget, including revenues and expenses;
(2) a list of the organization's governing body and its officers, showing business, professional and/or community affiliations;
(3) letters of support and letters from other agencies indicating their intent to collaborate (as appropriate);

(4) other documents the applicant feels supplement the above information, provided it is not duplicative of other material or information contained in the narratives or budget presentation;

(5) the most recent audited financial statements and;

(6) the most recent IRS determination letter.

Duration: Typically one year. Must reapply.

ADDRESS INQUIRIES TO:
Gary W. Freels, President
(See address above.)

THE ALLSTATE FOUNDATION   [1475]

2775 Sanders Road
Suite F-4
Northbrook, IL 60062-6127

E-MAIL ADDRESS:
grants@allstate.com

WEB SITE ADDRESS:
www.allstatefoundation.org

FOUNDED: 1952

AREAS OF INTEREST:
Teen safe driving and economic empowerment for victims of domestic violence.

TYPE:
Matching gifts; Project/program grants. Program support in the Foundation's areas of focus; matching gifts for higher education only.

YEAR PROGRAM STARTED: 1952

PURPOSE:
To assist deserving organizations serving the fields of teen safe drivers and economic empowerment for victims of domestic violence.

LEGAL BASIS:
Corporate foundation.

ELIGIBILITY:
Grants are made only to nonprofit 501(c)(3) organizations.

GEOGRAPHIC RESTRICTIONS:
United States.

FINANCIAL DATA:
Amount of support per award: National programs: $100,000; Local/regional grants: $5,000 to $20,000.

Total amount of support: $18,300,000 for the year 2011.

Matching fund requirements: For colleges and universities.

APPLICATION INFORMATION:
Information and guidelines are available online.

Duration: One year. Renewal based on program outcome and results.

PUBLICATIONS:
Guidelines.

IRS IDENTIFICATION NUMBER: 36-6116535

ADDRESS INQUIRIES TO:
See e-mail address above.

*PLEASE NOTE:
Unsolicited requests will not be accepted in 2014.

*SPECIAL STIPULATIONS:
Funding for domestic programs only.

THE CALIFORNIA ENDOWMENT

1000 North Alameda Street
Los Angeles, CA 90012
(213) 928-8645
(800) 449-4149
Fax: (213) 928-8818

E-MAIL ADDRESS:
destrada@calendow.org

WEB SITE ADDRESS:
www.calendow.org

TYPE:
Challenge/matching grants; Conferences/seminars; General operating grants; Project/program grants; Technical assistance.

See entry 1423 for full listing.

CAMPBELL FOUNDATION, INC.

705 York Road
Towson, MD 21204
(410) 828-1961
Fax: (410) 821-8814

E-MAIL ADDRESS:
lsperato@stoycpa.com

TYPE:
Capital grants; General operating grants; Project/program grants.

See entry 1111 for full listing.

CATHOLIC CHARITIES USA   [1476]

2050 Ballenger Avenue, Suite 400
Alexandria, VA 22314
(703) 549-1390
Fax: (703) 549-1656

E-MAIL ADDRESS:
mgonzales@catholiccharitiesusa.org

WEB SITE ADDRESS:
www.catholiccharitiesusa.org

AREAS OF INTEREST:
The aged, community services, homeless, emergency relief and family services.

TYPE:
Assistantships; Project/program grants.

PURPOSE:
To provide service to those in need and to advocate justice in societal structures.

LEGAL BASIS:
Nonprofit organization.

ELIGIBILITY:
Grants are only offered to the 1,700 Catholic Charities member agencies. Any organization which is not affiliated with Catholic Charities is ineligible for support.

GEOGRAPHIC RESTRICTIONS:
United States.

FINANCIAL DATA:
Amount of support per award: Varies depending on project and need of the geographic area being served.

Total amount of support: Varies.

APPLICATION INFORMATION:
Organizations should contact their local or diocesan chapters of Catholic Charities for application information and materials.

Duration: Up to five years.

CHRISTOPHER COLUMBUS FELLOWSHIP FOUNDATION   [1477]

110 Genesee Street
Suite 390
Auburn, NY 13021
(315) 258-0090
Fax: (315) 258-0093

E-MAIL ADDRESS:
judithmscolumbus@cs.com

WEB SITE ADDRESS:
www.columbusfdn.org

FOUNDED: 1992

AREAS OF INTEREST:
To encourage and support research, study and labor designed to produce new discoveries in all fields of endeavor for the benefit of mankind.

NAME(S) OF PROGRAMS:
● **Agriscience Awards**
● **Christopher Columbus Awards**
● **Homeland Security Award**
● **Life Sciences Awards**

TYPE:
Awards/prizes; Project/program grants; Seed money grants. In partnership with the American Farm Bureau Federation, the Foundation presents four Agriscience Awards. The mission of this partnership is to recognize, through monetary awards, an adult scientist, a current high school educator, and two current high school students who are judged to exemplify excellence in the field of agriscience and to highlight the importance of agriculture in the 21st century.

Christopher Columbus Awards are given to eight finalist teams of middle school students. The competition asks the students to identify a problem in their community and then solve it using the scientific method. The eight teams and their coaches win an all-expense-paid trip to Walt Disney World®, attend the Christopher Columbus Academy, vie for $2,000 cash for each team member, and one team wins the $25,000 Columbus Foundation Community Grant.

The Foundation presents one $25,000 Homeland Security Award to honor "cutting edge" innovations in the vast arena of homeland security. The award is presented in one of the following four fields: (1) Biological, Radiological, Nuclear, Chemical and Explosive Attacks; (2) Border and Transportation Security; (3) Cyber Security and Information Sharing and; (4) Emergency Responses to Natural and Man-made Disasters.

The Foundation presents four Life Sciences Awards. The purpose is to recognize, through monetary awards, an adult scientist, a current high school educator, and two current high school students who are judged to exemplify excellence in life sciences.

YEAR PROGRAM STARTED: 1996

PURPOSE:
To honor individuals whose accomplishments have had a significant impact on mankind, and encourage the youth in the U.S.

LEGAL BASIS:
Federal government agency.

GEOGRAPHIC RESTRICTIONS:
United States.

FINANCIAL DATA:
Amount of support per award: Agriscience Awards: One for $10,000, one for $5,000 and

two for $1,000. Christopher Columbus Awards: Two teams win $2,000 and gold medals (three- to four-member teams), and one team receives the $25,000 Columbus Foundation Community Grant. Homeland Security Award: $25,000. Life Sciences Awards: One for $10,000, one for $5,000 and two for $1,000.

Total amount of support: Approximately $284,000 per year.

NUMBER OF AWARDS: Agriscience: 4; Christopher Columbus: 3; Homeland Security: 1; Life Sciences: 4.

APPLICATION INFORMATION:
Contact the Foundation for information on each individual program application process.

TRUSTEES:
Dr. Maria Lombardo, Chairman
Cynthia Butler-McIntyre
Warren Hioki, Ph.D.
Kimberly A. Owens
Ronald Rapoport, Ph.D.
Sima Sarrafan
Peter Schaumber
Anthony C. Wisniewski

ADDRESS INQUIRIES TO:
Judith M. Shellenberger, Executive Director
(See address above.)

THE COMMONWEALTH FUND   [1478]
One East 75th Street
New York, NY 10021
(212) 606-3800

E-MAIL ADDRESS:
grants@cmwf.org

WEB SITE ADDRESS:
www.commonwealthfund.org

FOUNDED: 1918

AREAS OF INTEREST:
Supporting independent research on health care issues, and making grants to improve health care practice and policy.

NAME(S) OF PROGRAMS:
• **Affordable Health Insurance**
• **Commission on a High Performance Health System**
• **Health System Quality and Efficiency**
• **International Program in Health Policy and Innovation**
• **Patient-Centered Coordinated Care Program**
• **Payment and System Reform**

TYPE:
Project/program grants; Research grants; Research contracts.

YEAR PROGRAM STARTED: 1918

PURPOSE:
To promote a high-performing health care system that achieves better access, improved quality, and greater efficiency, particularly for society's most vulnerable, including low-income people, the uninsured, minority Americans, young children and elderly adults.

The Fund carries out this mandate by supporting independent research on health care issues and making grants to improve health care practice and policy. An international program in health policy is designed to stimulate innovative policies and practices in the U.S. and other industrialized countries.

LEGAL BASIS:
Private foundation.

ELIGIBILITY:
The Fund makes grants only to tax-exempt organizations and public agencies. No grants to individuals.

FINANCIAL DATA:
Amount of support per award: Varies.

Total amount of support: Projected $20,000,000 in grants for fiscal year 2013-14.

NUMBER OF APPLICANTS MOST RECENT YEAR:
870.

NUMBER OF AWARDS: 186.

REPRESENTATIVE AWARDS:
$258,582 to Harvard University to analyze the relationship between quality and efficiency in hospital care; $72,936 to Massachusetts General Hospital to assess the role of pay-for-performance in reducing racial and ethnic inequalities in health care.

APPLICATION INFORMATION:
The Fund requests letters of inquiry to initiate the grant application process. Applicants are encouraged to submit letters of inquiry using the online form. While the Fund will continue to accept letters of inquiry via regular mail and fax, such submissions will take longer to process than those received online. Letters of inquiry are acknowledged when received. Applicants are typically advised of the results of an initial staff review within two months. Program staff will contact applicants if more detailed information is required.

Duration: Typically one year, although some multiyear funding available.

Deadline: Applications may be submitted at any time.

IRS IDENTIFICATION NUMBER: 13-1635260

STAFF:
David Blumenthal, President
John E. Craig, Jr., Executive Vice President and Chief Operating Officer
Donald Moulds, Executive Vice President for Programs
Cathy A. Schoen, Senior Vice President for Policy, Research and Evaluation
Robin Osborn, Vice President and Director, International Program in Health Policy and Innovation
Barry A. Scholl, Vice President for Communications and Publishing
Andrea Landes, Vice President of Grants Management

BOARD OF DIRECTORS:
James R. Tallon, Jr., Chairman
Cristine Russell, Vice Chairman
Maureen Bisognano
David Blumenthal, M.D.
Sheila P. Burke, R.N.
Benjamin K. Chu, M.D.
Michael V. Drake, M.D.
Julio Frenk, M.D.
Kathryn D. Haslanger
Jane E. Henney, M.D.
Robert C. Pozen
Simon Stevens
William Y. Yun

ADDRESS INQUIRIES TO:
Andrea Landes
Vice President of Grants Management
(See address above.)

COMMUNITY FOUNDATION OF THE VERDUGOS   [1479]
111 East Broadway, Suite 200
Glendale, CA 91205
(818) 241-8040
Fax: (818) 241-8045

E-MAIL ADDRESS:
info@cfverdugos.org

WEB SITE ADDRESS:
www.cfverdugos.org

FOUNDED: 1956

AREAS OF INTEREST:
Arts and culture, children, education, health, homeless services, human services, senior services and environment.

TYPE:
Capital grants; Challenge/matching grants; Development grants; General operating grants; Project/program grants; Scholarships.

YEAR PROGRAM STARTED: 1956

PURPOSE:
To meet current and changing needs in the community.

LEGAL BASIS:
Community foundation.

ELIGIBILITY:
Eligible organizations must be schools or IRS 501(c)(3) tax-exempt.

GEOGRAPHIC RESTRICTIONS:
Burbank, Flintridge, Glendale, La Canada, La Crescenta, Montrose and Verdugo City, California.

FINANCIAL DATA:
Amount of support per award: Varies.

Total amount of support: $15,000 each grant cycle; $45,000 annually.

COOPERATIVE FUNDING PROGRAMS: Through restricted, donor-advised funds within the Foundation.

REPRESENTATIVE AWARDS:
$10,000 to The Salvation Army for ZONE after-school program; $15,000 to Glendale Adventist Medical Center toward cost of Omni Giraffe Bed for NICU; $10,000 to College View School toward cost of playground equipment for developmentally disabled children.

APPLICATION INFORMATION:
Guidelines and application form are available on the Foundation web site.

Duration: One year. Agency can reapply one year after the grant is made.

Deadline: February 1, May 15 and August 15.

PUBLICATIONS:
Annual report; quarterly newsletters.

IRS IDENTIFICATION NUMBER: 95-6068137

ADDRESS INQUIRIES TO:
Chief Executive Officer
(See address above.)

CORPORATION FOR NATIONAL AND COMMUNITY SERVICE   [1480]
1201 New York Avenue, N.W.
Washington, DC 20525
(202) 606-5000 ext. 6822
Fax: (202) 606-3475

E-MAIL ADDRESS:
info@cns.gov

WEB SITE ADDRESS:
www.nationalservice.gov
www.seniorcorps.gov

FOUNDED: 1971

AREAS OF INTEREST:
Volunteer service.

NAME(S) OF PROGRAMS:
- **Foster Grandparent Program**
- **Retired and Senior Volunteer Program (RSVP)**
- **Senior Companion Program**

TYPE:
Demonstration grants; General operating grants; Grants-in-aid; Project/program grants; Technical assistance. Grants to provide meaningful opportunities for low-income persons age 55 years and over, specifically providing person-to-person service to children with special needs as Foster Grandparents and providing services to adults with special needs as Senior Companions. The Retired and Senior Volunteer Program helps people 55 and older put their skills and life experience to work in their communities.

YEAR PROGRAM STARTED: 1965

PURPOSE:
To provide service opportunities for older Americans.

LEGAL BASIS:
Federal agency.

ELIGIBILITY:
State and local public agencies and private nonprofit organizations may apply.

GEOGRAPHIC RESTRICTIONS:
United States and territories.

FINANCIAL DATA:
Amount of support per award: Foster Grandparent Program: $328,000 average. Retired Senior Volunteer Program: $77,000 average. Senior Companion Program: $204,000 average.
Matching fund requirements: 10% for Foster Grandparent Program and Senior Companion Program. For Retired Senior Volunteer Program, 10-20-30%.

COOPERATIVE FUNDING PROGRAMS: Local public and private nonprofit agencies receive grants to sponsor and operate FGP, RSVP and SCP.

APPLICATION INFORMATION:
Contact the Corporation.
Duration: Three years with opportunity to amend annually.
Deadline: Varies.

PUBLICATIONS:
Grant application; guidelines.

IRS IDENTIFICATION NUMBER: 53-0260397

ENTERPRISE COMMUNITY PARTNERS   [1481]
One Whitehall Street, 11th Floor
New York, NY 10004
(212) 262-9575
Fax: (212) 262-9635

E-MAIL ADDRESS:
metlifeawards@enterprisecommunity.org

WEB SITE ADDRESS:
www.enterprisecommunity.org

FOUNDED: 1982

AREAS OF INTEREST:
Affordable housing.

NAME(S) OF PROGRAMS:
- **MetLife Foundation Awards for Excellence in Affordable Housing**

TYPE:
Awards/prizes; General operating grants. MetLife Awards will be made in two categories: 1) Supportive Housing and 2) Property and Asset Management.

YEAR PROGRAM STARTED: 1996

PURPOSE:
To see that all low-income people in the U.S. have the opportunity for fit and affordable housing and to move up and out of poverty into the mainstream of American life; to promote development and quality management of affordable housing.

GEOGRAPHIC RESTRICTIONS:
United States.

FINANCIAL DATA:
Amount of support per award: $50,000.
Total amount of support: $200,000.

COOPERATIVE FUNDING PROGRAMS: MetLife Foundation.

NUMBER OF AWARDS: 4 each year.

APPLICATION INFORMATION:
Contact the Foundation for application procedures.
Deadline: Varies.

PUBLICATIONS:
Annual report.

ADDRESS INQUIRIES TO:
See e-mail address above.

THE FEINSTEIN FOUNDATION   [1482]
37 Alhambra Circle
Cranston, RI 02905
(401) 467-5155
(401) 941-5913
Fax: (401) 941-0988

E-MAIL ADDRESS:
asf@feinsteinfoundation.org

WEB SITE ADDRESS:
www.feinsteinfoundation.org

AREAS OF INTEREST:
Ending hunger.

NAME(S) OF PROGRAMS:
- **Feinstein $1 Million Giveaway to Fight Hunger**

TYPE:
Challenge/matching grants. Each participating agency receives a share of $1,000,000 that represents their portion of the total amount reported to the Foundation that was raised by anti-hunger agencies using the Foundation's challenge in their fight to end hunger fund-raising.

PURPOSE:
To help nonprofit anti-hunger agencies nationwide raise funds.

LEGAL BASIS:
Nonprofit foundation.

ELIGIBILITY:
U.S. registered nonprofit 501(c)(3) agencies.

GEOGRAPHIC RESTRICTIONS:
United States.

FINANCIAL DATA:
Amount of support per award: Divided proportionately among all complying agencies with a maximum of $35,000 going to any one agency.

Total amount of support: $1,000,000.

NUMBER OF AWARDS: Varies.

APPLICATION INFORMATION:
The Foundation does not accept unsolicited requests for funding except from nonprofit agencies feeding the hungry.
Deadline: March 1 to April 30. Participating agencies must submit reports by May 12.

EXECUTIVE STAFF:
Alan Shawn Feinstein, Chief Executive Officer

ADDRESS INQUIRIES TO:
Alan Shawn Feinstein
Chief Executive Officer
(See address above.)

CARL M. FREEMAN FOUNDATION
36097 Sand Cove Road
Selbyville, DE 19975
(302) 436-3015

E-MAIL ADDRESS:
info@freemanfoundation.org

WEB SITE ADDRESS:
www.freemanfoundation.org

TYPE:
Capital grants; Challenge/matching grants; General operating grants.

See entry 451 for full listing.

THE GREAT BAY FOUNDATION   [1483]
100 Middle Street
Portland, ME 04101
(207) 773-9069

E-MAIL ADDRESS:
info@greatbayfoundation.org

WEB SITE ADDRESS:
www.greatbayfoundation.org

FOUNDED: 1998

AREAS OF INTEREST:
Social change.

TYPE:
General operating grants; Grants-in-aid; Project/program grants; Seed money grants. Grant program limited to projects that seek change on a fundamental systemic, institutional or community basis.

PURPOSE:
To improve the lives of children and families in Maine communities.

ELIGIBILITY:
Applicants must be 501(c)(3) organizations led by individuals who have an entrepreneurial attitude, drive and vision, and who work toward social change in the areas of economic development, education and health care. Grants are not made to individuals or religious organizations.

GEOGRAPHIC RESTRICTIONS:
Maine.

FINANCIAL DATA:
Amount of support per award: Up to $150,000.

Total amount of support: Varies.

APPLICATION INFORMATION:
Grant requests are considered only in response to an invitation by the Foundation. Unsolicited applications will not be accepted, considered, or responded to.

Duration: One year.

ADDRESS INQUIRIES TO:
Anne Dinsmore, Executive Director
(See address above.)

THE HEALTH FOUNDATION OF GREATER INDIANAPOLIS [1484]

429 East Vermont Street, Suite 300
Indianapolis, IN 46202-3698
(317) 630-1805
Fax: (317) 630-1806

E-MAIL ADDRESS:
bwilson@thfgi.org

WEB SITE ADDRESS:
www.thfgi.org

AREAS OF INTEREST:
Childhood obesity, HIV/AIDS and
school-based health.

TYPE:
Project/program grants.

PURPOSE:
To encourage organizations to improve the
health of people in greater Indianapolis,
especially those who are disadvantaged.

ELIGIBILITY:
Applicant must be a 501(c)(3) group,
organization or agency that provides
health-related programs or services within
Marion and the seven contiguous counties.
Must also function without discrimination or
segregation based on race, gender, age,
religion, national origin, sexual orientation,
disability, military or marital status in hiring,
termination, assignment and promotion of
staff, selection of board members or
provisions of services. No grants are made to
individuals. Nonsectarian religious programs
may apply.

GEOGRAPHIC RESTRICTIONS:
Marion County, Indiana and the seven
contiguous counties.

FINANCIAL DATA:
Amount of support per award: Varies.
Total amount of support: Approximately
$1,400,000 for the year 2012.

NUMBER OF APPLICANTS MOST RECENT YEAR:
20.

NUMBER OF AWARDS: 15.

APPLICATION INFORMATION:
Contact the Foundation prior to applying to
determine appropriateness of the proposal.
Duration: One year.
Deadline: Varies.

ADDRESS INQUIRIES TO:
Jason Grisell, Program Manager
(See address above.)

VICTOR AND LORRAINE HONIG FUND [1485]

405 14th Street, Suite 809
Oakland, CA 94612
(510) 834-2995
Fax: (510) 834-2998

E-MAIL ADDRESS:
grantsadmin@commoncounsel.org

WEB SITE ADDRESS:
www.commoncounsel.org

AREAS OF INTEREST:
Social change, community development,
environment, public policy and
empowerment.

TYPE:
General operating grants; Project/program
grants.

PURPOSE:
To support social change organizations which
reflect the communities in which they are
based; to expand community control over
economic, social and environmental decisions
affecting the communities' well-being; to
build a strong informed voice on public
policy issues.

LEGAL BASIS:
Family foundation.

ELIGIBILITY:
Grants made only to IRS 501(c)(3)
tax-exempt organizations. No grants are made
to social service programs offering ongoing
or direct delivery of services, medical,
educational or cultural institutions,
emergency funding, scholarship funds or
other aids to individuals, organizations which
have sophisticated fund-raising capabilities,
capital expenditure, construction or
renovation programs or programs undertaken
at government initiative. Priority is given to
grassroots community organizations in
low-income areas.

GEOGRAPHIC RESTRICTIONS:
California.

FINANCIAL DATA:
Amount of support per award: $1,000 to
$25,000.
Total amount of support: $468,000 for the
year 2011.

NUMBER OF APPLICANTS MOST RECENT YEAR:
50 to 100.

NUMBER OF AWARDS: 46 for the year 2011.

APPLICATION INFORMATION:
Letters of Inquiry and Proposals are by
invitation only.
Duration: Most grants are for one year.

ADDRESS INQUIRIES TO:
Grants Administrator
(See address above.)

A.V. HUNTER TRUST, INC. [1486]

650 South Cherry Street
Suite 535
Glendale, CO 80246
(303) 399-5450
Fax: (303) 399-5499

E-MAIL ADDRESS:
barbarahowie@avhuntertrust.org

WEB SITE ADDRESS:
www.avhuntertrust.org

FOUNDED: 1924

AREAS OF INTEREST:
Disabled, seniors, youth, and indigent.

TYPE:
General operating grants. Grants to
Colorado-based organizations in the priority
areas listed above.

YEAR PROGRAM STARTED: 1924

PURPOSE:
To give aid, comfort, support or assistance to
children or aged persons or indigent adults.

LEGAL BASIS:
Private foundation.

ELIGIBILITY:
Applicants must be organizations classified as
501(c)(3) by the IRS. The Trust will consider

only one request from an organization during
any 12-month period. Institutions or
organizations supported by tax-derived
monies, including those which have lost
governmental funding, will not be
considered. The Trustees will not consider
grants or loans to individuals, developmental
or start-up funds, research, publications, films
or other media projects, capital campaigns or
acquisitions, including construction and
renovations, education or scholarship aid,
grants to cover deficits or retirement of debt,
purchase of memberships or blocks of
tickets, endowments, recruiting and training
of staff or gathering and disseminating
information.

GEOGRAPHIC RESTRICTIONS:
Colorado.

FINANCIAL DATA:
Amount of support per award: $5,000 to
$30,000. Average: $15,000.
Total amount of support: $2,000,000
annually.

NUMBER OF AWARDS: 211 grants to
organizations and 417 grants to individuals
for the year 2013.

REPRESENTATIVE AWARDS:
$20,000 to Boys & Girls Clubs of San Luis
Valley; $7,500 to Greeley Transitional
Housing; $30,000 to Volunteers of America
Colorado Branch.

APPLICATION INFORMATION:
Detailed application information can be
obtained at the Trust web site or by calling
the telephone number listed above.

STAFF:
Barbara L. Howie, Executive Director
Charlotte A. Gillespie, Senior Program
Officer

BOARD OF TRUSTEES:
Allan B. Adams, President
Mary K. Anstine, Vice President
George C. Gibson, Treasurer
Bruce K. Alexander
W. Robert Alexander

ADDRESS INQUIRIES TO:
Barbara L. Howie, Executive Director
(See address above.)

THE STEWART HUSTON CHARITABLE TRUST

50 South First Avenue
Coatesville, PA 19320
(610) 384-2666
Fax: (610) 384-3396

E-MAIL ADDRESS:
admin@stewarthuston.org

WEB SITE ADDRESS:
www.stewarthuston.org

TYPE:
Capital grants; Challenge/matching grants;
General operating grants; Matching gifts;
Project/program grants.

See entry 814 for full listing.

THE HYAMS FOUNDATION [1487]

50 Federal Street, 9th Floor
Boston, MA 02110
(617) 426-5600
Fax: (617) 426-5696

E-MAIL ADDRESS:
info@hyamsfoundation.org

WEB SITE ADDRESS:
www.hyamsfoundation.org

FOUNDED: 1921

AREAS OF INTEREST:
Low-income and underserved populations;
low-income youth.

TYPE:
General operating grants; Project/program
grants; Technical assistance. General
operating, multiyear pledges, special projects,
technical assistance/consulting, unrestricted
grants in the following program areas:
(1) Affordable Housing: Public
policy/community organizing;
(2) Civic Engagement: Grassroots leadership
development, including teen organizing,
public policy/community organizing, voter
engagement and;
(3) Teen Development: Public
policy/community organizing.

PURPOSE:
To increase economic and social justice and
power within low-income communities in
Boston and Chelsea, MA.

LEGAL BASIS:
Nonprofit foundation.

ELIGIBILITY:
Applicants must be Massachusetts charitable
corporations, tax-exempt under Section
501(c)(3) and designated as not a private
foundation under Section 509(a). No grants
will be made to one organization for the
programs of another organization which has
not itself received both such determinations.
The Foundation ordinarily will consider only
one application from an organization in any
given 12-month period. However, a single
application may include a request for more
than one program or purpose.

Grants are not given to individuals,
educational institutions for standard
educational or capital programs, any
municipal, state or federal agency, hospital
capital campaigns, endowments and religious
organizations for sectarian religious purposes.

Grants are rarely made for curriculum
development, conferences, film production,
scholarships or to national or international
organizations.

GEOGRAPHIC RESTRICTIONS:
Boston and Chelsea, Massachusetts.

FINANCIAL DATA:
Amount of support per award: $30,000 to
$50,000.

Total amount of support: $5,400,000 for the
year 2013.

NUMBER OF APPLICANTS MOST RECENT YEAR:
Approximately 150.

APPLICATION INFORMATION:
Application form required. Organizations
which are unsure about whether they meet
the Foundation's funding priorities and
criteria are encouraged to submit a one-page
letter of interest to the Foundation. This letter
should describe the reason for seeking
support and the geographic area(s) and
population(s) to be served.

Application form is available online.

Duration: Typically one year. Multiyear
grants also given.

Deadline: March 1, September 1 and
December 1.

TRUSTEES:
Martella Wilson-Taylor, Chairman

Iris Gomez
Karen Mapp
Adam Seitchik

STAFF:
Elizabeth B. Smith, Executive Director
Angela Brown, Director of Programs
David Moy, Program Officer
Maria Mulkeen, Program Officer

ADDRESS INQUIRIES TO:
R. Shani Pankam, Grants Manager
(See address above.)

ITTLESON FOUNDATION, INC.   [1488]

15 East 67th Street
New York, NY 10065
(212) 794-2008
Fax: (212) 794-0351

WEB SITE ADDRESS:
www.ittlesonfoundation.org

FOUNDED: 1932

AREAS OF INTEREST:
Mental health, environment and AIDS.

TYPE:
Demonstration grants; Project/program
grants; Seed money grants. Seed money for
the start-up of innovative programs that will
improve the social welfare of citizens of the
U.S.

In the area of AIDS, the Foundation supports
cutting-edge prevention efforts. It is also
particularly interested in new model, pilot,
and demonstration efforts: addressing the
needs of underserved at-risk populations;
responding to the challenges facing
community-based AIDS service
organizations; providing meaningful
school-based sex education; making treatment
information accessible, available, and easily
understandable to those in need of it; and
addressing the psycho-social needs of those
infected and affected by AIDS, especially
adolescents.

In the area of environment, the Foundation
supports innovative pilot, model and
demonstration projects that will help move
individuals, communities and organizations
from environmental awareness to
environmental activism. The Foundation
seeks to: support the present generation of
environmental activists; educate and engage
the next generation; strengthen the
infrastructure of the environmental movement
with a particular focus on efforts at the
grassroots and statewide levels; and activate
new constituencies.

In the area of mental health, the Foundation
continues to support efforts to address the
needs of underserved populations. It also
seeks pilot, model and demonstration
projects: fighting the stigma associated with
mental illness; utilizing new knowledge and
current technological advances to improve
programs and services for people with mental
illness; bringing the full benefits of this new
knowledge and technology to those who
presently do not have access to them; and
advancing preventative mental health efforts,
especially those targeted to youth and
adolescents.

PURPOSE:
To launch innovative projects in the areas of
mental health, AIDS and the environment.

ELIGIBILITY:
Grants are available to nonprofit
organizations within the U.S. Preference is
given to pilot projects, test and demonstration
projects and applied research which ideally
should inform public policy, if successful.
The Foundation also supports dissemination
projects.

The Foundation does not usually support
capital building projects, endowments, grants
to individuals, scholarships or internships
(except as part of a program), or continuing
support to existing programs. Moreover, the
Foundation does not support programs of
direct service to individuals with only a local
focus or constituency. The Foundation does
not make international grants.

GEOGRAPHIC RESTRICTIONS:
United States.

FINANCIAL DATA:
Amount of support per award: Average
$20,000 to $70,000.

Total amount of support: $560,000 for the
year 2013.

NUMBER OF APPLICANTS MOST RECENT YEAR:
Approximately 500.

APPLICATION INFORMATION:
There are no application forms. Applicants
should write a brief letter to the Executive
Director describing the basic organization
and the work for which funds are being
sought, along with a budget and evidence of
tax-exempt status. If the activity falls within
the current scope of the Foundation's
interests, the applicant will be asked to
supply additional information as required.
Applicant should consult web site for current
year's focus.

Duration: Generally one year. Multiyear
when appropriate. No renewals.

Deadline: Letters of inquiry must be received
by September 1 for December meeting.

OFFICERS AND DIRECTORS:
H. Anthony Ittleson, Chairman and President
Pamela Syrmis, Vice President and Director
H. Davison, Treasurer
Anthony C. Wood, Secretary and Executive
Director
Andrew Auchincloss, Director
H. Philip Ittleson, Director
Stephanie Ittleson, Director
Christina Ittleson Smith, Director
Victor Syrmis, M.D., Director

ADDRESS INQUIRIES TO:
Anthony C. Wood, Executive Director
(See address above.)

JACKSONVILLE JAGUARS FOUNDATION

One EverBank Field Drive
Jacksonville, FL 32202
(904) 633-5437
Fax: (904) 633-5683

WEB SITE ADDRESS:
www.jaguars.com

TYPE:
General operating grants; Project/program
grants. Limited capital grants that target
economically and socially "at-risk" youths in
northeast Florida.

See entry 174 for full listing.

THE CARL W. AND CARRIE MAE JOSLYN CHARITABLE TRUST [1489]

c/o JPMorgan Private Client Services
2200 Ross Avenue, Floor 5
Dallas, TX 75201
(866) 836-6818

E-MAIL ADDRESS:
kelly.key.adams@jpmorgan.com

WEB SITE ADDRESS:
www.jpmorgan.com/onlinegrants

FOUNDED: 1975

AREAS OF INTEREST:
Children, elderly and handicapped persons of El Paso County, CO.

TYPE:
Project/program grants. Small project grants and general operating support.

YEAR PROGRAM STARTED: 1975

LEGAL BASIS:
Tax-exempt charitable trust.

ELIGIBILITY:
Organizations and individuals serving children, the elderly and handicapped persons in El Paso County, CO, are eligible to apply.

GEOGRAPHIC RESTRICTIONS:
El Paso County, Colorado.

FINANCIAL DATA:
Amount of support per award: $500 to $15,000.
Total amount of support: Approximately $55,000 to $65,000 annually.

NUMBER OF APPLICANTS MOST RECENT YEAR:
150.

NUMBER OF AWARDS: 30.

APPLICATION INFORMATION:
Application must be made online; paper applications will not be accepted.
Duration: One year. Nonrenewable.
Deadline: November 1.

ADDRESS INQUIRIES TO:
Kelly Adams, Trust Officer
JPMorgan
(See address above.)

LIBERTY HILL FOUNDATION [1490]

6420 Wilshire Boulevard
Suite 700
Los Angeles, CA 90048
(323) 556-7200
Fax: (323) 556-7240

E-MAIL ADDRESS:
info@libertyhill.org

WEB SITE ADDRESS:
www.libertyhill.org

FOUNDED: 1976

AREAS OF INTEREST:
Economic justice, environmental justice and LGBTQ justice.

NAME(S) OF PROGRAMS:
● **Fund for Change**
● **Wally Marks Leadership Institute for Change**
● **Queer Youth Fund**

TYPE:
General operating grants; Project/program grants; Scholarships; Seed money grants; Technical assistance. Fund for Change supports high-impact social change through

cultivating effective community leaders, seeding emerging organizations, and developing a base of grassroots activists within the areas of economic and racial justice, environmental justice and LGBTQ justice.

The Wally Marks Leadership Institute for Change invests in community leaders at the front lines of change with intensive on-the-job training for community organizers.

The Queer Youth Fund supports local, state and national nonprofit organizations that empower youth to improve their societal condition, promoting equality and justice. Youth are defined as 24 years old and younger.

YEAR PROGRAM STARTED: 1976

PURPOSE:
To advance social change through a strategic combination of grants, leadership training and campaigns.

LEGAL BASIS:
Public foundation.

ELIGIBILITY:
Fund for Change: The Foundation considers applications from nonprofit 501(c)(3) organizations, or those organizations having a fiscal sponsorship agreement with a nonprofit organization which complies with Liberty Hill's policy on fiscal sponsorship, in Los Angeles County, CA that actively work toward a more just distribution of resources and power, develop grassroots activism and leadership, are building their organizational infrastructure and promote a society free from discrimination.

The Foundation does not fund capital campaigns for land or buildings, individual efforts, films or video projects, profit making ventures, direct union organizing, electioneering for candidates in public office, one-time events or conferences that are not linked to social change organizing strategies, or projects that only serve communities outside Los Angeles County.

FINANCIAL DATA:
Amount of support per award: Fund for Change: $10,000 to $50,000. Queer Youth Fund: $100,000.

COOPERATIVE FUNDING PROGRAMS:
Donor-advised program.

APPLICATION INFORMATION:
Applications for Fund for Change must be submitted by mail or in person. Applications by e-mail or fax will not be accepted. Queer Youth Fund requires initial letter of intent.
Duration: One to five years.
Deadline: Varies.

PUBLICATIONS:
Guidelines; newsletter.

IRS IDENTIFICATION NUMBER: 51-0181191

STAFF:
Shane Goldsmith, Executive Director
Margarita Ramirez, Deputy Director of Grantmaking

ADDRESS INQUIRIES TO:
Shane Goldsmith, Executive Director
(See address above.)

THE AGNES M. LINDSAY TRUST

660 Chestnut Street
Manchester, NH 03104
(603) 669-1366
(866) 669-1366
Fax: (603) 665-8114

E-MAIL ADDRESS:
admin@lindsaytrust.org
proposals@lindsaytrust.org (for grants)

WEB SITE ADDRESS:
www.lindsaytrust.org

TYPE:
Capital grants; Scholarships. Awards grants for capital campaigns, capital items and renovation needs. Also, supports a number of health and welfare organizations, health projects, dental projects, special needs including blind, deaf and learning-disabled, elderly, children's hospitals, children's homes, youth organizations, youth and family services and summer camperships (summer enrichment programs). In addition, Trust supports colleges and universities and private secondary schools through scholarship aid.

See entry 1131 for full listing.

LUTHERAN FOUNDATION OF ST. LOUIS

8860 Ladue Road
Suite 200
St. Louis, MO 63124
(314) 231-2244
Fax: (314) 727-7688

E-MAIL ADDRESS:
info@lutheranfoundation.org

WEB SITE ADDRESS:
www.lutheranfoundation.org

TYPE:
Project/program grants.

See entry 817 for full listing.

M & M AREA COMMUNITY FOUNDATION

1101 11th Avenue, Suite One
Menominee, MI 49858-3018
(906) 864-3599
Fax: (906) 864-3657

E-MAIL ADDRESS:
info@mmcommunityfoundation.org

WEB SITE ADDRESS:
www.mmcommunityfoundation.org

TYPE:
Project/program grants; Scholarships; Training grants.

See entry 1322 for full listing.

RODERICK MACARTHUR FOUNDATION [1491]

9333 North Milwaukee Avenue
Niles, IL 60714
(847) 966-0143
Fax: (847) 581-8730

FOUNDED: 1976

AREAS OF INTEREST:
Protecting and encouraging freedom of expression, human rights, civil liberties and social justice.

TYPE:
Project/program grants. Project budgets, litigation and special projects.

YEAR PROGRAM STARTED: 1976

PURPOSE:
To support those working on programs and projects of interest to the Foundation, especially to maintain individual freedoms of expression and correct social injustices.

LEGAL BASIS:
Independent private foundation.

FINANCIAL DATA:
Amount of support per award: Varies.
Total amount of support: $6,370,000 for the year ended December 31, 2013.

NUMBER OF APPLICANTS MOST RECENT YEAR:
50.

NUMBER OF AWARDS: 7 for the year ended December 31, 2012.

REPRESENTATIVE AWARDS:
$4,500,000 to Harper's Magazine Foundation; $950,000 to American Dance Institute; $215,400 to Death Penalty Information Center.

APPLICATION INFORMATION:
Board-initiated only. Unsolicited requests are not accepted.
Duration: Varies according to project.

PUBLICATIONS:
Grants list.

IRS IDENTIFICATION NUMBER: 51-0214450

STAFF:
Marylou Bane, Administrator and Treasurer

BOARD OF DIRECTORS:
John R. MacArthur, Chairman
Robert Cordova, Vice Chairman
James Liggett, Director

ADDRESS INQUIRIES TO:
Marylou Bane
Administrator and Treasurer
(See address above.)

MAINE INITIATIVES   [1492]
P.O. Box 2248
Augusta, ME 04338
(207) 622-6294
Fax: (207) 622-6295

E-MAIL ADDRESS:
info@maineinitiatives.org

WEB SITE ADDRESS:
www.maineinitiatives.org

FOUNDED: 1993

AREAS OF INTEREST:
Supporting social change in Maine.

NAME(S) OF PROGRAMS:
● **Felder Fund for Art and Action**
● **Grants for Change**
● **Public Life Program**
● **Rapid Response "Lightning" Grants**

TYPE:
General operating grants; Seed money grants; Technical assistance. Grants provide funding to Maine groups advancing social, economic, and environmental justice at the grassroots level.

YEAR PROGRAM STARTED: 1994

PURPOSE:
To cultivate social, economic and environmental justice through grants and other support to grassroots organizations in Maine communities.

ELIGIBILITY:
Organization must be tax-exempt. Religious organizations are eligible but not for religious purposes.

GEOGRAPHIC RESTRICTIONS:
Maine.

FINANCIAL DATA:
Amount of support per award: Grants for Change: Up to $25,000 per year.
Total amount of support: Varies.

NUMBER OF APPLICANTS MOST RECENT YEAR:
Grants for Change: 50.

NUMBER OF AWARDS: 5 to 10.

APPLICATION INFORMATION:
Copies of IRS 501(c)(3) designation letters are requested. Contact the organization for application.
Duration: Grants for Change: Up to three years.
Deadline: Grants for Change: First Friday of February. Rapid Response Grants are reviewed on an ongoing basis.

PUBLICATIONS:
Newsletter; annual report.

IRS IDENTIFICATION NUMBER: 01-0484310

STAFF:
Charlie Bernstein, Executive Director

MAZON: A JEWISH RESPONSE
TO HUNGER   [1493]
10495 Santa Monica Boulevard
Suite 100
Los Angeles, CA 90025
(310) 442-0020
Fax: (310) 442-0030

E-MAIL ADDRESS:
mazonmail@mazon.org

WEB SITE ADDRESS:
www.mazon.org

FOUNDED: 1986

AREAS OF INTEREST:
Advocacy and education pertaining to hunger, emergency food assistance and food banks.

TYPE:
General operating grants; Project/program grants.

YEAR PROGRAM STARTED: 1986

PURPOSE:
To prevent and alleviate hunger among people of all faiths and backgrounds.

GEOGRAPHIC RESTRICTIONS:
United States and Israel.

FINANCIAL DATA:
Amount of support per award: Varies.
Total amount of support: Varies.

APPLICATION INFORMATION:
Applicants must submit a letter (maximum two pages) describing the agency and/or project, and request a grant application. A full grant application packet will be sent to organizations that best match the funding criteria and grantmaking priorities.
Duration: One year.

PUBLICATIONS:
Program announcement; guidelines.

ADDRESS INQUIRIES TO:
Elaine Himelfarb, Senior Program Officer
Marcy Kaplan, Program Officer
(See address above.)

MCKENZIE RIVER GATHERING
FOUNDATION   [1494]
1235 S.E. Morrison, Suite A
Portland, OR 97214
(503) 234-2338
Fax: (503) 232-1731

E-MAIL ADDRESS:
info@mrgfoundation.org

WEB SITE ADDRESS:
www.mrgfoundation.org

FOUNDED: 1976

AREAS OF INTEREST:
Community-based groups working for progressive social change, women, racial justice, low-income organizing, lesbian/gay, bi/trans, peace, international solidarity, environmental protection, economic justice and anti-bigotry.

NAME(S) OF PROGRAMS:
● **Critical Response Grants**
● **Public Interest Grants (General Fund)**
● **Travel Grants**

TYPE:
General operating grants; Project/program grants; Seed money grants; Travel grants. Funds special project grants and general support.

Critical Response Grants provide community-based groups with the additional capacity needed to organize a progressive response to an unexpected crisis or opportunity for organizing.

Travel Grants help MRG grantees make national and regional connections and develop the leadership and skills needed for effective organizational development and organizing.

YEAR PROGRAM STARTED: 1976

PURPOSE:
Social change.

LEGAL BASIS:
Nonprofit, tax-exempt 501(c)(3) public foundation.

ELIGIBILITY:
Organizations must do tax-exempt activities in the state of Oregon and fit criteria of social change work listed in fields of interest. No grants to individuals. The Foundation does not fund food co-ops, health centers or social services.

Travel Grants: Group applicant must have received an MRG General Fund or Peace Fund grant within the prior two years.

Grant applicants for the Critical Response Grant and the Travel Grant must have an organizational budget under $500,000 to be eligible.

GEOGRAPHIC RESTRICTIONS:
Oregon.

FINANCIAL DATA:
Amount of support per award: Critical Response Grants: Up to $2,000; General Fund: $2,000 to $20,000; Travel Grants: Up to $1,000.
Total amount of support: $470,000.

NUMBER OF APPLICANTS MOST RECENT YEAR:
100.

NUMBER OF AWARDS: 40.

REPRESENTATIVE AWARDS:
Center for Intercultural Organizing; Community Alliance of Tenants; Salem/Keizer Coalition for Equality.

APPLICATION INFORMATION:
Application forms and information are available upon request.
Duration: Six to 12 months.
Deadline: Critical Response Grants and Travel Grants have no application deadline, but are subject to exhaustion of annual funding monies. General Fund: August and February.

PUBLICATIONS:
Applying for a Grant from MRG.

OFFICERS:
Cassandra Villanueva, Chairperson

ADDRESS INQUIRIES TO:
Cris Lira, Grants Manager
(See address above.)

THE MCKNIGHT FOUNDATION [1495]
710 South Second Street
Suite 400
Minneapolis, MN 55401
(612) 333-4220
Fax: (612) 332-3833

E-MAIL ADDRESS:
info@mcknight.org

WEB SITE ADDRESS:
www.mcknight.org

FOUNDED: 1953

AREAS OF INTEREST:
Early literacy, region and communities, arts, international, environment, and research and applied sciences.

NAME(S) OF PROGRAMS:
- **Arts Program**
- **Education and Learning**
- **International**
- **Midwest Climate and Energy**
- **Mississippi River**
- **Neuroscience**
- **Region and Communities**
- **Research and Applied Sciences**

TYPE:
General operating grants; Project/program grants. The Research and Applied Sciences Programs are by invitation only.

YEAR PROGRAM STARTED: 1953

LEGAL BASIS:
Family foundation.

GEOGRAPHIC RESTRICTIONS:
Minnesota, with emphasis on the Minneapolis-St. Paul area, Mississippi, and select international areas of work.

FINANCIAL DATA:
Total amount of support: $86,573,933 (unaudited) for the year 2013.

NUMBER OF APPLICANTS MOST RECENT YEAR: 995.

NUMBER OF AWARDS: 403 for the year 2013.

APPLICATION INFORMATION:
Applications are available online.
Deadline: Initial Inquiry - Arts and Region and Communities: October 15, January 15, April 15 and July 15; Mississippi River: November 1, February 1, May 1 and August 1.

PUBLICATIONS:
Annual report, including grants list; grantmaking guidelines for all programs.

OFFICERS:
Kate Wolford, President
Richard J. Scott, Vice President of Finance and Compliance

DIRECTORS:
Ted Staryk, Chairperson
Anne Binger
Erika Binger
Meghan Binger Brown
Robert Bruininks
David Crosby
Bill Gregg
Debby Landesman
Perry Moriearty
Robert J. Struyk

ADDRESS INQUIRIES TO:
Stephanie Duffy
Director of Grants Administration
(See address above.)

MARIETTA MCNEILL MORGAN AND SAMUEL TATE MORGAN, JR. FOUNDATION [1496]
Bank of America
Philanthropic Management VA2-300-12-99
1111 East Main Street, 12th Floor
P.O. Box 26688
Richmond, VA 23261-6688
(804) 887-8763
Fax: (804) 887-8854

FOUNDED: 1959

AREAS OF INTEREST:
Specific capital projects of organizations only in the Commonwealth of Virginia.

TYPE:
Capital grants; Challenge/matching grants. Grants for capital only. No grants to individuals, for endowment funds or operating funds.

YEAR PROGRAM STARTED: 1959

LEGAL BASIS:
Private foundation.

ELIGIBILITY:
Nonprofit organizations in the Commonwealth of Virginia who are classified by IRS as tax-exempt and are not private foundations.

GEOGRAPHIC RESTRICTIONS:
Virginia.

FINANCIAL DATA:
Amount of support per award: $5,000 to $75,000 dispersed in a single payment; average $25,000.
Total amount of support: Varies.

COOPERATIVE FUNDING PROGRAMS: Other funding sources encouraged.

APPLICATION INFORMATION:
Applicant should write to the Foundation, requesting guidelines for application.
Duration: One year.
Deadline: May 1 and November 1. Award announcements late June and early February.

ADDRESS INQUIRIES TO:
Elizabeth D. Seaman, Advisor
(See address above.)

A.J. MUSTE MEMORIAL INSTITUTE [1497]
339 Lafayette Street
New York, NY 10012
(212) 533-4335

E-MAIL ADDRESS:
info@ajmuste.org

WEB SITE ADDRESS:
www.ajmuste.org

FOUNDED: 1974

AREAS OF INTEREST:
Peace and disarmament, social and economic justice, racial and sexual equality, and the labor movement.

TYPE:
Grants-in-aid. The Institute's regular grant fund annually funds international, national and local projects in the U.S. and around the world. It gives priority to those with small budgets and little chance of funding from more traditional sources. The Institute does not provide academic scholarships.

YEAR PROGRAM STARTED: 1974

PURPOSE:
To promote peace and disarmament, social and economic justice, racial and sexual equality, and the labor movement.

ELIGIBILITY:
The Institute funds projects which seek to advance nonviolent grassroots education and action for social and economic justice. The Institute does not make grants for general support of ongoing operations. It does not generally accept proposals from organizations with annual budgets over $500,000 or for projects with budgets over $50,000. It will also not accept a new request from a previously funded group for two years after a grant. Grants are not made to individuals and generally not to religious organizations or development projects.

FINANCIAL DATA:
Amount of support per award: Average grant: $2,000.
Total amount of support: Varies.

NUMBER OF AWARDS: Varies.

APPLICATION INFORMATION:
Complete information is available on the Institute web site.
Duration: Varies.
Deadline: Varies according to program.

ADDRESS INQUIRIES TO:
Jane Guskin, Program Director
(See address above.)

NATIONAL COUNCIL ON FAMILY RELATIONS [1498]
1201 West River Parkway
Suite 200
Minneapolis, MN 55454
(763) 781-9331
Fax: (763) 781-9348

E-MAIL ADDRESS:
info@ncfr.org

WEB SITE ADDRESS:
www.ncfr.org

FOUNDED: 1938

AREAS OF INTEREST:
Social work, family life education, child development, family science, sociology, psychology, family health, human ecology and religion.

NAME(S) OF PROGRAMS:
- **Affiliate Councils Award for Meritorious Service**
- **Margaret E. Arcus Outstanding Family Life Educator Award**
- **Felix Berardo Mentoring Award**

- **Jessie Bernard Outstanding Contribution to Feminist Scholarship Paper**
- **Jessie Bernard Outstanding Research Proposal**
- **Ernest W. Burgess Award**
- **Czaplewski Fellowship Award**
- **Reuben Hill Award**
- **Ruth Jewson Award**
- **John L. and Harriet P. McAdoo Award**
- **NCFR Student Award**
- **Ernest G. Osborne Award**
- **Marie Peters Award**
- **Anselm Straus Award for Qualitative Family Research**
- **Jan Trost Award**
- **Cindy Winter Award**

TYPE:
Awards/prizes. Awards given for contributions to the area of family relations. All of the awards, except the Reuben Hill Award and the Jessie Bernard initiatives, require NCFR membership. The Reuben Hill Award is a juried award.

YEAR PROGRAM STARTED: 1938

PURPOSE:
To support contributions in teaching, research and distinguished service in the area of family relations.

LEGAL BASIS:
501(c)(3) education and research association.

FINANCIAL DATA:
Amount of support per award: $200 to $1,500.
Total amount of support: Varies.

NUMBER OF AWARDS: 1 award each annually.

APPLICATION INFORMATION:
Application information is available on the web site.
Duration: One year.
Deadline: May 1 for most awards; April 15 for Jessie Bernard.

PUBLICATIONS:
Journal of Marriage and the Family; *Family Relations*; *Journal of Family Theory and Review.*

OFFICERS:
Paul R. Amato, President

ADDRESS INQUIRIES TO:
Jeanne Strand, Director of Governance and Operations
(See address above.)

OPEN SOCIETY INSTITUTE - BALTIMORE   [1499]
201 North Charles Street
Suite 1300
Baltimore, MD 21201
(410) 234-1091
Fax: (410) 234-2816

E-MAIL ADDRESS:
monique.dixon@opensocietyfoundations.org

WEB SITE ADDRESS:
www.osi-baltimore.org

AREAS OF INTEREST:
Criminal rehabilitation.

NAME(S) OF PROGRAMS:
- **Criminal Justice Program**

TYPE:
Project/program grants.

YEAR PROGRAM STARTED: 1998

PURPOSE:
To reduce Maryland's overuse of incarceration and its social and economic costs without compromising public safety.

LEGAL BASIS:
Foundation.

ELIGIBILITY:
Grants are made to organizations that have tax-exempt status under Section 501(c)(3) of the Internal Revenue Code. No grants are made to individuals.

GEOGRAPHIC RESTRICTIONS:
Baltimore City, Maryland.

FINANCIAL DATA:
Amount of support per award: Varies.
Total amount of support: Varies.

APPLICATION INFORMATION:
Applicants should submit a letter of inquiry of two to three pages which includes:
(1) a description of the program to be funded;
(2) the qualifications of the organization to carry out the program;
(3) the ways in which the program reflects the priorities of the Criminal Justice Program;
(4) the amount of the budget and the funds requested and;
(5) a copy of the IRS letter stating the organization's tax-exempt status.
Duration: Varies.

ADDRESS INQUIRIES TO:
Monique Dixon, Program Director
(See address above.)

PASADENA COMMUNITY FOUNDATION   [1500]
260 South Los Robles Avenue, Suite 119
Pasadena, CA 91101
(626) 796-2097
Fax: (626) 583-4738

E-MAIL ADDRESS:
jdevoll@pasadenacf.org

WEB SITE ADDRESS:
www.pasadenacf.org

FOUNDED: 1954

AREAS OF INTEREST:
Charitable organizations (Pasadena area only), children, youth and family, community development, environment education, arts and the humanities, health and people with special needs.

TYPE:
Capital grants; Project/program grants. Grants for non-recurring capital needs, such as equipment, building repairs and vehicles.

YEAR PROGRAM STARTED: 1954

PURPOSE:
To support charitable organizations in the Pasadena area.

LEGAL BASIS:
Nonprofit public benefit corporation.

ELIGIBILITY:
Applicants must be 501(c)(3) organizations. No personal grants to individuals, churches or schools. No grants out of the Pasadena area.

GEOGRAPHIC RESTRICTIONS:
Greater Pasadena area, California.

FINANCIAL DATA:
Amount of support per award: $1,725 to $50,000.

NUMBER OF APPLICANTS MOST RECENT YEAR:
132.

NUMBER OF AWARDS: 50.

REPRESENTATIVE AWARDS:
$8,000 to Bishop Gooden Home for kitchen improvements; $25,000 to Rosemary Children's Center for passenger van; $40,000 to Pasadena Enterprise Center for new roof and air conditioning.

APPLICATION INFORMATION:
Contact the Foundation.
Duration: One year.
Deadline: February 1.

PUBLICATIONS:
Application guidelines; formal application form; newsletter.

IRS IDENTIFICATION NUMBER: 20-0253310

ADDRESS INQUIRIES TO:
Jennifer Fleming DeVoll
Executive Director
(See address above.)

JAY AND ROSE PHILLIPS FAMILY FOUNDATION OF MINNESOTA   [1501]
615 1st Avenue, N.E.
Suite 330
Minneapolis, MN 55413-3061
(612) 623-1654
Fax: (612) 623-1653

E-MAIL ADDRESS:
info@phillipsfamilyfoundationmn.org

WEB SITE ADDRESS:
www.phillipsfamilyfoundationmn.org

FOUNDED: 1944

AREAS OF INTEREST:
Human services, education, employment, housing, transit, programs to combat discrimination, and programs to help people in poverty attain economic stability.

TYPE:
Project/program grants. Grants to improve organizational effectiveness.

YEAR PROGRAM STARTED: 1944

PURPOSE:
To provide support for organizations and projects that address unmet human and social needs; to help people in poverty attain economic stability.

LEGAL BASIS:
Private foundation.

ELIGIBILITY:
Grants are made to organizations that have tax-exempt status under Section 501(c)(3) of the Internal Revenue Code. No grants are made to individuals.

During times of severe economic hardship and financial distress, the Foundation's primary concern is in providing support for projects addressing unmet human and social needs.

Additional Funding Considerations: The Foundation's preference is to support projects that represent new thinking about community needs and innovative efforts that have the potential for long-term solutions to the problems being addressed.

GEOGRAPHIC RESTRICTIONS:
Minnesota.

FINANCIAL DATA:
Amount of support per award: $15,000 to $50,000.
Total amount of support: Varies.

NUMBER OF AWARDS: Varies.

APPLICATION INFORMATION:
Application information is available on the web site.
Duration: Typically one year.
Deadline: By invitation only.

PUBLICATIONS:
Annual report; application guidelines.

IRS IDENTIFICATION NUMBER: 27-4196509

ADDRESS INQUIRIES TO:
Tracy Lamparty
Grants and Operations Manager
(See address above.)

*SPECIAL STIPULATIONS:
Unsolicited requests are not accepted.

PLOUGH FOUNDATION   [1502]
62 North Main, Suite 201
Memphis, TN 38103
(901) 521-2779
Fax: (901) 529-4063

E-MAIL ADDRESS:
mail@ploughfoundation.org

WEB SITE ADDRESS:
www.ploughfoundation.org

FOUNDED: 1960

AREAS OF INTEREST:
Families in crisis, public education and youth, crime, health and economic development.

TYPE:
Capital grants; Challenge/matching grants; Project/program grants; Seed money grants.

YEAR PROGRAM STARTED: 1960

PURPOSE:
To make payments or distributions to charitable organizations or for charitable purposes which will benefit the greatest number of people in the City of Memphis and/or Shelby County, TN.

LEGAL BASIS:
Private, independent foundation.

ELIGIBILITY:
No grants for assistance to address a crisis management situation caused by poor initial planning, individuals and projects outside the Memphis/Shelby County (TN) area. No grants for funding for private schools K-12, funding for annual fund-raising, or to individuals.

GEOGRAPHIC RESTRICTIONS:
Shelby County, Tennessee.

FINANCIAL DATA:
Amount of support per award: Varies.
Total amount of support: Varies.

REPRESENTATIVE AWARDS:
University of Memphis; Memphis Child Advocacy Center; Memphis College of Art; Memphis Shelby Crime Commission.

APPLICATION INFORMATION:
A brief letter of three pages or less should be sent to the Foundation explaining the specific project for which funds are needed and the results anticipated if the funding is received. Organizations whose projects interest the Foundation will be invited to submit a full grant proposal.

Duration: One to three years.
Deadline: Concept letter must be received by January 1, April 1, July 1 and October 1 for review at quarterly board meetings.

PUBLICATIONS:
Brochure.

IRS IDENTIFICATION NUMBER: 23-7175983

BOARD OF TRUSTEES:
Diane Rudner, Chairperson
Patricia R. Burnham
Eugene J. Callahan
D.D. Eisenberg
Rick Masson
Johnny B. Moore
Peter Pettit
Jocelyn P. Rudner
James F. Springfield
Steven Wishnia

ADDRESS INQUIRIES TO:
Barbara Jacobs, Program Director
(See address above.)

PRITCHETT TRUST
BMO Harris Bank
417 North Broadway
Pittsburg, KS 66762
(414) 287-7317
Fax: (414) 287-8580

TYPE:
Project/program grants; Seed money grants.

See entry 1142 for full listing.

KATE B. REYNOLDS CHARITABLE TRUST   [1503]
128 Reynolda Village
Winston-Salem, NC 27106-5123
(336) 397-5500
Fax: (336) 723-7765

E-MAIL ADDRESS:
karenmm@kbr.org

WEB SITE ADDRESS:
www.kbr.org

FOUNDED: 1947

AREAS OF INTEREST:
Human services and health care for the financially disadvantaged.

NAME(S) OF PROGRAMS:
● **Health Care Division**
● **Poor and Needy Division**

TYPE:
Capital grants; Challenge/matching grants; Conferences/seminars; Demonstration grants; Fellowships; Project/program grants; Scholarships; Seed money grants; Technical assistance; Training grants; Research contracts. Capacity building. Through the Health Care Division, the Trust responds to health and wellness needs and invests in solutions that improve the quality of health for financially needy residents of North Carolina. This Division seeks impact through two program areas: Supporting Prevention and Providing Treatment.

Through the Poor and Needy Division, the Trust responds to basic life needs and invests in solutions that improve the quality of life for financially needy residents of Forsyth County. This Division seeks impact through two program areas: Increasing Self Reliance and Providing Basic Needs.

YEAR PROGRAM STARTED: 1947

PURPOSE:
To improve the quality of life and quality of health for the financially needy of North Carolina; to accelerate positive movement on critical community issues and to effect enduring systemic change.

LEGAL BASIS:
Private foundation.

ELIGIBILITY:
Organizations eligible for grants are those that have qualified for exemption under Section 501(c)(3) and are not private foundations or a Type III supporting organization. Grants are not made to individuals or for medical research. Advance consultations are required prior to accepting an application.

GEOGRAPHIC RESTRICTIONS:
North Carolina.

FINANCIAL DATA:
Amount of support per award: Average $20,000 to $200,000.

APPLICATION INFORMATION:
The Trust requires prospective applicants to call for an advance consultation prior to submitting an application. Applications are only accepted electronically.
Duration: One to seven years.
Deadline: Second Tuesday in February and August.

PUBLICATIONS:
Annual report; *CATALYST,* newsletter.

IRS IDENTIFICATION NUMBER: 56-6036515

STAFF:
Karen McNeil-Miller, President
Joel T. Beeson, Director, Administration and Grants
Lori V. Fuller, Director, Evaluation and Research
Allen J. Smart, Director, Health Care Division
Joe D. Crocker, Director, Poor and Needy Division
Alan G. Welch, Information Systems Manager
Abena K. Asante, Senior Program Officer

ADDRESS INQUIRIES TO:
Health Care Division:
Allen J. Smart, Director
(See address above.)

RURITAN NATIONAL FOUNDATION
5451 Lyons Road
Dublin, VA 24084
(540) 674-5431
Fax: (540) 674-2304

E-MAIL ADDRESS:
foundation@ruritan.org

WEB SITE ADDRESS:
www.ruritan.org

TYPE:
Grants-in-aid; Matching gifts. These programs allow Ruritan clubs to increase their financial assistance to a student of the club's choice. Ruritan clubs contribute $300 to the Foundation and, in turn, the Foundation will add to this amount for grants.

See entry 1586 for full listing.

RURITAN NATIONAL FOUNDATION [1504]

5451 Lyons Road
Dublin, VA 24084
(540) 674-5431
(877) 787-8727
Fax: (540) 674-2304

E-MAIL ADDRESS:
foundation@ruritan.org

WEB SITE ADDRESS:
www.ruritan.org

AREAS OF INTEREST:
Disaster relief.

NAME(S) OF PROGRAMS:
● **Operation We Care**

TYPE:
Project/program grants.

PURPOSE:
To provide aid to victims of situations
officially declared disasters by the state and
federal governments.

ELIGIBILITY:
Available to individuals in areas that are
officially declared disasters by the state and
federal governments.

GEOGRAPHIC RESTRICTIONS:
United States.

FINANCIAL DATA:
Amount of support per award: Grants vary in
amount, depending upon the needs and
nature of the request.
Total amount of support: Varies.

APPLICATION INFORMATION:
Application must be made to the local
Ruritan District Governor.

ADDRESS INQUIRIES TO:
Michael Chrisley, Executive Director
(See address above.)

SAILORS' SNUG HARBOR OF BOSTON [1505]

c/o GMA Foundations
77 Summer Street, 8th Floor
Boston, MA 02110-1006
(617) 391-3101
Fax: (617) 426-7087

E-MAIL ADDRESS:
rvictorin@gmafoundations.com

WEB SITE ADDRESS:
www.sailorssnugharbor.org

FOUNDED: 1852

AREAS OF INTEREST:
Elderly and fishing families.

TYPE:
General operating grants; Project/program
grants.

PURPOSE:
To help current and former Massachusetts
fishing families achieve sustainable
self-sufficiency during the current transition
period in their industry; to help Greater
Boston's low-income elderly population live
independently.

LEGAL BASIS:
Private foundation.

ELIGIBILITY:
Grants are made to organizations that have
tax-exempt status under Section 501(c)(3) of
the Internal Revenue Code. No grants are
made to individuals. Nonsectarian religious
programs may apply.

FINANCIAL DATA:
Amount of support per award: $5,000 to
$25,000; typical grant $10,000.
Total amount of support: Varies.

COOPERATIVE FUNDING PROGRAMS: Fishing
Communities Initiative of Island Foundation.

NUMBER OF APPLICANTS MOST RECENT YEAR:
60.

NUMBER OF AWARDS: 30 to 40.

APPLICATION INFORMATION:
Applications must be submitted online.
Duration: One year. Renewal by
reapplication.
Deadline: Late August for programs with a
fishing communities focus and mid-December
for programs with an elderly focus.

ADDRESS INQUIRIES TO:
Gracelaw Simmons, Foundation
Administrator
(See address above.)

GEORGE J. AND EFFIE L. SEAY MEMORIAL TRUST [1506]

1111 East Main Street, 12th Floor
Richmond, VA 23219
(804) 887-8763
Fax: (804) 887-8854

FOUNDED: 1959

AREAS OF INTEREST:
General philanthropic purposes with
emphasis on direct-service projects in
Virginia.

TYPE:
Project/program grants. Grants for specific
needs.

PURPOSE:
To enhance the quality of life in the
Commonwealth of Virginia.

LEGAL BASIS:
Private foundation.

ELIGIBILITY:
Nonprofit organizations only in the
Commonwealth of Virginia. No grants to
individuals or to endowment funds.

GEOGRAPHIC RESTRICTIONS:
Virginia.

FINANCIAL DATA:
Amount of support per award: $5,000 to
$15,000.
Total amount of support: Varies.
Matching fund requirements: Stipulated for
specific grants.

COOPERATIVE FUNDING PROGRAMS: Other
funding sources are encouraged.

APPLICATION INFORMATION:
Applicants should write to the Trust for
application guidelines.
Duration: Single payment grants made for
one year.
Deadline: May 1 and November 1. Award
announcement made in late June and early
February.

PUBLICATIONS:
Application guidelines.

ADDRESS INQUIRIES TO:
Elizabeth D. Seaman, Advisor
(See address above.)

*SPECIAL STIPULATIONS:
Grants made only to organizations in
Virginia.

WILLIAM G. AND MARIE SELBY FOUNDATION [1507]

1800 Second Street
Suite 954
Sarasota, FL 34236
(941) 957-0442
Fax: (941) 957-3135

E-MAIL ADDRESS:
ejones@selbyfdn.org

WEB SITE ADDRESS:
www.selbyfdn.org

FOUNDED: 1955

AREAS OF INTEREST:
Education, human services, the arts and
community improvement.

TYPE:
Capital grants; Scholarships.

YEAR PROGRAM STARTED: 1955

PURPOSE:
To improve the quality of life in the Sarasota
County area.

LEGAL BASIS:
Private foundation.

ELIGIBILITY:
501(c)(3) organizations.

GEOGRAPHIC RESTRICTIONS:
Charlotte, DeSoto, Manatee and Sarasota
counties, Florida.

FINANCIAL DATA:
Amount of support per award: Minimum
request: $10,000; average grant: $100,000.
Scholarships: Up to $7,000 per year.
Total amount of support: Approximately
$3,600,000 for fiscal year 2013.

APPLICATION INFORMATION:
Application information is available on the
web site.
Duration: Grants: Typically one year;
Scholarships: Up to four years.
Deadline: Grant Applications: February 1
and August 1. Notification May 1 and
December 1, respectively. Scholarships: April
1.

PUBLICATIONS:
Guidelines.

STAFF:
Sarah H. Pappas, President
Evan G. Jones, Grants and Scholarship
Manager

ADDRESS INQUIRIES TO:
Evan G. Jones
Grants and Scholarship Manager
(See address above.)

SHARE OUR STRENGTH [1508]

1030 15th Street, NW, Suite 1100 W
Suite 700
Washington, DC 20005
(202) 393-2925
(800) 969-4767
Fax: (202) 347-5868

E-MAIL ADDRESS:
grants@strength.org

WEB SITE ADDRESS:
www.strength.org

FOUNDED: 1984

AREAS OF INTEREST:
Domestic childhood hunger, hunger
prevention and alleviation limited to summer

meals, after-school meals, SNAP/WIC outreach, school breakfast and nutrition education.

NAME(S) OF PROGRAMS:
- **No Kid Hungry**

TYPE:
Project/program grants. Grants are focused on increasing participation in the federal nutrition programs, including summer meals, after-school meals, SNAP, WIC, school breakfast, and on nutrition education.

YEAR PROGRAM STARTED: 1984

PURPOSE:
To end childhood hunger in the United States.

LEGAL BASIS:
Nonprofit organization.

ELIGIBILITY:
Applicants must be 501(c)(3) organizations, schools/school districts, churches/faith-based organizations or other organizations/agencies eligible to receive grants.

GEOGRAPHIC RESTRICTIONS:
United States.

FINANCIAL DATA:
Amount of support per award: Average grant size $5,000 to $10,000.

APPLICATION INFORMATION:
Organizations that have received grants from Share Our Strength within the previous two years will be automatically notified of available grant opportunities. For all others, submit a Letter of Inquiry.
Duration: One year. Renewal possible.
Deadline: Varies.

PUBLICATIONS:
Annual report.

ADDRESS INQUIRIES TO:
Susan Berkun, Director, Grants
(See address above.)

SIERRA HEALTH FOUNDATION [1509]
1321 Garden Highway
Sacramento, CA 95833
(916) 922-4755
Fax: (916) 922-4024

E-MAIL ADDRESS:
info@sierrahealth.org

WEB SITE ADDRESS:
www.sierrahealth.org

FOUNDED: 1984

AREAS OF INTEREST:
Improving health outcomes and reducing health disparities.

NAME(S) OF PROGRAMS:
- **Conference and Convening Program**
- **Grizzly Creek Ranch Camp and Conference Center**
- **Health Leadership Program**
- **Healthy Sacramento Coalition**
- **Responsive Grants Program**
- **Sacramento Region Health Care Partnership**
- **Youth Pathways to Health**

TYPE:
Matching gifts; Project/program grants. Specific to funding opportunities - solicited.

YEAR PROGRAM STARTED: 1984

PURPOSE:
To invest in and serve as a catalyst for ideas, partnerships and programs that improve health and quality of life in northern California through convening, educating and strategic grantmaking.

LEGAL BASIS:
Private foundation.

ELIGIBILITY:
Applicant must be a public entity or designated 501(c)(3) organization by the IRS with 509(a)(1) or 509(a)(2) status. No grants to individuals, endowments or activities which exclusively benefit members of private or religious organizations.

GEOGRAPHIC RESTRICTIONS:
Northern California counties.

FINANCIAL DATA:
Amount of support per award: $1,000 to $100,000. Average $10,000.
Total amount of support: $2,890,116 for the year 2012.

NUMBER OF APPLICANTS MOST RECENT YEAR:
516.

NUMBER OF AWARDS: 108 for the year 2012.

PUBLICATIONS:
Healthy Youth Healthy Regions; Renewing Juvenile Justice.

IRS IDENTIFICATION NUMBER: 68-0050036

OFFICERS:
Chet P. Hewitt, President and Chief Executive Officer
Gil Alvarado, Vice President of Administration and Chief Financial Officer
Diane Littlefield, Vice President of Programs and Partnerships

BOARD OF DIRECTORS:
Jose Hermocillo, M.D., Chairman
David Gordon, Vice Chairman
Chet P. Hewitt
Nancy Lee
Robert Petersen, C.P.A.
Claire Pomeroy
Dr. Earl Washburn
Carol G. Whiteside

ADDRESS INQUIRIES TO:
See e-mail address above.

SOCIAL JUSTICE FUND NORTHWEST [1510]
1904 Third Avenue, Suite 806
Seattle, WA 98101
(206) 624-4081
Fax: (206) 382-2640

E-MAIL ADDRESS:
info@socialjusticefund.org

WEB SITE ADDRESS:
www.socialjusticefund.org

FOUNDED: 1978

AREAS OF INTEREST:
Funding community-based groups to promote social justice activities and organizations attempting to establish a society that is politically and economically democratic, equitable and environmentally sound.

CONSULTING OR VOLUNTEER SERVICES:
Facilitates regional networking and general foundation information.

TYPE:
General operating grants; Project/program grants; Seed money grants; Technical assistance; Training grants.

YEAR PROGRAM STARTED: 1978

PURPOSE:
To be a resource for organizations working for social justice in the states of Idaho, Montana, Oregon, Washington and/or Wyoming attempting to establish a society that is politically and economically democratic, equitable and environmentally just.

LEGAL BASIS:
Nonprofit, 501(c)(3), public foundation.

ELIGIBILITY:
Applicant must address fundamental issues facing Northwest/Northern Rockies or any organizations that work in and have a direct impact on the people of Idaho, Montana, Oregon, Washington and/or Wyoming. Considered are organizations that are led by the people most impacted.

GEOGRAPHIC RESTRICTIONS:
Idaho, Montana, Oregon, Washington and/or Wyoming.

FINANCIAL DATA:
Amount of support per award: Average grant: $10,000.
Total amount of support: Approximately $530,000 for the year 2013.

APPLICATION INFORMATION:
Application information is available on the web site.
Duration: Typically one year.
Deadline: Varies.

PUBLICATIONS:
Guidelines; monthly e-mail newsletter; annual report.

IRS IDENTIFICATION NUMBER: 91-1036971

BOARD OF DIRECTORS:
Molly Chidsey
Sashya Clark
Megan Do
Kegan Flaherty
Dina Flores-Breyer
Ubax Gardheere
Esther Handy
Jessan Hutchison-Quillian
Alice Ito
Michael McGinn
Burke Stansbury
Rich Stolz
Joaquin Uy
Abel Valladares

ADDRESS INQUIRIES TO:
Mijo Lee, Program Director
(See address above.)

IRVIN STERN FOUNDATION [1511]
4 East Ohio Street
Studio 22
Chicago, IL 60611
(312) 321-9402

E-MAIL ADDRESS:
christine@irvinstern.org

WEB SITE ADDRESS:
www.irvinstern.org

FOUNDED: 1957

AREAS OF INTEREST:
Human services, civic affairs and Jewish welfare.

TYPE:
General operating grants; Project/program grants.

PURPOSE:
To benefit social service organizations and enhance the welfare of Jewish communities.

LEGAL BASIS:
Family foundation.

ELIGIBILITY:
All organizations from outside the city of Chicago are by invitation only.

GEOGRAPHIC RESTRICTIONS:
Chicago, Illinois.

NUMBER OF APPLICANTS MOST RECENT YEAR:
65.

NUMBER OF AWARDS: 42.

APPLICATION INFORMATION:
Submit an online Letter of Inquiry or download a form and mail it to the Foundation at the address listed above.
Deadline: March 1 and September 1.

IRS IDENTIFICATION NUMBER: 36-6047947

STAFF:
Christine Flood, Grants Administrator

ADDRESS INQUIRIES TO:
Christine Flood, Grants Administrator
(See address and e-mail above.)

THE STODDARD CHARITABLE TRUST [1512]
370 Main Street
Suite 1250
Worcester, MA 01608
(508) 798-8621
Fax: (508) 791-6454

FOUNDED: 1939

AREAS OF INTEREST:
General charitable activities.

TYPE:
Capital grants. Grants to support activities in the Trustees' areas of interest.

YEAR PROGRAM STARTED: 1939

PURPOSE:
To provide funding to worthy causes in the Worcester, MA area and to help that community during times of need.

LEGAL BASIS:
Private, charitable foundation.

ELIGIBILITY:
Nonprofit organizations.

GEOGRAPHIC RESTRICTIONS:
Worcester, Massachusetts.

FINANCIAL DATA:
Amount of support per award: $5,000 to $2,000,000; average grant $10,000.
Total amount of support: $3,000,000 annually.

APPLICATION INFORMATION:
Submit requests for application procedures to the address above.
Duration: One year.
Deadline: March 1, June 1, September 1 and December 1.

OFFICERS AND TRUSTEES:
Warner S. Fletcher, Chairman
Judith S. King, Treasurer
Valerie S. Loring, Secretary

TRUSTEE:
Allen W. Fletcher, Trustee

ADDRESS INQUIRIES TO:
Warner S. Fletcher, Chairman
(See address above.)

THE SUMMIT FOUNDATION
111 A Lincoln Street
Breckenridge, CO 80424
(970) 453-5970
Fax: (970) 453-1423

E-MAIL ADDRESS:
tsfdirector@summitfoundation.org

WEB SITE ADDRESS:
www.summitfoundation.org

TYPE:
Capital grants; Challenge/matching grants; Endowments; General operating grants; Project/program grants; Scholarships; Technical assistance. The Foundation supports scholarship programs at Summit High School and neighboring community high schools. Scholarships are available to graduating seniors each year.

See entry 1385 for full listing.

SUNNEN FOUNDATION [1513]
7910 Manchester Avenue
St. Louis, MO 63143
(314) 781-2100

FOUNDED: 1953

AREAS OF INTEREST:
Grants for specific goal-oriented activities to protect reproductive and First Amendment rights and for youth and family services.

TYPE:
Capital grants; Challenge/matching grants; Development grants; Matching gifts; Project/program grants.

YEAR PROGRAM STARTED: 1953

LEGAL BASIS:
Private foundation.

ELIGIBILITY:
Limited to those organizations having tax-exempt status. No scholarship, research or travel grants are made to or for specific individuals.

GEOGRAPHIC RESTRICTIONS:
St. Louis, Missouri.

FINANCIAL DATA:
Assets of $13,808,000 (unaudited) as of December 31, 2013.
Amount of support per award: $2,500 to $100,000 for the year 2013.
Total amount of support: $421,160 for the year 2013.

NUMBER OF APPLICANTS MOST RECENT YEAR:
Approximately 30.

NUMBER OF AWARDS: 15 for the year 2013.

REPRESENTATIVE AWARDS:
$150,000 to Planned Parenthood Agencies.

APPLICATION INFORMATION:
The Sunnen Foundation has no formal application form. Proposal should include:
(1) summary page that describes the project and amount of funds requested;
(2) organizational background that includes mission, history, types of programs offered and constituencies served;
(3) project description that justifies the need, outlines specific goals, objectives and activities planned to meet the goals and objectives, a project time-line and specific methods of evaluation;
(4) project budget that notes anticipated expenses, including details of how the Sunnen Foundation funds will be used and anticipated income, including information

about other grantmakers approached for funding;
(5) organizational budget that notes the current year budget and proposed budget for project year(s) showing income and expenses, the organization's most recent audited financial statement and public and private sources of funds and;
(6) supporting documents that should include a list of current board members, annual report and evidence of 501(c)(3) status.

Five copies of the proposal should be submitted.
Duration: Varies.
Deadline: August 1. Proposals should be submitted in June or July.

PUBLICATIONS:
Guidelines.

IRS IDENTIFICATION NUMBER: 43-6029156

OFFICERS:
Kurt J. Kallaus, President and Director
Matthew S. Kreider, Vice President and Director
Susan S. Brasel, Treasurer and Director
Ruth Cardinale, Secretary and Director
Helen S. Sly, Director

ADDRESS INQUIRIES TO:
Kurt J. Kallaus, President
(See address above.)

TEAMMATES FOR KIDS FOUNDATION
1900 Wazee Street, Suite 205
Denver, CO 80202
(303) 759-9777

E-MAIL ADDRESS:
jason@tfkf.com

WEB SITE ADDRESS:
www.teammates4kids.com

TYPE:
Grants-in-aid. Foundation grants are directed to nonprofit organizations that specialize in working with children.

See entry 1149 for full listing.

TIDES FOUNDATION
P.O. Box 29198
San Francisco, CA 94129
(415) 561-6400
Fax: (415) 561-6401

E-MAIL ADDRESS:
info@tides.org

WEB SITE ADDRESS:
www.tides.org

TYPE:
General operating grants; Project/program grants.

See entry 1387 for full listing.

UNITED METHODIST HEALTH MINISTRY FUND [1514]
100 East First Street
Hutchinson, KS 67501
(620) 662-8586
Fax: (620) 662-8597

E-MAIL ADDRESS:
healthfund@healthfund.org

WEB SITE ADDRESS:
www.healthfund.org

FOUNDED: 1986

AREAS OF INTEREST:
Health care.

NAME(S) OF PROGRAMS:
- **Access to Health Care-System Change and Advocacy**
- **Healthy Congregations Program**
- **Healthy Nutrition and Physical Activity for Young Children**
- **Mental Health for Young Children**

TYPE:
Challenge/matching grants; Conferences/seminars; Demonstration grants; General operating grants; Project/program grants; Seed money grants; Technical assistance; Training grants.

YEAR PROGRAM STARTED: 1986

PURPOSE:
To advance health, healing and wholeness for persons within and beyond the bounds of the Kansas West Conference of the United Methodist Church.

LEGAL BASIS:
Church foundation.

ELIGIBILITY:
Grants are made:
(1) to organizations exempt from income tax under Section 501(c)(3) of the IRS Code;
(2) to governmental entities;
(3) for health care services and;
(4) for projects located in Kansas.

GEOGRAPHIC RESTRICTIONS:
Kansas.

FINANCIAL DATA:
Amount of support per award: Average grant $24,206 for the year 2013.

Total amount of support: $2,130,152 for the year 2013.

NUMBER OF APPLICANTS MOST RECENT YEAR:
100 for the year 2013.

NUMBER OF AWARDS: 88 for the year 2013.

REPRESENTATIVE AWARDS:
$700,000 to Kansas Hospital Education and Research Foundation to support the development of a Kansas Rural Health Systems Improvement Pilot Project; $100,454 to Kansas State University to continue development of A System for Obesity Prevention Through Childcare: HOP'N Child Development Online; $100,000 to Kansas Association for Infant and Early Childhood Mental Health to expand and enhance the Kansas workforce in the area of social and emotional development of young children by providing an Endorsement program which supports and recognizes mental health competencies for professionals who work with infants and toddlers and their families.

APPLICATION INFORMATION:
Application information is available by contacting the Fund.

Duration: Varies.

PUBLICATIONS:
Annual report; special publications.

IRS IDENTIFICATION NUMBER: 48-1019578

STAFF:
Kim Moore, President
Virginia Elliott, Vice President for Programs
Jeff Gamber, Technology Manager

ADDRESS INQUIRIES TO:
Virginia Elliott
Vice President for Programs
(See address above.)

*SPECIAL STIPULATIONS:
Preference for United Methodist Churches and agencies in Kansas.

WICHITA COMMUNITY FOUNDATION

301 North Main Street
Suite 100
Wichita, KS 67202
(316) 264-4880
Fax: (316) 264-7592

E-MAIL ADDRESS:
wcf@wichitacf.org

WEB SITE ADDRESS:
www.wichitacf.org

TYPE:
Project/program grants; Scholarships; Seed money grants.

See entry 1402 for full listing.

EDUCATION

Educational projects and research (general)

AMERICAN ASSOCIATION OF UNIVERSITY WOMEN EDUCATIONAL FOUNDATION
327 Second Street, Suite 103
Coralville, IA 52241
(319) 688-4334

E-MAIL ADDRESS:
aauw@scholarshipamerica.org

WEB SITE ADDRESS:
www.aauw.org

TYPE:
Project/program grants; Seed money grants.
See entry 1074 for full listing.

THE AMERICAN FOUNDATION FOR SUICIDE PREVENTION [1515]
120 Wall Street
29th Floor
New York, NY 10005
(212) 363-3500 ext. 2015
Fax: (212) 363-6237

E-MAIL ADDRESS:
grantsmanager@afsp.org

WEB SITE ADDRESS:
www.afsp.org

FOUNDED: 1987

AREAS OF INTEREST:
Suicide prevention.

NAME(S) OF PROGRAMS:
● **Pilot Grant**

TYPE:
Research grants.

PURPOSE:
To enable established investigators to pursue promising leads that emerge from their investigations and help develop preliminary data for the submission of larger funding requests to granting agencies.

ELIGIBILITY:
Grants are awarded to individuals affiliated with not-for-profit institutions or organizations in the U.S. and abroad. Grant applications are not accepted from for-profit organizations. Grant payments are made to the grantee institution and not the individual investigator.

FINANCIAL DATA:
Amount of support per award: Up to $30,000.

APPLICATION INFORMATION:
Applications must be submitted online at the Foundation web site.
Duration: One or two years.
Deadline: November 15.

ADDRESS INQUIRIES TO:
Jonathan Dozier-Ezell, Research Manager
(See address above.)

THE AMERICAN FOUNDATION FOR SUICIDE PREVENTION [1516]
120 Wall Street
29th Floor
New York, NY 10005
(212) 363-3500 ext. 2015
Fax: (212) 363-6237

E-MAIL ADDRESS:
grantsmanager@afsp.org

WEB SITE ADDRESS:
www.afsp.org

FOUNDED: 1987

AREAS OF INTEREST:
Suicide prevention.

NAME(S) OF PROGRAMS:
● **Postdoctoral Research Fellowships**

TYPE:
Fellowships; Research grants.

PURPOSE:
To sponsor full-time training projects by investigators who have recently received a Ph.D. degree.

ELIGIBILITY:
Postdoctoral Research Fellowships are awarded for full-time training projects by investigators who have received a Ph.D. degree within the preceding three years and have not had more than three years of fellowship support.

FINANCIAL DATA:
Amount of support per award: Up to $104,000 (stipend $46,000 per year and $6,000 per year institutional allowance).
Total amount of support: Up to $104,000.

APPLICATION INFORMATION:
Applications must be submitted online at the Foundation web site.
Duration: Two years.
Deadline: November 15.

ADDRESS INQUIRIES TO:
Jonathan Dozier-Ezell, Research Manager
(See address above.)

THE AMERICAN FOUNDATION FOR SUICIDE PREVENTION [1517]
120 Wall Street
29th Floor
New York, NY 10005
(212) 363-3500 ext. 2015
Fax: (212) 363-6237

E-MAIL ADDRESS:
grantsmanager@afsp.org

WEB SITE ADDRESS:
www.afsp.org

FOUNDED: 1987

AREAS OF INTEREST:
Suicide prevention.

NAME(S) OF PROGRAMS:
● **Distinguished Investigator Award**

TYPE:
Research grants.

PURPOSE:
To advance knowledge of suicide and the ability to prevent it; to fund new directions and initiatives in suicidology.

ELIGIBILITY:
Applicant must be an associate professor or higher with a proven history of research in the area of suicide.

FINANCIAL DATA:
Amount of support per award: $100,000 ($50,000 per year).

APPLICATION INFORMATION:
Applications must be submitted online at the Foundation web site.
Duration: Up to two years.
Deadline: November 15.

ADDRESS INQUIRIES TO:
Jonathan Dozier-Ezell, Research Manager
(See address above.)

THE AMERICAN FOUNDATION FOR SUICIDE PREVENTION [1518]
120 Wall Street
29th Floor
New York, NY 10005
(212) 363-3500 ext. 2015
Fax: (212) 363-6237

E-MAIL ADDRESS:
grantsmanager@afsp.org

WEB SITE ADDRESS:
www.afsp.org

FOUNDED: 1987

AREAS OF INTEREST:
Suicide prevention.

NAME(S) OF PROGRAMS:
● **Standard Research Grants**
● **Young Investigator Grants**

TYPE:
Research grants. Standard Research Grants are awarded to individual investigators. An additional annual stipend is available for mentors on Young Investigator Awards in which the investigator is at the level of Assistant Professor or lower.

PURPOSE:
To advance the knowledge of suicide and the ability to prevent it; to promote the study of clinical, biological and psychosocial aspects of suicide.

ELIGIBILITY:
Grants are awarded to not-for-profit organizations.

FINANCIAL DATA:
Amount of support per award: Up to $90,000 for a standard grant or $75,000, plus an additional $10,000 over two years for a mentor on Young Investigator Grant.

APPLICATION INFORMATION:
Applications must be submitted online at the Foundation web site.
Duration: One or two years.
Deadline: November 15.

ADDRESS INQUIRIES TO:
Jonathan Dozier-Ezell, Research Manager
(See address above.)

AMERICAN HONDA FOUNDATION [1519]
1919 Torrance Boulevard
Mailstop: 100-1W-5A
Torrance, CA 90501-2746
(310) 781-4090
Fax: (310) 781-4270

E-MAIL ADDRESS:
ahf@ahm.honda.com

WEB SITE ADDRESS:
www.foundation.honda.com

FOUNDED: 1984

AREAS OF INTEREST:
Youth education in the areas of science, technology, engineering, mathematics, environment, job training and literacy.

TYPE:
Project/program grants.

YEAR PROGRAM STARTED: 1984

PURPOSE:
To fund programs which strive to educate communities in the process of problem solving and planning; to educate minority youth in the areas of science and math.

LEGAL BASIS:
501(c)(3) corporate foundation.

ELIGIBILITY:
Applicants must be 501(c)(3) organizations, national in scope, impact and outreach and focused on youth and scientific education. To be considered for possible funding, programs related to youth and scientific education should be dedicated to improving the human condition of all mankind, soundly managed and administered by enthusiastic and dedicated individuals who approach their jobs in a youthful way, look to the future or foresightful programs, innovative and creative programs that propose untried methods which ultimately may result in providing solutions to the complex cultural, educational, scientific and social concerns currently facing American society, broad in scope, intent, impact and outreach, possess a high potential for success with a relatively low incidence of duplication of effort, operate from a position of financial soundness, in urgent need of funding from a priority basis (not necessarily financial need), i.e., the relative importance of the program or project to the public and represent a minimal risk in terms of venture capital investment.

Grants are not given to individuals or for scholarships, politics, fund-raising activities, religious activities, arts and culture, medical or educational research, sponsorships for nonprofit, or disaster relief.

No in-kind contributions from the Foundation. No donations of Honda products.

GEOGRAPHIC RESTRICTIONS:
United States.

FINANCIAL DATA:
Amount of support per award: $20,000 to $75,000 per year; $30,000 to $50,000 average.
Total amount of support: $1,700,000 for fiscal year 2014.

APPLICATION INFORMATION:
Grant application is accessible online. Grant requests should include:
(1) a description of the program for which the grant will be used;
(2) a copy of the IRS determination letter, 501(c)(3), designating the organization as a nonprofit, tax-exempt, public-supported charity;
(3) a copy of the organization's most recent Form 990 to the IRS;
(4) a list of the Board of Directors and a resolution from the Board which authorizes the request for a grant;
(5) a copy of the current budget for the entire organization, with comparisons to the last previous budget;
(6) a proposed budget utilizing the grant funds requested with line-item detail;
(7) audited financial statements for the last two years;
(8) a list of current contributions, with giving levels, particularly of other corporate sponsors and/or corporate foundations;
(9) a three- to five-year plan from the organization and;

(10) support materials (i.e., annual reports, press kits, brochures, flyers, press clippings, photos, etc.).
Duration: One year.
Deadline: November 1, February 1, May 1 and August 1.

ADDRESS INQUIRIES TO:
See e-mail address above.

*SPECIAL STIPULATIONS:
One proposal per year, per grant seeker.

AMERICAN INSTITUTE OF CERTIFIED PUBLIC ACCOUNTANTS (AICPA)   [1520]
220 Leigh Farm Road
Durham, NC 27707
(919) 402-2161
Fax: (919) 419-4705

E-MAIL ADDRESS:
scholarships@aicpa.org

WEB SITE ADDRESS:
www.thiswaytocpa.com/scholarships

AREAS OF INTEREST:
Accounting.

NAME(S) OF PROGRAMS:
● **AICPA Scholarship for Minority Accounting Students**

TYPE:
Scholarships.

YEAR PROGRAM STARTED: 1969

PURPOSE:
To provide financial assistance to minority students who show significant potential to become CPAs.

ELIGIBILITY:
An applicant must meet the following requirements:
(1) be an underrepresented minority in the accounting profession (e.g., Black or African American, Hispanic or Latino, Native American or Asian American);
(2) enrolled as a full-time undergraduate (12 semester-hours or equivalent) or a full-time graduate-level student (nine semester-hours or equivalent) for the 2013-14 academic year; an exception may be granted if the student plans to participate in an internship;
(3) pursuing an undergraduate- or graduate-level degree in an "accounting-related" major ("accounting-related" shall be as determined by Sponsor in Sponsor's sole discretion);
(4) planning to pursue the C.P.A. licensure but not presently be a C.P.A.;
(5) completed at least 30 semester-hours (or equivalent) of college coursework, including at least six semester-hours (or equivalent) in accounting, by end of spring 2013;
(6) applied to or been accepted into a public or private, 501(c) four-year college or university located in the U.S. or its territories; the business program must be accredited by the AACSB and/or ACBSP;
(7) maintained an overall and major grade point average of at least 3.0 (on a 4.0 scale);
(8) be an AICPA student affiliate member (or have submitted a new member application); those interested can apply on the web site at no cost;
(9) be a U.S. citizen or permanent resident (green card holder) and;
(10) have some financial need (i.e., not receiving a full or partial scholarship(s) and/or grant(s) that cover and/or exceed one's

educational expenses).
Note: AICPA staff and their family members are not eligible to receive this scholarship.

GEOGRAPHIC RESTRICTIONS:
United States and its territories.

FINANCIAL DATA:
Amount of support per award: Up to $3,000.
Total amount of support: Approximately $240,000 for the academic year 2013-14.

NUMBER OF AWARDS: Up to 80 per academic year.

APPLICATION INFORMATION:
Information is available online.
Duration: One year. Renewable.
Deadline: April 1.

ADDRESS INQUIRIES TO:
AICPA Scholarship for Minority Accounting Students Program (See e-mail address above.)

*SPECIAL STIPULATIONS:
Students selected to receive an AICPA scholarship must participate in the AICPA Legacy Scholars program, which includes performing at least eight hours of community service per semester to advocate for the CPA profession. Through their community service efforts, AICPA Legacy Scholars enhance their leadership and communication skills by building relationships with both aspiring and seasoned CPAs.

AMERICAN INSTITUTE OF CERTIFIED PUBLIC ACCOUNTANTS (AICPA)
220 Leigh Farm Road
Durham, NC 27707
(919) 402-4682
Fax: (919) 419-4705

E-MAIL ADDRESS:
scholarships@aicpa.org

WEB SITE ADDRESS:
www.aicpa.org

TYPE:
Fellowships. Awarded annually to full-time minority accounting scholars who demonstrate significant potential to become accounting educators.

See entry 1658 for full listing.

THE AMERICAN SOCIETY FOR NONDESTRUCTIVE TESTING, INC.   [1521]
1711 Arlingate Lane
Columbus, OH 43228
(614) 274-6003
(800) 222-2768 ext. 223 (U.S. and Canada)
Fax: (614) 274-6899

E-MAIL ADDRESS:
mthomas@asnt.org

WEB SITE ADDRESS:
www.asnt.org

FOUNDED: 1997

AREAS OF INTEREST:
Promotion of nondestructive testing.

NAME(S) OF PROGRAMS:
● **ASNT Faculty Grant Award**

TYPE:
Development grants. The Society sponsors an annual award that will provide grants to foster the development of nondestructive

testing and evaluation courses (NDT & NDE) as an integral part of its engineering curricula.

PURPOSE:
To support research and education in nondestructive testing; to increase public awareness of nondestructive testing's critical role in ensuring the safety and well-being of mankind.

LEGAL BASIS:
501(c)(3) corporation.

ELIGIBILITY:
Faculty members from ABET-accredited engineering programs are encouraged to submit proposals for this award.

FINANCIAL DATA:
Amount of support per award: $8,000.
Total amount of support: Up to $16,000.

NUMBER OF AWARDS: Up to 2.

APPLICATION INFORMATION:
Guidelines for submitting proposals are available online. Contact the ASNT administrative assistant for an application.
Duration: One year.
Deadline: December 1. Funding will begin the following July.

ADDRESS INQUIRIES TO:
Michelle Thomas, ASNT Administrative Assistant
(See address above.)

THE KATHRYN AMES FOUNDATION

c/o Pierson & Pierson
305 West Chesapeake Avenue, Suite 308
Towson, MD 21204
(410) 821-3006
Fax: (410) 821-3007

E-MAIL ADDRESS:
info@kathrynames.org

WEB SITE ADDRESS:
www.kathrynames.org

TYPE:
General operating grants; Project/program grants.

See entry 829 for full listing.

ARCHAEOLOGICAL INSTITUTE OF AMERICA

656 Beacon Street, 6th Floor
Boston, MA 02215
(617) 358-4184
Fax: (617) 353-6550

E-MAIL ADDRESS:
fellowships@aia.bu.edu

WEB SITE ADDRESS:
www.archaeological.org

TYPE:
Fellowships. The Fellowship supports projects pertaining to the archaeology of Portugal. These include, but are not limited to, research projects, colloquia, symposia, publication, research-related travel, or travel to academic meetings for the purpose of presenting papers on the archaeology of Portugal.

See entry 830 for full listing.

ARIZONA STATE UNIVERSITY [1522]

P.O. Box 870901
Tempe, AZ 85287-0901
(480) 727-6282
Fax: (480) 965-6712

E-MAIL ADDRESS:
janelle.kappes@asu.edu

WEB SITE ADDRESS:
www.students.asu.edu/lsp

AREAS OF INTEREST:
Leadership.

NAME(S) OF PROGRAMS:
• **ASU Leadership Scholarship Program**

TYPE:
Scholarships.

PURPOSE:
To recognize outstanding high school graduating seniors who have achieved excellence in leadership.

ELIGIBILITY:
Must have demonstrated leadership abilities, responsibilities, and potential in Key Club leadership and high school activities.

FINANCIAL DATA:
Amount of support per award: In-state: $9,000 per year; Out-of-state: $13,000 per year.

NUMBER OF AWARDS: 25 per year.

APPLICATION INFORMATION:
Guidelines are available on the University web site.
Duration: Eight consecutive semesters.
Deadline: December.

ADDRESS INQUIRIES TO:
Janelle Kappes, Assistant Director
(See address above.)

AXE-HOUGHTON FOUNDATION

c/o Foundation Source
55 Walls Drive, 3rd Floor
Fairfield, CT 06824
(800) 839-1754
Fax: (800) 421-6579

WEB SITE ADDRESS:
www.foundationcenter.org/grantmaker/axehoughton

TYPE:
Project/program grants.

See entry 653 for full listing.

BAT CONSERVATION INTERNATIONAL [1523]

P.O. Box 162603
Austin, TX 78716
(512) 327-9721
Fax: (512) 327-9724

E-MAIL ADDRESS:
grants2@batcon.org

WEB SITE ADDRESS:
www.batcon.org

FOUNDED: 1982

AREAS OF INTEREST:
Mammals, ecology, conservation and biology; specifically bats.

NAME(S) OF PROGRAMS:
• **BCI Student Scholarship**

TYPE:
Research grants; Scholarships. Support graduate students in research.

YEAR PROGRAM STARTED: 1990

PURPOSE:
To conserve bats and their habitat worldwide; to support research that specifically provides for bat conservation progress.

ELIGIBILITY:
Must be currently enrolled in a degree-granting program.

FINANCIAL DATA:
Amount of support per award: Up to $5,000.

NUMBER OF APPLICANTS MOST RECENT YEAR: 77.

NUMBER OF AWARDS: 24 for the year 2012.

APPLICATION INFORMATION:
Applications must be completed online.
Duration: One year.
Deadline: December 15.

IRS IDENTIFICATION NUMBER: 74-2553144

ADDRESS INQUIRIES TO:
Robert Locke, Grants Coordinator
(See address above.)

BATON ROUGE AREA FOUNDATION

402 North Fourth Street
Baton Rouge, LA 70802
(225) 387-6126
Fax: (225) 387-6153

E-MAIL ADDRESS:
jcarpenter@braf.org

WEB SITE ADDRESS:
www.braf.org

TYPE:
Capital grants; Challenge/matching grants; Conferences/seminars; Demonstration grants; Development grants; Matching gifts; Project/program grants; Scholarships; Seed money grants; Technical assistance; Training grants; Visiting scholars.

See entry 436 for full listing.

THE BAY AND PAUL FOUNDATIONS [1524]

17 West 94th Street, 1st Floor
New York, NY 10025
(212) 663-1115
Fax: (212) 932-0316

E-MAIL ADDRESS:
info@bayandpaulfoundations.org

WEB SITE ADDRESS:
www.bayandpaulfoundations.org

FOUNDED: 1962

AREAS OF INTEREST:
Arts in education and educational reform.

TYPE:
Challenge/matching grants; General operating grants; Project/program grants.

YEAR PROGRAM STARTED: 1962

PURPOSE:
To support a variety of programs that empower students through democracy, environmental stewardship, meaningful community service and the arts.

LEGAL BASIS:
Private foundation.

ELIGIBILITY:
Grants are made to organizations that have tax-exempt status under Section 501(c)(3) of the Internal Revenue Code. No grants are made to individuals and no grants are made to building campaigns or sectarian religious programs.

Additional information can be found on the Foundations web site.

FINANCIAL DATA:
Amount of support per award: Varies.
Total amount of support: $4,000,000.

NUMBER OF AWARDS: 70 to 80.

APPLICATION INFORMATION:
Proposals are accepted by invitation only. Unsolicited requests are not accepted.
Duration: One year; some multiyear.

IRS IDENTIFICATION NUMBER: 13-1991717

STAFF:
Dianne J. Daniels, Chief Operating Officer, Fiscal Officer
Michelle Graham, Senior Program Officer and Chief Program Administrator

BOARD OF DIRECTORS:
Frederick Bay, President and Chief Executive Officer
Corinne Steel, Director, Secretary
Rebecca Adamson, Director
David Bury, Director
Kenneth Hurwitz, Director
Khalis Williams, Director

*PLEASE NOTE:
Unsolicited requests are not accepted.

BAYER USA FOUNDATION

100 Bayer Road
Pittsburgh, PA 15205
(800) 422-9374
Fax: (412) 778-4430

E-MAIL ADDRESS:
karen.wirth@bayer.com

WEB SITE ADDRESS:
www.bayerus.com

TYPE:
General operating grants; Grants-in-aid; Project/program grants.
See entry 1815 for full listing.

BETHESDA LUTHERAN COMMUNITIES, INC. [1525]

600 Hoffmann Drive
Watertown, WI 53094
(920) 206-4428
Fax: (920) 206-7706 (Attn.: Chris Dovnik)

E-MAIL ADDRESS:
chris.dovnik@mailblc.org

WEB SITE ADDRESS:
bethesdalutherancommunities.org

AREAS OF INTEREST:
Developmental disabilities.

NAME(S) OF PROGRAMS:
• **Developmental Disabilities Scholastic Achievement Scholarships**

TYPE:
Scholarships.

PURPOSE:
To encourage Lutheran youth to develop God-pleasing attitudes and actions toward

people with individual differences, and to consider careers in the field of developmental disabilities services.

ELIGIBILITY:
Must be an active communicant member of a Lutheran church, have achieved sophomore status at a college or university, have a minimum 3.0 overall grade point average and have a career objective in the field of developmental disabilities services.

GEOGRAPHIC RESTRICTIONS:
United States and Canada.

FINANCIAL DATA:
Amount of support per award: $3,000.
Total amount of support: $6,000.

NUMBER OF APPLICANTS MOST RECENT YEAR:
21.

APPLICATION INFORMATION:
The application process includes a short, relevant essay, 100 hours of paid or volunteer work in the field of developmental disabilities, services, and letters of reference.
Deadline: April 16.

ADDRESS INQUIRIES TO:
Chris Dovnik, Coordinator
(See address above.)

BIBLIOGRAPHICAL SOCIETY OF AMERICA [1526]

P.O. Box 1537
Lenox Hill Station, NY 10021
(212) 734-2500
Fax: (212) 452-2710

E-MAIL ADDRESS:
bsa@bibsocamer.org

WEB SITE ADDRESS:
www.bibsocamer.org

FOUNDED: 1904

AREAS OF INTEREST:
Study of books and manuscripts.

NAME(S) OF PROGRAMS:
• **BSA Fellowship Program**

TYPE:
Fellowships. Stipend in support of travel, living and research expenses.

YEAR PROGRAM STARTED: 1983

PURPOSE:
To support bibliographical inquiry as well as research in the history of the book trades and in publishing history.

ELIGIBILITY:
Open to doctorates, postdoctorates and postgraduates. Applicants of any nationality can apply. Eligible topics may concentrate on books and documents in any field, but should focus on the book or manuscript (the physical object) as historical evidence. Such topics may include establishing a text or studying the history of book production, publication, distribution, collecting, or reading. Enumerative listings do not fall within the scope of this program.

FINANCIAL DATA:
Amount of support per award: Up to $2,000 per month.

APPLICATION INFORMATION:
Instructions on how to apply and application form are available on the Society's web site.
Duration: One to two months. Nonrenewable.
Deadline: December 15.

ADDRESS INQUIRIES TO:
Michele Randall, Executive Director
(See address above.)

THE BROWARD EDUCATION FOUNDATION, INC. [1527]

KC Wright Administration Building, 1st Floor
600 S.E. Third Avenue
Fort Lauderdale, FL 33301
(754) 321-2030
Fax: (754) 321-2706

E-MAIL ADDRESS:
jorene.jameson@browardschools.com

WEB SITE ADDRESS:
www.browardedfoundation.org

FOUNDED: 1983

AREAS OF INTEREST:
Education.

NAME(S) OF PROGRAMS:
• **Broward Advisors for Continuing Education (BRACE) Scholarship Fund**
• **The Florida Prepaid College Tuition Program**
• **Impact Teacher Grants**
• **Tools for Schools Broward**

TYPE:
Grants-in-aid; Scholarships. Broward Advisors for Continuing Education (BRACE) Scholarship Fund awards last-dollar scholarships to qualifying students who have exhausted all avenues for financial aid and still fall short of their monetary need to pursue a postsecondary education, including community college, university and vocational school.

The Florida Prepaid College Tuition Program purchases prepaid contracts through the state of Florida's Prepaid College Foundation. It provides a defined benefit college tuition contract for state universities, community colleges, and vocational/technical centers.

YEAR PROGRAM STARTED: 1983

PURPOSE:
To provide resources for students, teachers and other employees to help them achieve educational success.

LEGAL BASIS:
501(c)(3) education foundation.

GEOGRAPHIC RESTRICTIONS:
Broward County, Florida.

FINANCIAL DATA:
Amount of support per award: Varies.
Total amount of support: $1,100,000.

NUMBER OF APPLICANTS MOST RECENT YEAR:
1,300.

APPLICATION INFORMATION:
Contact the Foundation for specific application forms.
Duration: Varies.
Deadline: Varies.

PUBLICATIONS:
Financial report.

STAFF:
Jorene Jameson, Chief Executive Officer and President

ADDRESS INQUIRIES TO:
Coco Burns, Program Coordinator
(See address above.)

THE BROWN FOUNDATION, INC. [1528]

P.O. Box 130646
Houston, TX 77219-0646
(713) 523-6867
Fax: (713) 523-2917

E-MAIL ADDRESS:
bfi@brownfoundation.org

WEB SITE ADDRESS:
www.brownfoundation.org

FOUNDED: 1951

AREAS OF INTEREST:
Education, arts and humanities, civic/public affairs, medicine and science, and human services.

TYPE:
Assistantships; Capital grants; Challenge/matching grants; Fellowships; General operating grants; Matching gifts; Professorships; Project/program grants; Seed money grants.

YEAR PROGRAM STARTED: 1951

PURPOSE:
To distribute funds for public charitable purposes, principally for the support, encouragement and assistance to education, the arts and community service.

LEGAL BASIS:
Private foundation.

ELIGIBILITY:
Funding given to 501(c)(3) nonprofit institutions only. No grants to individuals.

GEOGRAPHIC RESTRICTIONS:
Primarily Texas.

FINANCIAL DATA:
Amount of support per award: Varies.
Total amount of support: $37,772,391 for fiscal year ended June 30, 2013.

APPLICATION INFORMATION:
Grant proposals must include the purpose of the organization requesting funds, tax-exempt determination letter, audited financial statement, summary of proposed project, budget and letter of approval from a chief administrator. Applications will not be processed until all required information is included.
Duration: Typically one year.

PUBLICATIONS:
Application guidelines.

OFFICERS AND TRUSTEES:
Nancy Negley, Chairman
Herman L. Stude, President
Louisa Sarofim, Vice President and Secretary
Nancy Abendshein
Holbrook Dorn
Will Mathis
John O'Connor
Elisa Pye
Christopher B. Sarofim

ADDRESS INQUIRIES TO:
Katy Hays, Chief Grants Officer
(See address above.)

FRITZ B. BURNS FOUNDATION [1529]

4001 West Alameda Avenue
Suite 203
Burbank, CA 91505
(818) 840-8802
Fax: (818) 840-0468

FOUNDED: 1955

AREAS OF INTEREST:
Education.

TYPE:
Capital grants; Scholarships. Grants are educational in nature. The emphasis is on buildings, equipment, endowments (not for operational expenses), scholarships, faculty fellowships, hospitals and hospital equipment and medical research.

YEAR PROGRAM STARTED: 1955

LEGAL BASIS:
Private foundation.

ELIGIBILITY:
Eligible organizations must have IRS 501(c)(3) not-for-profit status. Grants are not made to individuals or to religious organizations.

GEOGRAPHIC RESTRICTIONS:
Southern California, primarily Los Angeles County.

FINANCIAL DATA:
Amount of support per award: $500 to $100,000.
Total amount of support: Varies.

APPLICATION INFORMATION:
Applicant organizations must provide IRS 501(c)(3) documentation. Financial statements and a list of the organization's board of directors must be included with the application.
Duration: One year.
Deadline: September 30.

OFFICER:
Rex Rawlinson, President

ADDRESS INQUIRIES TO:
Rex Rawlinson, President
(See address above.)

BUSINESS SOLUTIONS ASSOCIATION EDUCATIONAL FOUNDATION [1530]

3601 East Joppa Road
Baltimore, MD 21234
(410) 931-8100
Fax: (410) 931-8111

E-MAIL ADDRESS:
info@businesssolutionsassociation.com

WEB SITE ADDRESS:
www.businesssolutionsassociation.com

AREAS OF INTEREST:
Education.

NAME(S) OF PROGRAMS:
● **Business Solutions Association Educational Foundation Scholarships**

TYPE:
Scholarships.

PURPOSE:
To assist students that are working in the office products industry with educational needs.

ELIGIBILITY:
Open to students that are already at college or starting in the fall, who are:
(1) employed by Business Solutions Association member company;
(2) a relative of an employee of Business Solutions Association member company;
(3) a member of a group affiliated with the office products industry or;
(4) a relative of a member of a group affiliated with the office products industry.

FINANCIAL DATA:
Amount of support per award: Up to $5,000.
Total amount of support: Varies.

APPLICATION INFORMATION:
Applicant must complete a Scholarship Application Form and mail it, along with attachments, to the address above. Form is available on the web site. The attachments which must accompany the completed form are:
(1) transcript of grades and credits through the most recent grading period (high school applicants) or transcripts covering a minimum of the previous two scholastic years;
(2) letter of recommendation from a person employed by a firm in the office products industry. This person should hold an executive or managerial position and;
(3) letter of recommendation from a teacher, professor or other educational professional.
Duration: One year. Renewal possible.
Deadline: March 31.

ADDRESS INQUIRIES TO:
Paula Kreuzburg, Associate Director
(See address above.)

THE CAYL INSTITUTE [1531]

31 Heath Street
Jamaica Plain, MA 02130
(617) 354-3820
Fax: (617) 354-3823

E-MAIL ADDRESS:
info@cayl.org

WEB SITE ADDRESS:
www.cayl.org

FOUNDED: 2004

NAME(S) OF PROGRAMS:
● **Early Educators Fellowship Initiative**

TYPE:
Fellowships. Established to help early education professionals develop the skills, relationships, and knowledge needed to bring about public policy change in early care and education.

YEAR PROGRAM STARTED: 2004

PURPOSE:
To develop and strengthen the movement for equity in education and child care.

ELIGIBILITY:
Applicants must be citizens or permanent residents of the U.S.

FINANCIAL DATA:
No stipend is granted; instead, three college credits from Cambridge College are awarded.

APPLICATION INFORMATION:
Applications are available online.
Duration: One calendar year.
Deadline: Varies.

STAFF:
Kate Amel, Operations Manager

ADDRESS INQUIRIES TO:
See e-mail address above.

CEMALA FOUNDATION [1532]

330 South Greene Street, Suite 101
Greensboro, NC 27401
(336) 274-3541
Fax: (336) 272-8153

E-MAIL ADDRESS:
cemala@cemala.org

WEB SITE ADDRESS:
www.cemala.org

FOUNDED: 1986

AREAS OF INTEREST:
Education, arts, health, human services, environment and public interest.

TYPE:
Capital grants; Challenge/matching grants; Conferences/seminars; Development grants; Fellowships; Grants-in-aid; Project/program grants; Seed money grants; Technical assistance; Training grants.

PURPOSE:
To better the quality of life for the citizens of Greensboro, NC.

LEGAL BASIS:
Private foundation.

ELIGIBILITY:
Eligible organizations must be IRS 501(c)(3) tax-exempt.

GEOGRAPHIC RESTRICTIONS:
Primarily Greensboro, North Carolina.

NUMBER OF APPLICANTS MOST RECENT YEAR:
78.

NUMBER OF AWARDS: 33.

APPLICATION INFORMATION:
Application is available online. A copy of IRS tax determination letter should be included.
Duration: Annual. Renewal possible.
Deadline: March 1 and September 1.

STAFF:
Susan Schwartz, Executive Director
Betty Day, Assistant Treasurer

THE COCA-COLA FOUNDATION, INC.   [1533]
P.O. Box 1734
Atlanta, GA 30301
(404) 676-2121

E-MAIL ADDRESS:
cocacolacommunityrequest@na.ko.com

WEB SITE ADDRESS:
www.cocacolacommunityrequest.com

FOUNDED: 1984

AREAS OF INTEREST:
Water stewardship, healthy and active lifestyles, community recycling and education.

TYPE:
Project/program grants.

PURPOSE:
To help develop and maintain vibrant, sustainable and local communities; to support initiatives and programs that respond in a meaningful way to community needs and priorities.

LEGAL BASIS:
Corporate foundation.

ELIGIBILITY:
Grants are made only to nonprofit 501(c)(3) or equivalent organizations. No grants to individuals, religious organizations or endeavors, or political, legislative, lobbying or fraternal organizations.

FINANCIAL DATA:
Amount of support per award: Varies.
Total amount of support: Varies.

APPLICATION INFORMATION:
Detailed instructions and application form are available online.
Duration: Typically one year.
Deadline: Requests accepted and reviewed on a year-round basis.

PUBLICATIONS:
Annual report.

COLAGE
4509 Interlake Avenue North
No. 180
Seattle, WA 98103
(855) 426-5243

E-MAIL ADDRESS:
colage@colage.org

WEB SITE ADDRESS:
www.colage.org

TYPE:
Awards/prizes; Scholarships. Grants and awards are offered to foster the growth of children, youth and adults of lesbian, gay, bisexual and transgender parents of all racial, ethnic and class backgrounds, by providing education, support and community on local and international levels.

See entry 985 for full listing.

THE COMMUNITY FOUNDATION FOR THE GREATER CAPITAL REGION   [1534]
6 Tower Place
Albany, NY 12203
(518) 446-9638
Fax: (518) 446-9708

E-MAIL ADDRESS:
jcuilla@cfgcr.org

WEB SITE ADDRESS:
www.cfgcr.org

AREAS OF INTEREST:
Education.

NAME(S) OF PROGRAMS:
• **Lou Rubin and Ike Cohen Memorial Scholarship**

TYPE:
Scholarships.

YEAR PROGRAM STARTED: 1968

PURPOSE:
To assist outstanding students in the extended periodical distributor industry family who plan to pursue postsecondary education in college and vocational programs.

LEGAL BASIS:
Community foundation.

ELIGIBILITY:
Applicants to the program must be dependent children of full-time employees of designated periodical wholesaler organizations, and/or national periodical distributors, and/or publishers in specified areas east of the Mississippi with one year of service. Eligible students must be high school seniors enrolling in a full-time undergraduate course of study at an accredited college, university, or vocational-technical school.

GEOGRAPHIC RESTRICTIONS:
Specified areas east of the Mississippi.

FINANCIAL DATA:
Amount of support per award: $2,500 for the year 2013.

Total amount of support: $5,000 for the year 2013.

NUMBER OF AWARDS: 1 or 2.

APPLICATION INFORMATION:
Applications are available from the Foundation at the address above.
Duration: One year.
Deadline: Early March.

ADDRESS INQUIRIES TO:
Jenna Cuilla, Donor Relations Manager
(See address above.)

COMMUNITY FOUNDATION OF THE LOWCOUNTRY, INC.   [1535]
4 Northridge Drive, Suite A
Hilton Head Island, SC 29926
(843) 681-9100
Fax: (843) 681-9101

E-MAIL ADDRESS:
foundation@cf-lowcountry.org

WEB SITE ADDRESS:
www.cf-lowcountry.org

FOUNDED: 1994

TYPE:
Community impact grants. Investment grants. Organization development grants.

PURPOSE:
To maintain and enhance the educational, social, culture, health, civic and environmental resources of the community.

LEGAL BASIS:
501(c)(3).

ELIGIBILITY:
501(c)(3) organizations.

GEOGRAPHIC RESTRICTIONS:
Hilton Head area, South Carolina.

FINANCIAL DATA:
Amount of support per award: Community Impact Grants: $5,000 to $50,000; Community Investment Grants: $100,000 up; Organizational Development Grants: Not to exceed $5,000.

Total amount of support: Approximately $3,000,000 for fiscal year 2012-13.

APPLICATION INFORMATION:
Applicants must attend a grants information session and register. In order to determine project eligibility, applicants are then required to meet with the Vice President for Grantmaking. Those eligible are invited to apply.
Duration: One year.
Deadline: April 1, August 1 and December 1.

ADDRESS INQUIRIES TO:
Dr. Cynthia Smith, Vice President for Grantmaking and Community Leadership
(See address above.)

CONSORTIUM OF COLLEGE AND UNIVERSITY MEDIA CENTERS   [1536]
601 East Kirkwood Avenue
Franklin Hall 0009
Bloomington, IN 47405-1223
(812) 855-6049
Fax: (812) 855-2103

E-MAIL ADDRESS:
ccumc@ccumc.org

WEB SITE ADDRESS:
www.ccumc.org

FOUNDED: 1971

AREAS OF INTEREST:
Media and technology services in higher education.

CONSULTING OR VOLUNTEER SERVICES:
Operation of media services.

NAME(S) OF PROGRAMS:
- **Donald A. Rieck Research Grant**

TYPE:
Awards/prizes; Demonstration grants; Project/program grants; Research grants. Financial support for research related to the production, selection, collection development, information retrieval, utilization, distribution, or management of instructional media, equipment or technology.

YEAR PROGRAM STARTED: 1978

PURPOSE:
To improve the quality, effectiveness, and efficiency of higher education by developing new knowledge and practices that improve leadership, knowledge, accessibility and utilization of media and academic technology to improve teaching and learning.

LEGAL BASIS:
University nonprofit association.

ELIGIBILITY:
Faculty, staff and students at constituent member institutions are eligible to apply for the annual Donald A. Rieck Research Grant. Research reports are presented at conferences.

Faculty, staff, graduate or undergraduate students from an accredited higher education institution can apply. Contact the Consortium for detailed eligibility requirements.

FINANCIAL DATA:
Grant funding must be processed through the host institution's research grant administration unit. Indirect overhead costs paid from the grant funding must not exceed 8%. Grant funds may not be used to augment the total salary or rate of salary of faculty during their regular academic appointment term, but may be used for "summer salary" for faculty to support the research activities or to augment the appointment of student investigators.
Amount of support per award: Up to $20,000.

NUMBER OF APPLICANTS MOST RECENT YEAR:
3.

NUMBER OF AWARDS: 1.

APPLICATION INFORMATION:
Application information is available on the web site.
Duration: Research projects should be in progress within six months of funding notification and be completed and reported on within 24 months. Project timelines that will be complete in less than 12 months from notification of funding are preferred.
Deadline: June 1. Announcement at the CCUMC Summer Board Meeting in July. Notification in August.

PUBLICATIONS:
Leader (CCUMC newsletter); *College & University Media Review* (CCUMC journal); Consortium directory; conference proceedings; annual report.

IRS IDENTIFICATION NUMBER: 51-0168225

BOARD OF DIRECTORS:
Sue Clabaugh, President

Pat Poet, President-Elect
John Fick, Treasurer
Brenda White, Secretary
Aileen Scales, Executive Director
Lyn McCurdy, Editor-in-Chief
Susan Brower
Cody Gregg
Ken Mangum
Doug McCartney
Sandie Miller
Robert Schmitt
Joey Wall

EXECUTIVE DIRECTOR:
Aileen Scales

ADDRESS INQUIRIES TO:
CCUMC Executive Office
(See e-mail address above.)

*SPECIAL STIPULATIONS:
Research results must be published in the *CCUMC College & University Media Review* journal and recipients are encouraged to submit a presentation proposal for a CCUMC Annual Conference.

COUNCIL ON TECHNOLOGY AND ENGINEERING TEACHER EDUCATION (CTETE)   [1537]
Technology and Engineering Education
Utah State University
Logan, UT 84322-6000
(435) 797-3642
Fax: (435) 797-2567

E-MAIL ADDRESS:
ed.reeve@usu.edu

WEB SITE ADDRESS:
www.ctete.org

FOUNDED: 1951

AREAS OF INTEREST:
Technology and engineering teacher education.

CONSULTING OR VOLUNTEER SERVICES:
NCATE state guideline preparation found on web site.

NAME(S) OF PROGRAMS:
- **Engineering and Technology Education**

TYPE:
Challenge/matching grants; Conferences/seminars; Project/program grants; Research grants; Travel grants; Research contracts. Field study support and curriculum development.

YEAR PROGRAM STARTED: 1996

PURPOSE:
To discover philosophical rationales, theoretical models, principles and/or practices that potentially increase the effectiveness and efficiency of pre-service or in-service engineering and technology teacher education.

LEGAL BASIS:
Special-interest foundation.

ELIGIBILITY:
Applicants must be members of the Council on Technology and Engineering Teacher Education.

FINANCIAL DATA:
Amount of support per award: Average $1,000.
Total amount of support: Varies.

NUMBER OF AWARDS: Varies.

APPLICATION INFORMATION:
Contact the Council for guidelines.

Duration: Typically one year.
Deadline: December 1.

ADDRESS INQUIRIES TO:
Dr. Edward Reeve, Past President
(See address above.)

THE DANA FOUNDATION
505 Fifth Avenue, Sixth Floor
New York, NY 10017
(212) 223-4040
Fax: (212) 317-8721

E-MAIL ADDRESS:
amarin@dana.org

WEB SITE ADDRESS:
www.dana.org

TYPE:
Awards/prizes; Challenge/matching grants; Project/program grants; Research grants. For the decade of the 1990s, the Foundation focused on brain research. Grants in these areas are made principally through competitive Clinical Hypotheses Programs in immuno-imaging, neuroimaging and brain-cardiovascular system interactions. These competitive grants programs support pilot testing of experimental and innovative ideas that in immunology and neuroscience research have the potential of advancing clinical applications. The Foundation also supports an invitational program in which leading scientists are invited to compete for research grants designed to improve immune system responses to biological agents.

The Foundation has supported advances in education throughout its history. Its current interest is focused primarily on professional development programs that foster improved teaching of the performing arts in public schools. Programs emphasize innovative training projects that are exported from, or imported to, New York City, Washington, DC, Los Angeles and their surrounding areas. Letters of intent are accepted on a rolling basis. Grantees are selected through a competitive process.

See entry 2254 for full listing.

FREDERICK DOUGLASS INSTITUTE FOR AFRICAN AND AFRICAN-AMERICAN STUDIES   [1538]
University of Rochester
Morey Hall 302
Rochester, NY 14627-0440
(585) 276-5744
Fax: (585) 256-2594

E-MAIL ADDRESS:
fdi@mail.rochester.edu

WEB SITE ADDRESS:
www.rochester.edu/college/aas/grad_programs

FOUNDED: 1986

AREAS OF INTEREST:
African and African-American studies and graduate education through advanced research at the University of Rochester.

NAME(S) OF PROGRAMS:
- **FDI Postdoctoral Fellowship**
- **FDI Predoctoral Dissertation Fellowship**

TYPE:
Awards/prizes; Conferences/seminars; Fellowships.

PURPOSE:
To promote the development of African and African-American studies and graduate education through advanced research at the University of Rochester; specifically, to support the completion of a project (FDI Postdoctoral Fellowship) and to support the completion of a dissertation (FDI Predoctoral Dissertation Fellowship).

ELIGIBILITY:
FDI Postdoctoral Fellowship: Open to scholars who hold a Ph.D. degree in a field related to the African and African-American experience.

FDI Predoctoral Dissertation Fellowship: Open to graduate students of any university who study aspects of the African and African-American experience.

FINANCIAL DATA:
Amount of support per award: Postdoctoral Fellowship: $40,000; Predoctoral Dissertation Fellowship: $26,000.

NUMBER OF APPLICANTS MOST RECENT YEAR: 85.

NUMBER OF AWARDS: 1 of each Fellowship.

APPLICATION INFORMATION:
Applicants to the Postdoctoral Fellowship must submit the following information online via www.rochester.edu/fort/fdi_postdoc:
(1) a completed FDI fellowship application form;
(2) a curriculum vitae;
(3) a three- to five-page description of the project (plus a short bibliography);
(4) a sample of published or unpublished writing on a topic related to the proposal and;
(5) three letters of recommendation that comment upon the value and feasibility of the work proposed, to be sent by the referees.

Applicants to the Predoctoral Dissertation Fellowship must submit the following information online via www.rochester.edu/fort/fdi_predoc:
(1) a completed FDI fellowship application form;
(2) a curriculum vitae;
(3) an official transcript showing completion of all preliminary coursework and qualifying examinations;
(4) the dissertation prospectus;
(5) a sample chapter from the dissertation and;
(6) three letters of recommendation to be sent out by the referees, including one from the dissertation supervisor, assessing the candidate's prospects for completing the project within a year.
Duration: September 1 to May 31.
Deadline: December 31.

EDUCATIONAL TESTING SERVICE   [1539]
660 Rosedale Road, MS 19-T
Princeton, NJ 08541
(609) 734-5543
Fax: (609) 734-5010

E-MAIL ADDRESS:
internfellowships@ets.org

WEB SITE ADDRESS:
www.ets.org/research/fellowships

FOUNDED: 1947

AREAS OF INTEREST:
Educational measurement and psychometrics, validity, natural language processing and speech technologies, cognitive psychology, learning theory, linguistics and computational linguistics, assessment design and development, teaching and classroom research, and statistics.

NAME(S) OF PROGRAMS:
- **ETS Postdoctoral Fellowship Award Program**

TYPE:
Fellowships.

YEAR PROGRAM STARTED: 1958

PURPOSE:
To provide research opportunities to individuals who hold a Doctorate in the fields indicated above; to increase the number of women and underrepresented minority professionals conducting research in educational measurement and related fields.

LEGAL BASIS:
Not-for-profit organization.

ELIGIBILITY:
Open to early career scholars who hold a Ph.D. or Ed.D. in one of the areas listed above. Individuals who have recently earned their doctoral degrees are invited to apply for a unique fellowship experience which combines working on cutting-edge ETS research projects and conducting independent research that is relevant to ETS goals.

FINANCIAL DATA:
Fellowship includes employee benefits, vacation, holidays and other paid leave in accordance with ETS policies. Also includes a $5,000 one-time relocation incentive for round-trip relocation expenses.
Total amount of support: Varies.

NUMBER OF APPLICANTS MOST RECENT YEAR: 30.

NUMBER OF AWARDS: Up to 2.

APPLICATION INFORMATION:
Application accepted online.
Duration: 12 months, with an option for second-year renewal upon mutual agreement.
Deadline: All application materials must be postmarked on or before February 1.

ADDRESS INQUIRIES TO:
See e-mail address above.

EDUCATIONAL TESTING SERVICE   [1540]
660 Rosedale Road, MS 19-T
Princeton, NJ 08541
(609) 734-5543
Fax: (609) 734-5010

E-MAIL ADDRESS:
internfellowships@ets.org

WEB SITE ADDRESS:
www.ets.org/research/fellowships.html

FOUNDED: 1947

AREAS OF INTEREST:
Educational measurement and psychometrics, validity, natural language processing and speech technologies, cognitive psychology, learning theory, linguistics and computational linguistics, teaching and classroom research, statistics and international large-scale assessments.

NAME(S) OF PROGRAMS:
- **Summer Internship Program for Graduate Students**

TYPE:
Internships. Interns in this eight- or 12-week program participate in research under the guidance of a senior ETS staff member in one of the areas of interest listed above. Interns also participate in seminars and workshops on a variety of topics.

YEAR PROGRAM STARTED: 1963

PURPOSE:
To provide research opportunities to individuals enrolled in a doctoral program in the fields described above; to increase the number of women and underrepresented minority professionals conducting research in educational measurement and related fields.

LEGAL BASIS:
Not-for-profit organization.

ELIGIBILITY:
Graduate students who are currently enrolled in a full-time doctoral program in one of the areas listed above and who have completed a minimum of two years of coursework toward their Ph.D. or Ed.D. prior to the program start date are eligible to apply.

GEOGRAPHIC RESTRICTIONS:
Princeton, New Jersey.

FINANCIAL DATA:
Amount of support per award: $6,000 salary and transportation allowance for relocating to and from the Princeton area; housing will be provided for interns commuting more than 50 miles.

Some projects may require a 12-week internship, for which the salary would be $9,000.

NUMBER OF APPLICANTS MOST RECENT YEAR: Average of 200.

NUMBER OF AWARDS: Approximately 15 to 20.

APPLICATION INFORMATION:
The application process opens in November. Applications must be submitted online.
Duration: Eight weeks in June and July, or 12 weeks from late May to mid-August.
Deadline: February 1. Applicants will be notified by April 1.

PUBLICATIONS:
Program announcement.

STAFF:
Georgiana Weingart, Fellowship Program Administrator

ADDRESS INQUIRIES TO:
See e-mail address above.

FEDERATION OF AMERICAN CONSUMERS AND TRAVELERS   [1541]
318 Hillsboro Avenue
P.O. Box 104
Edwardsville, IL 62025
(618) 656-0454
Fax: (618) 656-5369

E-MAIL ADDRESS:
vrolens@usafact.org

WEB SITE ADDRESS:
www.usafact.org

FOUNDED: 1984

AREAS OF INTEREST:
Education.

NAME(S) OF PROGRAMS:
- **Classroom and Community Grants**
- **Continuing Education Scholarships**

TYPE:
Project/program grants.

PURPOSE:
To help provide supplies or to otherwise support a classroom project for which funds may not be readily available somewhere else; to improve the teacher's ability to teach and the students'opportunity to learn.

ELIGIBILITY:
Classroom Grants: Any dues-paying member of FACT may nominate any teacher to apply for a grant. Only one nomination per year per member.

Continuing Education Scholarships: All applicants must be FACT members, their children or grandchildren.

Scholarships available to:
(1) current high school seniors;
(2) people who graduated from high school four or more years ago and are now planning to enroll in an undergraduate college, university or trade school program;
(3) students currently enrolled in an undergraduate college or university and;
(4) people who wish to attend a trade school or technical college.

GEOGRAPHIC RESTRICTIONS:
United States.

FINANCIAL DATA:
Amount of support per award: Classroom and Community Grants: $100 to $2,500; Continuing Education Scholarships: One $10,000 and one $2,500 award available in each of the four categories of eligibility for scholarships.

Total amount of support: Classroom and Community Grants: Approximately $130,000 since 1999; Continuing Education Scholarships: $865,000 since 1992.

APPLICATION INFORMATION:
Contact the Federation for guidelines.
Duration: Annual awards.
Deadline: Classroom and Community Grants: January, April, July and October; Continuing Education Scholarships: January 15.

ADDRESS INQUIRIES TO:
Vicki Rolens, Managing Director
(See address above.)

FLORIDA EDUCATION FUND   [1542]
201 East Kennedy Boulevard
Suite 1525
Tampa, FL 33602
(813) 272-2772 ext. 203
Fax: (813) 272-2784

E-MAIL ADDRESS:
fef.jackson@verizon.net

WEB SITE ADDRESS:
www.fefonline.org

FOUNDED: 1984

AREAS OF INTEREST:
Arts and sciences, mathematics, business, engineering, health sciences, nursing, visual and performing arts.

NAME(S) OF PROGRAMS:
● **McKnight Doctoral Fellowship**

TYPE:
Fellowships.

YEAR PROGRAM STARTED: 1984

PURPOSE:
To address the underrepresentation of African American and Hispanic faculty at colleges and universities in the state of Florida by increasing the pool of citizens qualified with Ph.D. degrees to teach at the college and university levels, thus expanding employment opportunities in the industry.

LEGAL BASIS:
Corporation.

ELIGIBILITY:
Applicants must be African American or Hispanic, U.S. citizens, and hold a minimum of a Bachelor's degree from a regionally accredited college or university. The Fellowship will be awarded only to persons who intend to seek the Ph.D. degree in one of the disciplines in the arts and sciences, mathematics, business or engineering.

FINANCIAL DATA:
Fellowships include a $12,000 stipend, plus up to $5,000 for tuition and fees. Any tuition and fees over $5,000 are waived.
Amount of support per award: $17,000 per year.
Total amount of support: Approximately $850,000.

NUMBER OF APPLICANTS MOST RECENT YEAR:
300.

NUMBER OF AWARDS: Up to 50 per academic year.

APPLICATION INFORMATION:
Online application is available at the web site.
Duration: Three years, with fourth and fifth years supported by the institution if necessary.
Deadline: January 15.

PUBLICATIONS:
Annual report.

ADDRESS INQUIRIES TO:
Charles Jackson, Program Manager
(See address above.)

FLORIDA STATE UNIVERSITY FOUNDATION   [1543]
2010 Levy Avenue
Building B, Suite 300
Tallahassee, FL 32310
(850) 644-6000
Fax: (850) 644-6211

WEB SITE ADDRESS:
www.foundation.fsu.edu

FOUNDED: 1851

AREAS OF INTEREST:
Information studies.

TYPE:
Assistantships; Awards/prizes; Conferences/seminars; Fellowships; Internships; Scholarships; Visiting scholars.

YEAR PROGRAM STARTED: 1973

PURPOSE:
To support educational excellence.

LEGAL BASIS:
University.

FINANCIAL DATA:
Amount of support per award: $500 to $6,300 per year.
Total amount of support: Varies.

NUMBER OF APPLICANTS MOST RECENT YEAR:
30.

APPLICATION INFORMATION:
Detailed information and application forms may be obtained from the web site.

Duration: Normally one year. Renewable for one year.
Deadline: January to March annually.

PUBLICATIONS:
Catalogs; brochures.

FOSTER CARE TO SUCCESS   [1544]
21351 Gentry Drive, Suite 130
Sterling, VA 20166
(571) 203-0270
Fax: (571) 203-0273

E-MAIL ADDRESS:
scholarships@fc2success.org
office@fc2success.org

WEB SITE ADDRESS:
www.fc2success.org

FOUNDED: 1981

AREAS OF INTEREST:
Foster children.

NAME(S) OF PROGRAMS:
● **Casey Family Scholars**
● **FCS Scholarship Fund**

TYPE:
Scholarships.

YEAR PROGRAM STARTED: 1986

PURPOSE:
To recognize outstanding scholarship and community service by a college student who has no family supporting their goals and efforts.

LEGAL BASIS:
501(c)(3), nonprofit organization.

ELIGIBILITY:
Applicants must be currently entering or enrolled in college or a vocational training program and:
(1) be currently in foster care or in foster care for one year at the time of their 18th birthday or high school graduation;
(2) have been adopted or taken into legal guardianship out of foster care after their 16th birthday or;
(3) have lost both parents to death before the age of 18 and not been subsequently adopted. In this instance, copies of the death certificate must be provided.

Applicants must be under the age of 25 on March 31 of the year in which they apply.

GEOGRAPHIC RESTRICTIONS:
United States.

FINANCIAL DATA:
Funds may be used for tuition, books, and approved living expenses.
Amount of support per award: $1,000 to $6,000.
Total amount of support: Varies.

NUMBER OF APPLICANTS MOST RECENT YEAR:
2,200.

NUMBER OF AWARDS: 75 new; 300 repeat recipients.

APPLICATION INFORMATION:
Information may be obtained from the address above or online from January 1 to March 31.
Duration: Annual awards. Recipients can reapply.

Deadline: March 31 for online application and postmark no later than April 15 for submission of additional materials required of applicant.

IRS IDENTIFICATION NUMBER: 52-1238437

STAFF:
Eileen McCaffrey, Chief Executive Officer

ADDRESS INQUIRIES TO:
Tina Raheem, Scholarship Director
(See address above.)

FOUNDATION FOR TECHNOLOGY AND ENGINEERING EDUCATION   [1545]

1914 Association Drive
Suite 201
Reston, VA 20191-1539
(703) 860-2100
Fax: (703) 860-0353

E-MAIL ADDRESS:
iteea@iteea.org

WEB SITE ADDRESS:
www.iteea.org

FOUNDED: 1939

AREAS OF INTEREST:
Technology education.

NAME(S) OF PROGRAMS:
* **Pittsco/Hearlihy/FTEE Grant Excellence in Teaching Technology and Engineering**

TYPE:
Grants-in-aid.

PURPOSE:
To encourage the integration of a quality technology program within the school curriculum.

ELIGIBILITY:
Applicant must be a teacher, elementary or secondary, who is successfully integrating technology and engineering education within the school curriculum and is a member of the ITEEA. An application above the elementary school level must be from a technology/engineering teacher.

FINANCIAL DATA:
Amount of support per award: $2,000.

NUMBER OF AWARDS: 1.

APPLICATION INFORMATION:
Applicants must submit an application package with four copies of the following required items:
(1) letter with explanation of the technology education program, how technology and engineering education is integrated with other academic projects, plans for using the grant and name, address, telephone, grade level and home address;
(2) school-based curriculum materials and/or a five- to 10-minute maximum video (MPEG, WMV, or AVI) illustrating how technology and engineering education is integrated with other academic subjects in the school and;
(3) three letters of recommendation which confirm the success of integrating technology and engineering education with other subjects. One letter must be from the principal and at least two from other academic teachers.

Deadline: December 1.

ADDRESS INQUIRIES TO:
Pittsco/Hearlihy/FTEE Grant
Foundation for Technology and Engineering Education
(See address above.)

FOUNDATION FOR TECHNOLOGY AND ENGINEERING EDUCATION   [1546]

1914 Association Drive
Suite 201
Reston, VA 20191-1539
(703) 860-2100
Fax: (703) 860-0353

E-MAIL ADDRESS:
iteea@iteea.org

WEB SITE ADDRESS:
www.iteea.org

FOUNDED: 1939

AREAS OF INTEREST:
Technology education.

NAME(S) OF PROGRAMS:
* **Maley/FTEE Scholarship Technology and Engineering Teacher Professional Development**

TYPE:
Scholarships.

PURPOSE:
To support teachers in their preparation to increase the positive outcomes of technology and engineering education.

ELIGIBILITY:
Criteria includes evidence of teaching success, plans for action research, recommendations, plans for professional development, ITEEA membership and the applicant's needs.

FINANCIAL DATA:
Amount of support per award: $1,000.

NUMBER OF AWARDS: 1.

APPLICATION INFORMATION:
Applicant must send an application package with four copies of the following required items:
(1) letter of application explaining plans for graduate study, plans for action research, the applicant's need and the school's name, address, telephone, grade level, and home address;
(2) official college transcript(s);
(3) documentation of acceptance into graduate school and;
(4) three letters of recommendation from among the following: undergraduate faculty, graduate faculty and school administration.

Deadline: December 1.

ADDRESS INQUIRIES TO:
Maley/FTEE Scholarship
Foundation for Technology and Engineering Education
(See address above.)

THE GAMBLE FOUNDATION   [1547]

1660 Bush Street, Suite 300
San Francisco, CA 94109
(415) 561-6540 ext. 222
Fax: (415) 561-6477

WEB SITE ADDRESS:
www.pfs-llc.net/gamble/gamble.html

FOUNDED: 1968

AREAS OF INTEREST:
Disadvantaged children and youth.

TYPE:
Project/program grants.

YEAR PROGRAM STARTED: 1968

PURPOSE:
To support academic enrichment programs and environmental education for disadvantaged youths; to promote a healthy and productive lifestyle.

LEGAL BASIS:
Private foundation.

ELIGIBILITY:
Grants are made to organizations that have tax-exempt status under Section 501(c)(3) of the Internal Revenue Code. No grants are made to individuals.

GEOGRAPHIC RESTRICTIONS:
San Francisco, Marin and Napa counties, California.

FINANCIAL DATA:
Amount of support per award: $5,000 to $20,000.
Total amount of support: Varies.

APPLICATION INFORMATION:
The Foundation encourages submission of proposals and attachments by e-mail. Additional instructions, such as required attachments, are available on the Foundation web site.
Duration: One to four years.
Deadline: February 1.

ADDRESS INQUIRIES TO:
Addie Lanier, Program Coordinator
(See address above.)

THE GOODRICH FOUNDATION   [1548]

4 Coliseum Centre
2730 West Tyvola Road
Charlotte, NC 28217-4578
(704) 423-7000
Fax: (704) 423-7011

E-MAIL ADDRESS:
grantinfo@goodrich.com

WEB SITE ADDRESS:
www.goodrich.com

FOUNDED: 1988

AREAS OF INTEREST:
Civic and community, education (with an emphasis on STEM), and health and human services.

TYPE:
Development grants; General operating grants; Grants-in-aid; Matching gifts; Project/program grants; Technical assistance; Training grants.

YEAR PROGRAM STARTED: 1988

PURPOSE:
To provide support to charitable organizations serving the public where Goodrich employees live and work.

LEGAL BASIS:
Corporate foundation.

ELIGIBILITY:
Grant applicants must be tax-exempt 501(c)(3) organizations as defined by the IRS. No grants to individuals.

GEOGRAPHIC RESTRICTIONS:
United States.

FINANCIAL DATA:
Amount of support per award: $5,000 to $100,000.

COOPERATIVE FUNDING PROGRAMS: Volunteer Bonus Program.

NUMBER OF APPLICANTS MOST RECENT YEAR: 1,500.

NUMBER OF AWARDS: 100.

APPLICATION INFORMATION:
Online application only.
Duration: Varies depending on project.
Deadline: March 1 and August 1.

OFFICERS:
Terrence Linnert, President
Jack Carmola, Vice President
Scott Kuechle, Treasurer
Kelly Chopus, Secretary

ADDRESS INQUIRIES TO:
Cynthia Forbes
Director of Community Relations
(See e-mail address above.)

HAMILTON FAMILY FOUNDATION   [1549]
200 Eagle Road
Suite 308
Wayne, PA 19087
(610) 293-2225
Fax: (610) 293-0967

E-MAIL ADDRESS:
nwingo@218enterprises.com

WEB SITE ADDRESS:
www.hamiltonfamilyfoundation.org

FOUNDED: 1992

AREAS OF INTEREST:
Education, youth and literacy-based education programs for underserved children and youth.

TYPE:
Challenge/matching grants; General operating grants; Project/program grants.

YEAR PROGRAM STARTED: 1996

PURPOSE:
To promote quality programs of education for economically underserved youth.

LEGAL BASIS:
Private foundation.

ELIGIBILITY:
Grants are made to organizations that have tax-exempt status under Section 501(c)(3) of the Internal Revenue Code. No grants are made to individuals.

GEOGRAPHIC RESTRICTIONS:
Philadelphia, Pennsylvania and surrounding counties.

FINANCIAL DATA:
Amount of support per award: $5,000 to $100,000.

APPLICATION INFORMATION:
Application form and guidelines are available on the Foundation web site.
Duration: One calendar year.
Deadline: November 1, February 1, May 1 and August 1.

STAFF:
Nancy Wingo, Executive Director

ADDRESS INQUIRIES TO:
Nancy Wingo, Executive Director
(See address above.)

HANNAFORD CHARITABLE FOUNDATION   [1550]
145 Pleasant Hill Road
Scarborough, ME 04074
(207) 885-3834
Fax: (207) 885-3051

WEB SITE ADDRESS:
www.hannaford.com

AREAS OF INTEREST:
Education, health through healthy communities and food security.

TYPE:
Capital grants; Project/program grants.

PURPOSE:
To provide financial support to nonprofit organizations dedicated to improving the communities where Hannaford operates.

LEGAL BASIS:
Private foundation.

ELIGIBILITY:
Preference for funding is given to organizations or programs that involve Hannaford associates and are located in Hannaford's marketing area, and have the potential to provide ongoing services to Foundation customers.

The Foundation does not offer support to individuals, tax-supported institutions or scholarship programs outside of their marketing area.

GEOGRAPHIC RESTRICTIONS:
Maine, Massachusetts, New Hampshire, New York and Vermont.

FINANCIAL DATA:
Amount of support per award: Varies.
Total amount of support: $1,200,000 for 2012.

NUMBER OF AWARDS: Varies.

APPLICATION INFORMATION:
Instructions on how to apply and what is required are available on the Foundation web site.
Duration: Typically one year.

HARBUS FOUNDATION   [1551]
Harvard Business School
Gallatin Hall D
Boston, MA 02163
(617) 495-6528
Fax: (617) 495-8619

E-MAIL ADDRESS:
info@harbusfoundation.org
general@harbus.org

WEB SITE ADDRESS:
www.harbusfoundation.org

FOUNDED: 1997

AREAS OF INTEREST:
Education, journalism and literacy.

TYPE:
Project/program grants. The Foundation, which was formed by the student-run Harbus News Corporation at Harvard Business School, seeks to give back to the community by supporting programs of educational development in the communities where students live and learn.

PURPOSE:
To support small, community-based organizations, individuals, or local schools with limited resources to establish and sustain new and innovative programs in the areas of literacy, journalism, and/or education.

ELIGIBILITY:
Proposals will be accepted from individuals and tax-exempt organizations as defined by Section 501(c)(3) of the Internal Revenue Code for purposes to be carried out within the greater Boston area.

The Foundation does not fund scholarships and fellowships, religious organizations for religious purposes, city or state governments, capital campaigns, for-profit organizations or purely personal needs.

GEOGRAPHIC RESTRICTIONS:
Greater Boston, Massachusetts area with priority given to the communities of Allston and Brighton.

FINANCIAL DATA:
Amount of support per award: $10,000.
Total amount of support: Varies.

APPLICATION INFORMATION:
Application for funding is by invitation only. However, if your organization aligns with the Foundation mission, send e-mail with a brief description of your organization and desired use of the Foundation resources.
Duration: One year. Renewal possible by reapplication for a maximum of three years.
Deadline: January 31.

PUBLICATIONS:
Brochure.

ADDRESS INQUIRIES TO:
Trustees
(See address above.)

THE PHIL HARDIN FOUNDATION   [1552]
2750 North Park Drive
Meridian, MS 39305
(601) 483-4282
Fax: (601) 483-5665

E-MAIL ADDRESS:
info@philhardin.org

WEB SITE ADDRESS:
www.philhardin.org

FOUNDED: 1964

AREAS OF INTEREST:
Education with special (but not exclusive) emphasis on pre-kindergarten.

TYPE:
Challenge/matching grants; Conferences/seminars; Endowments; Internships; Matching gifts; Project/program grants. Foundation's current primary focus is pre-kindergarten.

YEAR PROGRAM STARTED: 1964

PURPOSE:
To improve teaching and learning for Mississippians from grades pre-kindergarten to 12.

LEGAL BASIS:
Tax-exempt, private foundation.

ELIGIBILITY:
Tax-exempt organizations in and out of Mississippi for projects to improve the education of Mississippians. No individual grants.

GEOGRAPHIC RESTRICTIONS:
Mississippi.

FINANCIAL DATA:
Amount of support per award: $2,000 to $500,000.

Total amount of support: $1,500,000 per year for all programs.

Matching fund requirements: Stipulated with specific program.

COOPERATIVE FUNDING PROGRAMS: Economic Development Administration, Kresge Foundation, Mississippi Governor's Office of Job Development and Training, Texas Educational Association, Chisholm Foundation and CREATE.

NUMBER OF AWARDS: 26.

APPLICATION INFORMATION:
Proposals are to be based on current research and best practices. If not available, then prior approval to submit proposal must be obtained. Applications must be submitted online and include the following:
(1) IRS tax-exempt determination letter;
(2) list of board members, affiliations and contact information;
(3) most recent audited financial statement, including 990;
(4) copy of operating budget and;
(5) list of past and present funders.

The Foundation does not accept videotapes, faxed or e-mailed proposals.

Duration: One-time, one-year or multiyear grants and loans. Some renewals possible.

OFFICERS:
Robert Ward, President and Chairperson
R.B. Deen, Jr., Senior Vice President
Marty Davidson, Vice President for Investments
Steve Moore, Treasurer
Ronnie L. Walton, Secretary and General Counsel

DIRECTORS:
Dr. J.S. Covington
Marty Davidson
R.B. Deen, Jr.
Jim McGinnis
Steve Moore
Ronnie L. Walton
Robert Ward

ADDRESS INQUIRIES TO:
Sheryl Feltenstein
Administrative Assistant
(See address above.)

EDWARD W. HAZEN FOUNDATION
333 Seventh Avenue, 14th Floor
New York, NY 10001
(212) 889-3034
Fax: (212) 889-3039

E-MAIL ADDRESS:
hazen@hazenfoundation.org

WEB SITE ADDRESS:
www.hazenfoundation.org

TYPE:
Grants-in-aid; Project/program grants. In the area of Public Education, current programs support the strengthening of the connection between schools and community organizations, including school reform. The Foundation is primarily interested in parent organizing and training initiatives.

In the area of Youth Organizing, there is support for youth organizing around concrete social issues or issues of concern to youth.

For both Public Education and Youth Organizing, community-based projects directed toward middle and high school-age minority and low-income youth are given priority consideration.

There is limited support for Philanthropy and Special Projects including support for collaborative projects that encourage the growth of grantmaking.

See entry 1130 for full listing.

HEALTH RESOURCES AND SERVICES ADMINISTRATION [1553]
5600 Fishers Lane, Room 9-105
Rockville, MD 20857
(301) 443-4776
Fax: (301) 443-0846

E-MAIL ADDRESS:
dpolicy@hrsa.gov

WEB SITE ADDRESS:
www.hrsa.gov

AREAS OF INTEREST:
Health professions and nursing education.

NAME(S) OF PROGRAMS:
● **Scholarships for Disadvantaged Students**

TYPE:
Scholarships. Funds made available to eligible schools for the purpose of providing scholarships to full-time financially needy students from disadvantaged backgrounds. Students must apply at the financial aid office of school where enrolled or admitted for enrollment.

YEAR PROGRAM STARTED: 1991

LEGAL BASIS:
Government agency.

ELIGIBILITY:
Must be a citizen or permanent resident of the U.S. enrolled in a health profession or nursing program and be from a disadvantaged background.

GEOGRAPHIC RESTRICTIONS:
United States.

FINANCIAL DATA:
Amount of support per award: Varies.
Total amount of support: Varies.

NUMBER OF APPLICANTS MOST RECENT YEAR: 403.

NUMBER OF AWARDS: 99.

APPLICATION INFORMATION:
Contact student financial aid office at the school attended for application procedure.
Duration: Four years. Must reapply for additional funding after four years.

WILLIAM G. AND MYRTLE E. HESS CHARITABLE TRUST [1554]
c/o JPMorgan
1116 West Long Lake Road
Bloomfield Hills, MI 48302
Fax: (248) 645-5742

E-MAIL ADDRESS:
nayda.schwartz@jpmorgan.com

WEB SITE ADDRESS:
www.jpmorgan.com/onlinegrants

FOUNDED: 1969

AREAS OF INTEREST:
Science, education and charity.

TYPE:
General operating grants; Grants-in-aid; Project/program grants.

YEAR PROGRAM STARTED: 1969

PURPOSE:
To benefit organizations in Oakland County.

ELIGIBILITY:
Eligible organizations must be nonprofit, 501(c)(3) tax-exempt. Grants are not given to individuals or for religious or political purposes.

GEOGRAPHIC RESTRICTIONS:
Waterford and White Lake Townships in Oakland County, Michigan.

FINANCIAL DATA:
Amount of support per award: $1,000 to $10,000.

APPLICATION INFORMATION:
Applications are to be submitted online.
Deadline: April 30. Decisions on grant requests made annually in May.

ADDRESS INQUIRIES TO:
Nayda Schwartz, Vice President
(See address above.)

*PLEASE NOTE:
Applications received late will be held until the following year.

HUTCHINSON COMMUNITY FOUNDATION
One North Main Street
Suite 501
Hutchinson, KS 67501
(620) 663-5293
Fax: (620) 663-9277

E-MAIL ADDRESS:
info@hutchcf.org

WEB SITE ADDRESS:
www.hutchcf.org

TYPE:
Project/program grants; Seed money grants.

See entry 458 for full listing.

INTERNATIONAL ASSOCIATION OF ICE CREAM DISTRIBUTORS AND VENDORS [1555]
3601 East Joppa Road
Baltimore, MD 21234
(410) 931-8100
Fax: (410) 931-8111

E-MAIL ADDRESS:
info@iaicdv.org

WEB SITE ADDRESS:
www.iaicdv.org

FOUNDED: 1969

AREAS OF INTEREST:
The ice cream vending industry.

NAME(S) OF PROGRAMS:
● **IAICDV Annual Scholarship**

TYPE:
Scholarships.

YEAR PROGRAM STARTED: 1994

PURPOSE:
To cooperate for the improvement and stabilization of the ice cream vending industry.

ELIGIBILITY:
Applicant must be either an employee or child of an employee that is currently an active IAICDV member.

FINANCIAL DATA:
Amount of support per award: $3,000.
Total amount of support: $3,000.

NUMBER OF APPLICANTS MOST RECENT YEAR:
10.

NUMBER OF AWARDS: 1.

APPLICATION INFORMATION:
Contact the Association for detailed guidelines.
Duration: One-time award.
Deadline: June 30.

ADDRESS INQUIRIES TO:
IAICDV Scholarship Program
(See address above.)

INTERNATIONAL READING ASSOCIATION [1556]
800 Barksdale Road
Newark, DE 19714
(302) 731-1600
Fax: (302) 731-1057

E-MAIL ADDRESS:
exec@reading.org

WEB SITE ADDRESS:
www.reading.org

FOUNDED: 1956

AREAS OF INTEREST:
Reading and literacy through professional development, advocacy, partnership, research, and global literacy development.

NAME(S) OF PROGRAMS:
- **Grants for Literacy Projects in Countries with Developing Economies**
- **IRA Jerry Johns Outstanding Teacher Educator in Reading Award**
- **IRA Regie Routman Teacher Recognition Grant**
- **National Affiliate Conference Grants**

TYPE:
Awards/prizes; Research grants; Travel grants. Grants for Literacy Projects in Countries with Developing Economies: To assist in the funding of literacy projects and in the professional development of literacy educators. The fund also offers annual one-time grants to International Reading Association members from countries with developing economies who seek support for a literacy project in their own countries.

IRA Jerry Johns Outstanding Teacher Educator in Reading Award: Honors an outstanding college or university teacher of reading methods or reading-related courses. Nominees must be Association members, affiliated with a college or a university, and engaged in teacher preparation in reading at the undergraduate and/or graduate levels.

IRA Regie Routman Teacher Recognition Grant: Honors an outstanding mainstream, elementary classroom teacher dedicated to improving the teaching and learning of reading and writing, across the curriculum in real-world contexts in grades K-6 (ages 5-12). The grant may not be used for purchase of commercial programs.

National Affiliate Conference Grants: To assist national affiliates in good standing located in the countries the World Bank classifies as "economically developing" at the time of the application. The Grant is to support preconference planning, actual conference expenses, and/or postconference publication and reporting.

PURPOSE:
To promote reading by continuously advancing the quality of literacy instruction and research worldwide.

FINANCIAL DATA:
Amount of support per award: Grants for Literacy Projects: Up to $2,500; Jerry Johns: $1,000; National Affiliate Conference: $5,000; Regie Routman: $2,500.

APPLICATION INFORMATION:
Forms and guidelines can be obtained at the Association web site.
Deadline: Jerry Johns and Regie Routman: November 15; National Affiliate Conference: October 1 (12 months prior to the conference).

INTERNATIONAL READING ASSOCIATION [1557]
800 Barksdale Road
Newark, DE 19714
(302) 731-1600 ext. 423
Fax: (302) 731-1057

E-MAIL ADDRESS:
research@reading.org

WEB SITE ADDRESS:
www.reading.org

FOUNDED: 1956

AREAS OF INTEREST:
Reading and literacy through professional development, advocacy, partnership, research, and global literacy development.

NAME(S) OF PROGRAMS:
- **Jeanne S. Chall Research Fellowship**
- **Dina Feitelson Research Award**
- **Elva Knight Research Grant**
- **Outstanding Dissertation of the Year Award**
- **Helen M. Robinson Grant**
- **Steven A. Stahl Research Grant**
- **Teacher as Researcher Grant**

TYPE:
Awards/prizes; Fellowships; Grants-in-aid; Research grants. Jeanne S. Chall Research Fellowship is established to encourage and support reading research by promising scholars. Its special emphasis is to support research efforts in the areas of beginning reading, readability, reading difficulty, stages of reading development, the relation of vocabulary to reading, and diagnosing and teaching adults with limited reading ability.

Dina Feitelson Research Award is established to recognize an outstanding empirical study published in English in a refereed journal. The work should report on one or more aspects of literacy acquisition, such as phonemic awareness, the alphabetic principle, bilingualism, or cross-cultural studies of beginning reading. Works may be submitted by the author or anyone else.

Elva Knight Research Grant provides research in reading and literacy. Projects should be completed within two years and may be carried out using any research method or approach so long as the focus of the project is on research in reading or literacy.

Outstanding Dissertation of the Year Award is a grant from SchoolRise, LLC. Dissertations in reading or related fields are eligible for the competition. Studies using any research approach (ethnographic, experimental, historical, survey, etc.) are encouraged. Scholars must have completed their doctoral degree within the 12-month period prior to May 14 of the year in which application is being submitted.

Helen M. Robinson Grant is given annually to assist doctoral students at the early stages of their dissertation research in the areas of reading and literacy.

Steven A. Stahl Research Grant was established to encourage and support promising graduate students in their research. The grant will be awarded annually to a recipient with at least three years of teaching experience who is conducting classroom research (including action research) focused on improving reading instruction and children's reading achievement.

Teacher as Researcher Grant supports classroom teachers who undertake action research inquiries about literacy and instruction.

PURPOSE:
To promote reading by continuously advancing the quality of literacy instruction and research worldwide.

FINANCIAL DATA:
Amount of support per award: Jeanne S. Chall: $6,000; Dina Feitelson $500; Elva Knight $8,000; Outstanding Dissertation and Steven A. Stahl: $1,000; Helen M. Robinson: $1,200; Teacher as Researcher: Up to $4,000.
Total amount of support: Varies.

NUMBER OF AWARDS: 1 each annually. Research grants vary.

APPLICATION INFORMATION:
Application guidelines are available online.
Deadline: Jeanne S. Chall, Elva Knight, Helen M. Robinson, Steven A. Stahl and Teacher as Researcher: November 1; Dina Feitelson: September 1; Outstanding Dissertation: October 1.

PUBLICATIONS:
Application guidelines.

ADDRESS INQUIRIES TO:
Marcella Moore, Project Manager
Research Division
(See mailing address above.)

JELLISON BENEVOLENT SOCIETY [1558]
P.O. Box 145
Junction City, KS 66441-0145
(785) 762-5566

E-MAIL ADDRESS:
s_williams1948@yahoo.com

FOUNDED: 1947

AREAS OF INTEREST:
Higher education.

TYPE:
Scholarships.

PURPOSE:
To aid area students in pursuit of higher education.

LEGAL BASIS:
Private foundation.

ELIGIBILITY:
Must be a high school senior or older, preferably a resident of Geary County, KS.

GEOGRAPHIC RESTRICTIONS:
Geary County, Kansas.

FINANCIAL DATA:
Amount of support per award: $500 to
$1,500 per semester.

NUMBER OF APPLICANTS MOST RECENT YEAR:
75.

NUMBER OF AWARDS: 71.

APPLICATION INFORMATION:
Contact the Society for guidelines.
Duration: One year. Renewable by supplying
copy of grades above 2.0.
Deadline: June 20 and November 20.

IRS IDENTIFICATION NUMBER: 48-6106092

STAFF:
Dale Ann Clore, President
Susan E. Williams, Secretary

ADDRESS INQUIRIES TO:
Susan E. Williams, Secretary
(See address above.)

JEWISH COMMUNAL SERVICE ASSOCIATION OF NORTH AMERICA [1559]

25 Broadway
New York, NY 10004
(212) 284-6945
Fax: (212) 284-6566

E-MAIL ADDRESS:
info@jcsana.org

WEB SITE ADDRESS:
www.jcsana.org

FOUNDED: 1899

AREAS OF INTEREST:
Jewish communal services.

NAME(S) OF PROGRAMS:
• **Norman Edell Scholarship**
• **Graduate Student Network**
• **Local Groups Network**
• **Mandelkorn Distinguished Service Award**
• **Professional Development Programs**
• **Young Professional Award**

TYPE:
Awards/prizes; Conferences/seminars;
Internships. Support of local groups of
Jewish professionals.

YEAR PROGRAM STARTED: 1899

PURPOSE:
To enrich Jewish education in the communal
service field; to connect and enhance
professionals working on behalf of the
Jewish community.

LEGAL BASIS:
Nonprofit corporation.

GEOGRAPHIC RESTRICTIONS:
United States and Canada.

FINANCIAL DATA:
Amount of support per award: Varies.

NUMBER OF AWARDS: 5.

APPLICATION INFORMATION:
Contact the Association through its web site
for application procedures.

PUBLICATIONS:
Journal of Jewish Communal Service;
monthly newsletter.

EXECUTIVE DIRECTOR:
Brenda Gevertz, Executive Director

ADDRESS INQUIRIES TO:
Brenda Gevertz, Executive Director
(See e-mail address above.)

WALTER S. JOHNSON FOUNDATION [1560]

505 Montgomery Street, Suite 620
San Francisco, CA 94111-6529
(415) 283-1854
Fax: (415) 283-1840

E-MAIL ADDRESS:
info@wsjf.org

WEB SITE ADDRESS:
www.wsjf.org

AREAS OF INTEREST:
Transition-aged foster youth, college and
career technical education completion
strategies, and family economic success.

TYPE:
General operating grants; Project/program
grants; Seed money grants; Technical
assistance.

PURPOSE:
To strengthen public education and enhance
the well-being of children and youth.

LEGAL BASIS:
Private foundation.

ELIGIBILITY:
The Foundation does not consider proposals
for grants to individuals or religious
organizations for sectarian purposes. It also
does not provide funds for capital projects or
accept unsolicited proposals.

GEOGRAPHIC RESTRICTIONS:
Northern California and Washoe County,
Nevada.

FINANCIAL DATA:
Amount of support per award: Up to
$200,000.
Total amount of support: Average $4,000,000
annually.

APPLICATION INFORMATION:
Unsolicited proposals are not accepted.
Please contact Program Officer to discuss
invitation.
Duration: One-year to multiyear funding.

ADDRESS INQUIRIES TO:
Yali Lincroft, Program Officer
E-mail: yalilincroft@wsjf.org

WILLIAM R. KENAN, JR. CHARITABLE TRUST [1561]

360 Kenan Center Drive, Floor 5
Chapel Hill, NC 27599
(919) 962-0343
Fax: (919) 962-3331

FOUNDED: 1965

AREAS OF INTEREST:
Education.

TYPE:
Project/program grants.

PURPOSE:
To support educational programs of interest
to the Trust.

LEGAL BASIS:
Private foundation.

ELIGIBILITY:
The Foundation does not accept unsolicited
proposals.

GEOGRAPHIC RESTRICTIONS:
United States.

FINANCIAL DATA:
Amount of support per award: Varies.
Total amount of support: Varies.

APPLICATION INFORMATION:
Trustee's statement of guidelines, areas of
interest and required procedures are available
on request.
Duration: Varies.

ADDRESS INQUIRIES TO:
Executive Director
William R. Kenan, Jr. Charitable Trust
P.O. Box 3858
Chapel Hill, NC 27515-3858

CHARLES G. KOCH CHARITABLE FOUNDATION [1562]

1515 North Courthouse Road
Suite 200
Arlington, VA 22201
(703) 875-1770
Fax: (703) 875-1766

E-MAIL ADDRESS:
grants@charleskochfoundation.org

WEB SITE ADDRESS:
www.charleskochfoundation.org

FOUNDED: 1980

AREAS OF INTEREST:
Higher education, research, and professional
education programs.

TYPE:
Project/program grants; Seed money grants.

YEAR PROGRAM STARTED: 1980

PURPOSE:
To advance an understanding of how
economic freedom improves the well-being
of people around the world.

LEGAL BASIS:
Private foundation.

ELIGIBILITY:
The Foundation primarily makes grants to
Section 501(c)(3) public charities. The
Foundation does not support for-profit
corporations or individuals. Grant proposals
for capital construction, debt reduction, or
general fund-raising drives or events are
discouraged. The Foundation does not make
grants intended to support lobbying activities
or candidates for political office, and rarely
funds endowments.

GEOGRAPHIC RESTRICTIONS:
United States.

FINANCIAL DATA:
Amount of support per award: Varies
depending on program.

APPLICATION INFORMATION:
Organizations seeking grants must submit a
proposal online. If the proposal meets the
initial requirements, it is reviewed to assess
whether it fits within the Foundation's
priorities. Prospective grantees may be
contacted for further information.
Duration: Varies depending on needs and
nature of the request.
Deadline: Proposals are evaluated on a
rolling basis.

STAFF:
Brian Hooks, President
Vonda Holliman, Secretary and Treasurer
Logan Moore, Administrator
Matthew Brown, Policy Research Director

Elizabeth Brannen, Human Resource
Coordinator
Christopher Cardiff, Program Officer
Ryan Stowers, Program Officer

ADDRESS INQUIRIES TO:
Logan Moore, Foundation Administrator
(See address above.)

THE JEAN AND E. FLOYD KVAMME FOUNDATION [1563]

P.O. Box 2494
Saratoga, CA 95070
(408) 395-2829
Fax: (408) 354-0804

AREAS OF INTEREST:
Arts, charitable and cultural, education,
engineering school, health, medical research
and Christian religious organizations.

TYPE:
Capital grants; Development grants; General
operating grants; Project/program grants.

PURPOSE:
To support organizations and institutes that
promote arts, cultural, education, health,
medical, scientific and social advancement of
the international communities.

LEGAL BASIS:
Corporate contributions.

ELIGIBILITY:
Grants are made to organizations that have
tax-exempt status under Section 501(c)(3) of
the Internal Revenue Code and international
Christian organizations. No grants are made
to individuals.

GEOGRAPHIC RESTRICTIONS:
Northern California.

FINANCIAL DATA:
Amount of support per award: Varies.
Total amount of support: Varies.

APPLICATION INFORMATION:
Applicants must submit a brief (one-page)
letter outlining the purpose of the grant.
Further information may be obtained from
the Foundation.
Duration: One year. Renewal possible.

EXECUTIVE STAFF:
Jean Kvamme, President and Director

ADDRESS INQUIRIES TO:
Jean Kvamme, President and Director
(See address above.)

LEARNING FOR LIFE [1564]

1329 West Walnut Hill Lane
P.O. Box 152252
Irving, TX 75015-2225
(972) 580-2433
Fax: (972) 580-2137

E-MAIL ADDRESS:
dwilliam@lflmail.org

WEB SITE ADDRESS:
www.learningforlife.org/exploring

AREAS OF INTEREST:
Career opportunities, life skills, service
learning, character education and leadership
experience.

NAME(S) OF PROGRAMS:
● **Exploring Program**

TYPE:
Awards/prizes; Scholarships.

PURPOSE:
To provide experiences to help young people
mature and to prepare them to become
responsible and caring adults; to provide an
opportunity for youth to investigate the
meaning of interdependence in their personal
relationships and communities.

ELIGIBILITY:
Young men and women 15 to 20 years old or
14 years old, if they have completed the
eighth grade. Must be a participant in the
Learning for Life Exploring Program to
receive scholarship.

FINANCIAL DATA:
Amount of support per award: Varies per
award.
Total amount of support: Varies.

APPLICATION INFORMATION:
Guidelines are available on the web site.
Duration: One year. Must reapply.
Deadline: Varies per program.

MARSHALL COMMUNITY FOUNDATION [1565]

614 Homer Road
Marshall, MI 49068
(269) 781-2273
Fax: (269) 781-9747

E-MAIL ADDRESS:
info@marshallcf.org

WEB SITE ADDRESS:
www.marshallcf.org

FOUNDED: 1970

AREAS OF INTEREST:
Culture, education, environment and
recreation.

TYPE:
Project/program grants.

YEAR PROGRAM STARTED: 1985

PURPOSE:
To support projects that promote the
educational, recreational, environmental and
cultural development of the Marshall area
and Calhoun County.

LEGAL BASIS:
Community foundation.

ELIGIBILITY:
Grants are made to organizations that have
tax-exempt status under Section 501(c)(3)
and 509(a)(1) or (2) of the Internal Revenue
Code. Nonsectarian religious programs
meeting a general community need may
apply. No grants are made to individuals.

GEOGRAPHIC RESTRICTIONS:
Calhoun County, Michigan.

FINANCIAL DATA:
Amount of support per award: Varies.
Total amount of support: Varies.

APPLICATION INFORMATION:
Contact the Foundation for application.
Duration: One year.
Deadline: January 1, April 1, July 1 and
October 1.

ADDRESS INQUIRIES TO:
Sherry Anderson, Executive Director
(See address above.)

MCGRAW HILL FINANCIAL

1221 Avenue of the Americas, 47th Floor
New York, NY 10020-1095
(212) 512-6480
Fax: (212) 512-3611

E-MAIL ADDRESS:
susan.wallman@mhfi.com

WEB SITE ADDRESS:
www.mhfi.com

TYPE:
Matching gifts; Project/program grants. The
grants program places its strongest emphasis
on financial essentials and economic
empowerment. Contributions through
matching gifts are to colleges and
universities, to financial literacy, to adult
literacy organizations whose sole purpose is
the delivery or advancement of adult basic
skills instruction, and to arts and cultural
organizations providing matching gifts on a
1:1 basis.
See entry 1905 for full listing.

THE MUSTARD SEED FOUNDATION [1566]

7115 Leesburg Pike, Suite 304
Falls Church, VA 22043
(703) 524-5620

E-MAIL ADDRESS:
ljackson@msfdn.org

WEB SITE ADDRESS:
www.msfdn.org

FOUNDED: 1983

AREAS OF INTEREST:
Education and religion.

NAME(S) OF PROGRAMS:
● **Harvey Fellows Program**

TYPE:
Fellowships.

YEAR PROGRAM STARTED: 1992

PURPOSE:
To encourage students who are committed to
Jesus Christ to pursue vocations that are
culturally influential and to pursue vocational
credentials in the most prestigious graduate
programs; to validate exceptional abilities in
academics and leadership as gifts from God
worthy of cultivation and development.

LEGAL BASIS:
Nonprofit.

ELIGIBILITY:
The Harvey Fellows must be Christian
graduate students and attend a graduate
school program that is considered to be one
of the top five in a given subject area or
specialty in the world.

FINANCIAL DATA:
Amount of support per award: $12,000.
Total amount of support: Varies.

NUMBER OF AWARDS: Varies.

APPLICATION INFORMATION:
The application process has two stages. First,
the application must be completed and
submitted through the online application
system. No paper applications are accepted.
The online application does not need to be
completed all at once. Secondly, specific
required materials must be submitted via mail
(e.g., official transcripts, letters of
recommendation, test scores). All required
materials must be collected by the applicant,
bundled, and sent directly to the Foundation.
A complete list of the required documents
can be found on the Foundation's web site.
Duration: One year. Optional renewal.
Deadline: November 1.

THE NAACP LEGAL DEFENSE AND EDUCATIONAL FUND, INC.

40 Rector Street
5th Floor
New York, NY 10006
(212) 965-2225
Fax: (212) 226-7592

E-MAIL ADDRESS:
scholarships@naacpldf.org
mcorro@naacpldf.org

WEB SITE ADDRESS:
www.naacpldf.org/scholarships

TYPE:
Awards/prizes; Grants-in-aid; Internships; Scholarships. LDF Herbert Lehman Education Fund Scholarship Program: Scholarships for African-American high school seniors, high school graduates and college freshmen to attend four-year accredited colleges and universities.

LDF Earl Warren Legal Training Program: Scholarships for law students to attend three-year accredited law schools.

See entry 1030 for full listing.

THE NATIONAL ACADEMY OF EDUCATION [1567]

500 Fifth Street, N.W.
Washington, DC 20001
(202) 334-2093
Fax: (202) 334-2350

E-MAIL ADDRESS:
info@naeducation.org

WEB SITE ADDRESS:
www.naeducation.org

FOUNDED: 1965

AREAS OF INTEREST:
All aspects of educational research.

NAME(S) OF PROGRAMS:
- **National Academy of Education/Spencer Dissertation Fellowship**
- **National Academy of Education/Spencer Postdoctoral Fellowship**

TYPE:
Fellowships. The Dissertation Fellowship seeks to encourage a new generation of scholars from a wide range of disciplines and professional fields to undertake research relevant to the improvement of education. These fellowships support individuals whose dissertations show potential for bringing fresh and constructive perspectives to the history, theory or practice of formal or informal education anywhere in the world.

The Postdoctoral Fellowship is nonresidential and funds proposals that make significant scholarly contributions to the field of education. The program also develops the careers of its recipients through professional development activities involving National Academy of Education members.

PURPOSE:
To support early career scholars working in critical areas of education research.

LEGAL BASIS:
Private operating foundation.

ELIGIBILITY:
Dissertation Fellowship: The basic selection criteria are the importance of the research question to education, the quality of the research approach and feasibility of the work plan, and the applicant's future potential as a researcher and interest in educational research.

Postdoctoral Fellowship: Primary criterion for selection is promise as an educational research scholar, with special emphasis on potential to make a significant contribution to our understanding of education. Applicant must have received Ph.D., Ed.D. or equivalent degree in the past five years.

FINANCIAL DATA:
Dissertation Fellowship: The Fellowship funding is to support the writing of the dissertation only. The Fellowship funding must not be spent on data collection.

Postdoctoral Fellowship: Terms of the award do not permit institutional overhead. If the scholar transfers institutions, the grant transfers with him or her. The money may be spent toward any salary, supplies, etc., that aid the grantee in pursuing research described in the Fellowship application.

Amount of support per award: Dissertation Fellowship: $25,000 for one year. Postdoctoral Fellowship: $55,000 over one year, 18 months or two years.

NUMBER OF APPLICANTS MOST RECENT YEAR:
Dissertation Fellowship: Approximately 500 each year. Postdoctoral Fellowship: Approximately 300 each year.

NUMBER OF AWARDS: Dissertation Fellowship: 25. Postdoctoral Fellowship: 20.

APPLICATION INFORMATION:
Application material is available in early July.

Duration: Dissertation Fellowship: One or two years. Postdoctoral Fellowship: Up to two years.

Deadline: Dissertation Fellowship: Early October. Postdoctoral Fellowship: Early November.

NATIONAL CENTER FOR LEARNING DISABILITIES [1568]

381 Park Avenue South
Suite 1401
New York, NY 10016
(212) 545-7510
(888) 575-7373
Fax: (212) 545-9665

E-MAIL ADDRESS:
ncld@ncld.org

WEB SITE ADDRESS:
www.ld.org

FOUNDED: 1977

AREAS OF INTEREST:
Education and learning disabilities.

NAME(S) OF PROGRAMS:
- **Bill Ellis Teacher Preparation Award**

TYPE:
Awards/prizes.

YEAR PROGRAM STARTED: 1996

PURPOSE:
To recognize and award excellence in teaching by a general education teacher committed to helping all students, including those with learning disabilities, to learn successfully; to increase opportunities for all individuals with learning disabilities to achieve their potential.

LEGAL BASIS:
Nonprofit organization.

ELIGIBILITY:
Applicants must be general educators who would not otherwise be able to participate in professional meetings that focus on the needs of individuals with learning disabilities.

GEOGRAPHIC RESTRICTIONS:
United States.

FINANCIAL DATA:
Amount of support per award: $500.
Total amount of support: $500 annually.

NUMBER OF AWARDS: 1.

APPLICATION INFORMATION:
Information is available on the Center's web site.

ADDRESS INQUIRIES TO:
Sheldon H. Horowitz, Ed.D.
Director of LD Resources and Essential Information
E-mail: shhorowitz@ncld.org

NATIONAL CENTER FOR LEARNING DISABILITIES [1569]

381 Park Avenue South
Suite 1401
New York, NY 10016
(212) 545-7510
(888) 575-7373
Fax: (212) 545-9665

E-MAIL ADDRESS:
afscholarship@ncld.org

WEB SITE ADDRESS:
www.ncld.org

FOUNDED: 2001

AREAS OF INTEREST:
Education and learning disabilities.

NAME(S) OF PROGRAMS:
- **Allegra Ford Scholarship**
- **Anne Ford Scholarship**

TYPE:
Scholarships. Allegra Ford Scholarship is a one-time scholarship awarded to a graduating high school senior with a documented learning disability who will be enrolled in a two-year community college, a vocational or technical training program, or a specialized program for students with LD.

Anne Ford Scholarship is a four-year scholarship granted to a graduating high school senior with a documented learning disability who will be enrolled in a full-time Bachelor's degree program.

YEAR PROGRAM STARTED: 2001

PURPOSE:
To support a high school senior of high merit with an identified learning disability, who is pursuing an undergraduate degree.

LEGAL BASIS:
Nonprofit organization.

ELIGIBILITY:
Allegra Ford Scholarship applicant must:
(1) be a graduating high school senior who will be attending a two-year community college, a vocational/technical training program, or specialized program for students with LD;
(2) demonstrate financial need;
(3) provide most current documentation of an identified learning disability and;
(4) be a U.S. citizen.

Anne Ford Scholarship applicant must:
(1) be a graduating high school senior who will be attending a four-year Bachelor's

degree program;
(2) have an overall grade point average of 3.0 or higher on a four-point scale (or equivalent);
(3) provide most current documentation of an identified learning disability and;
(4) be a U.S. citizen.

GEOGRAPHIC RESTRICTIONS:
United States.

FINANCIAL DATA:
Amount of support per award: Allegra Ford Scholarship: $2,500. Anne Ford Scholarship: $10,000 ($2,500/year over four years).

NUMBER OF AWARDS: 1 of each award per year.

APPLICATION INFORMATION:
Application information is available on the web site.
Duration: Allegra Ford Scholarship: One-time scholarship. Anne Ford Scholarship: Four years.
Deadline: December 31 for both scholarships.

ADDRESS INQUIRIES TO:
Sheldon H. Horowitz, Ed.D., Director of LD Resources and Essential Information
E-mail: shhorowitz@ncld.org

*PLEASE NOTE:
For both scholarships: Attention-Deficit/Hyperactivity Disorder alone is not considered to be a learning disability; eligible candidates with AD/HD must also provide documentation of a specific learning disability.

*SPECIAL STIPULATIONS:
The scholars will be required to submit annual reports detailing their progress in school and describing their insights about their personal growth.

NATIONAL CENTER FOR LEARNING DISABILITIES [1570]
381 Park Avenue South
Suite 1401
New York, NY 10016
(212) 545-7510
(888) 575-7373
Fax: (212) 545-9665

E-MAIL ADDRESS:
ncld@ncld.org

WEB SITE ADDRESS:
www.ncld.org

FOUNDED: 2000

AREAS OF INTEREST:
Education and learning disabilities.

NAME(S) OF PROGRAMS:
● **Pete and Carrie Rozelle Award**

TYPE:
Awards/prizes.

YEAR PROGRAM STARTED: 1977

PURPOSE:
To recognize a school or school-related program that addresses the educational and social/emotional needs of all children, including those with learning disabilities. The award will allow for expanded programmatic and staff development opportunities that focus on incorporating effective research-based practices into classroom and schoolwide practice with preference given to programs that serve underprivileged and underserved communities, or programs that have demonstrated unique impact for students with learning disabilities.

LEGAL BASIS:
Nonprofit organization.

GEOGRAPHIC RESTRICTIONS:
United States.

FINANCIAL DATA:
Amount of support per award: $5,000.
Total amount of support: $5,000 annually.

NUMBER OF AWARDS: 1.

APPLICATION INFORMATION:
Contact the Center for application procedures.
Deadline: End of August to early September.

ADDRESS INQUIRIES TO:
Sheldon H. Horowitz, Ed.D., Director of LD Resources and Essential Information
E-mail: shhorowitz@ncld.org

NATIONAL COALITION OF BLACK MEETING PLANNERS (NCBMP) [1571]
4401 Huntchase Drive
Suite 126
Bowie, MD 20720
(301) 860-0200
Fax: (301) 860-0500

E-MAIL ADDRESS:
ncbmp.hq@verizon.net

WEB SITE ADDRESS:
www.ncbmp.com

FOUNDED: 1983

AREAS OF INTEREST:
Professional meeting planning and hospitality management.

TYPE:
Conferences/seminars; Scholarships.

YEAR PROGRAM STARTED: 1983

PURPOSE:
To be the preeminent organization in educating the African American meeting planner in all aspects of the meeting planning profession; to improve the meetings, conferences, exhibitions, and convocations that African Americans manage.

ELIGIBILITY:
Students seeking careers in meeting planning and enrolled in a hospitality management program.

GEOGRAPHIC RESTRICTIONS:
United States.

FINANCIAL DATA:
Amount of support per award: $1,000 to $2,500.
Total amount of support: $3,000 annually.

NUMBER OF AWARDS: 3.

APPLICATION INFORMATION:
Contact the Coalition for application procedures.
Duration: One-time award.
Deadline: November.

ADDRESS INQUIRIES TO:
Mrs. Ozzie Jenkins, Executive Director
(See address above.)

NATIONAL COUNCIL FOR THE SOCIAL STUDIES
8555 16th Street, Suite 500
Silver Spring, MD 20910
(301) 588-1800 ext. 107
Fax: (301) 588-2049

E-MAIL ADDRESS:
excellence@ncss.org

WEB SITE ADDRESS:
www.socialstudies.org

TYPE:
Awards/prizes; Grants-in-aid.
See entry 1859 for full listing.

NATIONAL COUNCIL FOR THE SOCIAL STUDIES
8555 16th Street, Suite 500
Silver Spring, MD 20910
(301) 588-1800 ext. 107
Fax: (301) 588-2049

E-MAIL ADDRESS:
excellence@ncss.org

WEB SITE ADDRESS:
www.socialstudies.org

TYPE:
Awards/prizes. Annual award for projects representing excellence and innovation in social studies education and having the potential of serving as a model for other teachers.
See entry 1860 for full listing.

NATIONAL COUNCIL FOR THE SOCIAL STUDIES
8555 16th Street, Suite 500
Silver Spring, MD 20910
(301) 588-1800 ext. 107
Fax: (301) 588-2049

E-MAIL ADDRESS:
excellence@ncss.org

WEB SITE ADDRESS:
www.socialstudies.org

TYPE:
Awards/prizes. Annual award honoring the outstanding performance of teachers, researchers, and other worthy individuals and programs.
See entry 1861 for full listing.

NATIONAL COUNCIL FOR THE SOCIAL STUDIES
8555 16th Street, Suite 500
Silver Spring, MD 20910
(301) 588-1800 ext. 107
Fax: (301) 588-2049

E-MAIL ADDRESS:
excellence@ncss.org

WEB SITE ADDRESS:
www.socialstudies.org

TYPE:
Awards/prizes. Annual award recognizing those who have distinguished themselves in defending the principles of academic freedom.
See entry 1862 for full listing.

NATIONAL COUNCIL FOR THE SOCIAL STUDIES
8555 16th Street, Suite 500
Silver Spring, MD 20910
(301) 588-1800 ext. 107
Fax: (301) 588-2049

E-MAIL ADDRESS:
excellence@ncss.org

WEB SITE ADDRESS:
www.socialstudies.org

TYPE:
Awards/prizes.

See entry 1863 for full listing.

NATIONAL COUNCIL FOR THE SOCIAL STUDIES

8555 16th Street, Suite 500
Silver Spring, MD 20910
(301) 588-1800 ext. 107
Fax: (301) 588-2049

E-MAIL ADDRESS:
excellence@ncss.org

WEB SITE ADDRESS:
www.socialstudies.org/fasse

TYPE:
Project/program grants. The grants are
intended to support collaborative projects that
demonstrate potential to enhance international
relationships and global perspectives in social
studies education. Funded projects will hold
promise for enhancing international and
cross-cultural understanding (e.g., through
global or international education, human
rights education, a focus on global issues,
global citizenship, etc.)

See entry 1864 for full listing.

NATIONAL EMERGENCY MEDICINE ASSOCIATION [1572]

P.O. Box 1039
Edgewood, MD 21040
(443) 922-7533
Fax: (888) 682-7947

E-MAIL ADDRESS:
info@nemahealth.org

WEB SITE ADDRESS:
www.nemahealth.org

FOUNDED: 1982

AREAS OF INTEREST:
Emergency medicine.

NAME(S) OF PROGRAMS:
● **Kids Do Matter (KDM)**
● **National Alzheimer's Council (NAC)**
● **National Heart Council (NHC)**
● **National Stroke Council (NSC)**

TYPE:
Awards/prizes; Capital grants;
Project/program grants; Research grants.

YEAR PROGRAM STARTED: 1982

PURPOSE:
To prevent injury or illness by addressing
health and social issues through education,
applied research, technology, and equipment.

LEGAL BASIS:
Educational nonprofit 501(c)(3).

ELIGIBILITY:
The granting of funds to applicants is
considered according to the following
priorities:
(1) first consideration to grants relating to
coronary trauma and heart wellness program;
(2) second consideration to grants relating to
all other types of trauma, vehicular trauma
and strokes and;
(3) third consideration to grants relating to
trauma prevention and the cause of trauma.

GEOGRAPHIC RESTRICTIONS:
United States.

FINANCIAL DATA:
Amount of support per award: Varies.

NUMBER OF APPLICANTS MOST RECENT YEAR:
5.

NUMBER OF AWARDS: 1.

REPRESENTATIVE AWARDS:
St. Agnes Hospital, Catonsville, MD, for
Chest Pain Emergency Clinic; National
Institute of Health, Bethesda, MD, for
research into coronary ischemia; Beth Israel
Medical Center, New York, NY, for research
in reversing effects of heart disease.

APPLICATION INFORMATION:
The proposal should be written in clear,
concise language with all technical terms
defined and should give a full description of
the project. The proposal should also include:
(1) purpose and services;
(2) a history of other similar projects and
their results;
(3) activities, benefits and desired results;
(4) amount requested, anticipated costs,
budget, and funding sources;
(5) annual report, financial statements and
background information of the sponsoring
organization;
(6) proof of tax-exempt status;
(7) qualifications of staff;
(8) list of Board members and;
(9) a plan for how information on the project
will be communicated to the public and how
NEMA will be credited.
Duration: Varies.
Deadline: Applications considered as
received.

PUBLICATIONS:
*Five Minute Guide to Heart Attack
Prevention and Survival; Five Minute Guide
to Stroke (Brain Attack) Prevention and
Survival;* wallet cards for Heart, Stroke and
Alzheimer's.

IRS IDENTIFICATION NUMBER: 52-1257429

OFFICERS:
Kelly Herzog, President/Chief Executive
Officer

ADDRESS INQUIRIES TO:
Kelly Herzog
President/Chief Executive Officer
(See address above.)

NATIONAL FOSTER PARENT ASSOCIATION

2021 East Hennepin Avenue
Suite 320
Minneapolis, MN 55413-1769
(512) 775-9781
(800) 557-5238
Fax: (253) 238-4252

E-MAIL ADDRESS:
info@nfpaonline.org

WEB SITE ADDRESS:
www.nfpaonline.org

TYPE:
Scholarships.

See entry 1138 for full listing.

NATIONAL INSTITUTE ON DRUG ABUSE   [1573]

6001 Executive Boulevard, Room 5232
MSC 9591
Bethesda, MD 20892-9591
(301) 443-6071
Fax: (301) 480-2485

E-MAIL ADDRESS:
ghimm@mail.nih.gov

WEB SITE ADDRESS:
www.nida.nih.gov

AREAS OF INTEREST:
Drug abuse and addiction.

TYPE:
Awards/prizes. The Institute supports a
variety of training and career development
grant awards. See
www.drugabuse.gov/researchtraining for a
complete listing.

PURPOSE:
To support research training and/or career
development.

ELIGIBILITY:
Specific eligibility criteria vary based on the
award.

GEOGRAPHIC RESTRICTIONS:
United States.

FINANCIAL DATA:
Amount of support per award: Varies.

ADDRESS INQUIRIES TO:
Mimi Ghim, Ph.D.
Deputy Coordinator of Research Training
(See address above.)

NATIONAL INSTITUTE ON DRUG ABUSE   [1574]

6001 Executive Boulevard, Room 3105
MSC 9567
Bethesda, MD 20892-9567
(301) 443-0441
Fax: (301) 480-8179

E-MAIL ADDRESS:
pg46n@nih.gov

WEB SITE ADDRESS:
www.nida.nih.gov

AREAS OF INTEREST:
Drug abuse, medicine and health disparity.

NAME(S) OF PROGRAMS:
● **Diversity-Promoting Institutions Drug
Abuse Research Program**

TYPE:
Project/program grants; Research grants.

PURPOSE:
To broaden and strengthen drug abuse
research in diversity-promoting; to achieve
health promotion and disease prevention.

ELIGIBILITY:
Organizations classified as 501(c)(3) by the
IRS can apply. No grants to individuals.

FINANCIAL DATA:
Amount of support per award: Varies, but not
to exceed direct costs of $350,000 per year.

APPLICATION INFORMATION:
Application form required. Applicants should
submit Public Health Service Form 398.
Additional information and appropriate forms
can be obtained online.

ADDRESS INQUIRIES TO:
Pamela Goodlow, Public Health Analyst
(See address above.)

NATIONAL MOLE DAY FOUNDATION

3896 Leaman Court
Freeland, MI 48623
(989) 964-8020

E-MAIL ADDRESS:
moleday@hotmail.com

WEB SITE ADDRESS:
www.moleday.org

TYPE:
Grants-in-aid. The George Hague Memorial Travel Award is given to financially support a young chemistry instructor (with two to five years of chemistry experience) in attending a biennial ChemEd conference.

The Maury Award is given to teachers to support student-centered Mole Day activities (promoting chemistry education).

The National Mole of the Year Award (MOTY) is given to a member of the National Mole Day Foundation who has contributed the most to furthering the cause of Mole Day and chemistry education.

See entry 2068 for full listing.

NATIONAL OCEANIC AND ATMOSPHERIC ADMINISTRATION [1575]

NOAA Chesapeake Bay Office
410 Severn Avenue, Suite 207
Annapolis, MD 21403
(410) 267-5660
Fax: (410) 267-5666

E-MAIL ADDRESS:
kevin.schabow@noaa.gov

WEB SITE ADDRESS:
chesapeakebay.noaa.gov

FOUNDED: 1985

AREAS OF INTEREST:
Stock assessment, multispecies, and ecosystem-based fisheries research in Chesapeake Bay.

NAME(S) OF PROGRAMS:
● **Chesapeake Bay Fisheries Research Program**

TYPE:
Project/program grants; Research grants; Research contracts.

YEAR PROGRAM STARTED: 1985

PURPOSE:
To support stock assessment, multispecies and ecosystem-based fisheries research in Chesapeake Bay.

LEGAL BASIS:
Government agency.

ELIGIBILITY:
Individuals who are U.S. citizens or residents and organizations, including religious, classified as 501(c)(3) by the IRS can apply.

GEOGRAPHIC RESTRICTIONS:
United States, with a focus on Chesapeake Bay/mid-Atlantic.

FINANCIAL DATA:
Amount of support per award: $400,000 average.

NUMBER OF APPLICANTS MOST RECENT YEAR: 26.

NUMBER OF AWARDS: 17.

APPLICATION INFORMATION:
Application information is available on the web site. RFPs released between December and February.
Duration: Multiyear.
Deadline: March/April time frame; varies each year.

PUBLICATIONS:
Application guidelines; annual report.

ADDRESS INQUIRIES TO:
Kevin Schabow, Grants Manager
National Marine Fisheries Service
(See address above.)

NATIONAL SCIENCE FOUNDATION

Directorate for Education and Human Resources
Division of Research on Learning in Formal and Informal Settings
4201 Wilson Boulevard, Suite 885 S
Arlington, VA 22230
(703) 292-8620
(703) 570-1975
Fax: (703) 292-9044; (703) 292-9046

E-MAIL ADDRESS:
acarroll@nsf.gov

WEB SITE ADDRESS:
www.nsf.gov

TYPE:
Conferences/seminars; Demonstration grants; Development grants; Project/program grants; Research grants; Training grants. With an emphasis on two-year colleges, the Advanced Technological Education (ATE) program focuses on the education of technicians for the high-technology fields that drive the nation's economy.

Discovery Research K-12 (DR K12) funds research, development and evaluation activities through knowledge generation and application to improve K-12 learning and teaching.

Informal Science Education (ISE) program invests in projects that develop and implement informal learning experiences designed to increase interest, engagement and understanding of science, technology, engineering and mathematics (STEM) by individuals of all ages and backgrounds, as well as projects that advance knowledge and practice of informal science education.

Innovative Technology Experiences for Students and Teachers (ITEST) is designed to increase the opportunities for students and teachers to learn about, experience, and use information technologies within the context of science, technology, engineering and mathematics (STEM), including Information Technology (IT) courses. It is in direct response to the concern about shortages of information technology workers in the U.S.

Research and Evaluation on Education in Science and Engineering (REESE) supports basic and applied research and evaluation that enhances science, technology, engineering and mathematics (STEM) learning and teaching.

See entry 1607 for full listing.

NATIVE AMERICAN COMMUNITY BOARD (NACB) [1576]

P.O. Box 572
Lake Andes, SD 57356-0572
(605) 487-7072
Fax: (605) 487-7964

E-MAIL ADDRESS:
charon@charles-mix.com

WEB SITE ADDRESS:
www.nativeshop.org

AREAS OF INTEREST:
Native American women.

NAME(S) OF PROGRAMS:
● **NACB Scholarship Fund**

TYPE:
Scholarships.

PURPOSE:
To support young women who show high potential and future promise and that are likely to have an impact on the community.

LEGAL BASIS:
Nonprofit tax-exempt 501(c)(3) organization.

ELIGIBILITY:
Must be a Yankton Sioux Tribally enrolled woman attending a college off of the reservation majoring in the fields of business, education, environmental studies, health, law/criminal justice or sociology.

GEOGRAPHIC RESTRICTIONS:
United States.

FINANCIAL DATA:
Amount of support per award: Varies.
Total amount of support: Varies.

NUMBER OF AWARDS: 4 or more per year.

APPLICATION INFORMATION:
Contact the NACB for application procedures.
Duration: One year.
Deadline: March 15 for Spring. November 15 for Fall.

ADDRESS INQUIRIES TO:
Charon Asetoyer, Executive Director
(See address above.)

THE NEA FOUNDATION [1577]

1201 16th Street, N.W.
Washington, DC 20036
(202) 822-7840
Fax: (202) 822-7779

E-MAIL ADDRESS:
info@neafoundation.org

WEB SITE ADDRESS:
www.neafoundation.org

AREAS OF INTEREST:
Public education.

TYPE:
Awards/prizes. Recognizes and awards the excellence demonstrated by educators nationwide.

PURPOSE:
To advance student achievement, through the unique strength of the Foundation's partnership with educators, by investing in public education that will prepare each of America's children to learn and thrive in a rapidly changing world.

FINANCIAL DATA:
Amount of support per award: State level: $750 gift to teacher's school and travel to Annual Salute to Excellence in Education Gala. Five finalists from the state level: $10,000 courtesy of the Horace Mann Educators Corporation. National awardee: $25,000 total from NEA Member Benefits Company.

APPLICATION INFORMATION:
Applicants must complete proposals through the Foundation's online grant system.
Deadline: May 1.

THE NEA FOUNDATION [1578]
1201 16th Street, N.W., Suite 416
Washington, DC 20036-3207
(202) 822-7840
Fax: (202) 822-7779

E-MAIL ADDRESS:
foundation_info@nea.org

WEB SITE ADDRESS:
www.neafoundation.org

FOUNDED: 1969

AREAS OF INTEREST:
Education.

NAME(S) OF PROGRAMS:
● **NEA Foundation Learning and
   Leadership Grants**
● **NEA Foundation Student Achievement
   Grants**

YEAR PROGRAM STARTED: 1999

PURPOSE:
To improve the academic achievement of
students in U.S. public schools and public
higher education institutions in any subject
area(s); to support public school teachers,
public education support professionals, and/or
faculty and staff in public institutions of
higher education.

ELIGIBILITY:
Applicants must be practicing U.S. public
school teachers in grades PreK-12, public
school education support professionals, or
faculty or staff at public higher education
institutions.

Preference will be given to members of the
National Education Association. The NEA
Foundation encourages grant applications
from education support professionals.

Learning and Leadership Grant: All
professional development must improve
practice, curriculum, and student
achievement. Decisions regarding the content
of the professional growth activities must be
based upon an assessment of student work
undertaken with colleagues, and must be
integrated into the institutional planning
process. Funds may not be used to pursue
degrees, pay direct costs, grant administration
fees, or salaries, or support travel costs or
conference fees for more than one person.

Student Achievement Grant: The proposed
work should engage students in critical
thinking and problem solving that deepens
their knowledge of standards-based subject
matter. The work should also improve
students' habits of inquiry, self-directed
learning, and critical reflection. Proposals for
work resulting in low-income and minority
student success with honors, advanced
placement, or other challenging curricula are
particularly encouraged. Funds may be used
for resource materials, supplies, equipment,
transportation, software, or
scholars-in-residence. Although some funds
may be used to support the professional
development necessary to implement the
project, the majority of grant funds must be
spent on materials or educational experiences
for students.

GEOGRAPHIC RESTRICTIONS:
United States.

FINANCIAL DATA:
Amount of support per award: Learning and
Leadership Grants: $2,000 (individuals) and
$5,000 (groups engaged in collegial study);
Student Achievement Grants: $2,000 and
$5,000.

NUMBER OF APPLICANTS MOST RECENT YEAR:
950.

NUMBER OF AWARDS: 170.

APPLICATION INFORMATION:
All proposals must be submitted through the
Foundation's online grant system.
Duration: Annual. Nonrenewable.
Deadline: February 1, June 1, October 15.

ADDRESS INQUIRIES TO:
Jesse Graytock, Grants Manager
(See address above.)

NELLIE MAE EDUCATION
FOUNDATION [1579]
1250 Hancock Street, Suite 205N
Quincy, MA 02169-4331
(781) 348-4200
Fax: (781) 348-4299

E-MAIL ADDRESS:
info@nmefoundation.org

WEB SITE ADDRESS:
www.nmefoundation.org

FOUNDED: 1998

AREAS OF INTEREST:
Systems change and student-centered
learning.

TYPE:
General operating grants; Matching gifts;
Research grants.

YEAR PROGRAM STARTED: 1998

PURPOSE:
To promote accessibility, quality and
effectiveness of education, especially for
underserved populations in the six New
England states.

LEGAL BASIS:
Public charity.

ELIGIBILITY:
Organizations must be 501(c)(3) or public
schools. Religious organizations may apply.
No grants are made to individuals.

GEOGRAPHIC RESTRICTIONS:
Connecticut, Maine, Massachusetts, New
Hampshire, Rhode Island and Vermont.

FINANCIAL DATA:
Amount of support per award: Varies.
Total amount of support: Varies.

APPLICATION INFORMATION:
Contact the Foundation for application
procedures.

ADDRESS INQUIRIES TO:
See e-mail address above.

NICSA [1580]
8400 Westpark Drive, 2nd Floor
McLean, VA 22102
(508) 485-1500
Fax: (508) 485-1560

E-MAIL ADDRESS:
info@nicsa.org

WEB SITE ADDRESS:
www.nicsa.org

FOUNDED: 1962

AREAS OF INTEREST:
Education.

NAME(S) OF PROGRAMS:
● **The NICSA/William T. Blackwell
   Scholarship Fund**

TYPE:
Scholarships.

PURPOSE:
To provide leadership and innovation in
educational programming and information
exchange within the operations sector of the
mutual fund industry worldwide; to recognize
outstanding students of the NICSA Family
with financial support for postsecondary
education.

ELIGIBILITY:
Applicants must be dependent children of
full-time employees of NICSA member
companies and be enrolled in or planning to
pursue a full-time course of study leading to
a Bachelor's degree from an accredited
four-year college or university.

FINANCIAL DATA:
Amount of support per award: $2,000 to
$5,000.
Total amount of support: Maximum of
$40,000 annually.

APPLICATION INFORMATION:
Application information is available on the
web site in the fall.
Duration: One-time award.
Deadline: January.

ADDRESS INQUIRIES TO:
The NICSA/William T. Blackwell
Scholarship Fund
Scholarship Management Services
One Scholarship Way, P.O. Box 297
St. Peter, MN 56082
Tel: (507) 931-1682

NORTH CAROLINA
GLAXOSMITHKLINE
FOUNDATION [1581]
5 Moore Drive
Research Triangle Park, NC 27709
(919) 483-2140
Fax: (919) 315-3015

E-MAIL ADDRESS:
info@ncgskfoundation.org

WEB SITE ADDRESS:
www.ncgskfoundation.org

FOUNDED: 1986

AREAS OF INTEREST:
Mathematics, science and health at all
educational and professional levels.

NAME(S) OF PROGRAMS:
● **Child Health Recognition Awards**
● **Ribbon of Hope**
● **Traditional Grants**
● **Women in Science Scholars Program**

TYPE:
Challenge/matching grants; Fellowships;
Professorships; Project/program grants;
Scholarships; Seed money grants. Support for
activities which help meet the educational
and health needs of today's society and
future generations.

Child Health Recognition Awards program
honors local health departments, public
health staff, and individuals for innovative,
collaborative programs that improve the lives
of North Carolina's children.

Ribbon of Hope provides one-time grants to
nonprofits for projects furthering health,
science and education in their communities.

The Traditional Grants program provides for larger grants that may be multiyear in nature, to support programs advancing health, science and education throughout the state of North Carolina.

Women in Science Scholars Program offers an educational opportunity to young women by coupling college scholarships with a mentoring program.

YEAR PROGRAM STARTED: 1986

PURPOSE:
To provide programs that emphasize the understanding and applications of health, science and education at all academic and professional levels; to seek out grant recipients representative of worthy causes that contribute to all well-being and quality of life.

LEGAL BASIS:
Corporate foundation.

ELIGIBILITY:
Ribbon of Hope: North Carolina community-based nonprofit, charitable organizations and institutions exempt under Section 501(c)(3) of the Internal Revenue Code are eligible to apply. Individuals may not apply. Nonprofits with proposals pertaining to health, science and education are encouraged to apply.

Traditional Grants: Grant applicants must be nonprofit, charitable organizations and institutions exempt under Section 501(c)(3) of the Internal Revenue Code. No grants are made to individuals, for construction or restoration projects, or for international programs. The primary focus of the Foundation is to provide seed funds for new and worthwhile educational programs. This policy does not preclude the consideration and possible funding of ongoing projects.

GEOGRAPHIC RESTRICTIONS:
North Carolina.

FINANCIAL DATA:
Amount of support per award: Ribbon of Hope: $25,000; Traditional Grants: $25,000 and up.
Total amount of support: $787,000 in new grants approved for the year 2013.

REPRESENTATIVE AWARDS:
Ribbon of Hope: Friends of the Great Smoky Mountains National Park, Haywood County, NC, to expand the internship program; Centers for Exceptional Children, Forsyth County, NC, to provide weekend respite care for families who care for medically fragile children; Montgomery Community College, Montgomery County, NC, to reach potential students who can benefit from its "GED to Degree" Program.

Traditional Grants: $1,760,000 to North Carolina A&T State University to develop a STEM Center of Excellence for Active Learning; $1,500,000 to North Carolina Central University for scholarship support for STEM majors, along with student and faculty support services; $160,000 to North Carolina Center for Public Policy Research to conduct a project to examine key issues affecting the rapidly growing aging population in the state.

APPLICATION INFORMATION:
Traditional Grants: Proposals should be accompanied by a cover letter signed by the president, director or equivalent official of the applicant organization. The application should also include an official certification from the IRS or other documentation of the

applicant institution's tax-exempt (501)(c)(3) status, an executive summary of the planned activities (not exceeding two double-spaced pages), a description of the objectives and explanation of the overall strategy of the proposed activities, and a detailed statement on the types of expenses for each activity proposed. Also, the applying organization should provide a summary of general information regarding itself, resumes of its program director and key personnel, and a summary of the organization's revenues and support during the past three fiscal years.
Duration: Ribbon of Hope: One-time grant; Traditional Grants: Up to five years.
Deadline: Ribbon of Hope: April 1 and October 1. Traditional Grants: January 1, April 1, July 1 and October 1.

PUBLICATIONS:
Annual report; application; brochure.

IRS IDENTIFICATION NUMBER: 58-1698610

OFFICERS:
Robert A. Ingram, Chairman
Margaret B. Dardess, President
Paul A. Holcombe, Jr., Secretary
Marilyn E. Foote-Hudson, Executive Director

ADDRESS INQUIRIES TO:
Marilyn E. Foote-Hudson, Executive Director
(See address above.)

OAK GROVE SCHOOL FOUNDATION [1582]
P.O. Box 150
South China, ME 04358
(207) 445-3333
(207) 872-5908
Fax: (207) 445-4477

E-MAIL ADDRESS:
nrshed@gmail.com

FOUNDED: 1989

AREAS OF INTEREST:
Education, secondary school curriculum development, limited secondary school scholarships, and some not-for-profits.

NAME(S) OF PROGRAMS:
• **Grants Program**
• **Tuition Assistance**

TYPE:
Demonstration grants; General operating grants; Grants-in-aid; Project/program grants; Scholarships. Scholarships are for Quaker schools.

YEAR PROGRAM STARTED: 1991

PURPOSE:
To foster secondary education innovation in proximate geographic area; to provide tuition assistance.

LEGAL BASIS:
Private foundation.

ELIGIBILITY:
Secondary schools and 501(c)(3) organizations in Central Maine. For tuition assistance, candidates may be either currently enrolled or accepted for enrollment in a Quaker secondary school and must be a resident of Maine or children or grandchildren of Oak Grove School or Oak Grove-Coburn School alumni/ae. In addition, children and grandchildren of former Oak Grove or Oak Grove-Coburn faculty and staff are eligible applicants.

GEOGRAPHIC RESTRICTIONS:
Central Maine.

FINANCIAL DATA:
Amount of support per award: $1,000 to $5,000.
Total amount of support: $100,000.

NUMBER OF APPLICANTS MOST RECENT YEAR: 107.

NUMBER OF AWARDS: 57.

APPLICATION INFORMATION:
Application available from the Foundation.
Duration: Up to three years.
Deadline: April 1.

IRS IDENTIFICATION NUMBER: 01-0211537

ADDRESS INQUIRIES TO:
Austin Law
(See address above.)

PANASONIC FOUNDATION, INC. [1583]
2 Riverfront Plaza, 11th Floor
Newark, NJ 07102
(201) 392-4132
(201) 271-3367

E-MAIL ADDRESS:
info@foundation.us.panasonic.com

WEB SITE ADDRESS:
www.panasonicfoundation.net

FOUNDED: 1984

AREAS OF INTEREST:
Pre-collegiate education and school reform.

NAME(S) OF PROGRAMS:
• **Collaboration for Innovation**
• **New Jersey Network of Superintendents**
• **Panasonic Foundation Partnership Program for School Reform**

TYPE:
Technical assistance. Collaboration for Innovation is an online community of practice serving 16 school districts all across the U.S.

The New Jersey Network of Superintendents, established December 2008, supports monthly meetings of district superintendents focused on improving teaching and learning for all students.

The Partnership Program was established with urban school districts serving large proportions of disadvantaged youth. The Foundation does not make grants, but rather it provides technical assistance to school districts with which it has formed a partnership.

YEAR PROGRAM STARTED: 1987

PURPOSE:
To partner with selected public school districts and their communities to break the links between race, poverty and educational outcomes by improving the academic and social success of all students: all means all!

LEGAL BASIS:
Corporate foundation.

GEOGRAPHIC RESTRICTIONS:
United States.

FINANCIAL DATA:
Amount of support per award: $35,000 to $70,000 per site.
Matching fund requirements: Districts in the Panasonic Partnership Program participate in the Foundation Leadership Associates

Program, which requires the district to assume the travel and lodging of at least four participants in two three-day-long events.

PUBLICATIONS:
Newsletter; brochure.

OFFICERS:
Michael Riccio, Treasurer
Gordon Kyvik, Assistant Treasurer
Sandra Karriem, Secretary

STAFF:
Larry Leverett, Executive Director
Scott Thompson, Assistant Executive Director
Kathleen Archetti, Planning Coordinator
Kaili Baucum, Senior Fellow

BOARD OF DIRECTORS:
Milton Chen, Chairman
Robert Marin
Kent McGuire
Deborah Meier
Sophie Sa
Steve Safier

ADDRESS INQUIRIES TO:
Larry Leverett, Executive Director
(See address above.)

PARENTS WITHOUT PARTNERS [1584]
1100-H Brandywine Boulevard
Zanesville, OH 43701
(740) 450-1332
Fax: (740) 452-2552

E-MAIL ADDRESS:
intl.hq@parentswithoutpartners.org

WEB SITE ADDRESS:
www.parentswithoutpartners.org

FOUNDED: 1957

AREAS OF INTEREST:
Education of children of single parents belonging to the organization.

NAME(S) OF PROGRAMS:
• **Parents Without Partners International Scholarship**

TYPE:
Scholarships.

PURPOSE:
To provide single parents and their children with an opportunity for enhancing personal growth, self-confidence, and sensitivity towards others by offering an environment for support, friendship and the exchange of parenting techniques.

LEGAL BASIS:
Nonprofit.

ELIGIBILITY:
Applicants must be dependent children, up to 25 years of age, of PWP members. Also, must be either in the senior class of any high school and planning to enter and have applied to a school of higher education for the following year, or be an undergraduate student at a college or trade school.

GEOGRAPHIC RESTRICTIONS:
United States and Canada.

FINANCIAL DATA:
Amount of support per award: Varies.
Total amount of support: Varies.

APPLICATION INFORMATION:
Contact PWP for guidelines.
Duration: One year. Nonrenewable.

ADDRESS INQUIRIES TO:
See e-mail address above.

THE MABEL LOUISE RILEY FOUNDATION [1585]
77 Summer Street, Eighth Floor
Boston, MA 02110
(617) 399-1850
Fax: (617) 399-1851

E-MAIL ADDRESS:
info@rileyfoundation.com

WEB SITE ADDRESS:
www.rileyfoundation.com

FOUNDED: 1972

AREAS OF INTEREST:
Emphasis on priority needs in social services and education, especially for youth, community development including cultural, housing and urban environmental programs.

TYPE:
Capital grants; Challenge/matching grants; Development grants; Project/program grants; Seed money grants; Training grants.

LEGAL BASIS:
Private foundation.

ELIGIBILITY:
Requests are considered only from corporations organized under the laws of Massachusetts for purposes to be carried out within Massachusetts and those who have a 501(c)(3) IRS determination.

GEOGRAPHIC RESTRICTIONS:
Greater Boston area, with a primary focus on the city of Boston, Massachusetts.

FINANCIAL DATA:
Amount of support per award: $50,000 to $100,000.
Total amount of support: $2,726,200 for the year 2013.

APPLICATION INFORMATION:
A brief two-page summary of proposal should be submitted before full proposal is submitted. If, after review of letter, the Trustees wish to see full proposal, applicant will be asked to submit one. All proposals should be prepared using the Common Proposal Format supplied by Associated Grantmakers of Massachusetts. However, all proposals should include a separate concise statement of purpose for which the grant is sought and of the program, staff, and specific budget necessary for its achievement. In addition, proposals should include:
(1) the organization's history, mission and services;
(2) current year's operating budget;
(3) the most recent audited financial statements;
(4) a complete copy of Form 990;
(5) a roster of the board of directors;
(6) a copy of the IRS tax-exemption letter and;
(7) where applicable, the resumes of the key staff people involved in the project.
Duration: One year. Renewals possible. Two-year waiting period is requested before applying again for those who have been awarded a grant.
Deadline: Meetings are held in March, June, September and December with deadlines for receipt of full grant proposals set 60 days prior to each meeting.

PUBLICATIONS:
Guidelines.

IRS IDENTIFICATION NUMBER: 04-6278857

TRUSTEES:
Grace Fey
Robert W. Holmes, Jr.

ADDRESS INQUIRIES TO:
Nancy A. Saunders, Administrator
(See address above.)

RURITAN NATIONAL FOUNDATION [1586]
5451 Lyons Road
Dublin, VA 24084
(540) 674-5431
Fax: (540) 674-2304

E-MAIL ADDRESS:
foundation@ruritan.org

WEB SITE ADDRESS:
www.ruritan.org

AREAS OF INTEREST:
Education.

NAME(S) OF PROGRAMS:
• **Build Your Dollars Grant**
• **Educational Grant Program**

TYPE:
Grants-in-aid; Matching gifts. These programs allow Ruritan clubs to increase their financial assistance to a student of the club's choice. Ruritan clubs contribute $300 to the Foundation and, in turn, the Foundation will add to this amount for grants.

PURPOSE:
To manage and maintain a trust for the encouragement, promotion, and financing of the charitable, educational, and benevolent principles and activities of Ruritan Clubs and of Ruritan National.

ELIGIBILITY:
Must be sponsored by a local Ruritan Club and have the endorsement of two members. Applicant should be pursuing a postsecondary education. Selection is based on financial need, character, scholarship and applicant's desire for higher education.

GEOGRAPHIC RESTRICTIONS:
United States.

FINANCIAL DATA:
Amount of support per award: Varies.
Total amount of support: Varies.

APPLICATION INFORMATION:
Applications for grant programs are available online.
Duration: Applicants must reapply each year.
Deadline: April 1.

ADDRESS INQUIRIES TO:
Michael Chrisley, Executive Director
(See address above.)

THE SCHOTT FOUNDATION FOR PUBLIC EDUCATION [1587]
678 Massachusetts Avenue, 8th Floor
Cambridge, MA 02139
(617) 876-7700
Fax: (617) 876-7702

E-MAIL ADDRESS:
info@schottfoundation.org

WEB SITE ADDRESS:
www.schottfoundation.org

FOUNDED: 1999

AREAS OF INTEREST:
K-12 education, early education, resource and fiscal equity.

TYPE:
General operating grants.

PURPOSE:
To develop and strengthen a broad-based and representative movement to achieve fully resourced and adequately funded high-quality preK-12 public education in Massachusetts and New York.

LEGAL BASIS:
501(c)(3).

ELIGIBILITY:
Funding to grassroots and other nonprofit organizations working to improve public education.

GEOGRAPHIC RESTRICTIONS:
Massachusetts and New York.

FINANCIAL DATA:
Amount of support per award: Varies.
Total amount of support: Varies.

NUMBER OF AWARDS: 50.

ADDRESS INQUIRIES TO:
Nakisha Lewis, Program Coordinator
(See address above.)

GEORGE J. AND EFFIE L. SEAY MEMORIAL TRUST

1111 East Main Street, 12th Floor
Richmond, VA 23219
(804) 887-8763
Fax: (804) 887-8854

TYPE:
Project/program grants. Grants for specific needs.

See entry 1506 for full listing.

SMITHSONIAN ENVIRONMENTAL RESEARCH CENTER

647 Contees Wharf Road
Edgewater, MD 21037
(443) 482-2217
Fax: (443) 482-2380

E-MAIL ADDRESS:
gustafsond@si.edu

WEB SITE ADDRESS:
www.serc.si.edu

TYPE:
Fellowships; Internships. The Program enables undergraduate and graduate students to work on specific projects under the direction of the Center's professional staff and is tailored to provide the maximum educational benefit to each participant. Graduate students and undergraduates may conduct independent projects with the approval of the staff member with whom they plan to study.

Subject matter of the projects includes terrestrial and estuarine environmental research within the disciplines of mathematics, chemistry, microbiology, botany, zoology, and environmental education.

Fellowships are offered annually at the postdoctoral, predoctoral and graduate levels.

Internships are offered three times per year at the undergraduate levels, recent graduate, or beginning Master's student.

See entry 2201 for full listing.

SPENCER FOUNDATION [1588]

625 North Michigan Avenue
Suite 1600
Chicago, IL 60611
(312) 337-7000
Fax: (312) 337-0282

E-MAIL ADDRESS:
abrinkman@spencer.org

WEB SITE ADDRESS:
www.spencer.org

FOUNDED: 1962

AREAS OF INTEREST:
Research on education as approached from scholars in the sciences, social sciences and humanities.

NAME(S) OF PROGRAMS:
- **Research Grant Program**

TYPE:
Research grants. Grants for research to expand knowledge and understanding of the problems and processes of education.

YEAR PROGRAM STARTED: 1970

PURPOSE:
To support research that gives promise of yielding new knowledge leading to the improvement of education, broadly defined.

LEGAL BASIS:
Independent foundation.

ELIGIBILITY:
The Foundation is interested in a wide variety of disciplinary and interdisciplinary approaches to the study of education. The principal investigator ordinarily must have an earned Doctorate in an academic discipline or in the field of education and must have an affiliation with a college or university, a research facility, or a cultural institution.

FINANCIAL DATA:
Amount of support per award: Varies.
Total amount of support: Approximately $14,000,000 annually.

NUMBER OF APPLICANTS MOST RECENT YEAR:
Approximately 1,000.

REPRESENTATIVE AWARDS:
$40,000 (over one year) to Mary Haywood Metz, University of Wisconsin-Madison, for "Models of School Organization: Comparing Understandings of School Organization Grounded in Ethnographics, Survey Research and the Federal 'No Child Left Behind Act';" $300,000 (over two years) to Jill V. Hamm et al., University of North Carolina at Chapel Hill, for "Correlations and Consequences of Growth in Mathematics Conceptual Understanding in Middle and High School."

APPLICATION INFORMATION:
Application procedures differ by program. Researchers seeking support should telephone for general program information.
Duration: Varies.

PUBLICATIONS:
Annual report.

OFFICERS:
Michael McPherson, President

BOARD OF DIRECTORS:
Deborah Loewenberg Ball, Chairman
Pamela Grossman
Carol Johnson
Michael McPherson
Richard Murnane
Stephen Raudenbush
Cybele Raver
Mario Small

Dennis Sullivan
Mark Vander Ploeg

ADDRESS INQUIRIES TO:
Annie Brinkman, Grants Manager
(See address above.)

SUBARU OF AMERICA FOUNDATION, INC. [1589]

2235 Route 70 West
Cherry Hill, NJ 08002
(856) 488-5099
Fax: (856) 488-3255

E-MAIL ADDRESS:
foundation@subaru.com

WEB SITE ADDRESS:
www.subaru.com/csr/soa-foundation.html

FOUNDED: 1984

AREAS OF INTEREST:
Education for children and youth and environmental stewardship for youth.

TYPE:
General operating grants; Project/program grants; Scholarships. Special programs; Employee matching gift program.

YEAR PROGRAM STARTED: 1984

PURPOSE:
To make a difference in the lives of young people by offering them enrichment and educational programs that support their academic needs.

LEGAL BASIS:
Corporate foundation.

ELIGIBILITY:
Consideration will be given primarily to nonprofit 501(c)(3) organizations in the communities located in and around National Headquarters and in the immediate surrounding areas of regional offices.

The Foundation does not permit contributions to religious, fraternal, veterans' or political associations, individual schools or special events, nor does it make grants to individuals, fund organizations outside the U.S., programs that benefit residents outside the U.S., or consider donation of vehicles.

FINANCIAL DATA:
Amount of support per award: Varies.
Matching fund requirements: Contributions for the matching gift program must be made by Subaru of America employees at a $25 minimum or $2,000 maximum per employee per fiscal year.

APPLICATION INFORMATION:
Application form is available online as a Word document. Grant application and all required supporting documentation must be submitted at the same time as one package and should be mailed to the address above to arrive by the deadline (not postmarked by the deadline). Grant applications with missing information or documentation will not be considered.
Deadline: Education programs: February 15. Environmental programs: July 31.

IRS IDENTIFICATION NUMBER: 22-2531774

STAFF:
Sandra E. Capell, Community Services Manager

ADDRESS INQUIRIES TO:
Sandra E. Capell
Community Services Manager
(See address above.)

TAILHOOK EDUCATIONAL
FOUNDATION   [1590]
9696 Business Park Avenue
San Diego, CA 92131
(858) 689-9223
Fax: (858) 578-8839

E-MAIL ADDRESS:
tag@tailhook.net

WEB SITE ADDRESS:
www.tailhook.net

FOUNDED: 1992

AREAS OF INTEREST:
Education.

NAME(S) OF PROGRAMS:
● **Tailhook Educational Foundation
Scholarship Award**

TYPE:
Scholarships. The Foundation awards
merit-based scholarships.

YEAR PROGRAM STARTED: 1992

PURPOSE:
To support dependents of the Naval Aviation
community with their educational needs.

LEGAL BASIS:
501(c)(3).

ELIGIBILITY:
The applicant or the applicant's
parent/grandparent/guardian must have served
in the U.S. Navy, U.S. Marine Corps, or U.S.
Coast Guard as a Naval Aviator, Naval Flight
Officer, or Designated Naval Aircrewman, or
served on board a U.S. Navy aircraft carrier
in any capacity as a member of ship's
company or assigned air wing.

GEOGRAPHIC RESTRICTIONS:
United States.

FINANCIAL DATA:
Amount of support per award: $2,000 to
$15,000.

NUMBER OF APPLICANTS MOST RECENT YEAR:
285.

NUMBER OF AWARDS: 87.

APPLICATION INFORMATION:
Application information is available on the
web site.
Duration: Multiyear.
Deadline: March 15.

IRS IDENTIFICATION NUMBER: 33-0487778

ADDRESS INQUIRIES TO:
The Tailhook Educational Foundation
P.O. Box 26626
San Diego, CA 92196-0626

TRIANGLE COMMUNITY
FOUNDATION   [1591]
324 Blackwell Street, Suite 1220
Durham, NC 27701
(919) 474-8370
Fax: (919) 941-9208

E-MAIL ADDRESS:
libby@trianglecf.org

WEB SITE ADDRESS:
www.trianglecf.org

AREAS OF INTEREST:
Projects of excellence.

TYPE:
Grants-in-aid; Scholarships. General
grantmaking.

YEAR PROGRAM STARTED: 1984

PURPOSE:
To expand philanthropy.

ELIGIBILITY:
Organizations, including religious, classified
as 501(c)(3) by the IRS can apply. No grants
to individuals.

GEOGRAPHIC RESTRICTIONS:
Chatham, Durham, Orange and Wake
counties, North Carolina.

FINANCIAL DATA:
Amount of support per award: Minimum
$250.

Total amount of support: Varies.

APPLICATION INFORMATION:
Application available online.
Duration: Grants are not renewable.

PUBLICATIONS:
Annual report.

ADDRESS INQUIRIES TO:
Libby Richards
Senior Community Programs Officer
(See address above.)

U.S. DEPARTMENT OF
EDUCATION   [1592]
International Education Programs Service
1990 K Street, N.W., 6th Floor
Washington, DC 20006-8521
(202) 502-7700
Fax: (202) 502-7859

E-MAIL ADDRESS:
amy.wilson@ed.gov

WEB SITE ADDRESS:
www.ed.gov/programs/iegpsirs

AREAS OF INTEREST:
International research and studies.

NAME(S) OF PROGRAMS:
● **International Research and Studies
Grant Program**

TYPE:
Development grants; Research grants.
Provides grants to IHEs, public and private
organizations, institutions and individuals to
support research and studies to determine
needs for increased or improved instructions
in foreign language, area studies or other
international fields, assess the utilization of
graduates supported under Title VI, compare
the effectiveness of strategies to
internationalize IHEs, evaluate more effective
methods of providing instruction and
achieving competency in foreign languages,
develop and publish language, area studies
and international studies materials and
develop foreign language performance tests
and assess their effectiveness.

Grant provides support for research and
studies, experimentation and development of
specialized instructional materials and the
publication of specialized materials
developed as a result of research conducted
under the program to improve foreign
language and area studies.

LEGAL BASIS:
Government agency.

ELIGIBILITY:
Applicants must be qualified researchers,
institutions of higher education, state
educational agencies, public school systems
or other educational and professional
organizations.

GEOGRAPHIC RESTRICTIONS:
United States.

FINANCIAL DATA:
Amount of support per award: $50,000 to
$200,000. Average $150,000.

Total amount of support: Approximately
$6,000,000.

NUMBER OF AWARDS: Varies each year.

APPLICATION INFORMATION:
All applications must be submitted
electronically.
Duration: Up to 36 months. Renewals of
grants which were not included in the
original negotiations will be considered in
competition with all other new applications.

ADDRESS INQUIRIES TO:
International and Foreign Language
Education
(See address above.)

U.S. DEPARTMENT OF
EDUCATION   [1593]
Institute of Education Sciences, Room 600E
555 New Jersey Avenue, N.W.
Washington, DC 20208
(202) 219-0644
Fax: (202) 219-1402

E-MAIL ADDRESS:
ellie.pelaez@ed.gov

WEB SITE ADDRESS:
ies.ed.gov

FOUNDED: 1972

AREAS OF INTEREST:
Basic and applied research, evaluations and
analyses in education practice and policy.

NAME(S) OF PROGRAMS:
● **Education Research**

TYPE:
Project/program grants; Research grants.
Grants competitions.

The Institute supports research on a diverse
set of student outcomes including: school
readiness for prekindergarten; academic
outcomes in kindergarten through Grade 12
that include learning, achievement, and
higher order thinking in the core academic
content areas of reading, writing,
mathematics, and science measured by
specific assessments (e.g.,
researcher-developed assessments,
standardized tests, grades, end of course
exams, exit exams) as well as course
completion, grade retention, high school
graduation and dropout rates; social skills,
dispositions, and behaviors that support
academic outcomes for students from
prekindergarten through high school; access
to, retention in, and completion of
postsecondary education; and reading,
writing, and mathematics skills for adult
learners (i.e., students at least 16 years old
and outside of the K-12 system). The
Institute supports research from
prekindergarten through Grade 12 for the
typically developing student. For
postsecondary and adult learners the Institute
supports research on typically developing
students and students with disabilities. The
Institute supports research on students with
disabilities from birth through high school
through a different grant program run by the
Institute's National Center for Special
Education Research.

LEGAL BASIS:
Public Law 92-318, as amended.

ELIGIBILITY:
Applicants must be colleges, universities, state departments of education, local education agencies, other public or private profit and nonprofit agencies, organizations, groups and individuals. Support is restricted to basic and applied research, planning studies, evaluations, investigations, experiments and developmental activities directly related to research in the field of education.

Most funds provide continuing support for long-term research and development programs. The remaining funds are used for new projects, announced as Grants Competitions in specific areas of interest.

FINANCIAL DATA:
Amount of support per award: Varies.
Total amount of support: Varies.

APPLICATION INFORMATION:
Application information is available on the web site.
Duration: Varies.
Deadline: Specific date changes each year, but application deadlines generally fall between June and September.

U.S. DEPARTMENT OF EDUCATION [1594]
Office of Career, Technical and Adult Education
550 12th Street, S.W., 11th Floor
Washington, DC 20202-7100
(202) 245-7700
Fax: (202) 245-7838

E-MAIL ADDRESS:
octae@ed.gov

WEB SITE ADDRESS:
www2.ed.gov/about/offices/list/octae

FOUNDED: 1965

AREAS OF INTEREST:
Adult basic education, basic literacy skills, English as a second language and adult secondary education.

CONSULTING OR VOLUNTEER SERVICES:
Technical assistance is provided to state educational agencies.

TYPE:
Grants-in-aid. The program provides grants to states to fund local programs of adult education and literacy services, including workplace literacy services, family literacy services, English language learning and integrated English literacy/civics education programs. Basic grants to all states including the District of Columbia as well as the Virgin Islands, American Samoa, Guam, Northern Mariana Islands and Palau.

YEAR PROGRAM STARTED: 1965

PURPOSE:
To provide educational opportunities for educationally disadvantaged adults.

LEGAL BASIS:
The Adult Education and Family Literacy Act (AEFLA), enacted as Title II of the Workforce Investment Act (WIA) of 1998, is the principal source of federal support for adult basic and literacy education programs for adults who lack basic skills, a high school diploma, or proficiency in English.

ELIGIBILITY:
Individuals and local providers cannot receive grant money directly from the Office of Vocational and Adult Education (OVAE).

Adult education and literacy programs are funded through federal grants to the states. The amount each state receives is based on a formula established by Congress. States, in turn, distribute funds to local eligible entities to provide adult education and literacy services.

The Division provides assistance to states to improve program quality and capacity.

GEOGRAPHIC RESTRICTIONS:
United States and its territories.

FINANCIAL DATA:
AEFLA funds are distributed by formula to states using census data on the number of adults (ages 16 and older) in each state who lack a high school diploma and who are not enrolled in school. States must match 25% of the federal contribution with state or local funds, but many states contribute considerably more.
Amount of support per award: Varies.
Matching fund requirements: 25% of grant award.

NUMBER OF APPLICANTS MOST RECENT YEAR: 57.

NUMBER OF AWARDS: 57.

APPLICATION INFORMATION:
Applicants interested in participating in the State-Administered Program should contact the appropriate state educational agency for information.
Duration: One year and continuing based on appropriations.

ADDRESS INQUIRIES TO:
Office of Career, Technical and Adult Education
Adult Education and Literacy Division
400 Maryland Avenue, S.W.
Washington, DC 20202-7100

U.S. DEPARTMENT OF EDUCATION [1595]
Office of English Language Acquisition, Language Enhancement and Academic Achievement
LBJ Education Building, Room 5C-140, MS-6510
400 Maryland Avenue, S.W.
Washington, DC 20202
(202) 401-1436
Fax: (202) 260-5496

E-MAIL ADDRESS:
libia.gill@ed.gov

WEB SITE ADDRESS:
www.ed.gov/offices/oela

AREAS OF INTEREST:
English language acquisition, language enhancement and academic achievement for Limited English Proficient (LEP) children.

NAME(S) OF PROGRAMS:
- **National Professional Development Program**
- **Native American and Alaska Native Children in School Program**

TYPE:
Formula grants. National Professional Development Program provides professional development activities intended to improve instruction for students with limited English proficiency (LEP) and assists education personnel working with such children to meet high professional standards.

Native American and Alaska Native Children in School Program provides grants to eligible entities that support language instruction education projects for limited English proficient (LEP) children from Native American, Alaska Native, native Hawaiian, and Pacific Islander backgrounds. The program is designed to ensure that LEP children master English and meet the same rigorous standards for academic achievement that all children are expected to meet. Funds may support the study of Native American languages.

YEAR PROGRAM STARTED: 1968

LEGAL BASIS:
Elementary and Secondary Education Act of 1965, as amended by No Child Left Behind Act of 2001.

ELIGIBILITY:
National Professional Development Program: Institutions of higher education in consortia with local education agencies or state education agencies may apply.

Native American and Alaska Native Children in School Program: Entities that operate the following kinds of elementary, secondary and postsecondary schools primarily for Native American children (including Alaska Native children) are eligible applicants under this program:
(1) Indian tribes;
(2) tribally sanctioned educational authorities;
(3) Native Hawaiian or Native American Pacific Islander native language educational organizations;
(4) elementary schools or secondary schools that are operated or funded by the Bureau of Indian Affairs (BIA), or a consortium of such schools;
(5) elementary schools or secondary schools operated under a contract with or grant from the BIA in consortium with another such school or a tribal or community organization and;
(6) elementary schools or secondary schools operated by the BIA and an institution of higher education (IHE), in consortium with elementary schools or secondary schools operated under a contract with or a grant from the BIA or a tribal or community organization.

GEOGRAPHIC RESTRICTIONS:
United States and its Commonwealths and territories.

STAFF:
Libia Gill, Assistant Deputy Director

ADDRESS INQUIRIES TO:
National Professional Development Program:
Samuel Lopez
Tel: (202) 401-1423

Native American and Alaska Native Children in School Program:
Trini Torres-Carrion
Tel: (202) 401-1445

U.S. DEPARTMENT OF STATE, FULBRIGHT TEACHER EXCHANGE PROGRAM [1596]
c/o Institute of International Education
1400 K Street, N.W., Suite 700
Washington, DC 20005
(202) 326-7678

E-MAIL ADDRESS:
fulbrightcte@iie.org

WEB SITE ADDRESS:
www.fulbrightteacherexchange.org

FOUNDED: 1946

AREAS OF INTEREST:
All subjects, including mathematics, science, English, English as a Second Language (ESL), foreign language and history. Subject and grade levels vary with each country.

NAME(S) OF PROGRAMS:
● **Fulbright Teacher Exchange Program**

TYPE:
Exchange programs; Travel grants.

YEAR PROGRAM STARTED: 1946

PURPOSE:
To increase mutual understanding between the people of the U.S. and the people of other countries through the funding of teacher and administrator exchanges.

LEGAL BASIS:
Mutual Educational and Cultural Exchange Act (Fulbright Hays Act) of 1961.

ELIGIBILITY:
Applicants must meet the following general requirements:
(1) current full-time teaching position;
(2) three years full-time teaching experience;
(3) U.S. citizenship;
(4) Bachelor's degree or higher and;
(5) English language fluency.

In addition, applicants must meet the specific subject and level requirements of the countries to which they apply. For some countries, fluency in the host country's language is required. Country-specific requirements are detailed in the application booklet.

FINANCIAL DATA:
In most cases, the U.S. teacher secures a leave of absence with pay from his or her home institution (as does the foreign teacher). Exchange grants include a summer orientation program and round-trip transportation for grantee only.
Amount of support per award: Varies.
Total amount of support: Varies.

APPLICATION INFORMATION:
Applications are available online.
Duration: Most programs last one academic year. Semester-long programs in India and the U.K.
Deadline: October 15 of the year preceding the grant year.

PUBLICATIONS:
Application booklet.

STAFF:
Tatiana Mackliff, Program Director

ADDRESS INQUIRIES TO:
See e-mail address above.

*PLEASE NOTE:
All programs are tentative and are subject to the availability of funds.

UNIVERSITY OF MANITOBA   [1597]
Faculty of Graduate Studies
500 University Centre
Winnipeg MB R3T 2N2 Canada
(204) 474-9836
Fax: (204) 474-7553

E-MAIL ADDRESS:
marcia.yoshida@umanitoba.ca

WEB SITE ADDRESS:
www.umanitoba.
ca/faculties/graduate_studies/funding

AREAS OF INTEREST:
Teaching and cutting-edge research.

NAME(S) OF PROGRAMS:
● **University of Manitoba Graduate Fellowships**

TYPE:
Fellowships. Any discipline taught at graduate level at the university.

PURPOSE:
To reward academic excellence.

ELIGIBILITY:
At the time of application, students do not need to have been accepted by the department or faculty, but at the time of taking up the award must be regular full-time graduate students who have been admitted to and registered in advanced degree programmes, e.g., Master's or Ph.D., but not pre-Master's in any field of study or faculty of the University of Manitoba. Students beyond the second year in the Master's programme or beyond the fourth year in the Ph.D. programme are not eligible to apply for or hold a University of Manitoba Fellowship.

FINANCIAL DATA:
Amount of support per award: $16,000 for Ph.D.; $12,000 for Master's.

APPLICATION INFORMATION:
Applicant must request information from the department to which he or she is applying at the University of Manitoba.

ADDRESS INQUIRIES TO:
Marcia Yoshida, Awards Officer
(See address above.)

VIETNOW NATIONAL   [1598]
1835 Broadway
Rockford, IL 61104
(815) 227-5100
Fax: (815) 227-5127

E-MAIL ADDRESS:
nationalhq@vietnow.com

WEB SITE ADDRESS:
www.vietnow.com

AREAS OF INTEREST:
Veterans.

TYPE:
Scholarships.

PURPOSE:
To provide financial assistance to college students of VietNow members.

ELIGIBILITY:
Applicant must be a child of a full member of VietNow.

FINANCIAL DATA:
Amount of support per award: Up to $2,000.
Total amount of support: Varies.

APPLICATION INFORMATION:
Contact the Organization for application procedures.
Duration: One year. Renewal by reapplication.
Deadline: April 1.

ADDRESS INQUIRIES TO:
Shawn Conrad, Office Manager or
Scholarship Committee
(See address above.)

DENNIS & PHYLLIS WASHINGTON FOUNDATION
P.O. Box 16630
Missoula, MT 59808
(406) 523-1300
Fax: (406) 523-1399

WEB SITE ADDRESS:
www.dpwfoundation.org

TYPE:
Project/program grants; Scholarships. Scholarship monies awarded to Montana's nine colleges and universities and seven Indian reservations.

See entry 1398 for full listing.

FRED B. AND RUTH B. ZIGLER FOUNDATION   [1599]
P.O. Box 986
Jennings, LA 70546-0986
(337) 824-2413
Fax: (337) 824-2414

E-MAIL ADDRESS:
frzigler@bellsouth.net

WEB SITE ADDRESS:
www.ziglerfoundation.org

AREAS OF INTEREST:
Education.

TYPE:
Project/program grants; Scholarships.

PURPOSE:
To benefit Jefferson-Davis Parish area.

LEGAL BASIS:
Private foundation.

ELIGIBILITY:
Grants are made to organizations that have tax-exempt status under Section 501(c)(3) of the Internal Revenue Code. No grants are made to individuals.

GEOGRAPHIC RESTRICTIONS:
Jefferson-Davis Parish area, Louisiana.

FINANCIAL DATA:
Amount of support per award: $12,000.
Total amount of support: Approximately $400,000.

NUMBER OF AWARDS: 30 for the year 2011.

APPLICATION INFORMATION:
Applicants must submit a brief letter outlining the purpose of the grant.
Duration: Up to four years.
Deadline: 30 days prior to the Board meeting. The Board meets every other month starting in January.

ADDRESS INQUIRIES TO:
Julie Berry, President
(See address above.)

Elementary and secondary education

ALTMAN FOUNDATION
521 Fifth Avenue
35th Floor
New York, NY 10175
(212) 682-0970

E-MAIL ADDRESS:
info@altman.org

WEB SITE ADDRESS:
www.altmanfoundation.org

TYPE:
Project/program grants.

See entry 1163 for full listing.

THE BELK FOUNDATION [1600]
2801 West Tyvola Road
Charlotte, NC 28217-4500
(704) 426-8396
Fax: (704) 357-1896

E-MAIL ADDRESS:
carol_shinn@belk.com

WEB SITE ADDRESS:
www.belkfoundation.org

FOUNDED: 1928

AREAS OF INTEREST:
Education.

TYPE:
General operating grants; Project/program grants; Research grants; Training grants. Core achievement in grades K-3; Teacher and Leader development.

PURPOSE:
To invest in schools and organizations that work aggressively to ensure all students graduate from high school and continue on an intentional path toward college, career and life.

ELIGIBILITY:
Charitable organizations, with 501(c)(3) status, located in communities where Belk associates live and work, with particular emphasis on Birmingham, AL; Atlanta, GA; and Charlotte, NC.

No grants made to individuals, private elementary or secondary schools, international programs and/or organizations, and organizations for the primary purpose of fund-raising.

GEOGRAPHIC RESTRICTIONS:
Birmingham, Alabama; Atlanta, Georgia; and Charlotte, North Carolina.

FINANCIAL DATA:
Amount of support per award: $5,000 to $500,000.

Total amount of support: Varies.

APPLICATION INFORMATION:
Applicant must complete online Eligibility Quiz. If prompted, applicant will submit Letter of Inquiry.

Deadline: April 1 and October 1.

STAFF:
Johanna Anderson, Executive Director
Carol Shinn, Program Associate

*PLEASE NOTE:
The Foundation dedicates its resources to two areas:
(1) Teaching and Leading and;
(2) K-3 Achievement.

*SPECIAL STIPULATIONS:
Currently the Foundation is only accepting Letters of Inquiry from organizations serving the communities of Birmingham, AL; Atlanta, GA; and Charlotte, NC.

THE LOUIS CALDER FOUNDATION
125 Elm Street
New Canaan, CT 06840
(203) 966-8925
Fax: (203) 966-5785

E-MAIL ADDRESS:
proposals@calderfdn.org

WEB SITE ADDRESS:
www.louiscalderfoundation.org

TYPE:
Capital grants; Project/program grants. Curriculum development.

See entry 1110 for full listing.

SAMUEL N. AND MARY CASTLE FOUNDATION [1601]
733 Bishop Street, Suite 1275
Honolulu, HI 96813
(808) 522-1101
Fax: (808) 522-1103

E-MAIL ADDRESS:
snandmarycastle@hawaii.rr.com

WEB SITE ADDRESS:
foundationcenter.org/grantmaker/castle

FOUNDED: 1894

AREAS OF INTEREST:
Early education and care, cultural arts, human services for children, and some maternal/child health support.

CONSULTING OR VOLUNTEER SERVICES:
Castle colleagues training for directors of early childhood centers.

TYPE:
Capital grants; Challenge/matching grants; Project/program grants.

YEAR PROGRAM STARTED: 1894

PURPOSE:
To support training for early childhood education professionals; to support early education, preschools, K-three schools, select K-three private schools (elementary), select K-three elementary independent schools, and select higher education programs in teacher training; to support select arts and culture projects.

LEGAL BASIS:
Private family foundation.

GEOGRAPHIC RESTRICTIONS:
Hawaii.

FINANCIAL DATA:
Amount of support per award: Typically $5,000 to $100,000.

Total amount of support: $1,715,500 for the year 2013.

Matching fund requirements: Varies.

NUMBER OF APPLICANTS MOST RECENT YEAR: 400.

NUMBER OF AWARDS: 65.

REPRESENTATIVE AWARDS:
$50,000 to Catholic Charities for families with children; $100,000 to Hawaiian Mission Children's Society for historical displays; $30,000 to KCAA for low-income tuition assistance for preschool students.

APPLICATION INFORMATION:
The applicant organization should review the Foundation's priorities and policies to determine whether it is eligible to be considered for funding and whether the type of activity proposed is in one of the Foundation's funding areas. Applicants are required to contact the Foundation's Executive Director by letter, e-mail, phone or personal visit before making fund application.

Proposals may be hand delivered or mailed and should include the following:
(1) proposal (one copy);
(2) one copy of each of the additional materials as defined on the Foundation's web site (e.g., IRS determination letter, audited financial statements);
(3) one- to two-page executive summary (two copies);
(4) budget (two copies) and;
(5) Board of Directors list (two copies).

Organizations which have submitted their charters, bylaws and 501(c)(3) may submit complete applications by e-mail attachment.

Applicant organizations should not bind their proposals or submit videos or other items which have not been requested by the Foundation.

Duration: One year. Renewal possible up to three years.

Deadline: February 1, June 1 and October 1.

PUBLICATIONS:
Annual report.

OFFICERS:
Dr. Robert Peters, President
Dr. Kittredge A. Baldwin, Vice President
James C. McIntosh, Vice President
Alfred L. Castle, Treasurer and Executive Director
Cynthia Quisenberry, Secretary

ADDRESS INQUIRIES TO:
Alfred L. Castle, Executive Director
(See address above.)

*PLEASE NOTE:
Applications must be prescreened before full submission.

HUGH AND HAZEL DARLING FOUNDATION
500 South Grand Avenue, 19th Floor
Los Angeles, CA 90071
(213) 683-5200
Fax: (213) 627-7795

TYPE:
Block grants; Capital grants; Challenge/matching grants; Matching gifts; Scholarships; Training grants.

See entry 1626 for full listing.

FIRSTENERGY [1602]
76 South Main Street
Akron, OH 44308
(330) 384-5022
Fax: (330) 761-4203

E-MAIL ADDRESS:
delores.jones@firstenergycorp.com

WEB SITE ADDRESS:
www.firstenergycorp.com/community

AREAS OF INTEREST:
Science, technology, engineering and mathematics education.

NAME(S) OF PROGRAMS:
● **STEM Grants Program**

TYPE:
Project/program grants. Project/program grants in the classroom setting.

YEAR PROGRAM STARTED: 1985

PURPOSE:
To encourage education in the sciences, technology, engineering and mathematics.

ELIGIBILITY:
Educators (grades preK-12) and youth group leaders in the service areas of FirstEnergy

and communities where FirstEnergy has facilities are encouraged to apply. Any creative project dealing with science, technology, engineering and mathematics is eligible. Projects that involve students directly, incorporate matching funds, community resources, interdisciplinary or team-teaching and involve various age groups are preferred. Teacher training projects are highly favored. Completed projects or those previously funded are not eligible.

GEOGRAPHIC RESTRICTIONS:
Maryland, New Jersey, Ohio, Pennsylvania and West Virginia.

FINANCIAL DATA:
Grants may be used to compensate experts who come to work with the students, but not to pay teachers or staff.
Amount of support per award: $500 maximum.
Total amount of support: Varies.

APPLICATION INFORMATION:
Submission must be filed on the appropriate application form. Contact the External Affairs Manager at your FirstEnergy office or the Community Involvement Department of FirstEnergy at the address listed above. A downloadable application is available online.
Duration: One school year.
Deadline: Usually third week in September.

PUBLICATIONS:
Bright Ideas for Educators.

ADDRESS INQUIRIES TO:
Community Involvement Department
(See address above.)

*SPECIAL STIPULATIONS:
Grants are only available to schools or groups in the FirstEnergy service area or in communities where it has facilities.

CHARLES HAYDEN FOUNDATION
140 Broadway, 51st Floor
New York, NY 10005
(212) 785-3677
Fax: (212) 785-3689

E-MAIL ADDRESS:
fdn@chf.org

WEB SITE ADDRESS:
www.charleshaydenfoundation.org

TYPE:
Capital grants; Challenge/matching grants; Project/program grants. Grant priorities focus on institutions and programs primarily serving youth at risk of not reaching their full potential, especially youth in low-income communities. Support is provided for youth development programs, charter schools, independent and parochial schools, and informal educational enrichment programs in institutions such as zoos, museums or libraries.

See entry 1129 for full listing.

INVESTED   [1603]
911 Eighth Avenue North
Seattle, WA 98109
(206) 352-1199
Fax: (206) 352-1203

E-MAIL ADDRESS:
support@invested.org

WEB SITE ADDRESS:
www.invested.org

FOUNDED: 1963

AREAS OF INTEREST:
Secondary education and personal needs for disadvantaged students.

NAME(S) OF PROGRAMS:
● **InvestED School Fund Program**

TYPE:
Grants-in-aid; Matching gifts.

YEAR PROGRAM STARTED: 1963

PURPOSE:
To support middle and senior high school aid program providing for grants to both accredited public and private schools (grades 6-12) within the state of Washington to enable these schools to assist individual students who have needs their families cannot afford.

LEGAL BASIS:
Public charity.

ELIGIBILITY:
Grants are restricted to a program aiding students in Washington state secondary schools.

School must submit year-end report May 1 to June 30 to be eligible for grant the following year.

GEOGRAPHIC RESTRICTIONS:
Washington state.

FINANCIAL DATA:
Amount of support per award: $200 to more than $3,500 per school.
Total amount of support: $379,315 for the year 2011.

APPLICATION INFORMATION:
Contact the Organization for guidelines.
Duration: One year. Renewable.
Deadline: June 30.

IRS IDENTIFICATION NUMBER: 23-7189670

DIRECTORS:
Lisa Schaures, President
Paul Ishii, First Vice President
Tom Gleason, Second Vice President
Jim Ivers, Treasurer
Pamela J. Hughes, Secretary
Dan Barritt
Darrell Bryan
Emory Bundy
Paul Condrat
Michael Dunn, Ed.D.
Nancy Fike
Tom Horton
Tanya Lamb
Martin Neeb
Roger Percy
Tom Rath
Kerry Thompson
Debbie Williams

ADDRESS INQUIRIES TO:
Executive Director
(See address above.)

MARTHA HOLDEN JENNINGS FOUNDATION   [1604]
The Halle Building
1228 Euclid Avenue, Suite 710
Cleveland, OH 44115-1811
(216) 589-5700
Fax: (216) 589-5730

WEB SITE ADDRESS:
www.mhjf.org

FOUNDED: 1959

AREAS OF INTEREST:
Ohio elementary and secondary education.

NAME(S) OF PROGRAMS:
● **Grants-to-Educators Program**
● **Open Grants**

TYPE:
Project/program grants. Project/program grants are for education only. Support to aide the improvement of elementary and secondary public school education in Ohio.

YEAR PROGRAM STARTED: 1959

PURPOSE:
To foster the development of individual capabilities of young people to the maximum extent through improving the quality of teaching in secular primary and secondary schools; to provide a means for greater accomplishment on the part of Ohio's teachers by encouraging creativity in teaching and bringing greater recognition to the teaching profession.

LEGAL BASIS:
Nonprofit foundation.

ELIGIBILITY:
For Grants-to-Educators, applicants must be teachers or public school administrators and are intended for classroom, schoolwide or districtwide projects. For other grants, applicants must be tax-exempt with 501(c)(3) status from the IRS.

Open Grants are available to any public school district, nonreligious private school working with public schools, or tax-exempt organization that assists elementary and secondary schools in Ohio. No grants for capital improvements or graduate study, and generally no grants for equipment or travel.

GEOGRAPHIC RESTRICTIONS:
Ohio.

FINANCIAL DATA:
Amount of support per award:
Grants-to-Educators: Up to $3,000; Open Grants: Varies depending on needs and nature of the request. Average: $15,000.
Total amount of support: $3,017,870 for the year 2013.

NUMBER OF AWARDS: 207 for the year 2013.

REPRESENTATIVE AWARDS:
$14,280 to Cory Rawson Local Schools, Rawson, OH, for Raising Achievement through Data; $11,340 to Kenston Local Schools, Chagrin Falls, OH, for Student Writer's Workshop; $12,340 to The Works, Newark, OH, for STEM Programs; $15,000 to Invent Now, North Canton, OH, for Camp Invention Program.

APPLICATION INFORMATION:
There are two funding categories within both the Grants-to-Educators and Open Grants programs: Excellent Teaching and Deep Learning; applicants need to understand the rationale behind these grant categories before completing a proposal. Applicants must indicate the category or categories for which they are seeking funds within each program.

There is a specific application for the Grants-to-Educators program which is available on the web site.
Mail the entire original (stapled) and nine copies in the above order to the Chairman, Distribution Committee; Martha Holden Jennings Foundation, at the above address.

There is no prescribed application form for Open Grants. Submit only the original grant proposal for consideration; grant requests

must not exceed 10 pages and must include:
(1) a one-page cover letter;
(2) a one-page executive summary;
(3) a detailed proposal (no more than six pages) for the project;
(4) a detailed one-page budget for the entire project;
(5) in the case of institutions proposing to provide services to schools, a letter indicating a need for the services and support for the project signed by the superintendent of schools of a targeted district and;
(6) a copy of the organization's IRS 501(c)(3) ruling (IRS ruling not needed for public schools); the IRS ruling is not considered part of the 10-page maximum.

Duration: One year. Proposal may be resubmitted for a second or third year.

Deadline: Proposals should be in by the 15th of the month preceding the month in which they are to be considered. If the 15th falls on a weekend or a holiday, requests must be submitted on the previous business day.

Grants-to-Educators: The Distribution Committee meets ten months a year (not in July or December).

Open Grants: The Board of Directors does not meet in February, July, October or December. Decisions on grant applications are generally communicated within two months of submission.

PUBLICATIONS:
Guidelines; *Pro-Excellentia.*

STAFF:
Dr. William T. Hiller, Executive Director

ADDRESS INQUIRIES TO:
Chairperson, Distribution Committee
(See address above.)

KLINGENSTEIN CENTER FOR INDEPENDENT SCHOOL LEADERSHIP [1605]

Teachers College, Columbia University
525 West 120th Street, Box 125
New York, NY 10027-6696
(212) 678-3156
Fax: (212) 678-3254

E-MAIL ADDRESS:
klingenstein@tc.columbia.edu

WEB SITE ADDRESS:
www.klingenstein.org

FOUNDED: 1977

AREAS OF INTEREST:
Leadership development for independent and international education.

NAME(S) OF PROGRAMS:
● **Klingenstein Heads Program**
● **Klingenstein Summer Institute**
● **Master's Degree in Educational Leadership**

TYPE:
Scholarships. The Klingenstein Heads Program gathers heads of independent and international schools from throughout the nation and the world for two weeks of intensive study among professional peers.

The Klingenstein Summer Institute gathers teachers in the beginning years of their careers for an exploration of teaching styles, educational philosophies and issues, and personal development.

The Master's Degree in Educational Leadership, with a focus in private school leadership, gathers independent school

teachers and administrators for a rigorous degree program. The Two Summers Master's Program is the two-summer version of the full-year degree program. The majority of students get generous tuition scholarships.

YEAR PROGRAM STARTED: 1978

PURPOSE:
To draw attention to outstanding leadership.

LEGAL BASIS:
Private foundation.

ELIGIBILITY:
Teachers and administrators working in an independent school with a nondiscriminatory admissions policy are eligible to apply. All programs are open to international applicants.

FINANCIAL DATA:
All programs offer tuition funding.
Amount of support per award: Varies.
Total amount of support: Varies.

APPLICATION INFORMATION:
Applicant must submit application, autobiographical information and recommendations from sponsoring school.
Duration: Varies.
Deadline: Klingenstein Heads of Schools Program: May 1; Summer Institute and Master's Degree: January 15; Two Summers Master's Program: November 1 of even-numbered years.

PUBLICATIONS:
Klingbrief.

ADDRESS INQUIRIES TO:
Assistant Director
(See address above.)

MEBANE CHARITABLE FOUNDATION, INC.

232 South Main Street
Mocksville, NC 27028
(336) 936-0041
Fax: (336) 936-0038

E-MAIL ADDRESS:
lcolbourne@mebanefoundation.com

WEB SITE ADDRESS:
www.mebanefoundation.com

TYPE:
Project/program grants.

See entry 1136 for full listing.

MITSUBISHI ELECTRIC AMERICA FOUNDATION [1606]

1560 Wilson Boulevard
Suite 1150
Arlington, VA 22209
(703) 276-8240

E-MAIL ADDRESS:
mea.foundation@meus.mea.com

WEB SITE ADDRESS:
www.meaf.org

FOUNDED: 1991

AREAS OF INTEREST:
People with disabilities, including education, employment, independence and community inclusion.

TYPE:
Demonstration grants; General operating grants; Internships; Matching gifts; Project/program grants; Seed money grants; Technical assistance; Training grants. Grants are offered to make a better world for all by

helping young people with disabilities to maximize their potential and participation in society.

YEAR PROGRAM STARTED: 1991

PURPOSE:
To help young people with disabilities maximize their potential and participation in society.

LEGAL BASIS:
Foundation.

ELIGIBILITY:
Applicants must meet criteria as stated in foundation guidelines. Priority given to applicants in communities where MEUS facilities are located.

GEOGRAPHIC RESTRICTIONS:
United States.

FINANCIAL DATA:
Amount of support per award: Average: $30,000.
Total amount of support: $490,000 for the year 2012.

NUMBER OF APPLICANTS MOST RECENT YEAR:
130.

NUMBER OF AWARDS: 9 for the year 2013.

REPRESENTATIVE AWARDS:
$55,000 to American Association of People with Disabilities to expand its Congressional internship program; $250,000 to Girls Scouts Council of the Nation's Capital for an Include All Girls initiative; $150,000 to the U.S. Business Leadership Network to support the Career Link Mentoring Program.

APPLICATION INFORMATION:
Submit a two-page concept paper (click on the "How to Apply" tab on the Foundation web site) including a budget summary and description of the need and objectives for the funds requested. Instructions for full proposals will be sent after initial screening. Concept papers are reviewed throughout the year.

Applicants are requested not to telephone the Foundation during the application process.
Duration: One to three years. Renewal possible on a case-by-case basis.
Deadline: June 1 to be considered for following year funding.

BOARD OF DIRECTORS:
Mike Corbo
Mike DeLano
Chris Gerdes
Jack Greaf
Shinji Harada
Brian Heery
Caitlin Helgeson
Nicole Johnson
Perry Pappous
David Rebmann
Katsuya Takamiya
Dr. Richard C. Waters
Jeff Whitelaw
Kenichiro Yamanishi

ADDRESS INQUIRIES TO:
Kevin R. Webb, Director
(See address above.)

NATIONAL ENDOWMENT FOR THE HUMANITIES

The Constitution Center
400 7th Street, S.W.
Washington, DC 20001
(202) 606-8424
Fax: (202) 606-8240

E-MAIL ADDRESS:
info@neh.gov

WEB SITE ADDRESS:
www.neh.gov

TYPE:
Conferences/seminars. Grants support summer seminars and national institutes in the humanities for college and school teachers. These faculty development activities are conducted at colleges and universities across the country. Lists of pending seminars and institutes are available from the program.

See entry 381 for full listing.

NATIONAL SCIENCE FOUNDATION   [1607]
Directorate for Education and Human Resources
Division of Research on Learning in Formal and Informal Settings
4201 Wilson Boulevard, Suite 885 S
Arlington, VA 22230
(703) 292-8620
(703) 570-1975
Fax: (703) 292-9044; (703) 292-9046

E-MAIL ADDRESS:
acarroll@nsf.gov

WEB SITE ADDRESS:
www.nsf.gov

FOUNDED: 1950

AREAS OF INTEREST:
Science, mathematics, technology education content; pedagogy; applied research; development of resources and tools for instruction, assessment, evaluation and informal science.

NAME(S) OF PROGRAMS:
● **Advanced Technological Education (ATE)**
● **Discovery Research K-12 (DR K12)**
● **Informal Science Education (ISE) (AISL)**
● **Innovative Technology Experiences for Students and Teachers (ITEST)**
● **Research and Evaluation on Education in Science and Engineering (REESE)**

TYPE:
Conferences/seminars; Demonstration grants; Development grants; Project/program grants; Research grants; Training grants. With an emphasis on two-year colleges, the Advanced Technological Education (ATE) program focuses on the education of technicians for the high-technology fields that drive the nation's economy.

Discovery Research K-12 (DR K12) funds research, development and evaluation activities through knowledge generation and application to improve K-12 learning and teaching.

Informal Science Education (ISE) program invests in projects that develop and implement informal learning experiences designed to increase interest, engagement and understanding of science, technology, engineering and mathematics (STEM) by individuals of all ages and backgrounds, as well as projects that advance knowledge and practice of informal science education.

Innovative Technology Experiences for Students and Teachers (ITEST) is designed to increase the opportunities for students and teachers to learn about, experience, and use information technologies within the context

of science, technology, engineering and mathematics (STEM), including Information Technology (IT) courses. It is in direct response to the concern about shortages of information technology workers in the U.S.

Research and Evaluation on Education in Science and Engineering (REESE) supports basic and applied research and evaluation that enhances science, technology, engineering and mathematics (STEM) learning and teaching.

PURPOSE:
To promote quality programs of education in mathematics, science and technology for all the nation's youth, and informal learning opportunities in these fields for youth and adults.

LEGAL BASIS:
The National Science Foundation Act of 1950, Public Law 81-507, as amended.

GEOGRAPHIC RESTRICTIONS:
United States.

FINANCIAL DATA:
Amount of support per award: Grants vary in amount, depending upon the needs and nature of the request and availability of funds.
Total amount of support: $180,000,000.

APPLICATION INFORMATION:
Contact the Foundation.
Duration: One to five years.
Deadline: Varies.

THE RADIANT PEACE FOUNDATION INTERNATIONAL, INC.   [1608]
P.O. Box 40822
St. Petersburg, FL 33743-0822
(727) 343-8212
Fax: (727) 343-8212

E-MAIL ADDRESS:
radiantpeaceintl@gmail.com

WEB SITE ADDRESS:
www.radiantpeace.org

FOUNDED: 1986

NAME(S) OF PROGRAMS:
● **Radiant Peace Education Awards**

TYPE:
Awards/prizes. Recognizes and awards children, teachers and schools for Radiant Peace essays, art, projects, and videos.

YEAR PROGRAM STARTED: 1990

PURPOSE:
To inspire, promote and encourage Radiant Peace worldwide.

LEGAL BASIS:
A 501(c)(3) nonprofit educational organization.

ELIGIBILITY:
All students grades one-12 including home schools and youth groups.

FINANCIAL DATA:
Amount of support per award: $25 to $500.
Total amount of support: Varies by year.

NUMBER OF AWARDS: Varies.

APPLICATION INFORMATION:
Invitations and guidelines posted online.
Deadline: December and April.

ADDRESS INQUIRIES TO:
Office Manager
(See address above.)

THOMAS B. AND ELIZABETH M. SHERIDAN FOUNDATION   [1609]
Executive Plaza II, Suite 704
11350 McCormick Road
Hunt Valley, MD 21031
(410) 771-0475

FOUNDED: 1962

AREAS OF INTEREST:
Education and cultural arts.

TYPE:
Development grants; General operating grants; Project/program grants. Grants to private secondary schools and the cultural arts in the Baltimore area.

PURPOSE:
To support private secondary schools and cultural organizations.

ELIGIBILITY:
Organizations, including parochial schools, classified as 501(c)(3) by the IRS can apply. No grants to individuals.

GEOGRAPHIC RESTRICTIONS:
Baltimore area, Maryland.

FINANCIAL DATA:
$16,159,232 in assets (market value) for the year ended December 31, 2012.
Amount of support per award: $50 to $310,000 for the year ended December 31, 2012.
Total amount of support: $770,050 for the year ended December 31, 2012.

NUMBER OF AWARDS: 12 for the year ended December 31, 2012.

SONY USA FOUNDATION, INC.   [1610]
550 Madison Avenue, 33rd Floor
New York, NY 10022-3211
(212) 833-6851

E-MAIL ADDRESS:
erin_amaty@sonyusa.com

WEB SITE ADDRESS:
www.sony.com/sca/corporate-responsibility

FOUNDED: 1972

AREAS OF INTEREST:
Arts, culture and technology, with primary focus in education; environmental issues; civic affairs; health and welfare.

TYPE:
General operating grants; Matching gifts; Product donations; Project/program grants.

YEAR PROGRAM STARTED: 1972

PURPOSE:
To meet the needs of the communities where Sony has a presence; to support national organizations which extend into Sony presence areas.

LEGAL BASIS:
Corporate foundation.

ELIGIBILITY:
No grants to individuals, political or religious organizations, labor unions, endowments, capital campaigns, lobbying groups, testimonial dinners, for-profit publications seeking advertisements and foreign or non-U.S. organizations.

GEOGRAPHIC RESTRICTIONS:
United States.

FINANCIAL DATA:
Amount of support per award: Varies.
Total amount of support: Varies.
Matching fund requirements: Sony matches contributions made by full-time employees to educational institutions, hospitals and cultural organizations.

APPLICATION INFORMATION:
Send brief letter describing organization, amount requested, objectives of organization, recent audited financial statement and proof of tax-exempt status. Phone calls not accepted, only written requests.
Duration: One year. Must reapply for continued support.
Deadline: Requests accepted throughout the year. Notification within three months.

PUBLICATIONS:
Contribution guidelines.

OFFICERS:
Mark Khalil, President

ADDRESS INQUIRIES TO:
Erin Amaty
Public Affairs Administrator
(See address above.)

STATE LIBRARY AND ARCHIVES OF FLORIDA
R.A. Gray Building
500 South Bronough Street
Tallahassee, FL 32399-0250
(850) 245-6600
Fax: (850) 245-6643

E-MAIL ADDRESS:
marian.deeney@dos.myflorida.com

WEB SITE ADDRESS:
info.florida.gov/bld/grants/Lsta/LSTA.html

TYPE:
Project/program grants. Project grants congruent with the state long-range plan.

See entry 740 for full listing.

W. CLEMENT & JESSIE V. STONE FOUNDATION [1611]
1100 Lake Street, Suite 202
Oak Park, IL 60301
(800) 288-4859

E-MAIL ADDRESS:
jeff@wcstonefnd.org

WEB SITE ADDRESS:
www.wcstonefnd.org

FOUNDED: 1958

AREAS OF INTEREST:
Education, early childhood and youth development.

TYPE:
Demonstration grants; Development grants; General operating grants; Project/program grants; Technical assistance; Training grants.

YEAR PROGRAM STARTED: 1958

PURPOSE:
To make the world a better place by supporting programs in education, early childhood and youth development.

ELIGIBILITY:
Grants are made to organizations that have tax-exempt status under Section 501(c)(3) of the Internal Revenue Code. Nonsectarian religious programs may apply. No grants are made to individuals.

GEOGRAPHIC RESTRICTIONS:
San Francisco Bay area, California; Chicago, Illinois; Boston, Massachusetts; New York City, New York; and Philadelphia, Pennsylvania.

FINANCIAL DATA:
Amount of support per award: $10,000 to $100,000, depending upon the program.
Total amount of support: $4,400,000 for the year 2013.

NUMBER OF AWARDS: 100.

REPRESENTATIVE AWARDS:
$70,000 to Youth Radio; $75,000 to Partners for School Innovation; $100,000 to Strategies for Children.

APPLICATION INFORMATION:
The Foundation does not accept unsolicited proposals. Organizations may call if they feel there is a strong match between their work and the Foundation's grantmaking priorities.
Duration: Typically one year.

IRS IDENTIFICATION NUMBER: 36-2498125

OFFICERS AND DIRECTORS:
Norman C. Stone, Chairman
Sandra Stone, President
Steven M. Stone, Treasurer
Michael A. Stone, Secretary
Tony Smith, Executive Director
Alex Knecht
Amy Stone
Barbara Stone
David Stone
Debbie Stone
Jamison Stone
Jennifer Stone
Norah Stone
Sara Stone
Chad Tingley

ADDRESS INQUIRIES TO:
Tony Smith, Executive Director
(See address above.)

TOSHIBA AMERICA FOUNDATION [1612]
1251 Avenue of the Americas, 41st Floor
New York, NY 10020
(212) 596-0620

E-MAIL ADDRESS:
foundation@tai.toshiba.com

WEB SITE ADDRESS:
www.taf.toshiba.com

FOUNDED: 1990

AREAS OF INTEREST:
Mathematics and science education for grades K-12.

TYPE:
Project/program grants.

YEAR PROGRAM STARTED: 1990

PURPOSE:
To improve science and math education at the pre-college level (grades K-12 only).

LEGAL BASIS:
Corporate foundation.

ELIGIBILITY:
Grants are made to private or public schools. Preference is given to programs or projects that take place in science or math classrooms. The Foundation does not fund grants for general operating costs, endowments, scholarships, conferences, summer programs, purchase of equipment (product or donations), sponsorships, or individuals.

GEOGRAPHIC RESTRICTIONS:
United States.

FINANCIAL DATA:
Amount of support per award: $1,000 to $20,000.
Total amount of support: Approximately $500,000.

NUMBER OF AWARDS: 150 annually.

APPLICATION INFORMATION:
Applications are available on the Foundation's web site.
Duration: One year.
Deadline: Grades K-5: October 1. Grades 6-12: February 1 and August 1 for requests more than $5,000.

IRS IDENTIFICATION NUMBER: 13-3596612

ADDRESS INQUIRIES TO:
Program Officer
(See address above.)

U.S. DEPARTMENT OF EDUCATION
Office of Indian Education
400 Maryland Avenue, S.W.
LBJ Building, 3E205
Washington, DC 20202-6335
(202) 260-3774
(202) 260-1454
Fax: (202) 260-7779

E-MAIL ADDRESS:
indian.education@ed.gov

WEB SITE ADDRESS:
www.ed.gov

TYPE:
Formula grants. Grants to provide financial assistance to LEAs and tribal schools to develop and carry out elementary and secondary school programs specially designed to meet the special educational and culturally related educational needs of Indian children.

See entry 1057 for full listing.

U.S. DEPARTMENT OF EDUCATION
Office of Postsecondary Education
TRIO Programs
1990 K Street, N.W., Room 7035
Washington, DC 20006
(202) 502-7586

E-MAIL ADDRESS:
OPE_TRIO@ed.gov

WEB SITE ADDRESS:
www.ed.gov/ope/trio

TYPE:
Project/program grants. There are three types of grants under the Upward Bound program: Regular Upward Bound Grants; Veterans Upward Bound Grants; and Upward Bound Math and Science Grants.

The Regular Upward Bound projects are designed to generate in participants the skills and motivation necessary for success in education beyond secondary school. The Veterans Upward Bound projects are designed to assist veterans in preparing for a program of postsecondary education. The Upward Bound Math and Science projects are designed to prepare high school students for postsecondary education programs that lead to careers in the fields of math and science.

See entry 1643 for full listing.

YOUTH FOR UNDERSTANDING USA

6400 Goldsboro Road
Suite 100
Bethesda, MD 20817
(240) 235-2100
(800) 833-6243
(866) 493-8872
Fax: (240) 235-2188

E-MAIL ADDRESS:
admissions@yfu.org

WEB SITE ADDRESS:
www.yfu-usa.org

TYPE:
Exchange programs; Grants-in-aid; Scholarships; Travel grants. Students on summer semester and year programs live with volunteer host families overseas. Students on semester and academic year programs also attend school. International students live and study at U.S. high schools or community colleges. Competitive, full and partial scholarships for Corporate, Finland-U.S. Senate, Japan-U.S. Senate Programs and Japan-America Friendship Scholars Program.

See entry 954 for full listing.

Higher education projects and research

ABEL FOUNDATION

1815 Y Street
Lincoln, NE 68508
(402) 434-1212
Fax: (402) 434-1799

WEB SITE ADDRESS:
www.abelfoundation.org

TYPE:
Capital grants; Matching gifts; Project/program grants.

See entry 1157 for full listing.

ADCO FOUNDATION   [1613]

c/o AA Shareholders Service Company, LLC
1060 First Avenue, Suite 400
King of Prussia, PA 19406
(610) 768-8020

AREAS OF INTEREST:
Higher education, communications, civic affairs, community funds, health and mental health.

TYPE:
General operating grants; Project/program grants; Seed money grants.

PURPOSE:
To promote higher education, physical and mental health.

ELIGIBILITY:
Grants are made to organizations that have tax-exempt status under Section 501(c)(3) of the Internal Revenue Code. No grants are made to individuals.

GEOGRAPHIC RESTRICTIONS:
Primarily New Jersey, New York and Pennsylvania.

FINANCIAL DATA:
Amount of support per award: $500 to $12,000.
Total amount of support: $45,000 for the year 2012.

NUMBER OF AWARDS: 4 for the year 2012.

APPLICATION INFORMATION:
Send a letter of inquiry to the Foundation, outlining the organization's goal and purposes, and the intended use and amount of the grant requested.
Duration: One year. Renewal possible.
Deadline: November 30.

ADDRESS INQUIRIES TO:
Barry Doney, Administrator
(See address above.)

AMERICAN FLORAL ENDOWMENT

1601 Duke Street
Alexandria, VA 22314
(703) 838-5211
Fax: (703) 838-5212

E-MAIL ADDRESS:
afe@endowment.org

WEB SITE ADDRESS:
www.endowment.org

TYPE:
Internships; Project/program grants; Research grants; Scholarships. The Endowment funds research and educational development in floriculture and environmental horticulture designed to produce solutions to industry needs and promote the growth and improvement of the floral industry for the benefit of the grower, wholesale, retail, allied segments and the general public.

The Endowment supports educational programs focused on attracting young people to the industry, and educational endeavors to identify and solve industry needs and/or challenges. The programs are divided into two major areas:
(1) paid floriculture internships/scholarships for full-time college students and;
(2) general educational grants to national programs.

See entry 2114 for full listing.

AMERICAN FOUNDATION FOR PHARMACEUTICAL EDUCATION (AFPE)   [1614]

6076 Franconia Road, Suite C
Alexandria, VA 22310-1758
(703) 875-3095
Fax: (703) 875-3098

E-MAIL ADDRESS:
info@afpenet.org

WEB SITE ADDRESS:
www.afpenet.org

FOUNDED: 1942

AREAS OF INTEREST:
Education.

NAME(S) OF PROGRAMS:
● **AFPE Predoctoral Fellowships in the Pharmaceutical Sciences**

TYPE:
Fellowships.

YEAR PROGRAM STARTED: 1942

PURPOSE:
To encourage an outstanding pharmacy school graduate to pursue an advanced degree in the pharmaceutical sciences.

ELIGIBILITY:
Applicant must have completed at least three semesters of graduate study toward the Ph.D. and have no more than three-and-a-half years remaining to obtain the Ph.D. degree in a graduate program in the pharmaceutical sciences administered by or affiliated with a U.S. school or college of pharmacy.

GEOGRAPHIC RESTRICTIONS:
United States.

FINANCIAL DATA:
Amount of support per award: $6,500 to $11,000.
Total amount of support: Varies.

NUMBER OF APPLICANTS MOST RECENT YEAR:
150.

NUMBER OF AWARDS: 42.

APPLICATION INFORMATION:
Application and guidelines are available online.
Duration: One year. Renewable.

ADDRESS INQUIRIES TO:
Sherri Hunter, Grants Manager
(See address above.)

AMERICAN FOUNDATION FOR PHARMACEUTICAL EDUCATION (AFPE)

6076 Franconia Road, Suite C
Alexandria, VA 22310-1758
(703) 875-3095
Fax: (703) 875-3098

E-MAIL ADDRESS:
info@afpenet.org

WEB SITE ADDRESS:
www.afpenet.org

TYPE:
Fellowships.

See entry 2536 for full listing.

AMERICAN FRIENDS OF THE ALEXANDER VON HUMBOLDT FOUNDATION   [1615]

1101 17th Street, N.W.
Suite 603
Washington, DC 20036
(202) 783-1907

E-MAIL ADDRESS:
info@americanfriends-of-avh.org

WEB SITE ADDRESS:
www.humboldt-foundation.de
americanfriends-of-avh.org

FOUNDED: 1953

AREAS OF INTEREST:
Postgraduate research in Germany.

NAME(S) OF PROGRAMS:
● **Humboldt Research Fellowship for Postdoctoral Researchers**

TYPE:
Fellowships. This program supports highly qualified scholars and scientists of all nationalities and disciplines so that they may carry out long-term research projects that the applicant has selected in cooperation with an academic host the applicant has selected at a research institution in Germany.

PURPOSE:
To support highly qualified scholars and scientists of all nationalities and disciplines so that they may carry out long-term research projects in Germany.

ELIGIBILITY:
Open to scientists and scholars who completed a doctoral degree within four years prior to the application submission date.

Fellowships are awarded on the basis of academic achievement, the quality and feasibility of the proposed research and the candidate's publications.

FINANCIAL DATA:
In addition to a monthly stipend, special allowances are available for accompanying family members, travel expenses and German language instruction.
Amount of support per award: EUR 2,650 monthly.
Total amount of support: Varies.

NUMBER OF AWARDS: Approximately 600 total fellowships for postdoctoral researchers and experienced researchers each year.

APPLICATION INFORMATION:
Application information is available on the web site.
Duration: Six to 24 months in Germany.
Deadline: Continuous. The review process takes several months, and the selection committee meets three times a year to review applications.

ADDRESS INQUIRIES TO:
Program Coordination
(See address above.) or

Alexander von Humboldt Stiftung
Jean-Paul-Strasse 12
D-53173 Bonn
Germany
Tel: 49 (0228) 833-0
Fax: 49 (0228) 833-199
E-mail: info@avh.de

AMERICAN LIBRARY ASSOCIATION (ALA) [1616]
50 East Huron Street
Chicago, IL 60611-2795
(312) 280-4279
(800) 545-2433 ext. 4279
Fax: (312) 280-3256

E-MAIL ADDRESS:
scholarships@ala.org

WEB SITE ADDRESS:
www.ala.org/educationcareers/scholarships

AREAS OF INTEREST:
Library science.

NAME(S) OF PROGRAMS:
- ALA/Century Scholarship
- ALSC/Bound-to-Stay-Bound Books Scholarship
- ALSC/Frederic G. Melcher Scholarship
- David H. Clift Scholarship
- Tom and Roberta Drewes Scholarship
- Mary V. Gaver Scholarship
- Miriam L. Hornback Scholarship
- Christopher J. Hoy/ERT Scholarship
- Tony B. Leisner Scholarship
- LITA/Christian Larew Memorial Scholarship
- LITA/LSSI Minority Scholarship
- LITA/OCLC Minority Scholarship
- Peter Lyman Memorial/SAGE Scholarships
- Cicely Phippen Marks Scholarship
- Spectrum Initiative Scholarship Program

TYPE:
Scholarships. ALA Century Scholarship is for an individual with a disability entering a Master's degree or Ph.D. program.

ALSC and Gaver Scholarships are for a youth services librarian.

Clift and Hoy/ERT are general scholarships.

Drewes, Hornback and Leisner Scholarships are for paid library support staff currently working in a library.

LITA/Christian Larew Memorial, LITA/LSSI Minority and LITA/OCLC Minority Scholarships are for librarians entering a Master's degree program.

Marks Scholarship is for a federal services librarian.

SAGE Scholarship is for a new media services librarian.

YEAR PROGRAM STARTED: 1996

PURPOSE:
To support library staff education.

ELIGIBILITY:
Applicants must be U.S. or Canadian citizens, or permanent residents thereof.

Applicants must demonstrate academic excellence, leadership qualities and evidence of commitment to a career in library service.

Applicants may not have completed more than 12 semester hours or the equivalent towards a Master's degree in library science prior to June 1.

GEOGRAPHIC RESTRICTIONS:
United States and Canada.

FINANCIAL DATA:
Amount of support per award: Varies.
Total amount of support: Varies.

NUMBER OF APPLICANTS MOST RECENT YEAR: 601 for the year 2012.

NUMBER OF AWARDS: 69 for the year 2012.

APPLICATION INFORMATION:
Application information is available on the web site.
Deadline: March 1.

STAFF:
Kimberly Redd, Program Officer

ADDRESS INQUIRIES TO:
Kimberly Redd, Program Officer
(See address above.)

THE AMERICAN-SCANDINAVIAN FOUNDATION [1617]
58 Park Avenue
New York, NY 10016
(212) 879-9779

E-MAIL ADDRESS:
grants@amscan.org

WEB SITE ADDRESS:
www.amscan.org

FOUNDED: 1910

AREAS OF INTEREST:
Cross-cultural exchange at an academic level.

NAME(S) OF PROGRAMS:
- Visiting Lectureships

TYPE:
Exchange programs. The Foundation invites U.S. colleges and universities to apply for funding to host a visiting lecturer from Norway or Sweden. Lectureships should be in the area of contemporary studies with an emphasis in one of the following areas: (1) public policy; (2) conflict resolution; (3) environmental studies; (4) multiculturalism and; (5) health care.

PURPOSE:
To promote international understanding through educational and cultural exchange between the U.S. and Scandinavia.

ELIGIBILITY:
The competition is open to all American colleges and universities. The award is appropriate for any department or interdisciplinary program with an interest in incorporating a Scandinavian focus. The lecturer must be a Norwegian or Swedish citizen and a scholar or expert in a field appropriate to the host department or program.

FINANCIAL DATA:
Amount of support per award: $20,000 teaching/research stipend plus a $5,000 travel stipend for lecture appearances outside home institution. Award also includes a J-1 visa sponsorship as a short-term scholar (up to six months) through the ASF Visitor Exchange Program.

APPLICATION INFORMATION:
Application and instructions are available on the Foundation web site.
Duration: One semester.
Deadline: Applicants are asked to submit a letter of intent by November 1. A full application must be submitted by the following February 1.

*SPECIAL STIPULATIONS:
The selected lecturer is expected to teach one course (undergraduate or graduate-level) and perform modest public activities (lectures, etc.) for which he or she will receive $20,000.

ARCHAEOLOGICAL INSTITUTE OF AMERICA [1618]
656 Beacon Street, 6th Floor
Boston, MA 02215
(617) 358-4184
Fax: (617) 353-6550

E-MAIL ADDRESS:
fellowships@aia.bu.edu

WEB SITE ADDRESS:
www.archaeological.org

FOUNDED: 1879

AREAS OF INTEREST:
Archaeological research and publication.

NAME(S) OF PROGRAMS:
- Helen M. Woodruff Fellowship of the AIA and the American Academy in Rome

TYPE:
Fellowships. A predoctoral or postdoctoral fellowship for study of archaeology and classical studies established by the Institute at the American Academy in Rome. Award supports a Rome Prize.

PURPOSE:
To promote the study of archaeology and classical studies.

ELIGIBILITY:
Applicant must be a citizen or permanent resident of the U.S.

GEOGRAPHIC RESTRICTIONS:
United States.

FINANCIAL DATA:
Amount of support per award: $10,000.
Total amount of support: $10,000.

NUMBER OF AWARDS: 1.

APPLICATION INFORMATION:
Applications must be sent to the American Academy in Rome; 7 East 60th Street; New York, NY 10022.
Duration: One year.
Deadline: November 1.

ADDRESS INQUIRIES TO:
Fellowship Coordinator
(See e-mail address above.)

ARCHITECTURAL LEAGUE OF NEW YORK
594 Broadway, Suite 607
New York, NY 10012
(212) 753-1722
Fax: (212) 486-9173

E-MAIL ADDRESS:
info@archleague.org

WEB SITE ADDRESS:
www.archleague.org

TYPE:
Research grants; Travel grants. The Deborah J. Norden Fund, established in 1995 in memory of architect and arts administrator Deborah Norden, awards travel/study grants to students and recent graduates in the field of architecture, architectural history, and urban studies.

See entry 413 for full listing.

ARCTIC INSTITUTE OF NORTH AMERICA [1619]
The University of Calgary
2500 University Drive, N.W., ES 1040
Calgary AB T2N 1N4 Canada
(403) 220-7515
Fax: (403) 282-4609

E-MAIL ADDRESS:
arctic@ucalgary.ca

WEB SITE ADDRESS:
www.arctic.ucalgary.ca

FOUNDED: 1945

AREAS OF INTEREST:
Arctic natural and social sciences.

NAME(S) OF PROGRAMS:
● AINA Grants-in-Aid

TYPE:
Grants-in-aid; Scholarships.

YEAR PROGRAM STARTED: 1945

PURPOSE:
To provide funding to young investigators, especially graduate students, to augment their research.

ELIGIBILITY:
Proposed projects can include field, library or office-intensive investigations. Although there is no limitation on the area of investigation, the Institute encourages applications focused on the natural sciences and social sciences, including anthropology and economics, in the North.

FINANCIAL DATA:
Funding can be used for travel, supplies, equipment and services, but not for salary or wages.
Amount of support per award: $1,000.
Total amount of support: Varies each year, depending on number of applications received.

NUMBER OF APPLICANTS MOST RECENT YEAR: 80.

NUMBER OF AWARDS: Varies.

APPLICATION INFORMATION:
Applications must be mailed to:
Arctic Institute of North America
University of Alaska, Rasmuson Library
P.O. Box 6808
Fairbanks, AK 99775-6808.
Deadline: February 1 (postmark).

PUBLICATIONS:
Arctic Journal.

ADDRESS INQUIRIES TO:
Arctic Institute of North America
(See e-mail address above.)

BARNES GROUP FOUNDATION
123 Main Street
Bristol, CT 06010
(860) 583-7070
Fax: (860) 589-7466

WEB SITE ADDRESS:
www.bginc.com

TYPE:
General operating grants; Scholarships. Employee scholarship program.

See entry 1177 for full listing.

CAESAR'S ENTERTAINMENT CORPORATION [1620]
One Caesar's Palace Drive
Las Vegas, NV 89109
(702) 407-6300
Fax: (702) 407-6520

WEB SITE ADDRESS:
www.caesars.com

AREAS OF INTEREST:
Education.

TYPE:
Matching gifts. The corporation matches employee contributions, dollar-for-dollar, to eligible colleges or universities.

YEAR PROGRAM STARTED: 1983

PURPOSE:
To encourage employees to support higher education by matching their gifts to institutions of greatest importance to them.

LEGAL BASIS:
Corporation.

ELIGIBILITY:
Regular, full-time employees of Caesar's or one of its operating units are eligible. Recipients of funding must be postsecondary institutions with nonprofit tax status, an appropriate regional or professional accreditation or licensing, a policy of nondiscrimination on the basis of sex, age, race or religion, and located within the U.S. or its possessions.

FINANCIAL DATA:
Amount of support per award: Up to $1,000 per employee, per year.

Total amount of support: Varies.

PUBLICATIONS:
Annual report.

OFFICERS:
Gary Loveman, Chairman and Chief Executive Officer

ADDRESS INQUIRIES TO:
Lindsay Garcia, Political Affairs and CSR Program Manager
(See address above.)

ROY J. CARVER CHARITABLE TRUST [1621]
202 Iowa Avenue
Muscatine, IA 52761-3733
(563) 263-4010
Fax: (563) 263-1547

E-MAIL ADDRESS:
info@carvertrust.org

WEB SITE ADDRESS:
www.carvertrust.org

FOUNDED: 1982

AREAS OF INTEREST:
Biomedical and scientific research; elementary, secondary and higher education; youth recreation.

TYPE:
Capital grants; Challenge/matching grants; Professorships; Project/program grants; Research grants; Scholarships.

YEAR PROGRAM STARTED: 1982

PURPOSE:
To support medical and scientific research, scholarships, general education and programs addressing the needs of youth.

LEGAL BASIS:
Trust.

ELIGIBILITY:
Eligible organizations must be IRS 501(c)(3) tax-exempt.

GEOGRAPHIC RESTRICTIONS:
Iowa and portions of western Illinois.

FINANCIAL DATA:
Amount of support per award: Varies.
Total amount of support: Varies.

APPLICATION INFORMATION:
Detailed information is available online.
Duration: Varies.
Deadline: February 15, May 15, August 15 and November 15.

ADDRESS INQUIRIES TO:
Troy K. Ross, Ph.D.
Executive Administrator
(See address above.)

CENTER FOR CALIFORNIA STUDIES, CAPITAL FELLOWS PROGRAMS
California State University, Sacramento
6000 J Street
Sacramento, CA 95819-6081
(916) 278-6906

E-MAIL ADDRESS:
calstudies@csus.edu

WEB SITE ADDRESS:
www.csus.edu/calst/judicial

TYPE:
Fellowships. Jointly sponsored by the Center for California Studies at California State University, Sacramento and the California

Judicial Council. Full-time fellowships for 10 fellows, 10 months and graduate units earned from California State University, Sacramento.

See entry 1990 for full listing.

CENTER FOR CALIFORNIA STUDIES, CAPITAL FELLOWS PROGRAMS

California State University, Sacramento
6000 J Street
Sacramento, CA 95819-6081
(916) 278-6906

E-MAIL ADDRESS:
calstudies@csus.edu

WEB SITE ADDRESS:
www.csus.edu/calst/senate

TYPE:
Fellowships. Jointly sponsored by the Center for California Studies at California State University, Sacramento and the California State Senate. Full-time fellowships for 18 fellows, 11 months and graduate units earned from California State University, Sacramento.

See entry 1991 for full listing.

CENTER FOR CALIFORNIA STUDIES, CAPITAL FELLOWS PROGRAMS

California State University, Sacramento
6000 J Street
Sacramento, CA 95819-6081
(916) 278-6906
Fax: (916) 278-5199

E-MAIL ADDRESS:
calstudies@csus.edu

WEB SITE ADDRESS:
www.csus.edu/calst/executive

TYPE:
Fellowships. Jointly sponsored by the Center for California Studies at California State University, Sacramento and the California governor. Full-time fellowships for 18 fellows, 10 months and six units of graduate study through California State University, Sacramento.

See entry 1992 for full listing.

CENTER FOR CALIFORNIA STUDIES, CAPITAL FELLOWS PROGRAMS

California State University, Sacramento
6000 J Street
Sacramento, CA 95819-6081
(916) 278-6906
Fax: (916) 278-5199

E-MAIL ADDRESS:
calstudies@csus.edu

WEB SITE ADDRESS:
www.csus.edu/calst/assembly_fellowship_program.html

TYPE:
Fellowships. Jointly sponsored by the Center for California Studies at California State University, Sacramento and the California State Assembly. Full-time fellowships for 18 fellows, 11 months and units of graduate study through California State University, Sacramento.

See entry 1993 for full listing.

CENTER FOR COMPARATIVE IMMIGRATION STUDIES AT THE UNIVERSITY OF CALIFORNIA-SAN DIEGO [1622]

9500 Gilman Drive, MC 0548
La Jolla, CA 92093-0548
(858) 822-4447
Fax: (858) 822-4432

E-MAIL ADDRESS:
ccis@ucsd.edu

WEB SITE ADDRESS:
ccis-ucsd.org

FOUNDED: 1999

AREAS OF INTEREST:
International and internal migration and refugee flows in all countries and immigrant ethnic minorities.

NAME(S) OF PROGRAMS:
● **Visiting Research Fellowship Program**

TYPE:
Fellowships.

YEAR PROGRAM STARTED: 1999

PURPOSE:
To systematically compare the historical and contemporary U.S. immigration experience with that of other labor-importing countries in other regions such as the Asia-Pacific, Latin America, Western Europe and Western Africa.

ELIGIBILITY:
Must be an advanced predoctoral or postdoctoral scholar researching and writing on any aspect of international migration and refugee flows, in any field of the social sciences, history, law and comparative literature. Must have current or former affiliation with a University of California campus.

NUMBER OF APPLICANTS MOST RECENT YEAR: 40.

NUMBER OF AWARDS: 1.

APPLICATION INFORMATION:
The applicant must complete a Fellowship Application Form and mail it, along with required attachments, to the address above.
Duration: Nine to 10 months, depending on the requirements of the project. Full academic year projects that are nine to 10 months are preferred.
Deadline: January 15. Details may be found on the web site.

STAFF:
Prof. David Fitzgerald
Prof. John Skrentny

ADDRESS INQUIRIES TO:
Fellowship Program
(See address above.)

*SPECIAL STIPULATIONS:
Fellowships must be held in residence at CCIS.

CORNELL UNIVERSITY

Society for the Humanities
A.D. White House
27 East Avenue
Ithaca, NY 14853-1101
(607) 255-9274
(607) 255-4086
Fax: (607) 255-1422

E-MAIL ADDRESS:
humctr@cornell.edu

WEB SITE ADDRESS:
www.arts.cornell.edu/sochum

TYPE:
Fellowships. Postdoctoral teaching-research fellowships in the humanities, each awarded for a two-year period. While in residence at Cornell, postdoctoral fellows hold department affiliation and have limited teaching duties and the opportunity for scholarly work.

See entry 364 for full listing.

COUNCIL FOR INTERNATIONAL EXCHANGE OF SCHOLARS (CIES) [1623]

1400 K Street, N.W.
Suite 700
Washington, DC 20005
(202) 686-6232
Fax: (202) 686-4029

E-MAIL ADDRESS:
jmcpeek@iie.org

WEB SITE ADDRESS:
www.cies.org

FOUNDED: 1947

AREAS OF INTEREST:
Distinguished chair lecturing awards.

NAME(S) OF PROGRAMS:
● **Fulbright Distinguished Chairs**

TYPE:
Awards/prizes. There are approximately 40 distinguished chair awards in 18 countries. Awards available in a wide variety of disciplines.

PURPOSE:
To promote mutual understanding and scholarship.

ELIGIBILITY:
Applicants must have a Ph.D. or equivalent professional degree; a terminal degree is required. Applicants should have a record of prominent scholarly achievement. U.S. citizenship required. Lecturing is in English.

FINANCIAL DATA:
Award benefits vary by country and generally include a monthly stipend, travel, and housing.
Amount of support per award: Varies.
Total amount of support: Varies.

APPLICATION INFORMATION:
Application must be submitted online.
Deadline: August 1.

COUNCIL FOR INTERNATIONAL EXCHANGE OF SCHOLARS (CIES) [1624]

1400 K Street, N.W.
Suite 700
Washington, DC 20005-2403
(202) 686-4000
Fax: (202) 362-3442

E-MAIL ADDRESS:
scholars@iie.org

WEB SITE ADDRESS:
www.cies.org/iea

FOUNDED: 1947

AREAS OF INTEREST:
Scholarly exchange.

NAME(S) OF PROGRAMS:
● **Fulbright International Education Administrators Program**

TYPE:
Conferences/seminars; Exchange programs;
Project/program grants; Research grants;
Travel grants. Through its short-term
seminars, the Fulbright International
Education Administrators Program can help
U.S. higher education administrators establish
lasting connections within the social, cultural
and education systems of other countries.
Selected administrators have the opportunity
to gain in-depth knowledge about the host
country's higher education system as well as
to establish networks of U.S. and
international colleagues. Grantees return
home with enhanced ability to serve
international students and encourage
prospective study-abroad students.

YEAR PROGRAM STARTED: 1947

PURPOSE:
To promote mutual understanding between
people of the U.S. and people of other
nations.

LEGAL BASIS:
Public Law 87-256, as amended, The Mutual
Educational and Cultural Exchange Act of
1961.

ELIGIBILITY:
Applicants must be U.S. citizens.

U.S.-India and U.S.-France IEA Programs are
open to experienced international education
administrators and senior administrators
responsible for enhancing the international
dimensions of their institutions.

U.S.-Japan IEA Program is open to
experienced international education
administrators and senior administrators
responsible for enhancing the international
dimensions of their institutions. Preference is
given to applicants who have not had
significant professional visits to Japan in the
last five years and who indicate an
institutional interest in increasing the number
of Japanese students on their campus.

U.S.-Korea IEA Program is open to
experienced international education
administrators and senior administrators
responsible for enhancing the international
dimensions of their institutions. Preference is
given to applicants who have an existing
population of Korean students on campus.

U.S.-Germany IEA Program is open to
experienced administrators in international
exchanges, foreign admissions, study-abroad,
international education, career services,
alumni affairs and development/fund-raising.

Applicants to any of these IEA programs are
not required to hold a Ph.D.

GEOGRAPHIC RESTRICTIONS:
United States.

FINANCIAL DATA:
Amount of support per award: Varies.

NUMBER OF APPLICANTS MOST RECENT YEAR:
Approximately 75.

NUMBER OF AWARDS: U.S.-France IEA: Up to
12; U.S.-Germany IEA: 20; U.S.-India IEA:
10; U.S.-Japan IEA: Up to 10; U.S.-Korea
IEA: 8.

APPLICATION INFORMATION:
Applicants must submit:
(1) adapted application form;
(2) project statement (not to exceed five
single-spaced pages);
(3) institutional statement (one to two pages);
(4) curriculum vitae (not to exceed six pages)
and;
(5) three references.

Duration: U.S.-India IEA: Two weeks in
March; U.S.-Japan and U.S.-Korea IEA: Two
weeks in June; U.S.-France and U.S.
Germany IEA: Two weeks in October.
Deadline: U.S.-Japan IEA and U.S.-Korea
IEA: November 3; U.S.-France IEA and
U.S.-Germany IEA: February 2; U.S.-India
IEA: August 1.

PUBLICATIONS:
Descriptive brochure; annual awards catalog;
annual report.

ADDRESS INQUIRIES TO:
Fulbright International Education
Administrators Program
(See e-mail and address above.)

GARDNER AND FLORENCE CALL COWLES FOUNDATION   [1625]
1915 Grand Avenue
Des Moines, IA 50309
(515) 284-8117
Fax: (515) 309-0704

AREAS OF INTEREST:
Higher education and private four-year
colleges in Iowa.

TYPE:
Capital grants; Project/program grants.

YEAR PROGRAM STARTED: 1936

PURPOSE:
To support four-year colleges in Iowa.

ELIGIBILITY:
Eligible organizations must be IRS 501(c)(3)
tax-exempt. No individual grants are given.

GEOGRAPHIC RESTRICTIONS:
Iowa.

FINANCIAL DATA:
Amount of support per award: Varies.

APPLICATION INFORMATION:
Contact the Foundation.
Duration: Varies.
Deadline: Spring and Fall. Call for dates.

STAFF:
Phyllis Mumford, Administrator

ADDRESS INQUIRIES TO:
Charles Edwards, Jr., President
(See address above.)

HUGH AND HAZEL DARLING FOUNDATION   [1626]
500 South Grand Avenue, 19th Floor
Los Angeles, CA 90071
(213) 683-5200
Fax: (213) 627-7795

FOUNDED: 1987

AREAS OF INTEREST:
Education.

TYPE:
Block grants; Capital grants;
Challenge/matching grants; Matching gifts;
Scholarships; Training grants.

YEAR PROGRAM STARTED: 1987

PURPOSE:
To support education in California, with
principle emphasis on legal education.

LEGAL BASIS:
Private foundation.

ELIGIBILITY:
Grants are made only to tax-exempt
501(c)(3) organizations. No grants are made
to individuals.

GEOGRAPHIC RESTRICTIONS:
California.

FINANCIAL DATA:
Amount of support per award: Varies.
Total amount of support: Varies.

NUMBER OF APPLICANTS MOST RECENT YEAR:
100.

NUMBER OF AWARDS: 44 for the year 2013.

REPRESENTATIVE AWARDS:
$125,000 to California Lutheran University;
$10,000 to Los Angeles Mission; $125,000
to UC Davis School of Law.

APPLICATION INFORMATION:
Send letter and literature.
Deadline: Applications accepted throughout
the year.

OFFICERS:
Richard L. Stack, Trustee

ADDRESS INQUIRIES TO:
Richard L. Stack, Trustee
(See address above.)

DELOITTE FOUNDATION   [1627]
10 Westport Road
Wilton, CT 06897
(203) 761-3413
Fax: (203) 423-6413

E-MAIL ADDRESS:
plevine@deloitte.com

WEB SITE ADDRESS:
www.deloitte.com/us/df

FOUNDED: 1928

AREAS OF INTEREST:
Higher education, specializing in accounting
and business.

TYPE:
Conferences/seminars; Fellowships; Matching
gifts; Professorships; Research grants.

YEAR PROGRAM STARTED: 1956

PURPOSE:
To support teaching and research in
accounting, business and related fields.

LEGAL BASIS:
Foundation.

ELIGIBILITY:
Doctoral Fellowship Program applicants must
be doctoral candidates pursuing a Ph.D. in
accounting at U.S. colleges and universities.

GEOGRAPHIC RESTRICTIONS:
United States.

FINANCIAL DATA:
Amount of support per award: Doctoral
Fellowship Program: $25,000.
Total amount of support: Fellowship:
$250,000 each year.

NUMBER OF APPLICANTS MOST RECENT YEAR:
61 for the year 2013.

NUMBER OF AWARDS: Doctoral Fellowship
Program: Up to 10.

APPLICATION INFORMATION:
Application required only for Doctoral
Fellowship Program and can be obtained
through head of university accounting
program. Send letter for other grant requests.
Duration: Doctoral Fellowship Program: Up
to two years.

Deadline: Doctoral Fellowships: October 15. Announcement in January. No deadline for Research Grants.

PUBLICATIONS:
Information brochure.

BOARD OF DIRECTORS:
Punit Renjen, Chairman
Shaun Budnik, President
Jennifer Steinmann, Secretary and Treasurer

ADDRESS INQUIRIES TO:
Peg Levine, Specialist
(See address above.)

HALBERT CENTRE FOR CANADIAN STUDIES [1628]

Canadian Friends of the Hebrew University
3080 Yonge Street, Suite 3020
P.O. Box 65
Toronto ON M4N 3N1 Canada
(416) 485-8000
(888) 432-7398 (Canada only)
Fax: (416) 485-8565

E-MAIL ADDRESS:
inquiry@cfhu.org

WEB SITE ADDRESS:
www.cfhu.org

FOUNDED: 1944

AREAS OF INTEREST:
Canadian studies.

NAME(S) OF PROGRAMS:
● **Halbert Centre for Canadian Studies Visiting Appointment**

TYPE:
Awards/prizes; Research grants; Visiting scholars.

YEAR PROGRAM STARTED: 1945

PURPOSE:
To emphasize the development of joint Israel-Canada research.

LEGAL BASIS:
Nonprofit.

ELIGIBILITY:
Applicants should hold university teaching positions in the social sciences, humanities or law. Applicants will be expected to combine broad teaching and research experience in their field with an ability to emphasize Canadian content. An expression of interest in participating in cooperative work to emphasize the development of joint Israel-Canada research will be of advantage to the applicant.

GEOGRAPHIC RESTRICTIONS:
Canada.

FINANCIAL DATA:
Remuneration includes economy-class return airfare, salary for four, five or nine months (as appropriate) at the rate of the Hebrew University equivalent to Canadian position and other benefits accruing to the position.
Total amount of support: Varies.

NUMBER OF AWARDS: 1.

PUBLICATIONS:
Program announcement.

STAFF:
Rami Kleinmann, National President

ADDRESS INQUIRIES TO:
Merle Goldman, Associate President and Chief Executive Officer
(See address above.)

THE HALLETT CHARITABLE TRUSTS [1629]

P.O. Box 39045
Edina, MN 55439
(952) 946-1229

E-MAIL ADDRESS:
halletttrusts@aol.com

WEB SITE ADDRESS:
www.halletttrusts.org

AREAS OF INTEREST:
Higher education, social services, children's services, health, economic and cultural services.

TYPE:
Project/program grants.

PURPOSE:
To directly impact the population of the community in a manner that will measurably enrich its educational, health, economic and cultural opportunities.

ELIGIBILITY:
Grants are made to organizations that have tax-exempt status under Section 501(c)(3) of the Internal Revenue Code. Nonsectarian religious programs may apply. No grants are made to individuals.

GEOGRAPHIC RESTRICTIONS:
Cuyuna Range area, Minnesota.

APPLICATION INFORMATION:
Minnesota Common Grant application form must be submitted to the address above.
Duration: Two years.
Deadline: October 1.

ADDRESS INQUIRIES TO:
Margaret M. Poley, Executive Director
(See address above.)

HALLIBURTON FOUNDATION, INC. [1630]

10200 Bellaire Boulevard
Houston, TX 77072-5206
(281) 575-3558
Fax: (281) 575-3570

E-MAIL ADDRESS:
brinda.maxwell@halliburton.com

WEB SITE ADDRESS:
www.halliburton.com

AREAS OF INTEREST:
Higher education and elementary/secondary education.

TYPE:
Matching gifts; Project/program grants.

LEGAL BASIS:
Corporate giving program.

ELIGIBILITY:
Applicants should be accredited junior colleges, colleges and universities or accredited elementary/secondary schools. Direct Grants are typically awarded to engineering departments or schools of colleges and universities. Grants include awards for faculty support.

No grants are awarded for building programs, financial assistance to students or support of student activities and organizations.

Grants are by invitation only.

GEOGRAPHIC RESTRICTIONS:
United States.

FINANCIAL DATA:
Amount of support per award: Varies.
Total amount of support: Varies.
Matching fund requirements: Contributions of directors, officers and employees of the Halliburton companies to accredited junior colleges, colleges/universities and elementary/secondary schools are matched 2:1 under certain conditions.

NUMBER OF AWARDS: Over 500.

APPLICATION INFORMATION:
Requests for support should be mailed to the address listed above. Lengthy proposals are not required.
Duration: One year.

PUBLICATIONS:
Guidelines.

ADDRESS INQUIRIES TO:
Brinda Maxwell, Administrator
(See address above.)

THE JOHN RANDOLPH HAYNES AND DORA HAYNES FOUNDATION [1631]

888 West Sixth Street, Suite 1150
Los Angeles, CA 90017-2737
(213) 623-9151
Fax: (213) 623-3951

E-MAIL ADDRESS:
info@haynesfoundation.org

WEB SITE ADDRESS:
www.haynesfoundation.org

FOUNDED: 1926

AREAS OF INTEREST:
Education and research in social sciences.

TYPE:
Fellowships; Research grants.

YEAR PROGRAM STARTED: 1926

PURPOSE:
To strengthen education and research in the social sciences into issues of the Los Angeles region.

LEGAL BASIS:
Independent private foundation.

ELIGIBILITY:
501(c)(3) organizations only.

GEOGRAPHIC RESTRICTIONS:
Los Angeles, California.

FINANCIAL DATA:
Amount of support per award: $5,000 to $400,000.
Total amount of support: Up to $3,000,000.

NUMBER OF APPLICANTS MOST RECENT YEAR: 50.

NUMBER OF AWARDS: 12.

REPRESENTATIVE AWARDS:
$50,000 to Center for the Study of Political Graphics; $30,000 to KPCC Southern California Public Radio; $18,800 to Los Angeles City Historical Society.

APPLICATION INFORMATION:
Application information is available on the web site.
Duration: One to two years.
Deadline: Varies.

PUBLICATIONS:
Annual report.

IRS IDENTIFICATION NUMBER: 95-1644020

BOARD OF TRUSTEES:
Jane G. Pisano, President

ADDRESS INQUIRIES TO:
William J. Burke, Administrative Director
(See address above.)

THE HOROWITZ FOUNDATION FOR SOCIAL POLICY

P.O. Box 7
Rocky Hill, NJ 08553-0007
(732) 445-2280

E-MAIL ADDRESS:
info@horowitz-foundation.org
applications@horowitz-foundation.org

WEB SITE ADDRESS:
www.horowitz-foundation.org

TYPE:
Awards/prizes; Research grants. Grants to doctoral candidates at the dissertation level with emphasis on policy-related studies.

See entry 1855 for full listing.

THE GEORGE A. AND ELIZA GARDNER HOWARD FOUNDATION   [1632]

80 Brown Street
Providence, RI 02912
(401) 863-2640
Fax: (401) 863-6280

E-MAIL ADDRESS:
howard_foundation@brown.edu

WEB SITE ADDRESS:
www.brown.edu/Howard_Foundation

FOUNDED: 1952

TYPE:
Fellowships. The Foundation awards a limited number of fellowships each year for independent projects in fields selected on a rotational basis.

YEAR PROGRAM STARTED: 1952

PURPOSE:
To aid the personal development of promising individuals at the crucial middle stages of their careers.

LEGAL BASIS:
Private foundation.

ELIGIBILITY:
Nominees should normally have the rank of assistant or associate professor or their nonacademic equivalents. Support is intended to augment paid sabbatical leaves, making it financially possible for grantees to have time off in which to pursue their projects, free of any other professional responsibilities. Accepted nominees should therefore be eligible for sabbaticals or other leave with guaranteed additional support.

The project undertaken by a Howard Fellow should also be comprehensible to persons outside the immediate field of specialization. Candidates, regardless of their country of citizenship, must be professionally based in the U.S. either by affiliation with an institution or by residence.

GEOGRAPHIC RESTRICTIONS:
United States.

FINANCIAL DATA:
Amount of support per award: $30,000 for the year 2013-14.
Total amount of support: Approximately $300,000.

NUMBER OF APPLICANTS MOST RECENT YEAR:
100.

NUMBER OF AWARDS: Approximately 10 per year.

APPLICATION INFORMATION:
Application information is available on the web site.
Duration: One academic year, July 1 to June 30.
Deadline: November 1.

ADMINISTRATION:
Christina Paxson, President of the University
Prof. William C. Crossgrove, Administrative Director
Peter Weber, Dean of the Graduate School
William W. Kenyon, Representative of the Trustees to the Board of Administration
Prof. John Bodel
Prof. Mary Clack
Prof. Forrest Gander
Prof. Douglas Nickel

BOARD OF TRUSTEES:
Bradford Gorham
Jane G. Gurzenda
Robert W. Kenyon
William W. Kenyon
Arthur H. Parker

ADDRESS INQUIRIES TO:
Prof. William C. Crossgrove
Administrative Director
George A. and Eliza
Gardner Howard Foundation
Box 1945
Brown University
Providence, RI 02912

THE FLETCHER JONES FOUNDATION   [1633]

117 East Colorado Boulevard
Suite 403
Pasadena, CA 91105
(626) 535-9506
Fax: (626) 535-9508

E-MAIL ADDRESS:
chris@fletcherjonesfdn.org

WEB SITE ADDRESS:
www.fletcherjonesfdn.org

FOUNDED: 1969

AREAS OF INTEREST:
Primarily, support to private independent colleges and universities in California.

TYPE:
Capital grants; Endowments; Fellowships; Grants-in-aid; Internships; Professorships; Project/program grants; Scholarships. Equipment grants. Academic programs.

YEAR PROGRAM STARTED: 1969

PURPOSE:
To assist private higher education in California.

LEGAL BASIS:
Private foundation.

ELIGIBILITY:
Grants are made to nonprofit, 501(c)(3) organizations. 90% of grants are for private colleges and universities in California. Grants are not made to carry on propaganda, to

influence legislation or elections, to promote voter registration, to political candidates, to political campaigns, or to organizations engaged in such activities. Grants are not made to individuals.

The Foundation generally does not favor requests for projects which should be financed by government agencies, nor does it normally make grants to operating funds, elementary or secondary schools, deficit financing, or contingencies.

GEOGRAPHIC RESTRICTIONS:
California.

FINANCIAL DATA:
Amount of support per award: Varies.

NUMBER OF AWARDS: 14 regular grants and 72 Trustee discretionary grants.

REPRESENTATIVE AWARDS:
$1,000,000 to Pomona College; $300,000 to Biola University.

APPLICATION INFORMATION:
A qualified, nonprofit organization which believes it meets the Foundation's criteria for a grant may wish to contact the Executive Director. Link to online application must be provided by the Executive Director after preliminary consultation.
Deadline: Applications are accepted throughout the year and reviewed quarterly.

IRS IDENTIFICATION NUMBER: 23-7030155

OFFICERS:
Peter Barker, President
Samuel P. Bell, Vice President
Patrick C. Haden, Vice President
Parker S. Kennedy, Vice President
Robert W. Kummer, Jr., Vice President
Dan Lungren, Vice President
Donald E. Nickelson, Vice President
Rockwell Schnabel, Vice President
Stewart R. Smith, Vice President
John D. Pettker, Secretary

TRUSTEES:
Peter Barker
Samuel P. Bell
Patrick C. Haden
Parker S. Kennedy
Robert W. Kummer, Jr.
Dan Lungren
Donald E. Nickelson
John D. Pettker
Rockwell Schnabel
Stewart R. Smith

STAFF:
Christine Sisley, Executive Director and Treasurer

ADDRESS INQUIRIES TO:
Christine Sisley
Executive Director and Treasurer
(See address above.)

ALICE AND JULIUS KANTOR CHARITABLE TRUST

809 North Bedford Drive
Beverly Hills, CA 90210
(310) 360-7541
Fax: (310) 360-7580

TYPE:
Development grants; Project/program grants; Research grants.

See entry 181 for full listing.

LUMINA FOUNDATION [1634]
30 South Meridian Street, Suite 700
Indianapolis, IN 46204-3503
(317) 951-5300
(800) 834-5756
Fax: (317) 951-5063

E-MAIL ADDRESS:
newinquiry@luminafoundation.org

WEB SITE ADDRESS:
www.luminafoundation.org

FOUNDED: 2000

AREAS OF INTEREST:
Promoting educational improvements and access. Focus beginning in 2013: Mobilizing to reach Goal 2025 and designing and building a 21st-century higher education system.

TYPE:
Project/program grants. The Foundation has worked with and made grants to many colleges, universities, peer foundations, associations and other organizations that work to improve student access and outcomes across the nation.

PURPOSE:
To help people achieve their potential by expanding access to and success in education beyond high school. Specific goal: To increase the proportion of Americans with high-quality college degrees, certificates and credentials to 60% by 2025.

ELIGIBILITY:
Organizations that are classified as tax-exempt under Section 501(c)(3) of the Internal Revenue Code and as public charities under Section 509(a)(1), (2) or (3) or to public organizations that are designated under Section 170(c) of the Code, not individuals. Grants will not be made to (a) supporting organizations controlled by disqualified persons to Lumina or (b) Type III supporting organizations that are not functionally integrated Type III supporting organizations (as defined in the Internal Revenue Code).

GEOGRAPHIC RESTRICTIONS:
United States and its territories.

FINANCIAL DATA:
Amount of support per award: Average grant amount: $200,000.
Total amount of support: More than $30,000,000 for the year 2012.

APPLICATION INFORMATION:
All unsolicited inquiries should be submitted as formal Letters of Inquiry (LOI) so that Foundation staff may carefully review the request. Preference is submission online. Full information can be found on the web site. Full proposals are by invitation.
Duration: One to three years; grant is not renewable.
Deadline: End of September for Letter of Inquiry.

MONROE-BROWN FOUNDATION [1635]
7950 Moorsbridge Road
Portage, MI 49024
(269) 324-5586
Fax: (269) 324-0686

E-MAIL ADDRESS:
jbaker@monroebrown.org

WEB SITE ADDRESS:
www.monroebrown.org

FOUNDED: 1984

AREAS OF INTEREST:
Higher education and economic development.

TYPE:
Development grants; Internships; Project/program grants; Scholarships.

PURPOSE:
To advance the public well-being through higher education and economic development.

LEGAL BASIS:
Private foundation.

ELIGIBILITY:
Organizations must qualify as a nonprofit under Section 501(c)(3) of the Internal Revenue Code.

GEOGRAPHIC RESTRICTIONS:
Kalamazoo, Michigan.

FINANCIAL DATA:
Amount of support per award: Varies.
Total amount of support: Varies.

APPLICATION INFORMATION:
Application information is available on the web site.
Duration: Varies.
Deadline: March 15, June 15, September 15 and December 15.

ADDRESS INQUIRIES TO:
Jane Baker, Director
(See address above.)

NATIONAL ASSOCIATION OF SCHOLARS [1636]
8 West 38th Street
Suite 503
New York, NY 10018
(917) 551-6770

E-MAIL ADDRESS:
contact@nas.org

WEB SITE ADDRESS:
www.nas.org

NAME(S) OF PROGRAMS:
- **The Barry R. Gross Memorial Award**
- **The Sidney Hook Memorial Award**
- **The Peter Shaw Memorial Award**

TYPE:
Awards/prizes. The Barry R. Gross Memorial Award rewards an NAS member for outstanding service to the cause of academic reform.

The Sidney Hook Memorial Award is given to an individual for distinguished contributions to the defense of academic freedom and the integrity of academic life.

The Peter Shaw Memorial Award recognizes exemplary writing on issues pertaining to higher education and American intellectual culture.

PURPOSE:
To enrich the substance and strengthen the integrity of scholarship and teaching.

ELIGIBILITY:
Candidates must be chosen by the Association.

FINANCIAL DATA:
Amount of support per award: Gross and Shaw Memorial Awards: $1,000; Hook Memorial Award: $2,500; for all three in addition, a plaque and travel expenses to attend the Association's National Conference and present a speech.

NATIONAL WILDLIFE FEDERATION
11100 Wildlife Center Drive
Reston, VA 20190-5362
(703) 438-6265
Fax: (703) 438-6468

E-MAIL ADDRESS:
fellows@nwf.org

WEB SITE ADDRESS:
www.nwf.org

TYPE:
Fellowships.

See entry 2192 for full listing.

SAMUEL ROBERTS NOBLE FOUNDATION, INC. [1637]
2510 Sam Noble Parkway
Ardmore, OK 73402
(580) 223-5810
Fax: (580) 224-6212

E-MAIL ADDRESS:
mkwilson@noble.org

WEB SITE ADDRESS:
www.noble.org

FOUNDED: 1945

AREAS OF INTEREST:
Higher education (primarily in Oklahoma) and health research.

TYPE:
Capital grants; Challenge/matching grants; General operating grants. Focus on capital funding for higher education and on health research and delivery systems.

LEGAL BASIS:
Private foundation.

ELIGIBILITY:
Organizations must be classified as 501(c)(3) by the IRS and are primarily located in Oklahoma. No loans or grants are made to individuals.

GEOGRAPHIC RESTRICTIONS:
Oklahoma.

FINANCIAL DATA:
Amount of support per award: Varies.
Total amount of support: Varies.

NUMBER OF APPLICANTS MOST RECENT YEAR:
136 grant requests for the year 2012.

NUMBER OF AWARDS: 28 grants approved for the year 2012.

APPLICATION INFORMATION:
Applicant organizations must send a letter of request summarizing the project prior to making a formal grant application. This letter should be addressed to Mary Kate Wilson, Director of Granting, at the address above.
Deadline: Letters of inquiry will be accepted until May 30.

IRS IDENTIFICATION NUMBER: 73-0606209

STAFF:
Mary Kate Wilson, Director of Granting
Samantha Ephgrave, Program Associate
Julie Barrick, Project Management Associate

ADDRESS INQUIRIES TO:
Mary Kate Wilson, Director of Granting
(See address above.)

NORTH CAROLINA ASSOCIATION OF EDUCATORS [1638]

NCAE Center for Instructional Advocacy
700 South Salisbury Street
Raleigh, NC 27601
(919) 832-3000 ext. 227
(800) 662-7924 ext. 227
Fax: (919) 829-1626

E-MAIL ADDRESS:
elic.senter@ncae.org

WEB SITE ADDRESS:
www.ncae.org

FOUNDED: 1970

AREAS OF INTEREST:
Teaching.

NAME(S) OF PROGRAMS:
● **Mary Morrow/Edna Richards Scholarship Fund**

TYPE:
Scholarships. To be used for college expenses in senior year.

YEAR PROGRAM STARTED: 1994

PURPOSE:
To aid worthy students who plan to teach in North Carolina after graduation.

LEGAL BASIS:
Nonprofit organization.

ELIGIBILITY:
The applicant must be in their junior year in a North Carolina college or university, planning to teach and willing to teach in the public schools of North Carolina for at least two years following graduation. Selection is based on character, personality, scholastic achievement, evidence of promise as a teacher and financial need.

GEOGRAPHIC RESTRICTIONS:
North Carolina.

FINANCIAL DATA:
Amount of support per award: $1,000 per year.
Total amount of support: Varies.

NUMBER OF APPLICANTS MOST RECENT YEAR:
Varies.

NUMBER OF AWARDS: Varies.

APPLICATION INFORMATION:
Application forms are mailed in Fall to the heads of the department of education in colleges in North Carolina, both state-supported and private. The department head is requested to give the application forms to two juniors of his or her selection.
Duration: One year.
Deadline: January 30 (postmark).

STAFF:
Elic A. Senter, Manager

ADDRESS INQUIRIES TO:
Elic A. Senter, Manager
NCAE Center for Instructional Advocacy
P.O. Box 27347
Raleigh, NC 27611
(See e-mail address above.)

PACIFIC FOUNDATION SERVICES [1639]

1660 Bush Street, Suite 300
San Francisco, CA 94109
(415) 561-6540
Fax: (415) 561-6477

WEB SITE ADDRESS:
www.pfs-llc.net

FOUNDED: 1984

AREAS OF INTEREST:
Minority education.

TYPE:
Challenge/matching grants; Demonstration grants; Project/program grants; Seed money grants.

YEAR PROGRAM STARTED: 1984

PURPOSE:
To support higher education, particularly within the minority and underprivileged community.

ELIGIBILITY:
Funding is available for eligible organizations who are IRS 501(c)(3) tax-exempt.

GEOGRAPHIC RESTRICTIONS:
San Francisco Bay area, California.

FINANCIAL DATA:
Amount of support per award: $10,000 to $25,000.
Total amount of support: $176,000.
Matching fund requirements: Generally 1:1.

NUMBER OF AWARDS: 10 to 12.

APPLICATION INFORMATION:
Guidelines are available on the Foundation web site.
Duration: Multiyear funding is subject to review.
Deadline: April 15 and October 15.

IRS IDENTIFICATION NUMBER: 94-2955164

ADDRESS INQUIRIES TO:
Hector Melendez, Managing Director
(See address above.)

RADCLIFFE INSTITUTE FOR ADVANCED STUDY, HARVARD UNIVERSITY [1640]

Radcliffe Institute Fellowship Program
Byerly Hall
8 Garden Street
Cambridge, MA 02138
(617) 496-1324
Fax: (617) 495-8136

E-MAIL ADDRESS:
fellowships@radcliffe.harvard.edu

WEB SITE ADDRESS:
www.radcliffe.harvard.edu/fellowship-program/how-apply

FOUNDED: 1960

NAME(S) OF PROGRAMS:
● **Radcliffe Institute Fellowship Program**

TYPE:
Fellowships. The Radcliffe Institute for Advanced Study is a scholarly community where individuals pursue advanced work across a wide range of academic disciplines, professions or creative arts. Within this broad purpose, and in recognition of Radcliffe's historic contributions to the education of women and to the study of issues related to women, the Radcliffe Institute sustains a continuing commitment to the study of women, gender and society, although applicants' projects need not focus on gender.

Radcliffe Institute Fellowships are designed to support scholars, scientists, artists and writers of exceptional promise and demonstrated accomplishment who wish to pursue independent work in academic and professional fields, and in the creative arts.

YEAR PROGRAM STARTED: 1961

PURPOSE:
To offer support to The Radcliffe Institute for Advanced Study Fellowship programs for a scholarly community where individuals pursue advanced work across a wide range of academic disciplines, professions and creative arts.

LEGAL BASIS:
Department of Harvard University, nonprofit.

ELIGIBILITY:
For all programs, residence in the Boston area and participation in the Institute community are required during the fellowship appointment.

GEOGRAPHIC RESTRICTIONS:
Boston and Cambridge, Massachusetts.

FINANCIAL DATA:
Additional funds provided for project expenses. Some support for relocation expenses provided when relevant. If so directed, Radcliffe will pay stipend to home institution.
Amount of support per award: Stipends up to $70,000 for one year.
Total amount of support: Varies.

NUMBER OF APPLICANTS MOST RECENT YEAR:
Over 1,000.

NUMBER OF AWARDS: Up to 50 fellowships.

APPLICATION INFORMATION:
Applications are available online in late Spring.
Duration: September 1 to May 31.
Deadline: October 1. For scientists: November 1.

ADDRESS INQUIRIES TO:
See e-mail address above.

*SPECIAL STIPULATIONS:
Fellows are expected to present their work-in-progress and to attend other fellows' events.

THE NELL J. REDFIELD FOUNDATION

P.O. Box 61
Reno, NV 89504
(775) 323-1373
Fax: (775) 323-4476

E-MAIL ADDRESS:
redfieldfoundation@yahoo.com

TYPE:
Capital grants; Challenge/matching grants; Development grants; Matching gifts; Project/program grants. Grants for higher education. Medical and social welfare for disadvantaged children and seniors.

See entry 275 for full listing.

GERTRUDE E. SKELLY CHARITABLE FOUNDATION [1641]

4600 North Ocean Boulevard
Suite 206
Boynton Beach, FL 33435
(561) 276-1008
Fax: (561) 272-2793

E-MAIL ADDRESS:
skelly@hhk.com

FOUNDED: 1991

AREAS OF INTEREST:
Nursing education and medical care for indigents.

TYPE:
Challenge/matching grants; Conferences/seminars; Internships; Project/program grants; Research grants; Scholarships; Training grants. Emergency grants for continued education.

YEAR PROGRAM STARTED: 1991

PURPOSE:
To provide scholarships for individuals to obtain educational opportunities and/or medical care.

LEGAL BASIS:
Private foundation.

ELIGIBILITY:
Eligible applicants are colleges and universities, and other IRS 501(c)(3) tax-exempt organizations. No grants are given to agencies which do not provide direct services or scholarships.

GEOGRAPHIC RESTRICTIONS:
United States.

FINANCIAL DATA:
Amount of support per award: Up to $50,000.
Total amount of support: $750,000 for the year 2013.
Matching fund requirements: Tailored to specific projects.

NUMBER OF APPLICANTS MOST RECENT YEAR: 85.

NUMBER OF AWARDS: 50.

APPLICATION INFORMATION:
Write to the address above for application guidelines.
Duration: One year.
Deadline: June 30. Award announcement the following January.

TRUSTEES:
Erik Edward Joh

ADDRESS INQUIRIES TO:
Erik Edward Joh, Trustee
(See address above.)

TARAKNATH DAS FOUNDATION [1642]
South Asia Institute
Columbia University
606 West 122nd Street, Room 213
New York, NY 10027
(212) 666-4282

WEB SITE ADDRESS:
www.columbia.edu/cu/sai/tdas.html

FOUNDED: 1930

AREAS OF INTEREST:
Indian national graduate students studying any field in a U.S. university.

TYPE:
Grants-in-aid.

YEAR PROGRAM STARTED: 1935

PURPOSE:
To promote friendly relations and cultural cooperation between the U.S. and India.

LEGAL BASIS:
Special interest foundation.

ELIGIBILITY:
Applicants are not limited by discipline or subject area. Applicants must be Indian

nationals (holding Indian passports) and must have completed at least one year of graduate study in the U.S.

FINANCIAL DATA:
Amount of support per award: $4,000 to $6,000.
Total amount of support: Approximately $25,000.

NUMBER OF APPLICANTS MOST RECENT YEAR: 20.

NUMBER OF AWARDS: About 4 annually.

APPLICATION INFORMATION:
Applicants must submit all application materials together. Only complete applications will be judged for the awards. Complete applications include:
(1) completed application form;
(2) transcript from most recent academic institution;
(3) three sealed letters of recommendation, including one from the applicant's academic advisor;
(4) academic plans of applicant and;
(5) photocopy of applicant's passport.
Duration: One year.
Deadline: August 1. Award announcement in late October.

ADDRESS INQUIRIES TO:
Leonard Gordon, Director
(See address above.)

U.S. DEPARTMENT OF EDUCATION
International Education Programs Service
1990 K Street, N.W.
Washington, DC 20006
(202) 502-7626
Fax: (202) 502-7859

WEB SITE ADDRESS:
www.ed.gov

TYPE:
Conferences/seminars; Demonstration grants; Development grants; Project/program grants; Research grants; Seed money grants; Training grants; Travel grants. The program assists institutions of higher learning in:
(1) innovation and improvement of international education curricula to serve the needs of the business community, including the development of new programs for nontraditional, midcareer or part-time students;
(2) development of programs to inform the public of increasing international economic interdependence and the role of U.S. business within the international economic system;
(3) internationalization of curricula at junior and community colleges, and at undergraduate and graduate schools of business;
(4) development of area studies programs and interdisciplinary international programs;
(5) establishment of export education programs through cooperative arrangements with regional and world trade centers and councils and with bilateral and multilateral trade associations;
(6) research for and development of teaching materials relating to international education, including language materials and facilities appropriate to business-oriented students;
(7) establishment of student and faculty fellowships and internships for training and education in international business activities;
(8) development of opportunities for business and other professional school junior faculty

to acquire or strengthen international skills and perspectives and;
(9) development of research programs on issues of common interest to institutions of higher education and private-sector organizations and associations engaged in promoting international economic activity.
See entry 1915 for full listing.

U.S. DEPARTMENT OF EDUCATION
Centers for International Business Education
1990 K Street, N.W., 6th Floor
Washington, DC 20006-8521
(202) 502-7622
Fax: (202) 502-7858

E-MAIL ADDRESS:
timothy.duvall@ed.gov

WEB SITE ADDRESS:
www2.ed.gov/programs/iegpscibe/index.html

TYPE:
Project/program grants. The program provides grants to eligible institutions of higher education or combinations of these institutions for planning, establishing and operating Centers for International Business Education.
See entry 1916 for full listing.

U.S. DEPARTMENT OF EDUCATION [1643]
Office of Postsecondary Education
TRIO Programs
1990 K Street, N.W., Room 7035
Washington, DC 20006
(202) 502-7586

E-MAIL ADDRESS:
OPE_TRIO@ed.gov

WEB SITE ADDRESS:
www.ed.gov/ope/trio

AREAS OF INTEREST:
Education for low-income youth.

NAME(S) OF PROGRAMS:
● **Upward Bound**

TYPE:
Project/program grants. There are three types of grants under the Upward Bound program: Regular Upward Bound Grants; Veterans Upward Bound Grants; and Upward Bound Math and Science Grants.

The Regular Upward Bound projects are designed to generate in participants the skills and motivation necessary for success in education beyond secondary school. The Veterans Upward Bound projects are designed to assist veterans in preparing for a program of postsecondary education. The Upward Bound Math and Science projects are designed to prepare high school students for postsecondary education programs that lead to careers in the fields of math and science.

YEAR PROGRAM STARTED: 1966

PURPOSE:
To generate participation skills and the motivation necessary for success in education beyond school.

LEGAL BASIS:
Title IV of the Higher Education Act of 1965, as amended.

GEOGRAPHIC RESTRICTIONS:
United States.

FINANCIAL DATA:

Amount of support per award: Estimated - Regular Upward Bound: $250,000 to $853,000 for year one. Average $350,000; Veterans Upward Bound: $250,000 to $543,000 for year one. Average $300,000; Upward Bound Math and Science: $250,000 to $354,000 for year one. Average $270,000.

NUMBER OF APPLICANTS MOST RECENT YEAR: 1,148.

NUMBER OF AWARDS: 791. Upward Bound Award for Math and Science: 130.

APPLICATION INFORMATION:
Official application materials are available from the address above.

Duration: Project periods of up to 60 months.

ADDRESS INQUIRIES TO:
Kenneth Waters, Program Specialist (See address above.)

U.S. DEPARTMENT OF EDUCATION   [1644]
International and Foreign Language Education Office
1990 K Street, N.W., Sixth Floor
Washington, DC 20006-8521
(202) 502-7626
Fax: (202) 502-7860

E-MAIL ADDRESS:
tanyelle.richardson@ed.gov

WEB SITE ADDRESS:
www.ed.gov/ope/iegps

NAME(S) OF PROGRAMS:
● **Undergraduate International Studies and Foreign Language Program**

TYPE:
Project/program grants; Seed money grants. Grants to plan, develop, and carry out a program to strengthen and improve undergraduate instruction in international studies and foreign languages. Projects primarily focus on curriculum and faculty development. Institutions of higher education and public and private nonprofit agencies and organizations may apply for funds to develop projects which have the potential for making an especially significant contribution to the improvement of undergraduate instruction in international and foreign language studies in the U.S.

YEAR PROGRAM STARTED: 1972

PURPOSE:
To assist institutions to internationalize the curriculum. Applicants may propose to initiate a global studies program or a program focusing on a single world area and its languages; to develop a program which focuses on issues or topics, such as environmental studies or international business; to combine the teaching of international studies with professional or preprofessional training; to integrate undergraduate studies with Master's degree programs; to combine international studies with teacher training programs.

LEGAL BASIS:
Title VI, section 604A, Higher Education Act, as amended in 1986.

ELIGIBILITY:
Proposals are invited from institutions of higher education, including universities and two- to four-year colleges, and consortia of such institutions. The proposed program should include plans to initiate new or revised courses in international studies or area studies, and to improve or expand instruction in foreign languages. The program should be comparative or interdisciplinary in nature and strengthen linkages among disciplines and professional fields.

GEOGRAPHIC RESTRICTIONS:
United States.

FINANCIAL DATA:
Amount of support per award: Single Institutions: Average $89,000 per year; Organizations, Associations and Institutional Consortia: Average $140,000 per year.

Total amount of support: $2,900,000 available for fiscal year 2014.

Matching fund requirements: Dollar-for-dollar primarily within in-kind contributions.

NUMBER OF APPLICANTS MOST RECENT YEAR: 92.

NUMBER OF AWARDS: Approximately 30.

APPLICATION INFORMATION:
Applications are required to be submitted electronically using the grants.gov system.

Duration: Single Institutions: Up to two years; Organizations, Associations and Institutional Consortia: Up to three years.

Deadline: Midsummer.

STAFF:
Tanyelle Richardson, Senior Program Officer

ADDRESS INQUIRIES TO:
Tanyelle Richardson, Senior Program Officer (See address above.)

*PLEASE NOTE:
Request program materials and project abstracts at the web site. If there are additional questions after consulting web site, call (202) 502-7626.

UCLA INSTITUTE OF AMERICAN CULTURES (IAC)
2329 Murphy Hall, Box 957244
Los Angeles, CA 90095-7244
(310) 825-6815
Fax: (310) 825-3994

E-MAIL ADDRESS:
iaccoordinator@conet.ucla.edu

WEB SITE ADDRESS:
www.iac.ucla.edu

TYPE:
Fellowships. Deals with arts and humanities, education and teacher training, fine arts, applied arts, law, social sciences, and sciences. The IAC, in cooperation with UCLA's four Ethnic Studies Research Centers (American Indian Studies Center, Asian American Studies Center, Bunche Center for African American Studies, and Chicano Studies Research Center), offers awards to visiting scholars to support research on African Americans, American Indians, Asian Americans and Chicanas/os.

See entry 1018 for full listing.

THE UNIVERSITY OF CALGARY   [1645]
Faculty of Graduate Studies
MacKimmie Library Tower, Room 213
2500 University Drive, N.W.
Calgary AB T2N 1N4 Canada
(403) 220-4938
Fax: (403) 289-7635

E-MAIL ADDRESS:
gsaward@ucalgary.ca

WEB SITE ADDRESS:
www.grad.ucalgary.ca

AREAS OF INTEREST:
Management.

NAME(S) OF PROGRAMS:
● **Robert A.Willson Doctoral Management Scholarship**

TYPE:
Awards/prizes; Scholarships.

PURPOSE:
To produce a noteworthy leader in management teaching and research who has a broad appreciation of management's role in society, both nationally and internationally.

ELIGIBILITY:
Open to candidates who, at the time of tenure, are registered in a full-time program leading to a doctoral degree in Management at the University of Calgary. While academic excellence is essential, candidates should also present evidence of leadership in their academic or professional background. Students with international experience and orientation will be particularly considered.

FINANCIAL DATA:
Amount of support per award: $8,000.
Total amount of support: $8,000.

COOPERATIVE FUNDING PROGRAMS: The donor of this scholarship program is the Haskayne School of Business.

NUMBER OF AWARDS: 1 per annum.

APPLICATION INFORMATION:
No application is required. The Haskayne School of Business will recommend a recipient on the basis of academic and professional leadership. The Graduate Coordinator will submit recommendations to the Graduate Scholarship Office. The recommendation is subject to final approval of the Graduate Scholarship Committee.

Duration: One year.
Deadline: May 15.

PUBLICATIONS:
Academic calendar.

ADDRESS INQUIRIES TO:
Graduate Scholarship Office (See address above.)

UNIVERSITY OF CALIFORNIA
President's Postdoctoral Fellowship Program
102 California Hall
UC Berkeley
Berkeley, CA 94720-1508
(510) 643-8235

E-MAIL ADDRESS:
ppfpinfo@berkeley.edu

WEB SITE ADDRESS:
ppfp.ucop.edu/info

TYPE:
Fellowships. Awarded for research conducted under faculty sponsorship on any one of the University of California's 10 campuses.

See entry 1020 for full listing.

UNIVERSITY OF TEXAS AT AUSTIN   [1646]
LBJ School of Public Affairs
P.O. Box Y
Austin, TX 78713-8925
(512) 471-4292
Fax: (512) 471-8455

E-MAIL ADDRESS:
lbjadmit@mail.utexas.edu

WEB SITE ADDRESS:
www.utexas.edu/lbj

AREAS OF INTEREST:
Public policy.

NAME(S) OF PROGRAMS:
• **Lyndon B. Johnson School of Public Affairs**

TYPE:
Assistantships; Fellowships. Merit fellowships are available to assist graduate students with financial support for education at the Master's and doctoral level.

ELIGIBILITY:
Applicants must be graduate students enrolled in Lyndon B. Johnson School of Public Affairs.

FINANCIAL DATA:
Amount of support per award: $4,000 to $50,000.

NUMBER OF AWARDS: 150.

APPLICATION INFORMATION:
Contact the University for application procedures.
Duration: One to two years. Grants not renewable.
Deadline: January 5.

ADDRESS INQUIRIES TO:
Office of Student Affairs and Programs (See address above.)

THE WABASH CENTER FOR TEACHING AND LEARNING IN THEOLOGY AND RELIGION

301 West Wabash Avenue
Crawfordsville, IN 47933
(765) 361-6047
Fax: (765) 361-6051

E-MAIL ADDRESS:
wabashcenter@wabash.edu

WEB SITE ADDRESS:
www.wabashcenter.wabash.edu

TYPE:
Conferences/seminars; Fellowships; Project/program grants; Research grants.

See entry 827 for full listing.

JEANNETTE K. WATSON FELLOWSHIP [1647]

11 Park Place, Suite 1503
New York, NY 10007
(212) 655-0201
Fax: (212) 843-0370

E-MAIL ADDRESS:
ckasabach@tjwf.org

WEB SITE ADDRESS:
www.jkwatson.org

TYPE:
Fellowships. The program offers 15 students each year, from 12 New York City colleges, the opportunity for paid internships for three consecutive summers. The internships offer closely supervised, challenging work from which the student can learn. The expectation is that three summers in different sectors (nonprofit organizations, public service and for-profit firms) in New York City and overseas will make fellows more compelling candidates for national fellowships, graduate admissions and good jobs.

YEAR PROGRAM STARTED: 2000

PURPOSE:
To develop talent, leadership and motivation for service.

ELIGIBILITY:
Applicant must:
(1) be enrolled at one of the invited colleges (Baruch College, Brooklyn College, City College, College of Staten Island, Hunter College, John Jay College, Lehman College, Long Island University-Brooklyn Campus, Marymount Manhattan College, Pace University-Manhattan Campus, Queens College, and St. John's University);
(2) be a second-semester freshman or a sophomore;
(3) not be older than 25 on March 1 of application year;
(4) be enrolled in a liberal arts program;
(5) be a U.S. citizen or a "green card" holder and;
(6) be willing to participate in three successive summer internships and their collateral summer and term-time seminars.

FINANCIAL DATA:
Amount of support per award: $5,000 for the first summer; $6,000 for each of the second and third summers.
Total amount of support: $255,000 annually.

APPLICATION INFORMATION:
Application information is available on the web site.
Duration: Three consecutive summer internships of 10 weeks plus year-round activities.
Deadline: February.

STAFF:
Chris Kasabach, Foundation Director
Jennifer Betancourt, Associate Director

THOMAS J. WATSON FELLOWSHIP PROGRAM [1648]

11 Park Place, Suite 1503
New York, NY 10017
(212) 245-8859
Fax: (212) 245-8860

E-MAIL ADDRESS:
tjw@tjwf.org

WEB SITE ADDRESS:
watsonfellowship.org

FOUNDED: 1968

AREAS OF INTEREST:
Independent study outside of the U.S. for graduating college seniors.

TYPE:
Fellowships. The Foundation provides Fellows an opportunity for a focused and disciplined "Wanderjahr" of their own devising or design-time in which to explore with thoroughness a particular interest, test their aspirations and abilities, view their lives and American society in greater perspective and concomitantly, to develop a more informed sense of international concern. The Fellowship experience is intended to provide Fellows an opportunity to immerse themselves in cultures other than their own for an entire year. The candidate's proposed project should involve investigation into an area of demonstrated concern and personal interest.

YEAR PROGRAM STARTED: 1968

PURPOSE:
To give exceptional college graduates the freedom to engage in a year of independent study, purposeful exploration and travel outside of the U.S. in order to enhance their capacity for resourcefulness, imagination, openness and leadership, and to foster their humane and effective participation in the world community.

LEGAL BASIS:
Private foundation.

ELIGIBILITY:
The Foundation welcomes applicants from a diverse range of backgrounds and academic disciplines. Only graduating seniors at participating institutions are eligible for nomination by their institution.

GEOGRAPHIC RESTRICTIONS:
United States.

FINANCIAL DATA:
Amount of support per award: $25,000 for single fellow; up to $35,000 if accompanied by a legal dependent.
Total amount of support: Varies.

NUMBER OF APPLICANTS MOST RECENT YEAR:
180.

NUMBER OF AWARDS: 40 each year.

APPLICATION INFORMATION:
Students must first be nominated by their college or university, and then compete on a national level. Application form required.
Duration: One year.
Deadline: Nominations and nominees' completed applications should arrive by first Tuesday in November. Announcement made in mid-March.

PUBLICATIONS:
Guidelines.

IRS IDENTIFICATION NUMBER: 13-6038151

STAFF:
Jennifer Ludovici, Assistant Director
Michele Amar, Project Manager

*SPECIAL STIPULATIONS:
All Fellows are required to maintain contact with the fellowship office during their year abroad. In addition to quarterly progress reports, they must submit a final evaluation of the Fellowship year together with a financial accounting of the expenditure of Fellowship funds. The Fellowship is taxable and must be reported by recipients as income. Taxes are not withheld by the Foundation.

TODD WEHR FOUNDATION [1649]

555 East Wells Street
Suite 1900
Milwaukee, WI 53202-3819
(414) 273-2100
Fax: (414) 223-5000

FOUNDED: 1954

AREAS OF INTEREST:
Education and inner-city Milwaukee capital projects for the benefit of children.

TYPE:
Capital grants.

ELIGIBILITY:
Organizations must have 501(c)(3) tax-exempt status. No grants to individuals.

GEOGRAPHIC RESTRICTIONS:
Wisconsin, with emphasis on Milwaukee.

FINANCIAL DATA:
  Amount of support per award: $10,000 to
  $50,000.

NUMBER OF AWARDS: 1 to 10.

APPLICATION INFORMATION:
  Send brief letter of inquiry along with full
  proposal.
  Duration: One to 10 years.
  Deadline: Applications accepted throughout
  the year.

ADDRESS INQUIRIES TO:
  Allan E. Iding, President
  (See address above.)

Scholar aid programs (all disciplines)

ALABAMA COMMISSION ON HIGHER EDUCATION   [1650]
100 North Union Street
Montgomery, AL 36104-3702
(334) 242-2273
Fax: (334) 242-2269

E-MAIL ADDRESS:
  cheryl.newton@ache.alabama.gov

WEB SITE ADDRESS:
  www.ache.alabama.gov

FOUNDED: 1977

AREAS OF INTEREST:
  Continuing higher education.

NAME(S) OF PROGRAMS:
  ● Senior Adult Scholarship Program

TYPE:
  Grants-in-aid; Scholarships. A free tuition
  program for senior citizens who meet the
  admission requirements.

ELIGIBILITY:
  Alabama residents who are 60 years of age
  or older and who attend public two-year
  postsecondary educational institutions in
  Alabama are eligible to apply.

GEOGRAPHIC RESTRICTIONS:
  Alabama.

APPLICATION INFORMATION:
  Applications can be obtained by contacting
  the financial aid office at any public two-year
  postsecondary educational institution in
  Alabama.

ADDRESS INQUIRIES TO:
  Cheryl B. Newton, Grants Coordinator
  (See address above.)

ALABAMA COMMISSION ON HIGHER EDUCATION   [1651]
100 North Union Street
Montgomery, AL 36104-3702
(334) 242-2273
Fax: (334) 242-2269

E-MAIL ADDRESS:
  cheryl.newton@ache.alabama.gov

WEB SITE ADDRESS:
  www.ache.alabama.gov

FOUNDED: 1977

AREAS OF INTEREST:
  Higher education.

NAME(S) OF PROGRAMS:
  ● Alabama National Guard Educational
    Assistance Program

TYPE:
  Awards/prizes. An award to be used for
  tuition, educational fees and books/supplies
  for Alabama National Guard members to
  attend a public or private postsecondary
  educational institution in Alabama.

YEAR PROGRAM STARTED: 1984

ELIGIBILITY:
  Students who are active members in good
  standing with a federally recognized unit of
  the Alabama National Guard are eligible to
  apply. Participants may receive federal
  veterans benefits, but must show a
  cost-less-aid amount of at least $25. Awards
  are based on need.

GEOGRAPHIC RESTRICTIONS:
  Alabama.

FINANCIAL DATA:
  Amount of support per award: Awards are
  limited to $500 per term and no more than
  $1,000 per year.

NUMBER OF AWARDS: 552 for the year 2012-13.

APPLICATION INFORMATION:
  Application forms are available from
  Alabama National Guard Units. Funds are
  limited, so students who are Guard members
  are encouraged to apply early. Forms must be
  signed by a representative of the Alabama
  Military Department and the financial aid
  officer at the college or university the student
  plans to attend.

ADDRESS INQUIRIES TO:
  Cheryl B. Newton, Grants Coordinator
  (See address above.)

ALABAMA COMMISSION ON HIGHER EDUCATION   [1652]
100 North Union Street
Montgomery, AL 36104-3702
(334) 242-2273
Fax: (334) 242-2269

E-MAIL ADDRESS:
  cheryl.newton@ache.alabama.gov

WEB SITE ADDRESS:
  www.ache.alabama.gov

FOUNDED: 1977

AREAS OF INTEREST:
  Higher education.

NAME(S) OF PROGRAMS:
  ● Alabama Student Assistance Program
  ● Alabama Student Grant Program

TYPE:
  Awards/prizes; Grants-in-aid; Scholarships.
  The Alabama Student Assistance Program is a
  need-based, state grant. Awards are limited
  to undergraduate work.

  The Alabama Student Grant Program is an
  award of grant assistance at an eligible
  independent Alabama college or university.
  Award is not based on need. Maximum
  amount available only when sufficient funds
  are available.

ELIGIBILITY:
  Applicants for the Alabama Student
  Assistance Program must be undergraduate
  students who are Alabama residents attending
  eligible Alabama institutions. 55 Alabama
  institutions participate in the program.

  Applicants for the Alabama Student Grant
  Program must be undergraduate students
  either half-time or full-time who are Alabama
  residents attending Amridge University,
  Birmingham-Southern College, Concordia
  College, Faulkner University, Huntington
  College, Judson College, Miles College,
  Oakwood College, Samford University, South
  University, Spring Hill College, Stillman
  College, U.S. Sports Academy or the
  University of Mobile.

GEOGRAPHIC RESTRICTIONS:
  Alabama.

FINANCIAL DATA:
  Amount of support per award: Student
  Assistance Program: $300 to $5,000; Student
  Grant Program: Up to $1,200.
  Total amount of support: ASAP: $2,972,568;
  ASGP: $1,588,330 for the year 2012-13.

NUMBER OF AWARDS: ASAP: 4,544; ASGP:
  5,585 for the year 2012-13.

APPLICATION INFORMATION:
  Application forms are available at the
  institution that the applicant is planning on
  attending.

ADDRESS INQUIRIES TO:
  Cheryl B. Newton, Grants Coordinator
  (See address above.)

THE ISABEL ALLENDE FOUNDATION   [1653]
116 Caledonia Street
Sausalito, CA 94965
(415) 289-0992
Fax: (415) 332-4149

E-MAIL ADDRESS:
  lori@isabelallendefoundation.org

WEB SITE ADDRESS:
  www.isabelallendefoundation.org

FOUNDED: 1996

NAME(S) OF PROGRAMS:
  ● Paula Scholarships

TYPE:
  Scholarships.

PURPOSE:
  To help dedicated individuals pursue their
  educational dreams.

ELIGIBILITY:
  Selected male and female students who
  would otherwise be unable to afford their
  education. Applicants must be U.S. citizens
  or residents. Students from all races and
  religions are eligible.

GEOGRAPHIC RESTRICTIONS:
  Marin County, California.

FINANCIAL DATA:
  Amount of support per award: $2,000 to
  $5,000.
  Total amount of support: Approximately
  $30,000.

APPLICATION INFORMATION:
  Unsolicited requests are not accepted.
  Applications must be made through 10,000
  Degrees Education Fund.
  Duration: One year.

ADDRESS INQUIRIES TO:
  Lori Barra, Executive Director
  (See address above.)

AMERICAN ASSOCIATION OF UNIVERSITY WOMEN

P.O. Box 4030
Iowa City, IA 52243-4030
(319) 337-1716
(800) 326-2289
Fax: (319) 337-1204

E-MAIL ADDRESS:
aauw@act.org

WEB SITE ADDRESS:
www.aauw.org

TYPE:
Fellowships. Awarded to women who are U.S. citizens or permanent residents and who intend to pursue a full-time course of study (during the fellowship year) in designated degree programs where women's participation has been traditionally low.

See entry 1071 for full listing.

AMERICAN COLLEGE OF MEDICAL PRACTICE EXECUTIVES   [1654]

104 Inverness Terrace East
Englewood, CO 80112-5306
(303) 799-1111 ext. 1259
Fax: (303) 784-6098

E-MAIL ADDRESS:
acmpe@mgma.com

WEB SITE ADDRESS:
www.mgma.com

FOUNDED: 1956

AREAS OF INTEREST:
Medical practice management.

TYPE:
Scholarships. Undergraduate and/or Graduate Scholarships are for individuals pursuing a degree relevant to medical practice management at accredited universities and colleges.

PURPOSE:
To support the continuous personal development of professionals in medical practice management through education and credentialing.

ELIGIBILITY:
Scholarships are available to individuals in graduate or undergraduate programs in health care administration. Preference in the selection of all scholarship recipients is given to individuals who either by past experience, current position, or future plans, demonstrate potential for contributing to the medical practice management profession. Applicants must be enrolled for the fall semester in which the award is made. The scholarship program is not intended to support clinical professions such as medicine, nursing, or physical therapy.

FINANCIAL DATA:
Amount of support per award: $1,000 to $5,000.
Total amount of support: Up to $45,000 per year.

NUMBER OF APPLICANTS MOST RECENT YEAR: 150 for the year 2011.

NUMBER OF AWARDS: 14 for the year 2011.

APPLICATION INFORMATION:
Applicants must apply online.
Duration: Varies.
Deadline: May 1.

ADDRESS INQUIRIES TO:
International Scholarship and Tuition Services, Inc.
Tel: (800) 310-4053 or

ACMPE Scholarship Fund, Inc.
Tel: (877) 275-6462 ext. 1205

AMERICAN COUNCIL FOR POLISH CULTURE (ACPC) [1655]

812 Lombard Street, No. 12
Philadelphia, PA 19147-1308
(215) 627-1391

E-MAIL ADDRESS:
dziecko2@comcast.net

WEB SITE ADDRESS:
www.polishcultureacpc.org

NAME(S) OF PROGRAMS:
- **ACPC Scholarship, Summer Studies in Poland**
- **Pulaski Scholarships for Advanced Studies**
- **Louis and Nellie Skalny Scholarships for Polish Studies**

TYPE:
Scholarships.

ELIGIBILITY:
ACPC Scholarship, Summer Studies in Poland: American of Polish descent entering junior or senior year at accredited college or university. Must have an ACPC affiliation.

Pulaski Scholarships for Advanced Studies: Applicant must be of Polish heritage and have completed at least two years in advanced studies at a U.S. university.

Skalny Scholarships for Polish Studies: Intended for students pursuing some Polish studies (major may be in other fields) at universities in the U.S. who have completed at least two years of college or university work. Scholarships awarded for the fall term.

FINANCIAL DATA:
Amount of support per award: ACPC Scholarship, Summer Studies in Poland: $2,000 toward transportation and tuition. Pulaski Scholarships for Advanced Studies: $5,000. Skalny Scholarships for Polish Studies: $3,000.

APPLICATION INFORMATION:
Instructions and application form, if required, are available online.
Deadline: ACPC Scholarship, Summer Studies in Poland: April 1. Pulaski Scholarships for Advanced Studies: March 15. Skalny Scholarships for Polish Studies: May 15.

ADMINISTRATION:
Deborah M. Majka, President

ADDRESS INQUIRIES TO:
ACPC Scholarship, Summer Studies in Poland: Camille Kopielski
Tel: (847) 394-2520.

Pulaski Scholarships for Advanced Studies: Mr. Marion W. Winters
Tel: (508) 949-0160
E-mail: mvwinters@charter.net.

Skalny Scholarships for Polish Studies: Deborah M. Majka
(See phone number and e-mail address above.)

AMERICAN COUNCIL OF THE BLIND   [1656]

2200 Wilson Boulevard, Suite 650
Arlington, VA 22201
(202) 467-5081
(800) 424-8666
Fax: (703) 465-5085

E-MAIL ADDRESS:
info@acb.org

WEB SITE ADDRESS:
www.acb.org

FOUNDED: 1961

AREAS OF INTEREST:
The needs, interests and concerns of blind and visually impaired people on the local, state and national level.

CONSULTING OR VOLUNTEER SERVICES:
The Council offers the following services: (1) information and referral on all aspects of blindness; (2) legal consultation and representation; (3) support to consumer advocates working on issues related to visual handicaps; (4) assistance in chapter development; (5) assistance in program development; (6) employment opportunities information; (7) speaker referral; (8) monitoring of existing service delivery systems, with advocacy for improvement when necessary; (9) representation on boards and advisory committees, both governmental and private; (10) consultation and assistance in technological research and; (11) national legislative hotline.

NAME(S) OF PROGRAMS:
- **American Council of the Blind Scholarships**

TYPE:
Assistantships; Awards/prizes; Internships; Scholarships. Scholarships for outstanding blind students enrolled in academic, vocational, technical or professional training programs beyond the high school level.

YEAR PROGRAM STARTED: 1982

PURPOSE:
To assist blind postsecondary students with educational expenses.

LEGAL BASIS:
Nonprofit membership organization.

ELIGIBILITY:
Applicants must be legally blind persons admitted or under consideration for admission to postsecondary training programs for the next school year, who are U.S. citizens or resident aliens and who have submitted a completed application and the required supporting materials.

GEOGRAPHIC RESTRICTIONS:
United States.

FINANCIAL DATA:
Amount of support per award: $500 to $3,000.
Total amount of support: $33,250.

NUMBER OF APPLICANTS MOST RECENT YEAR: 300.

NUMBER OF AWARDS: 25.

APPLICATION INFORMATION:
Applications must be submitted online. Applicant must submit completed application, certified transcript, autobiographical sketch, letter of recommendation from instructor, proof of acceptance by postsecondary school and proof of legal blindness.

Duration: One academic year. Nonrenewable, but recipient may reapply.

Deadline: Postmarked by March 1. Announcement June 1.

PUBLICATIONS:
Annual report; *Braille Forum*; *Student Advocate*.

IRS IDENTIFICATION NUMBER: 58-0914436

OFFICERS:
Kim Charlson, President
Jeff Thom, First Vice President
Marlaina Lieberg, Second Vice President

ADDRESS INQUIRIES TO:
Scholarship Coordinator
(See address above.)

AMERICAN FRIENDS OF THE ALEXANDER VON HUMBOLDT FOUNDATION   [1657]
1101 17th Street, N.W.
Suite 603
Washington, DC 20036
(202) 783-1907

E-MAIL ADDRESS:
info@americanfriends-of-avh.org

WEB SITE ADDRESS:
www.humboldt-foundation.de/web/programs-by-target-group.html

FOUNDED: 1953

AREAS OF INTEREST:
Scholarly research and academic cooperation through provision of awards and fellowships. All countries and all disciplines.

NAME(S) OF PROGRAMS:
● **Humboldt Research Awards for Foreign Scholars**

TYPE:
Awards/prizes. Research awards for outstanding achievements in the fields of humanities and social sciences, natural sciences, medicine and engineering sciences providing for visits to German research institutes.

YEAR PROGRAM STARTED: 1972

PURPOSE:
To strengthen scientific cooperation between foreign and German researchers.

LEGAL BASIS:
Government agency run according to private law.

ELIGIBILITY:
Open to internationally renowned scientists and scholars having full professor or equivalent standing.

FINANCIAL DATA:
Amount of support per award: Up to EUR 60,000, plus travel expenses for awardee and accompanying family members.
Total amount of support: Varies.

NUMBER OF AWARDS: Varies.

APPLICATION INFORMATION:
Awards are made by nomination and by eminent German scholars only. No direct applications are allowed.
Duration: Visits to German institutes from six to 12 months. No renewal of the award is possible, but recipient may be invited to Germany again.
Deadline: Nominations may be submitted at any time.

ADDRESS INQUIRIES TO:
See e-mail address above.

AMERICAN INDIAN COLLEGE FUND
8333 Greenwood Boulevard
Denver, CO 80221
(303) 426-8900
Fax: (303) 426-1200

E-MAIL ADDRESS:
scholarships@collegefund.org

WEB SITE ADDRESS:
collegefund.org

TYPE:
Scholarships.

See entry 1036 for full listing.

AMERICAN INDIAN GRADUATE CENTER
3701 San Mateo Boulevard, N.E.
Suite 200
Albuquerque, NM 87110
(505) 881-4584
Fax: (505) 884-0427

E-MAIL ADDRESS:
fellowships@aigcs.org

WEB SITE ADDRESS:
www.aigcs.org

TYPE:
Fellowships; Grants-in-aid; Scholarships. Grants on an academic year basis. Summer funding available to continuing students only; these are students who are currently in the fellowship program.

See entry 1037 for full listing.

AMERICAN INDIAN SCIENCE AND ENGINEERING SOCIETY (AISES)
2305 Renard, S.E.
Suite 200
Albuquerque, NM 87106
(505) 765-1052 ext. 103
(720) 552-6123

E-MAIL ADDRESS:
kcristiano@aises.org

WEB SITE ADDRESS:
www.aises.org/scholarships

TYPE:
Scholarships. AISES scholarships are intended to partially defray tuition and other educational expenses, thereby increasing access to higher education and improving college retention rates for AISES members.

AISES scholarships are made possible by corporations, government agencies, foundations, and individuals who wish to support the advancement of American Indians/Alaskan Natives. Scholarships are distributed in two disbursements and awarded for one academic year, unless otherwise specified. Recipients cannot receive more than one scholarship in any of the six programs.

Scholarships are also awarded to members of AISES who are American Indian/Alaskan Native college students who meet the eligibility requirements for each scholarship.

See entry 1038 for full listing.

AMERICAN INSTITUTE OF CERTIFIED PUBLIC ACCOUNTANTS (AICPA)
220 Leigh Farm Road
Durham, NC 27707
(919) 402-2161
Fax: (919) 419-4705

E-MAIL ADDRESS:
scholarships@aicpa.org

WEB SITE ADDRESS:
www.thiswaytocpa.com/scholarships

TYPE:
Scholarships.

See entry 1520 for full listing.

AMERICAN INSTITUTE OF CERTIFIED PUBLIC ACCOUNTANTS (AICPA)   [1658]
220 Leigh Farm Road
Durham, NC 27707
(919) 402-4682
Fax: (919) 419-4705

E-MAIL ADDRESS:
scholarships@aicpa.org

WEB SITE ADDRESS:
www.aicpa.org

AREAS OF INTEREST:
Accounting/doctoral program.

NAME(S) OF PROGRAMS:
● **AICPA Fellowship for Minority Doctoral Students**

TYPE:
Fellowships. Awarded annually to full-time minority accounting scholars who demonstrate significant potential to become accounting educators.

PURPOSE:
To ensure that C.P.As. of diverse backgrounds are visible in college and university classrooms; to increase the number of minority C.P.As. who serve as role models and mentors to young people in the academic environment.

ELIGIBILITY:
To be considered, applicants must meet the following requirements:
(1) have applied to a doctoral program and awaiting word on acceptance, or have been accepted into a doctoral program or already matriculated in a doctoral program and pursuing appropriate coursework;
(2) have earned a Master's degree and/or completed a minimum of three years of full-time experience in the practice of accounting;
(3) be a minority student of Black or African American, Hispanic or Latino, or Native American ethnicity;
(4) attend school on a full-time basis and plan to remain enrolled full-time until attaining one's doctoral degree;
(5) agree not to work full-time in a paid position or accept responsibility for teaching more than one course per semester as a teaching assistant, or dedicate more than one quarter of the time as a research assistant;
(6) be a C.P.A. or plan to pursue the C.P.A. credential and;
(7) be a U.S. citizen or permanent resident (green card holder).

GEOGRAPHIC RESTRICTIONS:
United States and its territories.

FINANCIAL DATA:
Amount of support per award: $12,000.

Total amount of support: Approximately $264,000 for the academic year 2013-14.

NUMBER OF AWARDS: 21 to 22.

APPLICATION INFORMATION:
Instructions are available online, or send an e-mail to the Institute.
Duration: One year. Renewable.
Deadline: April 1.

ADDRESS INQUIRIES TO:
AICPA Minority Doctoral Fellowship Program
(See address and e-mail above.)

AMERICAN LEGION AUXILIARY - DEPARTMENT OF WISCONSIN [1659]
2930 American Legion Drive
Portage, WI 53901
(608) 745-0124
Fax: (608) 745-1947

E-MAIL ADDRESS:
alawi@amlegionauxwi.org

WEB SITE ADDRESS:
www.amlegionauxwi.org

FOUNDED: 1921

AREAS OF INTEREST:
Scholar aid programs for children of Veterans.

NAME(S) OF PROGRAMS:
- **American Legion Auxiliary Badger Girls State Scholarships**
- **American Legion Auxiliary National Scholarships**
- **Child Welfare Scholarship**
- **Health Careers Scholarships**
- **Eileen Knox Memorial Scholarship**
- **Harry and Shirley Kuehl Foundation Scholarship**
- **H.S. and Angeline Lewis Scholarships**
- **Merit and Memorial Scholarships**
- **State President's Scholarships**
- **Della Van Deuren Scholarships**

TYPE:
Scholarships.

PURPOSE:
To enable students to secure Baccalaureate degrees.

ELIGIBILITY:
(1) Applicant must be a daughter, son, stepdaughter, stepson, wife or widow of a veteran;
(2) Granddaughters, grandsons, great-granddaughters, great-grandsons, step-granddaughters, step-grandsons, step-great-granddaughters, step-great-grandsons of a Wisconsin American Legion Auxiliary member may also apply;
(3) If the applicant is a member of a Wisconsin American Legion Auxiliary Unit, a Wisconsin American Legion Post or a Wisconsin Sons of The American Legion Squadron, they do not need to reside in Wisconsin;
(4) Applicant must be in need of financial help to continue their education;
(5) Applicant must have at least a 3.5 grade point average on a 4.0 grade base and;
(6) Applicant must be a resident of Wisconsin, except as noted in (3) above.

Applicant may apply for more than one scholarship, but can only receive one scholarship from the American Legion Auxiliary-Department of Wisconsin, awarded

on a one-time only basis, nonrenewable. School selected to attend must be an accredited school, but need not be located in Wisconsin. Judges reserve the right to determine the type of scholarship awarded and their decision is final.

GEOGRAPHIC RESTRICTIONS:
Wisconsin.

FINANCIAL DATA:
Amount of support per award: Varies depending on available funds.
Total amount of support: $27,000 for the year 2013.

NUMBER OF APPLICANTS MOST RECENT YEAR:
200.

NUMBER OF AWARDS: 30 for the year 2013.

APPLICATION INFORMATION:
Applicants must use only the application form designated for the year that they are applying for. For the Lewis, State President's, Merit and Memorial, Child Welfare, Health Careers and Registered Nurse Scholarships, one application form may be used regardless of how many programs an applicant may be eligible for.
Duration: One year.
Deadline: March 15.

ADDRESS INQUIRIES TO:
Bonnie Dorniak
Executive Secretary/Treasurer
(See address above.)

AMERICAN MEDICAL ASSOCIATION FOUNDATION [1660]
515 North State Street
Chicago, IL 60654
(312) 464-4200
Fax: (312) 464-4142

E-MAIL ADDRESS:
amafoundation@ama-assn.org

WEB SITE ADDRESS:
www.amafoundation.org

FOUNDED: 1950

AREAS OF INTEREST:
Public health and medical education.

CONSULTING OR VOLUNTEER SERVICES:
Raising awareness about low-health literacy.

NAME(S) OF PROGRAMS:
- **Excellence in Medicine**
- **Joan F. Giambalvo Memorial Scholarship**
- **Health Literacy Initiative**
- **Healthy Communities/Healthy America**
- **Healthy Living Grant Program**
- **Minority Scholars Award**
- **Physicians of Tomorrow Scholarship**
- **Scholars Fund**
- **Seed Grant Research Program**
- **Arthur N. Wilson, M.D. Scholarship**

TYPE:
Awards/prizes; Project/program grants; Research grants; Scholarships; Seed money grants. Excellence in Medicine Awards are given to recognize physicians and medical students who are improving the health of their communities and the lives of those who are most in need.

The Joan F. Giambalvo Memorial Scholarship is presented in conjunction with the AMA's Women Physicians Congress to provide a research grant to help researchers advance the progress of women in the

medical profession and identify and address the needs of women physicians and medical students.

Health Literacy Initiative seeks to provide awareness among physicians and health care providers to understand healthy literacy and its impact on patient safety.

Healthy Communities/Healthy America awards grants to existing, physician-led free clinics that provide free or low-cost medical care to underserved and uninsured populations.

Healthy Living Grant Program provides grants to support healthy lifestyles projects in the areas of nutrition, physical fitness, prescription medication safety and violence prevention.

The Minority Scholars Awards are given in collaboration with the AMA Minority Affairs Section to first- and second-year medical students from historically underrepresented minority groups in the medical profession.

The Physicians of Tomorrow Scholarships are awarded to promising fourth-year medical students based on financial need and academic excellence.

In partnership with the AMA Alliance, the Scholars Fund distributes tuition assistance funds to medical schools across the country.

The Seed Grant Research Program provides medical students, physician residents and fellows with grants to help them conduct basic science, applied or clinical research projects.

The Arthur N. Wilson, M.D. Scholarship is awarded to a medical student who is a graduate of a high school in southeast Alaska.

PURPOSE:
To advance public health and medical scholarship through philanthropic support of physician-directed initiatives.

LEGAL BASIS:
Public foundation.

GEOGRAPHIC RESTRICTIONS:
United States.

FINANCIAL DATA:
Amount of support per award: Joan F. Giambalvo Memorial Scholarship, Minority Scholars Award and Physicians of Tomorrow Scholarship: $10,000; Healthy Communities/Healthy America: Varies each year; Healthy Living Grant Program: $8,000; Arthur N. Wilson, M.D. Scholarship: $5,000; Scholars Fund: Varies by school; Seed Grant Research Program: $2,500.

PUBLICATIONS:
Brochure; program announcement; e-newsletter; quarterly newsletter.

ADDRESS INQUIRIES TO:
Krista Batey, Program Officer
(See address above.)

AMERICAN OSTEOPATHIC FOUNDATION
142 East Ontario Street, Suite 1450
Chicago, IL 60611-2864
(312) 202-8232
Fax: (312) 202-8216

E-MAIL ADDRESS:
vheck@aof.org

WEB SITE ADDRESS:
www.aof.org

TYPE:
Awards/prizes; Scholarships. Grants.

See entry 2522 for full listing.

AMERICAN OSTEOPATHIC FOUNDATION   [1661]
142 East Ontario Street, Suite 1450
Chicago, IL 60611
(312) 202-8232
(312) 202-8234
Fax: (312) 202-8216

E-MAIL ADDRESS:
vheck@aof.org

WEB SITE ADDRESS:
www.aof.org

FOUNDED: 1949

AREAS OF INTEREST:
Osteopathic medical education.

NAME(S) OF PROGRAMS:
● **McCaughan Heritage Scholarship**

TYPE:
Scholarships. Awarded annually to one rising
last-year student at each of the accredited
U.S. colleges of osteopathic medicine.

LEGAL BASIS:
Private foundation.

ELIGIBILITY:
Candidates for the McCaughan Heritage
Scholarship must demonstrate financial need,
outstanding academic and extracurricular
accomplishments, and strong commitment to
osteopathic philosophy during the last year of
school. Student must possess ability to work
harmoniously with fellow students and
faculty and show promise as an osteopathic
physician. The Foundation solicits
nominations from each school of osteopathic
medicine.

FINANCIAL DATA:
Amount of support per award: $5,000.

NUMBER OF AWARDS: 1.

APPLICATION INFORMATION:
Guidelines and application form are available
on the Foundation web site.
Duration: One year.
Deadline: April 30.

STAFF:
Stephen S. Downey, Executive Director
Vicki Heck, Director of Programs
Maggie K. Burton, Senior Development
Officer
Susan Laslie, Controller

ADDRESS INQUIRIES TO:
Vicki Heck
Director of Programs
(See address above.)

THE AMERICAN SOCIETY FOR NONDESTRUCTIVE TESTING, INC.   [1662]
1711 Arlingate Lane
Columbus, OH 43228
(614) 274-6003
(800) 222-2768
Fax: (614) 274-6899

E-MAIL ADDRESS:
mthomas@asnt.org

WEB SITE ADDRESS:
www.asnt.org

FOUNDED: 1941

AREAS OF INTEREST:
Nondestructive testing and engineering.

NAME(S) OF PROGRAMS:
● **Engineering Undergraduate Award**
● **Robert B. Oliver Scholarship**

TYPE:
Scholarships.

YEAR PROGRAM STARTED: 1998

PURPOSE:
To support research and education in
nondestructive testing and to increase public
awareness of nondestructive testing's critical
role in ensuring the safety and well-being of
mankind.

LEGAL BASIS:
501(c)(3) corporation.

ELIGIBILITY:
Engineering Undergraduate Award: Students
must be enrolled in an engineering program
of a university accredited by ABET or its
equivalent and choosing NDT as their field
of specialization.

Oliver Scholarship: Students must be
officially enrolled in an undergraduate
degree, associate degree, or postsecondary
certificate program, which includes studies in
NDT.

FINANCIAL DATA:
Amount of support per award: Engineering
Undergraduate Award: $3,000; Oliver
Scholarship: $2,500.

Total amount of support: Engineering
Undergraduate Award: $9,000; Oliver
Scholarship: $7,500.

NUMBER OF AWARDS: Up to 3 per year per
award.

APPLICATION INFORMATION:
Information and application are available
online.
Duration: One year.
Deadline: Engineering Undergraduate Award:
December 15. Oliver Scholarship: February
15.

ADDRESS INQUIRIES TO:
Michelle Thomas
ASNT Administrative Assistant
(See address above.)

AMERICAN SOCIETY OF ECHOCARDIOGRAPHY EDUCATION AND RESEARCH FOUNDATION (ASE)
210 Gateway Centre Boulevard, Suite 310
Morrisville, NC 27560
(919) 861-5574
Fax: (919) 882-9900

E-MAIL ADDRESS:
madilday@asecho.org

WEB SITE ADDRESS:
www.asecho.org

TYPE:
Awards/prizes; Scholarships. Scholarship
awards for students enrolled in a
cardiovascular ultrasound program accredited
by the Commission on Accreditation of
Allied Health Education Programs
(CAAHEP) in the U.S., or by an equivalent
Canadian or International ultrasound
program. Recipients are chosen based on
nomination of program directors, their letters
of support, personal accomplishments and
academic record.

See entry 2389 for full listing.

AMERICAN SOCIETY OF HEMATOLOGY
2021 L Street, N.W.
Suite 900
Washington, DC 20036
(202) 776-0544
Fax: (888) 719-7814

E-MAIL ADDRESS:
awards@hematology.org

WEB SITE ADDRESS:
www.hematology.org

TYPE:
Awards/prizes; Fellowships; Research grants;
Scholarships.

See entry 2235 for full listing.

THE AMERICAN SWEDISH INSTITUTE
2600 Park Avenue
Minneapolis, MN 55407
(612) 871-4907
Fax: (612) 871-8682

E-MAIL ADDRESS:
info@asimn.org

WEB SITE ADDRESS:
www.asimn.org

TYPE:
Scholarships; Travel grants. The Malmberg
Scholarship is awarded for up to one
academic year of study in Sweden.

See entry 897 for full listing.

AMVETS   [1663]
4647 Forbes Boulevard
Lanham, MD 20706-4380
(301) 459-9600
(877) 726-8387
Fax: (301) 459-7924

E-MAIL ADDRESS:
scholarships@amvets.org

WEB SITE ADDRESS:
www.amvets.org

FOUNDED: 1944

NAME(S) OF PROGRAMS:
● **AMVETS National Scholarship Program: Entering College Freshman Scholarship**
● **AMVETS National Scholarship Program: JROTC Scholarship**

TYPE:
Scholarships. National scholarship program
for high school seniors who are children or
grandchildren of veterans.

PURPOSE:
To make the goal of postsecondary education
more attainable for the children and
grandchildren of veterans by assisting
deserving students who might not otherwise
have the financial means to achieve their
educational goals.

ELIGIBILITY:
Applicant must:
(1) be a graduating high school senior
entering at the college freshman level in the
upcoming fall or be an active JROTC cadet
and currently a high school senior;
(2) have a minimum grade point average of
3.0 (or documented evidence of extenuating
circumstances that caused a lower grade

point average);
(3) be the child or grandchild of a U.S. veteran who is an AMVETS member, or if deceased, would have been eligible for AMVETS membership;
(4) be a U.S. citizen;
(5) demonstrate academic promise and financial need and;
(6) agree to authorize AMVETS to publicize their scholarship award, if they are selected.

GEOGRAPHIC RESTRICTIONS:
United States.

FINANCIAL DATA:
Amount of support per award: Entering College Freshman Scholarship: $4,000 ($1,000 per year of a four-year program); JROTC Scholarship: $1,000.

NUMBER OF AWARDS: Entering College Freshman Scholarship: 6; JROTC Scholarship: 1.

APPLICATION INFORMATION:
Applications must be sent via regular mail.
Duration: One to four years. Nonrenewable.
Deadline: April 30.

ADDRESS INQUIRIES TO:
Tiffany Hilton
National Programs Associate
(See address above.)

AMVETS   [1664]
4647 Forbes Boulevard
Lanham, MD 20706-4380
(301) 459-9600
(877) 726-8387
Fax: (301) 459-7924

E-MAIL ADDRESS:
scholarships@amvets.org

WEB SITE ADDRESS:
www.amvets.org

FOUNDED: 1944

NAME(S) OF PROGRAMS:
● **AMVETS/University of Phoenix Scholarship**

TYPE:
Scholarships. For U.S. veterans, active-duty service members, reservists, Guardsmen and their family members.

YEAR PROGRAM STARTED: 2007

PURPOSE:
To enable members of the active military, veterans, and their families to be successful and have a better quality of life for themselves and their families, starting with education.

ELIGIBILITY:
All veterans, service members, and family members are eligible to apply. Applicant must be a current member of the active military or an honorably discharged veteran or spouse, child or grandchild of these two groups and not be receiving 100% tuition reimbursement.

GEOGRAPHIC RESTRICTIONS:
United States.

FINANCIAL DATA:
Amount of support per award: $7,000 scholarship in the form of a noncash credit to the awardee's University Account to be used for tuition and fees only.

NUMBER OF AWARDS: Approximately 50 annually.

APPLICATION INFORMATION:
Applicants must submit a complete essay on one of the listed topics. All materials must be submitted by mail. Recipients will be selected by the Scholarship Committee, consisting of representatives from the University of Phoenix and AMVETS.
Duration: Varies. Nonrenewable.
Deadline: July 1.

ADDRESS INQUIRIES TO:
Tiffany Hilton
Programs Associate
(See address above.)

ARCHAEOLOGICAL INSTITUTE OF AMERICA   [1665]
656 Beacon Street, 6th Floor
Boston, MA 02215
(617) 358-4184
Fax: (617) 353-6550

E-MAIL ADDRESS:
fellowships@aia.bu.edu

WEB SITE ADDRESS:
www.archaeological.org

FOUNDED: 1879

AREAS OF INTEREST:
Archaeological research and publication.

NAME(S) OF PROGRAMS:
● **The AIA Publication Subvention Program**
● **Samuel H. Kress Grants for Research and Publication in Classical Art and Architecture**

TYPE:
Grants-in-aid. The AIA Publication Subvention Program offers subventions from the AIA's Bothmer Publication Fund in support of new book-length publications in the field of Greek, Roman, and Etruscan archaeology and art history.

Samuel H. Kress Grants for Research and Publication in Classical Art and Architecture funds publication preparation or research leading to publication undertaken by professional members of the AIA.

YEAR PROGRAM STARTED: 2002

PURPOSE:
To support the scholarly publication of archaeological works.

ELIGIBILITY:
Applicants must be members of the AIA.

FINANCIAL DATA:
Amount of support per award: AIA Publication Subvention Program: Up to $10,000; average $3,000 to $5,000. Samuel H. Kress Grants: $3,000.
Total amount of support: Varies.

NUMBER OF AWARDS: AIA Publication Subvention Program: 1 to 5; Samuel H. Kress Grants: 2.

APPLICATION INFORMATION:
Applications must be completed online. Full details are available on the Institute web site.
Duration: Typically one year.
Deadline: March 1 and November 1.

ADDRESS INQUIRIES TO:
Laurel Nilsen Sparks
Lecture and Fellowship Coordinator
(See address above.)

ARMENIAN GENERAL BENEVOLENT UNION   [1666]
55 East 59th Street
New York, NY 10022-1112
(212) 319-6383
Fax: (212) 319-6507

E-MAIL ADDRESS:
scholarship@agbu.org

WEB SITE ADDRESS:
www.agbu-scholarship.org

AREAS OF INTEREST:
Education.

NAME(S) OF PROGRAMS:
● **A.G.B.U. Scholarship Program**
● **Fellowship for U.S.-Based Study**
● **International Scholarships**
● **Performing Arts Fellowship**
● **Religious Studies Fellowship**

TYPE:
Fellowships; Scholarships.

PURPOSE:
To provide financial assistance to students of Armenian descent.

ELIGIBILITY:
Students must be of Armenian descent enrolled in college or university.

FINANCIAL DATA:
Amount of support per award: $1,500 to $7,500, depending on category.
Total amount of support: Approximately $700,000 annually.

NUMBER OF APPLICANTS MOST RECENT YEAR:
Over 1,000.

NUMBER OF AWARDS: Over 500.

APPLICATION INFORMATION:
Applications are available online.
Deadline: U.S. Fellowship: April 15; Performing Arts and Religious Studies Fellowships: May 15; International Scholarship: October 15 for study in Syria and France, May 31 for study in all other countries.

ADDRESS INQUIRIES TO:
Scholarship Program
(See address above.)

ASIAN AMERICAN JOURNALISTS ASSOCIATION   [1667]
5 Third Street
Suite 1108
San Francisco, CA 94103
(415) 346-2051
Fax: (415) 346-6343

E-MAIL ADDRESS:
naov@aaja.org

WEB SITE ADDRESS:
www.aaja.org

FOUNDED: 1981

AREAS OF INTEREST:
Journalism.

NAME(S) OF PROGRAMS:
● **Broadcast News Grant**
● **Stanford Chen Grant**
● **Vincent Chin Scholarships**
● **William Woo Print & Online News Grant**

TYPE:
Internships; Scholarships.

PURPOSE:
To encourage Asian-American students to pursue journalism careers.

ELIGIBILITY:
Must be a full-time college student or high school senior pursuing journalism as a major.

GEOGRAPHIC RESTRICTIONS:
United States.

FINANCIAL DATA:
Amount of support per award: Broadcast News Grant: $1,000 to $2,500; Stanford Chen Grant: $1,750; Vincent Chin Scholarships: $500; Print & Online News Grant: $1,000.
Total amount of support: Varies.

NUMBER OF APPLICANTS MOST RECENT YEAR:
100.

NUMBER OF AWARDS: 20.

APPLICATION INFORMATION:
Application information is available on the web site.
Duration: One year. Renewal possible.
Deadline: May.

ADDRESS INQUIRIES TO:
Nao Vang, Student Programs Coordinator (See address above.)

ASSOCIATION OF UNIVERSITIES AND COLLEGES OF CANADA   [1668]

350 Albert Street, Suite 600
Ottawa ON K1R 1B1 Canada
(613) 563-1236
Fax: (613) 563-9745

E-MAIL ADDRESS:
awards@aucc.ca

WEB SITE ADDRESS:
www.aucc.ca

FOUNDED: 1911

AREAS OF INTEREST:
Undergraduate education at a Canadian university.

NAME(S) OF PROGRAMS:
● **C.D. Howe Scholarships**

TYPE:
Scholarships. Applicable towards full-time studies for applicants entering the first year of a first Bachelor's degree program. There are no restrictions on the program of study or discipline. The program must be of a minimum three-year duration. Canadian educational institutions which have provincial degree-granting powers, or their affiliates, are eligible for this program.

YEAR PROGRAM STARTED: 1987

PURPOSE:
To assist Canadian students from Thunder Bay and the former federal constituency of Port Arthur to pursue an undergraduate degree in any field at a Canadian university.

LEGAL BASIS:
Nonprofit foundation.

ELIGIBILITY:
Each applicant must be a Canadian citizen or permanent resident and must be a resident of Thunder Bay or the former federal constituency of Port Arthur.

The Thunder Bay area includes the following school boards:
(1) Thunder Bay Catholic District School Board;
(2) Red Lake Combined Roman Catholic Separate School Board and;
(3) Superior North Catholic District School Board.

The former constituency of Port Arthur includes the following school boards:
(1) Lakehead District School Board;
(2) Superior Greenstone District School Board and;
(3) Conseil scolaire de district catholique des Aurores Boreales.
In most cases, applicant will be a student in the school boards mentioned above.

Applicant must also have a minimum cumulative average of 80% (or equivalent) over the last three semesters of available marks. Nonacademic courses such as career- or personal development-related courses will not be considered.

To be considered for renewal, scholarship recipients must maintain a full-time status, as defined by the educational institution, and must pass all courses and maintain a B average (or equivalent). They must also send the Association an official transcript at the end of each academic year. Students must complete and return the *Renewal Report* provided by the Association. Any changes of personal or academic status must also be transmitted to the AUCC.

GEOGRAPHIC RESTRICTIONS:
Canada.

FINANCIAL DATA:
Payment will be made by AUCC to the universities attended. Payment by the university will be according to the usual practice of the university.
Amount of support per award: $5,500 (CAN) annually.
Total amount of support: $11,000 (CAN) annually.

NUMBER OF AWARDS: Up to 2 entrance scholarships: one to a Thunder Bay student and one to a student from C.D. Howe's former constituency of Port Arthur.

APPLICATION INFORMATION:
Each applicant must provide:
(1) an official transcript of the last three semesters of available marks;
(2) two signed reference letters with the references' original signatures (one from a teacher and one from a person familiar with their volunteer/community involvement and/or extracurricular activities) and;
(3) one page (maximum 250 words) describing their volunteer/community involvement and/or extracurricular activities.

Note that a transcript will be considered acceptable only if it meets the following criteria:
(1) it is presented on the official paper of the institution and;
(2) it bears the appropriate signature(s) and/or seal of the institution.
Duration: Maximum of four years or until first degree is obtained, whichever occurs first.
Deadline: Postmarked by June 1.

PUBLICATIONS:
Program announcement.

ADDRESS INQUIRIES TO:
Higher Education Scholarships
Association of Universities and Colleges of Canada (AUCC)
Ref: C.D. Howe Scholarship Endowment Fund-Thunder Bay/Port Arthur Scholarship Program
(See street or e-mail addresses above.)

ASSOCIATION ON AMERICAN INDIAN AFFAIRS

966 Hungerford Drive, Suite 12-B
Rockville, MD 20850
(240) 314-7155
Fax: (240) 314-7159

E-MAIL ADDRESS:
lw.aaia@indian-affairs.org

WEB SITE ADDRESS:
www.indian-affairs.org

TYPE:
Scholarships.

See entry 1043 for full listing.

ASSOCIATION ON AMERICAN INDIAN AFFAIRS

966 Hungerford Drive, Suite 12-B
Rockville, MD 20850
(240) 314-7155
Fax: (240) 314-7159

E-MAIL ADDRESS:
lw.aaia@indian-affairs.org

WEB SITE ADDRESS:
www.indian-affairs.org

TYPE:
Grants-in-aid; Scholarships. Emergency Aid Scholarships are for full-time graduate and undergraduate students who are seeking a degree in any curriculum. This program is limited by the availability of scholarship funds.

See entry 1041 for full listing.

ASSOCIATION ON AMERICAN INDIAN AFFAIRS

966 Hungerford Drive, Suite 12-B
Rockville, MD 20850
(240) 314-7155
Fax: (240) 314-7159

E-MAIL ADDRESS:
lw.aaia@indian-affairs.org

WEB SITE ADDRESS:
www.indian-affairs.org

TYPE:
Scholarships.

See entry 1042 for full listing.

ASSOCIATION ON AMERICAN INDIAN AFFAIRS

966 Hungerford Drive, Suite 12-B
Rockville, MD 20850
(240) 314-7155
Fax: (240) 314-7159

E-MAIL ADDRESS:
lw.aaia@indian-affairs.org

WEB SITE ADDRESS:
www.indian-affairs.org

TYPE:
Scholarships. Offered to American Indian and Alaskan Native graduate and undergraduate students in any curriculum who are members of tribes that are not federally recognized.

See entry 1044 for full listing.

ALEXANDER GRAHAM BELL ASSOCIATION FOR THE DEAF AND HARD OF HEARING

3417 Volta Place, N.W.
Washington, DC 20007
(202) 337-5220
Fax: (202) 337-8314

E-MAIL ADDRESS:
financialaid@agbell.org

WEB SITE ADDRESS:
www.listeningandspokenlanguage.org

TYPE:
Scholarships.

See entry 981 for full listing.

BNSF RAILWAY FOUNDATION

2650 Lou Menk Drive
Fort Worth, TX 76131-2830
(817) 867-6458
Fax: (817) 352-7925

E-MAIL ADDRESS:
bnsffoundation@bnsf.com

WEB SITE ADDRESS:
www.bnsffoundation.org

TYPE:
Scholarships. Awarded annually to outstanding Native American high school seniors from funds provided by the Foundation, for up to four years or until undergraduate degree requirements are completed, whichever occurs first. Scholarship winners may attend any accredited college (two-year leading to a four-year degree) or university in the U.S.

See entry 1045 for full listing.

BNSF RAILWAY FOUNDATION

2650 Lou Menk Drive
Fort Worth, TX 76131-2830
(817) 867-6458
Fax: (817) 352-7925

E-MAIL ADDRESS:
bnsffoundation@bnsf.com

WEB SITE ADDRESS:
www.bnsffoundation.org

TYPE:
Scholarships. Scholarships awarded to high school graduates of Hispanic origin through the Hispanic College Fund (HCF).

See entry 1063 for full listing.

THE LYNDE AND HARRY BRADLEY FOUNDATION, INC. [1669]

1241 North Franklin Place
Milwaukee, WI 53202-2901
(414) 291-9915
Fax: (414) 291-9991

WEB SITE ADDRESS:
www.bradleyfdn.org

FOUNDED: 1942

AREAS OF INTEREST:
Humanities, social sciences and law.

NAME(S) OF PROGRAMS:
● **Bradley Fellowship Program**

TYPE:
Fellowships. To strengthen America's "intellectual infrastructure" at a higher-education level, providing useful assistance to young scholars during a critical phase in their education.

YEAR PROGRAM STARTED: 1986

PURPOSE:
To assist candidates to complete their studies, prepare manuscripts for publication, conduct research, and enhance their competitiveness in the job market.

ELIGIBILITY:
Selected candidates must be intelligent doctoral and postdoctoral fellows within the discretion of participating professors or nominators. The principal consideration is excellence and merit. Candidates must also be U.S. citizens or residents.

GEOGRAPHIC RESTRICTIONS:
United States.

FINANCIAL DATA:
Amount of support per award: Up to $25,000 per academic year.

APPLICATION INFORMATION:
Recipients must be nominated by participating professors or nominators.
Duration: One year.

ADDRESS INQUIRIES TO:
Dianne Sehler, Director of Academic, International and Cultural Programs
(See address above.)

BROADCAST EDUCATION ASSOCIATION

1771 N Street, N.W.
Washington, DC 20036-2891
(888) 380-7222
(202) 429-3935
Fax: (202) 775-2981

E-MAIL ADDRESS:
beamemberservices@nab.org

WEB SITE ADDRESS:
www.beaweb.org

TYPE:
Scholarships. BEA is the professional development association for professors, industry professionals and students involved in teaching and research related to radio, television and other electronic media. BEA administers nine scholarships annually, to honor broadcasters and the electronic media profession.

John Bayliss, Walter S. Patterson, and Abe Voron Scholarships: Study toward a career in radio.

Richard Eaton, Alexander M. Tanger, and Vincent T. Wasilewski Scholarships: Study in any area of broadcasting.

The BEA Two Year Award is for study at member schools offering only freshman and sophomore instruction, or for use at a four-year member school by a graduate of a BEA two-year campus. All other scholarships are awarded to juniors, seniors and graduate students at BEA Member institutions.

See entry 1924 for full listing.

BUREAU OF INDIAN EDUCATION

1849 C Street, N.W.
MS 3609 MIB
Washington, DC 20240
(202) 208-6123
Fax: (202) 208-3312

WEB SITE ADDRESS:
www.bie.edu

TYPE:
Fellowships; Scholarships.

See entry 1046 for full listing.

CALIFORNIA STUDENT AID COMMISSION [1670]

P.O. Box 419027
Rancho Cordova, CA 95741-9027
(888) 224-7268
Fax: (916) 464-8002

E-MAIL ADDRESS:
studentsupport@csac.ca.gov

WEB SITE ADDRESS:
www.calgrants.org

FOUNDED: 1955

NAME(S) OF PROGRAMS:
● **Cal Grants A, B and C**

TYPE:
Assistantships; Grants-in-aid. Grant A will help pay for tuition and fees at public and private colleges, and some private career colleges. Grant B provides low-income students with a living allowance and assistance with tuition and fees. Most five-year students receive an allowance for books and living expenses. Grant C helps pay for tuition and training costs at occupational or career technical schools.

YEAR PROGRAM STARTED: 1956

PURPOSE:
To assist with tuition and books for students attending college in California.

LEGAL BASIS:
California Education Code.

ELIGIBILITY:
Students must be U.S. citizen or eligible noncitizen and a California resident.

GEOGRAPHIC RESTRICTIONS:
California.

FINANCIAL DATA:
Amount of support per award: Grant A: Up to $12,192; Grant B: Up to $1,473 for first year; up to $6,945 for subsequent years; Grant C: $547.

NUMBER OF APPLICANTS MOST RECENT YEAR:
350,000.

NUMBER OF AWARDS: 75,000.

APPLICATION INFORMATION:
Students should submit the Free Application for Federal Student Aid (FAFSA) and a verified Cal Grant GPA. The FAFSA is available online.
Duration: Up to four years.

PUBLICATIONS:
Fund Your Future; *Financial Aid for Students*, booklet.

CALIFORNIA STUDENT AID COMMISSION [1671]

P.O. Box 419029
Rancho Cordova, CA 95741-9029
(888) 224-7268 Option 5
Fax: (916) 464-8002

E-MAIL ADDRESS:
specialized@csac.ca.gov

WEB SITE ADDRESS:
www.csac.ca.gov

FOUNDED: 1955

AREAS OF INTEREST:
Dependents of law enforcement personnel.

NAME(S) OF PROGRAMS:
● **Law Enforcement Personnel Dependents' Grant Program (LEPD)**

TYPE:
Grants-in-aid. The program provides need-based educational grants to dependents and spouses of California peace officers (Highway Patrol, police officers), Department of Corrections and California Youth Authority employees and permanent/full-time firefighters, employed by public entities who have been killed in the performance of duty or totally disabled as a result of an accident or injury caused by external violence or physical force incurred in the performance of duty.

Grant awards are for attendance at WASC-accredited colleges in California.

YEAR PROGRAM STARTED: 1969

LEGAL BASIS:
California Labor Code, Section 4709. State agency.

ELIGIBILITY:
Dependents and spouses of California peace officers.

GEOGRAPHIC RESTRICTIONS:
California.

FINANCIAL DATA:
Amount of support per award: $100 to $12,192; varies according to state budget.
Total amount of support: Varies.

NUMBER OF APPLICANTS MOST RECENT YEAR:
9.

APPLICATION INFORMATION:
Eligible students must file the following documents with the Specialized Programs Branch:
(1) a Law Enforcement Personnel Dependent's Grant application;
(2) a copy of the Student Aid Report (SAR), which is generated after filing a FAFSA;
(3) birth certificate (not required for spouse);
(4) the death certificate of the parent or spouse and the coroner's report (if appropriate), police report, and any other documentation that shows evidence that the death or total disability was caused by external violence or physical force incurred in the line of duty (for peace and law enforcement officers), by the direct action of an inmate (for officers and employees of the Department of Corrections and Rehabilitation), or in the performance of duty (for firefighters);
(5) findings of the Workers' Compensation Appeals Board or other evidence that the fatality or 100% disabling accident or injury was compensable under Division 4.0 and 4.5 (commencing with Section 6100) of the Labor Code and;
(6) proof of enrollment at a California postsecondary institution as described above for the applicable academic year.
Duration: Up to four years.

PUBLICATIONS:
Financial Aid for Students, booklet.

STAFF:
Diana Fuentes-Michel, Executive Director

ADDRESS INQUIRIES TO:
Diana Fuentes-Michel, Executive Director
(See address above.)

CALIFORNIA STUDENT AID COMMISSION [1672]

P.O. Box 419029
Rancho Cordova, CA 95741-9029
(888) 224-7268
Fax: (916) 464-8002

E-MAIL ADDRESS:
specialized@csac.ca.gov

WEB SITE ADDRESS:
www.csac.ca.gov
www.calgrants.org

FOUNDED: 1955

AREAS OF INTEREST:
Students pursuing teaching careers in critical teacher shortage areas and designated low-income schools.

NAME(S) OF PROGRAMS:
● **Assumption Program of Loans for Education (APLE)**

TYPE:
Loan forgiveness programs. Assumption of outstanding educational loan balances in return for the participant's service as a public school teacher in California designated shortage areas.

YEAR PROGRAM STARTED: 1986

PURPOSE:
To encourage outstanding students to become teachers and serve in critical teacher shortage areas.

LEGAL BASIS:
California Education Code.

ELIGIBILITY:
Applicants must:
(1) be legal residents of California;
(2) have completed a minimum of 60 semester or 90 quarter units prior to the fall term of the year of application;
(3) enroll in a program leading to a Baccalaureate degree or in an approved program of professional teacher preparation;
(4) have received, or have been approved to receive, Stafford Student Loans/Guaranteed Student Loans (GSL), Consolidation Loan Program loans or privately funded educational loans issued to students through institutions of higher education;
(5) be free of any obligation to repay any state or federal educational grant and not be in default on any state or federally insured educational loan;
(6) not have completed the coursework necessary to obtain an initial teaching credential;
(7) student must teach in a California public school within 36 months from the date they become eligible to receive their initial teaching credential and;
(8) student must provide eligible full-time teaching service under a regular full-time contract at a California public school for four consecutive years in their designated service area.

Additionally, credential teachers must teach at a public school ranked in the lowest two deciles on the Academic Performance Index, possess a clear multiple subject or single subject teaching credential or level II education specialist credential and be nominated through California County Office of Education. Service provided prior to entering into the program will not count towards assumption benefits.

GEOGRAPHIC RESTRICTIONS:
California.

FINANCIAL DATA:
CSAC will pay bonus amount of $1,000 each year of full-time, or part-time equivalent, teaching service provided in math, science, or education specialist instruction in low-performing schools.
Amount of support per award: Up to $11,000 to be issued by the Commission directly to lenders in the following manner: Up to $2,000 after completion of the first full school year of eligible full-time teaching service; Up to $3,000 for each of the second, third and fourth years of eligible teaching service.
Total amount of support: Based on the number of eligible teachers.

NUMBER OF AWARDS: 7,500 annually, pending legislative changes.

APPLICATION INFORMATION:
Applications may be obtained after April 1 through participating California colleges and universities offering approved teaching credential programs. Participating postsecondary institutions distribute applications, assess academic ability, select applicants, and are encouraged to promote applications by population underrepresented in the teaching profession.
Duration: Participants must maintain satisfactory progress and half-time enrollment to renew.
Deadline: June 30; however, will continue to receive applications after deadline until all allocations have been met.

PUBLICATIONS:
Program announcement.

ADDRESS INQUIRIES TO:
APLE
California Student Aid Commission
Specialized Programs Branch
(See address above.)

CANADIAN FRIENDS OF THE HEBREW UNIVERSITY [1673]

3080 Yonge Street, Suite 3020
Toronto ON M4N 3N1 Canada
(416) 485-8000
(888) 432-7398 (Canada only)
Fax: (416) 485-8565

E-MAIL ADDRESS:
mgoldman@cfhu.org
inquiry@cfhu.org

WEB SITE ADDRESS:
www.cfhu.org

FOUNDED: 1944

AREAS OF INTEREST:
Law, dentistry, social sciences, economics, humanities and the sciences.

TYPE:
Awards/prizes; Scholarships. The Canadian Friends of the Hebrew University sponsors Canadian college or university students who participate in programs at the Hebrew University of Jerusalem.

YEAR PROGRAM STARTED: 1944

PURPOSE:
To give the financial support necessary for Canadian students to study at Hebrew University in Jerusalem, Israel.

LEGAL BASIS:
Nonprofit.

ELIGIBILITY:
Applicants must be Canadian citizens or landed immigrants. Awards are given based on need.

GEOGRAPHIC RESTRICTIONS:
Canada.

FINANCIAL DATA:
Amount of support per award: $1,500 to $5,000.
Total amount of support: Varies.

NUMBER OF AWARDS: Varies.

APPLICATION INFORMATION:
Contact the Office of Academic Affairs at the address above.
Duration: At least one year.
Deadline: Announcement in May.

STAFF:
Rami Kleinmann, Chief Executive Officer and President

ADDRESS INQUIRIES TO:
Merle Goldman, Executive Vice President
(See address above.)

CANADIAN MERIT SCHOLARSHIP FOUNDATION   [1674]
460 Richmond Street West, Suite 502
Toronto ON M5V 1Y1 Canada
(416) 646-2120
(866) 544-2673
Fax: (416) 646-0846

E-MAIL ADDRESS:
info@cmsf.ca

WEB SITE ADDRESS:
www.cmsf.ca
www.loranaward.ca

FOUNDED: 1988

AREAS OF INTEREST:
Higher education.

NAME(S) OF PROGRAMS:
● **Loran Awards**

TYPE:
Scholarships. Grants for high school graduates about to enter a university in Canada.

PURPOSE:
To identify and support talented students who show promise of leadership and a strong commitment to service in the community; to fund these citizens to study on Canadian campuses, to the benefit of their future and ours.

ELIGIBILITY:
Applicant must:
(1) be in the graduating year of uninterrupted full-time studies in high school or CEGEP. Exceptions may be considered for those who have undertaken a gap year for academic pursuits or community service-based activities;
(2) present a minimum cumulative average of 85% and;
(3) hold Canadian citizenship or permanent resident status.

GEOGRAPHIC RESTRICTIONS:
Canada.

FINANCIAL DATA:
Amount of support per award: Varies.

APPLICATION INFORMATION:
Applications are available early September and can be downloaded from the Loran

Award web site. Students should speak to their guidance counselor about their school's nomination process.
Duration: Up to four years.

ADDRESS INQUIRIES TO:
Franca Gucciardi, Executive Director
(See address above.)

*PLEASE NOTE:
Loran Award Finalist and Provincial Awards are tenable at any public university in Canada. Loran Awards are tenable at participating Canadian consortium universities only.

THE CARSON SCHOLARS FUND, INC.   [1675]
305 West Chesapeake Avenue
Suite 310
Towson, MD 21204
(410) 828-1005
Fax: (410) 828-1007

E-MAIL ADDRESS:
katie@carsonscholars.org

WEB SITE ADDRESS:
carsonscholars.org

FOUNDED: 1994

AREAS OF INTEREST:
Education.

NAME(S) OF PROGRAMS:
● **Carson Scholarships**

TYPE:
Scholarships. The Carson Scholars Fund awards $1,000 college scholarships to students in grades 4-11 who excel academically and are dedicated to serving their communities.

PURPOSE:
To operate on the principle that if children could be taught early to excel, they would stay motivated and have a higher chance of educational success later in life.

ELIGIBILITY:
Students must be nominated by the principal at his or her school and only one student from each school is able to apply. Carson Scholars must have a grade point average of 3.75 and display humanitarian qualities through community service. Scholarships are awarded solely on the basis of academic achievements and humanitarian qualities, without regard to financial need or ethnicity. Carson Scholars must be U.S. citizens or residents.

GEOGRAPHIC RESTRICTIONS:
United States.

FINANCIAL DATA:
Scholarship winners receive the honor of being named "Carson Scholars" and are awarded an Olympic-sized medal and a trophy for their school. Winners receive a recognition package and an invitation to attend an awards banquet.
Amount of support per award: $1,000.

NUMBER OF AWARDS: 425 in 2013.

APPLICATION INFORMATION:
Students must be nominated by the principal of his or her school to compete. Only one student from each school is able to apply. Complete information is on the web site.
Duration: One-time award.
Deadline: Nominations open in October and close the beginning of January. Notification is made in March.

CATCHING THE DREAM
8200 Mountain Road, N.E.
Suite 203
Albuquerque, NM 87110
(505) 262-2351
Fax: (505) 262-0534

E-MAIL ADDRESS:
NScholarsh@aol.com

WEB SITE ADDRESS:
www.catchingthedream.org

TYPE:
Conferences/seminars; Fellowships; Scholarships; Technical assistance. CTD also works to improve Indian schools through a program of grants and technical assistance. This work has led to the development of 40 Exemplary Programs in Indian education since 1988. The annual Exemplary Institute is a meeting of these Exemplary Programs, where they teach other people how to develop similar programs.

MAST program makes grants of $5,000 to Indian high schools to improve their math and science teaching.

MESBEC Program consists of competitive scholarships for high-potential Native Americans studying in math, engineering, science, business, education and computers.

NALE Program consists of competitive scholarships for high-potential paraprofessional Native Americans who plan to complete their degrees and obtain credentials as teachers, counselors or administrators.

RAP makes grants to Indian schools to improve the reading ability of their students.

Tribal Business Management (TBM) Program consists of competitive scholarships for Native students in all fields of business.

See entry 1047 for full listing.

CHATHAM UNIVERSITY   [1676]
Woodland Road
Berry Hall
Pittsburgh, PA 15232
(412) 365-1825
Fax: (412) 365-1609

E-MAIL ADDRESS:
admission@chatham.edu

WEB SITE ADDRESS:
www.chatham.
edu/admission/aid/undergraduate/firstyear.cfm

FOUNDED: 1869

AREAS OF INTEREST:
Providing scholarship opportunities to students who have shown academic promise during their high school career and who are enrolled at Chatham University.

NAME(S) OF PROGRAMS:
● **The Chatham University Merit Scholarship Programs**

TYPE:
Awards/prizes; Endowments; Formula grants; General operating grants; Grants-in-aid; Internships; Scholarships. The Chatham University Merit Scholarship Programs include the Presidential, Trustee, Dean, and Founder, as well as Chatham Grants. Additional scholarship opportunities include the S-STEM Scholarship, the Heffer Family Scholarship, the Girl Scout Gold Scholarship, the Minna Kaufmann Ruud Music

Scholarship, the Eden Hall Scholarship for Sustainability, the AFS/YFU/Rotary International Scholarship, the Visual Arts Scholarship, the Interior Architecture Scholarship, the Girl Scout Leadership Award, the Legacy Award, the Family Heritage Award, the Phi Theta Kappa Scholarship, and the Rachel Carson Book Award.

YEAR PROGRAM STARTED: 1978

PURPOSE:
To attract outstanding students to Chatham University and to provide recognition of their academic performance.

ELIGIBILITY:
Chatham University Merit Scholars are chosen based on their performance in high school, grades, and SAT or ACT scores.

Grants are based strictly on need; many of the scholars are from families for whom the choice of a college such as Chatham would not be possible without this support.

FINANCIAL DATA:
Presidential Scholarship pays full tuition, including room and board.

Amount of support per award: Other Scholarships are from $1,000 per year to $16,000 per year (renewable based on minimum grade point average requirements and full-time enrollment).

Total amount of support: Varies.

NUMBER OF APPLICANTS MOST RECENT YEAR: 800.

APPLICATION INFORMATION:
All applicants must complete an application for admission to Chatham University which includes SAT or ACT scores, high school transcript, and application.

First-year students who choose not to submit the SAT/ACT will be required to submit a graded writing sample and resume or list of activities. Applicants will also have the option to submit a portfolio or special project/activity.

Duration: Four years of the undergraduate career, provided the high academic criteria expected of such scholars is maintained. Renewable annually based on grade point average of 3.0 or higher for Presidential Scholarship and 2.0 or higher for the other scholarships, and full-time enrollment.

Deadline: March 1.

STAFF:
Dr. Jennifer Burns, Director of Financial Aid

ADDRESS INQUIRIES TO:
Office of Enrollment Management
(See address above.)

CHINESE AMERICAN MEDICAL SOCIETY

41 Elizabeth Street
Suite 600
New York, NY 10013
(212) 334-4760
Fax: (646) 304-6373

E-MAIL ADDRESS:
jlove@camsociety.org

WEB SITE ADDRESS:
www.camsociety.org

TYPE:
Fellowships; Scholarships.

See entry 2253 for full listing.

# THE CLARK FOUNDATION					[1677]

One Rockefeller Plaza
New York, NY 10020
(607) 547-9927 (Cooperstown)
(212) 977-6900 (New York City)
Fax: (607) 547-8598

FOUNDED: 1931

NAME(S) OF PROGRAMS:
● **Clark Foundation Scholarship Program**

TYPE:
Scholarships. Undergraduate college scholarships.

YEAR PROGRAM STARTED: 1961

PURPOSE:
To assist Cooperstown area students in their pursuit of higher education.

LEGAL BASIS:
Nonprofit foundation.

ELIGIBILITY:
Individual undergraduate college scholarships are awarded to graduates of Central School, Cooperstown, NY and nine surrounding rural central school districts.

GEOGRAPHIC RESTRICTIONS:
Cooperstown and the nine surrounding New York rural central school districts of Cherry Valley-Springfield, Edmeston, Laurens, Milford, Mount Markham, Richfield Springs, Schenevus, Worcester and Owen D. Young.

FINANCIAL DATA:
Amount of support per award: Approximately $3,800.

Total amount of support: $3,660,000 for the year ended June 30, 2013.

NUMBER OF APPLICANTS MOST RECENT YEAR: 347.

NUMBER OF AWARDS: 183 new scholarships.

APPLICATION INFORMATION:
Students are recommended by their respective schools.

Duration: One year. Possible renewal each year for duration of undergraduate education.

Deadline: First week in February.

OFFICERS:
Jane Forbes Clark, President
Kevin S. Moore, Treasurer
Douglas Bauer, Executive Director and Secretary

ADDRESS INQUIRIES TO:
Gary Kuch, Director
Clark Foundation Scholarship Office
P.O. Box 427
Cooperstown, NY 13326

# COCA-COLA SCHOLARS FOUNDATION					[1678]

P.O. Box 442
Atlanta, GA 30301-0442
(800) 306-2653
Fax: (404) 733-5439

E-MAIL ADDRESS:
scholars@coca-cola.com

WEB SITE ADDRESS:
www.coca-colascholars.org

FOUNDED: 1986

AREAS OF INTEREST:
Enhancing educational opportunities in the U.S.

NAME(S) OF PROGRAMS:
● **Coca-Cola Scholars Program**

TYPE:
Scholarships. Coca-Cola Scholars Program is in two categories: National Scholars and Regional Scholars. They are awarded based on leadership, academics and community service.

YEAR PROGRAM STARTED: 1989

PURPOSE:
To enhance educational opportunities in the U.S. through scholarship awards and enrichment programs for young people who demonstrate, through academic excellence and leadership in their communities, their capacity for and commitment to making a difference in the world.

ELIGIBILITY:
Current high school (or home-schooled) seniors attending school in the U.S. (or select DoD schools). Applicant must not graduate prior to deadline.

GEOGRAPHIC RESTRICTIONS:
United States.

FINANCIAL DATA:
Program has awarded over $50,000,000 in scholarships since inception.

Amount of support per award: $10,000 regional and $20,000 national.

Total amount of support: Over $3,000,000 annually.

NUMBER OF APPLICANTS MOST RECENT YEAR: 50,000 to 100,000 annually.

APPLICATION INFORMATION:
Application must be submitted online.

Duration: Four or six years.

Deadline: October 31.

ADDRESS INQUIRIES TO:
See e-mail address above.

CONCORDIA UNIVERSITY [1679]

1455 de Maisonneuve Boulevard West
Graduate Awards Office, Room S-GM 930-49
Montreal QC H3G 1M8 Canada
(514) 848-2424 ext. 3809
(514) 848-2424 ext. 3801
Fax: (514) 848-2812

E-MAIL ADDRESS:
graduate-awards@concordia.ca

WEB SITE ADDRESS:
www.concordia.ca/offices/sgs.html

FOUNDED: 1974

AREAS OF INTEREST:
All disciplines.

NAME(S) OF PROGRAMS:
● **Concordia University Graduate Fellowships**

TYPE:
Assistantships; Awards/prizes; Conferences/seminars; Endowments; Fellowships; Scholarships. Postgraduate full-time fellowships.

PURPOSE:
To recruit highly qualified graduate students to Master's and doctoral programs.

ELIGIBILITY:
Candidates must be planning to pursue full-time Master's or doctoral studies at Concordia University. Academic merit is the prime consideration in the granting of the award.

All new admissions will be considered for awards.

GEOGRAPHIC RESTRICTIONS:
Canada.

FINANCIAL DATA:
Amount of support per award: $5,000 (CAN) to $45,000 (CAN) for three years.

NUMBER OF APPLICANTS MOST RECENT YEAR:
Over 1,000.

NUMBER OF AWARDS: 100 or more.

APPLICATION INFORMATION:
Applicants must submit a completed application form, statement of purpose, three letters of recommendation, and official transcripts of all university studies.
Duration: One to three years.

CONGRESSIONAL HISPANIC CAUCUS INSTITUTE
911 2nd Street, N.E.
Washington, DC 20002
(202) 543-1771
(800) 392-3532
Fax: (202) 546-2143

WEB SITE ADDRESS:
www.chci.org

TYPE:
Scholarships. The Institute's scholarship opportunities are afforded to Latino students in the U.S. who have a history of performing public service-oriented activities in their communities and who demonstrate a desire to continue their civic engagement in the future. There is no grade point average or academic major requirement. Students with excellent leadership potential are encouraged to apply.

See entry 1065 for full listing.

COOK FAMILY FOUNDATION
P.O. Box 278
Owosso, MI 48867-0278
(989) 725-1621
Fax: (989) 936-5910

E-MAIL ADDRESS:
tom@cookfamilyfoundation.org

WEB SITE ADDRESS:
www.cookfamilyfoundation.org

TYPE:
Capital grants; Challenge/matching grants; Demonstration grants; Development grants; Matching gifts; Project/program grants; Scholarships; Seed money grants; Technical assistance. Educational support.

See entry 1246 for full listing.

JACK KENT COOKE FOUNDATION   [1680]
44325 Woodridge Parkway
Lansdowne, VA 20176-5297
(855) 509-5253

E-MAIL ADDRESS:
scholarships@jkcf.org

WEB SITE ADDRESS:
www.jkcf.org

FOUNDED: 2000

AREAS OF INTEREST:
Education.

NAME(S) OF PROGRAMS:
● **College Scholarship Program**

● **Dissertation Fellowship Award**
● **Graduate Arts Award**
● **Undergraduate Transfer Scholarship**
● **Young Scholars Program**

TYPE:
Fellowships; Scholarships. College Scholarship Program is available to high-performing high school seniors with financial need who seek to attend and graduate from the nation's best four-year colleges and universities.

Dissertation Fellowship Award supports advanced doctoral students who are completing dissertations that further the understanding of the educational pathways and experiences of high-achieving, low-income students.

Graduate Arts Award enables students or recent alumni with exceptional artistic or creative promise and financial need to pursue up to three years of study at an accredited graduate institution in the U.S. or abroad.

Undergraduate Transfer Scholarship honors excellence by supporting outstanding community college students with financial need to transfer to and complete their Bachelor's degrees at the nation's top four-year colleges and universities.

Young Scholars Program seeks high-achieving, low- to moderate-income seventh-grade students, and cultivates their talents and abilities throughout high school by providing the personalized advising and financial support needed to secure challenging academic opportunities.

PURPOSE:
To help students of exceptional promise reach their full potential through education.

GEOGRAPHIC RESTRICTIONS:
United States.

FINANCIAL DATA:
Total assets of $623,028,000 for year ended May 31, 2012.

Amount of support per award: College Scholarship Program: Up to $30,000 per year. Dissertation Fellowship Award: Up to $25,000. Graduate Arts Award: Up to $50,000 per year. Undergraduate Transfer Scholarship: Up to $30,000 per year. Young Scholars Program: Varies.

Total amount of support: $20,071,000 for year ended May 31, 2012.

APPLICATION INFORMATION:
An application form needs to be completed. Application information is available on the web site.

Duration: College Scholarship Program: Up to four years. Dissertation Fellowship Award: Nine months and up to 18 months. Graduate Arts Award: Up to three years. Undergraduate Transfer Scholarship: Two to three years.

Deadline: College Scholarship Program: Opens late August; closes early November. Dissertation Fellowship Award: Opens October; closes early February. Graduate Arts Award: Opens early October; closes mid-/late November. Undergraduate Transfer Scholarship: Opens early September; closes mid-November. Young Scholars Program: Opens mid-June; closes late March.

DARTMOUTH COLLEGE
Office of Graduate Studies
Chavez/Eastman/Marshall
6062 Wentworth Hall
Hanover, NH 03755-3526
(603) 646-6578
Fax: (603) 646-8762

E-MAIL ADDRESS:
jane.b.seibel@dartmouth.edu

WEB SITE ADDRESS:
www.dartmouth.edu/~gradstdy/funding/fellowships

TYPE:
Exchange programs; Fellowships.

See entry 987 for full listing.

DAUGHTERS OF ITALY LODGE #2825   [1681]
14 South Jupiter Avenue
Clearwater, FL 33755
(727) 447-6890

E-MAIL ADDRESS:
vincenzad@verizon.net

WEB SITE ADDRESS:
www.daughtersofitaly.com

AREAS OF INTEREST:
Furtherance of education of Floridian students of Italian descent.

NAME(S) OF PROGRAMS:
● **Daughters of Italy Lodge #2825 Scholarship**

TYPE:
Scholarships. Open to full-time students at a Florida-accredited junior college, college or university or students graduating from high school.

PURPOSE:
To benefit worthy students of Italian descent that display academic excellence, leadership qualities and a financial need.

ELIGIBILITY:
Applicant must:
(1) be a Florida resident of Italian descent and a U.S. citizen;
(2) have a minimum grade point average of 3.0 (unweighted) and a minimum SAT total score of 1100, or must have an ACT Composite Score of 23 and;
(3) be a full-time student at a Florida-accredited junior college, college or university or a student graduating from high school.

GEOGRAPHIC RESTRICTIONS:
Florida.

FINANCIAL DATA:
Scholarship funds will not be released to any school until the Daughters of Italy Lodge #2825 Scholarship Chairperson receives a letter of acceptance from an accredited school and the recipient notifies the Chairperson in writing of her/his intent to enroll in the fall semester.
Amount of support per award: $1,000.

NUMBER OF AWARDS: 1.

APPLICATION INFORMATION:
Application, checklist and procedures may be accessed online. Applicants must include a 500-word essay on student's current and futuristic academic goals.
Duration: One year. Not renewable.
Deadline: End of March; exact date available online.

DAUGHTERS OF PENELOPE FOUNDATION, INC.

Supreme Headquarters
1909 Q Street, N.W., Suite 500
Washington, DC 20009
(202) 234-9741
Fax: (202) 483-6983

E-MAIL ADDRESS:
dophq@ahepa.org

WEB SITE ADDRESS:
www.dopfoundationinc.com

TYPE:
Scholarships.

See entry 1080 for full listing.

DAUGHTERS OF THE CINCINNATI   [1682]

20 West 44th Street, Room 508
New York, NY 10036
(212) 991-9945

E-MAIL ADDRESS:
scholarships@daughters1894.org

WEB SITE ADDRESS:
www.daughters1894.org

FOUNDED: 1894

NAME(S) OF PROGRAMS:
• **Daughters of the Cincinnati Scholarship Program**

TYPE:
Scholarships. Undergraduate scholarships.

YEAR PROGRAM STARTED: 1906

PURPOSE:
To assist high school seniors entering college with financial aid (annually for the four years).

LEGAL BASIS:
Nonprofit, tax-exempt organization.

ELIGIBILITY:
Applicant must be a senior in high school who is the daughter of a career officer commissioned in the regular Army, Navy, Air Force, Coast Guard or Marine Corps (active, retired or deceased). The daughters of officers in the Reserves, National Guard and State Militia are not eligible to apply for this scholarship.

FINANCIAL DATA:
Financial aid for tuition and/or living expense.
Amount of support per award: Average $3,000 to $5,000 annually.
Total amount of support: Varies.

NUMBER OF APPLICANTS MOST RECENT YEAR:
Approximately 200.

NUMBER OF AWARDS: Approximately 4 annually.

APPLICATION INFORMATION:
The application is accessible from the web site after supplying the parent's branch of service and rank.
Duration: Four years, or as long as the student attends college up to that length of time. Reviewed annually.
Deadline: Postmarked by March 15. Announcement in mid-May.

PUBLICATIONS:
Information sheet.

ADDRESS INQUIRIES TO:
Scholarship Administrator
(See address above.)

MICHAEL AND SUSAN DELL FOUNDATION   [1683]

P.O. Box 163867
Austin, TX 78716-3867
Fax: (512) 600-5501

E-MAIL ADDRESS:
info@msdf.org

WEB SITE ADDRESS:
www.msdf.org

NAME(S) OF PROGRAMS:
• **Dell Scholars Program**

TYPE:
Scholarships. Need-based scholarship that recognizes academic potential in lower-income and underserved students. Applicants must demonstrate a drive to succeed while overcoming personal obstacles.

PURPOSE:
To assist students who have worked hard to prepare themselves for higher education yet may have lower grade point averages and test scores because of adverse personal situations or surroundings.

ELIGIBILITY:
Applicants must:
(1) be high school seniors who have participated in a Michael and Susan Dell Foundation-approved college readiness program;
(2) be a U.S. citizen or legal permanent resident;
(3) have financial need confirmed through eligibility for a Federal Pell Grant;
(4) have a minimum 2.4 grade point average on a 4.0 scale and;
(5) be first generation college-bound.

Scholarship may be used at any accredited two- or four-year institution in the U.S. where credits can be earned towards a Baccalaureate degree, including community and junior colleges. Technical colleges and vocational programs are not eligible.

GEOGRAPHIC RESTRICTIONS:
United States.

FINANCIAL DATA:
Award may be applied to any cost of acquiring an education. Also provide other means of support, such as mentoring.
Amount of support per award: $20,000 over a maximum of six years.
Total amount of support: Varies.

APPLICATION INFORMATION:
All applications must be completed online. No paper applications will be accepted.
Duration: Up to six years.
Deadline: Application process opens in November and closes the following January 15.

THE EBELL OF LOS ANGELES   [1684]

743 South Lucerne Boulevard
Los Angeles, CA 90005-3707
(323) 931-1277 ext. 184
Fax: (323) 937-0272

E-MAIL ADDRESS:
Scholarship@ebelloflosangeles.com

WEB SITE ADDRESS:
www.ebellla.org

FOUNDED: 1894

AREAS OF INTEREST:
Higher education.

NAME(S) OF PROGRAMS:
• **Ebell/Flint Scholarship**

TYPE:
Scholarships.

YEAR PROGRAM STARTED: 1921

PURPOSE:
To support scholarships for qualified college students.

LEGAL BASIS:
Private foundation.

ELIGIBILITY:
To be eligible for an Ebell scholarship, applicants must be:
(1) United States citizen; if naturalized citizen, send proof;
(2) resident of Los Angeles County for one year or more and;
(3) Student attending an accredited Los Angeles County educational institution.

GEOGRAPHIC RESTRICTIONS:
Los Angeles County, California.

FINANCIAL DATA:
Amount of support per award: Four-year colleges: $5,000 per year (12 months) paid semi-annually in September and January; Two-year colleges: $3,000 per year.
Total amount of support: Over $200,000 annually.

NUMBER OF APPLICANTS MOST RECENT YEAR:
162.

NUMBER OF AWARDS: 58.

APPLICATION INFORMATION:
Guidelines and application form are available on the web site.
Duration: Three years or when the student graduates, whichever comes first.
Deadline: March 31.

IRS IDENTIFICATION NUMBER: 23-7049580

ADDRESS INQUIRIES TO:
See e-mail address above.

THE EISENHOWER FOUNDATION

200 S.E. 4th Street
Abilene, KS 67410
(785) 263-4751
(877) 746-4453 (toll-free phone)
Fax: (785) 263-6718

E-MAIL ADDRESS:
eisenhowerfoundation@nara.gov

WEB SITE ADDRESS:
www.dwighteisenhower.com
www.eisenhower.archives.
gov/travel_grants/travel_grants.html

TYPE:
Travel grants. Travel grants are awarded to individual researchers on a competitive basis to cover a portion of expenses while in Abilene, KS, using the presidential library.

See entry 1997 for full listing.

FEEA SCHOLARSHIP PROGRAM   [1685]

3333 South Wadsworth Boulevard
Suite 300
Lakewood, CO 80227
(303) 933-7580
Fax: (303) 933-7587

E-MAIL ADDRESS:
ngleason@feea.org

WEB SITE ADDRESS:
www.feea.org

AREAS OF INTEREST:
Education.

NAME(S) OF PROGRAMS:
● **Scholarship Program**

TYPE:
Scholarships. Merit-based scholarship competition program open exclusively to federal employees, their spouses and their children.

PURPOSE:
To financially aid hard-working federal employees, their spouses and their children in their college education.

ELIGIBILITY:
Must be a U.S. citizen and current civilian federal and/or postal employee (with at least three years of federal service), or their spouses or their children. Applicant must be a current high school senior who will be a college freshman by the fall of application or college student working toward an accredited degree and enrolled in a two- or four-year undergraduate, graduate or postgraduate program. All applicants must have a 3.0 cumulative grade point average unweighted on a 4.0 scale.

Current college freshmen must have a minimum 3.0 grade point average for the fall semester. Applicants who are dependents must be full-time students. Applicants who are federal employees may be part-time students.

GEOGRAPHIC RESTRICTIONS:
United States.

FINANCIAL DATA:
Amount of support per award: $500 to $5,000.

APPLICATION INFORMATION:
Application may be downloaded. Complete details may be viewed online. Applications should be submitted to the address above in a 9" x 12" (or larger) envelope, materials unbound and unfolded, along with a self-addressed, #10 envelope with current first-class postage.

Duration: One year. Must reapply for renewal.

Deadline: End of March.

ADDRESS INQUIRIES TO:
Niki Gleason
(See e-mail address above.)

*PLEASE NOTE:
Top student applicants have the opportunity to win one of three additional awards.

FINANCIAL SERVICE CENTERS OF AMERICA, INC. [1686]
Court Plaza South - East Wing
21 Main Street, Suite 101
Hackensack, NJ 07601
(201) 487-0412
Fax: (201) 487-3954

E-MAIL ADDRESS:
info@fisca.org

WEB SITE ADDRESS:
www.fisca.org

AREAS OF INTEREST:
Education to help unlock brighter futures for deserving and dedicated students.

NAME(S) OF PROGRAMS:
● **FiSCA National Scholarship Program**

TYPE:
Scholarships. The program offers scholarships for the freshman year of study. Criteria is based on academic achievement, leadership skills in school and the community, perseverance in the face of significant obstacles and an essay written expressly for the competition.

PURPOSE:
To benefit deserving college-bound high school seniors from families in areas served by its members.

ELIGIBILITY:
Scholarship program is open to college-bound high school seniors. Applicant must be a U.S. citizen, national or permanent resident. Candidates already in college and/or children or grandchildren of employees, officers or owners of FiSCA financial services locations are not eligible.

GEOGRAPHIC RESTRICTIONS:
United States and Puerto Rico.

FINANCIAL DATA:
Amount of support per award: Minimum of $2,000.

NUMBER OF AWARDS: Annually: Minimum of 2 in each of five regions.

APPLICATION INFORMATION:
The following materials are required of the applicant:
(1) application form (downloadable) completed in pen;
(2) official high school transcript, including first semester-year grades and test scores;
(3) two letters of recommendation (one from a community service organization and one from the applicant's school);
(4) description of applicant's community service activities and;
(5) an essay (200 words or less) that profiles a person or event that has influenced the applicant and how this has impacted an applicant's life.
Applications should be mailed to the regional committee chairman as listed on the web site.

Duration: One year; nonrenewable.

Deadline: Varies.

THE JAMES MARSTON FITCH CHARITABLE FOUNDATION
c/o The Neighborhood Preservation Center
232 East 11th Street
New York, NY 10003
(212) 252-6809
Fax: (212) 471-9987

E-MAIL ADDRESS:
info@fitchfoundation.org

WEB SITE ADDRESS:
www.fitchfoundation.org

TYPE:
Research grants. Richard Blinder Award was created to promote studies that explore the architecture of cultural buildings which integrate historic preservation and new construction - past, present and future; presented biennially.

Mid-Career Grant Program: This grant is the primary mission and the signature grant of this Foundation. The grants are intended to support projects of innovative original research or creative design that advance the practice of historic preservation in the U.S.

See entry 416 for full listing.

FLORIDA DEPARTMENT OF EDUCATION
Office of Student Financial Assistance
325 West Gaines Street, Suite 1314
Tallahassee, FL 32399-0400
(888) 827-2004
Fax: (850) 487-1809

E-MAIL ADDRESS:
osfa@fldoe.org

WEB SITE ADDRESS:
www.FloridaStudentFinancialAid.org

TYPE:
Scholarships. Financial assistance for descendants of the Rosewood family affected by the incidents of January 1923, to attend a state university, public community college or public postsecondary vocational-technical school.

See entry 1028 for full listing.

FLORIDA DEPARTMENT OF EDUCATION [1687]
Office of Student Financial Assistance
325 West Gaines Street, Suite 1314
Tallahassee, FL 32399-0400
(888) 827-2004
Fax: (850) 487-1809

E-MAIL ADDRESS:
osfa@fldoe.org

WEB SITE ADDRESS:
www.FloridaStudentFinancialAid.org

AREAS OF INTEREST:
Financial aid for Florida undergraduate students.

NAME(S) OF PROGRAMS:
● **Access to Better Learning and Education Grant Program (ABLE)**
● **Mary McLeod Bethune Scholarship Program (MMB)**
● **First Generation Matching Grant Program (FGMG)**
● **Florida Resident Access Grant (FRAG)**
● **Florida Student Assistance Grant Program (FSAG)**
● **Florida Work Experience Program (FWEP)**
● **Scholarships for Children and Spouses of Deceased or Disabled Veterans (CSDDV)**

TYPE:
Scholarships. The Access to Better Learning and Education (ABLE) Grant Program provides tuition assistance to Florida undergraduate students enrolled in degree programs at eligible private Florida colleges or universities. ABLE is a decentralized program, and each participating institution determines application procedures, deadlines and student eligibility.

The Mary McLeod Bethune Scholarships (MMB) are awarded to undergraduate students who meet scholastic requirements attending Bethune-Cookman University, Edward Waters College, Florida A&M University, or Florida Memorial University.

The First Generation Matching Grant Program (FGMG) provides need-based grants to degree-seeking, resident, undergraduate students who demonstrate financial need, are enrolled in participating postsecondary institutions, and whose parents have not earned Baccalaureate or higher degrees.

Florida Resident Access Grants (FRAG) are provided to full-time Florida undergraduates attending an eligible private, nonprofit Florida college or university.

The Florida Student Assistance Grant Program (FSAG) is a need-based grant program available to degree-seeking and certificate-seeking, resident, undergraduate students who demonstrate substantial financial need and are enrolled in participating postsecondary institutions.

The Florida Work Experience Program (FWEP) provides eligible Florida students the opportunity to secure work experiences that will complement and reinforce the students' educational and career goals.

Scholarships for Children and Spouses of Deceased or Disabled Veterans (CSDDV) provides scholarships for dependent children and unremarried spouses of Florida veterans who died as a result of service-connected injuries, diseases, or disabilities sustained while on active duty or have been certified by the Florida Department of Veterans' Affairs as having service-connected 100% total and permanent disabilities.

PURPOSE:
To provide financial assistance to Florida students continuing their education.

LEGAL BASIS:
State agency.

GEOGRAPHIC RESTRICTIONS:
Florida.

FINANCIAL DATA:
Amount of support per award: Varies per program.
Total amount of support: Varies.

APPLICATION INFORMATION:
Detailed program information can be found on the web site.

ADDRESS INQUIRIES TO:
See e-mail and phone number above.

FLORIDA DEPARTMENT OF EDUCATION   [1688]
Office of Student Financial Assistance
325 West Gaines Street, Suite 1314
Tallahassee, FL 32399-0400
(888) 827-2004
Fax: (850) 487-1809

E-MAIL ADDRESS:
osfa@fldoe.org

WEB SITE ADDRESS:
www.FloridaStudentFinancialAid.
org/SSFAD/bf

NAME(S) OF PROGRAMS:
● **Florida Bright Futures Scholarship Program**

TYPE:
Scholarships. The Florida Bright Futures Scholarship Program is the umbrella program for three state-funded scholarships based on academic achievement in high school: Florida Academic Scholars (FAS) Award, Florida Medallion Scholars (FMS) Award and Florida Gold Seal Vocational Scholars (GSV) Award.

PURPOSE:
To reward Florida's high school graduates who merit recognition of high academic achievement.

LEGAL BASIS:
State agency.

ELIGIBILITY:
Initial eligibility requirements to receive funding are as follows:
(1) be a Florida resident and a U.S. citizen or eligible noncitizen; student's residency and citizenship status are determined by the postsecondary institution; consult the financial aid office or admissions office of the institution one plans to attend;
(2) not owe a repayment or be in default under any state or federal grant, loan, or scholarship program unless satisfactory arrangements to repay have been made and;
(3) meet specific coursework and minimum grade point average and test score requirements.

GEOGRAPHIC RESTRICTIONS:
Florida.

FINANCIAL DATA:
Total amount of support: Varies.

APPLICATION INFORMATION:
Detailed program information can be found on the web site.
Duration: One year; renewable.
Deadline: Prior to high school graduation.

ADDRESS INQUIRIES TO:
State Scholarship and Grant Programs
(See address above.)

FLORIDA DEPARTMENT OF EDUCATION
Office of Student Financial Assistance
325 West Gaines Street, Suite 1314
Tallahassee, FL 32399-0400
(888) 827-2004
Fax: (850) 487-1809

E-MAIL ADDRESS:
osfa@fldoe.org

WEB SITE ADDRESS:
www.FloridaStudentFinancialAid.org

TYPE:
Challenge/matching grants; Grants-in-aid. Jose Marti Scholarship Challenge Grant Fund is a need-based merit scholarship that provides financial assistance to eligible students of Hispanic origin who will attend Florida public or eligible private institutions.

See entry 1067 for full listing.

FOUNDATION FOR TECHNOLOGY AND ENGINEERING EDUCATION   [1689]
1914 Association Drive
Suite 201
Reston, VA 20191-1539
(703) 860-2100
Fax: (703) 860-0353

E-MAIL ADDRESS:
iteea@iteea.org

WEB SITE ADDRESS:
www.iteea.org

FOUNDED: 1939

AREAS OF INTEREST:
Technology education.

NAME(S) OF PROGRAMS:
● **FTEE Undergraduate Scholarship**

TYPE:
Scholarships. The scholarship is for an undergraduate student majoring in technology and engineering education teacher preparation.

PURPOSE:
To support teacher preparation in technology and engineering education.

ELIGIBILITY:
Applicant must be a member of the International Technology and Engineering Educators Association and be a current, full-time undergraduate majoring in technology and engineering education teacher preparation. Applicant must not be a senior by application deadline.

FINANCIAL DATA:
Amount of support per award: $1,000.

NUMBER OF AWARDS: 1.

APPLICATION INFORMATION:
Applicants must submit the application package which consists of four copies of the following required items:
(1) letter of transmittal that includes a statement about personal interest in teaching technology and engineering and applicant's address with day and evening telephone numbers;
(2) resume or vitae which indicate career goals, current professional and college activities and achievements (maximum three pages);
(3) photocopy of college transcript (required 2.5 grade point average on 4.0 scale) and;
(4) three faculty letters of recommendation from among his or her professors and/or advisor.
Deadline: December 1.

ADDRESS INQUIRIES TO:
FTEE Undergraduate Scholarship
Foundation for Technology and Engineering Education
(See address above.)

FOUNDATION FOR TECHNOLOGY AND ENGINEERING EDUCATION   [1690]
1914 Association Drive
Suite 201
Reston, VA 20191-1539
(703) 860-2100
Fax: (703) 860-0353

E-MAIL ADDRESS:
iteea@iteea.org

WEB SITE ADDRESS:
www.iteea.org

FOUNDED: 1939

AREAS OF INTEREST:
Technology education.

NAME(S) OF PROGRAMS:
● **Litherland/FTEE Scholarship Undergraduate Major in Technology and Engineering Education**

TYPE:
Scholarships.

PURPOSE:
To assist an undergraduate student majoring in technology education and engineering teacher preparation.

ELIGIBILITY:
Applicant must be member of the International Technology and Engineering Educators Association and a current,

full-time undergraduate majoring in technology education and engineering teacher preparation. The student must not be a senior by application deadline. The award is based upon interest in teaching, academic ability, need and faculty recommendations.

FINANCIAL DATA:
Amount of support per award: $1,000.

NUMBER OF AWARDS: 1.

APPLICATION INFORMATION:
Applicants must submit an application package including four copies of the following required items:
(1) a letter of transmittal that includes a statement about his or her personal interest in teaching technology and engineering and applicant's address with day and evening telephone numbers;
(2) resume or vitae identifying career goals, current professional activities and achievements;
(3) photocopy of college transcript and;
(4) three faculty letters of recommendation from among his or her professors and/or advisor.
Deadline: December 1.

ADDRESS INQUIRIES TO:
Litherland/FTEE Scholarship
Foundation for Technology and
Engineering Education
(See address above.)

*SPECIAL STIPULATIONS:
Applicant must be a member of the ITEEA.

FREEDOM ALLIANCE   [1691]
22570 Markey Court, Suite 240
Dulles, VA 20166
(703) 444-7940
(800) 475-6620
Fax: (703) 444-9893

E-MAIL ADDRESS:
info@fascholarship.com

WEB SITE ADDRESS:
www.fascholarship.com

FOUNDED: 1990

AREAS OF INTEREST:
Scholarship aid to the children of American military personnel who have been killed or injured in military service.

NAME(S) OF PROGRAMS:
• **Freedom Alliance Scholarship Fund**

TYPE:
Scholarships. Freedom Alliance Scholarship Fund provides college scholarships to the sons and daughters of America's military heroes - those who sacrifice life or limb in defense of America's freedom.

YEAR PROGRAM STARTED: 1990

PURPOSE:
To honor the bravery and dedication exhibited by Americans in the U.S. armed forces who have sacrificed life and limb by providing educational scholarships to their children.

LEGAL BASIS:
501(c)(3) educational and charitable foundation.

ELIGIBILITY:
Students must be a dependent child of a service member who was killed or was permanently disabled (100% rating) in the line of duty, or who is currently certified as POW or MIA. The applicant must also be a senior in high school, a high school graduate, or enrolled in an institution of higher learning, including colleges, universities or vocational schools.

FINANCIAL DATA:
Amount of support per award: Varies.

NUMBER OF AWARDS: 277 for the year 2013.

APPLICATION INFORMATION:
Eligible students seeking a Freedom Alliance scholarship must first complete an application form. Applications will not be considered by the scholarship committee unless all required materials listed below accompany the application package:
(1) certificate of death/disability or proof of POW/MIA status as defined in the instructions;
(2) proof of dependency as defined in the instructions;
(3) 500-word essay as explained in the instructions;
(4) official transcripts from high school and all post-high school educational institutions;
(5) photo of applicant and;
(6) photo of parent.

DD Form 214 is also required in the case of a student whose parent is permanently disabled, in addition to the VA rating letter demonstrating permanent disability in the application packet.
Duration: Scholarships are awarded annually and are renewable for a total of four scholarships.

STAFF:
Thomas Kilgannon, President
Calvin Coolidge, Executive Director

BOARD OF DIRECTORS:
Hon. Ralph Smith, Chairman
Thomas Cook, Treasurer
Michael Mason
Jerry Morris
Rita Scott

FOUNDERS:
Lt Col Oliver L. North, USMC (Ret.),
Honorary Chairman
Lt Gen Edward J. Bronars, USMC

ADDRESS INQUIRIES TO:
Wanda Cruz, Program Assistant
(See address above.)

GOLDEN KEY INTERNATIONAL HONOUR SOCIETY, INC.   [1692]
1040 Crown Pointe Parkway
Suite 900
Atlanta, GA 30338
(678) 689-2200
(800) 377-2401

E-MAIL ADDRESS:
awards@goldenkey.org

WEB SITE ADDRESS:
www.goldenkey.org

AREAS OF INTEREST:
Nonprofit academic honors organization that recognizes the top 15% of juniors and seniors in all undergraduate fields.

NAME(S) OF PROGRAMS:
• **Business Achievement Awards**
• **Community Service Award**
• **Education Achievement Awards**
• **Engineering/Technology Achievement Awards**
• **GEICO Life Scholarship**
• **The Golden Key Graduate Scholarship Award**
• **Golden Key Research Grants**
• **Literary Achievement Awards**
• **Student Leader Award (Regional and International)**
• **Study Abroad Scholarships**
• **Visual and Performing Arts Achievement Awards**

TYPE:
Awards/prizes; Scholarships; Travel grants.
Business Achievement Awards: Recognize members who excel in the study of business.

Community Service Award: Recognizes one member for outstanding service to the community.

Education Achievement Awards: Recognize members who excel in the study of education.

Engineering/Technology Achievement Awards: Recognize members who excel in the study of engineering or technology.

GEICO Life Scholarship: Recognizes outstanding members who achieve academic excellence while balancing additional commitments such as family and/or career.

The Golden Key Graduate Scholar Award: Golden Key's premier scholarship program. Supports members' post-baccalaureate study at accredited universities anywhere in the world.

Golden Key Research Grants: Allow members to conduct thesis research and/or present their research at professional conferences or student research symposia.

Literary Achievement Awards: Recognize the literary talents of members in four categories: fiction, nonfiction, poetry and news writing.

Student Leader Awards: Regional Student Leader Awards recognizes one member in each region (10 U.S. regions) for outstanding commitment to the Society and display of effective campus and community leadership while maintaining superior academic performance.

Study Abroad Scholarships: Assists members who participate in a study abroad program.

Visual and Performance Arts Achievement Awards: Recognize the visual art talents of members in nine categories: painting, drawing, photography, sculpture, computer-generated art/graphic design/illustration, mixed media, instrumental performance, vocal performance, and dance.

PURPOSE:
To enable members to realize their potential.

ELIGIBILITY:
Open to Golden Key members.

FINANCIAL DATA:
Amount of support per award: $1,000 to $10,000.

APPLICATION INFORMATION:
Golden Key's scholarships and awards require a formal application. Each scholarship has a unique submission deadline and application process. Details about each of the scholarship programs can be found under the Scholarship and Award Listing on the web site. All scholarship submissions must be written in English.

ADDRESS INQUIRIES TO:
Scholarship Program Manager
(See address above.)

*SPECIAL STIPULATIONS:
Only Golden Key members may apply for these scholarships and awards.

GRADUATE EDUCATION OPPORTUNITY PROGRAM

Michigan State University
The Graduate School, 479 West Circle Drive
116 Linton Hall
East Lansing, MI 48824-1044
(517) 353-3262
Fax: (517) 353-3355

E-MAIL ADDRESS:
gradschool@grd.msu.edu

WEB SITE ADDRESS:
www.grad.msu.edu

TYPE:
Assistantships; Fellowships.

See entry 992 for full listing.

THE GREATER KANAWHA VALLEY FOUNDATION

Huntington Square, Suite 1600
900 Lee Street East
Charleston, WV 25301
(304) 346-3620
Fax: (304) 346-3640

E-MAIL ADDRESS:
sryder@tgkvf.org

WEB SITE ADDRESS:
www.tgkvf.org

TYPE:
Project/program grants; Scholarships.

See entry 1287 for full listing.

THE HIGHER EDUCATION STUDENT ASSISTANCE AUTHORITY   [1693]

P.O. Box 540
Trenton, NJ 08625
(609) 588-3268
Fax: (609) 588-2390

E-MAIL ADDRESS:
lsharp@hesaa.org

WEB SITE ADDRESS:
www.hesaa.org

FOUNDED: 1959

AREAS OF INTEREST:
State financial assistance for college students.

NAME(S) OF PROGRAMS:
● **Tuition Aid Grant (TAG)**

TYPE:
Grants-in-aid. The Higher Education Student
Assistance Authority (HESAA) is a New
Jersey authority that provides students and
families with the financial and informational
resources for students to pursue their
education beyond high school. With roots
dating back to 1959, HESAA's singular focus
has always been to benefit the students it
serves. HESAA provides state supplemental
loans, grants and scholarships. HESAA also
administers the state's college savings plan.

YEAR PROGRAM STARTED: 1969

PURPOSE:
To provide financial assistance to needy
students attending approved New Jersey
institutions. This is calculated by estimating
what a family can contribute from income
and assets plus a contribution from the
student's earnings and savings. The amount
and type of aid will depend upon program
eligibility, available funds and the degree of
need.

LEGAL BASIS:
New Jersey Higher Education Tuition Aid
Act.

ELIGIBILITY:
Applicants must be New Jersey residents for
at least 12 consecutive months prior to
receiving an award, and will be enrolled in
an approved New Jersey institution. Student
must be a U.S. citizen or eligible noncitizen
and be registered with the Selective Service,
if applicable. Grants are renewable annually
based upon satisfactory academic progress
and continued financial need. Students who
have received a Baccalaureate degree are not
eligible.

GEOGRAPHIC RESTRICTIONS:
New Jersey.

FINANCIAL DATA:
Amount of support per award: Award
amounts are based on the student's New
Jersey Eligibility Index, tuition charged and
appropriated funds.

NUMBER OF AWARDS: Based upon
appropriations.

APPLICATION INFORMATION:
Applicants must file the Free Application for
Federal Student Aid (FAFSA), which is
available online at www.fafsa.ed.gov, through
high school guidance and financial aid offices
or by calling, Tel: (800) 792-8670, available
from any location in New Jersey, Monday
through Friday, 9 A.M. to 5 P.M.
Duration: Renewable for four years of
undergraduate study providing eligibility
continues and an application is filed.
Deadline: October 1 for fall and spring
terms. March 1 for spring term only.
Renewals June 1 for fall and spring terms.

PUBLICATIONS:
*State and Federal Financial Aid Programs
for New Jersey Students,* brochure.

ADDRESS INQUIRIES TO:
Larry Sharp
Director, Grants and Scholarships
(See address above.)

THE HIGHER EDUCATION STUDENT ASSISTANCE AUTHORITY   [1694]

P.O. Box 540
Trenton, NJ 08625
(609) 588-3268
Fax: (609) 588-2390

E-MAIL ADDRESS:
lsharp@hesaa.org

WEB SITE ADDRESS:
www.hesaa.org

FOUNDED: 1959

AREAS OF INTEREST:
State financial assistance for college students.

NAME(S) OF PROGRAMS:
● **Survivor Tuition Benefits Program**

TYPE:
Grants-in-aid; Scholarships. The Higher
Education Student Assistance Authority
(HESAA) is a New Jersey authority that
provides students and families with the
financial and informational resources for
students to pursue their education beyond
high school. With roots dating back to 1959,
HESAA's singular focus has always been to
benefit the students it serves. HESAA

provides state supplemental loans, grants and
scholarships. HESAA also administers the
state's college savings plan.

YEAR PROGRAM STARTED: 1980

PURPOSE:
To benefit dependent children and surviving
spouses of New Jersey firefighters,
emergency service workers or law
enforcement officers who were killed in the
line of duty.

ELIGIBILITY:
Student must be a child or spouse of a New
Jersey firefighter, emergency service worker
or law enforcement officer killed in the line
of duty, who is resident of New Jersey,
attending an independent New Jersey
institution of higher education as an
undergraduate. Student must be a U.S. citizen
or eligible noncitizen.

GEOGRAPHIC RESTRICTIONS:
New Jersey.

FINANCIAL DATA:
Covers the cost of tuition at any New Jersey
public college or university. Students enrolled
at an independent New Jersey college or
university may receive up to the highest
tuition charged at a New Jersey public
institution.

APPLICATION INFORMATION:
Application information is available on the
HESAA web site.
Duration: Financial assistance is renewable
for four years of undergraduate study
providing eligibility for each program
continues and an application is filed.
Deadline: October 1 for fall and spring
terms. March 1 for spring term only.

PUBLICATIONS:
*State and Federal Financial Aid Programs
for New Jersey Students,* brochure.

THE HIGHER EDUCATION STUDENT ASSISTANCE AUTHORITY   [1695]

P.O. Box 540
Trenton, NJ 08625
(609) 588-3268
Fax: (609) 588-2228

E-MAIL ADDRESS:
clientservices@hesaa.org

WEB SITE ADDRESS:
www.hesaa.org

FOUNDED: 1959

AREAS OF INTEREST:
State financial assistance for college students.

NAME(S) OF PROGRAMS:
● **Law Enforcement Officer Memorial
   Scholarship**
● **New Jersey Student Tuition Assistance
   Reward Scholarship**
● **New Jersey Student Tuition Assistance
   Reward Scholarship II**
● **New Jersey World Trade Center
   Scholarship**

TYPE:
Scholarships. Law Enforcement Officer
Memorial Scholarship provides financial aid
for eligible children of law enforcement
officers killed in the line of duty.

New Jersey Student Tuition Assistance
Reward Scholarship provides access to higher
education for the state's highest achieving
students.

New Jersey Student Tuition Assistance Reward Scholarship II enables successful NJ STARS scholars to transfer to a New Jersey four-year college or university and earn a Bachelor's degree.

New Jersey World Trade Center Scholarship benefits dependent children and surviving spouses of New Jersey residents who were killed in or who died of the terrorist attacks against the U.S. on September 11, 2001.

PURPOSE:
To provide financial assistance to college students demonstrating academic proficiency.

GEOGRAPHIC RESTRICTIONS:
New Jersey.

APPLICATION INFORMATION:
Application information is available on the HESAA web site. NJ STARS/II applicants must file a FAFSA, which is available online through the HESAA web site, through high school guidance offices or college financial aid offices, or by calling 800-792-8670.

Deadline: New Jersey World Trade Scholarship: October 1 for Fall or full academic year; March 1 for Spring semester.

STAFF:
Larry Sharp, Director, Grants and Scholarships

HISPANIC SCHOLARSHIP FUND
1411 West 190th Street
Suite 325
Gardena, CA 90248
(877) 473-4636

E-MAIL ADDRESS:
info@hsf.net
gmsinfo@hsf.net

WEB SITE ADDRESS:
www.hsf.net
www.gmsp.org

TYPE:
Scholarships. Awarded to Hispanic community college, undergraduate and graduate students.

See entry 1068 for full listing.

HOLLAND & KNIGHT CHARITABLE FOUNDATION, INC.
P.O. Box 2877
Tampa, FL 33601-2877
(813) 227-8500

E-MAIL ADDRESS:
nativewriters@hklaw.com

WEB SITE ADDRESS:
foundation.hklaw.com

TYPE:
Awards/prizes; Scholarships. Young Native Writers Essay Contest is a writing contest for Native American high school students.

See entry 1050 for full listing.

HOLLAND & KNIGHT CHARITABLE FOUNDATION, INC.
P.O. Box 2877
Tampa, FL 33601-2877
(813) 227-8500

E-MAIL ADDRESS:
holocaust@hklaw.com

WEB SITE ADDRESS:
foundation.hklaw.com

TYPE:
Awards/prizes; Scholarships. The Holocaust Remembrance Project is a national essay contest for high school students designed to encourage and promote the study of the Holocaust.

See entry 598 for full listing.

THE HONOR SOCIETY OF PHI KAPPA PHI [1696]
7576 Goodwood Boulevard
Baton Rouge, LA 70806
(225) 388-4917 ext. 235
(800) 804-9880 ext. 235
Fax: (225) 388-4900

E-MAIL ADDRESS:
kpartin@phikappaphi.org

WEB SITE ADDRESS:
www.phikappaphi.org

FOUNDED: 1897

AREAS OF INTEREST:
Scholastic excellence in all academic fields.

NAME(S) OF PROGRAMS:
● **The Phi Kappa Phi Fellowship**

TYPE:
Fellowships. Support for the first year of graduate or professional school.

YEAR PROGRAM STARTED: 1932

PURPOSE:
To stimulate members of Phi Kappa Phi to go to graduate or professional school.

LEGAL BASIS:
Honor Society incorporated in Michigan, May 20, 1972. Authorized to operate in Louisiana, September 1978. Tax-exempt under IRS 501(c)(3). Companion organization, the Phi Kappa Phi Foundation, incorporated in California, December 17, 1969, as a Public Benefit Foundation, tax-exempt under IRS 501(c)(3).

ELIGIBILITY:
Applicant must be a member of Phi Kappa Phi, maintain high scholastic standing and be recommended by a chapter of Phi Kappa Phi.

GEOGRAPHIC RESTRICTIONS:
United States.

FINANCIAL DATA:
Amount of support per award: $5,000 or $15,000.
Total amount of support: $330,000.

COOPERATIVE FUNDING PROGRAMS: Awards made through Phi Kappa Phi Foundation, a companion organization to the Society.

NUMBER OF APPLICANTS MOST RECENT YEAR: 170.

NUMBER OF AWARDS: 56 (51 valued at $5,000 and 5 valued at $15,000) for the year 2013.

APPLICATION INFORMATION:
Completed application packet must be returned to the local chapter on or before the deadline.
Duration: One academic year. Nonrenewable.

IRS IDENTIFICATION NUMBER: 95-1856406

STAFF:
Kelli Partin, Programs Coordinator

ADDRESS INQUIRIES TO:
Kelli Partin, Programs Coordinator
(See address above.)

HORIZONS FOUNDATION
WID HORIZONS
2111 Wilson Boulevard, Suite 400
Arlington, VA 22201
(703) 522-1820
Fax: (703) 522-1885

E-MAIL ADDRESS:
jcasey@ndia.org

WEB SITE ADDRESS:
wid.ndia.org

TYPE:
Scholarships. The Horizons Foundation Scholarship Program is supported by accredited colleges and universities. Awards are made on an annual basis. The Foundation selects all scholarship recipients based on criteria it sets. Scholarships are awarded to applicants who require financial assistance, demonstrate strong academic credentials and a commitment to a career in national security.

See entry 1084 for full listing.

HORTICULTURAL RESEARCH INSTITUTE, INC. [1697]
1200 G Street, N.W.
Suite 800
Washington, DC 20005
(202) 695-2474
Fax: (888) 761-7883

E-MAIL ADDRESS:
tjodon@hriresearch.org

WEB SITE ADDRESS:
www.hriresearch.org

AREAS OF INTEREST:
Nursery, landscape research and horticulture.

NAME(S) OF PROGRAMS:
● **Carville M. Akehurst Memorial Scholarship**
● **Timothy Bigelow and Palmer W. Bigelow, Jr. Scholarship**
● **Muggets Scholarship**
● **Spring Meadow Nursery Scholarship**

TYPE:
Scholarships. The Carville M. Akehurst Memorial Scholarship was established by the Mid-Atlantic Nursery Trade Show, Inc. (MANTS) to provide scholarship opportunity to qualified students from Maryland, Virginia or West Virginia to help ensure the continuity of the nursery and landscape profession.

The Bigelow Scholarships provide aid to students from New England.

The Muggets Scholarship and the Spring Meadow Nursery Scholarship are intended to help aspiring students from across the U.S. obtain a degree in horticulture (nursery industry).

YEAR PROGRAM STARTED: 1988

PURPOSE:
To aid students seeking a career in the horticulture/nursery industry.

LEGAL BASIS:
Nonprofit organization.

ELIGIBILITY:
Carville M. Akehurst Memorial Scholarship: Applicant must be a resident of Maryland, Virginia or West Virginia, must be enrolled in an accredited undergraduate or graduate landscape/horticulture program or related discipline at a two- or four-year institution, must be currently enrolled in good standing,

with a good academic record, carry a full-time course load and must have at least a junior standing (four-year curriculum) or senior standing (two-year curriculum).

Bigelow Scholarship: Applicant must be a resident of one of the six New England states and be enrolled full-time in an accredited undergraduate or graduate landscape/horticulture program. Preference will be given to an applicant who plans to work in any aspect of the nursery industry following graduation. Preference will also be given to an applicant in financial need. Previous winners are not eligible for additional funding.

Muggets and Spring Meadow Nursery Scholarships: Applicant must be enrolled in an accredited undergraduate or graduate landscape horticulture program or related discipline at a two- or four-year institution (students in vocational agriculture programs are also eligible), must be currently enrolled in good standing, with a good academic record, and carry a full-time course load. Applicant must be a sophmore or senior at the start of the fall semester.

NUMBER OF APPLICANTS MOST RECENT YEAR:
Akehurst Memorial Scholarship: 10; Bigelow Scholarship: 10; Muggets Scholarship: 35; Spring Meadow Nursery Scholarship: 34.

NUMBER OF AWARDS: Carville M. Akehurst Memorial Scholarship: 2; All other scholarships: 1.

APPLICATION INFORMATION:
Applications are available online.
Duration: Bigelow Scholarship: One-time award.
Deadline: May 31.

IRS IDENTIFICATION NUMBER: 52-1052547

ADDRESS INQUIRIES TO:
Teresa Jodon, Executive Director
(See address above.)

ILLINOIS RESTAURANT ASSOCIATION EDUCATIONAL FOUNDATION   [1698]
33 West Monroe, Suite 250
Chicago, IL 60603
(312) 787-4000
Fax: (312) 845-1956

WEB SITE ADDRESS:
www.illinoisrestaurants.org

FOUNDED: 1973

AREAS OF INTEREST:
Foodservice/restaurant/hospitality.

NAME(S) OF PROGRAMS:
• **IRA Educational Foundation Scholarship Program**

TYPE:
Scholarships.

YEAR PROGRAM STARTED: 1973

PURPOSE:
To build the Illinois hospitality work force through the ProStart® curriculum, career exploration, workforce development and scholarships for high school students.

LEGAL BASIS:
Not-for-profit organization.

ELIGIBILITY:
Applicants must be permanent residents of the state of Illinois who are applying to or enrolled in an accredited culinary school,

college or university and who are enrolled full-time or substantial part-time, taking a minimum of nine credit hours each term, majoring in a culinary restaurant management or foodservice-related program.

GEOGRAPHIC RESTRICTIONS:
Illinois.

FINANCIAL DATA:
Scholarships provide assistance toward tuition and materials.
Amount of support per award: Minimum $1,000.

NUMBER OF AWARDS: 60.

APPLICATION INFORMATION:
Application forms are available on the web site.
Duration: One academic year. Renewal is not automatic.
Deadline: April 29.

IRS IDENTIFICATION NUMBER: 36-3271510

ADDRESS INQUIRIES TO:
Jenna Zera
Tel: 312-380-4117
Fax: 312-787-4792
(See address above.)

INDIANA COMMISSION FOR HIGHER EDUCATION, DIVISION OF STUDENT FINANCIAL AID   [1699]
W462 Indiana Government Center South
402 West Washington Street
Indianapolis, IN 46204
(888) 528-4719
Fax: (317) 232-3260

E-MAIL ADDRESS:
awards@che.in.gov

WEB SITE ADDRESS:
www.in.gov/che

FOUNDED: 1965

AREAS OF INTEREST:
Student financial aid.

NAME(S) OF PROGRAMS:
• **Mitch Daniels Early Graduation Scholarship**
• **EARN Indiana (State Work Study)**
• **Minority Teacher Scholarship**
• **National Guard Grant**
• **The Frank O'Bannon Grant**
• **Student Teaching Stipend for High-Needs Fields**
• **Student Teaching Stipend for Minorities**
• **21st Century Scholars Program**

TYPE:
Grants-in-aid; Project/program grants; Scholarships; Work-study programs. Monetary grants awarded annually toward the cost of tuition.

The Minority Teacher Scholarship was created to address the critical shortage of Black and Hispanic teachers in Indiana.

Student Teaching Stipend for High-Needs Fields is for students who plan to teach in "high-need" fields, which means a teaching specialty that affects the economic vitality of Indiana and in which there is a shortage of candidates.

Student Teaching Stipend for Minorities is for minority students (defined as Black and Hispanic) who plan to teach.

21st Century Scholars Program was created as Indiana's way of raising the educational aspirations of low- and moderate-income families.

YEAR PROGRAM STARTED: 1971

PURPOSE:
To provide financial assistance to students attending colleges within the state of Indiana.

LEGAL BASIS:
Indiana Scholarship Act, I.C. 20-12-21. I.C. 20-12-21.1.

ELIGIBILITY:
An applicant must be an Indiana resident, a U.S. citizen or eligible noncitizen and must attend an eligible institution located within the state of Indiana as a full-time undergraduate student (12 to 15 hours per term).

GEOGRAPHIC RESTRICTIONS:
Indiana.

FINANCIAL DATA:
Amount of support per award: Varies; Student Teaching Stipend for High-Needs Fields and Student Teaching Stipend for Minorities: Stipend up to $5,000 for students with a grade point average 3.5 on a 4.0 scale and $4,000 for students with a grade point average of 3.0 on a 4.0 scale.
Total amount of support: Varies.
Matching fund requirements: Only in EARN Indiana.

APPLICATION INFORMATION:
Free Application for Federal Student Aid (FAFSA) must be received by deadline for The Frank O'Bannon Grant.

21st Century Scholars Program: Must sign and submit pledge affirmation before March 10. File for state and federal financial aid by completing the FAFSA on time. Apply for admission and institutional financial aid at the Indiana college attending by the deadline for each college. Enroll as a full-time college student and maintain Indiana residency.
Duration: Four years. Reapplication required annually.
Deadline: The Frank O'Bannon Grant: March 10. Announcement in June. Minority Teacher Scholarship: October 4. Student Teaching Stipend: Beginning of the term in which they are teaching. 21st Century Scholars Program: March 10.

PUBLICATIONS:
Application guidelines.

STAFF:
Mary Jane Michalak, Associate Commissioner
Amanda Stanley, EARN Indiana Program Director
Eugene Johnson, Director of Student Awards

ADDRESS INQUIRIES TO:
State Student Assistance Commission
(See address above.)

INSTITUTE FOR THE INTERNATIONAL EDUCATION OF STUDENTS (IES)   [1700]
33 West Monroe Street
Suite 2300
Chicago, IL 60603-5405
(312) 944-1750
(800) 995-2300
Fax: (312) 944-1448

E-MAIL ADDRESS:
info@IESabroad.org

WEB SITE ADDRESS:
www.IESabroad.org

FOUNDED: 1950

AREAS OF INTEREST:
International education (JYA).

NAME(S) OF PROGRAMS:
- **The IES Abroad Boren and Gilman Scholarship Support Grants**
- **IES Abroad Merit-Based Scholarships**

TYPE:
Awards/prizes; Scholarships. The IES Abroad Boren and Gilman Scholarship Support Grants offer recipients of these prestigious scholarships the opportunity to apply for additional financial support.

IES Merit-Based Scholarships supplement U.S. college and university awards for undergraduates studying with IES Abroad in Argentina, Australia, Austria, Chile, China, Costa Rica, Ecuador, England, France, Germany, India, Ireland, Italy, Japan, Morocco, the Netherlands, New Zealand, South Africa, Spain and Turkey. Merit-Based Scholarships are available for proven strength and interest in fine arts, foreign language, high achievement, international business, international relations, leadership, science and urban issues. Diversity Scholarships are also available as are scholarships for students who attend historically Black colleges/universities.

Need-based grants available to students with demonstrated financial need.

All IES Abroad aid is available only to students from schools within the IES Abroad Consortium and who attend an IES Abroad program.

YEAR PROGRAM STARTED: 1950

PURPOSE:
To provide study opportunities abroad for qualified undergraduate students from U.S. colleges and universities.

LEGAL BASIS:
Not-for-profit educational organization organized under the laws of Illinois.

ELIGIBILITY:
IES Abroad Merit-Based Scholarships: To be eligible, candidates must have been accepted (or have made application) to an IES Abroad program, be at least 18 years of age, be working toward an academic degree, have approval of his or her home college or university and submit a merit-based scholarship application along with its accompanying pieces.

FINANCIAL DATA:
Amount of support per award: IES Abroad Merit-Based Scholarships: Up to $3,000. The IES Abroad Boren and Gilman Scholarship Support Grants: Fall and spring: $1,000 each; summer: $500 each.
Total amount of support: $2,356,616 in financial aid and scholarships for the 2013-14 academic year.

NUMBER OF APPLICANTS MOST RECENT YEAR:
Summer 2013: need-based aid, 140; Fall 2013: need-based aid, 256; merit-based aid, 416. Spring 2014: need-based aid, 248; merit-based aid, 586.

NUMBER OF AWARDS: Summer 2013: need-based aid, 107; Fall 2013: need-based aid, 220; merit-based aid, 53. Spring 2014: need-based aid, 220; merit-based aid, 45.

APPLICATION INFORMATION:
Applications may be submitted online or downloaded from the IES Abroad web site.

Duration: Academic year, one semester, or summer (need-based only). Nonrenewable.
Deadline: May 1 for fall semester and academic year; October 25 for spring semester; April 1 for summer.

PUBLICATIONS:
Annual report; IES Abroad Alumni Exchange Newsletter; IES Abroad catalogs; IES MAP©.

IRS IDENTIFICATION NUMBER: 36-2251912

GOVERNING BOARD:
Ezio Vergani, Chairperson
Dr. Loren J. Anderson
Mary Cahillane
James Crawford
Debora de Hoyos
Dr. Pamela Brooks Gann
John J. Gearen
Robert Hallworth
Rhonda Jordan
Thomas McDonald
Robert McNeill
Dr. Kathryn M. Moore
Dr. David Oxtoby
Dr. Marla Salmon
Alan Schwartz
Sheila A. Stamps
Peter E. Sundman
Monica Vachher

ADDRESS INQUIRIES TO:
Joseph Sevigny, Associate Vice President of Enrollment Management
(See address above.)

*SPECIAL STIPULATIONS:
Applicants must be admitted to an IES program and must attend a college or university that is part of the IES Abroad Consortium.

INTERNATIONAL ASSOCIATION OF FIRE CHIEFS FOUNDATION, INC. [1701]
4025 Fair Ridge Drive
Suite 300
Fairfax, VA 22033-2868
(703) 896-4822
Fax: (703) 273-9363

E-MAIL ADDRESS:
sbaroncelli@iafc.org

WEB SITE ADDRESS:
www.iafcf.org

FOUNDED: 1974

NAME(S) OF PROGRAMS:
- **International Association of Fire Chiefs Foundation Scholarship Program**

TYPE:
Scholarships. Scholarships for advanced study in fire science, fire department administration and operation, public administration or any fire-related program.

YEAR PROGRAM STARTED: 1974

PURPOSE:
To aid in better fire service administration and to support training in this area.

ELIGIBILITY:
Under the regulations, any member of the fire service who is a member of a state, county, provincial, municipal, community, industrial or federal fire department, and who has demonstrated proficiency as a member, is eligible to apply for a scholarship to a recognized institution of higher education of

his or her choice. Applicants must have the approval of their department chiefs. Dependents are not eligible.

GEOGRAPHIC RESTRICTIONS:
United States.

FINANCIAL DATA:
Amount of support per award: Generally $500 to $2,000, providing a maximum of this dollar amount toward tuition costs.
Total amount of support: Approximately $36,000 per year.

NUMBER OF APPLICANTS MOST RECENT YEAR:
Approximately 60.

NUMBER OF AWARDS: Approximately 21 awards annually.

APPLICATION INFORMATION:
Application information is available on the web site.
Duration: One year.
Deadline: June 1.

PUBLICATIONS:
Application guidelines.

ADDRESS INQUIRIES TO:
Sharon Baroncelli
Association Manager for Foundation
(See address above.)

INTERNATIONAL DEVELOPMENT RESEARCH CENTRE (IDRC)
150 Kent Street
Ottawa ON K1P 0B2 Canada
(613) 696-2098
Fax: (613) 236-4026

E-MAIL ADDRESS:
awards@idrc.ca

WEB SITE ADDRESS:
www.idrc.ca/awards

TYPE:
Awards/prizes. These awards are offered once a year and are intended for field research in one or more developing countries. Candidates must conduct their research in areas corresponding to IDRC's research priorities.

See entry 1304 for full listing.

IODE [1702]
40 Orchard View Boulevard, Suite 219
Toronto ON M4R 1B9 Canada
(416) 487-4416
Fax: (416) 487-4417

E-MAIL ADDRESS:
iodecanada@bellnet.ca

WEB SITE ADDRESS:
www.iode.ca

FOUNDED: 1900

AREAS OF INTEREST:
Education, social service and citizenship.

NAME(S) OF PROGRAMS:
- **War Memorial Scholarships**

TYPE:
Scholarships. Postgraduate scholarships tenable in any university in Canada and the Commonwealth.

YEAR PROGRAM STARTED: 1920

PURPOSE:
To provide scholarships for educational purposes as a memorial to Canadian men and women who gave their lives in defense of freedom during World Wars I and II.

LEGAL BASIS:
Charitable organization.

ELIGIBILITY:
Candidates must be Canadian citizens. At the time of application, candidates must be enrolled in at least the second year of a doctoral program.

GEOGRAPHIC RESTRICTIONS:
Canada and the Commonwealth.

FINANCIAL DATA:
Amount of support per award: $15,000 (CAN) for study in Canada and for study overseas within the Commonwealth.

NUMBER OF AWARDS: 5 annually.

APPLICATION INFORMATION:
A candidate must apply to the War Memorial Convener in the province in which the first degree was obtained. The names of Conveners change from year to year, but appear in the scholarship folder. Check web site for the application.
Duration: One year.
Deadline: Applications must reach the Convener of the province from which the first degree was obtained by December 1.

OFFICERS:
Hazel MacLeod, National War Memorial Officer

TRUSTEES:
E. Ann Mason, National President

THE JAPAN FOUNDATION, LOS ANGELES   [1703]
5700 Wilshire Boulevard
Suite 100
Los Angeles, CA 90036
(323) 761-7510
Fax: (323) 761-7517

E-MAIL ADDRESS:
culture@jflalc.org

WEB SITE ADDRESS:
www.jflalc.org

FOUNDED: 1983

AREAS OF INTEREST:
Japanese arts, culture and language education.

NAME(S) OF PROGRAMS:
* **Exhibitions Abroad Support Program**
* **Program for the Donation of Japanese Language Teaching Materials (for the United States)**
* **Translation and Publication Support Program**

TYPE:
Conferences/seminars; Exchange programs; Fellowships; Grants-in-aid; Product donations; Project/program grants; Research grants; Training grants; Visiting scholars.

PURPOSE:
To support grants that promote Japanese arts, culture, language and education.

ELIGIBILITY:
Candidates must be citizens or permanent residents of the U.S.

GEOGRAPHIC RESTRICTIONS:
United States.

FINANCIAL DATA:
Amount of support per award: Varies.
Total amount of support: Varies.

APPLICATION INFORMATION:
Guidelines are available online.

Duration: One year. No renewals.
Deadline: Varies.

THE JAPANESE AMERICAN CITIZENS LEAGUE (JACL) [1704]
1765 Sutter Street
San Francisco, CA 94115
(415) 921-5225
Fax: (415) 931-4671

E-MAIL ADDRESS:
ncwnp@jacl.org

WEB SITE ADDRESS:
www.jacl.org

FOUNDED: 1929

AREAS OF INTEREST:
Education, cultural preservation, and civil rights.

NAME(S) OF PROGRAMS:
* **JACL National Scholarship and Awards Program**

TYPE:
Scholarships. JACL offers more than 30 scholarships and student aid awards (financial aid).

Scholarship categories: Entering Freshman (High School Senior), Undergraduate, Graduate, Law, Creative and Performing Arts, Hagiwara Financial Aid.

YEAR PROGRAM STARTED: 1946

PURPOSE:
To recognize education as a key to greater opportunities for its members.

ELIGIBILITY:
Applicant must be a current National JACL member at either an individual or student/youth level. Applicants must be enrolled at an institution of higher learning within the U.S. at the undergraduate or graduate school level. Applicants may apply under only one scholarship category. Entering freshman applicants must be high school seniors. Creative and performing arts applicants cannot be professional artists.

FINANCIAL DATA:
Amount of support per award: $1,000 to $5,000.
Total amount of support: $60,000.

APPLICATION INFORMATION:
Information brochure and applications are posted on the JACL web site annually in November.
Duration: One year. Limited to a total of two awards.
Deadline: April 1.

ADDRESS INQUIRIES TO:
Scholarships Department
(See address above.)

JEWISH FAMILY AND CHILDREN'S SERVICES   [1705]
2150 Post Street
San Francisco, CA 94115
(415) 449-1226
Fax: (415) 848-7012
TDD: (415) 567-1044

E-MAIL ADDRESS:
michellel@jfcs.org

WEB SITE ADDRESS:
www.jfcs.org

FOUNDED: 1850

AREAS OF INTEREST:
Jewish individuals and their families, college tuition and expenses, vocational training and loans for business and professional endeavors.

NAME(S) OF PROGRAMS:
* **Educational Loans & Grants Program**

TYPE:
Grants-in-aid. Need-based loans and grants.

PURPOSE:
To provide educational loans and grants to Jewish students.

LEGAL BASIS:
Nonprofit.

ELIGIBILITY:
Applicants must be students of Jewish descent who have demonstrated academic achievement (generally demonstrated by a 2.75 grade point average on a 4.0 scale), financial need, broad-based extracurricular activities and in-depth community involvement and acceptance to an accredited college, university or vocational school.

GEOGRAPHIC RESTRICTIONS:
Marin, San Francisco, San Mateo, Santa Clara, or Sonoma counties, California.

FINANCIAL DATA:
Amount of support per award:
Graduate/Vocational Loans: Up to $6,000;
Loans: $4,500 to $5,000; Undergraduate Grants: $1,000 to $1,500.
Total amount of support: Up to $6,000 per student, per year.

NUMBER OF APPLICANTS MOST RECENT YEAR:
110.

NUMBER OF AWARDS: Varies per year.

APPLICATION INFORMATION:
Application information is available on the web site. Contact the organization's Director of Financial Aid Center for more information.
Duration: One academic year.
Deadline: Priority deadline: August 1; applications will be accepted until funding is exhausted.

PUBLICATIONS:
Program announcement.

ADDRESS INQUIRIES TO:
Michelle Lamphere
Director, JFCS Financial Aid Center
(See address above.)

MACKENZIE KING SCHOLARSHIP TRUST   [1706]
c/o J. Blom, Faculty of Law
1822 East Mall, University of British Columbia
Vancouver BC V6T 1Z1 Canada
(604) 822-4564
Fax: (604) 822-8108

E-MAIL ADDRESS:
mkingscholarships@law.ubc.ca

WEB SITE ADDRESS:
www.mkingscholarships.ca

FOUNDED: 1950

AREAS OF INTEREST:
Industrial and international relations.

NAME(S) OF PROGRAMS:
* **The Mackenzie King Traveling Scholarships**

TYPE:
Scholarships. For graduate study, either in the U.S. or the U.K., in the field of international or industrial relations (including the international or industrial aspects of law, history, politics or economics).

YEAR PROGRAM STARTED: 1950

LEGAL BASIS:
Private charitable trust.

ELIGIBILITY:
Applicants must be graduates of any Canadian university.

FINANCIAL DATA:
Amount of support per award:
Approximately $11,000 (CAN).

Total amount of support: Approximately $44,000 (CAN).

NUMBER OF APPLICANTS MOST RECENT YEAR:
150 for the 2011-12 academic year.

NUMBER OF AWARDS: 4 annually.

APPLICATION INFORMATION:
Applicants must submit completed application forms, all official transcripts and three letters of reference to the Canadian university from which they received their most recent degree, c/o the Faculty of Graduate Studies.

Deadline: February 1.

*SPECIAL STIPULATIONS:
Award may not be accepted if total scholarship support, including the award, exceeds expected tuition expense plus $16,000 (CAN).

MACKENZIE KING SCHOLARSHIP TRUST [1707]

c/o J. Blom, Faculty of Law
1822 East Mall, University of British Columbia
Vancouver BC V6T 1Z1 Canada
(604) 822-4564
Fax: (604) 822-8108

E-MAIL ADDRESS:
mkingscholarships@law.ubc.ca

WEB SITE ADDRESS:
www.mkingscholarships.ca

FOUNDED: 1950

AREAS OF INTEREST:
Graduate studies.

NAME(S) OF PROGRAMS:
● **The Mackenzie King Open Scholarship**

TYPE:
Scholarships. For full-time graduate studies in Canada or elsewhere, in any field.

YEAR PROGRAM STARTED: 1950

PURPOSE:
To assist graduates of Canadian universities pursue graduate study in any discipline anywhere in the world.

LEGAL BASIS:
Private charitable trust.

ELIGIBILITY:
Applicants must be graduates of any Canadian university.

FINANCIAL DATA:
Amount of support per award:
Approximately $9,000 (CAN).

Total amount of support: Approximately $9,000 (CAN) available annually.

NUMBER OF APPLICANTS MOST RECENT YEAR:
300 for 2011-12 academic year.

NUMBER OF AWARDS: Generally 1.

APPLICATION INFORMATION:
Applicants must submit completed application forms, all official transcripts and three letters of reference to the Canadian university from which they received their most recent degree, c/o Faculty of Graduate Studies.

Duration: Scholarships are tenable for one year.

Deadline: February 1.

*SPECIAL STIPULATIONS:
Award may not be accepted if total scholarship support, including the award, exceeds expected tuition expense plus $16,000 (CAN).

KNIGHTS OF COLUMBUS [1708]

P.O. Box 1670
New Haven, CT 06507-0901
(203) 752-4332
Fax: (203) 752-4103

WEB SITE ADDRESS:
www.kofc.org/scholarships

AREAS OF INTEREST:
Educational support.

NAME(S) OF PROGRAMS:
● **Educational Trust Scholarships**
● **Bishop Charles P. Greco Graduate Fellowships**
● **John W. McDevitt (Fourth Degree) Scholarships**
● **Pro Deo and Pro Patria Scholarships**

TYPE:
Fellowships; Project/program grants; Scholarships. Scholarships and fellowships are awarded to members of The Knights of Columbus in good standing, a son or daughter of such a member or deceased member, or to a member of the Columbian Squires.

The Educational Trust provides scholarships to sons and daughters of members who died or became permanently and totally disabled while serving in the military during a period of conflict or who died as a result of criminal violence directed against them while performing duties of full-time law enforcement officers or full-time firemen. The awards are for undergraduate studies in a four-year program leading to a Bachelor's degree at a Catholic college and include the amount not covered by other financial aid for tuition up to $25,000 per year.

The Bishop Greco Graduate Fellowships are for full-time graduate study leading to a Master's degree in a program for classroom teachers of persons with intellectual disabilities.

The John W. McDevitt (Fourth Degree) Scholarships are awarded to students entering the freshman class of undergraduate study at a Catholic college or university in the U.S.

For the Pro Deo and Pro Patria Scholarships, students must be entering the freshman class in a college program leading to a Bachelor's degree. Scholarships are available at The Catholic University of America in Washington, DC and to students entering other Catholic colleges in the U.S.

PURPOSE:
To provide support for community activities, education, the elderly, poor, disabled and victims of disasters; to provide financial assistance to children of members in good standing.

ELIGIBILITY:
For Educational Trust Scholarships, applicants must be:
(1) Children of a member in good standing who, while serving in the military forces of his country in a combat zone, specifically designated as such by the Board of Directors, is killed by hostile action or wounded by hostile action resulting within two years thereof in permanent and total disability; an application must be filed within two years of the death or determination of total and permanent disability of the member or;
(2) Children of a member in good standing who, while in the lawful performance of his duties as a full-time law enforcement officer or full-time firefighter, died as the result of criminal violence directed at him; an application must be filed within two years of the date of the death of the member.
A candidate for benefits is required to submit documents to establish eligibility.

For Bishop Greco Graduate Fellowships, applicants must be enrolled in a graduate study program leading to a Master's degree in a program designed for the preparation of classroom teachers of persons with intellectual disabilities. Membership requirements as listed for the scholarship above also apply for this award.

For McDevitt (Fourth Degree) Scholarships, applicants must be members in good standing of the Knights of Columbus or the wife, widow, son or daughter of such a member or deceased member.

For Pro Deo and Pro Patria Scholarships, applicants must be students entering in the freshman class in a Catholic college program leading to a Bachelor's degree. An applicant must be a member in good standing of the Knights of Columbus or the son or daughter of such a member, a deceased member or a member in good standing of the Columbian Squires.

GEOGRAPHIC RESTRICTIONS:
United States.

FINANCIAL DATA:
Amount of support per award: Bishop Greco Graduate Fellowships: $1,000 maximum per year; Educational Trust Scholarships: Up to $25,000 per year; McDevitt (Fourth Degree) Scholarships: $1,500; Pro Deo and Pro Patria Scholarships: $1,500 per year.

APPLICATION INFORMATION:
Application form required. Candidates are required to submit supporting documents to substantiate eligibility.

Duration: Pro Deo and Pro Patria and Educational Trust Scholarships: Up to four years. Greco Graduate Fellowship: Up to two years.

Deadline: May 1 for filing fellowship applications for the Bishop Greco Graduate Fellowships. March 1 for filing scholarship applications for the Pro Deo and Pro Patria Scholarships and McDevitt (Fourth Degree) Scholarships.

ADDRESS INQUIRIES TO:
Department of Scholarships
(See address above.)

*SPECIAL STIPULATIONS:
   Candidates for Educational Trust Fund
   scholarships will be required to submit
   supporting documents to substantiate the
   claim.

KOHL'S CORPORATION   [1709]

N56 W17000 Ridgewood Drive
Menomonee Falls, WI 53051
(262) 703-7000
Fax: (262) 703-6305

E-MAIL ADDRESS:
kohls@scholarshipamerica.org

WEB SITE ADDRESS:
www.kohls.scholarshipamerica.org

AREAS OF INTEREST:
   Education assistance and/or rewards for
   children who volunteer in the communities
   Kohl's serves.

NAME(S) OF PROGRAMS:
● **Kohl's Cares® Scholarship Program**

TYPE:
   Awards/prizes; Scholarships.

YEAR PROGRAM STARTED: 2001

PURPOSE:
   To recognize and reward youths whose
   volunteer efforts are making a difference in
   local communities Kohl's serves.

ELIGIBILITY:
   Students must be legal residence of the
   United States (except Hawaii) and must be
   between the ages of 6 and 18 and not yet a
   high school graduate. Each student must be
   nominated by someone age 21 years or older.
   Parents may nominate their own children.

   Winners will be chosen based on the benefits
   and outcomes of their volunteer service.

GEOGRAPHIC RESTRICTIONS:
   United States, except Hawaii.

FINANCIAL DATA:
   Amount of support per award: Store Level:
   $50 Kohl's gift card; Regional Level: $1,000
   scholarship; National winners will each
   receive a total of $10,000 in scholarships,
   plus Kohl's will donate $1,000 to a nonprofit
   of the student's choice.
   Total amount of support: $411,000
   anticipated for the year 2013.

NUMBER OF AWARDS: More than 2,300
anticipated for the year 2013.

APPLICATION INFORMATION:
   Guidelines and application form is available
   on the web site.
   Deadline: Nominations: March 15. Store
   winners announced in June. Regional and
   National winners announced in July.

THE KOSCIUSZKO
FOUNDATION, INC.   [1710]

15 East 65th Street
New York, NY 10065
(212) 734-2130

E-MAIL ADDRESS:
addy@thekf.org

WEB SITE ADDRESS:
www.thekf.org/scholarships/tuition/

FOUNDED: 1925

AREAS OF INTEREST:
   Scholarships and grants for graduate and
   postgraduate studies in the U.S.

NAME(S) OF PROGRAMS:
● **The Kosciuszko Foundation Tuition
   Scholarship**

TYPE:
   Scholarships. Offers funding to American
   citizens of Polish descent and to Polish
   citizens who have permanent residency status
   in the U.S. Scholarships are for Master's and
   Ph.D. students for full-time studies only.
   Undergraduate seniors may apply for a
   scholarship towards their first year of
   Master's-level studies. Americans (non-Polish
   descent) are eligible for graduate-level
   studies when majoring in Polish language,
   history or culture.

   All majors are supported, however, the
   Kosciuszko Foundation has special funding
   allocated in the following areas:
   law and engineering studies at DePaul
   University and nonpublic colleges and
   universities in the Chicagoland area and
   nonpublic Midwest colleges and universities
   (Illinois, Indiana, Iowa, Kansas, Michigan,
   Minnesota, Missouri, Nebraska, North
   Dakota, Ohio, South Dakota, and Wisconsin);
   Bayonne, NJ residents, with studies in
   nursing, teaching and business preferred;
   residents of Connecticut, particularly Fairfield
   and New Haven counties; Amsterdam, NY,
   Chicopee, MA and New Hampshire and;
   for violin and piano.

   Contact Foundation for additional funding
   opportunities.

YEAR PROGRAM STARTED: 1950

PURPOSE:
   To promote higher education of Americans of
   Polish descent and Polish studies.

LEGAL BASIS:
   501(c)(3) not-for-profit organization which is
   engaged in educational and cultural relations
   between the U.S. and Poland.

ELIGIBILITY:
   Applicants must:
   (1) be U.S. citizens of Polish descent or;
   (2) be Polish citizens who have legal
   permanent residency status in the U.S. or;
   (3) be Americans of non-Polish descent who
   are pursuing Polish majors and;
   (4) have a minimum grade point average of
   3.0.

   Scholarships will be awarded on the basis of
   academic excellence and evidence of
   identification with the Polish-American
   community. Financial need is taken into
   consideration. Scholarships are for full-time
   graduate study in the U.S. and certain
   programs in Poland.

   Within the parameters of the scholarship
   program are special opportunities for the
   studies in certain subject areas including
   journalism, nursing, teaching, business, piano
   performance, law, arts, social sciences and
   education.

GEOGRAPHIC RESTRICTIONS:
   United States and Poland.

FINANCIAL DATA:
   Amount of support per award: $1,000 to
   $7,000. Average: $3,100.
   Total amount of support: $228,250 for the
   academic year 2012-13.

NUMBER OF APPLICANTS MOST RECENT YEAR:
Over 100.

NUMBER OF AWARDS: 72.

APPLICATION INFORMATION:
   Applications are available online. Application
   materials include:

(1) application form;
(2) financial information form;
(3) statement of purpose;
(4) official transcripts of credit (three years
of academic work);
(5) two letters of recommendation from
professors or teachers discussing applicant's
academic performance;
(6) copy of acceptance letter for Master's
program of applicant's choice;
(7) proof of Polish descent and;
(8) two passport-size photos.

   Completed applications must be accompanied
   by a nonrefundable $35 application fee.
   Faxed applications and supporting materials
   are not accepted. Applications posted to the
   Internet in October are available through the
   deadline date.
   Duration: One academic year. Possible
   renewal for a second year upon reapplication.
   Deadline: January 5. Notification in May.
   Funding for the following academic year.

PUBLICATIONS:
   Guidelines; *KF Newsletter*; grants brochure;
   annual report.

IRS IDENTIFICATION NUMBER: 13-1628179

ADDRESS INQUIRIES TO:
   Tuition Scholarship Program
   (See address above.)

*SPECIAL STIPULATIONS:
   Scholarship checks are issued upon proof of
   full-time status.

MARCUS AND THERESA LEVIE
EDUCATION FUND   [1711]

Jewish Vocational Service
216 West Jackson Boulevard, Suite 700
Chicago, IL 60606-6921
(312) 673-3444
Fax: (312) 553-5544
TTY: (312) 444-2877

E-MAIL ADDRESS:
jvsscholarship@jvschicago.org

WEB SITE ADDRESS:
www.jvschicago.org

FOUNDED: 1959

AREAS OF INTEREST:
   Higher education for Jewish students in
   full-time academic programs in the helping
   professions, legally domiciled in the
   metropolitan Chicago (IL) area.

TYPE:
   Awards/prizes; Scholarships. Awards to
   individuals for the academic year.

YEAR PROGRAM STARTED: 1959

PURPOSE:
   To provide financial support to Jewish men
   and women for their full-time academic
   programs.

LEGAL BASIS:
   Tax-exempt private foundation.

ELIGIBILITY:
   Scholarships are awarded on the basis of
   financial need. Applicants must be full-time
   students of Jewish background,
   predominantly those legally domiciled in the
   metropolitan Chicago area. Applicants must
   have demonstrated career promise. Assistance
   is available for the fields listed below,
   including but not limited to:
   (1) the helping professions such as medicine,
   dentistry, social work, education, psychology,

the rabbinate and noncorporate areas of law;
(2) mathematics, engineering and other sciences and;
(3) communications within the College of Media at the University of Illinois at Urbana-Champaign.

Additional requirements:
(1) undergraduates entering or who have entered the junior year in career-specific programs which require no postgraduate education for professional-level employment in one of the professional areas mentioned above or;
(2) students entering or who have entered a graduate or professional school in a helping profession described above or;
(3) students in a vocational training program with a specific educational goal in the helping professions.

Newcomers who are refugees or asylees are encouraged to apply. Citizenship is not a prerequisite.

FINANCIAL DATA:
Total amount of support: Approximately $400,000 per year.

COOPERATIVE FUNDING PROGRAMS: Program is administered by the Jewish Vocational Service.

NUMBER OF APPLICANTS MOST RECENT YEAR: 150 for the year 2013.

NUMBER OF AWARDS: 91.

APPLICATION INFORMATION:
Application submission must include application form, budget worksheet, personal and financial data, IRS Form 1040, proof of (Cook County) legal domicility, two reference letters, autobiography and official academic transcript. Applicants must be available for a personal interview at Jewish Vocational Service offices located throughout the Chicago metropolitan area prior to April 20.

Applications are available in the fall and can be downloaded from the Jewish Vocational Service web site. (Click on "Scholarship Services.")

Duration: One academic year. Recipients may reapply for renewal.

Deadline: February 15 for submission of applications.

OFFICERS:
Sally Yarberry, Scholarship Coordinator

ADDRESS INQUIRIES TO:
Scholarship Coordinator
(See address and phone number above.)

*SPECIAL STIPULATIONS:
All applicants must be available for a personal interview at the Jewish Vocational Service offices located throughout the Chicago metropolitan area.

LOUISIANA DIVISION OF THE ARTS, DEPARTMENT OF CULTURE, RECREATION AND TOURISM

1051 North Third Street, Room 420
Baton Rouge, LA 70802
(225) 342-8200
Fax: (225) 342-8173

E-MAIL ADDRESS:
arts@crt.state.la.us

WEB SITE ADDRESS:
www.crt.state.la.us/arts

TYPE:
General operating grants; Technical assistance. Stabilization grants. Grants in a variety of programs are offered to arts organizations across the state.

Stabilization grants are offered in three levels of operating support to nonprofit arts organizations.

See entry 467 for full listing.

MARINE CORPS SCHOLARSHIP FOUNDATION, INC.   [1712]

909 North Washington Street
Alexandria, VA 22314
(703) 549-0060
Fax: (703) 549-9474

E-MAIL ADDRESS:
scholarship@mcsf.org

WEB SITE ADDRESS:
www.mcsf.org

FOUNDED: 1962

AREAS OF INTEREST:
Scholarships to children of Marines and children of former Marines.

TYPE:
Scholarships. Scholarships are for higher education (post-high school) college, trade or vocational school.

YEAR PROGRAM STARTED: 1962

PURPOSE:
To provide financial resources and the support of an extended community, ensuring that the children of Marines and eligible Navy Corpsmen have the opportunity to attend college and successfully achieve their goals.

LEGAL BASIS:
Nonprofit, tax-exempt corporation.

ELIGIBILITY:
Sons or daughters of Marines or children of former Marines. College or trade school. No graduate study.

Scholarships are for children of active duty, reserve, and honorably discharged Marines and Navy Corpsmen that serve with Marines. Applicants must be planning to attend, or already attending, an accredited college or vocational/technical institution, have a grade point average of at least 2.0, and pursuing their first degree or technical certificate. An income requirement must be met. Special funding is available for children of those who were wounded or killed in combat.

FINANCIAL DATA:
The Scholarship Foundation has provided over 30,000 scholarships valued at over $80,000,000 since 1962.

Amount of support per award: $1,500 to $10,000 per year; average $3,000.

Total amount of support: Over $6,600,000 for the 2013-14 academic year.

NUMBER OF APPLICANTS MOST RECENT YEAR: 2,273.

NUMBER OF AWARDS: 2,040.

APPLICATION INFORMATION:
Application available online beginning January 1.

Duration: One year. Renewable for up to three years. Recipients must reapply.

Deadline: March 1.

PUBLICATIONS:
Annual report; guidelines; yearbook; trifold; newsletter.

IRS IDENTIFICATION NUMBER: 22-1905062

STAFF:
Steven D. Peterson, Chief Operating Officer
Jeanna Adams, Assistant Director, Scholarship Programs
Matthew Rosales, Scholarship Programs Coordinator

ADDRESS INQUIRIES TO:
Director of Scholarship Programs
(See address above.)

*SPECIAL STIPULATIONS:
Cannot violate civil or campus law.

THURGOOD MARSHALL COLLEGE FUND   [1713]

4801 Woodway Drive
Suite 300 East
Houston, TX 77056
(202) 507-4851
Fax: (480) 287-9632

E-MAIL ADDRESS:
scholarships@tmcfund.org

WEB SITE ADDRESS:
www.thurgoodmarshallfund.org

FOUNDED: 1987

NAME(S) OF PROGRAMS:
● TMCF Scholarships

TYPE:
Scholarships. Scholarship for full-time students pursuing a degree at one of the 47 TMCF "member schools."

ELIGIBILITY:
Students must:
(1) be U.S. citizen pursuing a degree in any discipline at one of the 47 TMCF "member schools" on a full-time basis;
(2) demonstrate financial need and;
(3) demonstrate academic excellence and a commitment to community service with a high school or college grade point average of 3.0.

Awards are merit-based.

GEOGRAPHIC RESTRICTIONS:
United States.

FINANCIAL DATA:
Amount of support per award: Usually $6,200 split into two semesters: fall $3,100; spring $3,100.

NUMBER OF AWARDS: Approximately 300 per year.

APPLICATION INFORMATION:
Apply online only.

Duration: One academic year.

Deadline: Varies.

ADDRESS INQUIRIES TO:
See e-mail address above.

MARYLAND HIGHER EDUCATION COMMISSION   [1714]

Office of Student Financial Assistance
6 North Liberty Street
Baltimore, MD 21201
(410) 767-3109
(410) 767-3300
Fax: (410) 332-0250; (410) 332-0252

E-MAIL ADDRESS:
osfamail@mhec.state.md.us

WEB SITE ADDRESS:
www.mhec.state.md.us

FOUNDED: 1961

NAME(S) OF PROGRAMS:
- Maryland State Scholarships

TYPE:
Grants-in-aid; Scholarships; Loan forgiveness programs. The Educational Excellence Awards program is the state's largest need-based program. It has two components: the Educational Assistance Grant and the Guaranteed Access Grant. The Educational Assistance Grant is targeted to low- to moderate-income families and is based on financial need (40% of calculated financial need for four-year institutions, 60% for community colleges). The Guaranteed Access Grant is for very low-income high school students and requires a 2.5 high school grade point average (100% of student need up to a maximum of $16,100).

The Part-Time Grant supports part-time, degree-seeking, undergraduate students.

The Graduate and Professional School Scholarship provides support to full-time and part-time graduate and professional students in nursing, pharmacy, dentistry, law, medicine, veterinary science, and social work.

Senatorial Scholarships: Each member of the state senate may award scholarships each year.

Delegate Scholarships: Each member of the House of Delegates may award scholarships to students attending approved Maryland postsecondary institutions.

Maryland also offers a number of career/occupational and unique population financial assistance programs.

LEGAL BASIS:
Government agency.

ELIGIBILITY:
Candidate must be a resident of the state and generally enrolled or intending to enroll in a college or university in Maryland.

GEOGRAPHIC RESTRICTIONS:
Maryland.

FINANCIAL DATA:
Amount of support per award: Educational Assistance Grant: $400 to $3,000; Guaranteed Access Grant: Up to $16,100; Part-Time Grant: Up to $2,000; Graduate and Professional School Scholarship: Up to $5,000; Senatorial Scholarships: $400 to $9,700 annually per member of the state senate; Delegate Scholarships: $200 minimum award per member of the House of Delegates.
Total amount of support: Approximately $110,000,000 for all programs.

APPLICATION INFORMATION:
Use the Free Application for Federal Student Aid (FAFSA) or special program application.
Duration: Up to four years. Renewable.
Deadline: March 1 for state-administered, need-based aid program; other deadlines vary throughout the year.

PUBLICATIONS:
A Quick Guide to Cash for College and How to Get it; Student Guide to Higher Education and Financial Aid In Maryland; 6 Steps to Choosing the Right School.

ADDRESS INQUIRIES TO:
See e-mail address above.

MASSACHUSETTS MEDICAL SOCIETY (MMS)   [1715]
860 Winter Street
Waltham, MA 02451-1411
(800) 322-2303
Fax: (781) 893-8009

WEB SITE ADDRESS:
www.massmed.org

FOUNDED: 1954

NAME(S) OF PROGRAMS:
- **Massachusetts Medical Society International Health Studies Grant Program**
- **Massachusetts Medical Society (MMS) Scholars Program**
- **MMS Medical Information Technology Awards**
- **MMS Student Section Community Service Grants**

TYPE:
Awards/prizes; Grants-in-aid; Research grants; Scholarships. Massachusetts Medical Society International Health Studies Grant Program: Grants to defray the costs of study abroad.

Massachusetts Medical Society (MMS) Scholars Program: Awarded to two students from each of the four Massachusetts medical schools.

MMS Medical Information Technology Awards: Given annually to one medical student and one resident physician.

MMS Student Section Community Service Grants: Funding for each of two service projects per medical school chapter of the Section, per calendar year.

PURPOSE:
To advance medical knowledge; to develop and maintain the highest professional and ethical standards of medical practice and health care; to promote medical institutions formed on liberal principles for the health, benefit, and welfare of the citizens of the Commonwealth.

ELIGIBILITY:
Massachusetts Medical Society International Health Studies Grant Program: MMS member; preference given to applicants planning a career serving underprivileged populations. Massachusetts Medical Society (MMS) Scholars Program: MMS member; fourth-year students enrolled in a Massachusetts medical school. MMS Medical Information Technology Awards: MMS member; medical students, residents or fellows enrolled in one of the four Massachusetts Medical Schools or a Massachusetts hospital or training program. MMS Student Section Community Service Grants: Current medical student members of the MMS whose projects meet objectives in community and social service, public health activism and education or volunteer mentorship activities.

FINANCIAL DATA:
Amount of support per award: Massachusetts Medical Society International Health Studies Grant Program: $2,000. Massachusetts Medical Society (MMS) Scholars Program: $10,000. MMS Medical Information Technology Awards: $3,000 annually. MMS Student Section Community Service Grants: Up to $250.

NUMBER OF AWARDS: Massachusetts Medical Society International Health Studies Grant Program: 4. Massachusetts Medical Society

(MMS) Scholars Program: 8. MMS Medical Information Technology Awards: 1 medical student and 1 resident physician. MMS Student Section Community Service Grants: 2 service projects per medical school chapter of the Section, per calendar year.

APPLICATION INFORMATION:
Application information is available on the web site.
Deadline: Massachusetts Medical Society International Health Studies Grant Program: September 15. Massachusetts Medical Society (MMS) Scholars Program: January 17. MMS Medical Information Technology Awards: Mid-November annually.

PUBLICATIONS:
Application guidelines.

ADDRESS INQUIRIES TO:
Linda Howard, Regional Manager
Massachusetts Medical Society (MMS)
(See address above.)

MMS International Health Studies
Grant Program:
Jennifer Day, MMS and Alliance
Charitable Foundation Director
Tel: (781) 434-7044
E-mail: jday@mms.org.

MMS Scholars Program:
Applicant's Office of Student Affairs or
Thelma Tatten, Program Coordinator
MMS Department of Continuing Education
and Certification
Tel: (781) 434-7305
E-mail: ttatten@mms.org

MMS Medical Information Technology
Awards
Leon Q. Barzin, MMS Technical Program
Portfolio Director
Tel: (800) 322-2303 ext. 7048
E-mail: lbarzin@mms.org

MMS Student Section Community
Service Grants:
Colleen Hennessey, Academic Administrator
Tel: (800) 322-2303 ext. 7315
E-mail: chennessey@mms.org

MASSACHUSETTS OFFICE OF STUDENT FINANCIAL ASSISTANCE   [1716]
Office of Student Financial Assistance
454 Broadway, Suite 200
Revere, MA 02151
(617) 391-6070
Fax: (617) 727-0667

E-MAIL ADDRESS:
cmccurdy@osfa.mass.edu
osfa@osfa.mass.edu

WEB SITE ADDRESS:
www.osfa.mass.edu

FOUNDED: 1980

AREAS OF INTEREST:
Financial assistance to Massachusetts students.

NAME(S) OF PROGRAMS:
- **Cash Grant**
- **Gilbert Grants**
- **MASSGrants**

TYPE:
Grants-in-aid. Cash grant to assist needy students in meeting institutionally held charges such as mandatory fees and non-state-supported tuition. Designed as an

offset of the Tuition Waiver Program, these grants provide financial support to those individuals who would be denied the opportunity for higher education.

Gilbert Grants are based on financial need and awarded to Massachusetts residents enrolled in nonprofit private colleges.

MASSGrants are state grants in all undergraduate fields, based solely on financial need, renewable for up to four years of undergraduate study. State grants must be used at accredited institutions in Massachusetts and reciprocal states.

PURPOSE:
To assist those who are unable to meet the costs of postsecondary education.

ELIGIBILITY:
For Cash Grant, applicant must be a permanent legal resident of Massachusetts for one year prior to the academic year for which the grant is awarded, be a U.S. citizen or eligible noncitizen, and be in compliance with applicable laws. For Gilbert Grants, applicants must be permanent Massachusetts residents for at least one year, attending full-time in Massachusetts. MASSGrant applicants may attend school in Connecticut, Maine, Massachusetts, New Hampshire, Pennsylvania, Rhode Island, Vermont or Washington, DC.

GEOGRAPHIC RESTRICTIONS:
Primarily Massachusetts.

FINANCIAL DATA:
Amount of support per award: Cash Grant: Varies; Gilbert Grants: $200 to $2,500; MASSGrant: $300 to $1,600.

Total amount of support: Cash Grant: $26,000,000; Gilbert Grant: $16,000,000; MASSGrant: $37,000,000.

APPLICATION INFORMATION:
Applicants must file the Free Application for Federal Student Aid (FAFSA) after January 1.

Deadline: Cash Grant: May 1. Gilbert Grant is determined by college. MASSGrant: FAFSA by May 1.

PUBLICATIONS:
Guidelines.

ADDRESS INQUIRIES TO:
Clantha McCurdy
Senior Deputy Commissioner
(See address above.)

MEXICAN AMERICAN LEGAL DEFENSE AND EDUCATIONAL FUND

634 South Spring Street, 11th Floor
Los Angeles, CA 90014
(213) 629-2512
Fax: (213) 629-3120

E-MAIL ADDRESS:
lurquidi@maldef.org

WEB SITE ADDRESS:
www.maldef.org

TYPE:
Scholarships. Awarded annually to law students who have a demonstrated commitment to serving the Latino community with their law degree.

See entry 1985 for full listing.

MISSOURI DEPARTMENT OF HIGHER EDUCATION   [1717]

P.O. Box 1469
Jefferson City, MO 65102
(573) 751-2361
(800) 473-6757, option 4
Fax: (573) 751-6635

E-MAIL ADDRESS:
info@dhe.mo.gov

WEB SITE ADDRESS:
www.dhe.mo.gov

FOUNDED: 1986

NAME(S) OF PROGRAMS:
● **Missouri Higher Education Academic Scholarship Program ("Bright Flight")**

TYPE:
Scholarships. Provides undergraduate student financial aid to qualified Missouri students who wish to attend qualified Missouri institutions of higher education, both public and private.

PURPOSE:
To enable qualified full-time students to attend a participating postsecondary institution (public and private).

LEGAL BASIS:
RSMO Supp. 173.250. Government agency.

ELIGIBILITY:
Applicant must be a resident of Missouri and a U.S. citizen or permanent resident and enrolled in an eligible Missouri institution, be a high school senior who plans to enroll as a first-time, full-time student and have a composite score on the American College Testing Program (ACT) or the Scholastic Aptitude Test (SAT) in the top five percent of all Missouri students taking the tests.

Student must take the ACT or SAT assessment and receive the required test score on or before the June test date of their senior year. GED and home-schooled students may also qualify. The Missouri Department of Higher Education will obtain the ACT or SAT assessment records, whichever the student has taken, and will notify students, high schools and postsecondary institutions of scholarship awards. Scholarships may not be used for theology for divinity studies.

GEOGRAPHIC RESTRICTIONS:
Missouri.

FINANCIAL DATA:
Amount of support per award: Statutory maximum award for an academic year is $3,000 for the top three percent and $1,000 for the fourth/fifth percentile.

Total amount of support: Varies.

APPLICATION INFORMATION:
Contact the Department.

Duration: One academic year. Renewable annually until students have obtained a Baccalaureate degree or completed a total of 10 semesters.

Deadline: June.

ADDRESS INQUIRIES TO:
Information Center
(See address above.)

MISSOURI DEPARTMENT OF HIGHER EDUCATION   [1718]

P.O. Box 1469
Jefferson City, MO 65102-1469
(573) 751-2361
(800) 473-6757, option 4
Fax: (573) 751-6635

E-MAIL ADDRESS:
info@dhe.mo.gov

WEB SITE ADDRESS:
www.dhe.mo.gov

FOUNDED: 1986

NAME(S) OF PROGRAMS:
● **Access Missouri Financial Assistance Program**

TYPE:
Grants-in-aid. Undergraduate student financial aid to qualified Missouri students who wish to attend qualified Missouri institutions of higher education, both public and private.

YEAR PROGRAM STARTED: 2007

PURPOSE:
To enable full-time students to attend a participating postsecondary institution (public and private).

LEGAL BASIS:
Section 173.1101-173.1107, RSMo. Government agency.

ELIGIBILITY:
Initially, applicants must meet the following requirements:
(1) have a FAFSA on file by April 1;
(2) have any FAFSA corrections made by July 31 (school choices may be added until September 30);
(3) be a U.S. citizen or permanent resident and a Missouri resident;
(4) be enrolled full-time at a participating Missouri school;
(5) have an EFC of $12,000 or less and;
(6) not be pursuing a degree or certificate in theology or divinity.

Renewal students must continue to meet the eligibility requirements for initial students and additionally:
(1) be an undergraduate student enrolled full-time at a participating Missouri school. (Students with disabilities who are enrolled in at least six credit hours may be considered to be enrolled full-time);
(2) not have received the first Bachelor's degree, completed the required hours for a Bachelor's degree, or completed 150 semester credit hours;
(3) maintain a minimum cumulative grade point average of 2.5 and otherwise maintain satisfactory academic progress as defined by the applicant's school and;
(4) not have received an Access Missouri award for a maximum of five semesters at a two-year school or 10 semesters at any combination of two-year or four-year schools, whichever occurs first. (If Charles Gallagher or Missouri College Guarantee awardee in past semesters, those semesters are counted in the 10-semester limit, along with any semester in which the applicant has received an Access Missouri award).

GEOGRAPHIC RESTRICTIONS:
Missouri.

FINANCIAL DATA:
Amount of support per award: Award amounts are based on the type of school one is attending when award is received. If applicant transfers to a different school, his or her award amount may change based on the type of school to which he or she transfers. Public two-year: $300 to $1,000. Public four-year and Linn State Technical College: $1,000 to $2,150. Private: $2,000 to $4,600. (Note: Maximum award amounts

may be less than these figures; it depends on the amount of funding that is available for the program.)

Total amount of support: Varies.

NUMBER OF APPLICANTS MOST RECENT YEAR: 74,394.

NUMBER OF AWARDS: 43,000.

APPLICATION INFORMATION:
Contact the Department.

Duration: One academic year. Renewable.

Deadline: FAFSA on file by April 1.

ADDRESS INQUIRIES TO:
Information Center
(See address above.)

NATIONAL FEDERATION OF THE BLIND

NFB Scholarship Program
200 East Wells Street at Jernigan Place
Baltimore, MD 21230
(410) 659-9314 ext. 2415

E-MAIL ADDRESS:
scholarships@nfb.org

WEB SITE ADDRESS:
www.nfb.org/scholarships

TYPE:
Scholarships. Awarded on the basis of academic excellence and service to the community. Provides a one-time grant plus a continuing program of mentors and seminars for blind college students.

See entry 1002 for full listing.

NATIONAL INSTITUTE FOR LABOR RELATIONS RESEARCH   [1719]

5211 Port Royal Road
Suite 510
Springfield, VA 22151
(703) 321-9606 ext. 2231
Fax: (703) 321-7143

E-MAIL ADDRESS:
clj@nrtw.org

WEB SITE ADDRESS:
www.nilrr.org

FOUNDED: 1975

AREAS OF INTEREST:
Organization of public opposition to compulsory unionism in the education community.

NAME(S) OF PROGRAMS:
● **Applegate/Jackson Parks Future Teacher Scholarship**

TYPE:
Scholarships. Scholarship awarded annually to the education student who exemplifies dedication to principle and high professional standards.

YEAR PROGRAM STARTED: 1989

PURPOSE:
To promote awareness of compulsory unionism.

LEGAL BASIS:
Nonprofit 501(c)(3) organization.

ELIGIBILITY:
Applicants are limited to undergraduates and graduate students majoring in education in institutions of higher learning throughout the U.S. Applicants who will be considered must

demonstrate potential for successful completion of educational requirements in a college or university Department of Education program and the potential of successful application for a teaching license and demonstrate, by means of a written essay, an understanding of the individual freedom issue as it applies to the problem of compulsory unionism in the education community.

GEOGRAPHIC RESTRICTIONS:
United States.

FINANCIAL DATA:
Amount of support per award: $1,000 per scholarship.

Total amount of support: $1,000.

NUMBER OF APPLICANTS MOST RECENT YEAR:
Approximately 212.

NUMBER OF AWARDS: 1.

APPLICATION INFORMATION:
Applications may be submitted electronically. A total application will consist of a completed application form and a typewritten essay of approximately 500 words clearly demonstrating an interest in and a knowledge of the Right to Work principle as it applies to educators. All applicants will be requested to submit an official copy of his or her most recent transcript of grades.

Duration: One year. Nonrenewable.

Deadline: Applications must be postmarked on or by December 31 of calendar year.

ADDRESS INQUIRIES TO:
Cathy Jones, Scholarship Administrator
(See address above.)

*SPECIAL STIPULATIONS:
Applicant must be an education major attending college or have been admitted to an institution of higher learning in the U.S.

THE NATIONAL ITALIAN AMERICAN FOUNDATION [1720]

1860 19th Street, N.W.
Washington, DC 20009-5501
(202) 939-3116
Fax: (202) 483-2618

E-MAIL ADDRESS:
scholarships@niaf.org

WEB SITE ADDRESS:
www.niaf.org/scholarships

NAME(S) OF PROGRAMS:
● **NIAF Scholarship Program**

TYPE:
Scholarships. The National Italian American Foundation (NIAF) will award scholarships and grants to outstanding students for use during the following academic year. The awards will be made on the basis of academic merit and divided between two groups of students.

PURPOSE:
To assist Italian American students or those interested in Italian studies.

ELIGIBILITY:
Italian Americans studying any field, or students of any ethnic background studying Italian or Italian studies.

Italian American students who demonstrate outstanding potential and high academic achievements. The area of study is open.

Students from any ethnic background majoring or minoring in Italian language, Italian studies, Italian American studies or a related field, who demonstrate outstanding potential and high academic achievements.

GEOGRAPHIC RESTRICTIONS:
United States.

FINANCIAL DATA:
Each scholarship award can only cover tuition and university-provided room and board. Scholarship monies not used during one academic year are not transferable to the following academic year.

Amount of support per award: $2,000 to $10,000.

Total amount of support: Varies.

APPLICATION INFORMATION:
In order to be complete, an application must include the following:
(1) completed student application submitted online;
(2) Teacher Evaluation Form submitted online;
(3) an official school transcript submitted by mail and;
(4) FAFSA Financial Aid Form submitted by mail (optional).

Duration: One academic year.

Deadline: First Friday in March.

PUBLICATIONS:
Scholarship brochure.

ADDRESS INQUIRIES TO:
See e-mail address above.

NATIONAL JEWISH COMMITTEE ON SCOUTING   [1721]

1325 West Walnut Hill Lane
Irving, TX 75015
(972) 580-2097
Fax: (972) 580-2535

E-MAIL ADDRESS:
lee.shaw@scouting.org

WEB SITE ADDRESS:
www.jewishscouting.org

NAME(S) OF PROGRAMS:
● **Rick Arkans Eagle Scout Scholarship**
● **Chester M. Vernon Memorial Eagle Scout Scholarship**
● **Frank L. Weil Memorial Eagle Scout Scholarship**

TYPE:
Scholarships.

PURPOSE:
To promote Boy Scouting among Jewish youth; to help Jewish institutions and local council Jewish committees to provide Scouting opportunities for Jewish youth; to promote Jewish values in Scouting.

ELIGIBILITY:
Applicants must:
(1) be a registered, active member of a Boy Scout troop, Varsity Scout team, or Venturing crew;
(2) have received the Eagle Scout Award;
(3) be an active member of a synagogue and must have received the Ner Tamid or Etz Chaim religious emblem;
(4) have demonstrated practical citizenship in his synagogue, school, Scouting unit, and community and;
(5) be enrolled in an accredited high school and in his final year at the time of selection, except Scouts whose Eagle Scout boards of review are held the same year of their high

school graduation may apply in that calendar year. They may receive a scholarship one time only.

Applicants for Rick Arkans and Chester M. Vernon Memorial Eagle Scout Scholarships must also demonstrate financial need.

GEOGRAPHIC RESTRICTIONS:
United States.

FINANCIAL DATA:
Amount of support per award: Rick Arkans Eagle Scout Scholarship: $1,000; Chester M. Vernon Memorial Eagle Scout Scholarship: $1,000 per year for four years; Frank L. Weil Memorial Eagle Scout Scholarship: $1,000 first place award and two $500 second place awards.

NUMBER OF AWARDS: 6.

APPLICATION INFORMATION:
Applicants for the Arkans and Vernon Scholarships must submit a copy of the Free Application for Federal Student Assistance (FAFSA).

All sections of the scholarship application should be completed with as much information as possible. However, except for the required letter of recommendation (and FAFSA), no additional pages may be attached.

Deadline: Application submitted no later than February 28. Announcements by June 1.

ADDRESS INQUIRIES TO:
Lee Shaw, Staff Advisor
(See address above.)

NATIONAL SOCIETY DAUGHTERS OF THE AMERICAN REVOLUTION [1722]

1776 D Street, N.W.
Washington, DC 20006-5303
(202) 879-3292
Fax: (202) 879-3348

WEB SITE ADDRESS:
www.dar.org

FOUNDED: 1890

AREAS OF INTEREST:
Furthering the education of Native Americans.

NAME(S) OF PROGRAMS:
● **American Indian Scholarship**

TYPE:
Scholarships. Intended to help Native American college/university and technical school students at the undergraduate or graduate level.

PURPOSE:
To provide scholarship assistance to Native American students of any age or tribe, in any state, striving to get an education.

ELIGIBILITY:
Applicants must:
(1) be Native Americans (proof required by letter or proof papers) in financial need;
(2) be U.S. citizens/residents and;
(3) have a grade point average of 2.75 or higher.

Graduate students are eligible; however, undergraduate students are given preference.

GEOGRAPHIC RESTRICTIONS:
United States.

FINANCIAL DATA:
Amount of support per award: $4,000.

Total amount of support: Varies.

NUMBER OF AWARDS: Up to 20.

APPLICATION INFORMATION:
No phone or fax inquiries. Application may be made online.
Duration: No renewals.
Deadline: February 15.

NATIONAL SOCIETY DAUGHTERS OF THE AMERICAN REVOLUTION [1723]

1776 D Street, N.W.
Washington, DC 20006-5303
(202) 879-3292
Fax: (202) 879-3348

WEB SITE ADDRESS:
www.dar.org

FOUNDED: 1890

AREAS OF INTEREST:
Furthering the education of Native Americans.

NAME(S) OF PROGRAMS:
● **Frances Crawford Marvin American Indian Scholarship**

TYPE:
Scholarships. Intended to help Native American students enrolled full-time at a two- or four-year college or university.

PURPOSE:
To provide scholarship assistance to Native American students.

ELIGIBILITY:
Applicants must:
(1) be enrolled full-time at a two- or four-year college or university;
(2) be Native Americans (proof required by letter or proof papers);
(3) be U.S. citizens/residents;
(4) demonstrate financial need and academic achievement and;
(5) have a grade point average of 3.0 or higher.

A recipient may reapply and be considered along with members of the applicant pool.

GEOGRAPHIC RESTRICTIONS:
United States.

FINANCIAL DATA:
Amount of support per award: Up to $5,000.

NUMBER OF AWARDS: 1.

APPLICATION INFORMATION:
No phone or fax inquiries. Application may be made online.
Duration: Renewable upon reapplication.
Deadline: February 15.

NATIONAL SOCIETY OF ACCOUNTANTS SCHOLARSHIP FOUNDATION [1724]

1010 North Fairfax Street
Alexandria, VA 22314-1574
(703) 549-6400
(800) 966-6679
Fax: (703) 549-2984

E-MAIL ADDRESS:
members@nsacct.org

WEB SITE ADDRESS:
www.nsacct.org

AREAS OF INTEREST:
Accounting.

NAME(S) OF PROGRAMS:
● **The Stanley H. Stearman Award**

TYPE:
Scholarships.

PURPOSE:
To provide financial encouragement to students who select accounting as a career.

LEGAL BASIS:
501(c)(3) charitable organization.

ELIGIBILITY:
Must be an undergraduate accounting major who is a U.S. or Canadian citizen that attends a U.S.-accredited school and maintains a "B" or better overall grade point average. Also, must be the spouse, son, daughter, grandchild, niece, nephew, daughter-in-law or son-in-law of an active or retired NSA living or deceased member. The member must have held membership for at least one year prior to the annual distribution of applications in October.

GEOGRAPHIC RESTRICTIONS:
United States.

FINANCIAL DATA:
Amount of support per award: $2,000 per year.

NUMBER OF AWARDS: 1.

APPLICATION INFORMATION:
Applications and appraisal forms may be obtained by contacting Scholarship America at the address below, or online at the Foundation web site.
Duration: Not to exceed three years. This renewable award may extend through graduate studies.
Deadline: March 10 (postmark).

ADDRESS INQUIRIES TO:
National Society of Accountants
Scholarship Program
Scholarship America
One Scholarship Way
P.O. Box 297
St. Peter, MN 56082
Tel: (507) 931-1682

NATIONAL SOCIETY OF BLACK ENGINEERS [1725]

205 Daingerfield Road
Alexandria, VA 22314
(703) 549-2207
Fax: (703) 683-5312

E-MAIL ADDRESS:
scholarships@nsbe.org

WEB SITE ADDRESS:
www.nsbe.org

FOUNDED: 1975

AREAS OF INTEREST:
All areas of engineering.

TYPE:
Awards/prizes; Scholarships. The Society offers a variety of NSBE and corporate-sponsored scholarship and award opportunities to its precollege, collegiate undergraduate and graduate student members as well as technical professional members.

PURPOSE:
To increase the number of culturally responsible Black engineers who excel academically, succeed professionally and positively impact the community.

ELIGIBILITY:
For scholarships, applicant must:
(1) be an active, paid NSBE member and;

(2) submit one's transcript for grade point average confirmation to NSBE World Headquarters.

FINANCIAL DATA:
Amount of support per award: $500 to $10,000.
Total amount of support: Approximately $400,000 given annually in scholarships.

NUMBER OF AWARDS: Approximately 250 scholarships annually.

APPLICATION INFORMATION:
Application information is available on the web site; application must be made online.
Duration: One year; nonrenewable.
Deadline: Applications open in March with a deadline of June 1 and August with a deadline of November 30.

*SPECIAL STIPULATIONS:
Each scholarship recipient cannot be awarded more than two scholarships in a given program year. Members that apply for more than one scholarship that has an internship requirement must rank acceptance of scholarship for awarding, if selected as a recipient. (A member cannot accept both internships for a given time period; thus he or she must decide prior to selection which scholarship/internship they would want to accept in priority order.)

NATSO FOUNDATION   [1726]
1737 King Street
Suite 200
Alexandria, VA 22314
(703) 549-2100
Fax: (703) 684-4525

E-MAIL ADDRESS:
foundation@natso.com

WEB SITE ADDRESS:
www.natso.com/natsofoundation

FOUNDED: 1989

AREAS OF INTEREST:
Research, scholarships and public outreach.

NAME(S) OF PROGRAMS:
● **Bill Moon Scholarships**

TYPE:
Scholarships.

PURPOSE:
To aid travel plaza employees and their dependents with educational expenses.

ELIGIBILITY:
Must be an employee or a dependent of an employee of a travel plaza facility.

FINANCIAL DATA:
Amount of support per award: $5,000.
Total amount of support: Varies.

NUMBER OF APPLICANTS MOST RECENT YEAR: 30.

NUMBER OF AWARDS: 5.

APPLICATION INFORMATION:
Must submit application including transcript, essay, letter(s) of recommendation, and demonstration of need.
Duration: One semester.
Deadline: Varies.

ADDRESS INQUIRIES TO:
Taryn Brice-Rowland
Manager of Information and Research
(See address above.)

NBCC FOUNDATION, INC.   [1727]
3 Terrace Way
Greensboro, NC 27403
(336) 232-0376
Fax: (336) 232-0010

E-MAIL ADDRESS:
foundation@nbcc.org

WEB SITE ADDRESS:
www.nbccf.org

FOUNDED: 2005

AREAS OF INTEREST:
Philanthropy, mental health care, professional counseling, credentialing, scholarships and grant funding.

NAME(S) OF PROGRAMS:
● **NBCC Foundation Military Scholarship**
● **NBCC Foundation Minority Scholarships**
● **NBCC Foundation Rural Scholarship**
● **NBCC Minority Fellowships**

TYPE:
Fellowships; Scholarships. Academic scholarships for individuals pursuing a graduate-level degree in professional counseling.

YEAR PROGRAM STARTED: 2009

PURPOSE:
To increase the availability of counselors in underserved areas, with the current priority areas of minority, rural and military communities. Military Scholarship: To increase the number of counselors available to serve active duty service members and veterans. Minority Fellowship: To increase counseling resources available to underserved minority populations. Rural Scholarship: To increase access to needed counseling services in remote areas.

ELIGIBILITY:
Military Scholarship requirements:
(1) enrollment in good standing in a CACREP-accredited Master's degree counseling program; must have completed at least 18 credit-hours prior to application and carry at least six credit-hours during the current semester;
(2) prior or current active duty U.S. military service; veterans must have served in the military within the past five years and have received an honorable discharge;
(3) commitment to provide counseling services to service members and/or veterans for at least two years after graduation and;
(4) commitment to apply for the National Certified Counselor (NCC) credential prior to graduation.

Minority Fellowship requirements:
(1) U.S. citizen or permanent resident status;
(2) must not be receiving other federal funds or work for a federal agency; student loans are allowed;
(3) must hold the National Certified Counselor (NCC) credential;
(4) enrollment full-time and in good standing in a CACREP-accredited doctoral-level program;
(5) demonstrated knowledge and experience with racially and ethnically diverse populations and;
(6) commitment to provide mental health and/or substance abuse services to underserved minority populations in the private nonprofit and public sectors.

Minority Scholarship requirements:
(1) enrollment in good standing in a Master's-level counseling program accredited by the CACREP; must carry at least six credit-hours during the current semester and have completed at least 18 credit-hours;
(2) must possess substantial experience with ethnically, culturally and racially diverse communities;
(3) commitment to provide counseling services to underserved minority populations for at least two years after graduation and;
(4) commitment to apply for the National Certified Counselor (NCC) credential prior to graduation.

Rural Scholarship requirements:
(1) enrollment in good standing in a CACREP-accredited Master's degree counseling program; must have completed at least 18 credit-hours prior to application and carry at least six credit-hours during the current semester;
(2) residence in a rural area as defined by the Health Resources and Services Administration (HRSA); applicants must provide documentation of residence in a nonmetropolitan area as defined by HRSA;
(3) commitment to provide counseling services in a rural area for at least two years after graduation and;
(4) commitment to apply for the National Certified Counselor (NCC) credential prior to graduation.
CACREP stands for Council for Accreditation of Counseling and Related Educational Programs.

FINANCIAL DATA:
Financial awards go directly to recipients for any expenses associated with educational pursuit.
Amount of support per award: Military, Minority and Rural Scholarships: $5,000, subject to change upon annual review by NBCC Foundation Board of Trustees; Minority Fellowship: Up to $20,000.

APPLICATION INFORMATION:
Application information is available on the web site.
Duration: One-time scholarship award. Not renewable.
Deadline: Deadlines vary from year to year.

ADDRESS INQUIRIES TO:
Program Coordinator
(See address above.)

NEED
The Law and Finance Building
429 Fourth Avenue, 20th Floor
Pittsburgh, PA 15219
(412) 566-2760
Fax: (412) 471-6643

E-MAIL ADDRESS:
info@needld.org

WEB SITE ADDRESS:
www.needld.org

TYPE:
Internships; Matching gifts; Scholarships. Supplemental grants for postsecondary education at colleges and business, trade and technical schools.

See entry 1033 for full listing.

NEW JERSEY DEPARTMENT OF MILITARY AND VETERANS AFFAIRS [1728]

DVP-VBB
P.O. Box 340
Trenton, NJ 08625-0340
(609) 530-6854
Fax: (609) 530-6970

E-MAIL ADDRESS:
patty.richter@njdmava.state.nj.us

WEB SITE ADDRESS:
www.state.nj.us/military

FOUNDED: 1959

AREAS OF INTEREST:
State financial assistance for postsecondary students.

NAME(S) OF PROGRAMS:
● **Veterans Tuition Credit Program (VTCP)**

TYPE:
Grants-in-aid. Tuition assistance grant for attendance at any eligible undergraduate, graduate or vocational institution in the U.S.

YEAR PROGRAM STARTED: 1977

PURPOSE:
To provide tuition assistance to U.S. veterans of the Armed Forces of the U.S. who served on active duty between December 31, 1960 and May 7, 1975 who were, or are, eligible for federal veterans' educational assistance (G.I. Bill).

LEGAL BASIS:
Entitlement.

ELIGIBILITY:
Applicant must be a veteran of the armed forces of the U.S. who is or was eligible for veterans educational assistance pursuant to federal law and served on active duty in the armed forces of the U.S. between December 31, 1960 and May 7, 1975. Applicant must have been a legal New Jersey resident at the time of induction into the armed forces, or at the time of discharge from active duty or for at least one year prior to the time of application, excluding the time spent in active duty. If a veteran was not a New Jersey resident at time of induction or separation, veteran must provide documentation reflecting residency–copy of NJ Income Tax Return, letter from postmaster, home mortgage or apartment lease. Applicant must be currently enrolled in an approved state approving agency course of study at any eligible academic, professional or vocational institution in the U.S.

GEOGRAPHIC RESTRICTIONS:
New Jersey.

FINANCIAL DATA:
Amount of support per award: Eligible veterans may receive a maximum award of $400 a year for full-time attendance or $200 a year for half-time attendance as provided by regulations and available appropriations.

NUMBER OF APPLICANTS MOST RECENT YEAR: 17.

NUMBER OF AWARDS: Based upon appropriations.

APPLICATION INFORMATION:
Applications are available at campus Veterans Affairs offices or by calling the New Jersey Department of Military and Veterans Information Number, Tel: (888) 865-8387, available from any location in New Jersey, Monday through Friday, 8:30 A.M. to 4:30 P.M.

Duration: Eligible veterans may receive up to four academic years of payment.

Deadline: October 1 for fall and spring terms. March 1 for spring term only.

OFFICERS:
Robert Hughes, FD-FMB-BA

ADDRESS INQUIRIES TO:
Patricia Richter, Bureau Chief, VBB
(See address above.)

NEW JERSEY DEPARTMENT OF MILITARY AND VETERANS AFFAIRS [1729]

DVP-VBB
P.O. Box 340
Trenton, NJ 08625-0340
(609) 530-6854
Fax: (609) 530-6970

E-MAIL ADDRESS:
patty.richter@njdmava.state.nj.us

WEB SITE ADDRESS:
www.state.nj.us/military

FOUNDED: 1959

AREAS OF INTEREST:
State financial assistance for college students, 16 to 21 years of age.

NAME(S) OF PROGRAMS:
● **Prisoner of War/Missing in Action (POW/MIA) Program**

TYPE:
Grants-in-aid; Scholarships.

YEAR PROGRAM STARTED: 1978

LEGAL BASIS:
Entitlement.

ELIGIBILITY:
Applicants must be dependent children (any child born before, during or after the period of time its parent was a POW/MIA) of military service personnel who were officially declared "Prisoner of War" or "Person Missing in Action" after January 1, 1960. The POW or MIA must have been a resident of New Jersey at the time he or she entered the Armed Forces of the U.S. or whose official residence is New Jersey.

GEOGRAPHIC RESTRICTIONS:
New Jersey.

FINANCIAL DATA:
Amount of support per award: Full tuition costs will be paid on behalf of the eligible dependent to any New Jersey public or independent college or university upon certification of full-time enrollment.

APPLICATION INFORMATION:
Applications are available by contacting the New Jersey Department of Military and Veterans Affairs, Veterans Service Office, located in Mercer County.

Deadline: October 1 for fall and spring term benefits. March 1 for spring term benefits only.

OFFICERS:
Robert Hughes, FD-FMB-BA

ADDRESS INQUIRIES TO:
Patricia Richter, Bureau Chief, VBB
(See address above.)

NEW JERSEY OFFICE OF THE SECRETARY OF HIGHER EDUCATION [1730]

P.O. Box 542
Trenton, NJ 08625-0542
(609) 984-2709
Fax: (609) 633-8420

E-MAIL ADDRESS:
audrey.bennerson@njhe.state.nj.us

WEB SITE ADDRESS:
www.state.nj.us/highereducation/EOF/EOF_Description.shtml

FOUNDED: 1968

AREAS OF INTEREST:
State financial assistance for low-income, first-generation college students.

NAME(S) OF PROGRAMS:
● **The New Jersey Educational Opportunity Fund (EOF) Program**

TYPE:
Grants-in-aid. The Higher Education Student Assistance Authority (HESAA) is a New Jersey authority that provides students and families with the financial and informational resources for students to pursue their education beyond high school. With roots dating back to 1959, HESAA's singular focus has always been to benefit the students it serves. HESAA provides state supplemental loans, grants and scholarships. HESAA also administers the state's college savings plan.

Educational Opportunity Fund Grants (EOF) provide financial aid to eligible students from educationally and economically disadvantaged backgrounds at participating in-state institutions.

YEAR PROGRAM STARTED: 1968

PURPOSE:
To ensure meaningful access to higher education for those who come from backgrounds of economic and educational disadvantage.

LEGAL BASIS:
New Jersey Educational Opportunity Act of 1968.

ELIGIBILITY:
Applicants must be New Jersey residents for at least 12 consecutive months prior to receiving an award. Applicants must be full-time, matriculated students in an approved New Jersey college or university in an approved program of study. Household income cannot exceed established guidelines. The amount of the grant varies based on financial need, cost of attendance and available funding.

GEOGRAPHIC RESTRICTIONS:
New Jersey.

FINANCIAL DATA:
Amount of support per award: Dependent upon annual appropriations, financial need and cost of attendance.

Public four-year institution: $700 a semester. County/community college: $525 a semester. Independent college/university: $1,250 a semester.

Total amount of support: $23,293,919.

NUMBER OF AWARDS: 13,032 unduplicated.

APPLICATION INFORMATION:
All applicants for New Jersey grant assistance must file the Free Application for Federal Student Aid (FAFSA). EOF

applicants must also file an admissions application with a New Jersey college or university that participates in the EOF Program. Applications are available at high school guidance and college financial aid offices or by calling this toll-free phone number: (800) 792-8670, available from any location in New Jersey, Monday through Friday, 9 A.M. to 5 P.M.

Duration: Financial assistance is renewable for four years of undergraduate study providing student is making satisfactory academic progress, demonstrates unmet need, and an application is filed.

Deadline: October 1 for fall term and March 1 for spring term.

PUBLICATIONS:
State and Federal Financial Aid Programs for New Jersey Students, brochure.

ADDRESS INQUIRIES TO:
Audrey Bennerson
Statewide EOF Director
Office of the Secretary
of Higher Education
20 West State Street, Fourth Floor
P.O. Box 542
Trenton, NJ 08624-0542

NEW YORK STATE EDUCATION DEPARTMENT   [1731]
Scholarships and Grants
Education Building, Room 505 West
Albany, NY 12234
(518) 474-3719
Fax: (518) 474-7468

WEB SITE ADDRESS:
www.highered.nysed.gov/kiap/precoll

NAME(S) OF PROGRAMS:
- **Regents Physician Loan Forgiveness Award Program**
- **Scholarships for Academic Excellence**

TYPE:
Scholarships. Regents Physician Loan Forgiveness Award Program: Designed to increase the number of physicians practicing in areas of New York state designated by the Regents as having a shortage of physicians. Emphasis is placed on primary care.

Scholarships for Academic Excellence: For use only at colleges and universities within New York state. Students are nominated by their high schools for this award.

PURPOSE:
To encourage specially talented youth to continue their education.

GEOGRAPHIC RESTRICTIONS:
New York state.

FINANCIAL DATA:
Amount of support per award: Regents Physician Loan Forgiveness Award Program: Up to $10,000 per year for two years; Scholarships for Academic Excellence: $500 to $1,500.

Total amount of support: Varies.

NUMBER OF AWARDS: Regents Physician Loan Forgiveness Award Program: Minimum of 80; Scholarships for Academic Excellence; 2,000 $1,500 scholarships, 6,000 $500 scholarships.

APPLICATION INFORMATION:
Students must apply directly to the state education agency in their state of legal residence. Application forms are available through student's guidance counselor.

Duration: Regents Physician Loan Forgiveness Award Program: Two years.
Deadline: Varies.

NEW YORK STATE HIGHER EDUCATION SERVICES CORPORATION   [1732]
99 Washington Avenue
Albany, NY 12255
(888) 697-4372
Fax: (518) 474-3749

E-MAIL ADDRESS:
barbara.hochberg@hesc.ny.gov

WEB SITE ADDRESS:
www.hesc.ny.gov

FOUNDED: 1975

AREAS OF INTEREST:
Postsecondary student financial aid.

NAME(S) OF PROGRAMS:
- **Military Service Recognition Scholarship (MSRS)**
- **NYS Memorial Scholarships**

TYPE:
Grants-in-aid; Scholarships. Military Service Recognition Scholarship (MSRS) provides financial aid to children, spouses and financial dependents of members of the armed forces of the U.S. or of a state-organized militia who, at any time on or after August 2, 1990, while a New York state resident, died or became severely and permanently disabled while engaged in hostilities or training for hostilities. It is for study in New York state.

NYS Memorial Scholarships (NYS Memorial Scholarships for Families of Deceased Firefighters, Volunteer Firefighters, Police Officers, Peace Officers, and Emergency Medical Service Workers) provides financial aid to children, spouses and financial dependents of deceased members of these branches of public service who have died as the result of injuries sustained in the line of duty in service to the state of New York. It is for study in New York state.

The Corporation administers more than 25 grant, scholarship, award and other programs providing college financial aid for New York state residents.

YEAR PROGRAM STARTED: 2004

PURPOSE:
To provide special financial assistance for postsecondary study for children in certain categories.

LEGAL BASIS:
Article 13 of the Education Law. New York state agency.

ELIGIBILITY:
Students must:
(1) study at an approved postsecondary institution in New York state;
(2) have graduated from high school in the U.S., earned a GED, or passed a federally approved "Ability to Benefit" test as defined by the Commissioner of the State Education Department;
(3) be enrolled as a full-time student taking 12 or more credits per semester;
(4) be matriculated in an approved program of study and be in good academic standing;
(5) have at least a cumulative "C" average after receipt of two annual payments and;

(6) not be in default on a student loan guaranteed by HESC or any repayment of state awards.

GEOGRAPHIC RESTRICTIONS:
New York state.

FINANCIAL DATA:
Amount of support per award: Varies.
Total amount of support: Varies.

APPLICATION INFORMATION:
Applicants must complete and submit either the Military Service Recognition Scholarship Web Supplement or the NYS Memorial Scholarship Web Supplement. Be sure to print the Web Supplement confirmation, sign the supplement, and submit it along with the required documentation according to the instructions. FAFSA must be completed after eligibility is established and applicant has been assigned an account number.

Duration: Four years of full-time undergraduate study or five years of undergraduate study if the student is enrolled in an approved five-year program.
Deadline: June 30.

OFFICERS:
Angela Van Decker, Chairman

NEW YORK STATE HIGHER EDUCATION SERVICES CORPORATION   [1733]
99 Washington Avenue
Albany, NY 12255
(888) 697-4372
Fax: (518) 474-3749

E-MAIL ADDRESS:
danielle.freeman@hesc.ny.gov

WEB SITE ADDRESS:
www.hesc.ny.gov

FOUNDED: 1975

AREAS OF INTEREST:
Postsecondary student financial aid.

NAME(S) OF PROGRAMS:
- **NYS Aid for Part-Time Study (APTS)**

TYPE:
Grants-in-aid. College-based program providing grant assistance for eligible part-time students enrolled in approved undergraduate studies.

YEAR PROGRAM STARTED: 1984

PURPOSE:
To help pay tuition for eligible students enrolled in approved certificate or degree programs.

LEGAL BASIS:
State agency.

ELIGIBILITY:
To be considered for an award, a student must enroll part-time in a degree or an approved certificate program at a degree-granting institution, meet specific income limits, be a New York state resident, be either a U.S. citizen or eligible noncitizen, have a tuition charge of at least $100 per year, and not have used up Tuition Assistance Program (TAP) eligibility.

For this program, part-time study means being enrolled for at least three, but less than 12, semester-hours per semester, or four, but less than eight, credit hours per trimester. A participating college selects recipients from among eligible students.

GEOGRAPHIC RESTRICTIONS:
New York state.

FINANCIAL DATA:
Award amount is based on the student's need and the amount of money available at the institution.
Amount of support per award: Up to $2,000 per year.

APPLICATION INFORMATION:
Awards are made through each college offering the program. Students should contact the college financial aid office to find out how to apply at their school.
Duration: Renewable up to four years.
Deadline: Varies.

OFFICERS:
Angela Van Decker, Chairman

NEW YORK STATE HIGHER EDUCATION SERVICES CORPORATION   [1734]
99 Washington Avenue
Albany, NY 12255
(888) 697-4372
Fax: (518) 474-3749

E-MAIL ADDRESS:
barbara.hochberg@hesc.ny.gov

WEB SITE ADDRESS:
www.hesc.ny.gov

FOUNDED: 1975

AREAS OF INTEREST:
Postsecondary student financial aid.

NAME(S) OF PROGRAMS:
● **New York State Tuition Assistance Program (TAP)**

TYPE:
Grants-in-aid. New York's largest grant program, the Tuition Assistance Program helps eligible New York residents attending in-state postsecondary institutions pay for tuition. TAP grants are based on the applicant's and his or her family's New York state net taxable income.

YEAR PROGRAM STARTED: 1976

PURPOSE:
To partially defray tuition charges to students.

LEGAL BASIS:
Article 13 of the Education Law.

ELIGIBILITY:
Legal New York state residents who are U.S. citizens or eligible noncitizens, who are full-time students at an approved postsecondary institution in New York state, and who meet income eligibility limitations are eligible to apply.

GEOGRAPHIC RESTRICTIONS:
New York state.

FINANCIAL DATA:
Grant varies according to New York net taxable income of the applicant and the family. Student must attend an institution charging at least $200 annual tuition.
Amount of support per award: Up to $5,165.
Total amount of support: Varies.

NUMBER OF AWARDS: Unlimited.

APPLICATION INFORMATION:
Annual application is required. Applications will be sent to applicant after filing the Free Application for Federal Student Aid (FAFSA).
Duration: Up to four or five years of undergraduate study if the student is enrolled in an approved five-year program.

Deadline: June 30 of the current school year.

OFFICERS:
Angela Van Decker, Chairman

ADDRESS INQUIRIES TO:
Student Information
(See address above.)

THE CHARLOTTE W. NEWCOMBE FOUNDATION   [1735]
35 Park Place
Princeton, NJ 08542-6918
(609) 924-7022
Fax: (609) 252-1773

E-MAIL ADDRESS:
info@newcombefoundation.org

WEB SITE ADDRESS:
www.newcombefoundation.org

FOUNDED: 1979

AREAS OF INTEREST:
College scholarship funds to colleges and universities.

NAME(S) OF PROGRAMS:
● **Newcombe Fellowships**
● **Newcombe Scholarships for Mature Women**
● **Newcombe Scholarships for Students with Disabilities**
● **Special Scholarship Endowment Grants**

TYPE:
Challenge/matching grants; Endowments; Fellowships; Internships; Scholarships. Endowment challenges build up current Newcombe Scholarship Endowments at colleges in a Newcombe program.

Newcombe Fellowships are designed to encourage original and significant study of ethical and religious values in all areas of human endeavor. The selection process and all administration for this continuing fellowship program are handled by the Woodrow Wilson National Fellowship Foundation of Princeton, NJ. All doctoral requirements except the dissertation must be completed by November of the year preceding the Fellowship award. Student must be attending a graduate school in the U.S.

Newcombe Scholarships for Students with Disabilities are intended to recognize the extraordinary expenses these students incur because of their disabilities and to supplement other sources of aid. The Newcombe Foundation offers special disability expense scholarships, internship scholarships and partial tuition scholarships through the counseling offices of colleges which provide excellent support services for disabled students. Preference in this program is given to four-year colleges which render exceptional service to large numbers of disabled students. Eight colleges are in the Newcombe Program.

Newcombe Scholarships for Mature Women are for women age 25 and older who have completed half the credits required for their Bachelor's degrees. These scholarships are available at selected colleges which offer support services for mature women. Preference in this program is given to four-year colleges with excellent support services for mature women students. It is Foundation policy not to provide grants in this program to professional schools,

including theological seminaries and those training health care professionals; 31 colleges are in this program.

Special Scholarship Endowment Grants are awarded to selected institutions to benefit students from a specified economically disadvantaged population that the institution serves.

The Foundation makes no awards to individual students. All grants are made to colleges, universities and other institutions of higher education.

YEAR PROGRAM STARTED: 1981

PURPOSE:
To provide selected colleges and universities with scholarship funds for specifically targeted groups of students.

LEGAL BASIS:
Private.

ELIGIBILITY:
No grants to individuals. Scholarship aid only. No funds for program development staffing or support. The Foundation provides grants to colleges, universities and foundations to create scholarships for designated undergraduate and graduate students. No aid is available for postdoctoral fellowships.

GEOGRAPHIC RESTRICTIONS:
Scholarships for Disabled Students and Mature Women Scholarships are limited to Colleges in Delaware, Maryland, New Jersey, New York City, Pennsylvania and Washington, DC.

FINANCIAL DATA:
Amount of support per award: In three scholarship programs: $25,000 to $60,000 for the year 2012-13.
Total amount of support: $2,210,060 for the year 2012-13.
Matching fund requirements: Varies.

NUMBER OF APPLICANTS MOST RECENT YEAR:
43 (by invitation).

NUMBER OF AWARDS: 43.

REPRESENTATIVE AWARDS:
$41,000 to Misericordia University; $42,000 to Gwynedd-Mercy College; $47,000 to LaSalle University; $25,000 to Brooklyn College.

APPLICATION INFORMATION:
For Newcombe Fellowships, contact Woodrow Wilson National Fellowship Foundation, P.O. Box 5281, Princeton, NJ 08543-5281 for application materials. Tel: (609) 452-7007. Web site: www.woodrow.org.

For Newcombe Scholarships for Mature Women and Students with Disabilities, colleges within geographic area should contact the Foundation for applications. Individuals should contact their college of choice for availability of these scholarships.
Duration: Varies.
Deadline: Inquiries are accepted on an ongoing basis. Proposals by invitation.

PUBLICATIONS:
Annual report.

IRS IDENTIFICATION NUMBER: 23-2120614

STAFF:
Thomas N. Wilfrid, Executive Director
Jean Woodman, Administrative Associate
James H. Stocking, Financial and Technical Associate

ADDRESS INQUIRIES TO:
  Thomas N. Wilfrid, Executive Director
  (See address above.)

*PLEASE NOTE:
  No grants to individuals.

*SPECIAL STIPULATIONS:
  Grants are made to colleges and universities exclusively for student scholarships. Two programs (Mature Women and Students with Disabilities) are limited to colleges in Delaware, Maryland, New Jersey, New York City, Pennsylvania, and Washington, DC.

NORTH CAROLINA STATE EDUCATION ASSISTANCE AUTHORITY/COLLEGE FOUNDATION OF NORTH CAROLINA [1736]

P.O. Box 13663
Research Triangle Park, NC 27709-3663
(800) 700-1775
(866) 866-2362
Fax: (919) 248-6686

E-MAIL ADDRESS:
  programinformation@cfnc.org

WEB SITE ADDRESS:
  www.cfnc.org

AREAS OF INTEREST:
  Financial aid for North Carolina students.

TYPE:
  Grants-in-aid; Scholarships.

PURPOSE:
  To provide access to higher education and information for the citizens of North Carolina.

ELIGIBILITY:
  Varies with program. All applicants must be North Carolina residents and intend to use funds for tuition purposes only.

GEOGRAPHIC RESTRICTIONS:
  North Carolina.

FINANCIAL DATA:
  Amount of support per award: Varies.
  Total amount of support: Varies.

APPLICATION INFORMATION:
  Applications may be obtained online or by telephone request.
  Duration: Varies.
  Deadline: Varies.

ADDRESS INQUIRIES TO:
  NCSEAA Grants Training and Outreach
  (See address above.)

NORTH DAKOTA STATE BOARD FOR INDIAN SCHOLARSHIPS

1815 Schafer Street
Suite 202
Bismarck, ND 58501-1217
(701) 224-2647
Fax: (701) 224-5707

E-MAIL ADDRESS:
  ndfinaid@ndus.edu

WEB SITE ADDRESS:
  www.ndus.edu

TYPE:
  Scholarships. Grants to undergraduate and graduate Native American students in North Dakota colleges.

See entry 1054 for full listing.

NORTHERN CHAUTAUQUA COMMUNITY FOUNDATION [1737]

212 Lake Shore Drive West
Dunkirk, NY 14048
(716) 366-4892
Fax: (716) 366-3905

E-MAIL ADDRESS:
  nccf@nccfoundation.org

WEB SITE ADDRESS:
  www.nccfoundation.org

FOUNDED: 1986

AREAS OF INTEREST:
  Youth development and economic development.

TYPE:
  Challenge/matching grants; Project/program grants; Scholarships. Youth Development and Economic Development grants.

PURPOSE:
  To enhance the northern Chautauqua community.

LEGAL BASIS:
  Community foundation.

ELIGIBILITY:
  Applicants must be registered 501(c)(3) organizations that serve the northern Chautauqua County community.

GEOGRAPHIC RESTRICTIONS:
  Northern Chautauqua County, New York.

FINANCIAL DATA:
  Amount of support per award: $25 to $10,000.
  Total amount of support: Approximately $400,000.

APPLICATION INFORMATION:
  Call the Foundation for information.
  Deadline: Grants: March 1 and September 1.

PUBLICATIONS:
  Annual report; Spring and Fall newsletters.

IRS IDENTIFICATION NUMBER: 16-1271663

STAFF:
  Diane E. Hannum, Executive Director
  Eileen Dunn, Program Coordinator
  Nancy Mosier, Administrative Scholarship Coordinator
  John O. Wrigley, Accountant

ADDRESS INQUIRIES TO:
  Eileen Dunn, Program Coordinator
  (See address above.)

*SPECIAL STIPULATIONS:
  Scholarships to northern Chautauqua County residents only.

THE NRA FOUNDATION, INC. [1738]

11250 Waples Mill Road
Fairfax, VA 22030
(703) 267-1087
Fax: (703) 267-1083

E-MAIL ADDRESS:
  jebrayscholarship@nrahq.org

WEB SITE ADDRESS:
  nra.org

NAME(S) OF PROGRAMS:
  ● **Jeanne E. Bray Memorial Scholarship**

TYPE:
  Scholarships. For children of peace officers.

YEAR PROGRAM STARTED: 1988

PURPOSE:
  To assist children of peace officers, who are current NRA members, in furthering their education.

ELIGIBILITY:
  Must be an adult or junior member of the NRA and the son or daughter of a currently serving, full-time/deceased, full-time/retired, full-time, or disabled and retired commissioned peace officer who is also a current NRA member or was at the time of death. Eligible students can be senior high school students through senior college students. Applicants must have a satisfactory academic record and be enrolled full-time. Must be U.S. citizens or residents.

GEOGRAPHIC RESTRICTIONS:
  United States.

FINANCIAL DATA:
  Amount of support per award: Up to $10,000 or four years, whichever comes first.

NUMBER OF AWARDS: Varies.

APPLICATION INFORMATION:
  Applicant will need to contact Chandra Bolland to receive the personal reference forms.
  Duration: Up to four years.
  Deadline: November 15.

ADDRESS INQUIRIES TO:
  Chandra Bolland
  Jeanne E. Bray Memorial
  Scholarship Committee
  (See address above.)

OHIO BOARD OF REGENTS [1739]

Office of Financial Aid
25 South Front Street
Columbus, OH 43215
(614) 466-6000
Fax: (614) 752-5903

E-MAIL ADDRESS:
  wo_admin@regents.state.oh.us

WEB SITE ADDRESS:
  www.ohiohighered.org/ohio-war-orphans

NAME(S) OF PROGRAMS:
  ● **Ohio War Orphans Scholarship**

TYPE:
  Scholarships. Full-time undergraduate scholarships.

YEAR PROGRAM STARTED: 1954

PURPOSE:
  To enable children of disabled or deceased Ohio war veterans or children of Vietnam conflict MIAs or POWs to attend college.

LEGAL BASIS:
  State agency.

ELIGIBILITY:
  Applicant must be 16 to 25 years of age and a child of disabled or deceased Ohio war veteran or child of Vietnam conflict MIA or POW. Veteran parent must have at least a 60% combined disability rating. Applicant must also be enrolled as a full-time student in an eligible institution of higher education.

GEOGRAPHIC RESTRICTIONS:
Ohio.

FINANCIAL DATA:
Students attending Ohio nonprofit and profitmaking institutions of higher education will receive amounts no greater than the average amount paid for students attending public institutions; 93% tuition coverage at public institutions.
Amount of support per award: Varies.
Total amount of support: $4,753,907 for the year 2013.

NUMBER OF AWARDS: 747 for the year 2013.

APPLICATION INFORMATION:
Student must submit a completed application form.
Duration: Scholarships are automatically renewable for up to five years of undergraduate education.
Deadline: July 1. Announcements in early August.

STAFF:
Amber Brady, Program Manager

ADDRESS INQUIRIES TO:
Amber Brady, Program Manager
(See address above.)

OHIO BOARD OF REGENTS [1740]
Office of Financial Aid
25 South Front Street
Columbus, OH 43215
(614) 466-6000
Fax: (614) 752-5903

E-MAIL ADDRESS:
ocog_admin@regents.state.oh.us

WEB SITE ADDRESS:
www.ohiohighered.org/ocog

FOUNDED: 1963

NAME(S) OF PROGRAMS:
• **Ohio College Opportunity Grant Program (OCOG)**

TYPE:
General operating grants. Grants for college-bound students or current undergraduate students.

YEAR PROGRAM STARTED: 2006

PURPOSE:
To assist in achieving the goals of access and choice for low-income and middle-income students.

LEGAL BASIS:
State agency.

ELIGIBILITY:
Applicant must be an Ohio resident, demonstrate financial need, and be seeking an Associate's degree, a Bachelor's degree, or nursing diploma at an eligible institution.

GEOGRAPHIC RESTRICTIONS:
Ohio and Pennsylvania.

FINANCIAL DATA:
Amount of support per award: Varies.
Total amount of support: $86,048,204 for the year 2013.

NUMBER OF AWARDS: 94,479 for the year 2013.

APPLICATION INFORMATION:
Student must submit a Free Application for Federal Student Aid (FAFSA).
Duration: One academic year. Renewable for a maximum of five years of full-time study.

Deadline: October 1.

ADDRESS INQUIRIES TO:
Tamika Braswell, Program Manager
(See address above.)

OHIO NATIONAL GUARD SCHOLARSHIP PROGRAM [1741]
2825 West Dublin Granville Road
AGOH-SP
Columbus, OH 43235-2789
(614) 336-7143
(614) 336-7053
(888) 400-6484
Fax: (614) 336-7318

E-MAIL ADDRESS:
ongsp@ongsp.org

WEB SITE ADDRESS:
www.ongsp.org

FOUNDED: 1977

AREAS OF INTEREST:
Associate or undergraduate general education.

TYPE:
Scholarships. Grants for undergraduate students attending three credit hours or more.

YEAR PROGRAM STARTED: 1978

PURPOSE:
To encourage enlistment in Ohio National Guard.

LEGAL BASIS:
Ohio Revised Code. Nonprofit.

ELIGIBILITY:
Applicants must possess a high school diploma or a GED certificate and enlist, re-enlist or extend their current enlistment in a valid authorized or required MTOE/TDA (ARNG) or UMD (ANG) position for enlistment in Selective Reserve duty in the Ohio National Guard.

GEOGRAPHIC RESTRICTIONS:
Ohio.

FINANCIAL DATA:
Instructional and general fees paid 100% for student attending public institution.
Amount of support per award: Private Institution: $4,643 maximum per semester; $3,096 maximum per quarter. Public Institution: Varies.
Total amount of support: $16,000,000 annually.

NUMBER OF APPLICANTS MOST RECENT YEAR:
3,500.

APPLICATION INFORMATION:
An applicant must apply each term so that the application is received in the Scholarship Program Office no later than the established deadlines, which are no later than the close of business (4:30 P.M.).
Duration: Scholarships are renewable for up to four years of undergraduate education. Grants provide two years tuition assistance with three-year enlistment or four years tuition assistance with six-year enlistment.
Deadline: July 1 for fall; November 1 for winter/quarter, semester, trimester/spring semester; February 1 for spring quarter; April 1 for summer.

PUBLICATIONS:
Regulation AGOR 621-1 (Army); *35-1* (Air).

STAFF:
Afrika Alsup, Administrator

ADDRESS INQUIRIES TO:
Afrika Alsup, Administrator
(See address above.)

*SPECIAL STIPULATIONS:
Applicant must enlist in Ohio National Guard for not less than three years. Must enroll minimum three credit hours in degree-granting program.

ORDER SONS OF ITALY IN AMERICA, GRAND LODGE OF FLORIDA [1742]
18281 Fresh Lake Way
Boca Raton, FL 33498
(561) 479-2096

E-MAIL ADDRESS:
nana3028@aol.com

WEB SITE ADDRESS:
osiafl.org

FOUNDED: 1953

AREAS OF INTEREST:
Culture, charity and education.

TYPE:
Awards/prizes; Grants-in-aid; Scholarships. Scholarships are provided to high school students entering college.

Financial aid is given in support of charitable programs, such as Alzheimer's disease, Cooley's anemia, autism, and cancer.

YEAR PROGRAM STARTED: 1988

PURPOSE:
To share and help those in need; to support high school students entering college; to support charitable programs.

ELIGIBILITY:
Scholarship program: Applying student must be a U.S. citizen or resident who resides in the states of Florida or Georgia, be of Italian heritage, and achieve high scholastic grades.

Applying organizations must have 501(c)(3) not-for-profit status. No grants are made to religious organizations.

FINANCIAL DATA:
Amount of support per award: Scholarship program: $1,000 per student.

NUMBER OF APPLICANTS MOST RECENT YEAR:
42.

NUMBER OF AWARDS: Scholarship program: Varies with funding; 8 scholarships in 2012.

APPLICATION INFORMATION:
Scholarship application form can be obtained on the web site or at applying student's local high school. Completed application materials must be submitted to the State Scholarship Chairperson.
Duration: One-time awards. Grants are not renewable.
Deadline: March 31.

ADDRESS INQUIRIES TO:
Eva Mottola, State Scholarship Chairperson
(See telephone number above.)

PARAPSYCHOLOGY FOUNDATION, INC.
P.O. Box 1562
New York, NY 10021
(212) 628-1550
Fax: (212) 628-1559

E-MAIL ADDRESS:
info@parapsychology.org

WEB SITE ADDRESS:
www.parapsychology.org

TYPE:
Scholarships. Assists students attending an accredited college or university in pursuing the academic study of the science of parapsychology.

See entry 2585 for full listing.

PENNSYLVANIA HIGHER EDUCATION ASSISTANCE AGENCY   [1743]
1200 North Seventh Street
Harrisburg, PA 17102-1398
(717) 720-2800
(800) 692-7392 (Pennsylvania only)
Fax: (717) 720-3786

E-MAIL ADDRESS:
granthelp@pheaa.org

WEB SITE ADDRESS:
www.pheaa.org

FOUNDED: 1964

NAME(S) OF PROGRAMS:
• **Pennsylvania State Grant Program**

TYPE:
Grants-in-aid. The Pennsylvania State Grant Program allows eligible Pennsylvania residents to obtain financial assistance for undergraduate study at any PHEAA-approved institution of higher education. The Free Application for Federal Student Aid (FAFSA) serves as the program's application.

YEAR PROGRAM STARTED: 1964

PURPOSE:
To assist needy students in obtaining higher education.

LEGAL BASIS:
Government agency.

ELIGIBILITY:
The student applying for Pennsylvania State Grants must:
(1) meet criteria for financial need;
(2) be enrolled on at least a half-time basis in a PHEAA-approved undergraduate program of study and not already have a four-year (or more) undergraduate degree;
(3) be a high school graduate or the recipient of a GED;
(4) demonstrate academic progress (for continued aid) and;
(5) be a Pennsylvania resident (domiciliary).

Summer school students may also qualify for State Grant funds.

GEOGRAPHIC RESTRICTIONS:
Pennsylvania.

FINANCIAL DATA:
Amount of support per award: Varies annually.
Total amount of support: Varies annually due to appropriations, number of applicants, and financial strength of applying families.

NUMBER OF AWARDS: Approximately 185,000.

APPLICATION INFORMATION:
Submit the Free Application for Federal Student Aid (FAFSA). For faster processing, those applying can find out what they need to fill out the FAFSA and how to complete it by going online.
Duration: One academic year. Renewal contingent upon continued eligibility and financial need.
Deadline: Varies.

EXECUTIVE OFFICERS:
James L. Preston, President and Chief Executive Officer
Christine Zuzack, Vice President of State Grants and Special Programs

ADDRESS INQUIRIES TO:
Christine Zuzack, Vice President of State Grants and Special Programs
(See address above.)

THE PHI BETA KAPPA SOCIETY   [1744]
1606 New Hampshire Avenue, N.W.
Washington, DC 20009
(202) 745-3287
Fax: (202) 986-1601

E-MAIL ADDRESS:
awards@pbk.org

WEB SITE ADDRESS:
www.pbk.org

AREAS OF INTEREST:
Philosophy.

NAME(S) OF PROGRAMS:
• **The Romanell-Phi Beta Kappa Professorship in Philosophy**

TYPE:
Fellowships. Professorship awarded to scholars in the field of philosophy, without restriction to any one school of philosophical thought.

YEAR PROGRAM STARTED: 1983

PURPOSE:
To recognize not only distinguished achievement, but also the recipient's contribution or potential contribution to public understanding of philosophy.

ELIGIBILITY:
Scholar need not be a member of Phi Beta Kappa, but must be on the faculty of an institution sheltering a chapter of Phi Beta Kappa and must be nominated by that chapter.

GEOGRAPHIC RESTRICTIONS:
United States.

FINANCIAL DATA:
Amount of support per award: $7,500 stipend.

NUMBER OF AWARDS: 1 annually.

APPLICATION INFORMATION:
Recipient must be nominated by the chapter of Phi Beta Kappa at the institution in which they are on faculty.
Duration: One year. Nonrenewable.

STAFF:
Laura Hartnett, Coordinator of Administration

ADDRESS INQUIRIES TO:
Laura Hartnett
Coordinator of Administration
(See address above.)

*SPECIAL STIPULATIONS:
Recipient will be expected to give a series of three special lectures during the year of the Professorship. Such lectures are to be given at the sheltering institution and to be open to the general public as well as to the academic community.

PI GAMMA MU, INTERNATIONAL HONOR SOCIETY IN SOCIAL SCIENCE   [1745]
1001 Millington, Suite B
Winfield, KS 67156
(620) 221-3128
Fax: (620) 221-7124

E-MAIL ADDRESS:
executivedirector@pigammamu.org

WEB SITE ADDRESS:
www.pigammamu.org

FOUNDED: 1924

AREAS OF INTEREST:
Economics, history, political science, sociology, anthropology, international relations, social work, psychology, social philosophy, history of education and criminal justice, law and human/cultural geography.

NAME(S) OF PROGRAMS:
• **Pi Gamma Mu Scholarships**

TYPE:
Scholarships. Awarded for graduate study.

YEAR PROGRAM STARTED: 1951

PURPOSE:
To promote scholarship in the Society's areas of interest.

LEGAL BASIS:
Nonprofit.

ELIGIBILITY:
Applicants must be a member of Pi Gamma Mu.

FINANCIAL DATA:
Amount of support per award: $1,000 or $2,000.
Total amount of support: $13,000 annually.

NUMBER OF APPLICANTS MOST RECENT YEAR:
47.

NUMBER OF AWARDS: 10.

APPLICATION INFORMATION:
Resume, personal statement, transcript and three letters of recommendation required.
Duration: One year.
Deadline: February 15. Announcement May 1.

PUBLICATIONS:
Application guidelines.

OFFICERS:
Barry Friedman, President
C. Laurence Heck, First Vice President
Clara Small, Second Vice President
Janet Adamski, Secretary and Treasurer
Charles Hartwig, Chancellor
J.L. Kemp, Chancellor
Susan Kinsela, Chancellor
Yongsheng Wang, Chancellor

MINNIE STEVENS PIPER FOUNDATION   [1746]
1250 N.E. Loop 410, Suite 810
San Antonio, TX 78209-1539
(210) 525-8494
Fax: (210) 341-6627

E-MAIL ADDRESS:
mspf@mspf.org

WEB SITE ADDRESS:
www.mspf.org

FOUNDED: 1950

NAME(S) OF PROGRAMS:
• **Piper Professor Program**
• **Piper Scholar Program**
• **Student Loan Program**

TYPE:
Awards/prizes; Scholarships. Piper Professor Program: Annual awards to professors for superior teaching at the college level.

Piper Scholars: Four-year scholarships awarded to academically promising and superior high school seniors in amounts that assist them in attending the college or university of their choice within the state of Texas.

Student Loan Program: Loans to worthy and needy students at the junior, senior, undergraduate or graduate college level.

PURPOSE:
To support charitable, scientific, or educational undertakings by providing for, or contributing toward, the education of financially limited but worthy students; to assist young men and women residents of Texas, attending or wishing to attend colleges and universities in the state of Texas, to complete their education and obtain degrees; to contribute to community chests; to support any other nonprofit organization or activity dedicated to promoting the general welfare within the state of Texas.

LEGAL BASIS:
Private foundation with Letter Ruling under Section 4945 of the Tax Reform Act of 1969.

ELIGIBILITY:
Piper Professor Program: Candidates must be U.S. citizens and nominated through college/university President's office.

Piper Scholar Program: Participation is by invitation only to high schools in certain geographic areas. Student must be nominated by their high school counselor.

Student Loan Program: Must be full-time status. Restricted to Texas residents attending a college or university within the State of Texas.

GEOGRAPHIC RESTRICTIONS:
Texas.

FINANCIAL DATA:
Amount of support per award: Piper Professor Program: $5,000.

NUMBER OF AWARDS: Piper Professor Program: 10; Piper Scholar Program: 25.

APPLICATION INFORMATION:
Contact the Foundation.
Duration: Piper Scholar Program: Four years.

ADDRESS INQUIRIES TO:
Joyce M. Ellis, Executive Director
(See address above.)

*SPECIAL STIPULATIONS:
Piper Professor and Piper Scholars Programs are by invitation only.

THE PLANNING AND VISUAL EDUCATION PARTNERSHIP [1747]
4651 Sheridan Street, Suite 470
Hollywood, FL 33021
(954) 241-4800
(954) 241-4834
Fax: (954) 893-8375

E-MAIL ADDRESS:
pave@paveinfo.org

WEB SITE ADDRESS:
www.paveinfo.org

FOUNDED: 1992

AREAS OF INTEREST:
Retail design planning and visual merchandising.

TYPE:
Awards/prizes; Capital grants; Conferences/seminars; Internships; Product donations; Project/program grants; Scholarships. Student educational support.

PURPOSE:
To encourage students to study in the field of retail design and planning and visual merchandising.

FINANCIAL DATA:
Amount of support per award: PAVE the Way 3D Design Challenge: $13,500; Student Aid Program: $22,000; Student Design Competition: $5,000 for first place, $2,500 for second place, $1,500 for third place and $500 for honorable mention.
Total amount of support: $77,500 for the year 2013.

NUMBER OF AWARDS: 13.

ADDRESS INQUIRIES TO:
Dash Nagel, Managing Director
(See address above.)

PRESBYTERIAN CHURCH (U.S.A.) [1748]
100 Witherspoon Street
Louisville, KY 40202-1396
(888) 728-7228 ext. 5224
Fax: (502) 569-8766

E-MAIL ADDRESS:
finaid@pcusa.org

WEB SITE ADDRESS:
www.pcusa.org/financialaid

AREAS OF INTEREST:
Majors in health services/sciences, religious studies, sacred music, social services and social sciences.

NAME(S) OF PROGRAMS:
● **Student Opportunity Scholarship**

TYPE:
Scholarships. Need-based.

YEAR PROGRAM STARTED: 1956

PURPOSE:
To assist undergraduate juniors and seniors already in college, with preference to racial ethnic students seeking a degree with emphasis on the mission of PCUSA in the following disciplines: health services/sciences, religious studies, sacred music, social services and social sciences.

ELIGIBILITY:
Scholarship is open to African Americans, Asian Americans, Middle Eastern Americans, Hispanic Americans and Caucasians. Applicants must:
(1) demonstrate financial need;
(2) be a member of the Presbyterian Church (U.S.A.);
(3) be a sophomore, junior or senior already in college and;
(4) have a 2.5 grade point average to get in the program and a 2.5 grade point average to stay in.

GEOGRAPHIC RESTRICTIONS:
United States and Puerto Rico.

FINANCIAL DATA:
Amount of support per award: Up to $2,000 per academic year.
Total amount of support: Approximately $160,000 annually.

NUMBER OF APPLICANTS MOST RECENT YEAR:
120.

NUMBER OF AWARDS: 80.

APPLICATION INFORMATION:
Applications can be downloaded from the web site, beginning April 1.
Duration: Renewable up to three years depending on need and maintenance of a 2.5 grade point average.
Deadline: May 15 for "getting started" part; June 30 for financial information.

PUBLICATIONS:
Financial Aid Programs.

ADDRESS INQUIRIES TO:
Financial Aid for Service
(See address above.)

PRESBYTERIAN CHURCH (U.S.A.) [1749]
100 Witherspoon Street
Louisville, KY 40202-1396
(888) 728-7228 ext. 5224
Fax: (502) 569-8766

E-MAIL ADDRESS:
finaid@pcusa.org

WEB SITE ADDRESS:
www.pcusa.org/financialaid

NAME(S) OF PROGRAMS:
● **Samuel Robinson Essay Contest**

TYPE:
Awards/prizes. Essay contest, awarded to junior or senior undergraduate students enrolled full-time in one of the colleges/universities related to the Presbyterian Church (U.S.A.).

YEAR PROGRAM STARTED: 1940

PURPOSE:
To instill an interest in the work of the Presbyterian Church throughout the U.S.

LEGAL BASIS:
Nonprofit.

ELIGIBILITY:
Must be a member of the Presbyterian Church (U.S.A.) and a junior or senior attending a Presbyterian-related college or university.

GEOGRAPHIC RESTRICTIONS:
United States.

FINANCIAL DATA:
Amount of support per award: $1,500 to $5,000.
Total amount of support: Varies.

NUMBER OF APPLICANTS MOST RECENT YEAR:
15.

NUMBER OF AWARDS: Up to 15.

APPLICATION INFORMATION:
Applications by request only November 15 to March 15. Contact the Presbyterian Church (U.S.A.).
Duration: One-time award.
Deadline: April 1.

PUBLICATIONS:
Financial Aid Brochure.

ADDRESS INQUIRIES TO:
Financial Aid for Service
(See address above.)

*SPECIAL STIPULATIONS:
Open to Presbyterian students attending a Presbyterian-related school.

THE PRESS CLUB OF METROPOLITAN ST. LOUIS AND JOURNALISM FOUNDATION OF METROPOLITAN ST. LOUIS [1750]

c/o The Press Club of Metropolitan St. Louis
P.O. Box 410522
St. Louis, MO 63141
(314) 449-8029
Fax: (636) 203-2441

E-MAIL ADDRESS:
info@stlpressclub.org

WEB SITE ADDRESS:
stlpressclub.org

FOUNDED: 1956

AREAS OF INTEREST:
Journalism.

NAME(S) OF PROGRAMS:
- **Baseball Writers of America Scholarship**
- **Enterprise Journalism Fellowships**
- **Fleishman-Hillard, Inc. Scholarship**
- **Journalism Foundation Scholarships**
- **David Lipman Scholarship at the Missouri School of Journalism**
- **Missouri Professional Communicators Scholarships**
- **Press Club Media and Internship Scholarships**
- **Press Club of Metropolitan St. Louis Scholarships**
- **St. Louis Public Library Media Archives**
- **Times Newspapers and Webster University Journalism Scholarships**

TYPE:
Awards/prizes; Conferences/seminars; Development grants; Fellowships; Internships; Project/program grants; Scholarships; Seed money grants.

YEAR PROGRAM STARTED: 1970

PURPOSE:
To award scholarships to those entering sophomore, junior and senior years of college or graduate school preparing for journalism/communications careers at recognized schools, majoring in journalism, broadcasting, English or related fields; to award fellowships for journalists to do investigative stories for publication.

LEGAL BASIS:
Incorporated as nonprofit organization in state of Missouri.

ELIGIBILITY:
Applicant for scholarships must be at least a sophomore in college interested in a career in journalism and a St. Louis metropolitan area resident. Enterprise Journalism Fellowships: Journalists with an investigative project concerning the St. Louis region.

GEOGRAPHIC RESTRICTIONS:
St. Louis, Missouri and counties of Franklin, Jefferson, Lincoln, St. Charles, St. Louis and Warren, and Illinois counties of Bond, Clinton, Jersey, Madison, Monroe and St. Clair.

FINANCIAL DATA:
Amount of support per award: Varies.
Total amount of support: $30,000.

COOPERATIVE FUNDING PROGRAMS: Grants from member organizations.

NUMBER OF APPLICANTS MOST RECENT YEAR:
19.

NUMBER OF AWARDS: 14.

APPLICATION INFORMATION:
Scholarship applicant should submit an application from Journalism Foundation, college transcript, two letters of reference, writing samples and financial data.

Enterprise Journalism Fellowships: Journalist applicants prepare a description of story project, budget and where to be published.
Duration: One year. Renewable.
Deadline: May 3 for scholarships. Enterprise Journalism Fellowships applications are accepted on an ongoing basis.

PUBLICATIONS:
Courier, newsletter.

IRS IDENTIFICATION NUMBER: 43-1489003

STAFF:
Glenda Partlow, Executive Director
Laura Schnarr, Social Media and Website Coordinator

ADDRESS INQUIRIES TO:
Glenda Partlow
Executive Director, Press Club
(See address above.)

RONALD REAGAN PRESIDENTIAL FOUNDATION [1751]

40 Presidential Drive
Simi Valley, CA 93065
(805) 522-2977
Fax: (805) 520-9702

E-MAIL ADDRESS:
info@reaganfoundation.org

WEB SITE ADDRESS:
www.reaganfoundation.org/scholarships

FOUNDED: 1987

NAME(S) OF PROGRAMS:
- **GE-Reagan Foundation Scholarship Program**

TYPE:
Scholarships. The GE-Reagan Foundation Scholarship Program rewards college-bound students who demonstrate exemplary leadership, drive, integrity and citizenship with financial assistance to pursue higher education.

PURPOSE:
To honor the legacy and character of America's 40th president.

FINANCIAL DATA:
Amount of support per award: $10,000 for each scholarship.

NUMBER OF AWARDS: Up to 20 new scholarships each year.

APPLICATION INFORMATION:
Application information is available on the web site.
Duration: One academic year; renewable for up to three additional years.
Deadline: Application is available in the fall and is due in the winter. The scholarship will then be awarded for the next full academic year. Contact the Foundation for exact details.

ADDRESS INQUIRIES TO:
E-mail: ge-reagan@scholarshipamerica.org
Tel: 507-931-1682

SID RICHARDSON MEMORIAL FUND [1752]

309 Main Street
Fort Worth, TX 76102
(817) 336-0494
Fax: (817) 332-2176

E-MAIL ADDRESS:
sranelle@sidrichardson.org

FOUNDED: 1965

AREAS OF INTEREST:
Academic and vocational scholarships.

TYPE:
Scholarships. Scholarships are for both academic and vocational studies.

YEAR PROGRAM STARTED: 1965

LEGAL BASIS:
Tax-exempt.

ELIGIBILITY:
Limited funds are available to assist in defraying the cost of college education or of vocational training. These scholarships are awarded on a competitive basis according to academic achievement and/or financial need.

Those eligible to apply for a Sid Richardson Memorial Fund scholarship are direct descendants (children or grandchildren) of persons who qualified for Early Retirement, Normal Retirement, Disability Retirement, or Death Benefits from The Bass Retirement Plan (formerly The Retirement Plan For Employees of Bass Enterprises Production Co.), Retirement Plan for Employees of Barbnet/San Jose Cattle Co., Retirement Plan for Employees of City Center Development Co., City Club Retirement Plan, Retirement Plan for Employees of Richardson Aviation, G.P., Retirement Plan for Employees of Sid W. Richardson Foundation, or Retirement Plan for Employees of Sundance Square. Those eligible also include direct descendants (children or grandchildren) of persons presently employed with a minimum of three years' full-time service (as of March 31) with any of the following employers: Barbnet Investment Co., BEPCO, L.P., BOPCO, L.P., City Club of Fort Worth, Richardson Aviation, San Jose Cattle Co., Sid Richardson Carbon Co. (SRCE, L.P.), Sid W. Richardson Foundation, and Sundance Square Management, L.P.

FINANCIAL DATA:
Amount of support per award: $1,000 to $9,000 per student per academic year.
Total amount of support: Approximately $340,000.

NUMBER OF APPLICANTS MOST RECENT YEAR:
Varies.

NUMBER OF AWARDS: Varies.

APPLICATION INFORMATION:
Direct a written request for an application to Shanda Ranelle, Sid Richardson Memorial Fund, at the address, e-mail or fax number above. Include student name, address, e-mail and phone number, as well as the qualifying employee's name, Social Security number, qualifying company name and dates of employment as well as the relation to student.
Duration: Considered for renewal annually if a 2.0 grade point average is maintained for each semester.
Deadline: Completed applications must be postmarked no later than March 31 annually for the following academic year. Announcement of awards by May 31.

OFFICERS:
Pete Geren, President and Chief Executive Officer
Cindy Alexander, Treasurer
Shanda Ranelle, Secretary

ADDRESS INQUIRIES TO:
Shanda Ranelle, Coordinator
(See address above.)

JACKIE ROBINSON FOUNDATION
75 Varick Street, 2nd Floor
New York, NY 10013-1917
(212) 290-8600
Fax: (212) 290-8081

E-MAIL ADDRESS:
general@jackierobinson.org

WEB SITE ADDRESS:
www.jackierobinson.org

TYPE:
Conferences/seminars; Internships; Scholarships.

See entry 1011 for full listing.

THE ROTARY CLUB OF BRYN MAWR   [1753]
P.O. Box 84
Bryn Mawr, PA 19010

E-MAIL ADDRESS:
rbcuff@verizon.net

WEB SITE ADDRESS:
www.rotary7450.org

FOUNDED: 1969

AREAS OF INTEREST:
To serve others and satisfy Rotary principles.

NAME(S) OF PROGRAMS:
● **Harry H. Cabell Scholarship Program**

TYPE:
Awards/prizes; Scholarships.

YEAR PROGRAM STARTED: 1985

PURPOSE:
To recognize and reward college students who meet trust requirements.

LEGAL BASIS:
Not-for-profit society.

ELIGIBILITY:
Financial need, high academic standards and leadership qualities, service to others and achievement qualities are important factors in the decision process. Applicants must be in an area college or university.

GEOGRAPHIC RESTRICTIONS:
Metropolitan Philadelphia and surrounding counties.

FINANCIAL DATA:
Amount of support per award: $1,500 to $2,000.

Total amount of support: Varies.

NUMBER OF AWARDS: 2 to 4.

APPLICATION INFORMATION:
Application form must include recommendation from faculty, statement of good standing from dean, transcript of grades and 300-word essay.

Duration: One year. No renewals.

Deadline: Early March. Announcement approximately April 30.

ADDRESS INQUIRIES TO:
Richard Cuff, Scholarship Committee
Harry H. Cabell Scholarship Awards
(See address above.)

SACHS FOUNDATION
90 South Cascade Avenue
Suite 1410
Colorado Springs, CO 80903
(719) 633-2353
Fax: (719) 633-3663

E-MAIL ADDRESS:
lisa@sachsfoundation.org

WEB SITE ADDRESS:
sachsfoundation.org

TYPE:
Grants-in-aid; Scholarships.

See entry 1034 for full listing.

SCHOOL FOR ADVANCED RESEARCH   [1754]
P.O. Box 2188
Santa Fe, NM 87504-2188
(505) 954-7201
Fax: (505) 954-7214

E-MAIL ADDRESS:
scholar@sarsf.org

WEB SITE ADDRESS:
www.sarweb.org

FOUNDED: 1907

AREAS OF INTEREST:
Anthropology and allied disciplines in the humanities and social sciences.

NAME(S) OF PROGRAMS:
● **Summer Scholar Fellowships**

TYPE:
Fellowships. Eight-week summer residency program.

PURPOSE:
To promote the pursuit of research or writing projects that promote understanding of human behavior, culture, society, and the history of anthropology.

ELIGIBILITY:
Scholars in anthropology and related disciplines are invited to apply in order to pursue research or writing projects. Scholars whose projects relate to anthropological linguistics or to the history of anthropology are especially encouraged to apply. Both humanistically and scientifically oriented scholars are encouraged to apply.

FINANCIAL DATA:
Scholars are provided with a small stipend, free housing and office space, an allowance account, library support and other benefits.
Amount of support per award: Stipend up to $1,000 and an allowance up to $160.

COOPERATIVE FUNDING PROGRAMS: Ethel-Jane Westfeldt Bunting Foundation, William Y. and Nettie K. Adams Fellowship in the History of Anthropology, the Christopher Smeall Fellowship in Anthropological Linguistics, and the Cotsen Institute of Archaeology, University of California, Los Angeles.

NUMBER OF APPLICANTS MOST RECENT YEAR:
55 for the year 2011.

NUMBER OF AWARDS: 6.

APPLICATION INFORMATION:
Applicants should submit the following:
(1) cover sheet;
(2) letter describing the project, its significance, the status of the research, and what will be accomplished during the residency and;
(3) curriculum vitae.
Duration: Up to eight weeks.
Deadline: December 15. Awards will be announced within two months.

ADDRESS INQUIRIES TO:
Nicole Taylor
Director of Scholar Programs
(See address above.)

For overnight delivery:
660 Garcia Street
Santa Fe, NM 87505

SHASTRI INDO-CANADIAN INSTITUTE (SICI)
Room 1402, Education Tower
2500 University Drive, N.W.
Calgary AB T2N 1N4 Canada
(403) 220-7467
Fax: (403) 289-0100

E-MAIL ADDRESS:
sici@ucalgary.ca

WEB SITE ADDRESS:
www.sici.org

TYPE:
Fellowships. India Studies Fellowship Competition is intended to support candidates wishing to undertake research or training in India. The focus of study is subjects relating to India in the social sciences and humanities, including education, law, management, the arts, science, and technology.

See entry 941 for full listing.

HORACE SMITH FUND   [1755]
1441 Main Street, 6th Floor
Suite 620
Springfield, MA 01103
(413) 739-4222
Fax: (413) 739-1108

E-MAIL ADDRESS:
info@horacesmithfund.org

WEB SITE ADDRESS:
www.horacesmithfund.org

FOUNDED: 1899

AREAS OF INTEREST:
Education, scholarships and fellowships.

TYPE:
Fellowships; Scholarships.

YEAR PROGRAM STARTED: 1899

PURPOSE:
To help students obtain scholarships and fellowships.

ELIGIBILITY:
For scholarships, students must have graduated from a high school in Hampden County. For fellowships, students must be legal residents of Hampden County.

GEOGRAPHIC RESTRICTIONS:
Hampden County, Massachusetts.

FINANCIAL DATA:
Amount of support per award: Scholarships: $2,500 per year for four years; Fellowships: $4,000 per year for up to three years.

Total amount of support: Scholarships: $65,000; Fellowships: $16,000.

APPLICATION INFORMATION:
Applications are available in September.
Duration: One year. Renewable up to four years.
Deadline: Scholarships: December 20; Fellowships: February 1.

PUBLICATIONS:
Annual report; contributions policy; application guidelines.

ADDRESS INQUIRIES TO:
Josephine Sarnelli, Executive Director
(See address above.)

*SPECIAL STIPULATIONS:
Hampden County, Massachusetts residents only.

SOCIETY OF DAUGHTERS OF THE U.S. ARMY   [1756]
11804 Grey Birch Place
Reston, VA 20191-4223

FOUNDED: 1928

NAME(S) OF PROGRAMS:
• **Society of Daughters of the United States Army Scholarships**

TYPE:
Scholarships.

PURPOSE:
To help daughters or granddaughters (including adopted or step) of career warrant and commissioned Army officers (Warrant Officers through General) who are on active duty, retired after at least 20 years of active service, were medically retired, or died while on active duty or after eligible retirement.

LEGAL BASIS:
Nonprofit corporation.

ELIGIBILITY:
For the Roberts, Wagner, Prickett, Simpson and DUSA Scholarships, applicants must be a daughter or granddaughter (including step or adopted) of a career warrant (WO 1-5) or commissioned (2nd & 1st LT, CPT, MAJ, LTC, COL and BG, MG, LT or full General) officer of the U.S. Army who either:
(1) is currently on active duty;
(2) retired after at least 20 years of active service;
(3) was medically retired before 20 years of active service;
(4) died while on active duty or;
(5) died after retiring with 20 or more years of active service.

U.S. Army must have been the officer's primary occupation. These scholarships are for undergraduate study only and cover academic expenses only. Minimum grade point average is 3.0.

FINANCIAL DATA:
Amount of support per award: $1,000 per year.

NUMBER OF APPLICANTS MOST RECENT YEAR: 100.

NUMBER OF AWARDS: 8.

APPLICATION INFORMATION:
Mail one request with the officer's name, rank, component (active, reserve, retired), inclusive dates of active duty, and the relationship to the applicant, along with a stamped, self-addressed envelope, to the Scholarship Chairman. Do not send any

documentation. Requests for applications must be postmarked between November 1 and March 1 for awards in the next academic year. Office is closed between March 2 and October 31. Application is not available when office is closed. Application will not be sent without qualifying information.

Do not send by registered/certified or commercial mail; delivery will be delayed. All application submissions become the property of DUSA.
Duration: One year. The scholarships may be renewed annually for four years, provided a student maintains eligibility.
Deadline: March 1.

STAFF:
Mary P. Maroney, Chairman, Memorial and Scholarship Funds

ADDRESS INQUIRIES TO:
Mary P. Maroney, Scholarship Chairman
Daughters of the United States Army
(See address above.)

SOCIETY OF PHYSICS STUDENTS   [1757]
One Physics Ellipse
College Park, MD 20740-3843
(301) 209-3007
Fax: (301) 209-0839

E-MAIL ADDRESS:
sps@aip.org

WEB SITE ADDRESS:
www.spsnational.org

FOUNDED: 1968

AREAS OF INTEREST:
Physics.

NAME(S) OF PROGRAMS:
• **Society of Physics Students Leadership Scholarship**

TYPE:
Scholarships.

YEAR PROGRAM STARTED: 1985

PURPOSE:
To encourage the study of physics and the pursuit of high scholarship.

LEGAL BASIS:
Not-for-profit, 501(c)(3).

ELIGIBILITY:
Applicants must be full-time undergraduate students applying in at least their junior year (except for two-year college applicants who should apply after completing one semester of physics). Only Society of Physics Students members are eligible.

GEOGRAPHIC RESTRICTIONS:
United States.

FINANCIAL DATA:
Amount of support per award: $2,000 to $5,000.
Total amount of support: $41,000.

NUMBER OF APPLICANTS MOST RECENT YEAR: 29.

NUMBER OF AWARDS: 18.

APPLICATION INFORMATION:
Completed application form, official transcript of grades, and two letters of recommendation required.
Duration: One year. No renewals.
Deadline: February 15.

STAFF:
Toni Saucy, Director

ADDRESS INQUIRIES TO:
Toni Saucy, Director
(See address above.)

*SPECIAL STIPULATIONS:
Applicant must be an active member of the Society of Physics Students.

THE PAUL & DAISY SOROS FELLOWSHIPS FOR NEW AMERICANS   [1758]
224 West 57th Street
New York, NY 10019
(212) 547-6926
Fax: (212) 548-4605

E-MAIL ADDRESS:
pdsoros_fellows@sorosny.org

WEB SITE ADDRESS:
www.pdsoros.org

FOUNDED: 1997

AREAS OF INTEREST:
Financial aid for New Americans.

TYPE:
Fellowships.

PURPOSE:
To provide opportunities for continuing generations of able and accomplished New Americans to achieve leadership in their chosen fields.

ELIGIBILITY:
A New American is defined as an individual who:
(1) is a resident alien (i.e., holds a Green Card) or;
(2) has been naturalized as a U.S. citizen or;
(3) is the child of two parents who are both naturalized citizens.

The applicant must either have a Bachelor's degree or be in his or her final year of undergraduate study.

Upper age limit is 30 years by deadline.

GEOGRAPHIC RESTRICTIONS:
United States.

FINANCIAL DATA:
Amount of support per award: Fellow receives maintenance grant of $25,000 and a tuition grant of one-half tuition cost of U.S. graduate program attended, up to a maximum of $20,000 per annum.

NUMBER OF AWARDS: 30 per year.

APPLICATION INFORMATION:
Applications must be submitted via the online application system.
Duration: Up to two years.
Deadline: November 8.

ADDRESS INQUIRIES TO:
Yulian Ramos, Deputy Director
(See address above.)

*SPECIAL STIPULATIONS:
Must be 30 years old or younger by deadline in order to be eligible.

SOUTH CAROLINA HIGHER EDUCATION TUITION GRANTS COMMISSION   [1759]
115 Atrium Way
Suite 102
Columbia, SC 29223
(803) 896-1120
Fax: (803) 896-1126

E-MAIL ADDRESS:
jessica@sctuitiongrants.org

WEB SITE ADDRESS:
www.sctuitiongrants.com

FOUNDED: 1970

AREAS OF INTEREST:
Undergraduate student financial aid to eligible South Carolina residents attending in-state, independent colleges on a full-time basis.

CONSULTING OR VOLUNTEER SERVICES:
Assistance to South Carolina high schools and colleges with questions and problems pertaining to student financial aid.

NAME(S) OF PROGRAMS:
- **South Carolina Tuition Grants Program**

TYPE:
Grants-in-aid.

YEAR PROGRAM STARTED: 1970

PURPOSE:
To increase the level of college attendance in South Carolina and to better utilize the existing educational resources of the state; to give students a choice of attending the college that best meets their academic needs.

LEGAL BASIS:
Established by state statute.

ELIGIBILITY:
Applicant must be a South Carolina resident, demonstrate good moral character, be accepted by or enrolled full-time in an eligible South Carolina private college and have financial need. Incoming freshmen must rank in the upper three-quarters of their class or score 900 or higher on the re-centered SAT. Renewal applicants must complete at least 24 semester-hours per year.

GEOGRAPHIC RESTRICTIONS:
South Carolina.

FINANCIAL DATA:
Awards cannot exceed tuition and fees at the institution, the need of the student and the average per-pupil expenditure by the state at a public college.
Amount of support per award: $100 to $2,900 per year. Average grant $2,601 for the year 2012-13.
Total amount of support: $37,640,571 total state appropriations for the 2012-13 academic year.

NUMBER OF APPLICANTS MOST RECENT YEAR:
35,607 for the year 2012-13.

NUMBER OF AWARDS: 13,881 for the year 2012-13.

APPLICATION INFORMATION:
Application available online.
Duration: One year. Renewable if need continues for up to four years. Must reapply each year.
Deadline: June 30.

PUBLICATIONS:
Annual report; general brochure.

GRANTS COMMITTEE:
Dr. Walt Griffin, Chairman
Dr. Luns Richardson, Vice Chairman
Dr. David Norman, Secretary
Julie Carullo
Dr. Bill Jones
Dr. Stephen Jones
Dr. Cleveland Sellers
Dr. David Swinton
Dr. Henry Tisdale

ADDRESS INQUIRIES TO:
Earl L. Mayo, Jr.
(See address above.)

STATE COUNCIL OF HIGHER EDUCATION FOR VIRGINIA [1760]
James Monroe Building, 10th Floor
101 North 14th Street
Richmond, VA 23219
(804) 225-2600
Fax: (804) 225-2604

E-MAIL ADDRESS:
fainfo@schev.edu

WEB SITE ADDRESS:
www.schev.edu

FOUNDED: 1956

AREAS OF INTEREST:
Statewide coordination of higher education.

NAME(S) OF PROGRAMS:
- **Virginia Tuition Assistance Grant Program (TAGP)**

TYPE:
Grants-in-aid.

YEAR PROGRAM STARTED: 1973

PURPOSE:
To provide grants to all Virginia domiciliary residents who are undergraduate students enrolled full-time in participating private nonprofit colleges and universities in Virginia, regardless of financial need; to provide grants to graduate students in selected health-related degree programs.

LEGAL BASIS:
State agency. Program mandated by state law.

ELIGIBILITY:
Recipients must be domiciliary residents of Virginia who are enrolled full-time at an approved private college or university within the state. Not available at Virginia public institutions, for-profit institutions or non-Virginia institutions. Awards are not based on financial need. Students may not be enrolled in a program of religious training or theological education.

GEOGRAPHIC RESTRICTIONS:
Virginia.

FINANCIAL DATA:
Funding is specified biennially by the Appropriations Act.
Amount of support per award: Up to $3,200 per academic year, depending on amount of appropriation and number of recipients; $3,100 for the academic year 2013-14.
Total amount of support: $58,000,000 for the year 2012-13.

NUMBER OF AWARDS: Approximately 21,000.

APPLICATION INFORMATION:
Application is available from participating private colleges or universities in Virginia, or may be downloaded from the web site above.
Duration: Nine months (academic year). Renewals are reviewed by the institutions.
Deadline: July 31. September 14 for late applications.

ADDRESS INQUIRIES TO:
Applicants should contact the financial aid officer at the private Virginia college or university they plan to attend or see web site above.

SUDBURY FOUNDATION
326 Concord Road
Sudbury, MA 01776
(978) 443-0849
Fax: (978) 579-9536

E-MAIL ADDRESS:
contact@sudburyfoundation.org

WEB SITE ADDRESS:
www.sudburyfoundation.org

TYPE:
Project/program grants; Scholarships.

See entry 1383 for full listing.

SYRACUSE UNIVERSITY [1761]
Enrollment Management
212 Bowne Hall
Syracuse, NY 13244-1200
(315) 443-4492
Fax: (315) 443-3423

E-MAIL ADDRESS:
gradawd@syr.edu

WEB SITE ADDRESS:
www.syr.edu

AREAS OF INTEREST:
Student work/study programs.

NAME(S) OF PROGRAMS:
- **Syracuse University Graduate Assistantships**

TYPE:
Assistantships. Syracuse University Graduate Assistantships are of a teaching, research or administrative nature.

FINANCIAL DATA:
Amount of support per award: $13,000 minimum stipend plus up to 24 credit hours of tuition scholarship for the year 2014-15.

NUMBER OF AWARDS: Approximately 1,600 annually.

APPLICATION INFORMATION:
Applicants must apply through departments.
Duration: One year. Renewable, depending upon student's performance and need.

ADDRESS INQUIRIES TO:
See e-mail address above.

SYRACUSE UNIVERSITY [1762]
Enrollment Management
212 Bowne Hall
Syracuse, NY 13244-1200
(315) 443-4492
Fax: (315) 443-3423

E-MAIL ADDRESS:
gradawd@syr.edu

WEB SITE ADDRESS:
www.syr.edu

AREAS OF INTEREST:
Graduate university education.

NAME(S) OF PROGRAMS:
- **African American Graduate Fellowship**
- **Hursky Fellowship**
- **McNair Graduate Fellowship**
- **STEM Doctoral Fellowships**
- **Syracuse University Fellowship**

TYPE:
Fellowships.

PURPOSE:
To provide a full support package during a student's term of study.

ELIGIBILITY:

African American Graduate Fellowships: Awarded annually to new and continuing students across disciplines whose work supports that of the African American Studies Program.

Hursky Fellowship: Open to graduate students with a Ukrainian background whose area of study is the Ukraine or includes topics related to the Ukraine.

McNair Graduate Fellowship: Students must be either from an underrepresented group (African American, Hispanic or Native American) or a McNair Scholar at their undergraduate institution. Preference will be given to those in doctoral programs. Students will have already been admitted into a Syracuse University graduate program and must be formally nominated by their department for the award.

STEM Doctoral Fellowships: Science, technology, engineering and math disciplines. Open to members of an underrepresented group who are U.S. citizens or permanent residents.

Syracuse University Fellowships: Open to nationals of any country.

FINANCIAL DATA:
Amount of support per award: African American Graduate Fellowship, McNair Graduate Fellowship and Syracuse University Fellowship: $14,250 for Master's stipend plus full tuition; $23,830 for Ph.D. stipend plus full tuition; Hursky Fellowship: $15,000 stipend plus 24 credit hours of tuition; STEM Doctoral Fellowships: $23,830.

NUMBER OF AWARDS: African American Graduate Fellowship: 6 new per year; Hursky Fellowship: 1 new per year; McNair Graduate Fellowship: Up to 6 new per year; STEM Doctoral Fellowships: Up to 5 new per year (number of these fellowships may vary from year to year); Syracuse University Fellowship: Number of awards determined by each academic college, varies yearly.

APPLICATION INFORMATION:
Applicants must apply through admission application.
Duration: Varies by fellowship type, one to six years.
Deadline: January 1, unless earlier date determined by specific department.

ADDRESS INQUIRIES TO:
See e-mail address above.

TAMPA BAY TIMES FUND, INC. [1763]
490 First Avenue South
St. Petersburg, FL 33701
(727) 893-8780
Fax: (727) 892-2257

E-MAIL ADDRESS:
waclawek@tampabay.com

WEB SITE ADDRESS:
www.tampabay.com/scholarships

AREAS OF INTEREST:
Journalism.

NAME(S) OF PROGRAMS:
● **Career Journalism Scholarship**

TYPE:
Scholarships.

PURPOSE:
To identify worthy students who need additional resources to support their education in pursuing a journalism major in college and career after graduation.

ELIGIBILITY:
High school seniors in the Times' circulation area.

GEOGRAPHIC RESTRICTIONS:
Citrus, Hernando, Hillsborough, Pasco and Pinellas counties, Florida.

FINANCIAL DATA:
Amount of support per award: $2,500 annually.
Total amount of support: Average $10,000.

NUMBER OF AWARDS: Average 4 annually.

APPLICATION INFORMATION:
Applicant must submit:
(1) completed Questionnaire (two pages);
(2) short essay (500 to 800 words) describing journalism experience; if applicant does not have such experience, explain why interested in journalism as a career; also provide, on another sheet of paper, resume of achievements/awards;
(3) essay (1,000 to 1,500 words) reflecting how applicant has been affected by the work of journalists;
(4) letter detailing which college applicant plans to attend, total cost of education for that institution, other financial aid applied for or known to be received, and anything else pertinent to family's financial situation;
(5) portfolio of work (writing, web site, photography, design); no more than six examples and do not send originals; if applicant has no previous experience, send three samples of writing for class assignments and;
(6) three letters of recommendation, written and signed by teachers or others for whom applicant has done a substantial amount of writing, discussing the applicant's writing ability, strengths as a student, character, areas for improvement, and how applicant has demonstrated interest in journalism; each letter should have, at the top, applicant's name, teacher's name and teacher's phone number.
Duration: Up to four years. Must reapply.
Deadline: January 5.

ADDRESS INQUIRIES TO:
Nancy Waclawek, Director
(See address above.)

TAMPA BAY TIMES FUND, INC. [1764]
490 First Avenue South
St. Petersburg, FL 33701
(727) 893-8780
Fax: (727) 892-2257

E-MAIL ADDRESS:
waclawek@tampabay.com

WEB SITE ADDRESS:
www.tampabay.com/scholarships

NAME(S) OF PROGRAMS:
● **Barnes Scholarship**

TYPE:
Scholarships.

YEAR PROGRAM STARTED: 1999

PURPOSE:
To provide assistance to college-bound teens who have overcome significant obstacles in

their lives while remaining committed to academic achievement and community involvement.

ELIGIBILITY:
Applicants must be U.S. citizens or permanent residents, high school seniors in public or private schools in specific counties of Florida. Preference will be given to students whose parents have not graduated from a college or university and also to students who are applying to schools outside of Florida.

GEOGRAPHIC RESTRICTIONS:
Citrus, Hernando, Hillsborough, Pasco and Pinellas counties, Florida.

FINANCIAL DATA:
Amount of support per award: Up to $15,000 per year.
Total amount of support: Up to $60,000.

NUMBER OF AWARDS: 4 annually.

APPLICATION INFORMATION:
There are three parts to the application:

The first part includes basic information about the applicant, e.g., addresses of applicant and parents or guardians, phone numbers, e-mails, test scores, high school information, and colleges to which applicant has applied to or intends to apply.

The second part is a resume providing information about academic honors, classes taken, community service performed, extracurricular activities, employment, awards, athletics, and other activities that have been key in forming the applicant's life experience thus far.

The third part is an essay (250 to 1,000 words) describing the applicant's greatest obstacle in life and how it has been overcome.
Duration: Up to four years.
Deadline: October 15.

ADDRESS INQUIRIES TO:
Nancy Waclawek, Director
(See address above.)

TENNESSEE STUDENT ASSISTANCE CORPORATION [1765]
Parkway Towers, Suite 1510
404 James Robertson Parkway
Nashville, TN 37243-0820
(615) 741-1346
(800) 342-1663
Fax: (615) 741-6101

E-MAIL ADDRESS:
tsac.aidinfo@tn.gov

WEB SITE ADDRESS:
www.tn.gov/collegepays

FOUNDED: 1976

NAME(S) OF PROGRAMS:
● **Dependent Children Scholarship Program**
● **Graduate Nursing Loan-Forgiveness Program**
● **Christa McAuliffe Scholarship Program**
● **Ned McWherter Scholars Program**
● **Minority Teaching Fellows Program**
● **Tennessee Education Lottery Scholarship Program**
● **Tennessee Math & Science Teachers Loan Forgiveness Program**
● **Tennessee Student Assistance Award**
● **Tennessee Teaching Scholars Program**

TYPE:
Grants-in-aid; Scholarships; Loan forgiveness programs. Need-based grants for undergraduate Tennessee residents enrolled in an eligible Tennessee institution.

Dependent Children Scholarship Program provides aid for Tennessee residents who are dependent children of a Tennessee law enforcement officer, fireman or an emergency medical service technician who has been killed or totally and permanently disabled while performing duties within the scope of such employment.

Graduate Nursing Loan-Forgiveness Program is designed to encourage Tennessee residents who are nurses to become teachers and administrators in Tennessee nursing education programs. Participants in this program incur an obligation to enter a faculty or administrative position in a nursing education program, in Tennessee, immediately upon completion of the education program.

Christa McAuliffe Scholarship Program was established to encourage promising Tennesseans who have a commitment to teaching and inspiring young minds to explore and achieve their highest potential.

The Ned McWherter Scholars Program is intended to encourage academically superior Tennessee high school graduates to attend college in Tennessee.

Minority Teaching Fellows Program is intended to encourage talented minority Tennesseans to enter the teaching field in Tennessee.

Tennessee Education Lottery Scholarship Program is for those who have been a Tennessee resident for one year by September 1 of the year of application date.

Tennessee Math & Science Teachers Loan Forgiveness Program provides financial assistance to Tennessee public school teachers seeking an advanced degree in a math or a science, or a certification to teach a math or a science. Loan forgiveness requires employment in a Tennessee public school system two years for each year of the loan funding received.

Tennessee Student Assistance Award provides nonrepayable financial assistance to financially needy undergraduate students who are residents of Tennessee.

Tennessee Teaching Scholars Program is intended to encourage exemplary students to enter the teaching field in Tennessee.

YEAR PROGRAM STARTED: 1976

PURPOSE:
To provide grants based on financial need for Tennessee residents.

LEGAL BASIS:
State agency.

ELIGIBILITY:
Applicants for the Ned McWherter Scholars Program must be high school seniors with a 3.5 grade point average, a GED score of 570 and 29 ACT or 1280 SAT, and planning to attend an eligible Tennessee institution.

Applicants for the Minority Teaching Fellows Program are preferably high school seniors with a 2.75 grade point average and 18 ACT or be at the top 25% of their graduating class. Undergraduate applicants must have a 2.5 college grade point average.

Applicants for the Tennessee Education Lottery Scholarship Program must:
(1) be entering freshmen who are Tennessee residents for one year prior to application;
(2) enroll in a Tennessee public college/university or enroll in a Tennessee private college/university that is accredited by the Southern Association of Colleges and Schools and;
(3) be enrolled full-time (part-time prorated), leading to a certificate in the Tennessee Technology Centers or degree in approved colleges and universities. Satisfactory academic progress required.

Applicants for the Tennessee Teaching Scholars Program must be college juniors or seniors or post-Baccalaureate students admitted to teacher education programs in Tennessee colleges or universities and U.S. citizens.

GEOGRAPHIC RESTRICTIONS:
Tennessee.

FINANCIAL DATA:
Amount of support per award: Varies.
Matching fund requirements: For Ned McWherter Scholars Program, the institution must match $3,000.

NUMBER OF APPLICANTS MOST RECENT YEAR:
Ned McWherter Scholars: 900; Minority Teaching Fellows: 150; Tennessee Teaching Scholars: 400.

NUMBER OF AWARDS: Ned McWherter Scholars: 50; Minority Teaching Fellows: 29; Tennessee Education Lottery Scholarship Program: 40,000; Tennessee Teaching Scholars: 160.

APPLICATION INFORMATION:
Detailed information is available online.
Duration: Renewable each academic year.
Deadline: Ned McWherter Scholars: February 15; Minority Teaching Fellows: April 15; Tennessee Education Lottery Scholarship Program: September 1 for fall term, February 1 for spring and summer terms; Tennessee Teaching Scholars: April 15.

ADDRESS INQUIRIES TO:
See telephone numbers above.

*SPECIAL STIPULATIONS:
Loan Forgiveness Programs, Tennessee Teaching Scholars and Minority Teaching Fellows: Recipients agree to teach one year for each year of funding in a public Tennessee grades K-12 school or appropriate learning institution or repayment will be required.

TOURISM CARES   [1766]
275 Turnpike Street
Suite 307
Canton, MA 02021
(781) 821-5990 ext. 215
Fax: (781) 821-8949

E-MAIL ADDRESS:
amandad@tourismcares.org

WEB SITE ADDRESS:
www.tourismcares.org/student-resources

FOUNDED: 2005

AREAS OF INTEREST:
Travel and tourism, hospitality and sustainable tourism.

NAME(S) OF PROGRAMS:
- **Graduate Research Scholarships**
- **High School Scholarships**
- **Professional Development Scholarship Program**
- **Undergraduate or Graduate Scholarships**

TYPE:
Internships; Scholarships. Academic and Professional Development.

YEAR PROGRAM STARTED: 2005

PURPOSE:
To benefit society by preserving the travel experience for future generations by awarding academic and professional scholarships, internships, volunteering and mentoring opportunities to students of travel, tourism, and hospitality; by giving grants to cultural, historic and natural tourism-related sites worldwide; and by organizing volunteer efforts to restore tourism-related sites in need of care and rejuvenation.

LEGAL BASIS:
Nonprofit, tax-exempt 501(c)(3) public charity.

FINANCIAL DATA:
Amount of support per award: $1,000 to $5,000.
Total amount of support: $82,750 for the year 2012; more than $1,000,000 cumulative total since the beginning of the program.

NUMBER OF AWARDS: Varies.

APPLICATION INFORMATION:
Application process, FAQs and access to online-only applications are available at the web site.
Deadline: Varies.

PUBLICATIONS:
e-newsletter.

ADDRESS INQUIRIES TO:
Tourism Cares Scholarship Department
E-mail: scholarships@tourismcares.org

TUSKEGEE UNIVERSITY
1200 West Montgomery Road
Tuskegee, AL 36088
(334) 727-8375
Fax: (334) 724-4224

E-MAIL ADDRESS:
gsr@mytu.tuskegee.edu

WEB SITE ADDRESS:
www.tuskegee.edu

TYPE:
Fellowships.

See entry 2044 for full listing.

TWO TEN FOOTWEAR FOUNDATION   [1767]
Scholarship Department
1466 Main Street
Waltham, MA 02451
(800) 346-3210 ext. 1512
Fax: (781) 736-1555

E-MAIL ADDRESS:
scholarship@twoten.org

WEB SITE ADDRESS:
www.twoten.org

FOUNDED: 1939

AREAS OF INTEREST:
Footwear industry.

NAME(S) OF PROGRAMS:
- **Two Ten Footwear Foundation College Scholarship Program**

TYPE:
Scholarships. Offered to students affiliated with the footwear, leather or allied industries.

YEAR PROGRAM STARTED: 1969

PURPOSE:
To provide financial assistance to people in the footwear, leather and allied industries.

LEGAL BASIS:
Private foundation.

ELIGIBILITY:
Scholarship applicant must be affiliated with the footwear, leather or allied industries:
(1) either the student must be employed in the above industries, or have a parent (natural, step or adopted) who must be employed in these industries for a minimum of two years prior to January 1 (student must be considered a dependent);
(2) student must display financial need for college costs as calculated by the federal method of need analysis and the Two Ten Selection Committee;
(3) student must be a U.S. citizen or eligible noncitizen and;
(4) student must enroll at an accredited college, university, nursing or vocational/technical school, earning a two- or four-year undergraduate degree.

FINANCIAL DATA:
Amount of support per award: Generally, up to $3,000. There are also several larger awards available, as well as one super scholarship award of up to $15,000 of unmet need annually.

APPLICATION INFORMATION:
Contact the Foundation.
Duration: Up to four years.
Deadline: February 16.

ADDRESS INQUIRIES TO:
Scholarship Department
(See address above.)

*SPECIAL STIPULATIONS:
Eligible companies must do at least 50% of their business in footwear, or applicant or parent must work in a specific footwear division.

TWO TEN FOOTWEAR FOUNDATION   [1768]
1466 Main Street
Waltham, MA 02451
(800) 346-3210 ext. 1512
Fax: (781) 736-1555

E-MAIL ADDRESS:
scholarship@twoten.org

WEB SITE ADDRESS:
www.twoten.org

AREAS OF INTEREST:
Footwear design.

NAME(S) OF PROGRAMS:
● **Two Ten Footwear Foundation Design Scholarship Program**

TYPE:
Scholarships. Intended for students who are interested in pursuing a career in footwear design.

PURPOSE:
To provide financial aid to those studying footwear design.

ELIGIBILITY:
Applicant must:
(1) demonstrate an interest and commitment

to a career in footwear design;
(2) be a U.S. citizen or eligible noncitizen;
(3) display financial need as calculated by the federal method of need analysis and the Design Scholarship Selection Committee (applicant can estimate Expected Family Contribution at www.finaid.com) and;
(4) attend or plan to attend an approved postsecondary institution.

GEOGRAPHIC RESTRICTIONS:
United States.

FINANCIAL DATA:
Amount of support per award: Varies.
Total amount of support: Varies.

NUMBER OF AWARDS: Varies.

APPLICATION INFORMATION:
Applicants for consideration must submit a portfolio. Interested candidates must contact the director of scholarship for further information.
Duration: Up to four years.
Deadline: Varies.

ADDRESS INQUIRIES TO:
Kate Alley, Director of
Social Services and Scholarships
(See address above.)

U.S. DEPARTMENT OF EDUCATION   [1769]
Federal Student Aid Programs
830 First Street, N.E.
Washington, DC 20202
(800) 433-3243
TTY: (800) 730-8913

E-MAIL ADDRESS:
studentaid@ed.gov

WEB SITE ADDRESS:
www.studentaid.gov

AREAS OF INTEREST:
Student financial aid.

NAME(S) OF PROGRAMS:
● **Federal Supplemental Educational Opportunity Grant (FSEOG)**

TYPE:
Grants-in-aid. Federal Supplemental Educational Opportunity Grant (FSEOG) is a grant for undergraduate students with exceptional financial need. This grant does not need to be repaid. The program is administered directly by the financial aid office at each participating school and is therefore called "campus-based" aid. Not all schools participate.

PURPOSE:
To help undergraduates with exceptional financial need.

FINANCIAL DATA:
Amount of support per award: $100 to $4,000 a year, depending on student's financial need, when student applied, the amount of other aid student has received, and the availability of funds at student's school.

APPLICATION INFORMATION:
Student should check with his or her school's financial aid office to ascertain if the school offers the FSEOG.
Deadline: Each school sets its own deadlines for campus-based funds.

ADDRESS INQUIRIES TO:
Federal Student Aid Programs
P.O. Box 84
Washington, DC 20044

*PLEASE NOTE:
Each participating school receives a certain amount of FSEOG funds each year from the U.S. Department of Education's office of Federal Student Aid. Once the full amount of the school's FSEOG funds has been awarded to students, no more FSEOG awards can be made for that year.

U.S. DEPARTMENT OF EDUCATION   [1770]
Federal Student Aid Programs
830 First Street, N.E.
Washington, DC 20202
(800) 433-3243
TTY: (800) 730-8913

E-MAIL ADDRESS:
studentaid@ed.gov

WEB SITE ADDRESS:
www.studentaid.gov

AREAS OF INTEREST:
Student financial aid.

NAME(S) OF PROGRAMS:
● **Teacher Education Assistance for College and Higher Education (TEACH) Grant**

TYPE:
Grants-in-aid. Grant does not have to be repaid unless recipient fails to carry out the service obligation.

PURPOSE:
To help undergraduate, postbaccalaureate and graduate students with financial need.

ELIGIBILITY:
The TEACH Grant is intended for undergraduate, postbaccalaureate and graduate students who plan to become teachers. Recipient must sign Agreement to Serve saying he or she will teach full-time in a high-need field for four complete years (within eight years of completing the academic program) at an elementary school, secondary school or educational service agency serving children from low-income families.

FINANCIAL DATA:
Amount of support per award: Up to $4,000 per year. Undergraduate student: Total amount may not exceed $16,000. Graduate student: Total amount may not exceed $8,000.

ADDRESS INQUIRIES TO:
Federal Student Aid Programs
P.O. Box 84
Washington, DC 20044

U.S. DEPARTMENT OF EDUCATION   [1771]
Federal Student Aid Programs
830 First Street, N.E.
Washington, DC 20202
(800) 433-3243
TTY: (800) 730-8913

E-MAIL ADDRESS:
studentaid@ed.gov

WEB SITE ADDRESS:
www.studentaid.gov

AREAS OF INTEREST:
Student financial aid.

NAME(S) OF PROGRAMS:
● **Iraq and Afghanistan Service Grant**

TYPE:
Grants-in-aid. This Grant does not have to be repaid.

ELIGIBILITY:
Student applicants who meet the following conditions may be eligible for this Grant: (1) those not eligible for Pell Grants due to having less financial need than is required to receive Pell funds; (2) those whose parent or guardian died as a result of military service in Iraq or Afghanistan after September 11, 2001 and; (3) those who, at the time of the parent's or guardian's death, were less than 24 years old or were enrolled at least part-time at an institution of higher education.

FINANCIAL DATA:
Amount of support per award: Up to $5,080.50 per year.

ADDRESS INQUIRIES TO:
Federal Student Aid Programs
P.O. Box 84
Washington, DC 20044

U.S. DEPARTMENT OF EDUCATION [1772]
Federal Student Aid Programs
830 First Street, N.E.
Washington, DC 20202
(800) 433-3243
TTY: 800-730-8913

E-MAIL ADDRESS:
studentaid@ed.gov

WEB SITE ADDRESS:
www.studentaid.gov

AREAS OF INTEREST:
Student financial aid.

NAME(S) OF PROGRAMS:
• Pell Grant

TYPE:
Grants-in-aid. Student aid grants for higher education. Available almost exclusively to undergraduates. Grant does not have to be repaid.

YEAR PROGRAM STARTED: 1973

PURPOSE:
To help undergraduates pay for education after high school.

LEGAL BASIS:
Title IV, Higher Education Act of 1965, as amended.

ELIGIBILITY:
In general, the aid recipient must: (1) show financial need; (2) enroll as a regular student in an eligible degree or certificate program; (3) be a U.S. citizen or eligible noncitizen and; (4) meet the school's satisfactory academic progress standards in his or her course of study.

The student also must register with the Selective Service, if required.

FINANCIAL DATA:
Amount of support per award: Up to $5,730 for the 2014-15 award year. Amount depends on student's financial need, the cost of attendance (COA) at the student's school, status as full-time or part-time student and how long the student will be enrolled in the academic year in question. The financial aid office at student's college or career school will determine how much financial aid he or she is eligible to receive.

APPLICATION INFORMATION:
Applicants should contact the financial aid office at each school they are considering

attending to determine which forms must be submitted. Students can request a copy of the *Student Guide* at the toll-free phone number.
Duration: One year. Renewable. Student can receive Federal Pell Grant for no more than 12 semesters or the equivalent (roughly six years).

PUBLICATIONS:
Funding Education Beyond High School: The Guide to Federal Student Aid.

ADDRESS INQUIRIES TO:
Federal Student Aid Programs
P.O. Box 84
Washington, DC 20044

*PLEASE NOTE:
Applicant may receive only one Pell Grant in an award year, and may not receive Pell Grant funds from more than one school at a time.

U.S. DEPARTMENT OF EDUCATION [1773]
Federal Student Aid Programs
830 First Street, N.E.
Washington, DC 20202
(800) 433-3243
TTY: (800) 730-8913

E-MAIL ADDRESS:
studentaid@ed.gov

WEB SITE ADDRESS:
www.studentaid.gov

AREAS OF INTEREST:
Student financial aid.

NAME(S) OF PROGRAMS:
• Federal Work-Study

TYPE:
Work-study programs. Federal Work-Study program provides part-time jobs for undergraduate and graduate students with financial need. This allows them to earn money to help pay education expenses. Jobs can be on- or off-campus and are available to full-time or part-time students. Students are paid at least federal minimum wage. The money earned does not have to be repaid. The program is administered by schools participating in the Federal Work-Study Program. Interested students should check with their school's financial aid office to determine if their school does participate.

PURPOSE:
To enable students to earn a part of educational expenses.

LEGAL BASIS:
Government agency.

ELIGIBILITY:
In general, the aid recipient must: (1) show financial need; (2) be a U.S. citizen or eligible noncitizen with a valid Social Security number (SSN); (3) be working toward a degree or certificate in an eligible program; (4) demonstrate one is qualified to obtain a postsecondary education; (5) register (if not already done so) with the Selective Service, if one is a male between the ages of 18 and 25 and; (6) maintain satisfactory academic progress once in school.

FINANCIAL DATA:
Federal Work-Study wages will be at least the current federal minimum wage, but may be higher, depending on the type of work and the skills required. The total Federal

Work-Study award depends on when a student applies, one's level of need, and the funding level of one's school.
Amount of support per award: Varies.
Total amount of support: Varies.

APPLICATION INFORMATION:
The interested student should consult with his or her school's financial aid office.
Duration: One year. Renewable.

PUBLICATIONS:
Funding Your Education: The Guide to Federal Student Aid.

ADDRESS INQUIRIES TO:
Federal Student Aid Programs
P.O. Box 84
Washington, DC 20044

THE MORRIS K. UDALL AND STEWART L. UDALL FOUNDATION [1774]
130 South Scott Avenue
Tucson, AZ 85701
(520) 901-8564
Fax: (520) 901-8570

E-MAIL ADDRESS:
randler@udall.gov

WEB SITE ADDRESS:
www.udall.gov

FOUNDED: 1992

AREAS OF INTEREST:
Environment, including policy, engineering, science, education, urban planning and renewal, business, justice and economics; Native American health care and tribal public policy, including policy, engineering, science, education and business.

NAME(S) OF PROGRAMS:
• Udall Scholarship

TYPE:
Scholarships. The Udall Foundation seeks future leaders across a wide spectrum of environmental fields, including policy, engineering, science, education, urban planning and renewal, business, justice and economics.

The Udall Foundation also seeks future Native American and Alaska Native leaders in Native American health care and tribal public policy. Tribal policy includes fields related to tribal sovereignty, tribal governance, tribal law, Native American education, Native American justice, natural resource management, cultural preservation and revitalization, Native American economic development and other areas affecting Native American communities. Native American health care includes health care administration, social work, medicine and research into health conditions affecting Native American communities.

YEAR PROGRAM STARTED: 1996

PURPOSE:
To educate a new generation of Americans to preserve and protect their national heritage through studies in the environment, Native American health and tribal policy, and effective public policy conflict resolution.

LEGAL BASIS:
The Foundation is an executive branch agency. The President of the U.S. appoints its board of trustees with the advice and consent of the U.S. Senate.

ELIGIBILITY:
The scholarship awards are made on the basis of merit to two groups of students: (1) those who are college sophomores or juniors in the current academic year, have outstanding potential and who study the environment and related fields and; (2) Native American and Alaska Native students who are college sophomores or juniors in the current academic year, have outstanding potential and are in fields related to health care or tribal public policy.

FINANCIAL DATA:
Amount of support per award: Up to $5,000.
Total amount of support: Varies.

NUMBER OF APPLICANTS MOST RECENT YEAR:
490 for the year 2013.

NUMBER OF AWARDS: 50.

APPLICATION INFORMATION:
Application information is available on the web site.
Duration: One year.
Deadline: Approximately early March each year.

STAFF:
Paula Randler, Program Manager

ADDRESS INQUIRIES TO:
Paula Randler, Program Manager
(See address above.)

*SPECIAL STIPULATIONS:
Students must have support from a faculty or staff member at their college.

UNICO NATIONAL, INC. [1775]
271 U.S. Highway 46 West
Suite F-103
Fairfield, NJ 07004
(973) 808-0035
Fax: (973) 808-0043

E-MAIL ADDRESS:
uniconational@unico.org

WEB SITE ADDRESS:
www.unico.org

FOUNDED: 1922

NAME(S) OF PROGRAMS:
- **Basilone Postgraduate Scholarship**
- **Cottone Postgraduate Scholarship (Medical Only)**
- **William C. Davini Scholarship**
- **DiMattio Celli Undergraduate Study Abroad Program**
- **Major Don S. Gentile Scholarship**
- **Ella Grasso Literary Scholarship**
- **Theodore Mazza Scholarship**
- **Alphonse A. Miele Scholarship**
- **Bernard and Carolyn Torraco Nursing Scholarships**
- **Louise Torraco Memorial Scholarship for a Doctorate in Science**
- **Ralph J. Torraco Doctoral Scholarship for Music Study**
- **Ralph J. Torraco Doctoral Scholarship for the Study of Ancient Mediterranean History/Archaeology**

TYPE:
Scholarships. Postgraduate scholarships and undergraduate scholarships.

PURPOSE:
To give financial aid to students of outstanding merit so they may complete their education.

ELIGIBILITY:
Candidates must reside in the corporate limits of a city wherein an active chapter of

UNICO National is located. A graduating senior at any public or private school who is commencing undergraduate studies and who demonstrates financial need is eligible.

Scholarship candidates must be of Italian heritage, i.e., must have one parent or grandparent of Italian heritage. The extent to which a candidate has contributed to the life and welfare of school and/or community will be taken into account in the assessment of merit. UNICO member's children are eligible. Each chapter of UNICO National may submit applications for each of the UNICO Foundation scholarships.

A candidate for the undergraduate scholarships must be a citizen of the U.S. and have Italian heritage. An applicant must be a graduating senior at a public or private secondary school.

The Basilone Scholarship requires that the applicant be a senior in college or a graduate beginning postgraduate studies.

The Cottone Scholarship requires that a candidate be a college senior or graduate who is beginning postgraduate studies in the field of medicine or is currently enrolled in an accredited medical school in the U.S.

A candidate for either postgraduate program (Basilone or Cottone Scholarship) must be a U.S. citizen of Italian heritage.

A candidate for the Bernard and Carolyn Torraco Nursing Scholarship must currently be enrolled in an accredited nursing degree program in the U.S., completing core nursing courses, at one of the following: An Associate Degree School of Nursing; A Collegiate School of Nursing; A Diploma School of Nursing. Proof of enrollment must be provided. The candidate must have a minimum grade point average of 3.0 or B to qualify. Preference will be given to applicants demonstrating financial need.

A candidate for the Louise Torraco Memorial Scholarship for a Doctorate in Science must be enrolled as a Ph.D. candidate pursuing study of the physical sciences or life sciences. Nominee must hold U.S. citizenship.

Ralph J. Torraco Doctoral Scholarship for Music Study is given to students enrolled as Ph.D. candidates pursuing the study of music. Nominee must hold U.S. citizenship.

Ralph J. Torraco Doctoral Scholarship for the Study of Ancient Mediterranean History/Archaeology requires students to be enrolled as Ph.D. candidates pursuing study of the history and/or archaeology of ancient Mediterranean cultures. Nominees must hold U.S. citizenship.

FINANCIAL DATA:
Amount of support per award: Undergraduate and Basilone Postgraduate Scholarships: $1,500 per year; Cottone Postgraduate Scholarship: $5,000; DiMattio Celli Program: $1,250; Ella Grasso Scholarship: $1,000; Torraco Nursing Scholarship, Louise Toracco Memorial Scholarship and Ralph J. Torraco Doctoral Scholarships: $2,500.
Total amount of support: Varies.

NUMBER OF APPLICANTS MOST RECENT YEAR:
Approximately 140.

APPLICATION INFORMATION:
Applications for scholarships are available and must be acquired from and submitted through a participating, local UNICO

Chapter. Applicants may access the UNICO National web site and click on Find a Chapter.

Applicants for the Torraco Nursing Scholarship are required to submit the current FAFSA Student Aid Report (SAR).
Duration: Undergraduate and Basilone Postgraduate Scholarships: Maximum of four years; Cottone Postgraduate Scholarship: One-time only.
Deadline: April 15.

ADDRESS INQUIRIES TO:
National Scholarship Awards
(See address above.)

UNITED NEGRO COLLEGE FUND
1805 Seventh Street, N.W.
Washington, DC 20001
(800) 331-2244

E-MAIL ADDRESS:
scholarships@uncf.org

WEB SITE ADDRESS:
www.uncf.org

TYPE:
Fellowships; Internships; Scholarships; Technical assistance. The Fund, since its founding, has raised money for 39 private, historically Black colleges.

Faculty fellowship programs make it possible for hundreds of instructors to earn doctoral degrees.

Mentoring and internship opportunities are provided for hundreds of UNCF students.

Scholarships are offered to a pool of more than 60,000 talented students attending UNCF colleges and universities. The Fund oversees more than 450 scholarship programs in the following general categories:
(1) geographically based scholarships;
(2) scholarships based on academic major;
(3) scholarships based on merit and need and;
(4) financial aid for graduate study.

See entry 1035 for full listing.

UNIVERSITY OF ALBERTA [1776]
1-03 South Academic Building
Edmonton AB T6G 2G7 Canada
(780) 492-3264

E-MAIL ADDRESS:
jisabell@ualberta.ca

WEB SITE ADDRESS:
www.postdoc.ualberta.ca

FOUNDED: 1906

NAME(S) OF PROGRAMS:
- **Izaak Walton Killam Memorial Postdoctoral Fellowship**

TYPE:
Fellowships. Postdoctoral fellowships available in most fields to allow new or recent Ph.Ds. to undertake research at the University of Alberta.

YEAR PROGRAM STARTED: 1967

PURPOSE:
To contribute to the advancement of learning.

ELIGIBILITY:
Applicants must have recently completed a Ph.D. program or will do so in the immediate

future. Applicants who have received their Ph.D. degree from the University of Alberta or who will be on sabbatical leave or who hold or have held named postdoctoral fellowships at other institutions are not eligible. No restriction exists as to citizenship. No award can be taken up prior to completion of the Doctorate. Tenable only at the University of Alberta.

Killam Scholars should not be one-sided, and a sound character should complement their intellect.

FINANCIAL DATA:
Amount of support per award: $46,000 (CAN) per year, plus a one-time travel/research allowance of $4,000 (CAN).

NUMBER OF APPLICANTS MOST RECENT YEAR: 165.

NUMBER OF AWARDS: 4 annually.

APPLICATION INFORMATION:
Application information is available on the web site.
Duration: Two years.
Deadline: November.

UNIVERSITY OF ALBERTA   [1777]
1-03 South Academic Building
Edmonton AB T6G 2G7 Canada
(780) 492-3264

E-MAIL ADDRESS:
jisabell@ualberta.ca

WEB SITE ADDRESS:
www.postdoc.ualberta.ca

FOUNDED: 1906

NAME(S) OF PROGRAMS:
● **Grant Notley Memorial Postdoctoral Fellowship**

TYPE:
Fellowships. Postdoctoral fellowships for research in the politics, history, economy or society of western Canada or related fields.

PURPOSE:
To honor an illustrious Albertan by bringing to the University of Alberta active and promising young scholars who will do significant work in an area encompassed by Grant Notley's broad interests.

ELIGIBILITY:
Applicants must have recently completed a Ph.D. degree or will do so in the immediate future. No award can be taken up prior to completion of the Doctorate. Applicants should be active and promising young scholars who will perform significantly in fields associated with Grant Notley's broad interests in the politics, history, economy or society of western Canada or related fields. Applicants who have received their Ph.D. degree from the University of Alberta or who will be on sabbatical leave or who hold or have held named postdoctoral fellowships at other institutions are not eligible. Tenable only at the University of Alberta.

FINANCIAL DATA:
Amount of support per award: $46,000 (CAN) per year, plus a one-time travel/research allowance of $4,000 (CAN).

NUMBER OF AWARDS: 1 award offered annually.

APPLICATION INFORMATION:
Application information is available on the web site.

Duration: Two years.
Deadline: November.

THE UNIVERSITY OF BRITISH COLUMBIA   [1778]
Faculty of Graduate Studies
170-6371 Crescent Road
Vancouver BC V6T 1Z2 Canada
(604) 822-0976
Fax: (604) 822-5802

E-MAIL ADDRESS:
killam.fellowships@ubc.ca

WEB SITE ADDRESS:
www.grad.ubc.ca/awards

NAME(S) OF PROGRAMS:
● **Izaak Walton Killam Memorial Postdoctoral Research Fellowships**

TYPE:
Fellowships. Offered to allow researchers holding a Ph.D. or equivalent to devote full-time to research at the University of British Columbia.

YEAR PROGRAM STARTED: 1967

LEGAL BASIS:
University.

ELIGIBILITY:
Open to persons who have shown superior ability in research and have obtained, within two academic years of the anticipated commencement date of the Fellowship, a Ph.D. or equivalent at a university other than the University of British Columbia and who wish to pursue further study.

Fellowships are tenable only at the University of British Columbia. People holding faculty positions at universities or colleges are not eligible to apply.

Killam Postdoctoral Research Fellows are permitted to undertake teaching or other academic duties up to the equivalent of one six-credit (two-term) course over the two-year term of the Fellowship.

Citizens of any country may apply.

FINANCIAL DATA:
Amount of support per award: Stipend of up to $50,000 per annum plus a research/travel allowance of $4,000 over two years.
Total amount of support: Approximately $700,000 per year.

NUMBER OF APPLICANTS MOST RECENT YEAR: 150.

NUMBER OF AWARDS: 4 to 6 per year.

APPLICATION INFORMATION:
Applicant must first contact department of interest. Fellowships are awarded on the basis of applications submitted to UBC departments.
Duration: Fellowships are granted for two years, subject to review at the end of the first year.
Deadline: Mid-October to early November.

ADDRESS INQUIRIES TO:
Brendan Morey, Director
Graduate Awards and Development
(See address above.)

THE UNIVERSITY OF BRITISH COLUMBIA   [1779]
Faculty of Graduate Studies
170-6371 Crescent Road
Vancouver BC V6T 1Z2 Canada
(604) 822-0976
Fax: (604) 822-5802

E-MAIL ADDRESS:
graduate.awards@ubc.ca

WEB SITE ADDRESS:
www.grad.ubc.ca/awards

AREAS OF INTEREST:
All areas of advanced study.

NAME(S) OF PROGRAMS:
● **Affiliated Fellowships**

TYPE:
Fellowships. For postgraduate studies leading to a Master's or Doctorate degree at the University of British Columbia.

PURPOSE:
To allow outstanding students to devote full-time to research and study leading to a Master's or Doctorate degree.

LEGAL BASIS:
University.

ELIGIBILITY:
Citizens of any country may apply. Applicants must have outstanding academic records.

FINANCIAL DATA:
Amount of support per award: $1,000 to $30,000 (CAN) per annum.
Total amount of support: Approximately $600,000 (CAN) per annum.

NUMBER OF APPLICANTS MOST RECENT YEAR: Approximately 800.

NUMBER OF AWARDS: 50 per year.

APPLICATION INFORMATION:
Fellowships are awarded on the basis of applications submitted to graduate programs.
Duration: One or two years.
Deadline: Mid- to late September.

STAFF:
Brendan Morey, Director, Graduate Awards and Development

ADDRESS INQUIRIES TO:
Brendan Morey, Director
Graduate Awards and Development
(See address above.)

THE UNIVERSITY OF BRITISH COLUMBIA   [1780]
Faculty of Graduate Studies
170-6371 Crescent Road
Vancouver BC V6T 1Z2 Canada
(604) 822-0976
Fax: (604) 822-5802

E-MAIL ADDRESS:
graduate.awards@ubc.ca

WEB SITE ADDRESS:
www.grad.ubc.ca/awards

AREAS OF INTEREST:
Doctoral study in all disciplines.

NAME(S) OF PROGRAMS:
● **Four Year Doctoral Fellowships**

TYPE:
Fellowships.

YEAR PROGRAM STARTED: 2009

PURPOSE:
To attract and retain outstanding doctoral students by offering stable, base-level funding for the first four years of their Ph.D. studies and research.

ELIGIBILITY:
Open to doctoral students in any discipline. Citizens of any country may apply.

FINANCIAL DATA:
Ensures student receives financial support of at least $18,000 (CAN) per year plus tuition.

Total amount of support: Approximately $14,000,000.

NUMBER OF AWARDS: 200 new fellowships offered by graduate programs each year.

APPLICATION INFORMATION:
Applicant must first contact graduate program of interest. Fellowships are awarded on basis of nomination made by graduate program.

Duration: Four years.

Deadline: Most funding decisions made in January to March.

ADDRESS INQUIRIES TO:
Brendan Morey, Director
Graduate Awards and Development
(See address above.)

THE UNIVERSITY OF BRITISH COLUMBIA   [1781]

Faculty of Graduate Studies
170-6371 Crescent Road
Vancouver BC V6T 1Z2 Canada
(604) 822-0976
Fax: (604) 822-5802

E-MAIL ADDRESS:
graduate.awards@ubc.ca

WEB SITE ADDRESS:
www.grad.ubc.ca/awards

AREAS OF INTEREST:
Research-based Master's and doctoral studies.

NAME(S) OF PROGRAMS:
● **Graduate Student Initiative**

TYPE:
Scholarships.

YEAR PROGRAM STARTED: 2008

PURPOSE:
To provide funding for graduate students through entrance scholarships, multiyear funding packages, tuition awards, and scholarship top-ups.

LEGAL BASIS:
University.

ELIGIBILITY:
Citizens of any country may apply.

FINANCIAL DATA:
Amount of support per award: Set by graduate programs.
Total amount of support: $6,700,000.

APPLICATION INFORMATION:
Student should submit research proposal and academic record to the graduate department of interest.

Duration: Up to four years.

Deadline: Inquiry to graduate program of interest accepted throughout the year. Most funding decisions are made January to March.

ADDRESS INQUIRIES TO:
Brendan Morey, Director
Graduate Awards and Development
(See address above.)

THE UNIVERSITY OF CALGARY   [1782]

Faculty of Graduate Studies
MacKimmie Library Tower, Room 213
2500 University Drive, N.W.
Calgary AB T2N 1N4 Canada
(403) 220-4938
Fax: (403) 289-7635

E-MAIL ADDRESS:
gsaward@ucalgary.ca

WEB SITE ADDRESS:
www.grad.ucalgary.ca

FOUNDED: 1966

AREAS OF INTEREST:
Petroleum industry.

NAME(S) OF PROGRAMS:
● **The Archibald Waynne Dingman Memorial Graduate Scholarship**

TYPE:
Awards/prizes; Scholarships. Graduate scholarship for study in all areas relevant to the petroleum industry. Tenable at The University of Calgary. Award endowed through a bequest of the late Corinne Patteson.

ELIGIBILITY:
Open to qualified graduates of any recognized university who are registered in or admissible to a program leading to a Master's or doctoral degree at The University of Calgary.

FINANCIAL DATA:
Amount of support per award: $2,400 (CAN).
Total amount of support: $2,400 (CAN).

NUMBER OF AWARDS: 1.

APPLICATION INFORMATION:
Students should consult the Graduate Award Competition Guidelines and Application available online.

Duration: One year.

Deadline: February 1 to candidate's Graduate Program Office, unless program has an earlier deadline.

ADDRESS INQUIRIES TO:
Graduate Scholarship Office
(See address above.)

THE UNIVERSITY OF CALGARY   [1783]

Faculty of Graduate Studies
MacKimmie Library Tower, Room 213
2500 University Drive, N.W.
Calgary AB T2N 1N4 Canada
(403) 220-4938
Fax: (403) 289-7635

E-MAIL ADDRESS:
gsaward@ucalgary.ca

WEB SITE ADDRESS:
www.grad.ucalgary.ca

FOUNDED: 1966

NAME(S) OF PROGRAMS:
● **Queen Elizabeth II Graduate Scholarships**

TYPE:
Awards/prizes; Fellowships; Scholarships. Graduate scholarships and fellowships in all fields of study tenable at The University of Calgary.

ELIGIBILITY:
Open to qualified graduate students who are or will be, at the time of tenure, registered in a full-time Master's or doctoral program in the Faculty of Graduate Studies. Candidates must be either Canadian citizens or permanent residents and a resident of Alberta. Students whose awards begin in May are expected to carry out a full-time research program during the summer months.

This award cannot be held in addition to funding from a major award.

FINANCIAL DATA:
Amount of support per award: Master's level: Up to $10,800 (CAN); Doctoral level: Up to $15,000 (CAN).

NUMBER OF AWARDS: Varies.

APPLICATION INFORMATION:
Students should consult with their Graduate Program Office for application information.

Duration: One year.

Deadline: Students should consult with their Graduate Program Office for deadline information.

ADDRESS INQUIRIES TO:
Graduate Scholarship Office
(See address above.)

THE UNIVERSITY OF CALGARY   [1784]

Faculty of Graduate Studies
MacKimmie Library Tower, Room 213
2500 University Drive, N.W.
Calgary AB T2N 1N4 Canada
(403) 220-4938
Fax: (403) 289-7635

E-MAIL ADDRESS:
gsaward@ucalgary.ca

WEB SITE ADDRESS:
www.grad.ucalgary.ca

FOUNDED: 1966

AREAS OF INTEREST:
Medical sciences.

NAME(S) OF PROGRAMS:
● **William H. Davies Medical Research Scholarships**

TYPE:
Awards/prizes; Scholarships. Awards for study in the medical sciences. Tenable at The University of Calgary. Award endowed through a bequest of the late William H. Davies.

ELIGIBILITY:
Open to qualified graduates of any recognized university who will be registered in the Faculty of Graduate Studies at The University of Calgary. Successful candidates must contact their research program within the Faculty of Medicine; others cannot be considered. Awards are made solely on the basis of academic excellence.

FINANCIAL DATA:
Amount of support per award: $3,000 to $11,000 (CAN), depending upon the candidate's qualifications, experience and graduate program.

NUMBER OF AWARDS: Varies.

APPLICATION INFORMATION:
Information is available from the Faculty of Graduate Studies. Candidates should apply to the Associate Dean, Graduate Science Education, Faculty of Medicine. Recommendations from the Faculty of Medicine will be submitted for approval to the Graduate Scholarship Committee.

Duration: One year.

Deadline: June 15.

ADDRESS INQUIRIES TO:
Graduate Scholarship Office
(See address above.)

THE UNIVERSITY OF CALGARY   [1785]
Faculty of Graduate Studies
MacKimmie Library Tower, Room 213
2500 University Drive, N.W.
Calgary AB T2N 1N4 Canada
(403) 220-4938
Fax: (403) 289-7635

E-MAIL ADDRESS:
gsaward@ucalgary.ca

WEB SITE ADDRESS:
www.grad.ucalgary.ca

FOUNDED: 1966

NAME(S) OF PROGRAMS:
- **Izaak Walton Killam Predoctoral Scholarships**

TYPE:
Awards/prizes; Scholarships.

YEAR PROGRAM STARTED: 1967

PURPOSE:
To encourage advanced study, to increase the scientific and scholastic attainment of Canadians and to promote sympathetic understanding between Canadians and the peoples of other countries. Those receiving scholarships would likely contribute to the advancement of learning or win distinction in their profession.

ELIGIBILITY:
Scholarships are normally awarded to students who will be in their first, second, third or fourth year of Ph.D. studies during the tenure of the award. The recipients must be registered full-time in a doctoral program at the University of Calgary. Applicants must have completed at least one year of graduate study before taking up an award.

GEOGRAPHIC RESTRICTIONS:
Canada.

FINANCIAL DATA:
$3,000 of this award (a Killam Research Scholarship) is reserved to cover costs associated with special equipment, conferences and/or travel in direct connection with the Ph.D. research.
Amount of support per award: $36,000 (CAN).
Total amount of support: Varies.

NUMBER OF AWARDS: Varies.

APPLICATION INFORMATION:
In order to receive the Killam Research Scholarship portion of the award, the student must submit a letter outlining the proposed use of funds. This statement must be signed by the supervisor approving the use. No receipts are required.
Duration: One year. Renewable once upon presentation of evidence of satisfactory progress.
Deadline: February 1, unless candidate's graduate program office has an earlier deadline.

ADDRESS INQUIRIES TO:
Graduate Scholarship Office
(See address above.)

THE UNIVERSITY OF CALGARY   [1786]
Faculty of Graduate Studies
MacKimmie Library Tower, Room 213
2500 University Drive, N.W.
Calgary AB T2N 1N4 Canada
(403) 220-4938
Fax: (403) 289-7635

E-MAIL ADDRESS:
gsaward@ucalgary.ca

WEB SITE ADDRESS:
www.grad.ucalgary.ca

FOUNDED: 1966

AREAS OF INTEREST:
Cellular, molecular, microbial and biochemical biology.

NAME(S) OF PROGRAMS:
- **Bettina Bahlsen Memorial Graduate Scholarship**

TYPE:
Awards/prizes; Scholarships. Award for study in the fields of cellular, molecular, microbial or biochemical biology. Tenable at The University of Calgary, Department of Biological Sciences.

ELIGIBILITY:
Open to full-time graduate students entering or enrolled in a doctoral program in the Department of Biological Sciences. Selection will be based on academic excellence. Preference will be accorded to an international student and, if possible, to a student entering the first year of graduate studies.

FINANCIAL DATA:
Amount of support per award: $13,400 (CAN).
Total amount of support: $13,400 (CAN).

NUMBER OF AWARDS: 1.

APPLICATION INFORMATION:
Students should consult the Graduate Award Competition Guidelines and Application found at the web site.
Duration: One year. Possible renewal in open competition.
Deadline: February 1, unless the candidate's graduate program office has an earlier deadline.

ADDRESS INQUIRIES TO:
Graduate Scholarship Office
(See address above.)

THE UNIVERSITY OF CALGARY   [1787]
Faculty of Graduate Studies
MacKimmie Library Tower, Room 213
2500 University Drive, N.W.
Calgary AB T2N 1N4 Canada
(403) 220-4938
Fax: (403) 289-7635

E-MAIL ADDRESS:
gsaward@ucalgary.ca

WEB SITE ADDRESS:
www.grad.ucalgary.ca

FOUNDED: 1966

AREAS OF INTEREST:
Business and management.

NAME(S) OF PROGRAMS:
- **John Labatt Limited Scholarship**
- **ScotiaMcLeod Scholarship**

TYPE:
Awards/prizes; Scholarships. Awards for study in the fields of business, management and related areas. Tenable at the University of Calgary. Awards are endowed through gifts from John Labatt Limited and ScotiaMcLeod Inc. Matching grants provided from the Province of Alberta's Advanced Education Endowment Fund.

ELIGIBILITY:
Open to qualified graduate students who are registered in or admissible to the MBA program at The University of Calgary. Awardees must be engaged in full-time study during the tenure of the award.

FINANCIAL DATA:
Amount of support per award: Labatt Scholarship: $2,200 (CAN); ScotiaMcLeod Scholarship: $2,400 (CAN).

NUMBER OF AWARDS: 1 per award.

APPLICATION INFORMATION:
No applications are required.

Labatt Scholarship: Recommendations from the Director of the MBA Program, Haskayne School of Business will be forwarded to the Graduate Scholarship Office. The recommendation is subject to final approval of the Graduate Scholarship Committee.

ScotiaMcLeod Scholarship: The Associate Dean, Calgary MBA Program, Faculty of Management, will submit recommendations to the Graduate Scholarship Office. Recommendation is subject to final approval of the Graduate Scholarship Committee.
Duration: One year.
Deadline: May 15.

ADDRESS INQUIRIES TO:
Graduate Scholarship Office
(See address above.)

THE UNIVERSITY OF CALGARY   [1788]
Faculty of Graduate Studies
MacKimmie Library Tower, Room 213
2500 University Drive, N.W.
Calgary AB T2N 1N4 Canada
(403) 220-4938
Fax: (403) 289-7635

E-MAIL ADDRESS:
gsaward@ucalgary.ca

WEB SITE ADDRESS:
www.grad.ucalgary.ca

FOUNDED: 1966

NAME(S) OF PROGRAMS:
- **The University of Calgary Silver Anniversary Graduate Fellowships**

TYPE:
Awards/prizes; Fellowships. Graduate fellowships in all fields of study tenable in The Faculty of Graduate Studies at The University of Calgary. Award endowed by an anonymous donor and matched by the Province of Alberta.

ELIGIBILITY:
Open to qualified graduates of any recognized university who are registered in or admissible to a doctoral program at The University of Calgary. Candidates must be residents of Canada. Awards are granted on the basis of academic standing and demonstrated potential for advanced study and research.

FINANCIAL DATA:
  Amount of support per award: $16,000 to $20,000.
  Total amount of support: Varies.

NUMBER OF AWARDS: Varies depending on funds.

APPLICATION INFORMATION:
  Contact the University.
  Duration: One year. Renewable once upon presentation of evidence of satisfactory progress.
  Deadline: February 1, unless specific program has an earlier deadline.

ADDRESS INQUIRIES TO:
  Graduate Scholarship Office
  (See address above.)

THE UNIVERSITY OF CALGARY   [1789]

Faculty of Graduate Studies
MacKimmie Library Tower, Room 213
2500 University Drive, N.W.
Calgary AB T2N 1N4 Canada
(403) 220-4938
Fax: (403) 289-7635

E-MAIL ADDRESS:
  gsaward@ucalgary.ca

WEB SITE ADDRESS:
  www.grad.ucalgary.ca

FOUNDED: 1966

AREAS OF INTEREST:
  Creative writing in English, English literature, and related literary fields.

NAME(S) OF PROGRAMS:
  • **The A.T.J. Cairns Memorial Scholarship**

TYPE:
  Awards/prizes; Scholarships. Graduate scholarship tenable at The University of Calgary. Award endowed through the estate of the late A.T.J. Cairns, with a matching grant provided by the Province of Alberta's Advanced Education Endowment Fund.

ELIGIBILITY:
  Candidates must be registered in or admissible to a Master's or doctoral degree program in the Department of English.

FINANCIAL DATA:
  Amount of support per award: Up to $2,000.
  Total amount of support: Varies.

NUMBER OF AWARDS: Determined annually.

APPLICATION INFORMATION:
  Students interested in the award should apply to the Department of English in the first instance. Recommendations from the Department will be considered by the University Graduate Scholarship Committee.
  Duration: One year.
  Deadline: April 30.

ADDRESS INQUIRIES TO:
  Graduate Scholarship Office
  (See address above.)

THE UNIVERSITY OF CALGARY   [1790]

Faculty of Graduate Studies
MacKimmie Library Tower, Room 213
2500 University Drive, N.W.
Calgary AB T2N 1N4 Canada
(403) 220-4938
Fax: (403) 289-7635

E-MAIL ADDRESS:
  gsaward@ucalgary.ca

WEB SITE ADDRESS:
  www.grad.ucalgary.ca

FOUNDED: 1966

NAME(S) OF PROGRAMS:
  • **Graduate Faculty Council Scholarship**

TYPE:
  Awards/prizes; Scholarships. Graduate scholarship in all fields of study tenable at The University of Calgary. Award endowed by The University of Calgary Graduate Faculty Council.

ELIGIBILITY:
  Open to qualified full-time graduate students who are or will be, at the time of tenure, registered in a thesis-based doctoral program in the Faculty of Graduate Studies.

FINANCIAL DATA:
  Amount of support per award: $10,000 per annum.
  Total amount of support: Varies depending on funds available.

NUMBER OF AWARDS: Varies.

APPLICATION INFORMATION:
  Students should consult their Graduate Program Officer for application information.
  Duration: One year.
  Deadline: February 1.

ADDRESS INQUIRIES TO:
  Graduate Scholarship Office
  (See address above.)

THE UNIVERSITY OF CALGARY   [1791]

Faculty of Graduate Studies
MacKimmie Library Tower, Room 213
2500 University Drive, N.W.
Calgary AB T2N 1N4 Canada
(403) 220-4938
Fax: (403) 289-7635

E-MAIL ADDRESS:
  gsaward@ucalgary.ca

WEB SITE ADDRESS:
  www.grad.ucalgary.ca/awards

FOUNDED: 1966

AREAS OF INTEREST:
  Humanities.

NAME(S) OF PROGRAMS:
  • **Peter C. Craigie Memorial Scholarship**

TYPE:
  Awards/prizes; Scholarships. Graduate scholarship tenable at The University of Calgary. Award endowed by friends, family and colleagues of Peter Craigie, who was Vice President (Academic) at the University; matching grant provided from the Province of Alberta's Advanced Education Endowment Fund.

ELIGIBILITY:
  Open to full-time registrants who are registered in and have completed one term of study in a program of studies leading to a Master's degree in a department in the Faculty of Humanities. The recipient must have an outstanding scholastic record and have been or be involved in activities contributing to the general welfare of the University community.

FINANCIAL DATA:
  Amount of support per award: $3,300.

Total amount of support: $3,300.

NUMBER OF AWARDS: 1.

APPLICATION INFORMATION:
  Application information is available at the web site address.
  Duration: One year.
  Deadline: February 1.

ADDRESS INQUIRIES TO:
  Graduate Scholarship Office
  (See address above.)

THE UNIVERSITY OF CALGARY   [1792]

Faculty of Graduate Studies
MacKimmie Library Tower, Room 213
2500 University Drive, N.W.
Calgary AB T2N 1N4 Canada
(403) 220-4938
Fax: (403) 289-7635

E-MAIL ADDRESS:
  gsaward@ucalgary.ca

WEB SITE ADDRESS:
  www.grad.ucalgary.ca/awards

FOUNDED: 1966

AREAS OF INTEREST:
  Economics, geoscience, engineering and management.

NAME(S) OF PROGRAMS:
  • **Canadian Natural Resources Limited Graduate Scholarship**

TYPE:
  Awards/prizes; Scholarships. Graduate scholarship tenable at the University of Calgary. This Scholarship recognizes the importance training and education play in helping students take advantage of the career and economic prospects available in the oil and gas industry.

ELIGIBILITY:
  Open to candidates who at the time of tenure will be registered full-time in a thesis-based program in the Faculty of Graduate Studies at the University of Calgary.

FINANCIAL DATA:
  Amount of support per award: $4,475.
  Total amount of support: $4,475.

COOPERATIVE FUNDING PROGRAMS: Endowed by Canadian Natural Resources Ltd (formerly Sceptre Resources Limited); matching grant provided from the Province of Alberta's Advanced Education Endowment Fund.

NUMBER OF AWARDS: 1.

APPLICATION INFORMATION:
  Students should consult the Graduate Award Competition Guidelines. Application information is available at the web site address.
  Duration: One year.
  Deadline: February 1 to the candidate's graduate program office, unless the program has an earlier deadline.

ADDRESS INQUIRIES TO:
  Graduate Scholarship Office
  (See address above.)

THE UNIVERSITY OF CALGARY   [1793]

Faculty of Graduate Studies
MacKimmie Library Tower, Room 213
2500 University Drive, N.W.
Calgary AB T2N 1N4 Canada
(403) 220-4938
Fax: (403) 289-7635

E-MAIL ADDRESS:
gsaward@ucalgary.ca

WEB SITE ADDRESS:
www.grad.ucalgary.ca

AREAS OF INTEREST:
Natural resources, energy and environmental law.

NAME(S) OF PROGRAMS:
- **Faculty of Law Graduate Scholarship**

TYPE:
Awards/prizes; Scholarships.

ELIGIBILITY:
Open to students entering or enrolled in a full-time graduate program in the Faculty of Law. If, in the opinion of the University of Calgary Graduate Scholarship Selection Committee, no suitable applications are received, no awards will be made.

FINANCIAL DATA:
Amount of support per award: $7,400.
Total amount of support: $7,400.

COOPERATIVE FUNDING PROGRAMS: Endowed through contributions made to the Focus on Natural Resources Law Campaign; matching grant provided from the Province of Alberta.

NUMBER OF AWARDS: 1.

APPLICATION INFORMATION:
Application forms available from the Director, Graduate Programme, Faculty of Law. Awards will be recommended by a committee of the Faculty of Law based upon academic excellence. The Graduate Coordinator, Law, will submit recommendations to the Graduate Scholarship Office. The recommendation is subject to final approval of the Graduate Scholarship Committee.
Duration: One year. Nonrenewable.
Deadline: December 15.

PUBLICATIONS:
Academic calendar.

ADDRESS INQUIRIES TO:
Graduate Scholarship Office
(See address above.)

UNIVERSITY OF CALIFORNIA, LOS ANGELES [1794]
11353 Bunche Hall
Box 951487
Los Angeles, CA 90095-1487
(310) 206-6365
Fax: (310) 206-3555

E-MAIL ADDRESS:
burkle@international.ucla.edu

WEB SITE ADDRESS:
www.international.ucla.edu/burkle

FOUNDED: 1979

AREAS OF INTEREST:
International relations, law, development and globalization.

NAME(S) OF PROGRAMS:
- **Alice Belkin Memorial Scholarship**

TYPE:
Conferences/seminars; Fellowships; Internships; Research grants; Scholarships.

PURPOSE:
To support outstanding minority students in the field of international relations who need financial assistance.

ELIGIBILITY:
Granted to qualified graduate applicants who, in addition to outstanding leadership skills and academic achievement, demonstrate financial need.

Applicants must:
(1) have a minimum grade point average of 3.0 or higher;
(2) maintain a cumulative grade point average of 3.0 or higher during the academic year of award;
(3) be a currently enrolled minority graduate student with studies related to the fields of globalization or international relations at UCLA;
(4) be a citizen or permanent resident of the U.S. and;
(5) be a graduate student pursuing a J.D., MBA, Ph.D., LL.M., or M.A.

FINANCIAL DATA:
Amount of support per award: Up to $4,000.

NUMBER OF APPLICANTS MOST RECENT YEAR:
35.

NUMBER OF AWARDS: Up to 3.

APPLICATION INFORMATION:
Application form is available online. Application must include:
(1) statement of interest expressing personal background, career goals and confirming eligibility;
(2) resume or curriculum vitae;
(3) official transcript from UCLA (if this is applicant's first year at UCLA, he or she must include an official transcript from a prior institution);
(4) two letters of recommendation from professors, mentors and/or employers, preferably in a sealed/signed envelope and;
(5) complete list of other sources of financial support (including TAships and GSRs) applied for, pending and received up to the present.
Duration: One year.
Deadline: April and December.

ADDRESS INQUIRIES TO:
See e-mail address above.

UNIVERSITY OF KANSAS CHILD LANGUAGE DOCTORAL PROGRAM [1795]
1000 Sunnyside Avenue
Room 3031, Dole Center
Lawrence, KS 66045-7555
(785) 864-4570
Fax: (785) 864-4571

E-MAIL ADDRESS:
childlang@ku.edu

WEB SITE ADDRESS:
www.clp.ku.edu

AREAS OF INTEREST:
Early childhood education and language research.

NAME(S) OF PROGRAMS:
- **Child Language Doctoral Program**

TYPE:
Conferences/seminars; Research grants; Scholarships.

PURPOSE:
To train individuals on language impairment across the life span.

ELIGIBILITY:
Applicants must have U.S. citizenship or permanent residency status, admission to the Child Language Doctoral Program or Intercampus Program in Speech-Language-Hearing or a related program, submission of a significant research plan of high quality, demonstrated high academic achievements and potential, and research interests congruent with those of one or more of the training program faculty members.

FINANCIAL DATA:
Amount of support per award: $21,180 per year predoctoral award.

APPLICATION INFORMATION:
Applicants must submit:
(1) a curriculum vitae;
(2) a list of all courses taken in relevant areas such as language impairment of children, linguistics, psychology, special education, and speech and hearing sciences;
(3) a research plan describing the applicant's plans for research on language impairments of children;
(4) two official transcripts;
(5) names and phone numbers of three references who can evaluate the applicant's research potential;
(6) scores from the Graduate Record Examinations and;
(7) letter of intent stating willingness to participate in continuous research practicum.
Duration: One year.
Deadline: Beginning of February.

STAFF:
Dr. Mabel L. Rice, Director
Linda Mann, Program Assistant

ADDRESS INQUIRIES TO:
Dr. Mabel L. Rice, Director
(See address above.)

UNIVERSITY OF SOUTHERN CALIFORNIA [1796]
3720 South Flower Street, Third Floor
CUB 303
Los Angeles, CA 90089-0701
(213) 740-8207
(213) 740-7762
Fax: (213) 740-6070

E-MAIL ADDRESS:
jeri.muniz@usc.edu

WEB SITE ADDRESS:
www.usc.edu/research/dcg

AREAS OF INTEREST:
Art history.

TYPE:
Fellowships; Grants-in-aid.

PURPOSE:
To support graduate education in art history at USC.

ELIGIBILITY:
Admission to Ph.D. program in art history.

GEOGRAPHIC RESTRICTIONS:
California.

FINANCIAL DATA:
Amount of support per award: Varies.

APPLICATION INFORMATION:
Applicants must submit the Graduate School Application and the Supplemental Application form along with Graduate Record Exam (GRE) scores and letters of recommendation.
Duration: One year. Renewal possible based on academic progress.
Deadline: January.

ADDRESS INQUIRIES TO:
Contracts and Grants
(See address above.)

UNIVERSITY OF SOUTHERN CALIFORNIA   [1797]

USC Graduate School
3601 Watt Way, GFS 315
Los Angeles, CA 90089-1695
(213) 740-9033
Fax: (213) 740-9048

E-MAIL ADDRESS:
gradfllw@usc.edu

WEB SITE ADDRESS:
www.usc.edu/schools/GraduateSchool/

NAME(S) OF PROGRAMS:
● **Annenberg Graduate Fellowship
  Program**
● **Global Ph.D. Fellowship**
● **Provost's Ph.D. Fellowship Program**
● **Rose Hills Ph.D. Fellowship**

TYPE:
Fellowships. Merit fellowships. Fellowships
will be combined with matching funds from
individual schools to provide four or more
years of funding toward the Ph.D.

YEAR PROGRAM STARTED: 1982

PURPOSE:
To allow outstanding students to devote
full-time to research and study at USC
leading to a career in university teaching and
research.

LEGAL BASIS:
University.

ELIGIBILITY:
Excellent incoming Ph.D. applicants who
show outstanding promise for academic
careers in research and training.

FINANCIAL DATA:
Amount of support per award: $30,000 plus
tuition and mandatory fees.

NUMBER OF AWARDS: Up to 150 for the
2012-13 academic year.

APPLICATION INFORMATION:
Nomination by department only.
Duration: Two years, awarded annually with
at least two years subsequent
departmental/school support, based upon
continued superior performance.
Deadline: Varies.

PUBLICATIONS:
Program announcements.

ADDRESS INQUIRIES TO:
Kate Tegmeyer, Fellowship Coordinator
(See address above.)

UNIVERSITY OF SOUTHERN CALIFORNIA   [1798]

3601 Watt Way
Grace Ford Salvatori, Suite 227
Los Angeles, CA 90089-1695
(213) 740-1741

WEB SITE ADDRESS:
www.usc.edu/programs/ugprograms/
ugresearch/rose_hill.shtml

AREAS OF INTEREST:
Science and engineering.

NAME(S) OF PROGRAMS:
● **Rose Hills Foundation Summer Science
  and Engineering Fellowships**

TYPE:
Fellowships. Summer fellowship for
undergraduate students at USC supporting
full-time research in science or engineering.

PURPOSE:
The Rose Hills Foundation, which supports
nonprofit organizations for the benefit of the
people of southern California, has generously
provided funding for a limited number of
students who would like to obtain science
and engineering fellowships.

ELIGIBILITY:
Enrollment at USC during fall as a junior or
senior in a program leading to an
undergraduate degree in the life or natural
sciences or engineering. USC cumulative
grade point average of 3.0 or better.
(Preference will be given to students whose
grade point average is 3.5 or better.) U.S.
citizenship is required, with residency in
southern California. (A resident of southern
California is defined as a student whose
permanent address is south of the Tehachapi
Mountains.)

GEOGRAPHIC RESTRICTIONS:
Southern California.

FINANCIAL DATA:
Amount of support per award: Stipend of
$5,000.

NUMBER OF AWARDS: Average of 42 annually.

APPLICATION INFORMATION:
Online application. See web site for details
and submission.
Duration: Eight weeks, mid-May through
mid-August.
Deadline: End of March; announcement
before mid-April.

THE UNIVERSITY OF SOUTHERN MISSISSIPPI

118 College Drive, Box 5148
Hattiesburg, MS 39406
(601) 266-4349
Fax: (601) 266-6269

E-MAIL ADDRESS:
ellen.ruffin@usm.edu

WEB SITE ADDRESS:
www.lib.usm.edu/legacy/degrum/public_html/
html/research/re-fellowships.shtml

TYPE:
Fellowships. Keats/Domanska Research
Fellowship awards grants to scholars engaged
in projects based substantially on the
holdings of the de Grummond Children's
Literature Collection.

Rey Translation Fellowship is awarded to
hire translators (French, German, Portuguese
or Russian) for the purpose of translating the
H.A. and Margret Rey documents into
English to further facilitate use in research.

See entry 743 for full listing.

VERMONT STUDENT ASSISTANCE CORPORATION   [1799]

10 East Allen Street
Winooski, VT 05404-2601
(800) 642-3177 (continental U.S.)
(802) 655-9602 (Burlington area)
Fax: (802) 654-3765
TDD: (800) 281-3341

E-MAIL ADDRESS:
info@vsac.org

WEB SITE ADDRESS:
www.vsac.org

FOUNDED: 1965

AREAS OF INTEREST:
Students in need.

NAME(S) OF PROGRAMS:
● **Vermont Incentive Grants and
  Scholarships**
● **Vermont Outreach Programs**

TYPE:
Conferences/seminars; Grants-in-aid;
Scholarships. Grants and loans for students
enrolled in approved postsecondary
institutions.

YEAR PROGRAM STARTED: 1965

PURPOSE:
To ensure that all Vermonters have the
necessary financial and informational
resources to pursue their educational goals
beyond high school.

LEGAL BASIS:
Nonprofit, public corporation.

ELIGIBILITY:
For Incentive Grant, applicant must be a
Vermont resident, enrolled full-time at an
approved postsecondary institution, and must
meet need test.

For Part-Time Grant, applicant must be a
Vermont resident, taking fewer than 12 credit
hours, have not received a Bachelor's degree,
and must meet need test.

For Non-Degree Grant, applicant must be a
Vermont resident, not matriculated, and must
meet need test.

GEOGRAPHIC RESTRICTIONS:
Vermont.

FINANCIAL DATA:
Amount of support per award: Incentive
Grant: $1,730; Part-Time Grant: $484;
Non-Degree Grant: $1,801 for fiscal year
2013.
Total amount of support: $18,070,000 for
fiscal year 2013.

NUMBER OF APPLICANTS MOST RECENT YEAR:
23,562 for fiscal year 2013.

NUMBER OF AWARDS: 13,620 for fiscal year
2013.

APPLICATION INFORMATION:
Incentive grant application is required.
Duration: One academic year. Renewal
possible under annual reapplication.
Deadline: Applications accepted on a rolling
basis for all grants.

ADDRESS INQUIRIES TO:
VSAC Research Department
(See address above.)

VERTICAL FLIGHT FOUNDATION

217 North Washington Street
Alexandria, VA 22314
(703) 684-6777
Fax: (703) 739-9279

E-MAIL ADDRESS:
staff@vtol.org

WEB SITE ADDRESS:
www.vtol.org

TYPE:
Awards/prizes; Scholarships. Annual
scholarships to undergraduate senior,

Master's or Ph.D. students interested in pursuing careers in some technical aspect of helicopter or vertical flight engineering.

See entry 2630 for full listing.

WASHINGTON STUDENT ACHIEVEMENT COUNCIL [1800]

917 Lakeridge Way, S.W.
Olympia, WA 98502
(360) 753-7861
Fax: (360) 704-6247

E-MAIL ADDRESS:
sws@wsac.wa.gov

WEB SITE ADDRESS:
www.wsac.wa.gov

FOUNDED: 1969

AREAS OF INTEREST:
Postsecondary education planning and policy development, advisory board.

NAME(S) OF PROGRAMS:
- **Washington State Need Grant Program**
- **Washington State Work-Study Program**

TYPE:
Work-study programs. Subsidized employment opportunities.

YEAR PROGRAM STARTED: 1974

PURPOSE:
To provide financial assistance to needy students attending eligible postsecondary institutions in the state of Washington by stimulating and promoting their employment and to provide such needy students, wherever possible, with employment related to their academic pursuits.

LEGAL BASIS:
State agency.

ELIGIBILITY:
Applicants must demonstrate financial need, be enrolled or accepted for enrollment as at least half-time undergraduate, graduate or professional students and be capable, in the opinion of the institution, of maintaining good standing in a course of study while employed under the program.

GEOGRAPHIC RESTRICTIONS:
Washington state.

FINANCIAL DATA:
Amount of support per award: Varies.
Total amount of support: Approximately $7,500,000 for the 2012-13 academic year.

NUMBER OF AWARDS: 4,700 for the academic year 2012-13.

APPLICATION INFORMATION:
There is no separate application for this program. Students are awarded automatically by their school on the basis of their financial need as evidenced from their Free Application for Federal Student Aid (FAFSA) results.
Duration: Renewable.

STAFF:
Marlena Rae Robbins, Program Associate

ADDRESS INQUIRIES TO:
Financial Aid Office at the college or Washington Student Achievement Council (See address above.)

WASHINGTON UNIVERSITY [1801]

Graduate School of Arts and Sciences
One Brookings Drive
Campus Box 1187
St. Louis, MO 63130-4899
(314) 935-6831
Fax: (314) 935-4887

E-MAIL ADDRESS:
zafar@wustl.edu
graddvrs@artsci.wustl.edu

WEB SITE ADDRESS:
pages.wustl.edu/cgfp

FOUNDED: 1853

AREAS OF INTEREST:
Anthropology, architecture, art history, archaeology, biology, biomedical sciences, business administration, chemistry, Chinese/Japanese and comparative literature, creative writing, earth and planetary sciences, economics, education, engineering, English, fine arts, German, history, material science and engineering, mathematics, movement science, music, philosophy, physics, political science, psychology, romance languages, statistics, social work, and visual arts.

NAME(S) OF PROGRAMS:
- **The Chancellor's Graduate Fellowship Program at Washington University in St. Louis**

TYPE:
Fellowships; Research grants; Scholarships; Travel grants.

YEAR PROGRAM STARTED: 1991

PURPOSE:
To facilitate training for students interested in becoming college or university professors, and who can contribute to diversity on the Washington University campus.

LEGAL BASIS:
University.

ELIGIBILITY:
Open to students who are admissible into any of Washington University's Ph.D. programs in Arts and Sciences, Business, Engineering or Social Work. Also eligible are students admissible to other Washington University programs providing final disciplinary training for prospective college professors (e.g., M.F.A. in Creative Writing, M.F.A. in Art). Students must be able to contribute to the diversity on the Washington University campus.

Applicants must be in the process of receiving, or will receive, an undergraduate degree from a four-year institution in the U.S. International students may apply, as long as they meet all admissions criteria.

FINANCIAL DATA:
Amount of support per award: Doctoral candidates are provided stipends and allowances of $30,000 per twelve-month year for five years, plus full tuition scholarships, with a total value in excess of $120,000. This combines a fellowship stipend of $28,500 and a $1,500 educational allowance.

COOPERATIVE FUNDING PROGRAMS: Fellows will meet as a community on a regular basis to discuss trends and activities within their various disciplines. Scholars will lead discussions on a multitude of topics and the fellows will participate in an annual conference.

APPLICATION INFORMATION:
Application information is available on the web site.

Duration: Five years for doctoral candidates, contingent upon satisfactory academic progress. Two years for graduate students in MFA (in both Creative Writing and Visual Art) and March (Master of Architecture) programs.
Deadline: January 15 for application to a degree program. January 25 for application for Chancellor's Program.

PUBLICATIONS:
Program announcement.

ADDRESS INQUIRIES TO:
Rafia M. Zafar, Associate Dean
Graduate School of Arts and Sciences
(See address above.)

WASHINGTON UNIVERSITY [1802]

Graduate School of Arts and Sciences
Campus Box 1187
One Brookings Drive
St. Louis, MO 63130
(314) 935-6818
Fax: (314) 935-4887

E-MAIL ADDRESS:
cecilyhawksworth@wustl.edu

WEB SITE ADDRESS:
pages.wustl.edu/olinfellowship

FOUNDED: 1974

NAME(S) OF PROGRAMS:
- **Mr. and Mrs. Spencer T. Olin Fellowships for Women**

TYPE:
Fellowships. The Olin Fellowships are open to candidates for any of the following graduate and professional schools at Washington University: architecture, art, arts and sciences, business, engineering, medicine, and social work.

YEAR PROGRAM STARTED: 1974

PURPOSE:
To encourage women of exceptional promise to prepare for careers in higher education and the professions; to continue and extend the historically important contributions of Monticello College to the education of women; to extend the influence of Washington University by assisting in the advanced education of outstanding young women who are likely to make significant contributions to higher education and the professions.

LEGAL BASIS:
Joint program of a private foundation (The Monticello College Foundation) and of Washington University in St. Louis.

ELIGIBILITY:
Any female graduate of a Baccalaureate institution in the U.S. who plans to prepare for a career in higher education or the professions by full-time advanced study at Washington University is eligible to apply. Applicants are considered without regard to age, handicap, religious creed, race or national origin and only with regard to the excellence of their qualifications. Applicants must meet the admission requirements of the graduate or professional school of Washington University. Preference will be given to those who wish to study for the highest earned degree in their chosen field.

FINANCIAL DATA:
The Olin Fellowships are tenable only at Washington University. They carry awards which compare favorably in each discipline

with the most attractive financial aid offers available in that discipline at Washington University.

NUMBER OF APPLICANTS MOST RECENT YEAR: 363.

NUMBER OF AWARDS: 13.

APPLICATION INFORMATION:
A complete application consists of the following:
(1) an online information form;
(2) an uploaded curriculum vitae;
(3) an uploaded essay;
(4) uploaded transcript(s) and;
(5) three letters of recommendation, to be uploaded by recommenders.

Application materials must be submitted via the web site.
Duration: Given satisfactory academic achievement, awards are renewable for a period of four years or until the completion of the program of academic degree study, whichever is first.
Deadline: Applications, with all supporting documents, are due in the Office of the Graduate School of Arts and Sciences no later than January 25 preceding the academic year for which application has been made.

ADDRESS INQUIRIES TO:
Nancy P. Pope, Director
(See address above.)

WELLESLEY COLLEGE
Center for Work and Service
Green Hall 439A, 106 Central Street
Wellesley, MA 02481-8203
(781) 283-2347
Fax: (781) 283-3674

E-MAIL ADDRESS:
cws-fellowships@wellesley.edu

WEB SITE ADDRESS:
www.wellesley.edu/CWS

TYPE:
Fellowships; Research grants. The Anne Louise Barrett Fellowship is given preferably in music and primarily for study or research in musical theory, composition, or in the history of music, abroad or in the U.S.

The Margaret Freeman Bowers Fellowship is given for first year of study in the fields of social work, law, or policy/public administration, including MBA candidates with plans for a career in the field of social services.

The Eugene L. Cox Fellowship is for graduate study in medieval or renaissance history and culture abroad or in the U.S.

The Professor Elizabeth F. Fisher Fellowship is given for research or further study in geology or geography, including urban, environmental or ecological studies.

The Ruth Ingersoll Goldmark Fellowship is awarded for graduate study in English literature, English composition or in the classics.

The Horton-Hallowell Fellowship is awarded for graduate study in any field, preferably in the last two years of candidacy for the Ph.D. degree, or its equivalent, or for private research of equivalent standard.

The Peggy Howard Fellowship in Economics is given to provide financial aid for Wellesley students or alumnae continuing their study of economics. Administered by the economics faculty who may name one or two recipients depending on the income available.

The Edna V. Moffett Fellowship is given to a young alumna, preferably for a first year of graduate study in history.

The Alice Freeman Palmer Fellowship is awarded for study or research abroad or in the U.S.

The Kathryn Conway Preyer Fellowship is for advanced study in history.

The Vida Dutton Scudder Fellowship is given for study in the field of social science, political science or literature.

The Harriet A. Shaw Fellowship is given for study or research in music and the allied arts, in the U.S. or abroad.

Mary Elvira Stevens Traveling Fellowship is awarded for travel or study outside the U.S.

The Maria Opasnov Tyler '52 Scholarship is for graduate study in Russian studies.

The Sarah Perry Wood Medical Fellowship is awarded for the study of medicine at an accredited medical school approved by the American Medical Association.

The Fanny Bullock Workman Fellowship is given for graduate study in any field.

See entry 1097 for full listing.

WELLESLEY COLLEGE
Center for Work and Service
Green Hall 439A, 106 Central Street
Wellesley, MA 02481-8203
(781) 283-2347
Fax: (781) 283-3674

E-MAIL ADDRESS:
cws-fellowships@wellesley.edu

WEB SITE ADDRESS:
www.wellesley.edu/CWS

TYPE:
Fellowships; Scholarships. Awards are made to female applicants who plan for full-time graduate study for the coming year.

The Mary McEwen Schimke Scholarship is a supplemental award given to afford relief from household and child care expenses while pursuing graduate study.

The M.A. Cartland Shackford Medical Fellowship is given for study of medicine with a view to general practice, not psychiatry.

See entry 1098 for full listing.

WEST VIRGINIA HIGHER EDUCATION POLICY COMMISSION   [1803]
1018 Kanawha Boulevard East, Suite 700
Charleston, WV 25301
(304) 558-4016
Fax: (304) 558-5719

E-MAIL ADDRESS:
randerson@hepc.wvnet.edu

WEB SITE ADDRESS:
www.hepc.wvnet.edu

FOUNDED: 1969

AREAS OF INTEREST:
Education.

NAME(S) OF PROGRAMS:
● **West Virginia Higher Education Grant Program**

TYPE:
Grants-in-aid. Monetary grants awarded to undergraduate students attending approved institutions of higher education.

YEAR PROGRAM STARTED: 1968

PURPOSE:
To guarantee that the most able and needy students are given the opportunity to continue their program of self-improvement at the postsecondary level by assisting in the removal of financial barriers through monetary awards.

LEGAL BASIS:
West Virginia Higher Education Grant Program is a government program administered under the authority of West Virginia Code 18-C-5-1.

ELIGIBILITY:
An applicant must be a citizen of the U.S., have been a resident of West Virginia for at least one year immediately preceding the date of application for a grant or renewal of a grant, require financial assistance to pursue a college education, possess academic promise or be making satisfactory progress and enroll as a full-time undergraduate in an approved educational institution.

Grants are restricted to approved educational institutions located in West Virginia and Pennsylvania.

GEOGRAPHIC RESTRICTIONS:
West Virginia and Pennsylvania.

FINANCIAL DATA:
Amount of support per award: Up to $2,500.

Total amount of support: $39,019,864 total funding for student awards for academic year 2013-14 in state-appropriated funds, special fee revenues allocated by the governing Board.

NUMBER OF APPLICANTS MOST RECENT YEAR:
Approximately 60,000 for academic year 2013-14.

NUMBER OF AWARDS: Approximately 22,000 for academic year 2013-14.

APPLICATION INFORMATION:
Applicants must submit the Free Application for Federal Student Aid (FAFSA).

Duration: Total of eight semesters or 12 quarters. The eight semesters do not have to be consecutive. Receipt of a grant in a given year does not guarantee its continuance in a subsequent year even though eligibility may be maintained. Students must reapply each year.

Deadline: April 15. Awards announcement in early to mid-May.

IRS IDENTIFICATION NUMBER: 55-0517092

STAFF:
Rob Anderson, Executive Vice Chancellor for Administration
Brian Weingart, Senior Director of Financial Aid

ADDRESS INQUIRIES TO:
Brian Weingart
Senior Director of Financial Aid
(See address above.)

THE WOODROW WILSON NATIONAL FELLOWSHIP FOUNDATION [1804]

5 Vaughn Drive
Princeton, NJ 08540
(609) 452-7007 ext. 310

E-MAIL ADDRESS:
billmaier@woodrow.org

WEB SITE ADDRESS:
www.woodrow.org

FOUNDED: 1945

AREAS OF INTEREST:
Higher education.

NAME(S) OF PROGRAMS:
● **Charlotte W. Newcombe Doctoral Dissertation Fellowships**

TYPE:
Fellowships. Awards to support and encourage original and significant study of ethical and/or religious values in all areas of human endeavor.

YEAR PROGRAM STARTED: 1981

PURPOSE:
To encourage study of ethical or religious values.

LEGAL BASIS:
Publicly supported charity.

ELIGIBILITY:
Doctoral candidates enrolled in a U.S. university, located in the U.S., working on topics of religious or ethical values in the Humanities or Social Sciences may apply.

FINANCIAL DATA:
Amount of support per award: $25,000 for 12 months of dissertation writing.

COOPERATIVE FUNDING PROGRAMS: Program made available by funds from the Charlotte W. Newcombe Foundation.

NUMBER OF APPLICANTS MOST RECENT YEAR: 594.

NUMBER OF AWARDS: Minimum of 22.

APPLICATION INFORMATION:
Applications are accepted beginning September 1 and must be submitted electronically.
Duration: Tenure of the award is for the academic year following the announcement of the winners.
Deadline: November 15.

OFFICERS:
Arthur Levine, President

ADDRESS INQUIRIES TO:
E-mail: newcombe@woodrow.org

*SPECIAL STIPULATIONS:
Fellowship is for humanities and social sciences. Applicants in highly quantitative fields should not apply.

YOUNG MUSICIANS FOUNDATION (YMF)

244 South San Pedro Street
Suite 506
Los Angeles, CA 90012
(310) 859-7668
Fax: (310) 859-1365

E-MAIL ADDRESS:
info@ymf.org

WEB SITE ADDRESS:
www.ymf.org

TYPE:
Awards/prizes; Development grants; General operating grants; Internships; Project/program grants; Scholarships; Training grants. Mentor program. Financial assistance for private study and/or tuition at recognized musical institutions. Significant performance opportunity may be offered.

See entry 796 for full listing.

YOUNG MUSICIANS FOUNDATION (YMF)

244 South San Pedro Street
Suite 506
Los Angeles, CA 90012
(213) 617-7707
Fax: (213) 617-7706

E-MAIL ADDRESS:
info@ymf.org

WEB SITE ADDRESS:
www.ymf.org

TYPE:
Grants-in-aid; Scholarships. Each year, young musicians are selected through auditions to receive a grant for a series of coaching sessions with leading professional musicians from the Los Angeles (CA) area.

See entry 797 for full listing.

SCIENCES (multiple disciplines)

Sciences (multiple disciplines)

THE ACADEMY OF NATURAL SCIENCES OF PHILADELPHIA [1805]
1900 Benjamin Franklin Parkway
Philadelphia, PA 19103-1101
(215) 299-1065
Fax: (215) 299-1079

E-MAIL ADDRESS:
kepics@ansp.org

WEB SITE ADDRESS:
www.ansp.org/research

FOUNDED: 1812

AREAS OF INTEREST:
Research, exhibition and education in natural sciences.

NAME(S) OF PROGRAMS:
● **John J. and Anna H. Gallagher Fellowship**

TYPE:
Fellowships; Project/program grants; Research grants; Residencies; Training grants; Visiting scholars. The Gallagher Fellowship provides support for original postdoctoral or sabbatical research on the systematics of microscopic invertebrates, with priority for the study of rotifers.

YEAR PROGRAM STARTED: 1990

LEGAL BASIS:
Private, nonprofit natural science museum.

ELIGIBILITY:
Candidates must have a Ph.D. in zoology or in ecology, evolution and biodiversity from a major university. Applicants must provide a research proposal involving microscopic freshwater invertebrate animals, including development of expertise in one or more taxonomic groups and the names of three references who are acknowledged scholars in the field. Preference will be given to candidates specializing in Rotifera.

Work must take place primarily at the Academy of Natural Sciences of Philadelphia and/or in the field and should emphasize utilization of the Academy's collections of literature and specimens. Projects should be scaled for completion during the one-year duration of the fellowship.

FINANCIAL DATA:
Fellowship includes salary, benefits, travel expenses, field and laboratory supplies.
Total amount of support: $30,000 to $50,000.

NUMBER OF APPLICANTS MOST RECENT YEAR: 9.

NUMBER OF AWARDS: 1.

APPLICATION INFORMATION:
Research proposal should include:
(1) curriculum vitae;
(2) statement of research interests;
(3) a three- to five-page description of the project (including salary request, research project costs and a timeline) and;
(4) names and contact information of three references.
Duration: Up to 12 months.
Deadline: Proposals are accepted on a rolling basis.

ADDRESS INQUIRIES TO:
Kristen Kepics
Department Administrator
(See e-mail address above.)

ALABAMA ACADEMY OF SCIENCE, INC. [1806]
University of Alabama at Birmingham
Department of Chemistry, CHEM-201
Birmingham, AL 35297
(205) 934-8017
Fax: (205) 934-2543

E-MAIL ADDRESS:
krannich@uab.edu

WEB SITE ADDRESS:
www.alabamaacademyofscience.org

FOUNDED: 1924

AREAS OF INTEREST:
Chemistry, biology, archaeology, earth science, forestry, geography, conservation, physics, industry, economics, mathematics, computer science, anthropology, engineering, psychology, behavioral and social sciences, physical sciences, health sciences and ecology.

CONSULTING OR VOLUNTEER SERVICES:
Visiting Scientist Speaker Program for elementary schools, high schools and colleges.

NAME(S) OF PROGRAMS:
● **Gorgas Scholarship**
● **Mason Science Teaching Fellowships**
● **Student Research Grants**
● **Student Travel Awards**

TYPE:
Assistantships; Awards/prizes; Conferences/seminars; Fellowships; Project/program grants; Research grants; Scholarships; Travel grants; Visiting scholars. Grants to college and university students for small research projects and for travel to scientific meetings to present papers.

Fellowships are for teaching science for Alabama teachers.

The Gorgas Scholarships are awarded to high school senior students who were Alabama Science Scholar Search entrants for any Alabama college or university.

YEAR PROGRAM STARTED: 1924

PURPOSE:
To stimulate student science study and research; to promote the development of interested scientific matter in the state; to render public service in scientific matters.

LEGAL BASIS:
Tax-exempt membership organization.

ELIGIBILITY:
Open to individuals committed to the purpose of the Academy.

GEOGRAPHIC RESTRICTIONS:
Alabama.

FINANCIAL DATA:
Amount of support per award: MST Fellowship: $1,000 for teacher and $50 to $100 per award for student research; Student Research Grants: $250; Student Travel Awards: $50; $10,000 in scholarships to high school seniors.
Total amount of support: Up to $13,000 annually.

COOPERATIVE FUNDING PROGRAMS: Gorgas Scholarship Program is supported by the Alabama Power Foundation, Inc. All other programs are funded by membership dues, meeting registrations, exhibits, contributions and university memberships.

NUMBER OF AWARDS: MST Fellowship: 1 teacher award; Student Research Grants: 3 or 4; Student Travel Awards: 4 or 5.

APPLICATION INFORMATION:
Contact the Academy.
Duration: One year.
Deadline: Approximately February 1. Award announcement at annual meeting in March.

PUBLICATIONS:
Journal of the Alabama Academy of Sciences.

IRS IDENTIFICATION NUMBER: 063-6050246

OFFICERS:
Emanuel Waddell, President
Bettina Riley, Treasurer
Kevin Morse, Secretary

ADDRESS INQUIRIES TO:
Larry K. Krannich, Ph.D.
Executive Director
(See address above.)

ALBERTA INNOVATES - HEALTH SOLUTIONS
Suite 1500
10104 - 103 Avenue, N.W.
Edmonton AB T5J 4A7 Canada
(780) 423-5727
Fax: (780) 429-3509

E-MAIL ADDRESS:
health@albertainnovates.ca

WEB SITE ADDRESS:
www.aihealthsolutions.ca

TYPE:
Awards/prizes; Block grants; Conferences/seminars; Development grants; Fellowships; General operating grants; Project/program grants; Research grants; Scholarships; Training grants. Interdisciplinary team grants. Awards for personnel support, equipment purchase, conferences and workshops.

See entry 2215 for full listing.

ALTERNATIVES RESEARCH AND DEVELOPMENT FOUNDATION [1807]
801 Old York Road, Suite 316
Jenkintown, PA 19046
(215) 887-8076
Fax: (215) 887-0771

E-MAIL ADDRESS:
grants08@ardf-online.org

WEB SITE ADDRESS:
www.ardf-online.org

FOUNDED: 1990

AREAS OF INTEREST:
Development and validation of nonanimal methods in biomedical research, safety testing and education.

NAME(S) OF PROGRAMS:
- **Alternatives Research Grant Program**
- **William and Eleanor Cave Award**

TYPE:
Awards/prizes; Research grants.

YEAR PROGRAM STARTED: 1991

PURPOSE:
To develop and promote the use of alternatives to traditional uses of animals in biomedical research, testing and education.

ELIGIBILITY:
Nonsectarian religious programs may apply. Preference is given to organizations in the U.S. No grants are made to individuals.

FINANCIAL DATA:
Amount of support per award: $5,000 to $40,000.
Total amount of support: Varies.

APPLICATION INFORMATION:
Proposal with no indirect cost is preferred. Primary grant application should be no more than 15 pages, including the Alternatives Research Grant Program Application Form. Send five copies of the primary grant application and supplemental material.

Primary grant application is composed of:
(1) abstract (not to exceed 200 words) that describes the proposed research project and includes an explanation of how the work will contribute to reducing or replacing current uses of laboratory animals in biomedical research, product safety testings, or educational demonstrations;
(2) proposal that presents a clear research plan and includes sections on materials and methods, expected results, and a list of relevant references;
(3) description of how the proposed research will lead to a significant reduction or replacement of laboratory animals;
(4) detailed budget and justification for equipment and supplies;
(5) description of additional sources of funding for the project currently available or applied for. Also supply information about previous grant support in this project area during the past two years and;
(6) curriculum vitae for the principal investigator.

Supplemental material includes previous publications which directly support the current grant application and curriculum vitae (one page each) for up to three personnel involved other than the principal investigator.
Duration: One year.
Deadline: April 30.

ADDRESS INQUIRIES TO:
Sue Leary, President
(See address above.)

AMERICAN ASSOCIATION FOR THE ADVANCEMENT OF SCIENCE

1200 New York Avenue, N.W.
Washington, DC 20005
(202) 326-6645
Fax: (202) 371-9849

E-MAIL ADDRESS:
drossite@aaas.org

WEB SITE ADDRESS:
www.aaas.org/programs/education/MassMedia

TYPE:
Fellowships; Internships. Fellowships to primarily support graduate students in the fields of social, natural and physical sciences, mathematics, and engineering during the summer as intern reporters, researchers or production assistants in mass media organizations nationwide. Fellows will have the opportunity to observe and participate in the process by which events and ideas become news, improve their communication skills by learning to describe complex technical subjects in a manner understandable to the lay public, and increase their understanding of editorial decision making and the way in which information is effectively disseminated.

Each fellow will work for a specific media organization. Some will work for newspapers or magazines on news and feature writing assignments. Others may be involved in television or radio production.

See entry 1920 for full listing.

AMERICAN INSTITUTE OF CHEMICAL ENGINEERS (AICHE)   [1808]

120 Wall Street, 23rd Floor
New York, NY 10005-4020
(203) 702-7660
(646) 495-1348
Fax: (212) 591-8890

E-MAIL ADDRESS:
awards@aiche.org

WEB SITE ADDRESS:
www.aiche.org

AREAS OF INTEREST:
Chemical engineering.

NAME(S) OF PROGRAMS:
- **Food, Pharmaceutical and Bioengineering Division Award in Chemical Engineering**

TYPE:
Awards/prizes.

YEAR PROGRAM STARTED: 1970

PURPOSE:
To recognize an individual's outstanding chemical engineering contribution in the food, pharmaceutical and/or bioengineering industry.

LEGAL BASIS:
Professional association.

ELIGIBILITY:
Grants given to individuals. Contribution may have been made in industry, government, or academic areas, or with other organizations.

FINANCIAL DATA:
Amount of support per award: $4,000.
Total amount of support: $4,000.

NUMBER OF AWARDS: 1 annually.

APPLICATION INFORMATION:
Contact the Institute.
Deadline: February 15.

ADDRESS INQUIRIES TO:
Dr. Eleftherios Terry Papoutsakis, Director
Eugene DuPont Chair of Chemical Engineering
Delaware Biotechnology Institute
University of Delaware
15 Innovation Way
Newark, DE 19711
Tel: (302) 831-8376

THE AMERICAN MUSEUM OF NATURAL HISTORY   [1809]

Richard Gilder Graduate School
Central Park West at 79th Street
New York, NY 10024-5192
(212) 769-5017
Fax: (212) 769-5257

E-MAIL ADDRESS:
fellowships-rggs@amnh.org
mrios@amnh.org

WEB SITE ADDRESS:
rggs.amnh.org/pages/academics_and_research/
fellowship_and_grant_opportunities

FOUNDED: 1869

AREAS OF INTEREST:
Anthropology, paleontology and zoology.

NAME(S) OF PROGRAMS:
- **Collection Study Grants**
- **Lerner-Gray Grants for Marine Research**
- **Theodore Roosevelt Memorial Grants**

TYPE:
Grants-in-aid; Research grants. Collection Study Grants enable predoctoral and recent postdoctoral investigators to study any of the scientific collections at the American Museum in the departments of anthropology, earth and planetary sciences, entomology, herpetology, ichthyology, invertebrates, mammalogy, ornithology, and vertebrate paleontology.

The Lerner-Gray Grants for Marine Research provide support to highly qualified persons starting careers in marine zoology.

The Theodore Roosevelt Memorial Grants support research on North American fauna in wildlife conservation or natural history.

YEAR PROGRAM STARTED: 1976

PURPOSE:
To provide modest short-term awards to advanced graduate students and postdoctoral researchers who are commencing their careers in the fields of zoology, paleontology and anthropology.

ELIGIBILITY:
Applicants should be advanced graduate students and postdoctoral researchers who are beginning their careers in the interest areas listed above. Research projects need not be carried out at the American Museum.

FINANCIAL DATA:
Amount of support per award: $500 to $1,500.
Total amount of support: Varies.

NUMBER OF AWARDS: Average 45 per program.

APPLICATION INFORMATION:
Contact the Museum.
Duration: One year.
Deadline: Varies by grant.

ADDRESS INQUIRIES TO:
Maria Rios, Assistant Director
Fellowships and Student Affairs
(See address above.)

THE AMERICAN MUSEUM OF NATURAL HISTORY   [1810]

Richard Gilder Graduate School
Central Park West at 79th Street
New York, NY 10024-5192
(212) 769-5017
Fax: (212) 769-5257

E-MAIL ADDRESS:
fellowships-rggs@amnh.org
mrios@amnh.org

WEB SITE ADDRESS:
rggs.amnh.org/pages/academics_and_research/
fellowship_and_grant_opportunities

FOUNDED: 1869

AREAS OF INTEREST:
Vertebrate and invertebrate zoology,
paleozoology, anthropology, earth and
planetary sciences.

NAME(S) OF PROGRAMS:
- **Postdoctoral Research Fellowship
Program**

TYPE:
Fellowships.

YEAR PROGRAM STARTED: 1960

PURPOSE:
To advance the training of recent
postdoctoral investigators and established
scientists.

LEGAL BASIS:
Nonprofit.

ELIGIBILITY:
Provides training to postdoctoral investigators
and established scientists to carry out a
specific project, which must fit into the
Museum's areas of interest. Postdoctoral
Fellows are expected to be in residence at the
Museum.

FINANCIAL DATA:
Limited relocation, research, and publication
support is provided.

APPLICATION INFORMATION:
Applications require a project description
with bibliography, budget, curriculum vitae
including a list of publications, and letters of
recommendation.
Duration: Up to two years.
Deadline: November 15.

PUBLICATIONS:
*Grants and Fellowships of the American
Museum of Natural History,* booklet.

ADDRESS INQUIRIES TO:
Maria Rios, Assistant Director
Fellowships and Student Affairs
(See address above.)

AMERICAN SOCIETY FOR ENGINEERING EDUCATION

1818 N Street, N.W., Suite 600
Washington, DC 20036
(202) 649-3834

E-MAIL ADDRESS:
sffp@asee.org

WEB SITE ADDRESS:
sffp.asee.org

TYPE:
Fellowships. Research fellowship.

See entry 2642 for full listing.

AMERICAN TINNITUS ASSOCIATION (ATA)   [1811]

522 S.W. 5th Avenue
Suite 825
Portland, OR 97204
(503) 248-9985 ext. 211
(800) 634-8978 ext. 211
Fax: (503) 248-0024

E-MAIL ADDRESS:
research@ata.org

WEB SITE ADDRESS:
www.ata.org

FOUNDED: 1971

AREAS OF INTEREST:
Tinnitus.

NAME(S) OF PROGRAMS:
- **ATA Student Research Grant Program**
- **ATA Tinnitus Research Grant Program**

TYPE:
Research grants; Seed money grants.
Financially supports scientific studies about
tinnitus.

YEAR PROGRAM STARTED: 1980

PURPOSE:
To identify the mechanisms of tinnitus or to
improve tinnitus treatments.

ELIGIBILITY:
Tinnitus Research Grant: Postdoctorate.
Student Grant: Doctorate or medical student.
ATA will consider the subject of research,
quality of its design, potential for significant
advances in basic knowledge or clinical
application, available facilities and personnel
at the institution and qualifications of
investigators. Facility must be nonprofit.

GEOGRAPHIC RESTRICTIONS:
United States.

FINANCIAL DATA:
Amount of support per award: Tinnitus
Research Grant: Up to $150,000 ($50,000 per
year); Student Grant: $10,000.
Total amount of support: Up to $150,000.

APPLICATION INFORMATION:
In addition to the application form, applicants
must submit a concisely written research
proposal containing detailed descriptions of
the following elements:
(1) introduction, statement of the problem
and specific aims of the research;
(2) background and significance of the issue;
(3) relevant preliminary or pilot studies;
(4) the facility that will house the study
and/or administer the funds;
(5) discussion of relevant literature and,
where appropriate, standardized tinnitus
measures;
(6) outline of intended study procedures
including study design, sampling and
measurement data to be used, and description
of analysis and evaluation plan and;
(7) outcomes expected from the study and
the study's use.
Duration: Tinnitus Research Grant: Three
years. Student Grant: One year.
Deadline: June 30.

STAFF:
Daniel Born, Director, Research and Special
Projects

ADDRESS INQUIRIES TO:
Daniel Born, Director, Research and
Special Projects
(See address above.)

AMFAR, THE FOUNDATION FOR AIDS RESEARCH   [1812]

120 Wall Street, 13th Floor
New York, NY 10005-3908
(212) 806-1600
Fax: (212) 806-1601

E-MAIL ADDRESS:
grants@amfar.org

WEB SITE ADDRESS:
www.amfar.org

FOUNDED: 1985

AREAS OF INTEREST:
Research relevant to HIV/AIDS and projects
that extend the benefits of HIV/AIDS
research to vulnerable populations.

NAME(S) OF PROGRAMS:
- **GMT Initiative Grants**
- **Mathilde Krim Fellowships in Basic
Biomedical Research**
- **Research Grants**

TYPE:
Fellowships; Project/program grants;
Research grants. GMT Initiative Grants
provide support for HIV/AIDS research
relevant to communities of gay men, other
men who have sex with men, and transgender
persons worldwide. Proposed research must
be relevant to topics identified in current
RFPs.

Mathilde Krim Fellowships are grants made
to support two years of support for original
research conducted by outstanding
postdoctoral scientists and facilitate transition
to an independent research position.

Research Grants provide one year of support
for HIV/AIDS research relevant to topics
targeted in current RFPs. Investigators must
hold a doctoral degree and be affiliated with
a nonprofit research institution.

YEAR PROGRAM STARTED: 1985

PURPOSE:
To end the global AIDS epidemic through
innovative research; to fund research to
explore scientific approaches for preventing
and treating HIV infection and enhancing the
health and survival of people with
HIV/AIDS; to support global initiatives to
facilitate the development and
implementation of effective research,
treatment, prevention and education strategies
in developing countries; to support public
policy analysis and the advocacy of rational
and compassionate policies that promote
public health and protect the rights of people
threatened by HIV/AIDS; to support public
information programs to build awareness of
the continued threat HIV/AIDS poses and to
provide up-to-date medical, scientific and
prevention information to people with
HIV/AIDS, health care professionals and the
public.

LEGAL BASIS:
Not-for-profit public benefit corporation.

ELIGIBILITY:
Varies by program.

FINANCIAL DATA:
Since 1985, amfAR has invested more than
$388,000,000 in its mission and has awarded
more than 3,300 grants to research teams
worldwide.
Amount of support per award: GMT
Initiative Grants: Up to $250,000 as
appropriate to proposed research; Krim
Fellowships: Up to $150,000; Research
Grants: Up to $180,000.

APPLICATION INFORMATION:
The Foundation does not accept unsolicited
grant applications or requests. Requests for
Proposals details and downloadable forms are
available at the web site.
Duration: Krim Fellowships: Two years;
Research Grants: One year.
Deadline: Varies.

STAFF:
Rowena Johnston, Ph.D., Vice President,
Research
Kent Cozad, Director, Grants Administration
and Compliance
Kent Klindera, Director, GMT Initiative
Noza Zhumanova, Grants Administrator,
GMT Initiative
Jonathan Miller, Grants Administrator,
Research

ADDRESS INQUIRIES TO:
Grants Administration
(See address above.)

ARGONNE NATIONAL
LABORATORY   [1813]

Communications, Education and
Public Affairs Division
9700 South Cass Avenue
Argonne, IL 60439-4845
(630) 252-4114
Fax: (630) 252-3193

E-MAIL ADDRESS:
lisareed@anl.gov

WEB SITE ADDRESS:
www.dep.anl.gov

FOUNDED: 1968

AREAS OF INTEREST:
Basic physical and life sciences,
mathematics, computer science, engineering,
applied research relating to coal,
conservation, environmental impact and
technology, fission and fusion energy.

NAME(S) OF PROGRAMS:
● **Science Undergraduate Laboratory
  Internships**

TYPE:
Internships.

PURPOSE:
To encourage the further study of science.

LEGAL BASIS:
Research center of the U.S. Department of
Energy.

ELIGIBILITY:
Applicants must be U.S. citizens or
permanent resident aliens who are full-time
students at accredited U.S. colleges or
universities. In addition to their research
activities, participants are expected to attend
a series of seminars and tours dealing with
current topics in science and engineering.

GEOGRAPHIC RESTRICTIONS:
United States.

FINANCIAL DATA:
Amount of support per award: $500 per
week.
Total amount of support: Varies.

NUMBER OF APPLICANTS MOST RECENT YEAR:
100.

APPLICATION INFORMATION:
Applications must be submitted at the
Department of Energy web site.
Duration: 10 weeks during the summer; 15
weeks during fall or spring.
Deadline: Summer: January 10. Fall:
Approximately May 30. Spring: October 30.

ADDRESS INQUIRIES TO:
Lisa Reed, Program Coordinator
(See address above.)

ARGONNE NATIONAL
LABORATORY   [1814]

Communications, Education and
Public Affairs Division
9700 South Cass Avenue
Argonne, IL 60439-4845
(630) 252-4114
Fax: (630) 252-3193

E-MAIL ADDRESS:
lisareed@anl.gov

WEB SITE ADDRESS:
www.dep.anl.gov

FOUNDED: 1946

AREAS OF INTEREST:
Basic physical and life sciences,
mathematics, computer science and
engineering, applied research relating to coal,
conservation, environmental science and
energy technologies and fission and fusion
energy.

NAME(S) OF PROGRAMS:
● **Laboratory-Graduate Program**
● **Thesis Parts Program**

TYPE:
Fellowships. Laboratory Graduate Program
provides support for thesis research in
residence at Argonne.

Thesis Parts Program provides support for
partial dissertation research or to satisfy
practicum requirements at Argonne.

YEAR PROGRAM STARTED: 1968

PURPOSE:
To encourage the advanced study of science.

LEGAL BASIS:
Research center of the U.S. Department of
Energy.

ELIGIBILITY:
U.S. citizens or permanent residents are
eligible. Appointments are made to graduate
students who have completed all
requirements for their Master's or doctoral
degrees except for the dissertation. The
research must require resources not available
on campus.

GEOGRAPHIC RESTRICTIONS:
United States.

FINANCIAL DATA:
Amount of support per award:
Laboratory-Graduate Program provides
stipend, plus up to $10,500 per year tuition.
Thesis Parts Program provides per diem
amount.
Total amount of support: Varies.

NUMBER OF AWARDS: 15.

APPLICATION INFORMATION:
Applications must be submitted
electronically.
Duration: Laboratory-Graduate Program: Up
to one year. Renewable for a total of three
years.

ADDRESS INQUIRIES TO:
Lisa Reed, Program Coordinator
(See address above.)

BAYER USA FOUNDATION [1815]

100 Bayer Road
Pittsburgh, PA 15205
(800) 422-9374
Fax: (412) 778-4430

E-MAIL ADDRESS:
karen.wirth@bayer.com

WEB SITE ADDRESS:
www.bayerus.com

FOUNDED: 1953

AREAS OF INTEREST:
Education and workforce development,
environment and sustainability, health and
social services.

TYPE:
General operating grants; Grants-in-aid;
Project/program grants.

PURPOSE:
To take an active role in business
communities; to enhance the quality of life
for Bayer employees and neighbors.

LEGAL BASIS:
Corporate giving program.

ELIGIBILITY:
Proposed projects must impact at least one of
Bayer Corporation's business locations. No
grants to organizations without IRS 501(c)(3)
status, United Way-affiliated agencies for
general operating support, charitable dinners
and events, individuals, political
organizations, endowment funds, deficit
reduction, religious organizations, student
trips or exchange programs, community
advertising, athletic sponsorships or
telephone solicitations.

GEOGRAPHIC RESTRICTIONS:
United States and its territories.

FINANCIAL DATA:
Amount of support per award: Varies
depending on needs and nature of the
request.

APPLICATION INFORMATION:
Applications must be submitted online.
Deadline: Varies by location.

*SPECIAL STIPULATIONS:
Applicants should not telephone the
Foundation concerning their applications. All
questions should be e-mailed to
bayerusafoundation@bayer.com or submitted
in writing.

BROOKHAVEN WOMEN IN
SCIENCE

P.O. Box 183
Upton, NY 11973
(631) 344-2425
Fax: (631) 344-5676

E-MAIL ADDRESS:
bwisawards@bnl.gov

WEB SITE ADDRESS:
www.bnl.gov/bwis/scholarships.php

TYPE:
Awards/prizes; Scholarships. These
scholarships are offered to encourage women
to resume their formal education in the
natural sciences, engineering or mathematics.
See entry 1076 for full listing.

CARNEGIE INSTITUTION OF
WASHINGTON   [1816]

1530 P Street, N.W.
Washington, DC 20005
(202) 939-1120
Fax: (202) 939-1120

E-MAIL ADDRESS:
tmcdowell@ciw.edu

WEB SITE ADDRESS:
www.carnegiescience.edu

FOUNDED: 1902

AREAS OF INTEREST:
Astronomy, physics, chemistry, earth sciences, materials science, plant biology, developmental biology and global ecology.

NAME(S) OF PROGRAMS:
- **Predoctoral and Postdoctoral Fellowships at the Carnegie Institution**

TYPE:
Fellowships; Internships; Technical assistance; Visiting scholars; Research contracts. Predoctoral and Postdoctoral fellowships for research training in the fields of astronomy, geophysics, physics and related sciences, plant biology, genetics and developmental biology in residence at one of the Carnegie Institution's six operating centers.

YEAR PROGRAM STARTED: 1938

PURPOSE:
To encourage in the broadest and most liberal manner investigation, research and discovery and the application of knowledge to the improvement of mankind.

LEGAL BASIS:
Exempt under Section 501(c)(3) of the Internal Revenue Code.

ELIGIBILITY:
Qualified scientists who have obtained the doctoral degree or are in the process are eligible. Candidates are evaluated on the basis of academic record, recommendations of professors and associates and the complementing nature of their research to work in progress at the Carnegie department. Women and minorities are encouraged to apply.

FINANCIAL DATA:
Fellowships provide direct financial support and the use of the Institution's laboratory and observational facilities, including special equipment when needed. Travel funds may be included where long-distance travel is required to reach the Institution.
Amount of support per award: Varies by department.

APPLICATION INFORMATION:
Fellowship applications should be made to the Directors of the Departments of Carnegie Institution at the addresses listed below.
Duration: Fellowships are usually awarded for one year with the possibility of renewal for another year.
Deadline: Varies.

PUBLICATIONS:
Newsletter.

OFFICERS:
Richard A. Meserve, President
Cynthia Allen, Director of Administration and Finance

DIRECTORS:
Allan Spradling, Director, Department of Embryology
Christopher Field, Director, Department of Global Ecology
Wolf Frommer, Director, Department of Plant Biology
Richard Carlson, Acting Director, Department of Terrestrial Magnetism
George Cody, Acting Director, Geophysical Laboratory
Wendy Freedman, Director, Observatories of Carnegie

ADDRESS INQUIRIES TO:
Call first to determine to whom inquiry should be directed.

Dr. Allan C. Spradling
Director, Department of Embryology
3520 San Martin Drive
Baltimore, MD 21218 or

Dr. Christopher Field
Director, Department of Global Ecology
260 Panama Street
Stanford, CA 94305
Tel: (650) 462-1047 or

Dr. Wolf B. Frommer
Director, Department of Plant Biology
260 Panama Street
Stanford, CA 94305 or

Richard Carlson
Acting Director, Department of Terrestrial Magnetism
5241 Broad Branch Road, N.W.
Washington, DC 20015 or

George Cody
Acting Director, Geophysical Laboratory
5251 Broad Branch Road, N.W.
Washington, DC 20015 or

Dr. Wendy Freedman
Director, The Observatories of the Carnegie Institution
813 Santa Barbara Street
Pasadena, CA 91101

*SPECIAL STIPULATIONS:
Fellowships are tenable only at one of the Institution's facilities. No extracurricular grants.

EARTHWATCH INSTITUTE [1817]

114 Western Avenue
Boston, MA 02134
(800) 776-0188
Fax: (978) 461-2332

E-MAIL ADDRESS:
research@earthwatch.org

WEB SITE ADDRESS:
www.earthwatch.org/research

FOUNDED: 1971

AREAS OF INTEREST:
Any significant postdoctoral field research in the sciences, social sciences and humanities that can utilize teams of qualified assistant field volunteers, including animal behavior, archaeology, art and architecture, biodiversity and ecology, birds, coral reefs, culture and tradition, dinosaurs and other fossils, earth dynamics, endangered species, global change, health and nutrition, rain forests, resource management, sustainable development, whales, dolphins and other marine mammals, wildlife management, and climate change.

NAME(S) OF PROGRAMS:
- **Earthwatch Education Awards**
- **Earthwatch Funding for Field Research**

TYPE:
Research grants. Both personnel and financial support to field research projects. Volunteers pay to support the project and also work as research assistants to the scholars, usually for two- to three-week periods. Teams range in size from four to 20, with the average expedition using three to five teams. Since numbers of dollars vary directly with numbers of volunteers, applicants are urged to pay close attention to that relationship in their research design.

YEAR PROGRAM STARTED: 1971

PURPOSE:
To fund field research and additionally to promote public appreciation of the world's natural and cultural resources and of their interdependence, through participant-funding of significant research in the sciences and humanities.

LEGAL BASIS:
Incorporated as a nonprofit, tax-exempt organization, 501(c)(3) of the IRS Code.

ELIGIBILITY:
Applicants must hold Ph.D. or have had significant research experience as evidenced through publications or other accomplishments.

Proposals may be submitted by researchers of any nationality, covering work in any geographic region. Participation of host-country researchers or staff is strongly encouraged.

Grants vary according to project needs and are determined according to the total number of volunteer-participants that can be constructively utilized in the project.

FINANCIAL DATA:
Amount of support per award: $17,000 to $51,000. Average $850 per volunteer.
Total amount of support: $57,000,000.

NUMBER OF APPLICANTS MOST RECENT YEAR: 400.

APPLICATION INFORMATION:
Contact Earthwatch for application details.
Duration: Consider proposals for three or more years.
Deadline: Preliminary proposals are accepted year-round, and should be submitted 18 months in advance of fielding.

PUBLICATIONS:
Earthwatch, magazine; *Project Briefings;* proposal guidelines; grants list.

OFFICERS:
Mark Chandler, International Director of Research

ADDRESS INQUIRIES TO:
Research Department
(See address above.)

THE ELECTROCHEMICAL SOCIETY [1818]

65 South Main Street, Building D
Pennington, NJ 08534-2896
(609) 737-1902
(609) 737-1902 ext. 111
Fax: (609) 737-2743

E-MAIL ADDRESS:
ecs@electrochem.org
colleen.klepser@electrochem.org

WEB SITE ADDRESS:
www.electrochem.org

FOUNDED: 1902

AREAS OF INTEREST:
Advancement of the theory and practice of electrochemistry, electrometallurgy, solid-state science, electrothermics and allied subjects.

NAME(S) OF PROGRAMS:
- **ECS Summer Fellowships**

TYPE:
Awards/prizes; Conferences/seminars; Development grants; Fellowships; Grants-in-aid; Project/program grants;

Research grants; Training grants; Travel grants. Five summer fellowships granted annually for study in a college or university.

YEAR PROGRAM STARTED: 1928

PURPOSE:
To stimulate and encourage participation and education in the fields of electrochemical science and technology as well as other interests to the Society.

LEGAL BASIS:
Scientific, educational, nonprofit, tax-exempt organization.

ELIGIBILITY:
For Fellowships, the applicant must be a graduate student (between B.S. and Ph.D.) in a college or university who will continue studies following the summer months the award is given.

No limitations on sex, race, nationality or religion.

FINANCIAL DATA:
Amount of support per award: Varies upon approval from the Board of Directors; usually $5,000 each.
Total amount of support: Varies.

NUMBER OF APPLICANTS MOST RECENT YEAR:
50.

NUMBER OF AWARDS: Up to 5 Summer Fellowships annually.

APPLICATION INFORMATION:
Submit a brief statement of educational objectives, work accomplished on thesis, work planned, transcript of undergraduate and graduate work, two letters of recommendation and a letter of agreement not to hold other appointments or fellowships simultaneously.
Deadline: Fellowships: January 1. Notification for Fellowships will be made on or before June 1.

PUBLICATIONS:
Interface Magazine.

STAFF:
Colleen B. Klepser, Executive Administrator

ADDRESS INQUIRIES TO:
The Electrochemical Society
Awards/ECS
(See address above.)

THE ELECTROCHEMICAL SOCIETY   [1819]
65 South Main Street, Building D
Pennington, NJ 08534-2896
(609) 737-1902
(609) 737-1902 ext. 111
Fax: (609) 737-2743

E-MAIL ADDRESS:
ecs@electrochem.org
colleen.klepser@electrochem.org

WEB SITE ADDRESS:
www.electrochem.org/awards/

FOUNDED: 1902

AREAS OF INTEREST:
Advancement of the theory and practice of electrochemistry, electrometallurgy, solid-state science, electrothermics and allied subjects.

NAME(S) OF PROGRAMS:
- **Edward Goodrich Acheson Award**
- **Vittorio de Nora Award**
- **Henry B. Linford Award for Distinguished Teaching**
- **Gordon E. Moore Medal for Outstanding Achievement in Solid State Science and Technology**
- **Olin Palladium Award**
- **Charles W. Tobias Young Investigator Award**
- **Carl Wagner Memorial Award**

TYPE:
Awards/prizes. Edward Goodrich Acheson Award is for distinguished contributions to the advancement of any of the objects, purposes or activities of The Electrochemical Society.

Vittorio de Nora Award is for contributions to the field of electrochemical engineering and technology.

Henry B. Linford Award for Distinguished Teaching recognizes excellence in teaching in subject areas of interest to the Society.

Gordon E. Moore Medal for Outstanding Achievement in Solid State Science and Technology is for distinguished contributions to the field of solid state science.

Olin Palladium Award is for distinguished contributions to the field of electrochemical or corrosion science.

Charles W. Tobias Young Investigator Award recognizes outstanding scientific and/or engineering work in fundamental or applied electrochemistry or solid-state science and technology by a young scientist or engineer.

Carl Wagner Memorial Award recognizes a midcareer achievement and excellence in research areas of interest of the Society, and significant contributions in the teaching or guidance of students or colleagues in education, industry or government.

ELIGIBILITY:
Varies by award.

FINANCIAL DATA:
Varies by award.

Amount of support per award: Edward Goodrich Acheson Award: Gold medal, wall plaque, and prize of $10,000. Vittorio de Nora Award: Gold medal, wall plaque and prize of $7,500. Henry B. Linford Award for Distinguished Teaching: Silver medal, wall plaque and prize of $2,500. Olin Palladium Award: Palladium medal, wall plaque and prize of $7,500. Gordon E. Moore Medal for Outstanding Achievement in Solid State Science and Technology: Silver medal, wall plaque and prize of $7,500. Charles W. Tobias Young Investigator Award: Certificate, prize of $5,000, ECS Life Membership and travel assistance to the meeting of the award presentation (up to $1,000). Carl Wagner Memorial Award: ECS Life Membership, certificate, sterling silver medal, travel assistance to the meeting of award presentation (up to $1,000).

NUMBER OF APPLICANTS MOST RECENT YEAR: 5 to 10.

NUMBER OF AWARDS: Only 1 winner per award given in any of the award cycles.

APPLICATION INFORMATION:
Application information is available on the web site.
Deadline: Varies by award.

ADDRESS INQUIRIES TO:
E-mail: awards@electrochem.org

FATS AND PROTEINS RESEARCH FOUNDATION, INC.   [1820]
500 Montgomery Street
Suite 310
Alexandria, VA 22314
(703) 683-2633
Fax: (703) 683-2626

E-MAIL ADDRESS:
dmeeker@nationalrenderers.com

WEB SITE ADDRESS:
www.fprf.org

FOUNDED: 1962

AREAS OF INTEREST:
Use of rendered product in animal nutrition; feed safety and biosecurity of processes.

TYPE:
Research grants; Research contracts.

YEAR PROGRAM STARTED: 1962

PURPOSE:
To promote scientific and technological research into new and expanded uses for fats and proteins from animal by-products and processing technology; to encourage cooperative studies.

LEGAL BASIS:
Nonprofit foundation, 501(c)(6).

ELIGIBILITY:
Colleges, universities and research institutes with appropriate interests and capabilities are eligible to apply.

FINANCIAL DATA:
Amount of support per award: Average $35,000.
Total amount of support: $180,000 to $250,000 annually.

COOPERATIVE FUNDING PROGRAMS:
Encouraged.

NUMBER OF APPLICANTS MOST RECENT YEAR:
15.

NUMBER OF AWARDS: 6 for the year 2013.

APPLICATION INFORMATION:
Request proposal format from the above address or visit the web site. Prospective applicants should submit a brief outline of the proposed project (including background information, objectives, scope and mode of approach) along with a statement of the required budget and a brief biographical sketch of personnel to be involved in the research.
Duration: Varies.
Deadline: March 15 and September 15 for review of applications.

PUBLICATIONS:
Annual report; contributions policy; application guidelines.

IRS IDENTIFICATION NUMBER: 39-2497869

DIRECTORS:
David Kirstein, Chairman
Erika Weltzien, Vice Chairman
Nancy Cook, President

ADDRESS INQUIRIES TO:
Dr. David L. Meeker, Research Director
(See address above.)

FLORIDA EDUCATION FUND
201 East Kennedy Boulevard
Suite 1525
Tampa, FL 33602
(813) 272-2772 ext. 203
Fax: (813) 272-2784

E-MAIL ADDRESS:
fef.jackson@verizon.net

WEB SITE ADDRESS:
www.fefonline.org

TYPE:
Fellowships.

See entry 1542 for full listing.

FOUNDATION FOR SCIENCE AND DISABILITY

503 N.W. 89th Street
Gainesville, FL 32607
(352) 374-5774
Fax: (352) 374-5781

E-MAIL ADDRESS:
rmankin1@ufl.edu

WEB SITE ADDRESS:
stemd.org

TYPE:
Grants-in-aid; Research grants.

See entry 989 for full listing.

HARVARD TRAVELLERS CLUB, PERMANENT FUND   [1821]

P.O. Box 162
Lincoln, MA 01773
(781) 259-8665

E-MAIL ADDRESS:
jessepage@comcast.net

WEB SITE ADDRESS:
www.harvardtravellersclub.org

FOUNDED: 1937

AREAS OF INTEREST:
Various scientific fields.

TYPE:
Research grants. Small grants for research
projects.

PURPOSE:
To foster research and/or exploration which
involves travel.

LEGAL BASIS:
501(c)(3) nonprofit organization.

ELIGIBILITY:
Applicants must have ability to make a
competent contribution in the field of
research. The Fund does not pay travel
expenses unless it is intimately involved with
the research and/or exploration. Preference is
given to applicants working on advanced
degrees.

FINANCIAL DATA:
Amount of support per award: Up to $4,000.
Total amount of support: Varies.

APPLICATION INFORMATION:
Applicants should submit an explanation of
goals, an indication of ability, and a resume.
Duration: Usually one-time grant.
Deadline: End of February.

IRS IDENTIFICATION NUMBER: 04-6115589

TRUSTEES:
George P. Bates
Nils Bonde-Henriksen
Jesse R. Page

ADDRESS INQUIRIES TO:
Jesse R. Page, Trustee
(See address above.)

*SPECIAL STIPULATIONS:
No scholarships for study at educational
institutions.

THE HERB SOCIETY OF AMERICA, INC.

9019 Kirtland Chardon Road
Kirtland, OH 44094
(440) 256-0514
Fax: (440) 256-0541

E-MAIL ADDRESS:
herbs@herbsociety.org

WEB SITE ADDRESS:
www.herbsociety.org

TYPE:
Research grants. Cash award for research on
herbal projects.

See entry 2121 for full listing.

HISTORY OF SCIENCE SOCIETY

440 Geddes Hall
University of Notre Dame
Notre Dame, IN 46556
(574) 631-1194
Fax: (574) 631-1533

E-MAIL ADDRESS:
info@hssonline.org

WEB SITE ADDRESS:
www.hssonline.org

TYPE:
Awards/prizes. The Davis Prize honors books
in the history of science directed to a wide
public and was established through a
long-term pledge from Miles and Audrey
Davis.

The Joseph H. Hazen Education Prize
recognizes excellence in teaching in the
history of science.

The Levinson Prize is awarded in
even-numbered years to an outstanding book
in the life sciences and natural history.

The Pfizer Prize honors the best
English-language work related to the history
of science published in the preceding three
years.

The Nathan Reingold Prize is given for an
original essay in the history of science and
its cultural influences. Essay must be no
more than 8,000 words in length and
thoroughly documented.

The Margaret W. Rossiter History of Women
in Science Prize honors an outstanding book,
or in even-numbered years an article,
published in the preceding four years.

The Sarton Medal is given to an outstanding
historian of science selected from the
international scholarly community.

See entry 597 for full listing.

HISTORY OF SCIENCE SOCIETY

440 Geddes Hall
University of Notre Dame
Notre Dame, IN 46556
(574) 631-1194
Fax: (574) 631-1533

E-MAIL ADDRESS:
info@hssonline.org

WEB SITE ADDRESS:
www.hssonline.org

TYPE:
Awards/prizes. Prize for the best scholarly
article published in *Isis* during the past three
years.

See entry 596 for full listing.

ILLINOIS STATE ACADEMY OF SCIENCE   [1822]

c/o Illinois State Museum
502 South Spring Street
Springfield, IL 62706-5000
(217) 782-6436
Fax: (217) 782-1254

E-MAIL ADDRESS:
rmyers@museum.state.il.us

WEB SITE ADDRESS:
ilacadofsci.com

FOUNDED: 1907

AREAS OF INTEREST:
Promotion of science in the state of Illinois.

NAME(S) OF PROGRAMS:
● **Scientific Research Grants/Proposal Writing Contest**

TYPE:
Awards/prizes; Grants-in-aid; Project/program
grants; Research grants; Seed money grants.
Cash grants and certificates to Illinois college
or junior college students for writing a
scientific proposal and conducting the
proposed research.

YEAR PROGRAM STARTED: 1981

PURPOSE:
To promote science in the state of Illinois.

LEGAL BASIS:
Nonprofit organization.

ELIGIBILITY:
All public or private college or junior college
students in the state of Illinois who are
sponsored by a signing instructor are eligible.
ISAS membership is required. Proposals do
not have to be original. They can be a
spin-off of a lab experiment from class or
something the student is interested in as a
hobby.

GEOGRAPHIC RESTRICTIONS:
Illinois.

FINANCIAL DATA:
Total amount of support: Varies each year.

NUMBER OF AWARDS: Varies.

APPLICATION INFORMATION:
Students must submit application
electronically through the Academy's web
site.
Duration: One-time award. Renewable.
Deadline: November 1.

PUBLICATIONS:
*Transactions of the Illinois State Academy of
Science.*

IRS IDENTIFICATION NUMBER: 37-6043007

ADDRESS INQUIRIES TO:
Robyn Myers, Executive Secretary
(See address above.)

INSTITUTE OF FOOD TECHNOLOGISTS FOUNDATION

1025 Connecticut Avenue, N.W.
Suite 503
Washington, DC 20036
(312) 604-0284
Fax: (312) 416-7919

E-MAIL ADDRESS:
feedingtomorrow@ift.org

WEB SITE ADDRESS:
www.ift.org/scholarships

TYPE:
Scholarships. Freshman Scholarships and
Undergraduate Scholarships encourage
undergraduate enrollment in food science and
technology. Graduate Scholarships support
advanced study in the field of food science
and technology.

See entry 2610 for full listing.

INTERNATIONAL FOUNDATION FOR ETHICAL RESEARCH, INC. [1823]

53 West Jackson Boulevard, Suite 1552
Chicago, IL 60604
(312) 427-6025
Fax: (312) 427-6524

E-MAIL ADDRESS:
podonovan@navs.org
ifer@navs.org

WEB SITE ADDRESS:
www.ifer.org

FOUNDED: 1985

AREAS OF INTEREST:
Scientifically valid alternatives to the use of
animals in research, product testing, and
education.

TYPE:
Fellowships. Graduate Fellowships in Animal
Welfare support research in, but not limited
to, tissue, cell and organ cultures, clinical
studies using animals or humans,
epidemiological studies, enhanced use of
extensive tissue repositories and patient
databases, public education, and computer
modeling.

YEAR PROGRAM STARTED: 1997

PURPOSE:
To provide monetary assistance to graduate
students whose programs of study seem
likely to have impact on animal welfare.

LEGAL BASIS:
Nonprofit.

ELIGIBILITY:
Application is open to students enrolled in
Master's and Ph.D. programs in the sciences,
humanities, psychology, and journalism.

GEOGRAPHIC RESTRICTIONS:
United States.

FINANCIAL DATA:
Amount of support per award: Up to $12,500
stipend, plus up to $2,500 for supplies per
year.

APPLICATION INFORMATION:
Information and preproposal guidelines are
available from the Foundation.

Duration: The fellowships are renewable for
up to three years.

Deadline: March 15. Awards announced
October.

PUBLICATIONS:
Newsletter.

IRS IDENTIFICATION NUMBER: 22-2628153

STAFF:
Peter O'Donovan, Executive Director

ADDRESS INQUIRIES TO:
Peter O'Donovan, Executive Director
(See address above.)

INVENT NOW [1824]

3701 Highland Park, N.W.
North Canton, OH 44720-4535
(330) 849-6887
(800) 968-4332 (option 5)
Fax: (330) 762-6313

E-MAIL ADDRESS:
collegiate@invent.org

WEB SITE ADDRESS:
www.invent.org/collegiate

AREAS OF INTEREST:
Creative invention: science, engineering,
mathematics, technology and related fields.

NAME(S) OF PROGRAMS:
● **Collegiate Inventors Competition**

TYPE:
Awards/prizes. National competition in the
U.S. and Canada that recognizes and rewards
innovations, discoveries, and research by
college and university students and their
faculty advisors.

YEAR PROGRAM STARTED: 1990

PURPOSE:
To promote exploration in invention, science,
engineering, technology, and other creative
endeavors and provide a window on the
future technologies from which society will
benefit in the future.

ELIGIBILITY:
Open to students who are enrolled (or have
been enrolled) full-time in any U.S. or
Canadian college or university at least part of
the 12-month period prior to the date the
entry is submitted. In the case of a team
(maximum of four students), at least one
member must meet the full-time eligibility
criteria.

Entry must be the original idea and work
product of the student/advisor team, and must
not have been:
(1) made available to the public as a
commercial product or process or;
(2) patented or published more than one year
prior to the date of competition submission.

Entries must be written in English.

GEOGRAPHIC RESTRICTIONS:
United States and Canada.

FINANCIAL DATA:
Up to 12 finalists will win an
all-expense-paid trip in Fall 2014 to present
their work to a panel of expert judges.
Academic advisors of each of the top
winning teams will also receive a cash
award.

Amount of support per award: Up to
$15,000.

Total amount of support: Up to $100,000.

NUMBER OF APPLICANTS MOST RECENT YEAR:
Average 100.

NUMBER OF AWARDS: 6.

APPLICATION INFORMATION:
All entries must be submitted on the official
application form, which is available online.

Deadline: Mid-June.

ADDRESS INQUIRIES TO:
Collegiate Inventors Competition
(See address above.)

THE LALOR FOUNDATION, INC. [1825]

c/o GMA Foundations
77 Summer Street, Eighth Floor
Boston, MA 02110-1006
(617) 426-7080 ext. 323
Fax: (617) 426-7087

E-MAIL ADDRESS:
fellowshipmanager@gmafoundations.com

WEB SITE ADDRESS:
www.lalorfound.org

FOUNDED: 1935

AREAS OF INTEREST:
Basic postdoctoral research in mammalian
reproductive physiology and biochemistry
bearing on sterilization and/or prevention or
termination of pregnancy.

NAME(S) OF PROGRAMS:
● **The Lalor Foundation Postdoctoral
Fellowship Program**

TYPE:
Fellowships; Research grants. Fellowships are
for postdoctoral work.

Grants to institutions for basic postdoctoral
research in mammalian reproductive biology
as related to the regulation of fertility.

YEAR PROGRAM STARTED: 1937

PURPOSE:
To promote intensive research in mammalian
reproductive biology and to assist and
encourage young Ph.D. investigators in
academic positions to follow research careers
in reproductive physiology.

LEGAL BASIS:
Tax-exempt philanthropic foundation.

ELIGIBILITY:
Domestic institutions must be exempt from
federal income taxes under Section 501(c)(3)
of the Internal Revenue Code. Domestic and
foreign institutions must qualify under
Section 509(a)(1), (2) or (3). Individuals who
are nominated by the applicant institution
may be citizens of any country and should
have training and experience at least equal to
the Ph.D. or M.D. level. Potential fellows
may not have held the doctoral degree more
than two years.

The applicant institution may make its
nomination of a fellow from among its own
personnel or elsewhere, but, qualifications
being equal, candidates from other than the
proposing institution itself may carry modest
preference. The application must name the
institution's nominee for fellowship and
include his or her performance record.

FINANCIAL DATA:
Grants for coverage of fellowship stipend and
institutional expenses.

Amount of support per award: $45,000
(U.S.).

Total amount of support: $252,000 for fiscal
year 2013.

NUMBER OF APPLICANTS MOST RECENT YEAR:
30.

NUMBER OF AWARDS: 6 for fiscal year 2013.

APPLICATION INFORMATION:
One reference letter and two project reviews
are requested and IRS determination letter is
required.

Duration: One year. Renewable under some
circumstances.

Deadline: January 15. Notification by April
15.

IRS IDENTIFICATION NUMBER: 51-6000153

OFFICERS:
Cynthia B. Patterson, President
Christopher Burdick, Vice President
Lalor Burdick, Secretary and Treasurer

BOARD OF TRUSTEES:
Andrew G. Braun, Sc.D.
Christopher Burdick
Lalor Burdick
Carol Chandler, Esq.
Cynthia B. Patterson
Sally H. Zeckhauser

ADDRESS INQUIRIES TO:
Fellowship Manager
(See address above.)

LOS ALAMOS NATIONAL LABORATORY   [1826]

P.O. Box 1663
MS-P125
Los Alamos, NM 87545
(505) 664-6947 ext. 05004
Fax: (505) 606-5901

E-MAIL ADDRESS:
hrstaffing-postdocs@lanl.gov

WEB SITE ADDRESS:
www.lanl.gov/science/postdocs

FOUNDED: 1943

AREAS OF INTEREST:
Biosciences, chemistry, computing, Earth and space science, engineering, materials science, mathematics and physics.

NAME(S) OF PROGRAMS:
- **Richard P. Feynman Postdoctoral Fellowship in Theory and Computing**
- **J. Robert Oppenheimer Postdoctoral Fellowship**
- **Frederick Reines Postdoctoral Fellowship in Experimental Sciences**

TYPE:
Fellowships. The Distinguished Postdoctoral Fellowships provide the opportunity for the recipients to collaborate with LANL scientists and engineers on staff-initiated research. Candidates for these awards must display extraordinary ability in scientific research and show clear and definite promise of becoming outstanding leaders in the research they pursue.

YEAR PROGRAM STARTED: 1960

ELIGIBILITY:
Candidates must have a doctoral degree within the last five years or will have completed all Ph.D. requirements by commencement of their appointment. The Feynman and Reines Fellowships require the ability to obtain a DOE "Q" clearance, which normally requires U.S. citizenship.

Every candidate must be sponsored by a technical staff member before being reviewed by the Postdoctoral Committee.

FINANCIAL DATA:
A generous and comprehensive salary and benefits package is provided, including incoming relocation.
Amount of support per award: Feynman, Oppenheimer and Reines Postdoctoral Fellowships provide a starting salary of $106,000.

NUMBER OF AWARDS: Up to 2 in each fellowship category.

APPLICATION INFORMATION:
Details are available online.
Duration: Appointments are for three years.

Deadline: January.

ADDRESS INQUIRIES TO:
See e-mail address above.

MICHIGAN SOCIETY OF FELLOWS

University of Michigan
0540 Rackham Building
915 East Washington Street
Ann Arbor, MI 48109-1070
(734) 763-1259

E-MAIL ADDRESS:
society.of.fellows@umich.edu

WEB SITE ADDRESS:
www.societyoffellows.umich.edu

TYPE:
Fellowships. Fellows are appointed as Assistant Professors or Research Scientists in appropriate departments and as Postdoctoral Scholars in the Michigan Society of Fellows. They are expected to be in residence in Ann Arbor during the academic years of the fellowship, to teach for the equivalent of one academic year, to participate in the informal intellectual life of the Society, and to devote time to their independent research or artistic projects.

See entry 377 for full listing.

MICRON TECHNOLOGY FOUNDATION, INC.

8000 South Federal Way
P.O. Box 6
Boise, ID 83707-0006
(208) 363-3675
Fax: (208) 368-4435

E-MAIL ADDRESS:
mtf@micron.com

WEB SITE ADDRESS:
www.micron.com/foundation

TYPE:
Awards/prizes; Matching gifts; Professorships; Project/program grants; Research grants.

See entry 2096 for full listing.

MICROSCOPY SOCIETY OF AMERICA   [1827]

12100 Sunset Hills Road
Suite 130
Reston, VA 20190
(703) 234-4115
(800) 538-3672
Fax: (703) 435-4390

E-MAIL ADDRESS:
associationmanagement@microscopy.org

WEB SITE ADDRESS:
www.microscopy.org

FOUNDED: 1942

AREAS OF INTEREST:
Microscopy.

NAME(S) OF PROGRAMS:
- **Undergraduate Research Scholarship Program**

TYPE:
Scholarships.

PURPOSE:
To foster educational and research potential in full-time undergraduate students intent on pursuing microscopy as a career or major research tool.

LEGAL BASIS:
Nonprofit society.

ELIGIBILITY:
The applicant must be a full-time undergraduate student and must have achieved junior or senior standing by the time the work is initiated. Research must be completed prior to graduation. Scholarship funds must be expended within one year of award date.

Applicants may receive only one scholarship and may perform research at an institution other than the one in which the applicant is enrolled. Successful applicants must agree to furnish MSA with an abstract for publication in the Society Journal, *Microscopy & Microanalysis*, describing the results and status of their project within two months after the conclusion of the award period, to acknowledge the award in all resulting publications, and to provide reprints of any other resulting publications to the Society.

FINANCIAL DATA:
Amount of support per award: Up to $3,000.
Total amount of support: Varies.

NUMBER OF APPLICANTS MOST RECENT YEAR: 20.

NUMBER OF AWARDS: Average 5.

APPLICATION INFORMATION:
Required application form should include:
(1) a research proposal not to exceed three pages in length, including a brief introduction, a short methods section and description and itemized goals of the study;
(2) a budget indicating how the awarded funds will be expended;
(3) two letters of reference from scientists or university faculty familiar with the applicant's capabilities;
(4) a letter from the laboratory supervisor where the proposed research will be performed, confirming that the applicant and research project are acceptable;
(5) a curriculum vitae detailing previous education and/or training in microscopy and a brief statement of career goals and;
(6) a letter of recommendation from an MSA member.

An original and four copies of a completed application form and attachments are required, unless all materials are being submitted electronically.
Duration: One year. No renewals.
Deadline: December 31. Award announcement April 1.

PUBLICATIONS:
Program announcement.

ADDRESS INQUIRIES TO:
Business Office
MSA Undergraduate Research Scholarships
(See address above.)

MICROSCOPY SOCIETY OF AMERICA

12100 Sunset Hills Road
Suite 130
Reston, VA 20190
(703) 234-4115
(800) 538-3672
Fax: (703) 435-4390

E-MAIL ADDRESS:
associationmanagement@microscopy.org

WEB SITE ADDRESS:
www.microscopy.org

TYPE:
Awards/prizes; Conferences/seminars. Awards
to encourage attendance at the MSA Annual
Meeting by microscopists working in
developing countries who will travel to the
meeting. Several awards include free full
registration and attendance to the
proceedings.

See entry 2613 for full listing.

MICROSCOPY SOCIETY OF AMERICA [1828]

12100 Sunset Hills Road
Suite 130
Reston, VA 20190
(703) 437-4377
(800) 538-3672
Fax: (703) 435-4390

E-MAIL ADDRESS:
associationmanagement@microscopy.org

WEB SITE ADDRESS:
www.microscopy.org

FOUNDED: 1942

AREAS OF INTEREST:
All phases of microscopy.

NAME(S) OF PROGRAMS:
● **MSA Presidential Student Awards**

TYPE:
Awards/prizes; Conferences/seminars. Awards
are given to outstanding students selected on
the basis of the quality and originality of
their research abstracts submitted for the
Annual MSA Scientific Program. The award
consists of free registration for the meeting, a
copy of *Proceedings*, and an invitation to the
Sunday social event.

PURPOSE:
To promote student interest in microscopy
and exchange of information.

LEGAL BASIS:
Nonprofit.

ELIGIBILITY:
Applicants must be bona fide students at a
recognized college or university at the time
of the meeting. Awards are based on the
quality of the paper submitted for
presentation at the meeting and the applicant
must be the submitted paper's first author.
The paper may be submitted for platform or
poster presentation. Successful applicants
must present their papers personally at the
meeting in order to receive the award. They
are expected to attend and participate in the
entire meeting. Candidates should be juniors
or seniors at the time the work is initiated.
Former winners are ineligible.

GEOGRAPHIC RESTRICTIONS:
United States.

FINANCIAL DATA:
Awardees will be reimbursed up to $1,000
for travel (round-trip, lowest-fare, continental
U.S.) and lodging up to $100 per day for up
to five days.
Amount of support per award: Varies.
Total amount of support: Average $10,000.

APPLICATION INFORMATION:
Applications consist of a completed
Advanced Reservation Form, payment for
student registration, a supporting letter from
a member of MSA, preferably a research

advisor, attesting to the applicant's status,
and a scientific paper for presentation
accompanied by a completed Data Form.
Deadline: February 15.

PUBLICATIONS:
The MSA Proceedings.

ADDRESS INQUIRIES TO:
Presidential Student Award
(See address above.)

NATIONAL CENTER FOR ATMOSPHERIC RESEARCH [1829]

1850 Table Mesa Drive
Boulder, CO 80305
(303) 497-1328
Fax: (303) 497-1646

E-MAIL ADDRESS:
paulad@ucar.edu

WEB SITE ADDRESS:
www.asp.ucar.edu

FOUNDED: 1960

AREAS OF INTEREST:
Research in atmospheric sciences, including
such topics as atmospheric dynamics (on all
scales) and models, climate science, cloud
physics, atmospheric chemistry and radiation,
turbulence, upper-atmosphere physics, solar
and solar-terrestrial physics (including
ionospheric studies and aeronomy),
oceanography and atmospheric technology.
Also included are studies of the interaction of
the atmosphere with the oceans, the
cryosphere, the Earth's surface and human
society and application of biology, ecology,
geology, economics and political science
skills to atmospheric issues.

NAME(S) OF PROGRAMS:
● **Postdoctoral Fellowships at NCAR**

TYPE:
Fellowships. The fellowships cover a year's
appointment, with a likely extension to two
years, at NCAR to take advantage of its
educational programs and/or research
facilities in the broad field of atmospheric
sciences.

YEAR PROGRAM STARTED: 1964

PURPOSE:
To provide an opportunity for talented
scientists who have recently received their
Ph.Ds. to continue to pursue their research
interests and to develop expertise in new
areas; to enrich the research talent in the
atmospheric sciences by offering an
opportunity for highly qualified Ph.D.
physicists, chemists, applied mathematicians,
engineers and specialists from other
disciplines such as biology, geology, science
education, economics and geography, as well
as atmospheric science, to apply their
training to research in the atmospheric
sciences.

LEGAL BASIS:
Research institution operated by the nonprofit
University Corporation for Atmospheric
Research (UCAR) under sponsorship of the
National Science Foundation (NSF).

ELIGIBILITY:
Interested scientists who have received their
Ph.D. (or equivalent) are eligible. NCAR
encourages applications from women and
minorities. There are no restrictions for
foreign applicants.

Primary criteria in selection of postdoctoral
appointees are the applicant's scientific
capability and potential, originality and
independence, and the ability to take
advantage of the research opportunities at
NCAR.

Appointments are tenable only in residence
in Boulder, CO.

FINANCIAL DATA:
All appointees are eligible for life and health
insurance in addition to excellent retirement
benefits. Travel expenses to NCAR will be
reimbursed for the fellow and his or her
family. A small allowance for moving and
storage is provided. Scientific travel and
conference registration that costs up to
$3,500 each year is normally available.
Amount of support per award: Basic stipend
of $57,500 for the first year and $60,000 for
the second year.

NUMBER OF APPLICANTS MOST RECENT YEAR:
122.

NUMBER OF AWARDS: 7 to 9.

APPLICATION INFORMATION:
Contact the Center.
Duration: Two years.
Deadline: January 5, to be considered for
fellowship awards to begin the following
summer or fall. Selections announced in
April.

PUBLICATIONS:
Program announcement.

ADDRESS INQUIRIES TO:
Paula Fisher, Coordinator
Advanced Study Program
(See address above.)

*SPECIAL STIPULATIONS:
Appointments are tenable only in residence at
the National Center for Atmospheric
Research.

NATIONAL OCEANIC AND ATMOSPHERIC ADMINISTRATION [1830]

NOAA/Sea Grant, R/SG
1315 East-West Highway, SSMC-3, 11th Floor
Silver Spring, MD 20910
(301) 734-1066
(301) 734-1071
Fax: (301) 713-0799

WEB SITE ADDRESS:
www.seagrant.noaa.gov

FOUNDED: 1966

AREAS OF INTEREST:
Marine resource development.

NAME(S) OF PROGRAMS:
● **National Sea Grant College Program**

TYPE:
Research grants. Grants for research,
education and outreach in oceanography,
fisheries science and environmental studies;
marine commerce and engineering and
marine biotechnology; economic, legal and
sociological considerations related to the
management and development of natural
resources in the marine environment; and
development, conservation and economic
utilization of resources in the marine
environment.

The grant provides training and advisory
service activities in order to increase the
understanding, development and wise use of
ocean, coastal and Great Lakes resources.

The Secretary of Commerce, through NOAA, awards grants on a competitive basis for these purposes.

The program is carried out through a network of 30 Sea Grant programs, located in coastal and Great Lakes states, involving hundreds of universities nationwide.

YEAR PROGRAM STARTED: 1966

PURPOSE:
To promote wise utilization of marine and coastal resources.

LEGAL BASIS:
The National Sea Grant College and Program Act of 1966, Public Law 89-688, as amended. (33 U.S.C. 1121, et seq.)

ELIGIBILITY:
Universities and colleges, junior colleges, technical schools, institutes, laboratories and other public or private agencies with appropriate interests are eligible to apply.

FINANCIAL DATA:
Amount of support per award: Varies.
Total amount of support: Approximately $62,000,000 in grant funds per year.

APPLICATION INFORMATION:
Detailed information available upon request to the Administration.
Duration: Generally two years.
Deadline: Varies.

ADDRESS INQUIRIES TO:
Leon Cammen, Director
(See address above.)

NATIONAL RESEARCH COUNCIL OF CANADA [1831]

1200 Montreal Road, Building M-55
Room 369A
Ottawa ON K1A 0R6 Canada
(613) 949-4655
Fax: (613) 990-1286

E-MAIL ADDRESS:
info@nrc-cnrc.gc.ca
racoordinator.hrb@nrc-cnrc.gc.ca

WEB SITE ADDRESS:
careers-carrieres.nrc-cnrc.gc.ca
www.nrc-cnrc.gc.ca

FOUNDED: 1916

AREAS OF INTEREST:
Science and engineering.

NAME(S) OF PROGRAMS:
● **National Research Council Laboratories Research Associateships Program**

TYPE:
Assistantships. Research Associates will be appointed to the staff of the National Research Council on a term basis and will be offered salaries and benefits currently available to members of the continuing staff.

YEAR PROGRAM STARTED: 1975

PURPOSE:
To undertake, assist or promote scientific and engineering research to further Canada's economic and social development and to give promising scientists and engineers an opportunity to work on challenging research problems.

LEGAL BASIS:
Federal government agency.

ELIGIBILITY:
Recent graduates (within previous five years) at the Ph.D. level in physical or life science

or Master's level in engineering or in a program leading to the acquisition of one of these degrees and having demonstrated the ability to perform original research of a high quality in the chosen field. Open to nationals of all countries, although preference will be given to Canadians.

FINANCIAL DATA:
Amount of support per award: Ph.D. recruiting rate is $38,921 plus allowance of $8,000 per year.
Total amount of support: Varies.

NUMBER OF APPLICANTS MOST RECENT YEAR: 400.

NUMBER OF AWARDS: Varies.

APPLICATION INFORMATION:
Applicants must apply online. All applicants must submit university transcripts, two letters of recommendation, list of publications and resume. Application is valid for one year.
Duration: Two years. Renewal to a maximum of five years.

ADDRESS INQUIRIES TO:
Research Associates Program Coordinator
(See address above.)

NATIONAL SCIENCE FOUNDATION [1832]

Directorate for Education and
Human Resources
Division of Graduate Education
4201 Wilson Boulevard, Suite 875
Arlington, VA 22230
(703) 292-8694
Fax: (703) 292-9048

E-MAIL ADDRESS:
grfp@nsf.gov

WEB SITE ADDRESS:
www.nsfgrfp.org

FOUNDED: 1950

AREAS OF INTEREST:
Science, math and engineering.

NAME(S) OF PROGRAMS:
● **NSF Graduate Research Fellowship Program**

TYPE:
Fellowships. Awarded for graduate study leading to research-based Master's and doctoral degrees in the fields and programs of science and engineering supported by the National Science Foundation.

YEAR PROGRAM STARTED: 1952

PURPOSE:
To help ensure the vitality and diversity of the scientific and engineering workforce in the U.S. The program recognizes and supports outstanding graduate students who are pursuing research-based Master's and doctoral degrees in fields within NSF's mission. The GRFP provides three years of support for the graduate education of individuals who have demonstrated their potential for significant achievements in science and engineering research. The ranks of NSF Fellows include individuals who have made transformative breakthroughs in science and engineering research and have become leaders in their chosen careers and Nobel laureates.

LEGAL BASIS:
Government agency.

ELIGIBILITY:
Applicants for the GRFP are generally allowed to have completed no more than 12 months of full-time graduate study or its equivalent by August. Additional information is available on the Foundation web site.

GEOGRAPHIC RESTRICTIONS:
United States.

FINANCIAL DATA:
Amount of support per award: $132,000 per award; $44,000 annually (includes $32,000 stipend to the Fellow and $12,000 cost of education allowance to the institution), with up to three years of support.

NUMBER OF APPLICANTS MOST RECENT YEAR: 13,500.

NUMBER OF AWARDS: 2,000.

APPLICATION INFORMATION:
The following material is required from all applicants:
(1) personal, relevant background and future goals statement;
(2) graduate research plan statement;
(3) three reference letters and;
(4) academic transcripts.
Duration: Normal tenure is 12 months for each fellowship year. Availability of the second and third years of a three-year award is contingent upon certification by the fellowship institution that progress is being made and availability of appropriated funds.
Deadline: Applications must be filed early in November. Notification after mid-March of the following year.

ADDRESS INQUIRIES TO:
Graduate Research Fellowship Program
(See address above.)

*PLEASE NOTE:
Program eligibility requirements subject to change each year.

NATIONAL SCIENCE FOUNDATION [1833]

4201 Wilson Boulevard, Room 990
Arlington, VA 22230
(703) 292-7283
Fax: (703) 292-9068

E-MAIL ADDRESS:
fkronz@nsf.gov

WEB SITE ADDRESS:
www.nsf.gov

FOUNDED: 1950

AREAS OF INTEREST:
Ethical, value and policy issues in the interactions of science, technology and society, management of research and development.

NAME(S) OF PROGRAMS:
● **Science, Technology and Society**

TYPE:
Conferences/seminars; Fellowships; Project/program grants; Research grants; Training grants. Grants support research and educational projects, national meetings, dissemination efforts, cross-disciplinary study, dissertation research, small group training activities, dissertation improvement grants for graduate students, and postdoctoral fellowships. The proposals considered for support examine ethics, the conduct and impacts of science, engineering and technology, or undertake research to improve approaches and information for decision making concerning management and direction of research, science and technology.

YEAR PROGRAM STARTED: 1976

PURPOSE:
To provide educational opportunities for graduate students.

LEGAL BASIS:
Government agency.

ELIGIBILITY:
Individuals, universities and colleges.

FINANCIAL DATA:
Amount of support per award: Generally, $12,000 to $500,000.
Total amount of support: Approximately $7,000,000.

COOPERATIVE FUNDING PROGRAMS: National Institutes of Health; Department of Agriculture.

NUMBER OF APPLICANTS MOST RECENT YEAR: 400.

NUMBER OF AWARDS: 80.

APPLICATION INFORMATION:
Proposers should consult the SDEST Announcement 08-553 and appropriate NSF brochures such as Grant Proposal Guide, available from the address above.
Duration: One to four years.
Deadline: February 1 and August 1.

ADDRESS INQUIRIES TO:
Frederick Kronz, Program Director (See address above.)

NATIONAL SCIENCE
FOUNDATION   [1834]
Division of Polar Programs
4201 Wilson Boulevard, Suite 755
Arlington, VA 22230
(703) 292-8014
Fax: 703-292-9082

E-MAIL ADDRESS:
dfriscic@nsf.gov

WEB SITE ADDRESS:
www.nsf.gov

FOUNDED: 1950

AREAS OF INTEREST:
Antarctic natural sciences.

NAME(S) OF PROGRAMS:
● **U.S. Antarctic Research Program**

TYPE:
Fellowships; Project/program grants; Research grants. Grants for research projects in all fields of science pertinent to the Antarctic, including both field work in the Antarctic and study in the U.S. of already gathered data and specimens. Support is provided for research projects in astronomy, astrophysics, the behavioral sciences, biology, cartography, geology, glaciology, meteorology, oceanography, solid earth geophysics, upper atmospheric physics and magnetospheric physics. Logistics and support in Antarctica are arranged by the Foundation.

YEAR PROGRAM STARTED: 1959

PURPOSE:
To fund, coordinate and arrange for support of research in all fields of science pertinent to Antarctica.

LEGAL BASIS:
Federal agency under the National Science Foundation Act of 1950, Public Law 81-507, as amended. Also White House memo 6646 dated February 5, 1982.

ELIGIBILITY:
U.S. universities and colleges are the primary participants in the program. Other eligible participants include nonacademic research institutions, profit or nonprofit, and unaffiliated scientists or scientists employed by other federal agencies.

GEOGRAPHIC RESTRICTIONS:
United States.

FINANCIAL DATA:
Amount of support per award: Varies with need.
Total amount of support: Approximately $50,000,000.
Matching fund requirements: Grantee institutions are generally required to share in project costs by a contribution to any cost element in the project, direct or indirect.

NUMBER OF AWARDS: Approximately 50.

APPLICATION INFORMATION:
Applications are submitted in the form of a proposal with a detailed research plan and budget. Information concerning proposal preparation is available in the PAPPG, NSF 11-1, *Grant Proposal Guide, Antarctic Research Program Announcement and Proposal Guide* and NSF 11-532, *Antarctic Conservation Act of 1978.*
Duration: Average of two to four years depending on the quality of submissions and the availability of funds.
Deadline: Applications should be submitted by April 15.

ADDRESS INQUIRIES TO:
David Friscic, Tech Information Specialist (See address above.)

NATIONAL SCIENCE
FOUNDATION   [1835]
Division of Polar Programs
4201 Wilson Boulevard, Suite 755
Arlington, VA 22230
(703) 292-8014
Fax: (703) 292-9082

E-MAIL ADDRESS:
dfriscic@nsf.gov

WEB SITE ADDRESS:
www.nsf.gov

FOUNDED: 1950

AREAS OF INTEREST:
Arctic natural sciences and social sciences.

NAME(S) OF PROGRAMS:
● **Arctic Research Program**

TYPE:
Conferences/seminars; Research grants; Research contracts. Grants and contracts to support scientific research projects relating to the Arctic as well as the subsequent analysis of data. Research may be concerned with problems of marine research, including the polar pack ice; terrestrial biology, including analysis of the ecosystem; meteorology; solar-terrestrial physics; glaciology, including permafrost; geology and geophysics; social sciences; and data and information.

YEAR PROGRAM STARTED: 1971

PURPOSE:
To increase man's knowledge of the Arctic environment and its dynamic parameters; to increase cooperation in research with other agencies and nations having Arctic interests.

LEGAL BASIS:
The National Science Foundation Act of 1950, Public Law 81-507, as amended; Arctic Research and Policy Act of 1984.

ELIGIBILITY:
Proposals may be submitted by U.S. colleges and universities and by academically related nonprofit research organizations. Industry and other organizations are also eligible for support.

GEOGRAPHIC RESTRICTIONS:
United States.

FINANCIAL DATA:
Amount of support per award: Varies.
Total amount of support: Approximately $25,000,000 per year, depending on availability of funds.
Matching fund requirements: Cost sharing is not required.

NUMBER OF AWARDS: 75 per year, pending availability of funds.

APPLICATION INFORMATION:
Application information may be requested from the Foundation. Because of far-reaching scientific, logistic and international implications of Arctic research projects, it is essential that scientists specify all field needs when submitting proposals. Special procedures and a longer lead time apply to research proposed for Greenland. Proposers should also consult the Foundation's *Proposal and Award Procedures Guide* (PAPPG) (NSF 11-1).
Duration: Three years or more depending on the scientific merit and requirements of the project.
Deadline: October 18.

ADDRESS INQUIRIES TO:
David Friscic, Tech Information Specialist (See address above.)

THE ROYAL SOCIETY OF
CANADA   [1836]
Walter House
282 Somerset Street West
Ottawa ON K2P 0J6 Canada
(613) 991-6990 ext. 107
Fax: (613) 991-6996

E-MAIL ADDRESS:
awards@rsc-src.ca

WEB SITE ADDRESS:
www.rsc-src.ca

FOUNDED: 1883

AREAS OF INTEREST:
Arts and humanities, social sciences and the natural sciences.

NAME(S) OF PROGRAMS:
● **The Award in Gender Studies**
● **The Bancroft Award**
● **The Flavelle Medal**
● **The McLaughlin Medal**
● **The McNeil Medal**
● **The Lorne Pierce Medal**
● **The Miroslaw Romanowski Medal**
● **The Rutherford Memorial Medals**
● **The J.B. Tyrrell Historical Medal**
● **The Alice Wilson Award**

TYPE:
Awards/prizes. The Award in Gender Studies is intended to recognize significant contributions by a Canadian scholar in the humanities and social sciences to furthering our understanding of issues concerning gender.

The Bancroft Award is given for publication, instruction and research in the earth sciences that have conspicuously contributed to public understanding and appreciation of the subject.

The Flavelle Medal is awarded for an outstanding contribution to biological science during the preceding 10 years or for significant additions to a previous outstanding contribution to biological science.

The McLaughlin Medal is awarded for important research of sustained excellence in any branch of the medical sciences.

The McNeil Medal for the Public Awareness of Science is awarded to a candidate who has demonstrated outstanding ability to promote and communicate science to students and the public (in the broadest sense of the latter term) within Canada.

The Lorne Pierce Medal is awarded for an achievement of special significance and conspicuous merit in imaginative or critical literature written in either English or French (critical literature dealing with Canadian subjects has priority over critical literature of equal merit that does not deal with Canadian subjects).

The Miroslaw Romanowski Medal is awarded for significant contributions to the resolution of scientific aspects of environmental problems or for important improvements to the quality of an ecosystem in all aspects - terrestrial, atmospheric and aqueous - brought about by scientific means.

The Rutherford Memorial Medals are awarded for outstanding research in any branch of physics and chemistry.

The J.B. Tyrrell Historical Medal is awarded for outstanding work in the history of Canada.

The Alice Wilson Award is given to a woman of outstanding academic qualifications who is entering a career in scholarship or research at the postdoctoral level.

YEAR PROGRAM STARTED: 1955

PURPOSE:
To annually recognize Canadian citizens for contributions to Canadian academic excellence in various branches.

LEGAL BASIS:
Nonprofit.

ELIGIBILITY:
Awarded only to Canadian citizens or Canadian residents living in Canada for three years preceding the date of nomination.

GEOGRAPHIC RESTRICTIONS:
Canada.

APPLICATION INFORMATION:
Contact the Royal Society.
Duration: The Award in Gender Studies, The Bancroft Award, The Flavelle Medal, The Lorne Pierce Medal and The J.B. Tyrrell Historical Medal: Every two years. The McLaughlin, McNeil, Romanowski and Rutherford Memorial Medals and The Wilson Award: Every year.
Deadline: December 1.

ADDRESS INQUIRIES TO:
Sarah Pouliot
Officer, Institutional Members
(See address above.)

SIGMA DELTA EPSILON/GRADUATE WOMEN IN SCIENCE [1837]
P.O. Box 240607
St. Paul, MN 55124-0607
(952) 236-9112

E-MAIL ADDRESS:
gwised@mac.com

WEB SITE ADDRESS:
www.gwis.org

FOUNDED: 1922

AREAS OF INTEREST:
Science and research.

CONSULTING OR VOLUNTEER SERVICES:
A great deal of volunteering is provided by 18 chapters of the organization (e.g., science fair judges, girl scout support in science, etc.).

NAME(S) OF PROGRAMS:
● **SDE Fellowship Program**

TYPE:
Awards/prizes; Fellowships; Travel grants. Leadership Awards are given to Graduate Women in Science officers.

YEAR PROGRAM STARTED: 1935

PURPOSE:
To increase knowledge in the fundamental sciences; to encourage research careers in the sciences by women.

ELIGIBILITY:
Applicants must be enrolled as a graduate student or engaged in postdoctoral or early-stage academic research.

FINANCIAL DATA:
Applications are vetted for scientific expertise and financial need.
Amount of support per award: $5,000 to $10,000.
Total amount of support: Varies.

NUMBER OF APPLICANTS MOST RECENT YEAR:
223 for the year 2011-12.

NUMBER OF AWARDS: 10.

APPLICATION INFORMATION:
Information about the application process is available online.
Duration: One year. No renewals.
Deadline: January 15.

PUBLICATIONS:
GWIS Bulletin; *GWIS e-news*, monthly electronic newsletter.

ADDRESS INQUIRIES TO:
Ms. Dee M. McManus
National Executive Director
(See address above.)

SIGMA XI: THE SCIENTIFIC RESEARCH SOCIETY [1838]
3106 East NC Highway 54
Research Triangle Park, NC 27709
(919) 549-4691
Fax: (919) 549-0090

E-MAIL ADDRESS:
giar@sigmaxi.org

WEB SITE ADDRESS:
www.sigmaxi.org

FOUNDED: 1886

AREAS OF INTEREST:
The sciences, physical sciences, engineering, social, behavioral and life sciences.

NAME(S) OF PROGRAMS:
● **Grants-in-Aid of Research**

TYPE:
Grants-in-aid; Project/program grants; Research grants; Travel grants. Grants-in-aid to support research projects in any field of scientific investigation. Assistance is available for such research-related activities as travel to research location or supplies.

YEAR PROGRAM STARTED: 1921

PURPOSE:
To encourage scientific research.

LEGAL BASIS:
Nonprofit organization.

ELIGIBILITY:
Graduate and undergraduate students with proposals for specific research projects are eligible to apply. Student faculty advisor (first recommender) should be a full, active member of Sigma Xi to compete for Sigma Xi funds. NAS funds in the program are unrestricted and cover the physical, life and medical sciences (excluding the social sciences).

Grants do not cover overhead costs. No grants for publication/presentation costs, travel to meetings or stipends. Will fund travel to a research site.

FINANCIAL DATA:
Amount of support per award: Up to $1,000 for all areas of the sciences and engineering; Up to $5,000 for astronomy; Up to $2,500 for eye/vision research.
Total amount of support: Approximately $300,000.

COOPERATIVE FUNDING PROGRAMS: National Academy of Sciences.

APPLICATION INFORMATION:
Contact the Society for details.
Duration: Applicants may apply for a second grant after submitting a report on the outcome of the project supported by a first grant.
Deadline: Applications and supporting letters must be received by March 15 or October 15. Awards are announced within 12 weeks.

PUBLICATIONS:
Annual report; application guidelines.

ADDRESS INQUIRIES TO:
Kevin Bowen, Program Manager for Grants and Awards
(See address above.)

ALFRED P. SLOAN FOUNDATION
630 Fifth Avenue, Suite 2550
New York, NY 10111
(212) 649-1649
Fax: (212) 757-5117

E-MAIL ADDRESS:
boylan@sloan.org

WEB SITE ADDRESS:
www.sloanphds.org

TYPE:
Fellowships; Scholarships. Offers substantial scholarship support to underrepresented minority (African American, Hispanic American or Native American) students who are U.S. citizens and who are beginning their doctoral work in engineering, natural science and mathematics in selected departments at selected U.S. universities.

See entry 1013 for full listing.

ALFRED P. SLOAN FOUNDATION

630 Fifth Avenue, Suite 2550
New York, NY 10111
(212) 649-1649
Fax: (212) 757-5117

E-MAIL ADDRESS:
boylan@sloan.org

WEB SITE ADDRESS:
www.sloanphds.org

TYPE:
Fellowships; Scholarships. Offers substantial scholarship support to indigenous students (Native Americans, including American Indians, Native Alaskans and Native Hawaiians) who are beginning their Master's or doctoral work in engineering, natural science and mathematics in selected departments at selected U.S. universities.

See entry 1014 for full listing.

SMITHSONIAN INSTITUTION   [1839]

Office of Fellowships and Internships
470 L'Enfant Plaza, S.W., Suite 7102
MRC 902, P.O. Box 37012
Washington, DC 20013-7012
(202) 633-7070
Fax: (202) 633-7069

E-MAIL ADDRESS:
siofi@si.edu

WEB SITE ADDRESS:
www.si.edu/ofi

FOUNDED: 1846

AREAS OF INTEREST:
Animal behavior, ecology and environmental science, including an emphasis on the tropics; anthropology, including archaeology; astrophysics and astronomy; earth sciences and paleobiology; evolutionary and systematic biology; history of science and technology; history of art, especially American, contemporary, African and Asian art; 20th-century American crafts and decorative arts; social and cultural history of the U.S.; and folklore.

NAME(S) OF PROGRAMS:
- **Smithsonian Graduate Student Fellowships**
- **Smithsonian Postdoctoral Fellowships**
- **Smithsonian Predoctoral Fellowships**
- **Smithsonian Senior Fellowships**

TYPE:
Fellowships. Offered to qualified scholars for research to be conducted in residence at the Smithsonian in association with the staff, using collections and research facilities.

YEAR PROGRAM STARTED: 1964

PURPOSE:
To provide students and scholars in the sciences, arts and humanities with an opportunity for research utilizing the unique collections and facilities of the Smithsonian, while working with the institution's research staff.

LEGAL BASIS:
Act of Congress approved August 10, 1846; 20 U.S.C. 41 et seq.

ELIGIBILITY:
Smithsonian Fellowships are open to both U.S. citizens and foreign nationals. Fluency in English is required.

For the graduate fellowships, students must be formally enrolled and engaged in a graduate program of study at a degree-granting institution, have completed at least one semester and have not yet been advanced to candidacy if in a Ph.D. program.

For the predoctoral fellowships, students must be enrolled in a university as candidates for the Ph.D. or equivalent. At the time of appointment, the university must approve the undertaking of dissertation research at the Smithsonian and indicate that requirements for the Doctorate, other than the dissertation, have been met.

For the postdoctoral fellowships, applicants must have received the Ph.D., or equivalent, within seven years of the program deadline and must have completed the degree or certificate at the time the fellowship commences.

For the senior fellowships, applicants must have received the Ph.D., or equivalent, seven or more years before the program deadline.

Research must be conducted while in residence at the Smithsonian.

The Smithsonian Institution does not offer financial assistance for degree-granting programs at academic institutions. All forms of financial assistance are to support research in residence at the Smithsonian and its facilities.

FINANCIAL DATA:
Stipends are offered per calendar year and are prorated for terms of less than one year. Pre, Post and Senior Postdoctoral Fellows also receive research and travel allowances.
Amount of support per award: Graduate Fellowships: $6,500; Predoctoral Fellowships: $30,000; Postdoctoral and Senior Postdoctoral Fellowships: $45,000; Earth and Planetary Sciences Senior and Postdoctoral Fellowships: $50,000.

APPLICATION INFORMATION:
Official application materials are available upon request. Specify the fellowship corresponding to your academic level.
Duration: Graduate Fellowships: Ten weeks; Predoctoral, Postdoctoral and Senior Fellowships: Three to 12 months.
Deadline: January 15. Research appointments with or without fellowships may be conducted at any time during the year.

PUBLICATIONS:
Smithsonian Opportunities for Research and Study.

OFFICER:
Eric Woodard, Director

ADDRESS INQUIRIES TO:
Office of Fellowships and Internships
(See address above.)

SOCIETY FOR SCIENCE AND THE PUBLIC   [1840]

1719 N Street, N.W.
Washington, DC 20036
(202) 785-2255

E-MAIL ADDRESS:
sts@societyforscience.org

WEB SITE ADDRESS:
www.societyforscience.org

FOUNDED: 1942

AREAS OF INTEREST:
Sciences, mathematics, engineering and medicine.

NAME(S) OF PROGRAMS:
- **Intel Science Talent Search**

TYPE:
Awards/prizes. Competition for high school seniors excelling in science, math and engineering.

YEAR PROGRAM STARTED: 1942

PURPOSE:
To discover at the high school senior year level, those who have the potential to become the scientists, mathematicians and engineers of the future; to make the public aware of the impact that a quality science, mathematics or engineering education has on our future and the future of our nation.

LEGAL BASIS:
Nonprofit educational institution.

ELIGIBILITY:
Student must be in the last year of secondary school in the U.S., Puerto Rico, Guam, Virgin Islands, American Samoa, Wake and Midway Islands, the Marianas, DOD Schools or American schools abroad or for citizens studying abroad.

FINANCIAL DATA:
Amount of support per award: 10 four-year scholarships: one $100,000 ($25,000/year), one $75,000 ($18,750/year), one $50,000 ($12,500/year), one $40,000 ($10,000/year), one $30,000 ($7,500/year), two $25,000 ($6,250/year), three $20,000 ($5,000/year), and 30 $7,500 scholarships.
Total amount of support: Over $1,250,000.

APPLICATION INFORMATION:
Entries in the Intel Science Talent Search are submitted via an online application, with the exception of school transcripts, which must be mailed. Additional information is available on the Society web page.
Deadline: November.

ADDRESS INQUIRIES TO:
Caitlin Sullivan, Program Manager
(See address above.)

THE SOCIETY FOR THE SCIENTIFIC STUDY OF SEXUALITY   [1841]

881 Third Street, Suite B-5
Whitehall, PA 18052
(610) 443-3100
Fax: (610) 443-3105

E-MAIL ADDRESS:
thesociety@sexscience.org

WEB SITE ADDRESS:
www.sexscience.org

FOUNDED: 1957

AREAS OF INTEREST:
Sex research, sex therapy and sex education.

NAME(S) OF PROGRAMS:
- **Student Research Grants**

TYPE:
Grants-in-aid; Research grants. Cash award for two graduate student research projects per year.

YEAR PROGRAM STARTED: 1985

PURPOSE:
To assist with the development of quality graduate research projects in the area of sex research.

LEGAL BASIS:
Tax-exempt, private, not-for-profit corporation.

ELIGIBILITY:
Research conducted by Master's or doctoral students is eligible, although the project need not be restricted to thesis or doctoral projects. Students must be or become members of SSSS.

FINANCIAL DATA:
Amount of support per award: $1,000.
Total amount of support: $2,000.

NUMBER OF APPLICANTS MOST RECENT YEAR:
65.

NUMBER OF AWARDS: 2.

APPLICATION INFORMATION:
Students will be asked to submit a 10-page abstract of the proposed research and bibliography, along with proposed budget (one copy submitted electronically). Applications and further information may be obtained on the web site or from Dr. Peter Anderson at the address above.
Deadline: February 1 and June 1.

PUBLICATIONS:
Application guidelines.

IRS IDENTIFICATION NUMBER: 13-2642753

ADDRESS INQUIRIES TO:
Mandy Peters, Associate Director
(See address above.)

TOURETTE SYNDROME ASSOCIATION, INC.
42-40 Bell Boulevard
Suite 205
Bayside, NY 11361-2820
(718) 224-2999
Fax: (718) 279-9596

E-MAIL ADDRESS:
ts@tsa-usa.org

WEB SITE ADDRESS:
www.tsa-usa.org/research.html

TYPE:
Fellowships; General operating grants; Research grants; Seed money grants; Technical assistance. Research grants available for Ph.D. and M.D. researchers in the following categories:
(1) proposals in basic neuroscience specifically relevant to Tourette Syndrome and;
(2) clinical studies related to the etiology, pathophysiology and treatment of Tourette Syndrome.

Fellowships provide one-year postdoctoral training.

See entry 2483 for full listing.

U.S. ARMY RESEARCH OFFICE   [1842]
4300 South Miami Boulevard
Research Triangle Park, NC 27703
(919) 549-4272
(919) 549-0641
Fax: (919) 549-4388

E-MAIL ADDRESS:
patricia.j.fox8.civ@mail.mil

WEB SITE ADDRESS:
www.arl.army.mil

FOUNDED: 1951

AREAS OF INTEREST:
Biosciences, chemistry, electronics, engineering, environmental sciences, materials sciences, mathematical and computer sciences and physics.

TYPE:
Conferences/seminars; Research grants; Research contracts. Grants and contracts for scientific research in such areas of interest to the U.S. Army as chemistry, engineering, biology, mathematics, metallurgy and materials, physics, electronics and environmental sciences. Support is also provided for symposia on particular aspects of scientific investigation, the results of which further Department of the Army objectives.

YEAR PROGRAM STARTED: 1951

PURPOSE:
To increase knowledge of natural phenomena and environment in an attempt to solve problems in the physical, engineering, environmental and life sciences.

LEGAL BASIS:
Government agency.

ELIGIBILITY:
Organizations with appropriate interests are eligible to apply.

FINANCIAL DATA:
Amount of support per award: Grants and contracts vary in amount, depending upon the needs and nature of the request; $136,000 yearly average.
Total amount of support: $500,000,000 to $550,000,000 including both grants and contracts.

NUMBER OF APPLICANTS MOST RECENT YEAR:
Approximately 550.

NUMBER OF AWARDS: Approximately 350.

APPLICATION INFORMATION:
Research awards are selected from proposals submitted in response to an open-ended Broad Agency Announcement (BAA). Contractors interested in submitting proposals should go to the ARL web site and download the ARO BAA.
Duration: One to three years. Continuations possible if work has not been completed.
Deadline: Varies.

ADDRESS INQUIRIES TO:
Patty Fox, Chief
RDECOM Acquisitions Center
(See address above.)

U.S. DEPARTMENT OF ENERGY
3610 Collins Ferry Road
P.O. Box 880
Morgantown, WV 26507-0880
(412) 386-7406

E-MAIL ADDRESS:
vito.cedro@netl.doe.gov

WEB SITE ADDRESS:
www.grants.gov

TYPE:
Assistantships; Project/program grants; Research grants.

See entry 2665 for full listing.

U.S. DEPARTMENT OF THE NAVY   [1843]
Office of Naval Research, One Liberty Center
875 North Randolph Street, Suite 1425
Arlington, VA 22203-1995
(703) 696-4111
Fax: (703) 696-5940

E-MAIL ADDRESS:
onrpao@onr.navy.mil

WEB SITE ADDRESS:
www.onr.navy.mil

FOUNDED: 1946

AREAS OF INTEREST:
Advanced materials, ocean sciences, mathematics, information sciences, physics, electronics, chemistry, mechanics, cognitive and neural sciences.

NAME(S) OF PROGRAMS:
● **Basic Research Challenge Program**
● **University Research Initiative**
● **Young Investigator Program**

TYPE:
Research grants; Research contracts. ONR sponsors long-range scientific research, applied research and advanced technology development which offer potential for advancement and improvement of naval operations. Programs include physics, electronic and solid state sciences, mathematics, operations research, statistics and probability, information science, fluid dynamics, physiology, biochemistry, biophysics, microbiology, naval biology, cognitive and neural sciences research, personnel and training research, Arctic research, coastal sciences, earth and environmental physics, atmospheric sciences, metallurgy and ceramics research, chemistry, energy research, structural mechanics, physical and chemical oceanography, marine geology and geophysics, ocean biology, ocean acoustics and ocean engineering.

YEAR PROGRAM STARTED: 1946

PURPOSE:
To support research in various scientific fields including ocean science and physics.

LEGAL BASIS:
Public Law 588, as amended and Public Law 85-934, as amended.

ELIGIBILITY:
Nonprofit institutions of higher education and organizations whose primary purpose is the conduct of scientific research may apply for contracts or grants. Nonprofit and profit-making institutions, organizations or industrial establishments, as well as qualified individuals, are eligible for contract support.

FINANCIAL DATA:
Amount of support per award: Varies, depending upon the needs and nature of the request.
Total amount of support: Varies.

NUMBER OF APPLICANTS MOST RECENT YEAR:
Approximately 4,000 inquiries.

NUMBER OF AWARDS: Approximately 2,500 annually.

APPLICATION INFORMATION:
Before submitting a proposal, interested individuals are encouraged to assess the relevance of their research interests to Navy research priorities by consulting the ONR web page and talking to the relevant ONR Program Manager. Applications are submitted in the form of a proposal which should

include:
(1) general statement requesting consideration of the proposal;
(2) brief review of the scientific background of the proposed research;
(3) technical description of the project, including statement of objectives and scientific methods to be employed;
(4) description of available facilities;
(5) background of principal investigator(s) and associates;
(6) bibliography of pertinent publications;
(7) proposed duration of project and annual itemized budget;
(8) other research projects currently undertaken by the principal investigator;
(9) other agencies to whom the proposal is being submitted for possible financial support and;
(10) cost breakdown by year.

THE VAN SLYKE FOUNDATION [1844]
1850 K Street, N.W., Suite 625
Washington, DC 20006
(202) 857-0717
(800) 892-1400 ext. 1712
Fax: (202) 887-5093

E-MAIL ADDRESS:
skleinman@aacc.org

WEB SITE ADDRESS:
www.aacc.org

AREAS OF INTEREST:
Clinical laboratory science and study of outcomes of point-of-care testing (POCT).

NAME(S) OF PROGRAMS:
● **AACC Van Slyke Foundation Critical and Point-of-Care Testing Research Grant**

TYPE:
Research grants; Scholarships; Travel grants. Science Fair awards; Poster contest.

The Van Slyke Foundation is the American Association for Clinical Chemistry's philanthropic program.

PURPOSE:
To encourage and support deserving clinical laboratory scientists and students throughout the world.

FINANCIAL DATA:
Amount of support per award: $500.

NUMBER OF AWARDS: 1.

APPLICATION INFORMATION:
Application information is available on the web site.
Duration: One year. Renewable.
Deadline: March 15.

ADDRESS INQUIRIES TO:
Stephanie Kleinman, Foundation Coordinator (See address above.)

WEIZMANN INSTITUTE OF SCIENCE
Feinberg Graduate School of the Weizmann Institute of Science
P.O. Box 26
Rehovot 76100 Israel
(972-8) 9343843
(972-8) 9342924
Fax: (972-8) 9344114

E-MAIL ADDRESS:
postdoc@weizmann.ac.il

WEB SITE ADDRESS:
www.fgs.org.il

TYPE:
Fellowships. The Feinberg Graduate School of the Weizmann Institute of Science offers a limited number of postdoctoral fellowships in all areas of research in which the Weizmann Institute is engaged. The fellowships are offered in various fields of biology, chemistry, physics, biochemistry-biophysics, mathematics and computer science.

See entry 953 for full listing.

THE HELEN HAY WHITNEY FOUNDATION [1845]
20 Squadron Boulevard
Suite 630
New City, NY 10956-5247
(845) 639-6799
Fax: (845) 639-6798

E-MAIL ADDRESS:
hhwf@earthlink.net

WEB SITE ADDRESS:
www.hhwf.org

FOUNDED: 1947

AREAS OF INTEREST:
Biomedical sciences.

NAME(S) OF PROGRAMS:
● **Early Postdoctoral Research Fellowship Program in Biomedical Sciences**

TYPE:
Fellowships. Postdoctoral research fellowships.

YEAR PROGRAM STARTED: 1957

PURPOSE:
To provide beginning postdoctoral research training to young M.Ds. and Ph.Ds. to further their careers in research in biomedical sciences.

LEGAL BASIS:
Independent foundation.

ELIGIBILITY:
Candidates living in North America or foreign nationals that pursue their fellowship in the U.S., who hold the M.D., Ph.D. or equivalent degree, who are seeking beginning postdoctoral training in basic biomedical research and have no more than one year postdoctoral experience by July 15 are eligible. U.S. citizenship is not a requirement, but fellowships to resident noncitizens are awarded only for training in the U.S. Citizens may train abroad.

Applications from established scientists or advanced fellows will not be considered. Applicants who have already had one year's postdoctoral laboratory training at the time of deadline will not be considered for a Whitney Fellowship.

FINANCIAL DATA:
Amount of support per award: Fellowships provide stipends as follows: $49,000 for the first year, $50,000 for the second year and $51,000 for the third year, plus a $1,500 research allowance to the department for each year of tenure, travel to fellowship location and annual meeting of all fellows. Additionally, there is a dependent child allowance of $1,000 per each dependent child.

NUMBER OF APPLICANTS MOST RECENT YEAR:
400.

APPLICATION INFORMATION:
Online application is available at the Foundation web site.
Duration: Three years. Contingent upon satisfactory performance.
Deadline: Applications accepted April 1 to July 1. Fellowships begin the following April 1 through December 1.

PUBLICATIONS:
Annual report.

WOODS HOLE OCEANOGRAPHIC INSTITUTION [1846]
Clark Laboratory
360 Woods Hole Road
Education Office, MS #31
Woods Hole, MA 02543-1541
(508) 289-2219
Fax: (508) 457-2188

E-MAIL ADDRESS:
education@whoi.edu

WEB SITE ADDRESS:
www.whoi.edu

FOUNDED: 1930

AREAS OF INTEREST:
Research in biological oceanography, marine chemistry and geochemistry, marine geology and geophysics, applied ocean physics and engineering, physical oceanography and marine policy.

NAME(S) OF PROGRAMS:
● **Summer Student Fellowship Program in Oceanography**

TYPE:
Fellowships. Awards for independent research in oceanography/ocean engineering and marine policy projects pursued under the guidance of a member of the research staff of the Woods Hole Oceanographic Institution. Fellowship is for a 10- to 12-week summer study at Woods Hole Oceanographic Institution.

YEAR PROGRAM STARTED: 1954

PURPOSE:
To give a small group of qualified undergraduate science and engineering students experience that will enable them to determine whether they wish to devote lifetime careers to studying the oceans.

LEGAL BASIS:
Charter under the Commonwealth of Massachusetts.

ELIGIBILITY:
Applicant must be an undergraduate (junior) studying at a college or university in any fields of science or engineering with at least a tentative interest in oceanography.

FINANCIAL DATA:
Award includes weekly stipend, travel and housing allowance for WHOI housing.
Amount of support per award: Stipend of $540 per week.
Total amount of support: Varies.

APPLICATION INFORMATION:
Applications should be made to the Fellowship Committee at the address above. A complete application should include an application form, transcripts of college and university records, at least three personal references, a concise statement of the

applicant's research plans and interests, future education and career plans, and reasons for applying to the Institution.

Duration: 10 to 12 weeks.

Deadline: February 15. Notification by March 15.

STAFF:
Dr. James A. Yoder, Dean

ADDRESS INQUIRIES TO:
See e-mail address above.

SOCIAL SCIENCES

Social sciences (general)

AGENCY FOR HEALTHCARE RESEARCH AND QUALITY (AHRQ)
Office of Communications
and Knowledge Transfer
540 Gaither Road, 2nd Floor
Rockville, MD 20850
(301) 427-1104 (specify funding area)
(800) 518-4726

E-MAIL ADDRESS:
support@grants.gov

WEB SITE ADDRESS:
www.ahrq.gov

TYPE:
Conferences/seminars; Development grants; Fellowships; Project/program grants; Research grants; Training grants. Dissertation support highlighting primary care, market forces, cost containment, managed care, the cost of treating AIDS, the improvement of treatment for persons with HIV, rural health care, infant mortality, medical liability, malpractice reform, health care of the aged and disabled and policy studies.

See entry 1417 for full listing.

AMERICAN BAR FOUNDATION
750 North Lake Shore Drive, Fourth Floor
Chicago, IL 60611-4403
(312) 988-6517
Fax: (312) 988-6579

E-MAIL ADDRESS:
fellowships@abfn.org

WEB SITE ADDRESS:
www.americanbarfoundation.org

TYPE:
Fellowships. Residential fellowships at the ABF.

The American Bar Foundation is committed to developing the next generation of scholars in the field of law and social science. Since 1987, the Foundation has supported the dissertation research of a diverse group of graduate students from all social science disciplines and, in 1996, added a postdoctoral component to its fellowship program.

See entry 1970 for full listing.

AMERICAN BAR FOUNDATION
750 North Lake Shore Drive
Fourth Floor
Chicago, IL 60611
(312) 988-6517
Fax: (312) 988-6579

E-MAIL ADDRESS:
fellowships@abfn.org

WEB SITE ADDRESS:
www.americanbarfoundation.org

TYPE:
Fellowships; Internships.

See entry 970 for full listing.

BRETT FAMILY FOUNDATION   [1847]
1123 Spruce Street
Boulder, CO 80302
(303) 442-1200
Fax: (303) 442-1221

E-MAIL ADDRESS:
mike@brettfoundation.org

WEB SITE ADDRESS:
www.brettfoundation.org

FOUNDED: 2000

AREAS OF INTEREST:
Social justice, equal rights and access to opportunity for individuals and families.

NAME(S) OF PROGRAMS:
● **Social Justice Grant Program**

TYPE:
General operating grants.

PURPOSE:
To promote caring communities by investing in organizations throughout Colorado working for social justice and Boulder County nonprofits addressing the needs of underserved communities, primarily disadvantaged youth and their families.

ELIGIBILITY:
Applicants must be nonprofit 501(c)(3) organizations within the state of Colorado working to address the root causes of social, economic, gender, and racial inequities through strategies that challenge existing power structures and provide access to opportunity for individuals and families. No grants to individuals.

GEOGRAPHIC RESTRICTIONS:
Colorado.

FINANCIAL DATA:
Amount of support per award: $2,500 to $10,000.
Total amount of support: Social Justice Grant Program: $69,500; $437,550 in total grants for the year 2012.

APPLICATION INFORMATION:
Submit a letter of inquiry (up to three pages), unless requested to submit a full proposal by Foundation staff. A copy of current 501(c)(3) determination letter from the IRS must also be included.
Duration: One year. Must reapply.
Deadline: Social Justice: Letter of Inquiry, January 15. Full proposals, March 1.

ADDRESS INQUIRIES TO:
Claire Gilbert, Program Officer
(See address above.)

CANADIAN FEDERATION FOR THE HUMANITIES AND SOCIAL SCIENCES   [1848]
275 Bank Street, Suite 300
Ottawa ON K2P 2L6 Canada
(613) 238-6112 ext. 352
Fax: (613) 238-6114

E-MAIL ADDRESS:
aspp-paes@ideas-idees.ca

WEB SITE ADDRESS:
www.ideas-idees.ca

FOUNDED: 1941

AREAS OF INTEREST:
Social sciences and humanities.

NAME(S) OF PROGRAMS:
● **Awards to Scholarly Publications Program**

TYPE:
Grants-in-aid. Grants to support the publication of scholarly books in the social sciences and humanities.

YEAR PROGRAM STARTED: 1941

PURPOSE:
To assist the publication of books of advanced scholarship which are unlikely to be self-supporting.

LEGAL BASIS:
NGO, nonprofit.

ELIGIBILITY:
Manuscripts may be submitted by Canadian citizens or landed immigrants. The importance of a manuscript's contribution to scholarship is the sole basis for assessment. The following categories are not eligible: textbooks and anthologies, unrevised theses, fiction, poetry and incomplete manuscripts. Approved manuscripts must be published by recognized Canadian scholarly publishers.

GEOGRAPHIC RESTRICTIONS:
Canada.

FINANCIAL DATA:
Subventions are paid directly to publishers after an approved manuscript appears in print.
Amount of support per award: $8,000 per book.

NUMBER OF APPLICANTS MOST RECENT YEAR:
270.

NUMBER OF AWARDS: Approximately 185 per year.

APPLICATION INFORMATION:
Publishers usually apply on the behalf of authors, though authors may also apply directly. Visit the program web site to download the most up-to-date guidelines and application form.

PUBLICATIONS:
Application guidelines; application form.

OFFICERS:
Jessica Clark, Coordinator

ADDRESS INQUIRIES TO:
Jessica Clark, Coordinator, ASPP
(See address above.)

*SPECIAL STIPULATIONS:
Non-Canadians may be eligible for ASPP support if their work is on a Canadian subject and they are publishing with an eligible Canadian scholarly publisher.

CANADIAN INSTITUTE OF UKRAINIAN STUDIES
University of Alberta
430 Pembina Hall
Edmonton AB T6G 2H8 Canada
(780) 492-2972
Fax: (780) 492-4967

E-MAIL ADDRESS:
cius@ualberta.ca

WEB SITE ADDRESS:
www.cius.ca

TYPE:
Fellowships; Research grants; Scholarships.

See entry 585 for full listing.

COUNCIL FOR EUROPEAN STUDIES AT COLUMBIA UNIVERSITY
420 West 118th Street, MC 3307
New York, NY 10027
(212) 854-4172
Fax: (212) 854-8808

E-MAIL ADDRESS:
ces@columbia.edu

WEB SITE ADDRESS:
councilforeuropeanstudies.org

TYPE:
Awards/prizes; Fellowships. The CES Book
Award honors talented emerging scholars
with an award for the best first book on any
subject in European studies. The award is
given every two years.

Council for European Studies
Pre-Dissertation Research Fellowships are
intended to fund student's first major research
project in Europe.

First Article Prize awards one prize to a
scholar working in the humanities and one to
a scholar working in the social sciences.
These prizes will honor the writers of the
best first articles on European studies
published within a two-year period.

Mellon-CES Dissertation Completion
Fellowships are intended to facilitate the
timely completion of the doctoral degree by
late-stage graduate students focused on topics
in European studies.

See entry 835 for full listing.

CROSSROADS FUND   [1849]
3411 West Diversey Avenue, Suite 20
Chicago, IL 60647-1245
(773) 227-7676
Fax: (773) 227-7790

E-MAIL ADDRESS:
info@crossroadsfund.org

WEB SITE ADDRESS:
www.crossroadsfund.org

FOUNDED: 1981

AREAS OF INTEREST:
Social change.

TYPE:
General operating grants; Project/program
grants; Seed money grants; Technical
assistance.

PURPOSE:
To support grassroots organizations working
to alleviate underlying causes of social ills.

LEGAL BASIS:
Public foundation.

ELIGIBILITY:
Projects must be run by community
organizations or nonprofits. No individuals.
The Foundation only funds groups with
annual expenses under $300,000.

GEOGRAPHIC RESTRICTIONS:
Chicago, Illinois metropolitan area and
northwestern Indiana.

FINANCIAL DATA:
Amount of support per award: Up to
$10,000.
Total amount of support: $303,846 for the
year 2012.

APPLICATION INFORMATION:
Contact the Fund for guidelines.
Duration: One year.
Deadline: February 15.

PUBLICATIONS:
Application guidelines; newsletter; brochure;
annual report.

ADDRESS INQUIRIES TO:
Jane Kimondo, Program Director
(See address above.)

EARHART FOUNDATION   [1850]
2200 Green Road, Suite H
Ann Arbor, MI 48105
(734) 761-8592
Fax: (734) 761-2722

FOUNDED: 1929

AREAS OF INTEREST:
Graduate education and scholarly research in
the social sciences and humanities.

NAME(S) OF PROGRAMS:
● **Fellowship Research Grants**
● **Grants to Organizations**

TYPE:
Fellowships; Project/program grants.
Fellowship Research Grants allow the
advancement of knowledge through teaching,
lecturing and publication.

ELIGIBILITY:
For Fellowship Research Grants, applicants
must be associated with a nonprofit
educational or research institution and must
be citizens or permanent residents of the U.S.

For Grants to Organizations, applicants must
be publicly supported educational and
research organizations.

FINANCIAL DATA:
Amount of support per award: Varies.
Total amount of support: Varies.

APPLICATION INFORMATION:
Fellowship Research Grant applications must
include:
(1) a signed cover letter indicating the project
for which support is being requested, the
beginning and end date of the proposed grant
period, and the precise amount requested;
(2) a three- to five-page description of the
proposed research;
(3) an abstract of not more than one page,
single-spaced;
(4) the intended end use or publication;
(5) a budget and time schedule;
(6) a list of referrers;
(7) a statement about applications pending
elsewhere and;
(8) proof of U.S. citizenship or permanent
residency status.

Each award is for a specific purpose and
progress is monitored.

For Fellowship Research Grants and Grants
to Organizations, written inquiries are
preferable before a formal submission.

Applications must be submitted in hard copy.
Applications cannot be accepted
electronically.
Duration: Up to one year.
Deadline: Fellowship Research Grant
proposals should be submitted no less than
six months before commencement of the
projected work period.

PUBLICATIONS:
Summary report.

OFFICERS:
Dennis L. Bark, Chairman
John H. Moore, Vice Chairman
Ingrid A. Gregg, President
Kathleen B. Mason, Treasurer

ADDRESS INQUIRIES TO:
Montgomery B. Brown
Secretary and Director of Program
(See address above.)

EPILEPSY FOUNDATION OF
AMERICA   [1851]
8301 Professional Place East
Landover, MD 20785-8301
(301) 459-3700
(800) 332-1000
Fax: (301) 577-4941

E-MAIL ADDRESS:
grants@efa.org

WEB SITE ADDRESS:
www.epilepsyfoundation.org

FOUNDED: 1968

AREAS OF INTEREST:
Epilepsy research and training.

NAME(S) OF PROGRAMS:
● **Behavioral Sciences Student
    Fellowships**
● **Health Sciences Student Fellowships**

TYPE:
Fellowships. Offers qualified individuals an
opportunity to develop expertise in the area
of epilepsy research relative to the health
sciences through a three-month training
experience with involvement in an epilepsy
research project in either a clinical or
laboratory setting.

YEAR PROGRAM STARTED: 1975

PURPOSE:
To encourage students in vocational
rehabilitation and behavioral sciences to work
in the field of epilepsy.

LEGAL BASIS:
Nonprofit private foundation.

ELIGIBILITY:
The projects must be conducted at an
approved facility at a U.S. institution of the
student's choice and carried out during any
free period of the student's year. A preceptor
must accept responsibility for supervision of
the student and the project. Applications
from women and minorities are encouraged.

For the Behavioral Science Student
Fellowship, applicants must be actively
enrolled in a degree program at the time the
fellowship is to be undertaken. Both
undergraduate and graduate students are
eligible. Appropriate fields of study include
sociology, social work, psychology,
anthropology, nursing, economics, vocational
rehabilitation, counseling, political science
and others relevant to epilepsy research or
practice.

GEOGRAPHIC RESTRICTIONS:
United States.

FINANCIAL DATA:
Amount of support per award: Up to $3,000
depending upon the experience and
qualifications of the applicant and the scope
and duration of the proposed project.

APPLICATION INFORMATION:
Guidelines and application form are available
on the Foundation web site.
Duration: Three months.
Deadline: On or about March 21 for funding
during the same year.

ADDRESS INQUIRIES TO:
Research Department
(See address above.)

EPILEPSY FOUNDATION OF AMERICA [1852]
8301 Professional Place East
Landover, MD 20785-8301
(301) 459-3700
Fax: (301) 577-4941

E-MAIL ADDRESS:
grants@efa.org

WEB SITE ADDRESS:
www.epilepsyfoundation.org

FOUNDED: 1968

AREAS OF INTEREST:
Epilepsy research and training.

NAME(S) OF PROGRAMS:
● **Behavioral Sciences Postdoctoral Fellowship**

TYPE:
Fellowships. Awards for postdoctoral study through a one-year training experience in the area of epilepsy research. Appropriate fields of study for applications in the behavioral sciences include sociology, social work, psychology, anthropology, nursing, political science and others relevant to epilepsy research or practice.

YEAR PROGRAM STARTED: 1987

PURPOSE:
To offer qualified individuals an opportunity to develop expertise in the area of epilepsy research through a one-year training experience with involvement in an epilepsy research project.

LEGAL BASIS:
Private foundation.

ELIGIBILITY:
Individuals who have received their doctoral degree in a field of the social sciences by the time the fellowship commences and desire additional postdoctoral research experience in epilepsy may apply. Proposed projects must be carried out at an approved facility.

GEOGRAPHIC RESTRICTIONS:
United States.

FINANCIAL DATA:
Amount of support per award: Up to $40,000.

NUMBER OF APPLICANTS MOST RECENT YEAR:
1.

NUMBER OF AWARDS: 1.

APPLICATION INFORMATION:
Apply via Proposal Central which is available on the Foundation web site.
Duration: One year.
Deadline: On or about March 21 to be considered for funding during the same year.

ADDRESS INQUIRIES TO:
Research Department
(See address above.)

THE HARRY FRANK GUGGENHEIM FOUNDATION [1853]
25 West 53rd Street
16th Floor
New York, NY 10019-5401
(646) 428-0971
Fax: (646) 428-0981

E-MAIL ADDRESS:
info@hfg.org

WEB SITE ADDRESS:
www.hfg.org

FOUNDED: 1929

AREAS OF INTEREST:
Research on dominance, aggression and violence.

NAME(S) OF PROGRAMS:
● **The Harry Frank Guggenheim Foundation Research Grant**

TYPE:
Research grants. Support for projects which seek to advance and coordinate creative breakthroughs in the social and biological sciences relating to the study of dominance, violence and aggression.

YEAR PROGRAM STARTED: 1972

PURPOSE:
To further understanding of human social problems related to dominance, violence and aggression.

LEGAL BASIS:
Private, operating foundation.

ELIGIBILITY:
The Foundation awards research grants to individuals (or a few principal investigators at most) for individual projects and does not award grants to institutions for institutional programs.

Applicants for a research grant may be citizens of any country. While almost all recipients of a Foundation research grant possess a Ph.D., M.D., or equivalent degree, there are no formal degree requirements for the grant. The grant, however, may not be used to support research undertaken as part of the requirements for a graduate degree. Applicants need not be affiliated with an institution of higher learning, although most are college or university professors.

FINANCIAL DATA:
Amount of support per award: Usually $15,000 to $40,000 per year.
Total amount of support: Grants and Fellowships: $400,000 to $500,000.

NUMBER OF APPLICANTS MOST RECENT YEAR:
175.

NUMBER OF AWARDS: Approximately 10.

APPLICATION INFORMATION:
Guidelines and application form are available at the Foundation web site.
Duration: Usually one to two years. Renewal is possible if requested in original application, but not guaranteed.
Deadline: August 1 (received, not postmarked).

PUBLICATIONS:
Guidelines; Annual Report.

OFFICERS:
Josiah Bunting, III, President
Deirdre Hamill, Secretary-Treasurer
Karen Colvard, Program Director
Joel Wallman, Senior Program Officer

ADDRESS INQUIRIES TO:
Research Grants
(See address above.)

THE HARRY FRANK GUGGENHEIM FOUNDATION [1854]
25 West 53rd Street
16th Floor
New York, NY 10019-5401
(646) 428-0971
Fax: (646) 428-0981

E-MAIL ADDRESS:
info@hfg.org

WEB SITE ADDRESS:
www.hfg.org

FOUNDED: 1929

AREAS OF INTEREST:
Scholarly research on dominance, aggression and violence.

NAME(S) OF PROGRAMS:
● **The Harry Frank Guggenheim Foundation Dissertation Fellowship**

TYPE:
Fellowships. Awarded to individuals who will complete the writing of the dissertation within the award year. Support is for projects which seek to advance and coordinate creative breakthroughs in the social and biological sciences relating to the study of dominance, violence and aggression.

YEAR PROGRAM STARTED: 1990

PURPOSE:
To further understanding of human social problems related to violence, aggression and dominance.

LEGAL BASIS:
Private foundation.

ELIGIBILITY:
Fellowships are for students in the final year of their doctoral programs. They are designed to support the write-up stage of the dissertation. They are available to citizens of any country in the world.

Recipients of the Dissertation Fellowship must submit a copy of the dissertation, approved and accepted by their institution, within six months after the end of the award year. Any papers, books, articles, or other publications based on the research should also be sent to the Foundation.

FINANCIAL DATA:
Amount of support per award: $20,000.
Total amount of support: $200,000 each year.

NUMBER OF APPLICANTS MOST RECENT YEAR:
Average 225.

NUMBER OF AWARDS: Usually 10 each year.

REPRESENTATIVE AWARDS:
Amy Chasteen for "Constructing Rape;" James Hogue for "Bayonet Rule: Five Street Battles in New Orleans and the Rise and Fall of Radical Reconstruction;" David LeMarquand for "Tryptophan Depletion, Aggression, and Passive Avoidance Learning in Nonalcoholic Young Men with Paternal Family Histories of Alcoholism."

APPLICATION INFORMATION:
Guidelines and application forms are available on the web site.
Duration: Dissertation Fellowships are one-time awards and are not renewable.
Deadline: February 1.

PUBLICATIONS:
Guidelines and Report.

OFFICERS:
Josiah Bunting, III, President
Deirdre Hamill, Treasurer and Secretary
Karen Colvard, Program Director
Joel Wallman, Senior Program Officer

ADDRESS INQUIRIES TO:
Dissertation Fellowship
(See address above.)

THE JOHN RANDOLPH HAYNES AND DORA HAYNES FOUNDATION

888 West Sixth Street, Suite 1150
Los Angeles, CA 90017-2737
(213) 623-9151
Fax: (213) 623-3951

E-MAIL ADDRESS:
info@haynesfoundation.org

WEB SITE ADDRESS:
www.haynesfoundation.org

TYPE:
Fellowships; Research grants.

See entry 1631 for full listing.

THE HOROWITZ FOUNDATION FOR SOCIAL POLICY   [1855]

P.O. Box 7
Rocky Hill, NJ 08553-0007
(732) 445-2280

E-MAIL ADDRESS:
info@horowitz-foundation.org
applications@horowitz-foundation.org

WEB SITE ADDRESS:
www.horowitz-foundation.org

FOUNDED: 1997

AREAS OF INTEREST:
Social sciences, including anthropology, area studies, economics, political science, psychology, sociology, urban studies, as well as newer areas such as evaluation research.

TYPE:
Awards/prizes; Research grants. Grants to doctoral candidates at the dissertation level with emphasis on policy-related studies.

YEAR PROGRAM STARTED: 1997

PURPOSE:
To support the advancement of research and understanding in the major fields of the social sciences.

ELIGIBILITY:
Awards are only open to aspiring Ph.Ds. at the dissertation level whose project has received approval from their appropriate department head/university. Applicants are not required to be U.S. citizens or U.S. residents.

Preference will be given to projects that deal with contemporary issues in the social sciences and issues of policy relevance.

Awards are not allocated so as to insure a representative base of disciplines, but are approved solely on merit.

FINANCIAL DATA:
Amount of support per award: $5,000 to $7,500.

COOPERATIVE FUNDING PROGRAMS: Determined on a case-by-case basis.

NUMBER OF APPLICANTS MOST RECENT YEAR: 157 for the year 2011.

NUMBER OF AWARDS: Approximately 15 annually.

APPLICATION INFORMATION:
Applications can be obtained via download from Foundation web site.

Applications must be sent via e-mail to applications@horowitz-foundation.org. (Submission via e-mail is recommended for speedy processing.) Regular mail may also be used for supplemental materials.

All submitted applications, letters and documents must be in English. E-mail letters of support must be sent via the supporter's organizational e-mail account and, if possible, be displayed upon the letterhead with which the supporter is affiliated. Submitted materials become the property of the Foundation and will not be returned. Applicants should not send originals or other materials that cannot be replaced. Incomplete applications cannot be considered or processed.

Duration: One year. Nonrenewable.

Deadline: Applications and all required materials must be postmarked no later than January 31 of each year and received no later than February 10. Early submission is encouraged. Last-minute applicants cannot be advised of errors or omissions. Award winners will be announced in June of each year.

IRS IDENTIFICATION NUMBER: 31-1612153

BOARD OF TRUSTEES:
David J. Armor
James T. Bennett
Jonathan D. Breul
Mary E. Curtis
J. Christopher Mihm
Georgia Persons
Ray C. Rist
Rosalia Rodriguez-Garcia
Jeffrey Ian Ross
Rosemary A. Stevens
Jaan Valsiner
James Wright

ADDRESS INQUIRIES TO:
Mary E. Curtis
Chairman and Trustee
(See address above.)

INSTITUTE FOR ADVANCED STUDY   [1856]

Einstein Drive
Princeton, NJ 08540
(609) 734-8250
Fax: (609) 951-4457

E-MAIL ADDRESS:
donne@ias.edu

WEB SITE ADDRESS:
www.sss.ias.edu

FOUNDED: 1930

AREAS OF INTEREST:
Economics, political science, sociology, education, anthropology and history.

NAME(S) OF PROGRAMS:
● **School of Social Science Fellowships**

TYPE:
Fellowships; Residencies. Postdoctoral research fellowships at the School of Social Science. In 2014-15, the thematic focus will be "Egalitarianisms."

YEAR PROGRAM STARTED: 1970

PURPOSE:
To support fundamental research and scholarship in the social sciences and humanities.

LEGAL BASIS:
Private, nonprofit research center.

ELIGIBILITY:
Scholars of any nationality who have obtained their highest degree and whose work is relevant to any aspect of the social sciences are urged to apply.

FINANCIAL DATA:
Amount of support per award: Approximately $35,000 to $65,000.

Total amount of support: Varies.

Matching fund requirements: Institute strongly encourages applicants to apply for outside funds as well.

NUMBER OF APPLICANTS MOST RECENT YEAR: 220.

NUMBER OF AWARDS: 22.

APPLICATION INFORMATION:
Applications must be submitted online.

Duration: One academic year.

Deadline: November 1.

PUBLICATIONS:
Annual report.

STAFF:
Donne Petito, Administrative Officer

ADDRESS INQUIRIES TO:
School of Social Science
(See address above.)

*SPECIAL STIPULATIONS:
This is a residential (on-site) fellowship.

INSTITUTE FOR QUANTITATIVE SOCIAL SCIENCE, HARVARD UNIVERSITY   [1857]

Henry A. Murray Research Archive
318, CGIS Knafel Building
1737 Cambridge Street
Cambridge, MA 02138
(617) 496-6528
Fax: (617) 496-5149

E-MAIL ADDRESS:
mra_support@help.hmdc.harvard.edu

WEB SITE ADDRESS:
www.murray.harvard.edu

FOUNDED: 1976

AREAS OF INTEREST:
Social sciences, psychology and human development, and education.

NAME(S) OF PROGRAMS:
● **Jeanne Humphrey Block Dissertation Award**

TYPE:
Awards/prizes. The Block Dissertation Award is offered by the Henry A. Murray Research Archive.

YEAR PROGRAM STARTED: 1990

PURPOSE:
To support research that best embodies Henry A. Murray's commitment to the in-depth study of individuals in context, over time and from a variety of perspectives.

LEGAL BASIS:
University or research association.

ELIGIBILITY:
Applicant must be a Harvard Ph.D. candidate in the social sciences.

FINANCIAL DATA:
Amount of support per award: $2,500.
Total amount of support: $2,500.

NUMBER OF AWARDS: 1.

APPLICATION INFORMATION:
Detailed information and application guidelines are available upon request to the Institute.

Duration: One year.

Deadline: March 15.

PUBLICATIONS:
Program announcement.

IRS IDENTIFICATION NUMBER: 04-2103589

ADDRESS INQUIRIES TO:
E-mail: funding@lists.iq.harvard.edu

KAPPA OMICRON NU HONOR SOCIETY
4990 Northwind Drive
Suite 140
East Lansing, MI 48823-5031
(517) 351-8335
Fax: (517) 351-8336

E-MAIL ADDRESS:
dmitstifer@kon.org

WEB SITE ADDRESS:
www.kon.org

TYPE:
Fellowships; Project/program grants; Research grants; Scholarships. Awarded to members for graduate or postgraduate study and research in human sciences or one of its specializations at colleges or universities with strong research programs and supporting disciplines for the chosen major or topic.

See entry 2674 for full listing.

MADDIE'S FUND   [1858]
6160 Stoneridge Mall Road
Suite 120
Pleasanton, CA 94588
(925) 310-5450
Fax: (925) 310-5451

E-MAIL ADDRESS:
grants@maddiesfund.org

WEB SITE ADDRESS:
www.maddiesfund.org

AREAS OF INTEREST:
Animal welfare.

NAME(S) OF PROGRAMS:
- **Community Collaborative Grants**
- **Lifesaving Awards**
- **Medical Equipment Grants**
- **Shelter Medicine Programs**

TYPE:
Project/program grants.

PURPOSE:
To revolutionize the status and well-being of companion animals.

ELIGIBILITY:
Grants are made to organizations that have tax-exempt status under Section 501(c)(3) of the Internal Revenue Code, or that are government agencies, and that build coalitions in support of animal welfare and protection.

GEOGRAPHIC RESTRICTIONS:
United States.

APPLICATION INFORMATION:
Contact the Fund for guidelines.
Duration: Varies by program.

ADDRESS INQUIRIES TO:
Shelly Thompson, Grants Manager or Mary Smith, Vice President of Operations (See address above.)

THE NATIONAL ASSOCIATION OF BLACK SOCIAL WORKERS
2305 Martin Luther King Jr. Avenue, S.E.
Washington, DC 20020
(202) 678-4570
Fax: (202) 678-4572

E-MAIL ADDRESS:
harambee@nabsw.org

WEB SITE ADDRESS:
www.nabsw.org

TYPE:
Scholarships.

See entry 1032 for full listing.

NATIONAL COUNCIL FOR THE SOCIAL STUDIES   [1859]
8555 16th Street, Suite 500
Silver Spring, MD 20910
(301) 588-1800 ext. 107
Fax: (301) 588-2049

E-MAIL ADDRESS:
excellence@ncss.org

WEB SITE ADDRESS:
www.socialstudies.org

FOUNDED: 1921

AREAS OF INTEREST:
Social studies education.

NAME(S) OF PROGRAMS:
- **Exemplary Research in Social Studies**
- **Jean Dresden Grambs Distinguished Career in Social Studies**
- **The Larry Metcalf Exemplary Dissertation Award**
- **Outstanding Social Studies Teacher of the Year Awards**
- **Carter G. Woodson Book Awards**

TYPE:
Awards/prizes; Grants-in-aid.

PURPOSE:
To provide leadership, service and support for all social studies educators.

GEOGRAPHIC RESTRICTIONS:
United States.

FINANCIAL DATA:
Amount of support per award: Up to $3,000.
Total amount of support: Varies.

APPLICATION INFORMATION:
Applications must be submitted through the online system.
Deadline: May 31.

ADDRESS INQUIRIES TO:
Jordan Grote, Manager of External Relations (See address above.)

NATIONAL COUNCIL FOR THE SOCIAL STUDIES   [1860]
8555 16th Street, Suite 500
Silver Spring, MD 20910
(301) 588-1800 ext. 107
Fax: (301) 588-2049

E-MAIL ADDRESS:
excellence@ncss.org

WEB SITE ADDRESS:
www.socialstudies.org

FOUNDED: 1921

AREAS OF INTEREST:
Social studies education.

NAME(S) OF PROGRAMS:
- **Christa McAuliffe Reach for the Stars Award**

TYPE:
Awards/prizes. Annual award for projects representing excellence and innovation in social studies education and having the potential of serving as a model for other teachers.

YEAR PROGRAM STARTED: 1986

PURPOSE:
To help a social studies educator make his or her dream of innovative social studies a reality; to assist classroom teachers in developing and implementing imaginative, innovative, and illustrative social studies teaching strategies; to assist classroom teachers in supporting student implementation of innovative social studies, citizenship projects, field experiences, and community connections.

ELIGIBILITY:
NCSS membership is required. Applicant must be a full-time social studies teacher or social studies teacher educator currently engaged with K-12 students.

GEOGRAPHIC RESTRICTIONS:
United States.

FINANCIAL DATA:
Amount of support per award: $2,500.

NUMBER OF APPLICANTS MOST RECENT YEAR:
10.

NUMBER OF AWARDS: 1.

APPLICATION INFORMATION:
Applications must be submitted through the online system. No mail-in copies will be allowed. A complete proposal contains the following:
(1) cover page;
(2) 50- to 150-word project proposal abstract;
(3) project proposal and narrative description;
(4) professional resume (including current teaching assignment);
(5) two letters of support from applicant's supervisor acknowledging teaching status and support for the project (one letter may be from state or local social studies council);
(6) publicity outreach, including name, contact name, title and e-mail for a major local/community newspaper (up to two), district superintendent, and direct supervisor and;
(7) information release statement.

The project proposal and narrative description must include the following information:
(1) clear, concise statement of the project objectives;
(2) brief summary of project activities and timeline for completion;
(3) identification of population served, including relevant demographic information;
(4) budget showing how the funds will be used and if additional funds are being sought from other sources;
(5) brief explanation of how the award can facilitate the project;
(6) brief explanation of how the success of the project will be evaluated;
(7) description of the specific plan for sharing the project with local or state councils and with NCSS and;
(8) brief explanation of how the project can serve as a model for other teachers.

Deadline: May 31.

ADDRESS INQUIRIES TO:
Jordan Grote, Manager of External Relations (See address above.)

NATIONAL COUNCIL FOR THE SOCIAL STUDIES [1861]

8555 16th Street, Suite 500
Silver Spring, MD 20910
(301) 588-1800 ext. 107
Fax: (301) 588-2049

E-MAIL ADDRESS:
excellence@ncss.org

WEB SITE ADDRESS:
www.socialstudies.org

FOUNDED: 1921

AREAS OF INTEREST:
Social studies education.

NAME(S) OF PROGRAMS:
● **Grant for the Enhancement of Geographic Literacy**

TYPE:
Awards/prizes. Annual award honoring the outstanding performance of teachers, researchers, and other worthy individuals and programs.

PURPOSE:
To promote geography education in the schools; to enhance the geographic literacy of students at the classroom, district, or statewide level; to encourage integration of geography into the social studies curriculum/classroom.

ELIGIBILITY:
Programs, not individuals, individual lessons or units, which will enhance the geographic literacy of students at the classroom, district, or statewide levels. Recipients may be individuals or groups in school districts, public institutions, or universities.

GEOGRAPHIC RESTRICTIONS:
United States.

FINANCIAL DATA:
Amount of support per award: $2,500.

NUMBER OF APPLICANTS MOST RECENT YEAR:
10 to 12.

NUMBER OF AWARDS: 1.

APPLICATION INFORMATION:
Applications must be submitted through the online system. No mail-in copies will be allowed. A complete proposal includes the following:
(1) cover page;
(2) 150- to 200-word, double-spaced program abstract containing a clear and concise statement of the program's objective, a summary of the program activities and identification of the population served;
(3) five-page (maximum), double-spaced proposal;
(4) publicity outreach, including name, contact name, title, and e-mail for a major local/community newspaper (up to two), district superintendent, and direct supervisor and;
(5) information release statement (on cover page).

The project proposal must contain the following elements:
(1) concise rationale statement;
(2) complete program description that highlights specific geography skills and knowledge that will be introduced or reinforced;
(3) number of teachers and students served;
(4) specific criteria for and means of evaluating program effectiveness;
(5) statement of potential program impact after the first year;
(6) specific line-item budget for the program

grant and;
(7) curriculum vitae or professional resume for all key persons involved in the implementation of the grant.
Deadline: May 31.

ADDRESS INQUIRIES TO:
Jordan Grote, Manager of External Relations
(See address above.)

NATIONAL COUNCIL FOR THE SOCIAL STUDIES [1862]

8555 16th Street, Suite 500
Silver Spring, MD 20910
(301) 588-1800 ext. 107
Fax: (301) 588-2049

E-MAIL ADDRESS:
excellence@ncss.org

WEB SITE ADDRESS:
www.socialstudies.org

FOUNDED: 1921

AREAS OF INTEREST:
Social studies education.

NAME(S) OF PROGRAMS:
● **Defense of Academic Freedom Award**

TYPE:
Awards/prizes. Annual award recognizing those who have distinguished themselves in defending the principles of academic freedom.

PURPOSE:
To recognize and honor those who have distinguished themselves in defending the principles of academic freedom in specific controversies, in fostering academic freedom through advocacy, and in defending or advocating the freedom to teach and learn.

ELIGIBILITY:
Classroom teachers, professionals in other areas of education, students, parents, community groups, and members of other organizations who have engaged in or are currently engaged in activities that support academic freedom in the face of personal challenge or promote awareness of and support for academic freedom.

GEOGRAPHIC RESTRICTIONS:
United States.

FINANCIAL DATA:
Amount of support per award: $1,500.

APPLICATION INFORMATION:
Complete guidelines are available on the web site.
Deadline: March 21.

ADDRESS INQUIRIES TO:
Jordan Grote, Manager of External Relations
(See address above.)

NATIONAL COUNCIL FOR THE SOCIAL STUDIES [1863]

8555 16th Street, Suite 500
Silver Spring, MD 20910
(301) 588-1800 ext. 107
Fax: (301) 588-2049

E-MAIL ADDRESS:
excellence@ncss.org

WEB SITE ADDRESS:
www.socialstudies.org

FOUNDED: 1921

AREAS OF INTEREST:
Social studies education.

NAME(S) OF PROGRAMS:
● **Award for Global Understanding**

TYPE:
Awards/prizes.

PURPOSE:
To recognize a social studies educator (or a team of educators) who has made notable contributions in helping social studies students increase their understanding of the world.

ELIGIBILITY:
NCSS membership is required. Anyone may nominate. Nominees must be social studies educators who are affecting the global understanding of preK-12 students.

FINANCIAL DATA:
Amount of support per award: $2,000 cash award, up to $700 in transportation/lodging reimbursement, a complimentary NCSS conference registration, publicity for a session to present at the NCSS annual conference, and a commemorative gift.

NUMBER OF APPLICANTS MOST RECENT YEAR:
10.

NUMBER OF AWARDS: 1 annually.

APPLICATION INFORMATION:
Submissions must be made via the online application system. Nomination must include:
(1) cover page;
(2) letter of nomination written by the nominator which highlights the nominee's major strengths and accomplishments in infusing global perspectives and cross-cultural understanding into his or her current work assignment (not to exceed two single-spaced pages);
(3) curriculum vitae or professional resume prepared by the nominee;
(4) two letters supporting the nomination from two of the following: immediate supervisor, parents, academic teammates, State Social Studies Council, Local Social Studies Council, or other social studies professionals;
(5) nominee narrative describing in some detail how he or she meets the award criteria (not to exceed seven one-sided, single-spaced 8 1/2 x 11-inch pages of 12-point type);
(6) appendices of documentation for narrative which includes evidence of instructional planning (one lesson/unit plans), actual instruction (video or CD), as well as evidence of student work (sample projects, photos, videos/CDs, web sites, etc.), professional presentations, or publications;
(7) publicity outreach, including name, contact name, title and e-mail for a major local/community newspaper (up to two), district superintendent, and direct supervisor and;
(8) information release statement (on cover page).
Deadline: May 31.

ADDRESS INQUIRIES TO:
Jordan Grote, Manager of External Relations
(See address above.)

NATIONAL COUNCIL FOR THE SOCIAL STUDIES [1864]

8555 16th Street, Suite 500
Silver Spring, MD 20910
(301) 588-1800 ext. 107
Fax: (301) 588-2049

E-MAIL ADDRESS:
excellence@ncss.org

WEB SITE ADDRESS:
www.socialstudies.org/fasse

AREAS OF INTEREST:
Social studies education.

NAME(S) OF PROGRAMS:
- **FASSE-IA International Understanding Grants**

TYPE:
Project/program grants. The grants are intended to support collaborative projects that demonstrate potential to enhance international relationships and global perspectives in social studies education. Funded projects will hold promise for enhancing international and cross-cultural understanding (e.g., through global or international education, human rights education, a focus on global issues, global citizenship, etc.)

PURPOSE:
The Fund for the Advancement of Social Studies Education (FASSE) was created by the National Council for the Social Studies to support research and classroom application projects that improve social studies education and promote engaged, effective citizens. The International Assembly (IA) was founded upon a commitment to build international understanding and to share the activities and scholarship of global social studies educators.

ELIGIBILITY:
Members of NCSS from all geographic locations (i.e., U.S.-based and international) are encouraged to submit proposals. The primary grantee must be a member of NCSS. Upon awarding of the grant, he or she will be expected to join the International Assembly.

Grants are not made to individuals.

FINANCIAL DATA:
The International Assembly and the Fund for the Advancement of Social Studies Education will award up to three International Understanding Grants. The total of the three grants will not exceed $5,000.
Amount of support per award: Varies.
Total amount of support: $5,000.

NUMBER OF AWARDS: Up to 3 annually.

APPLICATION INFORMATION:
Complete application information and form is available on the web site.
Duration: Typically, one year.
Deadline: May 31.

NATIONAL COUNCIL ON FAMILY RELATIONS
1201 West River Parkway
Suite 200
Minneapolis, MN 55454
(763) 781-9331
Fax: (763) 781-9348

E-MAIL ADDRESS:
info@ncfr.org

WEB SITE ADDRESS:
www.ncfr.org

TYPE:
Awards/prizes. Awards given for contributions to the area of family relations. All of the awards, except the Reuben Hill Award and the Jessie Bernard initiatives, require NCFR membership. The Reuben Hill Award is a juried award.

See entry 1498 for full listing.

NATIONAL INSTITUTE OF MENTAL HEALTH   [1865]
Division of Adult Translational Research and Treatment Development (DATR)
6001 Executive Boulevard, Room 7111, MSC 9632
Bethesda, MD 20892-9632
(301) 443-3648

E-MAIL ADDRESS:
ftuma@nih.gov

WEB SITE ADDRESS:
www.nimh.nih.
gov/about/organization/datr/index.shtml

AREAS OF INTEREST:
Traumatic stress, violence (both perpetrators and victims) and disaster within the scope of the biological, behavioral, clinical, applied and psychosocial sciences.

NAME(S) OF PROGRAMS:
- **Research Training and Career Development Program**
- **Traumatic Stress Research Program**

TYPE:
Fellowships; Internships; Project/program grants; Research grants; Technical assistance; Training grants; Visiting scholars; Research contracts.

YEAR PROGRAM STARTED: 1969

PURPOSE:
To plan, support and administer programs of research, research training and resource development aimed at understanding the pathophysiology of mental illness and hastening the translation of behavioral science and neuroscience advances into innovations in clinical care.

LEGAL BASIS:
Section 301 of the Public Health Service Act, as amended; Public Law 78-410, 42 U.S.C. 241.

ELIGIBILITY:
Applicants can be any public or nonprofit institution such as a university, college, hospital or a community agency, unit of state or local government, an authorized unit of the federal government or a for-profit institution and/or entity.

GEOGRAPHIC RESTRICTIONS:
United States and its territories.

FINANCIAL DATA:
Amount of support per award: Small Grant Awards: $50,000 to $150,000 or more indirect costs per year. Average $120,000 to $160,000.

NUMBER OF APPLICANTS MOST RECENT YEAR: 60.

NUMBER OF AWARDS: 20.

APPLICATION INFORMATION:
Forms and instructions are available online.
Duration: Average three to five years.
Deadline: New research applications: February 1, June 1 and October 1. New research training applications: May 10.

NATIONAL SCIENCE FOUNDATION
4201 Wilson Boulevard, Room 990
Arlington, VA 22230
(703) 292-7283
Fax: (703) 292-9068

E-MAIL ADDRESS:
fkronz@nsf.gov

WEB SITE ADDRESS:
www.nsf.gov

TYPE:
Conferences/seminars; Fellowships; Project/program grants; Research grants; Training grants. Grants support research and educational projects, national meetings, dissemination efforts, cross-disciplinary study, dissertation research, small group training activities, dissertation improvement grants for graduate students, and postdoctoral fellowships. The proposals considered for support examine ethics, the conduct and impacts of science, engineering and technology, or undertake research to improve approaches and information for decision making concerning management and direction of research, science and technology.

See entry 1833 for full listing.

NATIONAL SOCIETY DAUGHTERS OF THE AMERICAN REVOLUTION [1866]
1776 D Street, N.W.
Washington, DC 20006-5303
(202) 879-3292
Fax: (202) 879-3348

E-MAIL ADDRESS:
scholarships@dar.org

WEB SITE ADDRESS:
www.dar.org

FOUNDED: 1895

AREAS OF INTEREST:
Political science, history, government and economics.

NAME(S) OF PROGRAMS:
- **Enid Hall Griswold Memorial Scholarship**

TYPE:
Scholarships. Undergraduate scholarships awarded to a deserving junior or senior accepted or enrolled in an accredited college or university in the U.S. who is majoring in either political science, history, government or economics.

YEAR PROGRAM STARTED: 1982

PURPOSE:
To provide ways and means to aid students to attain higher education.

LEGAL BASIS:
Incorporated historical society.

ELIGIBILITY:
Scholarships are awarded without regard to race, religion, sex or national origin. Candidates must be U.S. citizens and must attend an accredited college or university in the U.S. No affiliation or relationship to DAR is required for qualification. Awards are judged on the basis of academic excellence, commitment to field of study, as required, and financial need.

Candidate must major in political science, history, government or economics.

GEOGRAPHIC RESTRICTIONS:
United States.

FINANCIAL DATA:
Amount of support per award: $1,000.
Total amount of support: Varies.

NUMBER OF AWARDS: Varies.

APPLICATION INFORMATION:
Application information is available online.

Duration: One academic year. Nonrenewable.

Deadline: February 15.

PUBLICATIONS:
American Spirit, magazine.

ADDRESS INQUIRIES TO:
Office of the Reporter General
DAR Scholarship Committee
(See address above.)

PI GAMMA MU, INTERNATIONAL HONOR SOCIETY IN SOCIAL SCIENCE

1001 Millington, Suite B
Winfield, KS 67156
(620) 221-3128
Fax: (620) 221-7124

E-MAIL ADDRESS:
executivedirector@pigammamu.org

WEB SITE ADDRESS:
www.pigammamu.org

TYPE:
Scholarships. Awarded for graduate study.

See entry 1745 for full listing.

POVERTY & RACE RESEARCH ACTION COUNCIL   [1867]

1200 18th Street, N.W.
Suite 200
Washington, DC 20036
(202) 906-8025
Fax: (202) 842-2885

E-MAIL ADDRESS:
chartman@prrac.org

WEB SITE ADDRESS:
www.prrac.org

FOUNDED: 1991

AREAS OF INTEREST:
Poverty and race.

TYPE:
Research grants. Research on the intersection
of race and poverty must support an
advocacy plan.

YEAR PROGRAM STARTED: 2000

PURPOSE:
To generate, gather and disseminate
information and resources regarding the
intersection of race and poverty in the U.S.;
to promote the development and
implementation of policies and practices that
alleviate conditions caused by the interaction
of race and poverty.

LEGAL BASIS:
Nonprofit organization.

ELIGIBILITY:
Must be an advocate or social science
researcher and be a tax-exempt 501(c)(3)
organization or have a tax-exempt fiscal
sponsor.

GEOGRAPHIC RESTRICTIONS:
United States.

FINANCIAL DATA:
Amount of support per award: $10,000
maximum.

Total amount of support: Varies.

APPLICATION INFORMATION:
Applicants must submit a brief letter
outlining the purpose of the grant. Further
information is available online.

Duration: One-time. Must reapply.

PUBLICATIONS:
Poverty & Race, bimonthly newsletter;
journal; annual report; application guidelines.

IRS IDENTIFICATION NUMBER: 52-1705073

ADDRESS INQUIRIES TO:
Chester Hartman, Director of Research
(See address above.)

*SPECIAL STIPULATIONS:
Research must support planned advocacy
agenda.

SMITH RICHARDSON FOUNDATION, INC.   [1868]

60 Jesup Road
Westport, CT 06880
(203) 222-6222
Fax: (203) 222-6282

E-MAIL ADDRESS:
jhollings@srf.org

WEB SITE ADDRESS:
www.srf.org

FOUNDED: 1935

AREAS OF INTEREST:
Improvement of public policy in the fields of
social welfare, economic and regulatory
schemes and education issues; improvement
of American foreign policy, particularly as it
relates to national security.

NAME(S) OF PROGRAMS:
● **Domestic Public Policy Program**
● **International Security and Foreign
  Policy Program**

TYPE:
Conferences/seminars; Project/program
grants; Research grants. The Domestic Policy
Program primarily supports research on ways
to improve public policy in the fields of
social welfare, economic and regulatory
schemes and education issues. The program
has a particular interest in research that
examines the effectiveness of institutions
which serve children and families at-risk.

The Foreign Policy Program supports
projects in national security and defense
policy, in military history and strategy, in the
political, military and economic affairs of
Eastern Europe and the states of the former
Soviet Union, economic and security
developments in the Asia Pacific, and also in
international economic issues of vital interest
to American policymakers. The program aims
to define the nature of the post-cold war
security environment.

YEAR PROGRAM STARTED: 1935

PURPOSE:
To support and promote a vigorous and free
society.

LEGAL BASIS:
Private foundation.

ELIGIBILITY:
Organizations sponsoring projects appropriate
to the Foundation's interests are eligible. The
Foundation originates many of the grant
commitments which are made, and the vast
majority of unsolicited requests for funding
must be rejected. Because of fund limitations,
no grants are available for deficit funding of
previously established operations, projects
relating to building construction (i.e., "brick
and mortar"), programs related to the arts,
historic restoration projects, or research in
the physical sciences. No grants are made
directly to individuals or to advocacy

organizations. The Foundation does not
provide support for the operating costs of
direct-service programs or charities. The
Foundation rarely provides general support
for any organization or funding for
conferences and documentaries.

The Foundation awards grants for policy
research with national implications. Some
small grants are available to support
innovative service and educational programs
in Connecticut and North Carolina which
assist children and families at-risk. Nearly all
such local grants are solicited by the staff
and the Board of the Foundation. Service
programs in states other than Connecticut and
North Carolina are ineligible for funding.

GEOGRAPHIC RESTRICTIONS:
Connecticut and North Carolina.

FINANCIAL DATA:
Amount of support per award: Median grant:
$120,000.

APPLICATION INFORMATION:
The Foundation has a rigorous proposal
review process. The first step in the process
is the submission of a concept paper (not to
exceed five pages).

If the staff determines that a project warrants
further consideration under the Foundation's
guidelines, an applicant will be asked to
submit a full proposal that conforms to a
proposal template provided by the
Foundation.

Upon receipt of a grant application, the
Foundation will either mail or e-mail a
confirmation of receipt to the grant applicant.
The Foundation will respond to all grant
requests in a timely manner. However, given
the large number of grant proposals that it
receives, it cannot guarantee a response
within a specific time frame.

Requests for grants greater than $50,000 and
for multiyear grant support are made at one
of its regular board meetings. Requests for
grants of $50,000 or less are reviewed on an
ongoing basis and are handled as promptly as
possible.

Duration: Typically one year. Nonrenewable.

Deadline: Grants are reviewed on an ongoing
basis.

PUBLICATIONS:
Annual report.

IRS IDENTIFICATION NUMBER: 56-0611550

STAFF:
Dr. Nadia Schadlow, Senior Program Officer
Allan Song, Senior Program Officer
Mark Steinmeyer, Senior Program Officer
Olga Ramous, Grants Coordinator
Dale Stewart, Records Coordinator

OFFICERS AND TRUSTEES:
Peter L. Richardson, Chairman of the Board
Marin J. Strmecki, Ph.D., Senior Vice
President, Director of Programs
Ross F. Hemphill, Vice President and Chief
Financial Officer
Arvid R. Nelson, Ph.D., Secretary
W. Winburne King, III, General Counsel
Adele Richardson Ray
Peter L. Richardson
Stuart S. Richardson

ADDRESS INQUIRIES TO:
Domestic Policy or Foreign Policy Program
(See address above.)

THE ROYAL TOWN PLANNING INSTITUTE [1869]
41 Botolph Lane
London EC3R 8DL England
(020) 7929-9494
Fax: (020) 7929-9490

E-MAIL ADDRESS:
awards@rtpi.org.uk

WEB SITE ADDRESS:
www.rtpi.org.uk

FOUNDED: 1914

AREAS OF INTEREST:
Urban and regional planning, land use, transport and housing, industrial strategy on planning, rural planning, conservation and recreational planning.

NAME(S) OF PROGRAMS:
● **George Pepler International Award**

TYPE:
Travel grants. This biennial award is made to individuals under 30 years of age, who wish to visit Britain or, as residents of Britain, desire to visit another country for a short period to study the theory and practice of town and country planning or some particular aspect of planning.

YEAR PROGRAM STARTED: 1964

PURPOSE:
To provide an international travelling award for young people of any nationality who wish to visit another country in order to study town planning or a related subject.

LEGAL BASIS:
Charitable trust.

ELIGIBILITY:
Young people of any nationality under the age of 30 are eligible to apply. Professional qualifications are not necessary. Each applicant is required to complete a prescribed application form and submit to a panel of advisers a statement showing the nature of the study and suggested itinerary.

FINANCIAL DATA:
Amount of support per award: GBP 1,500 paid in two installments.

NUMBER OF APPLICANTS MOST RECENT YEAR:
15.

NUMBER OF AWARDS: 1.

APPLICATION INFORMATION:
Contact the Institute through its e-mail address for an entry form and details.
Duration: Three to four weeks.
Deadline: June 29.

ADDRESS INQUIRIES TO:
Awards Events Officer
(See address above.)

RUSSELL SAGE FOUNDATION [1870]
112 East 64th Street
New York, NY 10065
(212) 750-6000
Fax: (212) 371-4761

E-MAIL ADDRESS:
info@rsage.org

WEB SITE ADDRESS:
www.russellsage.org

FOUNDED: 1907

AREAS OF INTEREST:
Research in the future of work, cultural contact, immigration to the U.S. and social inequality.

TYPE:
Conferences/seminars; Research grants; Visiting scholars. Research awards. The Foundation currently pursues three principal programs:
(1) a program of research on the future of work, concerned principally with the causes and consequences of changes in the quality of low-wage work in the U.S. and other advanced economies;
(2) a program of research on current U.S. immigration focused on the adaptation of the second generation to American society and;
(3) a program on cultural contact that focuses on understanding and improving relations between racial and ethnic groups in schools, workplaces and neighborhood settings.

YEAR PROGRAM STARTED: 1907

PURPOSE:
To improve social and living conditions in the U.S. by conducting and supporting social science research relevant to public policy issues.

LEGAL BASIS:
Private operating foundation.

ELIGIBILITY:
The Foundation supports focused, empirical research projects under the direction of a principal investigator. Under the terms of the contract, the research must be coordinated through a fiscal agency (university, college or 501(c)(3) organization under the Internal Revenue Code).

The Foundation's awards are restricted to support for basic social science research within its announced programs. These currently include research on the future of work, immigration and the social psychology of social contact.

The Foundation conducts a Visiting Scholar program under which persons working in the areas of current interest to the Foundation join the staff for one year to consult and continue their own research and writing.

GEOGRAPHIC RESTRICTIONS:
United States.

FINANCIAL DATA:
Total amount of support: $6,500,000.

APPLICATION INFORMATION:
Applications for awards should be preceded by a letter of inquiry to the Foundation. Guidelines and other details are available on the web site.
Duration: Varies.
Deadline: Eight weeks prior to Board meetings to be held March 15 and August 15.

PUBLICATIONS:
Biennial report; scholarly books.

IRS IDENTIFICATION NUMBER: 13-1635303

OFFICERS:
Sheldon Danziger, President
Ivan Ramos, Director of Administration and Secretary

ADDRESS INQUIRIES TO:
Ivan Ramos, Director of Administration
(See address above.)

SOCIAL SCIENCES AND HUMANITIES RESEARCH COUNCIL OF CANADA [1871]
350 Albert Street
Ottawa ON K1P 6G4 Canada
(613) 943-7777
Fax: (613) 943-1329

E-MAIL ADDRESS:
fellowships@sshrc-crsh.gc.ca

WEB SITE ADDRESS:
www.sshrc-crsh.gc.ca

FOUNDED: 1977

AREAS OF INTEREST:
The development and support of research and research training in the social sciences and humanities.

NAME(S) OF PROGRAMS:
● **Doctoral Awards**

TYPE:
Awards/prizes; Fellowships; Scholarships. Through its Doctoral Awards program, SSHRC offers two types of funding for doctoral students:
(1) SSHRC Doctoral Fellowships and;
(2) Joseph-Armand Bombardier (JAB) Canada Graduate Scholarships (CGS) program–Doctoral Scholarships.

YEAR PROGRAM STARTED: 1977

PURPOSE:
To develop research skills and assist in the training of highly qualified personnel by supporting students who demonstrate a high standard of scholarly achievement in undergraduate and graduate studies in the social sciences and humanities.

LEGAL BASIS:
Government agency.

ELIGIBILITY:
Applicants must be Canadian citizens or permanent residents of Canada. SSHRC Doctoral Fellowships are tenable at any recognized university in Canada, or abroad, in which case the award holder has to have at least one previous degree from a Canadian university.

Joseph-Armand Bombardier Canada Graduate Scholarships-Doctoral Scholarships are tenable only at Canadian universities.

FINANCIAL DATA:
Amount of support per award: SSHRC Doctoral Fellowships: $20,000 (CAN) per year; Joseph-Armand Bombardier Canada Graduate Scholarships-Doctoral Scholarships: $35,000 (CAN) per year.

Total amount of support: SSHRC Doctoral Fellowship: Up to $80,000 (CAN) for four years; Joseph-Armand Bombardier Canada Graduate Scholarships-Doctoral Scholarships: $105,000 (CAN) for three years.

NUMBER OF APPLICANTS MOST RECENT YEAR:
4,969 total applicants from Canadian universities for the year 2011-12.

NUMBER OF AWARDS: SSHRC Doctoral Fellowships: 525; Joseph-Armand Bombardier Canada Graduate Scholarships-Doctoral Scholarships: 460 for the year 2011-12.

APPLICATION INFORMATION:
On university campuses, information may be obtained from the Dean or Faculty of Graduate Studies, the Office of Research Administration, the Registrar, or the Student Awards Office. Inquiries may also be addressed directly to the Research Training Portfolio of the Council, at the address above. Detailed program and application information is available online.

Duration: SSHRC Doctoral Fellowships: From six months to four years; Joseph-Armand Bombardier Canada Graduate Scholarships-Doctoral Scholarships: Three years.

Deadline: For applicants registered at a Canadian university, in the fall on the date set by the university; for other applicants, usually in mid-November.

OFFICERS AND STAFF:
Dr. Chad Gaffield, President
Dr. Brent Herbert-Copley, Vice President, Research Capacity
Gordana Krcevinac, Director, Research Training

ADDRESS INQUIRIES TO:
Research Training Portfolio
(See address above.)

SOCIAL SCIENCES AND HUMANITIES RESEARCH COUNCIL OF CANADA [1872]
350 Albert Street
Ottawa ON K1P 6G4 Canada
(613) 943-7777
Fax: (613) 943-1329

E-MAIL ADDRESS:
fellowships@sshrc-crsh.gc.ca

WEB SITE ADDRESS:
www.sshrc-crsh.gc.ca

FOUNDED: 1977

AREAS OF INTEREST:
The development and support of research, research training, and scholarly activities in the social sciences and humanities.

NAME(S) OF PROGRAMS:
● SSHRC Postdoctoral Fellowships

TYPE:
Fellowships. For Canadian citizens or permanent residents of Canada, to support postdoctoral research in the humanities and social sciences.

YEAR PROGRAM STARTED: 1977

PURPOSE:
To support promising new scholars in the social sciences and humanities and to assist them in establishing a research base at an important time in their research careers.

LEGAL BASIS:
Government agency.

ELIGIBILITY:
Competition is open to persons who have been awarded an earned Doctorate within the three years preceding competition closing date. Applicants must demonstrate that all doctoral requirements will be completed before the proposed starting date of tenure. Awards are for postdoctoral study or research within a university or research institution.

Applicants must be Canadian citizens or permanent residents of Canada living in the country at the time of application.

FINANCIAL DATA:
Amount of support per award: $38,000 (CAN) per year for one or two years, plus a one-time $5,000 (CAN) research allowance.
Total amount of support: Up to $81,000 (CAN).

NUMBER OF APPLICANTS MOST RECENT YEAR: 877 for the year 2011-12.

NUMBER OF AWARDS: 175 for the year 2011-2012.

APPLICATION INFORMATION:
Fellowships are tenable only at universities or other recognized research institutions in Canada or abroad. Applicants must present a significant and feasible program of postdoctoral research. Fellowships may not be used to obtain a degree. Fellows may be allowed to assume limited teaching duties, equivalent to one course per year. Detailed program and application information is available online.
Duration: Period of tenure is from 12 up to 24 months.
Deadline: Usually, in early or mid-October. Announcement usually between mid-February and early March.

OFFICERS AND STAFF:
Dr. Chad Gaffield, President
Dr. Brent Herbert-Copley, Vice President, Research Capacity
Gordana Krcevinac, Director, Research Training

ADDRESS INQUIRIES TO:
Research Training Portfolio
(See address above.)

SOCIAL SCIENCES AND HUMANITIES RESEARCH COUNCIL OF CANADA [1873]
350 Albert Street
Ottawa ON K1P 6G4 Canada
(613) 943-7777
Fax: (613) 943-1329

E-MAIL ADDRESS:
fellowships@sshrc-crsh.gc.ca

WEB SITE ADDRESS:
www.sshrc-crsh.gc.ca

FOUNDED: 1977

AREAS OF INTEREST:
The development and support of research and research training in the social sciences and humanities.

NAME(S) OF PROGRAMS:
● Bora Laskin National Fellowship in Human Rights Research

TYPE:
Fellowships. Awarded annually to encourage the development of expertise in the field of human rights. The research should emphasize themes and issues relevant to human rights in Canada. Research in all areas of the humanities and the social sciences, including journalism and law, is eligible. Of particular interest are multidisciplinary or interdisciplinary research projects. This award is intended for experienced researchers. It is not a research training fellowship.

YEAR PROGRAM STARTED: 1985

LEGAL BASIS:
Government agency.

ELIGIBILITY:
Candidates must be Canadian citizens or permanent residents of Canada. University and private scholars are eligible.

GEOGRAPHIC RESTRICTIONS:
Canada.

FINANCIAL DATA:
Amount of support per award: $45,000 (CAN) plus a $10,000 (CAN) accountable allowance for research and travel costs.
Total amount of support: $55,000 (CAN).

NUMBER OF APPLICANTS MOST RECENT YEAR: 6 for the year 2010-11.

NUMBER OF AWARDS: 1 in 2010-2011.

APPLICATION INFORMATION:
Detailed program and application information is available on the Council web site.
Duration: 12 months. Nonrenewable.

OFFICERS AND STAFF:
Dr. Chad Gaffield, President
Dr. Brent Herbert-Copley, Vice President, Program-Grants and Fellowships
Gordana Krcevinac, Director, Fellowships

ADDRESS INQUIRIES TO:
Research Training Portfolio
(See address above.)

SOCIAL SCIENCES AND HUMANITIES RESEARCH COUNCIL OF CANADA [1874]
350 Albert Street
Ottawa ON K1P 6G4 Canada
(613) 943-7777
Fax: (613) 943-1329

E-MAIL ADDRESS:
fellowships@sshrc-crsh.gc.ca

WEB SITE ADDRESS:
www.sshrc-crsh.gc.ca

FOUNDED: 1977

AREAS OF INTEREST:
The development and support of research and research training in the social sciences and humanities.

NAME(S) OF PROGRAMS:
● Joseph-Armand Bombardier Canada Graduate Scholarships Program - Master's Scholarships
● Master's Awards

TYPE:
Awards/prizes; Fellowships; Scholarships.

YEAR PROGRAM STARTED: 2003

PURPOSE:
To develop research skills and assist in the training of highly qualified personnel by supporting students who demonstrate a high standard of scholarly achievement in undergraduate and graduate studies in the social sciences and humanities.

LEGAL BASIS:
Government agency.

ELIGIBILITY:
Applicants must be Canadian citizens or permanent residents of Canada. Joseph-Armand Bombardier Canada Graduate Scholarships-Master's Scholarships are tenable only at Canadian universities.

FINANCIAL DATA:
Amount of support per award: Joseph-Armand Bombardier Canada Graduate Scholarships - Master's Scholarships: $17,500 (CAN) for one year only.
Total amount of support: Joseph-Armand Bombardier Canada Graduate Scholarships - Master's Scholarships: $17,500 (CAN).

NUMBER OF APPLICANTS MOST RECENT YEAR: 1,494 applicants from Canadian universities for the year 2011-12.

NUMBER OF AWARDS: 1,300 Joseph-Armand Bombardier Canada Graduate Scholarships - Master's Scholarships.

APPLICATION INFORMATION:
On university campuses, information may be obtained from the Dean or Faculty of Graduate Studies, the Office of Research

Administration, the Registrar, or the Student Awards Office. Inquiries may also be addressed directly to the Research Training Portfolio of the Council at the address above. Detailed program and application information is available online.

Duration: One year.

Deadline: For applicants registered at a Canadian university, in the fall on the date set by the university; for other applicants, usually in mid-November.

OFFICERS AND STAFF:
Dr. Chad Gaffield, President
Dr. Brent Herbert-Copley, Vice President, Research Capacity
Gordana Krcevinac, Director, Research Training

ADDRESS INQUIRIES TO:
Research Training Portfolio
(See address above.)

SOCIAL SCIENCES AND HUMANITIES RESEARCH COUNCIL OF CANADA   [1875]
350 Albert Street
Ottawa ON K1P 6G4 Canada
(613) 943-7777
Fax: (613) 943-1329

E-MAIL ADDRESS:
fellowships@sshrc-crsh.gc.ca

WEB SITE ADDRESS:
www.vanier.gc.ca

FOUNDED: 2008

AREAS OF INTEREST:
The development and support of research and research training in the social sciences and humanities.

NAME(S) OF PROGRAMS:
● **Vanier Canada Graduate Scholarships (CGS)**

TYPE:
Awards/prizes; Fellowships; Scholarships. For full-time doctoral students in the humanities and social sciences.

YEAR PROGRAM STARTED: 2008

PURPOSE:
To attract and retain world-class doctoral students by supporting students who demonstrate both leadership skills and a high standard of scholarly achievement in graduate studies in social sciences and humanities, natural sciences and engineering, and health.

LEGAL BASIS:
Government agency.

ELIGIBILITY:
Applicants can be citizens or permanent residents of Canada, as well as international students.

GEOGRAPHIC RESTRICTIONS:
Canada.

FINANCIAL DATA:
Amount of support per award: $50,000 (CAN) per year.
Total amount of support: $150,000 (CAN), up to three years.

NUMBER OF APPLICANTS MOST RECENT YEAR: 206 for the year 2011-2012.

NUMBER OF AWARDS: 55 for the year 2011-2012.

APPLICATION INFORMATION:
On university campuses, information may be obtained from the Dean or Faculty of

Graduate Studies, the Office of Research Administration, the Registrar, or the Student Awards Office. Inquiries may also be addressed directly to the Research Training Portfolio of the Council at the address above.

Duration: Two or three years.

Deadline: Nomination deadline is set by the university. SSHRC's deadline for nominations submitted by the universities is usually mid-November.

OFFICERS AND STAFF:
Dr. Chad Gaffield, President
Dr. Brent Herbert-Copley, Vice President, Research Capacity
Gordana Krcevinac, Director, Research Training

ADDRESS INQUIRIES TO:
Research Training Portfolio
(See address above.)

SOCIAL SCIENCES AND HUMANITIES RESEARCH COUNCIL OF CANADA   [1876]
350 Albert Street
Ottawa ON K1P 6G4 Canada
(613) 943-7777
Fax: (613) 943-1329

E-MAIL ADDRESS:
fellowships@sshrc-crsh.gc.ca

WEB SITE ADDRESS:
www.sshrc-crsh.gc.ca

FOUNDED: 2010

AREAS OF INTEREST:
The development and support of research, research training and scholarly activities in the social sciences and humanities.

NAME(S) OF PROGRAMS:
● **Banting Postdoctoral Fellowships**

TYPE:
Fellowships. For Canadian citizens, permanent residents of Canada and foreign citizens to support postdoctoral research in the humanities and social sciences.

YEAR PROGRAM STARTED: 2010

PURPOSE:
To support promising new scholars in the social sciences and humanities and to assist them in establishing a research base at an important time in their research careers.

LEGAL BASIS:
Government agency.

ELIGIBILITY:
Competition is open to persons who have been awarded an earned Doctorate within the three years preceding competition and applicants can be citizens or permanent residents of Canada, as well as international students.

Without exception, the Banting Postdoctoral Fellowships:
(1) are tenable only at the institution which supported the original application for the program;
(2) must be taken up no earlier than April 1 and no later than October 1 of the year following the application deadline and;
(3) are for two years from the date of up-take.

FINANCIAL DATA:
Amount of support per award: $70,000 (CAN) per year for two years.
Total amount of support: $140,000 (CAN).

NUMBER OF APPLICANTS MOST RECENT YEAR: 105 for the year 2011-12.

NUMBER OF AWARDS: 23.

APPLICATION INFORMATION:
On university campuses, information may be obtained from the Dean or Faculty of Graduate Studies, the Office of Research Administration, the Registrar, or the Student Awards Office.

Duration: Period of tenure is 24 months.

Deadline: Usually, in early or mid-November. Announcement usually at end of March.

OFFICERS AND STAFF:
Dr. Chad Gaffield, President
Dr. Brent Herbert-Copley, Vice President, Research Capacity
Gordana Krcevinac, Director, Research Training

ADDRESS INQUIRIES TO:
Research Training Portfolio
(See address above.)

THE SOCIETY FOR THE PSYCHOLOGICAL STUDY OF SOCIAL ISSUES (SPSSI)   [1877]
208 I Street, N.E.
Washington, DC 20002-4340
(202) 675-6956
Fax: (202) 675-6902

E-MAIL ADDRESS:
spssi@spssi.org
awards@spssi.org

WEB SITE ADDRESS:
www.spssi.org

FOUNDED: 1936

AREAS OF INTEREST:
Social psychology research.

NAME(S) OF PROGRAMS:
● **Gordon Allport Intergroup Relations Prize**

TYPE:
Awards/prizes. The Gordon Allport Intergroup Relations Prize honors the memory of the late Dr. Gordon W. Allport, a founder and past president of SPSSI.

LEGAL BASIS:
Independently incorporated society.

ELIGIBILITY:
Entries must be papers published during the calendar year preceding the year of submission. For the Award, submissions are limited to papers published in their primary form (e.g., appearing in print for print journals or online for online-only journals) with a formal publication date of the prior year. An individual or group may only submit one paper to SPSSI awards (including the Allport, Klineberg and Dissertation Awards) per award year (January 1 to December 31).

The award is given to "the best paper or article of the year on intergroup relations." Originality of the contribution, whether theoretical or empirical, will be given special weight. The research area of intergroup relations includes such dimensions as age, gender, and socioeconomic status, as well as ethnicity.

FINANCIAL DATA:
Amount of support per award: $1,000.

COOPERATIVE FUNDING PROGRAMS: The Award is sponsored by The Gordon W. Allport Memorial Fund of Harvard University and SPSSI.

APPLICATION INFORMATION:
Online submissions are the preferred method. Limit the number and size of files uploaded when applying online.

For hard-copy submissions, send five copies to SPSSI.

Duration: Annual award.

Deadline: June 15.

ADDRESS INQUIRIES TO:
Allport Award
(See address above.)

THE SOCIETY FOR THE PSYCHOLOGICAL STUDY OF SOCIAL ISSUES (SPSSI)   [1878]
208 I Street, N.E.
Washington, DC 20002-4340
(202) 675-6956
Fax: (202) 675-6902

E-MAIL ADDRESS:
spssi@spssi.org
awards@spssi.org

WEB SITE ADDRESS:
www.spssi.org

FOUNDED: 1936

AREAS OF INTEREST:
Social psychology research.

NAME(S) OF PROGRAMS:
● **Innovative Teaching Award**

TYPE:
Awards/prizes. SPSSI confers an annual award for innovative teaching in areas related to the psychological study of social issues. This award recognizes effective courses, assignments or classroom activities addressing social issues.

ELIGIBILITY:
Nominees should be SPSSI members who have developed innovative pedagogical products that aid in teaching the psychological study of social issues. Nominees may teach at graduate degree-granting institutions, Bachelor's-degree universities and colleges, two-year and community colleges, or as contingent or adjunct faculty.

FINANCIAL DATA:
Recipients will be recognized in the Teaching and Learning column in the SPSSI *Forward* newsletter. Honorable Mention awardees will receive one year of free SPSSI membership.
Amount of support per award: $1,000 and a plaque.

APPLICATION INFORMATION:
Application instructions are available on the web site.
Deadline: February 25.

ADDRESS INQUIRIES TO:
E-mail: awards@spssi.org

THE SOCIETY FOR THE PSYCHOLOGICAL STUDY OF SOCIAL ISSUES (SPSSI)   [1879]
208 I Street, N.E.
Washington, DC 20002-4340
(202) 675-6956
Fax: (202) 675-6902

E-MAIL ADDRESS:
awards@spssi.org

WEB SITE ADDRESS:
www.spssi.org

FOUNDED: 1936

AREAS OF INTEREST:
Social issues and psychology.

NAME(S) OF PROGRAMS:
● **Awards for Outstanding Teaching and Mentoring**

TYPE:
Awards/prizes. One award is given for a teacher/mentor from a program or department that grants Master's or doctoral degrees. Another award will be given to a teacher/mentor from a program or department that is undergraduate-only. The third award will be given to a teacher/mentor from contingent and/or community college faculty.

PURPOSE:
To recognize outstanding teaching in areas related to the psychological study of social issues.

LEGAL BASIS:
Independently incorporated society.

ELIGIBILITY:
Nominees should be SPSSI members who have made substantial contributions to students in the psychological study of social issues. To be eligible, individuals must have been teaching and/or mentoring students for at least five years full-time since the doctoral degree. Nominees may teach at graduate degree-granting institutions, Bachelor's degree universities and colleges, or two-year and community colleges. Self-nominations are encouraged.

FINANCIAL DATA:
Amount of support per award: $1,000 plus a plaque.

APPLICATION INFORMATION:
Application information is available on the web site.
Deadline: March 14.

PUBLICATIONS:
Application guidelines.

ADDRESS INQUIRIES TO:
SPSSI Central Office
(See address above.)

THE SOCIETY FOR THE PSYCHOLOGICAL STUDY OF SOCIAL ISSUES (SPSSI)   [1880]
208 I Street, N.E.
Washington, DC 20002-4340
(202) 675-6956
Fax: (202) 675-6902

E-MAIL ADDRESS:
awards@spssi.org
spssi@spssi.org

WEB SITE ADDRESS:
www.spssi.org/awards

FOUNDED: 1936

AREAS OF INTEREST:
Intergroup relations, social issues and psychology.

NAME(S) OF PROGRAMS:
● **The Applied Social Issues Internship Program**

TYPE:
Internships.

PURPOSE:
To encourage research that is conducted in cooperation with a community or government organization, public interest group or other not-for-profit entity that will benefit directly from the project.

LEGAL BASIS:
Independently incorporated society.

ELIGIBILITY:
College seniors, graduate students and first-year postdoctorates in psychology, applied social science, and related disciplines are eligible. Applicant must be an SPSSI member.

FINANCIAL DATA:
Amount of support per award: $300 to $2,500 to cover research costs, community organizing and, in unusual cases, a stipend for the intern.

COOPERATIVE FUNDING PROGRAMS: Cost sharing by sponsoring department or organization is desirable.

NUMBER OF APPLICANTS MOST RECENT YEAR:
20.

APPLICATION INFORMATION:
Application information may be obtained from the web site.
Deadline: April 25. Announcement by June 1.

ADDRESS INQUIRIES TO:
Anila Balkissoon
Administrative Coordinator
(See address above.)

THE SOCIETY FOR THE PSYCHOLOGICAL STUDY OF SOCIAL ISSUES (SPSSI)   [1881]
208 I Street, N.E.
Washington, DC 20002-4340
(202) 675-6956
Fax: (202) 675-6902

E-MAIL ADDRESS:
awards@spssi.org
spssi@spssi.org

WEB SITE ADDRESS:
www.spssi.org/awards

FOUNDED: 1936

AREAS OF INTEREST:
Intergroup relations, social issues and psychology.

NAME(S) OF PROGRAMS:
● **Clara Mayo Grants**

TYPE:
Research grants. Supports Master's theses and predissertation research on sexism, racism or prejudice, with preference given to students enrolled in a terminal Master's program.

PURPOSE:
To support Master's theses or predissertation research on aspects of sexism, racism or prejudice, with preference given to students enrolled in a terminal Master's program. Studies of the application of theory or the design of interventions or treatments to address these problems are welcome.

LEGAL BASIS:
Independently incorporated society.

ELIGIBILITY:
Individuals who are SPSSI members and who have matriculated in graduate programs in psychology, applied social science and related disciplines are eligible to apply. A

student who is applying for the Grants-In-Aid program may not apply for the Clara Mayo award in the same award year. Applicants may submit only one Mayo application per calendar year.

Studies of the application of theory or the design of interventions or treatments to address these problems are welcome. Proposals that include a college or university agreement to match the amount requested will be favored, but proposals without matching funds will also be considered.

FINANCIAL DATA:
Amount of support per award: $1,000 maximum.

NUMBER OF APPLICANTS MOST RECENT YEAR: 25.

NUMBER OF AWARDS: Up to 6 annually.

APPLICATION INFORMATION:
Application information is available on the web site.
Duration: One to two years.
Deadline: May 7.

ADDRESS INQUIRIES TO:
Anila Balkissoon
Administrative Coordinator
(See address above.)

THE SOCIETY FOR THE PSYCHOLOGICAL STUDY OF SOCIAL ISSUES (SPSSI) [1882]

208 I Street, N.E.
Washington, DC 20002-4340
(202) 675-6956
Fax: (202) 675-6902

E-MAIL ADDRESS:
spssi@spssi.org
awards@spssi.org

WEB SITE ADDRESS:
www.spssi.org/awards

FOUNDED: 1936

AREAS OF INTEREST:
Interests, intergroup relations, social issues and psychology.

NAME(S) OF PROGRAMS:
● **The SAGES Program**

TYPE:
Research grants. Program to encourage members 60 years of age and over and retired members to apply their knowledge to helping solve social problems or to assist policymakers to solve social problems. Proposals are invited that use social science research findings to address social problems through direct action projects, consulting with not-for-profit groups, or through preparing reviews of existing social science literature that could be used by policymakers.

LEGAL BASIS:
Independently incorporated society.

ELIGIBILITY:
Applicants must be retired SPSSI members. Members nearing retirement may be considered. Proposals will be evaluated in terms of how well they build on existing social science research and theory, the feasibility of the project, and the importance of the project.

FINANCIAL DATA:
Funding can be submitted for direct costs related to the project. This can be spent over a two-year period. Money can be used for

hiring staff (including clerical assistance), computing fees, travel, telephone, or other justifiable expenses. Funding cannot be used as a stipend for the applicant.
Amount of support per award: $1,000 to $10,000.

NUMBER OF APPLICANTS MOST RECENT YEAR: 5.

NUMBER OF AWARDS: 2 to 3 annually.

APPLICATION INFORMATION:
Application information may be obtained from the web site.
Duration: Up to two years.
Deadline: April 15. Announcement by May 15.

ADDRESS INQUIRIES TO:
Anila Balkissoon
Administrative Coordinator
(See address above.)

THE SOCIETY FOR THE PSYCHOLOGICAL STUDY OF SOCIAL ISSUES (SPSSI) [1883]

208 I Street, N.E.
Washington, DC 20002-4340
(202) 675-6956
Fax: (202) 675-6902

E-MAIL ADDRESS:
awards@spssi.org
spssi@spssi.org

WEB SITE ADDRESS:
www.spssi.org/awards

FOUNDED: 1936

AREAS OF INTEREST:
Intergroup relations, social issues and psychology.

NAME(S) OF PROGRAMS:
● **The Louise Kidder Early Career Award**

TYPE:
Awards/prizes. This award is named in honor of Louise Kidder for her early career accomplishments and contributions to SPSSI.

PURPOSE:
To recognize social issues researchers who have made substantial contributions to the field early in their careers.

LEGAL BASIS:
Independently incorporated society.

ELIGIBILITY:
Nominees should be investigators who have made substantial contributions to social issues research within five years of receiving a graduate degree and who have demonstrated the potential to continue such contributions. Nominees need not be current Society members.

FINANCIAL DATA:
Amount of support per award: $500 and plaque.

NUMBER OF APPLICANTS MOST RECENT YEAR: 10.

NUMBER OF AWARDS: 1.

APPLICATION INFORMATION:
Application information may be obtained from the web site.
Deadline: June 25.

ADDRESS INQUIRIES TO:
Anila Balkissoon
Administrative Coordinator
(See address above.)

THE SOCIETY FOR THE PSYCHOLOGICAL STUDY OF SOCIAL ISSUES (SPSSI) [1884]

208 I Street, N.E.
Washington, DC 20002-4340
(202) 675-6956
Fax: (202) 675-6902

E-MAIL ADDRESS:
spssi@spssi.org
awards@spssi.org

WEB SITE ADDRESS:
www.spssi.org

FOUNDED: 1936

AREAS OF INTEREST:
Social psychology research.

NAME(S) OF PROGRAMS:
● **SPSSI Grants-in-Aid**

TYPE:
Grants-in-aid.

YEAR PROGRAM STARTED: 1956

PURPOSE:
To support scientific research in social problem areas related to the basic interests and goals of SPSSI and particularly those that are not likely to receive support from traditional sources.

LEGAL BASIS:
Independently incorporated society.

ELIGIBILITY:
This year, SPSSI's Grants-in-Aid program will include a small number of grants earmarked especially in support of research related to SPSSI's current policy priorities: interpersonal violence, marriage equality, and immigration reform.

FINANCIAL DATA:
Funds are normally not provided for travel to conventions, travel or living expenses while conducting research, stipends of principal investigators, costs associated with manuscript preparation, or the indirect costs of institutions.
Amount of support per award: Usually, up to $2,000 for postdoctoral work and up to $1,000 for predoctoral work.
Total amount of support: Varies.
Matching fund requirements: Applicant is required to submit evidence of a request to match amount offered.

NUMBER OF APPLICANTS MOST RECENT YEAR: 35.

NUMBER OF AWARDS: 20.

APPLICATION INFORMATION:
Application information is available on the web site.
Duration: One year.
Deadline: October 25.

PUBLICATIONS:
Application guidelines.

ADDRESS INQUIRIES TO:
SPSSI Central Office
(See address above.)

THE SOCIETY FOR THE PSYCHOLOGICAL STUDY OF SOCIAL ISSUES (SPSSI) [1885]

208 I Street, N.E.
Washington, DC 20002-4340
(202) 675-6956
Fax: (202) 675-6902

E-MAIL ADDRESS:
awards@spssi.org
spssi@spssi.org

WEB SITE ADDRESS:
www.spssi.org

FOUNDED: 1936

AREAS OF INTEREST:
Intergroup relations, social issues and psychology.

NAME(S) OF PROGRAMS:
• **The Social Issues Dissertation Award**

TYPE:
Awards/prizes. The Social Issues Dissertation Award is given for the best psychological dissertation concerned with social issues. It is judged upon scientific excellence and potential application to social problems.

PURPOSE:
To award dissertations that best demonstrate scientific excellence and potential application to social problems.

LEGAL BASIS:
Independently incorporated society.

ELIGIBILITY:
Any doctoral dissertation in psychology (or in a social science with psychological subject matter) accepted between March 1 of the previous year and up to the deadline of the current year is eligible. Applicants must have successfully defended their dissertation prior to the current year's award deadline. An individual or group may only submit one paper to one SPSSI award (including the Allport, Klineberg and Dissertation Awards) per award year. Applicants may not submit to the Dissertation Prize more than one time.

FINANCIAL DATA:
Amount of support per award: First prize $1,000; Second prize $500.

APPLICATION INFORMATION:
Online applications are the preferred method. Limit the number and size of files uploaded when applying online. For hard-copy submissions, mail the complete application to SPSSI, at the address above; Attn: Social Issues Dissertation.

The application should include a 500-word summary of the dissertation. The summary should include title, rationale, methods, and results of dissertation, as well as its implications for social problems. Please also include a cover sheet that states the title of one's dissertation, applicant's name, postal and e-mail addresses, phone number and university granting the degree.

Deadline: May 20. Announcement of finalist status by July 15.

PUBLICATIONS:
Application guidelines.

STIFTELSEN RIKSBANKENS JUBILEUMSFOND
Kungstradgardsg. 18
SE-114 86 Stockholm Sweden
46 08-50 62 64 00
Fax: 46 08-50 62 64 31

E-MAIL ADDRESS:
rj@rj.se

WEB SITE ADDRESS:
www.rj.se

TYPE:
Conferences/seminars; Exchange programs; Fellowships; General operating grants; Project/program grants; Research grants; Travel grants; Visiting scholars.

See entry 401 for full listing.

DR. W.C. SWANSON FAMILY FOUNDATION, INC.   [1886]
2520 North 1500 West
Ogden, UT 84404
(801) 392-0360
Fax: (801) 392-0429

E-MAIL ADDRESS:
sff@swanfound.org

WEB SITE ADDRESS:
www.swanfound.org

AREAS OF INTEREST:
Education, literacy, religion, science and prevention of cruelty to children or animals.

TYPE:
Matching gifts; Product donations; Project/program grants.

YEAR PROGRAM STARTED: 1977

PURPOSE:
To provide support for charitable, religious, literacy, scientific or educational purposes and the prevention of cruelty to children or animals.

LEGAL BASIS:
Private foundation.

ELIGIBILITY:
Grants are made to organizations that have tax-exempt status under Section 501(c)(3) of the Internal Revenue Code. Nonsectarian religious programs may apply. No grants are made to individuals.

GEOGRAPHIC RESTRICTIONS:
Primarily Ogden City, Weber County and northern Utah.

FINANCIAL DATA:
Amount of support per award: Varies.
Total amount of support: Varies.

APPLICATION INFORMATION:
Grant application by invitation only. Contact the Foundation for guidelines.
Duration: One year. Renewal possible.

BOARD OF DIRECTORS:
Michael Fosmark
Jon Greiner
Tom Hanrahan
Annabel Hofer
W. Charles Swanson

ADVISORY BOARD:
Kim Dohrer
Marcy Korgenski
Cindy R. Purcell
Robin Stoddard
Tami Swanson
W. Charles Swanson

ADDRESS INQUIRIES TO:
Bridgett Tasker, Grants Administrator
(See address above.)

U.S. ARMY RESEARCH INSTITUTE FOR BEHAVIORAL AND SOCIAL SCIENCES   [1887]
Building 1464
6000 6th Street
Ft. Belvoir, VA 22060-5586
(703) 545-2410

E-MAIL ADDRESS:
jay.goodwin@us.army.mil
gerald.f.goodwin.civ@mail.mil

FOUNDED: 1940

AREAS OF INTEREST:
Leadership, interactive simulation training, individual performance and information comprehension, and social structures affecting army performance.

TYPE:
Fellowships; Visiting scholars; Work-study programs; Research contracts.

PURPOSE:
To contribute to the cumulative knowledge base in behavioral science, with an eye to building new technologies capable of improving the effectiveness of Army personnel and their units.

LEGAL BASIS:
Government agency.

ELIGIBILITY:
Both single-investigator and collaborative research efforts will be considered, and multidisciplinary approaches to a central problem are encouraged. Collaborative efforts may involve researchers at a single institution or in cooperating institutions and joint university/industry partnerships are welcomed. Interest is welcomed from the widest range of institutions, including historically Black colleges and universities and minority institutions.

No consideration will be given to applied research or investigations whose primary focus is on physiological or chemical mechanisms or psychopathology. Another consideration determining support for the research is the judgment that findings have the potential for feeding into development of new behavioral technologies capable of improving the effectiveness of Army personnel and their units.

FINANCIAL DATA:
Amount of support per award: Contract amounts vary according to funds available and Army requirements. Generally $100,000 to $800,000. Average $300,000 per year.
Total amount of support: $6,000,000 for the year 2013.

APPLICATION INFORMATION:
Interested individuals should seek ARI's Broad Agency Announcement, issued annually between January and June. Preliminary concept papers (three to five pages) as well as formal proposals may be submitted. Concept papers should describe the problem to be addressed, justify the effort's theoretical significance and uniqueness, briefly describe the approach to the problem and state potential benefits to the Army. An estimated budget and project duration should be included, along with brief vitae of the principal investigators.

Concept papers will be reviewed within ARI for their relevance to Army priorities, theoretical significance and technical merit. Offers of highly rated concept papers will be invited to submit formal proposals.
Duration: Maximum five years. Average three years.
Deadline: Varies.

PUBLICATIONS:
Program announcement.

STAFF:
Dr. Jay Goodwin, Ph.D., Chief of Foundational Science Research Unit

ADDRESS INQUIRIES TO:
Dr. Jay Goodwin, Ph.D.
Chief of Foundational Science Research Unit
(See address above.)

U.S. DEPARTMENT OF JUSTICE
Office of Juvenile Justice and
Delinquency Prevention
810 7th Street, N.W., 5th Floor
Washington, DC 20531
(202) 307-5911
Fax: (202) 307-2093

WEB SITE ADDRESS:
www.ojjdp.ncjrs.gov

TYPE:
Conferences/seminars; Development grants;
Fellowships; Internships; Project/program
grants; Research grants; Residencies; Visiting
scholars; Research contracts. Grants to
conduct research, evaluation and development
on juvenile justice and delinquency
prevention activities, including the
development of new or improved approaches,
techniques, systems and program models to
conduct behavioral research on the causes of
juvenile crime, means of, intervention and
prevention, and to evaluate juvenile programs
and procedures.

See entry 1412 for full listing.

WOODROW WILSON INTERNATIONAL CENTER FOR SCHOLARS
One Woodrow Wilson Plaza
1300 Pennsylvania Avenue, N.W.
Washington, DC 20004-3027
(202) 691-4170
Fax: (202) 691-4001

E-MAIL ADDRESS:
fellowships@wilsoncenter.org

WEB SITE ADDRESS:
www.wilsoncenter.org

TYPE:
Fellowships; Research grants; Residencies;
Scholarships; Visiting scholars. The Center
seeks to commemorate, through its residential
fellowship program of advanced research,
both the scholarly depth and the public
concerns of Woodrow Wilson. The Center
welcomes outstanding project proposals in
the social sciences and humanities on
national and/or international issues - topics
that intersect with questions of public policy
or provide the historical framework to illume
policy issues of contemporary importance.
The Center especially welcomes projects
likely to foster communication between the
world of ideas and the world of public
affairs.

Projects should have relevance to the world
of public policy. Fellows should be prepared
to interact with policymakers in Washington
and with the Center's staff working on
similar areas.

Fellowships are tenable in residence only at
the Woodrow Wilson International Center for
Scholars. The Center will not provide support
for research to be carried out elsewhere.
Fellows devote their full time to research and
writing.

See entry 405 for full listing.

CARTER G. WOODSON INSTITUTE FOR AFRICAN-AMERICAN AND AFRICAN STUDIES
University of Virginia
McCormick Road, 108 Minor Hall
Charlottesville, VA 22903
(434) 924-3109
Fax: (434) 924-8820

E-MAIL ADDRESS:
woodson@virginia.edu

WEB SITE ADDRESS:
www.virginia.edu/~woodson

TYPE:
Fellowships. The Woodson Institute offers
residential fellowships to predoctoral and
postdoctoral scholars. These fellowships are
designed to facilitate the completion of works
in progress by providing scholars with
unencumbered leave.

Afro-American and African Studies is
considered to cover Africa, Africans and
peoples of African descent in North, Central
and South America and the Caribbean, past
and present.

See entry 407 for full listing.

Business and economics

THE ACTUARIAL FOUNDATION
475 North Martingale Road, Suite 600
Schaumburg, IL 60173-2226
(847) 706-3535
Fax: (847) 706-3599

E-MAIL ADDRESS:
Scholarships@ActFnd.org

WEB SITE ADDRESS:
www.actuarialfoundation.org

TYPE:
Scholarships.

See entry 2092 for full listing.

AMERICAN INSTITUTE OF CERTIFIED PUBLIC ACCOUNTANTS (AICPA)   [1888]
Team 331
220 Leigh Farm Road
Durham, NC 27707
(919) 402-2161
Fax: (919) 402-4505

E-MAIL ADDRESS:
scholarships@aicpa.org

WEB SITE ADDRESS:
www.thiswaytocpa.com/scholarships

AREAS OF INTEREST:
Accounting, finance and information systems.

NAME(S) OF PROGRAMS:
- AICPA Accountemps Student Scholarship

TYPE:
Scholarships. Awarded to accounting majors
to encourage them to become a C.P.A.

PURPOSE:
To provide financial assistance to students
who are currently majoring in accounting,
finance or information systems; to encourage
students to consider careers in accounting
and business.

ELIGIBILITY:
An applicant must meet the following
requirements:
(1) pursuing an undergraduate- or
graduate-level degree in an
"accounting-related" major
("accounting-related" shall be as determined
by Sponsors in Sponsors' sole discretion);
(2) planning to pursue the C.P.A. licensure
but not presently be a C.P.A.;
(3) applied to or been accepted into a public
or private, 501(c) four-year college or
university located in the U.S. or its
territories; the business program must be
accredited by the AACSB and/or ACBSP;
(4) completed at least 30 semester-hours (or
equivalent) of college coursework, including
at least six semester-hours (or equivalent) in
accounting, by end of spring 2013;
(5) maintained an overall and major grade
point average of at least 3.0 (on a 4.0 scale);
(6) enrolled as a full-time undergraduate (12
semester-hours or equivalent) or a full-time
graduate-level student (nine semester-hours or
equivalent) for the 2013-14 academic year;
an exception may be made if one plans to
participate in an internship program;
(7) be an AICPA student affiliate member (or
have submitted a new member application);
those interested can apply on the web site at
no cost;
(8) be a U.S. citizen or permanent resident
(green card holder) and;
(9) have some financial need (i.e., not
receiving a full or partial scholarship(s)
and/or grant(s) that cover and/or exceed one's
educational expenses).
Note: AICPA and RHI/Accountemps staff
and their family members are not eligible to
receive this scholarship.

GEOGRAPHIC RESTRICTIONS:
United States.

FINANCIAL DATA:
Amount of support per award: $2,500.

NUMBER OF AWARDS: Up to 10.

APPLICATION INFORMATION:
Guidelines are available on the web site.
Duration: One year. Nonrenewable.
Deadline: April 1.

ADDRESS INQUIRIES TO:
See e-mail address above.

*SPECIAL STIPULATIONS:
Students selected to receive an AICPA
scholarship must participate in the AICPA
Legacy Scholars program, which includes
performing at least eight hours of community
service per semester to advocate for the
C.P.A. profession. Through their community
service efforts, AICPA Legacy Scholars
enhance their leadership and communication
skills by building relationships with both
aspiring and seasoned C.P.As.

AMERICAN INSTITUTE OF CERTIFIED PUBLIC ACCOUNTANTS (AICPA)   [1889]
Team 331
220 Leigh Farm Road
Durham, NC 27707
(919) 402-2161
Fax: (919) 402-4505

E-MAIL ADDRESS:
scholarships@aicpa.org

WEB SITE ADDRESS:
www.thiswaytocpa.com

AREAS OF INTEREST:
Accounting, finance and information systems.

NAME(S) OF PROGRAMS:
- **AICPA Foundation Two-Year Transfer Scholarship**

TYPE:
Scholarships. AICPA Foundation Two-Year Transfer Scholarship provides financial assistance to students who have earned an Associate's degree in business, accounting, finance or economics with a declared intent to major in accounting at a four-year college or university.

PURPOSE:
To provide financial assistance to students who are currently majoring in accounting, finance or information systems; to encourage students to consider careers in accounting and business.

ELIGIBILITY:
An eligible applicant must be/have:
(1) earned an Associate's degree in business, accounting, finance or economics with a declared intent to major in accounting or an "accounting-related field" at a four-year college or university ("accounting-related" shall be as determined by Sponsors in Sponsors' sole discretion);
(2) planning to pursue the C.P.A. licensure but not presently be a C.P.A.;
(3) proof of acceptance into a public or private, not-for-profit 501(c) four-year college or university located in the U.S. states or territories for the full upcoming academic year; the business program must be accredited by the AACSB and/or ACBSP; (exception may be granted, but not guaranteed, at the discretion of Sponsor; inquire at the e-mail address above if one is unsure of one's eligibility);
(4) maintained an overall and major grade point average of at least 3.0 (on a 4.0 scale);
(5) enrolled as a full-time undergraduate (12 semester hours or equivalent); (note: an exception may be made if one plans to participate in an internship program);
(6) an AICPA student affiliate member (or have submitted a new member application); one can apply online at no cost at the web site above;
(7) a U.S. citizen or permanent resident (green card holder) and;
(8) some financial need (i.e., not receiving a full or partial scholarship(s) and/or grant(s) that cover and/or exceed one's educational expenses).
Note: AICPA staff and their family members are not eligible to receive this scholarship.

GEOGRAPHIC RESTRICTIONS:
Applicant must be a United States citizen or permanent resident (green card holder).

FINANCIAL DATA:
Scholarship aid may be used only for the payment of expenses that directly relate to obtaining an accounting education (e.g., tuition, fees, room and board and/or books and materials only). Scholarship payments are sent directly to the student's financial aid office on behalf of the student.
Amount of support per award: $1,000 for one year.

NUMBER OF AWARDS: 5.

APPLICATION INFORMATION:
Guidelines are available on the web site. The application process is completed in two rounds.

Duration: One academic year. Awards are nonrenewable, and past recipients may not reapply.
Deadline: All applicants must submit a completed scholarship application (first round) by April 1 at 11:59 P.M. Students selected to advance to the second round will be notified via e-mail by May 1.

ADDRESS INQUIRIES TO:
See e-mail address above.

*SPECIAL STIPULATIONS:
Students selected to receive an AICPA scholarship must participate in the AICPA Legacy Scholars program, which includes performing at least eight hours of community service per semester to advocate for the C.P.A. profession. Through their community service efforts, AICPA Legacy Scholars enhance their leadership and communication skills by building relationships with both aspiring and seasoned C.P.As.

AMERICAN INSTITUTE OF CERTIFIED PUBLIC ACCOUNTANTS (AICPA)   [1890]
220 Leigh Farm Road
Durham, NC 27707
(919) 402-2161
Fax: (919) 419-4705

E-MAIL ADDRESS:
scholarships@aicpa.org

WEB SITE ADDRESS:
www.thiswaytocpa.com/scholarships

AREAS OF INTEREST:
Accounting.

NAME(S) OF PROGRAMS:
- **John L. Carey Scholarship**

TYPE:
Scholarships.

PURPOSE:
To provide financial assistance to liberal arts or other nonbusiness- related degree holders pursuing graduate studies in accounting and the C.P.A. designation; to encourage students with little or no previous accounting education to consider professional accounting careers.

ELIGIBILITY:
An applicant must meet the following requirements:
(1) have obtained a liberal arts or other nonbusiness undergraduate degree from a regionally accredited institution in the U.S. prior to enrolling in a graduate accounting program;
(2) have not earned more than 12 credits in accounting or business during his or her undergraduate program;
(3) planning to pursue the C.P.A. licensure but not presently be a C.P.A.;
(4) planning to pursue a graduate-level degree in an "accounting-related" major ("accounting-related" shall be as determined by Sponsor in Sponsor's sole discretion); this program will enable a student to sit for the C.P.A. exam;
(5) applied to or been accepted into a public or private, 501(c) four-year college or university located in the U.S. or its territories; the business program must be accredited by the AACSB and/or ACBSP;
(6) not actively participating in a graduate accounting program;
(7) enrolled as a full-time graduate-level student (nine semester-hours or equivalent)

for the 2013-14 academic year; an exception may be granted if one plans to participate in an internship program;
(8) be an AICPA student affiliate member (or have submitted a new member application) by the beginning of the 2013-14 academic year; those interested can apply on the web site at no cost;
(9) be a U.S. citizen or permanent resident (green card holder) and;
(10) have some financial need (i.e., not already be receiving a full or partial scholarship(s) that covers or exceeds one's educational expenses).
Note: AICPA staff and their family members are not eligible to receive this scholarship.

GEOGRAPHIC RESTRICTIONS:
United States and its territories.

FINANCIAL DATA:
Amount of support per award: $5,000.
Total amount of support: Up to $50,000 annually.

NUMBER OF AWARDS: Up to 10.

APPLICATION INFORMATION:
Guidelines are available on the web site.
Duration: One year. Nonrenewable.
Deadline: April 1.

ADDRESS INQUIRIES TO:
See e-mail address above.

*SPECIAL STIPULATIONS:
Students selected to receive an AICPA scholarship must participate in the AICPA Legacy Scholars program, which includes performing at least eight hours of community service per semester to advocate for the C.P.A. profession. Through their community service efforts, AICPA Legacy Scholars enhance their leadership and communication skills by building relationships with both aspiring and seasoned C.P.As.

APICS EDUCATIONAL AND RESEARCH FOUNDATION, INC.
8430 West Bryn Mawr Avenue
Suite 1000
Chicago, IL 60631-3439
(800) 444-2742 (customer service)
(773) 867-1777
Fax: (773) 639-3115

E-MAIL ADDRESS:
jstults@apics.org

WEB SITE ADDRESS:
www.apics.org/education/erfoundation

TYPE:
Awards/prizes; Conferences/seminars; Fellowships; Project/program grants; Research grants. Plossl Doctoral Dissertation Competition is in the area of business management.

Grants are also available at the postdoctoral, academic-practitioner level in the field of business.

See entry 2599 for full listing.

APPRAISAL INSTITUTE EDUCATION TRUST   [1891]
200 West Madison Street
Suite 1500
Chicago, IL 60606
(312) 335-4100
Fax: (312) 335-4134

E-MAIL ADDRESS:
educationtrust@appraisalinstitute.org

WEB SITE ADDRESS:
www.aiedtrust.org

NAME(S) OF PROGRAMS:
- **Appraisal Institute Education Trust Scholarship**

TYPE:
Scholarships. Graduate and undergraduate scholarships to help worthy and qualified students finance the cost of college work leading to a degree in the fields of real estate appraisal, land economics, real estate and allied fields.

PURPOSE:
To help finance the educational endeavors of individuals concentrating their studies in real estate appraisal, land economics, real estate or allied fields.

ELIGIBILITY:
Applicants must be citizens of the U.S., attending a full-time college, U.S. university or community college, and have the expressed intention of majoring in real estate evaluation and related subjects. Related subjects may include land economics, economics, economic geography, and others similarly related. Levels of education for the scholarship must be sophomore, junior, senior and graduate year of college.

Preference will be given to those applicants whose previous training and whose future course of study indicate that they intend to follow a field of endeavor which comes within the scope of the objectives of the Appraisal Institute. Applicants must also demonstrate qualities of leadership and scholarly attainments.

GEOGRAPHIC RESTRICTIONS:
United States.

FINANCIAL DATA:
Amount of support per award: Graduate: $2,000; Undergraduate: $1,000.

NUMBER OF AWARDS: Approximately 50 per year.

APPLICATION INFORMATION:
Scholarship applications are available on the web site.
Duration: One academic year.
Deadline: April 15 for the following academic year.

OFFICERS:
Fred Grubbe, Chief Executive Officer

ADDRESS INQUIRIES TO:
Scholarship Committee
(See address above.)

THE CONSORTIUM FOR GRADUATE STUDY IN MANAGEMENT [1892]
229 Chesterfield Business Parkway
Chesterfield, MO 63005
(636) 681-5553
(888) 658-6814
Fax: (636) 681-5499

WEB SITE ADDRESS:
www.cgsm.org

FOUNDED: 1966

NAME(S) OF PROGRAMS:
- **Consortium Fellowship**
- **Fellowships for Minorities in Management**

TYPE:
Fellowships. Graduate fellowships for minority students interested in management careers in business.

YEAR PROGRAM STARTED: 1967

PURPOSE:
To hasten the entry of minorities into management positions in business.

LEGAL BASIS:
Not-for-profit, IRS 501(c)(3) status.

ELIGIBILITY:
U.S. citizenship and permanent residence in the U.S. is required. African Americans, Hispanic Americans and Native Americans with Baccalaureate degrees are eligible to apply. The undergraduate degree need not be in business or economics.

Fellowships are tenable only at Consortium institutions, including University of California-Berkeley, Carnegie-Mellon University, Dartmouth College, Emory University, Indiana University (Bloomington), New York University, University of Michigan (Ann Arbor), University of North Carolina (Chapel Hill), University of Rochester, University of Southern California, University of Texas (Austin), University of Virginia, University of Wisconsin (Madison) and Washington University (St. Louis).

There are no fellowships awarded for part-time study.

FINANCIAL DATA:
The fellowship includes full tuition and required fees. Loans are also available for students who establish need in excess of the tuition.
Total amount of support: $26,000,000 for fiscal year 2013.

NUMBER OF APPLICANTS MOST RECENT YEAR: 1,000.

NUMBER OF AWARDS: 400.

APPLICATION INFORMATION:
Guidelines and application form are available on the web site.
Duration: Fellowships are awarded for a maximum of four semesters of full-time study.
Deadline: November 15 and January 5.

IRS IDENTIFICATION NUMBER: 43-0962198

STAFF:
Peter Aranda, Chief Executive Officer
Glenn Wilen, Vice President of Finance and Administration

DECA [1893]
1908 Association Drive
Reston, VA 20191
(703) 860-5000
Fax: (703) 860-4013

E-MAIL ADDRESS:
cindy_allen@deca.org

WEB SITE ADDRESS:
www.deca.org

FOUNDED: 1946

AREAS OF INTEREST:
Marketing education, management and entrepreneurship.

TYPE:
Scholarships.

YEAR PROGRAM STARTED: 1962

PURPOSE:
To further education and careers in marketing education, management and entrepreneurship.

LEGAL BASIS:
Nonprofit association.

ELIGIBILITY:
Applicant must be a current member of DECA.

GEOGRAPHIC RESTRICTIONS:
United States.

FINANCIAL DATA:
Amount of support per award: Varies.
Total amount of support: Varies.

NUMBER OF APPLICANTS MOST RECENT YEAR: 6,660.

NUMBER OF AWARDS: 150.

APPLICATION INFORMATION:
Information is available at the web site.
Duration: One year. Renewals are considered. Must reapply.
Deadline: January 16, 2015.

ADDRESS INQUIRIES TO:
Scholarship Department
(See address above.)

THE DIRECT MARKETING CLUB OF NEW YORK (DMCNY) [1894]
54 Adams Street
Garden City, NY 11530
(516) 746-6700
Fax: (516) 294-8141

E-MAIL ADDRESS:
info@dmcny.org

WEB SITE ADDRESS:
www.dmcny.org

FOUNDED: 1930

CONSULTING OR VOLUNTEER SERVICES:
Team of creative specialists is available for consulting or speaking.

NAME(S) OF PROGRAMS:
- **Boardroom Awards**
- **Silver Apple Award Scholarships**

TYPE:
Conferences/seminars; Grants-in-aid. Non-degree courses and seminars.

YEAR PROGRAM STARTED: 1977

PURPOSE:
To advance and promote the members' charitable, educational, scientific and literary interests, as well as their understanding and application of professional direct marketing practices.

LEGAL BASIS:
New York state not-for-profit corporation.

ELIGIBILITY:
Scholarships to students in direct marketing studies only. Grants made to universities only.

GEOGRAPHIC RESTRICTIONS:
Connecticut, New Jersey and New York.

FINANCIAL DATA:
Amount of support per award: $500 to $1,500.
Total amount of support: Approximately $3,500.

NUMBER OF AWARDS: 7.

APPLICATION INFORMATION:
Contact DMCNY for guidelines.
Duration: One year.

ADDRESS INQUIRIES TO:
Stuart Boysen, Director
(See address above.)

*SPECIAL STIPULATIONS:
The scholarship applicant's course of study
must be related to direct marketing.

ECONOMIC HISTORY
ASSOCIATION   [1895]
Economics Department
University of Arizona
Tucson, AZ 85721
(520) 621-4421

E-MAIL ADDRESS:
pfishback@eller.arizona.edu

WEB SITE ADDRESS:
www.eh.net/eha

FOUNDED: 1940

AREAS OF INTEREST:
Economic history.

NAME(S) OF PROGRAMS:
● Arthur H. Cole Grants-in-Aid

TYPE:
Grants-in-aid. Grants for advanced research
in any aspect of economic history.

YEAR PROGRAM STARTED: 1972

PURPOSE:
To support individual research in the field of
economic history or to supplement a major
fellowship.

LEGAL BASIS:
Nonprofit.

ELIGIBILITY:
Applicants must have completed their Ph.D.
and must be members of the Economic
History Association. Preference is given to
recent Ph.D. recipients.

FINANCIAL DATA:
Amount of support per award: Up to $5,000.

NUMBER OF APPLICANTS MOST RECENT YEAR:
20.

NUMBER OF AWARDS: 4.

APPLICATION INFORMATION:
Application information is available on the
Association web site.
Duration: One year.
Deadline: March 1.

PUBLICATIONS:
Annual newsletter; The Journal of Economic
History.

IRS IDENTIFICATION NUMBER: 13-6128711

THE EDUCATIONAL
FOUNDATION FOR WOMEN IN
ACCOUNTING   [1896]
136 South Keowee Street
Dayton, OH 45402-2241
(937) 424-3391
Fax: (937) 222-5794

E-MAIL ADDRESS:
info@efwa.org

WEB SITE ADDRESS:
www.efwa.org

FOUNDED: 1966

AREAS OF INTEREST:
Women in the accounting field.

NAME(S) OF PROGRAMS:
● Laurels Fund

● Michelle L. McDonald Scholarship
● Moss Adams LLP Scholarship
● Seattle ASWA Chapter Scholarship
● Women in Need Scholarship
● Women in Transition Scholarship

TYPE:
Scholarships. Laurels Fund provides a
one-year academic scholarship for women
pursuing a Ph.D. in accounting.

Women in Need Scholarship is available to
women in their third, fourth or fifth year of
academic pursuit who need the financial
support to complete their degrees. It is
renewable annually upon satisfactory
completion of course requirements.

Women in Transition Scholarship is intended
for women returning to school as freshmen to
earn a Bachelor's degree in accounting. It is
renewable annually upon satisfactory
completion of course requirements.

YEAR PROGRAM STARTED: 1966

PURPOSE:
To support the advancement of women in the
accounting profession through the funding of
education, research, career literature,
publications and other projects; to encourage
and enable women to enter the accounting
profession and empower them to achieve
equal opportunities and equal rewards.

LEGAL BASIS:
501(c)(3) organization.

ELIGIBILITY:
Women who are pursuing accounting degrees
at the undergraduate, graduate and
postgraduate levels.

GEOGRAPHIC RESTRICTIONS:
United States.

FINANCIAL DATA:
Amount of support per award: Varies.
Total amount of support: Varies.

NUMBER OF AWARDS: Vary annually.

APPLICATION INFORMATION:
Applications are available on the web site.
Duration: Laurels Fund, Michelle L.
McDonald, Moss Adams LLP and Seattle
ASWA Chapter Scholarships: One year;
Women in Need Scholarship: Two years;
Women in Transition Scholarship: Four
years.
Deadline: Laurels Fund: May 30. All others:
May 1.

ADDRESS INQUIRIES TO:
Kimberly Fantaci, Foundation Administrator
(See address above.)

ERNST & YOUNG
FOUNDATION   [1897]
200 Plaza Drive
Secaucus, NJ 07094
(201) 872-5686
(201) 872-2200
Fax: (866) 855-4960

E-MAIL ADDRESS:
ellen.glazerman@ey.com

WEB SITE ADDRESS:
www.ey.com

FOUNDED: 1937

AREAS OF INTEREST:
Higher education, with specific interests in
accounting and business.

TYPE:
Fellowships; Matching gifts; Scholarships.

YEAR PROGRAM STARTED: 1937

PURPOSE:
To support higher education.

LEGAL BASIS:
Public charity.

ELIGIBILITY:
No grants to individuals. No cold requests.

GEOGRAPHIC RESTRICTIONS:
United States and its territories.

FINANCIAL DATA:
Amount of support per award: Varies.
Total amount of support: Varies.
Matching fund requirements: Ernst & Young
Foundation will only match contributions to
an accredited college, junior college,
community college, university, graduate
school or professional school.

APPLICATION INFORMATION:
Contact the Foundation for details.
Duration: Varies.
Deadline: Grant requests are reviewed
continuously.

ADDRESS INQUIRIES TO:
Ellen Glazerman, Executive Director
(See address and e-mail above.)

FEDERATION OF AMERICAN
CONSUMERS AND
TRAVELERS   [1898]
318 Hillsboro Avenue
P.O. Box 104
Edwardsville, IL 62025
(618) 656-0454
(800) 872-3228
Fax: (618) 656-5369

E-MAIL ADDRESS:
vrolens@usafact.org

WEB SITE ADDRESS:
www.usafact.org

NAME(S) OF PROGRAMS:
● Community and Business Project
  Grants

TYPE:
Project/program grants; Seed money grants.

PURPOSE:
To support civic club, church, and
community projects that are nominated by
members.

ELIGIBILITY:
Projects are nominated by members.

GEOGRAPHIC RESTRICTIONS:
United States.

FINANCIAL DATA:
Amount of support per award: $100 to
$2,500, based on funding availability and the
needs of the specific proposal.
Total amount of support: Varies.

APPLICATION INFORMATION:
Contact the Federation for guidelines.
Duration: One-time award.
Deadline: January, April, July and October.

ADDRESS INQUIRIES TO:
Vicki Rolens, Managing Director
(See address above.)

4A'S
1065 Avenue of the Americas, 16th Floor
New York, NY 10018
(212) 682-2500
Fax: (212) 867-8329

E-MAIL ADDRESS:
maip@aaaa.org

WEB SITE ADDRESS:
maip.aaaa.org

TYPE:
Internships.

See entry 990 for full listing.

HAGLEY MUSEUM AND LIBRARY

Center for the History of
Business, Technology and Society
298 Buck Road
Wilmington, DE 19807
(302) 658-2400 ext. 243
Fax: (302) 655-3188

E-MAIL ADDRESS:
clockman@hagley.org

WEB SITE ADDRESS:
www.hagley.org

TYPE:
Fellowships; Research grants; Travel grants;
Visiting scholars. Grants to support
short-term research in the imprint,
manuscript, pictorial and artifact collections
of the Hagley Museum and Library.

The Henry Belin du Pont Dissertation
Fellowship in Business, Technology, and
Society supports research and writing by
candidates for doctoral degrees. Projects
should demonstrate superior intellectual
quality and make substantial use of Hagley's
collections.

Henry Belin du Pont Fellowships support
research in the collections of the museum
and library.

Hagley Exploratory Research Grant supports
a one-week visit by scholars who believe that
their project will benefit from Hagley
research collections, but need the opportunity
to explore them on-site to determine if a
Henry Belin du Pont research grant
application is warranted.

See entry 593 for full listing.

THE S.S. HUEBNER FOUNDATION FOR INSURANCE EDUCATION   [1899]

Department of Risk Management and Insurance
Georgia State University
35 Broad Street, Room 1135
Atlanta, GA 30303
(404) 413-7462
Fax: (404) 413-7499

E-MAIL ADDRESS:
cciccotello@gsu.edu

WEB SITE ADDRESS:
www.huebnerfoundation.org

FOUNDED: 1940

AREAS OF INTEREST:
Insurance and risk management.

TYPE:
The Foundation's program goals are:
(1) to support the Ph.D. program at Georgia
State University that is training the next
generation of scholars who will conduct
academic research on insurance economics
specifically and the efficient allocation of risk
in the economy more generally;
(2) to sponsor a periodic summer symposium
or occasional lecture series facilitated by

leading scholars designed to build
collaborative research relationships among
young researchers at Georgia State University
and elsewhere who are interested in
risk-related topics and;
(3) to provide assistance for professionals
who seek to develop the research skills
necessary to address contemporary insurance
and risk problems in such areas as regulation,
policy or industry practice.

YEAR PROGRAM STARTED: 1940

PURPOSE:
To advance university-level risk management
and insurance scholarship and learning.

APPLICATION INFORMATION:
Contact the Foundation for guidelines.

IRS IDENTIFICATION NUMBER: 23-6297325

ADDRESS INQUIRIES TO:
Conrad Ciccotello, J.D., Ph.D.
Executive Director
(See address above.)

INSTITUTE FOR SUPPLY MANAGEMENT   [1900]

2055 East Centennial Circle
Tempe, AZ 85284
(480) 752-6276
Fax: (480) 752-7890

E-MAIL ADDRESS:
nneibergall@ism.ws

WEB SITE ADDRESS:
www.ism.ws

FOUNDED: 1915

AREAS OF INTEREST:
Purchasing/supply management.

NAME(S) OF PROGRAMS:
● **ISM Dissertation Research Grant -
Phase 1 (Doctoral)**

TYPE:
Research grants. A limited number of grants
are available to doctoral candidates interested
in pursuing advanced study in industrial
and/or institutional purchasing, supply
management and closely related fields.

YEAR PROGRAM STARTED: 1984

PURPOSE:
To produce useful research that can be
applied to purchasing and supply
management; to help develop high-potential
academicians who will teach and conduct
research in purchasing and supply
management.

LEGAL BASIS:
501(c)(3) nonprofit educational and research
organization.

ELIGIBILITY:
Applicants must be doctoral candidates who
are pursuing a Ph.D. or D.B.A. in
purchasing, business, logistics, management,
economics, industrial engineering, or related
fields. Applicants must be enrolled full-time
in accredited U.S. universities.

GEOGRAPHIC RESTRICTIONS:
United States.

FINANCIAL DATA:
The stipend is allocated to the student for
support in conducting the research project
and related academic work. Payment is made
in two installments; one-half upon receipt of
a written statement from the dissertation
committee chairperson verifying that the
research project is approximately 50%

completed and one-half upon receipt of a
signed copy, by the dissertation committee,
of the dissertation.
Amount of support per award: Up to
$12,000.
Total amount of support: Up to $24,000.

NUMBER OF APPLICANTS MOST RECENT YEAR:
5.

NUMBER OF AWARDS: Up to 4, including partial.

APPLICATION INFORMATION:
Application forms and guidelines are
available at the web site.
Duration: Must be complete within three
years.
Deadline: March 31. Announcement on or
about June 30.

PUBLICATIONS:
Brochure.

ADDRESS INQUIRIES TO:
Nora Neibergall
Senior Vice President
Doctoral Grant Committee
(See address above.)

THE CALVIN K. KAZANJIAN ECONOMICS FOUNDATION, INC.   [1901]

P.O. Box 300
Dallas, PA 18612-0300
(570) 690-4629

E-MAIL ADDRESS:
director@kazanjian.org

WEB SITE ADDRESS:
www.kazanjian.org

FOUNDED: 1947

AREAS OF INTEREST:
Promoting the understanding of economics
and addressing the issue of economic
illiteracy.

TYPE:
Grants-in-aid. Grants for economic education.

PURPOSE:
To aid in bringing greater happiness and
prosperity to all through a better
understanding of economics.

ELIGIBILITY:
The Foundation will only give serious
consideration to those projects which directly
advance its immediate purposes and meet its
guidelines.

GEOGRAPHIC RESTRICTIONS:
United States.

FINANCIAL DATA:
Amount of support per award: $5,000 to
$50,000 per year.
Total amount of support: $400,000.

APPLICATION INFORMATION:
Guidelines and criteria are found on the web
site. Applicants must include:
(1) copy of an IRS nonprofit determination
letter;
(2) latest audited financial statement;
(3) list of board of trustees;
(4) annual budget and;
(5) project budget.
Duration: Varies.
Deadline: September 15 for December
review. February 15 for June review.

ADDRESS INQUIRIES TO:
Michael MacDowell, Managing Director
(See address above.)

*PLEASE NOTE:
The Foundation does not give scholarships.

KPMG FOUNDATION   [1902]
3 Chestnut Ridge Road
Montvale, NJ 07645-0435
(201) 307-7932
Fax: (201) 624-7763

E-MAIL ADDRESS:
tperino@kpmg.com

WEB SITE ADDRESS:
www.kpmgfoundation.org

FOUNDED: 1968

AREAS OF INTEREST:
Academic research, education and
professional development in the area of
business.

NAME(S) OF PROGRAMS:
● **KPMG Professorships**
● **Minority Accounting Doctoral
  Scholarships**
● **The PhD Project**

TYPE:
Conferences/seminars; Matching gifts;
Professorships; Project/program grants.
Special grants, made on the recommendations
of the Firm's college relations partners, are
for specific projects that create new
educational opportunities.

YEAR PROGRAM STARTED: 1968

PURPOSE:
To recognize outstanding achievement in
accounting education and research; to
recognize academic excellence and
community achievement; to help minority
students obtain careers in business and
industry; to promote research that will benefit
the profession now and in the future.

LEGAL BASIS:
Private foundation.

ELIGIBILITY:
The Foundation restricts grants to educational
purposes related to its firm's functional areas,
including accounting, auditing and tax.

GEOGRAPHIC RESTRICTIONS:
United States.

FINANCIAL DATA:
Amount of support per award: Minority
Accounting Doctoral Scholarships: $10,000.
Matching fund requirements: The Matching
Gift Program only matches employee/partner
gifts to colleges and universities from which
the donors are alumni or where KPMG
recruits. Minimum $50 for employees and
maximum $5,000 per institution per fiscal
year.

NUMBER OF APPLICANTS MOST RECENT YEAR:
15.

NUMBER OF AWARDS: 10.

APPLICATION INFORMATION:
Details available on the web site.
Duration: One year. Renewable for a total of
five years.
Deadline: Doctoral Scholarships: May 1.

PUBLICATIONS:
Annual report.

IRS IDENTIFICATION NUMBER: 13-6262199

BOARD OF TRUSTEES:
Jose Rodriguez, Chairperson
Bernard J. Milano, President
Theresa Ahlstrom

Kelli Brooks
Robert Fisher
Christine Griffith
Laurel Hammer
Kathy Hannan
Laura Hay
Tammy Hunter
Paul Knopp
Milford McGuirt
Bruce Pfau
Rebecca Sproule
French Taylor

ADDRESS INQUIRIES TO:
Tara Perino, Director
(See address above.)

LIBRA FUTURE FUND   [1903]
3 Canal Plaza, Suite 500
Portland, ME 04101
(207) 879-6280
Fax: (207) 879-6281

E-MAIL ADDRESS:
erik@librafoundation.org

WEB SITE ADDRESS:
www.librafoundation.org/libra-future-fund

FOUNDED: 2005

AREAS OF INTEREST:
Economic development and job opportunities
in Maine.

NAME(S) OF PROGRAMS:
● **Libra Future Fund Young Adult Grant
  Program**

TYPE:
Project/program grants. To promote economic
development and create job opportunities in
Maine.

YEAR PROGRAM STARTED: 2005

PURPOSE:
To capitalize upon the energy and creativity
that Maine's young people embody; to
combat youth out-migration by supporting
initiatives that increase the number of
Maine-based professional opportunities.

ELIGIBILITY:
Applicants must be 18 to 29 years of age,
reside in Maine at least eight months per
year, or be originally from Maine, but
attending school out of state.

GEOGRAPHIC RESTRICTIONS:
Maine.

FINANCIAL DATA:
Amount of support per award: $3,000 to
$5,000.
Total amount of support: Approximately
$40,000 for the year 2012.

APPLICATION INFORMATION:
Complete instructions can be found on the
Fund's web site.
Duration: One-time grant.
Deadline: April 1, July 1 and November 1.

ADDRESS INQUIRIES TO:
Erik Hayward, President
(See address above.)

THE GERALD LOEB AWARDS
UCLA Anderson School of Management
110 Westwood Plaza
Gold Hall, Suite B307
Los Angeles, CA 90095-1481
(310) 825-4478
Fax: (310) 825-4479

E-MAIL ADDRESS:
loeb@anderson.ucla.edu

WEB SITE ADDRESS:
www.loeb.anderson.ucla.edu

TYPE:
Awards/prizes. Awards to recognize business
and financial journalists for important
contributions to the understanding of
business, finance and the economy.
See entry 1942 for full listing.

MARKETING EDGE   [1904]
1120 Avenue of the Americas
New York, NY 10036-6700
(212) 768-7277 ext. 1512
Fax: (212) 790-1561

E-MAIL ADDRESS:
admin@marketingedge.org

WEB SITE ADDRESS:
www.marketingedge.org

FOUNDED: 1965

AREAS OF INTEREST:
Investing in the future of the
direct/interactive marketing field.

NAME(S) OF PROGRAMS:
● **Robert Kestnbaum Research Program**
● **Marketing EDGE Leadership
  Development Program**
● **Marketing EDGE Scholarship Program**
● **Shankar-Spiegel Award for the Best
  Dissertation Proposal in
  Direct/Interactive Marketing**

TYPE:
Awards/prizes; Conferences/seminars;
Exchange programs; Internships; Research
grants; Scholarships; Research contracts.
Robert Kestnbaum Research Program is
intended to generate leading-edge academic
research to impact the future of
direct/interactive marketing.

Marketing EDGE Leadership Development
Program offers qualified applicants the
opportunity to acquire valuable work
experience at a competitive salary during a
unique 12-month program.

Marketing EDGE Scholarship Program
provides education funding support to
undergraduate and graduate students
nationwide.

Shankar-Spiegel Award for the Best
Dissertation Proposal in Direct/Interactive
Marketing recognizes doctoral candidates
with the best dissertation proposal in
direct/interactive marketing. Doctoral students
from accredited doctoral programs are
eligible to receive this award.

YEAR PROGRAM STARTED: 1965

PURPOSE:
To nurture, maintain and grow talent
throughout the direct/interactive marketing
field; to educate students today in order to
enrich the talent pool in this field tomorrow.

LEGAL BASIS:
Nonprofit, tax-exempt organization.

ELIGIBILITY:
Varies by program.

GEOGRAPHIC RESTRICTIONS:
United States.

FINANCIAL DATA:
Amount of support per award: $1,000 to
$5,000.

APPLICATION INFORMATION:
Form and guidelines available online.

PUBLICATIONS:
Annual report; conference materials; *Journal of Interactive Marketing*®.

IRS IDENTIFICATION NUMBER: 13-6222757

STAFF:
Terri L. Bartlett, President
Marie Adolphe, Vice President, Program Development
Michelle Kennedy, Director, Development

ADDRESS INQUIRIES TO:
Terri L. Bartlett, President
(See address above.)

MCGRAW HILL FINANCIAL [1905]
1221 Avenue of the Americas, 47th Floor
New York, NY 10020-1095
(212) 512-6480
Fax: (212) 512-3611

E-MAIL ADDRESS:
susan.wallman@mhfi.com

WEB SITE ADDRESS:
www.mhfi.com

FOUNDED: 1979

AREAS OF INTEREST:
Corporate giving program: Financial essentials/economic empowerment.

CONSULTING OR VOLUNTEER SERVICES:
Employee Volunteer Grants and Global Volunteer Day Grants.

TYPE:
Matching gifts; Project/program grants. The grants program places its strongest emphasis on financial essentials and economic empowerment. Contributions through matching gifts are to colleges and universities, to financial literacy, to adult literacy organizations whose sole purpose is the delivery or advancement of adult basic skills instruction, and to arts and cultural organizations providing matching gifts on a 1:1 basis.

YEAR PROGRAM STARTED: 1979

PURPOSE:
To contribute to the vitality and well-being of the communities in which it is involved.

LEGAL BASIS:
Corporate giving program.

ELIGIBILITY:
Applicants must be organizations that qualify as public charities under the Internal Revenue Code 501(c)(3). Preference given to areas containing an employee base. Grants are not made to individual schools or school districts.

FINANCIAL DATA:
Amount of support per award: $5,000 to $25,000. Average grant $10,000.
Total amount of support: $4,100,000 for the year 2013.

APPLICATION INFORMATION:
Contact the organization for guidelines.
Duration: One year unless multiyear pledge. Reapply each year.

PUBLICATIONS:
Corporate annual report.

BOARD OF DIRECTORS:
Harold McGraw, III, Chairman
Sir Winfried F.W. Bischoff
William D. Green
Charles E. Haldeman, Jr.
Linda Koch Lorimer

Robert P. McGraw
Hilda Ochoa-Brillembourg
Douglas L. Peterson
Sir Michael Rake
Edward B. Rust, Jr.
Kurt L. Schmoke, Esq.
Sidney Taurel
Richard E. Thornburgh

ADDRESS INQUIRIES TO:
Susan A. Wallman
Manager, Corporate Contributions
(See address above.)

THE BURTON D. MORGAN FOUNDATION [1906]
22 Aurora Street
Hudson, OH 44236
(330) 655-1660
Fax: (330) 655-1673

E-MAIL ADDRESS:
drafferty@bdmorganfdn.org

WEB SITE ADDRESS:
www.bdmorganfdn.org

FOUNDED: 1967

AREAS OF INTEREST:
Free enterprise system, economics and entrepreneurship education.

TYPE:
Challenge/matching grants; Conferences/seminars; Endowments; General operating grants; Project/program grants.

YEAR PROGRAM STARTED: 1967

PURPOSE:
To strengthen the free enterprise system by investing in organizations and institutions that foster the entrepreneurial spirit.

LEGAL BASIS:
Private foundation.

ELIGIBILITY:
Grants are made to organizations recognized as public charities under the Internal Revenue Code Section 501(c)(3). The Foundation does not usually make multiyear grants and does not ordinarily consider grants to annual fund drives, units of government, or organizations and institutions which are primarily tax-supported, including state universities. Grants are not made to individuals.

GEOGRAPHIC RESTRICTIONS:
Primarily northeastern Ohio.

FINANCIAL DATA:
Amount of support per award: Varies.
Total amount of support: Varies.

COOPERATIVE FUNDING PROGRAMS: Blackstone LaunchPad Program; Northeast Ohio Collegiate Entrepreneurship Program.

NUMBER OF APPLICANTS MOST RECENT YEAR: 241 for the year 2012.

NUMBER OF AWARDS: 113 for the year 2012.

REPRESENTATIVE AWARDS:
$75,500 to Invent Now; $80,000 to Junior Achievement of North Central Ohio; $80,000 to Entrepreneurship Education Consortium; $56,000 to Northeast Ohio Technology Coalition; $40,000 to ideastream.

APPLICATION INFORMATION:
Before submitting a full proposal, organizations should send a letter of inquiry to the Foundation regarding the request. All letters of inquiry and applications must be submitted online through the Foundation's web site.

Duration: One year.
Deadline: Letter of Inquiry: February 1, May 1 and September 1. Full Proposal: March 1, June 1 and October 1.

PUBLICATIONS:
E-Spirit, newsletter; *Pipeline*, Foundation newsletter; *Venture Adventure*, e-newsletter.

IRS IDENTIFICATION NUMBER: 34-6598971

OFFICER:
Deborah D. Hoover, President

ADDRESS INQUIRIES TO:
Diane Rafferty, Executive Assistant
(See address above.)

THE NASDAQ OMX GROUP EDUCATIONAL FOUNDATION, INC. [1907]
805 King Farm Boulevard
Rockville, MD 20850
(301) 978-8738
(800) 842-0356
Fax: (301) 978-5055

E-MAIL ADDRESS:
foundation@nasdaq.com

WEB SITE ADDRESS:
www.nasdaqomx.com

FOUNDED: 1994

AREAS OF INTEREST:
Financial markets literacy.

TYPE:
Development grants; Fellowships; Project/program grants; Research grants; Seed money grants. The Foundation offers grants in the following areas:
(1) academic study or research;
(2) Ph.D. dissertation fellowships;
(3) curriculum development and;
(4) educational projects or programs.

PURPOSE:
To promote learning about capital formation, financial markets and entrepreneurship through innovative educational programs.

ELIGIBILITY:
The Foundation will accept proposals from educational institutions and organizations designated as tax-exempt according to Section 501(c)(3) of the Internal Revenue Code.

In limited cases, proposals from highly and specifically qualified individuals, only for the purpose of conducting independent academic study or research on financial markets, are accepted.

FINANCIAL DATA:
Amount of support per award: Varies.
Total amount of support: Varies.

APPLICATION INFORMATION:
Applicants must submit a letter of inquiry and be invited to submit a proposal.
Duration: One year, unless otherwise specified.
Deadline: Varies.

ADDRESS INQUIRIES TO:
Joan C. Conley, Senior Vice President and Corporate Secretary or
Angela Henson, Program Administrator
(See address above.)

NATIONAL ENDOWMENT FOR FINANCIAL EDUCATION (NEFE)   [1908]
1331 17th Street, Suite 1200
Denver, CO 80202
(303) 741-6333
Fax: (303) 220-0838

E-MAIL ADDRESS:
nefegrantrequest@nefe.org

WEB SITE ADDRESS:
www.nefe.org

FOUNDED: 1997

AREAS OF INTEREST:
Financial education for the American public.

NAME(S) OF PROGRAMS:
• **NEFE Fellows Program**
• **NEFE Grants Program**

TYPE:
Fellowships; Research grants. NEFE Fellows Program recruits qualified individuals from diverse backgrounds who share a common interest in working on projects within NEFE's broad scope of activities and in gaining nonprofit operations and management experience.

NEFE Grants Program awards grants for research projects that will expand the body of knowledge in the field of financial literacy.

YEAR PROGRAM STARTED: 1998

PURPOSE:
To help all Americans acquire the information and gain the skills necessary to take control of their personal finances.

ELIGIBILITY:
To be considered for a fellowship opportunity, candidates must be:
(1) in good standing with their academic institution and;
(2) a currently registered Master's degree-seeking student.

Grants are awarded to organizations that have been designated tax-exempt status according to Internal Revenue Code Section 501(c)(3) or its equivalent for colleges and universities. Grants are not awarded to:
(1) individuals;
(2) organizations that have not been designated tax-exempt under Section 501(c)(3) or its equivalent;
(3) organizations that discriminate on the basis of age, color, disability, marital status, nationality, race, religion, sex, sexual orientation, or veteran status;
(4) organizations and/or project principals and team members who fail to meet NEFE's Strategy Statement and Procedures requirements concerning the U.S.A. Patriot Act and related regulations;
(5) foreign organizations;
(6) international programs or projects or;
(7) organizations whose projects include re-grant of NEFE funding.

GEOGRAPHIC RESTRICTIONS:
United States.

FINANCIAL DATA:
Amount of support per award: NEFE Fellows Program: $3,000 to $6,000 per semester; NEFE Grants Program: Generally $100,000 up.
Total amount of support: Varies.

NUMBER OF APPLICANTS MOST RECENT YEAR:
NEFE Grants Program: 100.

NUMBER OF AWARDS: NEFE Grants Program: 3.

APPLICATION INFORMATION:
Fellowship Program does not accept unsolicited applications. Applicants to the Grant Program must first submit a Concept Inquiry Form. Those projects appearing to have strong potential will move to a proposal phase; applicants for those selected projects will be given further instruction at that time.
Duration: Varies.
Deadline: NEFE Fellows Program: Varies. NEFE Grants Program: First Tuesday in June and first Tuesday in December.

PUBLICATIONS:
NEFE Digest.

IRS IDENTIFICATION NUMBER: 84-0632115

ADDRESS INQUIRIES TO:
Grants Manager
(See address above.)

THE NATIONAL RESTAURANT ASSOCIATION EDUCATIONAL FOUNDATION   [1909]
175 West Jackson Boulevard
Suite 1500
Chicago, IL 60604-2814
(312) 715-6744

E-MAIL ADDRESS:
scholars@nraef.org

WEB SITE ADDRESS:
www.nraef.org/scholarships

FOUNDED: 1987

AREAS OF INTEREST:
Foodservice education and training.

NAME(S) OF PROGRAMS:
• **Professional Development for Educators Scholarship**

TYPE:
Training grants; Travel grants.

PURPOSE:
To support foodservice educators earning their Certified Secondary Educators Foodservice certification; to provide financial support to attend an NRA Summer Institute or participate in a "hands-on" industry work experience.

ELIGIBILITY:
Must be an educator of a restaurant and/or foodservice-related program in a secondary school and submit a signed letter of recommendation on school letterhead that also verifies employment by an immediate supervisor or program director. Applicants must be U.S. citizens/residents.

GEOGRAPHIC RESTRICTIONS:
United States.

FINANCIAL DATA:
Amount of support per award: $1,750.
Total amount of support: Varies.

NUMBER OF AWARDS: Varies.

APPLICATION INFORMATION:
Application information is available online.
Duration: Varies.

THE NATIONAL RESTAURANT ASSOCIATION EDUCATIONAL FOUNDATION
175 West Jackson Boulevard
Suite 1500
Chicago, IL 60604-2702
(800) 765-2122 ext. 6744
Fax: (312) 566-9733

E-MAIL ADDRESS:
scholars@nraef.org

WEB SITE ADDRESS:
www.nraef.org/scholarships

TYPE:
Scholarships. Provides scholarships for students who are pursuing an education and career in the foodservice industry.
See entry 2676 for full listing.

NATIONAL SOCIETY OF HISPANIC MBAS (NSHMBA)
450 East John Carpenter Freeway
Suite 200
Irving, TX 75062
(214) 596-9338
(877) 467-4622
Fax: (214) 596-9325

E-MAIL ADDRESS:
scholarships@nshmba.org

WEB SITE ADDRESS:
www.nshmba.org

TYPE:
Scholarships.
See entry 1006 for full listing.

PHI CHI THETA EDUCATIONAL FOUNDATION   [1910]
1508 East Beltline Road, Suite 104
Carrollton, TX 75006
(972) 245-7202

E-MAIL ADDRESS:
foundationinfo@phichitheta.org

WEB SITE ADDRESS:
www.phichitheta.org/foundation

FOUNDED: 1999

AREAS OF INTEREST:
Business and economics.

NAME(S) OF PROGRAMS:
• **Educational and Scholastic Advancement Programs**

TYPE:
Project/program grants; Scholarships.

YEAR PROGRAM STARTED: 2000

PURPOSE:
To promote the cause of higher business education for all people.

LEGAL BASIS:
Public charity, 501(c)(3) corporation.

ELIGIBILITY:
Open to students who are members of Phi Chi Theta in approved courses in colleges and universities in the U.S. leading to Bachelor's, Master's or doctoral degrees in the fields of business administration and/or economics. Applicants must have completed at least one semester of college-level study. Selection is based on scholastic achievement, motivation, leadership potential and financial need.

GEOGRAPHIC RESTRICTIONS:
United States.

FINANCIAL DATA:
Amount of support per award: $500 to $1,000.
Total amount of support: Varies.

NUMBER OF APPLICANTS MOST RECENT YEAR:
Over 20.

NUMBER OF AWARDS: Varies.

APPLICATION INFORMATION:
Applicants must submit an official transcript
and two letters of recommendation.
Duration: One year. Nonrenewable.
Deadline: May 1.

PUBLICATIONS:
Application guidelines.

IRS IDENTIFICATION NUMBER: 31-1672618

OFFICERS:
Gary Hodge, President
Mary Ellen Lewis, Treasurer

CHARLES SCHWAB FOUNDATION [1911]
211 Main Street, 16th Floor
San Francisco, CA 94105
(877) 408-5438
Fax: (415) 667-1593

E-MAIL ADDRESS:
charlesschwabfoundation@schwab.com

WEB SITE ADDRESS:
www.schwab.com

FOUNDED: 1993

AREAS OF INTEREST:
Financial education.

NAME(S) OF PROGRAMS:
● **Schwab Moneywise™**

TYPE:
General operating grants; Matching gifts;
Project/program grants. The Charles Schwab
Foundation awards strategic financial support
through direct grants to selected nonprofit
organizations that respond to local cultural
and social needs or support Schwab's
commitment to financial literacy. These
grants provide employees with a voice and
role in supporting the community groups they
care about most.

YEAR PROGRAM STARTED: 1993

PURPOSE:
To give back to communities by supporting
employee-selected causes and fostering
financial literacy through funding,
involvement and expertise.

LEGAL BASIS:
Corporate foundation.

ELIGIBILITY:
Applicants must meet at least one of the
following selection criteria:
(1) be recommended by an employee who is
an active volunteer in the organization;
(2) be performing community work that
corresponds to the Foundation's initiatives or;
(3) promote financial literacy.

Greater consideration will be given to those
organizations that already have Schwab
employee volunteer involvement. The more
employees involved, the greater the
opportunity to be considered for a direct
grant.

GEOGRAPHIC RESTRICTIONS:
United States.

FINANCIAL DATA:
Amount of support per award: $2,500 to
$25,000.
Total amount of support: Average $4,000,000
annually.
Matching fund requirements: Approximately
37% of Foundation's charitable contributions
are awarded as dollar-for-dollar matches to
employee charitable gifts. Matching gifts
must be initiated by employees.

NUMBER OF APPLICANTS MOST RECENT YEAR:
3,052.

NUMBER OF AWARDS: 2,454 including matching
grants for employee contributions.

APPLICATION INFORMATION:
See web site for complete information.
Deadline: Proposals are reviewed on a
quarterly basis.

PUBLICATIONS:
Program brochure with application
guidelines.

IRS IDENTIFICATION NUMBER: 94-1737782

ADDRESS INQUIRIES TO:
Direct Grant Program
(See address above.)

SIMON FRASER UNIVERSITY [1912]
Maggie Benston Student
Services Centre 1100
8888 University Drive
Burnaby BC V5A 1S6 Canada
(778) 782-3042
Fax: (778) 782-3080

E-MAIL ADDRESS:
gradstudies@sfu.ca

WEB SITE ADDRESS:
www.sfu.ca/dean-gradstudies.html

NAME(S) OF PROGRAMS:
● **SFU Teaching Assistantships**

TYPE:
Assistantships.

PURPOSE:
To provide financial support to the
University's students enrolled in a Master's
or Ph.D. program.

ELIGIBILITY:
Applicants must have already been accepted
into Master's or Ph.D. program. Most
teaching assistantships are available to visa
students, as well as Canadian citizens and
residents.

FINANCIAL DATA:
Amount of support per award: $2,500 to
$4,500 (CAN).

APPLICATION INFORMATION:
Contact the University.
Duration: One to two semesters, varying by
department.
Deadline: Varies by department.

ADDRESS INQUIRIES TO:
Specific Department of Enrollment
Simon Fraser University
(Request specific department's address.)

SIMON FRASER UNIVERSITY [1913]
Maggie Benston Student
Services Centre 1100
8888 University Drive
Burnaby BC V5A 1S6 Canada
(778) 782-3042
Fax: (778) 782-3080

E-MAIL ADDRESS:
gradstudies@sfu.ca

WEB SITE ADDRESS:
www.sfu.ca/dean-gradstudies.html

NAME(S) OF PROGRAMS:
● **SFU Graduate Fellowships**

TYPE:
Fellowships.

PURPOSE:
To offer financial support to the University's
students enrolled in a Master's or Ph.D.
program.

ELIGIBILITY:
Open to current or entering Master's or Ph.D.
program students with a grade point average
of 3.5 or above.

FINANCIAL DATA:
Amount of support per award: $3,125 to
$6,250 (CAN).

APPLICATION INFORMATION:
Contact the University.
Duration: One semester or more.
Deadline: April 15.

ADDRESS INQUIRIES TO:
Specific Department of Enrollment
Simon Fraser University
(Request specific department's address.)

SOCIETY OF ACTUARIES (SOA)
475 North Martingale Road
Suite 600
Schaumburg, IL 60173-2226
(847) 706-3509
Fax: (847) 273-8605

E-MAIL ADDRESS:
acoffelt@soa.org

WEB SITE ADDRESS:
www.soa.org/education/resources/academic-
initiatives/soa-doc-stipend.aspx

TYPE:
Awards/prizes; Scholarships. Society of
Actuaries' James C. Hickman Scholar
Doctoral Stipend Program is designed to
provide stipends to doctoral students who
will, through their studies, address research
and education needs of the profession,
including both the theoretical and practical
aspects.

See entry 2097 for full listing.

SOCIETY OF ACTUARIES (SOA)
475 North Martingale Road
Suite 600
Schaumburg, IL 60173-2226
(847) 706-3509
Fax: (847) 273-8605

E-MAIL ADDRESS:
acoffelt@soa.org

WEB SITE ADDRESS:
www.soa.org/education/resources/edu-
institution-grant/default.aspx

TYPE:
Awards/prizes; Development grants; General
operating grants; Project/program grants;
Research grants; Scholarships; Travel grants.
Grants to educational institutions.

See entry 2098 for full listing.

TRANSPORTATION CLUBS INTERNATIONAL SCHOLARSHIPS [1914]
Three Riverway, Suite 400
Houston, TX 77056
(877) 858-8627

E-MAIL ADDRESS:
Lynn.Donovick@martinmlp.com

WEB SITE ADDRESS:
www.transportationclubinternational.com

FOUNDED: 1922

NAME(S) OF PROGRAMS:
- **Ginger and Fred Deines Canada Scholarships**
- **Ginger and Fred Deines Mexico Scholarships**
- **Hooper Memorial Scholarship**
- **Denny Lydic Scholarship**
- **Texas Transportation Scholarship**
- **Alice Glaisyer Warfield Memorial Scholarship**
- **Charlotte Woods Memorial Scholarship**

TYPE:
Scholarships. Ginger and Fred Deines Canada Scholarship is awarded to a student of Canadian nationality and enrolled in a school in Canada or the U.S.

Ginger and Fred Deines Mexico Scholarship is awarded to a student of Mexican nationality and enrolled in a school in Mexico or the U.S.

The Hooper Memorial and Denny Lydic Scholarships are awarded to any student enrolled in an accredited institution of higher learning in a vocational or degree program.

Texas Transportation Scholarship is awarded to a student who has been enrolled in a school in Texas during some phase of his or her education (elementary, secondary or high school.)

Charlotte Woods Memorial Scholarship is awarded to a student who is a TCI member or a dependent of a member.

PURPOSE:
To encourage advanced vocational, undergraduate and graduate study in the field of transportation and traffic management.

ELIGIBILITY:
Offered to any student enrolled in an educational program in an accredited institution of higher learning in the U.S., Canada or Mexico offering courses in transportation, traffic management and related fields, i.e., marketing, economics, accounting, etc., who intends to prepare for a career in logistics, transportation, transportation management or related field. The awards will be based upon scholastic ability and potential, professional interest and character. Financial need will also be given consideration.

GEOGRAPHIC RESTRICTIONS:
United States, Canada and Mexico.

FINANCIAL DATA:
Amount of support per award: Varies.
Total amount of support: $12,000.

NUMBER OF APPLICANTS MOST RECENT YEAR:
25.

NUMBER OF AWARDS: 7.

APPLICATION INFORMATION:
In addition to a completed application form, supporting documents include:
(1) certified transcript directly from applicant's college/university;
(2) three letters of recommendation;
(3) small, current photograph (to be used for publication) and;
(4) 500-word essay explaining why the applicant has chosen transportation or an allied field as a career path, and outlining the objectives. Essay should be composed separately in Microsoft Word file only.
Application form is available at the web site.

Deadline: May 31.

ADDRESS INQUIRIES TO:
Lynn Donovick
(See address above.)

U.S. DEPARTMENT OF EDUCATION [1915]
International Education Programs Service
1990 K Street, N.W.
Washington, DC 20006
(202) 502-7626
Fax: (202) 502-7859

WEB SITE ADDRESS:
www.ed.gov

AREAS OF INTEREST:
International business education.

CONSULTING OR VOLUNTEER SERVICES:
Offers technical assistance.

NAME(S) OF PROGRAMS:
- **Business and International Education Program**

TYPE:
Conferences/seminars; Demonstration grants; Development grants; Project/program grants; Research grants; Seed money grants; Training grants; Travel grants. The program assists institutions of higher learning in:
(1) innovation and improvement of international education curricula to serve the needs of the business community, including the development of new programs for nontraditional, midcareer or part-time students;
(2) development of programs to inform the public of increasing international economic interdependence and the role of U.S. business within the international economic system;
(3) internationalization of curricula at junior and community colleges, and at undergraduate and graduate schools of business;
(4) development of area studies programs and interdisciplinary international programs;
(5) establishment of export education programs through cooperative arrangements with regional and world trade centers and councils and with bilateral and multilateral trade associations;
(6) research for and development of teaching materials relating to international education, including language materials and facilities appropriate to business-oriented students;
(7) establishment of student and faculty fellowships and internships for training and education in international business activities;
(8) development of opportunities for business and other professional school junior faculty to acquire or strengthen international skills and perspectives and;
(9) development of research programs on issues of common interest to institutions of higher education and private-sector organizations and associations engaged in promoting international economic activity.

YEAR PROGRAM STARTED: 1983

PURPOSE:
To improve the academic teaching and business curriculum at U.S. institutions of higher education; to conduct outreach activities that assist the U.S. business community to engage in international commerce.

LEGAL BASIS:
Government agency.

ELIGIBILITY:
U.S. institutions of higher education that have entered into agreements with U.S. business enterprises, trade organizations or associations engaged in international economic activity.

FINANCIAL DATA:
Amount of support per award: Average $80,000.
Matching fund requirements: 1:1.

COOPERATIVE FUNDING PROGRAMS: Assistance from parties to required "Agreement."

NUMBER OF APPLICANTS MOST RECENT YEAR:
Varies.

NUMBER OF AWARDS: Varies.

APPLICATION INFORMATION:
Applications for grants under this program are required to be submitted electronically using the Department's e-Grants system.
Duration: Two years.
Deadline: Varies.

STAFF:
Tanyelle Hawkins Richardson, Program Officer

ADDRESS INQUIRIES TO:
Program Officer
International Education Programs Service
(See address above.)

U.S. DEPARTMENT OF EDUCATION [1916]
Centers for International Business Education
1990 K Street, N.W., 6th Floor
Washington, DC 20006-8521
(202) 502-7622
Fax: (202) 502-7858

E-MAIL ADDRESS:
timothy.duvall@ed.gov

WEB SITE ADDRESS:
www2.ed.gov/programs/iegpscibe/index.html

AREAS OF INTEREST:
International business education.

CONSULTING OR VOLUNTEER SERVICES:
Offers technical assistance.

NAME(S) OF PROGRAMS:
- **Centers for International Business Education Program**

TYPE:
Project/program grants. The program provides grants to eligible institutions of higher education or combinations of these institutions for planning, establishing and operating Centers for International Business Education.

YEAR PROGRAM STARTED: 1989

PURPOSE:
To provide funding to schools of business for curriculum development, research, and training on issues of importance to U.S. trade and competitiveness.

LEGAL BASIS:
Government agency.

ELIGIBILITY:
An applicant must be an institution of higher education or a combination of such institutions that establishes a Center Advisory Council prior to the date that federal assistance is received. The Center Advisory Council shall conduct extensive planning prior to the establishment of the Center for International Business Education concerning the scope of the Center's activities and the design of its programs. Programs and

activities to be conducted by Centers for International Business Education must meet the programmatic requirements listed above.

FINANCIAL DATA:
Grant funds may be used to pay the federal share of costs of faculty and staff travel in foreign areas, regions or countries, teaching and research materials, curriculum planning and development, bringing visiting scholars and faculty to the center to teach or to conduct research, training and improvement of the staff for the purpose of and subject to such conditions as the Secretary finds necessary for carrying out the objectives of this program and other costs consistent with planning, establishing or operating a center.
Amount of support per award: $285,000 for the fiscal year 2014.
Total amount of support: $4,571,400 for the fiscal year 2014.

NUMBER OF APPLICANTS MOST RECENT YEAR:
Approximately 50 in fiscal year 2014.

NUMBER OF AWARDS: Approximately 16 for fiscal year 2014.

APPLICATION INFORMATION:
The Department of Education provides an application package upon request to the Office of Postsecondary Education. Applications become available in May.
Duration: Four years.
Deadline: June. Competition held every four years.

PUBLICATIONS:
Application guidelines; abstracts of grantees.

ADDRESS INQUIRIES TO:
Tim Duvall, Ph.D.
(See address above.)

THE UNIVERSITY OF CALGARY
Faculty of Graduate Studies
MacKimmie Library Tower, Room 213
2500 University Drive, N.W.
Calgary AB T2N 1N4 Canada
(403) 220-4938
Fax: (403) 289-7635

E-MAIL ADDRESS:
gsaward@ucalgary.ca

WEB SITE ADDRESS:
www.grad.ucalgary.ca

TYPE:
Awards/prizes; Scholarships. Awards for study in the fields of business, management and related areas. Tenable at the University of Calgary. Awards are endowed through gifts from John Labatt Limited and ScotiaMcLeod Inc. Matching grants provided from the Province of Alberta's Advanced Education Endowment Fund.
See entry 1787 for full listing.

UNIVERSITY OF NEBRASKA AT OMAHA [1917]
Mammel Hall, Room 300
6708 Pine Street
Omaha, NE 68182-0048
(402) 554-2303
Fax: (402) 554-3747

E-MAIL ADDRESS:
mba@unomaha.edu

WEB SITE ADDRESS:
cba.unomaha.edu/mba

AREAS OF INTEREST:
UNO Master's program.

NAME(S) OF PROGRAMS:
● **UNO Graduate Assistantships**

TYPE:
Assistantships. Graduate, MBA scholarships in all subjects.

ELIGIBILITY:
Graduate assistantships are available for qualified students who are enrolled in a graduate degree program in the College of Business Administration.

FINANCIAL DATA:
Amount of support per award: Waiver of tuition costs up to 12 hours of graduate credit per semester.

NUMBER OF APPLICANTS MOST RECENT YEAR:
25.

NUMBER OF AWARDS: 3.

APPLICATION INFORMATION:
Applicants should complete the Graduate Assistantship application that is available on the web site and submit it with a resume and letters of recommendation prior to the application deadline.
Deadline: July 1.

THE DEAN WITTER FOUNDATION [1918]
57 Post Street, Suite 510
San Francisco, CA 94104
(415) 981-2966
Fax: (415) 981-5218

E-MAIL ADDRESS:
admin@deanwitterfoundation.org

WEB SITE ADDRESS:
www.deanwitterfoundation.org

FOUNDED: 1952

AREAS OF INTEREST:
Research and higher education in finance, wildlife research and conservation projects, and K-12 education.

TYPE:
Challenge/matching grants; Fellowships; General operating grants; Internships; Matching gifts; Professorships; Project/program grants; Research grants; Scholarships; Seed money grants.

YEAR PROGRAM STARTED: 1952

PURPOSE:
To help fund research and higher education in areas of special interest to the Foundation, as well as K-12 education.

LEGAL BASIS:
Private foundation.

ELIGIBILITY:
Grants are made to tax-exempt 501(c)(3) institutions. No grants are made to individuals.

GEOGRAPHIC RESTRICTIONS:
Northern California.

FINANCIAL DATA:
Amount of support per award: $10,000 to $25,000.
Total amount of support: Approximately $850,000 for fiscal year ended June 30, 2013.

NUMBER OF APPLICANTS MOST RECENT YEAR:
100 for fiscal year ended June 30, 2012.

NUMBER OF AWARDS: 40 for fiscal year ended June 30, 2012.

APPLICATION INFORMATION:
Applicants should first submit a brief letter to the Consultant, explaining their program and its merits with estimated budget, personnel, time required to carry out the proposal, evidence of tax-exempt status, and a brief explanation of any other sources of support for the project, such as volunteer workers and matching funds commitments. If the project, program or institution falls within the priorities, interests and available funds of the Foundation, a more detailed proposal will be requested.
Duration: One year. Renewal possible.

OFFICERS AND TRUSTEES:
Dean Witter, III, President
Stephen Nessier, Vice President and Chief Financial Officer
Roland E. Tognazzini, Jr., Secretary
Deanne Gillette Violich, Trustee
Malcolm G. Witter, Trustee
William P. Witter, Trustee

ADDRESS INQUIRIES TO:
Kenneth J. Blum, Administrative Director
(See address above.)

ZONTA INTERNATIONAL FOUNDATION [1919]
1211 West 22nd Street, Suite 900
Oak Brook, IL 60523-3384
(630) 928-1400
Fax: (630) 928-1559

E-MAIL ADDRESS:
programs@zonta.org

WEB SITE ADDRESS:
www.zonta.org

FOUNDED: 1919

AREAS OF INTEREST:
Financial support for women of any nationality pursuing degrees in business leading to a business management career.

NAME(S) OF PROGRAMS:
● **Jane M. Klausman Women in Business Scholarships**

TYPE:
Awards/prizes; Scholarships. For women of any nationality pursuing degrees in business who demonstrate outstanding potential in the field of business.

YEAR PROGRAM STARTED: 1998

PURPOSE:
To provide financial support for women of any nationality pursuing degrees in business leading to a business management career.

LEGAL BASIS:
Incorporated in the state of Illinois as a nonprofit organization.

ELIGIBILITY:
Applicant must meet the following minimum requirements:
(1) be undertaking a business and/or business-related program at an accredited university, college or institute;
(2) be enrolled in at least the second year of an undergraduate program through the final year of a Master's program at the time the application is submitted; (applicants must still be attending school to receive this award in November);
(3) have achieved an outstanding academic record during her academic studies, including business-related subjects and;
(4) have demonstrated initiative, ambition and commitment to pursuing a career in

business and;
(5) be living or studying in a Zonta region/district.

FINANCIAL DATA:
The scholarship award may be used for tuition, books or living expenses at any university, college or institution offering accredited business courses and degrees.
Amount of support per award: $1,000 at the District Level and 12 scholarships for $7,000.
Total amount of support: Varies.

NUMBER OF APPLICANTS MOST RECENT YEAR: Varies.

NUMBER OF AWARDS: 32.

APPLICATION INFORMATION:
Applications must be completed in English. English translations must accompany all non-English documents. The Jane M. Klausman Women in Business Scholarship program operates at the club, district and international levels of Zonta International. To apply, contact the Zonta Club within the applicant's district/region for deadlines and an address to which to mail application. (Such contact information is also available on the web site.) Alternatively, one can e-mail one's name and contact information to Zonta International Headquarters at the address above. Applicants must be nominated by a local Zonta Club first.
Deadline: Must contact Zonta Club for deadlines.

ADDRESS INQUIRIES TO:
Martina Gamboa, Programs Coordinator
(See e-mail address above.)

Communications

AMERICAN ASSOCIATION FOR THE ADVANCEMENT OF SCIENCE   [1920]
1200 New York Avenue, N.W.
Washington, DC 20005
(202) 326-6645
Fax: (202) 371-9849

E-MAIL ADDRESS:
drossite@aaas.org

WEB SITE ADDRESS:
www.aaas.org/programs/education/MassMedia

FOUNDED: 1848

AREAS OF INTEREST:
Science-related issues in the media and public understanding and appreciation of science technology.

NAME(S) OF PROGRAMS:
● **Mass Media Science and Engineering Fellows Program**

TYPE:
Fellowships; Internships. Fellowships to primarily support graduate students in the fields of social, natural and physical sciences, mathematics, and engineering during the summer as intern reporters, researchers or production assistants in mass media organizations nationwide. Fellows will have the opportunity to observe and participate in the process by which events and ideas become news, improve their communication skills by learning to describe complex technical subjects in a manner understandable to the lay public, and increase their

understanding of editorial decision making and the way in which information is effectively disseminated.
Each fellow will work for a specific media organization. Some will work for newspapers or magazines on news and feature writing assignments. Others may be involved in television or radio production.

YEAR PROGRAM STARTED: 1974

PURPOSE:
To strengthen the relationship between science and technology and the media and to enhance coverage of science-related issues in the media in order to improve public understanding and appreciation of science and technology.

LEGAL BASIS:
Nonprofit association.

ELIGIBILITY:
Applicants must be American-born, naturalized citizens, or permanent residents. Non-U.S. citizens must have a valid work visa.

FINANCIAL DATA:
Fellowships include a weekly stipend, travel costs to and from the media site, and travel and expenses to attend a presummer orientation in Washington, DC, along with a wrap-up session.
Amount of support per award: $4,500 for a 10-week report.

NUMBER OF APPLICANTS MOST RECENT YEAR: Over 100.

NUMBER OF AWARDS: Typically 20.

APPLICATION INFORMATION:
In addition to the completed application form, candidates must submit a current resume, two writing samples, transcripts of undergraduate and graduate work, and three letters of recommendation. Transcripts and letters of recommendation must be submitted directly to the program. Applicants should be available for a telephone interview in March and be able to accept assignments anywhere in the U.S.
Duration: 10 weeks in the summer.
Deadline: January 15. Announcement in April.

STAFF:
Dione Rossiter, Ph.D., Manager, Mass Media Science and Engineering Fellows Program

ADDRESS INQUIRIES TO:
Dione Rossiter, Ph.D., Manager
(See address above.)

AMERICAN ASSOCIATION FOR THE ADVANCEMENT OF SCIENCE   [1921]
1200 New York Avenue, N.W.
Washington, DC 20005
(202) 326-6431
Fax: (202) 789-0455

E-MAIL ADDRESS:
elane@aaas.org

WEB SITE ADDRESS:
www.aaas.org/sjawards

FOUNDED: 1848

AREAS OF INTEREST:
Science and engineering.

NAME(S) OF PROGRAMS:
● **AAAS Kavli Science Journalism Awards**

TYPE:
Awards/prizes. U.S. awards for stories of life, physical and social sciences, engineering and mathematics, excluding the field of medicine, published in newspapers, general magazines, aired on radio and television, and online. Entries should be intended for general, nontechnical audiences. There is also an award open to journalists worldwide, recognizing excellence in science news reporting for children.

YEAR PROGRAM STARTED: 1945

PURPOSE:
To encourage newspaper, magazine, radio, television and online science writing.

LEGAL BASIS:
Nonprofit scientific organization.

ELIGIBILITY:
Qualified individuals may apply with appropriate single stories or series published in U.S. newspapers or general circulation magazines, or aired on radio and television. Reporters for international media outlets are eligible for the award for reporting on science for children. Awards may not be presented to the same entrant in any two consecutive years, and individuals who have already won three of the annual awards are no longer eligible to apply.
Must be published by a U.S.-based news outlet, with the exception of the international award for reporting on science for children.

FINANCIAL DATA:
Amount of support per award: $3,000.
Total amount of support: $24,000.

COOPERATIVE FUNDING PROGRAMS: Sponsored by The Kavli Foundation.

NUMBER OF APPLICANTS MOST RECENT YEAR: 485.

NUMBER OF AWARDS: 8 for the 2014 contest year. Seven awards in the U.S., one each for outstanding science writing in a newspaper with less than 100,000 circulation, a newspaper with over 100,000 daily circulation, in a general circulation magazine, on radio, television (two awards) and online. In addition, an international award for excellence in science news reporting for children, across all news media.

APPLICATION INFORMATION:
Online application information and FAQ can be found at the web site.
Deadline: August 1.

PUBLICATIONS:
Application guidelines.

OFFICERS:
Dr. Alan I. Leshner, Chief Executive Officer

ADDRESS INQUIRIES TO:
Earl Lane, AAAS Kavli Science Journalism Awards Administrator
(See address above.)

AMERICAN POLITICAL SCIENCE ASSOCIATION
1527 New Hampshire Avenue, N.W.
Washington, DC 20036
(202) 483-2512
Fax: (202) 483-2657

E-MAIL ADDRESS:
cfp@apsanet.org

WEB SITE ADDRESS:
www.apsanet.org/cfp

TYPE:
Fellowships. Awards to political science professors and journalists in early-career to midcareer status; the award provides an opportunity for support as a full-time aide to a member of the House or Senate or as a staff member for a Congressional committee.

See entry 1987 for full listing.

ART DIRECTORS CLUB, INC. [1922]
106 West 29th Street
New York, NY 10001
(212) 643-1440
Fax: (212) 643-4266

E-MAIL ADDRESS:
info@adcglobal.org

WEB SITE ADDRESS:
www.adcglobal.org

FOUNDED: 1920

AREAS OF INTEREST:
Art and graphic design, advertising, visual communications and media arts, art direction, creative arts, computer graphics, art and design education, industrial and environmental design and publication planning.

NAME(S) OF PROGRAMS:
- **ADC National Scholarships**

TYPE:
Awards/prizes; Conferences/seminars; Scholarships. Programs include the annual competition, exhibitions, publications, symposia, workshops, scholarships and other special events.

PURPOSE:
To promote excellence in the fields of visual communications through the support of young and aspiring talent nationwide.

LEGAL BASIS:
Not-for-profit association with an international membership.

ELIGIBILITY:
Applicants must be students at their sophomore or junior level enrolled in an accredited undergraduate program or in their last semester or quarter in a portfolio program and must be enrolled in schools in the U.S.

FINANCIAL DATA:
Amount of support per award: $2,500 to $3,500.
Total amount of support: Varies.

NUMBER OF AWARDS: Varies.

APPLICATION INFORMATION:
Students are required to submit five images of recent work (to be submitted online), a statement of purpose, a resume, a letter of recommendation from their professor, and an application.
Duration: One year.
Deadline: Late June to early July.

ADDRESS INQUIRIES TO:
Brendan Watson, Director of Education
(See address above.)

BENTON FOUNDATION [1923]
1250 Connecticut Avenue, N.W.
Suite 200
Washington, DC 20036
(202) 638-5770
Fax: (240) 235-5024

E-MAIL ADDRESS:
cgarcia@benton.org

WEB SITE ADDRESS:
www.benton.org

FOUNDED: 1948

AREAS OF INTEREST:
The use of media and information technology in solving social problems and strengthening communities.

NAME(S) OF PROGRAMS:
- **Media Policy and Public Service Media**

TYPE:
Technical assistance. Program is funded for preserving, protecting and strengthening the public benefits in America's media environment.

PURPOSE:
To articulate a public-interest vision for the digital age and to demonstrate the value of communications for solving social problems; to leverage media and technology in innovative ways as a means to strengthen communities.

LEGAL BASIS:
501(c)(3) private foundation.

FINANCIAL DATA:
Amount of support per award: $500 to $5,000.
Total amount of support: $250,000 for the year 2012.

APPLICATION INFORMATION:
By invitation only. The Foundation does not accept unsolicited grant applications.
Deadline: Varies.

ADDRESS INQUIRIES TO:
Cecilia Garcia, Executive Director
(See address above.)

BROADCAST EDUCATION ASSOCIATION [1924]
1771 N Street, N.W.
Washington, DC 20036-2891
(888) 380-7222
(202) 429-3935
Fax: (202) 775-2981

E-MAIL ADDRESS:
beamemberservices@nab.org

WEB SITE ADDRESS:
www.beaweb.org

FOUNDED: 1923

AREAS OF INTEREST:
Electronic media.

NAME(S) OF PROGRAMS:
- **John Bayliss Scholarship Fund**
- **Richard Eaton Foundation Award**
- **Walter S. Patterson Scholarship**
- **Alexander M. Tanger Scholarship**
- **Two Year/Community College BEA Award**
- **Abe Voron Scholarship**
- **Vincent T. Wasilewski Scholarship**

TYPE:
Scholarships. BEA is the professional development association for professors, industry professionals and students involved in teaching and research related to radio, television and other electronic media. BEA administers nine scholarships annually, to honor broadcasters and the electronic media profession.

John Bayliss, Walter S. Patterson, and Abe Voron Scholarships: Study toward a career in radio.

Richard Eaton, Alexander M. Tanger, and Vincent T. Wasilewski Scholarships: Study in any area of broadcasting.

The BEA Two Year Award is for study at member schools offering only freshman and sophomore instruction, or for use at a four-year member school by a graduate of a BEA two-year campus. All other scholarships are awarded to juniors, seniors and graduate students at BEA Member institutions.

YEAR PROGRAM STARTED: 1962

PURPOSE:
To secure mutual advantages that flow from a continuing relationship between broadcasters and institutions of higher learning which offer a high standard of training and guidance for those who plan to enter the electronic media.

LEGAL BASIS:
Private association.

ELIGIBILITY:
Scholarships will be awarded for full-time degree work for the full academic year. Scholarships must be used exclusively for tuition, student fees, university bookstore course purchases, dormitory and related items eligible to be charged to a student's official campus account. Current scholarship holders are not eligible for reappointment in the year following their award. In no case will any individual receive an award for more than two scholastic years. Winners must be full-time students for the entire academic year of the award. All scholarships must be applied to study at a campus where at least one department is a BEA institutional member.

The applicant should be able to show substantial evidence of superior academic performance and potential to be an outstanding electronic media professional. There should be compelling evidence that the applicant possesses high integrity and a well-articulated sense of personal and professional responsibility.

The Wasilewski Scholarship is intended for graduate students only.

FINANCIAL DATA:
Amount of support per award: John Bayliss and Richard Eaton Foundation Scholarships: $1,500 each; Patterson Scholarship: $1,750; Tanger and Voron Scholarships: $5,000 each; Two Year/Community College BEA Award: $1,500 each; Wasilewski Scholarship: $2,500.
Total amount of support: Varies.

NUMBER OF AWARDS: Bayliss, Eaton, Tanger, Voron, and Wasilewski Scholarships: 1 each; Patterson Scholarship and Two Year/Community College BEA Award: 2 each.

APPLICATION INFORMATION:
Scholarship applicants can obtain the official application forms from their campus faculty or download them from the Association web site. The forms ask for personal and academic data and transcripts, broadcast and other experience, a written statement of goals and supportive statements from three references, one of which must be an electronic media faculty member. The completed application should contain:
(1) four completed and collated copies of the main application form;
(2) waiver sheet (four copies);

(3) three letters of reference;
(4) college transcripts (one from each institution attended) and;
(5) NAB station employment/internship affidavit.
Do not send tapes, resumes, photos, etc. No faxed or e-mailed material will be accepted.

Completed applications should be sent to:
Dr. Peter B. Orlik, Scholarships, BEA
344 Moore Hall
Central Michigan University
Mount Pleasant, MI 48859
E-mail: orlik1pb@cmich.edu.

Duration: One academic year.

Deadline: Early October.

PUBLICATIONS:
Journal of Broadcasting & Electronic Media;
Journal of Radio Studies.

*SPECIAL STIPULATIONS:
All scholarships must be applied to study at a campus where at least one department is a BEA institutional member. Applications listing ineligible schools will be disqualified.

COLUMBIA JOURNALISM SCHOOL   [1925]
2950 Broadway, Room 303
New York, NY 10027-7004
(212) 854-6468
Fax: (212) 854-7701; (212) 854-3800

E-MAIL ADDRESS:
lsr21@columbia.edu

WEB SITE ADDRESS:
www.journalism.columbia.edu

FOUNDED: 1960

NAME(S) OF PROGRAMS:
• **Mike Berger Award**

TYPE:
Awards/prizes. A newspaper competition, covering the previous calendar year, open to reporters nationwide.

YEAR PROGRAM STARTED: 1960

PURPOSE:
To honor distinguished newspaper reporting in the tradition of the late Meyer Berger of the New York Times.

LEGAL BASIS:
University.

ELIGIBILITY:
All newspaper reporters across the country are eligible whether they report for dailies, weeklies, monthlies, newspaper magazines or online publications. Members of the ethnic press should submit copies of original stories with an English translation.

FINANCIAL DATA:
Winners receive a cash award along with a certificate and hotel and travel expenses to New York.
Amount of support per award: $1,500.

NUMBER OF AWARDS: 1 annually.

APPLICATION INFORMATION:
Nominations are solicited from the editors of all daily newspapers across the country, as well as ethnic, weekly and online publications. Judges request that a nominating exhibit include two copies of a letter from the editor, a brief biographical resume of the reporter, and two copies of not more than five clippings.

Deadline: Early March. Notification in the spring. Presented at Columbia University in May.

ADDRESS INQUIRIES TO:
Lisa Sara Redd
Associate Director
(See address above.)

COLUMBIA UNIVERSITY   [1926]
709 Pulitzer Hall
2950 Broadway
New York, NY 10027
(212) 854-3841
Fax: (212) 854-3342

E-MAIL ADDRESS:
pulitzer@pulitzer.org

WEB SITE ADDRESS:
www.pulitzer.org

FOUNDED: 1917

AREAS OF INTEREST:
Excellence in journalism, books, drama and music.

NAME(S) OF PROGRAMS:
• **Pulitzer Fellowships**
• **Pulitzer Prizes**

TYPE:
Awards/prizes; Fellowships. Awards in journalism, books and music.

Pulitzer Prizes in Journalism are awarded based on material appearing in a text-based U.S. newspaper or news site that publishes at least once a week during the year. Awards given for:
(1) meritorious public service by a newspaper through the use of its journalistic resources which may include editorials, cartoons, photographs, graphics and online material;
(2) local reporting of breaking news;
(3) investigative reporting by an individual or team, presented as a single article or series;
(4) explanatory journalism that illuminates a significant or complex subject, demonstrating mastery of the subject, lucid writing and clear presentation;
(5) local reporting;
(6) reporting on national affairs;
(7) reporting on international affairs, including United Nations correspondence;
(8) feature writing giving prime consideration to high literary quality and originality;
(9) commentary;
(10) criticism;
(11) editorial writing;
(12) cartoon or portfolio of cartoons;
(13) breaking news photography in black and white or color, which may consist of a photograph or photographs, a sequence or an album and;
(14) feature photography in black and white or color with the same stipulations as above.

Prizes in Letters are restricted to works first published in the U.S. during the year in book form and available for purchase by the general public. Awards given for:
(1) fiction by an American author, preferably dealing with American life;
(2) a play by an American author, preferably original in its source and dealing with American life, produced in the U.S. January 1 to December 31;
(3) appropriately documented book on the history of the U.S.;
(4) appropriately documented biography or autobiography by an American author;
(5) volume of original verse by an American author and;
(6) appropriately documented book of nonfiction by an American author that is not eligible for consideration in any other category.

A prize in music is given for distinguished musical composition by an American that has had its first performance in the U.S. during the year.

Four fellowships enable outstanding graduates to travel, report and study abroad. One fellowship is given to an outstanding graduate who wishes to specialize in drama, music, literary, film or television criticism.

YEAR PROGRAM STARTED: 1917

PURPOSE:
To recognize excellence in journalism, letters, drama and music.

LEGAL BASIS:
University.

ELIGIBILITY:
Competition for prizes is limited to work done during the calendar year ending December 31.

FINANCIAL DATA:
Amount of support per award: $10,000.
Total amount of support: $210,000.

NUMBER OF AWARDS: Fellowships: 5; Prizes in Drama: 1; Prizes in Journalism: 14; Prizes in Music: 1.

APPLICATION INFORMATION:
Application form and $50 handling fee required with entries.
Duration: One-time awards. Previous winners are eligible for consideration each year for any award.
Deadline: Prizes in Books: June 15 and October 1; Prizes in Drama and Prize in Music: December 31; Prizes in Journalism: January 25.

PUBLICATIONS:
Award announcement; brochure.

BOARD:
Danielle S. Allen
Randell Beck
Robert Blau
Lee C. Bollinger
Katherine Boo
Gail Collins
Steve Coll
John Daniszewski
Joyce Dehli
Junot Diaz
Stephen Engelberg
Paul A. Gigot
Sig Gissler
Aminda Marques Gonzales
Steven Hahn
Quiara Alegria Hudes
Eugene Robinson
Paul Tash
Keven Ann Willey

ADDRESS INQUIRIES TO:
The Pulitzer Prize Board
(See address above.)

COLUMBIA UNIVERSITY   [1927]
Graduate School of Journalism
2950 Broadway, Mail Code 3850
New York, NY 10027
(212) 854-2711
Fax: (212) 854-3900

E-MAIL ADDRESS:
tat5@columbia.edu

WEB SITE ADDRESS:
www.jrn.columbia.edu/knight-bagehot

FOUNDED: 1975

AREAS OF INTEREST:
Economics and business journalism for midcareer journalists.

NAME(S) OF PROGRAMS:
● **Knight-Bagehot Fellowship in Economics and Business Journalism**

TYPE:
Awards/prizes; Fellowships. Awarded to midcareer professional journalists to study business and economics at Columbia University.

YEAR PROGRAM STARTED: 1975

PURPOSE:
To improve the quality of business and economics journalism.

LEGAL BASIS:
University-affiliated fellowship program.

ELIGIBILITY:
Applicants must have at least four years' experience in journalism. Program is limited to journalists whose work regularly appears in the U.S. and Canada.

FINANCIAL DATA:
The Fellowship includes free tuition plus a stipend to cover living expenses.
Amount of support per award: $55,000.

NUMBER OF AWARDS: 10.

APPLICATION INFORMATION:
Submit two 1,000-word essays, one on the applicant's professional career and his or her interest in business and economics writing, and the other on a major business or economics trend. At least three letters of reference from individuals in a position to comment on the applicant's professional performance and at least five work samples must also be provided.
Duration: One academic year.
Deadline: March 1.

PUBLICATIONS:
Annual report.

ADDRESS INQUIRIES TO:
Terri Thompson, Director
Knight-Bagehot Fellowship
(See address above.)

COLUMBIA UNIVERSITY   [1928]
Graduate School of Journalism
2950 Broadway, Room 303
New York, NY 10027-7004
(212) 854-6468
Fax: (212) 854-7701; (212) 854-3800

E-MAIL ADDRESS:
lsr21@columbia.edu

WEB SITE ADDRESS:
www.journalism.columbia.edu

FOUNDED: 1960

AREAS OF INTEREST:
Environmental journalism.

NAME(S) OF PROGRAMS:
● **John B. Oakes Award**

TYPE:
Awards/prizes. Awarded for distinguished excellence in environmental journalism.

ELIGIBILITY:
To be considered for this Award, submitted articles must have been written between January 1 and December 31 of previous year.

The article must have been published in a U.S.-based publication. An online publication is acceptable.

GEOGRAPHIC RESTRICTIONS:
United States.

FINANCIAL DATA:
Amount of support per award: $5,000 prize, plus travel expenses to New York, NY, for the Awards luncheon at the Journalism School at Columbia University.

NUMBER OF AWARDS: 1 award yearly.

APPLICATION INFORMATION:
Application is available online.
Duration: Recipients of the Oakes Award can win it a second time.
Deadline: January 31.

ADDRESS INQUIRIES TO:
Lisa Sara Redd, Associate Director, Professional Prizes or
Laura Tejeda, Administrative Assistant, Professional Prizes
(See address above.)

COLUMBIA UNIVERSITY GRADUATE SCHOOL OF JOURNALISM   [1929]
Graduate School of Journalism
2950 Broadway, Room 303
New York, NY 10027
(212) 854-6468
Fax: (212) 854-7701; (212) 854-3800

E-MAIL ADDRESS:
lsr21@columbia.edu
cabotprizes@columbia.edu

WEB SITE ADDRESS:
www.jrn.columbia.edu

FOUNDED: 1939

AREAS OF INTEREST:
Journalism and inter-American relations.

NAME(S) OF PROGRAMS:
● **Maria Moors Cabot Prizes**

TYPE:
Awards/prizes. The prize program recognizes distinguished journalistic contributions to inter-American understanding. Prizes are awarded annually by the Trustees of Columbia University on recommendations made by the Dean of the Graduate School of Journalism and the Cabot Board.

YEAR PROGRAM STARTED: 1938

PURPOSE:
To recognize sustained and distinguished contributions of journalists to the advancement of understanding among the peoples of the Western Hemisphere.

LEGAL BASIS:
University.

ELIGIBILITY:
Although awards have been made to publishers or others in managerial positions, the board is particularly interested in working journalists throughout the Americas whose writings or broadcasts have contributed to mutual understanding and freedom of the press over a period of time.

GEOGRAPHIC RESTRICTIONS:
Western Hemisphere.

FINANCIAL DATA:
Amount of support per award: $5,000 and a Cabot medal, plus round-trip transportation to Columbia University for the award ceremonies.

NUMBER OF AWARDS: 5 for the year 2013.

APPLICATION INFORMATION:
The Committee appreciates the submission of two copies of all representative clippings, copies of broadcasts, books and of letters explaining why the nominee is especially deserving.
Deadline: March 16.

ADDRESS INQUIRIES TO:
Lisa Sara Redd, Program Manager
Professional Prizes
The Cabot Prize Program
(See address above.)

COUNCIL FOR THE ADVANCEMENT OF SCIENCE WRITING, INC.   [1930]
P.O. Box 910
Hedgesville, WV 25427
(304) 754-6786

E-MAIL ADDRESS:
diane@casw.org

WEB SITE ADDRESS:
www.casw.org

FOUNDED: 1959

AREAS OF INTEREST:
Writing about science, medicine, health, technology, energy, the environment, etc., for the general public via the mass media (distinct from technical writing or technical journalism).

NAME(S) OF PROGRAMS:
● **The Victor Cohn Prize for Excellence in Medical Science Reporting**
● **Rennie Taylor/Alton Blakeslee Fellowships for Graduate Study in Science Writing**

TYPE:
Awards/prizes; Fellowships. The Victor Cohn Prize salutes general excellence in medical science writing for the mass media. The prize, to be given annually, seeks to honor a writer for a body of work published or broadcast within the last five years which, for reasons of uncommon clarity, accuracy, breadth of coverage, enterprise, originality, insight and narrative power, has made a profound and lasting contribution to public awareness and understanding of critical advances in medical science and their impact on human health and well-being.

Rennie Taylor/Alton Blakeslee Fellowships support graduate students in science journalism and experienced reporters who wish to study science writing at the graduate level.

PURPOSE:
To increase public understanding of science by upgrading the quality and quantity of science and medical writing and by improving relationships between scientists and the press.

LEGAL BASIS:
Nonprofit 501(c)(3).

ELIGIBILITY:
The Victor Cohn Prize: Editors, colleagues, scientists and others familiar with the candidate's body of work may proffer nominations. Individuals may nominate themselves.

Rennie Taylor/Alton Blakeslee Fellowships: Journalists with two years of experience who wish to specialize in science writing will receive priority selection. Such applicants should be employed by daily newspapers, wire services, news magazines, radio stations, or television stations or networks. Students must have undergraduate degrees in science or journalism and prove to the satisfaction of a selection committee that they have the motivation and ability to pursue a career in science writing. Fellows may attend school full- or part-time.

Fellowships are not available to those who are pursuing or plan to pursue careers in public relations or public information work.

GEOGRAPHIC RESTRICTIONS:
United States.

FINANCIAL DATA:
Amount of support per award: The Victor Cohn Prize: $3,000 and a framed certificate; Rennie Taylor/Alton Blakeslee Fellowships: $2,000 to $5,000.

NUMBER OF APPLICANTS MOST RECENT YEAR:
Rennie Taylor/Alton Blakeslee Fellowships: 30.

NUMBER OF AWARDS: The Victor Cohn Prize: 1; Rennie Taylor/Alton Blakeslee Fellowships: 4.

APPLICATION INFORMATION:
For the Victor Cohn Prize, the nominator should submit no more than five examples of the candidate's journalistic efforts, all published or aired since January 2009. Books are not eligible. The letter of nomination should include an in-depth evaluation of the stories being submitted that, in the eyes of the nominator, make the candidate worthy of the prize and a biographical sketch of the candidate. Provide five copies of the published work, or standard audio or videocassettes (accompanied by typed or printed scripts). Nominations may be submitted online, or send the nomination package to The Victor Cohn Prize, CASW, at the address listed above.

Fellowship applications can be submitted online or by mail. The following items must be uploaded or three sets, collated and stapled, enclosed with the package:
(1) a complete resume;
(2) undergraduate transcript;
(3) at least one letter of recommendation;
(4) three writing samples;
(5) short statement on career goals and why applicant wants to study science writing;
(6) specific information on resources available at journalism school or university for study of science or science writing and;
(7) specific information on program and courses applicant plans to pursue.
Duration: One academic year. Nonrenewable.
Deadline: The Victor Cohn Prize: July 31. Rennie Taylor/Alton Blakeslee Fellowships: July 1.

PUBLICATIONS:
Guide to Careers in Science Writing.

IRS IDENTIFICATION NUMBER: 13-1953314

OFFICERS AND DIRECTORS:
Alan Boyle, President
Deborah Blum, Vice President
Tom Siegfried, Treasurer
Charles Petit, Secretary
Rosalind Reid, Executive Director
Lewis Cope
Barbara J. Culliton
Richard Harris
Maggie Koerth-Baker
Robin Lloyd
Betsy Mason
Miles O'Brien

Joann Rodgers
Cristine Russell
Carl Zimmer

ADDRESS INQUIRIES TO:
Rosalind Reid, Executive Director
(See address above.)

*SPECIAL STIPULATIONS:
United States citizens only.

COUNCIL ON FOREIGN RELATIONS   [1931]
58 East 68th Street
New York, NY 10065
(212) 434-9740
Fax: (212) 434-9870

E-MAIL ADDRESS:
fellowships@cfr.org

WEB SITE ADDRESS:
www.cfr.org/fellowships

FOUNDED: 1921

AREAS OF INTEREST:
International relations, international news, foreign policy, journalism, international journalism, war reporting, foreign affairs, international affairs, and international media.

NAME(S) OF PROGRAMS:
● **Edward R. Murrow Press Fellowship**

TYPE:
Fellowships. The Edward R. Murrow Press Fellow spends nine months full-time in residence at the Council on Foreign Relations' (CFR) headquarters in New York. The program enables the fellow to engage in sustained analysis and writing, expand his or her intellectual and professional horizons, and extensively participate in CFR's active program of meetings and events. The Fellow will be part of the David Rockefeller Studies Program, CFR's think tank, alongside the program's full-time, adjunct and visiting fellows, whose expertise extends across the broad range of significant foreign policy issues facing the U.S. and the international community.

YEAR PROGRAM STARTED: 1949

PURPOSE:
To promote the quality of responsible and discerning journalism that exemplified the work of Edward R. Murrow.

ELIGIBILITY:
The program is only open to applicants who have distinguished credentials in the field of journalism and who have covered international news as a working journalist for print, broadcast or online media widely available in the U.S. Applicants are limited to those individuals who are authorized to work in the U.S. and who will continue to be authorized for the duration of the Fellowship. CFR does not sponsor for visas.

FINANCIAL DATA:
The Fellow is considered an independent contractor rather than an employee of CFR, and is not eligible for employment benefits, including health insurance.
Amount of support per award: A stipend of $65,000, as well as a modest travel grant.

COOPERATIVE FUNDING PROGRAMS: CBS Foundation and Ford Foundation.

NUMBER OF AWARDS: 1 per year.

APPLICATION INFORMATION:
Interested candidates who meet the program's eligibility requirements can apply online

between January 1 and March 1 on an annual basis. Official selections and announcement of the award will be made in April.
Duration: Nine months, preferably beginning in September.
Deadline: March 1, 2015.

ADDRESS INQUIRIES TO:
See e-mail address or phone number above.

THE DOW JONES NEWS FUND   [1932]
4300 Route One North
South Brunswick, NJ 08852
(609) 452-2820
Fax: (609) 520-5804

E-MAIL ADDRESS:
djnf@dowjones.com

WEB SITE ADDRESS:
www.newsfund.org

FOUNDED: 1958

AREAS OF INTEREST:
Journalism.

NAME(S) OF PROGRAMS:
● **Business Reporting Interns, Sophomore and Junior Students**
● **Editing Intern Program for College Juniors, Seniors and Graduate Students**

TYPE:
Internships. Editing intern program for juniors, seniors and graduate college students who successfully complete a summer of work as beginning copy editors at newspapers.

PURPOSE:
To encourage students to consider careers in copy-editing.

LEGAL BASIS:
Nonprofit foundation.

ELIGIBILITY:
Applicants must be juniors, seniors or graduate students at any college who have a sincere interest in professional copy-editing news work. Working on a school publication is not a stated requirement, but highly recommended. Applicants must also be U.S. citizens.

GEOGRAPHIC RESTRICTIONS:
United States.

FINANCIAL DATA:
Interns will receive regular wages (minimum $350 per week) from the newspapers for which they work. After the summer of work, a $1,000 scholarship check is awarded to the intern's college, but only if that intern returns to school following the internship.
Amount of support per award: $1,000.
Total amount of support: $200,000 to $300,000, depending on number of interns selected and cost of pre-training course.

NUMBER OF APPLICANTS MOST RECENT YEAR:
700.

NUMBER OF AWARDS: Up to 125.

APPLICATION INFORMATION:
Applications available online September 1 to November 1.
Duration: Full summer.
Deadline: November 1.

OFFICERS:
Richard J. Levine, President
Paul Schmidt, Treasurer
Robin Gibson Sawyer, Secretary

STAFF:
Linda Shockley, Deputy Director
Diane Cohn, Director of Finance

DIRECTORS:
Don E. Carter
Thomas E. Engleman
Pamela Fisher
Ken Herts
Richard S. Holden
Mark H. Jackson
Diana Mitsu Klos
Neal Lipschutz
Laurence G. O'Donnell
Dr. Reginald Owens
Dr. Russell G. Todd

ADDRESS INQUIRIES TO:
Internship Coordinator
Editing Intern Programs
(See address above.)

FUND FOR INVESTIGATIVE JOURNALISM [1933]

529 14th Street, N.W.
13th Floor
Washington, DC 20045
(202) 662-7564

E-MAIL ADDRESS:
fundfij@gmail.com

WEB SITE ADDRESS:
www.fij.org

FOUNDED: 1969

AREAS OF INTEREST:
Promoting the work of investigative journalism.

TYPE:
Project/program grants. The Fund gives grants to investigative reporters working outside the protection and backing of major news organizations.

PURPOSE:
To provide funding for reporters engaged in investigative journalism.

FINANCIAL DATA:
Amount of support per award: Average grant: $5,000.
Total amount of support: Varies.

APPLICATION INFORMATION:
Applications are to be submitted online. Applicant must write a proposal letter outlining the story, what he or she expects to prove, how this will be done, and the sources for the proof. For projects, include the anticipated completion date.

The letter must be supported by a resume, a detailed budget to justify the size of the grant, no more than two writing samples or one sample chapter in the case of a book applicant, and a letter of commitment from an editor or publisher or an executive of a broadcast news operation or online news outlet stating that the project will be published or broadcast if completed according to the proposal.

A letter of commitment is required for all applicants and is a non-negotiable requirement. In the case of individuals seeking grants for books, a signed copy of a contract with a publisher is required and should be substituted for the commitment letter.
Deadline: Varies.

ADDRESS INQUIRIES TO:
Sandy Bergo, Executive Director
(See address above.)

RUTH HANCOCK SCHOLARSHIP FOUNDATION [1934]

95 St. Clair Avenue West
Suite 1103
Toronto ON M4V 1N6 Canada
(416) 729-1950
Fax: (416) 964-0771

E-MAIL ADDRESS:
breaume@acaweb.ca

WEB SITE ADDRESS:
www.bes.ca

FOUNDED: 1926

AREAS OF INTEREST:
Communications and marketing.

NAME(S) OF PROGRAMS:
● **Ruth Hancock Scholarships**

TYPE:
Awards/prizes; Scholarships. Scholarships to encourage talented, hard-working students to pursue careers in Canadian broadcasting.

PURPOSE:
To assist students in broadcast communication studies at community colleges and universities.

LEGAL BASIS:
Private.

ELIGIBILITY:
Open to Canadian citizens enrolled in a recognized communications course at a Canadian college or university.

GEOGRAPHIC RESTRICTIONS:
Canada.

FINANCIAL DATA:
Amount of support per award: $1,500.
Total amount of support: $4,500.

NUMBER OF AWARDS: 3.

APPLICATION INFORMATION:
Signed recommendation from course director or professor and a 500-word essay must be submitted with the application form.
Duration: One year. Recipients can reapply.
Deadline: June 30. Announcement in the fall.

ADDRESS INQUIRIES TO:
Bob Reaume, Vice President
Policy and Research
(See address above.)

WILLIAM RANDOLPH HEARST FOUNDATION [1935]

90 New Montgomery Street, Suite 1212
San Francisco, CA 94105
(415) 908-4560
Fax: (415) 243-0760

E-MAIL ADDRESS:
jwatten@hearstfdn.org

WEB SITE ADDRESS:
www.hearstawards.org

FOUNDED: 1948

AREAS OF INTEREST:
Writing, photojournalism and broadcast journalism.

NAME(S) OF PROGRAMS:
● **Journalism Awards Program**

TYPE:
Awards/prizes; Scholarships. Awards to the top 10 winners of 13 monthly competitions: six writing, three photo, two broadcast (TV and radio) and multimedia. Entrants must be journalism majors attending one of the 105 accredited schools of journalism. The schools receive a matching grant.

YEAR PROGRAM STARTED: 1960

PURPOSE:
To provide support, encouragement and assistance to education in journalism at the undergraduate college level.

LEGAL BASIS:
Nonprofit foundation.

ELIGIBILITY:
Participation in the program is open only to journalism majors who are undergraduates at the colleges and universities that are members of the Association of Schools of Journalism and Mass Communication.

GEOGRAPHIC RESTRICTIONS:
United States.

FINANCIAL DATA:
Amount of support per award: $1,000 to $2,600, depending upon placement of winners.
Total amount of support: Over $500,000 for the year 2012-13.

NUMBER OF APPLICANTS MOST RECENT YEAR: 1,000.

NUMBER OF AWARDS: 150 scholarships and grants.

APPLICATION INFORMATION:
Full application information may be obtained through individual departments of journalism at participating schools. A list of accredited schools is available at Hearst Foundation's San Francisco address.
Duration: Varies.
Deadline: Monthly during academic year.

STAFF:
Dino Dinovitz, Executive Director
Jan C. Watten, Program Director
Yasi Haerizadeh, Program Assistant

BOARD OF DIRECTORS:
William R. Hearst, III, President
James Asher
Annissa Balson
David Barrett
Frank A. Bennack, Jr.
John G. Conomikes
Ron Doerfler
George R. Hearst, Jr.
John R. Hearst, Jr.
Harvey Lipton
Gilbert C. Maurer
Mark Miller
Virginia Randt

ADDRESS INQUIRIES TO:
Jan C. Watten, Program Director
(See address above.)

THE SIDNEY HILLMAN FOUNDATION, INC. [1936]

12 West 31st Street
12th Floor
New York, NY 10001
(646) 448-6413

E-MAIL ADDRESS:
alex@hillmanfoundation.org

WEB SITE ADDRESS:
www.hillmanfoundation.org

FOUNDED: 1950

AREAS OF INTEREST:
Civil liberties, race relations, labor movement, social welfare, housing, economic security and international understanding.

NAME(S) OF PROGRAMS:
● **Hillman Prizes in Journalism**
● **Sidney Awards**

TYPE:
Awards/prizes. Monetary awards presented annually for outstanding contributions in the fields of daily or periodical journalism, nonfiction, radio and television, blogs and commentary.

YEAR PROGRAM STARTED: 1950

PURPOSE:
To recognize outstanding contributions to the field of journalism dealing with themes relating to the ideals which Sidney Hillman held throughout his life, including the protection of individual civil liberties, improved race relations, a strengthened labor movement, the advancement of social welfare, housing and economic security, greater world understanding and related problems.

LEGAL BASIS:
Private foundation.

ELIGIBILITY:
Only work published in English in the previous calendar year and distributed in the U.S. and Canada is eligible for consideration. Radio and television contributions must have been produced under professional auspices in the previous calendar year.

GEOGRAPHIC RESTRICTIONS:
United States and Canada.

FINANCIAL DATA:
Amount of support per award: Hillman Prize: $5,000; Sidney Award: $500.

NUMBER OF APPLICANTS MOST RECENT YEAR:
500.

NUMBER OF AWARDS: Hillman Prizes: 7; Sidney Awards: 12.

APPLICATION INFORMATION:
Material may be submitted by the author, his or her publication or publisher, or by anyone connected with it. The submission must be accompanied by a brief cover letter.
Deadline: Hillman Prizes: January 31. Sidney Awards: Last day of each month.

STAFF:
Alexandra Lescaze, Executive Director
Lindsay Beyerstein, Lead Writer

ADDRESS INQUIRIES TO:
Alexandra Lescaze, Executive Director
(See address above.)

INTER AMERICAN PRESS ASSOCIATION (IAPA)   [1937]
Jules Dubois Building
1801 S.W. 3rd Avenue, Suite 800
Miami, FL 33129
(305) 634-2465
Fax: (305) 635-2272

E-MAIL ADDRESS:
becas@sipiapa.org

WEB SITE ADDRESS:
www.sipiapa.org/becas

FOUNDED: 1942

AREAS OF INTEREST:
Press freedom.

NAME(S) OF PROGRAMS:
● **IAPA Scholarship Fund**

TYPE:
Exchange programs; Fellowships; Scholarships. Scholarships for American and Canadian working journalists, journalism graduates or journalism students to study in Latin America and for journalists who are citizens or residents of countries outside the U.S. or Canada to study in the U.S. or Canada.

YEAR PROGRAM STARTED: 1954

PURPOSE:
To support the exchange of journalists and journalism students between countries of the Western Hemisphere.

LEGAL BASIS:
Nonprofit association, tax-exempt under Internal Revenue Code 501(c)(3).

ELIGIBILITY:
Journalists or journalism school seniors or graduates between 21 and 35 years of age with a good command of the language they are to use. Students must have completed their degree before beginning the scholarship year.
Language ability for U.S. and Canadian candidates must be confirmed by a recognized authority in Spanish or Portuguese. Latin American candidates must take a TOEFL (Test of English as a Foreign Language).

FINANCIAL DATA:
U.S. and Canadian scholars will receive $20,000 for the duration of their stay abroad. Latin American and Caribbean scholars will receive $20,000 and a one-time round-trip airfare for the year.

NUMBER OF APPLICANTS MOST RECENT YEAR: 95.

NUMBER OF AWARDS: 4.

APPLICATION INFORMATION:
Application is available on the web site or by writing to the Association.
Duration: One academic year.
Deadline: October 2014/January 2015.

STAFF:
Julio E. Munoz, Executive Director
Mauricio J. Montaldo, Coordinator of Scholarship Fund

ADDRESS INQUIRIES TO:
Mauricio J. Montaldo
Coordinator of Scholarship Fund
(See address above.)

INTERNATIONAL DOCUMENTARY ASSOCIATION
3470 Wilshire Boulevard
Suite 980
Los Angeles, CA 90010
(213) 232-1660
Fax: (213) 232-1669

E-MAIL ADDRESS:
info@documentary.org

WEB SITE ADDRESS:
www.documentary.org

TYPE:
Awards/prizes; Internships. ABC News Videosource Award is awarded for the best use of news footage as an integral component in a documentary.

IDA/David L. Wolper Student Documentary Achievement Award recognizes exceptional achievement in nonfiction film and video production at the university level and brings greater public and industry awareness to the work of students in the documentary field.

The Pare Lorentz Award is awarded for films that demonstrate exemplary filmmaking while focusing on the appropriate use of the natural environment, justice for all and the illumination of pressing social problems.

See entry 462 for full listing.

INVESTIGATIVE REPORTERS AND EDITORS   [1938]
141 Neff Annex
Missouri School of Journalism
Columbia, MO 65211
(573) 882-6668
Fax: (573) 882-5431

E-MAIL ADDRESS:
rescntr@ire.org

WEB SITE ADDRESS:
www.ire.org

FOUNDED: 1975

AREAS OF INTEREST:
Journalism across all media.

NAME(S) OF PROGRAMS:
● **Investigative Reporters and Editors Contest**

TYPE:
Awards/prizes; Fellowships. Investigative Reporters and Editors Contest is an annual investigative reporting contest. The Tom Renner Award (one of the 18 categories of this Contest) is given to the best investigative reporting in print, broadcast or book form, covering crime and its impact on society.
IRE also offers fellowships to minority journalism students and professionals to attend IRE national or regional conferences. There are also fellowships available for small newspaper staffers and for journalism students.

PURPOSE:
To promote high-quality, in-depth journalism.

LEGAL BASIS:
University.

ELIGIBILITY:
Individual journalists and news organizations may submit entries for the Renner Award. No more than 10 stories can be entered. Entries that disregard the rules will be disqualified. Qualifications for IRE minority fellowships include financial need, references and answers to essay questions.

FINANCIAL DATA:
Amount of support per award: Renner Award: $500; Student Award: $250.
Total amount of support: Varies.

NUMBER OF APPLICANTS MOST RECENT YEAR: 430.

NUMBER OF AWARDS: 15.

APPLICATION INFORMATION:
Entry form required. Entrants must include three copies of the story or script cut and pasted or photocopied onto 8 1/2 x 11 inch paper with no foldovers. In addition, radio entries must be on audio CD and television entries on a DVD. Television and radio entries must include three copies of a transcript. For book entries, entrants must

send three copies of the published book. There is no limit on the number of entries allowed from individual journalists.

Deadline: Mid-January. Deadline for fellowships depends on conference dates.

PUBLICATIONS:
Program announcement; entry form.

IRS IDENTIFICATION NUMBER: 51-0166741

ADDRESS INQUIRIES TO:
Lauren Grandestaff, Contest Coordinator
(See address above.)

JOURNAL OF THE AMERICAN MEDICAL ASSOCIATION [1939]
330 North Wabash Avenue
Suite 39300
Chicago, IL 60611
(312) 464-4334
Fax: (312) 464-5824

E-MAIL ADDRESS:
robert.golub@jama-archives.org

WEB SITE ADDRESS:
www.jama.com

FOUNDED: 1847

AREAS OF INTEREST:
Public health, physician and health care personnel education and medical publications.

NAME(S) OF PROGRAMS:
● **Morris Fishbein Fellowship in Medical Editing**

TYPE:
Fellowships. Award granted to physicians exclusively as a one-year, full-time editorial fellowship with *The Journal of the American Medical Association*. The successful candidate will work with the editorial and production staff in all facets of editing and publishing a major weekly medical journal. At the completion of the program, it is expected that the candidate will be proficient in all aspects of manuscript selection, peer review, issue makeup, copy editing and styling, issue planning and managing, in addition to the many other elements of medical journal publication.

YEAR PROGRAM STARTED: 1978

PURPOSE:
To provide physicians with an opportunity to learn the editorial functions of a major medical journal.

LEGAL BASIS:
Not-for-profit organization serving members in the medical profession.

ELIGIBILITY:
Applicants must be physicians. Candidates also must have proven writing ability at the time of application because they will be required during the course of the year to prepare articles for publication. Although the fellow will work under the supervision of a physician-editor, ability to work independently is a must. Ability to use a resource library is a strong plus.

Fellow must live in Chicago during the 12-month full-time fellowship (July to June).

FINANCIAL DATA:
Amount of support per award: $54,000.
Total amount of support: $54,000 annually.

NUMBER OF APPLICANTS MOST RECENT YEAR: 12.

NUMBER OF AWARDS: 1 annually.

APPLICATION INFORMATION:
Application forms may be obtained from the address or e-mail listed above.
Duration: One year.
Deadline: Early January.

ADDRESS INQUIRIES TO:
Robert Golub, M.D., Deputy Editor
(See e-mail and address above.)

KAPPA TAU ALPHA [1940]
76 Gannett Hall
School of Journalism
University of Missouri
Columbia, MO 65211-1200
(573) 882-7685
Fax: (573) 884-1720

E-MAIL ADDRESS:
umcjourkta@missouri.edu

WEB SITE ADDRESS:
www.kappataualpha.org

FOUNDED: 1910

AREAS OF INTEREST:
Journalism research and mass communication.

NAME(S) OF PROGRAMS:
● **Frank Luther Mott KTA Research/Book Award**

TYPE:
Awards/prizes. Annual award for a published book concerned with journalism and mass communications research.

YEAR PROGRAM STARTED: 1944

PURPOSE:
To recognize the top book published in the field of journalism and mass communications research; to promote interest in Kappa Tau Alpha among students and faculty.

LEGAL BASIS:
National society honoring scholarship in journalism and mass communication.

ELIGIBILITY:
Qualified individuals may apply for the award with an appropriate book published during the year.

FINANCIAL DATA:
Amount of support per award: $1,000 and a plaque.

NUMBER OF APPLICANTS MOST RECENT YEAR: 28.

NUMBER OF AWARDS: 1 annually.

APPLICATION INFORMATION:
Interested applicants should submit six copies of the published work to be considered.
Deadline: Typically first Monday in December.

OFFICERS:
Peter J. Gade, President
Andrew Mendelson, Vice President
Dr. Keith P. Sanders, Executive Director

JUDGES:
Peter J. Gade
Andrew Mendelson
Dr. Keith P. Sanders

ADDRESS INQUIRIES TO:
Dr. Keith P. Sanders, Executive Director
(See address above.)

LIVINGSTON AWARDS [1941]
Wallace House, University of Michigan
620 Oxford Road
Ann Arbor, MI 48104
(734) 998-7575
Fax: (734) 998-7979

E-MAIL ADDRESS:
livawards@umich.edu

WEB SITE ADDRESS:
www.livawards.org

AREAS OF INTEREST:
Broadcast, print and online journalism.

NAME(S) OF PROGRAMS:
● **Livingston Awards for Young Journalists**

TYPE:
Awards/prizes.

YEAR PROGRAM STARTED: 1981

LEGAL BASIS:
Foundation.

ELIGIBILITY:
Entries must be directly related to current events or include new information about old events. Features and commentary are eligible. There are no awards for still photography.

Journalists who are 34 years old or younger as of December 31 and whose work appears in print, broadcast or online media may apply.

Submissions must consist of materials prepared in the ordinary course of the journalist's professional production. One entry per individual. Individuals may apply on their own, or be entered by their organization. Multiple by-lines are eligible, but all must meet age criteria. Materials prepared by journalists specifically for submission to the Livingston Awards will not qualify and may not be considered. Student media are not eligible.

All entries will be judged on the basis of either a single piece, or in the case of series, a maximum of three related pieces.

FINANCIAL DATA:
Amount of support per award: $10,000.
Total amount of support: $30,000.

NUMBER OF AWARDS: 3.

APPLICATION INFORMATION:
Detailed information is available online.
Deadline: February 1. Announcement in June.

PUBLICATIONS:
Program brochure.

STAFF:
Melissa Riley, Administrator

ADDRESS INQUIRIES TO:
See e-mail address above.

THE GERALD LOEB AWARDS [1942]
UCLA Anderson School of Management
110 Westwood Plaza
Gold Hall, Suite B307
Los Angeles, CA 90095-1481
(310) 825-4478
Fax: (310) 825-4479

E-MAIL ADDRESS:
loeb@anderson.ucla.edu

WEB SITE ADDRESS:
www.loeb.anderson.ucla.edu

FOUNDED: 1957

AREAS OF INTEREST:
Business, economic and financial news
writing and journalism.

TYPE:
Awards/prizes. Awards to recognize business
and financial journalists for important
contributions to the understanding of
business, finance and the economy.

YEAR PROGRAM STARTED: 1957

PURPOSE:
To recognize journalists who make significant
contributions to the understanding of business
and finance.

LEGAL BASIS:
University.

ELIGIBILITY:
Entries submitted must have been published
or broadcast for the first time during the
previous calendar year in the U.S.

FINANCIAL DATA:
Amount of support per award: $2,000; $500
Honorable Mention.
Total amount of support: $24,000 annually.

APPLICATION INFORMATION:
Application must be submitted online.

PUBLICATIONS:
Entry brochure.

ADDRESS INQUIRIES TO:
Jonathan Daillak, Program Manager
(See address above.)

MASSACHUSETTS INSTITUTE OF TECHNOLOGY   [1943]
MIT E19-623
77 Massachusetts Avenue
Cambridge, MA 02139-4307
(617) 253-3442
Fax: (617) 258-8100

E-MAIL ADDRESS:
knight-info@mit.edu

WEB SITE ADDRESS:
web.mit.edu/knight-science

AREAS OF INTEREST:
Science journalism.

NAME(S) OF PROGRAMS:
● **Knight Science Journalism Fellowships**

TYPE:
Fellowships. Nine months access to courses,
laboratories and researchers.

YEAR PROGRAM STARTED: 1983

PURPOSE:
To recognize excellence in explaining
science, medicine, technology and the
environment to the public; to provide a
deeper familiarity with the processes of
research and development to widen the
fellows' acquaintance with leading engineers,
scientists and medical researchers
experienced in explaining complex issues.

LEGAL BASIS:
University.

ELIGIBILITY:
Must have at least three years of full-time
experience covering science technology,
medicine or environment. Also consider
journalists who wish to gain expertise in
these fields and who have at least five years
of full-time experience.

FINANCIAL DATA:
Fellowship includes stipend. During their
residence, fellows may join an MIT affiliates
health plan.

Amount of support per award: $65,000
stipend.

COOPERATIVE FUNDING PROGRAMS: Sponsored
by the John S. and James L. Knight
Foundation.

NUMBER OF AWARDS: 10 to 12 annually.

APPLICATION INFORMATION:
Online submission only.
Duration: August 1 to May 31.
Deadline: March 1. Interviews will begin in
April with public announcement in early
May.

ADDRESS INQUIRIES TO:
Director
Knight Science Journalism Fellowships
(See address above.)

NATIONAL ASSOCIATION OF BROADCASTERS   [1944]
1771 N Street, N.W.
Washington, DC 20036-2800
(202) 429-5479
Fax: (202) 429-4199

E-MAIL ADDRESS:
irc@nab.org

WEB SITE ADDRESS:
www.nab.org

NAME(S) OF PROGRAMS:
● **Grants for Research in Broadcasting**

TYPE:
Research grants. Grants are intended to
stimulate interest in broadcast research,
especially research on economic, business,
social or policy issues of importance to the
U.S. commercial broadcast industry.

YEAR PROGRAM STARTED: 1967

PURPOSE:
To attract qualified personnel into the field of
broadcast research; to facilitate the training
of broadcast researchers; to assist individuals
already working in this area; to make
high-quality academic research available to
industry practitioners as well as other
academics.

LEGAL BASIS:
Nonprofit association.

ELIGIBILITY:
The competition is open to all academic
personnel and graduate students. Senior
undergraduates are invited to submit
proposals.

FINANCIAL DATA:
Monies are not to be used for overhead or
benefits.
Amount of support per award: Average
$5,000. More can be awarded if the project
merits additional funds.
Total amount of support: Up to $10,000.

NUMBER OF APPLICANTS MOST RECENT YEAR:
50.

NUMBER OF AWARDS: 4 to 6 annually.

APPLICATION INFORMATION:
Official application materials are available
upon request.
Duration: One year.
Deadline: Late January. Award notification
by April 1.

ADDRESS INQUIRIES TO:
Vice President
Research and Information
(See address above.)

NATIONAL ASSOCIATION OF FARM BROADCASTING FOUNDATION   [1945]
1100 Platte Falls Road
Platte City, MO 64079
(816) 431-4032
Fax: (816) 431-4087

E-MAIL ADDRESS:
aaron@nafb.com

WEB SITE ADDRESS:
www.nafbfoundation.com

AREAS OF INTEREST:
Agricultural journalism and communications.

NAME(S) OF PROGRAMS:
● **Ag Broadcast Scholarships**
● **Glenn Kummerow Memorial Scholarship**
● **The George and Jessie Logan Scholarship**

TYPE:
Scholarships. Since 1977, the NAFB
Foundation has provided financial support
and educational opportunities in the form of
college scholarships to assist students in
pursuit of careers in agricultural
communications. Currently the NAFB
Foundation offers three annual college
scholarships. These scholarships are
recognized at the National NAFB
Convention.

YEAR PROGRAM STARTED: 1975

PURPOSE:
To provide financial support and educational
opportunities for students in pursuit of
careers in agricultural communications.

ELIGIBILITY:
Must be at least junior-year college students
or in graduate school, enrolled in an
agricultural journalism/agricultural
communications curriculum, or plan to
transfer to a university which offers a
designated professional program of study in
agricultural radio-television broadcasting.
Selection is by application and is based on
agricultural communications aptitude and
leadership achievements, academic record
and career plans.

FINANCIAL DATA:
Winners receive an expense-paid trip to
attend the convention as part of the award.
Amount of support per award: Ag Broadcast
Scholarships: $4,000; Glenn Kummerow
Memorial Scholarship and George and Jessie
Logan Scholarship: $5,000.
Total amount of support: $14,000.

NUMBER OF AWARDS: 1 per award.

APPLICATION INFORMATION:
Applications are available in April on the
Foundation web site.
Duration: One school year.
Deadline: May 31.

STAFF:
Aaron Corbet, NAFB Member Services
Director

ADDRESS INQUIRIES TO:
Aaron Corbet
NAFB Member Services Director
(See address above.)

NATIONAL ASSOCIATION OF HISPANIC JOURNALISTS
1050 Connecticut Avenue, N.W.
10th Floor
Washington, DC 20036
(202) 662-7145
Fax: (202) 662-7144

E-MAIL ADDRESS:
alopez@nahj.org

WEB SITE ADDRESS:
www.nahj.org

TYPE:
Awards/prizes; Conferences/seminars; Fellowships; General operating grants; Internships; Matching gifts; Project/program grants; Research grants; Scholarships; Seed money grants; Training grants; Travel grants.

See entry 1001 for full listing.

NATIONAL ASSOCIATION OF SCIENCE WRITERS, INC.   [1946]
P.O. Box 7905
Berkeley, CA 94707
(510) 547-9500

E-MAIL ADDRESS:
director@nasw.org

WEB SITE ADDRESS:
www.nasw.org

FOUNDED: 1934

AREAS OF INTEREST:
Dissemination of scientific and medical information to a general lay audience and professional development for science writers.

NAME(S) OF PROGRAMS:
• **Science in Society Awards**

TYPE:
Conferences/seminars; Fellowships; Project/program grants; Seed money grants; Training grants; Travel grants. Separate monetary prizes and awards for writers in five categories:
(1) books;
(2) commentary or opinion;
(3) science reporting;
(4) science reporting for a local or regional market and;
(5) longform science reporting.

YEAR PROGRAM STARTED: 1972

PURPOSE:
To recognize investigative or interpretive reporting about the sciences and their impact on society.

LEGAL BASIS:
Professional membership organization.

ELIGIBILITY:
Any writer (or team) is eligible to submit not more than one entry in each category. Material may be single article or broadcast or a series. Books with a copyright date of 2014 are eligible. Works must be written or spoken, in English, intended for the layperson and published or broadcast in North America between January 1, 2014 and December 31, 2014.

GEOGRAPHIC RESTRICTIONS:
North America.

FINANCIAL DATA:
Amount of support per award: $2,500 and Certificates of Recognition in each category.

NUMBER OF APPLICANTS MOST RECENT YEAR: 200.

NUMBER OF AWARDS: 5 annually.

APPLICATION INFORMATION:
Details are available online.
Duration: One year.
Deadline: February 1.

ADDRESS INQUIRIES TO:
Tinsley Davis, Executive Director
(See address above.)

NATIONAL ENDOWMENT FOR THE HUMANITIES   [1947]
1100 Pennsylvania Avenue, N.W.
Washington, DC 20506
(202) 606-8269
Fax: (202) 606-8557

E-MAIL ADDRESS:
publicpgms@neh.gov

WEB SITE ADDRESS:
www.neh.gov

FOUNDED: 1965

AREAS OF INTEREST:
Scholarship, research, education and public programs in the humanities. In the act that established the Endowment, the term humanities includes, but is not limited to, the study of history, philosophy, languages, linguistics, literature, archaeology, jurisprudence, the history, theory and criticism of the arts, ethics, comparative religion and those aspects of the social sciences that employ historical or philosophical approaches.

NAME(S) OF PROGRAMS:
• **Public Programs**

TYPE:
Project/program grants. Grants support the planning and production of television and radio programs in the humanities intended for general audiences; the planning and implementation of exhibitions, the interpretation of historic sites and the production of related publications; multimedia components and educational programs and the planning and implementation of projects through the use of books, new technologies and other resources in the collections of libraries and archives in formats such as reading and discussion programs, lectures, symposia and interpretive exhibitions.

YEAR PROGRAM STARTED: 1969

PURPOSE:
To create an understanding and appreciation of the humanities among the general public.

LEGAL BASIS:
The National Foundation on the Arts and Humanities Act of 1965, Public Law 89-209, as amended.

ELIGIBILITY:
Nonprofit institutions, organizations and groups, including public television and radio stations and state humanities councils, are eligible for support.

GEOGRAPHIC RESTRICTIONS:
United States.

FINANCIAL DATA:
Amount of support per award: Varies.
Total amount of support: Varies.

NUMBER OF APPLICANTS MOST RECENT YEAR: 350.

NUMBER OF AWARDS: 75.

APPLICATION INFORMATION:
Prospective applicants are urged to submit a letter of inquiry which indicates an interest in the program and explains the general nature of the proposed project as well as its approximate cost. If appropriate, the applicant may then file a formal application for support.
Deadline: January, June and August.

PUBLICATIONS:
Annual report; *Grant Programs*; *Humanities Magazine*.

IRS IDENTIFICATION NUMBER: 52-1098584

ADDRESS INQUIRIES TO:
Division of Public Programs
(See address above.)

NATIONAL INSTITUTE FOR LABOR RELATIONS RESEARCH   [1948]
5211 Port Royal Road
Suite 510
Springfield, VA 22151
(703) 321-9606 ext. 2231
Fax: (703) 321-7143

E-MAIL ADDRESS:
info@research.org
CLJ@nrpw.org

WEB SITE ADDRESS:
www.nilrr.org

FOUNDED: 1985

AREAS OF INTEREST:
Research and analysis exposing the economic and social inequities of compulsory unionism.

NAME(S) OF PROGRAMS:
• **The William B. Ruggles Journalist Scholarship**

TYPE:
Scholarships. Unrestricted scholarship awarded annually to the student who exemplifies the dedication to principle and high journalistic standards of the late William B. Ruggles, the well-known and respected Texas journalist who contributed significantly to the Right to Work movement.

YEAR PROGRAM STARTED: 1974

PURPOSE:
To honor the late William B. Ruggles, former editorial page editor of *The Dallas Morning News*.

LEGAL BASIS:
Nonpartisan coalition of citizens.

ELIGIBILITY:
Applicants are limited to graduate or undergraduate students majoring in journalism in institutions of higher learning throughout the U.S. Graduating high school seniors may apply, if accepted to a journalism or communications school. To be considered, applicants must demonstrate the potential for a successful completion of educational requirements in an accredited journalism program and an understanding of voluntarism and of the problems of compulsory unionism.

GEOGRAPHIC RESTRICTIONS:
United States.

FINANCIAL DATA:
Amount of support per award: $2,000.
Total amount of support: $2,000 each year.

NUMBER OF APPLICANTS MOST RECENT YEAR: 50.

NUMBER OF AWARDS: 1 annually.

APPLICATION INFORMATION:
A total application will consist of a completed formal application form, available from the address above, an official grade transcript from essay finalists and a typewritten essay of approximately 500 words clearly demonstrating an interest in and a knowledge of the Right to Work principle. Application may be submitted electronically or by mail.
Deadline: Postmark by December 31. Announcement in April.

OFFICERS:
Mark Mix, Executive Vice President and Treasurer

ADDRESS INQUIRIES TO:
Cathy Jones
Journalism Scholarship Administrator
(See address above.)

NATIONAL PRESS FOUNDATION   [1949]

1211 Connecticut Avenue, N.W.
Suite 310
Washington, DC 20036
(202) 663-7280
Fax: (202) 530-2855

E-MAIL ADDRESS:
npf@nationalpress.org

WEB SITE ADDRESS:
www.nationalpress.org

AREAS OF INTEREST:
Journalism.

NAME(S) OF PROGRAMS:
- **Clifford K. and James T. Berryman Award for Editorial Cartoons**
- **Capitol Hill Issues Briefings**
- **The Feddie Award**
- **Paul Miller Washington Reporting Fellowship**
- **National Issues Programs**
- **Thomas L. Stokes Award**

TYPE:
Awards/prizes; Fellowships. International programs. The Feddie Award recognizes coverage of the impact of federal laws on local communities.

Paul Miller Washington Reporting Fellowship provides free professional development opportunities to nine, day-long monthly seminars to reporters new to covering Washington. Agency visits, briefings from officials and presentations by experts enable journalists to add depth and insight to topics they cover.

National Issues Programs offer free, all-expenses-paid fellowships to one- to four-day seminars on a variety of topics including Alzheimer's disease, cancer, and retirement.

PURPOSE:
To help journalists better understand the issues about which they write and broadcast.

ELIGIBILITY:
Clifford K. and James T. Berryman Award for Editorial Cartoons is open to editorial cartoonists of newspapers and magazines for work that exhibits power to influence public opinion, plus good drawing and striking effect.

Thomas L. Stokes Award is for the best writing in a daily newspaper on the subject of energy. The subject may be any form of energy - oil, gas, coal, nuclear, water, solar, etc. The writing may be reporting, analysis or comment. The work must have been published in a daily newspaper in the U.S. between January 1 and December 31.

FINANCIAL DATA:
Amount of support per award: Berryman Award: $2,500; Stokes Award: $1,000 and citation.

APPLICATION INFORMATION:
For the Berryman Award, applicants must submit three complete packets containing five cartoons (copies are acceptable), a supporting letter from an editor or supervisor and a brief biography.
Deadline: Berryman Award: October 1; Stokes Award: January 31.

STAFF:
Bob Meyers, President

NEW YORK STATE SENATE

Student Programs Office
80 South Swan Street, Suite 1426
Albany, NY 12247
(518) 455-2611
Fax: (518) 426-6827

E-MAIL ADDRESS:
students@nysenate.gov

WEB SITE ADDRESS:
www.nysenate.gov/department/student-programs

TYPE:
Assistantships; Fellowships; Internships. These fellowships are intended for the graduate/postgraduate/midcareer level. Stipends are for bipartisan opportunities to train in government while on-site in Albany, NY. Fellows spend almost a year immersed in the work of the Senate, learning techniques associated with policymaking and legislative process. Placement is usually to the office of an elected Senate member. The Senate Legislative Fellows Program, Biggane Fellowship, Roth Journalism Fellowship and Wiebe Public Service Fellowship constitute the Senate Graduate/Post-Graduate/Mid-Career Fellowships.

See entry 2010 for full listing.

THE NEWSPAPER GUILD-CWA   [1950]

501 Third Street, N.W.
6th Floor
Washington, DC 20001-2797
(202) 434-1162
Fax: (202) 434-1472

E-MAIL ADDRESS:
jhartman@cwa-union.org

WEB SITE ADDRESS:
www.newsguild.org

FOUNDED: 1933

AREAS OF INTEREST:
News industry, labor and free press.

NAME(S) OF PROGRAMS:
- **Heywood Broun Award**

TYPE:
Awards/prizes. Cash award and citation for outstanding journalistic achievement "in the spirit of Heywood Broun," the great newspaper columnist who founded The Newspaper Guild.

YEAR PROGRAM STARTED: 1941

PURPOSE:
To encourage and recognize individual journalistic achievement in this spirit by members of the working press, particularly if it helps right a wrong or correct an injustice, or shows an "abiding concern for the underdog and the underprivileged."

LEGAL BASIS:
Labor union.

ELIGIBILITY:
Journalistic work completed within the calendar year is eligible. Journalists working on behalf of newspapers, news services, news magazines, and radio and TV stations in the U.S., Canada and Puerto Rico are eligible. Managerial employees are not eligible, nor are publications and other employers as such, or entries on behalf of entire staffs that, in effect, constitute entries on behalf of a publication or employer.

Applicants may submit entries on their own or others' behalf. First consideration is given to entries on behalf of individuals or teams of no more than two persons.

GEOGRAPHIC RESTRICTIONS:
United States, Puerto Rico and Canada.

FINANCIAL DATA:
Amount of support per award: $5,000 plus a Guild citation; two awards of $1,000 for entries of substantial distinction, including one such award reserved specifically for a broadcast (radio or television) entry.
Total amount of support: $7,000.

NUMBER OF APPLICANTS MOST RECENT YEAR:
125.

NUMBER OF AWARDS: 1 annually.

APPLICATION INFORMATION:
Submit entries to the Broun Award Committee at the address above. There are no application forms, but each entry should be accompanied by a letter describing the circumstances under which the work was done and its results. To facilitate judging, entries and cover letters should be submitted in triplicate.
Deadline: Last Friday in January.

OFFICERS:
Bernard J. Lunzer, President
Carol Rothman, Secretary and Treasurer

ADDRESS INQUIRIES TO:
Broun Award Committee
(See address above.)

THE NEWSPAPER GUILD-CWA   [1951]

501 Third Street, N.W.
6th Floor
Washington, DC 20001-2797
(202) 434-7177
Fax: (202) 434-1472

E-MAIL ADDRESS:
dedmondson@cwa-union.org

WEB SITE ADDRESS:
www.newsguild.org

FOUNDED: 1933

AREAS OF INTEREST:
Union for journalists and related occupations in the newspaper industry.

NAME(S) OF PROGRAMS:
- **David S. Barr Award**

TYPE:
Awards/prizes; Scholarships.

YEAR PROGRAM STARTED: 1999

PURPOSE:
To recognize and encourage student journalists.

ELIGIBILITY:
The Award is open to all high school and college students. The journalistic work must have been published or broadcast in prior year and should focus on social justice.

FINANCIAL DATA:
Amount of support per award: High School Students: $1,000; College Students: $1,500.

NUMBER OF APPLICANTS MOST RECENT YEAR: 180.

NUMBER OF AWARDS: High School and College: 1 each.

APPLICATION INFORMATION:
Application form is available at the Guild web site. Entry must be mailed to TNG-CWA, along with four copies and the application form.
Duration: One-time award.
Deadline: Last Friday of January (postmark).

ADDRESS INQUIRIES TO:
Dominique Edmondson, Secretary to Collective Bargaining Department
David S. Barr Award
(See address above.)

NIEMAN FOUNDATION FOR JOURNALISM AT HARVARD [1952]
Walter Lippmann House
One Francis Avenue
Cambridge, MA 02138
(617) 495-2342
Fax: (617) 495-8976

E-MAIL ADDRESS:
ellen_tuttle@harvard.edu

WEB SITE ADDRESS:
www.nieman.harvard.edu

FOUNDED: 1938

AREAS OF INTEREST:
Journalism and investigative reporting.

NAME(S) OF PROGRAMS:
● **Worth Bingham Prize for Investigative Journalism**

TYPE:
Awards/prizes. Honors investigative reporting of stories of national significance where the public interest is being ill-served. These stories may involve state, local or national government, lobbyists or the press itself wherever there exists an "atmosphere of easy tolerance" that journalist Worth Bingham himself once described in his reporting on the nation's capital. The investigative reporting may cover actual violations of the law, rule or code; lax or ineffective administration or enforcement; or activities which create conflicts of interest, entail excessive secrecy or otherwise raise questions of propriety.

YEAR PROGRAM STARTED: 1967

PURPOSE:
To honor exceptional investigative reporting of stories of national significance where the public interest is being ill-served.

ELIGIBILITY:
All submissions must have been published in a U.S. newspaper or magazine or on the newspaper or magazine's web site during the calendar year. Web-based news organizations that follow a strict code of journalistic ethics and publish original reporting on a regular basis may also submit entries. No broadcast-only entries are allowed.

Entries may include a single story, a related series of stories, or up to three unrelated stories. Columns and editorials are eligible. Individuals are encouraged to submit their own entries. In the case of a series, at least half the individual stories must have been published during the contest year.

Winners in any one year will be eligible for future awards without restriction.

GEOGRAPHIC RESTRICTIONS:
United States.

FINANCIAL DATA:
Amount of support per award: $20,000 annually.

NUMBER OF AWARDS: 1.

APPLICATION INFORMATION:
Applicants should submit five copies of the entry, each with a completed entry blank. All entries must be accompanied by a $50 entry fee made payable to the Worth Bingham Memorial Fund.
Deadline: January for reports published the previous calendar year.

ADDRESS INQUIRIES TO:
Ellen Tuttle, Communications Officer
(See address above.)

NIEMAN FOUNDATION FOR JOURNALISM AT HARVARD [1953]
Walter Lippmann House
One Francis Avenue
Cambridge, MA 02138
(617) 495-2342
Fax: (617) 495-8976

E-MAIL ADDRESS:
ellen_tuttle@harvard.edu

WEB SITE ADDRESS:
www.nieman.harvard.edu

FOUNDED: 1938

AREAS OF INTEREST:
Journalism.

NAME(S) OF PROGRAMS:
● **Taylor Family Award for Fairness in Newspapers**

TYPE:
Awards/prizes. Established through gifts for an endowment by members of the Taylor family, which published *The Boston Globe* from 1872 to 1999.

PURPOSE:
To encourage fairness in news coverage by America's daily newspapers.

ELIGIBILITY:
Nominations are for a single article, editorial, commentary, photograph, or a series of stories, photographs, editorials, commentaries, or a body of work by an individual journalist. The work must have been published in a U.S. daily newspaper during the previous calendar year.

GEOGRAPHIC RESTRICTIONS:
United States.

FINANCIAL DATA:
Amount of support per award: $10,000.
Total amount of support: $10,000.

APPLICATION INFORMATION:
Anyone may submit a nomination. A completed application includes the application form, five copies of the work and a letter explaining why the entry is an exemplary example of fairness in newspapers. The letter must also explain how the work was developed, reported and presented to readers in the context of fairness.
Deadline: Mid- to late January.

ADDRESS INQUIRIES TO:
Communications Department
(See address above.)

NIEMAN FOUNDATION FOR JOURNALISM AT HARVARD [1954]
Walter Lippmann House
One Francis Avenue
Cambridge, MA 02138
(617) 495-2237
Fax: (617) 495-8976

E-MAIL ADDRESS:
nieman_applications@harvard.edu

WEB SITE ADDRESS:
www.nieman.harvard.edu

FOUNDED: 1938

AREAS OF INTEREST:
Journalism.

NAME(S) OF PROGRAMS:
● **Nieman Fellowships in Journalism**

TYPE:
Fellowships. Provides midcareer journalists with the opportunity to spend a year of study at Harvard University. Awards are for U.S. and international journalists.

YEAR PROGRAM STARTED: 1938

PURPOSE:
To provide an opportunity for journalists to deepen their knowledge in a field of specialty, broaden their knowledge in several areas, or prepare for a new journalistic assignment.

LEGAL BASIS:
A foundation of Harvard University.

ELIGIBILITY:
Print, broadcast and online reporters, editors, photographers, producers, editorial writers and cartoonists with at least five years of full-time, professional experience in the news media are invited to apply.

FINANCIAL DATA:
Nieman Fellows receive a stipend plus housing, child care and health insurance allowance, if appropriate.
Amount of support per award: $65,000 stipend.

NUMBER OF APPLICANTS MOST RECENT YEAR:
Approximately 300.

NUMBER OF AWARDS: Approximately 24 annually (12 to journalists from the U.S. and 12 to journalists from other countries).

APPLICATION INFORMATION:
Contact the Foundation.
Duration: 10 months.
Deadline: U.S. applications due January 31 for the academic year beginning in August. International applications are due December 1 for the academic year beginning the following August.

PUBLICATIONS:
Nieman Reports.

STAFF:
John Breen, Fellowship Administrator

ADDRESS INQUIRIES TO:
John Breen, Fellowship Administrator
(See address above.)

*SPECIAL STIPULATIONS:
Once candidates have been chosen and before their confirmation as Nieman Fellows by the Harvard Corporation, they must agree in writing to return at the end of the sabbatical year to the employer who granted the leave of absence, to refrain from professional work during the period of the Fellowship, to complete all the work in one academic course of their choice each semester, and to remain in residence in the Cambridge area each term while classes are in session.

THE ALICIA PATTERSON FOUNDATION   [1955]
1090 Vermont Avenue, N.W.
Suite 1000
Washington, DC 20005
(202) 393-5995
Fax: (301) 951-8512

E-MAIL ADDRESS:
info@aliciapatterson.org

WEB SITE ADDRESS:
www.aliciapatterson.org

FOUNDED: 1961

AREAS OF INTEREST:
Journalism.

NAME(S) OF PROGRAMS:
● **Fellowship Program for Journalists**

TYPE:
Fellowships. Awarded to working print journalists for six months or one year of travel and inquiry. On leave from their normal writing, editing or photographing duties, Fellows examine their chosen subjects (areas or problems of significant interest, foreign or domestic) and write quarterly articles for the *APF Reporter.* These articles may be reprinted.

YEAR PROGRAM STARTED: 1965

PURPOSE:
To provide a few talented and promising American journalists with the opportunity to pursue independent projects.

LEGAL BASIS:
Section 501(c)(3) of the IRS Code and Not For Profits Corporation Law: New York State.

ELIGIBILITY:
The program is open to U.S. citizens who are full-time print journalists or to non-U.S. citizens who work full-time for U.S. print publication, either in America or abroad.

GEOGRAPHIC RESTRICTIONS:
United States.

FINANCIAL DATA:
Amount of support per award: $20,000 stipend for six months or $40,000 stipend for the year.
Total amount of support: Varies.

NUMBER OF APPLICANTS MOST RECENT YEAR:
Varies.

NUMBER OF AWARDS: 7 to 10 per year.

REPRESENTATIVE AWARDS:
"The Impact of Budget Cuts on Civil Justice in America;" "Northeast India: Creatures and Cultures in Collision."

APPLICATION INFORMATION:
Application forms are available in June. Information may be requested from the address above throughout the year.
Duration: Fellowships support a one-year or six-month leave of absence. The fellowship typically begins within the first three months of the calendar year.
Deadline: October 1 (postmark).

PUBLICATIONS:
APF Reporter, quarterly magazine.

IRS IDENTIFICATION NUMBER: 13-6092124

ADDRESS INQUIRIES TO:
Margaret Engel
(See address above.)

THE PRESS CLUB OF METROPOLITAN ST. LOUIS AND JOURNALISM FOUNDATION OF METROPOLITAN ST. LOUIS
c/o The Press Club of Metropolitan St. Louis
P.O. Box 410522
St. Louis, MO 63141
(314) 449-8029
Fax: (636) 203-2441

E-MAIL ADDRESS:
info@stlpressclub.org

WEB SITE ADDRESS:
stlpressclub.org

TYPE:
Awards/prizes; Conferences/seminars; Development grants; Fellowships; Internships; Project/program grants; Scholarships; Seed money grants.

See entry 1750 for full listing.

PULLIAM JOURNALISM FELLOWSHIP   [1956]
P.O. Box 145
Indianapolis, IN 46206-0145
(317) 444-6001

E-MAIL ADDRESS:
russell.pulliam@indystar.com

WEB SITE ADDRESS:
www.indystar.com/pjf

FOUNDED: 1974

AREAS OF INTEREST:
Journalism awards.

TYPE:
Fellowships. Cash awards and on-the-job study at *The Indianapolis Star* or *The Arizona Republic,* which are owned by Gannett Co.

YEAR PROGRAM STARTED: 1974

PURPOSE:
To offer on-the-job experience, plus seminars and writing criticism, to college students seriously pursuing a newspaper journalism career.

LEGAL BASIS:
Corporate-sponsored.

ELIGIBILITY:
Applicants are generally college journalism majors or liberal arts majors with part-time

newspaper experience, outstanding character references, proven writing ability and a solid academic record.

GEOGRAPHIC RESTRICTIONS:
United States.

FINANCIAL DATA:
Amount of support per award: $6,500 ($650 per week for 10-week program).

NUMBER OF APPLICANTS MOST RECENT YEAR:
200.

NUMBER OF AWARDS: 25.

APPLICATION INFORMATION:
Brochures are available from the address above. View the instructions and download the application at the web site.
Duration: 10 weeks, June to August. No renewals.
Deadline: November 1.

PUBLICATIONS:
Brochure.

ADDRESS INQUIRIES TO:
Russ Pulliam, Director
(See address above.)

QUILL AND SCROLL FOUNDATION   [1957]
School of Journalism and
Mass Communication
The University of Iowa
100 Adler Journalism Building, Room E346
Iowa City, IA 52242-2004
(319) 335-3321
(319) 335-3457
Fax: (319) 335-3989

E-MAIL ADDRESS:
quill-scroll@uiowa.edu

WEB SITE ADDRESS:
www.quillandscroll.org

FOUNDED: 1926

AREAS OF INTEREST:
Journalism, high school media, media law and ethics, and scholastic journalism education.

CONSULTING OR VOLUNTEER SERVICES:
Coordinate judging of K-12 writing, journalism and media contests.

TYPE:
Research grants; Scholarships; Training grants. Grants for research projects in the field of high school journalism and school media.

YEAR PROGRAM STARTED: 1964

PURPOSE:
To improve the quality of secondary school journalism.

LEGAL BASIS:
Nonprofit special-interest foundation.

ELIGIBILITY:
Qualified scholars or educational departments with appropriate interests are eligible to apply.

GEOGRAPHIC RESTRICTIONS:
Primarily United States.

FINANCIAL DATA:
Support may be provided to cover partial or complete project costs.
Amount of support per award: $500 to $1,000.
Total amount of support: $6,000 for the year 2012-13.

NUMBER OF APPLICANTS MOST RECENT YEAR:
30 for the year 2012-13.

NUMBER OF AWARDS: 8 for the year 2012-13.

APPLICATION INFORMATION:
No official application forms are issued.
Prospective applicants should submit a letter
describing the proposed project in terms of
scope, objectives and financial need. Also
include a letter of support from project,
thesis adviser.
Duration: One-time award.
Deadline: May 10.

PUBLICATIONS:
Application guidelines.

IRS IDENTIFICATION NUMBER: 42-0795095

TRUSTEES:
Richard P. Johns, Chairperson
Julie Dodd, Vice Chairperson
Jack Dvorak
Thomas Eveslage
H.L. Hall
John Humenik
Lydia Ramos
George Rede
Sara Van Allen
Ann Visser
Jessica Young

OFFICER:
Vanessa Shelton, Executive Director

ADDRESS INQUIRIES TO:
Vanessa Shelton, Executive Director
(See address above.)

RADIO TELEVISION DIGITAL NEWS FOUNDATION   [1958]
The National Press Building
529 14th Street, N.W., Suite 1240
Washington, DC 20045
(202) 536-8356
Fax: (202) 223-4007

E-MAIL ADDRESS:
karenh@rtdna.org

WEB SITE ADDRESS:
www.rtdna.org

FOUNDED: 1946

AREAS OF INTEREST:
Electronic journalism.

NAME(S) OF PROGRAMS:
• **N.S. Biestock Fellowship**
• **Ed Bradley Scholarship**
• **Michele Clark Fellowship**
• **George Foreman Tribute to Lyndon B. Johnson**
• **Jacque I. Mimmotte Fellowship**
• **Vada and Barney Oldfield Fellowship for National Security Reporting**
• **Lou and Carole Prato Sports Reporting Scholarship**
• **The President's Scholarships**
• **Mike Reynolds Journalism Scholarship**
• **Abe Schecter Graduate Scholarship**
• **Carole Simpson Scholarship**
• **Pete Wilson Scholarship**

TYPE:
Fellowships; Scholarships. Awards for one
year of undergraduate and/or graduate study
in broadcast journalism.

YEAR PROGRAM STARTED: 1967

PURPOSE:
To aid in advanced learning of electronic
journalism.

LEGAL BASIS:
Incorporated.

ELIGIBILITY:
For scholarships, applicants must be officially
enrolled in college and have at least one full
academic year remaining, must be a fully
enrolled college sophomore or higher, may
apply for only one scholarship, and may be
enrolled in any major so long as their career
intent is television or radio news. Fellowships
are available to young professionals with
fewer than 10 years in the field. U.S. citizens
and international applicants are eligible.

FINANCIAL DATA:
Amount of support per award: Scholarships:
$1,000 to $10,000; Fellowships: $1,000 and
$2,500.

NUMBER OF APPLICANTS MOST RECENT YEAR:
500.

NUMBER OF AWARDS: Undergraduate: 7;
Graduate: 2; Fellowships: 4.

APPLICATION INFORMATION:
Application must be submitted online.
Duration: Scholarships: One year.
Deadline: Varies.

PUBLICATIONS:
Annual report.

IRS IDENTIFICATION NUMBER: 38-1860090

ADDRESS INQUIRIES TO:
Karen Hansen, Program Coordinator
(See address above.)

REPORTERS COMMITTEE FOR FREEDOM OF THE PRESS [1959]
1101 Wilson Boulevard
Suite 1100
Arlington, VA 22209-2275
(703) 807-2100
Fax: (703) 807-2109

E-MAIL ADDRESS:
rcfp@rcfp.org

WEB SITE ADDRESS:
www.rcfp.org

AREAS OF INTEREST:
First Amendment interests of the news
media.

NAME(S) OF PROGRAMS:
• **The Reporters Committee Legal Fellowship**

TYPE:
Fellowships. Legal fellows monitor
significant developments in First Amendment
media law, assist with legal defense requests
from reporters, prepare legal memoranda,
amicus briefs and other special projects. The
Fellowship focuses on media law.

YEAR PROGRAM STARTED: 1987

PURPOSE:
To promote legal research that helps protect
the First Amendment interests of the news
media.

ELIGIBILITY:
Candidates must have received a law degree
by August of the year the Fellowship begins.
Strong legal research and writing skills are
required, and a background in news reporting
is very strongly preferred.

FINANCIAL DATA:
Fellowship includes fully paid health
benefits.
Amount of support per award: $35,000.

APPLICATION INFORMATION:
Contact the Committee.

Duration: One year, September to August.
Deadline: February 1.

PUBLICATIONS:
News Media & the Law.

ADDRESS INQUIRIES TO:
Bruce Brown, Executive Director
(See address above.)

KURT SCHORK MEMORIAL FUND   [1960]
2475 Virginia Avenue
Suite 201
Washington, DC 20037
(202) 333-2545

E-MAIL ADDRESS:
enquiries@ksmfund.org

WEB SITE ADDRESS:
www.ksmfund.org

FOUNDED: 2001

AREAS OF INTEREST:
International journalism.

NAME(S) OF PROGRAMS:
• **Kurt Schork Awards in International Journalism**

TYPE:
Awards/prizes. Awards for print reporters
whose stories shed new light on controversial
issues. Two prizes are awarded each year,
one to a local reporter in a developing
country or nation in transition, and the other
to a freelance journalist covering
international news.

The awards are underwritten by the Kurt
Schork Memorial Fund and Reuters, and
administered by the Columbia University
Graduate School of Journalism.

YEAR PROGRAM STARTED: 2002

PURPOSE:
To honor Kurt Schork, an American freelance
journalist, killed in a military ambush while
on assignment for Reuters on May 24, 2000
in Sierra Leone.

ELIGIBILITY:
Local Reporter: Print journalists employed by
a local news outlet and residing in a
developing country or nation in transition
(non-OECD or EU countries), whose work
has been published in a local publication, are
eligible.

Freelance Journalist: All freelance print
journalists and those contracted by news
organizations are eligible.

Eligible Media: Entries are welcomed from
all types of print-based media including
newspapers and magazines and established
online publications.

FINANCIAL DATA:
Amount of support per award: $5,000.
Total amount of support: $10,000 annually.

NUMBER OF AWARDS: 2.

APPLICATION INFORMATION:
Complete information may be found on the
web site.
Deadline: May 31.

ADDRESS INQUIRIES TO:
See e-mail address above.

UNITED METHODIST COMMUNICATIONS [1961]
810 12th Avenue South
Nashville, TN 37203-4704
(888) 278-4862
Fax: (615) 742-5777

E-MAIL ADDRESS:
scholarships@umcom.org

WEB SITE ADDRESS:
www.umcom.org

FOUNDED: 1948

AREAS OF INTEREST:
Religion communications.

NAME(S) OF PROGRAMS:
● **The Stoody-West Fellowship**

TYPE:
Fellowships. Assists one United Methodist student in graduate study at an accredited U.S. college or university who intends to pursue a career in religious journalism.

YEAR PROGRAM STARTED: 1964

PURPOSE:
To enable the recipient to continue graduate studies in religion journalism; to promote a level of excellence in communication at the graduate level.

LEGAL BASIS:
Nonprofit.

ELIGIBILITY:
Applicant must be a member of The United Methodist Church who intends to pursue a career in religion journalism and is enrolled in graduate study at an accredited U.S. college or university (includes electronic and broadcast media as well as print). Employees of United Methodist Communications and members of the General Commission on Communication are not eligible for the Fellowship.

FINANCIAL DATA:
Amount of support per award: $6,000.
Total amount of support: $6,000.

NUMBER OF AWARDS: 1 annually.

APPLICATION INFORMATION:
Application forms are available online.

Applicant must submit:
(1) completed application form;
(2) official transcripts of schools attended, including evidence of enrollment as a graduate student in the journalism or communications department of a duly accredited college or university in the U.S.;
(3) three letters of recommendation;
(4) statement of interest and plans;
(5) three writing samples and;
(6) recent personal photograph.

If materials must be mailed, use the following address:
Stoody-West Fellowship Committee
United Methodist Communications
P.O. Box 320
Nashville, TN 37202-0320.

If submitting by FedEx or UPS, send to: Stoody-West Fellowship Committee, United Methodist Communications, at the street address above.

Duration: One academic year.
Deadline: March 15 (postmark).

PUBLICATIONS:
Application guidelines.

ADDRESS INQUIRIES TO:
Communications Ministry
(See address above.)

*PLEASE NOTE:
Religious journalism is interpreted to include news writing for secular press, church press and for church institutions. Appropriate news and journalism forms will be considered, including electronic and broadcast media, as well as print.

UNITED METHODIST COMMUNICATIONS
810 12th Avenue South
Nashville, TN 37203-4704
(888) 278-4862
Fax: (615) 742-5777

E-MAIL ADDRESS:
rjames@umcom.org

WEB SITE ADDRESS:
www.umcom.org

TYPE:
Fellowships; Scholarships. Award for junior or senior undergraduate study in religion journalism or mass communications. The term *communications* is meant to cover various media as audio-visual, electronic and print journalism.

See entry 1019 for full listing.

UNIVERSITY FILM AND VIDEO ASSOCIATION [1962]
Northern Illinois University
Communications
396 Kingsbury Drive
DeKalb, IL 60115

E-MAIL ADDRESS:
lvazquez@niu.edu

WEB SITE ADDRESS:
www.ufva.org

AREAS OF INTEREST:
Film, video and multimedia production.

NAME(S) OF PROGRAMS:
● **Carole Fielding Student Grants**

TYPE:
Block grants; Capital grants; Development grants; General operating grants; Project/program grants; Research grants; Seed money grants. Annual support for student projects in film, video and multimedia productions or research activities in historical, critical, theoretical or experimental studies in film or video.

YEAR PROGRAM STARTED: 1993

PURPOSE:
To support and promote student film and video makers.

LEGAL BASIS:
UFVA membership funded.

ELIGIBILITY:
An applicant must be a graduate or undergraduate student at the time the application is made, be sponsored by a faculty member who is an active member of the University Film and Video Association and agree to present, or have presented by his or her representative, a report on the project or production at the next annual meeting of the Association.

The judges reserve the right not to make an award if quality or quantity of submissions so justify.

FINANCIAL DATA:
Amount of support per award: Varies.

Total amount of support: $5,000 per year.

NUMBER OF APPLICANTS MOST RECENT YEAR:
90.

APPLICATION INFORMATION:
Applicants should submit six stapled and collated copies of their proposal to the Scholarship and Grants Office. The proposal must include a one-page description of the production or project which includes a statement of purpose, an indication of the resources available to complete the work and a summary of the proposed film, video production or study. If a narrative film is proposed, submit a copy of the script. A documentary proposal should include a short treatment. An experimental or animated film proposal should include a treatment (or script) and/or story boards. Also include a one-page budget, indicating what portion of the total project will be supported by this grant and a statement by a faculty member who is an active member of the University Film and Video Association assessing the feasibility of the project or production and indicating his or her willingness to serve as faculty supervisor or consultant.
Deadline: December 15. Announcements by March 31.

OFFICERS:
Norman Hollyn, President
Jennifer Machiorlatti, Executive Vice President
Bart Weiss, Editorial Vice President

ADDRESS INQUIRIES TO:
Laura Vazquez, UFVA Grants Office
(See e-mail address above.)

THE UNIVERSITY OF CALGARY [1963]
Faculty of Graduate Studies
MacKimmie Library Tower, Room 213
2500 University Drive, N.W.
Calgary AB T2N 1N4 Canada
(403) 220-4938
Fax: (403) 289-7635

E-MAIL ADDRESS:
gsaward@ucalgary.ca

WEB SITE ADDRESS:
www.grad.ucalgary.ca

FOUNDED: 1966

AREAS OF INTEREST:
Communications studies.

NAME(S) OF PROGRAMS:
● **Cogeco Inc. Graduate Scholarship**

TYPE:
Awards/prizes; Scholarships.

LEGAL BASIS:
University scholarship program.

ELIGIBILITY:
Applicants must be students admissible to or registered in a Master's program (either thesis-based or course-based) in the Communications Studies Programme at the University of Calgary. Awards will be made on the basis of academic excellence.

FINANCIAL DATA:
Amount of support per award: $6,200.
Total amount of support: $6,200.

COOPERATIVE FUNDING PROGRAMS: Scholarship is financed by Cogeco Inc.

NUMBER OF AWARDS: 1 each year.

APPLICATION INFORMATION:
Candidates should apply to the Master of Communications Studies Programme in the first instance. Recommendations from the Programme will be submitted to the University of Calgary Graduate Scholarship Office for approval. The recommendation is subject to final approval of the Graduate Scholarship Committee.

Duration: One year.

Deadline: February 1.

ADDRESS INQUIRIES TO:
Graduate Scholarship Office
(See address above.)

UNIVERSITY OF MICHIGAN [1964]
Knight-Wallace Fellows
Wallace House
620 Oxford Road
Ann Arbor, MI 48104-2635
(734) 998-7666
Fax: (734) 998-7979

E-MAIL ADDRESS:
kwfellows@umich.edu

WEB SITE ADDRESS:
www.kwfellows.org

AREAS OF INTEREST:
Arts, sciences and professions.

NAME(S) OF PROGRAMS:
● **Knight-Wallace Fellows**

TYPE:
Fellowships.

YEAR PROGRAM STARTED: 1973

PURPOSE:
To offer a full academic year in any field or fields at the University of Michigan.

LEGAL BASIS:
A part of the Provost's office at the University of Michigan.

ELIGIBILITY:
Eligibility extends to all full-time print, broadcast, online, photo and film journalists with five years' experience whose work appears regularly in U.S.-controlled news organizations. Freelancers are included. Work may be related or unrelated to professional objectives.

FINANCIAL DATA:
Fellowship also includes tuition and fees, plus travel expenses for our international news tours.

Amount of support per award: $70,000 stipend.

NUMBER OF APPLICANTS MOST RECENT YEAR: 120.

NUMBER OF AWARDS: 12 National.

APPLICATION INFORMATION:
Application form, a leave of absence (if possible) for the period of the Fellowship, and a support letter from direct supervisor is required. Two statements, an intellectual autobiography, and a proposed program of study must be included. Do not submit more than five examples of applicant's work.

Duration: Eight-month academic year, September to April.

Deadline: February 1. Announcement in May.

PUBLICATIONS:
The Journal of Knight-Wallace Fellows.

ADDRESS INQUIRIES TO:
Birgit Rieck, Assistant Director
(See address above.)

Labor

IMAGINE AMERICA FOUNDATION [1965]
12001 Sunrise Valley Drive
Suite 203
Reston, VA 20191
(571) 267-3015
Fax: (866) 734-5812

E-MAIL ADDRESS:
studentservices@imagine-america.org

WEB SITE ADDRESS:
www.imagine-america.org

FOUNDED: 1982

AREAS OF INTEREST:
Private career education.

NAME(S) OF PROGRAMS:
● **Imagine America Adult Skills Education Program (ASEP)**
● **Imagine America High School Scholarship Program**
● **Imagine America LDRSHIP Award**
● **Imagine America Military Award Program (MAP)**
● **Imagine America Promise Scholarship Program**

TYPE:
Awards/prizes; Scholarships; Research contracts. Sponsorships. Three scholarships are given to each high school listed on the Foundation web site above.

YEAR PROGRAM STARTED: 1982

PURPOSE:
To provide research, scholarship and training for America's career colleges.

LEGAL BASIS:
501(c)(3) nonprofit organization.

ELIGIBILITY:
Applicants must be graduating high school seniors. Applicants for Imagine America MAP must be honorably discharged, active duty, reservist or retired military.

GEOGRAPHIC RESTRICTIONS:
United States and Puerto Rico.

FINANCIAL DATA:
Amount of support per award: Varies.
Total amount of support: $75,000,000.

NUMBER OF AWARDS: More than 35,000.

PUBLICATIONS:
Imagine America's Guide to Career Colleges; *Imagine America's Student's Guide*; *A Profile of Career Colleges and Universities.*

ADDRESS INQUIRIES TO:
Lee Doubleday
Student Services Representative
(See address above.)

NATIONAL INSTITUTE OF STANDARDS AND TECHNOLOGY [1966]
U.S. Department of Commerce, NIST
100 Bureau Drive, Mail Stop 1650
Gaithersburg, MD 20899-1650
(301) 975-5603
Fax: (301) 840-5976

E-MAIL ADDRESS:
mfg@nist.gov
scott.mcnichol@nist.gov

WEB SITE ADDRESS:
www.nist.gov/mep

FOUNDED: 1901

AREAS OF INTEREST:
Advanced manufacturing technology.

NAME(S) OF PROGRAMS:
● **Manufacturing Extension Partnership**

TYPE:
Project/program grants.

YEAR PROGRAM STARTED: 1988

PURPOSE:
To establish, maintain and support manufacturing extension centers and services, the functions of which are to accelerate the usage of appropriate manufacturing technology by smaller U.S.-based manufacturing firms, and partner with the states in developing such technical assistance programs and services for their manufacturing base.

LEGAL BASIS:
Ominibus Trade and Competitiveness Act of 1988, Public Law 100-148, American Technology Preeminence Act of 1991.

ELIGIBILITY:
For extension services, eligible applicants should be U.S.-based nonprofit institutions or organizations or groups thereof. For extension service planning and pilot services agreements, eligible applicants shall be state governments and state-affiliated nonprofit organizations. For multistate regional planning and pilot services agreements, eligible applicants shall be state and local governments, representing either themselves or a consortium of states, and appropriate private or public nonprofit organizations, operating on behalf of a consortium of states or as a representative of states. Beneficiary shall be U.S.-based manufacturing firms, especially smaller companies.

FINANCIAL DATA:
Amount of support per award: Awards for manufacturing extension centers: $7,000,000 annually. Individual awards for extension service planning and pilot testing agreements: $25,000 to $100,000.

Total amount of support: Varies.

Matching fund requirements: Applicants must provide at least 50% of the capital, annual operating and maintenance funds required to create and maintain the center. Funds may be provided by any nonfederal source. A minimum of 50% of the applicant's share must be as cash of full-time personnel.

APPLICATION INFORMATION:
An applicant should consult the office or official designated as the single point of contact in his or her state for information on the process the state requires to be followed in applying for assistance, if the state has selected the program for review. For manufacturing extension centers, no formal preapplication is required, although applicants are advised to discuss their proposal during the early stages of development with NIST MEP regional managers. This portion of the program is excluded from coverage under E.O. 12372.

A *Federal Register* notice announcing the request for proposals from qualified organizations will be published when funds are available.

Duration: One year for extension service planning and pilot-testing agreements. Six years maximum for manufacturing extension centers. Agreements are renewed annually based upon positive evaluation and availability of funds.

Deadline: Notice of availability of funds and deadlines are published on cfda.gov.

ADDRESS INQUIRIES TO:
Scott McNichol, Team Leader
(See address above.)

U.S. DEPARTMENT OF HEALTH AND HUMAN SERVICES/ADMINISTRATION FOR CHILDREN AND FAMILIES/OFFICE OF FAMILY ASSISTANCE   [1967]

370 L'Enfant Promenade S.W.
5th Floor East
Washington, DC 20447
(202) 401-9275
Fax: (202) 205-5887

E-MAIL ADDRESS:
rachel.gwilliam@acf.hhs.gov

WEB SITE ADDRESS:
www.acf.hhs.gov/programs/ofa

FOUNDED: 1996

AREAS OF INTEREST:
Education, employment and support services, and financial assistance.

NAME(S) OF PROGRAMS:
● **Temporary Assistance for Needy Families (TANF)**

TYPE:
Block grants; Internships; Technical assistance. Block grants to states, the District of Columbia, territories, and federally recognized Indian tribes and Alaska Native Organizations for education, employment, training and supportive services to help eligible families move to work and self-sufficiency.

YEAR PROGRAM STARTED: 1996

PURPOSE:
To help needy families achieve self-sufficiency.

LEGAL BASIS:
Social Security Act, Title IV-A and Title IV-F, as amended (42 USC 602-603, 681-687 and 1302) and Public Law 100-485.

ELIGIBILITY:
Grants are awarded to states, the District of Columbia, territories, and federally recognized Indian tribes and Alaska Native Organizations based on a complete TANF plan. Statute precludes any grantees other than those stated above.

FINANCIAL DATA:
Amount of support per award: Calculated share of federal block grant.
Total amount of support: $16.5 billion.

PUBLICATIONS:
TANF Annual Report to Congress; policy announcements; program instructions; information memoranda.

ADDRESS INQUIRIES TO:
Rachel Gwilliam, Program Specialist
(See address above.)

U.S. DEPARTMENT OF LABOR   [1968]

Office of Apprenticeship
Room N-5311
200 Constitution Avenue, N.W.
Washington, DC 20210
(202) 693-2796
Fax: (202) 692-3799

E-MAIL ADDRESS:
ladd.john@dol.gov

WEB SITE ADDRESS:
www.doleta.gov/grants

FOUNDED: 1937

AREAS OF INTEREST:
Apprenticeship, skill and technical training.

CONSULTING OR VOLUNTEER SERVICES:
Provides technical assistance at no cost.

NAME(S) OF PROGRAMS:
● **National Apprenticeship System**

TYPE:
Technical assistance. Management and labor, along with government and the education system, work together at the national, state and local levels to formulate and promote effective apprenticeship programs. The program must be an organized, written plan embodying training and supervision of one or more apprentices in an apprenticeable occupation, as defined in 29 CFR 29.4 and subscribed to by a sponsor who has undertaken to carry out the apprenticeship program.

YEAR PROGRAM STARTED: 1937

PURPOSE:
To formulate, promote and publish labor standards necessary to safeguard the welfare of apprentices, encourage the inclusion of such standards in apprenticeship contracts, bring together employers and labor to create apprenticeship programs, cooperate with state agencies in formulating and promoting apprenticeship standards, and cooperate with the U.S. Department of Education on vocational education and related instruction in apprenticeship.

LEGAL BASIS:
National Apprenticeship Act of 1937 (P.L. 308-75); Title 29, CFR Part 30; Title 29, CFR Part 29.

ELIGIBILITY:
To be eligible as a sponsor, apprenticeship programs must meet the basic standards and established criteria set forth by the Secretary of Labor and may be registered upon request of the program sponsor. Registration of programs and apprentices in states having apprenticeship agencies recognized by the U.S. Department of Labor is performed by the state apprenticeship agencies. Programs in states not having recognized apprenticeship agencies will be registered by the Bureau of Apprenticeship and Training.

To be eligible as a beneficiary, applicants for apprenticeship must be at least 16 years of age. They must have the ability and aptitude to master the occupations and sufficient education to complete satisfactorily the required hours of related theoretical instruction.

GEOGRAPHIC RESTRICTIONS:
United States.

FINANCIAL DATA:
The Department of Labor does not finance apprenticeships. Program sponsors bear the expenses of the program.

NUMBER OF APPLICANTS MOST RECENT YEAR:
100,000.

APPLICATION INFORMATION:
Notices for accepting applications are published locally by apprenticeship program sponsors. Information may be obtained from local One Stop Centers or may be requested by contacting regional, state or area offices of the Office of Apprenticeship, U.S. Department of Labor, or the ETA Grants Office.

PUBLICATIONS:
Apprenticeship Past and Present; *National Apprenticeship Program.*

ADDRESS INQUIRIES TO:
Grants Department
Division of Grants and Contracts
(See address above.)

W.E. UPJOHN INSTITUTE FOR EMPLOYMENT RESEARCH   [1969]

300 South Westnedge Avenue
Kalamazoo, MI 49007-4686
(269) 343-5541
Fax: (269) 343-3308

E-MAIL ADDRESS:
communications@upjohn.org

WEB SITE ADDRESS:
www.upjohn.org

FOUNDED: 1945

AREAS OF INTEREST:
Policy-relevant research on employment and unemployment at the international, national, state and local levels. The Institute is also receptive to international studies for the purpose of drawing lessons for U.S. policy. Topics of interest include job creation, job stabilization, matching of jobs and people, alleviation of unemployment hazards, the political science of manpower programs and the quality of work life.

CONSULTING OR VOLUNTEER SERVICES:
Both consulting and volunteer services are available, though the latter are limited.

NAME(S) OF PROGRAMS:
● **Early Career Research Grants**

TYPE:
Conferences/seminars; Research grants; Visiting scholars; Research contracts. Early Career Research Grants are intended to provide resources to junior faculty (untenured and within six years of earning the Ph.D.) to carry out policy-related research on labor market issues. The Institute supports and encourages research on all issues related to labor markets and public workforce policy.

YEAR PROGRAM STARTED: 1976

PURPOSE:
To conduct research into the causes and effects of unemployment and measures for the alleviation of unemployment at the national, state and local levels.

LEGAL BASIS:
Public nonprofit organization.

ELIGIBILITY:
Grant proposals will be evaluated according to the following criteria:
(1) contribution to important labor market policy issues and to the professional literature;
(2) technical merit and;
(3) professional qualifications.

FINANCIAL DATA:

The Institute does not pay indirect costs but will entertain any legitimate research expense as part of the budget. Acceptable items include costs for professional, technical, and support personnel, data acquisition, materials and supplies, computer services, and travel. The Institute does not fund dissertation research although it does have a Dissertation Award program. Grant payments are made to the individual upon award.

Amount of support per award: Up to $5,000.

NUMBER OF APPLICANTS MOST RECENT YEAR:
52.

NUMBER OF AWARDS: 14.

APPLICATION INFORMATION:

Applicants should submit a proposal of up to 1,200 words (approximately four double-spaced pages) describing the proposed research and its relevance to labor market policy. The proposal should include an abstract and a brief budget. Applications must also include a current curriculum vita.

Applications submitted via regular mail are to be addressed to: Institute Grant Committee, W.E. Upjohn Institute for Employment Research, at the address above. Submissions by e-mail are accepted at the Institute's e-mail address.

Duration: Ordinarily one year, which includes research and writing of paper to be submitted to a scholarly journal.

Deadline: Applications: January 31. Announcement: March 1.

PUBLICATIONS:
Program announcement; proposal guidelines.

IRS IDENTIFICATION NUMBER: 38-1360419

TRUSTEES:
Donald R. Parfet, Chairman
Marilyn Schlack, Vice Chairman
Thomas W. Lambert, Secretary-Treasurer
John M. Dunn
William C. Richardson
Frank J. Sardone
Paul H. Todd
Amanda Van Dusen
B. Joseph White
Dr. Eileen Wilson-Oyelaran

ADDRESS INQUIRIES TO:
Randall W. Eberts, President
(See address above.)

*PLEASE NOTE:
Grant awards are essentially performance-based contracts. Applications for grants and all work submitted under grants become the property of the Institute. It is Institute policy to require submission of the research paper to its working paper series. Unaccepted proposals and rejected research papers will be returned upon request, without restrictions on further use by others. It is also Institute policy to encourage publication of the sponsored research in scholarly journals following submission of the research paper to the Institute. Submission of any material waives all rights to make any claim because of any use thereof by the W.E. Upjohn Unemployment Trustee Corporation, its agents and employees.

*SPECIAL STIPULATIONS:
Grant recipients are expected to write a research paper based on the funded work for submission to the Institute's working paper series, submit the paper to a peer-reviewed journal, and prepare a synopsis of the research for possible publication in the Institute's newsletter, *Employment Research.*

Law

AMERICAN ASSOCIATION OF LAW LIBRARIES
105 West Adams Street
Suite 3300
Chicago, IL 60603
(312) 939-4764
Fax: (312) 431-1097

E-MAIL ADDRESS:
membership@aall.org

WEB SITE ADDRESS:
www.aallnet.org

TYPE:
Scholarships. For study of law or librarianship, with support intended for prospective law librarians.

See entry 709 for full listing.

AMERICAN BAR FOUNDATION   [1970]
750 North Lake Shore Drive, Fourth Floor
Chicago, IL 60611-4403
(312) 988-6517
Fax: (312) 988-6579

E-MAIL ADDRESS:
fellowships@abfn.org

WEB SITE ADDRESS:
www.americanbarfoundation.org

FOUNDED: 1952

AREAS OF INTEREST:
Socio-legal research. Current research interests include: professionalism and the transformation of the legal profession in the U.S. and abroad, the impact of civil rights law on the economic progress of minorities, hate speech and its regulation, the influence of family and environmental factors on juvenile delinquency, the impact of public policy on the spread of the Internet, jury decision-making, historical analyses of labor and regulatory law, public interest lawyering and social reform, and sentencing judgement and the effect of victim impact evidence.

NAME(S) OF PROGRAMS:
● **ABF Fellowships in Law and Social Science**

TYPE:
Fellowships. Residential fellowships at the ABF.

The American Bar Foundation is committed to developing the next generation of scholars in the field of law and social science. Since 1987, the Foundation has supported the dissertation research of a diverse group of graduate students from all social science disciplines and, in 1996, added a postdoctoral component to its fellowship program.

YEAR PROGRAM STARTED: 1987

PURPOSE:
To encourage original and significant research on law, the legal profession and legal institutions.

LEGAL BASIS:
Private foundation.

ELIGIBILITY:
Applications are invited from outstanding students who are candidates for Ph.D. degrees in the social sciences, or who have completed their Ph.D. within the past two years. Proposed research must be in the general area of sociolegal studies or in social

scientific approaches to law, the legal profession or legal institutions. The research must address significant issues in the field and show promise of a major contribution to social scientific understanding of law and legal processes. Applicants must, at a minimum, have been admitted to candidacy for the Ph.D. before the commencement of the fellowship.

Minority applicants are especially encouraged.

In exceptional circumstances, candidates with a J.D. who have substantial social science training may also be considered.

GEOGRAPHIC RESTRICTIONS:
United States.

FINANCIAL DATA:
Fellows will receive a stipend for 12 months. Fellows may also request up to $1,500 each fellowship year for research support, including travel to conferences at which papers are presented. Relocation expenses of up to $2,500 may be reimbursed upon application.

Amount of support per award: $30,000 stipend.

NUMBER OF APPLICANTS MOST RECENT YEAR:
100.

NUMBER OF AWARDS: 2.

APPLICATION INFORMATION:
Applications must include:
(1) letter of application;
(2) statement describing research interests and achievements to date and plans for the fellowship period;
(3) two letters of reference;
(4) curriculum vitae;
(5) transcript of graduate record;
(6) sample of written work (conference paper, dissertation chapter or published article) and;
(7) Ph.D. candidates should include a copy of their dissertation proposal.

Duration: One year. Renewable for a second year subject to satisfactory progress and participation.

Deadline: December.

ADDRESS INQUIRIES TO:
Amanda Ehrhardt
Administrative Associate for Academic Affairs
(See address above.)

*PLEASE NOTE:
Fellowships are held in residence at the American Bar Foundation. Appointments to fellowships are full-time. Fellows are expected to participate fully in the academic life of the ABF so that they may develop close collegial ties with other scholars in residence.

AMERICAN COLLEGE OF LEGAL MEDICINE
1100 East Woodfield Road
Suite 350
Schaumburg, IL 60173-5125
(847) 969-0283
Fax: (847) 517-7229

E-MAIL ADDRESS:
info@aclm.org

WEB SITE ADDRESS:
www.aclm.org

TYPE:
Awards/prizes. The Hirsh Award is awarded to a law, dentistry, podiatry, nursing, pharmacy, health science, health care administration, or public health student.

See entry 2224 for full listing.

THE CANADIAN BAR ASSOCIATION [1971]
500-865 Carling Avenue
Ottawa ON K1S 5S8 Canada
(613) 237-2925
(800) 267-8860
Fax: (613) 237-0185

E-MAIL ADDRESS:
info@cba.org

WEB SITE ADDRESS:
www.cba.org

FOUNDED: 1914

AREAS OF INTEREST:
Law and the administration of justice, promoting access to justice and promotion of equality in the professional justice system.

NAME(S) OF PROGRAMS:
● **Viscount Bennett Fellowship**

TYPE:
Awards/prizes; Fellowships. Award is paid to one law student for legally oriented graduate study in an institution of higher learning anywhere, to be approved by selection committee.

YEAR PROGRAM STARTED: 1946

PURPOSE:
To encourage a high standard of legal education, training and ethics.

ELIGIBILITY:
Canadian citizens who have graduated from an approved law school in Canada or who, at the time of application, are pursuing final-year studies as undergraduate students at such approved law school. All applicants must be CBA members in good standing. Candidates must have completed and filed an application for graduate studies with the institution of higher learning of their choice before submitting the fellowship application to the CBA.

GEOGRAPHIC RESTRICTIONS:
Canada.

FINANCIAL DATA:
Amount of support per award: $40,000 (CAN) paid in two equal installments.
Total amount of support: $40,000 (CAN).

NUMBER OF APPLICANTS MOST RECENT YEAR:
44.

NUMBER OF AWARDS: 1 for the year 2012-13.

APPLICATION INFORMATION:
Applications may be secured from the address or web site above. Completed applications should be in writing, to the Senior Director of Communications.

Applications and the accompanying documents should be forwarded in a sealed envelope, addressed to:
Viscount Bennett Fellowship
c/o Marie Josee Lapointe
Senior Director of Communications.
Duration: One year. Nonrenewable.
Deadline: November 15 (postmark).

ADDRESS INQUIRIES TO:
Marie Josee Lapointe
Senior Director of Communications
(See address above.)

*SPECIAL STIPULATIONS:
As a condition of the Fellowship, recipient(s) of the Viscount Bennett Fellowship must submit a written report at midterm and at the end of the year of graduate study, and must submit a copy of their final thesis at year end.

CANADIAN INSTITUTE FOR ADVANCED LEGAL STUDIES [1972]
P.O. Box 43538, Leaside Post Office
1601 Bayview Avenue
Toronto ON M4G 4G8 Canada
(416) 429-3292
Fax: (416) 429-9805

E-MAIL ADDRESS:
info@canadian-institute.com

WEB SITE ADDRESS:
www.canadian-institute.com

FOUNDED: 1979

AREAS OF INTEREST:
Law.

NAME(S) OF PROGRAMS:
● **French Language Scholarship**
● **The Right Honourable Paul Martin, Sr. Scholarship**

TYPE:
Scholarships.

YEAR PROGRAM STARTED: 1983

PURPOSE:
French Language Scholarship: To study for the equivalent of a Master's or doctoral degree from a Canadian university at a European university where instruction is given in French.

The Right Honourable Paul Martin, Sr. Scholarship: To study for an L.L.M. at the University of Cambridge.

ELIGIBILITY:
French Language Scholarship: The Institute annually awards a scholarship for graduate studies in law toward a second-cycle or third-cycle diploma (the equivalent of a Master's or doctoral degree from a Canadian university) at a European university where instruction is given in French, to a person who has (in the four years before the candidate will commence the proposed studies) been awarded a Bachelor's degree in law from a Canadian university. An applicant must be accepted into a French-language European university for graduate studies in law in order to receive this Scholarship, although such acceptance need not be confirmed at the time of the application for the Scholarship or at the time that the Institute provides the candidate with notice that he or she has been selected to receive the Scholarship.

The Right Honourable Paul Martin, Sr. Scholarship: The Institute annually awards two full scholarships for graduate studies in law at the University of Cambridge (Cambridge, England) to candidates who have been awarded a law degree from a three- or four-year program at a faculty of law in a Canadian university in the four years before the candidate will commence his or her studies at the University of Cambridge

(supported by The Right Honourable Paul Martin Sr. Scholarship). An applicant must be accepted into the University of Cambridge and a College of the University of Cambridge for graduate studies in law in order to receive this Scholarship, although such acceptance need not be confirmed at the time of the application for the Scholarship nor at the time that the Institute provides the candidate with notice that he or she has been selected to receive the Scholarship.

FINANCIAL DATA:
French Language Scholarship: Scholarship includes full tuition and includes an allowance to cover a portion of living expenses and reasonable travel expenses to and from the European university, subject to any other awards received by the successful candidate. The Institute determines each year the maximum amount of the Scholarship, up to an amount of $20,000 for the 2014-15 academic year, and in so doing will take into account the tuition fees as well as the anticipated living expenses and travel expenses of the successful candidate.

The Right Honourable Paul Martin, Sr. Scholarship: Scholarships include tuition and college fees.
Total amount of support: French Language Scholarship: Approximately $20,000 (CAN). The Right Honourable Paul Martin, Sr. Scholarship: Approximately $25,000 (CAN).

NUMBER OF APPLICANTS MOST RECENT YEAR:
French Language Scholarship: (First Year) 4. The Right Honourable Paul Martin, Sr. Scholarship: 25.

NUMBER OF AWARDS: French Language Scholarship: 1. The Right Honourable Paul Martin, Sr. Scholarship: 2.

APPLICATION INFORMATION:
French Language Scholarship: Applications must include:
(1) curriculum vitae;
(2) a personal statement indicating why the applicant wishes to undertake graduate studies in law and why the applicant is suited to undertake such studies;
(3) a copy of transcripts for undergraduate and graduate studies, for studies in law or for a Bar Admission Course, as applicable;
(4) a maximum of three letters of reference and;
(5) a statement of tuition fees and anticipated living and travel expenses.

The Right Honourable Paul Martin, Sr. Scholarship: Applications must include:
(1) curriculum vitae;
(2) a personal statement indicating why the applicant wishes to undertake graduate studies in law at the University of Cambridge and why the applicant is suited to undertake such studies;
(3) a copy of transcripts for undergraduate and graduate studies, for studies in law and for a Bar Admissions Course, as applicable, and;
(4) a maximum of three letters of reference.

Applications may be submitted by mail, fax or electronic mail.
Duration: French Language Scholarship: One year. The Right Honourable Paul Martin, Sr. Scholarship: One year.
Deadline: The Right Honourable Paul Martin, Sr. Scholarship: Applications must be received no later than December 31 each year.

ADDRESS INQUIRIES TO:
See e-mail address above.

CIVIL JUSTICE FOUNDATION [1973]

777 6th Street, N.W.
Suite 200
Washington, DC 20001
(202) 965-3500
Fax: (866) 452-5269

E-MAIL ADDRESS:
civiljusticefoundation@yahoo.com

WEB SITE ADDRESS:
www.civiljusticefoundation.org

FOUNDED: 1986

AREAS OF INTEREST:
Advocacy for injury prevention.

TYPE:
Development grants; General operating
grants; Project/program grants. Funding for
progressive grassroots organizations focused
on models which seek to prevent consumer
injury and defend a consumer's access to
justice.

YEAR PROGRAM STARTED: 1986

PURPOSE:
To prevent harm to individuals by supporting
both organizations of injured consumers and
injury prevention research.

LEGAL BASIS:
501(c)(3) not-for-profit foundation.

ELIGIBILITY:
Applicants must be nonprofit organizations
and must provide a letter of tax-exempt
determination from the IRS. The Foundation
is committed to preventing consumer injury
and defending a consumer's access to justice
through grants to progressive grassroots
organizations seeking systemic change. The
Foundation is especially interested in
organizations or projects that find it difficult
to obtain funding from more traditional
sources because they are newly organized
and/or address a controversial problem. The
Foundation will not support organizations
with a current annual operating budget over
$500,000.

GEOGRAPHIC RESTRICTIONS:
United States and Canada.

FINANCIAL DATA:
Amount of support per award: Average:
$5,000 to $20,000.

NUMBER OF APPLICANTS MOST RECENT YEAR: 3
grant applications; 12 Letters of Proposal.

NUMBER OF AWARDS: 3 grants.

REPRESENTATIVE AWARDS:
$15,000 to Childhood Lead Action Project to
eliminate childhood lead poisoning in Rhode
Island through education, parent support and
advocacy; $10,000 to Kids in Danger to
advocate, promote and educate people about
children's product safety; $10,000 to Lead
Safe Bellows Falls: Parks Place Community
Center for lead poisoning prevention,
outreach and education program.

APPLICATION INFORMATION:
Applicants must submit a brief one- or
two-page letter to the Foundation, outlining
the intended project and supplying an
estimate of the funds involved. The
Foundation will select those to invite to
submit a full proposal. Unsolicited full
proposals will not be accepted or considered
for review.
Duration: Generally one to three years.
Deadline: February 15.

PUBLICATIONS:
Annual report; guidelines; fact sheet;
Branching Out, newsletter.

ENVIRONMENTAL LAW INSTITUTE [1974]

2000 L Street, N.W.
Suite 620
Washington, DC 20036-4919
(202) 939-3800
Fax: (202) 939-3868

E-MAIL ADDRESS:
law@eli.org

WEB SITE ADDRESS:
www.eli.org

FOUNDED: 1969

AREAS OF INTEREST:
Environmental law, management, and policy,
including economic and scientific aspects and
protection of natural areas.

CONSULTING OR VOLUNTEER SERVICES:
Variety of services including tuition
scholarships to continuing legal education
programs, consulting services and technical
assistance.

NAME(S) OF PROGRAMS:
● **Continuing Legal Education**
Scholarship Program

TYPE:
Scholarships. Tuition scholarships to annual
Environmental Law Course.

YEAR PROGRAM STARTED: 1970

PURPOSE:
To provide access to education on
environmental law and policy; to improve the
level of practice and raise the quality of
debate on key legal/policy questions.

LEGAL BASIS:
Nonprofit corporation, 501(c)(3).

ELIGIBILITY:
For annual Environmental Law Course/CLE
Scholarship Program, send letter of
application from public interest lawyers,
attorneys doing substantial pro bono work,
state and local government attorneys involved
in environmental law stating need and
expected benefit.

FINANCIAL DATA:
Amount of support per award:
Approximately $800 to $900 per scholarship
applicant approved.
Total amount of support: Approximately
$25,000 annually.

COOPERATIVE FUNDING PROGRAMS:
Environmental Law Conference with
ALI-ABA.

NUMBER OF APPLICANTS MOST RECENT YEAR:
Approximately 25.

NUMBER OF AWARDS: Approximately 25.

PUBLICATIONS:
Annual report; *Environmental Law Reporter*;
The Environmental Forum; *National Wetlands
Newsletter*.

IRS IDENTIFICATION NUMBER: 52-0901863

OFFICERS:
John Cruden, President

ADDRESS INQUIRIES TO:
See e-mail address above.

FOOD AND DRUG LAW INSTITUTE (FDLI) [1975]

1155 15th Street, N.W., Suite 800
Washington, DC 20005-2706
(202) 371-1420
Fax: (202) 371-0649

E-MAIL ADDRESS:
comments@fdli.org

WEB SITE ADDRESS:
www.fdli.org/resources/academics/h-thomas-
austern-memorial-writing-competition

FOUNDED: 1949

AREAS OF INTEREST:
Food and drug law issues.

NAME(S) OF PROGRAMS:
● **H. Thomas Austern Memorial Writing**
Competition-Food and Drug Law

TYPE:
Awards/prizes. The subject matter of the
competition is an in-depth analysis of a
current issue relevant to the food and drug
field, including a relevant case law, legislative
history and other authorities, particularly
where the U.S. Food and Drug
Administration is involved.

There are two categories of prizes:
(1) papers of 40 pages or less (including
appendices and footnotes) and;
(2) papers of more than 40 pages, but less
than 101 pages.

YEAR PROGRAM STARTED: 1978

PURPOSE:
To encourage law students interested in the
areas of law affecting foods, drugs, devices,
cosmetics and biologics; to provide a
marketplace for discussing food and drug law
issues.

LEGAL BASIS:
Nonprofit educational association.

ELIGIBILITY:
The level of study is postgraduate. Entrants
must currently be enrolled in a J.D. program
at any of the U.S. law schools.

GEOGRAPHIC RESTRICTIONS:
United States.

FINANCIAL DATA:
Amount of support per award: Both
categories: $4,000 first prize; $1,000 second
prize.
Total amount of support: $10,000.

NUMBER OF APPLICANTS MOST RECENT YEAR:
50.

NUMBER OF AWARDS: 4.

APPLICATION INFORMATION:
Applicants must submit all materials
electronically. Instructions can be found on
the web site.

PUBLICATIONS:
Food and Drug Law Journal.

THE HAGUE ACADEMY OF INTERNATIONAL LAW [1976]

Peace Palace
Carnegieplein 2
2517 KJ The Hague The Netherlands
(31-70) 302-4242

E-MAIL ADDRESS:
registration@hagueacademy.nl

WEB SITE ADDRESS:
www.hagueacademy.nl

FOUNDED: 1923

AREAS OF INTEREST:
Private and public international law.

NAME(S) OF PROGRAMS:
- **Doctoral Scholarships in International Law**

TYPE:
Project/program grants. Study programs. Residential scholarships for doctoral candidates from developing countries whose thesis, in private international law or public international law, is in the process of completion, who reside in their home country and who do not have access to scientific sources.

YEAR PROGRAM STARTED: 1923

PURPOSE:
To facilitate the completion of the theses through the use of the Academy, especially from the directors of studies and the use of the resources of the Library of the Peace Palace.

LEGAL BASIS:
Government agency.

ELIGIBILITY:
The candidates' doctoral thesis must be in the process of completion. Applicant must be a national of a developing country who is a resident in their own country.

FINANCIAL DATA:
Financial help in the form of a contribution towards travelling expenses may be granted to participants, taking into account the distance of their country of normal residence.
Amount of support per award: EUR 2,100.

NUMBER OF APPLICANTS MOST RECENT YEAR:
30.

NUMBER OF AWARDS: 4.

APPLICATION INFORMATION:
Applications should be accompanied by a recommendation from the professor under whose direction the thesis is being written which mentions the title of the thesis. It should also contain a CV, a copy of the highest degree certificate (translated in French or English) and a short letter giving reasons for application.
Duration: Two months from July 1 onward.
Deadline: March 1.

PUBLICATIONS:
Programme de la Session; Collected Courses, series of published lectures.

ADDRESS INQUIRIES TO:
Registration Office
(See address above.)

*SPECIAL STIPULATIONS:
The Academy will verify that recipients of scholarships are effectively resident in The Hague without interruption and that they use the Peace Palace Library on a regular basis.

No person may receive more than one scholarship.

THE HAGUE ACADEMY OF INTERNATIONAL LAW   [1977]
Peace Palace
Carnegieplein 2
2517 KJ The Hague The Netherlands
(31-70) 302-4242

E-MAIL ADDRESS:
registration@hagueacademy.nl

WEB SITE ADDRESS:
www.hagueacademy.nl

FOUNDED: 1923

AREAS OF INTEREST:
Private and public international law.

NAME(S) OF PROGRAMS:
- **Hague Academy of International Law Summer Courses**

TYPE:
Project/program grants; Scholarships. Study programs. A limited number of scholarships are given to cover tuition and living expenses while studying at the three-week summer session of the Hague Academy of International Law. Because of the limited number, granting of scholarships to attendees from every country is not possible.

YEAR PROGRAM STARTED: 1923

PURPOSE:
To support personal and effective participation of members in scientific work related to international law and international affairs.

ELIGIBILITY:
Candidates must have completed at least four years of university studies, which must have included lectures on International Law, or must hold a three-year law degree on the date of the opening of the courses.

FINANCIAL DATA:
Amount of support per award: EUR 1,150 (including registration fees of EUR 400) covering general expenses incurred during the three weeks of one of the teaching periods. Travelling expenses will not be refunded.

NUMBER OF APPLICANTS MOST RECENT YEAR:
680.

NUMBER OF AWARDS: 100.

APPLICATION INFORMATION:
Application for scholarship should be made through the online registration form. The application must contain an identity photograph, a curriculum vitae, a copy of the highest degree certificate (translated in English or French), a short letter giving reason for the application and a recommendation from a professor of international law, sent separately. Candidates must possess a satisfactory knowledge of either French or English, the working languages of the Academy.
Duration: Three weeks.
Deadline: Complete files of scholarship candidates should be in the possession of the Secretariat before March 1.

PUBLICATIONS:
Collected Courses, series of published lectures.

OFFICERS:
Prof. Yves Daudet, Secretary General of the Academy

ADDRESS INQUIRIES TO:
Registration Office
(See address above.)

*SPECIAL STIPULATIONS:
No person may receive more than one scholarship for the Summer Courses. Recipients of scholarships are required to attend the Academy's courses throughout the session.

THE HAGUE ACADEMY OF INTERNATIONAL LAW   [1978]
Peace Palace
Carnegieplein 2
2517 KJ The Hague The Netherlands
(31-70) 302 4242

E-MAIL ADDRESS:
registration@hagueacademy.nl

WEB SITE ADDRESS:
www.hagueacademy.nl

FOUNDED: 1923

AREAS OF INTEREST:
Public and private international law.

NAME(S) OF PROGRAMS:
- **Centre for Studies and Research in International Law and International Relations**

TYPE:
Project/program grants.

YEAR PROGRAM STARTED: 1957

PURPOSE:
To bring together young international lawyers of a high standard from all over the world, to undertake original research on a common general theme which is determined each year by the Academy.

ELIGIBILITY:
The program is open to academics or lawyers of a high standard. Applications are open only to those persons who hold advanced university degrees (a Doctorate or the Academy's diploma) or to those who provide evidence of their actual involvement, for at least three years, in international legal matters. Candidates must have real practical experience and an ability to undertake research. There are between 20 and 24 participants, half in the English-speaking section and half in the French-speaking section.

FINANCIAL DATA:
All participants receive a daily allowance of EUR 35 according to the length of the stay and the reimbursement of half of the travel expenses, up to a maximum of EUR 910.

NUMBER OF APPLICANTS MOST RECENT YEAR:
70.

NUMBER OF AWARDS: 10.

APPLICATION INFORMATION:
Candidates should send a curriculum vitae with, if applicable:
(1) a list of the publications;
(2) a copy of the law diplomas, translated into one of the two languages of the Academy (English or French);
(3) indication of the number of hours of international law courses attended, together with the results and marks obtained;
(4) a short letter giving reasons for the application and;
(5) a recommendation letter from a professor of international law sent separately.
Duration: Three weeks.
Deadline: April 1.

PUBLICATIONS:
Books of the Centre for Studies and Research - Hague Academy of International Law.

OFFICERS:
Prof. Yves Daudet, Secretary General

ADDRESS INQUIRIES TO:
Registration Office
(See address above.)

*PLEASE NOTE:
The research work undertaken at the Centre may be included in a collective work published by the Academy.

*SPECIAL STIPULATIONS:
In principle, no person may participate more than once in the Centre's activities. Each participant must write a report on a subject arising out of the general theme of the year, which will be determined by the director of studies. This report must be sent to the relevant director of studies, by mid-November at the latest.

THE HAGUE ACADEMY OF INTERNATIONAL LAW   [1979]

Peace Palace
Carnegieplein 2
2517 KJ The Hague The Netherlands
(31-70) 302 4242

E-MAIL ADDRESS:
registration@hagueacademy.nl

WEB SITE ADDRESS:
www.hagueacademy.nl

FOUNDED: 1923

AREAS OF INTEREST:
Public and private international law.

NAME(S) OF PROGRAMS:
● **External Programme**

TYPE:
Project/program grants. External Programme is held each year, in turn in Africa, Asia and Latin America, upon the invitation of host governments or international organizations. It is designed for approximately 20 participants from the countries in the region (who are resident in their own country), whose traveling expenses are usually financed by the Academy and whose accommodation is financed by the government of the host state or organization. In addition, a number of participants come from the host state itself.

YEAR PROGRAM STARTED: 1969

ELIGIBILITY:
This programme is aimed at persons having studied international law (young university teachers and young civil servants from the ministry of foreign affairs or other ministries), selected by the Secretary General in the name of the Curatorium on exclusively scientific criteria. Candidates should come from countries in the region of the host country. A list of the eligible nationalities is published every year.

FINANCIAL DATA:
All participants receive a daily allowance of $35 (U.S.) according to the length of the stay and the reimbursement of their travel expenses. The accommodation is provided by the host country.

NUMBER OF APPLICANTS MOST RECENT YEAR:
50.

NUMBER OF AWARDS: 20.

APPLICATION INFORMATION:
Candidates should send the following:
(1) a curriculum vitae;
(2) a copy of the law diplomas, translated into one of the two languages of the Academy (English or French);
(3) indication of the number of hours of international law courses attended, together with the results and marks obtained;
(4) a short letter giving reasons for the

application and;
(5) a recommendation letter from a professor of international law sent separately.

Duration: One week.

Deadline: July 15, 0:00 hours.

OFFICERS:
Prof. Yves Daudet, Secretary General

ADDRESS INQUIRIES TO:
Registration Office
(See address above.)

*SPECIAL STIPULATIONS:
One is not allowed to participate more than once in the External Programme. Candidates should reside in their home country when applying.

THE HISPANIC BAR ASSOCIATION OF D.C. FOUNDATION   [1980]

1640 Rhode Island Avenue, N.W.
Suite 600
Washington, DC 20036
(202) 466-8585
Fax: (202) 463-4803

E-MAIL ADDRESS:
fellowships@hbadc.org

WEB SITE ADDRESS:
www.hbadc.org

FOUNDED: 1995

AREAS OF INTEREST:
Law and public interest.

NAME(S) OF PROGRAMS:
● **The HBA-DC Foundation Fellowship**

TYPE:
Fellowships.

PURPOSE:
To provide students with valuable work experience and exposure to an area of public interest law.

ELIGIBILITY:
Eligible students are first- and second-year law students of law schools in the District of Columbia.

GEOGRAPHIC RESTRICTIONS:
District of Columbia and the metropolitan area.

FINANCIAL DATA:
Amount of support per award: $5,000.
Total amount of support: Varies.

NUMBER OF AWARDS: 3.

APPLICATION INFORMATION:
Application information is available on the web site.

ADDRESS INQUIRIES TO:
E-mail: foundation@hbadc.org

HISPANIC NATIONAL BAR FOUNDATION   [1981]

1900 K Street, N.W.
Suite 100
Washington, DC 20006
(202) 496-7206
Fax: (202) 496-7756

E-MAIL ADDRESS:
mprego@hnbf.org

WEB SITE ADDRESS:
www.hnbf.org

FOUNDED: 1987

AREAS OF INTEREST:
Promoting the legal education of persons of Hispanic heritage throughout the U.S. and Puerto Rico.

NAME(S) OF PROGRAMS:
● **HNBF Princeton Review Duard Bradshaw Memorial Scholarship**

TYPE:
Scholarships. Winners of the HNBF Princeton Review Duard Bradshaw Scholarship will receive a Princeton Review LSAT preparation course. The winner will enroll in the Accelerated LSAT course in their hometown. This course consists of 30 classroom hours and four full-length practice tests. It takes about four to five weeks to complete. Students will then take the July or September LSAT examination upon completion of the Accelerated LSAT course. Students must request special permission to apply this scholarship to the December test.

PURPOSE:
To provide tools and resources necessary to ensure full and equal opportunity for Hispanics to become leaders in the global community, thereby ensuring a brighter future for all.

LEGAL BASIS:
Section 501(c)(3) organization dedicated to charitable and educational purposes.

ELIGIBILITY:
Applicants must:
(1) be of Hispanic/Latino heritage;
(2) be a U.S. citizen or legal permanent resident;
(3) be a junior enrolled at least part-time in an accredited U.S. college or university;
(4) have a minimum cumulative grade point average of 2.75 on a 4.0 scale;
(5) demonstrate active participation and leadership in an undergraduate student Hispanic/Latino organization and;
(6) register for the July, September/October or December LSAT Examination upon acceptance of the Scholarship.

Relatives of HNBF board members or directors are not eligible.

FINANCIAL DATA:
Scholarship will cover the cost of an Accelerated LSAT Course, worth more than $1,000.

NUMBER OF AWARDS: 4.

APPLICATION INFORMATION:
Applicant must submit:
(1) an information sheet;
(2) a cover letter and resume;
(3) a personal essay and;
(4) a recommendation from a professor (sealed and mailed in with application packet).

Application materials must be mailed in one envelope to the Foundation.

Deadline: June 1.

ADDRESS INQUIRIES TO:
Mayda Prego, President
(See address above.)

HISPANIC NATIONAL BAR FOUNDATION   [1982]

1900 K Street, N.W.
Suite 100
Washington, DC 20006
(202) 496-7206
Fax: (202) 496-7756

E-MAIL ADDRESS:
mprego@hnbf.org

WEB SITE ADDRESS:
www.hnbf.org

FOUNDED: 1987

AREAS OF INTEREST:
Promoting the legal education of persons of
Hispanic heritage throughout the U.S. and
Puerto Rico.

NAME(S) OF PROGRAMS:
● **Future Latino Leaders Law Camp**

TYPE:
Conferences/seminars; Training grants.
Week-long program held by the Foundation
in Washington, DC which provides 25 to 30
Latino high school students with the
opportunity to learn more about the legal
profession. The Law Camp offers students
the chance to come to the nation's capital
and learn more about the college application
process, meet influential Latino leaders, and
tour national monuments and various
government agencies.

PURPOSE:
To provide tools and resources necessary to
ensure full and equal opportunity for
Hispanics to become leaders in the global
community, thereby ensuring a brighter
future for all.

LEGAL BASIS:
Section 501(c)(3) organization dedicated to
charitable and educational purposes.

ELIGIBILITY:
Applicants must meet the following criteria:
(1) be a high school student entering the
sophomore, junior or senior year, or be a
recent graduate;
(2) have an interest in learning about law
school and becoming a lawyer;
(3) be a U.S. citizen, legal permanent
resident or be a legal U.S. visitor with a
valid visa and passport and;
(4) have a demonstrated interest in helping
one's community and building one's
leadership skills.

FINANCIAL DATA:
There is no cost to participate in the Law
Camp. However, accepted students must pay
a $50 application fee, unless a waiver of this
fee is requested and granted. Students are
also responsible for arranging transportation
to Washington, DC. The cost of
transportation should not deter one from
applying. Upon acceptance to the program,
the Foundation is committed to working with
the attendee and his or her family in order to
ensure that person's ability to attend.
Amount of support per award: Valued at over
$3,000 per person.

NUMBER OF AWARDS: 25 to 30.

APPLICATION INFORMATION:
Application process begins on December 1.
Application can be completed online or sent
by mail and must include:
(1) Applicant Information Form;
(2) Rules and Regulations Form;
(3) essays;
(4) two letters of recommendation (from
teachers, counselors or employers);
(5) resume (may include community service,
leadership positions or civic activities);
(6) certified copy of academic record from
high school and;
(7) $50 application fee or fee waiver
approval.
Duration: Nine days.

Deadline: March 1. Notification in April.

ADDRESS INQUIRIES TO:
Program Coordinator
E-mail: info@hnbf.org

THURGOOD MARSHALL
COLLEGE FUND   [1983]
901 F Street, N.W., Suite 300
Washington, DC 20004
(202) 507-4851
Fax: (202) 448-1017

E-MAIL ADDRESS:
scholarships@tmcfund.org

WEB SITE ADDRESS:
www.thurgoodmarshallcollegefund.org

NAME(S) OF PROGRAMS:
● **The Sidney B. Williams, Jr. Intellectual
Property Law Scholarship**

TYPE:
Scholarships. Program for underrepresented
minority students who intend to enter the
intellectual property law field, to attend law
school.

PURPOSE:
To significantly increase the number of
underrepresented minorities working as
intellectual property law lawyers in both
private and corporate practice.

ELIGIBILITY:
Applicant must:
(1) be a U.S. citizen;
(2) be a member of an underrepresented
minority group;
(3) be currently enrolled in or have been
accepted to an ABA-accredited law school;
(4) have a demonstrated commitment to
developing a career in intellectual property
law and;
(5) be in need of financial assistance.

GEOGRAPHIC RESTRICTIONS:
United States.

FINANCIAL DATA:
Amount of support per award: $10,000 per
school year.

COOPERATIVE FUNDING PROGRAMS: This
Scholarship is administered by the Fund, and
it is offered through a partnership between
the Fund and the American Intellectual
Property Law Education Foundation.

NUMBER OF AWARDS: Varies.

APPLICATION INFORMATION:
Contact the Fund.
Duration: Up to three academic years. Must
reapply.
Deadline: Mid-March. Check online for
exact date.

ADDRESS INQUIRIES TO:
Deshuandra Walker
Student Support Services Manager
Thurgood Marshall College Fund
4801 Woodway Drive, Suite 300, East
Houston, TX 77056
Tel: (713) 574-4922
Fax: (202) 448-1017
(See e-mail address above.)

MCGILL UNIVERSITY   [1984]
Chancellor Day Hall
3644 Peel Street
Montreal QC H3A 1W9 Canada
(514) 398-6666
Fax: (514) 398-4659

E-MAIL ADDRESS:
staffappointments.law@mcgill.ca

WEB SITE ADDRESS:
www.mcgill.ca/law

AREAS OF INTEREST:
Law, especially pertaining to the Canadian
legal system and legal community.

NAME(S) OF PROGRAMS:
● **Maxwell Boulton Q.C. Fellowship**

TYPE:
Fellowships.

PURPOSE:
To provide younger scholars with an
opportunity to pursue a major research
project or to complete the research
requirement for a higher degree.

ELIGIBILITY:
Open to candidates who have completed
residency requirements for a doctoral degree
in law.

FINANCIAL DATA:
Amount of support per award: $30,000 to
$35,000 (CAN) per year.

NUMBER OF APPLICANTS MOST RECENT YEAR:
13.

NUMBER OF AWARDS: 1.

APPLICATION INFORMATION:
Information is available on the web site.
Duration: One year.
Deadline: February 1.

ADDRESS INQUIRIES TO:
See e-mail address above.

MEXICAN AMERICAN LEGAL
DEFENSE AND EDUCATIONAL
FUND   [1985]
634 South Spring Street, 11th Floor
Los Angeles, CA 90014
(213) 629-2512
Fax: (213) 629-3120

E-MAIL ADDRESS:
lurquidi@maldef.org

WEB SITE ADDRESS:
www.maldef.org

FOUNDED: 1968

AREAS OF INTEREST:
Law students.

NAME(S) OF PROGRAMS:
● **MALDEF Law School Scholarship**

TYPE:
Scholarships. Awarded annually to law
students who have a demonstrated
commitment to serving the Latino community
with their law degree.

YEAR PROGRAM STARTED: 1968

PURPOSE:
To promote social change through advocacy,
communications, community education, and
litigation in the areas of education,
employment, immigrant rights, and political
access.

LEGAL BASIS:
501(3)(c) charitable organization.

ELIGIBILITY:
All full-time law students with a
demonstrated commitment to serving the
Latino community with their law degrees,
attending school in the U.S., are eligible to
apply.

FINANCIAL DATA:
Amount of support per award: Varies; typically $5,000.
Total amount of support: Up to $50,000.

NUMBER OF APPLICANTS MOST RECENT YEAR: 100.

NUMBER OF AWARDS: 5 to 10.

APPLICATION INFORMATION:
Application forms are available on the web site.
Duration: One year. Renewable.
Deadline: Varies.

IRS IDENTIFICATION NUMBER: 74-1563270

REPORTERS COMMITTEE FOR FREEDOM OF THE PRESS

1101 Wilson Boulevard
Suite 1100
Arlington, VA 22209-2275
(703) 807-2100
Fax: (703) 807-2109

E-MAIL ADDRESS:
rcfp@rcfp.org

WEB SITE ADDRESS:
www.rcfp.org

TYPE:
Fellowships. Legal fellows monitor significant developments in First Amendment media law, assist with legal defense requests from reporters, prepare legal memoranda, amicus briefs and other special projects. The Fellowship focuses on media law.

See entry 1959 for full listing.

STATE OF RHODE ISLAND

Commission on State Government Internships
State House, Room 8AA
Providence, RI 02903
(401) 222-6782
Fax: (401) 222-4447

E-MAIL ADDRESS:
rgemma@rilin.state.ri.us

WEB SITE ADDRESS:
www.rilin.state.ri.us

TYPE:
Internships. Funding through General Assembly is also available. Internship opportunities for graduate and undergraduate students in the state government operation. Students are involved in executive, legislative and judicial assignments. The internship is viewed as an extension of the classroom and is seen as complementing and building upon the educational opportunities available on campuses.

This program has established a Summer Internship section, open to Rhode Island residents only, that begins in late June and concludes in August.

See entry 2016 for full listing.

THE UNIVERSITY OF CALGARY   [1986]

Faculty of Graduate Studies
MacKimmie Library Tower, Room 213
2500 University Drive, N.W.
Calgary AB T2N 1N4 Canada
(403) 220-4938
Fax: (403) 289-7635

E-MAIL ADDRESS:
gsaward@ucalgary.ca

WEB SITE ADDRESS:
www.grad.ucalgary.ca

FOUNDED: 1966

AREAS OF INTEREST:
Law.

NAME(S) OF PROGRAMS:
● **The Honourable N.D. McDermid Graduate Scholarship in Law**

TYPE:
Awards/prizes; Scholarships. Graduate scholarships in law tenable at The University of Calgary. Awards endowed by the McDermid Law Fund in memory of the late Honourable Neil Douglas McDermid, Q.C., who was a prominent member of the legal profession of Alberta and the Calgary community for many years.

PURPOSE:
To financially assist students who want to study law at the university.

LEGAL BASIS:
University.

ELIGIBILITY:
Graduate students entering or enrolled on a full-time basis in the graduate program in the Faculty of Law at The University of Calgary. If, in the opinion of the Faculty of Graduate Studies Scholarships Selection Committee, no suitable applications are received, no awards will be made.

GEOGRAPHIC RESTRICTIONS:
Canada.

FINANCIAL DATA:
Amount of support per award: $9,125 (award may be divided further to $4,562).
Total amount of support: $18,250.

NUMBER OF AWARDS: 2.

APPLICATION INFORMATION:
Application forms are available from the Dean's Office, Faculty of Law. Applications will be reviewed by a Committee of the Faculty of Law based upon academic excellence. The Graduate Coordinator, Law will submit recommendations to the Graduate Scholarship Office. The recommendation is subject to final approval of the Graduate Scholarship Committee.
Duration: One year; nonrenewable.
Deadline: December 15.

ADDRESS INQUIRIES TO:
Graduate Scholarship Office
(See address above.)

THE UNIVERSITY OF CALGARY

Faculty of Graduate Studies
MacKimmie Library Tower, Room 213
2500 University Drive, N.W.
Calgary AB T2N 1N4 Canada
(403) 220-4938
Fax: (403) 289-7635

E-MAIL ADDRESS:
gsaward@ucalgary.ca

WEB SITE ADDRESS:
www.grad.ucalgary.ca

TYPE:
Awards/prizes; Scholarships.

See entry 1793 for full listing.

Political science

AMERICAN POLITICAL SCIENCE ASSOCIATION   [1987]

1527 New Hampshire Avenue, N.W.
Washington, DC 20036
(202) 483-2512
Fax: (202) 483-2657

E-MAIL ADDRESS:
cfp@apsanet.org

WEB SITE ADDRESS:
www.apsanet.org/cfp

FOUNDED: 1903

AREAS OF INTEREST:
Political science.

NAME(S) OF PROGRAMS:
● **Congressional Fellowship Program**

TYPE:
Fellowships. Awards to political science professors and journalists in early-career to midcareer status; the award provides an opportunity for support as a full-time aide to a member of the House or Senate or as a staff member for a Congressional committee.

YEAR PROGRAM STARTED: 1953

PURPOSE:
To equip outstanding young political scientists and journalists with a better understanding of the national legislative process.

LEGAL BASIS:
Nonprofit association.

ELIGIBILITY:
Open to U.S. political scientists and journalists. Political scientists must have completed their Ph.D. within the last 15 years or are near completion. Applicant journalists must have a Bachelor's degree and between two and 10 years of full-time professional experience in newspaper, magazine, radio or television work. Special fellowships are available for Ph.D.-level scholars of any discipline or journalists with demonstrated professional interest in telecommunications.

Candidates who are not current residents of the U.S. must fund their own transportation to Washington to be interviewed should they be selected as finalists.

FINANCIAL DATA:
Amount of support per award: $38,000 stipend plus travel.
Total amount of support: Approximately $300,000.

NUMBER OF APPLICANTS MOST RECENT YEAR:
Varies.

NUMBER OF AWARDS: Varies.

APPLICATION INFORMATION:
Official application materials are available upon request to the Association or on the web site.
Duration: 10 months, November to August.
Deadline: December 1.

ADDRESS INQUIRIES TO:
Jeffrey Biggs, Director or
Veronica Jones, Manager
(See address above.)

AMERICAN POLITICAL SCIENCE ASSOCIATION [1988]

1527 New Hampshire Avenue, N.W.
Washington, DC 20036
(202) 483-2512
Fax: (202) 483-2657

E-MAIL ADDRESS:
minority@apsanet.org

WEB SITE ADDRESS:
www.apsanet.org

FOUNDED: 1903

AREAS OF INTEREST:
Political science.

NAME(S) OF PROGRAMS:
● **APSA Minority Fellows Program**

TYPE:
Fellowships; Grants-in-aid; Scholarships.
Awards to aid prospective African American,
Asian Pacific, Latino/Latina and Native
American political science students beginning
the doctoral study of political science.

YEAR PROGRAM STARTED: 1969

PURPOSE:
To increase the number of minority scholars
in the discipline; to assist minority students
in completing their doctorates by
concentrating not only on the recruitment of
minorities, but also on the retention of these
groups within the profession.

LEGAL BASIS:
Nonprofit association.

ELIGIBILITY:
Applicants must:
(1) be minority students applying to enter a
doctoral program in political science for the
first time;
(2) be members of one of the following
racial/ethnic minority groups: African
Americans, Asian Pacific Americans,
Latinos/Latinas, and Native Americans
(federal and state recognized tribes);
(3) demonstrate an interest in teaching and
potential for research in political science;
(4) be a U.S. citizen at time of award and;
(5) demonstrate financial need.

FINANCIAL DATA:
Amount of support per award: $4,000,
disbursed in two $2,000 payments, one at the
end of their first graduate year and one at the
end of their second, provided that they
remain in good academic standing.
Total amount of support: $48,000.

NUMBER OF APPLICANTS MOST RECENT YEAR:
30.

NUMBER OF AWARDS: 12.

APPLICATION INFORMATION:
Forms can be downloaded from the web site.
Duration: One year.

ADDRESS INQUIRIES TO:
Kimberly Mealy, Program Director
(See address above.)

AMERICAN POLITICAL SCIENCE ASSOCIATION [1989]

1527 New Hampshire Avenue, N.W.
Washington, DC 20036
(202) 483-2512
Fax: (202) 483-2657

E-MAIL ADDRESS:
grants@apsanet.org

WEB SITE ADDRESS:
www.apsanet.org

AREAS OF INTEREST:
Political science.

NAME(S) OF PROGRAMS:
● **Small Research Grant Program**

TYPE:
Project/program grants; Research grants;
Seed money grants; Technical assistance;
Travel grants. The Association Small
Research Grant Program supports research in
all fields of political science.

PURPOSE:
To support the research of political scientists
who are not employed at Ph.D.-granting
institutions and to help further the careers of
these scholars.

ELIGIBILITY:
Applicants must be Association members at
the time of application and when the funds
are dispersed. The principal investigator and
any coauthor must be one of the following:
(1) a faculty member at a college or
university that does not award a Ph.D. in
political science, public administration, public
policy, international relations, government or
politics and whose primary appointment is in
one of these departments or;
(2) a political scientist not affiliated with an
academic institution and is either (a)
unemployed or (b) working in a research
organization such as a think tank.

This grant does not provide support for
dissertation research or writing. Graduate
students are not eligible to apply. Applicants
do not have to be U.S. citizens or residents.

FINANCIAL DATA:
Funds may be used for such research
activities as:
(1) travel to archives;
(2) travel to conduct interviews;
(3) administration and coding of instruments;
(4) research assistance and;
(5) purchase of data-sets.

The following activities are excluded from
funding:
(1) travel to professional meetings;
(2) secretarial costs except for preparation of
the final manuscripts for publication and;
(3) salary support for the principal
investigator.
Overhead or indirect costs are not allowable
expenses.
Amount of support per award: Up to $2,500.

APPLICATION INFORMATION:
Complete proposal and application
procedures as well as sample proposals can
be found on the web site. Applicant should
send seven collated and stapled hard copies
to the address above (Attn: Small Research
Grant Competition).
Duration: One year; nonrenewable.
Deadline: February 1.

*SPECIAL STIPULATIONS:
Funds must be expended between the time
they are received (usually in May) and the
end of the following fiscal year (June 30).

ASHBURN INSTITUTE INC.

198 Okatie Village Drive
Suite 103, PMB 301
Bluffton, SC 29909
Fax: (843) 705-7643

E-MAIL ADDRESS:
info@ashburninstitute.org

WEB SITE ADDRESS:
www.ashburninstitute.org

TYPE:
Research grants; Scholarships.
See entry 831 for full listing.

CENTER FOR CALIFORNIA STUDIES, CAPITAL FELLOWS PROGRAMS [1990]

California State University, Sacramento
6000 J Street
Sacramento, CA 95819-6081
(916) 278-6906

E-MAIL ADDRESS:
calstudies@csus.edu

WEB SITE ADDRESS:
www.csus.edu/calst/judicial

FOUNDED: 1982

AREAS OF INTEREST:
California judicial system.

NAME(S) OF PROGRAMS:
● **Judicial Administration Fellowship Program**

TYPE:
Fellowships. Jointly sponsored by the Center
for California Studies at California State
University, Sacramento and the California
Judicial Council. Full-time fellowships for 10
fellows, 10 months and graduate units earned
from California State University, Sacramento.

YEAR PROGRAM STARTED: 1997

PURPOSE:
To enable fellows to conduct research,
advocate on behalf of the judiciary, develop
and implement programs, seek grants, and
engage in educational outreach, strategic
planning, and policy analysis.

ELIGIBILITY:
Must be 20 years of age by September 1 of
applying year and have a minimum four-year
Bachelor's degree with graduation by August
of applying year. Graduate, postgraduate and
midcareer applicants are welcome.

FINANCIAL DATA:
Fellowship includes monthly stipend plus
health, vision and dental benefits.
Amount of support per award: $1,972
monthly stipend.

NUMBER OF APPLICANTS MOST RECENT YEAR:
150.

NUMBER OF AWARDS: 10 annually.

APPLICATION INFORMATION:
Applications will only be accepted online.
Applicants must submit all transcripts, letters
of recommendation and two essays.
Duration: 10 months.
Deadline: Late February. Interviews in Los
Angeles and Sacramento in May. Fellowship
announcement in May.

ADDRESS INQUIRIES TO:
Megan Thorall, Program Director
(See address above.)

*SPECIAL STIPULATIONS:
International fellows must have a valid work
visa.

CENTER FOR CALIFORNIA STUDIES, CAPITAL FELLOWS PROGRAMS [1991]

California State University, Sacramento
6000 J Street
Sacramento, CA 95819-6081
(916) 278-6906

E-MAIL ADDRESS:
calstudies@csus.edu

WEB SITE ADDRESS:
www.csus.edu/calst/senate

FOUNDED: 1982

AREAS OF INTEREST:
California state government.

NAME(S) OF PROGRAMS:
● **California Senate Fellows Program**

TYPE:
Fellowships. Jointly sponsored by the Center for California Studies at California State University, Sacramento and the California State Senate. Full-time fellowships for 18 fellows, 11 months and graduate units earned from California State University, Sacramento.

PURPOSE:
To provide participants with insight into the legislative process, including exposing people with diverse life experiences and backgrounds to the legislative process and providing research and other professional staff assistance to the Senate.

ELIGIBILITY:
Must be 20 years of age by September 1 of applying year and have a minimum four-year Bachelor's degree with graduation by August of applying year. Graduate, postgraduate and midcareer applicants are welcome. Applicants need not be California residents; however, preference will be given to candidates who demonstrate knowledge of and commitment to the state.

FINANCIAL DATA:
Fellowship includes monthly stipend plus full health, vision and dental benefits.
Amount of support per award: $1,972 monthly stipend.

NUMBER OF APPLICANTS MOST RECENT YEAR:
400.

NUMBER OF AWARDS: 18 annually.

APPLICATION INFORMATION:
Applications will only be accepted online. Applicants must submit all transcripts, letters of recommendation and essay.
Duration: 11 months.
Deadline: Late February. Interviews in Los Angeles and Sacramento in May. Fellowship announcement in May.

ADDRESS INQUIRIES TO:
David Pacheco, Program Director
(See address above.)

*SPECIAL STIPULATIONS:
International fellows must have a valid work visa.

CENTER FOR CALIFORNIA STUDIES, CAPITAL FELLOWS PROGRAMS [1992]
California State University, Sacramento
6000 J Street
Sacramento, CA 95819-6081
(916) 278-6906
Fax: (916) 278-5199

E-MAIL ADDRESS:
calstudies@csus.edu

WEB SITE ADDRESS:
www.csus.edu/calst/executive

FOUNDED: 1982

AREAS OF INTEREST:
California state government.

NAME(S) OF PROGRAMS:
● **Executive Fellowship Program**

TYPE:
Fellowships. Jointly sponsored by the Center for California Studies at California State University, Sacramento and the California governor. Full-time fellowships for 18 fellows, 10 months and six units of graduate study through California State University, Sacramento.

YEAR PROGRAM STARTED: 1986

PURPOSE:
To provide an experiential learning opportunity in California state government, whereby Fellows gain valuable insight and experience in the realm of public policy and politics.

ELIGIBILITY:
Must be 20 years of age by September 1 of the applying year and have a minimum four-year Bachelor's degree with graduation by September 1 of the applying year. Graduate, postgraduate and midcareer applicants are welcome.

FINANCIAL DATA:
Fellowship includes monthly stipend plus medical, vision and dental benefits. Recipients also earn units of graduate credit.
Amount of support per award: $1,972 per month stipend.

NUMBER OF APPLICANTS MOST RECENT YEAR:
340.

NUMBER OF AWARDS: 18 annually.

APPLICATION INFORMATION:
Applications will only be accepted online. Applicants must submit all transcripts, letters of recommendation, a policy statement and a personal statement of interest.
Duration: 10 months.
Deadline: Late February. Interviews in Los Angeles and Sacramento, CA in May. Fellowship announced in May.

ADDRESS INQUIRIES TO:
Brian Aguilar, Program Director
(See address above.)

*SPECIAL STIPULATIONS:
International fellows must have a valid work visa.

CENTER FOR CALIFORNIA STUDIES, CAPITAL FELLOWS PROGRAMS [1993]
California State University, Sacramento
6000 J Street
Sacramento, CA 95819-6081
(916) 278-6906
Fax: (916) 278-5199

E-MAIL ADDRESS:
calstudies@csus.edu

WEB SITE ADDRESS:
www.csus.edu/calst/assembly_fellowship_program.html

FOUNDED: 1982

AREAS OF INTEREST:
California state government.

NAME(S) OF PROGRAMS:
● **Jesse M. Unruh Assembly Fellowship Program**

TYPE:
Fellowships. Jointly sponsored by the Center for California Studies at California State University, Sacramento and the California State Assembly. Full-time fellowships for 18 fellows, 11 months and units of graduate study through California State University, Sacramento.

PURPOSE:
To provide educational and governmental experience and assistance for legislators.

LEGAL BASIS:
University/government program funded by State Budget-General Budget Fund.

ELIGIBILITY:
Must be 20 years of age by September 1 of applying year and have a minimum four-year Bachelor's degree with graduation by August of applying year. Graduate, postgraduate and midcareer applicants are welcome.

FINANCIAL DATA:
In addition to the stipend, full medical, vision and dental benefits are provided.
Amount of support per award: $1,972 per month stipend.

NUMBER OF APPLICANTS MOST RECENT YEAR:
300.

NUMBER OF AWARDS: 18 annually.

APPLICATION INFORMATION:
Applicants must submit all transcripts, three letters of recommendation and two essays.
Duration: 11 months.
Deadline: Late February. Interviews in Los Angeles and Sacramento in May. Fellowship announcement in May.

ADDRESS INQUIRIES TO:
Pam Chueh, Program Director
(See address above.)

*SPECIAL STIPULATIONS:
International fellows must have a valid work visa.

CITY OF NEW YORK [1994]
Department of Citywide Administrative Services
One Centre Street, Room 2425
New York, NY 10007
(212) 386-0058
Fax: (212) 669-3688

E-MAIL ADDRESS:
bsimmons@dcas.nyc.gov

WEB SITE ADDRESS:
www.nyc.gov/fellowships

FOUNDED: 1969

AREAS OF INTEREST:
City government and New York City government.

NAME(S) OF PROGRAMS:
● **New York City Urban Fellows Program**

TYPE:
Fellowships. Stipend for full-time work in New York City government agencies. Fellows work closely with city officials on long- and short-term projects and attend weekly seminars to get an academic perspective on the workings and problems of local government. Assignments range over fields such as urban planning, housing, health and social sciences, economic and financial administration, youth service, intergovernmental relations, criminal justice, cultural affairs and innumerable others. Positions are at relatively high levels as assistants to administrators and staff within the various city agencies.

YEAR PROGRAM STARTED: 1969

PURPOSE:
To attract qualified college graduates to participate in a management training program in New York City government.

LEGAL BASIS:
City Government agency.

ELIGIBILITY:
As of September of the program year, applicants must be recent college graduates (no more than two full years out of college). Fellows participate on a full-time basis. A political science major is not required. Demonstrated interest in government is required. All students who are interested in pursuing a career in municipal government are encouraged to apply regardless of academic major or previous field of training.

FINANCIAL DATA:
A choice of paid health insurance plans is provided.
Amount of support per award: Currently $30,000 for nine-month duration (annualized to $40,000).

NUMBER OF APPLICANTS MOST RECENT YEAR:
Approximately 350.

NUMBER OF AWARDS: 25 to 30.

APPLICATION INFORMATION:
Application information is available on the web site.
Duration: Nine months, September to May.
Deadline: Second Friday in January.

PUBLICATIONS:
Application guidelines.

ADDRESS INQUIRIES TO:
Barbara Simmons, Executive Director
New York City Urban Fellows Program
(See address above.)

CONGRESSIONAL BLACK CAUCUS FOUNDATION, INC.
1720 Massachusetts Avenue, N.W.
Washington, DC 20036
(202) 263-2800
Fax: (202) 263-0846

E-MAIL ADDRESS:
info@cbcfinc.org

WEB SITE ADDRESS:
www.cbcfinc.org

TYPE:
Fellowships; Internships; Scholarships. The CBC Spouses Cheerios Brand Health Initiative Scholarship is intended to increase the number of minority students pursuing degrees in the fields of medicine, engineering, technology, nutrition and other health-related professions.

The CBC Spouses Education Scholarship Fund is a national program that awards scholarships to academically talented and highly motivated students who intend to pursue full-time undergraduate, graduate or doctoral degrees.

The CBCF Congressional Fellows Program helps participants gain invaluable experience as they assist in the development of legislative and public policy initiatives while working as congressional staff for a year. This program targets early career policy professionals who have completed a professional and/or graduate degree and have demonstrated commitment to improving the lives and services for individuals living in underserved communities. Fellows work on Capitol Hill in the office of a Congressional Black Caucus member.

The CBCF Congressional Internship Program provides undergraduate students with an in-depth orientation to Capitol Hill and the legislative process through actual work experience in the offices of Congressional Black Caucus Members. In this way interns prepare to become decision makers in the policymaking process.

See entry 1027 for full listing.

CONGRESSIONAL HISPANIC CAUCUS INSTITUTE
911 2nd Street, N.E.
Washington, DC 20002
(202) 543-1771
(800) 392-3532
Fax: (202) 546-2143

WEB SITE ADDRESS:
www.chci.org

TYPE:
Internships. Internships provide college students with a paid work placement in a congressional office or federal agency for a period of 12 weeks (Spring and Fall Programs) or eight weeks (Summer Program).

See entry 1064 for full listing.

CONGRESSIONAL HISPANIC CAUCUS INSTITUTE
911 2nd Street, N.E.
Washington, DC 20002
(202) 543-1771
(800) 392-3532
Fax: (202) 546-2143

WEB SITE ADDRESS:
www.chci.org

TYPE:
Fellowships. Graduate Fellowship Program offers exceptional Latinos who have earned a graduate degree or higher related to a chosen policy issue area within three years of program start date unparalleled exposure to hands-on experience in public policy.

Public Policy Fellowship offers talented Latinos who have earned a Bachelor's degree within two years of the program start date the opportunity to gain hands-on experience at the national level in public policy.

See entry 1066 for full listing.

THE DIRKSEN CONGRESSIONAL CENTER   [1995]
2815 Broadway
Pekin, IL 61554
(309) 347-7113
Fax: (309) 347-6432

E-MAIL ADDRESS:
fmackaman@dirksencenter.org

WEB SITE ADDRESS:
www.dirksencongressionalcenter.org

FOUNDED: 1963

AREAS OF INTEREST:
U.S. Congress and its leaders.

NAME(S) OF PROGRAMS:
● **Congressional Research Grants**

TYPE:
Research grants; Seed money grants; Travel grants. Financial awards to individuals conducting research about the U.S. Congress and its leaders.

YEAR PROGRAM STARTED: 1978

PURPOSE:
To foster study of Congress in order to enhance public understanding and appreciation of the legislative branch of the federal government.

LEGAL BASIS:
Independent, nonpartisan, not-for-profit research and educational organization.

ELIGIBILITY:
Open to anyone with a serious interest in studying Congress. The Center seeks applications specifically from political scientists, historians, biographers, scholars of public administration or American studies or journalists. Graduate students may also apply.

The program does not fund undergraduates or pre-Ph.D. study. Organizations are not eligible. No institutional overhead or indirect costs will be covered.

FINANCIAL DATA:
Amount of support per award: Up to $3,500.
Total amount of support: Up to $35,000 annually.

NUMBER OF APPLICANTS MOST RECENT YEAR:
70 or more.

NUMBER OF AWARDS: Approximately 12 per year.

APPLICATION INFORMATION:
Details on application are available on the web site.
Duration: Usually one year.
Deadline: March 1 postmark. Late-March announcement.

IRS IDENTIFICATION NUMBER: 36-6132816

BOARD OF DIRECTORS:
John A. Barra
Jeffrey L. Bernstein
Tim Butler
Dr. Michael D. Danner
Christopher Deverman
Barbara E. Drake
C. Lawrence Evans
William T. Fleming
David E. Glassman
Lincoln C. Hobson
Richard H. Hunt
Sue Ann Kortkamp
Drew Leman
Louis E. Miller
Carla J. Schaefer
Kay Sutton
Ed Whitaker

ADDRESS INQUIRIES TO:
Frank H. Mackaman
(See address above.)

*SPECIAL STIPULATIONS:
This program does not fund tuition.

DONNER CANADIAN FOUNDATION   [1996]
8 Prince Arthur Avenue, 3rd Floor
Toronto ON M5R 1A9 Canada
(416) 920-6400

E-MAIL ADDRESS:
mclean@donner.ca

WEB SITE ADDRESS:
www.donnerfoundation.org

FOUNDED: 1950

AREAS OF INTEREST:
Local and municipal government, school reform, environmental education and provincial fiscal policy.

TYPE:
Project/program grants.

PURPOSE:
To determine how government handles public assets in delivering public services.

LEGAL BASIS:
Private foundation.

ELIGIBILITY:
The Foundation only makes grants to charitable organizations under the Income Tax Act of Canada. Grants are usually made for specific projects. The Foundation does not make grants for ongoing expenses, the acquisition of capital (equipment, buildings, land, etc.), endowments, fund-raising drives or to cover budget deficits. The Foundation does not accept unsolicited proposals.

GEOGRAPHIC RESTRICTIONS:
Canada.

FINANCIAL DATA:
Amount of support per award: Varies.
Total amount of support: Approximately $3,000,000.

APPLICATION INFORMATION:
The Foundation does not regularly respond to letters of inquiry or unsolicited requests for funding. Charitable organizations may send the Foundation's Executive Director a two- to three-page description of their goals and programs and if there is a potential match between this work and the interests of the Foundation, staff will contact the charity for more information.
Duration: One year.

EXECUTIVE DIRECTOR:
Helen McLean

ADDRESS INQUIRIES TO:
Helen McLean, Executive Director
(See address above.)

*PLEASE NOTE:
The Foundation only provides support to organizations recognized as charitable by the Canada Revenue Agency.

THE EISENHOWER FOUNDATION [1997]
200 S.E. 4th Street
Abilene, KS 67410
(785) 263-4751
(877) 746-4453 (toll-free phone)
Fax: (785) 263-6718

E-MAIL ADDRESS:
eisenhowerfoundation@nara.gov

WEB SITE ADDRESS:
www.dwighteisenhower.com
www.eisenhower.archives.
gov/travel_grants/travel_grants.html

AREAS OF INTEREST:
Scholarly research in the fields of history, government, economics, communications and international affairs.

NAME(S) OF PROGRAMS:
• **Travel Grants**

TYPE:
Travel grants. Travel grants are awarded to individual researchers on a competitive basis to cover a portion of expenses while in Abilene, KS, using the presidential library.

PURPOSE:
To assist scholars' research of primary sources in such fields as history, government, economics, communications and international affairs so they may provide informed leadership in American national life.

ELIGIBILITY:
Applicants must be graduate-level students.

FINANCIAL DATA:
Grants are not retroactive and travel must occur within one year of award.
Amount of support per award: Up to $1,000, dependent upon the distance traveled and duration of stay in Abilene.

APPLICATION INFORMATION:
Applications may be accessed online.
Deadline: Varies.

*SPECIAL STIPULATIONS:
If grantee's research results in a thesis, dissertation, book or article, a copy of the final product must be submitted to the Eisenhower Library for its holdings.

GERALD R. FORD PRESIDENTIAL LIBRARY [1998]
1000 Beal Avenue
Ann Arbor, MI 48109
(734) 205-0578
Fax: (734) 205-0571

E-MAIL ADDRESS:
ford.library@nara.gov

WEB SITE ADDRESS:
www.fordlibrarymuseum.gov

AREAS OF INTEREST:
Domestic issues, foreign policy and politics of the 1970s.

NAME(S) OF PROGRAMS:
• **Research Travel Grant Program**

TYPE:
Research grants; Travel grants. Research Travel Grants are awarded biannually to scholars to help defray the expenses of travel to conduct archival research in the collections of the Ford Library. Library collections focus on federal policies, foreign relations, and politics in the 1970s.

PURPOSE:
To promote research in the holdings of the Ford Library.

ELIGIBILITY:
Overseas applicants are welcome to apply, but they are responsible for costs of travel from their home country to North America.

FINANCIAL DATA:
Amount of support per award: Up to $2,000.
Total amount of support: Approximately $40,000 annually.

NUMBER OF AWARDS: Varies.

APPLICATION INFORMATION:
Before applying, contact the Library for information about holdings related to your project. Applicants should submit the application form, a curriculum vitae, and a two- or three-page project proposal to the Library. The proposal should provide both a description of the project and the ways in which Ford Library resources can advance the research. Three professional references must submit supporting letters of recommendation.
Duration: Research to be conducted within one year notice of award.

Deadline: March 15 and September 15 (postmark).

ADDRESS INQUIRIES TO:
Jeremy P. Schmidt, Grants Coordinator
(See address above.)

*SPECIAL STIPULATIONS:
The Gerald R. Ford Foundation expects acknowledgment of its support in resulting publication(s) and a donated copy of same to the Gerald R. Ford Presidential Library.

GERALD R. FORD PRESIDENTIAL LIBRARY [1999]
1000 Beal Avenue
Ann Arbor, MI 48109
(734) 205-0555
Fax: (734) 205-0571

E-MAIL ADDRESS:
ford.library@nara.gov

WEB SITE ADDRESS:
www.fordlibrarymuseum.gov

FOUNDED: 1981

AREAS OF INTEREST:
The U.S. political process, broadly defined, since circa 1970. Of special interest is the role and analysis of public opinion in that process.

NAME(S) OF PROGRAMS:
• **Gerald R. Ford Scholar Award (Dissertation Award) in Honor of Robert M. Teeter**

TYPE:
Awards/prizes; Research grants. Annual award to a doctoral student doing dissertation research and writing on an aspect of the U.S. political process during the latter part of the 20th century. Robert Teeter spent over 30 years as a leader in public opinion analysis and campaign strategy, including the 1976 campaign of President Gerald R. Ford. The majority of written materials from Teeter's career are part of the Gerald R. Ford Presidential Library collections. The Robert M. Teeter Papers document public opinion analysis and political campaign strategy from 1972 to 2004. They also include NBC News and *Wall Street Journal* National Public Opinion Surveys from 1989 to 2004.

PURPOSE:
To promote research regarding the U.S. political process during the latter part of the 20th century.

ELIGIBILITY:
Applicants must have completed all requirements for the Ph.D. program (coursework and examinations) by the application deadline, except for the dissertation.

FINANCIAL DATA:
The Library will present the award when the recipient arrives at the Library to conduct research. The recipient determines use of the award money, including, but not limited to, travel, paper and audiovisual reproductions and administrative costs, and other research and writing expenses.
Amount of support per award: $5,000.

COOPERATIVE FUNDING PROGRAMS: The Award has been made possible by the generous support of the Teeter family and friends, and the United Parcel Service.

APPLICATION INFORMATION:
Applicants must submit each of the following:
(1) an abstract describing the dissertation (no

longer than 150 words);
(2) a five- to 10-page proposed plan of research;
(3) three letters of recommendation from individuals who can attest to the applicant's qualifications for the Award (one must be from their academic director that includes a statement approving the dissertation topic);
(4) unofficial transcripts from all graduate schools attended and;
(5) a curriculum vitae.

Deadline: April 10 annually. Awards are made each spring. Applications may be submitted at any time, but those received after the deadline will automatically be entered for the following year's award.

ADDRESS INQUIRIES TO:
Gerald R. Ford Scholar Award in Honor of Robert M. Teeter
(See address above.)

THE FUND FOR AMERICAN STUDIES   [2000]
1706 New Hampshire Avenue, N.W.
Washington, DC 20009
(202) 986-0384
Fax: (202) 986-8930

E-MAIL ADDRESS:
jfarley@tfas.org

WEB SITE ADDRESS:
www.tfas.org

FOUNDED: 1990

AREAS OF INTEREST:
Advancement of constitutional principles, a democratic society and a vibrant free enterprise system.

NAME(S) OF PROGRAMS:
● **The Robert Novak Journalism Fellowship Program**

TYPE:
Fellowships. One-year writing project on a topic of applicant's choosing, focusing on journalism supportive of American culture and a free society.

YEAR PROGRAM STARTED: 1994

PURPOSE:
To award grants to working print and online journalists who share the Foundation's mission.

ELIGIBILITY:
Applicants must be U.S. citizens and working journalists with less than 10 years of professional experience in print and online journalism and who share the mission to advance constitutional principles, a democratic society and a vibrant free enterprise system.

FINANCIAL DATA:
Amounts include funds for reimbursement of fellowship-related expenses.
Amount of support per award: $50,000 full-time gold fellowship and $25,000 part-time silver fellowship.
Total amount of support: Varies.

NUMBER OF AWARDS: Varies, depending upon funding available and the number of qualified applicants.

APPLICATION INFORMATION:
Contact the Foundation.
Duration: One year.
Deadline: February 11.

IRS IDENTIFICATION NUMBER: 13-6223604

ADDRESS INQUIRIES TO:
John W. Farley, Vice President of Fellowship Program
(See address above.)

THE HERITAGE FOUNDATION/B. KENNETH SIMON CENTER FOR AMERICAN STUDIES   [2001]
214 Massachusetts Avenue, N.E.
Washington, DC 20002
(202) 608-6203
Fax: (202) 675-1771

E-MAIL ADDRESS:
asjobs@heritage.org

WEB SITE ADDRESS:
www.heritage.org

AREAS OF INTEREST:
American political thought, history and public philosophy.

NAME(S) OF PROGRAMS:
● **Research Fellowship in American Studies**

TYPE:
Fellowships. The Research Fellowship in American Studies is for recent college graduates interested in political thought, history and public philosophy and how those ideas and principles relate to the issues and debates of current American politics. The Associate will work alongside Simon Center staff at The Heritage Foundation in Washington, DC.

PURPOSE:
Fellowship: To advance promising graduates who are interested in the prudent application of enduring principles to modern public policy debates and are committed to restoring limited constitutional government in the U.S.

ELIGIBILITY:
Individuals who are citizens or residents of the U.S.

GEOGRAPHIC RESTRICTIONS:
United States.

FINANCIAL DATA:
The position does not include employee benefits such as health insurance. The Associate is responsible for arranging his or her own living arrangements.
Amount of support per award: Salary of $36,000 (approximately $3,000 each month) in addition to a travel reimbursement and a book stipend related to the Associate's research project.

APPLICATION INFORMATION:
There is no application form. Mail or e-mail the following to the Simon Center for American Studies:
(1) resume or curriculum vitae;
(2) copy of undergraduate transcripts;
(3) two letters of recommendation (at least one from a professor in a relevant field);
(4) a brief statement describing applicant's interest in the Fellowship and what he or she hopes to achieve with it, his or her areas of study and longer-term goals (approximately 500 words) and;
(5) an academic writing sample (not to exceed 15 pages).
Duration: 12 months, beginning in June or July; nonrenewable.
Deadline: May.

*SPECIAL STIPULATIONS:
The Associate must reside in the Washington, DC area during the Fellowship and will work full-time at The Heritage Foundation for the length of the Fellowship.

HERBERT HOOVER PRESIDENTIAL LIBRARY ASSOCIATION, INC.   [2002]
302 Parkside Drive
West Branch, IA 52358
(800) 828-0475
Fax: (319) 643-2391

E-MAIL ADDRESS:
info@hooverassociation.org

WEB SITE ADDRESS:
www.hooverassociation.org

FOUNDED: 1954

NAME(S) OF PROGRAMS:
● **Herbert Hoover Presidential Travel Grant Program**

TYPE:
Travel grants. Money is only available for travel to the Hoover Presidential Library in West Branch, IA. The program seeks to encourage scholarly use of the holdings of the Herbert Hoover Presidential Library. It is specifically intended to promote the study of subjects of interest and concern to Herbert Hoover, Lou Henry Hoover, their associates and other public figures as reflected in the Library's 150 manuscript collections.

YEAR PROGRAM STARTED: 1978

PURPOSE:
To encourage graduate and postdoctoral scholarship consistent with Program objectives.

LEGAL BASIS:
Tax-exempt, privately supported educational foundation.

ELIGIBILITY:
Open on a competitive basis to all scholars whose research projects are consistent with Program objectives. Qualified nonacademic researchers are also encouraged to apply. The program is also open to qualified undergraduates and independent scholars/researchers.

FINANCIAL DATA:
Amount of support per award: Up to $1,500. The Association will consider larger requests for extended graduate and postgraduate research at the Library.
Total amount of support: Varies.

NUMBER OF APPLICANTS MOST RECENT YEAR: 8.

NUMBER OF AWARDS: 6.

APPLICATION INFORMATION:
Application materials are available on the web site or upon request from the Association. Applicants must consult with the archival staff concerning their topic prior to submitting a request for funding.
Duration: No grants made on a continuing basis. Reapplications for consecutive support periods are accepted. No more than two grants are allowed within a five-year period.
Deadline: March 1. Announcement April 30.

PUBLICATIONS:
Historical Materials in the Herbert Hoover Presidential Library.

ADDRESS INQUIRIES TO:
Delene W. McConnaha
Academic Programs Manager
(See address above.)

INSTITUTE FOR HUMANE STUDIES (IHS)   [2003]
3351 Fairfax Drive, MSN 1C5
Arlington, VA 22201-4432
(703) 993-4880
Fax: (703) 993-4890

E-MAIL ADDRESS:
ihs@ihs.gmu.edu

WEB SITE ADDRESS:
www.theihs.org

AREAS OF INTEREST:
Individual liberty.

NAME(S) OF PROGRAMS:
● **Humane Studies Fellowships**
● **Charles G. Koch Summer Fellowship**

TYPE:
Awards/prizes; Fellowships. Humane Studies Fellowships cover the fields of arts and humanities, fine and applied art, law, mass communication and information, religion and theology, or social and behavioral science.

Charles G. Koch Summer Fellowship deals with current public policy issues, career development workshops, writing projects with a professional editor, and the experience of spending a summer in a Washington, DC, or state-based policy community.

PURPOSE:
To assist graduate students worldwide with a special interest in individual liberty.

ELIGIBILITY:
Humane Studies Fellowships: Open to graduate students or undergraduate students with junior or senior standing in the next academic year at accredited colleges and universities.

Charles G. Koch Summer Fellowship: Undergraduates or recent graduates.

FINANCIAL DATA:
Amount of support per award: Humane Studies Fellowships: Up to $15,000; Charles G. Koch Summer Fellowship: $1,500 stipend plus housing assistance.
Total amount of support: Varies.

APPLICATION INFORMATION:
Application information is available on the web site.

ADDRESS INQUIRIES TO:
See e-mail address above.

THE INTERCOLLEGIATE STUDIES INSTITUTE   [2004]
3901 Centerville Road
Wilmington, DE 19807
(302) 652-4600
(800) 526-7022
Fax: (302) 652-1760

E-MAIL ADDRESS:
fellowships@isi.org

WEB SITE ADDRESS:
www.isifellowships.org

FOUNDED: 1953

AREAS OF INTEREST:
Education.

NAME(S) OF PROGRAMS:
● **Bache-Renshaw Fellowship**

● **Salvatori Fellowship**
● **Richard M. Weaver Fellowship**
● **Western Civilization Fellowship**

TYPE:
Awards/prizes; Fellowships; Scholarships.

PURPOSE:
To convey to successive generations of college students a better understanding of the values and institutions that sustain a free society.

LEGAL BASIS:
A nonprofit, nonpartisan, tax-exempt educational organization.

ELIGIBILITY:
Salvatori, Richard M. Weaver and Western Civilization Fellowships: An applicant must engage in graduate studies for the purpose of teaching at the college level. Those attending professional schools (such as law, business, medicine and divinity) are ineligible. Applicants must be U.S. citizens and college seniors or graduate students who are familiar with the Institute's mission and principles. Applicants may apply for more than one fellowship, but an applicant may receive only one during his or her academic career.

Recipients must be citizens of the U.S., but may study abroad.

FINANCIAL DATA:
Amount of support per award:
Bache-Renshaw Fellowship: $12,000 grant; Salvatori Fellowship: $10,000 grant; Weaver Fellowship: $1,000 book stipend, $5,000 stipend and payment of tuition at the school of his or her choice (either in the U.S. or abroad); Western Civilization Fellowship: $20,000 grant to pursue studies at the school of his or her choice.
Total amount of support: Varies.

NUMBER OF AWARDS: Bache-Renshaw, Salvatori and Western Civilization Fellowships: 1 per award; Richard M. Weaver Fellowship: Varies.

APPLICATION INFORMATION:
Application information is available on the web site.
Deadline: January 15.

ADDRESS INQUIRIES TO:
Academic Program Officer
Program and Fellowships
(See address above.)

THE JAPANESE AMERICAN CITIZENS LEAGUE (JACL) [2005]
1629 K Street, N.W.
Suite 400
Washington, DC 20006
(202) 223-1240

E-MAIL ADDRESS:
pouchida@jacl.org

WEB SITE ADDRESS:
www.jacl.org

FOUNDED: 1929

AREAS OF INTEREST:
Public service leadership development.

NAME(S) OF PROGRAMS:
● **Mike M. Masaoka Fellowship Fund Congressional Program**

TYPE:
Fellowships. Congressional fellowship established to help understand the importance of public service at the national level. The

Masaoka fellow serves in the Washington, DC office of a member of Congress in either the U.S. House of Representatives or the U.S. Senate.

YEAR PROGRAM STARTED: 1988

PURPOSE:
To develop leaders for public service.

ELIGIBILITY:
Candidates must be U.S. citizens who are graduating college seniors or students in graduate or professional programs. Preference will be given to those who have demonstrated commitment to Asian American and Pacific Islander (AAPI) issues, particularly those affecting the Japanese American community. Membership in the JACL is required. Communication skills, especially in writing, are important.

GEOGRAPHIC RESTRICTIONS:
United States.

FINANCIAL DATA:
Fellowship includes round-trip airfare from fellow's home to Washington, DC.
Amount of support per award: $2,200 to $2,500 monthly stipend.
Total amount of support: Up to $20,000.

NUMBER OF AWARDS: 1 annually.

APPLICATION INFORMATION:
Completed application materials may be sent via e-mail to policy@jacl.org.
Duration: Six to eight months.
Deadline: April. Announcement by June 1.

ADDRESS INQUIRIES TO:
Priscilla Ouchida, Executive Director
(See address above.)

THE LYNDON BAINES JOHNSON FOUNDATION   [2006]
2313 Red River Street
Austin, TX 78705-5702
(512) 232-2266
Fax: (512) 232-2285

E-MAIL ADDRESS:
grants@lbjfoundation.org

WEB SITE ADDRESS:
www.lbjfoundation.org

FOUNDED: 1969

AREAS OF INTEREST:
Support for the LBJ Presidential Library and the LBJ School of Public Affairs at The University of Texas.

NAME(S) OF PROGRAMS:
● **Middleton Fellowship in Presidential Studies**
● **Moody Research Grants**

TYPE:
Fellowships; Research grants.

YEAR PROGRAM STARTED: 1972

PURPOSE:
To defray living, travel and related expenses incurred while conducting research at the LBJ Library during the period for which the grant is awarded.

LEGAL BASIS:
Nonprofit organization.

ELIGIBILITY:
In accepting a grant, an applicant must agree to the following conditions:
(1) that the product of the research which is made possible through these funds will not be used for any political purpose;
(2) that the funds are for the purpose of

helping to defray expenses incurred while conducting research at the Johnson Library; (3) that the grant must be used in the grant period in which it is awarded and; (4) that the LBJ Foundation will be promptly provided with a copy of any publication, paper, article or book resulting from research made possible by this grant.

FINANCIAL DATA:
Amount of support per award: Middleton Fellowship: $5,000; Moody Research Grants: $600 to $3,000.

Total amount of support: Moody Research Grants: Approximately $30,000 per grant period.

NUMBER OF APPLICANTS MOST RECENT YEAR: 5 Middleton Fellowships and 28 Moody Research Grants for Spring 2014.

NUMBER OF AWARDS: Middleton Fellowship: 1; Moody Research Grants: 15.

APPLICATION INFORMATION:
Application forms must be accompanied by a written proposal. Candidates should state clearly and precisely how the holdings of the LBJ Library will contribute to the completion of the project.

Middleton Fellowship applicants are also required to submit three letters of recommendation.

Duration: Eight months for spring grant period. Six months for fall grant period.

Deadline: September 15 for January to August grant period. March 15 for June to December grant period.

IRS IDENTIFICATION NUMBER: 74-1774063

STAFF:
Amy Barbee, Executive Director
Stephanie Savage, Director of Grants and Programs

ADDRESS INQUIRIES TO:
Stephanie Savage
Director of Grants and Programs
Tel: (512) 232-2280
(See e-mail address above.)

NATIONAL ENDOWMENT FOR DEMOCRACY [2007]
1025 F Street, N.W.
Suite 800
Washington, DC 20004
(202) 378-9700
Fax: (202) 378-9407

E-MAIL ADDRESS:
info@ned.org

WEB SITE ADDRESS:
www.ned.org/grantseekers

FOUNDED: 1983

AREAS OF INTEREST:
Democracy throughout the world.

NAME(S) OF PROGRAMS:
● **National Endowment for Democracy Grants**

TYPE:
Project/program grants.

PURPOSE:
To strengthen democratic institutions throughout the world.

ELIGIBILITY:
Individuals and religious organizations are ineligible.

FINANCIAL DATA:
Amount of support per award: Average $50,000.

Total amount of support: Varies.

NUMBER OF AWARDS: Approximately 1,236 for the year 2012.

APPLICATION INFORMATION:
Application information is available on the web site.

Duration: One year. Renewable.

Deadline: Seven weeks prior to board meetings held in January, March, June and September.

NATIONAL FEDERATION OF REPUBLICAN WOMEN
124 North Alfred Street
Alexandria, VA 22314
(703) 548-9688
Fax: (703) 548-9836

E-MAIL ADDRESS:
mail@nfrw.org

WEB SITE ADDRESS:
www.nfrw.org

TYPE:
Internships; Scholarships. Dorothy Kabis Internship includes a six-week internship in Washington, DC, housing, travel and stipend.

National Pathfinder's Scholarships are given to the best nominated candidates.

Betty Rendel Scholarships are given to undergraduate women who are majoring in political science, government or economics.

See entry 1091 for full listing.

NEW YORK STATE ASSEMBLY INTERN COMMITTEE [2008]
Legislative Office Building, Room 104A
Albany, NY 12248
(518) 455-4704
Fax: (518) 455-4705

E-MAIL ADDRESS:
intern@assembly.state.ny.us

WEB SITE ADDRESS:
www.assembly.state.ny.us/internship

FOUNDED: 1971

AREAS OF INTEREST:
Government.

NAME(S) OF PROGRAMS:
● **Assembly Session Internships**

TYPE:
Internships. Program provides firsthand knowledge of the legislative process and functions. The interns are assigned research and administrative responsibilities in an Assembly office. They receive a practical educational experience and attend weekly classes. The Assembly benefits from the new ideas and fresh perspectives of the interns. All intern placements are in Albany, NY.

YEAR PROGRAM STARTED: 1971

PURPOSE:
To encourage talented students from all fields to learn about and get involved in state government.

LEGAL BASIS:
Government legislature.

ELIGIBILITY:
Applicants must be matriculated in a U.S. college or university degree program as

juniors or seniors. Applications are welcome from students in any academic field. Colleges generally award a full semester of credit for participation. International students should have academic requirements in the U.S. to be eligible.

FINANCIAL DATA:
Session interns receive a stipend and semester of college credit.

Amount of support per award: $4,500 session term.

NUMBER OF APPLICANTS MOST RECENT YEAR: 200.

NUMBER OF AWARDS: 150.

APPLICATION INFORMATION:
Applications are available from an Intern Program liaison officer on college campuses. Applications and all supporting documents must be submitted to the Intern Committee in a complete package.

The following documents must be included with the application:
(1) personal statement;
(2) official transcripts of all college courses completed and in progress;
(3) two letters of recommendation;
(4) a letter from an appropriate college official endorsing the student's participation and indicating the amount of credit to be granted by the college and;
(5) a concise writing sample.

Duration: January to mid-May.

Deadline: November 1.

STAFF:
Kathleen McCarty, Director, Assembly Intern Committee

ADDRESS INQUIRIES TO:
Kathleen McCarty, Director
Assembly Intern Committee
(See address above.)

NEW YORK STATE ASSEMBLY INTERN COMMITTEE [2009]
Legislative Office Building, Room 104A
Albany, NY 12248
(518) 455-4704
Fax: (518) 455-4705

E-MAIL ADDRESS:
intern@assembly.state.ny.us

WEB SITE ADDRESS:
www.assembly.state.ny.us/internship

FOUNDED: 1971

AREAS OF INTEREST:
Government.

TYPE:
Internships. Assignments designed to provide up to 10 graduate students with full-time work placements as Assembly researchers and policy analysts with all the responsibilities and expectations of such positions. The work placements are with Assembly leaders. The interns will have the opportunity to develop a better understanding of the legislative process while contributing new ideas and fresh perspectives to the legislative decision making process.

YEAR PROGRAM STARTED: 1976

PURPOSE:
To bring the expertise and thinking of the state's best graduate students into the legislative process.

LEGAL BASIS:
Government.

ELIGIBILITY:
All students matriculated in or who have recently completed a graduate degree program may apply. Students with expertise in a variety of public policy issues are being sought. Issues include public finance, education, environmental conservation, etc. Students must work full-time in the Assembly. International students should have academic requirements in the U.S. to be eligible. Credit can often be arranged by the school.

GEOGRAPHIC RESTRICTIONS:
New York state.

FINANCIAL DATA:
Amount of support per award: $11,500 per year.

NUMBER OF APPLICANTS MOST RECENT YEAR:
50.

NUMBER OF AWARDS: Up to 10 each year.

APPLICATION INFORMATION:
Applications are available from graduate schools, directly from the Assembly Intern Committee, or on the web site. Applications must include two letters of recommendation, a letter from graduate program dean or director, official transcripts, a writing sample and a personal statement.
Duration: Six months (January to June). Nonrenewable.
Deadline: November 1. Selection by December 1.

STAFF:
Kathleen McCarty, Director

ADDRESS INQUIRIES TO:
Kathleen McCarty, Director
(See address above.)

NEW YORK STATE SENATE [2010]
Student Programs Office
80 South Swan Street, Suite 1426
Albany, NY 12247
(518) 455-2611
Fax: (518) 426-6827

E-MAIL ADDRESS:
students@nysenate.gov

WEB SITE ADDRESS:
www.nysenate.gov/department/student-programs

FOUNDED: 1965

AREAS OF INTEREST:
New York state government and education which includes improved public access to and understanding of government, resulting in enhanced citizenship, career staffing, government administration and leadership.

CONSULTING OR VOLUNTEER SERVICES:
Placement in staff support roles in senate offices, ordinarily in the office of a senator. Also, host or travel to inform interested citizens, students and faculty; host or travel to government offices responsible for development or administration of similar programs.

NAME(S) OF PROGRAMS:
- **James L. Biggane Fellowship in Finance**
- **New York State Senate Legislative Fellows Program**
- **Richard J. Roth Journalism Fellowship**
- **Richard A. Wiebe Public Service Fellowship**

TYPE:
Assistantships; Fellowships; Internships. These fellowships are intended for the graduate/postgraduate/midcareer level. Stipends are for bipartisan opportunities to train in government while on-site in Albany, NY. Fellows spend almost a year immersed in the work of the Senate, learning techniques associated with policymaking and legislative process. Placement is usually to the office of an elected Senate member. The Senate Legislative Fellows Program, Biggane Fellowship, Roth Journalism Fellowship and Wiebe Public Service Fellowship constitute the Senate Graduate/Post-Graduate/Mid-Career Fellowships.

YEAR PROGRAM STARTED: 1965

PURPOSE:
To provide an opportunity for career experience and learning for graduate assistants, career recruitment among superior fellows, and citizenship training in general.

LEGAL BASIS:
Legislative authority.

ELIGIBILITY:
Graduate/Postgraduate/Midcareer Fellowships: In most cases, Fellows must be full-time matriculating graduate students in an accredited university during the immediately previous spring and fall semesters. Fellowships are open to all majors. Training in the history/politics/government of New York state is not required.

The Biggane Fellow may be a person in midcareer. Biggane applicants need not be currently enrolled in graduate-level study, but must have previous graduate-level experience. Legislative Fellows will be talented and skilled graduate/postgraduate students from a variety of academic disciplines.

The Roth Fellow may be a student with experience and/or intentions in the fields of communications, journalism and/or public relations.

The Wiebe Fellow may be a student with legal training and a variety of other backgrounds.

Applicants must be U.S. citizens. Students are not required to presently reside in New York state or attend school in New York state.

FINANCIAL DATA:
The stipend is distributed in biweekly installments prorated from the first day to the last day of enrollment. Some benefit options are available (health, dental, vision, life insurance, and the retirement program). Fellows are not Senate employees; they do not earn vacation or personal leave.

All Senate Fellowships are on-site in Albany, NY. Fellowships are not financial aid for academic work, on-campus or classroom study. Housing in Albany is the responsibility of the Fellow.
Amount of support per award:
Grant-in-Study stipend of $33,000 for the year 2014-15.

NUMBER OF APPLICANTS MOST RECENT YEAR:
65.

NUMBER OF AWARDS: Approximately 16 fellowships each year. Legislative Fellows Program: Up to 13; Biggane, Roth and Wiebe Fellowships: 1 each.

APPLICATION INFORMATION:
Applications must include the following:
(1) course work-in-progress list signed by campus official (if not on transcript);
(2) calling of Office of Student Programs to indicate one's intent to apply;
(3) policy proposal;
(4) rebuttal of policy proposal;
(5) statement of purpose;
(6) writing sample essay;
(7) resume or curriculum vitae;
(8) all official transcripts (graduate and undergraduate) and;
(9) three letters of reference from persons familiar with the applicant's character, academic and/or professional abilities (at least two from faculty members).
Duration: Approximately one year, September through mid-July. No renewals.
Deadline: April 28.

PUBLICATIONS:
Program announcement.

ADDRESS INQUIRIES TO:
Director, Office of Student Programs
New York State Senate
Legislative Office Building, Suite 1426
Albany, NY 12247

NEW YORK STATE SENATE [2011]
80 South Swan Street, Suite 1426
Albany, NY 12247
(518) 455-2611
Fax: (518) 426-6827

E-MAIL ADDRESS:
students@nysenate.gov

WEB SITE ADDRESS:
www.nysenate.gov/department/student-programs

FOUNDED: 1978

AREAS OF INTEREST:
State government internships for undergraduates.

NAME(S) OF PROGRAMS:
- **Undergraduate Session Assistants Program**

TYPE:
Assistantships; Internships. Annual undergraduate internship running second Thursday in January to third Wednesday in April.

YEAR PROGRAM STARTED: 1978

PURPOSE:
To provide on-site experience at the New York State Senate, Albany, NY.

ELIGIBILITY:
Each applicant must be a U.S. citizen matriculating full-time in an accredited, undergraduate degree program on a campus in New York State. The program is intended and designed for college juniors and seniors; exceptional sophomores may occasionally be selected. Freshmen are ineligible.

The Senate welcomes majors in all accredited disciplines. Training in the history/politics/government of New York is neither a prerequisite of nor an advantage to selection. Skill and ability, initiative, eagerness to learn, discretion and mature flexibility are essential for success.

Each student should demonstrate a 3.0 grade point average and meet the campus/departmental standard for off-campus study; full-time enrollment in the immediately previous spring (not summer) and current fall semester/previous two trimesters. Each standard is to be certified by the Campus Liaison Officer (CLO), student's academic advisor, chairman, dean, or other duly authorized campus official.

Placements are ordinarily to the offices of individual senators. Students may observe, participate in, and/or acquire experience with state government procedures. Combined participation in the program and legislative placement is for a minimum of 35 hours per week. Longer hours are possible and should be expected.

Each applicant must be able to earn campus-awarded credit for participation in the program to be eligible. On-campus faculty is responsible for academic advisement, evaluation, grading and granting of credit for their student participant(s) enrolled in this Senate program.

GEOGRAPHIC RESTRICTIONS:
New York state.

FINANCIAL DATA:
Arrangement of housing in Albany is the responsibility of the individual enrollee.
Amount of support per award: A stipend of $4,500 to offset costs of moving to and living in Albany.

NUMBER OF APPLICANTS MOST RECENT YEAR:
Approximately 50.

NUMBER OF AWARDS: Approximately 30.

APPLICATION INFORMATION:
Enrollment is on-site at the New York State Senate in Albany, NY. Applications are available on campus, from the Student Programs Office, or at the web site.

If there is no CLO on campus, contact Nicholas J. Parrella, Director of Programs, at the address listed above.
Duration: Approximately four months.
Deadline: The last Friday in October. Expect an earlier on-campus deadline if one's school has a Campus Liaison Officer (CLO). Announcement of selections is approximately mid-November.

STAFF:
Nicholas J. Parrella, Director of Student Programs
Kimberly Burke, Confidential Assistant

ADDRESS INQUIRIES TO:
Nicholas J. Parrella
Director of Student Programs
New York State Senate
Legislative Office Building, Suite 1426
Albany, NY 12247

PIPER FUND [2012]
15 Research Drive
Suite B
Amherst, MA 01002
(413) 256-0349
Fax: (413) 256-3536

E-MAIL ADDRESS:
grantsmanager@proteusfund.org

WEB SITE ADDRESS:
www.proteusfund.org

AREAS OF INTEREST:
Campaign finance reform in the American political system.

TYPE:
General operating grants; Project/program grants.

PURPOSE:
To help meet the needs of the growing movement for campaign finance reform in America.

GEOGRAPHIC RESTRICTIONS:
United States.

FINANCIAL DATA:
Amount of support per award: $10,000 to $50,000.
Total amount of support: Approximately $18,000,000 since inception. Over $1,000,000 for the year 2012.

APPLICATION INFORMATION:
Guidelines are available on the web site.
Duration: One year.

ADDRESS INQUIRIES TO:
Beery Adams-Jimenez, Grants Manager
(See address above.)

*SPECIAL STIPULATIONS:
Grants are by invitation only.

PRESIDENT'S COMMISSION ON WHITE HOUSE FELLOWSHIPS [2013]
712 Jackson Place, N.W.
Washington, DC 20503
(202) 395-4522
Fax: (202) 395-6179

E-MAIL ADDRESS:
whitehousefellows@whf.eop.gov

WEB SITE ADDRESS:
www.whitehouse.gov/fellows

FOUNDED: 1964

AREAS OF INTEREST:
Leadership and public service for young professionals.

NAME(S) OF PROGRAMS:
● **White House Fellowships**

TYPE:
Fellowships. The White House Fellows program is America's most prestigious program for leadership and public service. White House Fellowships offer exceptional young men and women firsthand experience working at the highest levels of the federal government.

White House Fellows typically spend a year working as full-time, paid special assistants to senior White House staff, the Vice President, cabinet secretaries and other top-ranking government officials. Fellows also participate in an education program consisting of roundtable discussions with renowned leaders from the private and public sectors, and trips to study U.S. policy in action both domestically and internationally. Fellowships are awarded on a strictly nonpartisan basis.

PURPOSE:
To give those who participate in the program firsthand, high-level experience with the workings of the federal government and to increase their sense of participation in national affairs.

ELIGIBILITY:
The following criteria apply:
(1) applicants must be U.S. citizens and not hold any foreign citizenships;
(2) employees of the federal government are not eligible unless they are career military personnel;
(3) applicants should be finished with their undergraduate education and working in their

chosen professions and;
(4) there are no formal age restrictions; however, the fellowship program was created to give selected Americans the experience of government service early in their careers.

The Commission awards fellowships on a strict nonpartisan basis and encourages balance and diversity in all aspects of the program.

GEOGRAPHIC RESTRICTIONS:
United States.

FINANCIAL DATA:
Fellows are eligible to purchase health insurance through the Federal Employee Health Benefit Plans.
Total amount of support: Approximately $100,000 for the year 2013-14. Military personnel, maintain their current salary and benefits.

NUMBER OF APPLICANTS MOST RECENT YEAR:
Up to 1,000.

NUMBER OF AWARDS: 11 to 19 fellowships per year.

APPLICATION INFORMATION:
Application must be submitted online and is available beginning in the Fall.
Deadline: Mid-January.

SARAH SCAIFE FOUNDATION, INC. [2014]
One Oxford Centre, Suite 3900
301 Grant Street
Pittsburgh, PA 15219-6401
(412) 392-2900

WEB SITE ADDRESS:
www.scaife.com

FOUNDED: 1941

AREAS OF INTEREST:
Domestic and international public policy issues.

TYPE:
Challenge/matching grants; Fellowships; General operating grants; Project/program grants; Seed money grants.

YEAR PROGRAM STARTED: 1941

PURPOSE:
To direct money to programs that address major domestic and international issues.

LEGAL BASIS:
Private foundation.

ELIGIBILITY:
The Foundation's grant program is directed primarily toward public policy programs that address major domestic and international issues. The Foundation does not make grants to individuals for any purpose or to nationally organized fund-raising groups.

FINANCIAL DATA:
Amount of support per award: Average $25,000 to $200,000.

REPRESENTATIVE AWARDS:
$200,000 to American Civil Rights Institute; $125,000 to Foundation for Individual Rights in Education, Inc.; $60,000 to New England Legal Foundation.

APPLICATION INFORMATION:
Initial inquiries to the Foundation should be in letter form signed by the organization's chief executive officer or authorized representative and have the approval of the organization's Board of Directors. The letter

should include a concise description of the purpose for which funds are requested, along with the related budget.

Applicant must also provide:
(1) latest audited financial statements and annual report;
(2) current annual budget;
(3) list of officers and directors and their major affiliations and;
(4) copy of current determination letter from the IRS evidencing tax-exempt status under Section 501(c)(3).

Duration: One year.

Deadline: Board meets quarterly in February, May, September and November. Notification within two to four weeks.

PUBLICATIONS:
Annual report.

OFFICERS:
Richard M. Scaife, Chairman
Michael W. Gleba, President
Barbara L. Slaney, Vice President and Treasurer
R. Daniel McMichael, Secretary

ADDRESS INQUIRIES TO:
Michael W. Gleba, President
(See address above.)

THE SOCIETY FOR THE PSYCHOLOGICAL STUDY OF SOCIAL ISSUES (SPSSI) [2015]
208 I Street, N.E.
Washington, DC 20002-4340
(202) 675-6956
Fax: (202) 675-6902

E-MAIL ADDRESS:
awards@spssi.org
spssi@spssi.org

WEB SITE ADDRESS:
www.spssi.org

FOUNDED: 1936

AREAS OF INTEREST:
Public policy, social issues, psychology and international relations.

NAME(S) OF PROGRAMS:
● **Otto Klineberg Intercultural and International Relations Award**

TYPE:
Awards/prizes. The Klineberg Award is given for the best paper or article of the year on intercultural or international relations.

PURPOSE:
To award the best paper or article of the year on intercultural or international relations.

LEGAL BASIS:
Independently incorporated society.

ELIGIBILITY:
Entries can be either unpublished manuscripts, in press papers, book chapters, or journal articles published no more than 18 months prior to the submission deadline. Entries cannot be returned. The competition is open to nonmembers and members of SPSSI. Graduate students are especially urged to submit papers. Submissions from across the social sciences are encouraged, however the paper must clearly demonstrate its relevance for psychological theory and research in the domain of intercultural and international relations.

FINANCIAL DATA:
Amount of support per award: $1,000.

NUMBER OF APPLICANTS MOST RECENT YEAR: 15.

NUMBER OF AWARDS: 1.

APPLICATION INFORMATION:
Online submissions are the preferred method. Please limit the number and size of files uploaded when applying online. For hard-copy submissions, send five (5) copies to the address listed above, "Attn: Klineberg Award."

Deadline: March 1.

PUBLICATIONS:
Program announcement; application guidelines.

STATE OF RHODE ISLAND [2016]
Commission on State Government Internships
State House, Room 8AA
Providence, RI 02903
(401) 222-6782
Fax: (401) 222-4447

E-MAIL ADDRESS:
rgemma@rilin.state.ri.us

WEB SITE ADDRESS:
www.rilin.state.ri.us

FOUNDED: 1969

NAME(S) OF PROGRAMS:
● **State Government Intern Program (Spring Semester Program)**
● **State Intern Summer Program**

TYPE:
Internships. Funding through General Assembly is also available. Internship opportunities for graduate and undergraduate students in the state government operation. Students are involved in executive, legislative and judicial assignments. The internship is viewed as an extension of the classroom and is seen as complementing and building upon the educational opportunities available on campuses.

This program has established a Summer Internship section, open to Rhode Island residents only, that begins in late June and concludes in August.

YEAR PROGRAM STARTED: 1969

PURPOSE:
To provide a link between the public and state government; to open a channel for the potential recruitment of personnel for state government internship; to supplement college and university course offerings in state and local government; to enable students to develop a knowledge of the structure and procedure of state government.

LEGAL BASIS:
Chapter 47, General Laws, state of Rhode Island.

ELIGIBILITY:
Spring semester interns are chosen by members of the faculties of 11 participating Rhode Island colleges and universities. Students must have junior or senior status. Summer applicants must be Rhode Island residents attending an out-of-state college or university.

FINANCIAL DATA:
Academic credit, up to a maximum of six credits, is available. For the Summer Internship, a student is required to work 35 hours per week and receives a monthly stipend.

Amount of support per award: $100 per week for eight weeks.

APPLICATION INFORMATION:
Interns are selected by the academic committee and referred to Intern Staff.

Duration: 12 weeks in the spring (one school semester) and eight weeks (July and August) for Summer Internship.

Deadline: November 15. May 15 for Summer Internship. Announcement by the end of May.

ADDRESS INQUIRIES TO:
Robert W. Gemma, Executive Director
(See address above.)

HATTON W. SUMNERS FOUNDATION [2017]
325 North St. Paul Street
Suite 3920
Dallas, TX 75201
(214) 220-2128
Fax: (214) 953-0737

E-MAIL ADDRESS:
info@hattonsumners.org

WEB SITE ADDRESS:
www.hattonsumners.org

FOUNDED: 1949

AREAS OF INTEREST:
Self-government, political science and democracy.

TYPE:
Challenge/matching grants; Conferences/seminars; Endowments; Fellowships; Internships; Project/program grants; Scholarships. Scholarship programs at selected universities and grants to support other educational activities for both students and adults, which are designed to create an appreciation and understanding for the U.S. executive, legislative and judicial processes.

YEAR PROGRAM STARTED: 1949

PURPOSE:
To encourage the study, teaching and research into the science and art of self-government so that the American people may understand the fundamental principles of democracy and be guided thereby in shaping governmental policies.

LEGAL BASIS:
Private charitable foundation.

GEOGRAPHIC RESTRICTIONS:
Arkansas, Kansas, Louisiana, Missouri, Nebraska, New Mexico, Oklahoma and Texas.

FINANCIAL DATA:
Amount of support per award: Varies.
Total amount of support: $2,400.000 for the year 2012.

NUMBER OF AWARDS: 47.

REPRESENTATIVE AWARDS:
$25,000 to Bill of Rights Institute, Arlington, VA, for constitutional seminars in Oklahoma and New Mexico; $35,000 to Project Vote Smart, Philipsburg, MT, for National Key Votes Database Project; $45,000 to Law Focused Education, Austin, TX, for Texas Citizen Bee Competition.

APPLICATION INFORMATION:
Grant applications must be in writing, but do not need to be formal. The Foundation does not accept applications via fax or e-mail.

Duration: One year. Occasional multiyear funding.

Deadline: August 1. Decision in October.

PUBLICATIONS:
Annual report.

STAFF:
Hugh C. Akin, Executive Director

ADDRESS INQUIRIES TO:
Hugh C. Akin, Executive Director
(See address above.)

HARRY S. TRUMAN LIBRARY
INSTITUTE   [2018]
500 West U.S. Highway 24
Independence, MO 64050
(816) 268-8248
Fax: (816) 268-8299

E-MAIL ADDRESS:
sullivan.hstli@gmail.com

WEB SITE ADDRESS:
www.trumanlibrary.org

FOUNDED: 1957

AREAS OF INTEREST:
Harry S. Truman and the Truman
administration.

NAME(S) OF PROGRAMS:
• **Dissertation Year Fellowships**
• **Research Grant**
• **Scholar's Award**
• **Harry S. Truman Book Award**

TYPE:
Awards/prizes; Fellowships; Grants-in-aid;
Research grants; Travel grants. The
Dissertation Year Fellowships are given to
encourage historical scholarship of the public
career of Harry S. Truman or the Truman
era. Support is given annually to one or two
graduate students who have completed the
dissertation research and are in the writing
stage. Preference will be given to projects
based on extensive research at the Truman
Library. Successful applicants will be
expected to deposit one copy of their
completed dissertation, or any publication
resulting therefrom, with the Truman Library.

Research Grants are intended to enable
graduate students as well as postdoctoral
scholars to come to the Library for one to
three weeks to use its archival facilities.

The Scholar's Award is given every other
year, even-numbered years only, to a scholar
engaged in a study of either the public career
of Harry S. Truman or some aspect of the
history of the Truman administration or of
the U.S. during that administration. The
scholar's work must be based on extensive
research at the Truman Library and must be
designed to result in the publication of a
book-length manuscript. One copy of such
book (and/or any other publication resulting
from work done under this award) shall be
deposited by the author with the Harry S.
Truman Library.

The Harry S. Truman Book Award is given
in even years for the best book dealing with
some aspect of history of the U.S. between
April 12, 1945 and January 20, 1953 or with
the public career of Harry S. Truman.

YEAR PROGRAM STARTED: 1959

PURPOSE:
To encourage study of the history of the
Truman administration and the public career
of Harry S. Truman; to promote the use of
the Truman Library as a national center for
historical scholarship.

ELIGIBILITY:
Undergraduate students, doctoral candidates
and postdoctoral scholars with appropriate
interests are eligible for support. Applicants
must be competent researchers with viable
topics for which pertinent materials are
available at the Truman Library.

FINANCIAL DATA:
Amount of support per award: Dissertation
Year Fellowships: $16,000 payable in two
installments; Research Grants: Up to $2,500;
Scholar's Award: Up to $30,000; Truman
Book Award: $2,500.

REPRESENTATIVE AWARDS:
Alonzo Hamby for "Man of the People: A
Life of Harry S. Truman;" Richard B. Frank
for "Downfall: The End of the Japanese
Imperial Empire;" Kari Frederickson for
"The Dixiecrat Revolt and the End of Solid
South, 1932-1968;" Stephen C. Schlesinger
for "Act of Creation: The Founding of the
United Nations;" John Lewis Gaddis for
"The Cold War: A New History."

APPLICATION INFORMATION:
Applicants for the Scholar's Award should
submit an application and proposal for
preliminary screening. If selected, applicants
must submit further information including a
list of Truman files already utilized or
planned to be utilized, a projected timeline
for completion, and projected income for the
academic year in which the award will be
announced. Applicants for Research Grants
may receive no more than two grants in this
category in any one five-year period.

For the Harry S. Truman Book Award, six
copies of each book entered must be
submitted to the Book Award Administrator.
Duration: Research Grants: One to three
weeks.
Deadline: Dissertation Year Fellowships:
February 1. Announcement first week of
April. Research Grants: April 1 and October
1. Results announced six weeks later.
Scholar's Award: December 15 for
preliminary screening. Decision by February
1. If selected, further information will be
requested with announcement by April 15.
Harry S. Truman Book Award: Books must
be received by January 20 in even-numbered
years.

PUBLICATIONS:
Program announcement; *Whistle Stop*,
newsletter.

OFFICERS:
John J. Sherman, Chairman of the Board
Clyde F. Wendel, Vice Chairperson
Roger A. Novak, Treasurer
Herb M. Kohn, Secretary

BOARD OF DIRECTORS:
Clifton Truman Daniel, Honorary
Chairperson
Carol Anderson
Alan Atterbury
Alex Burden
Kirk Carpenter
Michael J. Devine
John A. Dillingham
Robert P. Dunn
Susie S. Evans
Charles M. Foudree
Mary Ann Heiss
Mary Hunkeler
Allen L. Lefko
John A. MacDonald
Thomas R. McGee, Jr.
John P. McMeel
Larry L. McMullen

James B. Nutter, Jr.
Carol P. Powell
Page Branton Reed
Elizabeth T. Solberg
Charles S. Sosland
Jeannine Strandjord
Maurice A. Watson
David Williams

ADDRESS INQUIRIES TO:
Grants Administrator
(See address above.)

THE HARRY S. TRUMAN
SCHOLARSHIP
FOUNDATION   [2019]
712 Jackson Place, N.W.
Washington, DC 20006-4901
(202) 395-4831
Fax: (202) 395-6995

E-MAIL ADDRESS:
office@truman.gov

WEB SITE ADDRESS:
www.truman.gov

FOUNDED: 1975

AREAS OF INTEREST:
Local, state and national government service.

NAME(S) OF PROGRAMS:
• **Harry S. Truman Scholarship Program**

TYPE:
Awards/prizes. Awards for undergraduate
students who demonstrate outstanding
leadership potential, plan to pursue careers in
government or elsewhere in public service
and wish to attend graduate school to help
prepare for their careers. At least one Truman
Scholar is selected each year from each state,
the District of Columbia, Puerto Rico and,
considered as a single entity, Guam, the
Virgin Islands, American Samoa and the
Commonwealth of the Northern Mariana
Islands. Scholars may attend graduate schools
in the U.S. or in foreign countries.

YEAR PROGRAM STARTED: 1975

PURPOSE:
To develop increased opportunities for young
Americans to prepare for and pursue careers
in public service, whether it be at the local,
county, state or national level, through an
educational scholarship program. The
Foundation defines public service as
employment in government at any level,
including uniformed services, public-interest
organizations, non-governmental research
and/or educational organizations and
public-service oriented nonprofit
organizations such as those whose primary
purposes are to help needy or disadvantaged
persons or to protect the environment.

LEGAL BASIS:
Authorized by Congress in 1975; the sole
Federal memorial to President Harry S.
Truman.

ELIGIBILITY:
To be considered for nomination as a Truman
Scholar, a student must be:
(1) a full-time student as a junior at a
four-year institution pursuing a Bachelor's
degree;
(2) enrolled in a four-year accredited
institution of higher education;
(3) committed to a career in government or
in public service as defined above;
(4) in the upper quarter of his or her class
and;
(5) a U.S. citizen or, in the case of nominees

from American Samoa or the Commonwealth of the Northern Mariana Islands, a U.S. national.

FINANCIAL DATA:
The award may only be used for tuition, fees, books, room and board and other specifically approved expenses in graduate school.

Amount of support per award: Up to $30,000.

NUMBER OF APPLICANTS MOST RECENT YEAR: 600.

NUMBER OF AWARDS: 60 for the year 2013.

APPLICATION INFORMATION:
All candidates for scholarships are nominated by their institutions of higher education. The Foundation neither solicits nor accepts direct candidate applications. Each participating institution must appoint a faculty representative to serve as liaison between the institution and the Foundation. The Foundation's nomination and supporting information forms are available from faculty representatives.

Duration: Up to four years.

Deadline: February 3, 2015.

THE MORRIS K. UDALL AND STEWART L. UDALL FOUNDATION
130 South Scott Avenue
Tucson, AZ 85701
(520) 901-8561
Fax: (520) 901-8570

E-MAIL ADDRESS:
bravo@udall.gov

WEB SITE ADDRESS:
www.udall.gov

TYPE:
Internships. Congressional Internships: Native American college students work in congressional offices and the White House to gain a firsthand understanding of the federal government. They also take field trips and meet with congressional members, agency heads and cabinet secretaries.

See entry 1059 for full listing.

WOMEN'S POLICY, INC. (WPI)
409 12th Street, S.W.
Suite 310
Washington, DC 20024
(202) 554-2323

E-MAIL ADDRESS:
webmaster@womenspolicy.org

WEB SITE ADDRESS:
www.womenspolicy.org

TYPE:
Fellowships.

See entry 1103 for full listing.

Sociology and anthropology

AMERICAN SOCIOLOGICAL ASSOCIATION
1430 K Street, N.W.
Suite 600
Washington, DC 20005
(202) 383-9005 ext. 321
TDD: (202) 638-0981
Fax: (202) 638-0882

E-MAIL ADDRESS:
minority.affairs@asanet.org

WEB SITE ADDRESS:
www.asanet.org

TYPE:
Fellowships. Predoctoral training fellowships for minority-group members studying sociology.

See entry 975 for full listing.

L.S.B. LEAKEY FOUNDATION   [2020]
1003B O'Reilly Avenue
San Francisco, CA 94129-1359
(415) 561-4646
Fax: (415) 561-4647

E-MAIL ADDRESS:
grants@leakeyfoundation.org

WEB SITE ADDRESS:
www.leakeyfoundation.org

FOUNDED: 1968

AREAS OF INTEREST:
Human evolution, including research into the environments, archaeology and human paleontology of the Miocene, Pliocene and Pleistocene, into the behavior, morphology and ecology of the great apes and other primate species when it contributes to the development or testing of models of human evolution and into the ecology and adaptations of living hunter-gatherer peoples.

NAME(S) OF PROGRAMS:
● **Leakey Foundation Grants**

TYPE:
Research grants. The General Research Grants priority is normally given to the exploratory phase of promising new projects that most closely meet the stated purpose of the Foundation.

YEAR PROGRAM STARTED: 1968

PURPOSE:
To conduct research related to human origins.

LEGAL BASIS:
Public foundation 501(c)(3).

ELIGIBILITY:
Grants are made to senior scientists and postdoctoral students with professional qualifications and demonstrated capability in the area of human evolution. Graduate students must be advanced to candidacy (ABD) in order to be considered.

FINANCIAL DATA:
Amount of support per award: General Research Grants are awarded up to $15,000 for Ph.D. candidate students (ABD), and up to $22,000 for senior scientists and postdoctoral.

Total amount of support: Approximately $600,000 per year.

NUMBER OF AWARDS: Approximately 40 to 60 per year.

APPLICATION INFORMATION:
Guidelines and application forms are available on the Foundation's web site. Applications are submitted and accepted online only.

All applications must be for research projects related to understanding human evolution.

Duration: One year. Renewal possible for general research grants.

Deadline: Session One (Fall): July 15, with notification in mid-December. Session Two (Spring): January 5, with notification in May.

PUBLICATIONS:
Application guidelines; newsletter.

IRS IDENTIFICATION NUMBER: 95-2536475

ADDRESS INQUIRIES TO:
Paddy Moore, Grant/Program Officer
E-mail: paddy@leakeyfoundation.org

NATIONAL SCIENCE FOUNDATION   [2021]
4201 Wilson Boulevard
Arlington, VA 22230
(703) 292-7315
Fax: (703) 292-9068

E-MAIL ADDRESS:
dwinslow@nsf.gov

WEB SITE ADDRESS:
www.nsf.gov

FOUNDED: 1950

AREAS OF INTEREST:
Scientific research on the causes and consequences of human social and cultural variability.

NAME(S) OF PROGRAMS:
● **Cultural Anthropology Program**

TYPE:
Conferences/seminars; Grants-in-aid; Project/program grants; Research grants. The program supports a broad portfolio of research by both senior scholars and by graduate students.

YEAR PROGRAM STARTED: 1952

PURPOSE:
To support basic scientific research on the causes, consequences, and complexities of human social and cultural variability.

LEGAL BASIS:
National Science Foundation Act of 1950.

ELIGIBILITY:
The program does not fund research that takes as its primary goal improved clinical practice or applied policy.

Applicants may be colleges and universities on behalf of their staff members, nonprofit, U.S. nonacademic research institutions, such as independent museums, observatories, research laboratories, stock centers and similar organizations, private profit organizations, in exceptional circumstances, rarely, foreign institutions utilizing U.S. currency, and under special circumstances, unaffiliated U.S. scientists.

FINANCIAL DATA:
Support may cover salaries, research assistantships, staff benefits related directly to purpose, permanent equipment, travel, publication costs, computer costs and certain other direct and indirect costs.

Amount of support per award: $5,000 to
$300,000; average $150,000.

Total amount of support: Approximately
$3,000,000.

APPLICATION INFORMATION:
Application must be submitted online at
FastLane or Grants.gov.

Duration: 12 to 60 months, depending on the
scientific merit and requirements of the
project.

Deadline: August 15 and January 15.

STAFF:
Jeffrey Mantz, Program Director
Deborah Winslow, Ph.D., Program Director

ADDRESS INQUIRIES TO:
Deborah Winslow, Ph.D., Program Director
(See address above.)

NATIONAL SCIENCE
FOUNDATION   [2022]
Division of Behavioral and Cognitive Sciences
4201 Wilson Boulevard
Arlington, VA 22230
(703) 292-8759
Fax: (703) 292-9068

E-MAIL ADDRESS:
jyellen@nsf.gov

WEB SITE ADDRESS:
www.nsf.gov

NAME(S) OF PROGRAMS:
● **Archaeology Program**
● **Archaeometry Program**

TYPE:
Conferences/seminars; Grants-in-aid;
Project/program grants; Research grants. The
programs provide support for
anthropologically relevant archaeological
research at both a "senior" and
doctoral-dissertation level. It also funds
anthropologically significant archaeometric
research and high-risk exploratory research
proposals.

FINANCIAL DATA:
Maximum of $20,000 in direct costs to meet
expenses associated with doctoral dissertation
research.

Total amount of support: $700,000 for year
2012.

NUMBER OF AWARDS: Approximately 50
annually.

APPLICATION INFORMATION:
Complete details and application form is
available online at Grants.gov or FastLane.

Duration: Varies.

Deadline: Target dates: Archaeology: July 1
and December 20; Archaeometry: December
1; Dissertations: No deadline.

STAFF:
Dr. John E. Yellen, Program Director

ADDRESS INQUIRIES TO:
Dr. John E. Yellen, Program Director
(See address above.)

*PLEASE NOTE:
All proposals must be submitted online at
Grants.gov or FastLane.

SCHOOL FOR ADVANCED
RESEARCH   [2023]
P.O. Box 2188
Santa Fe, NM 87504-2188
(505) 954-7201
Fax: (505) 954-7214

E-MAIL ADDRESS:
scholar@sarsf.org
seminar@sarsf.org

WEB SITE ADDRESS:
www.sarweb.org

FOUNDED: 1907

AREAS OF INTEREST:
Anthropology and allied disciplines in the
humanities and social sciences.

NAME(S) OF PROGRAMS:
● **Advanced Seminar Program**
● **Resident Scholar Fellowships**

TYPE:
Conferences/seminars; Fellowships;
Residencies. Advanced Seminars promote
in-depth communication among scholars who
are at a critical stage of research on a
common topic and whose interaction has the
potential to move the discipline of
anthropology forward with new insights into
human evolution, behavior, culture or society,
including critical contemporary issues. Each
consists of 10 scholars who meet at SAR's
Santa Fe campus for five days of intense
discussion on a topic that provides new
insights into human evolution, behavior,
society or culture. Support is also available
for two- and three-day short seminars,
including a program funded by the National
Science Foundation for research team
seminars. Participants appraise ongoing
research, assess recent innovations in theory
and methods, and share data relevant to
broad problems in anthropology and related
disciplines.

Resident Scholar Fellowships are awarded
each year to scholars in anthropology and
related disciplines who have completed their
research and who need time to prepare
book-length manuscripts or doctoral
dissertations on topics important to the
understanding of humankind.

YEAR PROGRAM STARTED: 1973

PURPOSE:
To support advanced research in
anthropology and related disciplines.

LEGAL BASIS:
Private, nonprofit.

ELIGIBILITY:
Proposals are sought for the Advanced
Seminar Program.

Resident Scholar Program: Applications are
evaluated on the basis of the overall
excellence and significance of the proposed
project, clarity of presentation and the
applicant's academic accomplishments
relative to subdiscipline and career stage. The
program supports scholars whose work is
broad, synthetic and interdisciplinary and
promises to yield significant advances in
understanding human culture, behavior,
evolution or critical contemporary issues.
Projects that are narrowly focused
geographically and theoretically or that are
primarily methodological seldom receive
strong consideration. Each year the program
supports a mix of scholars with scientific and
humanistic orientations. Preference is given
to applicants whose research and analysis are
complete and who need time to prepare
manuscripts. Applicants for postdoctoral
fellowships must have their Ph.D. in hand at
time of application. Immediate dissertation
rewrites are not encouraged.

FINANCIAL DATA:
Advanced Seminars: SAR provides round-trip
coach airfare within the U.S., lodging and all
meals. Overseas airfare for up to two
participants may also be offered.

Resident scholars are provided with an office,
low-cost housing, a stipend, library assistance
and other benefits during a nine-month
tenure, from September through the
following May. Books written by scholars
may be considered for publication by SAR
Press.

Amount of support per award: Resident
Scholar Program: Maximum stipend of
$40,000.

Total amount of support: Varies.

COOPERATIVE FUNDING PROGRAMS: Funding for
the Resident Scholar Program is provided by
the Weatherhead Foundation, the Katrin H.
Lamon Endowment for Native American Art
and Education, the Anne Ray Charitable
Trust, the Henry Luce Foundation, the Vera
R. Campbell Foundation and the National
Endowment for the Humanities (NEH).

NUMBER OF APPLICANTS MOST RECENT YEAR:
158 for the year 2012.

NUMBER OF AWARDS: Advanced Seminars: 2 to
3 seminars annually (10 per seminar);
Resident Scholar Fellowships: 5 to 6
annually.

APPLICATION INFORMATION:
Submissions must be made via online
application process. Guidelines and
application form are available on the web
site.

Duration: Advanced Seminars: Five days;
Resident Scholar Fellowships: Nine months,
September 1 through May 31.

Deadline: Resident Scholar Program:
November 1. Announcement in March.

PUBLICATIONS:
Application guidelines.

OFFICERS:
Dr. Michael Brown, President and Chief
Executive Officer
Nicole Taylor, Director of Scholar Programs

ADDRESS INQUIRIES TO:
Cynthia Geoghegan, Program Coordinator
(See address above.)

SCHOOL FOR ADVANCED
RESEARCH   [2024]
P.O. Box 2188
Santa Fe, NM 87504-2188
(505) 954-7201
Fax: (505) 954-7214

E-MAIL ADDRESS:
staley@sarsf.org

WEB SITE ADDRESS:
www.sarweb.org

FOUNDED: 1907

AREAS OF INTEREST:
Anthropology and related disciplines in the
humanities and social sciences.

NAME(S) OF PROGRAMS:
● **J.I. Staley Prize**

TYPE:
Awards/prizes. Prize awarded annually to a
living author of a ground-breaking book that
exemplifies outstanding scholarship and
writing in anthropology. The award
recognizes innovative works that add new
dimensions to the understanding of the
human species.

YEAR PROGRAM STARTED: 1988

PURPOSE:
To acknowledge those innovative works that have gone beyond traditional frontiers and dominant schools of thought in anthropology and given new dimensions to our understanding of the human species; to honor books that cross subdisciplinary boundaries within anthropology and reach out in new and expanded interdisciplinary directions.

LEGAL BASIS:
Private, nonprofit.

ELIGIBILITY:
To be considered, a book must be currently in print and must have been in publication at least two years, but not more than eight years. Co-authored books may be nominated, but edited volumes and textbooks may not. The nomination must clearly be for a single book. The award is for one outstanding and influential publication, not for an author's lifetime achievement.

Nominated books are evaluated according to the following criteria:
(1) significant contribution to our understanding of humankind;
(2) innovative and rigorous thinking in terms of theory, research methods and/or application of findings;
(3) superior integration of subdisciplinary and/or interdisciplinary perspectives;
(4) exemplary writing and clarity of expression and;
(5) demonstrated or anticipated impact on the field of anthropology.

FINANCIAL DATA:
Amount of support per award: Cash award of $10,000.
Total amount of support: $10,000.

NUMBER OF APPLICANTS MOST RECENT YEAR:
41 for the year 2012.

NUMBER OF AWARDS: 1 annually.

REPRESENTATIVE AWARDS:
2011: Katherine Verdery, "The Vanishing Hectare: Property and Value in Postsocialist Transylvania" and Joel Robbins, "Becoming Sinners: Christianity and Moral Torment in a Papua New Guinea Society;" 2012: Sarah Blaffer Hrdy, "Mothers and Others: The Evolutionary Origins of Mutual Understanding;" 2013: Joao Biehl, "Vita: Life in a Zone of Social Abandonment."

APPLICATION INFORMATION:
Detailed information is available on the web site.
Duration: One-time award.
Deadline: Nominations may be submitted at any time throughout the year. Nominations received by October 1 will be considered for next year's prize.

OFFICERS:
Dr. Michael Brown, President and Chief Executive Officer
Nicole Taylor, Director of Scholar Programs

ADDRESS INQUIRIES TO:
Cynthia Geoghegan, Program Coordinator
(See address above.)

THE AMAURY TALBOT FUND [2025]
Royal Anthropological Institute
50 Fitzroy Street
London W1T 5BT England
(020) 7387 0455
Fax: (020) 7388 8817

E-MAIL ADDRESS:
admin@therai.org.uk

WEB SITE ADDRESS:
www.therai.org.uk/awards/prizes/the-amaury-talbot-prize-for-african-anthropology/

FOUNDED: 1948

AREAS OF INTEREST:
Nigeria or West Africa.

NAME(S) OF PROGRAMS:
- **Amaury Talbot Prize for African Anthropology**

TYPE:
Awards/prizes. Prize for a significant book, article or work of anthropological research relating to West Africa.

YEAR PROGRAM STARTED: 1948

PURPOSE:
To recognize and support valuable works dealing with African anthropological research.

LEGAL BASIS:
Created under the terms of the will of Mrs. Miriam Winifred Florence Talbot.

ELIGIBILITY:
Works of anthropological research concerning Africa which were published during a calendar year, to be received no later than January 31 in succeeding year, are eligible for the prize. Although works relating to any region of Africa may be submitted, preference is given first to works focusing on Nigeria, then to those dealing with any other section of West Africa or to publications relating to West Africa in general.

FINANCIAL DATA:
The amount of the prize is determined by income from investments and is therefore not constant.
Amount of support per award:
Approximately GBP 500 per annum.

NUMBER OF APPLICANTS MOST RECENT YEAR:
10.

NUMBER OF AWARDS: 1.

APPLICATION INFORMATION:
No official application form is required, but copies of the prospectus are available upon request to the Coordinator at the address above. Entries must be accompanied by three copies of the book, article or work in question. Entries will not be returned.
Deadline: March 31 in the year following publication.

ADDRESS INQUIRIES TO:
Amaury Talbot Prize Coordinator
Royal Anthropological Institute
(See address above.)

WENNER-GREN FOUNDATION FOR ANTHROPOLOGICAL RESEARCH, INC. [2026]
470 Park Avenue South
8th Floor
New York, NY 10016-6819
(212) 683-5000
Fax: (212) 683-9151

E-MAIL ADDRESS:
inquiries@wennergren.org

WEB SITE ADDRESS:
www.wennergren.org

FOUNDED: 1941

AREAS OF INTEREST:
All branches of anthropology, including cultural/social anthropology, ethnology, biological/physical anthropology, archaeology and anthropological linguistics, and closely related disciplines concerned with human origins, development and variation.

NAME(S) OF PROGRAMS:
- **Individual Research Grants**

TYPE:
Awards/prizes; Research grants. The Foundation offers Dissertation Fieldwork Grants, Post-Ph.D. Research Grants, and Hunt Postdoctoral Fellowships. Awards are available for basic research in all branches of anthropology. Grants are made to cover expenses or phases of a research project. The Foundation particularly invites projects employing comparative perspectives or integrating two or more subfields of anthropology.

The Hunt Postdoctoral Fellowship is awarded to scholars within 10 years of receipt of the Doctorate to aid the write-up of research results for publication.

Dissertation Fieldwork Grants are awarded to individuals to aid doctoral dissertation or thesis research.

Post-Ph.D. Research Grants are awarded to individual scholars holding the Doctorate or equivalent qualification in anthropology or a related discipline.

YEAR PROGRAM STARTED: 1941

PURPOSE:
To support anthropological research.

LEGAL BASIS:
Private operating foundation.

ELIGIBILITY:
Qualified scholars are eligible without regard to nationality or institutional affiliation for Dissertation Fieldwork, Post-Ph.D. Research Grants and Hunt Postdoctoral Fellowships.

Application for grants may be made by the scholar. Predoctoral grants application must be made jointly with a thesis advisor.

Dissertation Fieldwork Grants are for individuals enrolled in a doctoral program. These grants are contingent upon the applicant's successful completion of all requirements for the degree other than the dissertation/thesis.

Post-Ph.D. Research Grants are for individual scholars holding the Doctorate or equivalent qualification in anthropology or a related discipline.

Hunt Postdoctoral Fellowships are available to all scholars regardless of institutional affiliation and nationality. Applicants must have their Ph.D. in hand to apply and be within 10 years of receipt of their Doctorate.

FINANCIAL DATA:
Individual Research Grants, except for the Hunt Fellowship, are primarily for basic research. Grants cover research expenses directly related and essential to the project (i.e., travel, living expenses during fieldwork, equipment, supplies, research assistance and other relevant expenditures). Aid is not provided for salary and/or fringe benefits of applicant, tuition, nonproject personnel, travel to meetings, institutional overhead or institutional support. Expenses incurred prior to the effective date of an award will not be covered.

Amount of support per award: Dissertation Fieldwork Grants and Post Ph.D. Research Grants: Up to $20,000; May apply for a supplementary award, maximum $5,000. Hunt Fellowship: $40,000.

Total amount of support: Approximately $5,000,000.

NUMBER OF AWARDS: 148 for the year 2013.

APPLICATION INFORMATION:
Applicants are required to submit a formal application. Application forms must be submitted online through the Foundation's web site beginning three months prior to the application deadline.

Duration: Hunt Postdoctoral Fellowship: Up to one year (12 continuous months of full-time writing). Nonrenewable; Research Grants: Duration of the project.

Deadline: May 1 for funding during first half of the year. November 1 for projects scheduled to begin July or later. Announcement within six to eight months.

PUBLICATIONS:
Program announcement.

IRS IDENTIFICATION NUMBER: 13-1813827

OFFICERS:
Seth J. Masters, Chairman of the Board
Dr. John Immerwahr, Vice-Chairman
Dr. Leslie C. Aiello, President
Lauren Meserve, Treasurer
Maugha Kenny, Vice-President for Finance and Secretary

TRUSTEES:
Dr. Leslie C. Aiello
Dr. Ira Berlin
Cass Cliatt
Dr. Joan Girgus
Henry Gonzalez
Dr. John Immerwahr
Meredith Jenkins
Dr. Darcy Kelley
Seth J. Masters
Lauren Meserve
Dr. Ellen Mickiewicz
William B. Petersen
Dr. Barbara Savage
Lorraine Sciarra
Ted Seides
Deborah Wadsworth
Marissa Wesely

WENNER-GREN FOUNDATION FOR ANTHROPOLOGICAL RESEARCH, INC.   [2027]
470 Park Avenue South, 8th Floor
New York, NY 10016-6819
(212) 683-5000
Fax: (212) 683-9151

E-MAIL ADDRESS:
internationalprograms@wennergren.org

WEB SITE ADDRESS:
www.wennergren.org

FOUNDED: 1941

AREAS OF INTEREST:
All branches of anthropology, including cultural/social anthropology, ethnology, biological/physical anthropology, archaeology and anthropological linguistics, and closely related disciplines concerned with human origins, development and variation.

NAME(S) OF PROGRAMS:
● **Wadsworth International Fellowships**

TYPE:
Fellowships; Scholarships. Wadsworth International Fellowship is for scholars and students from developing countries undertaking study leading to a Ph.D. or equivalent doctoral degree at universities where they can receive international-level training in anthropology and its related subdisciplines. The main goals of these Fellowships are to expand and strengthen international ties and enhance anthropological infrastructure in countries where anthropology is underrepresented and where there are limited resources to send students overseas for training.

YEAR PROGRAM STARTED: 1980

PURPOSE:
To support anthropological study.

LEGAL BASIS:
Private operating foundation.

ELIGIBILITY:
Wadsworth International Fellowships are available only to students from countries where anthropology is underrepresented and where there are limited resources to send students overseas for training. Students must be in the early stages of their doctoral programs. Priority is given to applicants who have not already begun graduate training abroad, and who are likely to return to an academic position in their home country upon completion of their degree.

The applicant must have a Home Sponsor who is a member of the institution with which he or she is affiliated in the home country and a Host Sponsor who is a member of the institution in which the candidate plans to pursue training. The Host Sponsor must be willing to assume responsibility for overseeing the candidate's training.

FINANCIAL DATA:
Fellowships may be used to cover travel, living expenses, tuition, student fees, income taxes, research expenses, insurance, books and any other relevant categories of expenditure. Aid is not provided for salary and/or fringe benefits of applicant, family expenses or institutional overhead.

Amount of support per award: Up to $17,500 per year.

Total amount of support: Varies.

Matching fund requirements: Because the fellowship is intended as a partnership with the host institution in providing the fellow's training, it is expected that candidates will also be offered support by the institution.

NUMBER OF AWARDS: Approximately 5 per year.

APPLICATION INFORMATION:
The Foundation operates an online application submission procedure. Application forms and guidelines for completing these forms are available three months before each application deadline. Two printed copies of the application materials must also be mailed to the Foundation. Applications and supporting materials must be in English. The application asks for the following categories of information:
(1) general information about the applicant, the home institution and sponsor, and the host institution and sponsor;
(2) answers to three questions about the proposed plan of study, research interests, and professional goals and plans;
(3) a detailed budget;

(4) copies of official transcripts from the home institution (provide a translation if they are not in English);
(5) where applicable, the applicant must provide evidence of competency in the language of the country in which he/she will be pursuing training;
(6) curriculum vitae of the applicant and host sponsor and;
(7) the applicant should request letters from both the home sponsor and the host sponsor, to be sent directly to the Foundation. These letters must clearly identify the applicant by their full legal name. Applications cannot be processed unless both letters of recommendation are received by the application deadline.

Duration: One year. Possibility of renewal up to three additional years.

Deadline: March 1. Final decisions are made by May 1.

PUBLICATIONS:
Program announcement.

IRS IDENTIFICATION NUMBER: 13-1813827

OFFICERS:
Seth J. Masters, Chairman of the Board
Dr. Leslie C. Aiello, President

ADDRESS INQUIRIES TO:
International Program Office
(See address and e-mail above.)

WENNER-GREN FOUNDATION FOR ANTHROPOLOGICAL RESEARCH, INC.   [2028]
470 Park Avenue South, 8th Floor North
New York, NY 10016-6819
(212) 683-5000
Fax: (212) 683-9151

E-MAIL ADDRESS:
lobbink@wennergren.org

WEB SITE ADDRESS:
www.wennergren.org

FOUNDED: 1941

AREAS OF INTEREST:
All branches of anthropology, including cultural/social anthropology, ethnology, biological/physical anthropology, archaeology, anthropological linguistics, and closely related disciplines concerned with human origins, development and variation.

NAME(S) OF PROGRAMS:
● **Conference and Workshop Grants**
● **Wenner-Gren Symposium Program**

TYPE:
Conferences/seminars. Workshops.

PURPOSE:
To support anthropological research.

LEGAL BASIS:
Private operating foundation.

ELIGIBILITY:
The Foundation provides conference support in two forms. Conference and workshop grants are made to the organizer(s). Priority is given to public conferences sponsored by international scholarly organizations (e.g., the IUAES and EASA) that serve as their annual or periodic meetings and to working conferences that address broad research issues in anthropology and provide for intensive interaction among participants. Funds are not normally provided for panels or sessions that are part of larger meetings. Exceptions may be made for organizers who are applying for funds to aid the participation of scholars from developing countries.

The Foundation also sponsors and directly administers a limited number of conferences each year under the Wenner-Gren Symposium Program. These symposia are intended for topics of broad significance for anthropology. They are planned jointly by the organizer and the president and follow a specific format developed by the Foundation.

Requests by individuals to support their own travel to meetings are not accepted.

FINANCIAL DATA:
The Foundation pays all costs related to the Wenner-Gren Symposium and actively manages it, including sending out invitations and making travel arrangements.

Amount of support per award: Conference and Workshop Grants: $20,000.

Total amount of support: Varies.

NUMBER OF APPLICANTS MOST RECENT YEAR: 60.

NUMBER OF AWARDS: 15 to 20.

APPLICATION INFORMATION:
Consult the Foundation web site for application procedures. Guidelines include the following:
(1) Proposals for symposia should be received by the Foundation no less than 18 months before the proposed date for the symposium;
(2) Symposia must aim to make major theoretical or methodological interventions in current issues within anthropology, broadly construed;
(3) Symposia must also advance the Foundation's goal of fostering an international community of anthropologists by drawing participants from around the world;
(4) The Foundation prefers two organizers for the symposium, ideally from two different countries;
(5) The objectives of the symposium should be to coalesce and advance knowledge on the issue, to present and address divergent viewpoints, and to mark out directions for future research;
(6) Symposia should show the relevance of basic research in anthropology to analyzing the human condition, past and/or present and;
(7) Organizers choose the location from a list of suggested sites provided by the Foundation.

Duration: Length of particular conference.

Deadline: Conference and Workshop Grants: June 1 and December 1.

PUBLICATIONS:
Annual report.

IRS IDENTIFICATION NUMBER: 13-1813827

OFFICERS:
Seth J. Masters, Chairman
Dr. Leslie C. Aiello, President

ADDRESS INQUIRIES TO:
Laurie Obbink
Conference Program Associate
(See address above.)

WENNER-GREN FOUNDATION FOR ANTHROPOLOGICAL RESEARCH, INC. [2029]
470 Park Avenue South, 8th Floor
New York, NY 10016-6819
(212) 683-5000
Fax: (212) 532-1492

E-MAIL ADDRESS:
inquiries@wennergren.org

WEB SITE ADDRESS:
www.wennergren.org

AREAS OF INTEREST:
All branches of anthropology, including cultural/social anthropology, ethnology, biological/physical anthropology, archaeology and anthropological linguistics, and closely related disciplines concerned with human origins, development and variation.

NAME(S) OF PROGRAMS:
● **International Collaborative Research Grants**

TYPE:
Research grants. Projects normally should include one principal investigator from outside North America, Western Europe and Australia.

Grants are awarded to cover expenses of a specific research project. Applications are evaluated by two main criteria: the quality of the proposed research, and the potential benefits of the collaboration for international anthropology.

PURPOSE:
To encourage collaborations in which the principal investigators bring different and complementary perspectives, knowledge and/or skills.

ELIGIBILITY:
Individual scholars who hold the Doctorate or equivalent qualification in anthropology or a related discipline. The projects should contribute to anthropology as a discipline and provide new perspectives. Priority is given to new collaborations which create new partnerships between researchers.

FINANCIAL DATA:
Grants cover research expenses directly related and essential to the project (i.e., travel, living expenses during fieldwork, equipment, supplies, research assistance, expenses of communication between the investigators, and other relevant expenditures). Aid is not provided for salary and/or fringe benefits of applicants, tuition, non-project personnel, institutional overhead, or institutional support.

Amount of support per award: $35,000.

Total amount of support: Varies.

NUMBER OF AWARDS: 6.

APPLICATION INFORMATION:
Applications are available on the web site.

Deadline: June 1 and December 1.

OFFICERS:
Seth J. Masters, Chairman
Dr. Leslie C. Aiello, President

ADDRESS INQUIRIES TO:
International Program Office
E-mail:
internationalprograms@wennergren.org

*SPECIAL STIPULATIONS:
Application forms must be downloaded from the Foundation web site.

WHATCOM MUSEUM [2030]
121 Prospect Street
Bellingham, WA 98225
(360) 778-8968
Fax: (360) 778-8931

E-MAIL ADDRESS:
jgrant@cob.org

WEB SITE ADDRESS:
www.whatcommuseum.org

FOUNDED: 1973

AREAS OF INTEREST:
Linguistics.

NAME(S) OF PROGRAMS:
● **Jacobs Research Funds Small Grants Program**

TYPE:
Research grants. Grants are given for work on problems in language, social organization, political organization, religion, mythology, music and other arts, psychology and folk science.

YEAR PROGRAM STARTED: 1973

PURPOSE:
To support anthropological and linguistics research on the indigenous peoples of Canada, mainland U.S. and Mexico, with a focus on the Pacific Northwest.

ELIGIBILITY:
Formal academic credentials are not required. Applicants who are inexperienced in research should arrange for the collaboration or supervision of an appropriate and experienced research scholar.

GEOGRAPHIC RESTRICTIONS:
Canada, Mexico, United States and Pacific Northwest.

FINANCIAL DATA:
Amount of support per award: Individuals: $3,000; Group Grant: $6,000; Kinkade Grant: $9,000.

NUMBER OF APPLICANTS MOST RECENT YEAR: 35.

NUMBER OF AWARDS: 25.

APPLICATION INFORMATION:
Two letters in support of the applicant and the project are required. Applications are also accepted online.

Duration: One year. Must reapply for renewal.

Deadline: February 15 (postmark).

ADDRESS INQUIRIES TO:
Amy Geise, Museum Representative
(See address above.)

PHYSICAL SCIENCES

Physical sciences (general)

AMERICAN CHEMICAL SOCIETY [2031]

1155 16th Street, N.W.
Washington, DC 20036
(202) 872-4481
(800) 227-5558
Fax: (202) 872-6319

E-MAIL ADDRESS:
prfinfo@acs.org

WEB SITE ADDRESS:
www.acsprf.org

FOUNDED: 1944

AREAS OF INTEREST:
Fundamental research in chemistry, engineering and earth sciences which may impact the petroleum field.

NAME(S) OF PROGRAMS:
● **The Petroleum Research Fund**

TYPE:
Grants-in-aid; Research grants. The project may be in any field of pure science which may afford a basis for subsequent research directly connected with the petroleum field.

YEAR PROGRAM STARTED: 1944

PURPOSE:
To support advanced scientific education and fundamental research in the petroleum field.

LEGAL BASIS:
Private trust established in 1944 with contributions of seven petroleum companies.

ELIGIBILITY:
Grants are made to nonprofit scientific or educational institutions, such as universities, on behalf of projects of their regularly appointed faculty.

FINANCIAL DATA:
Amount of support per award: Up to $100,000 per year, depending upon the grant program.
Total amount of support: Varies.
Matching fund requirements: Varies.

APPLICATION INFORMATION:
Application information is available on the web site.
Duration: Up to two years.
Deadline: Five months prior to each scheduled meeting held in May and September.

PUBLICATIONS:
Annual report.

ADDRESS INQUIRIES TO:
Ronald Siatkowski, Director
(See address above.)

AMERICAN INDIAN SCIENCE AND ENGINEERING SOCIETY (AISES)

P.O. Box 9828
Albuquerque, NM 87119-9828
(505) 765-1052

E-MAIL ADDRESS:
info@aises.org

WEB SITE ADDRESS:
www.aises.org/Programs/
ScholarshipsandInternships/Scholarships

TYPE:
Scholarships.

See entry 1039 for full listing.

AMERICAN SOCIETY FOR MASS SPECTROMETRY [2032]

2019 Galisteo Street
Building I-1
Santa Fe, NM 87505
(505) 989-4517
Fax: (505) 989-1073

E-MAIL ADDRESS:
office@asms.org

WEB SITE ADDRESS:
www.asms.org

FOUNDED: 1969

AREAS OF INTEREST:
Mass spectrometry.

NAME(S) OF PROGRAMS:
● **ASMS Research Awards in Mass Spectrometry**

TYPE:
Project/program grants; Research grants.

YEAR PROGRAM STARTED: 1988

PURPOSE:
To promote academic research in mass spectrometry by young scientists.

LEGAL BASIS:
Nonprofit corporation.

ELIGIBILITY:
Grant applicants must be academic scientists within four years of joining the tenure track or research faculty of a North American university for research in mass spectrometry.

Applicants can be from any country, but must be on the faculty of a North American university when the award is made.

GEOGRAPHIC RESTRICTIONS:
North America.

FINANCIAL DATA:
Grants are made to the university in the name of the selected individual.
Amount of support per award: $35,000.
Total amount of support: $70,000 annually.

NUMBER OF APPLICANTS MOST RECENT YEAR:
15.

NUMBER OF AWARDS: 2.

APPLICATION INFORMATION:
Applicants should submit applications electronically in a PDF format including a curriculum vitae, list of current research support, three-page proposal, one-page fiscal proposal and justification, and two letters of recommendation. Proposals are ranked primarily on scientific merit and secondarily on effectiveness of proposed use of funds.
Duration: Varies.
Deadline: November 30.

IRS IDENTIFICATION NUMBER: 23-7050068

ADDRESS INQUIRIES TO:
See e-mail address above.

AMERICAN SOCIETY OF NAVAL ENGINEERS (ASNE)

1452 Duke Street
Alexandria, VA 22314-3458
(703) 836-6727
Fax: (703) 836-7491

E-MAIL ADDRESS:
jpierce@navalengineers.org

WEB SITE ADDRESS:
www.navalengineers.org

TYPE:
Scholarships. Stipend for tuition, fees and expenses to follow a full-time or co-op program of study that applies to naval engineering, such as naval architecture, marine engineering, ocean engineering, mechanical engineering, structural engineering, electrical engineering, electronic engineering and the physical sciences, as well as other programs leading to careers with civilian and military maritime organizations supporting and developing work and life at sea.

See entry 2647 for full listing.

ASPRS - THE IMAGING AND GEOSPATIAL INFORMATION SOCIETY [2033]

5410 Grosvenor Lane
Suite 210
Bethesda, MD 20814-2160
(301) 493-0290 ext. 101
Fax: (301) 493-0208

E-MAIL ADDRESS:
scholarships@asprs.org

WEB SITE ADDRESS:
www.asprs.org

FOUNDED: 1934

AREAS OF INTEREST:
Geospatial sciences, photogrammetry, remote sensing, geographic information systems (GIS) and Lidar supporting technologies.

NAME(S) OF PROGRAMS:
● **Robert E. Altenhofen Memorial Scholarship**
● **DigitalGlobe Foundation Award**
● **ERDAS Internship**
● **William A. Fischer Memorial Scholarship**
● **Ta Liang Memorial Award**
● **Paul R. Wolf Memorial Scholarship**
● **Z/I Imaging Scholarship**

TYPE:
Assistantships; Awards/prizes; Fellowships; Internships; Scholarships; Travel grants. Robert E. Altenhofen Memorial Scholarship is for undergraduate or graduate study in photogrammetry.

The DigitalGlobe Foundation Award is open to full-time undergraduate or graduate students at an accredited college or university in the U.S. or Canada with image processing facilities appropriate for conducting the proposed work.

ERDAS is an eight-week internship for graduate students in photogrammetry and remote sensing at the ERDAS facilities in Atlanta or elsewhere. The internship stipend includes an allowance for travel and living expenses.

William A. Fischer Memorial Scholarship is open to students pursuing graduate-level studies in remote sensing at an accredited institution.

Ta Liang Memorial Award is awarded to a graduate student in remote sensing to be used for research-related travel.

The Paul R. Wolf Memorial Scholarship is designed for prospective teachers in the general area of surveying, mapping or photogrammetry.

Z/I Imaging Scholarship is for a student who is currently pursuing graduate-level studies or who plans to enroll for graduate studies in a recognized college or university in the U.S. or elsewhere.

YEAR PROGRAM STARTED: 1960

PURPOSE:
To advance knowledge and improve understanding of mapping sciences; to promote the responsible applications of photogrammetry, remote sensing, geographic information systems (GIS) and supporting technologies.

LEGAL BASIS:
501(c)(3) organization.

ELIGIBILITY:
Applicant must be enrolled in an accredited college or university and in most cases be an active or student member of ASPRS.

GEOGRAPHIC RESTRICTIONS:
United States.

FINANCIAL DATA:
Amount of support per award: Robert E. Altenhofen Memorial Scholarship, William A. Fischer Memorial Scholarship, Ta Liang Memorial Award and Z/I Imaging Award: $2,000; DigitalGlobe Foundation Award: Potential value of up to $20,000; ERDAS Internship: $2,500 stipend, plus expenses; Paul R. Wolf Memorial Scholarship: $3,500.

NUMBER OF AWARDS: 1 per award.

APPLICATION INFORMATION:
Application information is available on the web site.
Duration: One year.
Deadline: All complete applications, including reference letters and transcripts, must be received at ASPRS no later than midnight, October 16, 2015.

PUBLICATIONS:
ASPRS Foundation Awards & Scholarships booklet.

STAFF:
Michael Hauck, Executive Director
Jesse Winch, Scholarship Administrator

ADDRESS INQUIRIES TO:
Awards and Scholarships
(See address and e-mail above.)

ASPRS - THE IMAGING AND GEOSPATIAL INFORMATION SOCIETY   [2034]
5410 Grosvenor Lane
Suite 210
Bethesda, MD 20814-2160
(301) 493-0290 ext. 101
Fax: (301) 493-0208

E-MAIL ADDRESS:
scholarships@asprs.org

WEB SITE ADDRESS:
www.asprs.org

FOUNDED: 1934

AREAS OF INTEREST:
Geospatial sciences, photogrammetry, remote sensing, geographic information systems (GIS) and supporting technologies.

NAME(S) OF PROGRAMS:
• **Abraham Anson Memorial Scholarship**
• **BAE Systems Award**
• **John O. Behrens Institute for Land Information (ILI) Memorial Scholarship**
• **Robert N. Colwell Memorial Fellowship**
• **Francis H. Moffitt Memorial Scholarship**
• **The Kenneth J. Osborn Memorial Scholarship**

TYPE:
Fellowships; Scholarships; Travel grants. Abraham Anson Memorial Scholarship is designed to encourage undergraduate students who have an exceptional interest in pursuing scientific research or education in geospatial science or technology related to photogrammetry, remote sensing, surveying and mapping to enter a professional field where they can use the knowledge of their discipline to excel in their profession.

BAE Systems Award is limited to papers describing civil (nonmilitary) applications of photogrammetry or remote sensing.

John O. Behrens Institute for Land Information (ILI) Memorial Scholarship is an undergraduate award established by the Institute for Land Information to encourage those who have an exceptional interest in pursuing scientific research or education in geospatial science or technology or land information systems/records to enter a professional field where they can use the knowledge of this discipline.

Robert N. Colwell Memorial Fellowship is made to a graduate student (Master's or Ph.D. level) currently enrolled or intending to enroll in a college or university in the U.S. or Canada, or a recently graduated (within three years of graduation) postdoctoral researcher, who is pursuing a program of study aimed at starting a professional career where expertise is required in remote sensing or other related geospatial information technologies.

Francis H. Moffitt Memorial Scholarship is for students currently enrolled or intending to enroll in a college or university in the U.S. or Canada, who are pursuing a program of study in surveying or photogrammetry leading to a career in the geospatial mapping profession.

The Kenneth J. Osborn Memorial Scholarship is made to an undergraduate student currently enrolled or intending to enroll in a college or university in the U.S., who is pursuing a program of study in preparation for entering the profession in the general area of surveying, mapping, photogrammetry or geospatial information and technology.

PURPOSE:
To advance knowledge and improve understanding of mapping sciences; to promote the responsible applications of photogrammetry, remote sensing, geographic information systems (GIS) and supporting technologies.

LEGAL BASIS:
501(c)(3) organization.

ELIGIBILITY:
Requirements vary with the program. Applicant must be enrolled in an accredited college or university and in most cases be an active or student member of ASPRS.

GEOGRAPHIC RESTRICTIONS:
United States and Canada.

FINANCIAL DATA:
Amount of support per award: Anson Memorial Scholarship, BAE Systems Award, Behrens Memorial Scholarship and Osborn Memorial Scholarship: $2,000; Colwell Memorial Fellowship: $5,500; Moffitt Memorial Scholarship: $4,500.

NUMBER OF APPLICANTS MOST RECENT YEAR:
100.

NUMBER OF AWARDS: 1 for each award.

APPLICATION INFORMATION:
Application information is available on the web site.
Duration: One year.
Deadline: Contact the Society for dates.

PUBLICATIONS:
ASPRS Awards and Scholarships booklet (including application form).

STAFF:
James R. Plasker, Executive Director

ADDRESS INQUIRIES TO:
See e-mail address above.

BUILDING AND FIRE RESEARCH LABORATORY   [2035]
National Institute of Standards and Technology
100 Bureau Drive, Stop 8660
Gaithersburg, MD 20899-8660
(301) 975-6598
Fax: (301) 975-4052

WEB SITE ADDRESS:
www.nist.gov/el/fire_grants.cfm

FOUNDED: 1974

AREAS OF INTEREST:
Exploratory fire research, furnishing flammability, fire performance and validation, smoke hazard calculation, fire growth and extinction, compartment fire models and fire safety performance.

NAME(S) OF PROGRAMS:
• **Fire Research Grants Program**

TYPE:
Research grants. The program includes the following: Fire Model and Application, Large Fire Research, Advanced Fire Measurement, Materials Fire Research, and Fire Sensing Equipment.

YEAR PROGRAM STARTED: 1981

PURPOSE:
To conduct research in the areas of fire analysis and prediction, fire metrology, fire fighting technology, integrated performance assessment, and materials and products.

LEGAL BASIS:
Public Law 93-498; Section 18.

ELIGIBILITY:
Institutions of higher education, hospitals, nonprofit organizations, commercial organizations, state, local, and Indian tribal governments, foreign governments, organizations under the jurisdiction of foreign governments, and international organizations are eligible. Joint programs with participation by more than one eligible entity are possible.

GEOGRAPHIC RESTRICTIONS:
United States.

FINANCIAL DATA:
Amount of support per award: Average $10,000 to $100,000 per award.

NUMBER OF APPLICANTS MOST RECENT YEAR:
30.

NUMBER OF AWARDS: 5 for the year 2012.

APPLICATION INFORMATION:
Application information is available on the web site.
Duration: One year. Renewals possible.

Deadline: As listed in *Federal Register* notice.

COOPERATIVE INSTITUTE FOR RESEARCH IN ENVIRONMENTAL SCIENCES (CIRES)

CIRES Building, Room 318
University of Colorado
Boulder, CO 80309-0216
(303) 492-1143
Fax: (303) 492-1149

E-MAIL ADDRESS:
info@cires.colorado.edu
karen.dempsey@cires.colorado.edu

WEB SITE ADDRESS:
cires.colorado.edu/collaboration/fellowships

TYPE:
Fellowships. The program provides opportunities for interactions between CIRES scientists and visiting fellows to pursue common research interests. CIRES research includes theoretical studies, laboratory experimentation, and field investigations which may affect the enhancement of air and water quality and prediction of weather climate fluctuations.

See entry 2175 for full listing.

INTERNATIONAL UNION FOR VACUUM SCIENCE, TECHNIQUE AND APPLICATIONS (IUVSTA)   [2036]

84 Oldfield Drive, Vicars Cross
Chester CH3 5LW England
44 1244 342675
Fax: 44 7005 860135

E-MAIL ADDRESS:
iuvsta.secretary.general@ronreid.me.uk

WEB SITE ADDRESS:
www.iuvsta.org

FOUNDED: 1958

AREAS OF INTEREST:
Scientific and technological fields of study or applications using vacuum.

NAME(S) OF PROGRAMS:
• **M.W. Welch International Scholarship**

TYPE:
Scholarships. Support for a scholar for one year working in a research laboratory abroad.

YEAR PROGRAM STARTED: 1965

PURPOSE:
To support younger scientists working abroad in vacuum science and technology.

LEGAL BASIS:
Scientific association.

ELIGIBILITY:
Applicants must submit a form outlining the research program and signed by the supervisor in the laboratory where the research is to be carried out to indicate the agreement of the laboratory and the proposed supervisor to the proposed studies.

Applicants must make arrangements for the proposed research program with a laboratory of their choice. The laboratory must be outside the applicant's native country. Strong preference will be given to applicants who propose to study in a foreign lab in which they have not yet studied. The research must be on a topic of vacuum science, technique

or application. It is expected that the successful applicant will be encouraged to publish most of the results in scientific and technical journals. Candidates for the scholarship should have at least a Bachelor's degree; a doctoral degree is preferred.

FINANCIAL DATA:
Award does not automatically include travel expenses. In principle, the successful applicant makes his or her own arrangements.
Amount of support per award:
Approximately $15,000 (U.S.).
Total amount of support: Approximately $15,000 (U.S.).

NUMBER OF APPLICANTS MOST RECENT YEAR:
14.

NUMBER OF AWARDS: 1 annually.

APPLICATION INFORMATION:
Application information is available online, or contact Dr. F.R. Shepherd, Administrator
3 Grierson Lane
Ottawa, ON K2W 1A6
Canada
E-mail: frank_shepherd@avs.org.
Duration: One year. Nonrenewable.
Deadline: April 30, 2014.

PUBLICATIONS:
Application guidelines.

ADDRESS INQUIRIES TO:
Dr. R.J. Reid
Secretary General IUVSTA
84 Oldfield Drive
Vicars Cross
Chester CH3 5LW
England
E-mail:
iuvsta.secretary.general@ronreid.me.uk

JILA   [2037]

440 UCB
University of Colorado at Boulder
Boulder, CO 80309-0440
(303) 492-7789
Fax: (303) 492-5235

E-MAIL ADDRESS:
kim.monteleone@jila.colorado.edu

WEB SITE ADDRESS:
jila.colorado.edu

FOUNDED: 1962

AREAS OF INTEREST:
Atomic and molecular physics, chemical physics, laser physics, astrophysics, optical physics, precision measurements, geophysical measurement and other closely related areas.

NAME(S) OF PROGRAMS:
• **Postdoctoral Research Associateships**
• **Visiting Fellowships**

TYPE:
Assistantships; Fellowships. Postdoctoral Research Associateships provide advanced research experience in the years immediately after the Ph.D. degree. Visiting Fellowships support research and study for experienced scientists.

YEAR PROGRAM STARTED: 1963

PURPOSE:
To further scientific exchange.

LEGAL BASIS:
Jointly sponsored by the University of Colorado at Boulder and the National Institute of Standards and Technology.

ELIGIBILITY:
Postdoctoral Research Associateships are awarded on the basis of the applicants' scholarly qualifications, promise as research scientists, and research interests and experience in relation to those specific ongoing research programs for which financial support is available. There are no restrictions as to citizenship except as may be imposed by conditions of individual contracts. Ph.D. required.

Visiting Fellowships are available to scientists with extensive research experience beyond the doctoral degree, although younger persons with significant scientific achievements are also encouraged to apply. Awards are based on the fields of scientific interest and the scholarly achievements or promise of the applicants. There are no restrictions as to citizenship.

APPLICATION INFORMATION:
Application information is available on the web site.
Deadline: Varies.

ADDRESS INQUIRIES TO:
Kim Monteleone, Coordinator
Visiting Scientists Program
(See address above.)

LINK FOUNDATION   [2038]

c/o Binghamton University Foundation
P.O. Box 6005
Binghamton, NY 13902-6005
(607) 777-2210
Fax: (607) 777-2533

WEB SITE ADDRESS:
www.linkfoundation.org

FOUNDED: 1953

AREAS OF INTEREST:
Energy, oceanographic, aerospace simulation research and fellowships.

NAME(S) OF PROGRAMS:
• **Energy Fellowship Program**
• **Oceanography Engineering Fellowship Program**
• **Simulation Fellowship Program**

TYPE:
Development grants; Fellowships; Internships; Research grants. Grants for research, development and training related to the mastery of air, sea and energy resources.

YEAR PROGRAM STARTED: 1953

PURPOSE:
To promote the general welfare through the advancement of scientific, technological and general educational projects.

ELIGIBILITY:
Nonprofit educational institutions and organizations with appropriate interests are eligible to apply. Grants are not awarded directly to individuals.

FINANCIAL DATA:
Amount of support per award: $3,700 to $27,000.

APPLICATION INFORMATION:
Information on applying for fellowships may be obtained from the administrators for the individual programs. Proof of an organization's tax-exempt status must accompany the application if not listed in the publication Cumulative List of Organizations described in Section 170(c) of the Internal Revenue Code.

The following documents must be submitted in the order indicated or they will not be accepted:
(1) cover sheet specific to the individual program;
(2) 500-word description of the project that places the research in the context of current activities in the field;
(3) two letters of recommendation, as specified for the individual program;
(4) two additional letters of reference (professional or educational);
(5) project objectives, timeline and projected budget (projected budget only for Energy Program) and;
(6) current resume.

Duration: Subject to annual review.

Deadline: January.

TRUSTEES:
Dr. Thomas F. Kelly, Chairman
Douglas R. Johnson, Treasurer
Jimmie Anne Haisley, Secretary
Dr. Andrew M. Clark
David Gdovin

ADDRESS INQUIRIES TO:
Dr. Thomas F. Kelly, Chairman
(See address above.)

NATIONAL RESEARCH COUNCIL OF THE NATIONAL ACADEMIES   [2039]
Fellowship and Research Associateship Programs
500 Fifth Street, N.W.
Washington, DC 20001
(202) 334-2760
Fax: (202) 334-2759

E-MAIL ADDRESS:
rap@nas.edu

WEB SITE ADDRESS:
www.nationalacademies.org/rap

AREAS OF INTEREST:
All fields in science and engineering.

NAME(S) OF PROGRAMS:
- **National Research Council Graduate, Postdoctoral and Senior Research Associateship Programs**

TYPE:
Fellowships. Research awards. Fellowships at the graduate, postdoctoral and senior levels for research-in-residence at U.S. federal laboratories and affiliated institutions.

YEAR PROGRAM STARTED: 1954

PURPOSE:
To provide research opportunities for qualified personnel.

LEGAL BASIS:
Not-for-profit agency.

ELIGIBILITY:
Citizens of the U.S. and foreign nationals may apply. Must have or expect to receive Ph.D., Sc.D. or other earned equivalent research Doctorate. Program also available for graduate-level applicants.

Awards are tenable only at participating U.S. federal laboratories and affiliated institutions.

FINANCIAL DATA:
Research Associateship awards include stipend, support for relocation and professional travel and health insurance.

Amount of support per award: Annual stipend for recent Ph.D. recipients: $45,000 to $80,000, with higher stipend for additional

experience. Annual entry-level stipend for graduate awards: $30,000, with higher stipend for additional experience.

Total amount of support: Varies.

NUMBER OF APPLICANTS MOST RECENT YEAR: 1,000.

NUMBER OF AWARDS: 275.

APPLICATION INFORMATION:
Application information is available on the web site.

Duration: One to three years.

Deadline: February 1, May 1, August 1 and November 1.

STAFF:
Dr. H. Ray Gamble, Director of Fellowships and Associateships

ADDRESS INQUIRIES TO:
Research Associateship Programs
(See address above.)

NATIONAL SCIENCE FOUNDATION   [2040]
Division of Atmospheric and Geospace Sciences
4201 Wilson Boulevard, Room 775S
Arlington, VA 22230
(703) 292-8520
Fax: (703) 292-9022

E-MAIL ADDRESS:
trozell@nsf.gov

WEB SITE ADDRESS:
www.nsf.gov

FOUNDED: 1950

AREAS OF INTEREST:
The Atmospheric Sciences program supports research to add new understanding of the behavior of the Earth's atmosphere and its interactions with the Sun. Included are studies of the physics, chemistry and dynamics of the Earth's upper and lower atmosphere and its space environment, research on climate processes and variations and studies to understand the natural global cycles of gases and particles in the Earth's atmosphere.

TYPE:
Conferences/seminars; Research grants.

YEAR PROGRAM STARTED: 1962

PURPOSE:
To continue to build a base of fundamental knowledge of the atmospheres of the Earth and other planets and of the Sun.

LEGAL BASIS:
Government agency.

ELIGIBILITY:
Proposals may be submitted by academic institutions, nonacademic and nonprofit research organizations, profitmaking and private research organizations and individuals. Occasionally, NSF sponsors efforts by other government agencies, particularly for field programs.

GEOGRAPHIC RESTRICTIONS:
United States and its territories.

FINANCIAL DATA:
Amount of support per award: Varies.
Total amount of support: Varies.

APPLICATION INFORMATION:
Application information is available on the web site.

Duration: Varies.

Deadline: Varies.

PUBLICATIONS:
NSF Guide to Programs.

ADDRESS INQUIRIES TO:
Tracy L. Rozell, Program Support Manager
(See address above.)

OAK RIDGE INSTITUTE FOR SCIENCE AND EDUCATION
P.O. Box 117
Oak Ridge, TN 37831-0117
(865) 574-7798
Fax: (865) 576-1609

E-MAIL ADDRESS:
ruth.keller@orau.org
science.education@orau.org

WEB SITE ADDRESS:
orise.orau.gov/sep/catalog.htm
see.orau.org

TYPE:
Internships. Full- and part-time appointments are available for a period of three to 12 months. Assignments afford students the opportunity to apply and practice theories and methods learned in the classroom. Program participants are assigned individual projects that relate to their academic majors, career goals, and the ongoing research and development missions of the facility. They make recommendations or reports regarding their findings or solutions to a staff member of the facility who provides guidance and advice, serves as their research advisor, and reviews their findings.

See entry 2661 for full listing.

RESEARCH CORPORATION FOR SCIENCE ADVANCEMENT [2041]
4703 East Camp Lowell Drive
Suite 201
Tucson, AZ 85712-1281
(520) 571-1111
Fax: (520) 571-1119

E-MAIL ADDRESS:
awards@rescorp.org

WEB SITE ADDRESS:
www.rescorp.org

FOUNDED: 1912

AREAS OF INTEREST:
University research and education in physics, chemistry and astronomy.

NAME(S) OF PROGRAMS:
- **Cottrell Scholar Awards**
- **Scialog: Solar Energy Conversion**
- **Single Investigator Cottrell College Science Awards**

TYPE:
Awards/prizes. Cottrell Scholar Awards recognize beginning faculty members in Ph.D.-granting universities who excel at teaching and research.

Scialog: Solar Energy Conversion funds transformative research in solar energy conversion at colleges and universities.

Single Investigator Cottrell Science Awards help early career faculty in primarily undergraduate institutions start a program of research.

PURPOSE:
To promote excellence in both research and teaching in science departments in colleges and universities.

LEGAL BASIS:
Operating foundation.

ELIGIBILITY:
Cottrell Scholar Awards: Applicants must be tenure-track assistant professors in a Ph.D.-granting department of astronomy, chemistry or physics who are in, or who will begin, their third academic year during the calendar year of application.

Scialog: Solar Energy Conversion: Faculty in U.S. colleges and universities.

Single Investigator Cottrell College Science Awards: Faculty in the first three years of first tenure-track appointment in a primarily undergraduate institution. Funds must be used for supplies, equipment, faculty summer stipends or student summer stipends.

The Corporation does not make awards to individuals or businesses. Proposals are only accepted from U.S. academic institutions.

GEOGRAPHIC RESTRICTIONS:
United States.

FINANCIAL DATA:
Cottrell Scholar and Scialog Awards: Grant awards can be used at discretion of awardee for most direct costs.

Amount of support per award: Cottrell Scholar Awards: $75,000; Scialog: Solar Energy Conversion: $100,000 to $250,000; Single Investigator Cottrell College Science Awards: $40,000.

Total amount of support: Varies.

Matching fund requirements: Single Investigator Cottrell College Science Awards: $15,000.

APPLICATION INFORMATION:
Application information is available on the web site.

Duration: Two years with a possible one-year no-cost extension.

PUBLICATIONS:
Annual report; newsletter; occasional publications and guidelines.

IRS IDENTIFICATION NUMBER: 13-1963407

OFFICERS:
Jack Pladziewicz, Interim President

BOARD OF DIRECTORS:
G. Scott Clemons
Peter K. Dorhout
Robert B. Hallock
Jonathan Hook
Brent Iverson
Gayle P.W. Jackson
Elizabeth McCormack
Patrick S. Osmer
David Wenner

ADDRESS INQUIRIES TO:
Science Advancement Program
(See address above.)

ALFRED P. SLOAN FOUNDATION   [2042]

630 Fifth Avenue
Suite 2550
New York, NY 10111-0242
(212) 649-1649

E-MAIL ADDRESS:
researchfellows@sloan.org

WEB SITE ADDRESS:
www.sloan.org

FOUNDED: 1934

AREAS OF INTEREST:
Science, technology, mathematics, computer science, economics, ocean sciences and neuroscience.

NAME(S) OF PROGRAMS:
● **Sloan Research Fellowships**

TYPE:
Fellowships. Research fellowships are awarded to young scholars in chemistry, computational and evolutionary molecular biology, computer science, economics, mathematics, neuroscience, physics, and ocean sciences. The Fellow need not pursue a specified research project and is free to change the direction of his or her research at any time.

YEAR PROGRAM STARTED: 1955

PURPOSE:
To identify and support promising young scientists at an early stage.

LEGAL BASIS:
Private foundation.

ELIGIBILITY:
Candidates are required to hold a Ph.D. (or equivalent) in chemistry, physics, mathematics, computer science, economics, computational and evolutionary molecular biology, neuroscience, or ocean sciences, and must be members of the regular faculty of a U.S. or Canadian college or university. They may be no more than six years from completion of the most recent Ph.D. or equivalent as of the year of their nomination, unless special circumstances are involved such as military service, a change of field, child rearing or for less than two years they have held a faculty appointment.

Applicant must be employed at a U.S. or Canadian institution.

GEOGRAPHIC RESTRICTIONS:
United States and Canada.

FINANCIAL DATA:
Each fellowship is administered by the Fellow's institution and is designed to allow the greatest possible freedom and flexibility in its use. The award may be used for equipment, technical assistance, professional travel, or any other activity directly related to the Fellow's research.

Amount of support per award: $50,000 over a two-year term.

Total amount of support: $5,310,000.

NUMBER OF APPLICANTS MOST RECENT YEAR:
700.

NUMBER OF AWARDS: 126 fellowships: 23 for physics, 23 for chemistry, 20 for mathematics, 16 for neuroscience, 16 for computer science, 8 for economics, 8 for ocean science, and 12 for computational and evolutionary molecular biology.

APPLICATION INFORMATION:
Candidates may not apply directly, but must be nominated by a department head or other senior scholar. The nominator should submit a letter describing the candidate's qualifications and must see that the Foundation receives three supporting letters directly from other scholars, preferably not at the same institution. A curriculum vitae, a list of scientific publications plus one copy of no more than two representative publications, and a one-page statement by the nominee describing his or her significant scientific work and immediate research plans should accompany the nomination form and letter.

Strong evidence in submitted publications and supporting letters of the nominee's independent creativity is one of the most important considerations in the review process.

Duration: Two years. One two-year extension is permitted on request.

Deadline: Selections are made in February. Nominations must be received no later than September 15 for awards to begin the following September.

PUBLICATIONS:
Brochure; annual report.

ADMINISTRATIVE OFFICERS AND STAFF:
Paul L. Jaskow, President
Leisle Lin, Financial Vice President and Secretary
Christopher T. Sia, Controller

SOCIETY FOR THE STUDY OF AMPHIBIANS AND REPTILES   [2043]

Department of Biological Sciences
University of Wisconsin-Whitewater
Whitewater, WI 53190
(262) 472-1069

E-MAIL ADDRESS:
kapferj@uww.edu

WEB SITE ADDRESS:
www.ssarherps.org/pages/GIH.php

AREAS OF INTEREST:
Herpetology.

NAME(S) OF PROGRAMS:
● **Grants in Herpetology**

TYPE:
Awards/prizes; Research grants. Awards are given in six categories: Conservation of Amphibians and/or Reptiles, Field Research, Laboratory Research, Herpetological Education, Travel and International Research.

PURPOSE:
To advance research, conservation, and education concerning amphibians and reptiles; to provide financial support for deserving individuals or organizations involved in herpetological research, education, or conservation.

ELIGIBILITY:
Applicants must be students and members of the SSAR with the exception of those applying for educational grants.

FINANCIAL DATA:
Amount of support per award: $500.
Total amount of support: $3,000.

NUMBER OF AWARDS: 6.

APPLICATION INFORMATION:
Applicants may only apply for one category and must designate to which of the six their proposal is submitted. Each proposal must include the following:
(1) title page;
(2) background and objects of the proposed project;
(3) methods of carrying out the project;
(4) complete project budget;
(5) brief resume or curriculum vitae of the applicant or project coordinator and;
(6) letter of support.

Duration: One-time award.

Deadline: December 15.

ADDRESS INQUIRIES TO:
Dr. Joshua M. Kapfer, Chairperson
(See address above.)

TUSKEGEE UNIVERSITY [2044]

1200 West Montgomery Road
Tuskegee, AL 36088
(334) 727-8375
Fax: (334) 724-4224

E-MAIL ADDRESS:
gsr@mytu.tuskegee.edu

WEB SITE ADDRESS:
www.tuskegee.edu

FOUNDED: 1881

AREAS OF INTEREST:
Postgraduate education in the sciences.

NAME(S) OF PROGRAMS:
● **Master's Program in Material Science and Engineering**
● **Ph.D. Program in Material Science and Engineering**

TYPE:
Fellowships.

YEAR PROGRAM STARTED: 1944

PURPOSE:
To enable students who might otherwise be unable to pursue Master's and doctoral degrees at Tuskegee University.

LEGAL BASIS:
University.

FINANCIAL DATA:
Amount of support per award: Master's Program: $18,000 stipend plus tuition and other fees for U.S. citizens; $15,000 stipend plus tuition and other fees for international students. Ph.D. Program: Up to $54,000 per year ($25,000 to $30,000 stipend plus tuition and other fees up to $24,000) for U.S. citizens; $20,000 to $25,000 stipend plus tuition and other fees for international students.

Total amount of support: Varies.

NUMBER OF AWARDS: Varies.

APPLICATION INFORMATION:
Application form is available online.
Duration: Three to five years, depending upon student's performance.
Deadline: February 1.

ADDRESS INQUIRIES TO:
Office of Graduate Studies and Research
John A. Kenney Hall
Suite 44-320, Tuskegee University
Tuskegee, AL 36088
(See e-mail address above.)

WILLIAM P. WHARTON TRUST [2045]

c/o Choate, Hall & Stewart
2 International Place
Boston, MA 02110
(617) 248-5000
Fax: (617) 248-4000

E-MAIL ADDRESS:
williampwhartontrust@choate.com

WEB SITE ADDRESS:
williamwharton.org

AREAS OF INTEREST:
Conservation and nature.

TYPE:
Project/program grants.

YEAR PROGRAM STARTED: 1976

PURPOSE:
To support projects that directly promote the study, conservation and appreciation of nature.

ELIGIBILITY:
Organizations must be 501(c)(3) tax-exempt. No funding for individuals.

FINANCIAL DATA:
Amount of support per award: $2,500 to $10,000.

Total amount of support: Approximately $200,000 annually.

NUMBER OF AWARDS: Approximately 30.

APPLICATION INFORMATION:
Complete application instructions are available on the Trust web site.

Astronomy and aerospace science

AMERICAN ASTRONOMICAL SOCIETY [2046]

2000 Florida Avenue, N.W.
Suite 400
Washington, DC 20009-1231
(202) 328-2010
Fax: (202) 234-2560

E-MAIL ADDRESS:
marvel@aas.org

WEB SITE ADDRESS:
www.aas.org

FOUNDED: 1899

AREAS OF INTEREST:
The advancement of astronomy and closely related branches of science.

NAME(S) OF PROGRAMS:
● **Chrétien International Research Grant**

TYPE:
Research grants. Research grant(s) with preference given to individuals of high promise who are otherwise unfunded.

YEAR PROGRAM STARTED: 1982

PURPOSE:
To further international collaborative projects in observational astronomy, with emphasis on long-term international visits and the development of close working relationship with astronomers in other countries.

LEGAL BASIS:
Nonprofit, scientific corporation.

ELIGIBILITY:
Astronomers with a Ph.D. or equivalent are eligible. Graduate students are not eligible.

FINANCIAL DATA:
Amount of support per award: Up to $20,000.

Total amount of support: $20,000 each year.

NUMBER OF APPLICANTS MOST RECENT YEAR: 20.

NUMBER OF AWARDS: 1.

APPLICATION INFORMATION:
Application and all supporting materials should be submitted electronically to Kelly Clark at grants@aas.org. Applications should include:
(1) a description of the research project (less than three pages in length), including an assessment of its importance to that particular subfield of astronomy and a statement enumerating all the aspects of international collaboration;
(2) a statement of the candidate's ability to do the proposed research, with special emphasis on international collaboration and foreign visits which have been arranged, including facilities available and observing time allocations, if any;
(3) the proposed budget, with brief justification for the amount requested;
(4) a description of other financial resources available;
(5) the candidate's curriculum vitae and bibliography of recent papers;
(6) two letters of reference from astronomers who know the candidate's work and;
(7) any special circumstances which might help in the decision process.
Duration: One year.
Deadline: Application due April 1. Announcement the following September.

ADDRESS INQUIRIES TO:
Kelly Clark
E-mail: grants@aas.org

AMERICAN ASTRONOMICAL SOCIETY [2047]

2000 Florida Avenue, N.W.
Suite 400
Washington, DC 20009-1231
(202) 328-2010
Fax: (202) 234-2560

E-MAIL ADDRESS:
marvel@aas.org

WEB SITE ADDRESS:
www.aas.org/grants/awards.html

FOUNDED: 1899

AREAS OF INTEREST:
Astronomy and closely related branches of science.

NAME(S) OF PROGRAMS:
● **Newton Lacy Pierce Prize in Astronomy**

TYPE:
Awards/prizes. Given to recognize outstanding achievement during the five years preceding the award in observational astronomical research based on measurements of radiation from an astronomical object. A monetary prize and certificate are awarded annually.

YEAR PROGRAM STARTED: 1974

LEGAL BASIS:
Nonprofit, scientific corporation.

ELIGIBILITY:
Applicants must be residents of North America (including Hawaii or Puerto Rico) or a member of a North American institution stationed abroad. Applicants should also be under 36 years of age.

FINANCIAL DATA:
Amount of support per award: $1,500.
Total amount of support: $1,500.

NUMBER OF AWARDS: 1.

APPLICATION INFORMATION:
Contact the Society regarding application materials and requirements.

PUBLICATIONS:
Program announcement.

ADDRESS INQUIRIES TO:
Dr. G. Fritz Benedict, Secretary
American Astronomical Society
University of Texas-Austin
McDonald Observatory
Austin, TX 78712-1083

ASTRONOMICAL SOCIETY OF THE PACIFIC [2048]
390 Ashton Avenue
San Francisco, CA 94112
(415) 337-1100
Fax: (415) 337-5205

E-MAIL ADDRESS:
awards@astrosociety.org

WEB SITE ADDRESS:
www.astrosociety.org

FOUNDED: 1889

AREAS OF INTEREST:
Astronomy and science education.

NAME(S) OF PROGRAMS:
● **Maria and Eric Muhlmann Award**

TYPE:
Awards/prizes.

YEAR PROGRAM STARTED: 1995

PURPOSE:
To improve significant observational research, possibly through advances in astronomical instrumentation, software or support infrastructure.

ELIGIBILITY:
Award is available to individuals. Applicants do not have to be U.S. citizens or residents.

FINANCIAL DATA:
Amount of support per award: $500 and plaque.
Total amount of support: $500 each year.

APPLICATION INFORMATION:
Sponsors should submit a two-page nomination giving strong support to the choice.
Duration: One year.
Deadline: January 1.

ADDRESS INQUIRIES TO:
Dr. Linda Shore, Executive Director
(See address above.)

ASTRONOMICAL SOCIETY OF THE PACIFIC [2049]
390 Ashton Avenue
San Francisco, CA 94112
(415) 337-1100
Fax: (415) 337-5205

E-MAIL ADDRESS:
jmanning@astrosociety.org

WEB SITE ADDRESS:
www.astrosociety.org

AREAS OF INTEREST:
Astronomy.

NAME(S) OF PROGRAMS:
● **Klumpke-Roberts Award**

TYPE:
Awards/prizes.

PURPOSE:
To recognize outstanding contributions to the public understanding and appreciation of astronomy.

ELIGIBILITY:
There are no restrictions on nominations for this award. The contributions may be in the form of popular books and articles; lectures; radio, TV or movie productions; or service to public education in astronomy of any other nature.

FINANCIAL DATA:
Award includes travel reimbursement and hotel accommodation to annual meeting.

Amount of support per award: $500 and plaque.

NUMBER OF APPLICANTS MOST RECENT YEAR:
12.

NUMBER OF AWARDS: 1.

APPLICATION INFORMATION:
Nominations only. Self-nominations are not accepted.
Deadline: January 1.

ADDRESS INQUIRIES TO:
James G. Manning, Executive Director
(See e-mail address above.)

ASTRONOMICAL SOCIETY OF THE PACIFIC [2050]
390 Ashton Avenue
San Francisco, CA 94112
(415) 337-1100
Fax: (415) 337-5205

E-MAIL ADDRESS:
jmanning@astrosociety.org

WEB SITE ADDRESS:
www.astrosociety.org

AREAS OF INTEREST:
Astronomy.

NAME(S) OF PROGRAMS:
● **Thomas Brennan Award for Outstanding Contributions to the Teaching of Astronomy in Grades 9-12**

TYPE:
Awards/prizes.

PURPOSE:
To recognize exceptional achievement related to the teaching of astronomy at the high school level.

ELIGIBILITY:
Nominees must reside in North America.

GEOGRAPHIC RESTRICTIONS:
North America.

FINANCIAL DATA:
Award includes travel reimbursement and hotel accommodation to annual meeting.
Amount of support per award: $500 and plaque.

NUMBER OF APPLICANTS MOST RECENT YEAR:
8.

NUMBER OF AWARDS: 1.

APPLICATION INFORMATION:
Nominations must be made on the Brennan Award form, available on the web site. Neither self-nominations nor nomination by a family member will be accepted.
Deadline: January 1.

ADDRESS INQUIRIES TO:
James G. Manning, Executive Director
(See e-mail address above.)

ASTRONOMICAL SOCIETY OF THE PACIFIC [2051]
390 Ashton Avenue
San Francisco, CA 94112
(415) 337-1100
Fax: (415) 337-5205

E-MAIL ADDRESS:
jmanning@astrosociety.org

WEB SITE ADDRESS:
www.astrosociety.org

AREAS OF INTEREST:
Astronomy and amateur astronomy.

NAME(S) OF PROGRAMS:
● **Amateur Achievement Award**
● **Las Cumbres Amateur Outreach Award**

TYPE:
Awards/prizes. Amateur Achievement Award recognizes significant observational or technological contributions to astronomy or amateur astronomy.

Las Cumbres Amateur Outreach Award honors outstanding educational outreach by an amateur astronomer to K-12 children and the interested lay public.

PURPOSE:
To award outstanding contribution or educational outreach in the field of astronomy or amateur astronomy.

ELIGIBILITY:
Amateur Achievement Award: Nominees must not be employed as professional astronomers.

Las Cumbres Amateur Outreach Award: Nominee must not receive compensation (other than expenses) for their activitiy and not receive the majority of their income from a profession in astronomy.

FINANCIAL DATA:
Awards include travel reimbursement and hotel accommodation to annual meeting.
Amount of support per award: $500 and plaque.

NUMBER OF APPLICANTS MOST RECENT YEAR:
11.

NUMBER OF AWARDS: 1 per award.

APPLICATION INFORMATION:
Nominations are made from the ASP Amateur Advisory Committee and by members of the astronomical community. Self-nominations or nomination by a family member will not be accepted. Letters of support are required.
Deadline: January 1. Announcements in spring.

ADDRESS INQUIRIES TO:
James G. Manning, Executive Director
(See e-mail address above.)

LUNAR AND PLANETARY INSTITUTE [2052]
3600 Bay Area Boulevard
Houston, TX 77058
(281) 486-2159
Fax: (281) 486-2127

E-MAIL ADDRESS:
internprogram@lpi.usra.edu

WEB SITE ADDRESS:
www.lpi.usra.edu

FOUNDED: 1968

AREAS OF INTEREST:
Study of lunar exploration, planetary remote sensing and spectroscopy, image processing, planetary geology and surface processes, impact studies, geophysical data analysis and modeling, physics and chemistry of planetary atmospheres, meteorites and sample analysis, interplanetary dust and presolar grains, minerology/petrology and astrobiology.

NAME(S) OF PROGRAMS:
● **Lunar Exploration Summer Intern Program**

TYPE:
Conferences/seminars; Internships; Scholarships; Travel grants.

YEAR PROGRAM STARTED: 1969

PURPOSE:
To promote and assist in the analysis and interpretation of lunar and planetary data.

ELIGIBILITY:
College graduate students in geology, planetary science, and related programs are eligible. Preference will be given to graduate students, but applications from excellent undergraduate students will be considered. Applicants will be considered for appointment without regard to race, creed, color, sex, national origin, age, handicap status or other non-merit factors.

FINANCIAL DATA:
Amount of support per award: Selected interns will receive a $5,000 stipend to cover the costs associated with being in Houston for the duration of the program. Additionally, U.S. citizens will receive up to $1,000 in travel expense reimbursement and foreign nationals will receive up to $1,500 in travel expense reimbursement.

APPLICATION INFORMATION:
Applications are only accepted using the electronic application form found on the Institute web site.
Duration: 10-week program, May through August.
Deadline: January.

ADDRESS INQUIRIES TO:
See e-mail address above.

MCDONNELL CENTER FOR THE SPACE SCIENCES
Washington University, Campus Box 1105
One Brookings Drive
St. Louis, MO 63130-4899
(314) 935-5332

E-MAIL ADDRESS:
trecia@physics.wustl.edu

WEB SITE ADDRESS:
mcss.wustl.edu

TYPE:
Fellowships. These fellowships are funded by a gift from the McDonnell Douglas Foundation to Washington University and provide tuition remission plus stipend for graduate students interested in pursuing research in the space sciences who are enrolled in the Washington University Departments of Physics or Earth and Planetary Sciences.

See entry 2623 for full listing.

NATIONAL CENTER FOR ATMOSPHERIC RESEARCH   [2053]
High Altitude Observatory
P.O. Box 3000
Boulder, CO 80307-3000
(303) 497-1598
Fax: (303) 497-1589

E-MAIL ADDRESS:
rivas@ucar.edu

WEB SITE ADDRESS:
www.hao.ucar.edu/people/visitors/newkirk.php

FOUNDED: 1940

AREAS OF INTEREST:
Solar physics, solar-terrestrial physics and related astrophysics. Specific research interests include coronal and interplanetary physics, solar activity and magnetic fields, the solar interior and terrestrial interactions.

NAME(S) OF PROGRAMS:
● **Newkirk Graduate Research Assistantships**

TYPE:
Assistantships.

PURPOSE:
To promote cooperative research between HAO and academic institutions by providing support for aspiring young scientists at formative stages in their careers.

ELIGIBILITY:
Applicants must be full-time graduate students enrolled in a university program leading to the Ph.D. Students must declare their intention of working on their thesis in cooperation with an HAO staff member and should expect to spend a significant fraction of their time in residence at HAO.

FINANCIAL DATA:
Total amount of support: $42,000.

APPLICATION INFORMATION:
Application includes transcripts of undergraduate and graduate courses, brief statement of goals and three letters of recommendation.
Duration: One-year term with possibility of renewals until completion of the Ph.D. degree.
Deadline: January.

PUBLICATIONS:
Brochure.

ADDRESS INQUIRIES TO:
Teresa Rivas
(See address above.)

NATIONAL RADIO ASTRONOMY OBSERVATORY   [2054]
520 Edgemont Road
Charlottesville, VA 22903-2475
(434) 296-0221
Fax: (434) 296-0385

E-MAIL ADDRESS:
jutley@nrao.edu

WEB SITE ADDRESS:
www.nrao.edu

FOUNDED: 1957

AREAS OF INTEREST:
Ground-based radio astronomy. Current areas of research include cosmology, theoretical and observational studies of radio sources, the interstellar and intergalactic medium, structure and dynamics of galactic and extragalactic sources, physics of HII regions, stars, solar system objects and astrometry.

NAME(S) OF PROGRAMS:
● **Jansky Fellowships at the NRAO**

TYPE:
Fellowships. Research appointments. Postdoctoral appointments with liberal support for research travel, data reduction and publication. Jansky Fellows may or may not be residents at NRAO sites.

YEAR PROGRAM STARTED: 1960

LEGAL BASIS:
Federally funded research organization.

ELIGIBILITY:
Fellows must have received their Ph.D. prior to beginning the appointment. Preference is given to recent Ph.D. recipients.

FINANCIAL DATA:
Vacation accrual, health insurance, a moving allowance and other benefits available.
Amount of support per award: Annual salary $63,000, plus $10,000 travel budget per year.

NUMBER OF APPLICANTS MOST RECENT YEAR: 98.

NUMBER OF AWARDS: 4 for the year 2013-14.

APPLICATION INFORMATION:
Application should include a curriculum vitae and a statement of the type of research activity to be undertaken at the NRAO. The applicant should request letters of recommendation from three references. These letters should be sent directly to the NRAO.
Duration: Two years. Possibility of renewal for a third year if mutually agreeable.
Deadline: On or around November 1 of each year.

PUBLICATIONS:
Program announcement.

ADDRESS INQUIRIES TO:
Jessica Utley
Science and Academic Affairs
(See address above.)

NATIONAL SCIENCE FOUNDATION   [2055]
Division of Astronomical Sciences
4201 Wilson Boulevard, Room 1045
Arlington, VA 22230
(703) 292-8820
Fax: (703) 292-9034

E-MAIL ADDRESS:
julvesta@nsf.gov

WEB SITE ADDRESS:
www.nsf.gov

FOUNDED: 1950

NAME(S) OF PROGRAMS:
● **Astronomy and Astrophysics Research Grants**

TYPE:
Awards/prizes; Challenge/matching grants; Conferences/seminars; Fellowships; Project/program grants; Research grants; Seed money grants; Travel grants; Research contracts. Broad base of support for fundamental research directed at explaining celestial objects and the cosmos in terms of physical principles.

Basic research support is provided under the following grant programs:

Planetary Astronomy - Objects studied in this program include the planets and their satellites, the asteroids and the comets. Ground-based observations are indispensable to the complete understanding of their structure, composition and origin.

Stellar Astronomy and Astrophysics - This program supports studies of the physical and chemical characteristics of the Sun and other stars, especially as they relate to the stars' past and future evolution. These studies make use of observations at many wavelengths, as well as laboratory measurements and theoretical modeling.

Galactic Astronomy - The topics studied in this program are the spatial and kinematics characteristics of the stars in our galaxy and the properties and distribution of the interstellar medium.

Extragalactic Astronomy and Cosmology - The objective of this program is the description of the nature, structure and evolution of external galaxies and quasars, as well as the implications of these data for the birth, expansion rate and future of the universe.

Advanced Technologies and Instrumentation - This program provides support for development of astronomical equipment at universities. In addition to supporting the acquisition of telescopes and auxiliary instrumentation, this program also supports the reduction of astronomical data by providing funds for minicomputers. Particular emphasis is being placed on the use of advanced technology detectors at radio, infrared and optical wavelengths.

PURPOSE:
To support research and education in astronomy and astrophysics.

LEGAL BASIS:
Government agency.

ELIGIBILITY:
NSF eligibility criteria apply.

GEOGRAPHIC RESTRICTIONS:
United States.

FINANCIAL DATA:
Amount of support per award: Varies.
Total amount of support: Varies.

APPLICATION INFORMATION:
Application information can be obtained from the Foundation.
Duration: Varies.
Deadline: November 15 for all Planetary, Stellar, Galactic and Extragalactic.

PUBLICATIONS:
Guide to Programs; *Grants for Scientific and Engineering Research.*

OFFICERS:
Jim Ulvestad, Division Director

ADDRESS INQUIRIES TO:
Jim Ulvestad, Division Director
(See address and e-mail above.)

SMITHSONIAN ASTROPHYSICAL OBSERVATORY [2056]

60 Garden Street
Mail Stop 67
Cambridge, MA 02138
(617) 495-7103
Fax: (617) 496-7589

E-MAIL ADDRESS:
predoc@cfa.harvard.edu

WEB SITE ADDRESS:
www.cfa.harvard.edu/opportunities/fellowships/predoc

FOUNDED: 1890

AREAS OF INTEREST:
Astrophysical research, including the fields of astronomy, astrophysics and planetary sciences.

NAME(S) OF PROGRAMS:
● **Predoctoral Research Fellowships**

TYPE:
Exchange programs; Fellowships; Internships. Predoctoral fellowships for thesis research. Fellowships are designed to allow students from other institutions throughout the world to do all or part of their thesis research at the Observatory. A wide variety of research projects may be proposed. About 300 scientific staff conduct research in observation, theory and instrumentation, and in nearly all areas related to astronomy.

YEAR PROGRAM STARTED: 1985

ELIGIBILITY:
Applicants must be enrolled in a Ph.D. program in appropriate fields (i.e., astronomy or astrophysics) and have completed all course work and examinations.

Applicants must be ready to begin dissertation research at the time of the award. They must have the approval of their department head at their home institution to conduct their thesis research at the Observatory. Students from any country are eligible.

FINANCIAL DATA:
Some funds may be available for relocation, travel and other expenses.
Amount of support per award: $33,204 for the year 2014.

NUMBER OF APPLICANTS MOST RECENT YEAR: 7 for the year 2013.

NUMBER OF AWARDS: 11 for the year 2012.

APPLICATION INFORMATION:
Application forms are available on the web site.
Duration: Six months. Renewable up to three years.
Deadline: Proposals are reviewed on an ongoing basis.

STAFF:
Charles R. Alcock, Director

ADDRESS INQUIRIES TO:
Christine Crowley
Fellowship Program Coordinator
(See address above.)

SMITHSONIAN ASTROPHYSICAL OBSERVATORY [2057]

Mail Stop 67
60 Garden Street
Cambridge, MA 02138
(617) 495-7103
Fax: (617) 496-7589

E-MAIL ADDRESS:
postdoc@cfa.harvard.edu

WEB SITE ADDRESS:
www.cfa.harvard.edu/opportunities/postdocs.html

FOUNDED: 1973

AREAS OF INTEREST:
Astrophysics, including the areas of theory, observation, instrumentation and/or laboratory research. Research programs at the Center are organized into seven divisions including atomic and molecular physics, high energy astrophysics, optical and infrared astronomy, radio and geoastronomy, solar, stellar and planetary sciences, theoretical astrophysics, and science education.

NAME(S) OF PROGRAMS:
● **Clay Postdoctoral Fellowship**

TYPE:
Fellowships. Postdoctoral fellowships for research in the Center's areas of interest.

YEAR PROGRAM STARTED: 1974

ELIGIBILITY:
Open to recent Ph.D. recipients with interests in any of the areas above.

FINANCIAL DATA:
Amount of support per award: Stipends of approximately $66,500; annual research budget of approximately $16,000 per appointee for the year 2014-15.

NUMBER OF APPLICANTS MOST RECENT YEAR: 254.

NUMBER OF AWARDS: 1 for the year 2014.

APPLICATION INFORMATION:
Application forms are available online.
Duration: Two years. Renewal possible for a third year.
Deadline: October 30.

PUBLICATIONS:
Observatory reports issue of the *Bulletin of the American Astronomical Society.*

STAFF:
Charles R. Alcock, Director

SPACE TELESCOPE SCIENCE INSTITUTE [2058]

3700 San Martin Drive
Baltimore, MD 21218
(410) 338-4574
Fax: (410) 338-4976

E-MAIL ADDRESS:
hfinquiry@stsci.edu

WEB SITE ADDRESS:
www.stsci.edu

FOUNDED: 1990

AREAS OF INTEREST:
Astronomy, astrophysics and related disciplines.

NAME(S) OF PROGRAMS:
● **Hubble Fellowship Program**

TYPE:
Fellowships. Provides a limited number of recent postdoctoral scientists of unusual promise and ability with the opportunity to pursue research of their choice at a participating U.S. astronomical institution designated as host institution by the scientist.

YEAR PROGRAM STARTED: 1990

PURPOSE:
To expand and strengthen the research work of the astronomical community.

ELIGIBILITY:
Applicants must have earned a Doctorate degree, three years prior to application, in physics, astronomy or a related discipline. Applicants can be any nationality. Candidates are selected on the basis of their research proposal, publications and academic achievement. No more than one fellow per year is approved for any one academic location.

Fellowships must be held at U.S. institutions.

FINANCIAL DATA:
Amount of support per award: Annual stipend of approximately $62,500, plus $16,000 per year for research expenses.
Total amount of support: Varies.

COOPERATIVE FUNDING PROGRAMS: Funded by the National Aeronautics and Space Administration (NASA).

NUMBER OF APPLICANTS MOST RECENT YEAR: 280 for the year 2013.

NUMBER OF AWARDS: 17.

APPLICATION INFORMATION:
Application information is available on the web site.

Duration: One year and two annual renewals contingent on satisfactory performance and availability of NASA funds.

Deadline: First week in November.

ADDRESS INQUIRIES TO:
Dr. Ron Allen, Program Director
Hubble Fellowship Program
(See address above.)

ZONTA INTERNATIONAL FOUNDATION   [2059]

1211 West 22nd Street, Suite 900
Oak Brook, IL 60523-3384
(630) 928-1400
Fax: (630) 928-1559

E-MAIL ADDRESS:
programs@zonta.org

WEB SITE ADDRESS:
www.zonta.org

FOUNDED: 1919

AREAS OF INTEREST:
Aerospace-related sciences or aerospace-related engineering.

NAME(S) OF PROGRAMS:
● **Amelia Earhart Fellowship**

TYPE:
Fellowships. Awarded annually to women for graduate study in aerospace-related sciences or aerospace-related engineering at any university or college offering accredited graduate courses and degrees.

YEAR PROGRAM STARTED: 1938

PURPOSE:
To encourage and support the study and research of women scientists and engineers throughout the world and to improve the status of women.

LEGAL BASIS:
Incorporated in the state of Illinois as a nonprofit organization.

ELIGIBILITY:
Women of any nationality who must meet the following minimum requirements:
(1) be registered in an accredited Ph.D./doctoral program in a qualifying area of science or engineering closely related to advanced studies in aerospace-related science or aerospace-related engineering; a letter of acceptance or verification of enrollment must be submitted with the application;
(2) demonstrate a superior academic record at a recognized university or college with accredited courses in aerospace-related studies as verified by transcripts and recommendations;
(3) provide evidence of a well-defined research program in aerospace-related science or aerospace-related engineering as described in the application essay, research and publications;
(4) clearly demonstrate the relationship of their research to aerospace and furnish verification of their research program through at least one of the reference letters required with the application (i.e., research supervisor or advisor must be one of the referees) and;

(5) be registered in a Ph.D./Doctorate program by the time the Fellowship is awarded.

The award may be used at any university or college offering accredited graduate courses and degrees in aerospace studies. Awards may be renewed for an additional year by a current Fellow and will undergo the same application and evaluation procedures as first-time applicants. Fellows may accept additional grants and scholarships from other sources.

Defense-related and postdoctoral research programs are not eligible for the Fellowship. Members and employees of Zonta International or the Zonta International Foundation are also not eligible to apply for the Fellowships.

FINANCIAL DATA:
Fellowship awards may be used for tuition, books, fees or living expenses.
Amount of support per award: $10,000 annually.

NUMBER OF AWARDS: 35 per year.

APPLICATION INFORMATION:
Applications can be secured from the Foundation web site. Elements to be included are biographical information, list of schools attended and degrees received, transcripts of grades and school verification form (on Foundation web site), employment history, plans for intended study, essay on academic and professional goals, and three recommendations from teachers or supervisors. Information other than transcripts and recommendations must be limited to the space provided. Attachments will not be considered.

The application must be completed in English. In addition, international applicants must provide English translations for all non-English documents.
Duration: One academic year. Recipient may reapply for a second year.
Deadline: November 15.

AWARDS COMMITTEE:
Sharon Langenbeck, Chairman

ADDRESS INQUIRIES TO:
Megan Radavich, Programs Manager
(See address above.)

Chemistry

AMERICAN CHEMICAL SOCIETY   [2060]

1155 16th Street, N.W.
Washington, DC 20036-4800
(202) 872-6283
Fax: (202) 776-8008

E-MAIL ADDRESS:
awards@acs.org

WEB SITE ADDRESS:
www.acs.org/nationalawards

FOUNDED: 1876

AREAS OF INTEREST:
Chemical.

CONSULTING OR VOLUNTEER SERVICES:
Volunteer services.

NAME(S) OF PROGRAMS:
● **Nakanishi Prize**

TYPE:
Awards/prizes. Award presented in the U.S. in odd years and Japan in even years.

YEAR PROGRAM STARTED: 1995

PURPOSE:
To recognize and stimulate significant work that extends chemical and spectroscopic methods to the study of important biological phenomena.

LEGAL BASIS:
Nonprofit association.

ELIGIBILITY:
Individuals can apply. There are no limits on age or nationality.

FINANCIAL DATA:
Amount of support per award: $5,000, plus up to $2,500 travel allowance, medallion with presentation box and certificate.

NUMBER OF APPLICANTS MOST RECENT YEAR: 6 for the year 2013.

NUMBER OF AWARDS: 1.

APPLICATION INFORMATION:
Application procedures are available online.
Duration: Nomination renewable.
Deadline: November 1.

ADDRESS INQUIRIES TO:
Office of Awards
(See address above.)

*SPECIAL STIPULATIONS:
Special consideration will be given for work that has contributed broadly on an international scope.

AMERICAN CHEMICAL SOCIETY   [2061]

1155 16th Street, N.W.
Washington, DC 20036-4800
(202) 872-6283
Fax: (202) 776-8008

E-MAIL ADDRESS:
awards@acs.org

WEB SITE ADDRESS:
www.acs.org/awards

FOUNDED: 1876

AREAS OF INTEREST:
Research in industrial and engineering chemistry and chemical engineering principles.

NAME(S) OF PROGRAMS:
● **E.V. Murphree Award in Industrial and Engineering Chemistry**

TYPE:
Awards/prizes.

YEAR PROGRAM STARTED: 1955

PURPOSE:
To stimulate fundamental research in industrial and engineering chemistry, the development of chemical engineering principles and their application to industrial processes.

LEGAL BASIS:
Nonprofit association.

ELIGIBILITY:
Individuals can apply. Nominee must have accomplished outstanding research of theoretical or experimental nature in fields of industrial chemistry or chemical engineering. There are no limits on age or nationality.

FINANCIAL DATA:
Amount of support per award: $5,000, certificate, and up to $1,000 travel expenses.

NUMBER OF APPLICANTS MOST RECENT YEAR:
12 for the year 2014.

NUMBER OF AWARDS: 1.

APPLICATION INFORMATION:
Application procedures are available online.
Duration: One year. Nominations renewable.
Deadline: November 1.

ADDRESS INQUIRIES TO:
Office of Awards
(See address above.)

AMERICAN NUCLEAR SOCIETY (ANS) [2062]
555 North Kensington Avenue
LaGrange Park, IL 60526
(708) 352-6611
Fax: (708) 352-0499

E-MAIL ADDRESS:
outreach@ans.org

WEB SITE ADDRESS:
www.ans.org

FOUNDED: 1954

AREAS OF INTEREST:
Radioanalytical chemistry or analytical
applications of nuclear science.

NAME(S) OF PROGRAMS:
● **James R. Vogt Radiochemistry Scholarship**

TYPE:
Scholarships. Scholarship award to recognize
one outstanding undergraduate student or one
graduate student pursuing a career in
radioanalytical chemistry or analytical
applications of nuclear science.

YEAR PROGRAM STARTED: 1987

ELIGIBILITY:
Applicants must have completed a minimum
of two years in an accredited undergraduate
program and be enrolled in a four-year
college or university in the U.S. and must be
U.S. citizens or possess a permanent resident
visa. Also open to first-year graduate
students. Academic accomplishments must be
substantiated by transcript. Graduate students
must have completed their first year of
graduate studies to be eligible. Applicants
must be sponsored by an ANS local section,
division, student branch, committee, member
or organization member.

FINANCIAL DATA:
Scholarship funds may be used by the
student to defray any bona fide education
costs including tuition, fees, books, room and
board.
Amount of support per award:
Undergraduate: $2,000; Graduate: $3,000.

NUMBER OF AWARDS: 1 annually.

APPLICATION INFORMATION:
Applications are made on a form available
from ANS headquarters at the address above.
The applicant must check the "Vogt" box on
the scholarship form to be considered for this
scholarship. Please provide a self-addressed,
stamped envelope. In addition, applicant must
include year in school, major and the school
he or she will be attending. Application is
available online.
Duration: One year. Nonrenewable.
Deadline: February 1.

ADDRESS INQUIRIES TO:
Scholarship Coordinator
(See address above.)

AMERICAN OIL CHEMISTS SOCIETY [2063]
2710 South Boulder Drive
Urbana, IL 61802-6996
(217) 359-2344
Fax: (217) 351-8091

E-MAIL ADDRESS:
awards@aocs.org

WEB SITE ADDRESS:
www.aocs.org

FOUNDED: 1909

AREAS OF INTEREST:
Lipid chemistry, biochemistry, fats, oils and
related materials, surfactants and detergents,
and personal care products.

NAME(S) OF PROGRAMS:
● **Stephen S. Chang Award**
● **Schroepfer Medal Award**
● **Supelco AOCS Research Award**

TYPE:
Awards/prizes.

YEAR PROGRAM STARTED: 1982

PURPOSE:
To annually recognize scientists,
technologists or engineers who have made
substantial accomplishments in lipid
chemistry, either by one major breakthrough
or by an accumulation of publications.

LEGAL BASIS:
Professional society.

ELIGIBILITY:
Nominations are accepted. Preference shall
be given to individuals who are actively
associated with research and who have made
discoveries that have influenced their fields of
endeavor.

FINANCIAL DATA:
Amount of support per award: Varies.

NUMBER OF APPLICANTS MOST RECENT YEAR:
15.

NUMBER OF AWARDS: Chang Award and
Supelco Award: 1 of each annually.
Schroepfer Medal: 1 biennially in
even-numbered years.

APPLICATION INFORMATION:
Nominations for the Chang Award must
include a letter from the nominator
describing the nominee's distinguished
accomplishments in basic research and how
they have been utilized by industry to help
improve or develop products related to lipids.
The nomination must include at least three
letters of recommendation and biographical
information, including the curriculum vitae.

Nominations for the Supelco Award consist
of the same supporting documentation as the
Chang Award.

Nominations for the Schroepfer Medal should
include a 300- to 1,000-word summary
describing the significance of the nominee's
accomplishments in the steriod field, a
current curriculum vitae including a full list
of publications, and two supporting letters.
Duration: One-time awards.
Deadline: October 15 for the Chang Award
and Schroepfer Medal; November 1 for the
Supelco Award.

PUBLICATIONS:
*INFORM: International News on Fats, Oils,
and Related Materials*; *JAOCS: Journal of
the American Oil Chemists' Society*; *Lipids*;
Journal of Surfactants and Detergents.

ADDRESS INQUIRIES TO:
Membership Department
(See address above.)

CANADIAN SOCIETY FOR CHEMICAL TECHNOLOGY [2064]
130 Slater Street
Suite 550
Ottawa ON K1P 6E2 Canada
(613) 232-6252 ext. 223
Fax: (613) 232-5862

E-MAIL ADDRESS:
awards@cheminst.ca

WEB SITE ADDRESS:
www.cheminst.ca/awards

AREAS OF INTEREST:
Chemistry, biochemistry, chemical
engineering technology or chemical
technology.

NAME(S) OF PROGRAMS:
● **Norman and Marion Bright Memorial Award**

TYPE:
Awards/prizes.

YEAR PROGRAM STARTED: 1980

PURPOSE:
To reward an individual who has made an
outstanding contribution in Canada to the
furtherance of chemical technology.

ELIGIBILITY:
The person honored must be either a
chemical sciences technologist or a person
from outside the field who had made a
significant or noteworthy contribution to its
advancement.

GEOGRAPHIC RESTRICTIONS:
Canada.

FINANCIAL DATA:
Amount of support per award: $500.

NUMBER OF AWARDS: 1.

APPLICATION INFORMATION:
Applicants must complete a nomination form.
Deadline: December 1.

ADDRESS INQUIRIES TO:
Gale Thirlwall, Awards Manager
(See address above.)

CANADIAN SOCIETY FOR CHEMISTRY [2065]
130 Slater Street
Suite 550
Ottawa ON K1P 6E2 Canada
(613) 232-6252 ext. 223
Fax: (613) 232-5862

E-MAIL ADDRESS:
awards@cheminst.ca

WEB SITE ADDRESS:
www.cheminst.ca/awards

AREAS OF INTEREST:
Biochemistry, organic and bioorganic
chemistry.

NAME(S) OF PROGRAMS:
● **CCUCC Chemistry Doctoral Award**

TYPE:
Awards/prizes. CCUCC Chemistry Doctoral
Award recognizes outstanding achievement
and potential in research by a graduate
student.

PURPOSE:
To recognize outstanding contributions by chemists for their research in a wide variety of fields.

ELIGIBILITY:
CCUCC Chemistry Doctoral Award is intended to recognize outstanding achievement and potential in research by a graduate student whose Ph.D. thesis in chemistry was formally accepted by a Canadian university in the 12-month period preceding the nomination deadline.

FINANCIAL DATA:
Amount of support per award: CCUCC Chemistry Doctoral Award: $2,000.
Total amount of support: Varies.

NUMBER OF AWARDS: CCUCC Chemistry Doctoral Award: 1.

APPLICATION INFORMATION:
Nominations for the CCUCC Chemistry Doctoral Award should include:
(1) letter of support by nominator;
(2) curriculum vitae (using NSERC guidelines);
(3) brief synopsis of doctoral thesis (10 pages double-spaced maximum) and;
(4) copy of the official thesis appraisal. There is an online submission of the nomination.
Deadline: CCUCC Chemistry Doctoral Award: September 15.

PUBLICATIONS:
Program announcement.

ADDRESS INQUIRIES TO:
Gale Thirlwall, Awards Manager
(See address above.)

GEORGETOWN UNIVERSITY   [2066]
Department of Chemistry
Box 571227
Washington, DC 20057-1227
(202) 687-6073
Fax: (202) 687-6209

E-MAIL ADDRESS:
chemad@georgetown.edu

WEB SITE ADDRESS:
chemistry.georgetown.edu

FOUNDED: 1789

AREAS OF INTEREST:
Graduate education in chemistry.

NAME(S) OF PROGRAMS:
● **Doctoral Program in Chemistry**

TYPE:
Assistantships; Awards/prizes; Conferences/seminars; Exchange programs; Fellowships; General operating grants; Professorships; Research grants; Scholarships; Visiting scholars; Work-study programs.

YEAR PROGRAM STARTED: 1924

PURPOSE:
To enable graduate students to earn a Ph.D. degree in chemistry, inorganic, organic, analytical, physical or theoretical chemistry, organometallic, synthetic, or nano-chemistry, biochemistry, or structural crystallography.

LEGAL BASIS:
University.

ELIGIBILITY:
Fellowships are open to nationals of any country and a Bachelor's degree or the equivalent is required.

FINANCIAL DATA:
Amount of support per award: $26,650 stipend, full-time tuition coverage and comprehensive individual medical insurance.

NUMBER OF APPLICANTS MOST RECENT YEAR: 95.

NUMBER OF AWARDS: 10.

APPLICATION INFORMATION:
Application information is available on the web site.
Duration: Nine months to one year. Renewable for as long as student continues good progress toward the degree.
Deadline: Although applications will be accepted at any time, priority deadline is January 15.

PUBLICATIONS:
Graduate Studies in Chemistry, booklet.

DIRECTORS:
Dr. YuYe J. Tong, Professor and Chairperson
Dr. Diana Glick, Professor
Dr. Steven Metallo, Professor

ADDRESS INQUIRIES TO:
Dr. YuYe J. Tong
Professor and Chairperson
(See address above.)

THE HAMNER INSTITUTES FOR HEALTH SCIENCES   [2067]
6 Davis Drive
Research Triangle Park, NC 27709
(919) 558-1331
Fax: (919) 558-1430

E-MAIL ADDRESS:
koverman@thehamner.org

WEB SITE ADDRESS:
www.thehamner.org

FOUNDED: 1974

AREAS OF INTEREST:
All areas of human health and related risk assessment.

NAME(S) OF PROGRAMS:
● **Postdoctoral Fellowship at The Hamner Institutes for Health Sciences**

TYPE:
Conferences/seminars; Fellowships; Internships; Visiting scholars.

YEAR PROGRAM STARTED: 1976

PURPOSE:
To train toxicologists and computational biologists.

LEGAL BASIS:
Nonprofit, 501(c)(3) organization.

ELIGIBILITY:
Candidate must have completed a doctoral degree in a bioscience or related field.

FINANCIAL DATA:
Amount of support per award: $40,000 to $44,000.

NUMBER OF APPLICANTS MOST RECENT YEAR: Over 30.

NUMBER OF AWARDS: 20 ongoing awards.

APPLICATION INFORMATION:
Application information is available on the web site.
Duration: One to three years. Renewal for second and third year contingent on satisfactory performance the first year.

PUBLICATIONS:
Annual report; *The Hamner Activities*, monthly; Index of The Hamner publications available on request.

BOARD OF DIRECTORS:
Charles Hamner, Chairman

ADDRESS INQUIRIES TO:
Human Resources Department
(See address above.)

NATIONAL MOLE DAY FOUNDATION   [2068]
3896 Leaman Court
Freeland, MI 48623
(989) 964-8020

E-MAIL ADDRESS:
moleday@hotmail.com

WEB SITE ADDRESS:
www.moleday.org

FOUNDED: 1991

AREAS OF INTEREST:
Chemistry education.

NAME(S) OF PROGRAMS:
● **The George Hague Memorial Travel Award**
● **The Maury Award**
● **National Mole of the Year Award (MOTY)**

TYPE:
Grants-in-aid. The George Hague Memorial Travel Award is given to financially support a young chemistry instructor (with two to five years of chemistry experience) in attending a biennial ChemEd conference.

The Maury Award is given to teachers to support student-centered Mole Day activities (promoting chemistry education).

The National Mole of the Year Award (MOTY) is given to a member of the National Mole Day Foundation who has contributed the most to furthering the cause of Mole Day and chemistry education.

PURPOSE:
To support Mole Day activities in classrooms, schools or communities.

ELIGIBILITY:
Must be a member of the National Mole Day Foundation and be involved with chemical education. Those receiving grants are not eligible again for the following three years.

FINANCIAL DATA:
Amount of support per award: The George Hague Memorial Travel Award: Up to $750; The Maury Award: Up to $200; National Mole of the Year Award (MOTY): $250.

APPLICATION INFORMATION:
Application information is available on the web site.
Deadline: Hague Award: March 1. Maury Award: June 1. National Mole of the Year Award: May 1 of odd-numbered years.

ADDRESS INQUIRIES TO:
Rebecca Talik, Executive Director
(See address above.)

THE UNIVERSITY OF SYDNEY   [2069]
Scholarships Office
Level 5, Jane Foss Russell Building G02
The University of Sydney N.S.W. 2006
Australia
(02) 8627 8112
Fax: (02) 8627 8485

E-MAIL ADDRESS:
research.training@sydney.edu.au

WEB SITE ADDRESS:
www.sydney.edu.au/scholarships/research

FOUNDED: 1850

AREAS OF INTEREST:
Chemistry in relation to agriculture and industry.

NAME(S) OF PROGRAMS:
● **Henry Bertie and Florence Mabel Gritton Postgraduate Research Scholarships/Fellowships**

TYPE:
Fellowships; Scholarships. Scholarships are awarded for research leading to a higher degree. Fellowships are available for postdoctoral research.

PURPOSE:
To promote the knowledge and study of chemistry in relation to industry and agriculture, including chemistry connected with electrical engineering, metallurgical chemistry and chemistry in its application to mining and the winning and treatment of minerals and natural products of the soil.

LEGAL BASIS:
University.

ELIGIBILITY:
Open to graduates of universities which are members of the Association of Commonwealth Universities or to graduates of any university who are either citizens of a Commonwealth country or who are permanent residents of Australia. Candidates for scholarships must hold at least a first class honours degree. Candidates for Fellowships must hold a Ph.D. degree.

Tenable at the University of Sydney.

FINANCIAL DATA:
Scholarship does not cover tuition fees payable by international students.
Amount of support per award: Scholarships: $24,653 AUD per annum for the year 2013; Fellowships: $78,252 to $83,998 AUD per annum.

NUMBER OF AWARDS: 6 scholarships for the year 2013.

APPLICATION INFORMATION:
Application information is available on the web site.
Duration: Scholarships: Two years for a Master's research degree and three years for a Ph.D.; Fellowships: Tenable for two years.
Deadline: Scholarships: Second week in January and second week in July. Fellowships: As vacancy occurs.

THE ROBERT A. WELCH FOUNDATION [2070]
5555 San Felipe
Suite 1900
Houston, TX 77056-2730
(713) 961-9884
Fax: (713) 961-5168

WEB SITE ADDRESS:
www.welch1.org

FOUNDED: 1954

AREAS OF INTEREST:
Basic research in chemistry.

NAME(S) OF PROGRAMS:
● **Departmental Grants**

● **Research Grants**
● **Welch Summer Scholar Program**

TYPE:
Research grants. Grants to support long-range fundamental research in the broad domain of chemistry.

The Welch Foundation supports chemical research at educational institutions within the state of Texas.

LEGAL BASIS:
Corporate.

ELIGIBILITY:
Full-time regular faculty members at Texas colleges or universities, who are tenured or on the tenured track, are eligible to apply for research grants.

GEOGRAPHIC RESTRICTIONS:
Texas.

FINANCIAL DATA:
Amount of support per award: Minimum $60,000 per year.
Total amount of support: Varies.

NUMBER OF AWARDS: Varies.

APPLICATION INFORMATION:
Application information is available on the web site.
Duration: Two years. Renewable.
Deadline: February 1.

IRS IDENTIFICATION NUMBER: 76-0343128

Earth sciences

AMERICAN ASSOCIATION OF PETROLEUM GEOLOGISTS FOUNDATION [2071]
1444 South Boulder
Tulsa, OK 74119
(855) 302-2743
Fax: (918) 560-2642

E-MAIL ADDRESS:
foundation@aapg.org

WEB SITE ADDRESS:
foundation.aapg.org

FOUNDED: 1917

AREAS OF INTEREST:
The science of geology, especially as it relates to the search and development of hydrocarbons and economic sedimentary minerals and/or to environmental geology as it pertains to the petroleum industry.

NAME(S) OF PROGRAMS:
● **AAPG Foundation Grants-in-Aid**

TYPE:
Grants-in-aid; Research grants.

YEAR PROGRAM STARTED: 1956

PURPOSE:
To foster research in the geosciences by providing support to graduate students in the earth sciences whose research has application to the search for and development of petroleum and energy mineral resources, and to related environmental geology issues.

LEGAL BASIS:
Special-interest foundation.

ELIGIBILITY:
Graduate students in the geological sciences are eligible to apply. Factors weighed in selection of successful applicants include

qualifications of the applicant as indicated by past performance, originality and imagination of the proposed project, support of the department in which the work is being done and perceived significance of the project to science and industry. The program focuses on support of qualified Master's candidates. Qualified doctoral candidates with expenses outside the usual scope of funding by other agencies are also encouraged to apply.

Grants are based on merit and, in part, on the financial needs of the applicant.

Applicants are eligible to receive awards twice as long as they remain qualified graduate students.

FINANCIAL DATA:
Grants are to be applied to selected expenses of graduate study such as a summer of field work, etc. Funds may not be used for tuition, room and board, capital expenses, to pay salaries or attend conferences.
Amount of support per award: Grants not to exceed $3,000.
Total amount of support: $207,750 for the year 2013-14.

NUMBER OF APPLICANTS MOST RECENT YEAR:
Over 375 for the year 2013-14.

NUMBER OF AWARDS: 91 for the year 2013-14.

APPLICATION INFORMATION:
Applications must be submitted electronically. A completed application includes:
(1) applicant name and contact information;
(2) academic and employment history;
(3) a project summary;
(4) description of the research project (limited to 300 words);
(5) project budget and funding request;
(6) disclose if applicant has been a previous recipient of an AAPG Foundation grant;
(7) name and e-mail address for two separate references qualified to endorse the applicant and project and;
(8) official academic transcripts from the last two years (or equivalent).
Duration: One year.
Deadline: January 31. Announcement in early April.

PUBLICATIONS:
Explorer, magazine; annual report; application guidelines.

IRS IDENTIFICATION NUMBER: 73-1298684

OFFICER:
David Curtiss, Executive Director
David Lange, Deputy Executive Director

ADDRESS INQUIRIES TO:
Tamra Campbell, Program Coordinator
(See address above.)

*PLEASE NOTE:
This program is intended for support of individuals only in earth sciences related to the petroleum industry.

THE AMERICAN GEOSCIENCES INSTITUTE (AGI) [2072]
4220 King Street
Alexandria, VA 22302-1502
(703) 379-2480 ext. 227
Fax: (703) 379-7563

E-MAIL ADDRESS:
wallacescholarship@agiweb.org

WEB SITE ADDRESS:
www.agiweb.org/scholarships/wallace

FOUNDED: 1948

AREAS OF INTEREST:
Major study in the fields of geology, geophysics, geochemistry, hydrology, meteorology, physical oceanography, planetary geology and earth-science education.

NAME(S) OF PROGRAMS:
● **Harriet Evelyn Wallace Scholarship**

TYPE:
Scholarships. The Harriet Evelyn Wallace Scholarship is available for female students pursuing a Master's or Doctorate degree at an accredited institution of higher education in a recognized geoscience program.

YEAR PROGRAM STARTED: 2013

PURPOSE:
To increase the participation of female students in the geosciences by providing financial support.

LEGAL BASIS:
Nonprofit, tax-exempt scientific federation.

ELIGIBILITY:
The successful applicant will be a thesis-based, full-time student and must be a U.S. citizen or permanent resident. Applicants will be evaluated on their probability of successfully completing a geoscience graduate program and transitioning into the geoscience profession following graduation. The successful applicant will have an undergraduate grade point average of 3.25 or higher and a graduate grade point average of 3.0 or higher. In addition, all applicants must be active members of at least one of AGI's professional member societies.

GEOGRAPHIC RESTRICTIONS:
United States.

FINANCIAL DATA:
Amount of support per award: $5,000 per year.

COOPERATIVE FUNDING PROGRAMS: Funding for the Wallace Scholarship is from a bequest by Harriet Evelyn Wallace, a founding member of the Geoscience Information Society of AGI.

NUMBER OF AWARDS: 2 per year.

APPLICATION INFORMATION:
Applications may be submitted beginning October 1. Applicants must submit unofficial Graduate Record Examination scores, all postsecondary unofficial academic transcripts, unofficial graduate academic transcripts (if applicable), curriculum vitae or resume, and a 500-word abstract about their research interests. If the applicant is intending on pursuing graduate school, she will need to send proof of acceptance in the program before the award is funded.
Duration: Up to two years.
Deadline: January 31.

ADDRESS INQUIRIES TO:
Workforce Development, Education, Outreach and Scholarship Coordinator
The American Geosciences Institute (AGI)
(See address above.)

AMERICAN METEOROLOGICAL SOCIETY
45 Beacon Street
Boston, MA 02108-3693
(617) 226-3907
Fax: (617) 742-8718

E-MAIL ADDRESS:
dfernandez@ametsoc.org

WEB SITE ADDRESS:
www.ametsoc.org

TYPE:
Fellowships; Scholarships. AMS Freshman Undergraduate Scholarship Program awards funding to high school seniors entering their freshman year of undergraduate study in the fall.

AMS Graduate Fellowship in the History of Science is awarded to a student wishing to complete a dissertation on the history of the atmospheric and related oceanic or hydrologic sciences.

AMS Graduate Fellowships are designed to attract students entering their first year of graduate study in the fall who wish to pursue advanced degrees in the atmospheric and related oceanic and hydrologic sciences.

AMS/Industry Minority Scholarships award funding to high school minority students who have been traditionally underrepresented in the sciences, especially Hispanic, Native American and Black/African American students.

AMS Named Scholarships are directed to students entering their final year of undergraduate study in the fall.

The Father James B. Macelwane Annual Awards in Meteorology are intended to stimulate interest in meteorology among college students through the submission of original student papers concerned with some phase of the atmospheric sciences. The student must be enrolled as an undergraduate at the time the paper was written.

See entry 2620 for full listing.

THE ASSOCIATION OF AMERICAN GEOGRAPHERS   [2073]
1710 16th Street, N.W.
Washington, DC 20009
(202) 234-1450
Fax: (202) 234-2744

E-MAIL ADDRESS:
grantsawards@aag.org

WEB SITE ADDRESS:
www.aag.org

FOUNDED: 1904

NAME(S) OF PROGRAMS:
● **AAG-IGIF Graduate Research Awards**
● **AAG-IGIF Student Paper Awards**
● **AAG-IGIF Student Travel Grants**

TYPE:
Research grants; Travel grants. AAG International Geographic Information Fund offers three types of awards:

Graduate Research Awards support research in any area of spatial analysis or geographic information science or systems.

Student Paper Awards are given in recognition of outstanding papers in any area of spatial analysis or geographic information science or systems that were given at a national and international conference or specialized meeting sponsored by recognized professional organizations.

Student Travel Grant supports travel to national and international symposia or specialized meetings sponsored by recognized professional organizations.

PURPOSE:
To support college and university student career development in the academic areas of applied spatial data analysis or geographic information systems (GIS).

ELIGIBILITY:
Full-time students currently registered in undergraduate or graduate degree programs providing a degree or explicit specialization in some area of applied spatial data analysis or GIS study at a duly accredited and recognized college, university or other educational institution located within the U.S.

FINANCIAL DATA:
Amount of support per award: Graduate Research Award: Up to $500; Student Paper Award: Up to $200; Student Travel Grant: Approximately $500.

APPLICATION INFORMATION:
Digital submissions are required for all applications.

For the Graduate Research Award, applicant must submit a proposal of no more than five pages which includes:
(1) an abstract of research intent;
(2) statement of problem and relevancy;
(3) context of proposed research in the literature;
(4) methodology/research design;
(5) anticipated results and significance of such results;
(6) schedule of research;
(7) budget and;
(8) a letter of recommendation from a faculty member.

For the Student Paper Award, applicant must submit:
(1) a copy of the full paper presented at the conference or event;
(2) a letter requesting consideration for the award and indicating the applicant's present status as a student and;
(3) in the case of papers already presented, evidence of the presentation of the paper or, in the case of papers yet to be presented, evidence of acceptance of the paper to the specific event selected by the applicant for presentation of the paper, clearly identifying the name and dates of the conference.

For the Student Travel Grant, applicants must submit:
(1) a letter of no more than three pages in length specifically addressing how the grant funds will be used, the career goals of the student and how these funds will assist in meeting those goals. This may be supplemented, if necessary, by no more than two pages of supporting illustrations;
(2) a letter from the student's faculty advisor including an endorsement from the chairperson of the applicable department or program;
(3) a brief curriculum vitae of the applicant and;
(4) a copy of the applicant's most recent transcript.
Deadline: December 31.

ADDRESS INQUIRIES TO:
See e-mail address above.

THE ASSOCIATION OF AMERICAN GEOGRAPHERS   [2074]
1710 16th Street, N.W.
Washington, DC 20009
(202) 234-1450
Fax: (202) 234-2744

E-MAIL ADDRESS:
grantsawards@aag.org

WEB SITE ADDRESS:
www.aag.org

FOUNDED: 1904

NAME(S) OF PROGRAMS:
- **AAG Research Grant**

TYPE:
Research grants. Small grant to support research and fieldwork.

PURPOSE:
To support research and fieldwork proposals which offer the prospect of obtaining substantial subsequent support from private foundations or federal agencies and that address questions of major importance to the discipline.

ELIGIBILITY:
Must be an AAG member for at least two years at the time of application. Grants can be used only for direct expenses of research; salary and overhead costs are not allowed. The committee will not approve awards for Master's or doctoral dissertation research.

FINANCIAL DATA:
Amount of support per award: Up to $1,000.

APPLICATION INFORMATION:
Digital submissions are required.
Deadline: December 31.

ADDRESS INQUIRIES TO:
See e-mail address above.

THE ASSOCIATION OF AMERICAN GEOGRAPHERS   [2075]
1710 16th Street, N.W.
Washington, DC 20009
(202) 234-1450
Fax: (202) 234-2744

E-MAIL ADDRESS:
grantsawards@aag.org

WEB SITE ADDRESS:
www.aag.org

FOUNDED: 1904

NAME(S) OF PROGRAMS:
- **AAG Dissertation Research Grants**

TYPE:
Research grants.

PURPOSE:
To provide financial assistance to candidates preparing doctoral dissertations in geography.

ELIGIBILITY:
Must be an AAG member for at least one year at the time of application, must not have a Doctorate at the time of the award, and have completed all Ph.D. requirements except the dissertation by the end of the semester or term following approval of the award. Dissertation supervisor must certify eligibility. The Paul Vouras Fund gives preference to minority student applicants.

FINANCIAL DATA:
Amount of support per award: Up to $500.

APPLICATION INFORMATION:
Digital submissions are required.
Deadline: December 31.

THE ASSOCIATION OF AMERICAN GEOGRAPHERS   [2076]
1710 16th Street, N.W.
Washington, DC 20009
(202) 234-1450
Fax: (202) 234-2744

E-MAIL ADDRESS:
grantsawards@aag.org

WEB SITE ADDRESS:
www.aag.org

FOUNDED: 1904

NAME(S) OF PROGRAMS:
- **AAG Globe Book Award for Public Understanding of Geography**
- **AAG Meridian Book Award for the Outstanding Scholarly Work in Geography**

TYPE:
Awards/prizes. AAG Globe Book Award is awarded annually to a book that conveys most powerfully the nature and importance of geography to the nonacademic world.

AAG Meridian Book Award is awarded annually to a book that makes an unusually important contribution to advancing the science and art of geography.

PURPOSE:
To award outstanding geographic authors.

ELIGIBILITY:
Books must be written or co-authored by a geographer. Books published in the previous calendar year are eligible.

FINANCIAL DATA:
Amount of support per award: $1,000.

APPLICATION INFORMATION:
Nomination statements (two-page maximum) should provide full contact information for the author(s) and the nominator(s), including e-mail addresses, and should document the ways the nominated work conveys the nature and importance of geography to the nonacademic world (Globe Book Award) or contributes to advancing the science and art of geography (Meridian Book Award). Nomination statements and four copies of each nominated book should be submitted.
Deadline: December 31.

ADDRESS INQUIRIES TO:
Attn: Globe Book Award or
Attn: Meridian Book Award
(See address and e-mail above.)

THE GEOLOGICAL SOCIETY OF AMERICA, INC.   [2077]
P.O. Box 9140
Boulder, CO 80301-9140
(303) 357-1028
Fax: (303) 357-1070

E-MAIL ADDRESS:
jrecio@geosociety.org
awards@geosociety.org

WEB SITE ADDRESS:
www.geosociety.org

FOUNDED: 1888

AREAS OF INTEREST:
Geoscience.

NAME(S) OF PROGRAMS:
- **GSA Research Grants**

TYPE:
Grants-in-aid; Project/program grants; Research grants; Seed money grants. Grants for projects contributing to the science of geology.

YEAR PROGRAM STARTED: 1933

PURPOSE:
To provide partial support of Master's and doctoral thesis research in earth science for graduate students.

LEGAL BASIS:
Private membership association.

ELIGIBILITY:
Qualified investigators with appropriate interests are eligible to apply. Graduate students apply for support of Master's or doctoral thesis work. The GSA strongly encourages women, minorities and persons with disabilities to participate in this grants program.

Applicants must be members of GSA.

GEOGRAPHIC RESTRICTIONS:
North and Central America.

FINANCIAL DATA:
Funds are intended as an aid to the research project and not to sustain entire research costs.
Amount of support per award: Grants vary in amount, depending upon the needs and nature of the request.

APPLICATION INFORMATION:
Official application materials are available online.
Duration: One year.
Deadline: Applications must be submitted electronically by February 1 for consideration at the spring review meeting.

PUBLICATIONS:
Annual report; application guidelines.

OFFICERS:
Jack Hess, Executive Officer

ADDRESS INQUIRIES TO:
Program Officer
Grants, Awards and Recognition
(See address above.)

INTERNATIONAL WOMEN'S FISHING ASSOCIATION SCHOLARSHIP TRUST   [2078]
P.O. Box 460387
Fort Lauderdale, FL 33346-0387

E-MAIL ADDRESS:
scholarship@iwfa.org

WEB SITE ADDRESS:
www.iwfa.org

FOUNDED: 1965

AREAS OF INTEREST:
Marine science.

NAME(S) OF PROGRAMS:
- **IWFA Scholarship Trust**

TYPE:
Scholarships. For postgraduate educational expense including tuition, supplies and books.

YEAR PROGRAM STARTED: 1965

PURPOSE:
To aid needy students who are seeking postgraduate degrees in marine science.

ELIGIBILITY:
Applicant must be a graduate student in marine science. Student must be matriculated at a school in the U.S.

FINANCIAL DATA:
Amount of support per award:
Approximately $500 per award.
Total amount of support: $24,250 for the year 2012.

NUMBER OF APPLICANTS MOST RECENT YEAR: 25.

NUMBER OF AWARDS: 32.

APPLICATION INFORMATION:
Application form may be downloaded from the Scholarship page on the web site above or obtained by sending written request to the Association.
Duration: One year.
Deadline: March 1.

ADDRESS INQUIRIES TO:
IWFA Scholarship Trustees
(See address above.)

*SPECIAL STIPULATIONS:
For graduate students in the Marine Science field only.

LUNAR AND PLANETARY INSTITUTE
3600 Bay Area Boulevard
Houston, TX 77058
(281) 486-2159
Fax: (281) 486-2127

E-MAIL ADDRESS:
internprogram@lpi.usra.edu

WEB SITE ADDRESS:
www.lpi.usra.edu

TYPE:
Conferences/seminars; Internships; Scholarships; Travel grants.
See entry 2052 for full listing.

THE MINERALOGICAL SOCIETY OF AMERICA   [2079]
3635 Concorde Parkway, Suite 500
Chantilly, VA 20151-1110
(703) 652-9950
Fax: (703) 652-9951

E-MAIL ADDRESS:
business@minsocam.org

WEB SITE ADDRESS:
www.minsocam.org

FOUNDED: 1919

AREAS OF INTEREST:
Crystallography, mineralogy and petrology.

NAME(S) OF PROGRAMS:
● **Research Grant in Crystallography, Mineral Physics or Chemistry and Mineralogy**
● **Student Research Grant in Mineralogy and Petrology**

TYPE:
Research grants. Grants supported through endowment funds.

YEAR PROGRAM STARTED: 1973

PURPOSE:
To encourage research in mineralogy, crystallography, geochemistry, and petrology.

ELIGIBILITY:
For the crystallography grant, applicant must have reached his or her 25th birthday, but not

yet have reached his or her 36th birthday, in the year the grant proposal is submitted, and must be an MSA Counselor. The mineralogy/petrology grant is limited to students.

FINANCIAL DATA:
The grant is for research-related expenses only. Travel to meetings, conferences, short courses, nonresearch field trips, tuition, nonresearch living (room and board) expenses, etc., are not suitable uses of the money. Neither should the money be used for salary or wages for the researcher.
Amount of support per award: $5,000.
Total amount of support: $15,000.

NUMBER OF APPLICANTS MOST RECENT YEAR: 56.

NUMBER OF AWARDS: 3.

APPLICATION INFORMATION:
Proposal submissions are to be made online.
Duration: One year.
Deadline: June 1.

IRS IDENTIFICATION NUMBER: 52-6044250

ADDRESS INQUIRIES TO:
Dr. J. Alex Speer, Executive Director
(See address above.)

NATIONAL ASSOCIATION OF GEOSCIENCE TEACHERS [2080]
c/o Science Education Resource Center
200 Division Street, Suite 210
Northfield, MN 55057
(507) 222-5634
Fax: (507) 222-5175

E-MAIL ADDRESS:
cmanduca@carleton.edu

WEB SITE ADDRESS:
www.nagt.org

FOUNDED: 1938

AREAS OF INTEREST:
Earth sciences.

NAME(S) OF PROGRAMS:
● **Dottie Stout Professional Development Grants**
● **Summer Field Course Scholarship**

TYPE:
Development grants; Scholarships. Dottie Stout Professional Development Grants will be awarded in support of the following activities:
(1) participation in earth science classes or workshops;
(2) attendance at professional scientific or science education meetings;
(3) participation in earth science field trips and;
(4) purchase of earth science materials for classroom use.

Summer Field Course Scholarship: Cash award for a summer field course in geology.

YEAR PROGRAM STARTED: 1970

PURPOSE:
To further geological education at the undergraduate level.

LEGAL BASIS:
Tax-exempt corporation.

ELIGIBILITY:
Dottie Stout Professional Development Grants: Community college faculty and K-12th grade teachers who teach one or more earth science courses and community college

students actively pursuing a career in the earth sciences are encouraged to apply for these awards.

Summer Field Course Scholarship: Applicants must be full-time students with a geology major. The chief criterion for selection is advanced students with distinguished academic records within the major.

FINANCIAL DATA:
Amount of support per award: Dottie Stout Professional Development Grants: $750 each to a community college faculty member, a community college student and a K-12th grade educator; Summer Field Course Scholarship: $500.
Total amount of support: Varies.

NUMBER OF APPLICANTS MOST RECENT YEAR:
Dottie Stout Professional Development Grants: 10; Summer Field Course Scholarships: 80.

NUMBER OF AWARDS: Dottie Stout Professional Development Grants: 4; Summer Field Course Scholarships: 18.

APPLICATION INFORMATION:
Application information is available at the web site.
Deadline: Dottie Stout Professional Development Grants: April 15; Summer Field Course Scholarship: February 16.

PUBLICATIONS:
Journal of Geoscience Education.

IRS IDENTIFICATION NUMBER: 74-6068050

OFFICERS:
Aida Awad, President
Cathy Manduca, Executive Director

NATIONAL CENTER FOR ATMOSPHERIC RESEARCH
1850 Table Mesa Drive
Boulder, CO 80305
(303) 497-1328
Fax: (303) 497-1646

E-MAIL ADDRESS:
paulad@ucar.edu

WEB SITE ADDRESS:
www.asp.ucar.edu

TYPE:
Fellowships. The fellowships cover a year's appointment, with a likely extension to two years, at NCAR to take advantage of its educational programs and/or research facilities in the broad field of atmospheric sciences.
See entry 1829 for full listing.

NATIONAL GEOGRAPHIC SOCIETY   [2081]
1145 17th Street, N.W.
Washington, DC 20036-4688
(202) 857-7000
Fax: (202) 429-5729

E-MAIL ADDRESS:
cre@ngs.org

WEB SITE ADDRESS:
www.nationalgeographic.com/field/grants-programs

FOUNDED: 1888

AREAS OF INTEREST:
Sciences pertinent to geography, including anthropology, archeology, astronomy, biology, botany, geography, geology, oceanography, paleontology and zoology.

NAME(S) OF PROGRAMS:
- **National Geographic Society Committee for Research and Exploration**

TYPE:
Grants-in-aid; Research grants; Seed money grants. Grants-in-aid for basic research in the sciences pertinent to geography (including, but not limited to, projects in geography). Support may also be provided for projects in these fields that depend on exploration. The Society is currently emphasizing multidisciplinary projects that address environmental issues.

YEAR PROGRAM STARTED: 1890

PURPOSE:
To support scientific field research and exploration through its Committee for Research and Exploration.

LEGAL BASIS:
Nonprofit.

ELIGIBILITY:
Applicants are expected to have advanced degrees (Ph.D. or equivalent) and be associated with an educational organization or institution. Independent researchers or those pursuing a Ph.D.-level degree may apply, but competition is keen and awards to non-Ph.D. applicants are rare. As a general rule, all applicants are expected to have published a minimum of three articles in peer-reviewed scientific journals. Individuals between the ages of 18 and 25 are invited to apply to the Young Explorers Program. These applicants are not expected to have advanced degrees but should have a record of prior experience as it pertains to their proposed project. Citizens of any country are eligible.

Grants normally are made only for field research. Laboratory work is supported only to the extent that it may be a necessary follow-up to Society-funded field research.

Grants are awarded on the basis of the project's scientific merit. All proposed projects must have both a geographical dimension and relevance to other scientific fields and be of broad scientific interest. The Committee pays special attention to the significance of the research proposal in terms of its relationship to major scientific questions or problems. The Committee's priorities favor research that relates to environmental concerns and has relevance to global geographic issues.

FINANCIAL DATA:
Society funds may be used for transportation, supplies, and daily subsistence. Capital equipment (generally defined as any item costing more than U.S. $500) must be individually justified. Laboratory expenses are acceptable, provided the laboratory work is a logical extension of the field research.
Amount of support per award: $20,000 to $25,000 per year.
Total amount of support: $3,000,000 budgeted for research program annually.
Matching fund requirements: National Geographic Society funds are intended to function as complementary support. The committee strongly encourages applicants to seek additional, concurrent funding from other agencies.

NUMBER OF APPLICANTS MOST RECENT YEAR: 976.

NUMBER OF AWARDS: Approximately 250 per year.

APPLICATION INFORMATION:
Prior to applying for a grant, each potential investigator must submit a preapplication, available on the web site, with a 500-word maximum length outlining the significance of the research and describing who will conduct the research and where it will occur. Also, a fieldwork schedule should be projected. Anticipated budgetary expenses must be itemized and, if necessary, justified. A curriculum vitae for each principal investigator, along with a list of his or her scholarly publications, should also be included.

A link to the full application will be e-mailed to those individuals whose project(s) are deemed appropriate for further formal review. Previous Society research grant recipients must comply with all grant obligations from past awards and must be up-to-date with any outstanding reports and/or financial accounting requirements before submitting applications for additional support.
Duration: One year.
Deadline: Applications may be submitted at any time.

PUBLICATIONS:
Program description; National Geographic Index 1888-1988.

NATIONAL OCEANIC AND ATMOSPHERIC ADMINISTRATION [2082]
1315 East West Highway, 12th Floor
Silver Spring, MD 20910-5603
(301) 734-1206
Fax: (301) 713-0517

E-MAIL ADDRESS:
cpogrants@noaa.gov

WEB SITE ADDRESS:
www.climate.noaa.gov

FOUNDED: 1966

AREAS OF INTEREST:
Climate and atmospheric research.

NAME(S) OF PROGRAMS:
- **Climate and Global Change Program**

TYPE:
Challenge/matching grants; Conferences/seminars; Formula grants.

PURPOSE:
To develop the knowledge required to establish a predictive capability for short- and long-term climate fluctuations and trends.

LEGAL BASIS:
Government agency.

ELIGIBILITY:
Applicants may be institutions of higher education, other nonprofits, commercial organizations, international organizations, state, local and Indian tribal governments. Federal agencies or institutions are ineligible.

FINANCIAL DATA:
Grants may be used for research and development, advisory services and operational systems as they relate to specific programs.
Amount of support per award: Up to $200,000.

Total amount of support: Approximately $56,000,000 in total funding annually.

NUMBER OF AWARDS: Estimated 70 annually.

APPLICATION INFORMATION:
Applications are to be submitted through grants.gov.
Duration: One to three years.

ADDRESS INQUIRIES TO:
Diane Brown
Grants Administration Team Leader
Climate Program Office
(See address above.)

NATIONAL OCEANIC AND ATMOSPHERIC ADMINISTRATION [2083]
National Marine Fisheries Service
263 13th Avenue South
St. Petersburg, FL 33701
(727) 824-5324
Fax: (727) 824-5364

E-MAIL ADDRESS:
dax.ruiz@noaa.gov
robert.sadler@noaa.gov

WEB SITE ADDRESS:
sero.nmfs.noaa.gov

AREAS OF INTEREST:
Southeast region.

NAME(S) OF PROGRAMS:
- **Cooperative Research Program Grants**
- **Marine Fisheries Initiative Grants**

TYPE:
Development grants; Research grants.

YEAR PROGRAM STARTED: 2003

PURPOSE:
To support research and development.

ELIGIBILITY:
Cooperative Research Program Grants: Applicants who are not commercial or recreational fishermen must have commercial or recreational fishermen participating in their project. There must be a written agreement with a fisherman describing the involvement in the project activity. Eligible applicants include institutions of higher education, other nonprofits, commercial organizations, state, local and Indian tribal governments and individuals. Federal agencies or institutions are not eligible. Foreign governments, organizations under the jurisdiction of foreign governments, and international organizations are excluded for purposes of this solicitation since the objective of the CRP is to optimize research and development benefits from U.S. marine fishery resources.

Marine Fisheries Initiative Grants are available to institutions of higher education, other nonprofits, commercial organizations, state, local and Indian tribal governments. Federal agencies or institutions are not eligible. Foreign governments, organizations under the jurisdiction of foreign governments, and international organizations are excluded for purposes of this solicitation since the objective of the MARFIN program is to optimize research and development benefits from U.S. marine fishery resources.

FINANCIAL DATA:
Amount of support per award: $25,000 to $175,000.

Total amount of support: $2,000,000 for the year 2014.

Matching fund requirements: Cost sharing is not required.

NUMBER OF AWARDS: 8 to 10.

APPLICATION INFORMATION:
Applications are available on grants.gov. New applicants should include IRS documentation.

Duration: Cooperative Research Program Grants: One year; Marine Fisheries Initiative Grants: One to three years.

Deadline: Announced in NOAA solicitation and grant opportunities index.

PUBLICATIONS:
Annual report.

ADDRESS INQUIRIES TO:
Cooperative Research Program Grants:
Dax Ruiz, Federal Grants Program Officer

Marine Fisheries Initiative Grants:
Robert Sadler, Federal Grants Program Officer
(See address above.)

NATIONAL OCEANIC AND ATMOSPHERIC ADMINISTRATION   [2084]
Ocean Exploration and Research Program
SSMC3, R/OER, Room 10210
1305 East-West Highway
Silver Spring, MD 20910
(301) 734-1014
Fax: (301) 713-4252

E-MAIL ADDRESS:
john.mcdonough@noaa.gov

WEB SITE ADDRESS:
oceanexplore.noaa.gov
explore.noaa.gov

AREAS OF INTEREST:
Marine research.

NAME(S) OF PROGRAMS:
● **Ocean Exploration and Research Program**

TYPE:
Project/program grants; Research grants.

ELIGIBILITY:
Eligible applicants are U.S. institutions of higher education, not-for-profit institutions, and federal, state, and local governments. Federal agencies may not charge salary or overhead.

GEOGRAPHIC RESTRICTIONS:
United States.

FINANCIAL DATA:
Amount of support per award: Varies by center.

Total amount of support: Varies.

APPLICATION INFORMATION:
Each National Undersea Research Center has its own proposal forms and guidelines. Specific locations and instructions are available online.

Duration: One year.

Deadline: Varies by center.

ADDRESS INQUIRIES TO:
John McDonough, Acting Director
(See address above.)

NATIONAL OCEANIC AND ATMOSPHERIC ADMINISTRATION   [2085]
Center for Satellite Applications and Research
National Environmental Satellite Data and Information Services
5830 University Research Court E/RA1
College Park, MD 20740
(301) 683-3511

E-MAIL ADDRESS:
heather.hay@noaa.gov

WEB SITE ADDRESS:
www.nesdis.noaa.gov

AREAS OF INTEREST:
Environmental sciences, application, data and education.

NAME(S) OF PROGRAMS:
● **Research in Remote Sensing of the Earth and Environment Grants**

TYPE:
Research grants.

PURPOSE:
To advance and promote applied research and technology development in satellite remote sensing of the earth and the atmosphere in support of national operational needs.

ELIGIBILITY:
Applicant must be any state university, college, institute or laboratory, public or private nonprofit, tax-exempt institution or consortium. No grants to individuals.

GEOGRAPHIC RESTRICTIONS:
United States.

FINANCIAL DATA:
Amount of support per award: $25,000 to $300,000.

Total amount of support: Varies.

Matching fund requirements: Varies.

APPLICATION INFORMATION:
Applications are available on grants.gov.

Duration: One to three years. Renewals possible.

Deadline: Posted online or published in *Federal Register.*

ADDRESS INQUIRIES TO:
Heather Hay, Administrator
(See address above.)

NATIONAL SCIENCE FOUNDATION   [2086]
Division of Earth Sciences, Room 785
4201 Wilson Boulevard
Arlington, VA 22230
(703) 292-8550
Fax: (703) 292-9025

E-MAIL ADDRESS:
pbrookin@nsf.gov

WEB SITE ADDRESS:
www.nsf.gov

FOUNDED: 1950

AREAS OF INTEREST:
Earth sciences.

TYPE:
Research grants. The Division of Earth Sciences supports proposals for research geared toward improving the understanding of the structure, composition, and evolution of the Earth and the processes that govern the formation and behavior of the Earth's materials.

YEAR PROGRAM STARTED: 1950

PURPOSE:
To create a better understanding of the Earth's changing environments and the natural distribution of its mineral, water and energy resources; to provide methods for predicting and mitigating the effects of geologic hazards such as earthquakes, volcanic eruptions, floods and landslides.

LEGAL BASIS:
Federal agency.

ELIGIBILITY:
Scientists and engineers, especially college and university faculty members, are eligible to apply.

GEOGRAPHIC RESTRICTIONS:
United States and its territories.

NUMBER OF APPLICANTS MOST RECENT YEAR:
1,600.

NUMBER OF AWARDS: 500.

APPLICATION INFORMATION:
Application information is available on the web site.

Duration: One to five years.

Deadline: Two or three deadlines per year as announced in the *National Science Foundation Bulletin.* At least six months should be allowed for review and processing of a proposal.

PUBLICATIONS:
Grant proposal guide (NSF 04-23).

ADDRESS INQUIRIES TO:
Division Director
(See address above.)

NATIONAL SCIENCE FOUNDATION   [2087]
Division of Ocean Sciences, Room 725
4201 Wilson Boulevard
Arlington, VA 22230
(703) 292-8580
Fax: (703) 292-9085

E-MAIL ADDRESS:
dconover@nsf.gov

WEB SITE ADDRESS:
www.nsf.gov

FOUNDED: 1950

NAME(S) OF PROGRAMS:
● **Ocean Section**

TYPE:
Research grants. Support for fundamental research in marine science, including physical oceanography and limnology, chemical oceanography, biological oceanography and marine geology, geophysics and ocean technology, with the objective of increasing knowledge and enhancing our understanding of the marine environment.

Most of the research supported is basic in character, although some applied research is also supported. This program also supports research workshops, symposia and conferences and purchases of scientific equipment related to projects supported.

YEAR PROGRAM STARTED: 1980

PURPOSE:
To improve understanding of the nature of the ocean and its influence on human activities and of human impacts on the marine environment.

LEGAL BASIS:
Government agency.

ELIGIBILITY:
Program is primarily for support of scientists in basic research in ocean sciences and instrumentation and the facilities to support it.

FINANCIAL DATA:
Amount of support per award: Varies.
Total amount of support: Varies.

APPLICATION INFORMATION:
Application information is available at the web site.
Duration: Varies.
Deadline: Proposals may be submitted at any time. Approximately six months are required for review and processing. Target dates are February 15 and August 15.

PUBLICATIONS:
Grants for Scientific and Engineering Research.

OFFICERS:
Deborah Bronk, Acting Division Director
Bilal Haq, Marine Geology and Geophysics
Eric Itsweire, Physical Oceanography
Don Rice, Chemical Oceanography

ADDRESS INQUIRIES TO:
Deborah Bronk, Acting Division Director
(See address above.)

NATIONAL SOCIETY OF PROFESSIONAL SURVEYORS (NSPS)

5119 Pegasus Court
Suite Q
Frederick, MD 21704
(240) 439-4615 ext. 106
Fax: (240) 439-4952

E-MAIL ADDRESS:
curtis.sumner@nsps.us.com

WEB SITE ADDRESS:
www.nsps.us.com

TYPE:
Scholarships. Berntsen International Scholarship in Surveying: Annual scholarship award for undergraduate study in four-year degree programs in surveying or in closely related degree programs such as geomatics or surveying engineering.

Berntsen International Scholarship in Surveying Technology: For students enrolled in two-year degree programs in surveying technology.

See entry 2657 for full listing.

NATIONAL SOCIETY OF PROFESSIONAL SURVEYORS (NSPS)

5119 Pegasus Court
Suite Q
Frederick, MD 21704
(240) 439-4615 ext. 106
Fax: (240) 439-4952

E-MAIL ADDRESS:
curtis.sumner@nsps.us.com

WEB SITE ADDRESS:
www.nsps.us.com

TYPE:
Scholarships. For students enrolled in four-year degree programs in surveying or in closely related degree programs such as geomatics or surveying engineering.

See entry 2656 for full listing.

NATIONAL SOCIETY OF PROFESSIONAL SURVEYORS (NSPS)

5119 Pegasus Court
Suite 2
Frederick, MD 21704
(240) 439-4615 ext. 106
Fax: (240) 439-4952

E-MAIL ADDRESS:
curtis.sumner@nsps.us.com

WEB SITE ADDRESS:
www.nsps.us.com

TYPE:
Scholarships.

See entry 2658 for full listing.

NATIONAL SOCIETY OF PROFESSIONAL SURVEYORS (NSPS) AMERICAN ASSOCIATION FOR GEODETIC SURVEYING (AAGS)

5119 Pegasus Court
Suite Q
Frederick, MD 21704
(240) 439-4615 ext. 106
Fax: (240) 439-4952

E-MAIL ADDRESS:
curtis.sumner@nsps.us.com

WEB SITE ADDRESS:
www.aagsmo.org

TYPE:
Fellowships. Annual fellowship award to support graduate study in a program with a significant focus on geodetic surveying or geodesy at a school of the recipient's choice.

See entry 2659 for full listing.

NATIONAL SOCIETY OF PROFESSIONAL SURVEYORS (NSPS) AMERICAN ASSOCIATION FOR GEODETIC SURVEYING (AAGS)

5119 Pegasus Court
Suite Q
Frederick, MD 21704
(240) 439-4615 ext. 106
Fax: (240) 439-4952

E-MAIL ADDRESS:
curtis.sumner@nsps.us.com

WEB SITE ADDRESS:
www.aagsmo.org

TYPE:
Scholarships. The award is intended for students enrolled in four-year degree programs in surveying or in closely related degree programs.

See entry 2660 for full listing.

V. KANN RASMUSSEN FOUNDATION [2088]

475 Riverside Drive, Suite 900
New York, NY 10115
(212) 812-4268
Fax: (212) 812-4299

E-MAIL ADDRESS:
ikrarup@vkrf.org

WEB SITE ADDRESS:
www.vkrf.org

FOUNDED: 1991

AREAS OF INTEREST:
Environment.

TYPE:
Challenge/matching grants; General operating grants; Project/program grants.

PURPOSE:
To emphasize environmental grantmaking, with special focus on collaboration across disciplines and among institutions.

LEGAL BASIS:
Private foundation.

ELIGIBILITY:
Eligible organizations must be IRS 501(c)(3) tax-exempt.

GEOGRAPHIC RESTRICTIONS:
United States.

FINANCIAL DATA:
Amount of support per award: Varies.
Total amount of support: Approximately $3,000,000 for the year ended June 30, 2012.

APPLICATION INFORMATION:
Application procedures can be found on the Foundation web site.
Duration: One to two years.
Deadline: Varies.

IRS IDENTIFICATION NUMBER: 22-3101266.

STAFF:
Irene Krarup, Associate Director and Head of Programs

ADDRESS INQUIRIES TO:
Irene Krarup, Associate Director and Head of Programs
(See address above.)

THE PERCY SLADEN MEMORIAL FUND

c/o The Linnean Society of London
Burlington House, Piccadilly
London W1J 0BF England
44 (0)20 7434 4479
Fax: 44 (0)20 7287 9364

E-MAIL ADDRESS:
info@linnean.org; gina@linnean.org

WEB SITE ADDRESS:
www.linnean.org

TYPE:
Awards/prizes; Project/program grants; Research grants; Travel grants. Field work grants in life and earth sciences (excludes any projects which are part of further education, e.g., a Doctorate or a Master's course).

See entry 2110 for full listing.

SOCIETY OF EXPLORATION GEOPHYSICISTS [2089]

8801 South Yale Avenue
Suite 500
Tulsa, OK 74137
(918) 497-5500
Fax: (918) 497-5560

E-MAIL ADDRESS:
scholarships@seg.org

WEB SITE ADDRESS:
www.seg.org/foundation
www.seg.org/scholarships

FOUNDED: 1956

AREAS OF INTEREST:
Applied geophysics.

NAME(S) OF PROGRAMS:
- **SEG Scholarship Program**

TYPE:
Scholarships. Undergraduate and graduate scholarships for the study of geophysics.

YEAR PROGRAM STARTED: 1956

PURPOSE:
To assist young people in pursuing careers in the field of applied geophysics.

LEGAL BASIS:
Nonprofit society.

ELIGIBILITY:
Applicant must intend to pursue a college course directed toward a career in applied geophysics and must have an interest in and aptitude for physics, mathematics, and geology. Applicants must be:
(1) a high school student with above-average grades planning to enter college the next fall term;
(2) an undergraduate college student whose grades are above average or;
(3) a graduate college student whose studies are directed toward a career in applied geophysics in operations, teaching or research.

FINANCIAL DATA:
Amount of support per award: $500 to $10,000 per academic year, averaging $3,500 per academic year.
Total amount of support: $474,392 for the academic year 2013.

NUMBER OF AWARDS: 175 for the academic year 2013.

APPLICATION INFORMATION:
Application must be submitted electronically. Transcripts and letters of recommendation may be submitted online or sent via regular mail. Results of aptitude tests are not required but should be included if taken.
Duration: One year. Renewable at the discretion of the SEG Scholarship Committee, subject to student's maintenance of satisfactory grades, funds available and continued study leading to a career in geophysics.
Deadline: March 1.

ADDRESS INQUIRIES TO:
Scholarship Coordinator
(See address above.)

*SPECIAL STIPULATIONS:
Certain scholarships carry additional qualifications specified by the scholarships' donors.

THE UNIVERSITY OF CALGARY   [2090]
Faculty of Graduate Studies
MacKimmie Library Tower, Room 213
2500 University Drive, N.W.
Calgary AB T2N 1N4 Canada
(403) 220-4938
Fax: (403) 289-7635

E-MAIL ADDRESS:
gsaward@ucalgary.ca

WEB SITE ADDRESS:
www.grad.ucalgary.ca/awards

NAME(S) OF PROGRAMS:
- **Harry and Laura Jacques Bursary**

TYPE:
Scholarships. Awarded to those involved in Master's (thesis-based) or doctoral work. The field of study is unrestricted.

ELIGIBILITY:
Open to candidates who at the time of tenure will be registered full-time in a thesis-based graduate program at the University of Calgary. Selection will be based on financial need and academic merit.

FINANCIAL DATA:
Amount of support per award: $3,200.
Total amount of support: $3,200.

NUMBER OF AWARDS: 1.

APPLICATION INFORMATION:
Students should consult the Graduate Award Competition Guidelines and Application available at the web site.
Duration: One year.
Deadline: February 1 to the candidate's graduate program office, unless the program has an earlier deadline.

ADDRESS INQUIRIES TO:
Graduate Scholarship Office
(See address above.)

Mathematics

THE ACTUARIAL FOUNDATION   [2091]
475 North Martingale Road
Suite 600
Schaumburg, IL 60173-2226
(847) 706-3500
Fax: (847) 706-3599

E-MAIL ADDRESS:
Scholarships@ActFnd.org

WEB SITE ADDRESS:
www.actuarialfoundation.org

FOUNDED: 1994

AREAS OF INTEREST:
Actuarial science, a branch of mathematics based on calculus, probability and statistics, as well as business economics.

NAME(S) OF PROGRAMS:
- **Actuarial Diversity Scholarship**

TYPE:
Scholarships. The Actuarial Diversity Scholarship was formed in 1977 as a joint effort of the Casualty Actuarial Society and the Society of Actuaries. In 2008, the scholarship was transferred to The Actuarial Foundation.

The scholarship promotes diversity in the profession through an annual scholarship program for Black/African American, Hispanic, Native North American and Pacific Islander students. The scholarship award recognizes and encourages academic achievements by awarding scholarships to full-time undergraduate students pursuing a degree that may lead to a career in the actuarial profession.

LEGAL BASIS:
Private- and corporate-funded.

ELIGIBILITY:
Each applicant must fulfill all of the following requirements:
(1) must have at least one birth parent who is a member of one of the following minority

groups: Black/African American, Hispanic, Native North American, or Pacific Islander;
(2) enrolled as a full-time undergraduate student at a U.S.-accredited educational institution during the application academic year;
(3) minimum grade point average of 3.0 (on a 4.0 scale), emphasis on math or actuarial courses;
(4) entering college freshmen must have a minimum ACT math score of 28 or SAT math score of 600 and;
(5) intent on pursuing a career in the actuarial profession.

GEOGRAPHIC RESTRICTIONS:
United States.

FINANCIAL DATA:
Amount of support per award: Varies by need.
Total amount of support: $72,000 for the year 2013.

NUMBER OF APPLICANTS MOST RECENT YEAR:
56 for the year 2013.

NUMBER OF AWARDS: 41 for the year 2013.

APPLICATION INFORMATION:
Applications are posted in early January. Application and guidelines are available online.
Duration: One academic year. Renewable based on academic performance.
Deadline: May.

IRS IDENTIFICATION NUMBER: 36-2136422

ADDRESS INQUIRIES TO:
Scholarship Coordinator
(See address above.)

*PLEASE NOTE:
Applicants must intend to pursue a career in the actuarial profession.

THE ACTUARIAL FOUNDATION   [2092]
475 North Martingale Road, Suite 600
Schaumburg, IL 60173-2226
(847) 706-3535
Fax: (847) 706-3599

E-MAIL ADDRESS:
Scholarships@ActFnd.org

WEB SITE ADDRESS:
www.actuarialfoundation.org

FOUNDED: 1994

AREAS OF INTEREST:
Actuarial science.

NAME(S) OF PROGRAMS:
- **Actuary of Tomorrow - Stuart A. Robertson Memorial Scholarship**

TYPE:
Scholarships.

YEAR PROGRAM STARTED: 2006

PURPOSE:
To recognize and encourage the academic achievements of undergraduate students pursuing a career in actuarial science.

ELIGIBILITY:
Applicant must:
(1) be a full-time undergraduate student entering as a sophomore, junior or senior in the fall term;
(2) have a minimum cumulative grade point average of 3.0 (on a 4.0 scale);
(3) have successfully completed two actuarial exams;

(4) attach a current unofficial copy of transcripts from attending college/university;
(5) provide a letter of recommendation supporting academic achievement, leadership and communication skills from professor or advisor;
(6) provide a letter of recommendation from an employer or previous employer and;
(7) submit a personal essay of approximately 500 words, focusing on why you want to be an actuary.

GEOGRAPHIC RESTRICTIONS:
United States.

FINANCIAL DATA:
Amount of support per award: $7,500.

NUMBER OF APPLICANTS MOST RECENT YEAR:
33 for the year 2013.

NUMBER OF AWARDS: 2 for the year 2013.

APPLICATION INFORMATION:
Application is available online. Applicant should meet the eligibility requirements.
Deadline: June 1. Notification by mail after August 1.

ADDRESS INQUIRIES TO:
Scholarship Coordinator
(See address and e-mail above.)

*SPECIAL STIPULATIONS:
Scholarships are awarded directly to the college/university of choice in the recipients' name.

AMERICAN MATHEMATICAL SOCIETY [2093]
201 Charles Street
Providence, RI 02904-2294
(800) 321-4267 ext. 4101
(401) 455-4101
Fax: (401) 455-4004

E-MAIL ADDRESS:
prof-serv@ams.org

WEB SITE ADDRESS:
www.ams.org

FOUNDED: 1888

AREAS OF INTEREST:
Research mathematics.

NAME(S) OF PROGRAMS:
● **American Mathematical Society Centennial Fellowship**

TYPE:
Fellowships. The AMS Centennial Research Fellowship Program makes awards annually to outstanding mathematicians to help further their careers in research.

YEAR PROGRAM STARTED: 1974

PURPOSE:
To help outstanding mathematicians further their careers in research.

LEGAL BASIS:
Nonprofit corporation.

ELIGIBILITY:
The primary selection criterion for the Centennial Fellowship is the excellence of the candidate's research. Preference will be given to candidates who have not had extensive fellowship support in the past. Recipients may not hold the Centennial Fellowship concurrently with another research fellowship such as a Sloan Fellowship, NSF Postdoctoral Fellowship, or Career Award. Under normal circumstances, the fellowship cannot be deferred. A recipient of the fellowship shall have held his or her

doctoral degree for at least three years and not more than 12 years at the inception of the award. Applications will be accepted from those currently holding a tenured, tenure-track, postdoctoral, or comparable (at the discretion of the selection committee) position at an institution in North America.

GEOGRAPHIC RESTRICTIONS:
North America.

FINANCIAL DATA:
Amount of support per award:
Approximately $80,000, plus about $8,000 for expenses.
Total amount of support: Varies.

COOPERATIVE FUNDING PROGRAMS: The Society has a matching program so that funds for at least one fellowship are guaranteed.

NUMBER OF AWARDS: 1 fellowship for the 2013-14 academic year.

APPLICATION INFORMATION:
Applications should include a cogent plan indicating how the fellowship will be used. The plan should include travel to at least one other institution and should demonstrate that the fellowship will be used for more than reduction of teaching at the candidate's home institution. The selection committee will consider the plan in addition to the quality of the candidate's research, and will try to award the fellowship to those for whom the award would make a real difference in the development of their research careers. Work in all areas of mathematics, including interdisciplinary work, is eligible.

Application forms can be accessed at the web site. For paper copies of the form, contact the Membership and Programs Department, American Mathematical Society, at the address or e-mail above, or phone (401) 455-4105.
Duration: One year. Nonrenewable.
Deadline: December 1. Announcement in February, or earlier if possible.

PUBLICATIONS:
Application guidelines.

OFFICERS:
David Vogan, President
Jane Hawkins, Treasurer
Zbigniew Nitecki, Associate Treasurer

ADDRESS INQUIRIES TO:
Associate Executive Director
(See address above.)

*SPECIAL STIPULATIONS:
Acceptance of the Fellowship cannot be postponed.

CONFERENCE BOARD OF THE MATHEMATICAL SCIENCES [2094]
1529 18th Street, N.W.
Washington, DC 20036
(202) 293-1170
Fax: (202) 293-3412

E-MAIL ADDRESS:
rosier@georgetown.edu

WEB SITE ADDRESS:
www.cbmsweb.org

FOUNDED: 1960

AREAS OF INTEREST:
Mathematical sciences.

NAME(S) OF PROGRAMS:
● **NSF-CBMS Regional Conferences in the Mathematical Sciences**

TYPE:
Conferences/seminars. Grants given jointly by NSF and the Conference Board for five-day conferences in the mathematical sciences.

YEAR PROGRAM STARTED: 1969

PURPOSE:
To stimulate interest and activity in mathematical research.

LEGAL BASIS:
A nonprofit professional society.

ELIGIBILITY:
Colleges or universities with at least some research competence in the field of the proposal are eligible to apply. Since a major goal of these conferences is to attract new researchers into the field of the conference and to stimulate new research activity, institutions that are interested in upgrading or improving their research efforts are especially encouraged to apply.

FINANCIAL DATA:
Grants for approximately 25 to 30 participants may include travel and lodging costs, director's and secretary's salaries, announcement costs and other miscellaneous expenses.
Amount of support per award: $33,000 to $35,000.

COOPERATIVE FUNDING PROGRAMS: Grants are given jointly with NSF.

APPLICATION INFORMATION:
Proposals must be submitted electronically via Fastlane to the Division of Mathematical Sciences (DMS) at NSF.
Duration: Five days during the summer or during a recess in the academic year.
Deadline: Mid- to late April. Announcement in October.

PUBLICATIONS:
Monographs of the conferences are available from the American Mathematical Society, the Society for Industrial and Applied Mathematics, the Institute of Mathematical Statistics and the American Statistical Association.

IBM THOMAS J. WATSON RESEARCH CENTER [2095]
Department of Business Solutions and Mathematical Sciences
1101 Kitchawan Road, Route 134
Yorktown Heights, NY 10598
Fax: (914) 945-3434

E-MAIL ADDRESS:
goldpost@us.ibm.com

WEB SITE ADDRESS:
www.research.ibm.com/goldstine

AREAS OF INTEREST:
Research in pure and applied mathematics and in theoretical and exploratory computer science.

NAME(S) OF PROGRAMS:
● **IBM Herman Goldstine Memorial Postdoctoral Fellowship for Research in Mathematical and Computer Sciences**

TYPE:
Fellowships.

YEAR PROGRAM STARTED: 1972

PURPOSE:
To provide scientists of outstanding ability an opportunity to advance their scholarship as resident department members at the IBM Thomas J. Watson Research Center.

ELIGIBILITY:
Applicant must have a Ph.D. in science, engineering or mathematics received within the last five years.

FINANCIAL DATA:
Allowance provided for moving expenses.
Amount of support per award: $95,000 to $115,000 per year, depending on the area and length of experience.

NUMBER OF AWARDS: Up to 2 per year.

APPLICATION INFORMATION:
Applications accepted via e-mail only.

Applicants are also responsible for arranging for three or more letters of recommendation, including one from the thesis advisor, that must also be e-mailed to the address above.

Duration: One year. Renewable for a second year if of mutual interest.

Deadline: Applications accepted November to January (exact dates vary).

ADDRESS INQUIRIES TO:
Chai Wah Wu, Research Staff Member
(See address above.)

MICRON TECHNOLOGY FOUNDATION, INC. [2096]

8000 South Federal Way
P.O. Box 6
Boise, ID 83707-0006
(208) 363-3675
Fax: (208) 368-4435

E-MAIL ADDRESS:
mtf@micron.com

WEB SITE ADDRESS:
www.micron.com/foundation

FOUNDED: 1999

AREAS OF INTEREST:
Education with an emphasis on math, science and engineering.

TYPE:
Awards/prizes; Matching gifts; Professorships; Project/program grants; Research grants.

YEAR PROGRAM STARTED: 2000

PURPOSE:
To support a wide range of projects and programs which promote the growth and enhance the quality of the community, with primary emphasis on youth and educational programs related to math and science.

LEGAL BASIS:
Private corporate foundation.

ELIGIBILITY:
Micron will consider projects or programs:
(1) which address an educational need, especially those which advance math and science;
(2) which impact a large number of people;
(3) which have long-term benefits and;
(4) which are in a geographic area where Micron has operations.

Micron generally does not address individual sponsorships or donations, requests for assistance with travel or lodging expenses, religious organizations requesting funds for purposes other than nondenominational education or organizations located in areas where Micron has no operations.

GEOGRAPHIC RESTRICTIONS:
Boise, Idaho and Manassas, Virginia.

FINANCIAL DATA:
Amount of support per award: Varies.
Total amount of support: Varies.
Matching fund requirements: Micron may match employee donations at a 1:1 ratio, K-12 up to $100 and higher education grants up to $1,000 per employee per calendar year to qualified educational institutions.

NUMBER OF AWARDS: Varies.

REPRESENTATIVE AWARDS:
Boise School District Educational Foundation; Boise State University; University of Idaho; University of Washington; Virginia Tech.

APPLICATION INFORMATION:
Supporting materials can be included with the application form, but may not be reviewed in their entirety.

Higher education grants by invitation only.
Duration: Varies.

IRS IDENTIFICATION NUMBER: 82-0516178

ADDRESS INQUIRIES TO:
Micron Technology Foundation, M/S 407
Community and Academic Relations
8000 South Federal Way, P.O. Box 6
Boise, ID 83707-0006

SOCIETY OF ACTUARIES (SOA) [2097]

475 North Martingale Road
Suite 600
Schaumburg, IL 60173-2226
(847) 706-3509
Fax: (847) 273-8605

E-MAIL ADDRESS:
acoffelt@soa.org

WEB SITE ADDRESS:
www.soa.org/education/resources/academic-initiatives/soa-doc-stipend.aspx

FOUNDED: 1949

AREAS OF INTEREST:
Actuarial science, a branch of mathematics based on calculus, probability and statistics, as well as business economics.

NAME(S) OF PROGRAMS:
● **Society of Actuaries' James C. Hickman Scholar Doctoral Stipend Program**

TYPE:
Awards/prizes; Scholarships. Society of Actuaries' James C. Hickman Scholar Doctoral Stipend Program is designed to provide stipends to doctoral students who will, through their studies, address research and education needs of the profession, including both the theoretical and practical aspects.

YEAR PROGRAM STARTED: 2009

PURPOSE:
To increase the number of academic actuaries who hold a Ph.D. and an actuarial designation, and who intend to pursue academic careers in the U.S. or Canada.

LEGAL BASIS:
Society-funded.

ELIGIBILITY:
Individuals who meet the following requirements may apply:
(1) enrolled full-time, have recently been admitted or are currently applying to a qualifying doctoral program in the U.S. or Canada; a qualifying doctoral program is one in actuarial science or a field related to actuarial science (e.g., business, demography, economics, financial economics, insurance, mathematics, risk management, statistics); applicants may apply at the same time they are applying for a doctoral program; if selected, these applicants will be awarded the stipend conditional upon enrollment in a qualifying doctoral program;
(2) hold a fellowship-level actuarial credential or are pursuing Associateship or Fellowship membership of an accrediting actuarial organization (i.e., CAS, CIA, FA, IA, IAA, SOA); applicants who are already Associate members (including those awarded the CERA designation) will be expected to pursue a Fellowship credential and;
(3) all applicants must have at least two actuarial exams passed.

While U.S. or Canadian citizenship is not expressly required, the applicant will attest to citizenship status on the application. An applicant's citizenship status may be used to evaluate the likelihood that the applicant will pursue an academic career in the U.S. or Canada.

FINANCIAL DATA:
The stipend is to be used at the discretion of the Ph.D. candidate for appropriate expenses related to the completion of the Ph.D. and the actuarial credential if not yet attained. Applicants should be aware that stipend funds are provided for qualified expenses (tuition, books, fees, etc.). Qualified expenses do not include room and board. Stipend funds not used for qualified expenses may be taxable. Please consult one's tax advisor if one has any questions.

Amount of support per award: Generally $20,000 per academic year.

Total amount of support: Varies.

NUMBER OF APPLICANTS MOST RECENT YEAR: 50.

NUMBER OF AWARDS: Varies.

APPLICATION INFORMATION:
Applicants must submit an application and supporting documentation that includes the following:
(1) Applicants currently applying to doctoral programs must provide the names of the schools/programs to which they have applied, and the intended field of study in each school/program. (If a stipend is awarded, it will be conditional on enrollment in the specified program and for the field of study proposed in the application.);
(2) Applicants already enrolled in a doctoral program will indicate how many years they have been studying, and approximately how many more years they believe they need to complete their Doctorate. They will also provide a statement from their supervisor or program director attesting to progess in their doctoral program and;
(3) Applicant must submit a Statement of Interest. This may be the same statement submitted for the doctoral program, but additional language should be added for this application to clearly explain their goals regarding teaching, research and contributions to the actuarial profession.

Duration: One academic year. Renewable up to four times based on satisfactory progress.

Deadline: Completed application forms and supporting materials must be received at the Society no later than February 15. Recipients will be announced April 15. Recipients must notify the Society of acceptance of the stipend by May 15.

PUBLICATIONS:
Application guidelines.

OFFICERS:
Mark J. Freedman, F.S.A., M.A.A.A., President

ADDRESS INQUIRIES TO:
SOA James C. Hickman Scholar Doctoral Stipend Program
(See address above.)

SOCIETY OF ACTUARIES (SOA) [2098]
475 North Martingale Road
Suite 600
Schaumburg, IL 60173-2226
(847) 706-3509
Fax: (847) 273-8605

E-MAIL ADDRESS:
acoffelt@soa.org

WEB SITE ADDRESS:
www.soa.org/education/resources/edu-institution-grant/default.aspx

FOUNDED: 1949

AREAS OF INTEREST:
Actuarial science, a branch of mathematics based on calculus, probability and statistics, as well as business economics.

NAME(S) OF PROGRAMS:
• **Society of Actuaries Educational Institution Grant**

TYPE:
Awards/prizes; Development grants; General operating grants; Project/program grants; Research grants; Scholarships; Travel grants. Grants to educational institutions.

YEAR PROGRAM STARTED: 1991

PURPOSE:
To provide financial support for the promotion and development of educational and research programs in actuarial science; to recognize the added value professional actuarial qualifications offer to actuarial teaching and research.

LEGAL BASIS:
Society-funded.

ELIGIBILITY:
A full-time faculty member at the applying institution must attain Associateship (ASA) status or Fellowship (FSA) status to qualify the institution for a grant.

Full-time faculty are defined as individuals employed by a college or university who are considered to be full-time members of the regular faculty by their employer. This does not include visiting faculty, adjuncts, graduate students or teaching assistants.

FINANCIAL DATA:
Amount of support per award: $5,000 one-time grant to an educational institution when a full-time faculty member attains ASA status; $7,500 one-time grant to an educational institution when a full-time faculty member attains FSA status.
Total amount of support: Varies.

NUMBER OF APPLICANTS MOST RECENT YEAR: 3.

NUMBER OF AWARDS: Varies.

APPLICATION INFORMATION:
Application form and details are available online.

Deadline: Applications for institution grants must be received within three years of the date the faculty member attains FSA or ASA status as indicated on the FSA or ASA diploma.

PUBLICATIONS:
Application guidelines.

OFFICERS:
Mark J. Freedman, F.S.A., M.A.A.A., President

ADDRESS INQUIRIES TO:
Educational Institution Grants (ASA/FSA Grants)
(See address above.)

Physics

AMERICAN INSTITUTE OF PHYSICS [2099]
One Physics Ellipse
College Park, MD 20740-3843
(301) 209-3099
Fax: (301) 209-0846

E-MAIL ADDRESS:
media@aip.org

WEB SITE ADDRESS:
www.aip.org/aip/writing

FOUNDED: 1931

AREAS OF INTEREST:
The advancement and diffusion of the knowledge of physics and its application to human welfare.

NAME(S) OF PROGRAMS:
• **American Institute of Physics Science Writing Award in Physics and Astronomy**

TYPE:
Awards/prizes. Four writing awards, one to a physicist, astronomer or member of an AIP society, one to a journalist for noteworthy writing about physics and astronomy in the print media, one to a journalist for noteworthy writing about physics and astronomy for broadcast media, and one for science writing aimed at children.

PURPOSE:
To stimulate distinguished reporting and writing that will improve public understanding of physics and astronomy.

ELIGIBILITY:
Entries must have been printed in any recognized international, national or local medium of communication such as newspapers, magazines or books. The media should normally be available to, and intended for, the general public. Purely scientific, technical and trade publications are excluded.

Entries must have been published or translated into English during the period one year immediately prior to the deadline date. No more than three entries may be submitted by any one individual. Persons other than the author may submit entries on behalf of an author in accordance with the rules.

FINANCIAL DATA:
Amount of support per award: $3,000.
Total amount of support: $9,000.

NUMBER OF APPLICANTS MOST RECENT YEAR: 75.

NUMBER OF AWARDS: 3.

APPLICATION INFORMATION:
Application information is available on the web site.

OFFICERS:
H. Frederick Dylla, Executive Director and Chief Executive Officer
Richard Baccante, Treasurer and Chief Financial Officer
Benjamin Snavely, Secretary
John Haynes, Senior Vice President, Publishing
Theresa C. Braun, Vice President, Human Resources
Catherine O'Riordan, Vice President, Physics Resource Center

ADDRESS INQUIRIES TO:
Jennifer Lauren Lee, Programs Coordinator
(See address above.)

AMERICAN VACUUM SOCIETY (AVS) [2100]
125 Maiden Lane, Room 1501
New York, NY 10038-4714
(212) 248-0200
Fax: (212) 248-0245

E-MAIL ADDRESS:
avsnyc@avs.org

WEB SITE ADDRESS:
www.avs.org

FOUNDED: 1953

AREAS OF INTEREST:
Vacuum science and technology, thin film research, vacuum metallurgy, surface physics, electronic materials and processing, plasma science and technology and applied surface science.

NAME(S) OF PROGRAMS:
• **Graduate Research Awards**
• **Russell and Sigurd Varian Award**
• **Nellie Yeoh Whetten Award**

TYPE:
Awards/prizes; Fellowships. Cash awards and a one-year fellowship in recognition of scientific promise or excellence in graduate studies in vacuum science.

The Whetten Award is offered to encourage and recognize participation by women in science and engineering.

PURPOSE:
To recognize and encourage excellence in graduate studies in the sciences and technologies of interest to the Society.

LEGAL BASIS:
Nonprofit 501(c)(3) organization.

ELIGIBILITY:
All awards are open to students engaged in graduate studies in major fields of the organization's interest at accredited graduate schools in North America.

For the Whetten Award, the nominee must be a registered female graduate student in an accredited academic institution at the time when the applications are due. Criteria for selection of the awardee are research and academic excellence.

FINANCIAL DATA:
Amount of support per award: Graduate Research Awards: $1,000 per award; $1,500 each for the Whetten Award and for the Varian Award, plus reimbursed travel support (up to $750 maximum) to attend the International Symposium.
Total amount of support: Varies.

NUMBER OF APPLICANTS MOST RECENT YEAR:
11.

NUMBER OF AWARDS: Graduate Research Awards: Approximately 3 annually; Varian Award and Whetten Award: 1 each per year.

ADDRESS INQUIRIES TO:
Angela Klink, Program Administrator
E-mail: angela@avs.org

MCDONNELL CENTER FOR THE SPACE SCIENCES

Washington University, Campus Box 1105
One Brookings Drive
St. Louis, MO 63130-4899
(314) 935-5332

E-MAIL ADDRESS:
trecia@physics.wustl.edu

WEB SITE ADDRESS:
mcss.wustl.edu

TYPE:
Fellowships. These fellowships are funded by a gift from the McDonnell Douglas Foundation to Washington University and provide tuition remission plus stipend for graduate students interested in pursuing research in the space sciences who are enrolled in the Washington University Departments of Physics or Earth and Planetary Sciences.

See entry 2623 for full listing.

NATIONAL SCIENCE FOUNDATION [2101]

Division of Physics
4201 Wilson Boulevard
Arlington, VA 22230
(703) 292-8890
Fax: (703) 292-9078

E-MAIL ADDRESS:
dcalwel@nsf.gov

WEB SITE ADDRESS:
www.nsf.gov

AREAS OF INTEREST:
Nuclear, theoretical, atomic and molecular, gravitational, and elementary particles, education and interdisciplinary research, physics of living systems, particle and nuclear astrophysics.

NAME(S) OF PROGRAMS:
● **Physics Research Grants**

TYPE:
Research grants.

ELIGIBILITY:
As specified in the NSF Grant Proposal Guidelines.

FINANCIAL DATA:
Amount of support per award: Varies.
Total amount of support: Varies.

APPLICATION INFORMATION:
Application information is available on the web site.
Duration: Typically one to five years. Renewals by reapplication.

Deadline: Varies according to program.

ADDRESS INQUIRIES TO:
Cognizant Program Director
Division of Physics
(See address above.)

SOCIETY OF PHYSICS STUDENTS [2102]

American Institute of Physics
One Physics Ellipse
College Park, MD 20740
(301) 209-3007
Fax: (301) 209-0839

E-MAIL ADDRESS:
sps@aip.org

WEB SITE ADDRESS:
www.spsnational.
org/programs/awards/research.htm

AREAS OF INTEREST:
Physics.

NAME(S) OF PROGRAMS:
● **Sigma Pi Sigma Undergraduate Research Awards**

TYPE:
Awards/prizes.

PURPOSE:
To promote interest in physics among students and the general public.

LEGAL BASIS:
Nonprofit.

ELIGIBILITY:
Must participate in annual competition and must be SPS member.

FINANCIAL DATA:
Amount of support per award: Up to $2,000.
Total amount of support: Varies.

COOPERATIVE FUNDING PROGRAMS: Funded through income from the Sigma Pi Sigma Trust Endowment Fund.

NUMBER OF AWARDS: Typically 6 to 10.

APPLICATION INFORMATION:
Submit a proposal to the Society which:
(1) contains a precise statement of the proposed Chapter activity;
(2) shows evidence of imaginative and thoughtful appraisal of the objectives of the SPS program and the ways in which the proposed activity would contribute towards those objectives;
(3) is written clearly and concisely in correct English;
(4) includes bibliographical references;
(5) contains a realistic budget totaling not more than $2,000 and;
(6) is signed by the advisor and officers of the Chapter.
Duration: One year.
Deadline: November 15.

STAFF:
Toni Saucy, Director

SOCIETY OF PHYSICS STUDENTS [2103]

One Physics Ellipse
College Park, MD 20740
(301) 209-3009
Fax: (301) 209-0839

E-MAIL ADDRESS:
sps@aip.org

WEB SITE ADDRESS:
www.spsnational.org

FOUNDED: 1968

AREAS OF INTEREST:
Physics.

NAME(S) OF PROGRAMS:
● **Future Faces of Physics Awards**

TYPE:
Awards/prizes.

YEAR PROGRAM STARTED: 2011

PURPOSE:
To promote interest in physics.

LEGAL BASIS:
Not-for-profit, 501(c)(3).

ELIGIBILITY:
Applicant must be a Society of Physics Students member.

FINANCIAL DATA:
Amount of support per award: Up to $300.
Total amount of support: Approximately $1,500 per year.

NUMBER OF APPLICANTS MOST RECENT YEAR:
5.

NUMBER OF AWARDS: 5.

APPLICATION INFORMATION:
Application information is available on the web site.
Duration: One year.
Deadline: November 15. Announcement January 1.

STAFF:
Dr. Gary White, Director

*SPECIAL STIPULATIONS:
Only one proposal may be submitted by an SPS chapter.

SOCIETY OF PHYSICS STUDENTS [2104]

One Physics Ellipse
College Park, MD 20740
(301) 209-3007
Fax: (301) 209-0839

E-MAIL ADDRESS:
sps@aip.org

WEB SITE ADDRESS:
www.spsnational.org

FOUNDED: 1968

AREAS OF INTEREST:
Physics.

NAME(S) OF PROGRAMS:
● **Marsh W. White Awards**

TYPE:
Awards/prizes.

YEAR PROGRAM STARTED: 1974

PURPOSE:
To promote interest in physics.

LEGAL BASIS:
Not-for-profit, 501(c)(3).

ELIGIBILITY:
Applicant must be a Society of Physics Students member.

FINANCIAL DATA:
Amount of support per award: Up to $300.
Total amount of support: Approximately $6,300 per year.

NUMBER OF APPLICANTS MOST RECENT YEAR:
35.

NUMBER OF AWARDS: 21.

APPLICATION INFORMATION:
Application information is available on the web site.

Duration: One year.

Deadline: November 15. Announcement January 1.

STAFF:
Tony Sauncy, Director

ADDRESS INQUIRIES TO:
See e-mail address above.

*SPECIAL STIPULATIONS:
Only one proposal may be submitted by an SPS chapter.

SOCIETY OF PHYSICS STUDENTS
One Physics Ellipse
College Park, MD 20740-3843
(301) 209-3007
Fax: (301) 209-0839

E-MAIL ADDRESS:
sps@aip.org

WEB SITE ADDRESS:
www.spsnational.org

TYPE:
Scholarships.

See entry 1757 for full listing.

LIFE SCIENCES

Life sciences (general)

AMERICAN UROGYNECOLOGIC FOUNDATION [2105]
2025 M Street, N.W., Suite 800
Washington, DC 20036
(202) 367-1167
Fax: (202) 367-2167

E-MAIL ADDRESS:
info@augs.org

WEB SITE ADDRESS:
www.augs.org

AREAS OF INTEREST:
Incontinence and pelvic dysfunctions.

NAME(S) OF PROGRAMS:
● **June Allyson Award**

TYPE:
Research grants.

PURPOSE:
To provide research training and experience for a candidate who exhibits significant evidence of talent and dedication to research.

ELIGIBILITY:
Applicant must:
(1) be an active, life, honorary or allied health member of AUGS;
(2) be a current fellow in either an accredited or non-accredited fellowship program;
(3) have a senior research mentor or mentoring team. Mentors or co-investigators need not be members of AUGS and;
(4) funding must remain at the same institution for the period of the research project.

FINANCIAL DATA:
The award may be used for purchases of equipment and supplies, laboratory tests, technician/research assistant salaries, Institutional Review Board costs, and/or statistical report. Salary support for the applicant is not allowed.
Amount of support per award: Up to $25,000.
Total amount of support: $25,000.

NUMBER OF APPLICANTS MOST RECENT YEAR:
Average 20 per year.

NUMBER OF AWARDS: 1.

APPLICATION INFORMATION:
Application requirements are available online.
Duration: One year.
Deadline: October 15.

ADDRESS INQUIRIES TO:
Tristan Wood, Senior Associate
(See e-mail address above.)

ANXIETY AND DEPRESSION ASSOCIATION OF AMERICA
8701 Georgia Avenue, Suite 412
Silver Spring, MD 20910
(240) 485-1001
Fax: (240) 485-1035

E-MAIL ADDRESS:
information@adaa.org

WEB SITE ADDRESS:
www.adaa.org

TYPE:
Conferences/seminars; Project/program grants; Research grants; Seed money grants; Travel grants.

See entry 2570 for full listing.

DAIRY RESEARCH INSTITUTE - NATIONAL DAIRY COUNCIL
10255 West Higgins Road
Suite 900
Rosemont, IL 60018-5616
(847) 803-2000
Fax: (847) 803-2077

E-MAIL ADDRESS:
chris.cifelli@rosedmi.com

WEB SITE ADDRESS:
www.driresearchsubmission.com

TYPE:
Research contracts. The National Dairy Council is the nutrition research, education and communications arm of Dairy Management Inc. On behalf of U.S. dairy farmers, the National Dairy Council provides science-based nutrition information to, and in collaboration with, a variety of stakeholders committed to fostering a healthier society, including health professionals, educators, school nutrition directors, academia, industry, consumers and media. The National Dairy Council comprises a staff of nutrition science researchers, registered dietitians and communications experts dedicated to educating the public on the health benefits of consuming milk and milk products throughout a person's lifespan.

See entry 2671 for full listing.

DJ & T FOUNDATION [2106]
9201 Wilshire Boulevard, Suite 204
Beverly Hills, CA 90210
(310) 278-1160
Fax: (310) 275-6202

E-MAIL ADDRESS:
will@prappascompany.com

WEB SITE ADDRESS:
www.djtfoundation.org

FOUNDED: 1995

AREAS OF INTEREST:
Animal population control.

TYPE:
Grants-in-aid. Fund grants to organizations that operate low-cost spay/neuter clinics or offer free or low-cost spay/neuter voucher programs.

YEAR PROGRAM STARTED: 1995

PURPOSE:
To fund nonprofit, low-cost spay and neuter clinics.

LEGAL BASIS:
Private foundation.

ELIGIBILITY:
Eligible organizations must be IRS 501(c)(3) tax-exempt.

GEOGRAPHIC RESTRICTIONS:
United States.

FINANCIAL DATA:
Amount of support per award: Varies.
Total amount of support: Varies.

NUMBER OF APPLICANTS MOST RECENT YEAR:
More than 200.

NUMBER OF AWARDS: 75 to 100.

APPLICATION INFORMATION:
Applications are available at the web site and must include a copy of the IRS tax determination letter.
Duration: Varies.

ADDRESS INQUIRIES TO:
DJ & T Foundation
(See address above.)

THE HAMNER INSTITUTES FOR HEALTH SCIENCES
6 Davis Drive
Research Triangle Park, NC 27709
(919) 558-1331
Fax: (919) 558-1430

E-MAIL ADDRESS:
koverman@thehamner.org

WEB SITE ADDRESS:
www.thehamner.org

TYPE:
Conferences/seminars; Fellowships; Internships; Visiting scholars.

See entry 2067 for full listing.

THE HASTINGS CENTER [2107]
21 Malcolm Gordon Road
Garrison, NY 10524
(845) 424-4040
Fax: (845) 424-4545

E-MAIL ADDRESS:
visitors@thehastingscenter.org

WEB SITE ADDRESS:
www.thehastingscenter.org

FOUNDED: 1969

AREAS OF INTEREST:
Ethical issues in medicine, health care and the life sciences. Recent research topics include biotechnology, death and dying, aging, neonatal care, allocation of resources, occupational health, health professional-patient relationships, chronic illness, rehabilitation medicine, AIDS, surrogate motherhood and artificial reproduction, organ transplantation, prospective payment systems, deinstitutionalization, nursing homes, animal experimentation, environmental protection, civic education and the professions and the public good.

NAME(S) OF PROGRAMS:
● **Visiting Scholars Program**

TYPE:
Residencies; Visiting scholars. Independent study. Some financial aid is available.

YEAR PROGRAM STARTED: 1969

PURPOSE:
To permit scholars and practitioners in the humanities or the sciences to conduct productive research on ethical issues in medicine, the life sciences and the professions.

LEGAL BASIS:
Nonprofit independent research association.

ELIGIBILITY:
Visiting Scholars Program is open to persons with a degree in the humanities, sciences, law or medicine and that are prepared to pursue their own independent research project in the Center's areas of interest.

FINANCIAL DATA:
Amount of support per award: Waiver of cost of apartment rental up to $600.
Total amount of support: Up to $600.

NUMBER OF APPLICANTS MOST RECENT YEAR:
35.

NUMBER OF AWARDS: 14.

APPLICATION INFORMATION:
Application information is available on the web site.

Duration: Two to eight weeks.

PUBLICATIONS:
Annual report; application guidelines; *Hastings Center Report*; *Hastings Center Books in Print*; *IRB: Ethics and Human Research*; *Bioethics Forum*.

ADDRESS INQUIRIES TO:
Visiting Scholars Program
(See address above.)

THOMAS F. AND KATE MILLER JEFFRESS MEMORIAL TRUST [2108]

Bank of America–Philanthropic Management
VA 2-300-12-92
1111 East Main Street, 12th Floor
Richmond, VA 23219
(804) 887-8773
Fax: (980) 233-7158

E-MAIL ADDRESS:
sarah.kay@ustrust.com

WEB SITE ADDRESS:
www.hria.org/tmfservices/tmfgrants.html

FOUNDED: 1981

AREAS OF INTEREST:
Astronomy, biosciences, chemistry, computer sciences, engineering, environmental sciences, material science, mathematics and physics.

NAME(S) OF PROGRAMS:
● **Jeffress Trust Awards Program in Interdisciplinary Research**

TYPE:
Research grants.

YEAR PROGRAM STARTED: 1982

PURPOSE:
To support basic research in chemical, medical, or other scientific fields at educational and research institutions in the Commonwealth of Virginia.

LEGAL BASIS:
Trust.

ELIGIBILITY:
Grants are made to tax-exempt institutions and organizations which are operated exclusively for charitable, scientific purposes. Grants are not made to private foundations.

GEOGRAPHIC RESTRICTIONS:
Virginia.

FINANCIAL DATA:
Amount of support per award: Up to $100,000 per year.
Total amount of support: $1,000,000.

NUMBER OF AWARDS: Up to 10.

APPLICATION INFORMATION:
Grant procedures and guidelines are available at the web site above.
Duration: One year.
Deadline: January 15.

PUBLICATIONS:
Guidelines.

ADDRESS INQUIRIES TO:
Sarah Kay
Vice President for Charitable Funds
Senior Philanthropic Relationship Manager
(See address above.)

NATIONAL EYE INSTITUTE

National Institutes of Health
5635 Fishers Lane, Suite 1300
Bethesda, MD 20892
(301) 451-2020
Fax: (301) 402-0528

WEB SITE ADDRESS:
www.nei.nih.gov

TYPE:
Conferences/seminars; Fellowships; Research grants; Training grants. Research Project Grants support individual investigators whose work is aimed at discovering means of improving the prevention, diagnosis and treatment of blinding and disabling eye and vision disorders.

Small Business Innovation Research Awards aim to stimulate technological innovations, to use small business to meet federal research-development needs that may ultimately lead to commercial products or services and to foster and encourage participation by minority and disadvantaged persons in technological innovations.

Areas of study include vision research, retinal diseases, corneal diseases, cataract, glaucoma, low vision and blindness rehabilitation, visual impairment and its rehabilitation, strabismus, amblyopia and visual processing.

See entry 2518 for full listing.

NATIONAL EYE INSTITUTE

5635 Fishers Lane, Suite 1300
Bethesda, MD 20892
(301) 451-2020
Fax: (301) 496-9997

E-MAIL ADDRESS:
wwd@nei.nih.gov

WEB SITE ADDRESS:
www.nei.nih.gov

TYPE:
Research grants; Research contracts.

See entry 2519 for full listing.

NATIONAL RESEARCH COUNCIL OF THE NATIONAL ACADEMIES

Fellowship and Research Associateship Programs
500 Fifth Street, N.W.
Washington, DC 20001
(202) 334-2760
Fax: (202) 334-2759

E-MAIL ADDRESS:
rap@nas.edu

WEB SITE ADDRESS:
www.nationalacademies.org/rap

TYPE:
Fellowships. Research awards. Fellowships at the graduate, postdoctoral and senior levels for research-in-residence at U.S. federal laboratories and affiliated institutions.

See entry 2039 for full listing.

KENNETH A. SCOTT CHARITABLE TRUST [2109]

c/o KeyBank Nonprofit Services
127 Public Square, 18th Floor
Cleveland, OH 44114-1306
(216) 752-3301

E-MAIL ADDRESS:
director@kennethscottcharitabletrust.org

WEB SITE ADDRESS:
www.kennethscottcharitabletrust.org

FOUNDED: 1995

AREAS OF INTEREST:
Animal welfare.

TYPE:
Project/program grants. Grants are available for animal welfare and humane education projects of national scope or significance anywhere in the U.S. Grants are available for localized projects of shelters and humane groups in Ohio and other Great Lakes states (only).

YEAR PROGRAM STARTED: 1995

PURPOSE:
To prevent cruelty to animals and promote the humane treatment of animals, particularly companion animals (dogs, cats) and other species commonly kept as household pets. Requests related to wildlife and animals in other settings may also be considered.

LEGAL BASIS:
Private foundation.

ELIGIBILITY:
Eligible organizations must be IRS 501(c)(3) tax-exempt. No grants to individuals.

GEOGRAPHIC RESTRICTIONS:
Ohio. Some grants in other Great Lakes states.

FINANCIAL DATA:
Amount of support per award: $15,000 average.
Total amount of support: $849,758 for the year 2013.

NUMBER OF AWARDS: 73 for the year 2013.

APPLICATION INFORMATION:
A query letter, e-mail or phone call to the Trust is required before submitting the application.
Duration: One year.
Deadline: March 15 and September 15 for Ohio proposals. December 15 and June 15 for National and Great Lakes proposals.

IRS IDENTIFICATION NUMBER: 34-7034544

ADDRESS INQUIRIES TO:
Dr. H. Richard Obermanns
Executive Director
(See address above.)

THE PERCY SLADEN MEMORIAL FUND [2110]

c/o The Linnean Society of London
Burlington House, Piccadilly
London W1J 0BF England
44 (0)20 7434 4479
Fax: 44 (0)20 7287 9364

E-MAIL ADDRESS:
info@linnean.org; gina@linnean.org

WEB SITE ADDRESS:
www.linnean.org

FOUNDED: 1904

AREAS OF INTEREST:
Natural sciences, with a focus of support on field work in the life and earth sciences, both through expeditions and individual research projects overseas.

NAME(S) OF PROGRAMS:
● **Percy Sladen Memorial Fund Grants**

TYPE:
Awards/prizes; Project/program grants; Research grants; Travel grants. Field work grants in life and earth sciences (excludes any projects which are part of further education, e.g., a Doctorate or a Master's course).

YEAR PROGRAM STARTED: 1904

PURPOSE:
To support field work away from usual country of residence.

LEGAL BASIS:
Registered charity.

ELIGIBILITY:
There are no restrictions in award of grants based on nationality, age, sex or prior qualifications. No grants for field work undertaken as part of a higher degree or general support for undergraduate expeditions.

FINANCIAL DATA:
Grants may be used toward a portion of total costs or for specific items of equipment. *Amount of support per award:* Generally, less than GBP 750.

APPLICATION INFORMATION:
Application form and referees reports are available from the Secretary to the Trustees at the address above. *Duration:* Grant must be taken up within one year of receipt. *Deadline:* January 30 and September 30.

ADDRESS INQUIRIES TO:
Gina Douglas
Secretary to the Trustees
(See address above.)

*SPECIAL STIPULATIONS:
No support for course work. No undergraduate expeditions. No grants for field work for completion of dissertations or higher degrees.

SOCIETY FOR THE STUDY OF AMPHIBIANS AND REPTILES
Department of Biological Sciences
University of Wisconsin-Whitewater
Whitewater, WI 53190
(262) 472-1069

E-MAIL ADDRESS:
kapferj@uww.edu

WEB SITE ADDRESS:
www.ssarherps.org/pages/GIH.php

TYPE:
Awards/prizes; Research grants. Awards are given in six categories: Conservation of Amphibians and/or Reptiles, Field Research, Laboratory Research, Herpetological Education, Travel and International Research.

See entry 2043 for full listing.

ROB AND BESSIE WELDER WILDLIFE FOUNDATION [2111]
10260 Welder Wildlife
Sinton, TX 78387
(361) 364-2643
Fax: (361) 364-2650

E-MAIL ADDRESS:
welderfoundation@welderwildlife.org

WEB SITE ADDRESS:
www.welderwildlife.org

FOUNDED: 1954

AREAS OF INTEREST:
Wildlife conservation, wildlife ecology, wildlife science and higher education (graduate level only).

TYPE:
Fellowships. Graduate research fellowships only in fields of wildlife ecology and management.

YEAR PROGRAM STARTED: 1956

PURPOSE:
To encourage and sponsor wildlife research and education.

LEGAL BASIS:
Private, nonprofit foundation.

ELIGIBILITY:
Graduate students at accredited universities seeking advanced degrees in the above-designated fields are eligible to apply. Undergraduates need not apply.

GEOGRAPHIC RESTRICTIONS:
Continental United States.

FINANCIAL DATA:
Fellowships are generally $1,500 (M.S.) to $1,700 (Ph.D.) per month, plus some funds for field supplies and travel. Living quarters are available for students doing research on the Foundation's refuge area near Sinton, TX, including utilities. *Amount of support per award:* Normally $20,000 per calendar year. *Total amount of support:* $100,000 available for the year 2014.

COOPERATIVE FUNDING PROGRAMS: The Foundation participates in cooperative funding for approvable proposals not adequately financed through other sources, if and when surplus funds are available.

NUMBER OF APPLICANTS MOST RECENT YEAR:
Over 20.

NUMBER OF AWARDS: 10.

APPLICATION INFORMATION:
Initial contact with the Foundation may be submitted in an abbreviated outline of the research problem, a preliminary estimate of expenses, and letter signed by a qualified member of the faculty at the parent university. If the Foundation staff thereafter entertains the matter further, a more complete proposal will be requested along with material concerning the proposed fellowship recipient. *Duration:* One year. May be renewed if progress is satisfactory. *Deadline:* October 1.

PUBLICATIONS:
Biennial report of staff and student activities.

IRS IDENTIFICATION NUMBER: 74-1381321

OFFICERS:
Terry Blankenship, Ph.D., Director
Selma Glasscock, Ph.D., Assistant Director

TRUSTEES:
Hughes C. Thomas
H.C. Weil
John J. Welder, V

ADDRESS INQUIRIES TO:
Terry Blankenship, Ph.D., Director
(See address above.)

*SPECIAL STIPULATIONS:
Priority will be given to research proposals involving studies on the Foundation's refuge area and/or in south Texas.

Agriculture, land resources, rural development

AGRICULTURAL HISTORY SOCIETY
MSU History Department
P.O. Box H
Mississippi State, MS 39762
(662) 268-2247

E-MAIL ADDRESS:
jgiesen@history.msstate.edu

WEB SITE ADDRESS:
www.aghistorysociety.org

TYPE:
Awards/prizes. The Everett E. Edwards Award is presented to the graduate student who submits the best manuscript on any aspect of agricultural history and rural studies during the current calendar year.

The Gilbert C. Fite Dissertation Award will be presented to the author of the best dissertation on any aspect of agricultural history completed during the current calendar year.

The Wayne D. Rasmussen Award is given to the author of the best article on agricultural history published by a journal other than *Agricultural History* during the current calendar year.

The Theodore Saloutos Book Award is presented to the author of a book on any aspect of agricultural history in the U.S. within the current year, broadly interpreted.

See entry 576 for full listing.

THE AMERICAN CHESTNUT FOUNDATION [2112]
160 Zillicoa Street, Suite D
Asheville, NC 28801
(828) 281-0047
Fax: (828) 253-5373

E-MAIL ADDRESS:
lisa@acf.org

WEB SITE ADDRESS:
www.acf.org

FOUNDED: 1983

AREAS OF INTEREST:
Chestnut research.

TYPE:
Research grants.

PURPOSE:
To restore the American chestnut to Eastern forests.

ELIGIBILITY:
Grants are reviewed on a case-by-case basis.

GEOGRAPHIC RESTRICTIONS:
United States.

FINANCIAL DATA:
Amount of support per award: $2,000 to $20,000. *Total amount of support:* Approximately $60,000 for the year 2012.

APPLICATION INFORMATION:
Send a letter of inquiry letter form, outlining the goal and purpose, the intended use, and amount of the grant requested.

Duration: Up to three years.
Deadline: Varies.

ADDRESS INQUIRIES TO:
Lisa Sousa
Director of Grants and Agreements
(See address above.)

AMERICAN FARM BUREAU FOUNDATION FOR AGRICULTURE [2113]

600 Maryland Avenue, S.W.
Suite 1000 West
Washington, DC 20024
(800) 443-8456
Fax: (202) 314-5121

E-MAIL ADDRESS:
foundation@fb.org

WEB SITE ADDRESS:
www.agfoundation.org

AREAS OF INTEREST:
Agricultural, consumer education, classroom, consumer and farm safety programs.

NAME(S) OF PROGRAMS:
• **White-Reinhardt Fund for Education**

TYPE:
Conferences/seminars; Project/program grants; Research contracts. Teacher Scholarships to National Conference.

YEAR PROGRAM STARTED: 1967

PURPOSE:
To initiate and finance education programs and projects.

GEOGRAPHIC RESTRICTIONS:
United States.

FINANCIAL DATA:
Amount of support per award: Teacher Scholarships: $1,000 to $1,500; Mini-grants: Up to $500.
Total amount of support: Varies.

APPLICATION INFORMATION:
Mini-grant applications must be completed and submitted to the State Farm Bureau president, Agriculture in the Classroom coordinator or administrator for signature. All applications will be pre-screened for compliance with grant proposal guidelines. Any grant not meeting guidelines will be eliminated from the judging process prior to examination by judges.
Duration: One year.
Deadline: November.

ADDRESS INQUIRIES TO:
Julia Recko, Program Coordinator
(See address above.)

AMERICAN FLORAL ENDOWMENT [2114]

1601 Duke Street
Alexandria, VA 22314
(703) 838-5211
Fax: (703) 838-5212

E-MAIL ADDRESS:
afe@endowment.org

WEB SITE ADDRESS:
www.endowment.org

FOUNDED: 1961

AREAS OF INTEREST:
Floricultural/environmental horticulture research and development funding in the U.S.

TYPE:
Internships; Project/program grants; Research grants; Scholarships. The Endowment funds research and educational development in floriculture and environmental horticulture designed to produce solutions to industry needs and promote the growth and improvement of the floral industry for the benefit of the grower, wholesale, retail, allied segments and the general public.

The Endowment supports educational programs focused on attracting young people to the industry, and educational endeavors to identify and solve industry needs and/or challenges. The programs are divided into two major areas:
(1) paid floriculture internships/scholarships for full-time college students and;
(2) general educational grants to national programs.

YEAR PROGRAM STARTED: 1961

PURPOSE:
To further the advancement of education and science in the field of floriculture through funding research and studies in the floriculture field, the results of which will be published; to finance scholarships and internships to students interested in floriculture.

LEGAL BASIS:
Not-for-profit, nongovernmental organization.

GEOGRAPHIC RESTRICTIONS:
United States.

FINANCIAL DATA:
Amount of support per award: Varies.
Total amount of support: Varies.

APPLICATION INFORMATION:
Contact the Endowment.
Duration: Typically one year; research grants can be multiyear.
Deadline: Varies.

PUBLICATIONS:
Update, quarterly newsletter; annual report.

AMERICAN SOCIETY FOR ENOLOGY AND VITICULTURE [2115]

1784 Picasso Avenue, Suite D
Davis, CA 95618-0551
(530) 753-3142
Fax: (530) 753-3318

E-MAIL ADDRESS:
society@asev.org

WEB SITE ADDRESS:
www.asev.org

FOUNDED: 1951

AREAS OF INTEREST:
A scientific society of enologists, viticulturists and others in the fields of wine and grape production, promoting technical advancement and integrated research in science and industry.

TYPE:
Scholarships. Awards for undergraduate or graduate students enrolled in enology or viticulture or in a curriculum which emphasizes a science basic to the wine and grape industry and who intend to pursue a career in research for the wine or grape industry after graduation from college or university.

PURPOSE:
To support education and research in enology, viticulture or related fields.

LEGAL BASIS:
Professional, scientific association.

ELIGIBILITY:
Undergraduate and graduate students who have been accepted at an accredited college or university in North America, are enrolled in an appropriate field of study and reside in North America may apply. Applicants must be at least junior level in academic status (60 quarter units or 45 semester units). Undergraduate students must have a minimum 3.0 overall grade point average on a scale of 4.0. Graduate students must have a minimum 3.2 overall grade point average on a scale of 4.0.

FINANCIAL DATA:
Amount of support per award: Varies each academic year.
Total amount of support: Varies each academic year.

APPLICATION INFORMATION:
Applications can be downloaded from the web site.
Duration: One academic year. Renewable in open competition.
Deadline: All completed forms, letters and transcripts must be received by March 1.

STAFF:
Lyndie M. Boulton, Executive Director

ADDRESS INQUIRIES TO:
Scholarship Committee
P.O. Box 1855
Davis, CA 95617-1855

CENTER FOR PLANT CONSERVATION [2116]

Missouri Botanical Garden
P.O. Box 299
St. Louis, MO 63166-0299
(314) 577-9450
(314) 577-9451
Fax: (314) 577-9456

E-MAIL ADDRESS:
cpc.temp@mobot.org

WEB SITE ADDRESS:
www.centerforplantconservation.org

FOUNDED: 1984

AREAS OF INTEREST:
Education.

NAME(S) OF PROGRAMS:
• **Catherine H. Beattie Fellowship for Conservation Horticulture**

TYPE:
Fellowships.

YEAR PROGRAM STARTED: 1984

PURPOSE:
To aid students who pursue research in the area of rare plant conservation.

ELIGIBILITY:
Must be a graduate student in biology, horticulture, or a related field conducting research on a rare or endangered U.S. plant. Preference is given to students focusing on the endangered flora of the Carolinas or the southeastern U.S.

FINANCIAL DATA:
Amount of support per award: $1,000 to $4,000.
Total amount of support: Varies.

NUMBER OF APPLICANTS MOST RECENT YEAR:
6.

NUMBER OF AWARDS: 1 to 2.

APPLICATION INFORMATION:
Applicants should submit the following:
(1) a two- to three-page proposal, which includes a description of the research project and how it relates to the student's academic and professional development;
(2) an itemized budget for the funds requested;
(3) a current resume;
(4) a letter of endorsement by an academic advisor from the institution where the student is pursuing graduate studies;
(5) the names of three additional persons qualified to describe the student's character and ability and;
(6) official transcripts for both undergraduate and graduate academic records.

Applicant should be prepared to write an article for CPC Newsletter, *Plant Conservation*.

Duration: Varies.

Deadline: November 30. Notification by March 31.

PUBLICATIONS:
Plant Conservation, newsletter.

THE CH FOUNDATION [2117]
P.O. Box 94038
Lubbock, TX 79493-4038
(806) 792-0448
Fax: (806) 792-7824

E-MAIL ADDRESS:
ksanford@chfoundation.com

WEB SITE ADDRESS:
www.chfoundationlubbock.com

FOUNDED: 1976

AREAS OF INTEREST:
Agriculture, community development, culture education, health, ranching, research, social services and youth.

TYPE:
Capital grants; Project/program grants.

YEAR PROGRAM STARTED: 1991

PURPOSE:
To support programs that meet the needs of and improve the quality of life.

ELIGIBILITY:
Grants are limited to organizations whose services benefit the Lubbock area of Texas. Grants are made to organizations that have tax-exempt status under Section 501(c)(3) of the Internal Revenue Code. No grants are made to individuals or political organizations.

GEOGRAPHIC RESTRICTIONS:
Lubbock, Texas and surrounding counties.

APPLICATION INFORMATION:
Contact the Foundation to determine the interest and appropriateness of a full proposal.

Duration: One year. Renewal possible.

Deadline: May 1. Disbursements are made in December.

PUBLICATIONS:
Application guidelines.

IRS IDENTIFICATION NUMBER: 75-1534816

ADDRESS INQUIRIES TO:
Kay Sanford, Grants Administrator
(See address above.)

FARM AID [2118]
501 Cambridge Street
Third Floor
Cambridge, MA 02141
(617) 354-2922
Fax: (617) 354-6992

E-MAIL ADDRESS:
grants@farmaid.org

WEB SITE ADDRESS:
www.farmaid.org/grants

FOUNDED: 1985

AREAS OF INTEREST:
Supporting organizations that help farm families stay on their land, build local markets, confront the threat of corporate control of agriculture, train new farmers and support farmer-to-farmer programs for more sustainable agricultural practices. Emergency and disaster assistance for farm families.

TYPE:
General operating grants; Project/program grants. Grants fall within three broad categories which make it possible for organizations to build long-term solutions to the problems farmers face.

Grant Categories:
(1) Growing the Good Food Movement: These grants fund organizations or projects that seek to strengthen what Farm Aid calls the Good Food Movement, the growing number of Americans reaching for and demanding family farm-identified, local, organic or humanely raised food. These grants build connections between farmers and consumers, creating new markets for family farmers.
(2) Helping Farmers Thrive: These grants fund organizations or projects that assist farmers transition to more sustainable and profitable farming practices, find alternative markets, or start a new farming operation as well as provide support services to farm families in crisis. These organizations are the core of the Farmer Resource Network which responds to individual farmers as well as regional events such as natural disasters.
(3) Taking Action to Change the System: These grants fund organizations or projects that promote fair farm policies and grassroots organizing campaigns to defend and bolster family farm-centered agriculture. These grants enable advocates to strengthen the voices of family farmers and promote their interests on a local, regional and national level.

YEAR PROGRAM STARTED: 1985

LEGAL BASIS:
Tax-exempt, charitable and educational organization.

ELIGIBILITY:
Applicants must be IRS 501(c)(3) nonprofit organizations and include a copy of their IRS 501(c)(3) tax-exempt verification letter. If organization does not have 501(c)(3) status, it must include the IRS 501(c)(3) letter and authorization from the organization acting as its fiscal agent.

The following types of projects are not eligible for Farm Aid funding:
(1) grants or loans to individuals;
(2) grants or loans to support commercial operation of a farming enterprise;
(3) production of book, film, television or radio projects;
(4) projects outside the U.S.;
(5) projects directed or substantially funded by government bodies (federal, state or

local), including Resource Conservation & Development Councils (RC & Ds);
(6) legal defense funds;
(7) capital campaigns, equipment purchases, endowments or deficit financing;
(8) historic preservation of farmland or buildings;
(9) lobbying to influence elections or legislation and;
(10) conferences, publications or research projects unless they are directly connected to ongoing program activities.

GEOGRAPHIC RESTRICTIONS:
United States.

FINANCIAL DATA:
Amount of support per award: Grants typically from $3,000 to $20,000; mostly $5,000 to $7,500.
Total amount of support: Varies.

NUMBER OF APPLICANTS MOST RECENT YEAR:
150.

NUMBER OF AWARDS: 45 or more.

APPLICATION INFORMATION:
Up-to-date application information is available on the web site.

Deadline: Proposals: August 1. Grants are awarded in December.

PUBLICATIONS:
Newsletter.

IRS IDENTIFICATION NUMBER: 36-3383233

ADDRESS INQUIRIES TO:
Alicia Harvie, Program Manager
(See address above.)

THE GARDEN CLUB OF AMERICA [2119]
14 East 60th Street, Third Floor
New York, NY 10022
(212) 753-8287
Fax: (212) 753-0134

E-MAIL ADDRESS:
grosscupscholarship@gmail.com

WEB SITE ADDRESS:
www.gcamerica.org

FOUNDED: 1913

AREAS OF INTEREST:
Horticulture or related field, or any endeavor in the field of gardening including conservation, historic preservation and plant conservation.

NAME(S) OF PROGRAMS:
● **Katharine M. Grosscup Scholarships**

TYPE:
Scholarships.

YEAR PROGRAM STARTED: 1981

PURPOSE:
To encourage the study of horticulture and related fields.

LEGAL BASIS:
Nonprofit national organization.

ELIGIBILITY:
Applicants must be college juniors, seniors, or graduate students who wish to pursue the study of horticulture and related fields.

GEOGRAPHIC RESTRICTIONS:
Indiana, Kentucky, Michigan, Ohio, Pennsylvania and West Virginia.

FINANCIAL DATA:
Amount of support per award: Up to $3,500.

NUMBER OF AWARDS: 2 or more.

APPLICATION INFORMATION:
Application available online. The Committee does not accept telephone inquiries.
Duration: One year.
Deadline: January 10.

PUBLICATIONS:
Program announcement.

ADDRESS INQUIRIES TO:
Grosscup Scholarship
c/o Leslie Marting
2513 Marlboro Road
Cleveland Heights, OH 44118

THE FRED C. GLOECKNER FOUNDATION, INC.   [2120]
600 Mamaroneck Avenue
Harrison, NY 10528
(914) 698-2300
Fax: (914) 698-0848

E-MAIL ADDRESS:
jsimone@fredgloeckner.com

WEB SITE ADDRESS:
www.gloecknerfoundation.org

FOUNDED: 1960

AREAS OF INTEREST:
Floriculture and related fields such as plant pathology, plant breeding, agricultural engineering, agricultural economics, entomology and plant physiology related to floriculture.

TYPE:
Assistantships; Project/program grants; Research grants.

YEAR PROGRAM STARTED: 1961

PURPOSE:
To support floriculture research and education.

LEGAL BASIS:
Nonprofit educational corporation.

ELIGIBILITY:
Grants are awarded to nonprofit institutions, primarily colleges and universities, for research and education projects in the above fields. Research in basic plant physiology unrelated to floriculture is not considered. Grants may include assistantships for qualified graduate students seeking an M.S. or Ph.D. in the above fields. Grants are not made directly to students.

GEOGRAPHIC RESTRICTIONS:
United States.

FINANCIAL DATA:
Amount of support per award: $2,000 to $12,000.
Total amount of support: Varies.

NUMBER OF APPLICANTS MOST RECENT YEAR:
45.

NUMBER OF AWARDS: 20.

REPRESENTATIVE AWARDS:
$8,000 to Miller B. McDonald, Ohio State University, for the development of seed quality tests for monitoring flower seed vigor and deterioration; $6,000 to Merriam Karlsson, University of Alaska, Fairbanks, for day and night temperature requirements for flowering and development of cyclamen; $9,700 to Bernard Rubinstein, University of Massachusetts, Amherst, for use of heat shock to preserve flowers not affected by

ethylene; $2,000 to Andrew Senesac, Cornell University, for preemergent weed control for transplanted field-grown cutflowers.

APPLICATION INFORMATION:
Applications are available from the Foundation office, or can be downloaded from the web site.
Duration: One year. Renewals possible.
Deadline: April 1.

PUBLICATIONS:
Annual report; application guidelines.

OFFICERS:
Paul L. Daum, President
Dr. Richard Craig, Vice President
Martin D. Kortjohn, Treasurer
Joseph A. Simone, Secretary

DIRECTORS:
Dr. Richard Craig
Margery Daughtery
Paul L. Daum
Dr. Paul Allen Hammer
J. Michael Klesa
Martin D. Kortjohn
Andrew Lee
Jay Sheely
Joseph A. Simone

ADDRESS INQUIRIES TO:
Joseph A. Simone, Secretary
(See address above.)

THE HERB SOCIETY OF AMERICA, INC.   [2121]
9019 Kirtland Chardon Road
Kirtland, OH 44094
(440) 256-0514
Fax: (440) 256-0541

E-MAIL ADDRESS:
herbs@herbsociety.org

WEB SITE ADDRESS:
www.herbsociety.org

FOUNDED: 1933

AREAS OF INTEREST:
Furthering the knowledge and use of herbs and contributing the results of the experience and research of its members to the records of horticulture, science, literature, history, art or economics.

CONSULTING OR VOLUNTEER SERVICES:
Volunteer services including maintenance of public gardens and workshops.

TYPE:
Research grants. Cash award for research on herbal projects.

YEAR PROGRAM STARTED: 1971

PURPOSE:
To promote the knowledge, use and delight of herbs through educational programs, research, and sharing the experiences of its members with the community.

LEGAL BASIS:
Tax-exempt, nonprofit corporation under IRS 501(c)(3).

ELIGIBILITY:
Students, professionals and individuals engaged in research on the horticultural, scientific and/or social applications or use of herbs throughout history.

Funding does not cover indirect costs, purchase or maintenance of durable computer, laboratory or office equipment, expenses related to tuition, textbooks, or conference attendance, private garden development, or travel to/from research site.

FINANCIAL DATA:
Total amount of support: Up to $5,000.

NUMBER OF APPLICANTS MOST RECENT YEAR:
30.

NUMBER OF AWARDS: Varies.

APPLICATION INFORMATION:
Applications should include the following:
(1) application form;
(2) professional vita, not to exceed two pages, listing qualifications for the project, academic degrees and honors;
(3) explanation, not to exceed 500 words, describing how the project will be completed, where the work will be done, and what facilities and equipment are available;
(4) detailed listing of all anticipated costs and;
(5) specific timeline for the project.
Successful applicants will be required to sign a Grant Acceptance Form prior to the award of a grant.
Duration: One year. No renewals.
Deadline: January 31. Announcement May 1.

PUBLICATIONS:
The Herbarist; newsletter; grant guidelines.

IRS IDENTIFICATION NUMBER: 34-1596261

ADDRESS INQUIRIES TO:
Research Grant
(See address above.)

*SPECIAL STIPULATIONS:
Under the terms of the grant, periodic progress reports are to be sent to the Research Grant Chairman. At the termination of the project, The Herb Society expects a complete copy of the finished product for the Herb Society Library and a summary of the work for publication in the Society's publication, *The Herbarist.* The Society reserves the right to reject or accept credit in any publication resulting from the grant.

HORTICULTURAL RESEARCH INSTITUTE, INC.   [2122]
2130 Stella Court
Columbus, OH 43215
(202) 789-2900
Fax: (202) 789-1893

E-MAIL ADDRESS:
josepha@americanhort.org

WEB SITE ADDRESS:
www.hriresearch.org

FOUNDED: 1962

AREAS OF INTEREST:
Nursery and landscape research.

NAME(S) OF PROGRAMS:
● **HRI Competitive Grants Program**

TYPE:
Grants-in-aid; Research grants; Scholarships; Seed money grants; Research contracts.

YEAR PROGRAM STARTED: 1974

PURPOSE:
To direct, fund, promote and communicate research which increases the quality and value of plants, improves the productivity and profitability of the nursery and landscape industry and protects and enhances the environment.

LEGAL BASIS:
501(c)(3).

ELIGIBILITY:
Proposals are evaluated on the basis of their relevance to the nursery industry.

GEOGRAPHIC RESTRICTIONS:
North America.

FINANCIAL DATA:
Amount of support per award: $5,000 to
$35,000 for the year 2014.
Total amount of support: $400,000 for the
year 2014.

NUMBER OF APPLICANTS MOST RECENT YEAR:
65.

NUMBER OF AWARDS: 16 for the year 2013.

APPLICATION INFORMATION:
Completed proposals must be submitted
using HRI's online application process. No
hard copies or e-mailed applications will be
accepted.
Deadline: June 1. Announcement in late
January/early February.

PUBLICATIONS:
Application guidelines.

IRS IDENTIFICATION NUMBER: 52-1052547

ADDRESS INQUIRIES TO:
Joseph Albano, Ph.D.
Research Programs Director
(See address above.)

HORTICULTURAL RESEARCH INSTITUTE, INC.

1200 G Street, N.W.
Suite 800
Washington, DC 20005
(202) 695-2474
Fax: (888) 761-7883

E-MAIL ADDRESS:
tjodon@hriresearch.org

WEB SITE ADDRESS:
www.hriresearch.org

TYPE:
Scholarships. The Carville M. Akehurst
Memorial Scholarship was established by the
Mid-Atlantic Nursery Trade Show, Inc.
(MANTS) to provide scholarship opportunity
to qualified students from Maryland, Virginia
or West Virginia to help ensure the continuity
of the nursery and landscape profession.

The Bigelow Scholarships provide aid to
students from New England.

The Muggets Scholarship and the Spring
Meadow Nursery Scholarship are intended to
help aspiring students from across the U.S.
obtain a degree in horticulture (nursery
industry).

See entry 1697 for full listing.

INTERNATIONAL DEVELOPMENT RESEARCH CENTRE (IDRC)   [2123]

150 Kent Street
Ottawa ON K1P 0B2 Canada
(613) 696-2098
Fax: (613) 236-4026

E-MAIL ADDRESS:
awards@idrc.ca

WEB SITE ADDRESS:
www.idrc.ca/awards

FOUNDED: 1970

AREAS OF INTEREST:
Forestry.

NAME(S) OF PROGRAMS:
● **John G. Bene Fellowship in
Community Forestry: Trees and People**

TYPE:
Awards/prizes; Fellowships. Fellowship
provides assistance to Canadian graduate
students undertaking research on the
relationship of forest resources to the social,
economic, cultural and environmental welfare
of people in developing countries.

PURPOSE:
To provide assistance to Canadian graduate
students undertaking research on the
relationship of forest resources to the social,
economic, cultural and environmental welfare
of people in developing countries.

LEGAL BASIS:
Public corporation.

ELIGIBILITY:
The successful candidate will be the one
whose work most benefits the lives of the
less privileged people in the developing
country. Applicants must:
(1) be Canadian citizens or hold permanent
residency status;
(2) be registered at a Canadian university at
the Master's or doctoral level;
(3) have an academic background that
combines forestry or agroforestry with social
sciences; applicants from interdisciplinary
programs may also be eligible, provided their
programs contain the specified elements;
(4) research proposal must be approved by
the research/thesis committee;
(5) provide evidence of affiliation with an
institution or organization in the region in
which the research will take place and;
(6) have completed course work and passed
comprehensive examinations by the time of
award tenure.

FINANCIAL DATA:
Amount of support per award: Up to $15,000
per year.
Total amount of support: Up to $15,000.

NUMBER OF APPLICANTS MOST RECENT YEAR:
Varies.

NUMBER OF AWARDS: 1 per year.

APPLICATION INFORMATION:
Applications must be submitted online from
the IDRC's competitions page.
Duration: Generally, three to 12 months.
Candidates may apply for renewal of funding
for a second year of field work. Renewals are
an exception.

PUBLICATIONS:
Program announcement.

ADDRESS INQUIRIES TO:
Fellowships and Awards
(See address above.)

*SPECIAL STIPULATIONS:
Proposed field research must take place in a
developing country.

LAND O'LAKES FOUNDATION

4001 Lexington Avenue North
Arden Hills, MN 55126
(651) 481-2123
Fax: (651) 481-2000

E-MAIL ADDRESS:
lrbotham@landolakes.com

WEB SITE ADDRESS:
www.foundation.landolakes.com

TYPE:
Scholarships. John Brandt Memorial
Scholarship Program is a $25,000 scholarship
available to graduate students pursuing
dairy-related degrees. One or two

scholarships are awarded annually to
deserving candidates who have demonstrated
exceptional commitment and aptitude toward
their field of study.

See entry 201 for full listing.

NATIONAL ASSOCIATION OF FARM BROADCASTING FOUNDATION

1100 Platte Falls Road
Platte City, MO 64079
(816) 431-4032
Fax: (816) 431-4087

E-MAIL ADDRESS:
aaron@nafb.com

WEB SITE ADDRESS:
www.nafbfoundation.com

TYPE:
Scholarships. Since 1977, the NAFB
Foundation has provided financial support
and educational opportunities in the form of
college scholarships to assist students in
pursuit of careers in agricultural
communications. Currently the NAFB
Foundation offers three annual college
scholarships. These scholarships are
recognized at the National NAFB
Convention.

See entry 1945 for full listing.

NATIONAL CATTLEMAN'S BEEF ASSOCIATION

9110 East Nichols Avenue
Centennial, CO 80112-3450
(830) 569-0046
Fax: (303) 770-6921

E-MAIL ADDRESS:
smcneill@beef.org

WEB SITE ADDRESS:
www.beefresearch.org

TYPE:
Grants-in-aid; Research grants; Research
contracts. Research contracts and
grants-in-aid for experimental projects in the
areas of:
(1) beef as part of a balanced diet;
(2) parity studies;
(3) health benefits of beef lipids and;
(4) contribution of beef nutrients to total diet.

Proposals solicited via specific RFPs (request
for proposals).

See entry 2675 for full listing.

NATIONAL DAIRY SHRINE   [2124]

P.O. Box 725
Denmark, WI 54208
(920) 863-6333
Fax: (920) 863-6333

E-MAIL ADDRESS:
info@dairyshrine.org

WEB SITE ADDRESS:
www.dairyshrine.org

FOUNDED: 1949

AREAS OF INTEREST:
Dairy production, research, milk products,
milk marketing, genetics and education.

NAME(S) OF PROGRAMS:
● **National Dairy Shrine Student
Recognition Program**

- **NDS Graduate Production Award**
- **NDS Progressive Dairy Producers Awards**
- **NDS/Core Scholarship**
- **NDS/DMI Milk Marketing Scholarships**
- **NDS/Iager Scholarship**
- **NDS/Kildee Scholarships**
- **NDS/Klussendorf Scholarship**
- **NDS/McCullough Scholarships**
- **NDS/McKown Scholarship**

TYPE:
Awards/prizes; Scholarships; Training grants. Awards made annually to students interested in careers in the dairy industry. Majors can include dairy science, animal science, agricultural economics, agricultural communications, agriculture education, food and nutrition.

YEAR PROGRAM STARTED: 1951

PURPOSE:
To encourage students to pursue careers in the dairy industry.

LEGAL BASIS:
Nonprofit corporation.

ELIGIBILITY:
National Dairy Shrine Student Recognition Program: Graduating seniors planning a career related to dairy-production agriculture who have demonstrated leadership skills, academic ability and interest in dairy cattle.

NDS/Core Scholarship: Applicants must be outstanding freshman college students at a four-year agricultural college.

NDS/DMI Milk Marketing Scholarships: Available to undergraduate students (except previous winners) during his or her sophomore or junior year with an explicit interest in dairy products marketing. The applicants must have at least a cumulative 2.5 grade point average on a 4.0 scale.

NDS Graduate Production Award: Available to a two- or four-year college graduate to finance replacement animals. Must have graduated four years prior.

NDS/Iager Scholarship: Open to outstanding second-year college dairy students in a two-year agricultural college.

NDS/Kildee Scholarships: Applicants must have placed in Top 25 at National Intercollegiate or National 4-H Dairy Judging Contests. Platinum winners in the last three National Dairy Challenge Contests may apply for Kildee Graduate Study Scholarships.

NDS/Klussendorf Scholarship: Open to students successfully completing their first, second or third years at a two- or four-year college or university in Dairy/Animal Science.

NDS/McCullough Scholarships: The applicant must be a high school graduating senior planning to enter a four-year college or university with intent to major in Dairy/Animal Science with a Communications emphasis or Agricultural Journalism with a Dairy/Animal Science emphasis and be a U.S. citizen.

NDS/McKown Scholarship: Open to students successfully completing their first, second or third year at a four-year college or university in Dairy/Animal Science.

NDS Progressive Dairy Producers: Must be 21 to 50 years of age. Two divisions: Small Herd Division (300 or less milking cows) and Large Herd Division (301 or more milking cows).

GEOGRAPHIC RESTRICTIONS:
United States.

FINANCIAL DATA:
Amount of support per award: National Dairy Shrine Student Recognition Program: $5,000 to $7,500; NDS/Core Scholarship and NDS/Iager Scholarship: $1,000; NDS/DMI Milk Marketing Scholarships: $1,500 and $1,000; NDS Graduate Production Award: $2,500; NDS/Kildee Scholarships: $6,000 graduate and $2,000 undergraduate; NDS/Klussendorf Scholarships: $3,500; NDS/McCullough Scholarships: $2,500 and $1,000; NDS/McKown Scholarship: $4,000; NDS Progressive Dairy Producers Awards: $2,000 each for educational travel.

Total amount of support: Over $40,000.

NUMBER OF APPLICANTS MOST RECENT YEAR:
125.

NUMBER OF AWARDS: National Dairy Shrine Student Recognition Program: 7 to 10; NDS/Core Scholarship and NDS Graduate Production Award: 2; NDS/DMI Milk Marketing Scholarships: 5 or 8 awards of $1,000 and 1 award of $1,500; NDS/Iager Scholarship: 2 or more; NDS/Kildee Scholarships: 2 graduate and 1 undergraduate; NDS/Klussendorf Scholarships and NDS/McKown Scholarship: 7; NDS/McCullough Scholarships: 1 award of $2,500 and 1 award of $1,000; NDS Progressive Dairy Producers Awards: 2.

APPLICATION INFORMATION:
All NDS scholarships and awards require the submission of a completed application form with additional requirements for some scholarships. Forms are available at the web site above. All requirements for the scholarship application and submission deadlines must be followed.
Duration: One year.
Deadline: Applications accepted March 1 to April 15 (postmarked). Announcements by July 1.

PUBLICATIONS:
Application form.

EXECUTIVE DIRECTOR:
David Selner

ADDRESS INQUIRIES TO:
David Selner, Executive Director
(See address above.)

*SPECIAL STIPULATIONS:
The second half of each scholarship will be awarded after successful completion of next year. Recipients will be asked to submit their most recent grade transcript and proof of enrollment in the first term of the following year.

NATIONAL FARMER'S ORGANIZATION   [2125]
528 Billy Sunday Road
Suite 100
Ames, IA 50010
(515) 292-2000
Fax: (866) 629-4853

E-MAIL ADDRESS:
nfo@nfo.org

WEB SITE ADDRESS:
www.nfo.org

AREAS OF INTEREST:
Agricultural careers.

NAME(S) OF PROGRAMS:
- **Farm Kids for College Scholarships**

TYPE:
Scholarships.

PURPOSE:
To assist students planning careers in agriculture and farming.

ELIGIBILITY:
Must be a high school senior that will major in an agricultural field at an accredited college or university.

FINANCIAL DATA:
Amount of support per award: $1,000.
Total amount of support: $3,000.

NUMBER OF AWARDS: 3.

APPLICATION INFORMATION:
Application information is available on the web site.
Duration: One year.
Deadline: February.

ADDRESS INQUIRIES TO:
Helene Bergren
Director of Communications
(See address above.)

NATIONAL PARK FOUNDATION
1201 Eye Street, N.W.
Suite 550B
Washington, DC 20005
(202) 354-6460
Fax: (202) 371-2066

E-MAIL ADDRESS:
ask-npf@nationalparks.org

WEB SITE ADDRESS:
www.nationalparks.org

TYPE:
Block grants; Challenge/matching grants; Research grants; Scholarships. Grants range from small seed or start-up programs to larger ones which continue successful projects. Grants enable the parks to obtain additional cash and in-kind contributions, such as products, service or volunteer time.

The Albright-Wirth Employee Development Fund underwrites advanced skills training, graduate education and other professional development programs for Park Service employees.

The Harry Yount National Park Ranger Award recognizes a Ranger for leadership, exemplary skills and dedication to the Park Ranger profession.

See entry 2190 for full listing.

NORTHEAST AGRICULTURAL EDUCATION FOUNDATION   [2126]
101 South Salina Street
Suite 400
Syracuse, NY 13202
(315) 671-0588
Fax: (315) 671-0589

E-MAIL ADDRESS:
info@northeastagriculture.org

WEB SITE ADDRESS:
www.northeastagriculture.org

FOUNDED: 1966

AREAS OF INTEREST:
Agriculture, civic and community.

TYPE:
Project/program grants.

PURPOSE:
To support nonprofit organizations dedicated to serving the interests of farmers and rural communities in the Northeast.

LEGAL BASIS:
Private foundation.

ELIGIBILITY:
Grants are made to nonprofit organizations that have tax-exempt status under Section 501(c)(3) of the Internal Revenue Code. No grants are made to individuals.

GEOGRAPHIC RESTRICTIONS:
Primarily northeastern United States.

FINANCIAL DATA:
Amount of support per award: Varies.

APPLICATION INFORMATION:
Complete Grant Summary Sheet and provide supporting documents. Full grant application package is available on web site.
Duration: Varies.
Deadline: Applications are accepted on a rolling basis. Grant requests should be submitted at least 90 to 120 days prior to date funding is needed.

PUBLICATIONS:
Background and application guidelines; application requirements; grant request summary.

ADDRESS INQUIRIES TO:
Mary Habib, Administrator
(See address above.)

*SPECIAL STIPULATIONS:
The Foundation does not fund recurring operating costs unless it is for programmatic start-up.

NORTHEASTERN LOGGERS' ASSOCIATION, INC. [2127]
3311 State Route 28
Old Forge, NY 13420-0069
(315) 369-3078
Fax: (315) 369-3736

E-MAIL ADDRESS:
mona@northernlogger.com

WEB SITE ADDRESS:
www.northernlogger.com

FOUNDED: 1952

AREAS OF INTEREST:
Forestry, wood science and technology.

NAME(S) OF PROGRAMS:
● **NELA Annual Scholarship Contest**

TYPE:
Scholarships. Essay scholarship contest.

YEAR PROGRAM STARTED: 1975

PURPOSE:
To provide support for students and employees of members.

LEGAL BASIS:
501(c)(6) giving program.

ELIGIBILITY:
Scholarships are available to the immediate families of individual members, or the immediate families of employees of Industrial and Associate Members of the Northeastern Loggers' Association. Applicants must be bound for or engaged in post-high school education and must be either seniors in high school graduating in the current year, students in two-year

Associate's degree or technical school programs or juniors/seniors in four-year Bachelor's degree programs.

GEOGRAPHIC RESTRICTIONS:
United States.

FINANCIAL DATA:
Amount of support per award: $500 to $1,000.
Total amount of support: $6,000.

NUMBER OF APPLICANTS MOST RECENT YEAR:
17.

NUMBER OF AWARDS: Up to 8 annually.

APPLICATION INFORMATION:
Applicants must prepare a 1,000-word essay (about four pages double-spaced) on the topic: "What It Means to Grow Up in the Forest Industry." The essay must be typed and the quality of the essay will be the primary determining factor for the award. Applicant must submit with the essay a completed application form, grade transcript, and report card information before the application deadline.

Application forms and additional information are also available on the Association web site.
Duration: One year.
Deadline: March 31. Notification in May.

ADDRESS INQUIRIES TO:
Mona Lincoln
Director, Safety and Training
(See address and e-mail above.)

JESSIE SMITH NOYES FOUNDATION
6 East 39th Street
12th Floor
New York, NY 10016
(212) 684-6577
Fax: (212) 689-6549

E-MAIL ADDRESS:
noyes@noyes.org

WEB SITE ADDRESS:
www.noyes.org

TYPE:
General operating grants; Project/program grants. Grants to tax-exempt institutions in the connected and overlapping areas of sustainable agriculture, toxics, reproductive rights, and New York City environment in order to achieve the Foundation's overall goal, which is to promote a sustainable and just social and natural system by supporting grassroots organizations and movements committed to this goal.

See entry 2194 for full listing.

RURAL HOUSING SERVICE [2128]
1400 Independence Avenue, S.W.
Room 2214
Washington, DC 20250
(202) 720-4780
Fax: (202) 720-6895

E-MAIL ADDRESS:
myron.wooden@wdc.usda.gov

WEB SITE ADDRESS:
www.rurdev.usda.gov

FOUNDED: 1949

AREAS OF INTEREST:
Rural development.

NAME(S) OF PROGRAMS:
● **Rural Housing Grants (Section 504)**

TYPE:
Grants-in-aid; Project/program grants. Grants to assist elderly, very low-income owner-occupants in rural areas to repair or improve their dwellings to make such dwellings safe and sanitary and remove hazards.

RHS is the credit agency for rural development in USDA. RHS has offices at the state, district and county levels which serve every county or parish in the 50 states, plus the western Pacific areas, Guam, Puerto Rico and the Virgin Islands.

YEAR PROGRAM STARTED: 1961

PURPOSE:
To assist applicants who are unable to repay a loan amortized at one percent over 20 years.

LEGAL BASIS:
42 U.S.C. 1474.

ELIGIBILITY:
Open to counties and towns or places of 10,000 or less within SMA's and towns or places of up to 20,000 outside SMA's. Areas classified as rural prior to October 1, 1990, with a population in excess of 10,000 are eligible if the area population is 25,000 or less.

Applicants must own and occupy houses in rural areas that need repair to remove health or safety hazards. Grant recipients must be 62 years of age or older, very low-income households (under 50% of median income) owner-occupants, and unable to pay for that cost of repair with a loan.

FINANCIAL DATA:
Amount of support per award: Lifetime assistance cannot exceed $7,500.

APPLICATION INFORMATION:
Applicants must apply at the local county Rural Development (RD) office. Awards are approved by Community Development Manager.

TREE RESEARCH & EDUCATION ENDOWMENT FUND [2129]
552 South Washington Street
Suite 109
Naperville, IL 60540
(630) 369-8300
Fax: (630) 369-8382

E-MAIL ADDRESS:
treefund@treefund.org

WEB SITE ADDRESS:
www.treefund.org

FOUNDED: 1975

AREAS OF INTEREST:
Research in areas of urban tree care, preservation and arboriculture education.

NAME(S) OF PROGRAMS:
● **Arboriculture Education Grant**
● **John Duling Grant**
● **Robert Felix Memorial Scholarship**
● **Hyland Johns Grant**
● **Jack Kimmel International Grant**
● **Ohio Chapter ISA Education Grant**
● **John Wright Memorial Scholarship**

TYPE:
Research grants; Scholarships; Seed money grants. Grants to further research relating to arboriculture. Scholarships are for arboriculture and horticulture students.

YEAR PROGRAM STARTED: 1976

PURPOSE:
To initiate and foster scientific investigation of problems concerned with the practice of arboriculture.

LEGAL BASIS:
Tax-exempt public-supported corporation, 501(c)(3) classification.

ELIGIBILITY:
Qualified persons who have a B.S. degree and are planning on graduate study for a Master's or Doctorate in a related field are eligible to apply for scholarship program. Scholarships available for undergraduate study focusing on arboriculture or horticulture.

GEOGRAPHIC RESTRICTIONS:
United States.

FINANCIAL DATA:
Grants do not pay for overhead expenses.
Amount of support per award: Scholarships: Up to $3,000; John Duling and Jack Kimmel Grants: Up to $10,000; Hyland Johns Grant: Up to $25,000.

NUMBER OF APPLICANTS MOST RECENT YEAR:
Varies.

NUMBER OF AWARDS: Varies.

APPLICATION INFORMATION:
Applications are to be completed online. Before applying for a grant, carefully read the Grant Guidelines. Applications that do not contain all the requested information may be denied.
Duration: John Duling Grant: One year; Hyland Johns and Jack Kimmel Grants: Multiyear.
Deadline: John Duling and Jack Kimmel Grants: October 1; Hyland Johns Grant: April 1.

PUBLICATIONS:
Application guidelines.

IRS IDENTIFICATION NUMBER: 37-1018692

STAFF:
M. Janet Bornancin, President/Chief Executive Officer
Mary DiCarlo, Manager, Development and Communications

ADDRESS INQUIRIES TO:
Barbara Duke, Office Manager
E-mail: bduke@treefund.org

*SPECIAL STIPULATIONS:
No part of grant can be used for overhead expenses.

U.S. DEPARTMENT OF AGRICULTURE
1400 Independence Avenue, S.W.
Stop 0513
Washington, DC 20250-0510
(202) 720-6221
Fax: (202) 720-4619

E-MAIL ADDRESS:
matthewponish@wdc.usda.gov

WEB SITE ADDRESS:
www.fsa.usda.gov

TYPE:
Grants-in-aid. Cost-share assistance with agricultural producers to rehabilitate agricultural lands damaged by natural disasters. Assistance may also be provided for carrying out emergency water conservation measures during periods of severe drought.
See entry 2206 for full listing.

U.S.-ISRAEL BINATIONAL AGRICULTURE RESEARCH AND DEVELOPMENT FUND (BARD) [2130]
P.O. Box 6
Bet Dagan 50250 Israel
(972)-3-9683366
Fax: (972)-3-9662506

WEB SITE ADDRESS:
www.bard-isus.com

FOUNDED: 1977

AREAS OF INTEREST:
Agriculture.

NAME(S) OF PROGRAMS:
● **Graduate Student Fellowship Program**
● **Senior Research Fellowship Program**
● **Vaadia-BARD Postdoctoral Fellowship Program**

TYPE:
Fellowships; Research grants; Visiting scholars.

YEAR PROGRAM STARTED: 1977

PURPOSE:
To promote cooperative agriculture research between the U.S. and Israel; to provide BARD with input into new research areas; to enhance scientific competence in these areas.

LEGAL BASIS:
Nonprofit organization. Governmental Associations in U.S. and Israel.

ELIGIBILITY:
Citizens of the U.S. or Israel who are established research scientists, Ph.D. students and young scientists from American or Israeli nonprofit research institutions, universities, or federal or state agencies are eligible.

GEOGRAPHIC RESTRICTIONS:
United States and Israel.

FINANCIAL DATA:
Amount of support per award: Graduate Student Fellowship: $1,500 per month, plus $2,000 to cover travel costs. Postdoctoral Fellowship: $37,000, plus $8,000 for fellows with dependents. Research Grant: Approximately $320,000 over three years. Senior Research Fellowship: $3,000 per month, plus one-time allocation of $2,000 for travel.
Total amount of support: $8,000,000 per year.

NUMBER OF APPLICANTS MOST RECENT YEAR:
100.

NUMBER OF AWARDS: 25.

APPLICATION INFORMATION:
For application information, consult with BARD office in Israel.
Duration: Graduate Student Fellowship: Three to six months. Postdoctoral Fellowship: One year; second year possible with agreement from mentor and shared on a matching basis between BARD and host lab. Research awards: Three years. Senior Research Fellowship: Two to 12 months.

Deadline: Research awards: Mid-September. Postdoctoral Fellowship, Senior Fellowship Program, and Graduate Student Fellowship Program: January 15.

PUBLICATIONS:
Application guidelines.

OFFICERS:
Edo Chalutz, Executive Director
Miriam Green, Controller

THE UNIVERSITY OF SYDNEY [2131]
Scholarships Office
Level 5, Jane Foss Russell Building G02
The University of Sydney N.S.W. 2006
Australia
(02) 8627 8112
Fax: (02) 8627 8485

E-MAIL ADDRESS:
research.training@sydney.edu.au

WEB SITE ADDRESS:
www.sydney.edu.au/scholarships/research

FOUNDED: 1850

AREAS OF INTEREST:
Agriculture and veterinary science or chemical engineering.

NAME(S) OF PROGRAMS:
● **F.H. Loxton Postgraduate Studentships**

TYPE:
Scholarships. Awarded for research leading to a higher degree. Tenable at the University of Sydney.

PURPOSE:
To enable a male graduate of any university to engage in postgraduate research at the University of Sydney, within the Faculty of Veterinary Science, Faculty of Agriculture and Environment, and the School of Chemical and Biomolecular Engineering.

LEGAL BASIS:
University.

ELIGIBILITY:
Open only to male graduates of any university enrolled in a higher degree by research in the Faculty of Veterinary Science, or Faculty of Agriculture and Environment, or the School of Chemical and Biomolecular Engineering at the University of Sydney.

FINANCIAL DATA:
Award does not cover tuition fees payable by international students. Relocation allowance within Australia and thesis allowance available.
Amount of support per award: $24,653 AUD per annum for the year 2013.

NUMBER OF AWARDS: Offered as vacancies occur.

APPLICATION INFORMATION:
Particulars are available from the Faculty of Agriculture and Environment, Faculty of Veterinary Science, or School of Chemical and Biomolecular Engineering, The University of Sydney.
Duration: Master's research degree: Two years; Ph.D. degree: Three years.
Deadline: Varies.

ADDRESS INQUIRIES TO:
The Faculty of Agriculture and Environment
E-mail: fae.pgscholarships@sydney.edu.au
The Faculty of Veterinary Science
E-mail: pgvetsci@vetsci.usyd.edu.au
School of Chemical and
Biomolecular Engineering

E-mail: timothy.langrish@sydney.edu.au
The University of Sydney
N.S.W. 2006 Australia

THE UNIVERSITY OF SYDNEY [2132]

Scholarships Office
Level 5, Jane Foss Russell Building G02
The University of Sydney N.S.W. 2006
Australia
(02) 8627 8112
Fax: (02) 8627 8485

E-MAIL ADDRESS:
research.training@sydney.edu.au

WEB SITE ADDRESS:
www.sydney.edu.au/scholarships/research

FOUNDED: 1850

AREAS OF INTEREST:
Any subject in the Faculty of Agriculture.

NAME(S) OF PROGRAMS:
- **Thomas Lawrance Pawlett Scholarship**
- **Christian Rowe Thornett Scholarship**
- **Alexander Hugh Thurburn Scholarship**

TYPE:
Scholarships. Awarded for postgraduate research. Tenable at the University of Sydney.

PURPOSE:
To encourage and promote scientific study in agriculture at the University of Sydney.

LEGAL BASIS:
University.

ELIGIBILITY:
Open to University of Sydney graduates, graduands, or persons holding equivalent qualification who are eligible for admission to candidature for a higher degree by research and thesis and who enroll as full-time candidates in the Faculty of Agriculture and Environment.

Scholarships may not be held concurrently with other awards or salaried position, except with the approval of the Faculty of Agriculture and Environment.

FINANCIAL DATA:
No assistance with travel costs of scholars taking up award from outside Australia. Award does not cover tuition fees payable by international students.

Amount of support per award: $24,653 AUD per annum for the year 2013.

NUMBER OF AWARDS: Offered as funds available.

APPLICATION INFORMATION:
Contact the University.

Duration: Tenable for two years for Master's candidate. Tenable for three years with the possibility of a six-month extension for Ph.D. candidate.

Deadline: October 31.

ADDRESS INQUIRIES TO:
The Faculty of Agriculture and Environment
The University of Sydney
N.S.W. 2006 Australia
Tel: (02) 8627 1002
E-mail: fae.pgscholarships@sydney.edu.au

USDA - RURAL UTILITIES SERVICE [2133]

1400 Independence Avenue, S.W.
Stop 1548
Washington, DC 20250
(202) 690-2670
Fax: (202) 720-0718

WEB SITE ADDRESS:
www.usda.gov/rus/water

FOUNDED: 1935

AREAS OF INTEREST:
Rural areas and towns that have a population of up to 10,000.

NAME(S) OF PROGRAMS:
- **Water and Waste Disposal Systems for Rural Communities**

TYPE:
Capital grants; Development grants; Project/program grants. Loans.

YEAR PROGRAM STARTED: 1965

PURPOSE:
To provide financial assistance for water and waste disposal facilities in rural areas and towns.

LEGAL BASIS:
Government agency.

ELIGIBILITY:
Only rural areas and cities and towns with populations under 10,000 are eligible.

Applicants must:
(1) be a public entity, nonprofit corporation or Indian tribe;
(2) be unable to obtain needed funds from other sources at reasonable rates and terms;
(3) have legal capacity and;
(4) have adequate security for loans.

FINANCIAL DATA:
Amount of support per award: Varies.

COOPERATIVE FUNDING PROGRAMS: Can cooperate with any other federal, state, local or private credit source.

APPLICATION INFORMATION:
Applicants must submit Form SF-424, application for federal assistance and state intergovernmental review comments and recommendations.

Deadline: Applications accepted throughout the year.

ADDRESS INQUIRIES TO:
Jacqueline M. Ponti-Lazaruk
Assistant Administrator
Water and Environmental Programs
(See address above.)

WOMAN'S NATIONAL FARM & GARDEN ASSOCIATION, INC. [2134]

9355 R.D. 11
Ottawa, OH 45875

E-MAIL ADDRESS:
SBTfellowship@aol.com

WEB SITE ADDRESS:
www.wnfga.org

FOUNDED: 1914

NAME(S) OF PROGRAMS:
- **Sarah Bradley Tyson Memorial Fellowship**

TYPE:
Fellowships; Internships; Scholarships. Awards for advanced study in the fields of agriculture, horticulture and allied subjects.

YEAR PROGRAM STARTED: 1928

PURPOSE:
To encourage better living around the world.

ELIGIBILITY:
Open to properly qualified young women (now including men) who have proven their ability by several years of experience. Awards have been made in recognition of leadership in cooperative extension work and initiative in scientific research.

The Fellowship is to be used for advanced study (Master's or Doctorate) at an educational institution of recognized standing within the U.S. It is to be chosen by the candidate and with the approval of the Fellowship Committee.

FINANCIAL DATA:
Amount of support per award: $1,000. Checks are made out to the student's university and mailed to the student.

APPLICATION INFORMATION:
There are no application forms. A letter of application should be sent to the Chairman of the Committee. The letter of application should contain:
(1) an account of the applicant's educational training;
(2) a statement, in full, of the object in view and the plan of study;
(3) a certificate/transcript from the registrar of the school, college or university awarding the degree or degrees received by the applicant;
(4) testimonials as to character, ability, personality and scholarship;
(5) theses, papers or reports of investigations, published or unpublished, if available; these will be returned if postage is sent for that purpose; confidential letters sent to the Committee are retained;
(6) a health certificate; (a doctor's handwritten note on prescription paper, verifying good health of the student, will suffice;) and;
(7) a small recent photograph.

Duration: One year.

Deadline: Applications and recommendations for the Fellowship must be received not later than April 15 of the year to be awarded.

IRS IDENTIFICATION NUMBER: 52-6073829

OFFICERS:
Julia Siefker, President
Molly Hammerle, A & O Treasurer
Susan Hunt, E & C Treasurer
Aileen LaBret, Corresponding Secretary
Judy Henning, Recording Secretary
Mary Bertolini, Advisor

ADDRESS INQUIRIES TO:
Mrs. Harold L. Matyn
Chairman, Fellowship Committee
Woman's National Farm
& Garden Association, Inc.
3801 Riverview Terrace, South
East China Township, MI 48054

*SPECIAL STIPULATIONS:
The acceptance of the Fellowship implies the obligation on the part of the student to devote herself or himself unreservedly to study or research as outlined in her or his application, and to submit any proposed change in her or his plan to the Chairman for approval.

Biology

THE ACADEMY OF NATURAL SCIENCES OF PHILADELPHIA   [2135]

1900 Benjamin Franklin Parkway
Philadelphia, PA 19103-1195
(215) 299-1065
Fax: (215) 299-1079

E-MAIL ADDRESS:
kepics@ansp.org

WEB SITE ADDRESS:
www.ansp.org/research/jessupinfo.html

FOUNDED: 1812

AREAS OF INTEREST:
Research, exhibition and education in natural sciences.

NAME(S) OF PROGRAMS:
● **Jessup Fellowship**
● **McHenry Fellowship**

TYPE:
Fellowships. The Jessup Fellowship is for research support in any specialty in which the curatorial staff of the Academy have expertise. The McHenry Fellowship is for botanical research support.

PURPOSE:
To promote research in the natural sciences.

ELIGIBILITY:
The Jessup Fellowships are awarded competitively to students wishing to conduct studies at the postgraduate, doctoral and postdoctoral levels under the supervision or sponsorship of a member of the curatorial staff of the Academy. The Fellowships are not available for undergraduate study. These Fellowships are restricted to those who wish to conduct their study at the Academy and are intended to assist predoctoral and postdoctoral students within several years of receiving their Ph.Ds.

FINANCIAL DATA:
Round-trip travel costs up to a total of $500 for North American (including Mexico and the Caribbean) applicants and $1,000 for applicants from other parts of the world may be available, but cannot be guaranteed. The provision of scientific supplies and equipment is the responsibility of the student and the sponsoring curator.
Amount of support per award: Stipend for subsistence of $375 per week.

APPLICATION INFORMATION:
Applicant is responsible to submit his or her application in time and to be sure that the three letters of recommendation also reach the Fund Chairman in time. One of these letters of recommendation must be from the Academy curator overseeing or sponsoring the student.

Application form and supporting information should be sent to Dr. Edward Daeschler, Jessup-McHenry Fund Committee, using the address above.

Duration: Two to 16 weeks.

Deadline: Applications for grants will be considered in March and October of each year. Applicants wishing to do their research between April 1 and October 31 should apply by March 1; those wishing to work between November 1 and March 31 should apply by October 1.

*SPECIAL STIPULATIONS:
Fellowship awardees are expected to give a seminar after their arrival and are encouraged to publish at least some of their work accomplished at the Academy.

AMERICAN ASSOCIATION OF ZOO KEEPERS   [2136]

8476 East Speedway
Suite 204
Tucson, AZ 85710-1728
(520) 298-9688
Fax: (520) 298-9688

E-MAIL ADDRESS:
ed.hansen@aazk.org

WEB SITE ADDRESS:
www.aazk.org

FOUNDED: 1968

AREAS OF INTEREST:
Animal care and the promotion of animal keeping as a profession.

NAME(S) OF PROGRAMS:
● **Zoo Keeper Grants in Zoology**

TYPE:
Research grants; Scholarships; Training grants; Travel grants. Grants in the area of zoology, with emphasis on contributions to improving animal management.

YEAR PROGRAM STARTED: 1980

PURPOSE:
To provide funds for original keeper-initiated research of behavioral and/or biomedical topics and general zoological park management principles.

LEGAL BASIS:
Nonprofit corporation.

ELIGIBILITY:
Candidates must be full-time, permanent keepers in the zoo and aquarium profession and must be AAZK professional members in good standing.

GEOGRAPHIC RESTRICTIONS:
United States and Canada.

FINANCIAL DATA:
Amount of support per award: Up to $1,000.
Total amount of support: $2,000 per year.

NUMBER OF APPLICANTS MOST RECENT YEAR:
5.

NUMBER OF AWARDS: 4 annually.

APPLICATION INFORMATION:
Applications consist of an application form, brief research proposal and resume. Application materials and further information are available from the Committee chairperson or can be downloaded from the web site.
Duration: One year. One-year extension is possible with status report and Committee approval.
Deadline: March 1. Successful applicants are notified within three months of the deadline.

PUBLICATIONS:
Application guidelines.

IRS IDENTIFICATION NUMBER: 23-7274856

BOARD OF DIRECTORS:
Bob Cisneros, President
Penny Jolly, Vice President
Ed Hansen, Chief Executive Officer/Chief Financial Officer
Wendy Lenhart
Kelly Wilson
Deana Wlaz

ADDRESS INQUIRIES TO:
Ed Hansen, Chief Executive Officer/Chief Financial Officer
(See address above.)

*SPECIAL STIPULATIONS:
Research results must be presented to the AAZK membership by either an oral presentation at an AAZK conference, a paper published in *Animal Keepers' Forum* or a research summary report published in *Animal Keepers' Forum.*

THE AMERICAN MUSEUM OF NATURAL HISTORY   [2137]

Richard Gilder Graduate School
Central Park West at 79th Street
New York, NY 10024-5192
(212) 769-5017
Fax: (212) 769-5257

E-MAIL ADDRESS:
mrios@amnh.org
info-rggs@amnh.org

WEB SITE ADDRESS:
rggs.amnh.org

FOUNDED: 1869

AREAS OF INTEREST:
Education of Ph.D. candidates in scientific disciplines.

NAME(S) OF PROGRAMS:
● **Graduate Student Fellowship Program**

TYPE:
Fellowships. An educational partnership with selected universities dedicated to the training of Ph.D. candidates. The university exercises educational jurisdiction over the program and awards the degree. The museum curator serves as a graduate advisor, co-major professor, or major professor. The student benefits by having the staff and facilities of both the university and the museum in order to carry on his or her training and research programs. Joint programs are with the following universities:
(1) Columbia University in vertebrate and invertebrate paleontology, earth and planetary sciences, and evolutionary biology;
(2) Cornell University in entomology;
(3) City University of New York in evolutionary biology and the biological anthropology programs and;
(4) New York University in molecular biology.

PURPOSE:
To encourage bright and promising students to enter the fields of science in which the museum participates.

ELIGIBILITY:
Applicants must have a Bachelor's degree and be able to fulfill university admission requirements, including TOEFL and Graduate Record Examinations. The program is not open to candidates for the Master's degree.

FINANCIAL DATA:
Fellowships cover stipend, tuition and health insurance.
Amount of support per award: Varies.
Total amount of support: Varies.

APPLICATION INFORMATION:
All applications are to be completed online only. All materials, including reference letters, must be submitted electronically, using the forms provided on the web site. Complete instructions are available on the web site.

Duration: One year. Renewable annually for up to four years.

Deadline: December 15.

PUBLICATIONS:
Program announcement; application.

ADDRESS INQUIRIES TO:
Maria Dickson, Assistant Director
Fellowships and Student Affairs
(See address above.)

AMERICAN ORCHID SOCIETY [2138]

Fairchild Tropical Botanic Garden
10901 Old Cutler Road
Coral Gables, FL 33156
(305) 740-2010

E-MAIL ADDRESS:
theaos@aos.org

WEB SITE ADDRESS:
www.aos.org

FOUNDED: 1921

AREAS OF INTEREST:
Orchid research.

NAME(S) OF PROGRAMS:
● **American Orchid Society Grants for Orchid Research**

TYPE:
Awards/prizes; Block grants; Capital grants; Development grants; Grants-in-aid; Research grants. Grants and research contracts for experimental projects and applied and fundamental research pertaining to orchids and grants-in-aid to graduate students engaged in research on orchids. Support is given in such areas relevant to orchids as biological research (including taxonomy, anatomy, genetics, physiology development, tissue culture and pathology), conservation and education.

YEAR PROGRAM STARTED: 1966

PURPOSE:
To advance the scientific study of orchids in every aspect; to assist in the publication of scholarly and popular scientific literature on orchids.

LEGAL BASIS:
Corporation.

ELIGIBILITY:
Qualified research personnel associated with accredited institutions of higher learning or appropriate research institutes may apply for research grants. Support is not restricted to individuals or institutions within the U.S. The salary of established scientists is not supported. Qualified graduate students with appropriate interests may apply for grants in support of their research. If justified, their salary may be supported.

In general, travel to collect orchids is not supported. Other types of travel may be supported on a case-by-case basis.

FINANCIAL DATA:
Grants and research contracts vary in amount, depending upon the needs and nature of the request and the potential for securing additional funds from other sources.

Amount of support per award: $500 to $12,000 per year.

APPLICATION INFORMATION:
As a first step, prospective applicants should submit a brief letter outlining the objectives and general plans of the project. If

appropriate, an application form and project outline for request of a grant will then be supplied to provide the applicant with further detailed information.

Duration: Although the duration of each grant depends upon the particular project, most grants are awarded for one year with the possibility of renewal. In all cases, the maximum grant period is three years.

Deadline: February 1.

PUBLICATIONS:
Application guidelines.

ADDRESS INQUIRIES TO:
Ron McHatton, Director of Education
(See address above.)

*SPECIAL STIPULATIONS:
Research application must involve orchids.

AMERICAN SOCIETY FOR MICROBIOLOGY [2139]

Education Department
1752 N Street, N.W.
Washington, DC 20036
(202) 942-9283
Fax: (202) 942-9329

E-MAIL ADDRESS:
fellowships@asmusa.org

WEB SITE ADDRESS:
www.asm.org/cdcfellowship
www.asm.org/urc
www.asm.org/postdocs

FOUNDED: 1899

AREAS OF INTEREST:
Biological research.

NAME(S) OF PROGRAMS:
● **ASM/CDC Postdoctoral Research Fellowship Program**
● **Undergraduate Research Capstone Program**

TYPE:
Fellowships. ASM/CDC Postdoctoral Research Fellowship Program: The American Society for Microbiology and Centers for Disease Control and Prevention (ASM/CDC) Postdoctoral Research Fellowship Program is a comprehensive training program which provides opportunities to participate in interdisciplinary training on global public health issues. Fellows will perform research at one of the Centers for Disease Control and Prevention (CDC) locations.

Undergraduate Research Capstone Program: This fellowship encourages students to pursue careers or advanced degrees in the microbiological sciences by providing an opportunity to participate in a research project at their institution and gain experience in presenting their results. The fellowship allows students to conduct research in the summer with an ASM member faculty mentor and present the results at the ASM General Meeting the following year.

PURPOSE:
To promote study and research in microbiology; to increase the number of underrepresented and historically excluded undergraduate students completing doctoral degrees in microbiology.

LEGAL BASIS:
Private, nonprofit science organization.

ELIGIBILITY:
ASM/CDC Postdoctoral Research Fellowship Program: Applicant must have a Ph.D.

Undergraduate Research Capstone Program: Prospective applicants must:
(1) have conducted research in microbiology prior to applying;
(2) have participated in an undergraduate summer research program at a U.S.-based institution and;
(3) submit a research abstract for presentation to the ASM General Meeting.

Preference will be given to juniors and seniors.

GEOGRAPHIC RESTRICTIONS:
United States.

FINANCIAL DATA:
Amount of support per award: ASM/CDC Postdoctoral Research Fellowship Program: Up to $46,106 annual stipend, up to $3,000 annually in health benefits for a maximum of two years, up to $500 for relocation benefits, and up to $2,000 annually for professional development for a maximum of two years; Undergraduate Research Capstone Program: A two-year ASM student membership, and up to $1,000 travel support to attend the ASM General Meeting.

Total amount of support: Varies.

APPLICATION INFORMATION:
Application information is available on the web site.

Duration: ASM/CDC Postdoctoral Research Fellowship Program: Two years; Undergraduate Research Fellowship: Minimum 12 weeks.

Deadline: ASM/CDC Postdoctoral Research Fellowship Program: January 15; Undergraduate Research Capstone Program: December 1.

PUBLICATIONS:
Application guidelines.

ADDRESS INQUIRIES TO:
See e-mail address above.

AMERICAN SOCIETY FOR MICROBIOLOGY [2140]

Education Department
1752 N Street, N.W.
Washington, DC 20036
(202) 942-9283
Fax: (202) 942-9329

E-MAIL ADDRESS:
fellowships@asmusa.org

WEB SITE ADDRESS:
www.asm.org/watkins

FOUNDED: 1899

AREAS OF INTEREST:
Microbiology.

NAME(S) OF PROGRAMS:
● **ASM Robert D. Watkins Graduate Research Fellowships**

TYPE:
Fellowships. This fellowship encourages underrepresented and historically excluded graduate students to conduct research in the microbiological sciences.

YEAR PROGRAM STARTED: 1980

PURPOSE:
To help increase the number of underrepresented and historically excluded groups completing doctoral degrees in microbiology.

LEGAL BASIS:
Private, nonprofit science organization.

ELIGIBILITY:
Fellowships are available to graduate students enrolled in a full-time Ph.D. program in microbiology at an accredited U.S. institution of higher learning who are from an underrepresented and historically excluded group. Applicants must be U.S. citizens or permanent residents, ASM student members, been formally admitted and have successfully completed the first year as a doctoral candidate.

GEOGRAPHIC RESTRICTIONS:
United States.

FINANCIAL DATA:
Funds cannot be used for tuition and fees.
Amount of support per award: $63,000 ($21,000 annual stipend).
Total amount of support: Varies.

NUMBER OF AWARDS: 6 for the year 2013.

APPLICATION INFORMATION:
Applications are available online. Students must apply electronically.
Duration: Up to three years.
Deadline: May 1.

PUBLICATIONS:
Application guidelines.

ADDRESS INQUIRIES TO:
See e-mail address above.

ATLANTIC SALMON FEDERATION   [2141]
P.O. Box 5200
St. Andrews NB E5B 3S8 Canada
(506) 529-1385
Fax: (506) 529-4985

E-MAIL ADDRESS:
jcarr@asf.ca

WEB SITE ADDRESS:
www.asf.ca

FOUNDED: 1948

AREAS OF INTEREST:
Conservation of Atlantic salmon and its habitat through programs in education, research, enhancement, restoration and international cooperation.

NAME(S) OF PROGRAMS:
● Olin Fellowships

TYPE:
Awards/prizes; Block grants; Capital grants; Demonstration grants; Fellowships; General operating grants; Grants-in-aid; Internships; Project/program grants; Research grants; Scholarships; Training grants; Travel grants; Visiting scholars; Work-study programs. Fellowships are offered to individuals seeking to improve their knowledge or skills in advanced fields while looking for solutions to current problems in Atlantic salmon biology, management or conservation.

YEAR PROGRAM STARTED: 1971

PURPOSE:
To further salmon conservation.

LEGAL BASIS:
Tax-exempt, nonprofit organization.

ELIGIBILITY:
Applicants must be legal residents of the U.S. or Canada. The Fellowships are tenable at any accredited university or research laboratory or in an active management program and may be applied toward a wide range of endeavors including salmon management, graduate study and research. Applicants need not be enrolled in a degree program.

FINANCIAL DATA:
Amount of support per award: $1,000 to $3,000.
Total amount of support: Varies.

NUMBER OF APPLICANTS MOST RECENT YEAR: 2.

NUMBER OF AWARDS: 2.

APPLICATION INFORMATION:
Information and application forms may be obtained from the address above, from Atlantic Salmon Federation, P.O. Box 807, Calais, ME 04619 or from the web site.
Duration: One year.
Deadline: Applications must be received at the St. Andrews office by March 15. Applicants will be advised of awards by May 15.

PUBLICATIONS:
Atlantic Salmon Journal; annual report.

OFFICERS:
Bill Taylor, President
Hon. M.A. Meighen, Q.C., Chairman, ASF (Canada)
R.J. Warren, Chairman, ASF (U.S.)

ADDRESS INQUIRIES TO:
Ellen Merrill, Executive Assistant
Research and Environment
(See address above.)

CALIFORNIA ACADEMY OF SCIENCES   [2142]
Department of Invertebrate Zoology and Geology
55 Music Concourse Drive
San Francisco, CA 94118
(415) 379-5270

E-MAIL ADDRESS:
rmooi@calacademy.org
ssi-bi@calacademy.org

WEB SITE ADDRESS:
www.calacademy.org
research.calacademy.org/opportunities/ssi

FOUNDED: 1853

AREAS OF INTEREST:
Biology, anthropology, aquatic biology, botany, entomology, geology, herpetology, ichthyology, invertebrate zoology, mammalogy, ornithology and paleontology.

NAME(S) OF PROGRAMS:
● Summer Systematics Institute

TYPE:
Internships. Matches students with Academy scientists to work on specific research projects. May include laboratory and molecular components.

YEAR PROGRAM STARTED: 1995

PURPOSE:
To allow students to gain hands-on experience in the labs and collections archive.

ELIGIBILITY:
Applicants must be junior- or senior-level undergraduates who are U.S. citizens, with a "B" average or better and demonstrated participation in a wide range of campus activities.

FINANCIAL DATA:
Travel costs up to $500 to San Francisco will be reimbursed and a subsistence allowance of $2,100 is given for housing and food. Research costs, publication costs, and travel to return to CAS or to a conference are supported.
Amount of support per award: $3,600 stipend for the internship period.
Total amount of support: Varies.

NUMBER OF APPLICANTS MOST RECENT YEAR: 150.

NUMBER OF AWARDS: 7 to 10.

APPLICATION INFORMATION:
Application information is available through either web site.
Duration: Full-time (40 hours per week) for eight weeks (mid-June to mid-August).
Deadline: Mid-February.

PUBLICATIONS:
Program announcement.

IRS IDENTIFICATION NUMBER: 94-1156258

STAFF:
Dr. Rich Mooi, REU Site Director

ADDRESS INQUIRIES TO:
Dr. Rich Mooi, REU Site Director
(See address above.)

COLUMBIA UNIVERSITY   [2143]
College of Physicians and Surgeons
630 West 168th Street, P & S 2-401
New York, NY 10032
(212) 305-7970

E-MAIL ADDRESS:
horwitzprize@columbia.edu

WEB SITE ADDRESS:
www.cumc.columbia.edu/horwitz/index.html

FOUNDED: 1754

NAME(S) OF PROGRAMS:
● The Louisa Gross Horwitz Prize

TYPE:
Awards/prizes. An annual prize designed to honor a major scientific contribution in basic research to the fields of biology or biochemistry.

YEAR PROGRAM STARTED: 1967

PURPOSE:
To honor a scientific investigator, or group of investigators, whose contributions to knowledge in either of these fields are deemed worthy of special recognition.

ELIGIBILITY:
The prize is open to scientists for outstanding basic research in the fields of biology or biochemistry.

NUMBER OF AWARDS: 3.

APPLICATION INFORMATION:
Nomination must include the name, title, mailing address and e-mail address of the nominee and nominator, along with the following supporting documents:
(1) curriculum vitae;
(2) biographical sketch;
(3) 500-word research summary;
(4) 500-word research significance and;
(5) key publications list.
Deadline: January 31.

ADDRESS INQUIRIES TO:
See e-mail address above.

CONSERVATION AND RESEARCH FOUNDATION

P.O. Box 909
Shelburne, VT 05482-0909
(802) 985-4106

E-MAIL ADDRESS:
minda@holdahl.com

WEB SITE ADDRESS:
conservationresearch.wordpress.com

TYPE:
Research grants; Seed money grants.

See entry 2174 for full listing.

THE ENTOMOLOGICAL FOUNDATION [2144]

1020 Regent Street
Madison, WI 53715
(608) 232-1410
Fax: (608) 232-1440

E-MAIL ADDRESS:
ipmworks@ipminstitute.org

WEB SITE ADDRESS:
www.entfdn.org

FOUNDED: 1991

AREAS OF INTEREST:
Entomology.

NAME(S) OF PROGRAMS:
● **Henry and Sylvia Richardson Research Grant**

TYPE:
Research grants.

YEAR PROGRAM STARTED: 1989

PURPOSE:
To provide research funds to postdoctoral members who have at least one year of promising work experience, who are undertaking research in selected areas of entomology and have demonstrated a high level of scholarship.

ELIGIBILITY:
Candidates must be members of Entomological Society of America (ESA), postdoctoral students and working in insect control by attractants, repellents, biological controls, thermo controls, or chemical controls. Second priority is given to those students working in insect control of medical or veterinary importance. When there are no suitable candidates in the above, candidates working in areas of physiology or toxicology may be considered. Candidates must have an overall grade point average equivalent to 3.0 on a 4.0 scale.

FINANCIAL DATA:
Amount of support per award: Varies.
Total amount of support: Varies.

COOPERATIVE FUNDING PROGRAMS: Research grant is funded by interest earned from the Richardson Endowment Fund.

NUMBER OF AWARDS: 1 annually.

APPLICATION INFORMATION:
The entire nomination package, not to exceed 20 pages, must be submitted electronically. Paper nominations will not be accepted. Nominators must provide:
(1) CV-related items, as outlined on the Foundation's web site;
(2) letter of nomination;
(3) letter of application describing eligibility;
(4) two-page description of research in one of the areas defined above;
(5) two letters of recommendation, one from a major professor and one from a previous instructor and;
(6) official graduate-level and postgraduate transcripts. Mail transcripts to the address listed above.

Duration: One academic year.

Deadline: July 1.

PUBLICATIONS:
Guidelines.

ADDRESS INQUIRIES TO:
Tom Green, Acting President
(See address above.)

THE ENTOMOLOGICAL FOUNDATION [2145]

1020 Regent Street
Madison, WI 53715
(608) 232-1410
Fax: (608) 232-1440

E-MAIL ADDRESS:
ipmworks@ipminstitute.org

WEB SITE ADDRESS:
www.entfdn.org

FOUNDED: 1991

AREAS OF INTEREST:
Entomology.

NAME(S) OF PROGRAMS:
● **Jeffery P. LaFage Graduate Student Research Award**

TYPE:
Awards/prizes; Research grants.

YEAR PROGRAM STARTED: 1992

PURPOSE:
To encourage research by graduate students in the field of the biology and control of termites and other insect pests of the urban environment.

ELIGIBILITY:
Grant is awarded to a graduate student who proposes innovative research to significantly advance or contribute to the knowledge of the biology or control of pests of the urban environment, especially termites or other wood-destroying organisms. The applicant must be a candidate for a Master's or Ph.D. degree at an accredited university. The grant is open to students throughout the world.

Priority will be given to proposals demonstrating a creative and realistic approach to the fields of interest. The recipient is encouraged to present the research results at an ESA meeting and is required to acknowledge the grant award in any publications resulting from these funds.

FINANCIAL DATA:
Grant may be used for salaries, equipment, supplies or travel to initiate, accelerate, augment, or expand a research project.
Amount of support per award: Varies.
Total amount of support: Varies.

NUMBER OF AWARDS: 1.

APPLICATION INFORMATION:
All nomination packages must be submitted electronically. The entire nomination package must not exceed 20 pages, including letters of nomination or recommendation and publication lists. Paper nominations and printed letters sent in lieu of electronic versions will not be accepted.

Duration: Grant is renewable.

Deadline: July 1.

PUBLICATIONS:
Guidelines.

ADDRESS INQUIRIES TO:
Tom Green, Acting President
(See address above.)

*SPECIAL STIPULATIONS:
Science must be related to entomology.

JOHN E. FOGARTY INTERNATIONAL CENTER [2146]

Division of International Training and Research
Building 31, B2C39
31 Center Drive, MSC 2220
Bethesda, MD 20892-2220
(301) 496-1653
Fax: (301) 402-0779

WEB SITE ADDRESS:
www.fic.nih.gov

AREAS OF INTEREST:
International biomedical, behavioral and social sciences health research and collaboration.

NAME(S) OF PROGRAMS:
● **Fogarty International Research Collaboration Award (FIRCA)**

TYPE:
Research grants. A small grants program to support biomedical, behavioral and social sciences health research.

PURPOSE:
To facilitate collaborative research efforts between U.S. and foreign scientists and their colleagues in low- and middle-income countries.

ELIGIBILITY:
Applications are encouraged for research collaboration with investigators in sub-Saharan African countries.

FINANCIAL DATA:
These small grants will provide funds to the foreign collaborator, through the U.S. grantee institution, for equipment, supplies and research support at his or her home institution and for travel expenses for both the U.S. Principal Investigator and the foreign collaborator.
Amount of support per award: $50,000 in direct costs for up to three years.

NUMBER OF APPLICANTS MOST RECENT YEAR:
Approximately 100 per year.

NUMBER OF AWARDS: Approximately 20 per year.

APPLICATION INFORMATION:
Detailed information is available online.
Duration: Up to three years.
Deadline: Varies.

PUBLICATIONS:
Program announcement.

ADDRESS INQUIRIES TO:
Xinghzhu Liu, Program Director
(See address above.)

THE HARRY FRANK GUGGENHEIM FOUNDATION

25 West 53rd Street
16th Floor
New York, NY 10019-5401
(646) 428-0971
Fax: (646) 428-0981

E-MAIL ADDRESS:
info@hfg.org

WEB SITE ADDRESS:
www.hfg.org

TYPE:
Fellowships. Awarded to individuals who will complete the writing of the dissertation within the award year. Support is for projects which seek to advance and coordinate creative breakthroughs in the social and biological sciences relating to the study of dominance, violence and aggression.

See entry 1854 for full listing.

THE HARRY FRANK GUGGENHEIM FOUNDATION
25 West 53rd Street
16th Floor
New York, NY 10019-5401
(646) 428-0971
Fax: (646) 428-0981

E-MAIL ADDRESS:
info@hfg.org

WEB SITE ADDRESS:
www.hfg.org

TYPE:
Research grants. Support for projects which seek to advance and coordinate creative breakthroughs in the social and biological sciences relating to the study of dominance, violence and aggression.

See entry 1853 for full listing.

HUMAN FRONTIER SCIENCE PROGRAM ORGANIZATION [2147]
12 Quai St. Jean
BP 10034
67080 Strasbourg Cedex France
(33) 3-88-21-51-26 (Grants)
(33) 3-88-21-51-27 (Fellowships)
Fax: (33) 3-88-32-88-97

E-MAIL ADDRESS:
grant@hfsp.org
fellow@hfsp.org

WEB SITE ADDRESS:
www.hfsp.org

FOUNDED: 1989

AREAS OF INTEREST:
Interdisciplinary research into the complex mechanisms of biological functions.

NAME(S) OF PROGRAMS:
● **Career Development Award**
● **Cross-Disciplinary Fellowships**
● **Long-Term Fellowships**
● **Program Grants**
● **Young Investigator Grants**

TYPE:
Fellowships; Project/program grants; Research grants. Career Development Awards are to help former HFSP Fellows set up their own independent laboratories in the home country or another HFSP member country.

Cross-Disciplinary Fellowships are modeled on the Long-Term Fellowships but are specifically for scientists with Ph.Ds. in non-biological disciplines who seek training in the life sciences.

Long-Term Fellowships are for young scientists within three years of obtaining their Ph.D. who wish to broaden their scientific experience in a foreign laboratory.

Program Grants are collaborative research projects for interdisciplinary teams of researchers in different countries at any stage of their career.

Young Investigator Grants are collaborative research projects for interdisciplinary teams of young researchers who are within the first five years of their first independent positions and located in different countries.

YEAR PROGRAM STARTED: 1989

PURPOSE:
To foster international collaboration and postdoctoral training at the frontiers of the life sciences.

LEGAL BASIS:
Not-for-profit association.

ELIGIBILITY:
Scientists from all countries can apply, but with some restrictions. The principal investigator of grants must be from a member country. Fellowship candidates from nonmember countries can only apply to work in a member country.

Career Development Award competition is only open to former HFSP fellows.

FINANCIAL DATA:
Amount of support per award: Varies, depending upon the size of the grant team or the host country of the fellowship.

NUMBER OF APPLICANTS MOST RECENT YEAR:
Career Development Awards: 55; Cross-Disciplinary Fellowships: 67; Long-Term Fellowhips: 680; Young Investigator Grants and Program Grants: 799 letters of intent, 95 full applications.

NUMBER OF AWARDS: Career Development Awards: 8; Cross-Disciplinary Fellowships: 2; Long-Term Fellowships: 80; Program Grants: 25; Young Investigator Grants: 8.

APPLICATION INFORMATION:
Application information is available on the web site.
Duration: Up to three years.

PUBLICATIONS:
Annual report.

ADDRESS INQUIRIES TO:
For fellowships: fellow@hfsp.org
For grants: grant@hfsp.org

INTERNATIONAL CRANE FOUNDATION, INC. [2148]
E-11376 Shady Lane Road
Baraboo, WI 53913
(608) 356-9462
Fax: (608) 356-9465

E-MAIL ADDRESS:
cranes@savingcranes.org

WEB SITE ADDRESS:
www.savingcranes.org

FOUNDED: 1973

AREAS OF INTEREST:
Aviculture, crane ecology and conservation education.

CONSULTING OR VOLUNTEER SERVICES:
Work with individuals who have specific questions regarding crane propagation, restoration of natural habitats, or conservation education on an informal basis and as the need arises.

TYPE:
Internships. Formal stipended internship programs in the fields of aviculture, crane ecology and conservation education.

YEAR PROGRAM STARTED: 1980

PURPOSE:
To act as the world center for the study and preservation of cranes and their natural habitats.

LEGAL BASIS:
Nonprofit corporation.

ELIGIBILITY:
College sophomores through recent college graduates in biology, zoology, botany or education who have a willingness to work at a variety of tasks and can work in a self-directed manner.

FINANCIAL DATA:
Amount of support per award: $550 stipend per month, plus housing.

NUMBER OF APPLICANTS MOST RECENT YEAR:
Approximately 80.

NUMBER OF AWARDS: 11.

APPLICATION INFORMATION:
Letter of application indicating interest, relevant coursework and experience, plus three references. An interview will be required, although a phone interview may suffice.
Duration: Three to nine months. Must submit additional application for renewal.

IRS IDENTIFICATION NUMBER: 39-1187711

ADDRESS INQUIRIES TO:
See e-mail address above.

THE JACKSON LABORATORY [2149]
600 Main Street
Bar Harbor, ME 04609
(207) 288-6272
Fax: (207) 288-6697

E-MAIL ADDRESS:
training@jax.org

WEB SITE ADDRESS:
www.jax.org

FOUNDED: 1929

AREAS OF INTEREST:
Mammalian genetics.

NAME(S) OF PROGRAMS:
● **Postdoctoral Program at the Jackson Laboratory**

TYPE:
Fellowships. Research participation at the postdoctoral level in cancer genetics, developmental genetics, hematology and immunology and other fields of mammalian biology. Support is for research training at the Jackson Laboratory.

PURPOSE:
To support postdoctoral research training in mammalian genetics.

LEGAL BASIS:
Private institution.

ELIGIBILITY:
An applicant must be a recent recipient of the Ph.D., M.D., D.V.M. or equivalent degree. An applicant for a training grant appointment must be either a citizen of the U.S. or a foreign national holding a visa permitting permanent residence in the U.S.

FINANCIAL DATA:
Program includes full benefits.

Amount of support per award: $37,740 to $52,068 in stipends, depending upon years of postdoctoral experience.

Total amount of support: Varies.

APPLICATION INFORMATION:
Applications must include a curriculum vitae and three letters of recommendation.

Duration: Appointments are for one year. Renewable for up to two years.

Deadline: Applications accepted throughout the year.

ADMINISTRATIVE OFFICERS:
Dr. Robert Braun, Vice President for Research

ADDRESS INQUIRIES TO:
Dr. Robert Braun
Vice President for Research
(See address above.)

*SPECIAL STIPULATIONS:
Appointments tenable only at the Jackson Laboratory.

LIFE SCIENCES RESEARCH FOUNDATION (LSRF) [2150]
Lewis Thomas Laboratories
Washington Road
Princeton University
Princeton, NJ 08544
(609) 649-3997

E-MAIL ADDRESS:
sdirenzo@princeton.edu

WEB SITE ADDRESS:
www.lsrf.org

FOUNDED: 1984

AREAS OF INTEREST:
Biological sciences.

NAME(S) OF PROGRAMS:
• **Three-Year Postdoctoral Fellowships**

TYPE:
Fellowships.

YEAR PROGRAM STARTED: 1984

PURPOSE:
To offer research support for aspiring scientists.

LEGAL BASIS:
Private organization.

ELIGIBILITY:
Fellowship applicants must be graduates with M.D. or Ph.D. degrees in any field of the biological sciences. Awards are based solely on the quality of the individual applicant's previous accomplishments and on the merit of his or her proposal for postdoctoral research. All U.S. citizens are eligible to apply with no restrictions on the laboratory of their choice. (Foreign applicants will be eligible for study in U.S. laboratories.)

No applicant with a contracted, salaried position (such as assistant professor) is eligible to apply.

FINANCIAL DATA:
Stipend includes salary, fringe benefits, travel to the host institution and to the annual meeting and research expenses.

Amount of support per award: $57,000 per year.

Total amount of support: $2,736,000 to $3,078,000.

NUMBER OF APPLICANTS MOST RECENT YEAR: 900.

NUMBER OF AWARDS: 20.

APPLICATION INFORMATION:
Application should include the following:
(1) abstract of the proposal (200 words or less);
(2) curriculum vitae (three-page maximum);
(3) research proposal (five-page maximum);
(4) letter from supervisor and;
(5) three letters of reference.

All documents are to be uploaded online as either Microsoft Word or PDF files. Further details can be found on the Foundation's web site.

Duration: Three years.

Deadline: October 1.

ADDRESS INQUIRIES TO:
Susan DiRenzo, Assistant Director
(See address above.)

MARINE BIOLOGICAL LABORATORY [2151]
Office of Research and Programs
7 MBL Street
Woods Hole, MA 02543
(508) 289-7173
Fax: (508) 289-7934

E-MAIL ADDRESS:
researchprograms@mbl.edu

WEB SITE ADDRESS:
www.mbl.edu

FOUNDED: 1888

AREAS OF INTEREST:
Cellular and molecular physiology, molecular biology, developmental biology, neurobiology, innate immunity, ecology, parasitology, microbiology, pharmacology, toxicology, cancer biology, regenerative biology, aging, molecular evolution, microbial biology, sensory physiology, aquaculture, metabolic diseases, environmental science, climate change, and plant physiology.

NAME(S) OF PROGRAMS:
• **Marine Biological Laboratory Research Awards**

TYPE:
Research grants.

PURPOSE:
To provide funding to scientists interested in conducting research projects in various scientific areas.

LEGAL BASIS:
Nonprofit organization.

ELIGIBILITY:
Applicants must be independent investigators. Working scientists must be willing to come to the Laboratory for a minimum six-week stay to conduct independent research in areas of interest to the Laboratory. Sabbaticals are encouraged.

FINANCIAL DATA:
Amount of support per award: Varies.

Total amount of support: Varies.

Matching fund requirements: Strongly encouraged from home institution.

COOPERATIVE FUNDING PROGRAMS: APA, ASCB and HHMI.

NUMBER OF AWARDS: Varies.

APPLICATION INFORMATION:
Application information is available on the web site.

Duration: Varies.

Deadline: December 15.

IRS IDENTIFICATION NUMBER: 04-2104690

ADDRESS INQUIRIES TO:
Office of Research and Programs
(See address above.)

MICROSCOPY SOCIETY OF AMERICA [2152]
12100 Sunset Hills Road, Suite 130
Reston, VA 20190-3221
(703) 234-4115
(800) 538-3672
Fax: (703) 435-4390

E-MAIL ADDRESS:
associationmanagement@microscopy.org

WEB SITE ADDRESS:
www.microscopy.org/awards

FOUNDED: 1942

AREAS OF INTEREST:
Microscopy.

NAME(S) OF PROGRAMS:
• **MSA Professional Technical Staff Awards**

TYPE:
Awards/prizes; Conferences/seminars.

PURPOSE:
To stimulate attendance for those who ordinarily might not participate; to encourage employers to support their staff in professional activities.

LEGAL BASIS:
Special interest society.

ELIGIBILITY:
Applicants must have been current members of MSA for three years prior to the time of the annual meeting. Awards are based on the quality of the paper submitted for presentation at the meeting. Abstracts will be judged by the MSA Technologist's Forum. The applicant must be the first author of the submitted paper.

Successful applicants must present their papers personally at the meeting in order to receive the award. They are expected to attend and participate in the entire meeting. Former winners will not be eligible for another award.

FINANCIAL DATA:
Amount of support per award: The award consists of complimentary full registration for the annual meeting including a copy of *Proceedings* and the Sunday evening social event. In addition, MSA will reimburse awardees up to $1,000 for travel, lodging and other expenses.

Total amount of support: Varies.

NUMBER OF AWARDS: Up to 4.

APPLICATION INFORMATION:
Applications shall consist of a copy of the abstract and data form to be sent to the Technologist's Forum Committee and a supporting letter from the applicant's employer, manager or supervisor, attesting to the applicant's status as a full-time, professional staff member.

Duration: One-time award.

Deadline: Typically February 15.

STAFF:
Bob Dziuban, Managing Director
Ashley Carey, Program Manager

ADDRESS INQUIRIES TO:
Bob Dziuban, Managing Director
(See address above.)

MOUNT DESERT ISLAND BIOLOGICAL LABORATORY [2153]
P.O. Box 35
Salsbury Cove, ME 04672
(207) 288-9880 ext. 102
Fax: (207) 288-2130

E-MAIL ADDRESS:
jmedlin@mdibl.org

WEB SITE ADDRESS:
www.mdibl.org

FOUNDED: 1898

AREAS OF INTEREST:
Biological, toxicological and biomedical sciences, and environmental health.

NAME(S) OF PROGRAMS:
• **The High School Research Fellowship**
• **Summer Research Fellowships for Undergraduate Faculty and Students**
• **David W. Towle Fellowship**

TYPE:
Fellowships; Internships. Faculty fellowship awards are made to teacher scientists with primary responsibilities at the undergraduate level. Summer research awards are given to scientists through a New Investigator Award (NIA) program. Undergraduate fellowships are available to student trainees.

The High School Research Fellowship program is a mentored laboratory experience for Maine high school students interested in biology, medicine or research and runs six to eight weeks in the summer.

The David W. Towle Fellowship is intended for graduate students from both U.S. and international institutions to spend the summer at MDIBL working on their thesis.

YEAR PROGRAM STARTED: 1898

PURPOSE:
To enhance scientific training in the biological sciences.

LEGAL BASIS:
Nonprofit research institute.

ELIGIBILITY:
Applicants for faculty fellowships must have an earned Doctorate and be actively engaged in biological research. Applicants for undergraduate fellowships must have had a minimum of one year of biology and one year of chemistry. Undergraduate minorities are encouraged to apply.

FINANCIAL DATA:
Student fellowships cover housing, travel and research costs in addition to a summer stipend. Faculty fellowships cover housing and laboratory costs.

Amount of support per award: Faculty Fellowships: Up to $12,000; Undergraduate Fellowships: Up to $6,000.

Total amount of support: Varies.

COOPERATIVE FUNDING PROGRAMS: Grants are made possible with support from private sources, the National Science Foundation and the National Institutes of Health.

APPLICATION INFORMATION:
Complete application information can be found on the Laboratory web site.

Duration: One to four months during the summer.
Deadline: Varies.

IRS IDENTIFICATION NUMBER: 01-0202467

ADDRESS INQUIRIES TO:
Education Coordinator
(See address above.)

MUSEUM OF COMPARATIVE ZOOLOGY [2154]
Harvard University, OEB Administration
26 Oxford Street, Room 108
Cambridge, MA 02138
(617) 495-2460
Fax: (617) 496-8308

E-MAIL ADDRESS:
grants@oeb.harvard.edu

WEB SITE ADDRESS:
www.mcz.harvard.edu/grants_and_funding/ernst-mayr-travel.html

FOUNDED: 1858

AREAS OF INTEREST:
Comparative zoology.

NAME(S) OF PROGRAMS:
• **Ernst Mayr Grants in Animal Systematics**

TYPE:
Awards/prizes; Research grants; Travel grants.

YEAR PROGRAM STARTED: 1984

PURPOSE:
To enable animal systematists to make short visits to museums for research needed to complete taxonomic revisions and monographs; to stimulate taxonomic work on neglected taxa, including those with numerous poorly described species, genera and families known to have many undescribed species in institutional collections, taxa for which it is unknown what proportion of the nominal species are synonyms, and difficult genera without keys.

ELIGIBILITY:
Preference is given to studies that use the Museum of Comparative Zoology collections, although applications to work at other museums also will be considered.

FINANCIAL DATA:
Grants may cover travel, lodging and meals for up to a few months while conducting research at the museums, services purchased from the host institution, research supplies, etc.

Amount of support per award: $1,000 average.
Total amount of support: Varies.

NUMBER OF APPLICANTS MOST RECENT YEAR: 42.

NUMBER OF AWARDS: 24,

APPLICATION INFORMATION:
Proposals should consist of an application form which includes a short project description and explicit statement of the goals of the research, itinerary, and budget, a curriculum vitae, and three letters of support. All applications should be written in English. Proposals may be submitted through standard mail to the address above or electronically to the e-mail listed above. Submissions through standard mail must include five copies of the proposal materials and must be received by the deadline.

Duration: Must be used within one year.
Deadline: April 1 and October 15. Announcements typically within two months following the application deadline.

STAFF:
Catherine Weisel, Museum Projects Coordinator

ADDRESS INQUIRIES TO:
Catherine Weisel
Museum Projects Coordinator
(See address and e-mail above.)

*SPECIAL STIPULATIONS:
Each grantee is required to submit a written report summarizing the scientific accomplishments achieved with the award within one month of travel completion.

MYCOLOGICAL SOCIETY OF AMERICA [2155]
P.O. Box 1897
Lawrence, KS 66044
(785) 865-9402
(800) 627-0326
Fax: (785) 843-6153

E-MAIL ADDRESS:
msa@allenpress.com

WEB SITE ADDRESS:
msafungi.org

FOUNDED: 1931

AREAS OF INTEREST:
The study of fungi.

NAME(S) OF PROGRAMS:
• **Backus Award**
• **Forest Fungal Ecology Award**
• **Martin-Baker Research Awards**
• **Mentor Student Travel Awards**
• **MSA Graduate Fellowship**
• **NAMA Memorial Graduate Fellowship**
• **John W. Rippon Research Award**
• **Clark T. Rogerson Research Award**
• **Alexander H. and Helen V. Smith Research Fund**

TYPE:
Awards/prizes; Conferences/seminars; Fellowships; Travel grants. Supplementary grant for an outstanding candidate awarded in addition to any fellowship, scholarship or assistantship support from other sources to further graduate studies in the field of mycology.

LEGAL BASIS:
Nonprofit organization.

ELIGIBILITY:
Applicants must be student members of the Mycological Society of America. In selecting the recipient of the Fellowship, consideration is given to scholastic merit, research ability and promise shown as a future mycologist.

FINANCIAL DATA:
Amount of support per award: Approximately $2,000 per fellowship; $1,000 for Backus Award.
Total amount of support: Approximately $15,000 annually.

APPLICATION INFORMATION:
Application information is available on the web site.
Duration: One year. Nonrenewable.
Deadline: February 15.

PUBLICATIONS:
Mycologia, research journal; *Inoculum,* newsletter.

NATIONAL ALOPECIA AREATA FOUNDATION [2156]

14 Mitchell Boulevard
San Rafael, CA 94903
(415) 472-3780
Fax: (415) 472-5343

E-MAIL ADDRESS:
info@naaf.org

WEB SITE ADDRESS:
www.naaf.org

FOUNDED: 1981

AREAS OF INTEREST:
Baldness, hair loss and alopecia areata.

TYPE:
Research grants.

YEAR PROGRAM STARTED: 1985

PURPOSE:
To support research to find an acceptable
treatment and studies that will lead to an
eventual cure for alopecia areata.

ELIGIBILITY:
Must be an Institute Review Board-approved
researcher who has submitted a proposal
about alopecia areata or hair biology. No
funding for established investigators.

FINANCIAL DATA:
Salaries only fellows, assistants, residents and
technicians.
Amount of support per award: $10,000 to
$50,000.
Total amount of support: Over $6,000,000
since inception of program.

COOPERATIVE FUNDING PROGRAMS: Joint grants
with other organizations.

NUMBER OF APPLICANTS MOST RECENT YEAR:
Varies.

NUMBER OF AWARDS: Varies.

APPLICATION INFORMATION:
Contact the Foundation for application
procedures.
Duration: One year.

ADDRESS INQUIRIES TO:
Jeanne Rappoport, Vice President
Administration and Meetings
(See address above.)

NATIONAL SCIENCE FOUNDATION [2157]

Division of Molecular & Cellular Biosciences
(BIO/MCB)
4201 Wilson Boulevard, Room 655 S
Arlington, VA 22230
(703) 292-8440
Fax: (703) 292-9061

WEB SITE ADDRESS:
www.nsf.gov

FOUNDED: 1950

AREAS OF INTEREST:
Biochemistry, biophysics, genetics and cell
biology.

NAME(S) OF PROGRAMS:
● **Division of Molecular and Cellular
Biosciences Programs**

TYPE:
Conferences/seminars; Project/program
grants; Research grants; Seed money grants.
The Division of Molecular and Cellular
Biosciences at the National Science
Foundation has the following clusters:

Molecular Biophysics, which encourages
proposals such as the following areas of
research:
(1) general principles of the relationship
between structure, dynamics and function of
biomolecules and;
(2) fundamental principles governing
biomolecular interactions and mechanisms.

Cellular Dynamics and Function, which
encourages proposals such as the following
areas of research:
(1) predictive understanding of the behavior
of living cells through integration of
modeling and experimentation;
(2) integrative cellular function across broad
spatiotemporal scales, from single molecules
to whole cells and;
(3) origin, evolution and function of cells,
organelles and microcompartments.

Genetic Mechanisms, which encourages
proposals such as the following areas of
research:
(1) gene expression, including epigenetics
and RNA-mediated regulation;
(2) chromosome dynamics, DNA replication,
repair, recombination and inheritance and;
(3) evolution of genes and genomes.

Systems and Synthetic Biology, which
encourages proposals such as the following
areas of research:
(1) systems-level, theory-driven analysis of
regulatory, signaling and metabolic networks;
(2) synthetic biology to address fundamental
biological questions including the origin of
life, minimal cell, emergent behavior in
complex systems, robustness in design and
organization and;
(3) tool development to facilitate systems and
synthetic biology studies.

YEAR PROGRAM STARTED: 1992

PURPOSE:
To increase our store of knowledge in these
fields and enhance our understanding of the
scientific aspects of major problems
confronting the nation.

LEGAL BASIS:
National Science Foundation Act of 1950,
Public Law 81-507, as amended.

ELIGIBILITY:
The principal recipients of scientific research
project support are academic institutions and
nonprofit research institutions. Grants may
also be awarded to other types of institutions
and to individuals. In these cases, preliminary
inquiry should be made to the cognizant
program officer before a proposal is
submitted. Support may be provided to
projects involving a single scientist or to
projects covering the activities of a number
of scientists. Awards are made for projects
confined to a single disciplinary area and for
projects which cross or merge disciplinary
interests. Clinically oriented research is not
supported.

APPLICATION INFORMATION:
Application information is available on the
web site.
Duration: Varies.
Deadline: Contact Foundation for specific
dates.

PUBLICATIONS:
Brochures.

DIRECTORS:
Dr. Parag R. Chitnis, Division Director

ADDRESS INQUIRIES TO:
Cognizant Program Officer

NATIONAL SCIENCE FOUNDATION [2158]

Division of Environmental Biology
4201 Wilson Boulevard, Room 635N
Arlington, VA 22230
(703) 292-8480
Fax: (703) 292-9064

E-MAIL ADDRESS:
pfirth@nsf.gov
sedaniel@nsf.gov

WEB SITE ADDRESS:
www.nsf.gov/bio/deb/about.jsp

FOUNDED: 1950

AREAS OF INTEREST:
Ecology, ecosystem science, population
biology and systematic biology, and
biodiversity inventories cluster.

NAME(S) OF PROGRAMS:
● **Division of Environmental Biology**

TYPE:
Conferences/seminars; Research grants;
Training grants; Travel grants.

PURPOSE:
To increase our store of knowledge in these
fields and enhance our understanding of the
scientific aspects of major problems
confronting the nation.

LEGAL BASIS:
National Science Foundation Act of 1950,
Public Law 81-507, as amended.

ELIGIBILITY:
The principal recipients of scientific research
project support are academic institutions and
nonprofit research institutions. Grants may
also be awarded to other types of institutions
and to individuals. In these cases, preliminary
inquiry should be made to the cognizant
program officer before a proposal is
submitted. Support may be provided to
projects involving a single scientist or to
projects covering the activities of a number
of scientists. Awards are made for projects
confined to a single disciplinary area and for
projects which cross or merge disciplinary
interests.

FINANCIAL DATA:
Amount of support per award: $108,000
average.

NUMBER OF APPLICANTS MOST RECENT YEAR:
2,500.

NUMBER OF AWARDS: 500.

APPLICATION INFORMATION:
Application information is available on the
web site.
Duration: 12 to 60 months, depending on the
scientific merit and requirements of the
project.
Deadline: January 9 and July 9.

PUBLICATIONS:
Awards list; program description.

ADDRESS INQUIRIES TO:
Penny Firth, Deputy Division Director
(See address above.)

SOCIETY FOR DEVELOPMENTAL BIOLOGY [2159]

9650 Rockville Pike
Bethesda, MD 20814-3998
(301) 634-7815
Fax: (301) 634-7825

E-MAIL ADDRESS:
sdb@sdbonline.org

WEB SITE ADDRESS:
www.sdbonline.org

FOUNDED: 1939

AREAS OF INTEREST:
Developmental biology.

NAME(S) OF PROGRAMS:
- **Edwin G. Conklin Medal**
- **Developmental Biology-SDB Lifetime Achievement Award**
- **John Doctor Best Education Poster Award**
- **Viktor Hamburger Outstanding Educator Prize**
- **Latin American-Caribbean Scholarships**
- **Non-SDB Education Activities Grant**
- **Non-SDB Meeting Grants**
- **SDB Boot Camp for New Faculty**
- **SDB Travel Awards**
- **Teaching Faculty Travel Grants**

TYPE:
Awards/prizes; Conferences/seminars; Scholarships.

PURPOSE:
To further the study of development in all organisms and at all levels; to represent and promote communication among students of development; to promote the field of developmental biology.

ELIGIBILITY:
Must be a student or investigator studying in the field of developmental biology.

For the Latin American Award, student must study in Latin America or the Caribbean.

FINANCIAL DATA:
Amount of support per award: Latin American-Caribbean Scholarships: $2,000; John Doctor Best Education Poster Award: $1,000; Teaching Faculty Travel Grants: $500; Student/Postdoctoral Travel Awards: Varies.

Total amount of support: Varies.

NUMBER OF AWARDS: Latin American-Caribbean Scholarships: 6.

APPLICATION INFORMATION:
Nomination instructions and application guidelines may be obtained from the Society's web site.
Duration: One-time award. Reapplication possible for grants and scholarships.
Deadline: Varies.

ADDRESS INQUIRIES TO:
Ida Chow, Executive Officer
(See address above.)

SOCIETY FOR THE STUDY OF AMPHIBIANS AND REPTILES

Department of Biological Sciences
University of Wisconsin-Whitewater
Whitewater, WI 53190
(262) 472-1069

E-MAIL ADDRESS:
kapferj@uww.edu

WEB SITE ADDRESS:
www.ssarherps.org/pages/GIH.php

TYPE:
Awards/prizes; Research grants. Awards are given in six categories: Conservation of

Amphibians and/or Reptiles, Field Research, Laboratory Research, Herpetological Education, Travel and International Research.

See entry 2043 for full listing.

THE UNIVERSITY OF CALGARY

Faculty of Graduate Studies
MacKimmie Library Tower, Room 213
2500 University Drive, N.W.
Calgary AB T2N 1N4 Canada
(403) 220-4938
Fax: (403) 289-7635

E-MAIL ADDRESS:
gsaward@ucalgary.ca

WEB SITE ADDRESS:
www.grad.ucalgary.ca

TYPE:
Awards/prizes; Scholarships. Award for study in the fields of cellular, molecular, microbial or biochemical biology. Tenable at The University of Calgary, Department of Biological Sciences.

See entry 1786 for full listing.

THE WETLANDS INSTITUTE   [2160]

1075 Stone Harbor Boulevard
Stone Harbor, NJ 08247-1424
(609) 368-1211
Fax: (609) 368-3871

E-MAIL ADDRESS:
research@wetlandsinstitute.org

WEB SITE ADDRESS:
www.wetlandsinstitute.org

FOUNDED: 1969

AREAS OF INTEREST:
Mid-Atlantic coastal organisms and environments.

NAME(S) OF PROGRAMS:
- **Coastal Conservation Research Program**

TYPE:
Internships. Summer internships for field research on mid-Atlantic coastal organisms and environments at the Wetlands Institute.

YEAR PROGRAM STARTED: 1969

PURPOSE:
To involve undergraduate students in a wide variety of research projects pertaining to coastal environments.

LEGAL BASIS:
Nonprofit organization that conducts research and education.

ELIGIBILITY:
Applicants should have a minimum of one year college education. A science major is desired, but not required.

GEOGRAPHIC RESTRICTIONS:
United States.

FINANCIAL DATA:
Amount of support per award: Varies with project.
Total amount of support: Varies.

NUMBER OF APPLICANTS MOST RECENT YEAR: 40.

NUMBER OF AWARDS: 10.

APPLICATION INFORMATION:
Contact the Institute for guidelines.

Duration: Minimum of 10 weeks, starting last week of May.
Deadline: March 1.

IRS IDENTIFICATION NUMBER: 23-7046783

ADDRESS INQUIRIES TO:
See e-mail address above.

WHITEHALL FOUNDATION, INC.   [2161]

125 Worth Avenue
Suite 220
Palm Beach, FL 33480
(561) 655-4474
Fax: (561) 655-1296

E-MAIL ADDRESS:
email@whitehall.org

WEB SITE ADDRESS:
www.whitehall.org

FOUNDED: 1937

AREAS OF INTEREST:
Exclusive focus on assisting basic research in vertebrate (excluding clinical) and invertebrate neurobiology in the U.S.

TYPE:
Grants-in-aid; Research grants. Research grants are available to established scientists of all ages working at accredited institutions in the U.S.

The grants-in-aid program is designed for researchers at the assistant professor level who experience difficulty in competing for research funds because they have not yet become firmly established. Grants-in-aid will also be made to senior scientists.

YEAR PROGRAM STARTED: 1937

PURPOSE:
To assist scholarly research in the life sciences; to assist those dynamic areas of basic biological research that are not heavily supported by federal agencies or other foundations with specialized missions.

LEGAL BASIS:
Not-for-profit corporation.

ELIGIBILITY:
Grants-in-aid: All applications will be judged on the scientific merit and innovative aspects of the proposal, as well as on past performance and evidence of the applicant's continued productivity.

Research grants: Applications will be judged on the scientific merit and the innovative aspects of the proposal, as well as on the competence of the applicant.

The Foundation does not award funds to investigators who have substantial existing or potential support (even if it is for an unrelated purpose), and applications may be held in abeyance until the results of other funding decisions are determined. In general, the Foundation currently defines "substantial" as approximately $200,000 per year (including both direct and indirect expense but excluding the principal investigator's salary). The principal investigator must hold no less than the position of assistant professor, or the equivalent, in order to make application.

GEOGRAPHIC RESTRICTIONS:
United States.

FINANCIAL DATA:
Amount of support per award: Research Grants: $30,000 to $75,000 per year; Grants-in-aid: Up to $30,000.

APPLICATION INFORMATION:
The first step in the proposal process is the submission of a Letter of Intent, which includes the following:
(1) cover page on institutional letterhead including investigator's full name, academic rank and institutional affiliation, complete U.S. mail and e-mail addresses, telephone and fax numbers, title of the project (not to exceed 60 characters), type of grant requested, and a table of all current and pending funding including grant title, source, total amount of direct and indirect costs per year, length in years, percent effort expended on the project and notification date if the application is still pending and;
(2) research abstract of the proposed research project (not to exceed two pages and 600 words). Investigator's last name must be placed on the top right corner of each page. Do not include any reprints, curriculum vitaes, or letters of reference.

On the basis of this letter, the Whitehall Foundation's scientific advisory staff will determine whether or not the proposed research project will continue to the application process.

Letters of Intent will not be accepted via e-mail.
Duration: Grants-in-aid: One year. Research Grants: Up to three years; a renewal grant with a maximum of two years is possible, but it will be awarded on a competitive basis.

IRS IDENTIFICATION NUMBER: 13-5637595

ADDRESS INQUIRIES TO:
Whitehall Foundation, Inc.
P.O. Box 3423
Palm Beach, FL 33480

*PLEASE NOTE:
The Foundation encourages the use of electronic mail. All correspondence and reports should be sent to the e-mail address above. The Letter of Intent must be submitted in hard copy on institutional letterhead.

WILSON ORNITHOLOGICAL SOCIETY [2162]
Museum of Zoology
University of Michigan
1109 Geddes Avenue
Ann Arbor, MI 48109-1079
(734) 764-0457

E-MAIL ADDRESS:
wos@salve.edu

WEB SITE ADDRESS:
www.wilsonsociety.org/awards/wosawards.html

FOUNDED: 1888

AREAS OF INTEREST:
Ornithology.

NAME(S) OF PROGRAMS:
• **Louis Agassiz Fuertes Award**
• **George A. Hall/Harold Mayfield Award**
• **Paul A. Stewart Award**
• **Student Travel Awards**
• **Alexander Wilson Student Presentation Award**

TYPE:
Grants-in-aid. Fuertes, Hall/Mayfield and Stewart Awards provide for the promotion and encouragement of field research on birds. A research proposal is required.

Student Travel Awards provide funds for students to attend the annual meeting.

Alexander Wilson Student Presentation Award is given to the best student paper presented at the annual meeting.

YEAR PROGRAM STARTED: 1947

PURPOSE:
To promote the scientific study of birds.

LEGAL BASIS:
Corporation.

ELIGIBILITY:
Each award requires a willingness of the awardee to report results of the research as an oral or poster paper at an annual meeting of the Wilson Ornithological Society.

Louis Agassiz Fuertes Award: Available to all ornithologists, although graduate students and young professionals are preferred. Any avian research is eligible.

George A. Hall/Harold Mayfield Award: Limited to independent researchers without access to funds and facilities available at colleges, universities or governmental agencies, and is restricted to nonprofessionals, including high school students. Any kind of avian research is eligible.

Paul A. Stewart Awards: Preference will be given to proposals for studies of bird movements based on banding, analysis of recoveries and returns of banded birds, with an emphasis on economic ornithology.

Student Travel Awards: Students presenting an oral paper or poster at WOS Annual Meeting are invited to apply.

FINANCIAL DATA:
Amount of support per award: Fuertes Award: $2,500; Hall/Mayfield Award: $1,000; Stewart Award: $500.

NUMBER OF APPLICANTS MOST RECENT YEAR:
102.

NUMBER OF AWARDS: Fuertes Award: 2; Hall/Mayfield Award: 1; Stewart Award: 8.

APPLICATION INFORMATION:
Requirements and application instructions are available on the Society web site.
Duration: One-time grant. Nonrenewable.
Deadline: February 1.

PUBLICATIONS:
Wilson Journal of Ornithology; *Wilson Bulletin*; *Guide to Graduate Programs in Ornithology*; *Manual of Ornithology*.

Environment

ACORN FOUNDATION [2163]
c/o Common Counsel Foundation
405 14th Street, Suite 809
Oakland, CA 94612
(510) 834-2995
Fax: (510) 834-2998

E-MAIL ADDRESS:
info@commoncounsel.org
grantsadmin@commoncounsel.org

WEB SITE ADDRESS:
www.commoncounsel.org

FOUNDED: 1978

AREAS OF INTEREST:
A sustainable ecological future and a healthy global environment.

TYPE:
General operating grants.

YEAR PROGRAM STARTED: 1978

PURPOSE:
To advance community-based organizations working for environmental conservation, sustainability and environmental justice.

ELIGIBILITY:
The Foundation makes grants to grassroots organizations. Organizational budget must be $400,000 or less. The Foundation is particularly interested in small and innovative community-based projects that engage in community organizing in order to:
(1) preserve and restore habitats supporting biological diversity and wildlife;
(2) advocate for environmental justice, particularly in low-income and indigenous communities and;
(3) prevent or remedy toxic pollution.

GEOGRAPHIC RESTRICTIONS:
Western and southern United States and Appalachia.

FINANCIAL DATA:
Amount of support per award: $5,000 to $10,000.

NUMBER OF APPLICANTS MOST RECENT YEAR:
More than 100.

NUMBER OF AWARDS: 10 to 14 per year.

APPLICATION INFORMATION:
Organizations that meet the eligibility and funding criteria are encouraged to submit a letter of inquiry form.
Duration: 12 months.
Deadline: January 15 and June 15 for spring and fall grantmaking meetings.

ADDRESS INQUIRIES TO:
Grants Administrator
(See address above.)

ALASKA CONSERVATION FOUNDATION [2164]
911 West Eighth Avenue
Suite 300
Anchorage, AK 99501
(907) 276-1917
Fax: (907) 274-4145

E-MAIL ADDRESS:
grants@alaskaconservation.org

WEB SITE ADDRESS:
www.alaskaconservation.org

AREAS OF INTEREST:
Conservation, ecosystem and lands protection, marine conservation, linking conservation with the economy and organizational effectiveness.

NAME(S) OF PROGRAMS:
• **Rapid Response Grant**

TYPE:
Awards/prizes; General operating grants; Internships; Project/program grants.

YEAR PROGRAM STARTED: 1977

PURPOSE:
To allow for a timely response to fast-breaking environmental issues of statewide or national importance.

ELIGIBILITY:
Incorporated, tax-exempt organizations, non-incorporated organizations, and individuals may apply for funding.

GEOGRAPHIC RESTRICTIONS:
Alaska.

FINANCIAL DATA:
Amount of support per award: $2,500 to
$10,000.
Total amount of support: $3,500,000 for the
year 2012.

APPLICATION INFORMATION:
Contact the Program Officer to determine if
the project fits within the grantmaking
program. ACF will invite full proposals to
appropriate projects. Rapid Response projects
must address an issue of statewide or
national importance. If invited, proposals to
the Rapid Response Fund should provide a
compelling narrative/justification, a clear
timeline, a detailed budget, and have a good
chance for success.
Duration: Up to six months.

EXECUTIVE DIRECTOR:
Ann Rothe

ADDRESS INQUIRIES TO:
See e-mail address above.

ALASKA CONSERVATION
FOUNDATION   [2165]
911 West Eighth Avenue
Suite 300
Anchorage, AK 99501
(907) 276-1917
Fax: (907) 274-4145

E-MAIL ADDRESS:
grants@alaskaconservation.org

WEB SITE ADDRESS:
www.alaskaconservation.org

FOUNDED: 1980

AREAS OF INTEREST:
Conservation, ecosystem and lands
protection, marine conservation, linking
conservation with the economy and
organizational effectiveness.

NAME(S) OF PROGRAMS:
● **ACF General Grants**
● **Alaska Native Fund**

TYPE:
General operating grants; Internships;
Project/program grants.

YEAR PROGRAM STARTED: 1980

PURPOSE:
To build strategic leadership and support for
Alaskan efforts to take care of wild lands,
water and wildlife, which sustain diverse
cultures, healthy communities and prosperous
economies.

LEGAL BASIS:
501(c)(3) public foundation.

ELIGIBILITY:
Incorporate, tax-exempt organizations,
non-incorporated organizations and
individuals may apply for funding.

Alaska Native Fund: Must perform work that
aligns with the priority environmental issues
and core strategies supported by the Fund
and be an Alaska Native individual, Tribe or
other Alaska Native nonprofit organization
(with Alaska Native majority on the Council
or Board of Directors).

GEOGRAPHIC RESTRICTIONS:
Alaska.

FINANCIAL DATA:
Amount of support per award: Alaska Native
Fund: $10,000 to $20,000; General Grants:
Up to $25,000.

APPLICATION INFORMATION:
Contact the Program Officer to determine if
the project fits within the grantmaking
program. ACF will invite full proposals to
appropriate projects.
Duration: Varies.
Deadline: Varies.

IRS IDENTIFICATION NUMBER: 92-0061466

EXECUTIVE DIRECTOR:
Ann Rothe

ADDRESS INQUIRIES TO:
See e-mail address above.

*SPECIAL STIPULATIONS:
ACF funds only in Alaska.

AMERICAN ACADEMY IN
ROME   [2166]
7 East 60th Street
New York, NY 10022
(212) 751-7200
Fax: (212) 751-7220

E-MAIL ADDRESS:
info@aarome.org

WEB SITE ADDRESS:
www.aarome.org

FOUNDED: 1894

AREAS OF INTEREST:
Landscape architecture.

NAME(S) OF PROGRAMS:
● **The Rome Prize Fellowship in
Landscape Architecture**

TYPE:
Awards/prizes; Fellowships; Residencies.
Provides a residential year at the American
Academy in Rome for an American
landscape architect for advanced study, travel
and association with other fellows in the arts
and humanities.

YEAR PROGRAM STARTED: 1920

PURPOSE:
To provide American landscape architects
with a special opportunity for advanced study
in Rome.

LEGAL BASIS:
Nonprofit, national organization.

ELIGIBILITY:
Applicants must hold an accredited degree in
landscape architecture, or equivalent
experience.

GEOGRAPHIC RESTRICTIONS:
United States.

FINANCIAL DATA:
Award consists of stipend, plus housing and
meals allowance.
Amount of support per award: $15,000 for
six-month fellowship; $28,000 for 11-month
fellowship.
Total amount of support: $90,000.

NUMBER OF APPLICANTS MOST RECENT YEAR:
22.

NUMBER OF AWARDS: 2 annually.

APPLICATION INFORMATION:
Applications are submitted electronically.
Duration: Six months or 11 months.
Deadline: November 1. Announcement in
April.

PUBLICATIONS:
Program announcement.

STAFF:
Mark Robbins, President
Shawn Miller, Program Director

ADDRESS INQUIRIES TO:
Program Director
(See address above.)

AMERICAN ALPINE CLUB [2167]
710 10th Street
Suite 100
Golden, CO 80401
(303) 384-0110
Fax: (303) 384-0111

E-MAIL ADDRESS:
grants@americanalpineclub.org
jmiller@americanalpineclub.org

WEB SITE ADDRESS:
www.americanalpineclub.org

FOUNDED: 1902

AREAS OF INTEREST:
Mountaineering, mountain environment and
polar regions.

NAME(S) OF PROGRAMS:
● **McNeill-Nott Climbing Award**
● **Mountain Fellowship**
● **Research Grants**
● **Lyman Spitzer Cutting Edge Climbing
Award**

TYPE:
Project/program grants; Research grants;
Travel grants. Grants to support research in
Arctic and alpine environments. Funds may
also be used to assist in publication or other
dissemination of the results of such research.

The Mountain Fellowship encourages young
American climbers under 26 years of age to
go into remote areas and seek out climbs
more difficult than they might ordinarily be
able to do.

YEAR PROGRAM STARTED: 1945

PURPOSE:
To encourage and broaden scientific research
in mountains and the polar regions.

LEGAL BASIS:
Membership organization.

ELIGIBILITY:
Individuals engaged in appropriate research
are eligible to apply.

FINANCIAL DATA:
Amount of support per award: Varies.
Total amount of support: Over $50,000
annually.

APPLICATION INFORMATION:
Application information is available on the
web site.
Duration: One-time grant. New application
required for ongoing projects.
Deadline: McNeill-Nott Climbing Award and
Lyman Spitzer Cutting Edge Climbing
Award: January 1. Announcement within four
to six weeks. Mountaineering Fund Grants:
April 1 and November 1. Notification eight
to 10 weeks after deadline. Research Grants:
March 1.

PUBLICATIONS:
Application guidelines.

ADDRESS INQUIRIES TO:
Janet Miller, Grants Manager
E-mail: jmiller@americanalpineclub.org

AMERICAN WATER RESOURCES ASSOCIATION [2168]

4 West Federal Street
Middleburg, VA 20118-1612
(540) 687-8390
Fax: (540) 687-8395

E-MAIL ADDRESS:
info@awra.org

WEB SITE ADDRESS:
www.awra.org

FOUNDED: 1964

AREAS OF INTEREST:
Water resources.

NAME(S) OF PROGRAMS:
● **Richard A. Herbert Memorial Educational Fund**

TYPE:
Scholarships.

YEAR PROGRAM STARTED: 1980

PURPOSE:
To advance multidisciplinary water resources management and research.

ELIGIBILITY:
Applicant must be a national AWRA member who is enrolled in a program related to water resources. May be a full-time undergraduate student working towards an undergraduate degree or a full-time graduate student.

The undergraduate scholarship will be awarded to the student most qualified by academic performance. Measures of academic performance include the cumulative grade point average, relevance of the student's curriculum to water resources, and leadership in extracurricular activities related to water resources. The graduate scholarship will be awarded to the student most qualified by academic and/or research performance.

FINANCIAL DATA:
Amount of support per award: $2,000.
Total amount of support: $4,000.

NUMBER OF APPLICANTS MOST RECENT YEAR: 3 undergraduate and 7 graduate applications.

NUMBER OF AWARDS: 4.

APPLICATION INFORMATION:
Submit a title page and summary of academic interests and achievements, extracurricular interests, and career goals as they relate to the selection criteria. Summaries must be limited to two pages. Include three letters of reference, a transcript of all college courses (undergraduate and graduate), and the applicant's full name, permanent mailing address, e-mail address, and a phone number at which applicant may be reached.
Duration: One year.
Deadline: April 22.

ADDRESS INQUIRIES TO:
AWRA Scholarship Coordinator
(See address above.)

BEN & JERRY'S FOUNDATION

30 Community Drive
South Burlington, VT 05403-6828
(802) 846-1500
Fax: (802) 846-1610

E-MAIL ADDRESS:
info@benandjerrysfoundation.org

WEB SITE ADDRESS:
www.benandjerrysfoundation.org

TYPE:
General operating grants; Project/program grants. Grants to nonprofit organizations which facilitate progressive social change by addressing the underlying conditions of societal and/or environmental problems using organizing as a strategy to create change.

See entry 982 for full listing.

BONNEVILLE ENVIRONMENTAL FOUNDATION [2169]

240 S.W. First Avenue
Portland, OR 97204-3503
(503) 248-1905
Fax: (503) 248-1908

E-MAIL ADDRESS:
info@b-e-f.org

WEB SITE ADDRESS:
www.b-e-f.org

FOUNDED: 1998

AREAS OF INTEREST:
Environmental conservation and the development of new sources of renewable energy.

NAME(S) OF PROGRAMS:
● **Model Watershed Program**
● **Renewable Energy Program**

TYPE:
Grants-in-aid. Model Watershed Program is intended to restore ecological integrity and native fish populations in watersheds across the western U.S.

Renewable Energy Program supports school solar projects and other renewable energy technologies that are taken up by utility and community-based renewable energy projects.

PURPOSE:
To support watershed restoration programs; to develop new sources of renewable energy.

ELIGIBILITY:
The Foundation does not fund residential projects.

FINANCIAL DATA:
Amount of support per award: Varies.
Total amount of support: Varies.

APPLICATION INFORMATION:
Complete application information is available on the Foundation web site.
Duration: Varies.

STAFF:
Angus Duncan, President
Dick Wanderscheid, Vice President for Renewable Energy Program
Todd Reeve, Chief Executive Officer
Robert Warren, Director, Model Watershed Program

BRAINERD FOUNDATION [2170]

1601 Second Avenue
Suite 610
Seattle, WA 98101
(206) 448-0676
Fax: (206) 448-7222

E-MAIL ADDRESS:
info@brainerd.org

WEB SITE ADDRESS:
www.brainerd.org

FOUNDED: 1995

AREAS OF INTEREST:
Environment.

NAME(S) OF PROGRAMS:
● **Grassroots Fund Grants**
● **Opportunity Fund Grants**

TYPE:
General operating grants; Matching gifts; Project/program grants; Training grants.

YEAR PROGRAM STARTED: 1995

PURPOSE:
To protect the environment of the Northwest and build broad citizen support for conservation.

ELIGIBILITY:
Organizations must be nonprofit classified as 501(c)(3) public charities by the IRS or Canadian organizations deemed equivalent by the Foundation.

GEOGRAPHIC RESTRICTIONS:
British Columbia and Yukon Territory, Canada; Alaska, Idaho, Montana, Oregon and Washington, United States.

FINANCIAL DATA:
Grants may be used to cover costs associated with, but not limited to, grassroots outreach, media strategies, litigation, scientific and economic studies, computer networking, and organizational capacity building.
Amount of support per award: Program Grants: $15,000 to $50,000; Grassroots Fund Grants: Up to $10,000; Opportunity Fund Grants: Up to $3,000.
Total amount of support: Varies.

APPLICATION INFORMATION:
Proposals by invitation only. One- to three-page letters of inquiry are accepted on a rolling basis. Each inquiry is weighed on its merits and strategic value, and on how it fits with guidelines. If a program officer invites a full proposal, a specific deadline will be given.
Duration: One year. Occasionally two.

STAFF:
Ann Krumboltz, Executive Director
Jim Owens, Senior Program Officer

BRUNSWICK PUBLIC FOUNDATION [2171]

One Northfield Court
Lake Forest, IL 60045
(847) 735-4344
Fax: (847) 735-4330

E-MAIL ADDRESS:
services@brunswick.com

WEB SITE ADDRESS:
www.brunswick.com

FOUNDED: 1998

AREAS OF INTEREST:
Environmental waterways.

TYPE:
Project/program grants.

PURPOSE:
To support community development primarily through contributions to preselected local United Way organizations; to support organizations that enhance the country's water resources for the recreational use by the public through proposals invited by the Foundation trustees.

ELIGIBILITY:
Grants are made to organizations that have tax-exempt status under Section 501(c)(3) of

the Internal Revenue Code. Nonsectarian religious programs may apply. No grants are made to individuals.

FINANCIAL DATA:
Amount of support per award: $5,000 to $100,000.
Total amount of support: $270,000 for the year 2012.

NUMBER OF AWARDS: 25.

APPLICATION INFORMATION:
Contact the Foundation for guidelines.
Duration: One year.
Deadline: March 15, July 15 and October 15.

IRS IDENTIFICATION NUMBER: 36-4195390

STAFF:
Lisa DeBartolo, Coordinator

BOARD OF DIRECTORS:
Jim Hubbard
David Knight
B. Russell Lockridge

ADDRESS INQUIRIES TO:
Lisa DeBartolo, Coordinator
(See address above.)

*SPECIAL STIPULATIONS:
By invitation only.

THE BULLITT FOUNDATION   [2172]

1501 East Madison
Seattle, WA 98122
(206) 343-0807
Fax: (206) 343-0822

E-MAIL ADDRESS:
info@bullitt.org

WEB SITE ADDRESS:
www.bullitt.org

FOUNDED: 1952

AREAS OF INTEREST:
Environment.

NAME(S) OF PROGRAMS:
• **Ecosystem Services**
• **Energy Industry and Technology**
• **Leadership and Civic Engagement**
• **Urban Ecology**

TYPE:
Development grants; General operating grants; Matching gifts; Project/program grants; Technical assistance; Training grants.

YEAR PROGRAM STARTED: 1952

PURPOSE:
To safeguard the natural environment by promoting responsible human activities and sustainable communities in the Pacific Northwest.

LEGAL BASIS:
Private foundation.

ELIGIBILITY:
Applicants must be organizations that have nonprofit tax status with clear, significant and achievable goals, as well as a cogent strategy to realize them. The trustees favor projects that avoid excessive reliance on any one source of funding. The Foundation cannot fund political elections or lobbying activities involving specific legislation. The Foundation does not fund university overhead costs or capital projects.

GEOGRAPHIC RESTRICTIONS:
Pacific Northwest, including Idaho, western Montana, Oregon and Washington state, coastal rainforests in Alaska and British Columbia, Canada.

FINANCIAL DATA:
Amount of support per award: Grants: $5,000 to $200,000; $35,000 average.
Total amount of support: $4,471,700 in grants for the year 2013.
Matching fund requirements: Employee and trustee donations will be matched.

NUMBER OF AWARDS: 125 for the year 2012.

REPRESENTATIVE AWARDS:
$50,000 to Justice Alliance Education Fund; $100,000 to Climate Solutions; $30,000 to Duwamish River Cleanup Coalition; $25,000 to Ecotrust.

APPLICATION INFORMATION:
An organization must first submit a proposal inquiry via the web site.

If invited, the organization must then submit a proposal. To apply for a grant, an organization must include:
(1) the Grant Request Cover Sheet, available upon request, and attach it to proposal. Be as clear as possible in identifying anticipated results for the project year. Try to answer the questions: "What is going to be better about the environment as a result of the project? How will the organization measure how successful the project has been?" Include measurable goals that directly relate to the Foundation's environmental priorities;
(2) a brief project description (no longer than five pages) defending the significance of the initiative and prospects for success. Relate the proposal to the Foundation's stated priorities. Grants are made on an annual (not multiyear) basis, so emphasize objectives for the project year. Identify the methods and criteria to be used to measure or determine results. Videos or other tapes are not encouraged unless necessary to describe the project;
(3) a work plan and timetable for the one-year funding period;
(4) a brief history of the accomplishments of the applicant organization and why it is best suited to address the stated need;
(5) the qualifications of those who will bear primary responsibility for the success of the initiative and the share of their time they will devote to the project;
(6) a list of the officers and directors of the organizations;
(7) a copy of the IRS determination letter verifying the tax-exempt status of the organization;
(8) a detailed budget of the project and the general budget of the sponsoring organization;
(9) an audited statement for the prior year or the IRS 990 report and;
(10) a detailed funding plan for the financial resources needed for the project, including other prospective sources of support.
Duration: One year. Renewal possible but not automatic; reapplication is necessary.
Deadline: Proposal inquiry: March 15 and November 15.

PUBLICATIONS:
Guidelines.

IRS IDENTIFICATION NUMBER: 91-6027795

TRUSTEES AND OFFICERS:
Maud Daudon, Chairperson
Harriet Bullitt, Vice Chairperson
Denis Hayes, President
Jabe Blumenthal, Treasurer
Rod Brown, Secretary
Howard Frumkin
Frank Greer

Martha Konsgaard
Michael Parham
Douglass Raff

ADDRESS INQUIRIES TO:
Program Officer
(See e-mail or address above.)

LIZ CLAIBORNE ART ORTENBERG FOUNDATION   [2173]

650 5th Avenue
15th Floor
New York, NY 10019
(212) 333-2536
Fax: (212) 956-3531

E-MAIL ADDRESS:
lcaof@lcaof.org

WEB SITE ADDRESS:
www.lcaof.org

FOUNDED: 1984

AREAS OF INTEREST:
Integration of conservation and development in the rural landscape.

TYPE:
Challenge/matching grants; Development grants; General operating grants; Project/program grants; Research grants; Seed money grants.

PURPOSE:
To conserve nature and relieve human distress; to redress the breakdown in the processes linking nature and humanity.

ELIGIBILITY:
The Foundation funds modest, carefully designed field projects, primarily in developing countries. No funding for general support or to underwrite institutional overhead. Local people should have a substantial proprietary interest in the project.

GEOGRAPHIC RESTRICTIONS:
Northern Rockies region of the United States.

FINANCIAL DATA:
Amount of support per award: $10,000 to $100,000.
Total amount of support: $4,200,000 for fiscal year 2013.

REPRESENTATIVE AWARDS:
$142,000 to African Conservation Centre for Amboseli Research and Conservation Program in Kenya and Tanzania; $49,030 to Wildlife Conservation Society for Tiger Conservation Program in Cambodia; $90,000 to Panthera Corporation for Jaguar Conservation Program in Brazil.

APPLICATION INFORMATION:
Contact the Foundation for guidelines.
Duration: One year.

PUBLICATIONS:
The View from Airlie; MONTANA: People and the Economy; brochure; Next Year Country-View from Red Lodge; 9 Case Studies on the Interior West of U.S.

TRUSTEES:
Victor Kovner
Alison Richard

DIRECTORS:
Douglas Chadwick
William Conway
William deBuys
Ullas Karanth
Grant Parker

George Schaller
David Western

ADDRESS INQUIRIES TO:
James Murtaugh, Program Director
Lori Cohen, Program Coordinator
(See address above.)

*PLEASE NOTE:
The Foundation is not accepting unsolicited proposals at this time.

COLUMBIA UNIVERSITY
Graduate School of Journalism
2950 Broadway, Room 303
New York, NY 10027-7004
(212) 854-6468
Fax: (212) 854-7701; (212) 854-3800

E-MAIL ADDRESS:
lsr21@columbia.edu

WEB SITE ADDRESS:
www.journalism.columbia.edu

TYPE:
Awards/prizes. Awarded for distinguished excellence in environmental journalism.

See entry 1928 for full listing.

CONSERVATION AND RESEARCH FOUNDATION [2174]
P.O. Box 909
Shelburne, VT 05482-0909
(802) 985-4106

E-MAIL ADDRESS:
minda@holdahl.com

WEB SITE ADDRESS:
conservationresearch.wordpress.com

FOUNDED: 1953

AREAS OF INTEREST:
Conservation and enlightened use of renewable natural resources, encouragement of related research in the biological sciences and promotion of methods to limit human fertility.

NAME(S) OF PROGRAMS:
● **Research and Conservation Grants**

TYPE:
Research grants; Seed money grants.

YEAR PROGRAM STARTED: 1953

PURPOSE:
To promote the conservation of the Earth's natural resources and deepen the understanding of the intricate relationship between people and the environment that supports them; to promote methods of limiting human reproduction.

LEGAL BASIS:
Public foundation.

ELIGIBILITY:
Grants to organizations and individuals engaged either in biological research or in conservation activities that might have a beneficial effect on environmental quality.

Appropriate background and credentials required. With respect to research, normally only those investigations that might, for one reason or another, be ineligible to receive funding from conventional granting agencies will be considered.

Grants do not cover institutional overhead.

Foundation does not provide funding for scholarships or fellowships.

FINANCIAL DATA:
Indirect costs usually not allowed.
Amount of support per award: Grants rarely exceed $5,000.
Total amount of support: $42,500 for the year 2013.

COOPERATIVE FUNDING PROGRAMS:
Occasionally required.

NUMBER OF AWARDS: 10 for the year 2013.

REPRESENTATIVE AWARDS:
$1,000 to Population Media Center; $2,000 to Western Lands Project; $2,000 to Connecticut River Council; $2,500 to Wild Earth Guardians; $500 to Living Oceans.

APPLICATION INFORMATION:
Proposals accepted only by invitation. A letter of inquiry with one-page abstract of proposal and budget may be submitted.
Deadline: August 31.

PUBLICATIONS:
Annual report; policy statement (available on web site).

IRS IDENTIFICATION NUMBER: 04-605-1843

OFFICERS:
Dr. Mary G. Wetzel, President
Myron Sopher, Treasurer
Dr. Philip M. Lintilhac, Secretary

TRUSTEES:
Dr. Tobias Baskin
Dr. Jon D. Erickson
Dr. Patricia Erickson
Richard H. Goodwin, Jr.
Crea S. Lintilhac
Dr. Philip M. Lintilhac
Dr. Ernesto Mendez
William N. Ryerson
Dr. Louise M. Tritton
Dr. Thomas C. Vogelmann
Dr. Mary G. Wetzel
Alexander T. Wilson

ADDRESS INQUIRIES TO:
Dr. Philip M. Lintilhac, Secretary
(See address above.)

COOPERATIVE INSTITUTE FOR RESEARCH IN ENVIRONMENTAL SCIENCES (CIRES) [2175]
CIRES Building, Room 318
University of Colorado
Boulder, CO 80309-0216
(303) 492-1143
Fax: (303) 492-1149

E-MAIL ADDRESS:
info@cires.colorado.edu
karen.dempsey@cires.colorado.edu

WEB SITE ADDRESS:
cires.colorado.edu/collaboration/fellowships

FOUNDED: 1967

AREAS OF INTEREST:
Physics, chemistry and dynamics of the earth system; global and regional environmental change; climate system monitoring, diagnostics, and modeling; development and application of remote sensing and in-situ measurement techniques for the earth and its atmosphere, cryosphere, ecosystems, and oceans.

NAME(S) OF PROGRAMS:
● **CIRES Visiting Fellowship Program in Environmental Sciences**

TYPE:
Fellowships. The program provides opportunities for interactions between CIRES scientists and visiting fellows to pursue common research interests. CIRES research includes theoretical studies, laboratory experimentation, and field investigations which may affect the enhancement of air and water quality and prediction of weather climate fluctuations.

YEAR PROGRAM STARTED: 1968

PURPOSE:
To provide support for scientists from around the world to visit CIRES and collaborate in a variety of research projects.

LEGAL BASIS:
Sponsored jointly by the University of Colorado and National Oceanic and Atmospheric Administration.

ELIGIBILITY:
Applicants must be Ph.D. scientists at all levels; faculty planning sabbatical leave and recent Ph.D. recipients are especially encouraged to apply. Priority is given to candidates with research experience at institutions outside the Boulder scientific community. The program is open to scientists of all countries. The University of Colorado is committed to diversity and equality in education and employment.

FINANCIAL DATA:
Amount of support per award: Stipend is flexible based on research experience.

NUMBER OF AWARDS: 16.

APPLICATION INFORMATION:
Applicant must send a resume, publications list and a brief (two- to four-page) description of the proposed research. In addition, candidates should request three letters of recommendation, to be sent directly to CIRES, from persons familiar with their qualifications. Postdoctoral-level applicants must also submit undergraduate and graduate transcripts.
Duration: One year. No renewal. Appointments can begin at any time during the year.
Deadline: December 31. Selection the following March.

ADDRESS INQUIRIES TO:
Karen Dempsey
Human Resources Coordinator
(See address above.)

THE ENERGY FOUNDATION [2176]
301 Battery Street, 5th Floor
San Francisco, CA 94111
(415) 561-6700
Fax: (415) 561-6709

E-MAIL ADDRESS:
energyfund@ef.org

WEB SITE ADDRESS:
www.ef.org

FOUNDED: 1991

AREAS OF INTEREST:
Energy efficiency and renewable energy.

TYPE:
Project/program grants. Promotes energy efficiency and renewable energy. Grants awarded in areas involving power, buildings, transportation, and climate programs.

YEAR PROGRAM STARTED: 1991

PURPOSE:
To assist in a national, and ultimately a global, transition to a sustainable future by promoting energy efficiency and renewable energy.

LEGAL BASIS:
Public charity 501(c)(3).

ELIGIBILITY:
501(c)(3) organizations only. No grants to individuals or for-profit organizations. Projects must have broad regional or national implications. No grants to religious organizations, political parties or for development of technology. No research and development or demonstration grants.

GEOGRAPHIC RESTRICTIONS:
United States and China.

FINANCIAL DATA:
Amount of support per award: Varies.
Total amount of support: Approximately $75,000,000 in grant payments for the year 2012.

NUMBER OF APPLICANTS MOST RECENT YEAR:
850 for the year 2012.

NUMBER OF AWARDS: 576 for the year 2012.

REPRESENTATIVE AWARDS:
$100,000 to the American Council for an Energy Efficient Economy to advance light and heavy duty vehicle standards and promote vehicle electrification; $80,000 to Renew Missouri to promote energy efficiency in Missouri; $50,000 to the Natural Resources Defense Council, Inc., to promote advanced codes and standards.

APPLICATION INFORMATION:
There is no fixed format for proposals. However, applications are available online. Applicant should include a statement of problem to be addressed, target audience, timeline, project budget, history of organization and intended mission and goals.
Duration: Typically one year. Renewal possible.

PUBLICATIONS:
Annual report.

IRS IDENTIFICATION NUMBER: 94-3126848

BOARD OF DIRECTORS:
Mark Burget
Robert Crane
Larry Goulder
Eric Heitz
Khee Poh Lam
Alan Lloyd
Kris Mayes
Bill Ritter, Jr.
William Ruckelshaus
Philip R. Sharp
Noa Staryk
Michael Wang
Hongjun Zhang

ADDRESS INQUIRIES TO:
Jason Mark, Senior Vice President and Director of U.S. Programs
(See address above.)

ENVIRONMENTAL LAW INSTITUTE
2000 L Street, N.W.
Suite 620
Washington, DC 20036-4919
(202) 939-3800
Fax: (202) 939-3868

E-MAIL ADDRESS:
law@eli.org

WEB SITE ADDRESS:
www.eli.org

TYPE:
Scholarships. Tuition scholarships to annual Environmental Law Course.

See entry 1974 for full listing.

FISHAMERICA FOUNDATION [2177]
1001 North Fairfax Street, Suite 501
Alexandria, VA 22314
(703) 519-9691
Fax: (703) 519-1872

E-MAIL ADDRESS:
fishamerica@asafishing.org

WEB SITE ADDRESS:
www.fishamerica.org

FOUNDED: 1983

AREAS OF INTEREST:
Environment and conservation.

NAME(S) OF PROGRAMS:
● **Fisheries Conservation and Research Projects**

TYPE:
Challenge/matching grants; Project/program grants; Research grants; Seed money grants.

YEAR PROGRAM STARTED: 1983

PURPOSE:
To provide funding for on-the-ground projects aimed at enhancing fish populations, restoring fish habitat, improving water quality and advancing fisheries research to improve sportfishing success.

LEGAL BASIS:
Public foundation, 501(c)(3).

ELIGIBILITY:
Any nonprofit tax-exempt organization including conservation organizations, sporting clubs, civic groups, and local and state agencies can apply.

GEOGRAPHIC RESTRICTIONS:
United States and Canada.

FINANCIAL DATA:
Amount of support per award: Average $15,000 per grant.
Total amount of support: $682,241 for conservation and research projects for fiscal year 2011.
Matching fund requirements: 1:1.

NUMBER OF APPLICANTS MOST RECENT YEAR:
162.

NUMBER OF AWARDS: 22.

REPRESENTATIVE AWARDS:
$50,000 to Elizabeth River Project, Portsmouth, VA, to improve fisheries habitat along the Elizabeth River in the Chesapeake Bay watershed; $7,512 to Rural Human Services of Crescent City, CA, to improve fisheries habitat in the Lower Klamath watershed by installing instream habitat structures, stabilizing eroding streambanks, and revegetating the riparian buffer along Sultan Creek; $14,600 to Idaho Department of Fish and Game to improve fish habitat in the Little Salmon River watershed.

APPLICATION INFORMATION:
Applicants should submit application, letter of support from the appropriate state resource agency biologist, and evidence of nonprofit status.
Duration: One year.

PUBLICATIONS:
Guidelines and application.

IRS IDENTIFICATION NUMBER: 36-3219015

BOARD OF DIRECTORS:
Gregg Wollner, Chairman
Dave Bulthuis, Vice Chairman
Jim Hubbard, Treasurer
Donn Schaible, Secretary
Thomas Dammrich
John Doerr
Ken Hammond
Kirk Immens
Martin MacDonald
Jeff Marble
Chris Megan
Dave Pfeiffer
Dick Pool
Tom Rolls
Paul Schluter
Aledia Hunt Tush
K.C. Walsh
Nick Wiley
Gary Zurn

ADDRESS INQUIRIES TO:
Grants Manager
(See address above.)

THE GARDEN CLUB OF AMERICA [2178]
14 East 60th Street, Third Floor
New York, NY 10022
(212) 753-8287
Fax: (212) 753-0134

E-MAIL ADDRESS:
scholarships@gcamerica.org

WEB SITE ADDRESS:
www.gcamerica.org

FOUNDED: 1913

AREAS OF INTEREST:
Horticulture, botany, landscape architecture and environmental studies.

NAME(S) OF PROGRAMS:
● **GCA Interchange Fellowship in Horticulture and Martin McLaren Scholarship**

TYPE:
Exchange programs; Fellowships. A graduate academic year in the U.S. for a British student and a work-study program for an American at universities and botanical gardens in the U.K. in fields related to horticulture, botany and landscape design.

YEAR PROGRAM STARTED: 1948

PURPOSE:
To foster British-American relations through the interchange of scholars in horticulture, botany, landscape architecture and environmental studies.

LEGAL BASIS:
Nonprofit, national organization.

ELIGIBILITY:
Open to men or women who are American citizens not older than 26 at the time of application. Applicants must have earned a B.A. or B.S. degree prior to the start of the Fellowship. They must be single and unaccompanied.

GEOGRAPHIC RESTRICTIONS:
United States.

FINANCIAL DATA:
The Fellowship covers the cost of tuition, travel expenses, board, lodging and incidental college expenses. It also provides an allowance for personal needs.
Amount of support per award: Varies.

COOPERATIVE FUNDING PROGRAMS: Sponsored jointly by the Garden Club of America and the Martin McLaren Scholarship in Horticulture, which is administered through the Institute of Horticulture.

NUMBER OF APPLICANTS MOST RECENT YEAR: 8.

NUMBER OF AWARDS: 2 annually.

APPLICATION INFORMATION:
Application form must be accompanied by: (1) one essay describing the applicant, including biographical data, how the applicant first became interested in horticulture, hobbies and special interests, travel in the U.S. and abroad, and applicant's ability to speak a foreign language; (2) one essay stating the reasons for applying for this scholarship, the specific field to be studied while in England, and what the applicant expects to gain and contribute, should he or she be awarded this scholarship; (3) copy of official college transcript and; (4) four letters of recommendation, including one from a college professor who knows the applicant well, and one from a personal reference (not a member of the applicant's family and not connected with the applicant's academic career). Please furnish names and addresses of those who are writing these recommendations.
Duration: 10-month program.
Deadline: February 1.

PUBLICATIONS:
Program announcement.

ADDRESS INQUIRIES TO:
Martin McLaren Scholarship:
Danielle Lella, Administrator
The Garden Club of America
Interchange Fellowship
(See address above.)

Interchange Fellowship (funds British student):
Marjorie Noel
E-mail: mclarenscholarship@rhs.org.uk

THE GARDEN CLUB OF AMERICA [2179]
14 East 60th Street, Third Floor
New York, NY 10022
(212) 753-8287
Fax: (212) 753-0134

E-MAIL ADDRESS:
scholarships@gcamerica.org

WEB SITE ADDRESS:
www.gcamerica.org

FOUNDED: 1913

AREAS OF INTEREST:
Plant preservation and tropical botany.

NAME(S) OF PROGRAMS:
- **The Anne S. Chatham Fellowship in Medicinal Botany**
- **Garden Club of America Awards in Tropical Botany**
- **The Frances M. Peacock Scholarship for Native Bird Habitat**

TYPE:
Research grants. Anne S. Chatham Fellowship in Medicinal Botany: Grant to enable study in medicinal botany.

GCA Awards in Tropical Botany: Grants to enable field study in tropical botany.

Frances M. Peacock Scholarship for Native Bird Habitat: Financial assistance to college seniors and graduate students to study habitat-related issues that will benefit threatened or endangered bird species and lend useful information for land management decisions.

YEAR PROGRAM STARTED: 1983

PURPOSE:
Anne S. Chatham Fellowship in Medicinal Botany: To protect and preserve knowledge about the medicinal use of plants by providing research support in the field of ethnobotany.

GCA Awards in Tropical Botany: To promote the preservation of tropical forests by enlarging the body of botanists with field experience.

Frances M. Peacock Scholarship for Native Bird Habitat: To study areas in the U.S. that provide winter or summer habitat for threatened and endangered native birds.

LEGAL BASIS:
Nonprofit, national organization.

ELIGIBILITY:
Chatham Fellowship in Medicinal Botany: Open to Ph.D. candidates and recent Ph.Ds.

GCA Awards in Tropical Botany: Open to Ph.D. candidates who will be carrying on field work in the tropics as a part of their doctoral dissertation research. Preference will be given to applications from those graduate students indicating that they have a long-term commitment to conservation of the forests. Nationality is not a criterion.

Peacock Scholarship for Native Bird Habitat: College seniors and graduate students.

GEOGRAPHIC RESTRICTIONS:
United States.

FINANCIAL DATA:
Amount of support per award: Chatham Fellowship in Medicinal Botany: $4,000; GCA Awards in Tropical Botany: $5,500; Peacock Scholarship for Native Bird Habitat: $4,000.

Total amount of support: Varies each year depending on funds.

NUMBER OF APPLICANTS MOST RECENT YEAR: 15.

NUMBER OF AWARDS: Chatham Fellowship in Medicinal Botany: 1; GCA Awards in Tropical Botany: 2 annually; Peacock Scholarship for Native Bird Habitat: 1.

APPLICATION INFORMATION:
Applications should include:
(1) a curriculum vitae for the student, including graduate and undergraduate transcripts;
(2) a two-page outline of the proposed research and a letter of recommendation from the advisor, which should include an evaluation of the student's progress to date and plans for the future and;
(3) evidence of foreign language capability, if necessary for country of research.

Further information regarding the GCA Awards in Tropical Botany is available from the World Wildlife Fund at the address below.

Duration: One year.
Deadline: Chatham Fellowship in Medicinal Botany: February 1; GCA Awards in Tropical Botany and Peacock Scholarship for Native Bird Habitat: January 15.

PUBLICATIONS:
Program announcement.

STAFF:
Danielle Lella, Administrator

ADDRESS INQUIRIES TO:
Awards in Tropical Botany:
Andrea Santy
World Wildlife Fund
1250 24th Street, N.W., Suite 500
Washington, DC 20037
Tel: (202) 495-4447

Chatham Fellowship:
Dr. Robert E. Magill
Missouri Botanical Garden
P.O. Box 299
St. Louis, MO 63166
Tel: (314) 577-9503

Peacock Scholarship:
Scott Sutcliffe
Cornell Lab of Ornithology
159 Sapsucker Woods Road
Ithaca, NY 14850
Fax: (607) 254-2415

THE GARDEN CLUB OF AMERICA [2180]
14 East 60th Street, Third Floor
New York, NY 10022
(212) 753-8287
Fax: (212) 753-0134

E-MAIL ADDRESS:
scholarships@gcamerica.org

WEB SITE ADDRESS:
www.gcamerica.org

FOUNDED: 1913

AREAS OF INTEREST:
Conservation, historic preservation and plant conservation, and tropical plant study.

NAME(S) OF PROGRAMS:
- **Catherine Beattie Fellowship**
- **The GCA Award in Coastal Wetland Studies**
- **The Loy McCandless Marks Scholarship in Tropical Ornamental Horticulture**

TYPE:
Fellowships. Beattie Fellowship: Research grant to a graduate student in the horticultural field to conduct field research on the biology and management of rare plants in conjunction with the programs of the Center for Plant Conservation headquartered at the Missouri Botanical Garden.

GCA Award in Coastal Wetland Studies: Seeks to promote wetland conservation through the support of young scientists in their field work and research.

Loy McCandless Marks Scholarship in Tropical Ornamental Horticulture: Affords a graduate student, or advanced undergraduate, an opportunity to study tropical ornamental horticulture at an appropriate foreign institution specializing in the study of tropical plants. Scholarship is given biennially in even years.

YEAR PROGRAM STARTED: 1983

PURPOSE:
Beattie Fellowship: To promote conservation of rare and endangered flora in the U.S.

The GCA Award in Coastal Wetland Studies: To promote wetlands conservation through the support of young scientists in their field work and research.

Loy McCandless Marks Scholarship in Tropical Ornamental Horticulture: To foster the study of tropical plants and their use in horticulture and landscape architecture.

LEGAL BASIS:
Nonprofit, national organization.

ELIGIBILITY:
Beattie Fellowship: Preference is given to graduate students whose projects focus on the endangered flora of the Carolinas and the southeastern U.S.

GCA Award in Coastal Wetland Studies: Graduate students.

Loy McCandless Marks Scholarship in Tropical Ornamental Horticulture: Graduate students and advanced undergraduates.

GEOGRAPHIC RESTRICTIONS:
United States.

FINANCIAL DATA:
Amount of support per award: Beattie Fellowship: Up to $4,000; GCA Award in Coastal Wetland Studies: $5,000; Loy McCandless Marks Scholarship in Tropical Ornamental Horticulture: $2,000.

NUMBER OF AWARDS: Beattie Fellowship, GCA Award in Coastal Wetland Studies and Loy McCandless Marks Scholarship in Tropical Ornamental Horticulture: 1 annually.

APPLICATION INFORMATION:
Guidelines and application form are available online.
Duration: One year.
Deadline: Beattie Fellowship: November 30; GCA Award in Coastal Wetland Studies: January 15; Loy McCandless Marks Scholarship in Tropical Ornamental Horticulture: January 15 in even years only.

PUBLICATIONS:
Program announcement.

ADDRESS INQUIRIES TO:
Beattie Fellowship:
Kathryn Kennedy
President and Executive Director
The Center for Plant Conservation
Missouri Botanical Garden
P.O. Box 299
St. Louis, MO 63166-0299

Loy McCandless Marks Scholarship and GCA Awards:
Danielle Lella, Administrator
The Garden Club of America
(See address above.)

THE GARDEN CLUB OF AMERICA [2181]
14 East 60th Street, Third Floor
New York, NY 10022
(212) 753-8287
Fax: (212) 753-0134

E-MAIL ADDRESS:
scholarships@gcamerica.org

WEB SITE ADDRESS:
www.gcamerica.org

FOUNDED: 1913

AREAS OF INTEREST:
Conservation, historic preservation and plant conservation.

NAME(S) OF PROGRAMS:
● GCA Awards for Summer Environmental Studies

TYPE:
Scholarships.

YEAR PROGRAM STARTED: 1964

PURPOSE:
To encourage studies and careers in the environmental field.

LEGAL BASIS:
Nonprofit, national organization.

ELIGIBILITY:
Open to a qualified undergraduate entering a summer program following the freshman, sophomore, and junior years.

FINANCIAL DATA:
Amount of support per award: $2,000.

NUMBER OF AWARDS: 4 or more.

APPLICATION INFORMATION:
Application guidelines and form are available online.
Deadline: January 10.

PUBLICATIONS:
Program announcement.

ADDRESS INQUIRIES TO:
Magda Cruz, Liaison
Scholarship Committee-Summer Studies
(See address above.)

GREAT LAKES PROTECTION FUND [2182]
1560 Sherman Avenue
Suite 880
Evanston, IL 60201
(847) 425-8150
Fax: (847) 424-9832

E-MAIL ADDRESS:
info@glpf.org

WEB SITE ADDRESS:
www.glpf.org

FOUNDED: 1989

AREAS OF INTEREST:
To identify, demonstrate and promote regional action to enhance the health of the Great Lakes ecosystem.

NAME(S) OF PROGRAMS:
● Great Lakes Protection Fund

TYPE:
Demonstration grants; Development grants; Seed money grants.

YEAR PROGRAM STARTED: 1990

PURPOSE:
To support projects that identify, demonstrate and promote regional action to enhance the health of the Great Lakes ecosystem.

LEGAL BASIS:
Nonprofit, multi-state endowment.

ELIGIBILITY:
The Great Lakes Protection Fund can support a wide variety of applicants. Nonprofit organizations (including environmental organizations, trade associations, and universities), for-profit businesses, government agencies, and individuals are eligible for Fund support. Successful applicants must maintain open access to certain project data, records and information.

All applicants must comply with the Fund's guidelines, show that the proposed work has clear public benefit to the Great Lakes basin, and that any related financial benefits will accrue to the public good. Government agencies must show that Fund support is not being used to replace or duplicate public funds.

FINANCIAL DATA:
Amount of support per award: Varies.
Total amount of support: Varies.

REPRESENTATIVE AWARDS:
$435,000 over 24 months to the Delta Institute to develop a series of tools to track and measure the full extent of the environmental impacts associated with specific reduction actions. Working with 13 facilities in Michigan, the team expects to reduce water use by over 15 million gallons per day, to eliminate almost 3 million tons of solid waste, reduce CO_2 emissions by over 11,000 tons, reduce emissions of criteria air pollutants by 150,000 pounds, and reduce hazard chemical use by over 200,000 gallons each year. The tools developed will provide a more accurate account of how on-site energy efficiency actions translate into "real" air pollutant reductions at a power generating facility. In conjunction with a panel of Sustainability Institute Fellows, the team will verify these ecosystem impacts and identify third-party transactions to retire the benefits.

APPLICATION INFORMATION:
The first step is the submission of a brief proposal that summarizes the proposed project. The following documents must be included:
(1) completed applicant cover sheet;
(2) preproposal document, no more than three pages, describing the environmental outcome, proposed work, key personnel and financial plan and;
(3) a resume of the project's manager (no more than two pages).

Preproposal documents can be submitted by e-mail to preproposal@glpf.org or send six copies addressed to Preproposal Application, Great Lakes Protection Fund, at the address above.
Duration: Multiyear.

PUBLICATIONS:
Annual report; guidelines for funding; summary papers.

STAFF:
Russell Van Herik, Executive Director
Robert Eder, Vice President and Director of Finance and Administration
David Rankin, Vice President and Director of Programs
Amy Elledge, Communications Manager
Stephanie Lindeloff, Project Development Manager
Shannon Donley, Project Implementation Manager

BOARD MEMBERS:
Patty Birkholz
Lori Boughton
Kathleen Brown
Matthew Driscoll
Frederick Dudderar
Michael Elmendorf
Edwin Hammett
Richard Hylant
Ken Johnson
Jeffrey Logan
Richard Meeusen
Craig Shaver
Debra Shore
Mauree Smyth

ADDRESS INQUIRIES TO:
E-mail: startaconversation@glpf.org

THE JACOB AND TERESE HERSHEY FOUNDATION [2183]

2121 San Felipe
Suite 122
Houston, TX 77019
(713) 529-7611
Fax: (713) 529-7613

E-MAIL ADDRESS:
judithboyce@jthershey.org
teresethershey@jthershey.org

FOUNDED: 1961

AREAS OF INTEREST:
Animal protection, conservation, environmental, open space and parks, environmental education, land acquisition and human population control.

TYPE:
Capital grants; Conferences/seminars; Development grants; General operating grants; Matching gifts; Project/program grants; Seed money grants. Land acquisition for conversation.

YEAR PROGRAM STARTED: 1961

PURPOSE:
To promote preservation and conservation of land, forests, streams, wetlands and habitat existing in a natural state and the defense of such resources; to establish, conserve and preserve parks and open space for public use; to help provide care facilities for animals and birds, both domestic and wild; to aid education efforts to promote environmental literacy and comprehension of the complexities of the web of life, particularly in museums and through citizen nonprofit organizations with similar purpose; to promote efforts toward population control.

LEGAL BASIS:
Private foundation.

ELIGIBILITY:
Grants are made to organizations that have tax-exempt status under Section 501(c)(3) of the Internal Revenue Code. Grants are not made to medical or religious institutions or groups, or to individuals. No grants for galas or parties. Multiple funding sources are encouraged.

GEOGRAPHIC RESTRICTIONS:
Southwestern Colorado; Austin and Houston, Texas areas.

FINANCIAL DATA:
Amount of support per award: $2,000 to $7,500.
Total amount of support: $350,000 to $400,000.

NUMBER OF APPLICANTS MOST RECENT YEAR:
85.

NUMBER OF AWARDS: 60.

APPLICATION INFORMATION:
Submit written applications only. No general solicitations or bulk mailings. Keep the application simple. One copy only.

Contact the Foundation for one-page grant guidelines.

Duration: One year. May reapply.

Deadline: April 15 and September 15. Applicant will receive an acknowledgement of receipt of application, as well as the date of the meeting at which it will be considered.

IRS IDENTIFICATION NUMBER: 74-6039126

EXECUTIVE DIRECTOR:
Judith Boyce

ADDRESS INQUIRIES TO:
Judith Boyce, Executive Director
(See address above.)

THE HUDSON RIVER FOUNDATION [2184]

17 Battery Place, Suite 915
New York, NY 10004
(212) 483-7667
Fax: (212) 924-8325

E-MAIL ADDRESS:
info@hudsonriver.org

WEB SITE ADDRESS:
www.hudsonriver.org

FOUNDED: 1981

AREAS OF INTEREST:
Environmental, ecological and public policy aspects of the Hudson River estuary.

NAME(S) OF PROGRAMS:
- **Hudson River Fund**
- **Hudson River Improvement Fund**
- **New York City Environmental Fund**

TYPE:
Capital grants; Fellowships; Research grants; Travel grants. The Hudson River Fund was created to meet the critical need for an independent institution to sponsor scientific research programs that would contribute to the development of sound public policy concerning the River's ecological system. The Hudson River Fund makes grants in five categories: Hudson River Research Grants, Travel Grants, Expedited Grants, Hudson River Graduate Fellowships, and Tibor T. Polgar Fellowships.

The Hudson River Improvement Fund supports projects to enhance public use and enjoyment of the Hudson River's natural, scenic and cultural resources. The emphasis of the Improvement Fund is on physical projects requiring capital construction, development, or improvement.

The New York City Environmental Fund proposes to foster "restoration, care, public enjoyment of, and education about New York City's natural resources."

YEAR PROGRAM STARTED: 1983

PURPOSE:
To make science integral to decision-making with regard to the Hudson River and its watershed; to support competent stewardship of this extraordinary resource.

LEGAL BASIS:
Private foundation.

ELIGIBILITY:
Research must be focused on Hudson River.

FINANCIAL DATA:
Amount of support per award: Graduate Fellowships: Up to $11,000 for one year, plus up to $1,000 toward supplies (doctoral students); up to $15,000 for one year, plus up to $1,000 for supplies (Master's students). Polgar Fellowships: $3,800, plus $1,000 for equipment and supplies.
Total amount of support: Varies.

NUMBER OF APPLICANTS MOST RECENT YEAR:
60 for research grants.

NUMBER OF AWARDS: 11.

APPLICATION INFORMATION:
Guidelines available online.
Duration: One to two years for fellowships.
Deadline: Contact the Foundation.

PUBLICATIONS:
Annual Program Plan; *Hudson River Fund: Call for Proposals.*

EXECUTIVE DIRECTOR:
Clay Hiles

ILLINOIS CLEAN ENERGY COMMUNITY FOUNDATION [2185]

2 North LaSalle Street, Suite 1140
Chicago, IL 60602
(312) 372-5191
Fax: (312) 372-5190

E-MAIL ADDRESS:
dobrien@illinoiscleanenergy.org

WEB SITE ADDRESS:
www.illinoiscleanenergy.org

FOUNDED: 1999

AREAS OF INTEREST:
Improving the environmental quality of life in the state of Illinois and natural habitat preservation.

TYPE:
Grants-in-aid; Project/program grants. The Foundation provides financial support in two principal ways:
(1) Grantmaking: The Foundation provides grants on a competitive basis, in response to proposals submitted by organizations in accord with the Foundation's announced strategic priorities and the application process described below. The Foundation can provide several different types of financial support, including grants.
(2) Direct Initiatives: The Foundation identifies strategic opportunities to undertake large-scale, high-impact projects and special initiatives that further its program objectives in energy efficiency, renewable energy and natural areas conservation.

YEAR PROGRAM STARTED: 2001

PURPOSE:
To invest in clean energy development and land preservation efforts, working with communities and citizens to improve environmental quality in Illinois.

LEGAL BASIS:
Independent, nonprofit grantmaking institution.

ELIGIBILITY:
The Foundation provides funding to tax-exempt organizations, including governmental entities. The Foundation will not provide funding for remediation of environmentally impaired properties, technology research, promotion of proprietary products, reoccurring operating costs, political campaigns or lobbying, capital campaigns or support for an organization's endowment, or projects undertaken by individuals.

GEOGRAPHIC RESTRICTIONS:
Illinois.

FINANCIAL DATA:
Amount of support per award: $2,000 to $500,000.
Total amount of support: Approximately $13,000,000 in total grants awarded for the year 2012.

APPLICATION INFORMATION:
Guidelines available on the web site.
Duration: One to two years.

ADDRESS INQUIRIES TO:
Bob Romo, Senior Program Officer
(See address above.)

INTERNATIONAL CRANE FOUNDATION, INC.
E-11376 Shady Lane Road
Baraboo, WI 53913
(608) 356-9462
Fax: (608) 356-9465

E-MAIL ADDRESS:
cranes@savingcranes.org

WEB SITE ADDRESS:
www.savingcranes.org

TYPE:
Internships. Formal stipended internship
programs in the fields of aviculture, crane
ecology and conservation education.

See entry 2148 for full listing.

LANDSCAPE ARCHITECTURE FOUNDATION   [2186]
1129 20th Street, N.W.
Suite 202
Washington, DC 20036
(202) 331-7070 ext. 16
Fax: (202) 331-7079

E-MAIL ADDRESS:
scholarships@lafoundation.org

WEB SITE ADDRESS:
www.lafoundation.org/scholarships

FOUNDED: 1966

AREAS OF INTEREST:
The profession of landscape architecture.

NAME(S) OF PROGRAMS:
- **ASLA Council of Fellows Scholarship**
- **EDSA Minority Scholarship**
- **Hawaii Chapter David T. Woolsey Scholarship**
- **Steven G. King Play Environments Scholarship**
- **Landscape Forms Design for People Scholarship**
- **Olmsted Scholars Program**
- **Courtland Paul Scholarship**
- **Peridian International/Rae L. Price, FASLA Scholarship**
- **Rain Bird Intelligent Use of Water Scholarship**
- **Douglas Dockery Thomas Fellowship in Garden History and Design**

TYPE:
Fellowships; Scholarships. Awards for
undergraduate and graduate students pursuing
an education in landscape architecture.

PURPOSE:
To assist students enrolled in programs of
landscape architecture.

LEGAL BASIS:
Nonprofit, tax-exempt foundation.

ELIGIBILITY:
Open to undergraduate and graduate students
currently enrolled in a professional degree
program in landscape architecture. Available
to students in financial need who show
promise and commitment to the profession.

GEOGRAPHIC RESTRICTIONS:
United States and Canada.

FINANCIAL DATA:
Amount of support per award: Olmsted
Scholars Program: $25,000 for graduate

winner and $15,000 for undergraduate
winner; $1,000 for finalist. All others: $2,000
to $5,000.
Total amount of support: $85,000.

NUMBER OF APPLICANTS MOST RECENT YEAR:
150.

NUMBER OF AWARDS: 17.

APPLICATION INFORMATION:
Application information is available on the
web site.
Duration: One academic year.
Deadline: Douglas Dockery Thomas
Fellowship: February 1. All others: February
15.

PUBLICATIONS:
Guidelines.

ADDRESS INQUIRIES TO:
Heather Whitlow, Director of Programs
and Communications
(See address and e-mail above.)

THE LEF FOUNDATION
P.O. Box 382066
Cambridge, MA 02238-2066
(617) 492-5333
Fax: (617) 868-5603

E-MAIL ADDRESS:
sara@lef-foundation.org

WEB SITE ADDRESS:
www.lef-foundation.org

TYPE:
Project/program grants; Seed money grants.
Program development.

See entry 418 for full listing.

MARSHALL COMMUNITY FOUNDATION
614 Homer Road
Marshall, MI 49068
(269) 781-2273
Fax: (269) 781-9747

E-MAIL ADDRESS:
info@marshallcf.org

WEB SITE ADDRESS:
www.marshallcf.org

TYPE:
Project/program grants.

See entry 1565 for full listing.

MONSANTO FUND   [2187]
800 North Lindbergh Boulevard, A2N
St. Louis, MO 63167
(314) 694-5322
Fax: (314) 694-7658

E-MAIL ADDRESS:
monsanto.fund@monsanto.com

WEB SITE ADDRESS:
www.monsantofund.org

FOUNDED: 1964

AREAS OF INTEREST:
Improving nutritional well-being through
agriculture, science education, the
environment and Monsanto communities.

TYPE:
Project/program grants.

PURPOSE:
To improve the Earth's ecosystem - including
clean water, clean air, productive land and

thriving biodiversity - and the well-being of
her people by supporting projects in the
focus areas.

ELIGIBILITY:
Applicants must be nonprofit 501(c)(3) or
units of government 170(c)(1). Proposed
projects must fit within one of the focus
areas. Must be an experienced, established
and reputable organization (not a start-up
organization), financially sound with a
diverse funding base, and be audited
annually.

Grants are not given to religious
organizations.

FINANCIAL DATA:
Amount of support per award: $2,500 to
$250,000.
Total amount of support: Varies.

APPLICATION INFORMATION:
Application information is available online.
Duration: One to two years.
Deadline: Varies.

NATIONAL FISH AND WILDLIFE FOUNDATION   [2188]
1133 15th Street, N.W.
Suite 1100
Washington, DC 20005
(202) 857-0166
Fax: (202) 857-0162

E-MAIL ADDRESS:
info@nfwf.org

WEB SITE ADDRESS:
www.nfwf.org

FOUNDED: 1984

AREAS OF INTEREST:
Conservation of natural resources including
fish, wildlife and plants.

TYPE:
Challenge/matching grants; Formula grants;
Matching gifts; Project/program grants;
Scholarships.

YEAR PROGRAM STARTED: 1986

PURPOSE:
To conserve natural resources through habitat
protection, environmental education, natural
resource management, species conservation
and leadership training for conservation
professionals.

LEGAL BASIS:
Private 501(c)(3) organization.

ELIGIBILITY:
Must be a 501(c)(3) organization. No grants
to individuals.

FINANCIAL DATA:
With $49,000,000 in federal funds and
$147,000,000 in private contributions and
grantee matching funds, the Foundation's
total conservation investments topped
$197,000,000 for the year 2013.
Amount of support per award: Varies.
Matching fund requirements: At least 1:1,
preference for higher leverage.

NUMBER OF APPLICANTS MOST RECENT YEAR:
Varies.

NUMBER OF AWARDS: Varies.

REPRESENTATIVE AWARDS:
$100,000 to Iowa Department of Natural
Resources to restore 1,254 acres of
bottomland hardwood forest in northeast
Iowa on former agricultural lands. The
project is working to reduce forest
fragmentation, enhance water quality, and

improve critical habitat for neo-tropical birds and other wildlife; $400,000 to Conservation Fund to reduce nutrient and sediment runoff entering Rockymarsh Run – a tributary to the Potomac River and ultimately the Chesapeake Bay; $87,800 to Environmental Defense to develop and implement 12 habitat restoration projects on 250 acres of private lands in New York, Maryland, and Pennsylvania. Restoration will help recover the federally endangered bog turtle population as well as other rare species that rely on fens and other shallow wetlands.

APPLICATION INFORMATION:
Information on application can be obtained from the Foundation.
Duration: Support usually lasts for one year. Renewals are on a case-by-case basis.
Deadline: Contact the Foundation for exact dates.

PUBLICATIONS:
Annual report; application guidelines.

IRS IDENTIFICATION NUMBER: 52-1384129

STAFF:
Robert Menzi, Executive Vice President, Finance and Operations
Claude Gascon, Ph.D., Executive Vice President, Science, Evaluation and Programs
Jeff Trandahl, Executive Director/Chief Executive Officer

BOARD OF DIRECTORS:
Dan Ashe
Michael L. Campbell
J. Michael Cline
Lance Conn
Ray Dalio
John V. Faraci, Jr.
Caroline Getty
J.J. Healy
George C. (Tim) Hixon
Patsy Ishiyama
Christopher M. James
Paul Tudor Jones, II
James P. Kelley
Eaddo H. Kiernan
Carl R. Kuehner, III
Reuben Mark
Charles D. McCrary
Don J. McGrath
R. King Milling
Ruth O'Donnell Mutch
David Perkins
Chad Pike
Amy Robbins Towers
Edwin Rodriguez, Jr.
Thomas L. Strickland
Kathryn D. Sullivan
John A. Tomke
Victoria J. Tschinkel
John E. von Schlegell
Steven A. Williams

ADDRESS INQUIRIES TO:
Appropriate Partnership Office Director
(See address above.)

NATIONAL INSTITUTE OF ENVIRONMENTAL HEALTH SCIENCES   [2189]
Division of Extramural Research and Training, MD K3-05
111 T.W. Alexander Drive
Research Triangle Park, NC 27709
(919) 541-3289
Fax: (919) 541-2843

E-MAIL ADDRESS:
mastin@niehs.nih.gov

WEB SITE ADDRESS:
www.niehs.nih.gov

FOUNDED: 1966

AREAS OF INTEREST:
Research on environmental agents and chemicals and their effects on human health.

NAME(S) OF PROGRAMS:
• **Environmental Health Sciences Research and Training Grants**

TYPE:
Conferences/seminars; Demonstration grants; Development grants; Fellowships; Project/program grants; Research grants; Training grants. NIEHS pursues its mission by supporting basic and applied research on the consequences of the exposure of humans to potentially toxic or harmful agents in the environment.

Research of interest encompasses studies that relate to the biological effects of environmental chemicals and physical factors including such agents as hazardous gases, suspended particles, aerosols, industrial by-products and intermediates, heavy metals, trace elements, food additives, adulterants and pesticides. Physical factors include noise, light, heat, microwaves and other forms of nonionizing radiation.

Research Training Programs support individuals at both the predoctoral and postdoctoral levels in the areas of environmental toxicology, environmental pathology, environmental mutagenesis and environmental epidemiology.

YEAR PROGRAM STARTED: 1966

PURPOSE:
To support research and research training in environmental health.

LEGAL BASIS:
Government agency authorized under Section 301(d), Public Health Services Act; 42 U.S.C. 241; 42 C.F.R. 52.

ELIGIBILITY:
Universities, research institutes and other public or private institutions may apply on behalf of qualified researchers. Small businesses may apply for SBIR grants.

GEOGRAPHIC RESTRICTIONS:
United States.

FINANCIAL DATA:
Funds are provided, as available, for all allowable expenses associated with approved research projects.
Amount of support per award: Varies.
Total amount of support: Varies.

APPLICATION INFORMATION:
Guidelines available on the web site.
Duration: Total grant project periods may not exceed five years and are renewable on a competitive basis at the end of the project period. Average project period length is currently four years.
Deadline: Varies with the specific grant.

PUBLICATIONS:
Fact book; special announcements.

STAFF:
Dr. Carol Shreffler, Health Science Administrator

ADDRESS INQUIRIES TO:
J. Patrick Mastin, Ph.D.
Deputy Director
(See address above.)

NATIONAL PARK FOUNDATION   [2190]
1201 Eye Street, N.W.
Suite 550B
Washington, DC 20005
(202) 354-6460
Fax: (202) 371-2066

E-MAIL ADDRESS:
ask-npf@nationalparks.org

WEB SITE ADDRESS:
www.nationalparks.org

FOUNDED: 1967

AREAS OF INTEREST:
Diversity, climate change, and natural and historic preservation and protection

NAME(S) OF PROGRAMS:
• **Active Trails**
• **Albright-Wirth Grants Program**
• **America's Best Idea**
• **The Junior Ranger Program**
• **Parks Climate Challenge**
• **Parks Stewards Program**
• **Transportation Scholars**
• **Harry Yount National Park Ranger Award**

TYPE:
Block grants; Challenge/matching grants; Research grants; Scholarships. Grants range from small seed or start-up programs to larger ones which continue successful projects. Grants enable the parks to obtain additional cash and in-kind contributions, such as products, service or volunteer time.

The Albright-Wirth Employee Development Fund underwrites advanced skills training, graduate education and other professional development programs for Park Service employees.

The Harry Yount National Park Ranger Award recognizes a Ranger for leadership, exemplary skills and dedication to the Park Ranger profession.

YEAR PROGRAM STARTED: 1967

PURPOSE:
To help fund important conservation, preservation, and education efforts on-the-ground in the National Parks.

LEGAL BASIS:
Nonprofit organization.

ELIGIBILITY:
All grants are made directly for projects in the national park system. Grants will fund educational projects, field training for volunteers and interns, resource conservation, historic preservation, interpretation programs for park visitors, outreach programs, and park projects conducted by park friends, cooperating associations or academic institutions.

The grants program will not fund the purchase of vehicles or maintenance equipment, new construction or large-scale improvements to buildings, infrastructure construction or maintenance of roads and utilities, base salaries of full-time NPS staff, advocacy or litigation, or the start-up costs of friends groups.

FINANCIAL DATA:
Amount of support per award: $5,000 to $50,000.
Total amount of support: Varies.
Matching fund requirements: Varies.

APPLICATION INFORMATION:
Applications accepted only from national park units. Complete information is available online.
Duration: Usually one year. Renewal applications permitted.
Deadline: Varies.

PUBLICATIONS:
Annual report.

IRS IDENTIFICATION NUMBER: 52-1086761

OFFICERS:
Hon. Sally Jewell, Chairman and Secretary of the Interior
Ellen S. Alberding, Vice Chairman
Peter Knight, Treasurer
John Jarvis, Secretary, Director National Park Service

STAFF:
Neil Mulholland, President and Chief Executive Officer
Mary Dickson, Chief Financial Officer

ADDRESS INQUIRIES TO:
See e-mail address above.

NATIONAL WILDLIFE FEDERATION   [2191]
11100 Wildlife Center Drive
Reston, VA 20190
(202) 797-6638

E-MAIL ADDRESS:
wallacee@nwf.org

WEB SITE ADDRESS:
www.nwf.org

FOUNDED: 1936

AREAS OF INTEREST:
Conservation of wildlife and other natural resources.

NAME(S) OF PROGRAMS:
● **Conservation Internships**

TYPE:
Fellowships; Internships. National Wildlife Federation offers a variety of education internships in which the intern would assist with conservation education and outreach activities.

YEAR PROGRAM STARTED: 1989

PURPOSE:
To educate, inspire, and assist individuals and organizations to conserve wildlife and other natural resources.

LEGAL BASIS:
Nonprofit organization able to carry on a defined amount of lobbying.

ELIGIBILITY:
A background in ecology, the environment, educational programming or public policy is desirable. Applicants must be reliable, energetic and willing to accept responsibilities.

GEOGRAPHIC RESTRICTIONS:
United States.

FINANCIAL DATA:
Amount of support per award: $400 per week, plus core benefits.
Total amount of support: Varies.

NUMBER OF AWARDS: Varies.

APPLICATION INFORMATION:
Application information is available on the web site or upon request to the Intern Program Coordinator.

Duration: 24 to 48 weeks.
Deadline: Varies.

ADDRESS INQUIRIES TO:
Elizabeth Wallace
Intern Program Coordinator
(See address above.)

NATIONAL WILDLIFE FEDERATION   [2192]
11100 Wildlife Center Drive
Reston, VA 20190-5362
(703) 438-6265
Fax: (703) 438-6468

E-MAIL ADDRESS:
fellows@nwf.org

WEB SITE ADDRESS:
www.nwf.org

FOUNDED: 1936

AREAS OF INTEREST:
Global warming impacts and solutions.

NAME(S) OF PROGRAMS:
● **Campus Ecology Fellowships**
● **Emerging Leaders Fellowships**

TYPE:
Fellowships.

YEAR PROGRAM STARTED: 1973

PURPOSE:
To give well-qualified and highly motivated individuals substantive practical experience.

LEGAL BASIS:
Nonprofit organization able to carry on a defined amount of lobbying.

ELIGIBILITY:
Campus Ecology Fellowships: Undergraduate or graduate students from any college or university in the U.S. may apply. Applications are invited from students in all disciplines and are not limited to environmental studies majors. Current and former employees of National Wildlife Federation and former NWF Campus Ecology Fellows are ineligible to apply. Former NWF interns are eligible to apply following one year from their final work date. Applications from students who have been nominated by a formal group or committee working on climate and other sustainability projects on campus will receive special consideration. A nomination process is especially encouraged where more than one student may be interested in applying for NWF's Campus Ecology Fellowship. The applicant must be enrolled in school throughout the duration of the 15-month grant period.

Emerging Leaders Fellowships are open to postgraduate, young professionals (ages 21 to 35) interested in career development and leadership opportunities within the conservation movement.

GEOGRAPHIC RESTRICTIONS:
United States.

FINANCIAL DATA:
Amount of support per award: Campus Ecology Fellowships: Up to $2,000 to offset project expenses for undergraduates; Up to $5,000 for graduates. Emerging Leaders Fellowships: Up to $2,000 stipend.
Total amount of support: Varies.

COOPERATIVE FUNDING PROGRAMS: Kendeda Sustainability Fund of the Tides Foundation, Kendeda Fund, Nathan Cummings Foundation, Town Creek Foundation.

NUMBER OF APPLICANTS MOST RECENT YEAR:
Approximately 400.

NUMBER OF AWARDS: Varies.

APPLICATION INFORMATION:
Information is available on the web site.
Duration: 15 months.
Deadline: Varies.

PUBLICATIONS:
Program description.

OFFICERS:
Larry Schweiger, President and Chief Executive Officer

ADDRESS INQUIRIES TO:
Fellowships
(See address above.)

NEW YORK SEA GRANT INSTITUTE   [2193]
121 Discovery Hall
Stony Brook University
Stony Brook, NY 11794-5001
(631) 632-6905
Fax: (631) 632-6917

E-MAIL ADDRESS:
nyseagrant@stonybrook.edu

WEB SITE ADDRESS:
www.nyseagrant.org

FOUNDED: 1971

AREAS OF INTEREST:
Coastal resource management, fisheries biology, contaminants and environmental quality, environmental processes and marine economics, seafood use and technology, recreation and tourism, human dimensions, marine aquaculture, youth education, biotech, and coastal processes.

TYPE:
Awards/prizes; Conferences/seminars; Development grants; Endowments; Fellowships; Internships; Project/program grants; Research grants; Scholarships; Technical assistance; Travel grants. Principally grants for laboratory and field studies, publications and communication and curriculum development.

YEAR PROGRAM STARTED: 1971

PURPOSE:
To foster the wise use and development of coastal resources through research, education and training.

LEGAL BASIS:
A cooperative research and education activity of the State University of New York and Cornell University, as well as NOAA's National Sea Grant College Program.

ELIGIBILITY:
Applicant must be a member of the faculty of an institution of higher learning or of a nonprofit organization. Projects must address issues relevant to New York state. In most cases, applicants are affiliated with New York institutions.

FINANCIAL DATA:
Amount of support per award: Varies.
Total amount of support: $1,000,000.
Matching fund requirements: Matching funds equal to 50% of funds requested must be provided by applicant from non-federal sources.

NUMBER OF APPLICANTS MOST RECENT YEAR:
Around 100 for most biennial solicitations.

NUMBER OF AWARDS: Approximately 10 per year.

APPLICATION INFORMATION:
Application information is available on the web site.

Duration: One year. Continuation possible.

Deadline: Biennial with occasional out-of-cycle.

OFFICERS:
William Wise, Interim Director
Cornelia G. Schlenk, Assistant Director

ADDRESS INQUIRIES TO:
Cornelia G. Schlenk, Assistant Director
(See address above.)

JESSIE SMITH NOYES FOUNDATION [2194]
6 East 39th Street
12th Floor
New York, NY 10016
(212) 684-6577
Fax: (212) 689-6549

E-MAIL ADDRESS:
noyes@noyes.org

WEB SITE ADDRESS:
www.noyes.org

FOUNDED: 1947

AREAS OF INTEREST:
Sustainable agriculture, toxics, reproductive rights, environmental justice, and environment in New York City.

TYPE:
General operating grants; Project/program grants. Grants to tax-exempt institutions in the connected and overlapping areas of sustainable agriculture, toxics, reproductive rights, and New York City environment in order to achieve the Foundation's overall goal, which is to promote a sustainable and just social and natural system by supporting grassroots organizations and movements committed to this goal.

PURPOSE:
To support programs that promote a sustainable and just social and natural system.

LEGAL BASIS:
Family foundation.

ELIGIBILITY:
The Foundation makes grants to tax-exempt organizations with 501(c)(3) classification from the IRS for work within the U.S. to individuals. It will not consider requests for endowments, capital construction, general fund-raising, deficit financing or scholarships, fellowships, loans or grants to individuals. The Foundation does not make grants for research or give support to conferences, seminars, media events, or workshops, unless they are an integral part of a broader program, does not generally make grants for college- and university-based programs, and does not provide support for the production and development of television and media programming.

GEOGRAPHIC RESTRICTIONS:
United States.

FINANCIAL DATA:
Amount of support per award: Varies.

NUMBER OF APPLICANTS MOST RECENT YEAR:
Approximately 350 letters of inquiry received each year.

NUMBER OF AWARDS: Approximately 100 per year.

REPRESENTATIVE AWARDS:
$25,000 to Alaska Community Action on Toxins, Anchorage, AK; $15,000 to Families United for Racial and Economic Equality, Brooklyn, NY; $25,000 to ACCESS/Women's Health Rights Coalition, Oakland, CA; $30,000 to National Campaign for Sustainable Agriculture, Pine Bush, NY.

APPLICATION INFORMATION:
The first step should be a letter of inquiry of no more than three pages. The Foundation welcomes the opportunity to meet with prospective grantees, but prefers to wait until after it receives a letter to determine if the meeting will be useful.

Letters of inquiry are reviewed by the program staff who determine if requests meet the Foundation's funding priorities. Those not meeting the priorities are declined. Requests that meet the priorities are given further consideration and a full proposal may be requested. Proposals should be submitted to the Foundation only upon request.

Duration: Varies.

Deadline: Letters of inquiry are accepted at any time. If a proposal is requested, it is assigned to one of the Foundation's three board meetings.

IRS IDENTIFICATION NUMBER: 13-5600408

OFFICERS:
Victor De Luca, President

STAFF:
Millie Buchanan, Program Officer
Wilma Montanez, Program Officer
Margaret Segall, Director of Administration

ADDRESS INQUIRIES TO:
Victor De Luca, President
(See address above.)

PATAGONIA INC. [2195]
259 West Santa Clara
Ventura, CA 93001
(805) 643-8616
Fax: (805) 643-2367

E-MAIL ADDRESS:
inquiries@patagonia.com

WEB SITE ADDRESS:
www.patagonia.com

AREAS OF INTEREST:
Preservation and protection of the natural environment.

NAME(S) OF PROGRAMS:
● **Environmental Grant Program**

TYPE:
General operating grants; Product donations; Project/program grants. Funds to help local groups working to protect local habitats and to force the government to abide by its own laws in regards to biodiversity and ecosystem protection.

YEAR PROGRAM STARTED: 1987

PURPOSE:
To assist groups who strive to preserve and restore the natural environment.

LEGAL BASIS:
Private corporation giving program.

ELIGIBILITY:
Applicants must be 501(c)(3) tax-exempt organizations. No grants for scientific

research, video, television or media projects or more general environmental education efforts.

GEOGRAPHIC RESTRICTIONS:
United States, Canada, Europe, Japan and South America.

FINANCIAL DATA:
Company pledges one percent of yearly sales or 10% of pre-tax profits, whichever is higher, to grassroots environmental groups. Total amount varies yearly, thus grant distribution is based on the sales volume achieved for the previous six months, as grants are distributed twice yearly.

Amount of support per award: $3,000 to $12,000.

APPLICATION INFORMATION:
Application information is available on the web site.

Duration: One year. Applicants must reapply for continued funding.

Deadline: Proposals must be submitted no later than April 30 or August 31. Grants distributed in September and January, respectively.

PUBLICATIONS:
Program guidelines.

ADDRESS INQUIRIES TO:
Lisa Myers
Environmental Grants Manager
(See address above.)

*PLEASE NOTE:
Phone calls are discouraged.

PEW FELLOWS PROGRAM IN MARINE CONSERVATION [2196]
Pew Environment Group
901 E Street, N.W., 10th Floor
Washington, DC 20004
(202) 540-6850

WEB SITE ADDRESS:
www.pewmarinefellows.org

FOUNDED: 1988

AREAS OF INTEREST:
Marine conservation.

TYPE:
Fellowships.

YEAR PROGRAM STARTED: 1990

PURPOSE:
To support innovative, applied projects aimed at developing and implementing solutions to critical challenges facing the world's oceans.

LEGAL BASIS:
Public trust.

ELIGIBILITY:
Applicant must work in the field of research, education, communications, advocacy or policy, and must be nominated.

FINANCIAL DATA:
Amount of support per award: $150,000 over three years, to be applied to a specific project.

Total amount of support: $750,000 per year.

NUMBER OF APPLICANTS MOST RECENT YEAR:
Approximately 35.

NUMBER OF AWARDS: 5 individuals or teams.

REPRESENTATIVE AWARDS:
Rohan Arthur, Nature Conservation Foundation; Yimnang Golbuu, Palau International Coral Reef Center; Anne Salomon, Simon Fraser University.

APPLICATION INFORMATION:
Applications are by nomination only. Unsolicited applications are not accepted.
Duration: Three years.
Deadline: Varies.

PUBLICATIONS:
Program guidelines; newsletter.

ADDRESS INQUIRIES TO:
Polita Glynn, Program Director
(See address above.)

*SPECIAL STIPULATIONS:
The Foundation does not accept unsolicited proposals.

RESOURCES FOR THE FUTURE   [2197]
1616 P Street, N.W.
Washington, DC 20036-1400
(202) 328-5000
Fax: (202) 939-3460

E-MAIL ADDRESS:
info@rff.org

WEB SITE ADDRESS:
www.rff.org

AREAS OF INTEREST:
Economics, policy sciences or issues relating to the environment and natural resources of energy.

NAME(S) OF PROGRAMS:
● **Joseph L. Fisher Dissertation Fellowships**
● **The Walter O. Spofford, Jr., Memorial Internship**

TYPE:
Awards/prizes; Fellowships; Internships. Joseph L. Fisher Dissertation Fellowships are in support of doctoral dissertation research on issues related to the environment, natural resources or energy.

The Walter O. Spofford, Jr., Memorial Internship is a paid internship for graduate students.

PURPOSE:
Joseph L. Fisher Dissertation Fellowships: To support graduate students in the final year of their dissertation research.

ELIGIBILITY:
Joseph L. Fisher Dissertation Fellowships: Candidates must have completed the preliminary examinations for the Doctorate not later than February 1 prior to the application deadline. Resources for the Future particularly encourages women and members of minority groups to apply. RFF's primary research disciplines are economics and other social sciences. Proposals originating in these fields will have the greatest likelihood of success. Proposals from the physical or biological sciences must have an immediate and obvious link to environmental policy matters.

The Walter O. Spofford, Jr., Memorial Internship: Candidates should be highly motivated and in the first or second year of graduate training in the social or natural sciences. Candidates should also have outstanding policy analysis and writing skills. They should also have a special interest in Chinese environmental issues.

FINANCIAL DATA:
Under the Tax Reform Act of 1986, most, if not all, of this stipend will probably be taxable income. This Fellowship is intended to be the principal source of support for graduate students in the final year of their dissertation research. The Fellowship will be reduced by the amount of any other financial assistance other than tuition support. Financial assistance must be disclosed to RFF. No additional support will be provided for travel, data acquisition, or other dissertation-related expenses.

If necessary, support for travel expenses and visa assistance can be provided for the Spofford Internship.

Amount of support per award: Joseph L. Fisher Dissertation Fellowships: $18,000 stipend for the academic year; Walter O. Spofford, Jr. Memorial Internship: $375 stipend per week.

NUMBER OF AWARDS: 1 Fisher Fellowship and 1 Spofford Internship.

APPLICATION INFORMATION:
Joseph L. Fisher Dissertation Fellowships: Graduate students interested in applying should submit the following:
(1) a completed application form;
(2) a cover letter;
(3) curriculum vitae;
(4) a graduate transcript;
(5) a one-page abstract of the dissertation;
(6) a technical summary of the dissertation not to exceed 2,500 words in length (not including the bibliography);
(7) a letter from the department chair or other university official certifying the student's doctoral candidacy and;
(8) two letters of recommendation from faculty members on the student's dissertation committee.
The technical summary should describe clearly the aim of the dissertation, its significance in relation to the existing literature, and the research methods and data to be used. RFF cannot provide written evaluations of proposals.

The Walter O. Spofford, Jr., Memorial Internship: Students should submit a completed application form, a cover letter describing their areas of interest, a resume, and a recent transcript. Applicants must have proof of eligibility to be employed in the U.S. One letter of recommendation from a faculty member should be sent directly by the professor to RFF. Transcripts and recommendation letters should be sent either by e-mail to spofford-award@rff.org with the name of the applicant in the subject field, or by post mail to: Coordinator for Academic Programs-Spofford Award, Resources for the Future, at the address above.

Duration: Joseph L. Fisher Dissertation Fellowships: One year; The Walter O. Spofford, Jr., Memorial Internship: Summer.

RESOURCES FOR THE FUTURE   [2198]
1616 P Street, N.W.
Washington, DC 20036-1400
(202) 328-5000
Fax: (202) 939-3460

E-MAIL ADDRESS:
info@rff.org

WEB SITE ADDRESS:
www.rff.org

FOUNDED: 1952

AREAS OF INTEREST:
Research and public education in development, conservation, economics, the use of natural resources and in the quality of the environment.

NAME(S) OF PROGRAMS:
● **Gilbert F. White Postdoctoral Fellowship Program**

TYPE:
Awards/prizes; Fellowships; Internships; Research grants; Residencies; Visiting scholars. Resident fellowships in honor of Gilbert F. White, internationally known statesman of science, for postdoctoral research in one of three divisions: the Energy and Natural Resources Division, the Quality of the Environment Division, or the Center for Risk Management.

YEAR PROGRAM STARTED: 1980

PURPOSE:
To support research in areas related to natural resources, energy, or the environment.

LEGAL BASIS:
Private, nonprofit research organization.

ELIGIBILITY:
Open to individuals in any discipline who will have completed their doctoral requirements by the beginning of the 2013-14 academic year. Selection criteria include the proposed research program and how it will fit with RFF work in progress. Teaching and/or research experience at the postdoctoral level is preferred, though not essential. Individuals holding positions in government, as well as at academic institutions, are eligible.

FINANCIAL DATA:
Fellows receive an annual stipend based upon their current salary, plus research support, office facilities at RFF, and an allowance of up to $1,000 for moving or living expenses. This stipend may be supplemented from other sources if the supplement does not divert the fellow from his or her research. Fellowships do not provide medical insurance or other RFF fringe benefits. Neither Social Security nor tax payments are deducted from the stipend.

Amount of support per award: Varies.
Total amount of support: Varies.

NUMBER OF APPLICANTS MOST RECENT YEAR:
12.

NUMBER OF AWARDS: 1.

APPLICATION INFORMATION:
No application form is required. Candidates should submit the following:
(1) brief letter of application and a curriculum vitae including educational background, professional experience and honors/awards received;
(2) list of publications and description of significant research completed, but not published;
(3) statement of proposed research (not more than 10 double-spaced pages) with hypothesis, objective, methods to be used, anticipated benefit, and how the work relates to current RFF research;
(4) project budget and;
(5) three letters of recommendation from fellow faculty members or colleagues.

With the exception of letters of recommendation, all materials should be sent electronically as Word documents to white-award@rff.org. Reference letters should be sent by mail to the Coordinator for Academic Programs-White Award at the address listed above.

Duration: 11 months.
Deadline: February. Announcement in April.

PUBLICATIONS:
Guidelines.

IRS IDENTIFICATION NUMBER: 53-0220900

OFFICERS:
Philip R. Sharp, President

ADDRESS INQUIRIES TO:
Coordinator for Academic Programs
(See address above.)

RESOURCES FOR THE FUTURE [2199]
1616 P Street, N.W.
Washington, DC 20036-1400
(202) 328-5000
Fax: (202) 939-3460

E-MAIL ADDRESS:
info@rff.org

WEB SITE ADDRESS:
www.rff.org

AREAS OF INTEREST:
Economics, policy sciences or issues relating to the environment and natural resources of energy.

NAME(S) OF PROGRAMS:
• **John V. Krutilla Research Stipend**

TYPE:
Research grants. Stipend can be used for summer salary support, to pay for research assistance, or for any other legitimate research expenses.

PURPOSE:
To provide research assistance.

ELIGIBILITY:
Open to young scholars who have a recently awarded doctoral degree (no more than five years beyond receipt of Ph.D.).

FINANCIAL DATA:
Amount of support per award: $5,500.

APPLICATION INFORMATION:
No application form is required. Individuals interested in applying should submit:
(1) a short description of the proposed research (no more than five typed pages, double-spaced; references do not count in the page total);
(2) a curriculum vitae and;
(3) one letter of recommendation that can comment on the candidate's past research and proposed project in specific terms; the letter of recommendation should be sent separately and should identify the name of the individual who is applying for the Krutilla research award.

All application materials must be sent electronically as Word documents to krutilla-award@rff.org. Mark the transmitted e-mail's subject as Krutilla Research Award.
Duration: One year.
Deadline: Last day of February. Announcement in April.

THE RUSSELL FAMILY FOUNDATION [2200]
3025 Harborview Drive
Gig Harbor, WA 98335
(253) 858-5050
Fax: (253) 851-0460

E-MAIL ADDRESS:
info@trff.org

WEB SITE ADDRESS:
www.trff.org

FOUNDED: 1999

AREAS OF INTEREST:
Environmental sustainability.

TYPE:
Project/program grants. Grants focused regionally on Puget Sound, environmental education and green business practices.

PURPOSE:
To implement strategies that raise awareness and understanding of our environment and the importance of protecting it.

ELIGIBILITY:
Organizations must be 501(c)(3) or nonprofit entities such as public schools and school districts, and must be located in and/or provide services within the Puget Sound region. No grants to individuals.

GEOGRAPHIC RESTRICTIONS:
Western Washington state (Clallam, Jefferson, King, Kitsap, Mason, Pierce, San Juan, Skagit, Snohomish, Thurston and Whatcom Island counties).

FINANCIAL DATA:
Amount of support per award: Average grant: $30,000.

APPLICATION INFORMATION:
Submit letter of inquiry through Foundation's online grantmaking system. Full proposals are accepted by invitation only.
Duration: One year. Renewal by reapplication.
Deadline: Letter of inquiry: January, July and October.

ADDRESS INQUIRIES TO:
Linsey Sauer, Grants Manager
(See address above.)

SMITHSONIAN ENVIRONMENTAL RESEARCH CENTER [2201]
647 Contees Wharf Road
Edgewater, MD 21037
(443) 482-2217
Fax: (443) 482-2380

E-MAIL ADDRESS:
gustafsond@si.edu

WEB SITE ADDRESS:
www.serc.si.edu

FOUNDED: 1975

AREAS OF INTEREST:
Environmental research and environmental education.

NAME(S) OF PROGRAMS:
• **Professional Training**

TYPE:
Fellowships; Internships. The Program enables undergraduate and graduate students to work on specific projects under the direction of the Center's professional staff and is tailored to provide the maximum educational benefit to each participant. Graduate students and undergraduates may conduct independent projects with the approval of the staff member with whom they plan to study.

Subject matter of the projects includes terrestrial and estuarine environmental research within the disciplines of mathematics, chemistry, microbiology, botany, zoology, and environmental education.

Fellowships are offered annually at the postdoctoral, predoctoral and graduate levels.

Internships are offered three times per year at the undergraduate levels, recent graduate, or beginning Master's student.

YEAR PROGRAM STARTED: 1972

PURPOSE:
To offer undergraduate and graduate-level students a unique opportunity to gain exposure to and experience in environmental research.

LEGAL BASIS:
Research unit of the Smithsonian Institution.

ELIGIBILITY:
Applicants must be qualified students from academic institutions in the U.S. or abroad. The SERC will accept applications from interested individuals who are in a position to commit themselves fully to the completion of a project. Selection is based upon the student's academic credentials, extent of relevant training or experience, letters of recommendation and the congruence of the student's expressed goals with those of the Professional Training Program.

FINANCIAL DATA:
Dorm space is available for $105 per week and does not include board. Space is limited.
Amount of support per award: Interns receive $500 per week.
Total amount of support: $45,000 postdoctoral/senior stipend; $30,000 predoctoral stipend; $6,500 graduate student; research allowances are additional.

NUMBER OF APPLICANTS MOST RECENT YEAR:
39 fellowship applicants and 489 internship applicants for the year 2013.

NUMBER OF AWARDS: 3 to 4 fellowships and 30 to 40 internships for the year 2013.

APPLICATION INFORMATION:
Application materials and additional information regarding fellowships can be obtained from the Smithsonian Institution Office of Fellowships and Grants, E-mail: siofg@ofg.si.edu.
Duration: Intern Appointments: Generally 12 to 16 weeks; Fellowships: One year, with renewal.
Deadline: Spring Session: November 15; Summer Session: February 1; Fall Session: June 1; Fellowships: January 15.

PUBLICATIONS:
Application guidelines.

STAFF:
Anson H. Hines, Director
Patrick Megonigal, Deputy Director
Daniel Gustafson, Jr., Professional Training Coordinator

ADDRESS INQUIRIES TO:
Daniel Gustafson, Jr.
Professional Training Coordinator
(See address above.)

SOIL AND WATER CONSERVATION SOCIETY [2202]
945 S.W. Ankeny Road
Ankeny, IA 50023-9764
(515) 289-2331
Fax: (515) 289-1227

E-MAIL ADDRESS:
swcs@swcs.org

WEB SITE ADDRESS:
www.swcs.org

AREAS OF INTEREST:
Soil, water and related natural resource management.

NAME(S) OF PROGRAMS:
- **Kenneth E. Grant Research Scholarship**

TYPE:
Research grants. Provides financial aid to members of the Society for graduate-level research on a specific conservation topic that will help the Society carry out its mission of fostering the science and the art of soil, water, and related natural resource management to achieve sustainability.

PURPOSE:
To foster the science and the art of soil, water and related natural resource management to achieve sustainability; to promote and practice an ethic recognizing the interdependence of people and the environment.

ELIGIBILITY:
Open to members of the Society who have demonstrated integrity, ability and competence to complete the specified study topic. Applicants must be eligible for graduate work at an accredited institution and show reasonable need for financial assistance. Must be members of the Society for at least one year.

FINANCIAL DATA:
Amount of support per award: Up to $1,300.

NUMBER OF AWARDS: 1.

APPLICATION INFORMATION:
Applicants must submit a proposal and evidence of their ability to meet eligibility requirements. There are no specific application forms.
Duration: One year.
Deadline: February 12.

THE ROBERT & PATRICIA SWITZER FOUNDATION   [2203]
P.O. Box 293
Belfast, ME 04915-0293
(207) 338-5654
Fax: (207) 338-5655

E-MAIL ADDRESS:
erin@switzernetwork.org

WEB SITE ADDRESS:
www.switzernetwork.org

FOUNDED: 1987

AREAS OF INTEREST:
Environment.

NAME(S) OF PROGRAMS:
- **Switzer Environmental Fellowship Program**

TYPE:
Fellowships; Project/program grants. Annual fellowship to recognize environmental leaders who have the ability and determination to make a significant impact on environmental quality.

YEAR PROGRAM STARTED: 1987

PURPOSE:
To support highly talented graduate students in California and New England whose studies are directed toward improving environmental quality and who demonstrate leadership in their field.

ELIGIBILITY:
Applicants must meet the following criteria:
(1) be a U.S. citizen;
(2) be enrolled in an accredited institution in California or New England and;
(3) have strong academic qualifications.

Master's degree candidates must have completed at least one semester of course work.

Ph.D. candidates must have completed at least three years of doctoral work or passed their qualifying exams.

GEOGRAPHIC RESTRICTIONS:
California and New England.

FINANCIAL DATA:
Amount of support per award: $15,000, paid in two equal installments, the first in June and the second in late January or early February.
Total amount of support: $300,000.

NUMBER OF APPLICANTS MOST RECENT YEAR:
300.

NUMBER OF AWARDS: 20 annually; 10 in California and 10 in New England.

APPLICATION INFORMATION:
Application information is available on the web site.
Duration: One year.
Deadline: January 10.

ADDRESS INQUIRIES TO:
Erin Lloyd, Program Officer
(See address above.)

TOURISM CARES   [2204]
275 Turnpike Street
Suite 307
Canton, MA 02021
(781) 821-5990
Fax: (781) 821-8949

WEB SITE ADDRESS:
www.tourismcares.org/grants

FOUNDED: 2005

AREAS OF INTEREST:
Travel and tourism; hospitality; sustainable tourism; conservation, preservation or restoration; cultural heritage tourism; responsible tourism; educational programs and interpretive programs.

NAME(S) OF PROGRAMS:
- **Worldwide Grant Program**

TYPE:
Project/program grants. Grants to nonprofit, tax-exempt organizations.

As part of its mission, Tourism Cares distributes charitable grants to worthy tourism-related 501(c)(3) nonprofit organizations worldwide to conserve, preserve or restore sites of exceptional cultural, historic or natural significance. The program goals call for a balanced distribution to U.S. and non-U.S. recipients.

YEAR PROGRAM STARTED: 1999

PURPOSE:
To benefit society by preserving the travel experience for future generations by awarding academic and professional scholarships to students of travel, tourism, and hospitality; by giving grants to cultural, historic and natural tourism-related sites worldwide; and by organizing volunteer efforts to restore tourism-related sites in need of care and rejuvenation.

LEGAL BASIS:
Nonprofit, tax-exempt 501(c)(3) public charity.

ELIGIBILITY:
Grant recipients must be organizations classified as nonprofit and tax-exempt under Section 501(c)(3) of the U.S. Internal Revenue Code or, in the case of non-U.S. organizations, must function as the equivalent. Site must be a cultural, historic or natural tourism-related site of exceptional significance. The project or program must be "brick-and-mortar" capital improvements or educational programs that enhance the way the site is interpreted.

FINANCIAL DATA:
Amount of support per award: Typical grants are $10,000.

Total amount of support: Tourism Cares has supported nearly $2,500,000, not including the additional impact of matching funds, which Tourism Cares encourages Worldwide Grant applicants to secure.

Matching fund requirements: Preference is given to projects or programs with secured matching or challenge-grant funding from a source external to one's organization at the time of the grant request, but it is not a requirement.

NUMBER OF AWARDS: Varies.

APPLICATION INFORMATION:
Detailed application information can only be obtained online.
Duration: 12 months.
Deadline: Detailed information is available at the web site.

PUBLICATIONS:
e-newsletter.

IRS IDENTIFICATION NUMBER: 20-2013457

ADDRESS INQUIRIES TO:
Tourism Cares Grants Department
E-mail: grants@tourismcares.org

TOWN CREEK FOUNDATION, INC.   [2205]
121 North West Street
Easton, MD 21601
(410) 763-8171
Fax: (410) 763-8172

E-MAIL ADDRESS:
info@towncreekfdn.org

WEB SITE ADDRESS:
www.towncreekfdn.org

FOUNDED: 1981

AREAS OF INTEREST:
The environment and climate change.

TYPE:
General operating grants; Matching gifts; Project/program grants.

YEAR PROGRAM STARTED: 1981

PURPOSE:
To seek a healthy natural and sustainable environment, through public education, citizen action and advocacy.

LEGAL BASIS:
Private, tax-exempt foundation.

ELIGIBILITY:
501(c)(3) tax-exempt organizations are eligible for support. The Foundation does not make grants to individuals, organizations considered to be "private foundations," primary and secondary schools, hospitals or

health care institutions, religious organizations or capital and building fund campaigns. It does not make grants to colleges or universities except when some aspect of their work is an integral part of a program supported by the Foundation. It does not fund research, scholarship programs, conferences not part of a program supported by the Foundation, or publication of books and periodicals, or visual or performing arts.

GEOGRAPHIC RESTRICTIONS:
United States. Mid-Atlantic region.

FINANCIAL DATA:
Amount of support per award: Average: $40,000 to $50,000.
Total amount of support: $6,428,500 for the year 2013.

NUMBER OF AWARDS: 82 grants for the year 2013.

REPRESENTATIVE AWARDS:
$40,000 to Apollo Alliance; $100,000 to Chesapeake Bay Foundation; $75,000 to Living on Earth.

APPLICATION INFORMATION:
Online application required. Guidelines are available online.
Duration: One year.
Deadline: Spring: Letter of Intent/Inquiry: November. Invited Proposals: December.

Summer: Letter of Intent/Inquiry: March. Invited Proposals: April.

IRS IDENTIFICATION NUMBER: 52-1227030

TRUSTEES AND OFFICERS:
Jennifer Stanley, President
Lisa A. Stanley, Vice President
Philip E.L. Dietz, Jr., Secretary and Treasurer
Donald Boesch
Betsy Taylor

U.S. DEPARTMENT OF AGRICULTURE [2206]
1400 Independence Avenue, S.W.
Stop 0513
Washington, DC 20250-0510
(202) 720-6221
Fax: (202) 720-4619

E-MAIL ADDRESS:
matthewponish@wdc.usda.gov

WEB SITE ADDRESS:
www.fsa.usda.gov

FOUNDED: 1933

AREAS OF INTEREST:
The conservation of the nation's soil, forest and water resources.

CONSULTING OR VOLUNTEER SERVICES:
Technical assistance is provided by federal and state agencies cooperating with this program.

NAME(S) OF PROGRAMS:
• **Emergency Conservation Program (ECP)**

TYPE:
Grants-in-aid. Cost-share assistance with agricultural producers to rehabilitate agricultural lands damaged by natural disasters. Assistance may also be provided for carrying out emergency water conservation measures during periods of severe drought.

YEAR PROGRAM STARTED: 1957

PURPOSE:
To provide emergency funding and technical assistance for farmers and ranchers to rehabilitate farmland damaged by natural disasters and for carrying out emergency water conservation measures in periods of severe drought.

LEGAL BASIS:
Government agency, authorized by P.L. 95-334, August 1978.

ELIGIBILITY:
Applicants are limited to agricultural producers, such as owners, landlords, tenants or sharecroppers of farms or ranches used to produce grains, row crops, livestock, vegetables, hay, orchards, vineyards, seed crops or other agricultural commodities commercially.

All landowners, regardless of race, sex, religion, marital status, disability, color, age or national origin, may apply for cost-sharing.

GEOGRAPHIC RESTRICTIONS:
United States.

FINANCIAL DATA:
Amount of support per award: Maximum of $200,000 per person.
Matching fund requirements: Producers are required to contribute the difference between the cost-share amount and the total cost of each ECP practice.

ADDRESS INQUIRIES TO:
Contact the nearest FSA County Office where your land is located.

U.S. ENVIRONMENTAL PROTECTION AGENCY [2207]
Office of Enforcement and Compliance Assurance
1200 Pennsylvania Avenue, N.W.
Washington, DC 20460
(202) 566-1980
Fax: (202) 564-0085

E-MAIL ADDRESS:
simpson.julie@epa.gov

WEB SITE ADDRESS:
www.epa.gov/compliance/state/grants/fifra.html

FOUNDED: 1970

AREAS OF INTEREST:
Pesticides enforcement.

NAME(S) OF PROGRAMS:
• **Pesticide Enforcement Cooperative Agreements**

TYPE:
Grants-in-aid; Project/program grants.

YEAR PROGRAM STARTED: 1977

PURPOSE:
To develop and maintain comprehensive pesticide programs that address all aspects of pesticide enforcement and special pesticide initiatives; to sponsor cooperative surveillance monitoring and analytical procedures; to encourage regulatory activities within the states and tribes.

LEGAL BASIS:
Federal Insecticide, Fungicide and Rodenticide Act, as amended; P.L. 92-516; 7 U.S.C. 136 et seq. as amended by P.L. 94-140, Section 23(a) and 95-396.

ELIGIBILITY:
State agencies having pesticide enforcement responsibilities in each state, territory and possession of the U.S., including the District of Columbia and Indian tribes.

The applicant must supply evidence of legal authority to conduct pesticide enforcement activities and a workable program adopted for the agency.

Each application will be reviewed according to the following criteria:
(1) the need for the development, improvement and/or maintenance of a comprehensive pesticides enforcement program within the state;
(2) the relative amount of pesticide production, formulation and use in the state and the potential risk to human health and the environment from pesticide misuse or abuse;
(3) the potential of the cooperative agreement to have a long-term beneficial impact on human health and the environment resulting from the comprehensive enforcement program and;
(4) the past level and effectiveness of the state pesticide regulatory program.

FINANCIAL DATA:
Amount of support per award: Varies by state, territory and tribe.
Matching fund requirements: 15% state match.

NUMBER OF AWARDS: Approximately 75.

APPLICATION INFORMATION:
It is advisable to preapply by having an informal meeting with the regional program office concerning program preparation. Prior to approval of any grants, the official State Pesticides Regulatory Agency must coordinate local pesticide enforcement efforts. The standard application forms furnished by the federal agency and OMB Circular No. A-102 must be used for this program. Completed applications and other required forms should be submitted to the appropriate EPA Regional Office.
Duration: Usually 12 months.

ADDRESS INQUIRIES TO:
Julie Simpson
(See address above.)

U.S. ENVIRONMENTAL PROTECTION AGENCY [2208]
Office of Superfund Remediation and Technology Innovation (5204P)
1200 Pennsylvania Avenue, N.W.
Washington, DC 20460
(703) 603-8835
Fax: (703) 603-9104

E-MAIL ADDRESS:
singer.yolanda@epamail.epa.gov

WEB SITE ADDRESS:
www.epa.gov/superfund

FOUNDED: 1970

AREAS OF INTEREST:
Cleanup of hazardous waste releases into the environment.

NAME(S) OF PROGRAMS:
• **Superfund State and Indian Tribe Core Program Cooperative Agreements**
• **Superfund State, Political Subdivision, and Indian Tribe Site-Specific Cooperative Agreements**

TYPE:
Project/program grants. Superfund State and Indian Tribe Core Program Cooperative Agreements: This program seeks to effectively implement the statutory requirements of the Comprehensive Environmental Response, Compensation, and Liability Act (CERCLA), Section 121(f) for state involvement. It is intended to provide funds to conduct CERCLA activities which are not assignable to specific sites, but support a recipient's site-specific response program.

Superfund State, Political Subdivision, and Indian Tribe Site-Specific Cooperative Agreements: This program proposes to: (1) conduct site characterization activities at potential or confirmed hazardous waste sites; (2) undertake response planning and implementation actions at sites on the National Priorities List (NPL) to clean up the hazardous waste sites that are found to pose hazards to human health and; (3) effectively implement the statutory requirements of CERCLA 121(f) which mandates substantial and meaningful state involvement.

YEAR PROGRAM STARTED: 1981

PURPOSE:
To undertake removal actions at NPL and non-NPL sites to protect the public from the release of hazardous materials; to conduct preremedial activities to determine if sites require listing on the NPL; to perform remedial planning and remedial implementation actions in response to releases on the NPL; to clean up the hazardous waste sites that are found to pose the most imminent threat to human health; to support state involvement in the Superfund program.

LEGAL BASIS:
Comprehensive Environmental Response, Compensation and Liability Act of 1980 (Superfund) (P.L. 96-510), as amended by The Superfund Amendments and Reauthorization Act of 1986 (SARA) (P.L. 99-499), The Small Business Liability Relief and Brown Fields Revitalization Act (PL 107-118).

ELIGIBILITY:
States (and political subdivisions thereof), commonwealths, U.S. territories and possessions, and federally recognized Indian tribal governments, including intertribal consortia.

GEOGRAPHIC RESTRICTIONS:
United States and its territories.

FINANCIAL DATA:
Amount of support per award: Superfund State and Indian Tribe Core Program Cooperative Agreements: $7,202 to $552,983; average award amount: $189,960. Superfund State, Political Subdivision, and Indian Tribe Site-Specific Cooperative Agreements: $188,000 to $3,500,000; average: $308,157.

ADDRESS INQUIRIES TO:
Yolanda Singer, Environmental Scientist Site Assessment Remedy Decisions Branch (See address above.)

U.S. SOCIETY ON DAMS
1616 17th Street, Suite 483
Denver, CO 80202
(303) 628-5430
Fax: (303) 628-5431

E-MAIL ADDRESS:
stephens@ussdams.org

WEB SITE ADDRESS:
www.ussdams.org

TYPE:
Scholarships.

See entry 2666 for full listing.

UNIVERSITY OF PITTSBURGH [2209]
Pymatuning Laboratory of Ecology
13142 Hartstown Road
Linesville, PA 16424
(814) 273-0416
Fax: (814) 683-2302

E-MAIL ADDRESS:
pymlab@pitt.edu

WEB SITE ADDRESS:
www.pitt.edu/~biology/pymatuning.htm

FOUNDED: 1949

AREAS OF INTEREST:
Ecology research.

NAME(S) OF PROGRAMS:
● **Leasure K. Darbaker Prize in Botany**
● **McKinley Research Fund**
● **Pape Research Fund**

TYPE:
Research grants. The Leasure K. Darbaker Prize in Botany is an annual award available for support of botanically related studies at the graduate or postdoctoral level.

The G. McKinley Research Fund and the Pape Research Fund of the Pittsburgh Foundation provide grants for support of graduate and postdoctoral research in ecology. Several are awarded each summer.

LEGAL BASIS:
Department of the University of Pittsburgh.

ELIGIBILITY:
Proposals are welcome at all academic graduate and postdoctoral levels for research in any area of ecology.

Awards are granted for work to be carried out at the facility in northwestern Pennsylvania.

FINANCIAL DATA:
Funds for travel, equipment, supplies, assistants and room and board at the laboratory may be included.
Amount of support per award: Up to $3,000 per award.
Total amount of support: Varies.

APPLICATION INFORMATION:
Application information can be found at the web site.
Deadline: February 7.

PUBLICATIONS:
Application guidelines.

ADDRESS INQUIRIES TO:
Chris Davis, Assistant Director
(See address above.)

THE UNIVERSITY OF SYDNEY [2210]
Scholarships Office
Level 5, Jane Foss Russell Building G02
The University of Sydney N.S.W. 2006
Australia
(02) 8627 8112
Fax: (02) 8627 8485

E-MAIL ADDRESS:
research.training@sydney.edu.au

WEB SITE ADDRESS:
www.sydney.edu.au/scholarships/research

FOUNDED: 1850

AREAS OF INTEREST:
Water conservation.

NAME(S) OF PROGRAMS:
● **Richard Claude Mankin Scholarship**

TYPE:
Scholarships. Postdoctoral award for research and postgraduate for research leading to a higher degree. Tenable at the University of Sydney.

YEAR PROGRAM STARTED: 1973

PURPOSE:
To promote research related to water conservation at the University of Sydney.

LEGAL BASIS:
University.

ELIGIBILITY:
Candidates may be of postgraduate or postdoctoral standing at the University of Sydney.

FINANCIAL DATA:
The scholarship does not cover tuition fees payable by international students.
Amount of support per award: $24,653 AUD per annum for the year 2013.

NUMBER OF AWARDS: 1 offered as vacancy occurs and funds are available.

APPLICATION INFORMATION:
Application information is available on the web site.
Duration: Two years for Master's candidate. Up to three and one-half years for Ph.D. candidate.
Deadline: Second week in January and second week in July.

VIRGINIA ENVIRONMENTAL ENDOWMENT [2211]
919 East Main Street, Suite 1070
Richmond, VA 23219
(804) 644-5000
Fax: (804) 644-0603

E-MAIL ADDRESS:
info@vee.org

WEB SITE ADDRESS:
www.vee.org

FOUNDED: 1977

AREAS OF INTEREST:
Environmental improvement.

NAME(S) OF PROGRAMS:
● **Kanawha and Ohio River Valleys Program**
● **Virginia Program**

TYPE:
Challenge/matching grants; Demonstration grants; Project/program grants; Research grants; Seed money grants; Research contracts. Provides grants to projects that demonstrate feasibility, innovation and appropriateness to the Endowment's purpose and priorities. Improvement of the quality of the environment in the Commonwealth of Virginia, especially water quality research and monitoring; land conservation; Chesapeake Bay conservation, research and education; and environmental education.

Programs addressing water quality and the effects of water pollution on public health and the environment in the Kanawha River and Ohio River valleys of Kentucky and West Virginia.

YEAR PROGRAM STARTED: 1977

PURPOSE:
To improve the quality of the environment by using its capital to encourage all sectors to work together to prevent pollution, conserve natural resources and promote environmental literacy.

LEGAL BASIS:
Tax-exempt, grantmaking organization 501(c)(4).

ELIGIBILITY:
The Endowment makes grants to nonprofit, tax-exempt, charitable organizations and institutions, and occasionally to governmental agencies. It encourages requests for specific projects that promise measurable results to improve the environment. Applicants should describe specifically how they propose to measure the success of a grant project. Grant funds are not provided for general support, overhead, indirect costs, capital projects, land purchases, building construction or renovation, endowments, lawsuits or to individuals.

GEOGRAPHIC RESTRICTIONS:
The state of Virginia and the Kanawha and Ohio River valleys of Kentucky and West Virginia.

FINANCIAL DATA:
Reviewed asset value: $16,884,918 as of March 31, 2013.
Amount of support per award: Varies.
Total amount of support: $452,617 for fiscal year ended March 31, 2013.
Matching fund requirements: At least a 1:1 match is normally required.

COOPERATIVE FUNDING PROGRAMS: The Endowment welcomes opportunities for collaboration.

NUMBER OF APPLICANTS MOST RECENT YEAR: 69.

NUMBER OF AWARDS: 29 for fiscal year ended March 31, 2013.

APPLICATION INFORMATION:
Two copies of the complete proposal, signed by the organization's chief executive officer or board chairman, must be received by the deadline date. The Endowment does not review or comment on preliminary proposals.

Each proposal must include the following information:
(1) a cover letter identifying the applicant, project title, grant request, matching funds, project schedule, and whether the proposal is being submitted to the Virginia Program or the Kanawha and Ohio River Valleys Program;
(2) a project description, limited to five pages, clearly stating the need for the project, goals and objectives and how they will be achieved, how project results will be measured, and relationship to other work being done in the field;
(3) a description of the organization, names and qualifications of key project staff, a list of the members of the governing board, the current operating budget, and a copy of the current tax-exempt ruling from the IRS, if applicable;
(4) a line-item budget for the proposed project showing total project costs, the

amount and proposed allocation of grant funds requested from the Endowment, and all sources and amounts of matching funds, which must equal or exceed the requested grant;
(5) the project schedule, with specific beginning and ending dates for requested grant support and;
(6) a detailed plan for evaluating and disseminating project results, for continuing project activities, and for raising future financial support.

Proposals may not be submitted by facsimile or by e-mail.

For delivery by U.S. Mail, address to Joseph Maroon, Executive Director, Virginia Environmental Endowment, P.O. Box 790, Richmond, VA 23218-0790.
Duration: Stipulated with specific projects. One year preferred.
Deadline: Kanawha and Ohio River Valleys Program: June 15; Virginia Program: June 15 and December 1. Proposals must be received by 5 P.M. Board decisions about proposals are normally made in April and October.

PUBLICATIONS:
Annual report, including guidelines.

IRS IDENTIFICATION NUMBER: 54-1041973

STAFF:
Joseph Maroon, Executive Director

DIRECTORS:
Robin D. Baliles
Dixon M. Butler
Landon Hilliard
Lawrence Kochard
Anna L. Lawson
Nina Randolph
Robert B. Smith, Jr.

ADDRESS INQUIRIES TO:
Joseph Maroon, Executive Director
(See address above.)

*SPECIAL STIPULATIONS:
No preliminary proposal reviews are provided; full proposals are required.

WEEDEN FOUNDATION   [2212]
35 Adams Street
Bedford Hills, NY 10507
(914) 864-1375
Fax: (914) 864-1377

E-MAIL ADDRESS:
weedenfdn@weedenfdn.org

WEB SITE ADDRESS:
www.weedenfdn.org

FOUNDED: 1963

AREAS OF INTEREST:
Biodiversity, population and environment, natural resource conservation and consumption.

NAME(S) OF PROGRAMS:
● **Consumption**
● **Domestic Biodiversity**
● **International Biodiversity**
● **Population**

TYPE:
General operating grants; Project/program grants.

YEAR PROGRAM STARTED: 1963

PURPOSE:
To address the adverse impact of exploding human population and overuse of natural resources on the biological fabric of the planet.

LEGAL BASIS:
Nonprofit, family foundation.

ELIGIBILITY:
Applicants must be nonprofit, tax-exempt organizations with 501(c)(3) status or international equivalent.

GEOGRAPHIC RESTRICTIONS:
Bolivia, Central Siberia, Chile and the Pacific Northwest.

FINANCIAL DATA:
Amount of support per award: Average: $15,000 to $25,000.
Total amount of support: Varies.

NUMBER OF APPLICANTS MOST RECENT YEAR: 100 for the year 2012.

NUMBER OF AWARDS: 80 for the year 2012.

REPRESENTATIVE AWARDS:
$20,000 to IPAS; $20,000 to Center for a New American Dream; $20,000 to Forest Ethics.

APPLICATION INFORMATION:
Applicants should submit a letter of inquiry. Foundation will request a full proposal, if interested.
Duration: One year. Renewal possible.
Deadline: Varies.

IRS IDENTIFICATION NUMBER: 94-6109313

STAFF:
Donald A. Weeden, Executive Director
Emily Rodriguez, Research Assistant

BOARD OF DIRECTORS:
Norm Weeden, Ph.D., President
Bob Weeden, Treasurer
Leslie Weeden, Secretary
Barbara Daugherty
Christina Roux
Alan Weeden
Donald E. Weeden
Jack D. Weeden
John D. Weeden
William Weeden

ADDRESS INQUIRIES TO:
Donald A. Weeden, Executive Director
(See address above.)

THE WILDLIFE CONSERVATION SOCIETY   [2213]
2300 Southern Boulevard
Bronx, NY 10460
(718) 220-5100
Fax: (718) 364-4275

E-MAIL ADDRESS:
fellowship@wcs.org

WEB SITE ADDRESS:
programs.wcs.org/grants
www.wcs.org

FOUNDED: 1895

AREAS OF INTEREST:
Wildlife conservation, wildlands, communities, threatened wildlife and ecosystems.

NAME(S) OF PROGRAMS:
● **Research Fellowship Program**

TYPE:
Awards/prizes; Fellowships; Project/program grants; Research grants. Awards small grants to field research projects leading to the conservation of threatened wildlife and wildlife habitat.

YEAR PROGRAM STARTED: 1993

PURPOSE:
To support individual research projects that lead to concrete advances in the understanding and conservation of wildlife or wildlands.

LEGAL BASIS:
Nonprofit organization.

ELIGIBILITY:
Project must demonstrate strong scientific merit, as well as direct relevance to wildlife conservation. No support for conferences, travel to scientific meetings, legal actions, construction of permanent field stations, tuition, salaries, overhead costs, major laboratory expenses, gene storage, vehicle purchase, captive breeding, or computer equipment. Stipends are not funded; however, investigators who have no other source of support may receive modest living expenses. Faculty and/or research advisors should not be listed as a principal investigator unless they plan to carry out the majority of the field work.

The program supports marine or terrestrial field research in Africa, Asia, and Latin America (including Mexico). While all applications to work in Asian, African, and Latin American countries are currently considered, the Society encourages applications from nationals from the following countries: Algeria, Argentina, Azerbaijan, Bolivia, Brazil, China, Colombia, Egypt, Georgia, India, Indonesia, Libya, Malaysia, Pakistan, Russia, Trinidad and Tobago, Turkey and Venezuela. Proposals are accepted for research in North America only from Native Americans and First Nation people. Must conduct work on Native lands or on issues of direct relevance to wildlife or on species governed by treated intertribal agreement.

FINANCIAL DATA:
Amount of support per award: Maximum $20,000.

APPLICATION INFORMATION:
Proposals can be submitted in English, Spanish or French, but the coversheet and abstract must be in English. Application and procedures are available online.
Duration: One year.
Deadline: March 15 and September 15. Final decisions are announced at the end of June and December.

PUBLICATIONS:
Application guidelines.

THE DEAN WITTER FOUNDATION
57 Post Street, Suite 510
San Francisco, CA 94104
(415) 981-2966
Fax: (415) 981-5218

E-MAIL ADDRESS:
admin@deanwitterfoundation.org

WEB SITE ADDRESS:
www.deanwitterfoundation.org

TYPE:
Challenge/matching grants; Fellowships; General operating grants; Internships; Matching gifts; Professorships; Project/program grants; Research grants; Scholarships; Seed money grants.

See entry 1918 for full listing.

Medicine (multiple disciplines)

A-T CHILDREN'S PROJECT   [2214]
5300 West Hillsboro Boulevard
Suite 105
Coconut Creek, FL 33073
(954) 481-6611
Fax: (954) 725-1153

E-MAIL ADDRESS:
grants@atcp.org
info@atcp.org

WEB SITE ADDRESS:
www.atcp.org

FOUNDED: 1993

AREAS OF INTEREST:
Projects that, while drawing on basic discoveries, apply innovative and novel strategies for suggesting, developing and evaluating specific disease-modifying and symptomatic interventions for ataxia-telangiectasia (A-T); clinical studies for A-T.

NAME(S) OF PROGRAMS:
● A-T Postdoctoral Fellowship Award
● A-T Research Grant Program

TYPE:
Research grants.

YEAR PROGRAM STARTED: 1993

PURPOSE:
To accelerate first-rate, international scientific research in an attempt to help find a cure or life-improving therapies for children with ataxia-telangiectasia.

ELIGIBILITY:
Open to all ages and nationalities. Proposal for grant must have direct relevance to ataxia-telangiectasia.

Applicants should be aware that meritorious proposals may be rejected if:
(1) the proposed research is too far from being relevant to a therapeutic intervention;
(2) the A-T Children's Project's Scientific Advisory Board finds the research redundant and in no need of validation;
(3) the proposed research is likely to happen anyway, without the A-T Children's Project's support and;
(4) the research cannot realistically be achieved with the proposed budget.

FINANCIAL DATA:
Amount of support per award: Up to $75,000 per year.
Total amount of support: Varies.

APPLICATION INFORMATION:
Detailed information can be found on the organization web site. A Letter of Intent is not required. However, prior to submission of a full-length proposal, applicants seeking Scientific Advisory Board input may submit a Letter of Intent directly to the Science Coordinator at cynthia@atcp.org. This letter, not to exceed two pages, should include a brief abstract describing the proposed research, specific aims and an estimated budget.

Applicants must submit an electronic copy of their proposal in either MSWord or PDF formats to grants@atcp.org.
Duration: One to two years.
Deadline: September 1 and March 1 of each calendar year.

ADDRESS INQUIRIES TO:
Dr. Cynthia Rothblum-Oviatt
Science Coordinator
E-mail: cynthia@atcp.org

ALBERTA INNOVATES - HEALTH SOLUTIONS   [2215]
Suite 1500
10104 - 103 Avenue, N.W.
Edmonton AB T5J 4A7 Canada
(780) 423-5727
Fax: (780) 429-3509

E-MAIL ADDRESS:
health@albertainnovates.ca

WEB SITE ADDRESS:
www.aihealthsolutions.ca

FOUNDED: 2010

AREAS OF INTEREST:
Supporting biomedical and health research at Alberta universities, affiliated institutions, and other medical and technology-related institutions.

NAME(S) OF PROGRAMS:
● AIHS Catalyst Opportunities
● AIHS Collaborative Research and Innovation Opportunities
● AIHS Conference Grants
● AIHS HYRS Program
● AIHS Industry Partnered Translational Fund
● AIHS Sustainability Funding Opportunity
● AIHS Training and Early Career Development Programs
● Alberta Cancer Grants Program
● Campus Alberta/AIHS Translational Health Chairs
● Knowledge Exchange Grants
● Knowledge-to-Action Grant
● Partnership for Research and Innovation in the Health System (PRIHS)

TYPE:
Awards/prizes; Block grants; Conferences/seminars; Development grants; Fellowships; General operating grants; Project/program grants; Research grants; Scholarships; Training grants. Interdisciplinary team grants. Awards for personnel support, equipment purchase, conferences and workshops.

YEAR PROGRAM STARTED: 2010

PURPOSE:
To promote research in medical and health sciences and implement means of using the scientific resources of the medical sciences in Alberta.

LEGAL BASIS:
Funding agency created by an act of the Alberta legislature.

ELIGIBILITY:
Most awards tenable only in Alberta.

GEOGRAPHIC RESTRICTIONS:
Alberta.

FINANCIAL DATA:
Grants are made on a year-round basis from interest revenue earned on an original endowment of $300,000,000.
Amount of support per award: Stipulated with individual awards.
Total amount of support: Approximately $70,000,000 for the fiscal year 2011-12.

Matching fund requirements: Stipulated with applicable awards.

APPLICATION INFORMATION:
Application forms and guidelines are available from the Research Services Offices of Alberta universities and on the AIHS web site.
Duration: Varies by program.
Deadline: Varies by program.

PUBLICATIONS:
Guidelines for Grants and Awards.

ADDRESS INQUIRIES TO:
Ryan Perry, Director, Programs
(See address above.)

*SPECIAL STIPULATIONS:
Awards are to be held in Alberta, or if held outside Alberta, are to be sponsored by an Alberta university.

THE JOHN W. ALDEN TRUST

c/o Rackemann, Sawyer & Brewster
160 Federal Street, 15th Floor
Boston, MA 02110-1700
(617) 951-1108
Fax: (617) 542-7437

E-MAIL ADDRESS:
smonahan@rackemann.com

WEB SITE ADDRESS:
www.cybergrants.com/alden

TYPE:
Capital grants; Challenge/matching grants; Conferences/seminars; Demonstration grants; Development grants; Matching gifts; Project/program grants; Research grants; Scholarships; Seed money grants; Technical assistance; Training grants. Grants will normally be made for specific projects rather than general operating expenses.

See entry 1106 for full listing.

ALZHEIMER'S DRUG DISCOVERY FOUNDATION   [2216]

57 West 57th Street
Suite 904
New York, NY 10019
(212) 901-8000
Fax: (212) 901-8010

E-MAIL ADDRESS:
hfillit@alzdiscovery.org

WEB SITE ADDRESS:
www.alzdiscovery.org

FOUNDED: 2004

AREAS OF INTEREST:
Drug discovery and development for Alzheimer's disease, related dementias and cognitive decline.

NAME(S) OF PROGRAMS:
• **Novel Approaches to Drug Discovery in Alzheimer's Disease**

TYPE:
Awards/prizes; Conferences/seminars; Research grants.

PURPOSE:
To promote the research and development of therapies to identify, treat and prevent cognitive decline, Alzheimer's disease and related dementias.

LEGAL BASIS:
Nonprofit Delaware corporation 501(c)(3) public charity.

ELIGIBILITY:
Applicant must be a university medical center or early-stage biotechnology company.

FINANCIAL DATA:
Amount of support per award: $150,000 to $300,000 per year.
Total amount of support: Varies.

NUMBER OF APPLICANTS MOST RECENT YEAR: 250.

NUMBER OF AWARDS: 37.

APPLICATION INFORMATION:
Complete instructions are available on the Foundation web site.
Duration: One to two years.
Deadline: Letters of intent accepted on an ongoing basis. Applications due quarterly.

ADDRESS INQUIRIES TO:
Niyati Thakker, Grants Manager
(See address above.)

AMERICAN ACADEMY OF FACIAL PLASTIC AND RECONSTRUCTIVE SURGERY (AAFPRS)   [2217]

Educational and Research Foundation
for the AAFPRS
310 South Henry Street
Alexandria, VA 22314
(703) 299-9291
Fax: (703) 299-8898

E-MAIL ADDRESS:
matkins@aafprs.org

WEB SITE ADDRESS:
www.aafprs.org

FOUNDED: 1964

AREAS OF INTEREST:
Physician education in cosmetic and reconstructive surgery of the face, head and neck.

CONSULTING OR VOLUNTEER SERVICES:
Combined Otolaryngology Research Efforts (C.O.R.E.).

NAME(S) OF PROGRAMS:
• **Leslie Bernstein Resident Research Grants**

TYPE:
Research grants; Seed money grants. Cash award toward research by a resident member in facial plastic and reconstructive surgery.

YEAR PROGRAM STARTED: 1983

PURPOSE:
To stimulate resident research in projects that are well conceived and scientifically valid.

LEGAL BASIS:
Professional association of independent members.

ELIGIBILITY:
Applicant must be an AAFPRS member. Residents at any level may apply, even if the research work will be done during their fellowship year.

FINANCIAL DATA:
Grant money must be used for direct costs; only 10% of monies can be used for indirect cost.
Amount of support per award: $5,000.
Total amount of support: $10,000.

NUMBER OF APPLICANTS MOST RECENT YEAR: 15.

NUMBER OF AWARDS: Up to 2.

APPLICATION INFORMATION:
Applicants must submit a letter of intent. Guidelines are available from AAFPRS.
Duration: One to two years.
Deadline: January 15. Announcement in August.

PUBLICATIONS:
Guidelines; application form.

IRS IDENTIFICATION NUMBER: 36-2952891

ADDRESS INQUIRIES TO:
Maria Atkins
Manager, Membership Services
(See address above.)

AMERICAN ACADEMY OF FACIAL PLASTIC AND RECONSTRUCTIVE SURGERY (AAFPRS)   [2218]

Educational and Research Foundation
for the AAFPRS
310 South Henry Street
Alexandria, VA 22314
(703) 299-9291
Fax: (703) 299-8898

E-MAIL ADDRESS:
matkins@aafprs.org

WEB SITE ADDRESS:
www.aafprs.org

FOUNDED: 1964

AREAS OF INTEREST:
Physician education in cosmetic and reconstructive surgery of the face, head and neck.

CONSULTING OR VOLUNTEER SERVICES:
Combined Otolaryngology Research Efforts (C.O.R.E.).

NAME(S) OF PROGRAMS:
• **Leslie Bernstein Investigator Development Grant**

TYPE:
Project/program grants; Research grants; Seed money grants. Support for the work of a young faculty member conducting significant clinical or laboratory research in facial plastic surgery and training resident surgeons in research. Funded by a donation from Leslie Bernstein, M.D., D.D.S., to the AAFPRS Foundation.

YEAR PROGRAM STARTED: 1983

PURPOSE:
To support work of a young faculty member in Facial Plastic Surgery conducting significant clinical or laboratory research and involved in the training of resident surgeons in research.

LEGAL BASIS:
Professional association of independent members.

ELIGIBILITY:
Applicants must be Academy members. Research proposals are subject to the following conditions:
(1) a sponsor, either an Academy Fellow or the investigator's department chairman, is required;
(2) the parent institution must provide professional support and;
(3) the research plan must incorporate a resident or residents in the research activities.

FINANCIAL DATA:
Grant monies must be used for direct costs; only 10% can be used for indirect cost.

Amount of support per award: $15,000.
Total amount of support: $15,000.

NUMBER OF APPLICANTS MOST RECENT YEAR:
2.

NUMBER OF AWARDS: 1.

APPLICATION INFORMATION:
Applicants must submit a letter of intent. The
official entry form must be completed and
submitted with the proposal. Failure to
comply with the particular requirements and
format outlined in the guidelines may result
in disqualification.
Duration: Three years.
Deadline: January 15 each year.
Announcement in August.

PUBLICATIONS:
Grants and awards brochure.

IRS IDENTIFICATION NUMBER: 36-2952891

ADDRESS INQUIRIES TO:
Maria Atkins
Manager, Membership Services
(See address above.)

AMERICAN ACADEMY OF FACIAL PLASTIC AND RECONSTRUCTIVE SURGERY (AAFPRS)   [2219]

Educational and Research Foundation
for the AAFPRS
310 South Henry Street
Alexandria, VA 22314
(703) 299-9291
Fax: (703) 299-8898

E-MAIL ADDRESS:
matkins@aafprs.org

WEB SITE ADDRESS:
www.aafprs.org

FOUNDED: 1964

AREAS OF INTEREST:
Physician education in cosmetic and
reconstructive surgery of the face, head and
neck.

CONSULTING OR VOLUNTEER SERVICES:
Combined Otolaryngology Research Efforts
(C.O.R.E.).

NAME(S) OF PROGRAMS:
● **Leslie Bernstein Research Grant**

TYPE:
Project/program grants; Research grants;
Seed money grants. Research award for
Academy members, funded by income from
a donation by Leslie Bernstein, M.D., D.D.S.,
to the Academy's Foundation.

YEAR PROGRAM STARTED: 1988

PURPOSE:
To encourage original research projects
which will advance facial plastic and
reconstructive surgery.

LEGAL BASIS:
Professional association of independent
members.

ELIGIBILITY:
Applicants must be AAFPRS members
undertaking research that will advance facial
plastic and reconstructive surgery. The
primary criteria are that the research be
original and have direct application to facial
plastic surgery.

FINANCIAL DATA:
Grants may be used as seed money for
research projects.

Amount of support per award: $25,000.
Total amount of support: $25,000.

NUMBER OF AWARDS: 1.

APPLICATION INFORMATION:
Proposals should be typed (double-spaced)
and include the following information:
(1) investigator's curriculum vitae;
(2) brief statement of the specific aims of the
investigator's research project, not to exceed
150 words;
(3) brief review of the significance of the
work performed by the investigator and/or
others, not to exceed two pages;
(4) a detailed description of research
procedures including the experimental design,
justification of sample size, outcome
measures and methods of analysis including
justification of each item;
(5) budget for the research award;
(6) description of facilities;
(7) certification of institutional conformity to
the U.S. Government Guidelines for Human
and Animal Experimentation and;
(8) application must be submitted through
C.O.R.E. program.
Duration: Three years.
Deadline: January 15 for review.
Announcement in August.

PUBLICATIONS:
Grants and awards brochure.

IRS IDENTIFICATION NUMBER: 36-2952891

ADDRESS INQUIRIES TO:
Maria Atkins
Manager, Membership Services
(See address above.)

AMERICAN ACADEMY OF FACIAL PLASTIC AND RECONSTRUCTIVE SURGERY (AAFPRS)   [2220]

Educational and Research Foundation
for the AAFPRS
310 South Henry Street
Alexandria, VA 22314
(703) 299-9291 ext. 234
Fax: (703) 299-8898

E-MAIL ADDRESS:
info@aafprs.org

WEB SITE ADDRESS:
www.aafprs.org

AREAS OF INTEREST:
Facial plastic and reconstructive surgery.

NAME(S) OF PROGRAMS:
● **Community Service Award**
● **John Dickinson Teacher of the Year
  Award**
● **Sir Harold Delf Gillies Award**
● **F. Mark Rafaty Memorial Award**
● **Residency Travel Award**
● **John Orlando Roe Award**
● **Ben Shuster Memorial Award**
● **Ira Tresley Research Award**
● **William K. Wright Award**

TYPE:
Awards/prizes; Fellowships; Travel grants.
Community Service Award may be presented
annually to an AAFPRS member who has
distinguished himself/herself by providing
and/or making possible free medical service
to the poor in his/her community.

John Dickinson Teacher of the Year Award
honors an AAFPRS fellow member for
sharing knowledge about facial plastic and
reconstructive surgery with the effective use
of audiovisuals in any one year.

Sir Harold Delf Gillies Award is presented
each year to the graduate fellow who submits
the best basic science research paper written
during fellowship.

The F. Mark Rafaty Memorial Award may be
presented each year to an AAFPRS member
who has made outstanding contributions to
facial plastic and reconstructive surgery.

The Residency Travel Award is presented to
the most outstanding paper in facial plastic
and reconstructive surgery, primarily authored
by a resident or medical student in training.
The paper must be submitted by February 1
for consideration, and to be presented at the
Annual Fall Meeting.

The John Orlando Roe Award is presented
each year to the graduate fellow who submits
the best clinical research paper written during
fellowship.

The Ben Shuster Memorial Award is
presented for the most outstanding research
paper by a resident or fellow in training on
any clinical work or research in facial plastic
and reconstructive surgery delivered at a
national meeting (or its equivalent) between
March 1 and the following February 28. Each
entrant must be the sole or senior author and
an AAFPRS member.

The Ira Tresley Research Award recognizes
the best original research in facial plastic
surgery by an AAFPRS member who has
been board-certified for at least three years.
Papers presented at a national meeting (or its
equivalent) between March 1 and the
following February 28 are eligible for this
award.

William Wright Award may be presented
each year to an AAFPRS member who has
made outstanding contributions to facial
plastic and reconstructive surgery.

PURPOSE:
To support research in facial and
reconstructive plastic surgery.

LEGAL BASIS:
Foundation.

ELIGIBILITY:
Applicants must be AAFPRS members,
except medical students may apply for
Resident Travel Award.

GEOGRAPHIC RESTRICTIONS:
United States.

FINANCIAL DATA:
Amount of support per award: $1,000;
Residency Travel Award: $500.

Total amount of support: $5,000.

NUMBER OF AWARDS: Residency Travel Award:
Up to 2; All others: 1.

APPLICATION INFORMATION:
Contact AAFPRS for application information.
Deadline: February 1.

PUBLICATIONS:
Application form.

STAFF:
Stephen C. Duffy, Executive Vice President
Ann K. Jenne, Director, Development and
Humanitarian Programs
Rita Chua Magness, Director, Marketing and
Publications
Fatima E. El-Porter, Manager, Fellowship
Programs

Ollie Edwards, Manager, Meetings and
Exhibits
Maria Atkins, Manager, Membership
Services

ADDRESS INQUIRIES TO:
Awards Coordinator
(See address above.)

AMERICAN ACADEMY OF FAMILY PHYSICIANS FOUNDATION [2221]

11400 Tomahawk Creek Parkway
Leawood, KS 66211
(913) 906-6000
Fax: (913) 906-6095

E-MAIL ADDRESS:
sgoodman@aafp.org

WEB SITE ADDRESS:
www.aafpfoundation.org

FOUNDED: 1958

AREAS OF INTEREST:
Family physician practice and training.

NAME(S) OF PROGRAMS:
- **Joint Grant Awards Program**
- **Pfizer Teacher Development Award**

TYPE:
Awards/prizes; Research grants; Scholarships;
Seed money grants; Training grants. The
AAFP/F, through the Joint Grant Awards
Program, is primarily interested in supporting
research projects conducted by family
physicians on topics relevant to family
medicine. Funds are available for both formal
grant proposals as well as less formal
applications for research stimulation studies.

The Pfizer Teacher Development Award
provides community-based family physicians
who are committed to teaching family
medicine part-time a scholarship to attend
skill-building opportunities and a stipend for
their teaching center.

PURPOSE:
To strengthen research in family medicine.

LEGAL BASIS:
Foundation.

ELIGIBILITY:
The Joint Grant Awards Program seeks
proposals requesting grant support for family
medicine research. Those eligible to receive a
grant include individual family physicians,
family medicine organizations or
associations, family medicine residency
programs, departments of family medicine
and educational and health care institutions
or organizations which will use the program
support exclusively for research projects
directly involving and impacting on family
medicine. Examples of activities that will not
normally be considered for grant support are
designing a curriculum, supporting a seminar,
or production of an instructional videotape.
At least one investigator on the research team
must be a member of AAFP.

For the Pfizer Teacher Development Award,
eligible applicants must be AAFP members
who are no more than seven years out of
family medicine residency and who have
entered or plan to enter part-time teaching of
family medicine.

GEOGRAPHIC RESTRICTIONS:
United States.

FINANCIAL DATA:
Amount of support per award: Varies.

NUMBER OF AWARDS: Varies.

APPLICATION INFORMATION:
All programs require application forms
and/or letters of intent.

For the Pfizer Teacher Development Award,
applicants must submit an application form
and a curriculum vitae, a letter of verification
of qualifications from applicant's family
practice residency program director, a
recommendation letter and reference form
from two faculty members of the residency
program, either full-time, part-time or
voluntary members, and a letter of
verification from the administration of the
program in which the applicant is teaching.
Duration: Varies.
Deadline: Joint Grant Awards: December 1
and June 3; Pfizer Teacher Development
Award: April 30.

PUBLICATIONS:
Program announcement; application packet.

OFFICERS:
Mary Jo Welker, M.D., President
Jane A. Weida, M.D., Vice President
Craig Doane, Executive Director

STAFF:
Angie Holmes, Senior Manager, Grants and
Awards
Sondra Goodman, Grants and Programs
Manager

ADDRESS INQUIRIES TO:
Joint Grant Awards: Angie Holmes
Senior Manager, Grants and Awards
Pfizer Award: Sondra Goodman
Grants and Programs Manager
(See address above.)

AMERICAN AGING ASSOCIATION [2222]

1700 K Street, N.W., Suite 740
Washington, DC 20006
(202) 293-2856
Fax: (202) 955-8394

E-MAIL ADDRESS:
contact@americanagingassociation.org

WEB SITE ADDRESS:
www.americanagingassociation.org

FOUNDED: 1970

AREAS OF INTEREST:
Biomedical gerontology.

NAME(S) OF PROGRAMS:
- **Paul Glenn Award**
- **Walter Nicolai Award in Biomedical Gerontology**

TYPE:
Awards/prizes; Conferences/seminars; Travel
grants. One first prize and one runner-up for
each award annually.

Paul Glenn Award: For meritorious research
in the area of biomedical gerontology by a
postdoctoral fellow.

Walter Nicolai Award: For meritorious basic
biologic aging research by a graduate or
medical student.

PURPOSE:
To promote biological aging research.

ELIGIBILITY:
Nominees must be graduate or medical
students. Each nomination must have a
sponsor. A nomination may be made by any
member of a society associated with aging
research. The sponsor may reside in the U.S.,
Canada or Mexico.

GEOGRAPHIC RESTRICTIONS:
North America.

FINANCIAL DATA:
Awards include a citation and cash prize.
Amount of support per award: $500 for first
place and $250 for each runner-up.
Total amount of support: $1,500 annually.

NUMBER OF AWARDS: 2 per award.

APPLICATION INFORMATION:
Nominations should include four copies of a
six- to 10-page report of the research being
nominated, sponsor's letter commenting on
the significance of the work and candidate's
curriculum vitae with current address.
Duration: One-time award.
Deadline: March 1.

PUBLICATIONS:
*AGE, the Journal of the American Aging
Association,* quarterly; *Age News Quarterly.*

IRS IDENTIFICATION NUMBER: 23-7364654

ADDRESS INQUIRIES TO:
Kate Reinert, Administrator
(See address above.)

AMERICAN ASSOCIATION FOR HAND SURGERY [2223]

500 Cummings Center
Suite 4550
Beverly, MA 01915
(978) 927-8330
Fax: (978) 524-8890

E-MAIL ADDRESS:
contact@handsurgery.org

WEB SITE ADDRESS:
www.handsurgery.org

FOUNDED: 1970

AREAS OF INTEREST:
Hand surgery and hand therapy.

TYPE:
Research grants. International hand therapy
outreach.

AAHS/PSF Combined Pilot Research Grant
supports the preliminary or pilot phase of
scientific research projects.

YEAR PROGRAM STARTED: 1970

PURPOSE:
To promote education and research; to foster
creativity and innovation in basic and/or
clinical research in all areas pertinent to hand
surgery and hand therapy.

ELIGIBILITY:
Applications are open to AAHS members
and candidates for membership. Residents
and fellows sponsored by an AAHS member
are also eligible to apply. One of the
co-investigators must be an Active or
Affiliate AAHS member. AAHS therapist and
surgeon members are eligible to apply for the
Vargas International Hand Therapy Teaching
Award.

FINANCIAL DATA:
Amount of support per award: AAHS/PSF
Combined Pilot Research Grant: Up to
$10,000; Vargas International Hand Therapy
Teaching Award: Up to $5,000 in
reimbursement for mission expenses.

COOPERATIVE FUNDING PROGRAMS: Match grant
with Plastic Surgery Foundation.

APPLICATION INFORMATION:
Application information is available on the web site.
Duration: AAHS/PSF Combined Pilot Research Grant: One year.

ADDRESS INQUIRIES TO:
See e-mail address above.

AMERICAN COLLEGE OF LEGAL MEDICINE   [2224]

1100 East Woodfield Road
Suite 350
Schaumburg, IL 60173-5125
(847) 969-0283
Fax: (847) 517-7229

E-MAIL ADDRESS:
info@aclm.org

WEB SITE ADDRESS:
www.aclm.org

FOUNDED: 1960

AREAS OF INTEREST:
Legal medicine.

NAME(S) OF PROGRAMS:
● **American College of Legal Medicine's Student Writing Competition in Law, Medicine and Bioethics**

TYPE:
Awards/prizes. The Hirsh Award is awarded to a law, dentistry, podiatry, nursing, pharmacy, health science, health care administration, or public health student.

PURPOSE:
To promote interdisciplinary cooperation and an understanding of issues where law and medicine converge.

ELIGIBILITY:
Must be a student at an accredited school of law, medicine, dentistry, podiatry, nursing, pharmacy, health science, health care, administration, or public health that has written an outstanding original paper on Legal Medicine.

FINANCIAL DATA:
Amount of support per award: Hirsh Award: $1,000 first prize, $500 second prize and $250 third prize.
Total amount of support: $1,750.

NUMBER OF AWARDS: 3.

APPLICATION INFORMATION:
Contact the College.
Deadline: January 1. Announcements in August.

ADDRESS INQUIRIES TO:
Sue O'Sullivan, Administrative Director
(See address above.)

AMERICAN FEDERATION FOR AGING RESEARCH (AFAR)   [2225]

55 West 39th Street
16th Floor
New York, NY 10018
(212) 703-9977
(888) 582-2327
Fax: (212) 997-0330

E-MAIL ADDRESS:
grants@afar.org

WEB SITE ADDRESS:
www.afar.org

FOUNDED: 1981

AREAS OF INTEREST:
Aging research.

NAME(S) OF PROGRAMS:
● **Rosalinde and Arthur Gilbert Foundation/AFAR New Investigator Awards in Alzheimer's Disease**
● **Julie Martin Mid-Career Awards in Aging Research**

TYPE:
Awards/prizes; Research grants. The Rosalinde and Arthur Gilbert Foundation/AFAR New Investigator Awards in Alzheimer's Disease supports research in areas in which more scientific investigation is needed to improve the prevention, diagnosis and treatment of Alzheimer's Disease.

The Julie Martin Mid-Career Award in Aging Research encourages outstanding midcareer scientists who have not been engaged in aging research but whose research is relevant and could lead to novel approaches to aging.

PURPOSE:
To support basic biomedical research that promotes healthier aging and advances the understanding of the aging process and its associated diseases and disorders; to encourage the training of new scientists and physicians in geriatric research and in the practice of geriatric medicine.

LEGAL BASIS:
Private foundation.

ELIGIBILITY:
Rosalinde and Arthur Gilbert Foundation/AFAR New Investigator Awards in Alzheimer's Disease: Junior faculty in the U.S. and Israel who conduct research on Alzheimer's Disease or healthy brain aging.

Julie Martin Mid-Career Awards in Aging Research: Outstanding midcareer scientists whose research has the potential for high payoff in advancing the understanding of basic aging.

GEOGRAPHIC RESTRICTIONS:
United States.

FINANCIAL DATA:
Amount of support per award: Rosalinde and Arthur Gilbert Foundation/AFAR New Investigator Awards in Alzheimer's Disease: $100,000; Julie Martin Mid-Career Awards in Aging Research: $550,000.

NUMBER OF AWARDS: Rosalinde and Arthur Gilbert Foundation/AFAR New Investigator Awards in Alzheimer's Disease: Up to 5; Julie Martin Mid-Career Awards in Aging Research: 2.

APPLICATION INFORMATION:
Required application form is available on the web site.
Duration: Rosalinde and Arthur Gilbert Foundation/AFAR New Investigator Awards in Alzheimer's Disease: One to two years; Julie Martin Mid-Career Awards in Aging Research: Four years.
Deadline: Mid-December.

PUBLICATIONS:
Program announcement.

STAFF:
Stephanie Lederman, Executive Director
Nancy O'Leary, Director, Development
Odette van der Willik, Director, Grant Programs
Hattie Herman, Program Officer
Catherine Cullar, Administrative Manager

ADDRESS INQUIRIES TO:
Hattie Herman, Program Officer
(See address above.)

AMERICAN FEDERATION FOR AGING RESEARCH (AFAR)   [2226]

55 West 39th Street, 16th Floor
New York, NY 10018
(212) 703-9977
(888) 582-2327
Fax: (212) 997-0330

E-MAIL ADDRESS:
grants@afar.org

WEB SITE ADDRESS:
www.afar.org

FOUNDED: 1981

AREAS OF INTEREST:
Biomedical aging research.

NAME(S) OF PROGRAMS:
● **Glenn/AFAR Scholarships for Research in the Biology of Aging**

TYPE:
Scholarships.

PURPOSE:
To support basic biomedical research that promotes healthier aging and advances the understanding of the aging process and its associated diseases and disorders; to encourage the training of new scientists and physicians in geriatric research and in the practice of geriatric medicine.

LEGAL BASIS:
Private foundation.

ELIGIBILITY:
Open to graduate students enrolled in M.D., D.O., Ph.D. or combined-degree programs.

GEOGRAPHIC RESTRICTIONS:
United States.

FINANCIAL DATA:
Amount of support per award: $5,000.

APPLICATION INFORMATION:
Application form is available on the web site.
Duration: Three- to six-month research project.

STAFF:
Stephanie Lederman, Executive Director
Nancy O'Leary, Director, Development
Odette van der Willik, Director, Grant Programs
Hattie Herman, Program Officer
Catherine Cullar, Administrative Manager

ADDRESS INQUIRIES TO:
Hattie Herman, Program Officer
(See address above.)

AMERICAN FEDERATION FOR AGING RESEARCH (AFAR)   [2227]

55 West 39th Street
16th Floor
New York, NY 10018
(212) 703-9977
(888) 582-2327
Fax: (212) 997-0330

E-MAIL ADDRESS:
grants@afar.org

WEB SITE ADDRESS:
www.afar.org

FOUNDED: 1981

AREAS OF INTEREST:
Biomedical aging research.

NAME(S) OF PROGRAMS:
- **AFAR Research Grants**
- **Paul Beeson Career Development Awards in Aging Research Program**
- **Glenn/AFAR Breakthroughs in Gerontology Awards**
- **Medical Student Training in Aging Research Program (MSTAR)**

TYPE:
Fellowships; Research grants; Scholarships; Training grants. The AFAR Research Grants are given to provide one to two years of support for junior faculty to do research that will serve as the basis for longer-term research efforts.

The Paul Beeson Career Development Awards in Aging Research Program is intended to bolster the current and severe shortage of academic physicians who have the combination of medical, academic and scientific training relative to caring for older people.

The Glenn/AFAR Breakthroughs in Gerontology Awards are to provide timely support to a small number of pilot research programs that may be of relatively high risk but which offer significant promise of yielding transforming discoveries in the fundamental biology of aging.

Medical Student Training in Aging Research Program (MSTAR) provides medical students, early in their training, with an enriching experience in aging-related research and geriatrics, under the mentorship of top experts in the field. Students participate in an eight- to 12-week structured research, clinical and didactic program in geriatrics.

PURPOSE:
To support basic biomedical research that promotes healthier aging and advances the understanding of the aging process and its associated diseases and disorders; to encourage the training of new scientists and physicians in geriatric research and in the practice of geriatric medicine.

LEGAL BASIS:
Private foundation.

ELIGIBILITY:
For the AFAR Research Grants, applicants must be junior faculty (M.Ds. and Ph.Ds.).

Paul Beeson Career Development Awards in Aging Research Program applicants are clinically trained individuals who are pursuing research careers in aging.

For the Glenn/AFAR Breakthroughs in Gerontology Awards, qualified applicants must be full-time faculty members at the rank of assistant professor or higher who can demonstrate a strong record of independence.

The Medical Student Training in Aging Research Program (MSTAR) is intended for medical students and is built on the Medical Student Geriatric Scholars Program.

GEOGRAPHIC RESTRICTIONS:
United States.

FINANCIAL DATA:
Amount of support per award: AFAR Research Grants: Up to $100,000; Paul Beeson Career Development Awards in Aging Research: $200,000 per year; Glenn/AFAR Breakthroughs in Gerontology Awards: Up to $200,000.

NUMBER OF AWARDS: AFAR Research Grants: Up to 10; Paul Beeson Career Development Awards in Aging Research: Up to 10; Glenn/AFAR Breakthroughs in Gerontology Awards: 2.

APPLICATION INFORMATION:
Required application form is available on the web site.

Duration: One to two years. Up to five years for Beeson Award.

Deadline: Mid-December.

PUBLICATIONS:
Program announcement.

STAFF:
Stephanie Lederman, Executive Director
Odette van der Willik, Director, Grant Programs
Hattie Herman, Program Officer
Catherine Cullar, Administrative Manager

ADDRESS INQUIRIES TO:
Hattie Herman, Program Officer
(See address above.)

AMERICAN KIDNEY FUND   [2228]
11921 Rockville Pike, Suite 300
Rockville, MD 20852
(800) 638-8299
(866) 300-2900 (Spanish/English HelpLine)
Fax: (301) 881-0898

E-MAIL ADDRESS:
helpline@kidneyfund.org

WEB SITE ADDRESS:
www.kidneyfund.org

FOUNDED: 1971

AREAS OF INTEREST:
Treatment, prevention and cure of kidney disease.

NAME(S) OF PROGRAMS:
- **Clinical Scientist in Nephrology (CSN)**

TYPE:
Fellowships.

YEAR PROGRAM STARTED: 1989

PURPOSE:
To provide aid in the treatment, prevention and care of kidney disease.

ELIGIBILITY:
Applicant must be a nephrologist in a current academic setting.

GEOGRAPHIC RESTRICTIONS:
United States and its territories.

FINANCIAL DATA:
Amount of support per award: Up to $80,000 per year.

Total amount of support: Up to $160,000.

NUMBER OF APPLICANTS MOST RECENT YEAR: 11.

NUMBER OF AWARDS: 1.

APPLICATION INFORMATION:
Complete application information may be found on the web site.

Duration: One to two years.

Deadline: December 1.

ADDRESS INQUIRIES TO:
Susan McDonough, Senior Director of Health Initiatives and Education
(See address above.)

AMERICAN KIDNEY FUND   [2229]
11921 Rockville Pike, Suite 300
Rockville, MD 20852
(800) 638-8299
(866) 300-2900 (Spanish/English HelpLine)
Fax: (301) 881-0898

E-MAIL ADDRESS:
helpline@kidneyfund.org

WEB SITE ADDRESS:
www.kidneyfund.org

FOUNDED: 1971

AREAS OF INTEREST:
Treatment, prevention and cure of kidney disease.

NAME(S) OF PROGRAMS:
- **Patient Services Grants: Safety Net Grant Program**

TYPE:
Grants-in-aid; Product donations. Medical Grants. Provides financial assistance to qualified dialysis patients who are referred by their physicians and social workers for treatment-specific expenses such as transportation, over-the-counter medicines, medication co-payments, kidney donor expenses, mobility aids and nutritional supplements.

YEAR PROGRAM STARTED: 1971

PURPOSE:
To provide aid in the treatment, prevention, and cure of kidney disease.

ELIGIBILITY:
Based on financial need. Kidney dialysis and transplant patients living in the U.S. are eligible. Additional requirements are available online.

GEOGRAPHIC RESTRICTIONS:
United States and its territories.

FINANCIAL DATA:
Amount of support per award: $100 per year.

APPLICATION INFORMATION:
Applications must be submitted online via Grants Management System. Applications must be completed by the patient and a dialysis or transplant renal professional. Paper applications will no longer be accepted.

Duration: Renewable 12 months from the check date of the last grant.

IRS IDENTIFICATION NUMBER: 23-7124261

ADDRESS INQUIRIES TO:
Patient Services Department
Tel: (800) 795-3226
(See address above.)

AMERICAN MEDICAL ASSOCIATION FOUNDATION
515 North State Street
Chicago, IL 60654
(312) 464-4200
Fax: (312) 464-4142

E-MAIL ADDRESS:
amafoundation@ama-assn.org

WEB SITE ADDRESS:
www.amafoundation.org

TYPE:
Awards/prizes; Project/program grants; Research grants; Scholarships; Seed money grants. Excellence in Medicine Awards are given to recognize physicians and medical students who are improving the health of their communities and the lives of those who are most in need.

The Joan F. Giambalvo Memorial Scholarship is presented in conjunction with the AMA's Women Physicians Congress to provide a research grant to help researchers advance the progress of women in the medical profession and identify and address the needs of women physicians and medical students.

Health Literacy Initiative seeks to provide awareness among physicians and health care providers to understand healthy literacy and its impact on patient safety.

Healthy Communities/Healthy America awards grants to existing, physician-led free clinics that provide free or low-cost medical care to underserved and uninsured populations.

Healthy Living Grant Program provides grants to support healthy lifestyles projects in the areas of nutrition, physical fitness, prescription medication safety and violence prevention.

The Minority Scholars Awards are given in collaboration with the AMA Minority Affairs Section to first- and second-year medical students from historically underrepresented minority groups in the medical profession.

The Physicians of Tomorrow Scholarships are awarded to promising fourth-year medical students based on financial need and academic excellence.

In partnership with the AMA Alliance, the Scholars Fund distributes tuition assistance funds to medical schools across the country.

The Seed Grant Research Program provides medical students, physician residents and fellows with grants to help them conduct basic science, applied or clinical research projects.

The Arthur N. Wilson, M.D. Scholarship is awarded to a medical student who is a graduate of a high school in southeast Alaska.

See entry 1660 for full listing.

AMERICAN MEDICAL TECHNOLOGISTS   [2230]
10700 West Higgins Road
Suite 150
Rosemont, IL 60018
(847) 823-5169
(800) 275-1268
Fax: (847) 823-0458

E-MAIL ADDRESS:
mail@americanmedtech.org

WEB SITE ADDRESS:
www.americanmedtech.org

FOUNDED: 1939

AREAS OF INTEREST:
Students pursuing studies as medical technologist, medical laboratory technician, medical laboratory assistant, medical administrative specialist, medical assistant, dental assistant, or phlebotomist.

NAME(S) OF PROGRAMS:
- **AMT Student Scholarships**

TYPE:
Scholarships.

YEAR PROGRAM STARTED: 1969

PURPOSE:
To assist students to complete the training to work in clinical laboratories and doctors' offices.

ELIGIBILITY:
The following criteria apply:
(1) applicant must be a graduate of, or a senior in, an accredited high school (G.E.D. also acceptable);
(2) applicant must be enrolled in a school accredited by an accrediting agency recognized by the U.S. Department of Education and;
(3) applicant's course of study must lead to a career in one of the disciplines (medical technologist, medical laboratory technician, medical laboratory assistant, medical administrative specialist, medical assistant, dental assistant, or phlebotomist) certified by the American Medical Technologists; applicants pursuing careers other than those certified by the American Medical Technologists will not be accepted.

Winners of the scholarship must furnish proof of being either a student in good standing or enrolled for entrance into the fall program of an accredited school. The award may only be used to defray tuition costs, and will be sent directly to the school of the recipient's choice. Applicant must provide evidence of financial need and career goals.

GEOGRAPHIC RESTRICTIONS:
United States.

FINANCIAL DATA:
Amount of support per award: $500.
Total amount of support: $2,500.

NUMBER OF APPLICANTS MOST RECENT YEAR:
75.

NUMBER OF AWARDS: 5 annually.

APPLICATION INFORMATION:
Detailed information is available online.
Deadline: Application form must be completed and received by April 1 to be considered for the current year's scholarship.

PUBLICATIONS:
Application form.

ADDRESS INQUIRIES TO:
Linda Halblander
Scholarship Program Coordinator
(See address above.)

*SPECIAL STIPULATIONS:
The award may only be used to defray tuition costs, and will be sent directly to the school of the recipient's choice.

AMERICAN MEDICAL WOMEN'S ASSOCIATION, INC.   [2231]
12100 Sunset Hills Road
Suite 130
Reston, VA 20190
(703) 234-4069
Fax: (703) 435-4390

E-MAIL ADDRESS:
associatedirector@amwa-doc.org

WEB SITE ADDRESS:
www.amwa-doc.org

FOUNDED: 1915

AREAS OF INTEREST:
Women physicians, women medical students and women's health.

NAME(S) OF PROGRAMS:
- **American Women's Hospitals Service (AWHS)**

TYPE:
Awards/prizes; Conferences/seminars; General operating grants; Project/program

grants; Training grants; Travel grants. Support for clinics serving the poor in medically underserved areas, scholarships and loans to qualifying women medical students, and continuing medical education for physicians in areas related to women's health.

YEAR PROGRAM STARTED: 1915

PURPOSE:
To advance women in medicine and improve women's health through advocacy, leadership, education, expertise and mentoring, and strategic alliances.

LEGAL BASIS:
AMWA: 501(c)(6) corporation. AWHS: 501(c)(3) foundation.

ELIGIBILITY:
Open to women who are enrolled in accredited medical schools in the U.S.

GEOGRAPHIC RESTRICTIONS:
United States.

BOARD OF DIRECTORS:
Farzanna Haffizulla, M.D., President

ADDRESS INQUIRIES TO:
Katherine He
(See address above.)

THE AMERICAN PORPHYRIA FOUNDATION   [2232]
4900 Woodway Drive
Suite 780
Houston, TX 77056-1837
(713) 266-9617
Fax: (713) 840-9552

E-MAIL ADDRESS:
porphyrus@aol.com

WEB SITE ADDRESS:
www.porphyriafoundation.com

AREAS OF INTEREST:
Porphyria.

TYPE:
Research grants.

PURPOSE:
To improve the health and well-being of individuals and families affected by porphyria.

ELIGIBILITY:
Qualified investigators involved in porphyria research.

FINANCIAL DATA:
Amount of support per award: $5,000 to $10,000.
Total amount of support: Varies.

APPLICATION INFORMATION:
Send a two-page summary of proposed research and research experience to the Foundation.
Duration: Typically one year.

PUBLICATIONS:
Newsletters.

ADDRESS INQUIRIES TO:
Desiree Lyon Howe, Executive Director
(See address above.)

AMERICAN ROENTGEN RAY SOCIETY   [2233]
44211 Slatestone Court
Leesburg, VA 20176
(703) 729-3353
Fax: (703) 729-4839

E-MAIL ADDRESS:
info@arrs.org

WEB SITE ADDRESS:
www.arrs.org

FOUNDED: 1900

AREAS OF INTEREST:
Diagnostic radiology.

NAME(S) OF PROGRAMS:
● **ARRS Annual Scholarship Program**

TYPE:
Scholarships.

YEAR PROGRAM STARTED: 1992

PURPOSE:
To provide resources needed to acquire knowledge, skills and training in the areas that are vital to radiology but have traditionally been outside the scope of diagnostic radiology.

ELIGIBILITY:
Candidates must have earned an M.D. or D.O. from an accredited institution. Also, must have completed all residencies or fellowship training or equivalent, full-time appointment as instructor, assistant professor or equivalent for no more than five years beyond training. Appointment must be in a department of radiology, nuclear medicine, ultrasound or radiation oncology.

Scholar may choose a one-year program requiring a minimum 80% time commitment, or a two-year program requiring a minimum 50% time commitment.

FINANCIAL DATA:
Funds distributed to individual's institution.
Amount of support per award: $140,000.
Total amount of support: Varies.

NUMBER OF AWARDS: 1.

APPLICATION INFORMATION:
Submission of a curriculum vitae, summary of qualifications, goals and purposes of the study, estimated budget, and a statement from department regarding applicant's goals and commitment ensuring applicant's return to faculty upon completion.
Duration: One or two years.
Deadline: November.

ADDRESS INQUIRIES TO:
Samantha Schmidt
Education Administrative Assistant
(See address above.)

AMERICAN SOCIETY FOR CLINICAL PATHOLOGY   [2234]
33 West Monroe, Suite 1600
Chicago, IL 60603
(312) 541-4954
Fax: (312) 541-4767

E-MAIL ADDRESS:
andrew.sauer@ascp.org

WEB SITE ADDRESS:
www.ascp.org/scholarships

FOUNDED: 1922

AREAS OF INTEREST:
Laboratory medicine.

NAME(S) OF PROGRAMS:
● **ASCP Scholarships**

TYPE:
Scholarships.

PURPOSE:
To encourage and support individuals interested in laboratory professions.

LEGAL BASIS:
Professional society.

ELIGIBILITY:
ASCP Scholarships are offered to eligible final-year students in Medical Technologist (MT), Medical Laboratory Technician (MLT), Cytotechnologist (CT), Histotechnician (HT), Histotechnologist (HTL) and Pathologist Assistant (PA) programs. An applicant must be enrolled in an NAACLS- or CAAHEP-accredited program, in the final clinical year of education and a U.S. citizen or permanent U.S. resident. Applicants must also have a minimum 2.8 grade point average on a 4.0 scale.

Scholarship selection criteria include academic achievement, leadership abilities and community activities, professional goals, and endorsements from faculty and community leaders.

GEOGRAPHIC RESTRICTIONS:
United States.

FINANCIAL DATA:
Amount of support per award: $1,000.
Total amount of support: Approximately $50,000 per year.

NUMBER OF APPLICANTS MOST RECENT YEAR: 400.

NUMBER OF AWARDS: 50 for the year 2013.

APPLICATION INFORMATION:
Application form required. Contact the Society.
Duration: One year. Nonrenewable.
Deadline: November 15, 2014.

PUBLICATIONS:
Announcement.

ADDRESS INQUIRIES TO:
Siemens-ASCP Scholarship Program
(See address above.)

AMERICAN SOCIETY OF HEMATOLOGY   [2235]
2021 L Street, N.W.
Suite 900
Washington, DC 20036
(202) 776-0544
Fax: (888) 719-7814

E-MAIL ADDRESS:
awards@hematology.org

WEB SITE ADDRESS:
www.hematology.org

FOUNDED: 1985

AREAS OF INTEREST:
Hematology, basic and clinical/translational research.

NAME(S) OF PROGRAMS:
● **Fellow Scholar Award**
● **Junior Faculty Scholar Award**

TYPE:
Awards/prizes; Fellowships; Research grants; Scholarships.

PURPOSE:
To support hematologists who have chosen a career in research.

ELIGIBILITY:
Fellows must have more than two years, but less than six years, postdoctoral research training at the time of application. Junior

Faculty applicants must be within the first two years of their initial tenure-track faculty appointment as Assistant Professor at the time of application.

GEOGRAPHIC RESTRICTIONS:
United States and Canada.

FINANCIAL DATA:
Amount of support per award: $150,000 for a Junior Faculty Scholar Award or $100,000 for a Fellow Scholar Award. These awards can be spread over two or three years with an annual maximum not to exceed $75,000 for junior faculty and $50,000 for fellows.
Total amount of support: Approximately $2,300,000.

APPLICATION INFORMATION:
A letter of intent is required before submission of full proposal. Contact the Society for details.
Duration: Two to three years.
Deadline: Mandatory Letter of Intent: Late April/early May; Application: August 1.

ADDRESS INQUIRIES TO:
Lisa Fanning
Awards and Diversity Programs Manager
(See address above.)

AMERICAN SOCIETY OF HEMATOLOGY   [2236]
2021 L Street, N.W.
Suite 900
Washington, DC 20036
(202) 776-0544
Fax: (888) 724-0513

E-MAIL ADDRESS:
training@hematology.org

WEB SITE ADDRESS:
www.hematology.org

AREAS OF INTEREST:
Hematology.

NAME(S) OF PROGRAMS:
● **Trainee Research Award Program**

TYPE:
Awards/prizes. Each scholarship provides the medical school with funds to cover the expenses for students to complete a program and travel support for students to attend the ASH annual meeting.

PURPOSE:
To provide medical students, residents, and selected undergraduates with an introduction to the specialty of hematology by encouraging them to take time during their medical school curriculum to work on a project with a hematologist.

ELIGIBILITY:
Medical students, residents, and selected undergraduates in the United States, Mexico and Canada.

GEOGRAPHIC RESTRICTIONS:
United States, Mexico and Canada.

FINANCIAL DATA:
Amount of support per award: $4,000 cash award and $1,000 travel stipend for annual meeting.
Total amount of support: $200,000 for the year 2012.

APPLICATION INFORMATION:
The institution is responsible for selecting student participants. Contact the Society for additional application information.
Duration: Varies.
Deadline: Mid-March.

ADDRESS INQUIRIES TO:
Joe Basso, Training Manager
(See address above.)

AMERICAN SOCIETY OF
HYPERTENSION   [2237]
45 Main Street
Suite 712
Brooklyn, NY 11201
(212) 696-9099
Fax: (347) 916-0267

E-MAIL ADDRESS:
awards@ash-us.org

WEB SITE ADDRESS:
www.ash-us.org

AREAS OF INTEREST:
Hypertension and related cardiovascular
disease.

TYPE:
Awards/prizes; Research grants.

PURPOSE:
To organize and conduct educational
activities designed to promote and encourage
the development, advancement, and exchange
of scientific information in all aspects of
research, diagnosis, and treatment of
hypertension and related cardiovascular
diseases.

GEOGRAPHIC RESTRICTIONS:
North America.

FINANCIAL DATA:
Amount of support per award: $500 to
$10,000.
Total amount of support: Varies.

APPLICATION INFORMATION:
Contact the Society.
Duration: Typically one year.

STAFF:
Ashley Buron, Program Coordinator
Scientific Meetings and Professional Affairs

ADDRESS INQUIRIES TO:
Ashley Buron, Program Coordinator
Scientific Meetings and Professional Affairs
(See address above.)

AMERICAN VETERINARY
MEDICAL ASSOCIATION   [2238]
AVMA Governmental Relations Division
1910 Sunderland Place, N.W.
Washington, DC 20036
(800) 321-1473
Fax: (202) 842-4360

E-MAIL ADDRESS:
fellowship@avma.org

WEB SITE ADDRESS:
www.avma.org/fellowship

AREAS OF INTEREST:
Veterinary medicine.

NAME(S) OF PROGRAMS:
• **AVMA Fellowship**

TYPE:
Fellowships.

YEAR PROGRAM STARTED: 1988

PURPOSE:
To support AVMA members to serve as a
congressional or executive branch fellow for
one year in a personal or committee office of
the U.S. Congress.

LEGAL BASIS:
Association.

ELIGIBILITY:
Applicants must be AVMA members and
U.S. citizens who demonstrate special
competence in an area of veterinary
medicine, possess a broad professional
background and exhibit an interest in
applying scientific knowledge to solve
societal/public policy problems.

Applicants must be articulate, literate,
adaptable and capable of working on a wide
range of policy issues.

Fellows must serve in Washington, DC.

FINANCIAL DATA:
Amount of support per award:
Approximately $77,000 plus expenses and up
to $6,000 in health insurance premiums.

NUMBER OF APPLICANTS MOST RECENT YEAR:
30 for the year 2013-14.

NUMBER OF AWARDS: 3 for the year 2013-14.

APPLICATION INFORMATION:
Applicants must submit:
(1) a letter of intent;
(2) a curriculum vitae;
(3) two letters of reference from professional
colleagues;
(4) a letter of support from the applicant's
local, state, specialty or allied veterinary
medical organization and;
(5) a personal statement (not to exceed 750
words) describing the applicant's
qualifications, commitment to veterinary
medicine and why the fellowship is desired.
Duration: One year.
Deadline: Usually second Friday in February.

PUBLICATIONS:
Program announcement.

IRS IDENTIFICATION NUMBER: 36-6117739

ADDRESS INQUIRIES TO:
See e-mail address above.

ANIMAL ASSISTANCE
FOUNDATION   [2239]
405 Urban Street
Suite 340
Lakewood, CO 80228
(303) 744-8396
Fax: (303) 744-7065

E-MAIL ADDRESS:
rogerhaston@aaf-fd.org

WEB SITE ADDRESS:
www.aaf-fd.org

FOUNDED: 1975

AREAS OF INTEREST:
Companion animal overpopulation,
operational optimization, adoption and
permanent homes, cruelty prevention and
intervention, innovation and ingenuity and
companion animals and unwanted horse
issues.

TYPE:
Capital grants; General operating grants;
Project/program grants. Operating and service
grants. The Foundation offers charitable
support through its grantmaking program to
organizations located within the state of
Colorado or an agency that has a direct
impact on animals and their owners in
Colorado. Direct impact on animals and their
owners in Colorado applies to institutions
conducting studies that result in new science,
practice or knowledge significantly affecting
animals living in Colorado.

YEAR PROGRAM STARTED: 1975

PURPOSE:
To provide leadership and support to make
Colorado the Model State for animal welfare
through philanthropy toward animals.

LEGAL BASIS:
Private foundation.

ELIGIBILITY:
In considering grant requests, the Foundation
values proposals that:
(1) are located in Colorado or that have a
direct impact on animals and their owners in
Colorado;
(2) have a measurable impact on animal
welfare;
(3) fit within the key focus areas for AAF
and;
(4) include additional funding from other
sources.

Grants are not given to individuals. Eligible
applicants must be a unit of government or
recognized as an IRS 501(c)(3) tax-exempt
organization and must propose an activity
compatible with the Foundation's mission.
(Groups designated by the IRS as Type III
supporting organizations, however, are not
eligible to apply.) Religious organizations are
not eligible.

The Foundation does not fund individuals,
pets of individuals, debt retirement, indirect
administrative costs, start-up costs,
endowments or political campaigns.

GEOGRAPHIC RESTRICTIONS:
Colorado.

FINANCIAL DATA:
Amount of support per award: Varies.
Total amount of support: More than $541,600
in grants for the year 2012.
Matching fund requirements: Varies.

NUMBER OF APPLICANTS MOST RECENT YEAR:
100.

NUMBER OF AWARDS: 88 (54 Model State and
34 Service Grant recipients).

REPRESENTATIVE AWARDS:
$5,000 to Fort Collins Cat Rescue; $10,000
to Humane Society of Weld County.

APPLICATION INFORMATION:
If Foundation has indicated it will accept
applicant's proposal, the following criteria
must be met:
(1) Applications must be typed,
computer-generated or legibly printed;
(2) Applicant must submit one original,
unbound, and in a form that can be readily
copied (unstapled or not in a folder or
notebook) and;
(3) One electronic copy of the application
(plus attachments) must be submitted.

Send the original grant application and
attachments via mail to the address above
and also an electronic copy of the application
and attachments to info@aaf-fd.org.
Duration: One to two years. Renewable with
reapplication.
Deadline: Last Friday in March and
September.

PUBLICATIONS:
Annual report.

IRS IDENTIFICATION NUMBER: 84-0715412

ADDRESS INQUIRIES TO:
Letters of inquiry and formal proposals
should be addressed to:
Grant Committee: Application
and Information

Animal Assistance Foundation
E-mail: info@aaf-fd.org
(See address or phone number above.)

*SPECIAL STIPULATIONS:
Eligible organizations are asked to submit only one proposal per year. If funded, programs are eligible to request a second year's funding.

APLASTIC ANEMIA AND MDS INTERNATIONAL FOUNDATION [2240]
100 Park Avenue, Suite 108
Rockville, MD 20850
(301) 279-7202
(800) 747-2820
Fax: (301) 279-7205

E-MAIL ADDRESS:
help@aamds.org

WEB SITE ADDRESS:
www.aamds.org

FOUNDED: 1983

AREAS OF INTEREST:
Aplastic anemia, myelodysplastic syndrome (MDS) and paroxysmal nocturnal hemoglobinuria (PNH).

NAME(S) OF PROGRAMS:
• AA&MDSIF Research Grant Program

TYPE:
Research grants.

YEAR PROGRAM STARTED: 1983

PURPOSE:
To support research related to aplastic anemia, myelodysplastic syndrome (MDS) and paroxysmal nocturnal hemoglobinuria (PNH).

ELIGIBILITY:
Qualified investigators affiliated with appropriate institutions are eligible to apply.

FINANCIAL DATA:
Amount of support per award: $30,000 per year.

APPLICATION INFORMATION:
Applications must be submitted electronically.
Duration: Two years. Second-year funding pending approval by Medical Board.
Deadline: February 28.

STAFF:
Alice Houk, Director of Health Professional Programs

ADDRESS INQUIRIES TO:
Alice Houk
Director of Health Professional Programs
(See address above.)

ARTHRITIS NATIONAL RESEARCH FOUNDATION (ANRF) [2241]
200 Oceangate, Suite 830
Long Beach, CA 90802
(800) 588-2873
(562) 437-6808
Fax: (562) 437-6057

E-MAIL ADDRESS:
hbelisle@curearthritis.org

WEB SITE ADDRESS:
www.curearthritis.org

FOUNDED: 1952

AREAS OF INTEREST:
Research related to arthritis.

NAME(S) OF PROGRAMS:
• ANRF Arthritis Research Grants

TYPE:
Research grants; Travel grants. ANRF Arthritis Research Grants are intended to support basic and clinical research focusing on rheumatic and related autoimmune diseases, such as osteoarthritis and rheumatoid arthritis.

YEAR PROGRAM STARTED: 1952

PURPOSE:
To support basic and clinical research related to arthritis.

ELIGIBILITY:
Applicants must hold an M.D. and/or Ph.D. degree or equivalent. Applicants need not be U.S. citizens, but must conduct their research at U.S. nonprofit institutions.

FINANCIAL DATA:
No overhead expenses funded.
Amount of support per award: $50,000 to $100,000.
Total amount of support: $1,050,000 for fiscal year 2013-14.

COOPERATIVE FUNDING PROGRAMS: American Federation for Aging Research (AFAR).

NUMBER OF APPLICANTS MOST RECENT YEAR: 69 for fiscal year 2013-14.

NUMBER OF AWARDS: 15 for fiscal year 2013-14.

REPRESENTATIVE AWARDS:
$75,000 to study the role of autoantibodies in pulmonary manifestations of inflammatory arthritis.

APPLICATION INFORMATION:
A standard cover sheet and budget page are required and provided on the Foundation's web site. Application must be submitted online along with two hard copies, one original and one copy.
Duration: One year. May apply for second year of funding.
Deadline: January 15 or next business day.

IRS IDENTIFICATION NUMBER: 95-6043953

STAFF:
Helene Belisle, Executive Director

ADDRESS INQUIRIES TO:
See e-mail address above.

AUTISM SPEAKS [2242]
1060 State Road, 2nd Floor
Princeton, NJ 08540
(609) 228-7313
Fax: (609) 430-9163

E-MAIL ADDRESS:
jnew@autismspeaks.org

WEB SITE ADDRESS:
www.autismspeaks.org

FOUNDED: 1994

AREAS OF INTEREST:
Autism.

NAME(S) OF PROGRAMS:
• Family Services Community Grants
• Meixner Translational Postdoctoral Fellowships
• Weatherstone Predoctoral Fellowships
• Suzanne & Bob Wright Trailblazer

TYPE:
Fellowships; Project/program grants; Research grants. Research grants that are in line with Autism Speaks research priorities.

YEAR PROGRAM STARTED: 1994

PURPOSE:
To fund global biomedical research into the causes, prevention, treatment and cure for autism; to raise public awareness about autism and its effects on individuals, families and society.

LEGAL BASIS:
National nonprofit, tax-exempt organization.

ELIGIBILITY:
Science grants: Open to investigators at established research institutions.

GEOGRAPHIC RESTRICTIONS:
United States.

FINANCIAL DATA:
Amount of support per award: Varies.
Total amount of support: Varies.

NUMBER OF APPLICANTS MOST RECENT YEAR:
Family Services: 500; Science: 440.

NUMBER OF AWARDS: Varies.

APPLICATION INFORMATION:
All proposals must be submitted online via Autism Speaks grants administration site. Current information and RFAs can be found at the web site.
Duration: Varies.
Deadline: Varies.

IRS IDENTIFICATION NUMBER: 20-2329938

ADDRESS INQUIRIES TO:
Joan New, Grants Manager
(See address above.)

Family Services: Serena Selkin
Grants Manager
E-mail: sselkin@autismspeaks.org

BATTEN DISEASE SUPPORT AND RESEARCH ASSOCIATION [2243]
1175 Dublin Road
Columbus, OH 43215
(614) 973-6011
(800) 448-4570
Fax: (866) 648-8718

E-MAIL ADDRESS:
mfrazier@bdsra.org

WEB SITE ADDRESS:
www.bdsra.org

FOUNDED: 1987

AREAS OF INTEREST:
Batten Disease, NCL and Kufs Disease.

NAME(S) OF PROGRAMS:
• Batten Disease Research Grant

TYPE:
Fellowships; Research grants; Seed money grants.

YEAR PROGRAM STARTED: 1994

PURPOSE:
To maximize the opportunities of victims of Batten to lead as normal lives as possible; to provide a parent communication network, information and emotional support to families of persons with Batten Disease; to educate lay persons and professionals about the special needs of victims and their families; to act as a national registry for NCL researchers throughout the world.

ELIGIBILITY:
Applications will be reviewed based upon the quality of the proposed science, the probability of achieving the specific aims proposed and the likelihood of securing federal funding for continued research.

APPLICATION INFORMATION:
Write or call the Foundation to determine the interest and appropriateness of a full proposal.
Duration: One to two years.
Deadline: May 15.

IRS IDENTIFICATION NUMBER: 91-1397792

STAFF:
Margie Frazier, Executive Director

ADDRESS INQUIRIES TO:
Margie Frazier, Executive Director
(See address above.)

*SPECIAL STIPULATIONS:
Grants must not be used to cover indirect or overhead costs.

BRIGHAM AND WOMEN'S HOSPITAL

75 Francis Street
Boston, MA 02115
(617) 732-8422
Fax: (617) 582-6112

E-MAIL ADDRESS:
bwhdeland@partners.org

WEB SITE ADDRESS:
www.brighamandwomens.
org/delandfellowship

TYPE:
Fellowships.

See entry 1421 for full listing.

BURROUGHS WELLCOME FUND   [2244]

21 T.W. Alexander Drive
Research Triangle Park, NC 27709
(919) 991-5100
Fax: (919) 991-5160

E-MAIL ADDRESS:
info@bwfund.org

WEB SITE ADDRESS:
www.bwfund.org

FOUNDED: 1955

AREAS OF INTEREST:
Biomedical research.

NAME(S) OF PROGRAMS:
- **Career Awards at the Scientific Interface**
- **Career Awards for Medical Scientists**
- **Institutional Program Unifying Population and Laboratory Based Sciences**
- **Investigators in the Pathogenesis of Infectious Disease**
- **Preterm Birth Initiative**

TYPE:
Awards/prizes; Conferences/seminars; Research grants. Career Awards at the Scientific Interface bridge advanced postdoctoral training and the first three years of faculty service. These awards are intended to foster the early career development of researchers with backgrounds in the physical/mathematical/computational sciences whose work addresses biological questions.

Career Awards for Medical Scientists provide funds to bridge advanced postdoctoral/fellowship training and the early years of faculty service. This award addresses the ongoing problem of increasing the number of physician scientists and will help facilitate the transition to a career in research.

Institutional Program Unifying Population and Laboratory Based Sciences provides funds to unite the population and computational sciences and the laboratory-based biological sciences. The award supports the training of researchers working between existing research concentrations in population approaches to human health and in basic biological sciences.

Investigators in the Pathogenesis of Infectious Disease provides awards for opportunities for accomplished investigators at the assistant professor level to study pathogenesis, with a focus on the intersection of human and microbial biology. The program is intended to shed light on the overarching issues of how human hosts handle infectious challenge.

Preterm Birth Initiative brings together a diverse interdisciplinary group with expertise in genetics/genomics, immunology, microbiology and proteomics along with the more traditional areas of parturition research such as maternal fetal medicine, obstetrics and pediatrics to address the scientific issues related to preterm birth.

PURPOSE:
To advance the medical sciences by supporting research and other scientific and educational activities; to help scientists early in their careers develop as independent investigators; to advance fields in the basic medical sciences that are undervalued or in need of particular encouragement.

GEOGRAPHIC RESTRICTIONS:
United States and Canada.

FINANCIAL DATA:
Amount of support per award: Career Awards at the Scientific Interface: $500,000; Career Awards for Medical Scientists: $700,000; Institutional Program Unifying Population and Laboratory Based Sciences: $2,500,000; Investigators in Pathogenesis of Infectious Disease: $500,000; Preterm Birth Initiative: Up to $600,000.
Total amount of support: Approximately $25,000,000 in grants awarded annually.

APPLICATION INFORMATION:
Contact the Fund.
Duration: Preterm Birth Initiative: Four years. All others: Five years.
Deadline: Varies.

PUBLICATIONS:
FOCUS, newsletter; *Career Development Guides,* annual report.

IRS IDENTIFICATION NUMBER: 23-7225395

ADDRESS INQUIRIES TO:
Burroughs Wellcome Fund
P.O. Box 13901
Research Triangle Park, NC 27709-3901

CANADIAN BLOOD SERVICES   [2245]

1800 Alta Vista Drive
Ottawa ON K1G 4J5 Canada
(613) 739-2408
Fax: (613) 739-2201

E-MAIL ADDRESS:
cilla.perry@blood.ca

WEB SITE ADDRESS:
www.blood.ca

AREAS OF INTEREST:
Research in transfusion science.

NAME(S) OF PROGRAMS:
- **Canadian Blood Services Trainee Awards Graduate Fellowship Program**
- **Canadian Blood Services Trainee Awards Postdoctoral Fellowship**

TYPE:
Fellowships.

PURPOSE:
To attract and support young investigators to initiate or continue training in the field of transfusion science; to foster careers related to transfusion science in Canada.

ELIGIBILITY:
Graduate Fellowship: Open to graduate students who are undertaking full-time research training leading to a Ph.D. degree. Students registering solely for a Master's degree will not be considered.

Postdoctoral Fellowship: Candidates must hold a recent Ph.D., M.D., D.D.S., D.V.M. or equivalent.

GEOGRAPHIC RESTRICTIONS:
Canada.

FINANCIAL DATA:
Amount of support per award: Graduate Fellowship: $21,000 per annum (CIHR guidelines); Postdoctoral Fellowship: $40,000 per annum (CIHR guidelines).
Total amount of support: Graduate Fellowship: Approximately $300,000; Postdoctoral Fellowship: Approximately $200,000.

NUMBER OF APPLICANTS MOST RECENT YEAR:
15 Graduate Fellowship and 8 Postdoctoral Fellowship for the year 2012.

NUMBER OF AWARDS: 8 Graduate Fellowships and 4 Postdoctoral Fellowships for the year 2012.

APPLICATION INFORMATION:
Candidates are required to submit application form GFP-01 for Graduate Fellowship or RD40 for Postdoctoral Fellowship.
Duration: Two years. Renewal to maximum of four years for Graduate Fellowship and three years for Postdoctoral Fellowship.
Deadline: Graduate Fellowship Program: May 17 and November 15; Postdoctoral Fellowship: July 2.

ADDRESS INQUIRIES TO:
Cilla Perry
Manager, Research and Development
(See address above.)

*SPECIAL STIPULATIONS:
Awards must be held in Canada.

CANADIAN INSTITUTES OF HEALTH RESEARCH (CIHR)   [2246]

160 Elgin Street, 9th Floor
Address Locator 4809A
Ottawa ON K1A 0W9 Canada
(613) 954-1968
(888) 603-4178 (press 1)
Fax: (613) 954-1800

E-MAIL ADDRESS:
info@cihr-irsc.gc.ca

WEB SITE ADDRESS:
www.cihr-irsc.gc.ca

FOUNDED: 2000

AREAS OF INTEREST:
Basic, applied and clinical research in
Canada in the health sciences.

NAME(S) OF PROGRAMS:
● **Canada Graduate Scholarships
Master's Awards**

TYPE:
Awards/prizes; Scholarships. Intended to
provide special recognition and support to
students who are pursuing a Master's degree
in a health-related field in Canada. These
candidates are expected to have an
exceptionally high potential for future
research achievement and productivity.

YEAR PROGRAM STARTED: 2003

PURPOSE:
To help ensure a reliable supply of highly
qualified personnel to meet the needs of
Canada's knowledge economy.

LEGAL BASIS:
Government agency.

ELIGIBILITY:
The program is open to Canadian citizens
and permanent residents. At the time of the
CIHR deadline for application, candidates
must have completed or be in the last year of
a Bachelor's degree or have been registered
for no more than 10 months as a full-time
student in a Master's program. Only those
students engaged in full-time Master's
programs in which research is a major
component are eligible for support. Awards
will take effect only after the recipient has
registered in a full-time Master's program.

Persons with a health professional degree
who seek support for Master's research
training are eligible to apply, but should also
consult the guidelines for the CIHR
Fellowships program. Those eligible for both
have the option of applying to either program
but not to both in the same year (i.e.,
September through August).

GEOGRAPHIC RESTRICTIONS:
Canada.

FINANCIAL DATA:
Amount of support per award: $17,500
(CAN).
Total amount of support: Varies.

APPLICATION INFORMATION:
Contact the Institutes.
Duration: One year. Nonrenewable.
Deadline: February 1.

ADDRESS INQUIRIES TO:
Joane Delage, Program Coordinator
(See address above.)

*SPECIAL STIPULATIONS:
Awards must be taken up between July 1 and
October 1 following the offer of award and
must commence at the beginning of the
semesters, September 1 and January 1.

CANADIAN INSTITUTES OF
HEALTH RESEARCH
(CIHR)   [2247]
160 Elgin Street, 9th Floor
Address Locator 4809A
Ottawa ON K1A 0W9 Canada
(613) 952-0763
Fax: (613) 954-1800

E-MAIL ADDRESS:
info@cihr-irsc.gc.ca

WEB SITE ADDRESS:
www.cihr-irsc.gc.ca

FOUNDED: 1969

AREAS OF INTEREST:
Basic, applied and clinical research in
Canada in the health sciences.

NAME(S) OF PROGRAMS:
● **Frederick Banting and Charles Best
Canada Graduate Scholarship-Doctoral
Awards**

TYPE:
Scholarships.

PURPOSE:
To provide special recognition and support to
students who are pursuing a doctoral degree
in a health-related field in Canada.

ELIGIBILITY:
The program is open to Canadian citizens
and permanent residents of Canada. Only
those students engaged in full-time research
training in a Canadian graduate school are
eligible for support.

GEOGRAPHIC RESTRICTIONS:
Canada.

FINANCIAL DATA:
Amount of support per award: $30,000
(CAN) annual stipend, plus an annual
research allowance of $5,000.
Total amount of support: Varies.

NUMBER OF APPLICANTS MOST RECENT YEAR:
1,365.

NUMBER OF AWARDS: 180.

APPLICATION INFORMATION:
Application information is available on the
web site.
Duration: Three years.
Deadline: October 15.

ADDRESS INQUIRIES TO:
Deputy Director
Doctoral Research Awards
(See address above.)

CANADIAN INSTITUTES OF
HEALTH RESEARCH
(CIHR)   [2248]
160 Elgin Street, 9th Floor
Address Locator 4809A
Ottawa ON K1A 0W9 Canada
(613) 952-0763
Fax: (613) 954-1800

E-MAIL ADDRESS:
info@cihr-irsc.gc.ca

WEB SITE ADDRESS:
www.cihr-irsc.gc.ca

FOUNDED: 1969

AREAS OF INTEREST:
Basic, applied and clinical research in
Canada in the health sciences.

NAME(S) OF PROGRAMS:
● **Doctoral Research Award**

TYPE:
Awards/prizes; Training grants. The program
aims to attract and retain world-class doctoral
students by supporting students who
demonstrate a high standard of scholarly
achievement in graduate studies in the social
sciences and humanities, natural sciences and
engineering, and health, as well as leadership
skills.

YEAR PROGRAM STARTED: 1997

PURPOSE:
To support promising doctoral students.

LEGAL BASIS:
Government agency.

ELIGIBILITY:
Canadian citizens, permanent residents and
international students.

GEOGRAPHIC RESTRICTIONS:
Canada.

FINANCIAL DATA:
Amount of support per award: $50,000
(CAN) per year.

COOPERATIVE FUNDING PROGRAMS: Natural
Sciences and Engineering Research Council
of Canada; Social Sciences and Humanities
Research Council of Canada.

NUMBER OF APPLICANTS MOST RECENT YEAR:
Approximately 166 annually.

NUMBER OF AWARDS: 55 to 56.

APPLICATION INFORMATION:
The university must provide a nomination
letter for each student it wishes to nominate.
The letter must provide a high-level rationale
for the nomination, explaining why the
university is nominating the student for the
award, and how the institution will support
the nominee in the development of his or her
potential.
Duration: Three years maximum.
Nonrenewable.
Deadline: Typically October.

ADDRESS INQUIRIES TO:
Deputy Director
Doctoral Research Awards
(See address above.)

*SPECIAL STIPULATIONS:
Awards must be taken up within 12 months
of the date of offer.

CANADIAN INSTITUTES OF
HEALTH RESEARCH
(CIHR)   [2249]
160 Elgin Street, 9th Floor
Address Locator 4809A
Ottawa ON K1A 0W9 Canada
(613) 954-1968
Fax: (613) 954-1800

E-MAIL ADDRESS:
fellowships@cihr-irsc.gc.ca

WEB SITE ADDRESS:
www.cihr-irsc.gc.ca

FOUNDED: 1969

AREAS OF INTEREST:
Health research sciences.

NAME(S) OF PROGRAMS:
● **Fellowship Program**

TYPE:
Fellowships. Postdoctoral fellowships.

YEAR PROGRAM STARTED: 1969

PURPOSE:
To provide support for highly qualified
candidates to add to their experience by
engaging in research either in Canada or
abroad.

LEGAL BASIS:
Government agency.

ELIGIBILITY:
A candidate must hold, or be completing, a Ph.D. or a health professional degree (or equivalent). The health professional degree must be in a regulated health profession such as medicine, dentistry, pharmacy, optometry, veterinary medicine, chiropractic, nursing or rehabilitative science.

For those with a Ph.D. degree (or equivalent), or a Ph.D. and health professional degree, the maximum period of support is three years, and candidates will only be eligible for support until the end of their fifth year of post-Ph.D. training.

For individuals that do not hold a health professional degree, awards will take effect only after the recipient has completed all requirements of the Ph.D. program, including the oral examination.

Candidates with more than three years of post-Ph.D. research training by the competition deadline are not eligible to apply. Any interruption in a candidate's post-Ph.D. research training will be taken into account in determining eligibility.

An applicant may not hold more than three years of federal award funding (e.g., SSHRC, NSERC, CIHR) to undertake postdoctoral studies. Recipients already holding a postdoctoral award from a federal source for a term of three years are not eligible to apply.

Individuals wishing to undertake post-Ph.D. research training in the same research environment (e.g., same department, supervisor or co-supervisor) in which they received their Ph.D. are not eligible for an award.

Candidates with a health professional degree may propose a program of research leading to a Master's or Ph.D. degree; however, registration in a graduate program is not a requirement.

FINANCIAL DATA:
Amount of support per award: $21,000 to $55,000 (CAN) per year, plus $5,000 research allowance per year.
Total amount of support: Varies.

NUMBER OF APPLICANTS MOST RECENT YEAR: 1,200 for the year 2011-12.

NUMBER OF AWARDS: 170 for the year 2011-12.

APPLICATION INFORMATION:
Guidelines will be made available to the public in July.
Duration: One to five years, depending on degree held.
Deadline: October.

PUBLICATIONS:
Annual Report of the President; Grants and Awards Guide.

STAFF:
Joane Delage

ADDRESS INQUIRIES TO:
Joane Delage
Program Coordinator
(See address above.)

CANADIAN LIVER FOUNDATION

3100 Steeles Avenue East
Suite 801
Markham ON L3R 8T3 Canada
(416) 491-3353
(800) 563-5483
Fax: (905) 752-1540

E-MAIL ADDRESS:
clf@liver.ca

WEB SITE ADDRESS:
www.liver.ca

TYPE:
Research grants.

See entry 2410 for full listing.

CANADIAN LIVER FOUNDATION   [2250]

3100 Steeles Avenue East
Suite 801
Markham ON L3R 8T3 Canada
(416) 491-3353
(800) 563-5483
Fax: (905) 752-1540

E-MAIL ADDRESS:
clf@liver.ca

WEB SITE ADDRESS:
www.liver.ca

FOUNDED: 1969

AREAS OF INTEREST:
Research and education into the causes, diagnosis, prevention and treatment of diseases of the liver.

NAME(S) OF PROGRAMS:
● **Canadian Liver Foundation Graduate Studentships**

TYPE:
Scholarships.

PURPOSE:
To enable academically superior students to undertake full-time studies in a Canadian university in a discipline relevant to the Foundation's objectives.

LEGAL BASIS:
Registered Canadian charity.

ELIGIBILITY:
Candidates must be accepted into a full-time university graduate science program in a medically related discipline related to a Master's or doctoral degree and hold a record of superior academic performance in studies relevant to the proposed training.

Candidates must be sponsored by a faculty supervisor with a record of productive medical research and sufficient, competitively acquired research funding to ensure the satisfactory conduct of the student's research during the term of the award.

GEOGRAPHIC RESTRICTIONS:
Canada.

FINANCIAL DATA:
Amount of support per award: $20,000 (CAN) per year.

NUMBER OF APPLICANTS MOST RECENT YEAR: 11 for the year 2012.

NUMBER OF AWARDS: 3 for the year 2012.

APPLICATION INFORMATION:
Contact the Foundation.
Duration: Two academic years. Nonrenewable. Upon approval, transfer from an M.Sc. programme to a Ph.D. programme will permit the student to renew for the total of four years of support.
Deadline: March 31, for awards to become tenable the following September 1.

PUBLICATIONS:
Program description and guidelines.

STAFF:
Billie Potkonjak, Research Grants Administrator

ADDRESS INQUIRIES TO:
Billie Potkonjak
Research Grants Administrator
(See address above.)

CANADIAN LIVER FOUNDATION   [2251]

3100 Steeles Avenue East
Suite 801
Markham ON L3R 8T3 Canada
(416) 491-3353
(800) 563-5483
Fax: (905) 752-1540

E-MAIL ADDRESS:
clf@liver.ca

WEB SITE ADDRESS:
www.liver.ca

FOUNDED: 1969

AREAS OF INTEREST:
Research and education into the causes, diagnosis, prevention and treatment of diseases of the liver.

NAME(S) OF PROGRAMS:
● **Summer Studentships**

TYPE:
Scholarships.

PURPOSE:
To provide an opportunity for a limited number of well-motivated students with records of strong academic performance to participate in liver-related research in Canada.

LEGAL BASIS:
Registered Canadian charity.

ELIGIBILITY:
Applicants must be registered at a Canadian institution in an undergraduate degree program.

GEOGRAPHIC RESTRICTIONS:
Canada.

FINANCIAL DATA:
Amount of support per award: $4,000 (CAN) for any three summer months (May through August).

NUMBER OF APPLICANTS MOST RECENT YEAR: 6 for the year 2012.

NUMBER OF AWARDS: 2 for the year 2012.

APPLICATION INFORMATION:
Guidelines and application forms are available in hospitals and universities through the office of Research Administration, on the Foundation web site, or from the address above.
Duration: Each award will be for any three summer months (May to August).
Deadline: March 31.

PUBLICATIONS:
Program description and guidelines.

STAFF:
Billie Potkonjak, Research Grants Administrator

ADDRESS INQUIRIES TO:
Billie Potkonjak
Research Grants Administrator
(See address above.)

CANADIAN SOCIETY FOR MEDICAL LABORATORY SCIENCE [2252]

33 Wellington Street North
Hamilton ON L8R 1M7 Canada
(905) 528-8642
Fax: (905) 528-4968

E-MAIL ADDRESS:
memserv@csmls.org

WEB SITE ADDRESS:
www.csmls.org

FOUNDED: 1937

AREAS OF INTEREST:
Continuing education and medical research.

TYPE:
Scholarships. Available to students involved in the clinical phase of their medical lab technology training program. Students must be enrolled in general medical laboratory technology, cytotechnology, or clinical genetics studies leading to CSMLS certification.

YEAR PROGRAM STARTED: 1937

ELIGIBILITY:
Applicants must be enrolled with the CSMLS as a student member and be a Canadian citizen or permanent resident.

GEOGRAPHIC RESTRICTIONS:
Canada.

FINANCIAL DATA:
Amount of support per award: $500 (CAN).
Total amount of support: $2,000 (CAN).

COOPERATIVE FUNDING PROGRAMS: Program is made possible by the generous support of Ortho-Clinical Diagnostics, BD Biosciences and Cowan Insurance Brokers.

NUMBER OF APPLICANTS MOST RECENT YEAR: 2.

NUMBER OF AWARDS: 2.

APPLICATION INFORMATION:
Contact the Society.
Duration: Varies depending on award. Generally nonrenewable.
Deadline: October 1.

ADDRESS INQUIRIES TO:
Katherine Coles, Executive Assistant
(See e-mail address above.)

*SPECIAL STIPULATIONS:
Must be a student enrolled in an accredited training program in Canada.

CHINESE AMERICAN MEDICAL SOCIETY [2253]

41 Elizabeth Street
Suite 600
New York, NY 10013
(212) 334-4760
Fax: (646) 304-6373

E-MAIL ADDRESS:
jlove@camsociety.org

WEB SITE ADDRESS:
www.camsociety.org

FOUNDED: 1963

AREAS OF INTEREST:
Medicine.

NAME(S) OF PROGRAMS:
- **CAMS Scholarship Program**
- **Medical Student Summer Research Fellowship**

TYPE:
Fellowships; Scholarships.

YEAR PROGRAM STARTED: 1973

PURPOSE:
To promote the scientific association of medical professionals of Chinese descent; to advance medical knowledge and scientific research with emphasis on aspects unique to the Chinese; to establish scholarships to medical and dental students and to provide endowments to medical schools and hospitals of good standing; to promote the health status of Chinese Americans.

LEGAL BASIS:
A nonprofit, charitable, educational, and scientific society.

ELIGIBILITY:
Candidates must currently be in their first, second or third year of medical or dental school in a U.S.-accredited medical or dental school when applying. Candidates must reside in the U.S. at the time of application either as an alien student or citizen of the U.S. Students who have just been accepted into medical or dental school at the time of application are not eligible.

FINANCIAL DATA:
Amount of support per award: Scholarships: $1,500 to $2,000; Research Fellowships: $3,200 to $4,000.
Total amount of support: $10,000 to $15,000.

NUMBER OF AWARDS: Scholarships: 4 to 6; Research Fellowships: Up to 3.

APPLICATION INFORMATION:
Contact the Society.
Duration: One-time award.
Deadline: April 30.

STAFF:
Ms. Jamie Love, Administrator

ADDRESS INQUIRIES TO:
Warren W. Chin, M.D.
Executive Director
(See address above.)

COLLEGE OF PHYSICIANS OF PHILADELPHIA

Francis Clark Wood Institute
for the History of Medicine
19 South 22nd Street
Philadelphia, PA 19103-3097
(215) 399-2305
Fax: (215) 561-6477

E-MAIL ADDRESS:
ssereda@collegeofphysicians.org

WEB SITE ADDRESS:
www.collegeofphysicians.org

TYPE:
Travel grants; Visiting scholars. This program allows scholars to conduct short-term research in the College's Library and/or Mutter Museum.

See entry 586 for full listing.

CUREPSP FOUNDATION FOR PSP/CBD AND RELATED BRAIN DISEASES

30 East Padonia Road
Suite 201
Timonium, MD 21093
(410) 785-7004
Fax: (410) 785-7009

E-MAIL ADDRESS:
bantum@curepsp.org

WEB SITE ADDRESS:
www.curepsp.org

TYPE:
Research grants.

See entry 2460 for full listing.

THE DANA FOUNDATION [2254]

505 Fifth Avenue, Sixth Floor
New York, NY 10017
(212) 223-4040
Fax: (212) 317-8721

E-MAIL ADDRESS:
amarin@dana.org

WEB SITE ADDRESS:
www.dana.org

FOUNDED: 1950

AREAS OF INTEREST:
Science, health and education, with a current focus on neuroscience research.

NAME(S) OF PROGRAMS:
- **Clinical Neuroscience Research**
- **David Mahoney Neuro-Imaging Program**

TYPE:
Awards/prizes; Challenge/matching grants; Project/program grants; Research grants. For the decade of the 1990s, the Foundation focused on brain research. Grants in these areas are made principally through competitive Clinical Hypotheses Programs in immuno-imaging, neuroimaging and brain-cardiovascular system interactions. These competitive grants programs support pilot testing of experimental and innovative ideas that in immunology and neuroscience research have the potential of advancing clinical applications. The Foundation also supports an invitational program in which leading scientists are invited to compete for research grants designed to improve immune system responses to biological agents.

The Foundation has supported advances in education throughout its history. Its current interest is focused primarily on professional development programs that foster improved teaching of the performing arts in public schools. Programs emphasize innovative training projects that are exported from, or imported to, New York City, Washington, DC, Los Angeles and their surrounding areas. Letters of intent are accepted on a rolling basis. Grantees are selected through a competitive process.

YEAR PROGRAM STARTED: 1950

PURPOSE:
To strengthen and improve the quality of science, health and education.

LEGAL BASIS:
Private, independent philanthropic foundation.

ELIGIBILITY:
The Foundation, in general, makes its grants in accordance with the following policies: (1) it supports programs in science, health and education; carefully defined objectives in each field guide its grantmaking; (2) in many cases, it requires grantee institutions to share the cost of a project or raise matching funds; (3) it makes no grants directly to individuals; (4) it does not support annual operating budgets of organizations, deficit reduction, capital campaigns or individual sabbaticals

and;
(5) it does not schedule meetings with applicants, other than by specific invitation initiated by the Foundation.

GEOGRAPHIC RESTRICTIONS:
United States.

FINANCIAL DATA:
Amount of support per award: $200,000 to $300,000.
Total amount of support: Varies by program.
Matching fund requirements: Most awards for matching grants require grant recipients to raise a significant portion of the financing necessary for the proposed project.

NUMBER OF APPLICANTS MOST RECENT YEAR:
500.

NUMBER OF AWARDS: Varies.

APPLICATION INFORMATION:
Requests for Proposals (RFPs) for the Clinical Neuroscience Research Program are sent to the deans of all U.S. medical schools and other invited institutions.

Inquiries for grant support should be in the form of a two-page letter describing:
(1) goal(s) of the project;
(2) need the project would meet and its fit with the Foundation's priorities in health or education;
(3) means to be used to achieve the project's goal(s);
(4) capabilities of the institution to undertake the project and the qualifications of the project's proposed director and;
(5) estimated cost and proposed methods of financing the project, including the institution's intended contribution.

Letters of inquiry should be mailed to the Foundation. No proposals submitted by fax will be accepted. If the Foundation determines that an inquiry fits its interests, a full proposal will be requested. Supporting materials should not be submitted until requested. A full proposal should be accompanied by documents establishing the applicant's Internal Revenue Code 501(c)(3) tax-exempt status.
Duration: Up to three years. Renewals are rare.
Deadline: Varies.

PUBLICATIONS:
Annual report; *Dana Report,* newsletter; application guidelines.

IRS IDENTIFICATION NUMBER: 06-6036761

BOARD OF DIRECTORS:
Edward F. Rover, Chairman
Clark M. Whittemore, Jr., Secretary and Treasurer
Edward Bleier
Wallace L. Cook
Charles A. Dana, III
Steven E. Hyman, M.D.
LaSalle D. Leffall, Jr., M.D.
Hildegarde E. Mahoney
Ann McLaughlin-Korologos
Herbert J. Siegel

ADMINISTRATION:
Edward F. Rover, President
Jane Nevins, Vice President
Barbara E. Gill, Vice President, Communications
Burton M. Mirsky, Vice President, Finance

ADDRESS INQUIRIES TO:
Angie Marin, Grant Officer
(See address above.)

DERMATOLOGY FOUNDATION   [2255]
1560 Sherman Avenue
Suite 870
Evanston, IL 60201-4808
(847) 328-2256
Fax: (847) 328-0509

E-MAIL ADDRESS:
dfgen@dermatologyfoundation.org

WEB SITE ADDRESS:
www.dermatologyfoundation.org

FOUNDED: 1964

AREAS OF INTEREST:
Cancer and other diseases of the skin, hair and nails.

TYPE:
Fellowships; Project/program grants; Research grants. Research funding in the form of career development grants, fellowships, project/program grants and research grants for academic investigators in the early stages of their careers.

There are 12 research award categories. Career development awards include Physician Scientist, Dermatologic Surgery, Health Care Policy, Medical Dermatology, Psoriasis, Science of Human Appearance and Women's Health Issues. Dermatologist Investigator and Pediatric Dermatology Fellowships. Various Patient-Directed and Research Grants available.

YEAR PROGRAM STARTED: 1964

PURPOSE:
To advance the research careers of young individuals in dermatology and cutaneous biology, with the emphasis on research benefiting the dermatology community at large.

LEGAL BASIS:
Nonprofit charitable organization.

GEOGRAPHIC RESTRICTIONS:
United States.

FINANCIAL DATA:
Amount of support per award: Career development awards: Average $55,000; Fellowships: Average $30,000 to $45,000; Grants: Average $20,000.
Total amount of support: $3,100,000 in research funding for the year 2013.

NUMBER OF AWARDS: 67.

APPLICATION INFORMATION:
Forms are available only on the Foundation web site.
Duration: One year. Renewal possibilities vary.
Deadline: October 15. Announcement midwinter at the annual meeting of the American Academy of Dermatology.

PUBLICATIONS:
Annual report; *Dermatology Focus,* scientific publication.

IRS IDENTIFICATION NUMBER: 04-6115524

OFFICERS:
Bruce U. Wintroub, M.D., Chairman, Board of Trustees
Richard L. Edelson, M.D., President
Michael D. Tharp, M.D., Vice President
Stuart R. Lessin, M.D., Secretary/Treasurer

ADDRESS INQUIRIES TO:
Sandra R. Benz, Executive Director
(See address above.)

EDWIN H. EDDY FAMILY FOUNDATION   [2256]
Wells Fargo Bank Minnesota
222 West Superior Street
Duluth, MN 55802
(218) 723-2615
Fax: (218) 722-9158

AREAS OF INTEREST:
Communicative disorders, research, rehabilitation and treatment.

TYPE:
Matching gifts; Project/program grants; Research grants; Scholarships; Technical assistance.

PURPOSE:
To promote medical research and rehabilitative medicine in the city of Duluth, MN, and the surrounding area.

LEGAL BASIS:
Private foundation.

ELIGIBILITY:
Grants are not made to individuals. A qualifying organization must have 501(c)(3) not-for-profit status.

Scholarships are provided for students in an accredited graduate program of communication disorders at University of Minnesota, Duluth. Applicants for scholarships must be citizens or residents of the U.S. The award will be strictly scholarship and not traineeship. Only full-time students qualify. Applicants must meet a minimum overall grade point average (currently 3.3) to qualify for a scholarship.

GEOGRAPHIC RESTRICTIONS:
Duluth, Minnesota and the surrounding area.

FINANCIAL DATA:
Amount of support per award: Scholarships: $1,000 to graduate-level students for each of five semesters for first-year graduate students and three semesters for second-year graduate students.
Total amount of support: Approximately $25,000 annually.

NUMBER OF AWARDS: 5 annually.

APPLICATION INFORMATION:
Grant applicant organization must request guidelines, then submit a proposal which includes the IRS 501(c)(3) letter of determination.

Scholarship applicants must provide the Foundation a completed application form and a certified copy of the most recent transcript from present or previous institution attended.
Duration: Scholarships: Per semester. Renewable.

TRUSTEE:
Karl Wasson, Trustee

ADDRESS INQUIRIES TO:
Karl Wasson, Trustee
Edwin H. Eddy Family Foundation
(See address above.)

EMERGENCY MEDICINE FOUNDATION   [2257]
1125 Executive Circle
Irving, TX 75038-2522
(800) 798-1822 ext. 3217
Fax: (972) 580-2816

E-MAIL ADDRESS:
info@emfoundation.org

WEB SITE ADDRESS:
www.emfoundation.org

FOUNDED: 1972

AREAS OF INTEREST:
Emergency medicine research.

TYPE:
Research grants; Technical assistance.
Policy-based research awards in emergency
medicine.

YEAR PROGRAM STARTED: 1972

PURPOSE:
To promote education and research in
emergency medicine.

ELIGIBILITY:
Must be an emergency medicine researcher.

GEOGRAPHIC RESTRICTIONS:
United States.

FINANCIAL DATA:
Amount of support per award: $2,400 to
$150,000.
Total amount of support: Varies.

NUMBER OF APPLICANTS MOST RECENT YEAR:
75.

NUMBER OF AWARDS: 13.

APPLICATION INFORMATION:
Contact the Foundation.
Duration: One year.
Deadline: Varies.

IRS IDENTIFICATION NUMBER: 75-2331221

STAFF:
Cathey Wise, Director

ADDRESS INQUIRIES TO:
Cynthia Singh, Director of
Grant and Foundation Development
(See address above.)

FOUNDATION FOR ANESTHESIA EDUCATION AND RESEARCH [2258]
200 First Street, S.W., WF6-674
Rochester, MN 55905
(507) 538-7884
Fax: (507) 284-0291

E-MAIL ADDRESS:
jody.clikeman@faer.org

WEB SITE ADDRESS:
www.faer.org

AREAS OF INTEREST:
Anesthesiology, critical care, pain, and all
areas of perioperative medicine.

NAME(S) OF PROGRAMS:
● **FAER Health Services Research Grant**
● **FAER Mentored Research Training Grant**
● **FAER Research Education Grant**
● **FAER Research Fellowship Grant**

TYPE:
Fellowships; Research grants; Training
grants. These grants are designed to create
opportunities for physicians to excel in an
exceedingly competitive environment and to
eventually acquire NIH funding.

PURPOSE:
To provide research grant funding for
promising investigators to train in clinical,
basic science and translational anesthesiology
research.

ELIGIBILITY:
FAER Mentored Research Training Grant:
Applicants must be instructors or assistant
professors who are within 10 years of their
initial appointment.

FAER Research Education Grant: Open to
anesthesiology residents or faculty.

FAER Research Fellowship Grant: Open to
anesthesiology residents after CA-1 training
and six months of clinical scientist track.

A 20-member committee consisting of both
clinical and basic science anesthesiologists
reviews proposals. Clinical and outcomes
projects are encouraged.

GEOGRAPHIC RESTRICTIONS:
United States.

FINANCIAL DATA:
Amount of support per award: $50,000 to
$175,000.
Total amount of support: $2,000,000
annually.

NUMBER OF APPLICANTS MOST RECENT YEAR:
57.

NUMBER OF AWARDS: 17.

APPLICATION INFORMATION:
Contact the Foundation.
Deadline: February 15.

IRS IDENTIFICATION NUMBER: 52-1494164

ADDRESS INQUIRIES TO:
Denham S. Ward, M.D., Ph.D., President
(See address above.)

THE FOUNDATION OF THE AMERICAN SOCIETY OF NEURORADIOLOGY [2259]
800 Enterprise Drive, Suite 205
Oak Brook, IL 60523
(630) 574-0220
Fax: (630) 574-0661

E-MAIL ADDRESS:
executive@asnr.org

WEB SITE ADDRESS:
foundation.asnr.org

FOUNDED: 1995

AREAS OF INTEREST:
Neuroradiology.

TYPE:
Research grants.

YEAR PROGRAM STARTED: 1962

PURPOSE:
To disseminate scientific and educational
information about neuroradiology.

ELIGIBILITY:
Applicant must be a member of the
American Society of Neuroradiology.

FINANCIAL DATA:
Amount of support per award: Up to
$60,000.

NUMBER OF AWARDS: 3 to 4.

APPLICATION INFORMATION:
Contact the Organization for application
procedures.
Duration: One year. Some renewals.
Deadline: October.

PUBLICATIONS:
American Journal of Neuroradiology.

STAFF:
Stephanie Walsh, Director of Development

ADDRESS INQUIRIES TO:
James B. Gantenberg, Executive Director
(See address above.)

THE MICHAEL J. FOX FOUNDATION FOR PARKINSON'S RESEARCH [2260]
Grand Central Station
P.O. Box 4777
New York, NY 10163-4777
(212) 509-0995
Fax: (212) 509-2390

E-MAIL ADDRESS:
research@michaeljfox.org

WEB SITE ADDRESS:
www.michaeljfox.org

FOUNDED: 2000

AREAS OF INTEREST:
Medical research and Parkinson's disease.

TYPE:
Conferences/seminars; Research grants.

YEAR PROGRAM STARTED: 2000

PURPOSE:
To find a cure for Parkinson's disease
through an aggressively funded research
agenda; to ensure the development of
improved therapies for those living with
Parkinson's today.

LEGAL BASIS:
501(c)(3).

ELIGIBILITY:
Varies depending on research program.

FINANCIAL DATA:
Amount of support per award: Varies.
Total amount of support: Varies.

APPLICATION INFORMATION:
The Foundation has implemented an
electronic grant submission and review
system that will enable research to be funded
quickly and efficiently. Applicants should
consult the Foundation web site for
information.
Duration: Varies.
Deadline: Varies.

PUBLICATIONS:
Accelerating the Cure, newsletter; *Fox Flash,*
e-newsletter; annual report; progress report.

IRS IDENTIFICATION NUMBER: 13-4141945

STAFF:
Deborah W. Brooks, Co-Founder and
Executive Vice Chairman
Todd Sherer, Ph.D., Chief Executive Officer
Alison Urkowitz, Vice President of Research
Operations
Brian Fiske, Vice President of Research
Programs
Mark Frasier, Vice President of Research
Programs

ADDRESS INQUIRIES TO:
Brian Fiske
Vice President of Research Programs
(See address above.)

THE PARKER B. FRANCIS FELLOWSHIP PROGRAM [2261]
8427 S.E. 35th Street
Mercer Island, WA 98040
(206) 462-9224

E-MAIL ADDRESS:
dsnapp@u.washington.edu

WEB SITE ADDRESS:
www.francisfellowships.org

FOUNDED: 1951

AREAS OF INTEREST:
Research related to lung biology, pulmonary disease and respiratory medicine.

TYPE:
Fellowships. Awarded for postdoctoral lung research and training.

YEAR PROGRAM STARTED: 1975

PURPOSE:
To enable qualified postdoctoral candidates to devote the major part of their professional effort in research related to pulmonary disease.

LEGAL BASIS:
Private foundation.

ELIGIBILITY:
M.D. or Ph.D. candidates may hold any relevant doctoral degree (e.g., M.D., Ph.D., Sc.D., D.V.M., D.P.H.) and an aptitude and proficiency in research. Candidates must be citizens of the U.S., Canada or Mexico, or have documentation towards securing citizenship.

GEOGRAPHIC RESTRICTIONS:
North America.

FINANCIAL DATA:
Funds to be used for stipends and fringe benefits, with up to $2,000 per year as a travel allowance.
Amount of support per award: $156,000.

NUMBER OF AWARDS: 15 to 18.

APPLICATION INFORMATION:
Contact the Program.
Duration: Three years.
Deadline: October of each year.

STAFF:
Deborah Snapp, Administrator

ADDRESS INQUIRIES TO:
Thomas R. Martin, M.D., Director
(See address above.)

*SPECIAL STIPULATIONS:
Only two applications will be accepted from a department per year. Support is provided for only three Fellows in a department at any one time.

FRAXA RESEARCH FOUNDATION   [2262]
10 Prince Place
Newburyport, MA 01950
(978) 462-1866

E-MAIL ADDRESS:
info@fraxa.org

WEB SITE ADDRESS:
www.fraxa.org

FOUNDED: 1994

AREAS OF INTEREST:
Medical research aimed at the treatment of Fragile X Syndrome.

NAME(S) OF PROGRAMS:
● **FRAXA Grants and Fellowships**

TYPE:
Fellowships; Research grants; Research contracts.

YEAR PROGRAM STARTED: 1994

PURPOSE:
To promote research aimed at finding a specific treatment for Fragile X Syndrome; to provide funds for postdoctoral fellowships and investigator-initiated grants.

FINANCIAL DATA:
Amount of support per award: Up to $45,000 per year for fellowships. No limit on grants.

NUMBER OF APPLICANTS MOST RECENT YEAR:
Approximately 40 for the year 2013.

NUMBER OF AWARDS: 25 for the year 2013.

APPLICATION INFORMATION:
Application form, plus a one-page initial inquiry letter.
Duration: One year. Renewable.
Deadline: February 1.

PUBLICATIONS:
Newsletter; e-mail updates.

IRS IDENTIFICATION NUMBER: 04-3222167

OFFICER:
Katherine Clapp, President

FRIENDS OF JOSE CARRERAS INTERNATIONAL LEUKEMIA FOUNDATION   [2263]
1100 Fairview Avenue North
Suite D5-100
P.O. Box 19024
Seattle, WA 98109-1024
(206) 667-7108
Fax: (206) 667-6124

E-MAIL ADDRESS:
friendsjc@carreras-foundation.org

WEB SITE ADDRESS:
www.carreras-foundation.org

FOUNDED: 1990

AREAS OF INTEREST:
Leukemia and related hematologic diseases research.

NAME(S) OF PROGRAMS:
● **Research Fellowships**

TYPE:
Fellowships.

YEAR PROGRAM STARTED: 1990

PURPOSE:
To cure leukemia and allied diseases by providing funding for medical research to young investigators.

LEGAL BASIS:
501(c)(3).

ELIGIBILITY:
Candidates must hold an M.D. or Ph.D. degree and have completed at least three years postdoctoral training, but must be less than 10 years past their first doctoral degree when the award begins. There are no restrictions based on nationality, but only one application will be considered from each sponsoring institution. Candidates must be committed to the research goals of the Foundation, must be able to devote at least 60% of their time to the project and must have a sponsoring institution with the academic environment to provide adequate support for the proposed project.

FINANCIAL DATA:
Amount of support per award: $50,000 per year.

NUMBER OF AWARDS: 1 annually.

APPLICATION INFORMATION:
All applications must be typed, single-spaced, in English and must follow the format specified in the application packet. All forms must be completed and space restrictions adhered to. Request for application forms will not be considered after October 15. Application forms will not be sent by fax. Do not contact the Foundation for results. Reapplication by unsuccessful candidates will be necessary for the following year.
Duration: Three years.
Deadline: Early November. Announcement in January.

ADDRESS INQUIRIES TO:
Karen Carbonneau, Administrator
(See address or e-mail above.)

FSH SOCIETY, INC.   [2264]
64 Grove Street
BBRI Room 353
Watertown, MA 02472
(617) 658-7878
Fax: (617) 658-7879

E-MAIL ADDRESS:
june.kinoshita@fshsociety.org

WEB SITE ADDRESS:
www.fshsociety.org

FOUNDED: 1991

AREAS OF INTEREST:
Facioscapulohumeral Muscular Dystrophy.

TYPE:
Conferences/seminars; Fellowships; Project/program grants; Research grants; Seed money grants; Travel grants.

YEAR PROGRAM STARTED: 1998

PURPOSE:
To promote research on and disperse information on Facioscapulohumeral Muscular Dystrophy.

LEGAL BASIS:
501(c)(3) organization.

ELIGIBILITY:
Applications may be submitted by domestic or foreign for-profit and nonprofit organizations, public and private, such as universities, colleges, hospitals, laboratories, units of state and local governments, and eligible agencies of the federal government.

FINANCIAL DATA:
Total amount of support: $30,000 to $45,000 per year.

NUMBER OF APPLICANTS MOST RECENT YEAR:
9.

NUMBER OF AWARDS: 5.

APPLICATION INFORMATION:
Contact the Society.
Duration: One year.
Deadline: February 1 and August 1.

PUBLICATIONS:
FSH Watch Newsletter; patient information on FSHD (English and Spanish).

IRS IDENTIFICATION NUMBER: 52-1762747

STAFF:
Daniel Paul Perez, President
June Kinoshita, Executive Director

ADDRESS INQUIRIES TO:
June Kinoshita, Executive Director
(See address above.)

GLAUCOMA RESEARCH FOUNDATION

251 Post Street, Suite 600
San Francisco, CA 94108
(415) 986-3162
Fax: (415) 986-3763

E-MAIL ADDRESS:
research@glaucoma.org

WEB SITE ADDRESS:
www.glaucoma.org

TYPE:
Project/program grants; Research grants.

See entry 2514 for full listing.

THE GRAYSON-JOCKEY CLUB RESEARCH FOUNDATION [2265]

821 Corporate Drive
Lexington, KY 40503
(859) 224-2850
Fax: (859) 224-2853

E-MAIL ADDRESS:
ebowen@jockeyclub.com

WEB SITE ADDRESS:
www.grayson-jockeyclub.org

FOUNDED: 1940

AREAS OF INTEREST:
Race horses, veterinary medicine and research for all horses.

TYPE:
Research grants. Supports equine medical research.

PURPOSE:
To promote research in veterinary medicine and in the breeding, raising and handling of horses.

LEGAL BASIS:
Nonprofit foundation.

ELIGIBILITY:
The principal investigator should have some professional rank and salary from the institution involved, or hold some grade of Research Professorship with salary from the institution. Research interest must be relevant to the equine, particularly in regard to, but not limited to, cardiopulmonary disorders, infectious diseases, musculoskeletal disorders, and reproduction.

FINANCIAL DATA:
Amount of support per award: Average $50,000.
Total amount of support: Approximately $1,000,000 annually.

NUMBER OF APPLICANTS MOST RECENT YEAR: 60.

NUMBER OF AWARDS: 15.

APPLICATION INFORMATION:
The Foundation will only accept the online application. See web site for complete information.
Duration: One or two years.
Deadline: October 1. Announcement April 1.

PUBLICATIONS:
Application; guidelines; *Research Today*, newsletter.

OFFICERS:
Dell Hancock, Chairman
A. Gary Lavin, D.V.M., Vice Chairman
Edward L. Bowen, President
Nancy C. Kelly, Vice President of Development/Secretary
Laura Barillaro, Treasurer

ADDRESS INQUIRIES TO:
Edward L. Bowen, President
(See address above.)

HEALTH RESOURCES AND SERVICES ADMINISTRATION [2266]

Primary Care Medical Education Branch
Division of Medicine and Dentistry
5600 Fishers Lane, Room 9A-27
Rockville, MD 20857
(301) 443-6190
Fax: (301) 443-1945

WEB SITE ADDRESS:
bhpr.hrsa.gov/grants/default.htm

TYPE:
Residencies; Training grants. Grants to assist in meeting the cost of planning, developing, operating or participating in approved graduate training programs in the field of medicine. The program assists residency programs in the promotion of physicians who are trained for and will enter the practice of medicine.

YEAR PROGRAM STARTED: 1972

PURPOSE:
To improve and expand access to quality health care for all.

LEGAL BASIS:
Section 747(a) of the PHS Act, as amended by the Health Professions Education Extension Amendments of 1992, Public Law 102-408.

ELIGIBILITY:
Hospitals, accredited schools of medicine and osteopathy and/or public or private nonprofit entities providing health or educational programs are eligible.

GEOGRAPHIC RESTRICTIONS:
United States.

FINANCIAL DATA:
Grants may include support for the program only or support of both the program and trainees who plan to specialize or work in the practice of family medicine.

NUMBER OF AWARDS: Varies.

APPLICATION INFORMATION:
Applicants are required to apply for this funding opportunity electronically through www.grants.gov.

All applications are competitively reviewed and evaluated.
Duration: One to three years. Renewal permitted.

HEALTHY MINDS CANADA [2267]

2 Toronto Street
5th Floor
Toronto ON M5C 2B6 Canada
(416) 351-7757
Fax: (416) 351-7765

E-MAIL ADDRESS:
admin@healthymindscanada.ca

WEB SITE ADDRESS:
www.healthymindscanada.ca

FOUNDED: 1980

AREAS OF INTEREST:
Biomedical research targeted in psychiatric disorders and addiction in Canada.

NAME(S) OF PROGRAMS:
- **HMC Partnership Awards - Children's Mental Health**
- **Open Minds Across Canada**
- **Youth Summit**

TYPE:
Awards/prizes; Conferences/seminars; Project/program grants; Research grants.

YEAR PROGRAM STARTED: 2012

PURPOSE:
To promote meritorious research into the neurobiology of psychiatric disorders and addictions, schizophrenia mood disorders, anxiety disorders (e.g., posttraumatic stress disorder) and addiction and co-morbidity.

ELIGIBILITY:
Research grant applicants must have a primary academic appointment with a Canadian university or teaching hospital and have Canadian immigrant status. Fellowship is awarded to a CIHR-funded researcher (Ph.D./M.D. level) in children's mental health. Funding for events and conferences is restricted to registered Canadian charities.

GEOGRAPHIC RESTRICTIONS:
Canada.

FINANCIAL DATA:
Amount of support per award: Up to $5,000 per annum per research grant or event.

NUMBER OF AWARDS: 2.

APPLICATION INFORMATION:
Contact Healthy Minds Canada.
Duration: One year.
Deadline: Contact the Foundation for details.

ADDRESS INQUIRIES TO:
Grants Officer
(See address above.)

THE LARRY L. HILLBLOM FOUNDATION, INC. [2268]

755 Baywood Drive, Suite 180
Petaluma, CA 94954
(707) 762-6691
Fax: (707) 762-6694

E-MAIL ADDRESS:
som@llhf.org

WEB SITE ADDRESS:
www.llhf.org

AREAS OF INTEREST:
Medical research on diabetes mellitus and diseases associated with aging.

NAME(S) OF PROGRAMS:
- **Fellowship Research Grants**
- **Start-Up Research Grants**

TYPE:
Assistantships; Block grants; Endowments; Fellowships. Fellowship Research Grants are intended to enable qualified institutions to provide postdoctoral research fellowship training to qualified applicants in one of the two areas of stated interest to the Foundation.

Start-Up Research Grants are offered to qualified institutions to enable them to select and assist qualified researchers to initiate independent research careers.

YEAR PROGRAM STARTED: 2000

PURPOSE:
To provide philanthropic support exclusively for charitable, religious, scientific, literary and educational purposes.

ELIGIBILITY:
Eligible organizations must have 501(c)(3) status.

GEOGRAPHIC RESTRICTIONS:
Primarily, California.

FINANCIAL DATA:
Amount of support per award: Fellowship Grants: Up to $60,000 per year; Start-Up Grants: Up to $70,000 per year.
Total amount of support: Varies.

NUMBER OF APPLICANTS MOST RECENT YEAR:
Varies.

NUMBER OF AWARDS: Varies.

APPLICATION INFORMATION:
Contact the Foundation.
Duration: Up to three years.
Deadline: Early January. Notification by June.

HIMSS FOUNDATION   [2269]
33 West Monroe Street, Suite 1700
Chicago, IL 60603-5616
(312) 915-9277
(312) 664-4467
Fax: (312) 664-6143

E-MAIL ADDRESS:
scholarship@himss.org

WEB SITE ADDRESS:
www.himss.org

FOUNDED: 1961

AREAS OF INTEREST:
Health care information and management systems.

NAME(S) OF PROGRAMS:
● **HIMSS Foundation Scholarship Program**

TYPE:
Awards/prizes; Conferences/seminars; Fellowships; Internships; Research grants; Scholarships.

YEAR PROGRAM STARTED: 1986

PURPOSE:
To recognize students who have the potential to be future leaders in the health care information management systems industry.

ELIGIBILITY:
Applicant must be a student in an accredited degree-granting institution, a junior when the scholarship is awarded, and a student member of the Healthcare Information and Management Systems Society. Previous winners are not eligible, although the undergraduate winner is eligible if pursuing a graduate degree.

FINANCIAL DATA:
An all-expense-paid trip to the HIMSS annual conference is awarded in addition to grant.
Amount of support per award: $5,000.
Total amount of support: Varies.

NUMBER OF APPLICANTS MOST RECENT YEAR:
120.

NUMBER OF AWARDS: 11 for the year 2013.

APPLICATION INFORMATION:
See web site for complete information.
Duration: One year.
Deadline: Applications are accepted annually August 1 to October 15.

ADDRESS INQUIRIES TO:
Fritze Roberts
Program Manager, Professional Development
Tel: (312) 915-9233
(See address above.)

MAXIMILIAN E. & MARION O. HOFFMAN FOUNDATION, INC.   [2270]
970 Farmington Avenue, Suite 203
West Hartford, CT 06107
(860) 521-2949
Fax: (860) 561-5082

AREAS OF INTEREST:
Education, medicine and the arts.

TYPE:
Project/program grants.

PURPOSE:
To provide funding to 501(c)(3) nonprofits conducting projects in education, medicine, and the arts.

LEGAL BASIS:
Nonprofit private foundation.

ELIGIBILITY:
Applicants must be 501(c)(3). No grants to individuals.

GEOGRAPHIC RESTRICTIONS:
United States, with preference to Connecticut.

FINANCIAL DATA:
Amount of support per award: Varies depending on needs and nature of the request.

APPLICATION INFORMATION:
Submit Letter of Inquiry with copy of 501(c)(3).
Duration: One year. Some multiyear grants. Renewal possible by reapplication.
Deadline: The Board of Directors meets four to six times a year to consider requests.

PUBLICATIONS:
Application form.

ADDRESS INQUIRIES TO:
Marion Barrak, President
(See address above.)

HOWARD HUGHES MEDICAL INSTITUTE   [2271]
Medical Research Fellows Program
4000 Jones Bridge Road
Chevy Chase, MD 20815
(800) 448-4882 ext. 6708
Fax: (240) 497-2314

E-MAIL ADDRESS:
medfellows@hhmi.org

WEB SITE ADDRESS:
www.hhmi.org/medfellowships

FOUNDED: 1953

AREAS OF INTEREST:
Fundamental biomedical research and science education.

NAME(S) OF PROGRAMS:
● **Medical Research Fellows Program**

TYPE:
Fellowships.

YEAR PROGRAM STARTED: 1989

PURPOSE:
To strengthen and expand the pool of medically trained researchers.

LEGAL BASIS:
Medical research organization.

ELIGIBILITY:
Applicant must attend a medical, dental or veterinary school located in the U.S., not in a Ph.D. or M.D./Ph.D. or other combined professional degree/Ph.D. program. Applicant must plan to spend a year full-time in fundamental biomedical research.

FINANCIAL DATA:
Amount of support per award: $29,000 stipend, $5,500 research allowance, and $5,500 Fellow's allowance.

NUMBER OF APPLICANTS MOST RECENT YEAR:
250 for the year 2013.

NUMBER OF AWARDS: 60 for the year 2013.

APPLICATION INFORMATION:
Online application requires the following information:
(1) educational background;
(2) prior research experience;
(3) research plan;
(4) mentor's endorsement and reference letters and;
(5) undergraduate academic transcript data.
Duration: One year.
Deadline: January 11. Announcement at the end of March.

IRS IDENTIFICATION NUMBER: 59-0735717

ADDRESS INQUIRIES TO:
Melanie Daub, Program Officer
(See address above.)

IMMUNE DEFICIENCY FOUNDATION
40 West Chesapeake Avenue
Suite 308
Towson, MD 21204
(866) 939-7568
Fax: (410) 321-0293

E-MAIL ADDRESS:
tcaulder@primaryimmune.org

WEB SITE ADDRESS:
www.usidnet.org

TYPE:
Travel grants; Visiting scholars.
See entry 2337 for full listing.

INTERNATIONAL ANESTHESIA RESEARCH SOCIETY (IARS)   [2272]
44 Montgomery Street
Suite 1605
San Francisco, CA 94104
(415) 296-6900
Fax: (415) 296-6901

E-MAIL ADDRESS:
info@iars.org

WEB SITE ADDRESS:
www.iars.org

FOUNDED: 1922

AREAS OF INTEREST:
Anesthesia.

NAME(S) OF PROGRAMS:
● **Anesthesiology Teaching Recognition Awards**
● **Frontiers in Anesthesia Research Award**
● **IARS Mentored Research Awards**

TYPE:
Research grants. Education awards.

YEAR PROGRAM STARTED: 1983

ELIGIBILITY:
Applicant must be a member of the IARS.

FINANCIAL DATA:
Amount of support per award:
Anesthesiology Teaching Recognition
Awards: $1,000 and $15,000 Innovation in
Education grant; Frontiers in Anesthesia
Research Award: $750,000, in three annual
installments; IARS Mentored Research
Awards: $150,000.

NUMBER OF APPLICANTS MOST RECENT YEAR:
Anesthesiology Teaching Recognition
Awards: 18 for the year 2014; Frontiers in
Anesthesia Research Award: 38 for the year
2012; IARS Mentored Research Awards: 44
for the year 2014.

NUMBER OF AWARDS: Anesthesiology Teaching
Recognition Awards: 2 annually; Frontiers in
Anesthesia Research Award: 1 triennially;
IARS Mentored Research Awards: 4
annually.

APPLICATION INFORMATION:
Interested applicants should visit the IARS
web site. Instructions and applications can be
submitted online.
Duration: Anesthesiology Teaching
Recognition Awards: One year; Frontiers in
Anesthesia Research Award: Three years;
IARS Mentored Research Awards: Two
years.
Deadline: Anesthesiology Teaching
Recognition Awards: Late in calendar year,
annually; Frontiers in Anesthesia Research
Award: Late in calendar year, given every
three years; IARS Mentored Research
Awards: Early in the calendar year, annually.

PUBLICATIONS:
Anesthesia & Analgesia, journal.

ADDRESS INQUIRIES TO:
Tom Cooper, Executive Director
(See address above.)

INTERNATIONAL COLLEGE OF SURGEONS [2273]
1516 North Lake Shore Drive
Chicago, IL 60610-1694
(312) 560-5006
Fax: (312) 787-1683

E-MAIL ADDRESS:
max@icsglobal.org

WEB SITE ADDRESS:
www.icsglobal.org

AREAS OF INTEREST:
Medical research and surgery.

NAME(S) OF PROGRAMS:
● **ICS Scholarship**

TYPE:
Scholarships.

PURPOSE:
To support education and research.

ELIGIBILITY:
Open to surgeons around the world traveling
to developed nations to further their
education.

FINANCIAL DATA:
Amount of support per award: $500 to
$2,000.
Total amount of support: Varies.

NUMBER OF APPLICANTS MOST RECENT YEAR:
Varies.

NUMBER OF AWARDS: Varies.

APPLICATION INFORMATION:
Send request to ICS.
Duration: Varies.

ADDRESS INQUIRIES TO:
Max Downham, Executive Director
(See address above.)

INTERNATIONAL MYELOMA FOUNDATION (IMF) [2274]
12650 Riverside Drive, Suite 206
North Hollywood, CA 91607-3421
(818) 487-7455
Fax: (818) 487-7454

E-MAIL ADDRESS:
theimf@myeloma.org

WEB SITE ADDRESS:
www.myeloma.org

FOUNDED: 1990

AREAS OF INTEREST:
Myeloma.

NAME(S) OF PROGRAMS:
● **Brian D. Novis Research Grants**

TYPE:
Internships; Research grants; Travel grants.

YEAR PROGRAM STARTED: 1995

PURPOSE:
To promote research into better treatments,
management, prevention and a cure for
myeloma.

LEGAL BASIS:
Nonprofit organization.

ELIGIBILITY:
Open to junior researchers or senior
researchers working in the field of multiple
myeloma. Junior researchers must have
completed postdoctoral studies or clinical
fellowships no later than August 1 of the
application year and must have the ability to
devote a minimum of 50% of his or her time
to research during the award year. Also, must
provide a completed application with
evidence of a meritorious research project.

FINANCIAL DATA:
Amount of support per award: Junior
researchers: $50,000; Senior researchers:
$80,000.
Total amount of support: Varies each year.

APPLICATION INFORMATION:
Applications can be downloaded from the
Foundation's web site.
Duration: One year. Renewable upon
reapplication.
Deadline: August 1 (postmarked) for the
following year's program.

PUBLICATIONS:
Myeloma Today, newsletter.

STAFF:
Susie Novis, President
Lisa Paik, Vice President of Clinical
Education and Research Initiatives

ADDRESS INQUIRIES TO:
Lisa Paik, Vice President of Clinical
Education
and Research Initiatives or
Danielle Loi
(See address above.)

ROBERT WOOD JOHNSON FOUNDATION [2275]
Route One and College Road East
Princeton, NJ 08543-2316
(877) 843-7953
Fax: (609) 627-7582

E-MAIL ADDRESS:
mail@rwjf.org

WEB SITE ADDRESS:
www.rwjf.org

FOUNDED: 1972

AREAS OF INTEREST:
Childhood obesity, health insurance coverage,
human capital, pioneer, public health,
quality/equality, and vulnerable populations.

TYPE:
Project/program grants; Research grants. The
Foundation supports training, education,
research (excluding biomedical research) and
projects that demonstrate the effective
delivery of health care services. Rather than
paying for individual care, the Foundation
concentrates on health care systems and the
conditions that promote better health.

Grantees include hospitals, medical, nursing,
and public schools, professional associations,
research organizations, state and local
government agencies, and community groups.

The Foundation grants in seven areas:
(1) Childhood Obesity focuses on reversing
the childhood obesity epidemic by 2015;
(2) Health Insurance Coverage focuses on
ensuring that everyone in America has stable,
affordable care coverage;
(3) Human Capital supports programs that
assure the nation has a diverse, well-trained
leadership and workforce in health and health
care;
(4) Pioneer aims to spur potentially
breakthrough improvements in the future of
health and health care;
(5) Public Health supports programs that
strengthen the practice of public health;
(6) Quality/Equality supports programs
helping communities set and achieve
ambitious goals to improve quality of health
and;
(7) Vulnerable Populations supports ideas to
help overcome longstanding health
challenges.

YEAR PROGRAM STARTED: 1972

PURPOSE:
To improve the health and health care of all
Americans; to improve health care – how it
is delivered, how it is paid for, and how well
it does for patients and their families.

LEGAL BASIS:
Private foundation.

ELIGIBILITY:
Preference is given to tax-exempt, public
agencies under Section 501(c)(3). The
Foundation does not fund general operating
expenses or existing deficits, endowments or
capital costs, basic biomedical research, drug
therapies or devices research, international
programs or institutions, direct support of
individuals, or lobbying of any kind.

In addition, the Foundation rarely makes
grants for conferences, unless they relate
clearly to the Foundation's goals, or for
publications and media projects, except those
that grow out of one of the Foundation's
grant programs.

GEOGRAPHIC RESTRICTIONS:
United States.

FINANCIAL DATA:
Assets of approximately $10 billion.
Amount of support per award: Varies.
Total amount of support: Varies.

COOPERATIVE FUNDING PROGRAMS: Robert Wood Johnson Foundation Local Funding Partnerships.

NUMBER OF APPLICANTS MOST RECENT YEAR: Varies.

NUMBER OF AWARDS: Varies.

REPRESENTATIVE AWARDS:
$18,734,344 to Sports4Kids to support National Expansion of Sports4Kids: A Program that Promotes Physical Activity and Play at Schools (phase 2); $15,959,747 to University of Illinois at Chicago Health Research and Policy Centers to support Bridging the Gap: Research Informing Practice and Policy for Healthy Youth Behavior; $8,563,940 to Kaiser Foundation Research Institute to support expediting the study of the genetic and environmental determinants of health.

APPLICATION INFORMATION:
Applicants should initiate the process of applying for an unsolicited grant by submitting a three-page online brief proposal using the application form provided on the Foundation's web site.

The Foundation accepts proposals online only.
Duration: Varies.
Deadline: Varies.

OFFICERS:
Hon. Thomas H. Kean, Chairman, Board of Trustees
Risa Lavizzo-Mourey, M.D., M.B.A., President and Chief Executive Officer
John R. Lumpkin, M.D., Senior Vice President and Director Health Care Group
James S. Marks, M.D., M.P.H., Senior Vice President and Director Health Group
Katherine Hatton, Vice President, General Counsel and Secretary
David L. Waldman, Vice President, Human Resources and Administration
Albert O. Shar, Ph.D., Vice President, Information Technology
David Colby, Ph.D., Vice President, Research and Evaluation
Peggi Einhorn, Chief Financial Officer and Treasurer
Brian S. O'Neil, Chief Investment Officer
Robin E. Mockenhaupt, Chief of Staff
Mary E. Castria, Controller

ADDRESS INQUIRIES TO:
Lydia Ryba, Manager
Office of Proposal Management
P.O. Box 2316
Princeton, NJ 08543-2316

ROBERT J. KLEBERG, JR. AND HELEN C. KLEBERG FOUNDATION [2276]

700 North St. Mary's Street
Suite 1200
San Antonio, TX 78205
(210) 271-3691
Fax: (210) 299-1541

E-MAIL ADDRESS:
cathyf@alexventures.com

WEB SITE ADDRESS:
www.klebergfoundation.org

AREAS OF INTEREST:
Biomedical research, health and education.

TYPE:
Project/program grants; Research grants.

PURPOSE:
To provide financial support for research projects or actual programs in the area of biomedical research, education, health and welfare.

LEGAL BASIS:
Private foundation.

ELIGIBILITY:
Applicants must be IRS 501(c)(3) organizations. No grants to individuals. No grants for endowments, deficit financing, ongoing operating expenses, community organizations outside of Texas, indirect costs or overhead for research projects.

GEOGRAPHIC RESTRICTIONS:
United States.

FINANCIAL DATA:
Amount of support per award: Varies.
Total amount of support: Varies.

APPLICATION INFORMATION:
Guidelines are available online. Applicants are required to send a proposal including background of the organization, description of the proposed project, detailed project budget, amount requested, evidence of tax-exempt status and a statement of approval of the request for funds signed by the chief administrator of the organization.
Duration: One year. Reapply for additional funding. Research grants can be multiyear.
Deadline: Mid-April for consideration in June; mid-October for consideration in December.

PUBLICATIONS:
Guidelines.

ADDRESS INQUIRIES TO:
Cathy Friese, Grant Coordinator
(See address above.)

THE JACOB AND VALERIA LANGELOTH FOUNDATION [2277]

275 Madison Avenue, 33rd Floor
New York, NY 10016
Fax: (212) 687-8877

E-MAIL ADDRESS:
info@langeloth.org

WEB SITE ADDRESS:
www.langeloth.org

AREAS OF INTEREST:
Health care.

TYPE:
Demonstration grants; Project/program grants; Research grants.

PURPOSE:
To promote and support effective and creative programs, practices and policies related to healing from illness, accident, physical, social or emotional trauma; to extend the availability of programs that promote healing to underserved populations.

ELIGIBILITY:
Grants are made to organizations that have tax-exempt status under Section 501(c)(3) of the Internal Revenue Code and that are health care providers, academic research institutions or community-based organizations. Grants are made nationwide, with a specific interest in New York state.

GEOGRAPHIC RESTRICTIONS:
Primarily New York state.

FINANCIAL DATA:
Amount of support per award: Varies.
Total amount of support: Varies.

APPLICATION INFORMATION:
Applications must be submitted online. Organizations may submit more than one application, but each project requires a separate registration and user name. The process involves the following steps:
(1) project registration;
(2) letter of intent invitation;
(3) letter of intent submission;
(4) proposal invitation and;
(5) proposal submission.

Applicants will be notified via e-mail at each step.
Duration: Up to three years.
Deadline: April 1 and October 1.

STAFF:
Scott Moyer, President
Andrea Fionda, Program Officer
Melissa Houston, Grants Manager

ADDRESS INQUIRIES TO:
Scott Moyer, President
(See address above.)

*SPECIAL STIPULATIONS:
Foundation does not accept unsolicited proposals.

LEUKEMIA RESEARCH FOUNDATION

3520 Lake Avenue
Suite 202
Wilmette, IL 60091
(847) 424-0600
Fax: (847) 424-0606

E-MAIL ADDRESS:
info@lrfmail.org

WEB SITE ADDRESS:
www.leukemia-research.org

TYPE:
Research grants. The goal of the grant program is to support new investigators. It funds scientists and physicians around the world.

See entry 2441 for full listing.

LOVELACE RESPIRATORY RESEARCH INSTITUTE

2425 Ridgecrest Drive, S.E.
Albuquerque, NM 87108
(505) 348-9400
Fax: (505) 348-4966

E-MAIL ADDRESS:
aescovedo@lrri.org

WEB SITE ADDRESS:
www.lrri.org

TYPE:
Fellowships. Training program in respiratory tract disease caused by environmental agents.

See entry 2338 for full listing.

LOWE SYNDROME ASSOCIATION [2278]

P.O. Box 864346
Plano, TX 75086-4346
(972) 733-1338

E-MAIL ADDRESS:
info@lowesyndrome.org

WEB SITE ADDRESS:
www.lowesyndrome.org

FOUNDED: 1982

AREAS OF INTEREST:
Medical research pertaining to Lowe
Syndrome.

NAME(S) OF PROGRAMS:
- **The Leland McSpadden Memorial Fund for Medical and Scientific Research**

TYPE:
Research grants. Supports research leading to
a better understanding of the metabolic basis
of Lowe Syndrome, to better treatments of
the major complications of Lowe Syndrome,
to the prevention of Lowe Syndrome, and/or
to a cure for Lowe Syndrome.

YEAR PROGRAM STARTED: 1983

PURPOSE:
To foster communication among families; to
promote a better understanding of Lowe
Syndrome and the potential of individuals
with this condition; to provide information,
and encourage and support medical research
relating to Lowe Syndrome.

ELIGIBILITY:
Researchers of all types are invited to send
applications, including but not limited to,
universities, hospitals, and other nonprofit
organizations with interest in research in
areas specified by the Association.

FINANCIAL DATA:
Amount of support per award: Up to
$25,000.

NUMBER OF APPLICANTS MOST RECENT YEAR:
1.

APPLICATION INFORMATION:
Contact the Association.
Duration: One year.
Deadline: Receipt of research proposals:
When RFPs are issued.

ADDRESS INQUIRIES TO:
Deborah Jacobs, President
(See address above.)

LUPUS FOUNDATION OF AMERICA, INC.   [2279]
2000 L Street, N.W., Suite 410
Washington, DC 20036
(202) 349-1155
Fax: (202) 349-1156

WEB SITE ADDRESS:
www.lupus.org/rfa/finzifellowships

FOUNDED: 1977

AREAS OF INTEREST:
Lupus research.

NAME(S) OF PROGRAMS:
- **Basic, Clinical and Translational Research Grant Programs**
- **Gina Finzi Memorial Student Summer Fellowship Program**

TYPE:
Research grants. Summer Fellowship.

YEAR PROGRAM STARTED: 1977

ELIGIBILITY:
Applicants whose home institutions are in the
U.S., Canada or Mexico may apply.

GEOGRAPHIC RESTRICTIONS:
North America.

FINANCIAL DATA:
No indirect costs.
Amount of support per award: Gina M. Finzi
Memorial Student Summer Fellowships offer
a $4,000 award. Other awards on varying
topics (including neuropsychiatric lupus,
pediatric lupus, reproductive issues in lupus,
cutaneous lupus, stem cells in lupus research,
and lupus nephritis) offer awards of $50,000
to $100,000.

APPLICATION INFORMATION:
Guidelines and form available at the
Foundation web site.
Duration: Finzi Student Fellowships are for
one summer. Other awards are for one year.
Deadline: Research Grants: April 30.
Awarded October 1; Student Summer
Fellowships: March 31. Awarded in May.

ADDRESS INQUIRIES TO:
Research Program Manager
(See address above.)

JOSIAH MACY JR. FOUNDATION   [2280]
44 East 64th Street
New York, NY 10065
(212) 486-2424
Fax: (212) 644-0765

E-MAIL ADDRESS:
info@macyfoundation.org

WEB SITE ADDRESS:
www.macyfoundation.org

FOUNDED: 1930

AREAS OF INTEREST:
Health care, health professions and medical
education.

NAME(S) OF PROGRAMS:
- **Board Grants**
- **Macy Faculty Scholars**
- **President's Grants**

TYPE:
Conferences/seminars; Demonstration grants;
Development grants; Matching gifts;
Project/program grants. Major interest in
education for careers in medicine or medical
science. Special programs on preparation of
minority groups for health professions and
teamwork among and between health
professions.

YEAR PROGRAM STARTED: 1930

PURPOSE:
To fund activities in medical and other health
professional education.

LEGAL BASIS:
Private foundation.

ELIGIBILITY:
Applicants must be qualified not-for-profit
institutions with appropriate interests. No
grants are made directly to individuals, nor
for building, annual fund appeals or medical
research.

GEOGRAPHIC RESTRICTIONS:
United States.

FINANCIAL DATA:
Amount of support per award: Varies based
on need.
Matching fund requirements: Foundation
matches gifts from full-time employees,
directors and officers only to charitable
organizations.

APPLICATION INFORMATION:
Contact the Foundation for details.

Duration: Varies.

PUBLICATIONS:
Annual report; conference proceedings.

STAFF:
Peter Goodwin, MBA, Chief Operating
Officer and Treasurer
Karen A. Butler
Eric Hoffman
Yasmine Legendra, MPA
Stephen C. Schoenbaum, M.D.
Ellen Witzkin

BOARD OF DIRECTORS:
William H. Wright, II, Chairman
George E. Thibault, M.D., President
David Blumenthal, M.D.
George Campbell, Jr., Ph.D.
Linda Cronenwett, Ph.D., R.N.
Harvey Fineberg, M.D., Ph.D.
Linda P. Fried, M.D.
John W. Frymoyer, M.D.
Henry P. Johnson
Judith B. Krauss, R.N.
Herbert Pardes, M.D.
Paul G. Ramsey, M.D.
George Erik Rupp, Ph.D.
Gregory Warner

ADDRESS INQUIRIES TO:
Foundation President
(See address above.)

MAP INTERNATIONAL   [2281]
4700 Glynco Parkway
Brunswick, GA 31525
(912) 265-6010
Fax: (912) 265-6170

E-MAIL ADDRESS:
info@map.org

WEB SITE ADDRESS:
www.map.org

FOUNDED: 1954

AREAS OF INTEREST:
Community health development.

NAME(S) OF PROGRAMS:
- **MAP International Medical Fellowship**

TYPE:
Travel grants. Fellowship for medical
education.

YEAR PROGRAM STARTED: 1971

PURPOSE:
To encourage lifelong involvement in global
health issues by providing selected medical
students firsthand exposure in a Christian
context to the health, social and cultural
characteristics of a developing world
community.

LEGAL BASIS:
Nonprofit organization.

ELIGIBILITY:
Grants are available for senior medical
students. Applicants must attend an approved
medical school in North America.

FINANCIAL DATA:
Grant pays 100% of the lowest airfare to the
country they will be serving.
Amount of support per award: Varies.
Total amount of support: Varies.

NUMBER OF APPLICANTS MOST RECENT YEAR:
14.

NUMBER OF AWARDS: 12.

APPLICATION INFORMATION:
Application form required. Contact organization for other application requirements.
Duration: Minimum eight weeks.
Deadline: March 1. Announcement May 1.

PUBLICATIONS:
Annual report; application forms.

IRS IDENTIFICATION NUMBER: 36-2586390

ADDRESS INQUIRIES TO:
MAP Fellows Coordinator
(See address above.)

MARCH OF DIMES
FOUNDATION   [2282]
1275 Mamaroneck Avenue
White Plains, NY 10605
(914) 997-4555
Fax: (914) 997-4560

E-MAIL ADDRESS:
researchgrants@marchofdimes.com

WEB SITE ADDRESS:
www.marchofdimes.com
researchgrants.marchofdimes.com (online application system)

FOUNDED: 1938

AREAS OF INTEREST:
Prevention of birth defects, the amelioration of their consequences and the improvement of the outcome of pregnancy.

NAME(S) OF PROGRAMS:
• **Research Grants Program**

TYPE:
Research grants. Grants for research in human birth defects.

The March of Dimes defines a birth defect as any abnormality of structure or function, whether inherited or acquired in utero and presenting in infancy or early childhood. Deviations from reproductive health of women and men as an underlying basis of birth defects (i.e., preconceptional events, perinatal course and premature births) are appropriate subjects for research support. The Foundation does not accept applications dealing with infertility.

YEAR PROGRAM STARTED: 1974

PURPOSE:
To support programs designed to gain new knowledge about the mechanisms that cause birth defects and to find ways of controlling or preventing them.

LEGAL BASIS:
Tax-exempt 501(c)(3) organization.

ELIGIBILITY:
In considering grant applications, the March of Dimes takes into account purpose of the research program and plan of study, qualifications, experience and abilities of the persons who are to supervise and participate in the proposed program, and facilities available.

Qualified scientists, with faculty appointments or equivalent, at universities, hospitals and research institutions (not-for-profit or for-profit) are invited to submit applications for research grants relevant to the Foundation's mission. This encompasses basic biological processes governing differentiation and development, genetics and genomics of these processes, clinical studies, reproductive health and environmental toxicology, and social and behavioral studies concerning cognitive and behavioral risks that affect outcomes of pregnancy, the perinatal period, and subsequent child development.

Applications will be directed to one of three committees whose respective foci are:
(1) cell lineage and differentiation, developmental biology;
(2) gene discovery, biological mechanisms, translational medicine and;
(3) social and behavioral sciences involving family units; this includes genes, toxicants, social determinants that adversely affect language or behavior, especially if involving premature infants or children with birth defects.

FINANCIAL DATA:
The budget does not ordinarily cover the salary expenses of the Principal Investigator or those of other faculty, but does provide salary support for technical help.
Amount of support per award:
Approximately $100,000 per year for a three-year grant.

NUMBER OF APPLICANTS MOST RECENT YEAR:
354 for the year 2012.

NUMBER OF AWARDS: 39 for the year 2012.

REPRESENTATIVE AWARDS:
$314,965 to Michael Fant, M.D., Ph.D., University of South Florida, College of Medicine, for "PLAC1 in Placental Development and Function;" $292,508 to Mark K. Abe, M.D., University of Chicago, for "Mitogen Activated Protein Kinase p38alpha in Lung Branching Morphogenesis;" $294,093 to Emily Feinberg, Sc.D., C.P.N.P., Boston University School of Public Health, for "Reducing Risk After An Adverse Pregnancy Outcome: Addressing Maternal Depression During Internatal Periods."

APPLICATION INFORMATION:
Potential applicants should electronically submit the required administrative information and a Letter of Intent addressed to the Senior Vice President for Research and Global Programs via the Foundation's online application system. The Letter of Intent must include the following information in this order:
(1) title of proposal;
(2) hypothesis;
(3) preliminary data;
(4) précis of specific aims and methods of procedure;
(5) plan for evaluating results;
NOTE: Items 1-5 should not exceed three pages;
(6) current financial support: list each current grant or contract for the conduct of this research; if there is no other support, state "NONE" and;
(7) if the applicant is already a recipient of a current March of Dimes research grant or a Basil O'Connor Starter Scholar Research Award, include a summary of its progress (not to exceed one page).

The Letters of Intent will be evaluated by a scientific advisory committee, and full applications will be invited from those whom the committee recommends.
Duration: Grants are usually awarded for a three-year period, but may be made for a lesser time if it is appropriate.
Deadline: The online Letter of Intent process must be completed by April 30. The scientific advisory committee's selection will be transmitted no later than July 15. Complete application (from those selected): September 15. Applicants will be informed of the decisions regarding these applications no later than the following April 30. Funding initiated June 1.

PUBLICATIONS:
Program announcement; grants list.

ADDRESS INQUIRIES TO:
Joe Leigh Simpson, M.D.
Senior Vice President for Research and Global Programs
(See address above.)

MARCH OF DIMES
FOUNDATION   [2283]
1275 Mamaroneck Avenue
White Plains, NY 10605
(914) 997-4555
Fax: (914) 997-4560

E-MAIL ADDRESS:
researchgrants@marchofdimes.com

WEB SITE ADDRESS:
www.marchofdimes.com
researchgrants.marchofdimes.com (online application system)

FOUNDED: 1938

AREAS OF INTEREST:
Prevention of birth defects, the amelioration of their consequences and the improvement of the outcome of pregnancy.

NAME(S) OF PROGRAMS:
• **Prematurity Research Initiative (PRI)**

TYPE:
Research grants. The March of Dimes defines a birth defect as any abnormality of structure or function, whether inherited or acquired in utero, presenting in infancy or early childhood. Deviations from reproductive health as an underlying basis of birth defects are also included. Thus preconceptual events, prenatal course, and premature births are appropriate subjects for research support.

This program seeks to advance knowledge in this specific area of prematurity research. The March of Dimes seeks applications requesting grant support for projects related to cause(s) (etiology) of normal labor and preterm labor. The intent is to provide new insights into preventing preterm births; in most cases the cause (and thus potential prevention) remains elusive. Emphasis is upon proposals using technology of or encompassing contemporary technologies of genetic, molecular biology and gene-environment interactions. Especially encouraged are proposals from established investigators heretofore not involved in prematurity prevention research and wishing to enter the prematurity domain.

YEAR PROGRAM STARTED: 2005

PURPOSE:
To provide new insights into the large, and increasing, proportion of preterm deliveries in which the cause (and thus the means of prevention) remains elusive.

LEGAL BASIS:
Tax-exempt 501(c)(3) organization.

ELIGIBILITY:
Applicants must be members of not-for-profit institutions.

FINANCIAL DATA:
The budget does not ordinarily cover the salary expenses of the Principal Investigator or those of other faculty, but does provide salary support for technical help.

Amount of support per award: Approximately $100,000 per year for a three-year grant.

NUMBER OF APPLICANTS MOST RECENT YEAR: 37 for the year 2013.

NUMBER OF AWARDS: 5 for the year 2013.

REPRESENTATIVE AWARDS:
$350,272 to Nihar Ranjan Nayak, D.V.M., Ph.D., Stanford University School of Medicine, for "VEGF Regulation of Placental sFlt-1 Production and Its Relevance to the Etiology of Preeclampsia;" $389,939 to Tippi C. MacKenzie, M.D., University of California, San Francisco, for "The Role of Maternal T Cells in Preterm Labor;" $345,952 to Sarah K. England, Ph.D., Washington University, for "Mechanisms Underlying Myometrial Smooth Muscle Relaxation During Pregnancy."

APPLICATION INFORMATION:
Potential applicants should electronically submit the required administrative information and a Letter of Intent addressed to the Senior Vice President for Research and Global Programs via the Foundation's online application system. The Letter of Intent must include the following information in this order:
(1) title of proposal;
(2) hypothesis;
(3) preliminary data;
(4) précis of specific aims and methods of procedure;
(5) plan for evaluating results;
NOTE: Items 1-5 should not exceed three pages;
(6) current financial support: list each current grant or contract for the conduct of this research; if there is no other support, state "NONE" and;
(7) if the applicant is already a recipient of a current March of Dimes research grant or a Basil O'Connor Starter Scholar Research Award, include a summary of its progress (not to exceed one page).

The Letter of Intent will be evaluated and full applications will be solicited from those who are selected.

Duration: Grants are usually awarded for a three-year period, but may be for a lesser time if it is appropriate.

Deadline: The online Letter of Intent process must be completed by April 15. The Foundation's decision will be transmitted to the candidates no later than May 15. Those who are invited to submit a full application will have to do so by July 15. Evaluation will be performed in November or December. The applicants will be informed of the decisions regarding their applications no later than February 1 of the following year, with funding initiated on March 1 of that year.

PUBLICATIONS:
Program policies and grants list.

ADDRESS INQUIRIES TO:
Joe Leigh Simpson, M.D.
Senior Vice President for Research and Global Programs
(See address above.)

*PLEASE NOTE:
The Foundation does not accept applications dealing with infertility.

Please adhere to the instructions precisely. Any letter that does not follow this precise format will not be included in the review process.

MARCH OF DIMES FOUNDATION   [2284]
1275 Mamaroneck Avenue
White Plains, NY 10605
(914) 997-4555
Fax: (914) 997-4560

E-MAIL ADDRESS:
researchgrantssupport@marchofdimes.com

WEB SITE ADDRESS:
www.marchofdimes.com
researchgrants.marchofdimes.com (online application system)

FOUNDED: 1938

AREAS OF INTEREST:
Prevention of birth defects, the amelioration of their consequences and the improvement of the outcome of pregnancy.

NAME(S) OF PROGRAMS:
- **Basil O'Connor Starter Scholar Research Award**

TYPE:
Research grants. The March of Dimes defines a birth defect as any abnormality of structure or function, whether inherited or acquired in utero and presenting in infancy or early childhood. Deviations from reproductive health of women and men as an underlying basis of birth defects (i.e., preconceptional events, perinatal course and premature births) are appropriate subjects for research support.

The applicants' research interests should be in agreement with those of the mission of the March of Dimes: to improve the health of babies by preventing birth defects, premature birth and infant mortality.

Relevance is interpreted broadly to include fundamental cell biology (embryogenesis, cell lineage, differentiation), genetics and genomics, fundamental cellular and clinical pathogenesis of disorders of importance to mothers and infants, biomedical engineering and imaging, and social and behavioral aspects.

YEAR PROGRAM STARTED: 1973

PURPOSE:
To support young scientists just embarking on their independent research careers.

LEGAL BASIS:
Tax-exempt 501(c)(3) organization.

ELIGIBILITY:
Award is intended to be an initial independent grant to young investigators. Eligibility is thus restricted.

Each application should be accompanied by a Letter of Support from a Nominator. The Nominator should first vouch for a candidate's having an unrestricted faculty position and lab space. Ph.D. applicants should be no more than eight years past their degree. Successful applicants have traditionally had four to six years of postdoctoral training or other faculty-mentored work, but not more than eight years. For M.D. or M.D./Ph.D. applicants, the same four-eight year timeline applies, but begins upon completion of the last year of clinical training required for medical specialty board certification. Requests for exceptions (e.g., pregnancy and

maternity leave) should be directed to the Senior Vice President for Research and Global Programs.

March of Dimes takes into account the purpose of the research program and plan submitted, qualifications, experience and abilities of the persons who are to supervise and participate in the proposed program and the facilities available.

FINANCIAL DATA:
Grants do not cover the recipient's salary, but may provide salary support for technical help.

Amount of support per award: $75,000 per year for two years.

NUMBER OF APPLICANTS MOST RECENT YEAR: 108 for the year 2013.

NUMBER OF AWARDS: 30 for the year 2013.

REPRESENTATIVE AWARDS:
$150,000 to Gregory Charles Rogers, Ph.D., University of Arizona, Arizona Cancer Center, for "Cellular Control of Centriole Assembly: Elucidating the Mechanisms of Polo-like Kinase 4 Activity;" $150,000 to Craig Thomas Miller, Ph.D., University of California at Berkeley, for "Genetic Analysis of Craniofacial Patterning in Sticklebacks;" $150,000 to Yi Xing, Ph.D., University of Iowa, for "Genomic Signatures of Gene Expression and Alternative Splicing in Preterm Labor."

APPLICATION INFORMATION:
The entire process must be completed online via the March of Dimes online application system.

The following information is required from the candidate:
(1) title of the proposed research project;
(2) candidate's name, academic appointment, mailing address, telephone and fax numbers and e-mail address;
(3) candidate's curriculum vitae in NIH format and;
(4) Letter of Intent (template provided) for the proposed research.

This Letter of Intent must include the following information in this order:
(1) title of proposal;
(2) hypothesis;
(3) preliminary data;
(4) précis of specific aims and methods of procedure;
(5) plan for evaluating results and;
(6) current financial support: list each current grant or contract for the conduct of this research; if there is no other support, state "NONE."
NOTE: Items 1-6 should not exceed three pages.

Information required from the Nominator: Deans, Chairpersons of Departments or Directors of Institutes/Centers may submit nominations for this award, addressed to the Senior Vice President for Research and Global Programs. Included should be the Nominator's name, academic appointment, mailing address, telephone and fax numbers and e-mail address. The Letter of Nomination should be submitted via the online application system. It should explicitly contain information about the candidate's faculty appointment, independence, and facilities available, including his or her laboratory space.

Letters of Intent will be reviewed initially by the Senior Vice President for Research and Global Programs for adherence to eligibility.

Those eligible will be subjected to a preliminary selection process to identify a pool suitable for a committee to analyze critically. Those selected will then be invited to submit a full application. The scientific advisory committee will then conduct its review of the proposals.

Duration: Programs are approved for two years.

Deadline: Nominations: March 15. Proposals: By June 30. Reviewed in October for February 1 funding cycle.

PUBLICATIONS:
Program announcement and grants list.

NATIONAL OFFICERS:
LaVerne H. Council, D.B.A., Chairperson
Jennifer L. Howse, Ph.D., President
Richard Mulligan, Executive Vice
President/Chief Operating Officer
Alfred Childs, Treasurer
David R. Smith, M.D., Secretary
David Horne, Assistant Treasurer
Lisa Bellsey, Esq., Assistant Secretary
Edward R.B. McCabe, M.D., Ph.D., Medical Director

ADDRESS INQUIRIES TO:
Joe Leigh Simpson, M.D.
Senior Vice President for Research and Global Programs
(See address above.)

*PLEASE NOTE:
The Foundation does not accept applications dealing with infertility.

*SPECIAL STIPULATIONS:
Basil O'Connor applicants may not be recipients of a major grant (e.g., an R01, or other grant exceeding $200,000 a year) at the time of the application. If an application for such other grant is under review, eligibility for Basil O'Connor remains so long as it has not been awarded at the time of March of Dimes review. Applicants who have transition faculty-mentored awards (e.g., K99/R00) are welcome, if they have completed the mentored portion. If not, application should be deferred. Candidates may not simultaneously submit an application for any other March of Dimes research program. Those who have previously submitted an application to the March of Dimes are not eligible for a Basil O'Connor Award unless permission has been explicitly given; however, application for a regular research grant is welcomed.

MAYO CLINIC   [2285]
Mayo School of Graduate Medical Education
200 First Street, S.W.
Rochester, MN 55905
(507) 284-1196
Fax: (507) 538-3267

E-MAIL ADDRESS:
pathologyeducation@mayo.edu

WEB SITE ADDRESS:
www.mayo.edu/msgme

AREAS OF INTEREST:
Surgical and medical pathology, including bone and soft tissue pathology, cardiovascular pathology, cytopathology, GI/liver pathology, breast pathology, and renal pathology.

NAME(S) OF PROGRAMS:
● **Surgical Pathology Fellowships**

TYPE:
Fellowships. Available subspecialty fellowships include bone and soft tissue

pathology, cardiovascular pathology, cytopathology, gastrointestinal pathology, hematopathology, neuropathology, pulmonary pathology and surgical pathology. Each fellowship will give ample opportunity to diagnose and work with a large diverse volume of tissue specimens. Fellows will assist Mayo's staff consultants with projects and will be encouraged to initiate and participate in clinical pathology and basic research studies for publication and presentation at national meetings. Fellows will also develop and present studies at conferences and seminars and may assist in teaching pathology residents, medical students and fellows from other departments. Each specialty fellowship consists of a one-year program except neuropathology, which is a two-year appointment. Combined fellowships are also possible.

PURPOSE:
To promote the belief that physicians need to work together, teach and learn from others and conduct research to provide sustained, excellent patient care.

LEGAL BASIS:
Hospital.

ELIGIBILITY:
Applicants must have a medical degree with U.S. or Canadian specialty training in anatomic pathology for all specialty fellowships.

FINANCIAL DATA:
Fellows will be permitted 15 days each year for vacation. Fellows will also receive a stipend and benefits package including a comprehensive medical care plan, short-term disability insurance, voluntary family life insurance, dental assistance plan, professional liability coverage and excess personal liability insurance. Since Fellows are encouraged to present research at regional and national meetings, Mayo will pay authorized expenses to attend that meeting within the U.S.

Amount of support per award: Varies depending on experience and fellowship.

NUMBER OF AWARDS: 1 in each specialty except for surgical pathology, which has 9 fellows.

APPLICATION INFORMATION:
To apply for a Mayo fellowship, applicants need to submit:
(1) a completed Mayo School of Graduate Medical Education application form;
(2) official college, graduate school and medical school transcripts;
(3) an official record of board scores;
(4) a dean's letter and two other letters of recommendation;
(5) curriculum vitae and personal statement;
(6) a valid ECFMG certificate if the applicant has graduated from a medical school outside of the U.S. or Canada and;
(7) a letter of recommendation from the residency program director.

If an applicant is considered for an appointment, they will be asked to visit Mayo Clinic Rochester for an interview with the program director and selected faculty. Interviews are conducted from December through March each year.

Duration: One year for specialties and two years for neuropathology.

Deadline: January 1 of the year preceding appointment.

BENJAMIN AND MARY SIDDONS MEASEY FOUNDATION   [2286]
P.O. Box 258
Media, PA 19063
(610) 566-5800
Fax: (610) 566-8197

FOUNDED: 1958

AREAS OF INTEREST:
Medical education in Philadelphia area processed through Philadelphia medical schools only.

NAME(S) OF PROGRAMS:
● **Medical Education Grants**

TYPE:
Challenge/matching grants; Fellowships; Grants-in-aid.

YEAR PROGRAM STARTED: 1958

PURPOSE:
To advance medical education of physicians.

LEGAL BASIS:
1958 Trust Document.

ELIGIBILITY:
Grants are made through accredited medical schools in the immediate Philadelphia, PA area. Individual applications are not accepted by the Foundation; institutions only.

GEOGRAPHIC RESTRICTIONS:
Philadelphia, Pennsylvania area.

FINANCIAL DATA:
Amount of support per award: $7,500 to $500,000.

Total amount of support: $2,160,000 for the year 2013.

NUMBER OF APPLICANTS MOST RECENT YEAR:
10.

APPLICATION INFORMATION:
Application is by letter. Organizations must provide 501(c)(3) tax-exempt information.

Duration: One year. Nonrenewable.

Deadline: Two weeks prior to quarterly meetings held in March, June, September and December.

IRS IDENTIFICATION NUMBER: 23-6298781

STAFF:
James C. Brennan, Esq., Manager
M.S. Donaldson, Esq., Secretary

ADDRESS INQUIRIES TO:
James C. Brennan, Esq., Manager and Counsel
(See address above.)

*SPECIAL STIPULATIONS:
No applications to Foundation directly.

MEDICAL LIBRARY ASSOCIATION
65 East Wacker Place
Suite 1900
Chicago, IL 60601-7246
(312) 419-9094
Fax: (312) 419-8950

E-MAIL ADDRESS:
grants@mlahq.org

WEB SITE ADDRESS:
www.mlanet.org/awards

TYPE:
Fellowships; Scholarships. Awarded for study and doctoral work in health sciences librarianship.

Thomson Reuters/MLA Doctoral Fellowship is awarded biennially. It was established by the Institute for Scientific Information (ISI) and is administered by the MLA.

See entry 729 for full listing.

NATIONAL ALOPECIA AREATA FOUNDATION
14 Mitchell Boulevard
San Rafael, CA 94903
(415) 472-3780
Fax: (415) 472-5343

E-MAIL ADDRESS:
info@naaf.org

WEB SITE ADDRESS:
www.naaf.org

TYPE:
Research grants.

See entry 2156 for full listing.

NATIONAL BRAIN TUMOR SOCIETY   [2287]
55 Chapel Street
Suite 200
Newton, MA 02458
(617) 924-9997
Fax: (617) 924-9998

E-MAIL ADDRESS:
research@braintumor.org

WEB SITE ADDRESS:
www.braintumor.org

FOUNDED: 1981

AREAS OF INTEREST:
Brain tumor treatment.

CONSULTING OR VOLUNTEER SERVICES:
Research, advocacy/public policy, and patient care.

NAME(S) OF PROGRAMS:
● **NBTF Brain Tumor Research Grants**

TYPE:
Awards/prizes; Project/program grants; Research grants.

YEAR PROGRAM STARTED: 1981

PURPOSE:
To provide information and support for brain tumor patients, family members, and health care professionals; to support innovative research into better treatment options and a cure for brain tumors.

ELIGIBILITY:
For clinical grants, applicants must be qualified research investigators with a Ph.D. or higher level practicing neuroscience at U.S. or Canadian medical centers. Quality of Life researcher need not be Ph.D., but must hold at least a Master's degree.

Grant monies cannot be used for general administrative costs, debt reduction, or indirect costs of the project.

GEOGRAPHIC RESTRICTIONS:
United States and Canada.

FINANCIAL DATA:
Total amount of support: $500,000 to $750,000.

NUMBER OF APPLICANTS MOST RECENT YEAR:
100.

NUMBER OF AWARDS: 12.

APPLICATION INFORMATION:
Contact the Society for application form and guidelines.
Duration: One year. Renewal possible.

IRS IDENTIFICATION NUMBER: 94-2876985

ADDRESS INQUIRIES TO:
Carrie Treadwell, Director of Research
(See address above.)

NATIONAL HEART, LUNG AND BLOOD INSTITUTE (NHLBI)
National Institutes of Health
Grants Operations Branch, Room 7160
6701 Rockledge Drive, MSC-7926
Bethesda, MD 20892-7926
(301) 435-0144
Fax: (301) 480-3310

E-MAIL ADDRESS:
whitesa@nhlbi.nih.gov

WEB SITE ADDRESS:
www.nhlbi.nih.gov/funding/index.htm
www.grants.nhlbi.nih.gov

TYPE:
Conferences/seminars; Fellowships; Project/program grants; Research grants; Training grants; Loan forgiveness programs. Career awards and other grant mechanisms to foster research on heart, vascular and lung diseases, and to develop scientists in these areas. Also, small business grants. Loan forgiveness programs are for research.

See entry 2397 for full listing.

THE NATIONAL HEMOPHILIA FOUNDATION   [2288]
116 West 32nd Street, 11th Floor
New York, NY 10001
(212) 328-3727
Fax: (212) 328-3799

E-MAIL ADDRESS:
awang@hemophilia.org

WEB SITE ADDRESS:
www.hemophilia.org

FOUNDED: 1948

AREAS OF INTEREST:
Biochemistry, genetics, hematology, microbiology, orthopedics, psychiatry and other disciplines related to hemophilia and other bleeding disorders.

NAME(S) OF PROGRAMS:
● **Judith Graham Pool Postdoctoral Research Fellowships in Bleeding Disorders**

TYPE:
Development grants; Fellowships; Research grants. Support for research in clinical and/or basic sciences in areas relating to problems in hemophilia and other bleeding disorders.

Judith Graham Pool Postdoctoral Research Fellowships are designed to support research studies of high scientific merit and relevance to hemophilia. They are awarded through professional and graduate schools, or research institutions.

YEAR PROGRAM STARTED: 1972

PURPOSE:
To encourage and support hemophilia-related and other bleeding disorders research.

LEGAL BASIS:
Voluntary, nonprofit health organization.

ELIGIBILITY:
Applicants must have completed doctoral training and must enter the fellowship program from a doctoral, postdoctoral, internship or residency training program. This is not a research grant program for established investigators or faculty members.

GEOGRAPHIC RESTRICTIONS:
United States.

FINANCIAL DATA:
All money is to be used for salary and up to $750 for travel. No overhead is paid to any institution, except with the consent of the grantee and from his or her stipend.
Amount of support per award: $42,000 per year.
Total amount of support: Varies.

NUMBER OF AWARDS: 1.

APPLICATION INFORMATION:
Interested candidates must submit a Letter of Intent. This should be a brief letter identifying the researcher, their mentor, institution, and a description of the proposed research project. Letters of Intent should include an NIH-style curriculum vitae or biosketch for both candidate and mentor. After review, candidates may be invited to submit a full application.
Duration: Up to two years. Renewal contingent upon review of fellow's six-month progress report.

STAFF:
Val Bias, Chief Executive Officer
Neil Frick, Vice President, Clinical Research and Information Services
Angelina Wang, Director of Research and Medical Information

ADDRESS INQUIRIES TO:
Angelina Wang, Director of Research and Medical Information
(See address above.)

NATIONAL INSTITUTE OF ENVIRONMENTAL HEALTH SCIENCES
Division of Extramural Research and Training, MD K3-05
111 T.W. Alexander Drive
Research Triangle Park, NC 27709
(919) 541-3289
Fax: (919) 541-2843

E-MAIL ADDRESS:
mastin@niehs.nih.gov

WEB SITE ADDRESS:
www.niehs.nih.gov

TYPE:
Conferences/seminars; Demonstration grants; Development grants; Fellowships; Project/program grants; Research grants; Training grants. NIEHS pursues its mission by supporting basic and applied research on the consequences of the exposure of humans to potentially toxic or harmful agents in the environment.

Research of interest encompasses studies that relate to the biological effects of environmental chemicals and physical factors including such agents as hazardous gases, suspended particles, aerosols, industrial by-products and intermediates, heavy metals, trace elements, food additives, adulterants and pesticides. Physical factors include noise, light, heat, microwaves and other forms of nonionizing radiation.

Research Training Programs support individuals at both the predoctoral and postdoctoral levels in the areas of environmental toxicology, environmental pathology, environmental mutagenesis and environmental epidemiology.

See entry 2189 for full listing.

NATIONAL INSTITUTE OF GENERAL MEDICAL SCIENCES   [2289]

National Institutes of Health
45 Center Drive, MSC 6200
Bethesda, MD 20892-6200
(301) 496-7301
Fax: (301) 402-0224

E-MAIL ADDRESS:
info@nigms.nih.gov

WEB SITE ADDRESS:
www.nigms.nih.gov

FOUNDED: 1962

AREAS OF INTEREST:
Basic biomedical research.

NAME(S) OF PROGRAMS:
- **Division of Biomedical Technology, Bioinformatics, and Computational Biology**
- **Division of Cell Biology and Biophysics**
- **Division of Genetics and Developmental Biology**
- **Division of Pharmacology, Physiology, and Biological Chemistry**
- **Division of Training, Workforce Development, and Diversity**

TYPE:
Fellowships; Project/program grants; Research grants; Training grants; Research contracts. Grants to support research on the structure and function of cells and cell organelles. Research to gain knowledge that will lead to the prevention, therapy and control of genetic diseases, as well as research to increase knowledge of drug action in order to increase safety of administration and diminish toxicity. Grants also given for research in biophysics and the physiological sciences and in certain clinical areas, particularly anesthesiology and trauma and burns. All of the research programs also support research training.

In addition, the Institute has special research training programs designed to increase the diversity of the biomedical and behavioral research workforce.

YEAR PROGRAM STARTED: 1962

PURPOSE:
To support basic biomedical research that lays the foundation for advances in disease diagnosis, treatment, and prevention; to help provide the most critical element of good research: well-prepared scientists.

LEGAL BASIS:
Part of a government agency under the PHS Act, various sections, and various public laws.

ELIGIBILITY:
For Research Grants, applicants must be academic institutions, teaching hospitals, public agencies, nonprofit organizations and for-profit corporations.

National Research Service Awards for the above areas may be made to individuals for postdoctoral training or nonprofit institutions for the training of individuals at the predoctoral and postdoctoral level.

For Small Business Innovative Research Program, applicants must be qualified small businesses to stimulate technological innovation in areas of interest to the Institute.

FINANCIAL DATA:
Total amount of support: $2.6 billion for fiscal year 2013.

NUMBER OF AWARDS: 5,134 NIGMS-funded research grants for fiscal year 2013.

APPLICATION INFORMATION:
The appropriate application forms and instructions may be obtained from and submitted to:
The Division of Extramural Outreach and Information Resources
Office of Extramural Research
National Institutes of Health, Room 6207
6701 Rockledge Drive, MSC 7910
Bethesda, MD 20892-7910
Tel: (301) 435-0714
E-mail: grantsinfo@nih.gov.
Duration: Varies.
Deadline: Varies by program.

STAFF:
Ann Dieffenbach, Public Information Officer

ADDRESS INQUIRIES TO:
Office of Communications
and Public Liaison
(See address above.)

NATIONAL INSTITUTE OF GENERAL MEDICAL SCIENCES   [2290]

Division of Training, Diversity
& Workforce Development
45 Center Drive, Room 2AS-37
MSC 6200
Bethesda, MD 20892-6200
(301) 594-3900
Fax: (301) 480-2753

E-MAIL ADDRESS:
zlotnikh@nigms.nih.gov

WEB SITE ADDRESS:
www.nigms.nih.gov

FOUNDED: 1972

NAME(S) OF PROGRAMS:
- **Minority Biomedical Research Support Awards**

TYPE:
Development grants; Research grants; Technical assistance. Grants to assist eligible institutions to strengthen the institutions' biomedical research capabilities and provide opportunities to students to engage in biomedical or behavioral research and other activities in preparation for Ph.D. training in these areas.

YEAR PROGRAM STARTED: 1972

PURPOSE:
To increase the number of faculty, students, and investigators who are members of groups underrepresented in the biomedical and behavioral sciences who are engaged in research in these fields.

LEGAL BASIS:
Public Health Service Act of 1944 as amended, Section 301(c); U.S.C. 241.d.

ELIGIBILITY:
Applicant must be located in a state, the District of Columbia or a U.S. territory, and be a public or private university, four-year college or other institution offering undergraduate, graduate or health

professional degrees with more than 50% minority enrollment, a public or private nonprofit four-year college or other institution offering undergraduate, graduate or health professional degrees, with a significant enrollment (but not necessarily more than 50%) derived from ethnic minorities, if the secretary of DHHS determines that the institution is committed to encouragement and assistance to ethnic minority faculty, students and investigators, or an Indian tribe with a recognized governing body which performs substantial government functions or an Alaska Regional Corporation (ARC) as defined in the Alaska Native Claims Settlement Act and located in a state, the District of Columbia, Puerto Rico, the Virgin Islands, the Canal Zone, Guam, American Samoa or the Trust Territory of the Pacific Islands.

GEOGRAPHIC RESTRICTIONS:
United States and its territories.

FINANCIAL DATA:
Amount of support per award: $135,000 to $2,000,000.

COOPERATIVE FUNDING PROGRAMS: Co-funding with other NIH Institutes.

APPLICATION INFORMATION:
Detailed information is available from the Branch Chief.
Duration: Typically three to four years.

ADDRESS INQUIRIES TO:
Dr. Hinda Zlotnik, Branch Chief
(See address above.)

NATIONAL INSTITUTE OF GENERAL MEDICAL SCIENCES   [2291]

Natcher Building, MSC 6200
45 Center Drive, 2AS-13C
Bethesda, MD 20892-6200
(301) 594-0828
Fax: (301) 480-2004

E-MAIL ADDRESS:
preuschp@nigms.nih.gov

WEB SITE ADDRESS:
www.nigms.nih.gov

AREAS OF INTEREST:
Basic biomedical research.

NAME(S) OF PROGRAMS:
- **Medical Scientist Training Program**

TYPE:
Grants-in-aid; Training grants. The goal of this program is to prepare its graduates to function independently in both clinical practice and scientific research. MSTP has over 40 participating programs.

YEAR PROGRAM STARTED: 1964

PURPOSE:
To support research training leading to the combined M.D.-Ph.D. degree.

ELIGIBILITY:
Applicants must be U.S. domestic institutions.

GEOGRAPHIC RESTRICTIONS:
United States.

FINANCIAL DATA:
Many institutions supplement the basic stipend provided by the MSTP grant. Trainees incur no payback obligation.

Amount of support per award: $22,032 stipend, plus tuition allowance of up to $21,000, travel allowance of $300, and $4,200 for equipment, supplies and health care for the year 2012.

Total amount of support: Varies.

NUMBER OF AWARDS: 932 for the year 2012.

APPLICATION INFORMATION:
Individuals who wish to enter the program should contact the program office at the participating institution(s) of their choice directly for curriculum information and admission requirements. Interested institutions should contact the NIGMS program director. Institutions should include the standard Form 424.

Applications guidelines are available online.

Duration: Maximum six years, although the course of study for the combined degree may take longer. Continued support conditional upon annual review and availability of funds to the institution.

Deadline: January 25, May 25 and September 25. Grant awarded only once per year.

NATIONAL INSTITUTES OF HEALTH   [2292]
Office of Extramural Research
9000 Rockville Pike
Bethesda, MD 20892
(301) 435-0714
TTY: (301) 451-5936

E-MAIL ADDRESS:
grantsinfo@nih.gov

WEB SITE ADDRESS:
grants.nih.gov/grants/guide/pa-files/PA-11-113.html

FOUNDED: 1930

AREAS OF INTEREST:
Biomedical research and improvement of human health.

NAME(S) OF PROGRAMS:
- **Ruth L. Kirschstein National Research Service Awards (NRSA) for Individual Postdoctoral Fellows (Parent F32)**

TYPE:
Fellowships; Research grants; Training grants. This individual postdoctoral research training fellowship is to provide support to promising fellowship applicants with the potential to become productive, independent investigators in scientific health-related research fields relevant to the missions of participating NIH Institutes and Centers.

PURPOSE:
To help ensure that a diverse pool of highly trained scientists is available in appropriate scientific disciplines to address the nation's biomedical, behavioral and clinical research needs.

ELIGIBILITY:
Eligible organizations: Higher education institutions, nonprofits other than institutions of higher education, for-profit organizations, governments and other (non-U.S.) entities.

Eligible Individuals: Applicant - Project Director/Principal Investigator (PD/PI) - must be a citizen or a noncitizen national of the U.S. or have been lawfully admitted for permanent residence.

Before the award can be activated, the candidate will have received a Ph.D., M.D., D.O., D.C., D.D.S., D.V.M., O.D., D.P.M.,

Sc.D., Eng.D., Dr.P.H., DNSc., N.D., Pharm.D., D.S.W., Psy.D., or equivalent doctoral degree from an accredited domestic or foreign institution.

GEOGRAPHIC RESTRICTIONS:
United States and its territories.

FINANCIAL DATA:
Award budgets are composed of stipends, tuition and fees, and institutional allowance. NIH does not separately reimburse indirect costs (also known as Facilitates and Administrative - or F and A - Costs) for fellowships. Costs for administering fellowships are part of institutional allowance.

NUMBER OF AWARDS: Varies.

APPLICATION INFORMATION:
Guidelines and detailed information are available on the NIH web site. Paper applications will not be accepted.

Duration: Varies; up to three years for individuals.

*SPECIAL STIPULATIONS:
Conformance to all requirements (both in the Application Guide and the Funding Opportunity Announcement (FOA)) is required and strictly enforced.

At the time of award, individuals are required to pursue their research training on a full-time basis, normally defined as 40 hours per week or as specified by the sponsoring institution in accordance with its own policies.

NATIONAL INSTITUTES OF HEALTH   [2293]
Office of Extramural Research (OER)
9000 Rockville Pike
Bethesda, MD 20892
(301) 435-0714
TTY: (301) 451-5936

E-MAIL ADDRESS:
grantsinfo@nih.gov

WEB SITE ADDRESS:
www.nih.gov

FOUNDED: 1887

AREAS OF INTEREST:
Biomedical research and improvement of human health.

NAME(S) OF PROGRAMS:
- **Mentored Clinical Scientist Research Career Development Award (Parent K08)**

TYPE:
Research grants. This program prepares qualified individuals for careers that have a significant impact on the health-related research needs of the nation.

PURPOSE:
To help ensure that a diverse pool of highly trained scientists are available in appropriate scientific disciplines to address the nation's biomedical, behavioral and clinical research needs.

LEGAL BASIS:
Public Health Service Act, Section 301(c).

ELIGIBILITY:
Eligible organizations include higher education institutions, nonprofits other than institutions of higher education, for-profit organizations, different domestic levels of

government, Native American tribal organizations and faith-based or community-based organizations.

Eligible individuals (program director/principal investigator) must be a citizen or a noncitizen national of the U.S. or have been lawfully admitted for permanent residence. They must have a clinical doctoral degree (e.g., M.D., D.D.S., D.M.D., D.O., D.C., O.D., N.D., D.V.M., Pharm.D., or, in certain clinical disciplines, Ph.D.). The K08 award may be used by candidates with different levels of prior research training and at different stages in their career development.

GEOGRAPHIC RESTRICTIONS:
United States.

APPLICATION INFORMATION:
Applications must be submitted electronically. Paper applications will not be accepted.

Duration: Up to five years.

NATIONAL INSTITUTES OF HEALTH   [2294]
Office of Extramural Research
9000 Rockville Pike
Bethesda, MD 20892
(301) 435-0714
TTY: (301) 451-5936

E-MAIL ADDRESS:
grantsinfo@nih.gov

WEB SITE ADDRESS:
grants.nih.gov/grants/guide/pa-files/PA-11-114.html

FOUNDED: 1930

AREAS OF INTEREST:
Biomedical research and improvement of human health.

NAME(S) OF PROGRAMS:
- **Ruth L. Kirschstein National Research Service Awards (NRSA) for Individual Senior Fellows (Parent F33)**

TYPE:
Fellowships. This program is intended to provide senior fellowship support to experienced scientists who wish to make major changes in the direction of their research careers or who wish to broaden their scientific background by acquiring new research capabilities as independent investigators in research fields relevant to the missions of the participating NIH Institutes and Centers.

PURPOSE:
To help ensure that a diverse pool of highly trained scientists is available in appropriate scientific disciplines to address the nation's biomedical, behavioral and clinical research needs.

LEGAL BASIS:
An agency of the U.S. Public Health Service.

ELIGIBILITY:
Eligible organizations: Higher education institutions, nonprofits other than institutions of higher education, for-profit organizations, governments and other (non-U.S.) entities.

Eligible Individuals: The Project Director/Principal Investigator must have had at least seven subsequent years of relevant research or professional experience and will have established an independent research career. By the time of the award, that individual must be a citizen or a noncitizen national of the U.S. or have been lawfully admitted for permanent residence.

GEOGRAPHIC RESTRICTIONS:
United States.

FINANCIAL DATA:
Award budgets are composed of stipends, tuition and fees, and institutional allowance. NIH does not separately reimburse indirect costs (also known as Facilitates and Administrative - or F and A - Costs) for fellowships. Costs for administering fellowships are part of institutional allowance.

NUMBER OF AWARDS: Varies.

APPLICATION INFORMATION:
Contact the National Institutes of Health. Paper applications will not be accepted.
Duration: Typically, up to two years.

*SPECIAL STIPULATIONS:
Conformance to all requirements (both in the Application Guide and the Funding Opportunity Announcement (FOA)) is required and strictly enforced.

At the time of award, individuals are required to pursue their research training on a full-time basis, normally defined as 40 hours per week or as specified by the sponsoring institution in accordance with its own policies.

NATIONAL INSTITUTES OF HEALTH   [2295]
National Center for Research Resources
6701 Democracy Boulevard
Room 958, Building One
Bethesda, MD 20892
(301) 435-0772
Fax: (301) 480-3659

E-MAIL ADDRESS:
sig@mail.nih.gov

WEB SITE ADDRESS:
www.ncrr.nih.gov

FOUNDED: 1930

AREAS OF INTEREST:
Biomedical research and improvement of human health.

NAME(S) OF PROGRAMS:
● **Shared Instrumentation Grant Program**

TYPE:
Project/program grants.

YEAR PROGRAM STARTED: 1982

PURPOSE:
To provide research institutions the opportunity to obtain expensive (over $100,000 per item) commercially available instruments to be shared by groups of NIH-funded investigators.

LEGAL BASIS:
An agency of the U.S. Public Health Service.

ELIGIBILITY:
Federal agencies, foreign institutions and for-profit institutions are not eligible.

FINANCIAL DATA:
Amount of support per award: Maximum award is $600,000.
Total amount of support: $42,000,000 for fiscal year 2012.

NUMBER OF AWARDS: Varies.

APPLICATION INFORMATION:
Contact the National Institutes of Health.
Duration: One year. No renewals.
Deadline: Usually the last week in March.

ADDRESS INQUIRIES TO:
Shared Instrumentation Grant Program
(See address above.)

NATIONAL MEDICAL FELLOWSHIPS, INC.   [2296]
347 Fifth Avenue, Suite 510
New York, NY 10016
(212) 483-8880
Fax: (212) 483-8897

E-MAIL ADDRESS:
scholarships@nmfonline.org

WEB SITE ADDRESS:
www.nmfonline.org

FOUNDED: 1946

AREAS OF INTEREST:
Minority medical students and the health care of low-income and minority communities.

NAME(S) OF PROGRAMS:
● **Aetna Foundation/NMF Healthcare Leadership Program**
● **Hugh J. Andersen Scholarship**
● **California Community Service-Learning Program**
● **Emergency Scholarship Fund**
● **GE/NMF International Medical Scholars Program**
● **GE-NMF Primary Care Leadership Program (PCLP)**
● **Monash/Scott Medical Student Scholarship Program**
● **United Health Foundation/Diverse Medical Scholars Program**

TYPE:
Awards/prizes; Fellowships; Scholarships. Aetna Foundation/NMF Healthcare Leadership Program is a highly successful national program that awards 10 second- and third-year minority medical students who demonstrate leadership potential through commitment to service. Target cities are Los Angeles, Chicago and New York City.

GE/NMF International Medical Scholars Program supports for the next three years in Ghana and Kenya a mentored service-learning clinical experience for U.S. fourth-year medical students to improve patient care in district hospitals, including a new focus on building site capacity on public health/disease-prevention issues.

GE-NMF Primary Care Leadership Program (PCLP) is a transformational, multiyear, multimillion-dollar program that will provide community service scholarships for medical students, nursing and health professions students in eight key U.S. states during its first two program years.

Monash/Scott Medical Student Scholarship Program was, with funding and leadership from The Chicago Community Trust, conceived to help Chicago meet its need for culturally competent physician-leaders by 2040. Service scholarships are provided to second- and third-year students in Chicago medical schools, and residency scholarships to students who have completed medical school and matched as residents in the Chicago area.

YEAR PROGRAM STARTED: 1946

PURPOSE:
To improve the health of low-income and minority communities by increasing the number of minority physicians and addressing the special needs of these communities.

LEGAL BASIS:
Nonprofit corporation.

ELIGIBILITY:
Varies by program.

FINANCIAL DATA:
Amount of support per award: Varies.
Total amount of support: Varies.

NUMBER OF APPLICANTS MOST RECENT YEAR:
Varies.

NUMBER OF AWARDS: Varies.

APPLICATION INFORMATION:
Guidelines and official application materials are available at the organization web site.
Duration: Varies by program.
Deadline: Varies by program.

BOARD OF DIRECTORS:
Daniel T. McGowan, Chairman
Paula Madison, Vice Chairperson
Stephen N. Keith, M.D., M.S.P.H., Treasurer and Secretary

ADDRESS INQUIRIES TO:
Programs Operations and Management
(See address above.)

THE NATIONAL ORGANIZATION FOR RARE DISORDERS   [2297]
55 Kenosia Avenue
Danbury, CT 06813-1968
(203) 744-0100
Fax: (203) 798-2291

E-MAIL ADDRESS:
research@rarediseases.org

WEB SITE ADDRESS:
www.rarediseases.org

FOUNDED: 1983

AREAS OF INTEREST:
Rare "orphan" disease.

NAME(S) OF PROGRAMS:
● **Restricted Research Program**

TYPE:
Research grants; Seed money grants. The Restricted Research Program provides seed money grants to academic scientists studying new treatments or diagnostic tests for rare diseases.

PURPOSE:
To promote the diagnosis, treatment and cure of rare disorders through programs of education, advocacy, service and research.

ELIGIBILITY:
Must be an academic scientist. IRB approval and a copy of informed consent is necessary if the study involves human, and NIH Recombinant DNA Advisory Committee review or waiver of review if human gene therapy is involved.

FINANCIAL DATA:
Overhead and indirect costs are not awarded.
Amount of support per award: Minimum $30,000.
Total amount of support: Varies.

NUMBER OF APPLICANTS MOST RECENT YEAR:
Approximately 25.

NUMBER OF AWARDS: 1 to 5.

APPLICATION INFORMATION:
Submit a letter of intent, curriculum vitae, one-page abstract, and a brief budget. Full proposals by invitation only. Requests for proposals announcements typically posted online in early March of each year.

Duration: One to two years.

Deadline: Typically early to mid-May.

ADDRESS INQUIRIES TO:
Stefanie Putkowski, R.N.
Research Program Administrator
The National Organization
for Rare Disorders
P.O. Box 1968
Danbury, CT 06813-1968

*SPECIAL STIPULATIONS:
Reports and communication must be written in English and adhere to the most recent guidelines set forth by the National Institutes of Health.

NATIONAL SOCIETY DAUGHTERS OF THE AMERICAN REVOLUTION [2298]

1776 D Street, N.W.
Washington, DC 20006-5303
(202) 879-3292

WEB SITE ADDRESS:
www.dar.org

FOUNDED: 1895

AREAS OF INTEREST:
Medicine and psychiatric nursing.

NAME(S) OF PROGRAMS:
● **Irene and Daisy MacGregor Memorial Scholarship**

TYPE:
Scholarships.

YEAR PROGRAM STARTED: 1991

PURPOSE:
To provide ways and means to aid students in attaining higher education.

LEGAL BASIS:
Incorporated historical society.

ELIGIBILITY:
Scholarships are awarded without regard to race, religion, sex or national origin. All four-year scholarships must be for consecutive years and are renewable only upon review and approval of annual transcript. Candidates must be U.S. citizens and must attend or plan to attend an accredited college or university in the U.S. No affiliation or relationship to DAR is required for qualification, but candidate must be sponsored by a local DAR Chapter. Awards are judged on the basis of academic excellence, commitment to field of study, as required, and financial need.

The MacGregor Memorial Scholarship is awarded to students of high scholastic standing and character who have been accepted into or are pursuing an approved course of study to become a medical doctor (not pre-med) at an approved, accredited medical school.

This MacGregor Memorial Scholarship is also available to students who have been accepted into or who are pursuing an approved course of study in the field of psychiatric nursing, graduate level, at medical schools, colleges or universities. There is a preference to females "if equally qualified."

FINANCIAL DATA:
Amount of support per award: $5,000 annually for up to four consecutive years, with a maximum of $20,000.

APPLICATION INFORMATION:
To obtain a scholarship application packet, send a self-addressed, stamped #10 business-size envelope to Office of the Reporter General, DAR Scholarship Committee, at the address listed above.

No affiliation or relationship with the NSDAR is necessary, unless specifically stated, to apply for a scholarship.

Included with the application packet is the list of DAR State Scholarship Chairmen. All scholarship applicants are required to have a letter of sponsorship from a chapter. Individuals interested in obtaining a letter of sponsorship from a local chapter are encouraged to contact the DAR State Chairman.

Duration: Up to four consecutive years. Annual transcript review required for renewal and award.

Deadline: April 15.

PUBLICATIONS:
American Spirit, magazine.

ADDRESS INQUIRIES TO:
Office of the Reporter General
DAR Scholarship Committee
(See address above.)

NORTH AMERICAN SPINE SOCIETY (NASS) [2299]

8320 St. Moritz Drive
Spring Grove, IL 60081
(630) 230-3691
Fax: (630) 230-3791

E-MAIL ADDRESS:
kjames@spine.org

WEB SITE ADDRESS:
www.spine.org

FOUNDED: 1985

AREAS OF INTEREST:
Disorders and functions of the human spine.

NAME(S) OF PROGRAMS:
● **Clinical Traveling Fellowship**
● **Research Grant**
● **Research Traveling Fellowship**
● **Young Investigator Grants**

TYPE:
Awards/prizes; Fellowships; Research grants. Clinical Traveling Fellowship: At least one month to be spent in three to five different medical centers studying spine techniques.

Research Traveling Fellowship: At least five months at one medical center, other than the one in which the applicants currently practice. This Fellowship primarily covers the cost of travel and housing.

Research Grant: This grant is for investigative research on the spine.

Young Investigator Grant: This grant is for projects in basic science, clinical or translational.

YEAR PROGRAM STARTED: 1989

PURPOSE:
To advance quality spine care through education, research and advocacy; to encourage and support basic and clinical science that is performed with integrity and

with a goal towards improving quality spine care for patients and understanding underlying disorders.

ELIGIBILITY:
Qualified investigators are eligible to apply. Applicants for Fellowships must have the approval of the institution and recommendation of the department head where the research training will be conducted.

FINANCIAL DATA:
Amount of support per award: $50,000 to $100,000.

Total amount of support: Varies.

NUMBER OF APPLICANTS MOST RECENT YEAR:
183.

NUMBER OF AWARDS: Fellowships: 2; Research Grants: 7.

APPLICATION INFORMATION:
Contact the Organization for application procedures. Budget restrictions are available when requesting an application.

Duration: Two years.

Deadline: Letters of Proposals for Grants: First week in February. Invited Grants and Fellowships: First week in May.

ADDRESS INQUIRIES TO:
Karen James, Manager of Research and Quality Improvement
(See address above.)

ORTHOPAEDIC RESEARCH AND EDUCATION FOUNDATION [2300]

6300 North River Road
Suite 700
Rosemont, IL 60018-4261
(847) 698-9980
Fax: (847) 698-7806

E-MAIL ADDRESS:
mcrae@oref.org

WEB SITE ADDRESS:
www.oref.org

FOUNDED: 1955

AREAS OF INTEREST:
Musculoskeletal research.

NAME(S) OF PROGRAMS:
● **OREF Clinical Research Award**

TYPE:
Awards/prizes.

YEAR PROGRAM STARTED: 1996

PURPOSE:
To award outstanding research related to clinical musculoskeletal disease or injury.

LEGAL BASIS:
Special-interest foundation, 501(c)(3).

ELIGIBILITY:
Individual applicants must be members of the AAOS, ORS, Canadian Orthopaedic Association, Canadian ORS or sponsored by a member.

FINANCIAL DATA:
Amount of support per award: $20,000.

Total amount of support: $20,000.

NUMBER OF APPLICANTS MOST RECENT YEAR:
6.

NUMBER OF AWARDS: 1.

APPLICATION INFORMATION:
Submission guidelines are available on the web site.

Duration: One-time award.

Deadline: July 1.

PUBLICATIONS:
Annual report; application guidelines.

ADDRESS INQUIRIES TO:
Kenya D. McRae, J.D., Ph.D.
Vice President of Grants
(See address above.)

ORTHOPAEDIC RESEARCH AND EDUCATION FOUNDATION [2301]

6300 North River Road
Suite 700
Rosemont, IL 60018-4261
(847) 698-9980
Fax: (847) 698-7806

E-MAIL ADDRESS:
mcrae@oref.org
marino@oref.org

WEB SITE ADDRESS:
www.oref.org

FOUNDED: 1955

AREAS OF INTEREST:
Orthopaedic research.

NAME(S) OF PROGRAMS:
● **Career Development Grants**

TYPE:
Research grants. Grants for scientific research in orthopaedic surgery.

YEAR PROGRAM STARTED: 1984

PURPOSE:
To encourage a commitment to scientific research in orthopaedic surgery.

LEGAL BASIS:
501(c)(3) special-interest foundation.

ELIGIBILITY:
Candidates must have completed residency in orthopaedic surgery and have demonstrated a sustained interest in research, as well as excellence in clinical training. Letters of nomination and support must offer convincing evidence of the candidate's potential to develop as an investigator.

GEOGRAPHIC RESTRICTIONS:
United States.

FINANCIAL DATA:
Amount of support per award: Up to $75,000 per year. Budget may include salary support.
Total amount of support: Varies.

APPLICATION INFORMATION:
Contact the Foundation.
Duration: Up to three years, conditional upon annual review.
Deadline: Fall. Announcement the following February or March.

PUBLICATIONS:
Annual report; application guidelines.

ADDRESS INQUIRIES TO:
Mary Marino, Grants Manager
(See address above.)

*SPECIAL STIPULATIONS:
Applicant must be working in the U.S. only.

ORTHOPAEDIC RESEARCH AND EDUCATION FOUNDATION [2302]

6300 North River Road
Suite 700
Rosemont, IL 60018-4261
(847) 698-9980
Fax: (847) 698-7806

E-MAIL ADDRESS:
mcrae@oref.org

WEB SITE ADDRESS:
www.oref.org

FOUNDED: 1955

AREAS OF INTEREST:
Orthopaedic surgery research.

NAME(S) OF PROGRAMS:
● **Resident Clinician-Scientist Training Grant**

TYPE:
Research grants. Grants to prepare residents for a career with research as a major component.

YEAR PROGRAM STARTED: 1961

PURPOSE:
To encourage the research interests and meritorious projects of residents and fellows in approved orthopaedic programs.

LEGAL BASIS:
501(c)(3) special-interest foundation.

ELIGIBILITY:
Candidates must be residents or fellows in approved orthopaedic programs.

GEOGRAPHIC RESTRICTIONS:
United States.

FINANCIAL DATA:
Grants provide funds for supplies and expenses, but not for resident salary or travel.
Amount of support per award: Up to $20,000.
Total amount of support: Varies.

APPLICATION INFORMATION:
Applications are available on the web site from May until September.
Duration: One year.
Deadline: Mid-September. Announcement the following February or March.

PUBLICATIONS:
Annual report; application guidelines.

ADDRESS INQUIRIES TO:
Kenya McRae, Ph.D., J.D.
Vice President of Grants
(See address above.)

*SPECIAL STIPULATIONS:
Resident must be working in the U.S.

OSTEOGENESIS IMPERFECTA FOUNDATION [2303]

804 West Diamond Avenue
Suite 210
Gaithersburg, MD 20878
(301) 947-0083
Fax: (301) 947-0456

E-MAIL ADDRESS:
bonelink@oif.org

WEB SITE ADDRESS:
www.oif.org

FOUNDED: 1970

AREAS OF INTEREST:
Osteogenesis imperfecta medical research.

NAME(S) OF PROGRAMS:
● **Clinical Seed Grants**
● **Michael Geisman Fellowships**
● **Seed Grants**

TYPE:
Fellowships; Research grants; Seed money grants. Clinical Seed Grants are designed to study people with osteogenesis imperfecta and their families.

Michael Geisman Fellowships: Applicants must be in academic institutions and the work must be done under the supervision of a mentor with training and experience in osteogenesis imperfecta (OI) or a related field.

Seed Grants are for basic or clinical studies with relevance to OI.

YEAR PROGRAM STARTED: 1970

PURPOSE:
To expand understanding and identify improved treatments for osteogenesis imperfecta.

LEGAL BASIS:
Nonprofit organization.

ELIGIBILITY:
Applicants for the fellowship must be postdoctoral fellows in academic institutions and the work must be done under the supervision of a mentor with appropriate training and experience in this or related field.

FINANCIAL DATA:
Amount of support per award: Clinical Seed Grants: Up to $120,000; Michael Geisman Fellowships: Up to $50,000 per year ($35,000 toward the investigator's salary and up to $15,000 per year for supplies); Seed Grants: Up to $60,000.

APPLICATION INFORMATION:
Applicants should submit an original application with 10 copies. The application should include an abstract for a lay audience, budget, education, previous research experience, professional training, publications and a research plan. Electronic submissions are accepted.
Duration: Clinical Seed Grants: One-time funding for two years; Michael Geisman Fellowships: One year with possible renewal; Seed Grants: One-time funding for one year.
Deadline: December 1.

PUBLICATIONS:
Annual report; application guidelines; bimonthly newsletter.

IRS IDENTIFICATION NUMBER: 23-7076021

ADDRESS INQUIRIES TO:
OIF Research Department
(See address above.)

OXALOSIS AND HYPEROXALURIA FOUNDATION [2304]

201 East 19th Street, Suite 12-E
New York, NY 10003
(212) 777-0470
(800) 643-8699
Fax: (212) 777-0471

E-MAIL ADDRESS:
kimh@ohf.org

WEB SITE ADDRESS:
www.ohf.org

FOUNDED: 1989

AREAS OF INTEREST:
Hyperoxaluria and oxalosis.

NAME(S) OF PROGRAMS:
● **OHF Research Grant**

TYPE:
Research grants. The Research Grant program assists investigators, new or established, who have research projects for which they need support.

PURPOSE:
To fund grants which will increase the understanding of hyperoxaluria and oxalosis and improve the clinical management and treatment of these diseases.

ELIGIBILITY:
Applications are accepted from anywhere in the world. There are no citizenship requirements.

FINANCIAL DATA:
Funds may be used for salaries for the investigators, technical assistance, special equipment, animals, supplies and travel.
Amount of support per award: Up to $160,000.
Total amount of support: Varies.

APPLICATION INFORMATION:
All applications must be made on the OHF forms. OHF prefers that applications be submitted electronically as an attachment and e-mailed to grantapp@ohf.org. Appendices, if included, may also be submitted electronically. Additionally, one original paper copy of the application must be submitted to the OHF Office address listed above. Applications or supporting material received after the deadline will not be considered, regardless of the date of postmark.
Duration: Up to two years.
Deadline: November 15.

ADDRESS INQUIRIES TO:
Kim Hollander, Executive Director
(See address above.)

OXNARD FOUNDATION   [2305]
5 Royal St. George Road
Newport Beach, CA 92660
(949) 644-4160
Fax: (949) 644-4171
E-MAIL ADDRESS:
covlineage@gmail.com
AREAS OF INTEREST:
General medical research.
TYPE:
Matching gifts; Research grants.
PURPOSE:
To help continue medical research in the areas of concern for the Foundation.
ELIGIBILITY:
IRS 501(c)(3) tax-exempt organizations, schools and hospitals.
GEOGRAPHIC RESTRICTIONS:
California, New Mexico and Tennessee.
FINANCIAL DATA:
Amount of support per award: $35,000 to $50,000.
Total amount of support: Varies.
APPLICATION INFORMATION:
Applicants should first send a letter and include a copy of the IRS tax determination letter.
Duration: One year. Renewal by reapplication.
Deadline: Applications are reviewed at Board meetings in February, June and November.
ADDRESS INQUIRIES TO:
Christopher Veitch, President
(See address above.)

PHARMACEUTICAL RESEARCH AND MANUFACTURERS OF AMERICA FOUNDATION, INC.   [2306]
950 F Street, N.W.
Suite 300
Washington, DC 20004
(202) 572-7756
Fax: (202) 572-7799
E-MAIL ADDRESS:
foundation@phrma.org
WEB SITE ADDRESS:
www.phrmafoundation.org
AREAS OF INTEREST:
Health outcomes and pharmaceutical research.
NAME(S) OF PROGRAMS:
● **Predoctoral Fellowships in Health Outcomes**
TYPE:
Fellowships.
YEAR PROGRAM STARTED: 2002
PURPOSE:
To support promising students during their thesis research.
ELIGIBILITY:
Full-time, in-residence Ph.D. candidates in the fields of health outcomes enrolled in U.S. schools of medicine, pharmacy, dentistry, or schools of public health are eligible to apply. Students must have completed two years of study and start their thesis research by the time the award is activated. Applicants must be U.S. citizens or permanent residents. Applications are to be submitted by an accredited U.S. school.
GEOGRAPHIC RESTRICTIONS:
United States.
FINANCIAL DATA:
Award is made to the university on behalf of the fellow. Annual stipend payable monthly for one to two years. $500 per year may be used for incidentals directly associated with thesis research preparation.
Amount of support per award: Maximum $50,000 ($25,000 per year).
NUMBER OF AWARDS: 2 budgeted.
APPLICATION INFORMATION:
Contact the Foundation.
Duration: Two years.
Deadline: Deadline and announcement date are available online.
PUBLICATIONS:
Brochure.
BOARD OF DIRECTORS:
Elias A. Zerhouni, M.D., Chairman
John Castellani
Thomas O. Daniel, M.D.
G. Mikael Dolsten, M.D., Ph.D.
Glenn J. Gormley, M.D., Ph.D.
Jan M. Lundberg, Ph.D.
Michael Rosenblatt, M.D.
Moncef Slaoui, Ph.D.
Tadataka Yamada, M.D.
ADVISORY COMMITTEE:
Darrell R. Abernethy, M.D., Ph.D., Chairman
Terry L. Bowlin, Ph.D.
Jean Paul Gagnon, Ph.D.
Michael J. Hageman, Ph.D.
Michael N. Liebman, Ph.D.
ADDRESS INQUIRIES TO:
Predoctoral Fellowships in Health Outcomes
(See address above.)

PHARMACEUTICAL RESEARCH AND MANUFACTURERS OF AMERICA FOUNDATION, INC.   [2307]
950 F Street, N.W.
Suite 300
Washington, DC 20004
(202) 572-7756
Fax: (202) 572-7799
E-MAIL ADDRESS:
foundation@phrma.org
WEB SITE ADDRESS:
www.phrmafoundation.org
AREAS OF INTEREST:
Informatics.
NAME(S) OF PROGRAMS:
● **Postdoctoral Fellowships in Informatics**
TYPE:
Fellowships.
YEAR PROGRAM STARTED: 2002
PURPOSE:
To support postdoctoral career development activities of individuals preparing to engage in research that will bridge the gap between experimental and computational approaches in genomic and biomedical studies.
ELIGIBILITY:
Applicants must hold a Ph.D. degree in the field of study logically or functionally related to the proposed postdoctoral activities, or expect to receive the Ph.D. before activating the award. Must also have firm commitment from an accredited U.S. university and be a U.S. citizen or permanent resident.
GEOGRAPHIC RESTRICTIONS:
United States.
FINANCIAL DATA:
Annual stipend made to the institution on behalf of the fellow.
Amount of support per award: Maximum $80,000 ($40,000 per year).
NUMBER OF AWARDS: 2 budgeted.
APPLICATION INFORMATION:
Applications are to be submitted at the Foundation web site.
Duration: One to two years.
Deadline: September 1. Announcement December 15.
PUBLICATIONS:
Brochure.
ADDRESS INQUIRIES TO:
Postdoctoral Fellowships in Informatics
(See address above.)
*SPECIAL STIPULATIONS:
Second year contingent upon progress report approved by the Foundation and submission of a financial report.

PHARMACEUTICAL RESEARCH AND MANUFACTURERS OF AMERICA FOUNDATION, INC.   [2308]
950 F Street, N.W.
Suite 300
Washington, DC 20004
(202) 572-7756
Fax: (202) 572-7799
E-MAIL ADDRESS:
foundation@phrma.org

WEB SITE ADDRESS:
www.phrmafoundation.org

AREAS OF INTEREST:
Health outcomes, informatics,
pharmacology/toxicology and pharmaceutics.

NAME(S) OF PROGRAMS:
- **Sabbatical Fellowships in Health Outcomes**
- **Sabbatical Fellowships in Informatics**
- **Sabbatical Fellowships in Pharmaceutics**
- **Sabbatical Fellowships in Pharmacology/Toxicology**

TYPE:
Fellowships.

YEAR PROGRAM STARTED: 2002

PURPOSE:
To provide support for individuals engaged in a multidisciplinary research training program that will create or extend their credentials in the fields of health outcomes, informatics, pharmacology/toxicology or pharmaceutics.

ELIGIBILITY:
Varies by program.

GEOGRAPHIC RESTRICTIONS:
United States.

FINANCIAL DATA:
Amount of support per award: $40,000.
Matching fund requirements: Matching funds must be provided by the institution.

NUMBER OF AWARDS: 1 budgeted for each program.

APPLICATION INFORMATION:
Applications are to be submitted at the Foundation web site.
Duration: One year.
Deadline: Pharmaceutics and Health Outcomes: October 1. All others: September 1. Announcement: December 15.

PUBLICATIONS:
Brochure.

ADDRESS INQUIRIES TO:
Sabbatical Fellowships
(See address above.)

PHARMACEUTICAL RESEARCH AND MANUFACTURERS OF AMERICA FOUNDATION, INC.   [2309]
950 F Street, N.W.
Suite 300
Washington, DC 20004
(202) 572-7756
Fax: (202) 572-7799

E-MAIL ADDRESS:
foundation@phrma.org

WEB SITE ADDRESS:
www.phrmafoundation.org

AREAS OF INTEREST:
Pharmacology and toxicology.

NAME(S) OF PROGRAMS:
- **Postdoctoral Fellowship in Pharmacology/Toxicology**

TYPE:
Fellowships.

YEAR PROGRAM STARTED: 2002

PURPOSE:
To support postdoctoral career development activities of individuals prepared (or preparing) to engage in research that

integrates information on molecular or cellular mechanisms of action with information on the effect of an agent in the intact organism.

ELIGIBILITY:
Applicants must hold a Ph.D. degree or appropriate terminal research Doctorate in a field of study logically or functionally related to the proposed postdoctoral activities, or expect to receive the Ph.D. before activating the award. They must also have a firm commitment from an accredited U.S. university and be a U.S. citizen or permanent resident.

GEOGRAPHIC RESTRICTIONS:
United States.

FINANCIAL DATA:
Stipend is made to the institution on behalf of the fellow.
Amount of support per award: Maximum $80,000 ($40,000 per year).

NUMBER OF AWARDS: 2 budgeted.

APPLICATION INFORMATION:
Applications are to be submitted at the Foundation web site.
Duration: Two years.
Deadline: September 1. Announcement December 15.

PUBLICATIONS:
Brochure.

ADDRESS INQUIRIES TO:
Postdoctoral Fellowship in Pharmacology/Toxicology
(See address above.)

*SPECIAL STIPULATIONS:
Second year is contingent upon a progress report approved by the Foundation and submission of a financial report.

PHARMACEUTICAL RESEARCH AND MANUFACTURERS OF AMERICA FOUNDATION, INC.   [2310]
950 F Street, N.W.
Suite 300
Washington, DC 20004
(202) 572-7756
Fax: (202) 572-7799

E-MAIL ADDRESS:
foundation@phrma.org

WEB SITE ADDRESS:
www.phrmafoundation.org

FOUNDED: 1965

AREAS OF INTEREST:
Health outcomes.

NAME(S) OF PROGRAMS:
- **Postdoctoral Fellowship in Health Outcomes**

TYPE:
Fellowships. This program provides stipend to well-trained graduates from Pharm.D., M.D., and Ph.D. programs who seek to further develop and refine research skills through formal postdoctoral training.

YEAR PROGRAM STARTED: 2002

PURPOSE:
To encourage graduates from Ph.D. programs in health outcomes to continue their research skills through formal postdoctoral training.

LEGAL BASIS:
501(c)(3) organization.

ELIGIBILITY:
Applicant must be a graduate from Pharm.D., M.D. or Ph.D. program.

Before an individual is eligible to apply for a PHRMA Foundation award, he or she must first have a firm commitment from a U.S. university. Applications must be submitted by an accredited school in the U.S. and all applicants should either be a U.S. citizen or permanent resident.

GEOGRAPHIC RESTRICTIONS:
United States.

FINANCIAL DATA:
Amount of support per award: Maximum $110,000 ($55,000 per year).

NUMBER OF APPLICANTS MOST RECENT YEAR:
10.

NUMBER OF AWARDS: 1 budgeted.

APPLICATION INFORMATION:
Contact the Foundation.
Duration: Two years.
Deadline: Deadline and announcement date will be available online.

PUBLICATIONS:
Brochure.

IRS IDENTIFICATION NUMBER: 52-6063009

ADVISORY COMMITTEE:
Darrell R. Abernethy, M.D., Ph.D., Chairman
Terry L. Bowlin, Ph.D.
Jean Paul Gagnon, Ph.D.
Michael J. Hageman, Ph.D.
Michael N. Liebman, Ph.D.

ADDRESS INQUIRIES TO:
Postdoctoral Fellowship
in Health Outcomes
(See address above.)

PHARMACEUTICAL RESEARCH AND MANUFACTURERS OF AMERICA FOUNDATION, INC.
950 F Street, N.W.
Suite 300
Washington, DC 20004
(202) 572-7756
Fax: (202) 572-7799

E-MAIL ADDRESS:
foundation@phrma.org

WEB SITE ADDRESS:
www.phrmafoundation.org

TYPE:
Project/program grants; Research grants; Seed money grants. Starter grants to support research in the fields of pharmacology, clinical pharmacology, drug toxicology, pharmaceutics, informatics and health outcomes.

See entry 2542 for full listing.

DR. AND MRS. ARTHUR WILLIAM PHILLIPS CHARITABLE TRUST   [2311]
P.O. Box 316
Oil City, PA 16301
(814) 676-2736
Fax: (814) 677-5701

FOUNDED: 1979

AREAS OF INTEREST:
Primarily medical centers, research and education.

TYPE:
Project/program grants.

PURPOSE:
To support many varied projects.

ELIGIBILITY:
Organizations must be:
(1) IRS 501(c)(3) tax-exempt;
(2) located in northwestern Pennsylvania;
(3) able to raise the balance of necessary funding from other sources and;
(4) able to show evidence of financial responsibility that will insure the completion and success of the project.

GEOGRAPHIC RESTRICTIONS:
Northwestern Pennsylvania.

FINANCIAL DATA:
Amount of support per award: Varies.
Total amount of support: Approximately $600,000.

APPLICATION INFORMATION:
Applications should be made in triplicate and include a short history of the organization, the need for the project, the annual budget for the project, other helpful financial budgetary information and a copy of their 501(c)(3).
Duration: Typically one year.

IRS IDENTIFICATION NUMBER: 25-6201015

TRUSTEES:
Larry S. Adams
Edith Gilmore Letcher
Robert W. McFate

ADDRESS INQUIRIES TO:
Robert W. McFate, Trustee
(See address above.)

PLASTIC SURGERY FOUNDATION (PSF) [2312]
ASPS/PSF
444 East Algonquin Road
Arlington Heights, IL 60005
(847) 228-9900
Fax: (847) 709-7506

E-MAIL ADDRESS:
research@plasticsurgery.org

WEB SITE ADDRESS:
www.thepsf.org/research/grant-applications

AREAS OF INTEREST:
Basic/translational research, clinical, or health services research.

NAME(S) OF PROGRAMS:
• **National Endowment for Plastic Surgery**
• **Pilot Research Grant**
• **Research Fellowship**

TYPE:
Awards/prizes. National Endowment for Plastic Surgery: This grant is designed to support projects that address clinically relevant, immediate issues facing the practice of plastic surgery. The Endowment encourages the specialty to be proactive in identifying research opportunities; it also quickly responds to changing demands within the field of plastic surgery. Sponsoring institutions, as well as individuals, are encouraged to apply for this specific type of funding.

Pilot Research Grant: This program is designed to promote advancement and innovation in plastic surgery. These grants provide "seed" funding and allow researchers to conduct preliminary studies related to plastic surgery science; they also set the stage for investigators to apply for external funding sources.

Research Fellowship: These grants encourage research and academic career development in plastic surgery. This program is designed for those who wish to supplement one year of clinical training for a research experience and can be utilized for training in any area of plastic surgery. Fellowship to be used for salary support only.

ELIGIBILITY:
National Endowment Grant and Pilot Research Grant: Applicants must be M.D., D.O., or Ph.D. and hold a full-time position in a Department of Plastic Surgery or equivalent and be an active or candidate member of ASPS (if currently in plastic surgery training, sponsorship from an active ASPS member).

Research Fellowship: Applicants must be an M.D. or D.O. and hold a full-time position in a Department of Plastic Surgery or equivalent. Applicants must be residents or within five years of initial faculty appointment and must be an active or candidate member of ASPS, or in training, with the sponsorship of an active ASPS member.

FINANCIAL DATA:
Amount of support per award: National Endowment for Plastic Surgery Grant: Up to $50,000; Pilot Research Grant: Up to $10,000; Research Fellowship: Up to $50,000.
Total amount of support: Varies.

NUMBER OF AWARDS: Varies.

APPLICATION INFORMATION:
Application instructions can be found on the Foundation web site.
Duration: One year.
Deadline: December; check online for exact date.

POST-POLIO HEALTH INTERNATIONAL [2313]
4207 Lindell Boulevard
Suite 110
St. Louis, MO 63108-2930
(314) 534-0475
Fax: (314) 534-5070

E-MAIL ADDRESS:
director@post-polio.org

WEB SITE ADDRESS:
www.post-polio.org

FOUNDED: 1995

AREAS OF INTEREST:
Neuromuscular respiratory diseases and post-poliomyelitis.

NAME(S) OF PROGRAMS:
• **The Research Fund**

TYPE:
Research grants; Seed money grants. The Research Fund supports the work of researchers investigating the late effects of poliomyelitis and/or neuromuscular respiratory disease through one of two grants:

The Thomas Wallace Rogers Memorial Respiratory Research Grant: To study the cause(s) and treatment of neuromuscular respiratory insufficiency and the effects of long-term home mechanical ventilation.

The Post-Poliomyelitis Research Grant: This grant is to study the cause(s), treatment and management of the problem of the late effects of polio.

The award is for two years. The next call for proposals will be in 2016.

YEAR PROGRAM STARTED: 2000

PURPOSE:
To help support researchers, scientists, and clinicians worldwide to investigate the cause, treatment, and management of post-poliomyelitis and neuromuscular respiratory disease; to seek scientific information leading to eventual amelioration of the consequences of poliomyelitis and/or neuromuscular respiratory diseases.

LEGAL BASIS:
Not-for-profit organization.

ELIGIBILITY:
Applicants must be affiliated with an institution or organization. Citizens of all countries may apply. Applications, however, must be in English. Proposals will not be accepted via fax. The research may be quantitative and/or qualitative and follow sound and appropriate research standards relevant to the subject matter. The research findings must relate to improving the quality of life for people with disabilities. Preference will be given to innovative or original research.

FINANCIAL DATA:
Funding does cover indirect costs to a maximum of $3,000/year.
Amount of support per award: $50,000 a year; accepts proposals for up to two years; maximum of $100,000.

NUMBER OF APPLICANTS MOST RECENT YEAR: 11.

NUMBER OF AWARDS: 1.

APPLICATION INFORMATION:
Contact the organization.
Duration: Up to two years.

IRS IDENTIFICATION NUMBER: 34-0961952

ADDRESS INQUIRIES TO:
Joan L. Headley, Executive Director
(See address above.)

THE ELISABETH SEVERANCE PRENTISS FOUNDATION [2314]
c/o PNC Bank
1900 East Ninth Street
Mailstop B7-YB13-03-1
Cleveland, OH 44114
(216) 222-2760
Fax: (216) 222-2410

E-MAIL ADDRESS:
john.baco@pnc.com

WEB SITE ADDRESS:
www.esprentissfoundation.org

FOUNDED: 1944

AREAS OF INTEREST:
Medical research, public health, hospital assistance for capital improvements, operation, management and administration.

TYPE:
Capital grants; Project/program grants. Project grants, educational support grants and building improvement grants in related medical areas.

YEAR PROGRAM STARTED: 1944

PURPOSE:
To promote and improve medical services, especially within Cuyahoga County (OH) for all individuals.

LEGAL BASIS:
Charitable foundation.

ELIGIBILITY:
Grant request must fall within restrictions of general purpose requirements, must not be for individuals for scholarships, fellowships, grants-in-aid or other personal purposes and must not be for redistribution by national foundations. Most favorable consideration will be given to those requests from applicants for purposes within the Cuyahoga County (OH) area. The Foundation strongly favors grant requests for specific projects over those requesting general operating support.

GEOGRAPHIC RESTRICTIONS:
Greater Cleveland, Ohio.

FINANCIAL DATA:
Total assets of $71,194,552 as of December 31, 2011.
Total amount of support: $3,015,500 for the year ended December 31, 2011.

APPLICATION INFORMATION:
There is no set form, but sufficient information and facts with supporting data should be given in the application to permit the Board of Managers to make a fair decision based on full and complete information. Applicant should also include six copies of each pertinent document being sent.
Duration: Support will continue, with annual installments, until requested grant has been satisfied. Grants are renewable.
Deadline: April 15 and October 15. Announcement after May and November semiannual board meetings.

ADDRESS INQUIRIES TO:
Richard Mack, Secretary
(See address above.)

PULMONARY FIBROSIS FOUNDATION   [2315]
230 East Ohio Street
Suite 304
Chicago, IL 60611
(888) 733-6741
Fax: (866) 587-9158

E-MAIL ADDRESS:
info@pulmonaryfibrosis.org

WEB SITE ADDRESS:
www.pulmonaryfibrosis.org

AREAS OF INTEREST:
Research of and treatment for pulmonary fibrosis.

NAME(S) OF PROGRAMS:
• **Clinical Research in Pulmonary Fibrosis Program**

TYPE:
Matching gifts. Supports postdoctoral research for studies in the clinical investigation of pulmonary fibrosis.

YEAR PROGRAM STARTED: 2000

PURPOSE:
To improve the quality of life of those affected by pulmonary fibrosis; to provide funding for research and treatment of pulmonary fibrosis.

ELIGIBILITY:
Researchers by invitation only.

FINANCIAL DATA:
Amount of support per award: Varies.

Total amount of support: Nearly $3,000,000 over the last 10 years.

IRS IDENTIFICATION NUMBER: 84-1558631

ADDRESS INQUIRIES TO:
Patti Tuomey, Chief Operating Officer
(See address above.)

RADIOLOGICAL SOCIETY OF NORTH AMERICA RESEARCH AND EDUCATION FOUNDATION   [2316]
820 Jorie Boulevard
Oak Brook, IL 60523-2251
(630) 571-7816
Fax: (630) 571-7837

E-MAIL ADDRESS:
swalter@rsna.org

WEB SITE ADDRESS:
www.rsna.org/foundation

FOUNDED: 1915

AREAS OF INTEREST:
Radiology.

NAME(S) OF PROGRAMS:
• **Research Seed Grant**

TYPE:
Seed money grants. Research Seed Grant support is available for any area of research related to the radiologic sciences.

PURPOSE:
To enable investigators to gain experience in defining objectives and testing hypotheses in preparation for major grant applications to corporations, foundations and governmental agencies.

ELIGIBILITY:
Applicants must be RSNA members at the time of application.

FINANCIAL DATA:
Research Seed Grant is to support the preliminary or pilot phase of scientific projects, not to supplement major funding already secured. No salary support for the principal investigator will be provided.
Amount of support per award: Up to $40,000.
Total amount of support: Varies.

APPLICATION INFORMATION:
Applications are completed using the online Grant Application System. A printed, signed copy must be sent and received in the Foundation office on or before the posted deadline date.
Duration: One year.
Deadline: January 15.

ADDRESS INQUIRIES TO:
Scott Walter
Assistant Director, Grant Administration
(See address above.)

RADIOLOGICAL SOCIETY OF NORTH AMERICA RESEARCH AND EDUCATION FOUNDATION   [2317]
820 Jorie Boulevard
Oak Brook, IL 60523-2251
(630) 571-7816
Fax: (630) 571-7837

E-MAIL ADDRESS:
swalter@rsna.org

WEB SITE ADDRESS:
www.rsna.org/foundation

FOUNDED: 1915

AREAS OF INTEREST:
Radiology.

NAME(S) OF PROGRAMS:
• **Research Medical Student Grant**

TYPE:
Research grants. Research Medical Student Grant is for any area of research related to the radiologic sciences.

PURPOSE:
To make radiology research opportunities possible for medical students and to encourage them, early in their medical careers, to consider academic radiology as an important option for their future.

ELIGIBILITY:
Applicants must be RSNA members at the time of application.

FINANCIAL DATA:
Funds are intended to secure protected time for the recipient and may not be used for nonpersonnel research expenses.
Amount of support per award: $3,000.
Total amount of support: Approximately $75,000.
Matching fund requirements: $3,000 to be matched by the sponsoring department ($6,000 total) as a stipend for the medical student.

NUMBER OF AWARDS: 25.

APPLICATION INFORMATION:
Applications are completed using the online Grant Application System. A printed, signed copy must be sent and received in the Foundation office on or before the posted deadline date.
Duration: 10 weeks full-time (or equivalent).
Deadline: February 1.

ADDRESS INQUIRIES TO:
Scott Walter
Assistant Director, Grant Administration
(See address above.)

RADIOLOGICAL SOCIETY OF NORTH AMERICA RESEARCH AND EDUCATION FOUNDATION   [2318]
820 Jorie Boulevard
Oak Brook, IL 60523-2251
(630) 571-7816
Fax: (630) 571-7837

E-MAIL ADDRESS:
swalter@rsna.org

WEB SITE ADDRESS:
www.rsna.org/foundation

FOUNDED: 1915

AREAS OF INTEREST:
Radiology.

NAME(S) OF PROGRAMS:
• **Education Scholar Grant**

TYPE:
Training grants. Any area of education related to the radiologic sciences.

PURPOSE:
To fund individuals in radiology or related disciplines who are seeking an opportunity to develop their expertise in radiologic education; to develop teachers in radiology who can share their knowledge with the radiology community.

ELIGIBILITY:
Applicants must be RSNA members at the time of application.

FINANCIAL DATA:
Educational Scholar Grant to be used as part-time salary support and for educational expenses.

Amount of support per award: Up to $75,000.

APPLICATION INFORMATION:
Applications are completed using the online Grant Application System. A printed, signed copy must be sent and received in the Foundation office on or before the posted deadline date.

Duration: One year. In exceptional cases, grants for up to two years will be considered.

Deadline: January 10.

ADDRESS INQUIRIES TO:
Scott Walter
Assistant Director, Grant Administration
(See address above.)

RADIOLOGICAL SOCIETY OF NORTH AMERICA RESEARCH AND EDUCATION FOUNDATION [2319]
820 Jorie Boulevard
Oak Brook, IL 60523-2251
(630) 571-7816
Fax: (630) 571-7837

E-MAIL ADDRESS:
swalter@rsna.org

WEB SITE ADDRESS:
www.rsna.org/foundation

FOUNDED: 1915

AREAS OF INTEREST:
Radiology.

NAME(S) OF PROGRAMS:
● **RSNA/AUR/APDR/SCARD Radiology Education Research Development Grant**

TYPE:
Research grants.

PURPOSE:
To encourage innovation and improvement in health sciences education by providing research opportunities to individuals in pursuit of advancing the science of radiology education; to help in building a critical mass of radiology education researchers and promote the careers of persons advancing the science of radiology education.

ELIGIBILITY:
Grants are awarded to any person, at any level of career development, affiliated with a radiology department. Applicants must be members of one or more of the sponsoring organizations.

FINANCIAL DATA:
Grants can be used to help cover the costs of research materials, research assistant support and limited primary investigator salary support.

Amount of support per award: Up to $10,000.

Total amount of support: Varies.

COOPERATIVE FUNDING PROGRAMS:
Co-sponsored by the Radiological Society of North America (RSNA), Association of University Radiologists (AUR), Association

of Program Directors in Radiology (APDR), and Society of Chairmen of Academic Radiology Departments (SCARD).

APPLICATION INFORMATION:
Application procedures are available online.

Duration: One year.

Deadline: January 10.

ADDRESS INQUIRIES TO:
Scott Walter
Assistant Director, Grant Administration
(See address above.)

RADIOLOGICAL SOCIETY OF NORTH AMERICA RESEARCH AND EDUCATION FOUNDATION [2320]
820 Jorie Boulevard
Oak Brook, IL 60523-2251
(630) 571-7816
Fax: (630) 571-7837

E-MAIL ADDRESS:
swalter@rsna.org

WEB SITE ADDRESS:
www.rsna.org/foundation

FOUNDED: 1915

AREAS OF INTEREST:
Radiology.

NAME(S) OF PROGRAMS:
● **RSNA Research Scholar Grant**

TYPE:
Research grants.

PURPOSE:
To support junior faculty members who have completed the conventional resident/fellowship training programs but have not yet been recognized as independent investigators.

ELIGIBILITY:
Any area of research related to the radiologic sciences is eligible for Research Scholar Grant support. Applicants must be nominated by their department chair.

GEOGRAPHIC RESTRICTIONS:
North America.

FINANCIAL DATA:
Amount of support per award: $150,000 ($75,000 per year).

Total amount of support: Varies.

NUMBER OF APPLICANTS MOST RECENT YEAR: 20.

NUMBER OF AWARDS: 2 to 10.

APPLICATION INFORMATION:
Applications may be obtained from the Foundation web site.

Duration: Two years.

Deadline: January 15.

ADDRESS INQUIRIES TO:
Scott Walter
Assistant Director, Grant Administration
(See address above.)

*SPECIAL STIPULATIONS:
Applicant must commit to devoting 40% of time to granted project.

RADIOLOGICAL SOCIETY OF NORTH AMERICA RESEARCH AND EDUCATION FOUNDATION [2321]
820 Jorie Boulevard
Oak Brook, IL 60523-2251
(630) 571-7816
Fax: (630) 571-7837

E-MAIL ADDRESS:
swalter@rsna.org

WEB SITE ADDRESS:
www.rsna.org/foundation

FOUNDED: 1915

AREAS OF INTEREST:
Radiology.

NAME(S) OF PROGRAMS:
● **Research Resident/Fellow Grant**

TYPE:
Research grants. Grants will be awarded for diverse types of projects in the radiologic sciences including basic science and clinical research studies. This program is not intended to fund Ph.D. postdoctoral projects, nor to support those whose primary aim is to obtain practical experience in clinical radiology.

PURPOSE:
To provide young investigators not yet professionally established in the radiologic sciences an opportunity to gain further insight into scientific investigation and to develop competence in research techniques and methods.

ELIGIBILITY:
At the time of application, the applicant must:
(1) be an RSNA member;
(2) be a resident or fellow in a department of radiology, radiation oncology or nuclear medicine within a North American educational institution;
(3) have completed the internship year (PGY-1) and at least six months of specialty training in the radiologic sciences (PGY-2) for the resident grant, or be in the last year of, or have completed, the prescribed residency training for the fellow grant. (If awarded, applicant must be in a fellowship position during the period of grant support);
(4) be certified by the American Board of Radiology or equivalent, or on track for certification;
(5) not have been principal investigator on grant/contract amounts totaling more than $60,000 in a single calendar year (includes support from single or combined grants or contracts from any source including government, private or industrial/commercial sources);
(6) not be agent(s) of any for-profit, commercial company in the radiologic sciences (applies to applicant/co-principal investigator);
(7) not submit more than one research or education grant application to the RSNA Research and Education Foundation per year;
(8) not have concurrent RSNA grants and;
(9) devote at least 50% of applicant's time to granted project.

Acceptance of an award from another source for the same project is prohibited unless one source provides only salary support and the other source provides only support for nonpersonnel research expenses.

FINANCIAL DATA:
Funds may be used for salary and/or nonpersonnel research expenses.

Amount of support per award: $50,000 salary support for one-year Research Fellow project or $30,000 salary support for one-year Research Resident project.

Total amount of support: Varies.

NUMBER OF APPLICANTS MOST RECENT YEAR: 71.

NUMBER OF AWARDS: 15 to 30.

APPLICATION INFORMATION:
Applications are completed online using the Online Grant Application System. A printed, signed copy must be received in the Foundation office on or before the posted deadline date.

Duration: One year; however, residents may opt for a six-month, full-time research project.

Deadline: January 15.

ADDRESS INQUIRIES TO:
Scott Walter
Assistant Director, Grant Administration
(See address above.)

V. KANN RASMUSSEN FOUNDATION
475 Riverside Drive, Suite 900
New York, NY 10115
(212) 812-4268
Fax: (212) 812-4299

E-MAIL ADDRESS:
ikrarup@vkrf.org

WEB SITE ADDRESS:
www.vkrf.org

TYPE:
Challenge/matching grants; General operating grants; Project/program grants.

See entry 2088 for full listing.

FANNIE E. RIPPEL FOUNDATION   [2322]
14 Maple Avenue, Suite 200
Morristown, NJ 07960
(973) 540-0101
Fax: (973) 540-0404

E-MAIL ADDRESS:
pmacbain@rippelfoundation.org

WEB SITE ADDRESS:
rippelfoundation.org

FOUNDED: 1953

TYPE:
Project/program grants.

PURPOSE:
To seed innovation, catalyze change and create model processes that will lead to improvements in health.

LEGAL BASIS:
Private foundation.

ELIGIBILITY:
Organizations, associations, institutions and hospitals are eligible. No grants are made to individuals.

FINANCIAL DATA:
Amount of support per award: Varies.
Total amount of support: $3,000,000 to $4,000,000 per year.

NUMBER OF APPLICANTS MOST RECENT YEAR:
Varies.

NUMBER OF AWARDS: Average 8 to 12 per year.

APPLICATION INFORMATION:
When a grant proposal is requested, the following materials are required:
(1) written project proposal, including problem statement, project objectives, planned measures of success and timeline;
(2) profiles or resumes of key staff members;
(3) project and agency budget;
(4) IRS determination letter of 501(c)(3) status;
(5) most recent 990 tax return and;
(6) most recent audited financial statement, with auditor's management letter.

IRS IDENTIFICATION NUMBER: 22-1559427

OFFICERS:
John D. Campbell, Chairman
Laura K. Landy, President and Chief Executive Officer
Chana Fitton, Treasurer
Elizabeth Christopherson, Secretary

TRUSTEES:
Edward Ahart
John D. Campbell
Elizabeth Christopherson
Elliott Fisher
Laura K. Landy
David Surrenda

ADDRESS INQUIRIES TO:
Patricia MacBain, Office Manager
(See address above.)

*PLEASE NOTE:
Unsolicited proposals are not being accepted at this time.

SAVOY FOUNDATION   [2323]
230 Foch Street
St.-Jean-sur-Richelieu QC J3B 2B2 Canada
(450) 358-9779
Fax: (450) 346-1045

E-MAIL ADDRESS:
epilepsy@savoy-foundation.ca

WEB SITE ADDRESS:
www.savoy-foundation.ca

FOUNDED: 1971

AREAS OF INTEREST:
Epilepsy and medical research.

TYPE:
Fellowships; Research grants; Scholarships.

PURPOSE:
To promote research on epilepsy.

ELIGIBILITY:
Studentships will be awarded to meritorious applicants wishing to acquire training and pursue research in a biomedical discipline, the health sciences or social sciences related to epilepsy. To be eligible, the candidate must have a good university record (B.Sc., M.D. or equivalent diploma) and have ensured that a qualified researcher affiliated to a university and/or hospital will supervise his or her work. Concomitant registration in a graduate program (M.Sc. or Ph.D.) is encouraged.

Post-Doctoral and Clinical Research Fellowships will be awarded to scientists or medical specialists (Ph.D. or M.D.) wishing to carry out a full-time research project in the field of epilepsy.

Research Grants are available to clinicians and/or established scientists working on epilepsy or related subjects.

Studentships, fellowships, and grants are available to Canadian researchers, to foreign nationals or for projects conducted in Canada.

GEOGRAPHIC RESTRICTIONS:
Canada.

FINANCIAL DATA:
Amount of support per award: Studentships: $15,000 (CAN) per year. An annual sum of $1,000 will be allocated to the laboratory or institution as additional support for the research project. Post-Doctoral and Clinical Research Fellowships: $30,000. Research Grants: Up to $23,000.

Total amount of support: More than $250,000 (CAN) per year.

NUMBER OF APPLICANTS MOST RECENT YEAR:
49.

NUMBER OF AWARDS: 13.

APPLICATION INFORMATION:
Application information is available on the web site.

Duration: Studentships: One year. Renewable for a maximum duration of four years; Post-Doctoral and Clinical Research Fellowships: One year. Nonrenewable; Research grants generally are not renewable.

Deadline: January 15 (postmark). If January 15 falls on a weekend or holiday, the Foundation will consider the next working day as the deadline.

EXECUTIVE COMMITTEE:
George M. Savoy, President
Caroline Savoy, Vice President/Secretary
Alain Barbeau, Secretary and Treasurer

ADDRESS INQUIRIES TO:
Caroline Savoy, Secretary
(See address above.)

SCLERODERMA FOUNDATION   [2324]
300 Rosewood Drive, Suite 105
Danvers, MA 01923
(978) 463-5843 ext. 248
(800) 722-4673
Fax: (978) 463-5809

E-MAIL ADDRESS:
tsperry@scleroderma.org

WEB SITE ADDRESS:
www.scleroderma.org

FOUNDED: 1998

AREAS OF INTEREST:
Scleroderma.

NAME(S) OF PROGRAMS:
• **Scleroderma Foundation Research Grants**

TYPE:
Research grants.

YEAR PROGRAM STARTED: 1998

PURPOSE:
To support research in the area of scleroderma.

ELIGIBILITY:
Applicants must be principal investigators.

GEOGRAPHIC RESTRICTIONS:
United States for new and established investigators; international for established investigators only.

FINANCIAL DATA:
Amount of support per award: $150,000.

Total amount of support: Average $1,000,000 annually.

NUMBER OF APPLICANTS MOST RECENT YEAR: 39.

NUMBER OF AWARDS: Average 7.

APPLICATION INFORMATION:
Applicants must use the application form following NIH guidelines.
Duration: Established investigators: Two years; New investigators: Three years.
Deadline: September 15 annually. Deadline is subject to change. Call or visit the web site to verify deadline date.

PUBLICATIONS:
Quarterly magazine; literature.

IRS IDENTIFICATION NUMBER: 52-1375827

STAFF:
Tracey O'Connell Sperry, National Director of Development and Research

ADDRESS INQUIRIES TO:
Tracey O'Connell Sperry
National Director of
Development and Research
(See address above.)

SCLERODERMA FOUNDATION [2325]
300 Rosewood Drive, Suite 105
Danvers, MA 01923
(978) 463-5843 ext. 248
(800) 722-4673
Fax: (978) 463-5809

E-MAIL ADDRESS:
tsperry@scleroderma.org

WEB SITE ADDRESS:
www.scleroderma.org

FOUNDED: 1998

AREAS OF INTEREST:
Scleroderma.

NAME(S) OF PROGRAMS:
● **Scleroderma Foundation Multi-Center Collaborative Research Grant**

TYPE:
Research grants.

PURPOSE:
To support and enhance collaborations between two or more scleroderma centers to advance significant research on scleroderma.

ELIGIBILITY:
Applicants must be principal investigators.

GEOGRAPHIC RESTRICTIONS:
United States only.

FINANCIAL DATA:
Amount of support per award: $500,000.
Total amount of support: $500,000.

NUMBER OF APPLICANTS MOST RECENT YEAR: 6.

NUMBER OF AWARDS: 1.

APPLICATION INFORMATION:
Contact the Foundation.
Duration: Two years.
Deadline: Letter of Intent due September 2. Application: September 15.

PUBLICATIONS:
Quarterly magazine; literature.

IRS IDENTIFICATION NUMBER: 52-1375827

STAFF:
Tracey O'Connell Sperry, National Director of Development and Research

ADDRESS INQUIRIES TO:
Tracey O'Connell Sperry
National Director of
Development and Research
(See address above.)

SMITH FAMILY AWARDS PROGRAM FOR EXCELLENCE IN BIOMEDICAL RESEARCH [2326]
95 Berkeley Street, Second Floor
Boston, MA 02116
(617) 279-2240 ext. 702

E-MAIL ADDRESS:
glockwood@hria.org

WEB SITE ADDRESS:
www.tmfgrants.org/smith

FOUNDED: 1991

AREAS OF INTEREST:
Basic biomedical science including physics, chemistry and engineering with a focus on biomedical research.

TYPE:
Research grants.

YEAR PROGRAM STARTED: 1991

PURPOSE:
To provide research grants for newly independent junior faculty.

ELIGIBILITY:
Detailed information is available on the web site.

GEOGRAPHIC RESTRICTIONS:
Massachusetts, Yale University and Brown University.

FINANCIAL DATA:
Amount of support per award: $300,000 over three years.
Total amount of support: $1,500,000 for five new awards each year.

COOPERATIVE FUNDING PROGRAMS: Principal funding provided by the Richard and Susan Smith Family Foundation with contributing support from other donors.

NUMBER OF APPLICANTS MOST RECENT YEAR: 54 for the year 2013.

NUMBER OF AWARDS: 7 for funding cycle 2013-16.

REPRESENTATIVE AWARDS:
"Understanding Information-encoding During Salamander Limb Regeneration;" "Dissecting Motor Pattern Generating Circuits in Walking Drosophila;" "Learning How to See: A Biological and Computational Investigation of How Visual Cortex Learns and Develops;" "Bacterial Regulators of Immunity and Their Modulation of Host Transcription Factors."

APPLICATION INFORMATION:
Information and forms are available on the web site.
Duration: Three years. Nonrenewable.
Deadline: Early September to July 16.

PUBLICATIONS:
Application guidelines; directory of grant recipients (online); summaries of current and previous funded projects.

ADDRESS INQUIRIES TO:
Senior Program Officer
(See address above.)

THE SOCIETY FOR INVESTIGATIVE DERMATOLOGY [2327]
526 Superior Avenue East
Suite 540
Cleveland, OH 44114-1999
(216) 579-9300
Fax: (216) 579-9333

E-MAIL ADDRESS:
sid@sidnet.org

WEB SITE ADDRESS:
www.sidnet.org

FOUNDED: 1938

AREAS OF INTEREST:
Skin biology, skin disease, and publication and results of skin research.

CONSULTING OR VOLUNTEER SERVICES:
Advocacy for biomedical research.

NAME(S) OF PROGRAMS:
● **Albert M. Kligman Fellowship Fund Award**

TYPE:
Awards/prizes; Conferences/seminars; Fellowships; Research grants; Travel grants. Awards will be used to support resident, fellow and medical student travel to the Society's annual meetings to present their scientific work.

YEAR PROGRAM STARTED: 1973

PURPOSE:
To encourage trainees to become skin scientists; to encourage the best and brightest young scholars to become members of the research community in dermatology and to participate in the activities of the Society.

LEGAL BASIS:
Tax-exempt.

ELIGIBILITY:
Applicants must hold the M.D. or Ph.D. Project must be skin-/skin disease-related. Preceptor is required. One year of work minimum.

FINANCIAL DATA:
No indirect costs.
Amount of support per award: $25,000.

NUMBER OF AWARDS: Approximately 20.

APPLICATION INFORMATION:
Information on application can be obtained from the address above.
Duration: One year.
Deadline: Contact the Society for exact dates.

IRS IDENTIFICATION NUMBER: 23-1361165

OFFICERS:
Thomas Kupper, M.D., President

SOCIETY OF CARDIOVASCULAR ANESTHESIOLOGISTS
2209 Dickens Road
Richmond, VA 23230
(804) 282-0084
Fax: (804) 282-0090

E-MAIL ADDRESS:
sca@societyhq.com

WEB SITE ADDRESS:
www.scahq.org

TYPE:
Research grants.

See entry 2401 for full listing.

SOCIETY OF NUCLEAR MEDICINE AND MOLECULAR IMAGING (SNMMI)   [2328]

1850 Samuel Morse Drive
Reston, VA 20190-5316
(703) 652-6780
Fax: (703) 708-9015

E-MAIL ADDRESS:
kpadley@snmmi.org

WEB SITE ADDRESS:
www.snmmi.org/grants

FOUNDED: 1969

AREAS OF INTEREST:
Nuclear medicine.

NAME(S) OF PROGRAMS:
- **Mitzi & William Blahd, M.D. Pilot Research Grant**
- **Bradley-Alavi Student Fellowship**

TYPE:
Awards/prizes; Fellowships; Research grants; Seed money grants. Mitzi & William Blahd, M.D. Pilot Research Grant: This grant is designed to help a basic or clinical scientist in the early stages of his or her career conduct research that may lead to further funding.

Bradley-Alavi Student Fellowship: This program is designed to provide an introduction to, and to stimulate students' interest in, molecular imaging and nuclear medicine by supporting awardees' full-time participation in clinical or basic research activities for three months (or less).

YEAR PROGRAM STARTED: 1969

PURPOSE:
To advance excellence in health care through education and research in nuclear medicine by the provision of grants and awards.

LEGAL BASIS:
Tax-exempt, nonprofit organization.

ELIGIBILITY:
For the Mitzi & William Blahd, M.D. Pilot Research Grant, the following applicant requirements apply:
(1) basic or clinical scientists with an advanced degree, such as M.D., Ph.D. or equivalent;
(2) awardee must hold a full-time position in an educational/training institution when the award starts (faculty and trainees are eligible);
(3) applicant must be no more than five years post-nuclear medicine/-molecular imaging training (training can include residency, M.D./Ph.D. training or postdoctoral training);
(4) the research may be done in any country;
(5) applicant must not have served as the principal investigator of a peer-reviewed grant for more than $50,000 in a single calendar year and;
(6) preference will be given to individuals who have demonstrated great potential for a research career in the field of nuclear medicine/molecular imaging and whose research focuses on translational in vivo studies that include radionuclide imaging or therapy.

Bradley-Alavi Student Fellowship: An applicant from any country may apply, and must:
(1) be enrolled in a medical, pharmacy or graduate school, or be an undergraduate student demonstrating outstanding interest in nuclear medicine and/or molecular imaging research and;

(2) carry out fellowship during a three-month period between May 1 and December 31, 2014.

FINANCIAL DATA:
This grant may be used for salary support of the principal investigator, as well as direct costs of supplies and equipment. Support is not provided for salaries of other research personnel, or for indirect costs.
Amount of support per award: Mitzi & William Blahd, M.D. Pilot Research Grant: $25,000; Bradley-Alavi Student Fellowship: $3,000 each over three months.

COOPERATIVE FUNDING PROGRAMS: Mitzi & William Blahd, M.D. Pilot Research Grant is made possible by support from the Education and Research Foundation for Nuclear Medicine and Molecular Imaging.

The Bradley-Alavi Student Fellowship program is made possible through a grant from the Education and Research Foundation for Nuclear Medicine and Molecular Imaging.

NUMBER OF APPLICANTS MOST RECENT YEAR:
Mitzi & William Blahd, M.D. Pilot Research Grant: 8. Bradley-Alavi Student Fellowship: 15.

NUMBER OF AWARDS: Mitzi & William Blahd, M.D. Pilot Research Grant: 1. Bradley-Alavi Student Fellowship: 3 to 5.

APPLICATION INFORMATION:
Mitzi & William Blahd, M.D. Pilot Research Grant: The application must be completed in its entirety and submitted along with:
(1) principal investigator's current curriculum vitae;
(2) a research abstract and a detailed research proposal not to exceed 10 pages, excluding references;
(3) one letter of recommendation from the program director or research supervisor;
(4) one letter of recommendation from a professional colleague and;
(5) applicant must be a member of SNMMI at the time of award.

Bradley-Alavi Student Fellowship: The application must be completed in its entirety and submitted along with:
(1) a current curriculum vitae;
(2) a detailed research proposal not to exceed two pages, excluding references;
(3) a completed evaluation from the nuclear medicine faculty advisor overseeing the research (preceptor) and;
(4) at least one (preferably two) support letters from others involved in the applicant's educational/research experience; the applicant's preceptor may submit a letter of support; however, it must not be the sole letter received; letters of support must be received by the application deadline in order to be accepted.
Duration: Mitzi & William Blahd, M.D. Pilot Research Grant: One year. Bradley-Alavi Student Fellowship: Three months or less.
Deadline: Mitzi & William Blahd, M.D. Pilot Research Grant: January 31, 2015. Bradley-Alavi Student Fellowship: March 31, 2015.

OFFICERS:
Virginia Pappas, Chief Executive Officer

ADDRESS INQUIRIES TO:
Kristi C. Padley
Development Manager
(See telephone number
or e-mail address above.)

*SPECIAL STIPULATIONS:
Mitzi & William Blahd, M.D. Pilot Research Grant: No grantee may receive more than one research grant in any one year. Likewise no other grant request will be considered until a satisfactory summary of an earlier grant is received.

SOCIETY OF NUCLEAR MEDICINE AND MOLECULAR IMAGING (SNMMI)   [2329]

1850 Samuel Morse Drive
Reston, VA 20190-5316
(703) 652-6780
Fax: (703) 708-9015

E-MAIL ADDRESS:
kpadley@snmmi.org

WEB SITE ADDRESS:
www.snmmi.org/grants

FOUNDED: 1969

AREAS OF INTEREST:
Nuclear medicine.

NAME(S) OF PROGRAMS:
- **Paul Cole Technologist Scholarships**
- **PDEF Mickey Williams Technologist Minority Student Scholarships**

TYPE:
Scholarships. Scholarships support education of nuclear medicine technology students.

YEAR PROGRAM STARTED: 1969

PURPOSE:
To enhance the standards, further the progress, encourage research and improve practice in the field of nuclear medicine.

LEGAL BASIS:
Tax-exempt, 501(c)(3) nonprofit organization.

ELIGIBILITY:
To be eligible, all candidates must be active members of the SNMMI, demonstrate financial need, and have maintained a cumulative grade point average of 2.5 or better on a 4.0 scale, with evidence of high academic performance.

Applicants for the Paul Cole Scholarship must be enrolled in or accepted into an institution accredited through the Joint Review Committee on Educational Programs in Nuclear Medicine Technology (NRCNMT). The award is open to students in Associate, Baccalaureate, and certificate level programs.

Applicants for the PDEF Mickey Williams Minority Student Scholarship must be of African American, Native American, Hispanic American, Asian American or Pacific Islander descent. U.S. residency status of U.S. citizen, U.S. national, or U.S. permanent resident is required. Individuals with a visitor, student, or G-series visa are not eligible. The applicant must be currently enrolled in or accepted into an entry-level nuclear medicine technology program at the time of application. Award is open to students in Associate- and Baccalaureate-level programs only. Individuals with previous certificates or degrees in nuclear medicine sciences are not eligible.

Applicant must be a member of the SNMMI-TS. Students receive free membership.

GEOGRAPHIC RESTRICTIONS:
United States and Canada.

FINANCIAL DATA:
The scholarship may be used for tuition, or for other expenses if no tuition is charged.
Amount of support per award: Paul Cole Technologist Scholarships: $1,000; PDEF Mickey Williams Technologist Minority Student Scholarships: $2,500.
Total amount of support: $20,000 for the year 2014.

NUMBER OF APPLICANTS MOST RECENT YEAR:
100.

NUMBER OF AWARDS: Paul Cole Technologist Scholarships:15 for the year 2014; Mickey Williams Technologist Minority Student Scholarships: 2 for the year 2014.

APPLICATION INFORMATION:
Applications will not be considered unless the following have been received by the application deadline:
(1) a completed application, which includes the applicant's personal and financial information and the nuclear medicine technology program information;
(2) official transcripts of all formal education (high school transcripts are not necessary if transcripts of college-level work are submitted) issued directly from the institution's registrar's office;
(3) an applicant statement, not to exceed one page, in DOC or PDF format that can be attached to the application. The brief statement should describe the applicant's educational aspirations and financial need for scholarship assistance and;
(4) a completed evaluation from the program director, whose information will be requested in the "Program Director Evaluation" section of the application.
Duration: One year.
Deadline: December 31, 2014.

ADDRESS INQUIRIES TO:
Kristi C. Padley
Development Manager
(See telephone number
or e-mail address above.)

SOCIETY OF RADIOLOGISTS IN ULTRASOUND   [2330]
1891 Preston White Drive
Reston, VA 20191
(703) 858-9210
Fax: (703) 880-0295

E-MAIL ADDRESS:
info@sru.org

WEB SITE ADDRESS:
www.sru.org

AREAS OF INTEREST:
Diagnostic ultrasound.

TYPE:
Research grants.

PURPOSE:
To fund clinical ultrasound research projects.

ELIGIBILITY:
Applicants must be members of the Society of Radiologists in Ultrasound. Membership requirements include board certification in diagnostic radiology with majority of the member's practice being in diagnostic ultrasound.

FINANCIAL DATA:
Funds are made payable to applicant's institution.
Total amount of support: Up to $25,000.

NUMBER OF APPLICANTS MOST RECENT YEAR:
4.

NUMBER OF AWARDS: 1.

APPLICATION INFORMATION:
Submit a curriculum vitae, a five-page summary of proposed project and a proposed budget.
Duration: Varies.

ADDRESS INQUIRIES TO:
Susan Roberts, Executive Director
(See address above.)

TASTE AND SMELL CLINIC   [2331]
Center for Molecular Nutrition
and Sensory Disorders
5125 MacArthur Boulevard, N.W., Suite 20
Washington, DC 20016
(202) 364-4180
Fax: (202) 364-9727

E-MAIL ADDRESS:
doc@tasteandsmell.com

WEB SITE ADDRESS:
www.tasteandsmell.com

FOUNDED: 1969

AREAS OF INTEREST:
Taste and smell, clinical treatment of patients with taste and smell disorders, growth factors in relationship to stem cell maturation and development, saliva, salivary diagnostics, salivary proteins, functional magnetic imaging of the brain, transcranial magnetic stimulation of the brain, nasal mucus physiology and pathology, and nasal mucus diagnostics.

CONSULTING OR VOLUNTEER SERVICES:
The Taste and Smell Dysfunction Foundation.

NAME(S) OF PROGRAMS:
* **Taste and Smell Disorders Internship Program**

TYPE:
Assistantships; Conferences/seminars; Exchange programs; Fellowships; Internships; Research grants; Scholarships; Training grants; Visiting scholars; Work-study programs. The Taste and Smell Disorders Internship Program is offered to provide internships and programs to evaluate and treat patients with taste and smell dysfunctions.

YEAR PROGRAM STARTED: 1975

PURPOSE:
To provide internships and other programs to evaluate and treat patients with taste and smell dysfunctions; to study salivary and nasal mucus proteins; to support biochemists and physicians interested in cognitive neurology who want to come work with the clinic.

LEGAL BASIS:
Private organization.

ELIGIBILITY:
Preference to individuals from the Washington, DC metropolitan area.

FINANCIAL DATA:
Amount of support per award: Varies depending on need and tasks required.
Total amount of support: $20,000 to $60,000 per year.

COOPERATIVE FUNDING PROGRAMS: Taste and Smell Dysfunction Foundation.

NUMBER OF APPLICANTS MOST RECENT YEAR:
3.

NUMBER OF AWARDS: 1.

APPLICATION INFORMATION:
Resume and three letters of recommendation from scientific mentors are required.
Duration: One year. Renewable for second and third year.
Deadline: June 30.

STAFF:
R.I. Henkin, Director
S. Holen, Staff Scientist
S.J. Potolicchio, Senior Scientist in Neurology
L.M. Levy, Senior Scientist in Neuro-radiology

ADDRESS INQUIRIES TO:
R.I. Henkin, Director
(See address above.)

U.S. DEPARTMENT OF THE NAVY   [2332]
Navy Bureau of Medicine and Surgery
Accessions Department
8955 Wood Road, Suite 13132
Bethesda, MD 20889-5628
(301) 319-4059
(301) 295-9950

E-MAIL ADDRESS:
oh@med.navy.mil

WEB SITE ADDRESS:
www.med.navy.mil/sites/navmedmpte/accessions/Pages/default.aspx

FOUNDED: 1972

AREAS OF INTEREST:
Medicine, dentistry, optometry, and clinical psychology.

CONSULTING OR VOLUNTEER SERVICES:
Navy Recruiting Command.

NAME(S) OF PROGRAMS:
* **Navy Health Professions Scholarship Program (HPSP)**

TYPE:
Scholarships. This is an educational support program for individuals pursuing graduate degrees in professional medical programs and who have a desire to serve in the U.S. Navy following graduation.

YEAR PROGRAM STARTED: 1972

PURPOSE:
To provide officers for the Navy who are trained in these disciplines.

LEGAL BASIS:
Authorized by Public Law 92-426.

ELIGIBILITY:
Applicants must be:
(1) U.S. citizens (dual citizenship not permitted);
(2) physically qualified for a commission in the U.S. Navy and;
(3) accepted into an accredited school in the U.S. or Puerto Rico.

Eligible degree programs include medicine-allopathic (M.D.) or osteopathic (D.O.), dentistry (D.D.S. or D.M.D.), optometry (O.D.), and APA-accredited Ph.D. and Psy.D. degree programs.

GEOGRAPHIC RESTRICTIONS:
United States and Puerto Rico.

FINANCIAL DATA:
Amount of support per award: Scholarship includes full tuition (no upper limit) and allowable fees, reimbursement for all

required books, supplies and equipment (some limits apply), $20,000 signing bonus (medicine and dentistry only), monthly stipend of $2,157 (taxable), full pay and allowances of an ensign (O-1) for 45 days per year (about $4,500), and reimbursement for student's health insurance if required by school.

Total amount of support: Over $115,000,000 in tuition and stipends. Part of annual Congressional appropriation.

NUMBER OF APPLICANTS MOST RECENT YEAR: 500 for medical; 200 for dental.

NUMBER OF AWARDS: 330.

APPLICATION INFORMATION:
Must apply through Navy Recruiting Command.
Duration: Two to four years, according to year level upon entry. Acceptance of the program requires continuous participation until graduation. Dental scholarships are the same as medical scholarships.
Deadline: Rolling acceptance for medical, dental and optometry. Clinical psychology applications: January.

STAFF:
Dr. Sandra Yerkes, Program Manager

ADDRESS INQUIRIES TO:
See e-mail address above.

*SPECIAL STIPULATIONS:
For Scholarship awardees, one year of active duty (not in training) is required for each year of the Scholarship, with a three-year minimum.

THE UNIVERSITY OF CALGARY
Faculty of Graduate Studies
MacKimmie Library Tower, Room 213
2500 University Drive, N.W.
Calgary AB T2N 1N4 Canada
(403) 220-4938
Fax: (403) 289-7635

E-MAIL ADDRESS:
gsaward@ucalgary.ca

WEB SITE ADDRESS:
www.grad.ucalgary.ca

TYPE:
Awards/prizes; Scholarships. Awards for study in the medical sciences. Tenable at The University of Calgary. Award endowed through a bequest of the late William H. Davies.

See entry 1784 for full listing.

THE UNIVERSITY OF SYDNEY   [2333]
Scholarships Office
Level 5, Jane Foss Russell Building G02
The University of Sydney N.S.W. 2006
Australia
(02) 8627 8112
Fax: (02) 8627 8145

E-MAIL ADDRESS:
research.training@sydney.edu.au

WEB SITE ADDRESS:
www.sydney.edu.au/scholarships/research

FOUNDED: 1850

AREAS OF INTEREST:
Medicine.

NAME(S) OF PROGRAMS:
● **Sydney Medical School Postgraduate Research Scholarships**

TYPE:
Scholarships. For research leading to a higher degree. Tenable in the Sydney Medical School at the University of Sydney.

PURPOSE:
To promote and encourage research in the medical sciences at the University of Sydney.

LEGAL BASIS:
University.

ELIGIBILITY:
Available to full-time research candidates, normally Ph.D., in any department or research unit associated with the Sydney Medical School at the University of Sydney. Applicants must be either Australian citizens or permanent residents of Australia.

GEOGRAPHIC RESTRICTIONS:
Australia.

FINANCIAL DATA:
Amount of support per award: $23,728 AUD per annum for the year 2012.

NUMBER OF AWARDS: Varies according to availability of funds.

APPLICATION INFORMATION:
Contact the University for guidelines.
Duration: One year. Renewal for second and third year subject to satisfactory progress.

ADDRESS INQUIRIES TO:
Scholarships Officer
Sydney Medical School (A27)
The University of Sydney
N.S.W. 2006 Australia
E-mail: scholarships@med.usyd.edu.au

*PLEASE NOTE:
Very few awards are available and competition for them is extremely keen. They are awarded strictly on academic merit and only graduates with First Class Honours or equivalent qualifications (e.g., graduation magna cum laude) will be considered.

THE VALLEY FOUNDATION   [2334]
16450 Los Gatos Boulevard, Suite 210
Los Gatos, CA 95032
(408) 358-4545
Fax: (408) 358-4548

E-MAIL ADDRESS:
admin@valley.org

WEB SITE ADDRESS:
www.valley.org

FOUNDED: 1984

AREAS OF INTEREST:
Medical services and health care for lower-income households, the arts, senior citizens, education and research.

TYPE:
Project/program grants.

YEAR PROGRAM STARTED: 1984

PURPOSE:
To provide funding for nonprofit organizations in Santa Clara County, CA, with an emphasis in the medical field.

LEGAL BASIS:
Nonprofit foundation.

ELIGIBILITY:
Qualified 501(c)(3) charitable organizations. No individuals or political organizations.

GEOGRAPHIC RESTRICTIONS:
Santa Clara County, California.

FINANCIAL DATA:
The Foundation prefers to avoid grants which provide more than one-half of an organization's total budget in a 12-month period, usually expecting community and applicant commitment to a project through local cost sharing.
Amount of support per award: $10,000 to $100,000.

REPRESENTATIVE AWARDS:
$100,000 to Opera San Jose to fund artist salaries for the inaugural season at the California Theatre; $100,000 to Walden West School Foundation to fund Science Learning Center project; $25,000 to Diabetes Society of Santa Clara Valley to fund diabetes educational camps.

APPLICATION INFORMATION:
Guidelines are available on the Foundation web site.
Duration: Varies, but multiple-year requests are discouraged. Organizations which have received funding must wait at least one full year before submitting another application. Organizations that did not make it to the full LOI full proposal cycle can reapply on the anniversary of their first LOI submission.
Deadline: February 20, May 20, August 20 and November 20.

PUBLICATIONS:
Application guidelines.

IRS IDENTIFICATION NUMBER: 94-1584547

STAFF:
Vaskie Turner, Administrator

BOARD OF TRUSTEES:
Phillip R. Boyce, Chairman
Richard Sieve, M.D., Vice Chairman
Daniel P. Doore, Treasurer
Herbert Kain, M.D., Secretary
Arthur A. Basham, M.D.
Joseph Parisi

ADDRESS INQUIRIES TO:
Vaskie Turner, Administrator
(See address above.)

FRANKLIN H. AND RUTH L. WELLS FOUNDATION
3607 Rosemont Avenue, Suite 404
Camp Hill, PA 17011
(717) 763-1157

E-MAIL ADDRESS:
mgibbons989@verizon.net

TYPE:
Project/program grants; Seed money grants. Seed money grants are primarily for new programs.

See entry 1155 for full listing.

Allergy, immunology, infectious diseases

AMERICAN ACADEMY OF ALLERGY ASTHMA & IMMUNOLOGY   [2335]
555 East Wells Street, Suite 1100
Milwaukee, WI 53202-3823
(414) 272-6071
Fax: (414) 272-6070

E-MAIL ADDRESS:
info@aaaai.org

WEB SITE ADDRESS:
www.aaaai.org

FOUNDED: 1943

AREAS OF INTEREST:
Allergy and immunology.

NAME(S) OF PROGRAMS:
• **Travel Grant Awards**

TYPE:
Travel grants. Travel funds to attend the
Academy's annual scientific meeting.

PURPOSE:
To advance the knowledge and practice of
allergy by discussion at meetings, by
fostering the education of students and the
public, by encouraging union and cooperation
among those engaged in this field and by
promoting and stimulating research and study
in allergy.

LEGAL BASIS:
Nonprofit.

ELIGIBILITY:
Travel grants for the annual meeting are
awarded to member fellows-in-training in the
field of allergy and immunology. The grants
will be awarded on the basis of merit as
judged by the committee. Individuals with a
faculty appointment will not be considered.

GEOGRAPHIC RESTRICTIONS:
United States and Canada.

FINANCIAL DATA:
Amount of support per award: Up to $800
for travel to the annual meeting for first- and
second-year fellows-in-training; up to $650
for third- or fourth-year fellows-in-training;
up to $1,100 for applicants who submit an
abstract which is accepted for presentation.

APPLICATION INFORMATION:
Applicants who have not previously been
awarded this grant should submit an
application form, available on request from
the Academy.

ADDRESS INQUIRIES TO:
Mariana Duran, Program Coordinator
(See address above.)

ARTHRITIS NATIONAL RESEARCH FOUNDATION (ANRF)
200 Oceangate, Suite 830
Long Beach, CA 90802
(800) 588-2873
(562) 437-6808
Fax: (562) 437-6057

E-MAIL ADDRESS:
hbelisle@curearthritis.org

WEB SITE ADDRESS:
www.curearthritis.org

TYPE:
Research grants; Travel grants. ANRF
Arthritis Research Grants are intended to
support basic and clinical research focusing
on rheumatic and related autoimmune
diseases, such as osteoarthritis and
rheumatoid arthritis.

See entry 2241 for full listing.

CANCER RESEARCH INSTITUTE
One Exchange Plaza
55 Broadway, Suite 1802
New York, NY 10006
(212) 688-7515
(800) 992-2623
Fax: (212) 832-9376

E-MAIL ADDRESS:
grants@cancerresearch.org

WEB SITE ADDRESS:
www.cancerresearch.org

TYPE:
Fellowships; Research grants; Training
grants.

See entry 2430 for full listing.

DYSTROPHIC EPIDERMOLYSIS BULLOSA RESEARCH ASSOCIATION OF AMERICA, INC. (DEBRA) [2336]
75 Broad Street
Suite 300
New York, NY 10004
(212) 868-1573 ext. 110
Fax: (212) 868-9296

E-MAIL ADDRESS:
staff@debra.org

WEB SITE ADDRESS:
www.debra.org

FOUNDED: 1980

AREAS OF INTEREST:
Research into the causes, treatment and cure
of EB and other genetic disorders of the skin.

NAME(S) OF PROGRAMS:
• **DEBRA International Research Grants**

TYPE:
Research grants. Financial aid for EB
families in crisis.

YEAR PROGRAM STARTED: 1980

PURPOSE:
To provide opportunity to advance research
into the effects, causes, treatments and cure
for epidermolysis bullosa.

ELIGIBILITY:
Peer-reviewed grants made to full-time or
part-time researchers.

GEOGRAPHIC RESTRICTIONS:
United States.

FINANCIAL DATA:
Reimbursement of medical expenses
according to DEBRA funds available.
Amount of support per award: Varies.
Total amount of support: Varies.

APPLICATION INFORMATION:
Guidelines may be obtained from the
organization at the address above.
Duration: One to three years.

IRS IDENTIFICATION NUMBER: 11-2519726

ADDRESS INQUIRIES TO:
Brett Kopelan, Executive Director
(See address above.)

IMMUNE DEFICIENCY FOUNDATION [2337]
40 West Chesapeake Avenue
Suite 308
Towson, MD 21204
(866) 939-7568
Fax: (410) 321-0293

E-MAIL ADDRESS:
tcaulder@primaryimmune.org

WEB SITE ADDRESS:
www.usidnet.org

AREAS OF INTEREST:
Immunodeficiency diseases.

NAME(S) OF PROGRAMS:
• **U.S. Immunodeficiency Network**

TYPE:
Travel grants; Visiting scholars.

YEAR PROGRAM STARTED: 2003

PURPOSE:
To improve the diagnosis and treatment of
patients with primary immunodeficiency
diseases through research and education.

ELIGIBILITY:
Open to researchers whose work focuses on
identifying the causes and treatment of
primary immunodeficiency diseases.

GEOGRAPHIC RESTRICTIONS:
United States.

FINANCIAL DATA:
Amount of support per award: Generally up
to $2,000.
Total amount of support: $1,500,000.

APPLICATION INFORMATION:
Contact the Foundation for guidelines.
Duration: Up to five years. Renewed
annually.

ADDRESS INQUIRIES TO:
Tara Caulder
USIDNET Registry Manager
(See address above.)

MAGIC JOHNSON FOUNDATION, INC.
9100 Wilshire Boulevard
Suite 700, East Tower
Beverly Hills, CA 90212
(310) 246-4400
Fax: (310) 246-1106

WEB SITE ADDRESS:
www.magicjohnson.org

TYPE:
Project/program grants; Scholarships;
Technical assistance.

See entry 177 for full listing.

LOVELACE RESPIRATORY RESEARCH INSTITUTE [2338]
2425 Ridgecrest Drive, S.E.
Albuquerque, NM 87108
(505) 348-9400
Fax: (505) 348-4966

E-MAIL ADDRESS:
aescovedo@lrri.org

WEB SITE ADDRESS:
www.lrri.org

FOUNDED: 1947

AREAS OF INTEREST:
Respiratory diseases.

NAME(S) OF PROGRAMS:
• **Postdoctoral Training Program**

TYPE:
Fellowships. Training program in respiratory
tract disease caused by environmental agents.

YEAR PROGRAM STARTED: 1947

PURPOSE:
To provide research into prevention, treatment and cure of respiratory disease.

LEGAL BASIS:
Private research organization.

ELIGIBILITY:
Programs are tailored to individuals. Laboratory research or pathogenesis of disease can focus on one of several disciplinary areas, including cell biology, molecular biology, biochemistry, immunology, pathology, physiology, radiobiology or aerosol science, depending on interests and qualifications. Applicants must be U.S. citizens or permanent residents or eligible for a visa.

GEOGRAPHIC RESTRICTIONS:
United States.

FINANCIAL DATA:
Fellowship includes stipend and health insurance, relocation allowance, tuition and fees.
Amount of support per award: Varies.
Total amount of support: Varies.

NUMBER OF APPLICANTS MOST RECENT YEAR: 26.

NUMBER OF AWARDS: 4.

APPLICATION INFORMATION:
Application form required. Contact Institute for application guidelines.
Duration: One year. Renewable for second and third year.

ADDRESS INQUIRIES TO:
Amber Escovedo, SPHR
Human Resources Manager
(See address above.)

ROBERT MAPPLETHORPE FOUNDATION, INC.
477 Madison Avenue, 15th Floor
New York, NY 10022-5835
(212) 755-3025
Fax: (212) 941-4764

E-MAIL ADDRESS:
joree@mapplethorpe.org

WEB SITE ADDRESS:
www.mapplethorpe.org

TYPE:
Project/program grants. Funds medical research in the fight against AIDS and HIV infection and supports the promotion of photography as a fine art, embracing exhibitions, acquisitions, and publications.

See entry 470 for full listing.

NATIONAL FOUNDATION FOR INFECTIOUS DISEASES [2339]
7201 Wisconsin Avenue
Bethesda, MD 20814
(301) 656-0003
Fax: (301) 907-0878

E-MAIL ADDRESS:
info@nfid.org

WEB SITE ADDRESS:
www.nfid.org

FOUNDED: 1973

AREAS OF INTEREST:
Research, education and prevention of infectious diseases.

NAME(S) OF PROGRAMS:
- **NFID Advanced Vaccinology Course Travel Grants**
- **NFID Traveling Professorship in Rural Areas**

TYPE:
Awards/prizes; Fellowships; Travel grants.

PURPOSE:
To support research leading to the causes, cures and prevention of infectious diseases; to encourage and sponsor public and professional educational programs.

LEGAL BASIS:
Nonprofit, tax-exempt foundation with 501(c)(3) status.

ELIGIBILITY:
NFID Advanced Vaccinology Course Travel Grant: Applicant must have made separate application to the course.

NFID Traveling Professorship in Rural Areas: Applicant must be board-certified in infectious diseases and be a U.S. citizen.

FINANCIAL DATA:
NFID Advanced Vaccinology Course Travel Grant is meant to defray expenses related to attending the course, including registration, airfare, ground transportation, lodging, meals and incidentals. Grant payment for the NFID Traveling Professorship in Rural Areas may be used for travel expenses, handout production and supplies. Personal honorarium will not exceed $5,000 of the grant.
Amount of support per award: NFID Advanced Vaccinology Course Travel Grant: $4,000; NFID Traveling Professorship in Rural Areas: $10,000.

COOPERATIVE FUNDING PROGRAMS: NFID Advanced Vaccinology Course Travel Grant: sanofi pasteur, NFID Traveling Professorship in Rural Areas: NFID Steven R. Mostow Endowment for Outreach Programs.

APPLICATION INFORMATION:
Applicant must submit original application and two copies (four copies for Traveling Professorship) addressed to the Grants Manager at the address above.
Duration: NFID Traveling Professorship in Rural Areas: Five full working days, either continuous or intermittent, to be completed within one year of grant assignment.

IRS IDENTIFICATION NUMBER: 23-7198530

EXECUTIVE DIRECTOR:
Marla Dalton

Dentistry

THE AMERICAN ACADEMY OF ESTHETIC DENTISTRY [2340]
303 West Madison Street
Suite 2650
Chicago, IL 60606
(312) 981-6770
Fax: (312) 265-2908

E-MAIL ADDRESS:
info@estheticacademy.org

WEB SITE ADDRESS:
www.estheticacademy.org

FOUNDED: 1975

AREAS OF INTEREST:
Dentistry.

NAME(S) OF PROGRAMS:
- **AAED Esthetic Dentistry Research Grants**

TYPE:
Research grants.

YEAR PROGRAM STARTED: 1993

PURPOSE:
To promote the integration of dental esthetics into the total spectrum of oral health care.

ELIGIBILITY:
Applicant must be a graduate student or young untenured faculty at the instructor or assistant professor level at an accredited dental school.

GEOGRAPHIC RESTRICTIONS:
United States, Canada and Puerto Rico.

FINANCIAL DATA:
Amount of support per award: Up to $5,000.

NUMBER OF APPLICANTS MOST RECENT YEAR: 8.

NUMBER OF AWARDS: 1 per year.

APPLICATION INFORMATION:
Contact the Academy for application procedures.
Duration: One year.
Deadline: End of May.

ADDRESS INQUIRIES TO:
Joe Jackson, Executive Director
(See address above.)

AMERICAN ACADEMY OF IMPLANT DENTISTRY (AAID) FOUNDATION [2341]
211 East Chicago Avenue
Suite 750
Chicago, IL 60611
(312) 335-1550
Fax: (312) 335-9090

E-MAIL ADDRESS:
afshin@aaid.com

WEB SITE ADDRESS:
www.aaid.com

FOUNDED: 1979

AREAS OF INTEREST:
Dental implant research.

NAME(S) OF PROGRAMS:
- **Humanitarian Project Support**
- **Research Award**
- **Student Research Grant**

TYPE:
Awards/prizes; Project/program grants; Research grants. Humanitarian Project Support is available to those 501(c)(3) organizations who support the handicapped or disabled and medically-at-risk in need of dental implant.

Research Award provides limited support for meritorious dental implant research projects which determine the feasibility of a larger research project. This may be described as the conduct of pilot studies or venture research to develop and test new techniques and procedures, to carry out a small clinical or animal research project and to analyze existing data.

Student Research Grant is available for all graduate dental students. Research must be related to dental implant.

YEAR PROGRAM STARTED: 1981

PURPOSE:
To provide limited support for meritorious dental implant research projects.

LEGAL BASIS:
Research foundation.

ELIGIBILITY:
Investigators from any scientific discipline and at any stage of their career may apply for a Research Award. These awards are appropriated for new investigators and those changing areas of research or resuming research careers.

Student Research Grant is available to postgraduate dental students for implant-related research studies.

FINANCIAL DATA:
Grants may be used for supplies, small items of equipment and salary for technical and support personnel.

Amount of support per award: Humanitarian Project Support: Up to $5,000; Small Research Award: Up to $25,000 (total project costs); Student Research Grant: Up to $2,500 per year.

Total amount of support: $78,000.

NUMBER OF APPLICANTS MOST RECENT YEAR:
36.

NUMBER OF AWARDS: Research Award: 1 to 3; Student Research Grant: Up to 8.

APPLICATION INFORMATION:
Required documentation includes abstract of research plan, budget estimate, explanation of the project, including its specific aims, significance, experimental design and methods, sequence of events and time schedule and a complete bibliography, curriculum vitae and a list of all co-investigators and consultants.

Duration: Student Research Grant: Up to two years. Nonrenewable.

Deadline: Research Award: August 1. Student Research Grant: May 1.

PUBLICATIONS:
Guidelines.

OFFICERS:
Jaime Lozada, D.D.S., Chairman
Sharon Bennett, Chief Executive Officer

ADDRESS INQUIRIES TO:
F. Afshin Alavi, Chief Financial Officer
(See address above.)

AMERICAN ASSOCIATION FOR DENTAL RESEARCH [2342]
1619 Duke Street
Alexandria, VA 22314-3406
(703) 548-0066
Fax: (703) 548-1883

E-MAIL ADDRESS:
sherren@iadr.org

WEB SITE ADDRESS:
www.aadronline.org

AREAS OF INTEREST:
Dental research.

NAME(S) OF PROGRAMS:
● **AADR/Johnson & Johnson Healthcare Products Hatton Competition**

TYPE:
Awards/prizes. For junior investigators (junior, senior and postdoctoral) who exhibit potential for a productive career in dental research.

PURPOSE:
To advance research and increase knowledge for the improvement of oral health; to support and represent the oral health research community; to facilitate the communication and application of research findings.

ELIGIBILITY:
Applicants must be U.S. citizens or non-citizen nationals of the U.S. (or who have been lawfully admitted for permanent residence at the time of submission of the abstract - those with a "green card") or persons of other nationalities whose research is performed in the U.S. Must be an AADR member. There is no age limit for entrants in the AADR competition.

FINANCIAL DATA:
Amount of support per award: First prize: $1,000; Second prize: $500.

Total amount of support: $4,500.

NUMBER OF AWARDS: 3 First Prizes and 3 Second Prizes.

APPLICATION INFORMATION:
Details of the abstract to be submitted are available on the web site.

Deadline: Early October.

ADDRESS INQUIRIES TO:
Sheri S. Herren
Awards, Fellowships and Grants Manager
(See address above.)

AMERICAN ASSOCIATION FOR DENTAL RESEARCH [2343]
1619 Duke Street
Alexandria, VA 22314-3406
(703) 548-0066
Fax: (703) 548-1883

E-MAIL ADDRESS:
sherren@iadr.org

WEB SITE ADDRESS:
www.aadronline.org

AREAS OF INTEREST:
Basic and clinical research related to oral health.

NAME(S) OF PROGRAMS:
● **Student Research Fellowships**

PURPOSE:
To advance research and increase knowledge for the improvement of oral health; to support and represent the oral health research community; to facilitate the communication and application of research findings.

ELIGIBILITY:
Applicant must be enrolled in an accredited D.D.S./D.M.D. or hygiene program in a dental institution and must be sponsored by a faculty member. Students should not have received their degree, nor should they in the year of award. Applicant may have an advanced degree in a basic science subject. Must be an AADR member.

GEOGRAPHIC RESTRICTIONS:
United States.

FINANCIAL DATA:
Amount of support per award: $2,700.

Total amount of support: Varies.

NUMBER OF AWARDS: 20 for the year 2013.

APPLICATION INFORMATION:
Proposals will follow the general format of the Public Health Service Grant Application Form PHS 398, which is to be used only as a guideline. Each proposal must include the following:
(1) objectives, describing what the research is intended to accomplish and the hypothesis to be tested;
(2) background and significance;
(3) preliminary data, if any;
(4) materials and methods, including statistical management of data;
(5) literature cited;
(6) resource information, facilities and equipment to be used for the research project;
(7) other support for applicant and sponsor and;
(8) for those projects involving Recombinant DNA/Recombinant DNA Molecules, an indication that the project adheres to the current NIH Guidelines for Research Involving Recombinant DNA Molecules.

The following documents must also be included:
(1) cover letter from the applicant's sponsor, indicating the dental school's and the sponsor's support of the proposed research;
(2) curriculum vitae, not to exceed two pages, outlining the student's career up to the time of application;
(3) copy of the sponsor's biographical sketch in NIH format, not to exceed two pages and;
(4) documentation that the project has been approved by the Institutional Review Board for projects involving human subjects or vertebrate animals.

Proposals longer than four pages (PDF) and/or 1,400 words will not be considered.

Deadline: January.

ADDRESS INQUIRIES TO:
Sheri S. Herren
Awards, Fellowships and Grants Manager
(See address above.)

AMERICAN ASSOCIATION FOR DENTAL RESEARCH [2344]
1619 Duke Street
Alexandria, VA 22314-3406
(703) 548-0066
Fax: (703) 548-1883

E-MAIL ADDRESS:
sherren@iadr.org

WEB SITE ADDRESS:
www.aadronline.org

AREAS OF INTEREST:
Clinical research in periodontology.

NAME(S) OF PROGRAMS:
● **William B. Clark Fellowship in Clinical Research**

TYPE:
Fellowships.

PURPOSE:
To advance research and increase knowledge for the improvement of oral health; to support and represent the oral health research community; to facilitate the communication and application of research findings.

ELIGIBILITY:
Applicant must have completed first professional degree, should be appointed at an accredited dental school or academic research center in U.S., and must be a member of AADR.

GEOGRAPHIC RESTRICTIONS:
United States.

FINANCIAL DATA:
Amount of support per award: $5,000.

Total amount of support: $5,000.

APPLICATION INFORMATION:
Applicants must submit the following:
(1) letter stating their interest in applying for the award;
(2) three- to four-page (double-spaced) overview of their proposed areas of training, including how the experience will affect future research to be conducted by the applicant;
(3) brief description of the facility which will provide the training and;
(4) letter of support from the proposed mentor.
Deadline: October.

ADDRESS INQUIRIES TO:
Sheri S. Herren
Awards, Fellowships and Grants Manager
(See address above.)

AMERICAN ASSOCIATION FOR DENTAL RESEARCH [2345]
1619 Duke Street
Alexandria, VA 22314-3406
(703) 548-0066
Fax: (703) 548-1883

E-MAIL ADDRESS:
sherren@iadr.org

WEB SITE ADDRESS:
www.aadronline.org

AREAS OF INTEREST:
Dental research.

NAME(S) OF PROGRAMS:
● **William J. Gies Award**

TYPE:
Awards/prizes. For the best paper published in the *Journal of Dental Research* during the preceding year.

PURPOSE:
To advance research and increase knowledge for the improvement of oral health; to support and represent the oral health research community; to facilitate the communication and application of research findings.

FINANCIAL DATA:
Amount of support per award: $1,000.
Total amount of support: $1,000.

APPLICATION INFORMATION:
Information on the nomination process is available on the web site.
Deadline: Early October.

ADDRESS INQUIRIES TO:
Sheri S. Herren
Awards, Fellowships and Grants Manager
(See address above.)

AMERICAN ASSOCIATION OF WOMEN DENTISTS [2346]
216 West Jackson Boulevard, Suite 625
Chicago, IL 60606
(312) 263-1822
(800) 920-2293
Fax: (312) 750-1203

E-MAIL ADDRESS:
info@aawd.org

WEB SITE ADDRESS:
www.aawd.org

FOUNDED: 1921

AREAS OF INTEREST:
Dentistry.

NAME(S) OF PROGRAMS:
● **Colgate Research Scholarship**

● **Procter & Gamble Research Award for Postdoctoral Students**
● **Smiles for Success Program**

TYPE:
Awards/prizes; Scholarships. Colgate Research Scholarships support AAWD member/junior or senior dental students who are involved in dental research.

Proctor & Gamble Research Award for Postdoctoral Students provides a scholarship for research projects involving women's oral health.

Smiles for Success Program helps women in transition from welfare to work by providing low- or no-cost dental work.

PURPOSE:
To encourage women dental students who contribute to the school, to dentistry or dental health who are in need of financial assistance.

ELIGIBILITY:
Applicants must be dentists or junior/senior dental students.

FINANCIAL DATA:
Amount of support per award: Varies.
Total amount of support: Varies.

COOPERATIVE FUNDING PROGRAMS:
Scholarships are donated by Colgate Company and other organizations and members.

APPLICATION INFORMATION:
Contact the Association for detailed guidelines.
Duration: One year.
Deadline: Applications for Colgate Research Scholarship are accepted January to April. Applications for Proctor and Gamble Research Award are accepted April to August. Smiles for Success Program applications are accepted year-round.

PUBLICATIONS:
Chronicle; Women's Dental Journal.

ADDRESS INQUIRIES TO:
Debbie Gidley, Executive Director
(See address above.)

AMERICAN DENTAL ASSISTANTS ASSOCIATION [2347]
35 East Wacker Drive
Suite 1730
Chicago, IL 60601-2211
(312) 541-1550 ext. 200
Fax: (312) 541-1496

E-MAIL ADDRESS:
adaahelp@aol.com

WEB SITE ADDRESS:
www.dentalassistant.org

FOUNDED: 1923

AREAS OF INTEREST:
Dental assisting.

NAME(S) OF PROGRAMS:
● **Juliette A. Southard/Oral-B Laboratories Scholarship Program**

TYPE:
Scholarships. Tuition scholarships awarded to dental assisting students interested in furthering their education.

YEAR PROGRAM STARTED: 1946

PURPOSE:
To provide financial assistance for highly qualified applicants pursuing dental assisting education.

LEGAL BASIS:
Nonprofit professional organization.

ELIGIBILITY:
Applicants must be high school graduates or equivalent and enrolled in a dental assisting program. Candidates will be considered on the basis of academic achievement, ability, interest in dentistry and personal attributes. Must be a member of the ADAA.

GEOGRAPHIC RESTRICTIONS:
United States.

FINANCIAL DATA:
Amount of support per award: Varies.
Total amount of support: Varies.

NUMBER OF AWARDS: 10 for the year 2013.

APPLICATION INFORMATION:
Applicants must submit academic transcripts (high school and/or college), proof of acceptance into an accredited program and a letter of intent to pursue a long-range career in dental assisting. Two letters of reference are also required.
Duration: One year.
Deadline: March 15.

STAFF:
Lawrence H. Sepin, Executive Director

ADDRESS INQUIRIES TO:
Scholarship Committee
(See address above.)

AMERICAN DENTAL HYGIENISTS' ASSOCIATION INSTITUTE FOR ORAL HEALTH [2348]
444 North Michigan Avenue
Suite 3400
Chicago, IL 60611
(312) 440-8900 ext. 261 or 770
(800) 735-4916
Fax: (312) 467-1806

E-MAIL ADDRESS:
institute@adha.net

WEB SITE ADDRESS:
www.adha.org/institute

FOUNDED: 1927

AREAS OF INTEREST:
Dental hygiene.

NAME(S) OF PROGRAMS:
● **ADHA Institute Dental Hygiene Scholarships**

TYPE:
Scholarships. The Graduate Scholarship Program awards licensed dental hygienists who are, or will be, enrolled as graduate students in a program leading to a Master's or doctoral degree in dental hygiene or dental hygiene education. There is also an undergraduate scholarship program.

YEAR PROGRAM STARTED: 1986

PURPOSE:
To invest in the future careers of dental hygiene students by ensuring that they will be of exceptional quality and dedication.

LEGAL BASIS:
501(c)(3) public charity, as described in Sections 509(1)(1)-170(b)(1)(A)(vi) of the Internal Revenue Code.

GEOGRAPHIC RESTRICTIONS:
United States.

FINANCIAL DATA:
Amount of support per award: $1,000 to $2,000.

Total amount of support: $60,000 for the year 2013.

APPLICATION INFORMATION:
Applications can only be downloaded from the web site.

Duration: Scholarships are awarded for a period of one academic year.

Deadline: February 1.

PUBLICATIONS:
Annual report.

ADDRESS INQUIRIES TO:
Jessica Mitton, Development Manager (See address above.)

HISPANIC DENTAL ASSOCIATION FOUNDATION [2349]
1111 14th Street, N.W., Suite 1100
Washington, DC 20005
(202) 629-3628
Fax: (202) 629-3802

E-MAIL ADDRESS:
hispanicdental@hdassoc.org

WEB SITE ADDRESS:
www.hdassoc.org

FOUNDED: 1990

AREAS OF INTEREST:
Oral health careers.

NAME(S) OF PROGRAMS:
● **A-dec Scholarship**
● **Colgate-Palmolive Scholarship**
● **Procter & Gamble Scholarship**
● **Dr. Juan D. Villarreal Scholarship**

TYPE:
Awards/prizes; Conferences/seminars; Internships; Product donations; Scholarships.

YEAR PROGRAM STARTED: 1990

PURPOSE:
To encourage entry of Hispanics into oral health careers.

ELIGIBILITY:
Students must have permanent resident status in the U.S., be current student members of the Hispanic Dental Association, and attending U.S. dental schools.

Colgate-Palmolive Scholarships are open to student members of the Association who have been accepted into or are currently enrolled in an accredited Master's program in a dentistry-related field. Students must have an undergraduate or graduate degree in an oral health-related field (dental hygienist, dentistry, etc.) from the U.S. or abroad.

Dr. Juan D. Villarreal Scholarships are open to student members of the Association who have been accepted into or are currently enrolled in an accredited dental school or dental hygiene program in the state of Texas. The student may be at any stage of the undergraduate program, first through fourth years.

FINANCIAL DATA:
Amount of support per award:
Colgate-Palmolive Scholarships: Up to $10,000; Dr. Juan D. Villarreal Scholarships: $1,000 for Dental students and $500 for Dental Hygiene student.

Total amount of support: Varies.

NUMBER OF APPLICANTS MOST RECENT YEAR: 45.

NUMBER OF AWARDS: Colgate-Palmolive Scholarships: Varies; Dr. Juan D. Villarreal Scholarships: 2 for Dental students and 1 for Dental Hygiene student.

APPLICATION INFORMATION:
Application can be downloaded from the web site.

Duration: One year. Renewal possible by reapplication.

Deadline: May 1.

STAFF:
Carolina Galeano, Membership and Communications Coordinator

ADDRESS INQUIRIES TO:
E-mail: scholarships@hdassoc.org

INTERNATIONAL ASSOCIATION FOR DENTAL RESEARCH [2350]
1619 Duke Street
Alexandria, VA 22314-3406
(703) 548-0066
Fax: (703) 548-1883

E-MAIL ADDRESS:
sherren@iadr.org

WEB SITE ADDRESS:
www.iadr.org

AREAS OF INTEREST:
Original research in the area of oral health, basic, clinical and applied studies.

NAME(S) OF PROGRAMS:
● **Colgate Oral Health Research Award**

YEAR PROGRAM STARTED: 1998

PURPOSE:
To advance research and increase knowledge for the improvement of oral health; to support and represent the oral health research community; to facilitate the communication and applications of research findings.

ELIGIBILITY:
The nominee must be a member of IADR or the Oral Health Research Group. Work considered for this award should have resulted in publications in scientific, peer-reviewed journals. Researchers who are currently under contract with Colgate-Palmolive Company are not eligible to participate. Preference is given to dental hygienists.

FINANCIAL DATA:
Amount of support per award: $2,000.

Total amount of support: $2,000.

NUMBER OF AWARDS: 1.

APPLICATION INFORMATION:
Nominations must include a curriculum vitae that provides supporting evidence that the nominee has conducted original research. A letter of nomination should highlight the major reasons and specific research for which the individual is being nominated. Submit nominations electronically to Award Chair.

ADDRESS INQUIRIES TO:
Frances Doherty Genco
Award Chairperson
E-mail: fgenco@gmail.com or
Sheri S. Herren
Awards, Fellowships and Grants Manager
(See e-mail address above.)

NATIONAL INSTITUTE OF DENTAL AND CRANIOFACIAL RESEARCH (NIDCR) [2351]
National Institutes of Health
6701 Democracy Boulevard, Room 688
Bethesda, MD 20892
(301) 496-4263
Fax: (301) 402-7033

E-MAIL ADDRESS:
friedenla@nidcr.nih.gov

WEB SITE ADDRESS:
www.nidcr.nih.gov/careersandtraining

FOUNDED: 1948

AREAS OF INTEREST:
Dental, craniofacial health and research.

NAME(S) OF PROGRAMS:
● **Individual NRSA Postdoctoral Fellowships (F-32)**

TYPE:
Fellowships. Provides up to three years of support for trainees at academic institutions to broaden their scientific background or extend their potential for research in health-related areas.

YEAR PROGRAM STARTED: 1974

PURPOSE:
To develop individuals for careers in oral health research.

LEGAL BASIS:
Public Health Service Act as amended, Section 301c; 42 CFR 61; 42 U.S.C. 288a.

ELIGIBILITY:
Applicants must be citizens, non-citizen nationals or permanent residents of the U.S. at the time of the award and have a Ph.D., M.D., D.D.S., D.O., D.V.M. or equivalent degree prior to the beginning date of the proposed fellowship.

GEOGRAPHIC RESTRICTIONS:
United States.

FINANCIAL DATA:
Stipend level is based on number of years of postdoctoral experience. Additional funds are available for other training-related expenses.

Amount of support per award: Stipend levels are $42,000 to $55,272. Up to $7,850 per 12 months for institutional allowances.

Total amount of support: Varies.

APPLICATION INFORMATION:
Detailed information can be obtained from the Institute.

Duration: One, two or three years.

Deadline: April 8, August 8 and December 8.

ADDRESS INQUIRIES TO:
Leslie Frieden
Extramural Training Officer
(See address above.)

NATIONAL INSTITUTE OF DENTAL AND CRANIOFACIAL RESEARCH (NIDCR) [2352]
National Institutes of Health
6701 Democracy Boulevard, 6th Floor
Bethesda, MD 20892-4878
(301) 435-7908
Fax: (301) 480-8319

E-MAIL ADDRESS:
jatkinso@mail.nih.gov

WEB SITE ADDRESS:
www.nidcr.nih.gov

FOUNDED: 1948

AREAS OF INTEREST:
Multiple areas of research with the goal of improving oral and craniofacial health.

NAME(S) OF PROGRAMS:
- **AIDS**
- **Behavioral/Social Science Research**
- **Biotechnology/Regenerative Medicine**
- **Clinical Research/Clinical Trials**
- **Computational Science**
- **Conference Grants**
- **Epidemiology/Population Research**
- **Genetic Studies**
- **Health Literacy Research**
- **International Health**
- **Neurobiology/Pain**
- **Oral Cancer**
- **Oral Health Disparities Research**
- **Teeth and Bone**
- **Women's Health**

TYPE:
Conferences/seminars; Project/program grants; Research grants; Research contracts. Grants made to individual investigators for the support of clinical and nonclinical research projects bearing on oral health conditions.

YEAR PROGRAM STARTED: 1948

PURPOSE:
To develop methods for preventing and treating oral diseases and conditions through research related to oral and craniofacial health.

LEGAL BASIS:
Public Health Service Act as amended, Section 301c; 42 CFR 61; 42 U.S.C. 288a.

ELIGIBILITY:
Open to scientists at universities, hospitals, laboratories and other public, nonprofit or profit institutions. Applications are competitively rated on the basis of scientific merit and grants must be approved by the National Advisory Dental Research Council.

FINANCIAL DATA:
Grant funds may be used for salaries of professional and nonprofessional personnel, equipment, supplies, travel, other approved expenditures and indirect costs.
Amount of support per award: Varies.

APPLICATION INFORMATION:
Contact the Institute for detailed information.
Duration: Two to five years.

OFFICERS:
Dr. Martha Somerman, Institute Director

NATIONAL INSTITUTE OF DENTAL AND CRANIOFACIAL RESEARCH (NIDCR)   [2353]
National Institutes of Health
6701 Democracy Boulevard, Room 688
Bethesda, MD 20892
(301) 496-4263
Fax: (301) 402-7033

E-MAIL ADDRESS:
friedenla@nidcr.nih.gov

WEB SITE ADDRESS:
www.nidcr.nih.gov/careersandtraining

FOUNDED: 1948

AREAS OF INTEREST:
Biomedical and behavioral research.

NAME(S) OF PROGRAMS:
- **Individual NRSA Senior Fellowship Award (F-33)**

TYPE:
Fellowships. Provides health research training for experienced scientists, enabling them to update their skills or make changes in the direction of their career.

YEAR PROGRAM STARTED: 1979

PURPOSE:
To provide opportunities for experienced scientists to make major changes in the direction of their research careers, to enlarge their scientific background, to acquire new research capabilities, or to enlarge their command of an allied research field.

LEGAL BASIS:
Section 472 of the Public Health Service Act as amended (42 U.S.C. 2981-1).

ELIGIBILITY:
Applicants must be citizens, non-citizen nationals or permanent residents of the U.S. at the time of the award. Applicants must be at least seven years beyond the qualifying doctoral degree and have a sponsoring institution and mentor.

GEOGRAPHIC RESTRICTIONS:
United States.

FINANCIAL DATA:
A stipend is provided. Additional funds are available for other training-related expenses.
Amount of support per award: Stipend of $55,272. Up to $7,850 per 12 months for institutional allowances.
Total amount of support: Varies.

NUMBER OF AWARDS: 3.

APPLICATION INFORMATION:
Detailed information can be obtained from the Institute.
Duration: Up to two years.
Deadline: April 8, August 8 and December 8.

ADDRESS INQUIRIES TO:
Leslie Frieden
Extramural Training Officer
(See address above.)

Internal medicine

A.S.P.E.N. RHOADS RESEARCH FOUNDATION
8630 Fenton Street
Suite 412
Silver Spring, MD 20910
(301) 920-9146
Fax: (301) 587-2365

E-MAIL ADDRESS:
carolw@nutritioncare.org

WEB SITE ADDRESS:
www.nutritioncare.org

TYPE:
Research grants. Annual support for nutritional research.

See entry 2402 for full listing.

AMERICAN SOCIETY OF HEMATOLOGY   [2354]
2021 L Street, N.W.
Suite 900
Washington, DC 20036
(202) 776-0544
Fax: (888) 719-7814

E-MAIL ADDRESS:
awards@hematology.org

WEB SITE ADDRESS:
www.hematology.org

AREAS OF INTEREST:
Scientific abstracts.

NAME(S) OF PROGRAMS:
- **Abstract Achievement Award**
- **Outstanding Abstract Achievement Award**

TYPE:
Awards/prizes; Travel grants.

PURPOSE:
To offer need- and merit-based awards to select individuals in order to help defray annual meeting travel expenses.

ELIGIBILITY:
Abstract Achievement Award: Applicants must be undergraduate students, medical students, graduate students, resident physicians, and postdoctoral fellows who are both first author and presenter of an abstract.

Outstanding Abstract Achievement Award: Awards are offered to the first authors/presenters of abstracts that receive the highest score in the categories of undergraduate student, medical student, graduate student, resident physician, and postdoctoral fellow.

FINANCIAL DATA:
Amount of support per award: $500.
Total amount of support: Varies.

APPLICATION INFORMATION:
Contact the Society for application procedures.
Duration: One-time award.

ADDRESS INQUIRIES TO:
Lisa Fanning
Awards and Diversity Programs Manager
(See address above.)

AMERICAN SOCIETY OF NEPHROLOGY   [2355]
1510 H Street, N.W.
Suite 800
Washington, DC 20005
(202) 640-4660
Fax: (202) 478-2117

E-MAIL ADDRESS:
email@asn-online.org

WEB SITE ADDRESS:
www.asn-online.org

AREAS OF INTEREST:
Nephrology.

NAME(S) OF PROGRAMS:
- **The M. James Scherbenske Grant**

TYPE:
Research grants.

PURPOSE:
To provide bridge funding for investigators from R01 to R01 whose application was scored, but not funded.

ELIGIBILITY:
Applicant must have submitted a competitive renewal R01 application that was scored but not funded. Cannot have more than $75,000 of total extramural research funding (direct costs) as a principal investigator, co-principal investigator, and/or collaborating investigator with paid percent effort. Applicant must be an active member of the ASN and hold an M.D., Ph.D., or equivalent degree. The

applicant's membership must be current with dues fully paid no later than February 1 of the calendar year in which the application is submitted. Appointment to full-time faculty must be confirmed in writing by the Department Chair, indicating the date of first full-time faculty appointment, and providing assurance that the department will provide needed resources for conducting independent research (laboratory and office space, salary support, and protected research time of at least 75%). Additionally, applicants will be considered ineligible should they submit more than one ASN grant application during any particular grants cycle.

GEOGRAPHIC RESTRICTIONS:
North and Central America.

FINANCIAL DATA:
Amount of support per award: $75,000.

NUMBER OF AWARDS: 1 to 2.

APPLICATION INFORMATION:
Only online applications will be accepted.
Duration: One year.
Deadline: November, March and June.

ADDRESS INQUIRIES TO:
E-mail: grants@asn-online.org

AMERICAN SOCIETY OF NEPHROLOGY [2356]
1510 H Street, N.W.
Suite 800
Washington, DC 20005
(202) 640-4660
Fax: (202) 478-2117

E-MAIL ADDRESS:
email@asn-online.org

WEB SITE ADDRESS:
www.asn-online.org

AREAS OF INTEREST:
Nephrology.

NAME(S) OF PROGRAMS:
- **Carl W. Gottschalk Research Scholar Grant**
- **John Merrill Grant in Transplantation**
- **Norman Siegel Research Scholar Grant**

TYPE:
Research grants. The Gottschalk, Merrill and Siegel Grants are part of the Career Development Grant program.

PURPOSE:
To enhance and assist the study and practice of nephrology; to provide a forum for the promulgation of research; to meet the professional and continuing education needs of its members; to foster the independent careers of young investigators in biomedical research related to nephrology and transplantation.

ELIGIBILITY:
Merrill and Gottschalk Grants: Applicants must be active ASN members and hold an M.D., Ph.D., or equivalent degree. At the time of submission, the applicant's membership must be current and their dues paid. Appointment to full-time faculty must be confirmed in writing by the department chair, indicating the date of first full-time faculty appointment, and providing assurance that the department will provide needed resources for conducting independent research. Additionally, applicants will be considered ineligible should they submit more than one ASN grant application during any particular grants cycle.

GEOGRAPHIC RESTRICTIONS:
North America.

FINANCIAL DATA:
Amount of support per award: $100,000 per year.

APPLICATION INFORMATION:
Only online applications will be accepted.
Duration: Two years.
Deadline: December to January.

ADDRESS INQUIRIES TO:
E-mail: grants@asn-online.org

AMERICAN SOCIETY OF NEPHROLOGY [2357]
1510 H Street, N.W.
Suite 800
Washington, DC 20005
(202) 640-4660
Fax: (202) 478-2117

E-MAIL ADDRESS:
email@asn-online.org

WEB SITE ADDRESS:
www.asn-online.org

AREAS OF INTEREST:
Nephrology.

NAME(S) OF PROGRAMS:
- **ASN Student Scholar Grant**

TYPE:
Fellowships.

PURPOSE:
To enable selected medical students with an interest in either basic or clinical research to engage in continuous full-time research.

ELIGIBILITY:
Applicants must be currently enrolled in a U.S. medical school and in good standing. Applicants already receiving other sources of stipend support are not eligible.

The mentor must be an ASN member and must submit a program of study for the applicant. An award period can be a summer, semester, academic year, or any other 10- to 52-week period of continuous full-time research.

GEOGRAPHIC RESTRICTIONS:
United States and Canada.

FINANCIAL DATA:
Amount of support per award: Stipend of $400 per week, plus $100 per week provided to the principal investigator's lab to cover expenses and up to $1,500 to attend the ASN meeting following the research period.

APPLICATION INFORMATION:
Only online applications will be accepted.
Duration: 10 to 52 weeks.
Deadline: March and September.

ADDRESS INQUIRIES TO:
E-mail: grants@asn-online.org

AMERICAN SOCIETY OF NEPHROLOGY [2358]
1510 H Street, N.W.
Suite 800
Washington, DC 20005
(202) 640-4660
Fax: (202) 478-2117

E-MAIL ADDRESS:
email@asn-online.org

WEB SITE ADDRESS:
www.asn-online.org

AREAS OF INTEREST:
Nephrology.

NAME(S) OF PROGRAMS:
- **ASN Research Fellowships**

TYPE:
Fellowships. ASN Research Fellowships: The Society especially encourages applications from women and members of underrepresented minorities.

PURPOSE:
To fund fellows to conduct original, meritorious research projects, fostering, under the direction of a sponsor, the training of fellows who are highly motivated to make contributions to the understanding of kidney biology and disease.

ELIGIBILITY:
To apply for an ASN Research Fellowship, a candidate:
(1) must hold an M.D., D.O., Ph.D. or the equivalent degree;
(2) may not have completed more than three years of research training after the completion of the M.D. or D.O. degree or equivalent, or one year of postdoctoral research training after the Ph.D. degree (at the time of the activation of the award);
(3) cannot have or have had at any time a faculty position at any academic institution;
(4) must complete research under the direction and mentorship of a sponsor;
(5) must be a member of ASN at the time of the fellowship application; the sponsor of the candidate must also be an ASN member at the time of the fellowship application;
(6) cannot hold another full fellowship award such as another foundation fellowship or grant or a postdoctoral research fellowship from the National Institutes of Health; however, a candidate's institutions may supplement the support provided by ASN;
(7) must be working in North or Central America during the fellowship period and;
(8) must commit a minimum of 75% time to research during the fellowship period.

GEOGRAPHIC RESTRICTIONS:
North America.

FINANCIAL DATA:
Funds must be used for salary support (including fringe benefits) and cannot be used for project costs, travel expenses or overhead costs.

Amount of support per award: $50,000 per year for up to two years.

APPLICATION INFORMATION:
Only online applications will be accepted.
Duration: Up to two years. Second-year funding is contingent on a satisfactory progress report.
Deadline: December to January.

CANCER FEDERATION, INC. [2359]
711 West Ramsey Street
Banning, CA 92220
(951) 849-4325
Fax: (951) 849-0156

E-MAIL ADDRESS:
info@cancerfed.org

WEB SITE ADDRESS:
www.cancerfed.org

FOUNDED: 1977

AREAS OF INTEREST:
Cancer.

TYPE:
Awards/prizes; Research grants; Scholarships; Seed money grants. The Federation has five basic programs: research, biology, scholarships, publishing (books, a magazine, a newsletter, and other materials) and patient aid.

YEAR PROGRAM STARTED: 1977

PURPOSE:
To fund research in cancer immunology and scholarships; to serve cancer patients and their families; to provide patient aid.

LEGAL BASIS:
Member supported charity.

ELIGIBILITY:
Candidates must major in biology or natural sciences.

FINANCIAL DATA:
Total amount of support: $600,000.

NUMBER OF APPLICANTS MOST RECENT YEAR:
50.

NUMBER OF AWARDS: 60 scholarships.

APPLICATION INFORMATION:
Scholar is chosen by institution.
Duration: One year. Renewal possible by reapplication. Scholarships are one-time only.
Deadline: Varies according to sponsoring institution.

PUBLICATIONS:
Challenge, magazine; *CF Newsletter*; *Four Women Against Cancer*; and several others.

IRS IDENTIFICATION NUMBER: 95-3133568

ADDRESS INQUIRIES TO:
John Steinbacher, Chief Executive Officer
P.O. Box 1298
Banning, CA 92220

CHILDREN'S TUMOR FOUNDATION [2360]
120 Wall Street
16th Floor
New York, NY 10005
(212) 344-6633
Fax: (212) 747-0004

E-MAIL ADDRESS:
slarosa@ctf.org

WEB SITE ADDRESS:
www.ctf.org

AREAS OF INTEREST:
Neurofibromatosis research.

NAME(S) OF PROGRAMS:
• **Drug Discovery Initiative Award**
• **NF Clinic Network (CTF-NFCN)**
• **Young Investigator Awards**

TYPE:
Conferences/seminars; Research grants; Seed money grants; Travel grants; Research contracts. Clinic support grants.

PURPOSE:
To improve the health and well-being of individuals and families affected by neurofibromatosis.

ELIGIBILITY:
Drug Discovery Initiative Award: Applicants should have an M.D., Ph.D., or equivalent degree and access to all resources needed. Applicants from academia and the private sector are welcome, and partnerships between the two are encouraged. Applications are welcomed from all qualified individuals worldwide.

NF Clinic Network: Any clinic in the U.S. that sees NF patients may apply to be a CTF-NFCN Affiliate Clinic.

Young Investigator Award: Open to graduate students, postdoctoral fellows and young investigators no more than four years past completion of their M.D./Ph.D. training. The Investigator can be a graduate student or postdoctoral fellow associated with the laboratory of a more senior researcher, who acts as the research sponsor.

FINANCIAL DATA:
Amount of support per award: Drug Discovery Initiative Award: Up to $75,000; NF Clinic Network: Up to $6,000 per year; Young Investigator Award: Commensurate with experience.
Total amount of support: Young Investigator Award: $64,000 to $110,000.

NUMBER OF APPLICANTS MOST RECENT YEAR:
Young Investigator Award: Approximately 30.

NUMBER OF AWARDS: Young Investigator Award: Approximately 8.

APPLICATION INFORMATION:
Application information is available on the web site. Applications may be submitted online.
Duration: Young Investigator Award: Up to two years.
Deadline: Young Investigator Award: January to February.

IRS IDENTIFICATION NUMBER: 13-2298956

STAFF:
Annette Bakker, President and Chief Scientific Officer

ADDRESS INQUIRIES TO:
Salvatore La Rosa
Director of Research
(See address above.)

CYSTIC FIBROSIS CANADA [2361]
2323 Yonge Street
Suite 800
Toronto ON M4P 2C9 Canada
(416) 485-9149
(800) 378-2233 (Canada only)
Fax: (416) 485-0960

E-MAIL ADDRESS:
info@cysticfibrosis.ca

WEB SITE ADDRESS:
www.cysticfibrosis.ca

FOUNDED: 1960

AREAS OF INTEREST:
Cystic fibrosis.

TYPE:
Fellowships; General operating grants; Grants-in-aid; Research grants; Scholarships; Training grants; Travel grants. Studentships; Summer studentships.

A limited number of competitive fellowships are offered by the Organization each year for basic or clinical research training in areas of the biomedical or behavioral sciences pertinent to cystic fibrosis.

Research grants are intended to facilitate the scientific investigation of all aspects of cystic fibrosis.

Scholarships provide salary support for a limited number of exceptional investigators, offering them an opportunity to develop outstanding cystic fibrosis research programs, unhampered by heavy teaching or clinical loads.

A limited number of competitive studentships are offered by the Organization each year to: (1) highly qualified graduate students who are registered for a higher degree, and who are undertaking full-time research training in areas of the biomedical or behavioral sciences relevant to cystic fibrosis or; (2) highly qualified students who are registered in a joint M.D./M.Sc. or M.D./Ph.D. program.

YEAR PROGRAM STARTED: 1961

PURPOSE:
To further research on cystic fibrosis.

LEGAL BASIS:
Nonprofit organization.

ELIGIBILITY:
Research Grants: A principal investigator should hold a recognized, full-time faculty appointment in a relevant discipline at a Canadian university or hospital. Under exceptional circumstances, and at the discretion of the Scientific Review Panel, research grant applications from other individuals may be evaluated on a case-by-case basis, with significant emphasis placed on the degree of independence of the applicant, and on the institutional commitments to this individual.

Scholarship applications are restricted to candidates who have received their first faculty appointment within the preceding five calendar years. Applicants must hold an M.D. or Ph.D. degree, and must be sponsored by the chairman of the appropriate department and by the dean of the faculty. A commitment should be provided by the nominating institution, stating that the institution intends to continue to support the Scholar following the completion of the award.

Fellowships: Individuals who hold M.D. or Ph.D. degrees are eligible to apply. Medical graduates should have already completed basic residency training, and must be eligible for Canadian licensure. Applications for clinical fellowships must have a strong research component in the proposed program. Fellowships are not awarded for residency-type clinical training. Applicants who have already completed six or more years of postgraduate study or training are not eligible for Cystic Fibrosis Canada fellowships.

Studentships are awarded for studies at the Master's or doctoral level. If a student receiving support for studies leading to a Master's degree elects to continue to a Doctorate degree, he or she must reapply for an initial Cystic Fibrosis Canada studentship at the doctoral level. Students are expected to spend at least 75% of their time on the research training described in their application. Awards are tenable only at Canadian universities.

GEOGRAPHIC RESTRICTIONS:
Canada.

FINANCIAL DATA:
Scholarship, Fellowship and Studentship awards follow prevailing Canadian rates.
Amount of support per award: Varies.
Total amount of support: Varies.

COOPERATIVE FUNDING PROGRAMS: CIHR Partnerships, CFC-UBC Clinician Scientist at Saint Paul's, CFC-SMH Adult CF Research Chair.

NUMBER OF APPLICANTS MOST RECENT YEAR: 93.

NUMBER OF AWARDS: 14.

APPLICATION INFORMATION:
Copies of the Organization's Grants and Awards Guide are available. Applications should be submitted on the forms provided by the Organization. The guidelines and application forms must be closely followed.
Duration: Varies.
Deadline: Varies.

PUBLICATIONS:
Annual report; *Grants and Awards Guide*, English/French booklet; application guidelines.

ADDRESS INQUIRIES TO:
E-mail: researchprograms@cysticfibrosis.ca

CYSTIC FIBROSIS CANADA [2362]
2221 Yonge Street
Suite 601
Toronto ON M4S 2B4 Canada
(416) 485-9149
(800) 378-2233 (Canada only)
Fax: (416) 485-0960

E-MAIL ADDRESS:
info@cysticfibrosis.ca

WEB SITE ADDRESS:
www.cysticfibrosis.ca

FOUNDED: 1960

AREAS OF INTEREST:
Cystic fibrosis.

NAME(S) OF PROGRAMS:
● **Clinic Incentive Grants**

TYPE:
Grants-in-aid; Seed money grants. Clinic Incentive Grants are intended to enhance the standard of clinical care available to Canadians with cystic fibrosis, by providing funds to initiate a comprehensive program for cystic fibrosis patient care, research and teaching, or to strengthen an existing program.

YEAR PROGRAM STARTED: 1961

PURPOSE:
To help establish a comprehensive program for patient care, research, and teaching in cystic fibrosis.

LEGAL BASIS:
Nonprofit organization.

ELIGIBILITY:
Grants may be made to medical schools or hospitals in Canada. Program potential, regional need, relative need of the institution for assistance and special medical and technical advantages will be considered.

GEOGRAPHIC RESTRICTIONS:
Canada.

FINANCIAL DATA:
Grant payments will be made at the beginning of each quarter. Limited funding is available for related travel.
Total amount of support: Varies.

APPLICATION INFORMATION:
Application information is available on the web site.

Duration: One year. Grants are to be renegotiated annually.
Deadline: October 1.

ADDRESS INQUIRIES TO:
Ian D. McIntosh
Program Director, Healthcare
(See address above.)

HISTIOCYTOSIS ASSOCIATION [2363]
332 North Broadway
Pitman, NJ 08071
(856) 589-6606
Fax: (856) 589-6614

E-MAIL ADDRESS:
info@histio.org

WEB SITE ADDRESS:
www.histio.org

FOUNDED: 1986

AREAS OF INTEREST:
Histiocytosis, hemophagocytic lymphohistiocytosis, Langerhans cell histiocytosis, and histiocytic disorders.

NAME(S) OF PROGRAMS:
● **Research Grant Program**

TYPE:
Project/program grants; Research grants; Seed money grants.

YEAR PROGRAM STARTED: 1989

PURPOSE:
To fund worthy scientific research projects; to educate physicians and scientists; to encourage and support symposia into histiocytic disorders; to directly participate in research projects; to encourage publication of scientific information.

ELIGIBILITY:
Must be a tax-exempt, nonprofit medical research organization with researchers working in the field of histiocytosis research.

FINANCIAL DATA:
Amount of support per award: Up to $50,000 for one-year grants.
Total amount of support: Varies.

NUMBER OF APPLICANTS MOST RECENT YEAR: 23.

NUMBER OF AWARDS: 6.

APPLICATION INFORMATION:
Application can be downloaded from the web site.
Duration: Up to one year.
Deadline: July 1.

IRS IDENTIFICATION NUMBER: 22-2827069

STAFF:
Jeffrey Toughill, President and Chief Executive Officer

ADDRESS INQUIRIES TO:
Jeffrey Toughill
President and Chief Executive Officer
(See address above.)

THE LEUKEMIA & LYMPHOMA SOCIETY [2364]
1311 Mamaroneck Avenue
Suite 310
White Plains, NY 10605
(914) 821-8301
Fax: (914) 821-3290

E-MAIL ADDRESS:
researchprograms@lls.org

WEB SITE ADDRESS:
www.lls.org

AREAS OF INTEREST:
Leukemia, lymphoma and myeloma.

NAME(S) OF PROGRAMS:
● **Career Development Program**

TYPE:
Fellowships; Research grants; Scholarships. The Career Development Program provides awards intended to meet the specific needs of investigators at different stages of their research careers. The five awards, Fellow, Scholar, Scholar in Clinical Research, Special Fellow and Special Fellow in Clinical Research, provide stipends to investigators, allowing them to devote themselves to research bearing on leukemia, lymphoma and myeloma.

YEAR PROGRAM STARTED: 1949

PURPOSE:
To cure leukemia, lymphoma, Hodgkin's disease and myeloma; to improve the quality of life of patients and their families; to support individuals pursuing careers in basic or clinical research in leukemia, lymphoma and myeloma.

ELIGIBILITY:
Qualified investigators affiliated with appropriate institutions are eligible to apply. Applicants must have the approval of the institution and recommendation of the department head where the research training will be conducted. Ph.D. or M.D. status is required.

FINANCIAL DATA:
Amount of support per award: $165,000 for three years for Fellows; $550,000 for five years for Scholars and Scholars in Clinical Research; $195,000 for three years for Special Fellows and Special Fellows in Clinical Research.

APPLICATION INFORMATION:
Guidelines are available on the web site.
Duration: Renewable for up to five years at the level of Scholar and three years at the level of Special Fellow and Fellow.
Deadline: Preliminary application: September 15. Full application: October 1.

ADDRESS INQUIRIES TO:
Sammy Hattar
Director of Research Administration
(See address above.)

THE LEUKEMIA & LYMPHOMA SOCIETY [2365]
1311 Mamaroneck Avenue
Suite 310
White Plains, NY 10605
(914) 821-8301
Fax: (914) 821-3290

E-MAIL ADDRESS:
researchprograms@lls.org

WEB SITE ADDRESS:
www.lls.org

AREAS OF INTEREST:
Leukemia, lymphoma and myeloma.

NAME(S) OF PROGRAMS:
● **Translational Research Program**

TYPE:
Research grants. Translational Research Program is intended to encourage and provide support for new and novel clinical

research. The goal of the program is to accelerate transfer of findings from the laboratory to clinical application.

YEAR PROGRAM STARTED: 1996

PURPOSE:
To encourage and provide early-stage support for clinical research in leukemia, lymphoma, and myeloma, with the intention of developing innovative approaches to treatment, diagnosis or prevention; to support projects that translate laboratory findings to clinical application.

ELIGIBILITY:
Ph.D. or M.D. status is required. Candidates must be affiliated with a non-federal public or private nonprofit institution engaged in cancer-related research.

FINANCIAL DATA:
Amount of support per award: $200,000 annually.

COOPERATIVE FUNDING PROGRAMS: National Career Institutes; Academic, Public, Private, Partnership Program (AP4).

APPLICATION INFORMATION:
Guidelines are available on the web site.
Duration: Three years. In special cases these may be renewed for two years.
Deadline: Preliminary application: March 1. Full application: March 15.

ADDRESS INQUIRIES TO:
Sammy Hattar
Director of Research Administration
(See address above.)

THE LEUKEMIA & LYMPHOMA SOCIETY   [2366]
1311 Mamaroneck Avenue
Suite 310
White Plains, NY 10605
(914) 821-8301
Fax: (914) 821-3290

E-MAIL ADDRESS:
researchprograms@lls.org

WEB SITE ADDRESS:
www.lls.org

AREAS OF INTEREST:
Leukemia, lymphoma, Hodgkin's disease and myeloma.

NAME(S) OF PROGRAMS:
● **Marshall A. Lichtman Specialized Center of Research Program**

TYPE:
Research grants. The grant supports scientific core laboratories required by the component research programs, so as to provide access to key high technology to support facilities that might not otherwise be available to individual research programs.

PURPOSE:
To support research programs that are focused on any aspect of leukemia, lymphoma, Hodgkin's disease and myeloma in order to foster interactions, cooperation, and to enhance interdisciplinary research among the participants.

ELIGIBILITY:
Applications may be submitted by individuals holding an M.D., Ph.D., or equivalent degree, working in domestic or foreign nonprofit organizations, such as universities, colleges, hospitals or laboratories. Applications may be multi-institutional in nature. Applicants need

not be U.S. citizens, and there are no restrictions on applicant age, race, gender or creed.

FINANCIAL DATA:
Expenses for administrative staff (including secretarial) costs cannot exceed one full-time equivalent for the Center per year. Travel costs for all investigators cannot exceed $10,000 per year for the Center. The aggregate of office supplies and telephone costs cannot exceed $6,000 per year for the Center.
Amount of support per award: Up to $1,250,000 annually.

APPLICATION INFORMATION:
Guidelines are available on the web site.
Duration: Five years.
Deadline: Letter of Intent: November 1. Notification sent to those selected for full application submission by December 31. Application: March 15.

ADDRESS INQUIRIES TO:
Sammy Hattar
Director of Research Administration
(See address above.)

LYMPHOMA RESEARCH FOUNDATION   [2367]
115 Broadway, Suite 1301
New York, NY 10006
(212) 349-2910
Fax: (212) 349-2886

E-MAIL ADDRESS:
researchgrants@lymphoma.org

WEB SITE ADDRESS:
www.lymphoma.org

FOUNDED: 2001

AREAS OF INTEREST:
Lymphoma research.

CONSULTING OR VOLUNTEER SERVICES:
Many volunteer-based Chapters throughout the country.

NAME(S) OF PROGRAMS:
● **Clinical Investigator - Career Development Awards**
● **Focus Area Grants: CLL/SLL**
● **Focus Area Grants: DLBCL**
● **Focus Area Grants: Follicular Lymphoma Research Grants**
● **Focus Area Grants: Mantle Cell Lymphoma Correlative Grants**
● **Postdoctoral Fellowships**

TYPE:
Conferences/seminars; Fellowships; Research grants; Training grants.

YEAR PROGRAM STARTED: 1992

PURPOSE:
To develop novel therapeutic strategies for the treatment of lymphoma.

LEGAL BASIS:
Nonprofit organization.

ELIGIBILITY:
Career Development Award applicants should be advanced fellows or junior faculty up to the level of assistant professor and must also possess at least two years of training in hematology and/or oncology, plus clinical experience managing patients with lymphoma. Applicants must be licensed physicians at a clinical research institution in the U.S. or Canada for the duration of the LRF Clinical Investigator Grant.

Focus Area Grant applicants should be licensed Senior Researchers. These are awarded to experienced researchers pursuing the development of novel and innovative treatments.

Postdoctoral Fellowship applicants must have completed two years of their fellowship, or not more than two years as a junior faculty instructor or assistant professor at the start of the award period, and hold an M.D., Ph.D., or equivalent degree. Applicants must be affiliated with a sponsoring institution in the U.S. or Canada for the duration of the LRF Grant. Citizenship is not required.

FINANCIAL DATA:
Amount of support per award: Career Development Awards: $75,000 per year; Focus Area Grants: Up to $250,000; Postdoctoral Fellowships: $50,000 in year one and $55,000 in year two.

Total amount of support: Varies.

NUMBER OF APPLICANTS MOST RECENT YEAR: 105.

NUMBER OF AWARDS: 15 grants for the year 2012.

REPRESENTATIVE AWARDS:
$225,000 to Paul M. Barr, M.D., University of Rochester Medical Center, NY for "Targeting B cell receptor signaling in non-Hodgkin lymphoma;" $250,000 to Catherine Wu, M.D., Dana-Farber Cancer Institute, MA for "The role of mutatuons in RNA splicing pathway genes in chronic lymphocytic leukemia;" $750,000 to Arash Alizadeh, M.D., Ph.D., Stanford University, CA for "Single cell characterization of clonal evolution in follicular lymphoma."

APPLICATION INFORMATION:
E-mail the Foundation for application procedures.
Duration: Career Development Awards and Focus Area Grants: Three years; Postdoctoral Fellowships: Two years.
Deadline: Varies.

IRS IDENTIFICATION NUMBER: 95-4335088

BOARD OF DIRECTORS:
Steven J. Prince, Chairman
Tom Condon, Treasurer
Jerry Freundlich, Secretary
John P. Leonard, M.D., Chairman, Scientific Advisory Board
Morton Coleman, M.D., Chairman, Medical Affiliates Board
Joseph R. Bertino, M.D.
Errol M. Cook
Robert E. Fischer
Barbara Freundlich
Marnie Gordon
Keith Hoogland
Bob McAuley
John A. Nelson
Leigh Olson
Miriam Phalen
Donna Reinbolt
Leonard M. Rosen
Sheri Rosenfeld
Michael Werner

ADDRESS INQUIRIES TO:
Mickey DiFabrizio
Research Department Coordinator
(See telephone number listed above.)

NATIONAL HEADACHE FOUNDATION [2368]

820 North Orleans, Suite 411
Chicago, IL 60610-3132
(312) 274-2650
(888) 643-5552
Fax: (312) 640-9049

E-MAIL ADDRESS:
info@headaches.org

WEB SITE ADDRESS:
www.headaches.org

FOUNDED: 1970

AREAS OF INTEREST:
Headache and pain.

TYPE:
Research grants. Support for research in the field of headache and pain.

YEAR PROGRAM STARTED: 1970

PURPOSE:
To enhance the health care of individuals with headache; to provide a source of help to families, physicians and allied health care professionals who treat them, and to the public; to provide educational and informational resources, supporting headache research, and advocating for the understanding of headache as a legitimate neurobiological disease.

LEGAL BASIS:
Nonprofit organization.

ELIGIBILITY:
Investigators from departments of neurology and pharmacology are invited to apply. Submissions from other departments and individual investigators are also welcome. No funding for overhead, salaries, rent or indirect expenses. Grants may be used for data analysis, interpretation, reading of results, etc.

GEOGRAPHIC RESTRICTIONS:
United States.

FINANCIAL DATA:
Full or partial funding may be granted.
Amount of support per award: Varies depending on project.

NUMBER OF APPLICANTS MOST RECENT YEAR: 9.

NUMBER OF AWARDS: 2 for the year 2013-14.

REPRESENTATIVE AWARDS:
$15,000 to Beth Israel Deaconess Medical Center for Activity of Meningeal Sensory Neurons: Excitatory vs. Inhibitory Mechanisms in Sensitization; $10,000 to University of Iowa for Does Pregnancy Reduce Light Aversion in a Mouse Model of Migraine?; $10,000 to University of Missouri Kansas City for Novel Mechanism Underlying the Pathophysiology of Visual Impairment During Migraine Headaches.

APPLICATION INFORMATION:
Applicants must submit abstract of research proposal on Foundation form as well as protocol and proposed budget. Proposed projects will be evaluated at the winter board meeting of the NHF.
Duration: One year.
Deadline: October 1. Announcement December 1.

PUBLICATIONS:
Program announcement.

ADDRESS INQUIRIES TO:
Mary A. Franklin, Director of Operations
(See address above.)

NATIONAL HEART, LUNG AND BLOOD INSTITUTE (NHLBI) [2369]

Division of Blood Diseases and Resources
National Institutes of Health
6701 Rockledge Drive, Suite 9030
Bethesda, MD 20892
(301) 435-0080
Fax: (301) 480-0867

E-MAIL ADDRESS:
hootsw@nhlbi.nih.gov

WEB SITE ADDRESS:
www.nhlbi.nih.gov

FOUNDED: 1948

AREAS OF INTEREST:
Research on the causes, prevention, and treatment of nonmalignant blood diseases, including anemias, sickle cell disease, and thalassemia; premalignant processes such as myelodysplasia and myeloproliferative disorders; hemophilia and other abnormalities of hemostasis and thrombosis; and immune dysfunction.

NAME(S) OF PROGRAMS:
● **Blood Diseases and Resources Research**

TYPE:
Conferences/seminars; Demonstration grants; Fellowships; Grants-in-aid; Project/program grants; Training grants; Research contracts. Funding encompasses a broad spectrum of research ranging from basic biology to medical management of blood diseases.

YEAR PROGRAM STARTED: 1972

PURPOSE:
To develop programs that will reduce the morbidity and mortality caused by blood diseases, lead to the primary prevention of these diseases and ensure the availability of adequate supplies of safe and efficacious blood products.

LEGAL BASIS:
Public Health Service Act, Section 301(e) and Section 412; Public Law 78-410, as amended; 42 U.S.C. 241; 42 U.S.C. 287a; Public Health Service Act, Section 472; Public Law 78-410, as amended; 42 U.S.C. 289 1-1.

ELIGIBILITY:
Any nonprofit organization engaged in biomedical research and institutions (or companies) organized for profit may apply for grants with the exception of National Research Service Awards. Only citizens and non-citizen nationals are eligible for support by research training and career development programs. Other mechanisms are not restricted.

FINANCIAL DATA:
Grants may support salaries, equipment, supplies, travel and patient hospitalization as required to perform the research effort.
Amount of support per award: Varies by the type of grant.
Total amount of support: $450,000,000.

APPLICATION INFORMATION:
Application information is available on the web site.
Duration: One to five years. Renewable through reapplication.
Deadline: Varies.

PUBLICATIONS:
Annual report.

DIRECTORS:
W. Keith Hoots, Director
Donna DiMichele, M.D., Deputy Director

RESEARCH STAFF:
Harvey Luksenburg, M.D., Branch Chief, Blood Diseases Branch
Simone Glynn, M.D., Chief, Transfusion Medicine and Cellular Therapeutics Branch

ADDRESS INQUIRIES TO:
Division of Blood Diseases and Resources
(See address above.)

NEURO-DEVELOPMENTAL TREATMENT ASSOCIATION [2370]

1540 South Coast Highway
Suite 203
Laguna Beach, CA 92651
(800) 869-9295
Fax: (949) 376-3456

E-MAIL ADDRESS:
membership@ndta.org

WEB SITE ADDRESS:
www.ndta.org

AREAS OF INTEREST:
Neuro-Developmental Treatment.

TYPE:
Research grants.

PURPOSE:
To support the investigation of the effectiveness of Neuro-Developmental Treatment with pediatric and adult populations.

ELIGIBILITY:
Qualified investigators affiliated with appropriate institutions are eligible to apply. Applicants must have the approval of the institution and recommendation of the department head where the research training will be conducted.

FINANCIAL DATA:
The grant does not pay indirect, overhead or salary reimbursement costs.
Amount of support per award: Up to $5,000.

NUMBER OF AWARDS: Typically 1 annually.

APPLICATION INFORMATION:
Send requests for a grant application and guidelines to:
Janet Powell, Ph.D., OT
University of Washington
Division of Occupational Therapy
1959 Northeast Pacific Street, Box 356490
Seattle, WA 98195
E-mail: jmpowell@u.washington.edu.
Deadline: December 1.

ADDRESS INQUIRIES TO:
Mark Toof, Associate Director
(See address above.)

THE NEUROPATHY ASSOCIATION [2371]

60 East 42nd Street
Suite 942
New York, NY 10165
(212) 692-0662
Fax: (212) 692-0668

E-MAIL ADDRESS:
info@neuropathy.org
npires@neuropathy.org

WEB SITE ADDRESS:
www.neuropathy.org

FOUNDED: 1995

AREAS OF INTEREST:
Disorders of the peripheral nervous system.

CONSULTING OR VOLUNTEER SERVICES:
Volunteer services.

TYPE:
Research grants.

YEAR PROGRAM STARTED: 1995

PURPOSE:
To support research into the causes and treatment of peripheral neuropathies; to provide support through education and sharing information and experiences related to peripheral neuropathy.

LEGAL BASIS:
501(c)(3).

ELIGIBILITY:
Open to medical doctors working in a neurological research program in the area of neuropathy.

FINANCIAL DATA:
Amount of support per award: $40,000.

NUMBER OF APPLICANTS MOST RECENT YEAR:
12.

NUMBER OF AWARDS: 2.

APPLICATION INFORMATION:
Write or call the Foundation to determine the interest and appropriateness of a full proposal.
Duration: Up to two years.
Deadline: September.

ADDRESS INQUIRIES TO:
Natacha Pires
Director, Medical and Public Affairs
(See address above.)

Cardiovascular and pulmonary

AMERICAN COLLEGE OF CARDIOLOGY [2372]
2400 N Street, N.W.
Washington, DC 20037
(202) 375-6648
Fax: (202) 375-6842

E-MAIL ADDRESS:
jberman@acc.org

WEB SITE ADDRESS:
www.cardiosource.org/researchawards

AREAS OF INTEREST:
Cardiology.

NAME(S) OF PROGRAMS:
● **ACCF/Merck Research Fellowships in Cardiovascular Disease**

TYPE:
Awards/prizes; Development grants; Endowments; Fellowships; Internships; Project/program grants; Research grants; Scholarships; Seed money grants; Technical assistance; Training grants; Travel grants; Visiting scholars; Work-study programs; Research contracts.

PURPOSE:
To advance research in cardiovascular disease.

ELIGIBILITY:
Anyone currently in an adult cardiology fellowship training program recognized by the Accreditation Council for Graduate Medical Education or the American Osteopathic Association and who has the recommendation and agreement of their training program director and institution is eligible to apply. Preference is given to individuals who have had no more than two years of prior full-time experience either in clinical or basic research.

GEOGRAPHIC RESTRICTIONS:
United States and Canada.

FINANCIAL DATA:
Fellowships must be used only for salary support.
Amount of support per award: $70,000 for one year of salary support.

NUMBER OF AWARDS: 4.

APPLICATION INFORMATION:
Guidelines and application form are available online.
Duration: One year.
Deadline: September.

ADDRESS INQUIRIES TO:
Julia Berman, Senior Specialist
(See e-mail address above.)

AMERICAN COLLEGE OF CARDIOLOGY [2373]
2400 N Street, N.W.
Washington, DC 20037
(202) 375-6613
Fax: (202) 375-6842

E-MAIL ADDRESS:
krobertson@acc.org

WEB SITE ADDRESS:
www.cardiosource.org/researchawards

AREAS OF INTEREST:
Cardiology.

NAME(S) OF PROGRAMS:
● **ACC Young Investigators Awards Competition**

TYPE:
Awards/prizes. Awarded in four categories:
(1) Clinical Investigations, Congenital Heart Disease and Cardiac Surgery;
(2) Physiology, Pharmacology, and Pathology;
(3) Molecular and Cellular Cardiology and;
(4) Cardiovascular Health Heart Outcome and Population Genetics.

PURPOSE:
To encourage and recognize young scientific investigators of promise.

ELIGIBILITY:
Any physician or scientist presently in a residency or fellowship training program or who has been in such a program within the past three years, medical students, and Ph.D. candidates are eligible to apply.

FINANCIAL DATA:
Amount of support per award: First Place: $2,000; Second Place: $1,000; Honorable Mention: $500.
Total amount of support: $18,000.

APPLICATION INFORMATION:
Guidelines and application form are available online.
Deadline: October.

ADDRESS INQUIRIES TO:
Kristin Robertson
Senior Specialist, Member Strategy
(See address above.)

AMERICAN COLLEGE OF CARDIOLOGY [2374]
2400 N Street, N.W.
Washington, DC 20037
(202) 375-6648
Fax: (202) 375-6842

E-MAIL ADDRESS:
jberman@acc.org

WEB SITE ADDRESS:
www.cardiosource.org/researchawards

AREAS OF INTEREST:
Cardiology.

NAME(S) OF PROGRAMS:
● **ACCF/William F. Keating, Esq. Endowment Award for Hypertension and Peripheral Vascular Disease**

TYPE:
Awards/prizes; Research grants. This is a career development award.

PURPOSE:
To recognize and provide financial support for research efforts by outstanding young cardiovascular scholars; to encourage junior faculty in the early phases of their careers in the field of cardiology.

ELIGIBILITY:
The award recipient must meet the following qualifications:
(1) will hold the rank of instructor or assistant professor at the time of the initiation of the award and have completed adult, pediatric, surgical cardiology fellowship training in a program approved by the Accreditation Council for Graduate Medical Education or the American Osteopathic Association;
(2) is a member or is eligible to become a member of the American College of Cardiology (ACC);
(3) is no more than five years out of training;
(4) has the recommendation and agreement of his or her division chief and his or her chief's assurance that the award's support will provide protected time for the applicant to pursue his or her research program and;
(5) has an agreement with his or her institution that the full amount of the award will be designated for the salary support.

GEOGRAPHIC RESTRICTIONS:
United States and Canada.

FINANCIAL DATA:
Award funds can only be used for salary support. They cannot be used for any institutional or indirect costs.
Amount of support per award: $70,000.

NUMBER OF AWARDS: 1 per year.

APPLICATION INFORMATION:
Guidelines and application form are available online.

ADDRESS INQUIRIES TO:
Julia Berman, Senior Specialist
(See e-mail address above.)

AMERICAN COLLEGE OF CARDIOLOGY [2375]
2400 N Street, N.W.
Washington, DC 20037
(202) 375-6648
Fax: (202) 375-6842

E-MAIL ADDRESS:
jberman@acc.org

WEB SITE ADDRESS:
www.cardiosource.org/researchawards

AREAS OF INTEREST:
Cardiology.

NAME(S) OF PROGRAMS:
• **ISCTR-ACCF Cardiovascular Translational Research Scholarship**

TYPE:
Awards/prizes; Research grants; Scholarships. This is a career development award. The program is intended for a physician with a strong interest in developing a career in cardiovascular translational research.

PURPOSE:
To encourage junior faculty in the early phases of their careers in the field of cardiology; to enable the awardee to develop skills and expertise in translating basic biological and device concepts into clinical application.

ELIGIBILITY:
The Scholarship applicant must meet the following qualifications:
(1) have completed one year of previous interventional cardiology;
(2) is a member or is eligible to become a member of the ACC and ISCTR and;
(3) will spend the duration of the Scholarship at an institution that has the ability to perform translational research (conducts both preclinical and clinical research).

GEOGRAPHIC RESTRICTIONS:
United States and Canada.

FINANCIAL DATA:
Award funds can only be used for salary support. They cannot be used for any institutional or indirect costs.
Amount of support per award: $70,000 for one year of salary support.

NUMBER OF AWARDS: 1 per year.

ADDRESS INQUIRIES TO:
Julia Berman, Senior Specialist
(See e-mail address above.)

AMERICAN HEART ASSOCIATION [2376]

AHA National Center
7272 Greenville Avenue
Dallas, TX 75231-4596
(214) 360-6104
Fax: (214) 706-1969

E-MAIL ADDRESS:
apply@heart.org

WEB SITE ADDRESS:
my.americanheart.org

FOUNDED: 1948

AREAS OF INTEREST:
Research broadly related to cardiovascular disease and stroke, and research in clinical, basic science, bioengineering or biotechnology, and public health problems.

NAME(S) OF PROGRAMS:
• **Postdoctoral Fellowship**

TYPE:
Fellowships. Supports individuals before they are ready for some stage of independent research.

PURPOSE:
To help a trainee initiate a career in cardiovascular and stroke research while obtaining significant research results under the supervision of a sponsor or mentor.

ELIGIBILITY:
Applicants must:
(1) be a U.S. citizen or permanent resident;
(2) be individuals before they are ready for some stage of independent research;
(3) have M.D., Ph.D., D.O., D.V.M. (or equivalent) at activation and;
(4) have five years or less postdoctoral research experience at time of activation.

GEOGRAPHIC RESTRICTIONS:
United States.

FINANCIAL DATA:
Amount of support per award: Varies per initiative for each geographical area.

APPLICATION INFORMATION:
Guidelines and application form are available on the web site.
Duration: Two years. Must reapply for third year.
Deadline: July.

ADDRESS INQUIRIES TO:
See e-mail address above.

AMERICAN HEART ASSOCIATION [2377]

AHA National Center
7272 Greenville Avenue
Dallas, TX 75231-4596
(214) 360-6104
Fax: (214) 706-1969

E-MAIL ADDRESS:
apply@heart.org

WEB SITE ADDRESS:
my.americanheart.org

FOUNDED: 1948

AREAS OF INTEREST:
Research broadly related to cardiovascular disease and stroke, and research in clinical, basic science, bioengineering or biotechnology, and public health problems.

NAME(S) OF PROGRAMS:
• **Predoctoral Fellowship**

TYPE:
Fellowships.

PURPOSE:
To help students initiate careers in cardiovascular and stroke research by providing research assistance and training.

ELIGIBILITY:
Applicants must meet the following criteria:
(1) be a U.S. citizen or permanent resident;
(2) be post-Baccalaureate, predoctoral M.D., Ph.D., D.O., D.V.M. (or equivalent) student seeking research training with a sponsor/mentor prior to embarking on a research career and;
(3) be a full-time student working toward their degree.

GEOGRAPHIC RESTRICTIONS:
United States.

FINANCIAL DATA:
Amount of support per award: Varies per initiative for each geographical area.

APPLICATION INFORMATION:
Guidelines and application form are available on the web site.
Duration: One to two years. Must reapply for third year.
Deadline: July.

ADDRESS INQUIRIES TO:
See e-mail address above.

AMERICAN HEART ASSOCIATION [2378]

AHA National Center
7272 Greenville Avenue
Dallas, TX 75231-4596
(214) 360-6104
Fax: (214) 706-1969

E-MAIL ADDRESS:
apply@heart.org

WEB SITE ADDRESS:
my.americanheart.org

FOUNDED: 1948

AREAS OF INTEREST:
Research broadly related to cardiovascular disease and stroke, and clinical, basic science, bioengineering or biotechnology, and public health problems.

NAME(S) OF PROGRAMS:
• **Beginning Grant-in-Aid**

TYPE:
Grants-in-aid. Beginning grant-in-aid for all basic disciplines as well as epidemiological, community and clinical investigations that bear on cardiovascular and stroke problems.

PURPOSE:
To promote the independent status of promising beginning scientists.

ELIGIBILITY:
Applicant must:
(1) be a U.S. citizen or permanent resident;
(2) at time of application have M.D., Ph.D., D.O., D.V.M. or equivalent initiating independent research career;
(3) hold position of assistant professor (or equivalent) or higher at activation and;
(4) have faculty/staff appointment at activation and meet institutional requirements for grant submission at time of application.

GEOGRAPHIC RESTRICTIONS:
United States.

FINANCIAL DATA:
Amount of support per award: Varies per initiative for each geographical area.

APPLICATION INFORMATION:
Guidelines and application form are available on the web site.
Duration: Two years. Possible one to two years upon reapplication.
Deadline: July.

ADDRESS INQUIRIES TO:
See e-mail address above.

AMERICAN HEART ASSOCIATION [2379]

AHA National Center
7272 Greenville Avenue
Dallas, TX 75231-4596
(214) 360-6104
Fax: (214) 706-1969

E-MAIL ADDRESS:
apply@heart.org

WEB SITE ADDRESS:
my.americanheart.org

FOUNDED: 1948

AREAS OF INTEREST:
Research broadly related to cardiovascular disease and stroke, and research in clinical, basic science, bioengineering or biotechnology, and public health problems.

doctoral degree;
(2) meet institutional requirements for grant submission;
(3) be a U.S. citizen, permanent resident, pending permanent resident, or have one of the following visas: E-3, H-1B, J-1, O-1 or TN and;
(4) at the time of award activation, have a faculty (or faculty equivalent) appointment. This award is not intended for postdoctoral fellows or others in research training positions.

Eligibility for the grant is not restricted based upon experience level or seniority. Seniority will not be used as a criterion in evaluating an application's merit.

FINANCIAL DATA:
Amount of support per award: $75,000 per year (including 10% indirect costs).

APPLICATION INFORMATION:
Guidelines and application form are available on the web site.
Duration: Two years.
Deadline: Mid-July.

AMERICAN HEART ASSOCIATION [2383]
AHA National Center
7272 Greenville Avenue
Dallas, TX 75231-4596
(214) 360-6104
Fax: (214) 706-1969

E-MAIL ADDRESS:
apply@heart.org

WEB SITE ADDRESS:
my.americanheart.org

FOUNDED: 1948

AREAS OF INTEREST:
Research broadly related to cardiovascular function and disease and stroke, or related to clinical, basic science, bioengineering or biotechnology, and public health problems, including multidisciplinary efforts.

NAME(S) OF PROGRAMS:
● **National Established Investigator Award**

TYPE:
Research grants. Candidates for this award have a demonstrated commitment to cardiovascular or cerebrovascular science as indicated by prior publication history and scientific accomplishments. A candidate's career is expected to be in a rapid growth phase.

PURPOSE:
To support midcareer investigators with unusual promise and an established record of accomplishments.

ELIGIBILITY:
Proposals are encouraged from all basic disciplines as well as epidemiological, behavioral, community and clinical investigations that bear on cardiovascular and stroke problems.

At the time of application, the applicant must:
(1) have an M.D., Ph.D., D.O. or equivalent doctoral degree;
(2) be a faculty/staff member;
(3) meet institutional requirements for grant submission;
(4) have current national-level funding as a principal investigator (or co-PI) on an R01 grant or its equivalent;

(5) be a U.S. citizen or permanent resident and;
(6) at the time of award activation be at least four years, but no more than nine years, since the first faculty/staff appointment at the assistant professor level or equivalent (including, but not limited to, research assistant professor, research scientist, staff scientist, etc.). Instructor positions (or equivalent positions) do not count toward the four or nine years of eligibility.

Research awards are limited to nonprofit institutions, including medical, osteopathic and dental schools, veterinary schools, schools of public health, pharmacy schools, nursing schools, universities and colleges, public and voluntary hospitals and other nonprofit institutions that can demonstrate the ability to conduct the proposed research. Applications will not be accepted for work with funding to be administered through any federal institution or work to be performed by a federal employee, except for Veterans Administration employees.

Funding is prohibited for awards at non-U.S. institutions.

FINANCIAL DATA:
Amount of support per award: $80,000 per year (including up to 10% indirect costs).

APPLICATION INFORMATION:
Guidelines and application form are available on the web site.
Duration: Five years. No renewals.
Deadline: Mid-July.

AMERICAN HEART ASSOCIATION [2384]
AHA National Center
7272 Greenville Avenue
Dallas, TX 75231-4596
(214) 360-6104
Fax: (214) 706-5255

E-MAIL ADDRESS:
apply@heart.org

WEB SITE ADDRESS:
my.americanheart.org

FOUNDED: 1948

AREAS OF INTEREST:
Reducing disability and death from cardiovascular diseases and stroke; clinical, basic science, bioengineering/biotechnology, and public health problems; epidemiological, community and clinical investigations that bear on cardiovascular and stroke problems.

NAME(S) OF PROGRAMS:
● **National Clinical Research Program**
● **National Scientist Development Grant**

TYPE:
Awards/prizes; Development grants; Research grants. National Clinical Research Program is intended to encourage early career investigators who have appropriate and supportive mentoring relationships to engage in high-quality introductory and pilot clinical studies that will guide future strategies for reducing cardiovascular disease and stroke while fostering new research in clinical and translational science, and encouraging community- and population-based activities.

National Scientist Development Grant is intended to support highly promising beginning scientists in their progress toward independence by encouraging and adequately funding research projects that can bridge the

gap between completion of research training and readiness for successful competition as an independent investigator.

YEAR PROGRAM STARTED: 1997

PURPOSE:
To support research activities broadly related to cardiovascular function and disease, stroke, or to related basic science, clinical, bioengineering/biotechnology and public health problems.

LEGAL BASIS:
Research association.

ELIGIBILITY:
Applicant must be U.S. citizen or permanent resident.

National Clinical Research Program: Open to health care professionals with a Master's or post-Baccalaureate doctoral degree, including M.P.H., R.N., Pharm.D., M.D., D.O. or Ph.D. Interdisciplinary research teams are eligible. Applicant must meet institutional requirements for grant submission at time of application.

National Scientist Development Grant: At the time of application, applicant must hold an M.D., Ph.D., D.O., D.V.M. or equivalent post-Baccalaureate doctoral degree and meet institutional requirements for grant submission. At the time of award activation, applicant must hold a faculty-staff position up to and including the rank of assistant professor (or equivalent). Applications may be submitted for review in the final year of a postdoctoral research fellowship or in the initial years of the first faculty/staff appointment. No more than four years can have elapsed since an applicant's first faculty/staff appointment (after receipt of doctoral degree) at the assistant professor level or its equivalent (including, but not limited to, research assistant professor, research scientist, staff scientist, etc.).

GEOGRAPHIC RESTRICTIONS:
United States.

FINANCIAL DATA:
Amount of support per award: Up to $35,000 per year (50%) of direct costs may be used for salary/fringe benefits, including allowance of up to $5,000 for mentor, indirect cost of $7,000 (10%), project support of up to $3,000 for travel and $5,000 computer limit, up to a maximum of $77,000 per year.

APPLICATION INFORMATION:
Guidelines and application form are available on the web site.
Duration: National Clinical Research Program: Two years. National Scientist Development Grant: Four years.
Deadline: July.

ADDRESS INQUIRIES TO:
See e-mail address above.

THE AMERICAN LEGION NATIONAL HEADQUARTERS
P.O. Box 1055
Indianapolis, IN 46206
(317) 630-1323
Fax: (317) 630-1369

E-MAIL ADDRESS:
scholarships@legion.org

WEB SITE ADDRESS:
www.legion.org

TYPE:
Scholarships. Grants for registered nurses.
See entry 2485 for full listing.

AMERICAN LUNG ASSOCIATION   [2385]
21 West 38th Street, Floor 3
New York, NY 10018-2254

E-MAIL ADDRESS:
research@lung.org

WEB SITE ADDRESS:
www.lung.org

FOUNDED: 1904

AREAS OF INTEREST:
Research and education for the prevention
and control of lung disease.

NAME(S) OF PROGRAMS:
● **Dalsemer Research Grant**

TYPE:
Research grants.

PURPOSE:
To support research in interstitial lung
disease.

LEGAL BASIS:
Nonprofit.

ELIGIBILITY:
At the time of application, applicant must:
(1) hold a doctoral degree and be assured of
a faculty appointment or equivalent with
demonstrated institutional commitment
(salary support, research space) by the start
of the award;
(2) have completed two years of postdoctoral
research training;
(3) be U.S. citizens or foreign nationals
holding one of the following visa
immigration statuses: permanent resident
(Green Card), exchange visitor (J-1),
temporary worker in a specialty occupation
(H-1, H-1B), Canadian or Mexican citizen
engaging in professional activities (TC or
TN), or temporary worker with extraordinary
abilities in the sciences (O-1). Non-citizens
must submit a notarized copy of proof of
visa immigration status and;
(4) be employed by a U.S. institution.

Grantee organizations must be recognized
academic or other nonprofit research entities.

Medical residents, those presently enrolled in
a degree program (e.g., graduate students),
and established investigators are not eligible
to apply.

FINANCIAL DATA:
Amount of support per award: $40,000 per
year.

NUMBER OF AWARDS: 1 to 2.

APPLICATION INFORMATION:
Application information is available on the
web site.
Duration: Up to two years.
Deadline: Varies.

PUBLICATIONS:
Program announcement.

ADDRESS INQUIRIES TO:
See e-mail address above.

AMERICAN LUNG ASSOCIATION   [2386]
21 West 38th Street, Floor 3
New York, NY 10018-2254

E-MAIL ADDRESS:
research@lung.org

WEB SITE ADDRESS:
www.lung.org

FOUNDED: 1904

AREAS OF INTEREST:
Adult pulmonary medicine, lung biology,
pediatric pulmonary medicine, and research
and education for the prevention and control
of lung disease.

NAME(S) OF PROGRAMS:
● **Senior Research Training Fellowships**

TYPE:
Fellowships.

YEAR PROGRAM STARTED: 1948

PURPOSE:
To prevent lung disease and promote lung
health through research, education and
advocacy.

LEGAL BASIS:
Nonprofit foundation.

ELIGIBILITY:
At the time of application, an applicant must
hold a doctoral degree and must work in an
academic or not-for-profit institution. M.D. or
D.O. applicants must be in their third or
fourth year of fellowship training. Ph.D.
applicants must be in their first or second
year of postdoctoral training.

GEOGRAPHIC RESTRICTIONS:
United States.

FINANCIAL DATA:
Amount of support per award: $32,500 per
year.

APPLICATION INFORMATION:
Application information is available on the
web site.
Duration: Up to two years.
Deadline: November.

PUBLICATIONS:
Program announcement.

ADDRESS INQUIRIES TO:
See e-mail address above.

AMERICAN LUNG ASSOCIATION   [2387]
21 West 38th Street, Floor 3
New York, NY 10018-2254

E-MAIL ADDRESS:
research@lung.org

WEB SITE ADDRESS:
www.lung.org

FOUNDED: 1904

AREAS OF INTEREST:
Research and education for the prevention
and control of lung disease.

NAME(S) OF PROGRAMS:
● **Biomedical Research Grants**

TYPE:
Research grants.

YEAR PROGRAM STARTED: 1921

PURPOSE:
To prevent lung disease and promote lung
health through research, education and
advocacy.

LEGAL BASIS:
Nonprofit foundation.

ELIGIBILITY:
Intended for junior investigators researching
the mechanisms of lung disease and general
lung biology.

FINANCIAL DATA:
Amount of support per award: $40,000 per
year.

APPLICATION INFORMATION:
Application information is available on the
web site.
Duration: Up to two years.
Deadline: November.

PUBLICATIONS:
Program announcement.

ADDRESS INQUIRIES TO:
See e-mail address above.

AMERICAN LUNG ASSOCIATION   [2388]
21 West 38th Street, Floor 3
New York, NY 10018-2254

E-MAIL ADDRESS:
research@lung.org

WEB SITE ADDRESS:
www.lung.org/research

FOUNDED: 1904

AREAS OF INTEREST:
Research and education for the prevention
and control of lung disease.

NAME(S) OF PROGRAMS:
● **Lung Health Dissertation Grant**

TYPE:
Research grants.

LEGAL BASIS:
Nonprofit organization.

ELIGIBILITY:
Grant is intended for predoctoral support for
students with an academic career focus
and/or nurses pursuing a doctoral degree.
Research areas of particular interest to the
Association include psychosocial, behavioral,
health services, health policy,
epidemiological, biostatistical and educational
matters related to lung disease. Applicants
must be matriculating in a full-time doctoral
program. Individuals with an M.D. seeking a
Ph.D. are not eligible.

Applicant must be a U.S. citizen or
permanent resident or have a valid working
visa. Research must be conducted in the U.S.

GEOGRAPHIC RESTRICTIONS:
United States.

FINANCIAL DATA:
Amount of support per award: Up to $21,000
($16,000 stipend and $5,000 for research
support).

NUMBER OF APPLICANTS MOST RECENT YEAR: 8
to 10 for the year 2012.

NUMBER OF AWARDS: 1.

APPLICATION INFORMATION:
Application information is available on the
web site.
Duration: Up to two years.
Deadline: November. Contact Association for
exact date.

ADDRESS INQUIRIES TO:
Elizabeth Lancet
Assistant Vice President of Research
(See address above.)

AMERICAN SOCIETY OF ECHOCARDIOGRAPHY EDUCATION AND RESEARCH FOUNDATION (ASE) [2389]

210 Gateway Centre Boulevard, Suite 310
Morrisville, NC 27560
(919) 861-5574
Fax: (919) 882-9900

E-MAIL ADDRESS:
madilday@asecho.org

WEB SITE ADDRESS:
www.asecho.org

AREAS OF INTEREST:
Cardiovascular ultrasound.

NAME(S) OF PROGRAMS:
* **The Alan D. Waggoner Student Scholarship Award**

TYPE:
Awards/prizes; Scholarships. Scholarship awards for students enrolled in a cardiovascular ultrasound program accredited by the Commission on Accreditation of Allied Health Education Programs (CAAHEP) in the U.S., or by an equivalent Canadian or International ultrasound program. Recipients are chosen based on nomination of program directors, their letters of support, personal accomplishments and academic record.

YEAR PROGRAM STARTED: 2001

PURPOSE:
To promote excellence in cardiovascular ultrasound and its application to patient care through education, advocacy, research, innovation and service to its members and the public.

ELIGIBILITY:
Applicants must be actively enrolled in a cardiac ultrasound program accredited by CAAHEP (U.S.) or by an equivalent Canadian or international ultrasound program at the time of the scholarship selection. International candidates will need to submit information describing equivalency of program to CAHHEP standards and/or course work that follows the National Education Curriculum for Sonography (NEC).

FINANCIAL DATA:
Scholarship includes complimentary registration for the recipient to attend the ASE's Annual Scientific Sessions, and limited travel support.
Amount of support per award: $1,000, plus annual meeting travel support up to $500.

NUMBER OF AWARDS: Varies.

APPLICATION INFORMATION:
Submissions must include:
(1) nomination from program directors;
(2) completed application;
(3) two letters of nomination addressing the applicant's personal accomplishments and academic achievements, with at least one letter from an ASE member;
(4) reference letter from their program director and;
(5) a copy of the applicant's curriculum vitae or resume.

The official application form is available on the web site.
Duration: One-time award. Nonrenewable.

AMERICAN SOCIETY OF ECHOCARDIOGRAPHY EDUCATION AND RESEARCH FOUNDATION (ASE FOUNDATION) [2390]

2100 Gateway Centre Boulevard
Suite 310
Morrisville, NC 27560
(919) 861-5574
Fax: (919) 882-9900

E-MAIL ADDRESS:
foundation@asecho.org

WEB SITE ADDRESS:
www.asefoundation.org

FOUNDED: 1975

AREAS OF INTEREST:
Cardiovascular diseases, cardiovascular ultrasound, echocardiography, and cardiovascular imaging.

NAME(S) OF PROGRAMS:
* **ASE Foundation Research Awards**

TYPE:
Research grants.

PURPOSE:
To support innovative and meritorious echocardiographic research activities that demonstrate the relevance of echocardiography in the changing health care environment, and that promote new and innovative applications of the technology.

ELIGIBILITY:
Detailed information is available on the Foundation web site.

FINANCIAL DATA:
Amount of support per award: Varies.
Total amount of support: Varies.

NUMBER OF AWARDS: Varies.

APPLICATION INFORMATION:
Application information is available on the web site.
Duration: Varies.
Deadline: Varies.

ADDRESS INQUIRIES TO:
ASE Foundation Research Awards
(See address above.)

THE CANADIAN LUNG ASSOCIATION (CLA) [2391]

1750 Courtwood Crescent
Suite 300
Ottawa ON K2C 2B5 Canada
(613) 569-6411 ext. 262
Fax: (613) 569-8860

E-MAIL ADDRESS:
research@lung.ca

WEB SITE ADDRESS:
www.lung.ca

FOUNDED: 1958

AREAS OF INTEREST:
Prevention and control of lung disease including asthma, emphysema, chronic bronchitis, tuberculosis and lung cancer; air pollution and smoking.

NAME(S) OF PROGRAMS:
* **Canadian Thoracic Society Fellowship**
* **Canadian Thoracic Society Studentship**

TYPE:
Fellowships. The Society offers a number of fellowships and studentships to support research training in pulmonary disease.

YEAR PROGRAM STARTED: 1959

PURPOSE:
To permit physicians and those holding Doctorate degrees in the health sciences to be funded for a period of research training so they may contribute to Canadian work in the area of respiratory disease.

LEGAL BASIS:
Not-for-profit, incorporated.

ELIGIBILITY:
A candidate/applicant must hold, or be completing, a Ph.D. or a health professional degree (or equivalent). The health professional degree must be in a field such as medicine, dentistry, pharmacy, optometry, veterinary medicine, chiropractic, nursing or rehabilitative science. For individuals that do not hold a health professional degree, awards will take effect only after the recipient has completed all requirements of the Ph.D. program, including the oral examination.

These awards are normally held at Canadian institutions. Canadian citizens and permanent residents may apply for awards to be held outside Canada. Candidates who are neither Canadian citizens nor permanent residents may apply only for awards to be held in Canada.

FINANCIAL DATA:
Amount of support per award: Fellowships: $45,000 to $55,000 (CAN) per year; Studentships: $21,000 (CAN) per year.
Total amount of support: Varies.

COOPERATIVE FUNDING PROGRAMS: Partnerships include CIHR and the pharmaceutical industry (peer review only).

NUMBER OF APPLICANTS MOST RECENT YEAR:
41 for the year 2012.

NUMBER OF AWARDS: Approximately 6 each year.

APPLICATION INFORMATION:
Application information is available on the web site.
Duration: One to two years. Competitive renewal.
Deadline: January 31.

PUBLICATIONS:
Canadian Respiratory Journal.

ADDRESS INQUIRIES TO:
The Canadian Thoracic Society
c/o Michelle McEvoy, Manager of Research
(See address above.)

THE CANADIAN LUNG ASSOCIATION (CLA)

1750 Courtwood Crescent
Suite 300
Ottawa ON K2C 2B5 Canada
(613) 569-6411 ext. 262
Fax: (613) 569-8860

E-MAIL ADDRESS:
research@lung.ca

WEB SITE ADDRESS:
www.lung.ca/crhp-pcsr/research-recherche_e.php

TYPE:
Fellowships; Research grants. Fellowships are offered to registered nurses pursuing postgraduate education with a major component of the program involving respiratory nursing practice, physiotherapists pursuing postgraduate training with respiratory research as the major component, and respiratory therapists pursuing

postgraduate education with a major component of the program involving respiratory therapy practice.

Grants for research and feasibility studies are offered to registered nurses undertaking research investigations related to nursing management of patients with respiratory disease and symptoms. Grants are also offered to physiotherapists undertaking investigations related to management of patients with respiratory disease. Respiratory therapists undertaking research investigations related to the management of patients with respiratory disease and symptoms may also qualify.

See entry 2488 for full listing.

THE CHEST FOUNDATION [2392]
2595 Patriot Boulevard
Glenview, IL 60026
(224) 521-9525

E-MAIL ADDRESS:
lfulton@chestnet.org

WEB SITE ADDRESS:
www.onebreath.org

FOUNDED: 1935

AREAS OF INTEREST:
All aspects of chest medicine and surgery.

NAME(S) OF PROGRAMS:
- **ACCP/Alfred Soffer Research Award**
- **ACCP Young Investigator Award**
- **Alpha-1 Foundation/CHEST Foundation Clinical Research Award in COPD and Alpha-1 Antitrypsin (AAT) Deficiency**
- **The Roger C. Bone Advances in End-of-Life Care Award**
- **The CHEST Foundation Clinical Research Award in Pulmonary Arterial Hypertension**
- **The CHEST Foundation Clinical Research Award in Women's Health**
- **Clinical Research Trainee Awards**
- **Distinguished Scholar Awards in Respiratory Health, Critical Care and Thrombosis**
- **Humanitarian Project Development Grants**
- **Humanitarian Recognition Awards**
- **The OneBreath Clinical Research Award for Lung Cancer**

TYPE:
Awards/prizes; Development grants. Awards for abstracts on all aspects of chest medicine and surgery (circulation, respiration, thoracic-cardiovascular surgery, critical care and related disciplines) presented at the Annual Scientific Assembly held usually in late October each year.

ACCP/Alfred Soffer Research Awards are given for the two papers judged best in scientific quality.

ACCP Young Investigator Awards are given to investigators who are in residency or fellowship programs or who have completed their fellowship program within the last five years and whose abstracts are judged to describe outstanding original scientific research.

Clinical Research Trainee Awards are granted to six physicians enrolled in a subspecialty training program with the best proposal for a clinical research project.

Humanitarian Project Development Grants and Humanitarian Recognition Awards are granted to ACCP members who have demonstrated professional dedication to the community.

YEAR PROGRAM STARTED: 1996

PURPOSE:
To provide resources to advance the prevention and treatment of diseases of the chest: asthma, tuberculosis, end-of-life issues, smoking prevention and chronic obstructive pulmonary disease.

LEGAL BASIS:
Supporting organization.

ELIGIBILITY:
Investigators from outside the U.S. are welcome, provided abstracts and presentations are in English. Abstracts must be original and should not have been presented nationally or published elsewhere in manuscript form prior to the Annual Scientific Assembly.

The ACCP/Alfred Soffer Research Award is open to M.D. and non-M.D. investigators at all academic levels and to investigators in both basic and clinical research.

The ACCP Young Investigator Award is open to investigators who are in residency or fellowship programs or who have completed their fellowship programs within the last five years. Co-authors are permitted, but the presenting young investigator must be the primary contributor. An abstract in any area of chest medicine and surgery is eligible.

Clinical Research Awards are open to U.S. and Canadian ACCP members.

FINANCIAL DATA:
Amount of support per award: ACCP/Alfred Soffer Research Award: $1,000 each; ACCP Young Investigator Award: $1,000 each to defray travel costs; Clinical Research Trainee Awards: $10,000 each; Clinical Research Awards in partnership with other foundations and associations: $20,000 to $50,000 for one year.
Total amount of support: $500,000.

COOPERATIVE FUNDING PROGRAMS: Alpha-1 Foundation; The American Society of Transplantation.

NUMBER OF APPLICANTS MOST RECENT YEAR: Abstracts: Over 400; Clinical Research: Over 50.

NUMBER OF AWARDS: ACCP/Alfred Soffer Research Award: 2; ACCP Young Investigator Award: 20; Clinical Research Trainee Awards: 6; Humanitarian Project Development Grants: 2; Humanitarian Recognition Awards: 5 to 10; All other awards in partnership with other foundations and associations: 1 each.

APPLICATION INFORMATION:
Contact the Foundation for guidelines.
Duration: One-time award.
Deadline: May 1.

PUBLICATIONS:
Call for Abstracts, brochure; also in *Ads in CHEST*, monthly publication of The American College of Chest Physicians (ACCP).

IRS IDENTIFICATION NUMBER: 36-3286520

ADDRESS INQUIRIES TO:
Lee Ann Fulton, Project Manager
(See address above.)

*SPECIAL STIPULATIONS:
Award recipients are expected to attend the Annual International Scientific Assembly of the ACCP, which usually occurs at the end of October.

GREENBURG-MAY FOUNDATION
146 Central Park West
New York, NY 10023
(212) 451-3200

TYPE:
Development grants; Research grants. Social services.

See entry 2438 for full listing.

HEART AND STROKE FOUNDATION OF CANADA [2393]
222 Queen Street
Suite 1402
Ottawa ON K1P 5V9 Canada
(613) 569-4361
Fax: (613) 569-3278

E-MAIL ADDRESS:
research@hsf.ca

WEB SITE ADDRESS:
www.hsf.ca/research

FOUNDED: 1956

AREAS OF INTEREST:
Cardiovascular/cerebrovascular research.

NAME(S) OF PROGRAMS:
- **Grant-in-Aid**

TYPE:
Grants-in-aid. Grants to support projects in areas of cardiovascular/cerebrovascular research.

YEAR PROGRAM STARTED: 1958

PURPOSE:
To reduce the morbidity and mortality from cardiovascular/cerebrovascular disease in Canada.

LEGAL BASIS:
Nonprofit.

ELIGIBILITY:
Qualified investigators affiliated with appropriate institutions are eligible.

GEOGRAPHIC RESTRICTIONS:
Canada.

FINANCIAL DATA:
Amount of support per award: Varies, depending upon the needs and nature of the request.

APPLICATION INFORMATION:
Current guidelines and official application materials may be obtained online.
Duration: One to three years.
Deadline: Applications should be received in their complete form by September 1 for awards normally becoming effective on July 1 of the following year.

ADDRESS INQUIRIES TO:
Research Department
(See e-mail address above.)

HEART AND STROKE FOUNDATION OF CANADA [2394]

222 Queen Street
Suite 1402
Ottawa ON K1P 5V9 Canada
(613) 569-4361
Fax: (613) 569-3278

E-MAIL ADDRESS:
research@hsf.ca

WEB SITE ADDRESS:
www.hsf.ca/research

FOUNDED: 1956

AREAS OF INTEREST:
Cardiovascular and cerebrovascular research.

NAME(S) OF PROGRAMS:
● **New Investigator**

TYPE:
Awards/prizes; Scholarships. The New Investigator is the senior award offered by the Foundation.

YEAR PROGRAM STARTED: 1958

PURPOSE:
To reduce the morbidity and mortality from cardiovascular disease in Canada.

LEGAL BASIS:
Nonprofit.

ELIGIBILITY:
Individuals who have clearly demonstrated excellence during their predoctoral and postdoctoral training in cardiovascular or cerebrovascular research are eligible.

GEOGRAPHIC RESTRICTIONS:
Canada.

FINANCIAL DATA:
Amount of support per award: $60,000 (CAN) including employer's portion of fringe benefits.

APPLICATION INFORMATION:
Official application materials may be obtained from the web site.
Duration: Varies.
Deadline: September 1, to become tenable July 1 of the following year.

ADDRESS INQUIRIES TO:
Research Department
(See e-mail address above.)

HEART AND STROKE FOUNDATION OF CANADA [2395]

222 Queen Street
Suite 1402
Ottawa ON K1P 5V9 Canada
(613) 569-4361
Fax: (613) 569-3278

E-MAIL ADDRESS:
research@hsf.ca

WEB SITE ADDRESS:
www.hsf.ca/research

FOUNDED: 1956

AREAS OF INTEREST:
Cardiovascular and cerebrovascular research.

NAME(S) OF PROGRAMS:
● **Research Fellowship**

TYPE:
Fellowships.

YEAR PROGRAM STARTED: 1958

PURPOSE:
To attract and foster the young investigator to initiate and/or continue training and competence in scientific method in a chosen area of the cardiovascular and cerebrovascular fields.

LEGAL BASIS:
Nonprofit organization.

ELIGIBILITY:
Intended for applicants with a Ph.D., M.D., or equivalent degree in cardiovascular or cerebrovascular field. Refer to guidelines for specific eligibility criteria.

GEOGRAPHIC RESTRICTIONS:
Canada.

FINANCIAL DATA:
Amount of support per award: Up to $50,000 (CAN) per year.

APPLICATION INFORMATION:
Official application materials may be obtained from the web site.
Duration: Two to three years.
Deadline: November 1 for fellowships normally becoming tenable on July 1 of the following year.

ADDRESS INQUIRIES TO:
Research Department
(See e-mail address above.)

NATIONAL BLOOD FOUNDATION [2396]

8101 Glenbrook Road
Bethesda, MD 20814-2749
(301) 215-6552
Fax: (301) 215-5751

E-MAIL ADDRESS:
nbf@aabb.org

WEB SITE ADDRESS:
www.aabb.org/nbf

FOUNDED: 1983

AREAS OF INTEREST:
Blood banking, blood safety, transfusion medicine, tissue transplantation, cellular therapy, and patient blood management.

NAME(S) OF PROGRAMS:
● **Scientific Research Grants Program**

TYPE:
Awards/prizes; Development grants; Seed money grants. Basic medical research grants.

The focus of the NBF's Scientific Research Grants Program is to support early career researchers in the field of transfusion medicine, to include aspects of immunology, hematology, tissue and transplantation medicine, cellular therapies, emerging infectious disease, immunohematology, donor health and recruitment and retention, implementation of technological advances, and patient blood management. Priority is given to young investigators and innovative new projects with the potential to have a practical impact on patients and donors in transfusion medicine and cellular therapies.

YEAR PROGRAM STARTED: 1985

PURPOSE:
To actively support the leadership role of the AABB in establishing and promoting the highest standards of care for patients and donors by funding basic and applied scientific research, administrative research/projects, professional education in all aspects of blood banking, transfusion medicine, cellular therapies and patient blood management.

LEGAL BASIS:
Nonprofit association.

ELIGIBILITY:
Each applicant/researcher must be a doctor (M.D. or Ph.D.) or transfusion medicine or cellular therapies professional. Priority will be given to innovative, new projects. Funding will not be given to any one investigator more than two times. Awards will not be made to increase the funding available for currently funded research projects.

FINANCIAL DATA:
Grant awards may not cover indirect costs. Equipment expenditures cannot exceed $8,000 per grant.
Amount of support per award: Up to $75,000.

NUMBER OF APPLICANTS MOST RECENT YEAR: 47.

NUMBER OF AWARDS: 5.

APPLICATION INFORMATION:
Required application forms are available from the Foundation. Electronic submission required as pdf (size restrictions). Application fee of $150 if applicant is not an AABB individual member.
Duration: One to two years.
Deadline: December 31. Announcement in June for funds to be distributed in July.

PUBLICATIONS:
Application; program announcement.

IRS IDENTIFICATION NUMBER: 36-2384118

ADDRESS INQUIRIES TO:
Amy Quiggins, Manager
(See address above.)

NATIONAL HEART, LUNG AND BLOOD INSTITUTE (NHLBI) [2397]

National Institutes of Health
Grants Operations Branch, Room 7160
6701 Rockledge Drive, MSC-7926
Bethesda, MD 20892-7926
(301) 435-0144
Fax: (301) 480-3310

E-MAIL ADDRESS:
whitesa@nhlbi.nih.gov

WEB SITE ADDRESS:
www.nhlbi.nih.gov/funding/index.htm
www.grants.nhlbi.nih.gov

FOUNDED: 1948

AREAS OF INTEREST:
Diseases of the heart, blood vessels, lung and blood, sleep disorders, clinical use of blood and blood resources, and transfusion medicine.

TYPE:
Conferences/seminars; Fellowships; Project/program grants; Research grants; Training grants; Loan forgiveness programs. Career awards and other grant mechanisms to foster research on heart, vascular and lung diseases, and to develop scientists in these areas. Also, small business grants. Loan forgiveness programs are for research.

YEAR PROGRAM STARTED: 1948

PURPOSE:
To support research into the causes, improved diagnosis, treatment and prevention of

cardiovascular diseases in arteriosclerosis, hypertension, cardiovascular disease, coronary heart disease, peripheral vascular disease, arrhythmias, heart failure and shock, congenital and rheumatic heart disease, cardiomyopathies and infections of the heart, circulatory assistance and AIDS.

LEGAL BASIS:
Public Health Service Act, Sections 301(c), 412 and 472.

ELIGIBILITY:
Any nonprofit or for-profit organization engaged in biomedical research may apply. An individual may apply for a fellowship award. Some restrictions may apply to foreign grantee institutions.

FINANCIAL DATA:
Amount of support per award: Varies by type of award.

APPLICATION INFORMATION:
Application information is available on the web site.
Duration: Varies.
Deadline: Varies.

PUBLICATIONS:
NHLBI Fact Book; Annual Report of Director, NHLBI.

OFFICER:
Suzanne White, Chief Grants Management Officer

ADDRESS INQUIRIES TO:
Suzanne White
Chief Grants Management Officer
(See address above.)

NATIONAL HEART, LUNG AND BLOOD INSTITUTE (NHLBI)   [2398]
Two Rockledge Centre, Suite 10042
6701 Rockledge Drive, MSC 7952
Bethesda, MD 20892-7952
(301) 435-0233
Fax: (301) 480-3547

E-MAIL ADDRESS:
nhlbi@nhlbi.nih.gov

WEB SITE ADDRESS:
www.nhlbi.nih.gov

FOUNDED: 1948

AREAS OF INTEREST:
Pulmonary research, prevention, education and training programs in pulmonary diseases.

NAME(S) OF PROGRAMS:
● **Lung Diseases Research**

TYPE:
Project/program grants. Cooperative agreements.

YEAR PROGRAM STARTED: 1970

PURPOSE:
To use available knowledge and technology to solve specific disease problems of the lungs; to promote further studies on the structure and function of the lung; to achieve improvement in the prevention and treatment of lung diseases.

LEGAL BASIS:
Public Health Service Act, Section 301, 422 and 487, as amended, Public Laws 78-410 and 99-158, 42 U.S.C. 241, 42 U.S.C. 285, and 42 U.S.C. 288, as amended.

ELIGIBILITY:
Any nonprofit or for-profit organization engaged in biomedical research may apply

for grants with the exception of NRSAs. An individual may apply for an NRSA or, in some cases, may qualify for a research grant if adequate facilities in which to perform the research are available.

Some grants are available to U.S. citizens or institutions only.

FINANCIAL DATA:
Grants may support salaries, equipment, supplies, travel, and patient hospitalization as required to perform the research effort.

APPLICATION INFORMATION:
Research grant applications are submitted on designated forms to the Center for Scientific Review, National Institutes of Health, Bethesda, MD 20892. Forms for individual NRSA applications may be obtained from and submitted to the Office of Research Manpower, Center for Scientific Review, National Institutes of Health, Bethesda, MD 20892. For some special grant programs, applicants may be advised to submit directly to the Review Branch, Division of Extramural Affairs, National Heart, Lung, and Blood Institute, Bethesda, MD 20892. The standard application forms, as furnished by PHS and required by 45 CFR, Part 92, must be used for this program.
Duration: One to five years. Renewable.

PUBLICATIONS:
Annual Program Report.

STAFF:
Gary H. Gibbons, Director, Division of Lung Diseases

ADDRESS INQUIRIES TO:
Gary H. Gibbons, Director
Division of Lung Diseases
(See address above.)

THE POTTS MEMORIAL FOUNDATION   [2399]
P.O. Box 1015
Hudson, NY 12534
(518) 851-2292

FOUNDED: 1922

AREAS OF INTEREST:
Tuberculosis.

TYPE:
Fellowships; Grants-in-aid; Research grants; Seed money grants. At present, the program allows the Foundation to provide for the care, treatment and rehabilitation of persons afflicted with tuberculosis by methods selected by the trustees. This may include maintenance, operation of hospitals, research, vocational counseling and guidance, scholarships, subsidies for education and training, job placement, grants to hospitals and charitable institutions and the operation of sheltered workshops.

YEAR PROGRAM STARTED: 1922

PURPOSE:
To help people who are battling tuberculosis.

LEGAL BASIS:
Nonprofit corporation.

FINANCIAL DATA:
Amount of support per award: $1,000 to $30,000.

NUMBER OF APPLICANTS MOST RECENT YEAR:
Under 50.

NUMBER OF AWARDS: 10 to 15.

APPLICATION INFORMATION:
A letter of request and proposal should be furnished in as much detail as possible, including a detailed budget, to the Foundation. Eight (8) copies would be appreciated.
Duration: One year.
Deadline: 30 days prior to May 15 and October 15.

OFFICERS:
Brian Daggett, M.D., President
Kathleen A. McDonough, Ph.D., Vice President
Sidney D. Richter, Treasurer
Donna D. Klose, Secretary

TRUSTEES:
John Chan, M.D.
Joseph J. Fusco, M.D.
Richard Gullot, M.D.
Anthony Malanga, M.D.
Donna O'Hare, M.D.

ADDRESS INQUIRIES TO:
Donna D. Klose, Secretary
(See address above.)

THE SARNOFF CARDIOVASCULAR RESEARCH FOUNDATION   [2400]
731 Walker Road
Suite G2
Great Falls, VA 22066
(703) 759-7600
(888) 472-7663
Fax: (703) 759-7838

E-MAIL ADDRESS:
dboyd@sarnofffoundation.org

WEB SITE ADDRESS:
www.sarnofffoundation.org

FOUNDED: 1981

AREAS OF INTEREST:
Cardiovascular research.

NAME(S) OF PROGRAMS:
● **Sarnoff Fellowship Program**
● **Sarnoff Scholar Fellow-to-Faculty Transition Award**

TYPE:
Awards/prizes; Fellowships. Research Fellowship and Award.

PURPOSE:
To give medical students the opportunity to spend a year conducting intensive work in a biomedical research laboratory; to provide financial support to former Sarnoff Fellows committed to pursuing a career in cardiovascular research.

ELIGIBILITY:
Sarnoff Fellowship Program is for medical students enrolled in any accredited medical school in the U.S. who have completed their second or third year of medical school. Applicants enrolled in an M.D./Ph.D. program are ineligible.

Sarnoff Scholar Fellow-to-Faculty Transition Award applicant must be a former Sarnoff Fellow pursuing a career in cardiovascular research. Applicants may apply during the second half of their post-residency training/fellowship program and/or overlapping with the first two junior faculty years.

GEOGRAPHIC RESTRICTIONS:
United States.

FINANCIAL DATA:

Amount of support per award: Fellowship: $30,000 stipend and $5,500 allowance for travel and moving expenses, health insurance and computer equipment; Scholar: $50,000 in direct costs per year for salary support, $10,000 per year research supply budget and maximum of 10% indirect costs paid to the institution for handling the award.

Total amount of support: Varies.

NUMBER OF AWARDS: Fellowship: Up to 18 annually; Scholar: 1 annually.

APPLICATION INFORMATION:

Applicants to the Fellowship Program must submit the following:
(1) one-page personal statement describing scholarly interests and career plans;
(2) three-page essay on the applicant's cardiovascular topic of interest;
(3) completed application form and signed statement of confidentiality;
(4) official medical school transcript;
(5) curriculum vitae;
(6) recommendation from the applicant's sponsor;
(7) two additional recommendations and;
(8) any other material that the applicant determines is appropriate to support the application.

Duration: Fellowship: One year; Scholar: Two years.

Deadline: Fellowship and Scholar: January 9.

ADDRESS INQUIRIES TO:

Dana Boyd, Executive Director
(See address above.)

SOCIETY OF CARDIOVASCULAR ANESTHESIOLOGISTS [2401]

2209 Dickens Road
Richmond, VA 23230
(804) 282-0084
Fax: (804) 282-0090

E-MAIL ADDRESS:
sca@societyhq.com

WEB SITE ADDRESS:
www.scahq.org

AREAS OF INTEREST:
Cardiothoracic and vascular anesthesia.

NAME(S) OF PROGRAMS:
- **Roizen & Anesthesia Research Foundation New Investigator Grant**
- **SCA Starter Grants**
- **SCA-IARS Mid-Career Grant**

TYPE:
Research grants.

PURPOSE:
To promote excellence in patient care through education and research in perioperative care for patients undergoing cardiothoracic and vascular procedures.

ELIGIBILITY:
Grant applicants must be a member of Society of Cardiovascular Anesthesiologists and hold an M.D. or Ph.D. degree.

No part of the grant may be used for salary support of the principal investigator (or fellows or residents), travel or tuition expenses of the principal investigator, patient costs (except to pay for pertinent laboratory studies), consultant costs, alterations or renovations.

FINANCIAL DATA:

Amount of support per award: $25,000 to $50,000 per year.

Total amount of support: Up to $100,000 per recipient, depending on which grant is applied for.

NUMBER OF APPLICANTS MOST RECENT YEAR:
21.

NUMBER OF AWARDS: Maximum of 5 each year.

APPLICATION INFORMATION:
Application information is available on the web site.

Duration: Up to two years.

Deadline: Varies.

IRS IDENTIFICATION NUMBER: 72-0863580

ADDRESS INQUIRIES TO:
Dana B. Gibson, Executive Director
(See address above.)

Metabolism, gastroenterology, nephrology

A.S.P.E.N. RHOADS RESEARCH FOUNDATION [2402]

8630 Fenton Street
Suite 412
Silver Spring, MD 20910
(301) 920-9146
Fax: (301) 587-2365

E-MAIL ADDRESS:
carolw@nutritioncare.org

WEB SITE ADDRESS:
www.nutritioncare.org

FOUNDED: 1975

AREAS OF INTEREST:
Metabolic issues and nutrition support therapy.

TYPE:
Research grants. Annual support for nutritional research.

YEAR PROGRAM STARTED: 1992

PURPOSE:
To support research projects in nutrition support therapy and metabolic issues by young and new investigators.

LEGAL BASIS:
Nonprofit foundation.

ELIGIBILITY:
Applicants are encouraged from the fields of medicine, dietetics, nursing and pharmacy. Grants are only given to individuals. There are no citizenship requirements. A.S.P.E.N. membership is required.

FINANCIAL DATA:

Amount of support per award: Up to $25,000.

Total amount of support: Up to $130,000 annually.

NUMBER OF AWARDS: Up to 4 at $25,000; 1 at $16,000; 2 at $5,000.

APPLICATION INFORMATION:
Application form required. Contact the Foundation for additional information.

Duration: One year. Renewal possible up to two years.

Deadline: September 8.

PUBLICATIONS:
Application guidelines.

ADDRESS INQUIRIES TO:
Carol Woodside, Research Coordinator
(See address above.)

AMERICAN DIABETES ASSOCIATION [2403]

1701 North Beauregard Street
Alexandria, VA 22311
(703) 549-1500 ext. 2362
Fax: (703) 621-3759

E-MAIL ADDRESS:
grantquestions@diabetes.org

WEB SITE ADDRESS:
www.professional.diabetes.org/grants

FOUNDED: 1940

AREAS OF INTEREST:
Programs serving the needs of people with diabetes, their families, researchers, clinicians and the diabetic health care team.

CONSULTING OR VOLUNTEER SERVICES:
Various support and education programs carried out at affiliate level. Research program on national level.

NAME(S) OF PROGRAMS:
- **Basic Science Award**
- **Career Development Award**
- **Clinical Research and Epidemiological Award**
- **Clinical Scholars Award**
- **Clinical Scientist Training Award**
- **Distinguished Clinical Scientist Award**
- **Innovation Award**
- **Junior Faculty Award**
- **Mentor-Based Postdoctoral Fellowship Program**
- **Mentor-Based Postdoctoral Minority Fellowship**
- **Translational Research Award**

TYPE:
Fellowships; Research grants; Training grants.

YEAR PROGRAM STARTED: 1955

PURPOSE:
To aid in the search for a cure and prevention of diabetes; to help those with diabetes complications.

LEGAL BASIS:
Nonprofit voluntary health organization.

ELIGIBILITY:
Applicants for all awards, except the Clinical Scholars and Clinical Scientist Training Awards, must have M.D., Ph.D., Pharm.D., D.P.M. or D.O. degrees or appropriate health or science-related degrees, and must hold full-time or clinical faculty positions or the equivalent at university-affiliated institutions within the U.S. or its possessions. For all programs, applicants must be U.S. citizens or permanent residents. For Career Development Award, applicants must have an assistant professor-level faculty appointment. For the Junior Faculty Award, applicants can have any level of faculty appointment up to Associate Professor. For the Mentor-Based Postdoctoral Minority Fellowship, underrepresented minorities are defined as those minorities who are underrepresented in the area of biomedical and behavioral research. These minority groups include African Americans, Hispanics, Pacific Islanders, American Indian and Alaskan Natives.

GEOGRAPHIC RESTRICTIONS:
United States.

FINANCIAL DATA:
Amount of support per award: Basic Science Award: Up to $115,000 per year; Career Development Award: Approximately $172,500 per year; Clinical Research and Epidemiological Award: $200,000 per year; Clinical Scholars Award and Clinical Scientist Training Award: $30,000 per year; Distinguished Clinical Scientist Award: $200,000 per year; Innovation Award: $50,000 per year; Junior Faculty Award: Up to $138,000 per year, plus up to $10,000 per year towards repayment of the principal on loans for a doctoral degree (M.D. or Ph.D.); Mentor-Based Postdoctoral Fellowship: Approximately $45,000 per year; Mentor-Based Postdoctoral Minority Fellowships: $45,000 per year; Translational Research Award: Up to $200,000 per year.

NUMBER OF APPLICANTS MOST RECENT YEAR:
1,000.

APPLICATION INFORMATION:
Applicants for all grants must submit application forms, a nontechnical description of the research project of less than 200 words and a scientific abstract of the proposal of no more than 200 words.

Duration: Career Development Award: Five years. Nonrenewable; Clinical Research Grant and Junior Faculty Award: Three years; Innovation Award: Two years; Mentor-Based Postdoctoral Fellowship: Four years; Mentor-Based Postdoctoral Minority Fellowship: Two to three years; Research Award: Up to three years.

Deadline: Basic Science Award, Career Development Award, Clinical Research Grant, Innovation Award, and Junior Faculty Award: January 15 and July 15. Clinical Scholars Program, Clinical Scientist Training, Distinguished Clinical Scientist, and all Postdoctoral Fellowship Awards: January 15.

PUBLICATIONS:
Annual reports.

OFFICERS:
L. Hunter Limbaugh, Chairman of the Board
Geralyn Spollett, M.S.N., ANP-CS, President, Health Care and Education
Vivian Fonseca, M.D., President, Medicine and Science

ADDRESS INQUIRIES TO:
Priya Selvakumar
Associate Director Research Programs
(See address above.)

AMERICAN GASTROENTEROLOGICAL ASSOCIATION (AGA) [2404]

4930 Del Ray Avenue
Bethesda, MD 20814
(301) 222-4012
Fax: (301) 652-3890

E-MAIL ADDRESS:
awards@gastro.org

WEB SITE ADDRESS:
www.gastro.org/research/find-funding

FOUNDED: 1990

AREAS OF INTEREST:
Gastroenterology and related fields.

NAME(S) OF PROGRAMS:
● **AGA R. Robert and Sally D. Funderburg Research Award in Gastric Cancer**

TYPE:
Research grants. Recognition award for an established investigator working on novel approaches in gastric cancer, including the fields of gastric mucosal cell biology, regeneration and regulation of cell growth (not as they relate to peptic ulcer disease or repair), inflammation as precancerous lesions, genetics of gastric carcinoma, oncogenes in gastric epithelial malignancies, epidemiology of gastric cancer, etiology of gastric epithelial malignancies or clinical research in diagnosis or treatment of gastric carcinoma.

YEAR PROGRAM STARTED: 1990

PURPOSE:
To support an established investigator in the field of gastric biology which enhances our fundamental understanding of gastric cancer pathobiology in order to develop a cure for the disease.

LEGAL BASIS:
Nonprofit foundation.

ELIGIBILITY:
Candidates must hold faculty positions at accredited North American institutions. Candidates may not hold other exclusively salary support awards on a similar topic from other agencies. In recognition of their underrepresentation in gastroenterology-related fields, women and minorities are strongly encouraged to apply. Applicant must also be a member of the AGA.

Awardees will be selected based on the novelty, feasibility and significance of the proposal, attributes of the candidate and the likelihood that support will lead the applicant toward a research career in the field of gastric cancer biology. Preference will be given to novel approaches.

GEOGRAPHIC RESTRICTIONS:
North America.

FINANCIAL DATA:
Funds are to be used for the salary, support, equipment and supplies of the investigator, to promote his or her involvement in the field. No indirect costs will be allowed.
Amount of support per award: $50,000 per year.

NUMBER OF APPLICANTS MOST RECENT YEAR:
12 for the year 2013.

NUMBER OF AWARDS: 1.

APPLICATION INFORMATION:
Application forms can be obtained online.
Duration: Two years.
Deadline: Late August.

PUBLICATIONS:
Announcements.

ADDRESS INQUIRIES TO:
Wykenna S.C. Vailor
Senior Manager, Research Affairs and Awards
(See address above.)

AMERICAN GASTROENTEROLOGICAL ASSOCIATION (AGA) [2405]

4930 Del Ray Avenue
Bethesda, MD 20814
(301) 222-4012
Fax: (301) 652-3890

E-MAIL ADDRESS:
awards@gastro.org

WEB SITE ADDRESS:
www.gastro.org/research/find-funding

FOUNDED: 1990

AREAS OF INTEREST:
Gastroenterology and related fields.

NAME(S) OF PROGRAMS:
● **AGA Research Scholar Award**

TYPE:
Research grants. Awards for young investigators working in any area of gastroenterology, hepatology or in related areas.

YEAR PROGRAM STARTED: 1990

PURPOSE:
To provide salary support or, in special circumstances, research support to ensure that a major proportion of time is protected for research scholarship. The overall objective is to enable young investigators to develop independent productive research careers in gastroenterology-related fields.

LEGAL BASIS:
Nonprofit foundation.

ELIGIBILITY:
The applicant must hold a full-time faculty position at a North American university or professional institute at the time of application. Applicant also must be a member of the AGA. The award is not intended for fellows, but for young faculty who have demonstrated unusual promise and have some record of accomplishment in research. Emphasis will be on support of physician-investigators who have a high potential to develop independent productive research careers in gastroenterology and hepatology. Nonphysician candidates with a Ph.D. will also be considered. Established investigators are not appropriate candidates. Candidates must devote at least 70% of their effort to research related to the gastrointestinal tract or liver. Candidates should be early in their careers and, commonly, will have recently completed their fellowship training. In recognition of their underrepresentation in gastroenterology-related fields, one award is reserved for a minority candidate.

Applicants cannot hold or have held, prior to receiving the first payment of this award, an R01, R29, K-series award, VA career development award, or any award with similar objectives from non-federal sources. However, awards or grants obtained after receipt of the Research Scholar Award support by the RSA would be required to forfeit the remaining balance of award.

GEOGRAPHIC RESTRICTIONS:
North America.

FINANCIAL DATA:
Amount of support per award: $180,000 ($90,000 per year).

COOPERATIVE FUNDING PROGRAMS: Jointly sponsored by the American Gastroenterological Association and participating pharmaceutical corporations.

APPLICATION INFORMATION:
Application forms can be obtained online.
Duration: Two years.
Deadline: October for awards to begin the following July.

ADDRESS INQUIRIES TO:
Wykenna S.C. Vailor
Senior Manager, Research Affairs and
Awards
(See address above.)

AMERICAN GASTROENTEROLOGICAL ASSOCIATION (AGA) [2406]

4930 Del Ray Avenue
Bethesda, MD 20814
(301) 222-4012
Fax: (301) 652-3890

E-MAIL ADDRESS:
awards@gastro.org

WEB SITE ADDRESS:
www.gastro.org/research/find-funding

FOUNDED: 1990

AREAS OF INTEREST:
Gastroenterology and related fields.

NAME(S) OF PROGRAMS:
- **AGA Student Research Fellowship Award**

TYPE:
Research grants. Financial support for
individuals to obtain research experience by
spending some time in an active research
environment. The proposed subjects of
investigation should be related to a problem
in digestive disease or nutrition. This award
is not intended to provide salary for lab
technicians.

YEAR PROGRAM STARTED: 1990

PURPOSE:
To stimulate interest in research careers in
digestive diseases by providing salary support
for research projects.

LEGAL BASIS:
Nonprofit foundation.

ELIGIBILITY:
Candidates may be high school students or
undergraduate students at accredited North
American (U.S. or Canada) institutions and
must be in full-time research with a preceptor
for a minimum of 10 weeks. Candidates
holding advanced degrees must be enrolled
as undergraduate students. In recognition of
their underrepresentation in
gastroenterology-related fields, women and
minorities are strongly encouraged to apply.
Candidates may not hold similar salary
support awards from other agencies, e.g.,
American Liver Foundation and/or Crohn's
and Colitis Foundation.

The preceptor must be a full-time faculty
member who directs a research project in a
gastroenterology-related area at an accredited
North American institution. In addition,
he/she must be an individual member of the
AGA.

Awardees will be selected based on novelty,
feasibility and significance of the proposal,
attributes of the candidate, the record of the
preceptor, evidence of institutional
commitment and the laboratory environment.

GEOGRAPHIC RESTRICTIONS:
North America.

FINANCIAL DATA:
Amount of support per award: $2,500 for
high school students and undergraduates;
$3,000 for medical students and graduate
students.

NUMBER OF APPLICANTS MOST RECENT YEAR:
43 for the year 2013.

NUMBER OF AWARDS: 26 for the year 2013.

APPLICATION INFORMATION:
Application forms can be obtained online.
Duration: Eight to 10 weeks minimum
during the year.
Deadline: March for awards to begin the
following July.

PUBLICATIONS:
Announcement.

ADDRESS INQUIRIES TO:
Wykenna S.C. Vailor
Senior Manager, Research Affairs and
Awards
(See address above.)

*SPECIAL STIPULATIONS:
Applicants must be sponsored by an AGA
member.

AMERICAN GASTROENTEROLOGICAL ASSOCIATION (AGA) [2407]

4930 Del Ray Avenue
Bethesda, MD 20814
(301) 222-4012
Fax: (301) 652-3890

E-MAIL ADDRESS:
awards@gastro.org

WEB SITE ADDRESS:
www.gastro.org/research/find-funding

FOUNDED: 1990

AREAS OF INTEREST:
Gastroenterology and related fields.

NAME(S) OF PROGRAMS:
- **Elsevier Pilot Research Award**

TYPE:
Research grants. Research initiative grants for
investigators to work in gastroenterology- or
hepatology-related areas.

YEAR PROGRAM STARTED: 1990

PURPOSE:
To provide non-salary funds to new
investigators starting their research careers to
help them establish their independence; to
support pilot projects that represent new
research directions for established
investigators, with the intent of stimulating
research in gastroenterology- or
hepatology-related areas by permitting
investigators to obtain new data which can
ultimately provide the basis for subsequent
grant applications of more substantial funding
and duration.

LEGAL BASIS:
Nonprofit foundation.

ELIGIBILITY:
Open to investigators with M.Ds. or Ph.Ds.
(or equivalent), who must hold faculty
positions at accredited North American
institutions. They may not hold awards on a
similar topic from other agencies. Applicant
must also be a member of the AGA. In
recognition of their underrepresentation in
gastroenterology-related fields, women and
minorities are strongly encouraged to apply.

Proposals will be selected on the basis of
novelty, importance, feasibility, environment,
commitment of the institution and overall
likelihood that the projects will lead to more
substantial, subsequent grant applications. For

clinical projects, prior IRB approval must be
obtained and that documentation must
accompany submission of the application.

GEOGRAPHIC RESTRICTIONS:
North America.

FINANCIAL DATA:
Funds may be used for salary (for lab
personnel and technicians only), supplies or
equipment. Indirect costs are not allowed.
Amount of support per award: $25,000 per
year.

NUMBER OF APPLICANTS MOST RECENT YEAR:
Varies.

NUMBER OF AWARDS: 1.

APPLICATION INFORMATION:
Application information is available on the
web site.
Duration: One year.
Deadline: January 16.

ADDRESS INQUIRIES TO:
Wykenna S.C. Vailor
Senior Manager, Research Affairs and
Awards
(See address above.)

THE ELI AND EDYTHE BROAD FOUNDATION [2408]

Broad Medical Research Program
10900 Wilshire Boulevard, 12th Floor
Los Angeles, CA 90024-6532
(310) 954-5091
Fax: (310) 954-5092

E-MAIL ADDRESS:
info@broadmedical.org

WEB SITE ADDRESS:
www.broadmedical.org

FOUNDED: 2001

AREAS OF INTEREST:
Understanding and treating inflammatory
bowel disease.

NAME(S) OF PROGRAMS:
- **Broad Medical Research Program**

TYPE:
Research grants; Seed money grants.
Designed to stimulate innovative research
that will lead to both the prevention and
successful therapy of inflammatory bowel
disease.

YEAR PROGRAM STARTED: 2001

PURPOSE:
To understand and treat inflammatory bowel
disease.

ELIGIBILITY:
Grants will only be awarded to nonprofit
organizations, such as universities, hospitals
and research institutes.

FINANCIAL DATA:
Amount of support per award: Average
$114,082 per year.
Total amount of support: $3,438,825 for the
year 2012.

NUMBER OF APPLICANTS MOST RECENT YEAR:
103.

NUMBER OF AWARDS: 20 new awards.

APPLICATION INFORMATION:
Applicants should submit a brief Letter of
Interest (up to three pages, not including
attachments) as the initial request for
funding. Investigators whose Letters of
Interest fit the Program's criteria and areas of
interest will be invited to submit a full grant
application.

The following information is part of the three-page limit:
(1) title of the project;
(2) specific hypothesis or question to be investigated;
(3) methodology;
(4) data analysis and;
(5) anticipated outcomes.

Additionally, applicants are required to:
(1) state why the project fits the Program's criteria, including its relevance and likely benefits to patients with inflammatory bowel disease in the next several years;
(2) attach the investigator's curriculum vitae(s) or biographical sketch(es);
(3) briefly describe the laboratory or clinical environment;
(4) indicate the estimated total budget and the period for which funding is requested and;
(5) provide the principal investigator's e-mail and postal addresses.

Supportive information, such as references, preliminary data or recent publications, may be included. These will not be counted as part of the three-page limit.

Duration: Up to two years.

IRS IDENTIFICATION NUMBER: 95-4686318

ADDRESS INQUIRIES TO:
See e-mail address above.

CANADIAN DIABETES ASSOCIATION   [2409]
National Life Building
522 University Avenue, Suite 1400
Toronto ON M5G 2R5 Canada
(416) 363-3373 ext. 7085
Fax: (416) 363-7465

E-MAIL ADDRESS:
info@diabetes.ca

WEB SITE ADDRESS:
www.diabetes.ca

FOUNDED: 1953

AREAS OF INTEREST:
Medical research into the causes and cure of diabetes.

NAME(S) OF PROGRAMS:
● **Charles H. Best Research Fund**

TYPE:
Research grants. Support for ongoing research into better ways to treat diabetes and ultimately cure it.

YEAR PROGRAM STARTED: 1975

PURPOSE:
To promote the health of Canadians through diabetes research, education, service and advocacy.

LEGAL BASIS:
Nonprofit.

ELIGIBILITY:
Individuals and groups may apply for research programs in Canada only.

GEOGRAPHIC RESTRICTIONS:
Canada.

FINANCIAL DATA:
Total amount of support: Varies.

APPLICATION INFORMATION:
Guidelines and application form are available on the web site.
Duration: One to three years.
Deadline: February 1.

ADDRESS INQUIRIES TO:
Jovita Sundaramoorthy
Vice President, Research and Education
(See address above.)

CANADIAN LIVER FOUNDATION   [2410]
3100 Steeles Avenue East
Suite 801
Markham ON L3R 8T3 Canada
(416) 491-3353
(800) 563-5483
Fax: (905) 752-1540

E-MAIL ADDRESS:
clf@liver.ca

WEB SITE ADDRESS:
www.liver.ca

FOUNDED: 1969

AREAS OF INTEREST:
Research and education into the causes, diagnosis, prevention and treatment of diseases of the liver.

NAME(S) OF PROGRAMS:
● **Canadian Liver Foundation Operating Grant**

TYPE:
Research grants.

YEAR PROGRAM STARTED: 1970

PURPOSE:
To support research projects directed towards a defined objective, conducted by an investigator working alone or in collaboration with others.

LEGAL BASIS:
Registered Canadian charity.

ELIGIBILITY:
Hepatobiliary research investigators who hold an academic appointment in a Canadian university or affiliated institution are eligible to apply. Clinical investigators and basic scientists will be considered.

The applicant must designate the institution in which he or she holds an academic appointment. The institution is considered by the Foundation to be responsible for the provision of space, facilities, furniture and general services for the conduct of the research project described.

GEOGRAPHIC RESTRICTIONS:
Canada.

FINANCIAL DATA:
Amount of support per award: $60,000 (CAN) per year.
Total amount of support: Varies depending on the number of suitable candidates and the funds available.

NUMBER OF APPLICANTS MOST RECENT YEAR: 43 for the year 2012.

NUMBER OF AWARDS: 6 for the year 2012.

REPRESENTATIVE AWARDS:
Dr. Laura Arbour, University of British Columbia, "Genetic studies of primary biliary cirrhosis in First Nations peoples of the Pacific Northwest Coast;" Dr. Norman Kneteman, University of Alberta, "Transcriptional regulation of hepatic genes in response to hepatitis C infection and treatment with interferon alpha 2b;" Dr. Diana Mager, University of Alberta, "Altered fat metabolism as a mechanism for hepatic steatosis in children with non-alcoholic fatty liver disease."

APPLICATION INFORMATION:
Grant application criteria and forms are available on the web site.
Duration: Two years.
Deadline: March 31, for awards to become tenable the following September 1.

PUBLICATIONS:
Program description and guidelines.

STAFF:
Billie Potkonjak, Research Grants Administrator

ADDRESS INQUIRIES TO:
Billie Potkonjak
Research Grants Administrator
(See address above.)

CANADIAN LIVER FOUNDATION
3100 Steeles Avenue East
Suite 801
Markham ON L3R 8T3 Canada
(416) 491-3353
(800) 563-5483
Fax: (905) 752-1540

E-MAIL ADDRESS:
clf@liver.ca

WEB SITE ADDRESS:
www.liver.ca

TYPE:
Scholarships.

See entry 2251 for full listing.

CANADIAN LIVER FOUNDATION
3100 Steeles Avenue East
Suite 801
Markham ON L3R 8T3 Canada
(416) 491-3353
(800) 563-5483
Fax: (905) 752-1540

E-MAIL ADDRESS:
clf@liver.ca

WEB SITE ADDRESS:
www.liver.ca

TYPE:
Scholarships.

See entry 2250 for full listing.

COOLEY'S ANEMIA FOUNDATION, INC.   [2411]
330 7th Avenue
Suite 200
New York, NY 10001-5264
(212) 279-8090 ext. 201
(800) 522-7222
Fax: (212) 279-5999

E-MAIL ADDRESS:
info@cooleysanemia.org

WEB SITE ADDRESS:
www.cooleysanemia.org

FOUNDED: 1954

AREAS OF INTEREST:
Cooley's anemia and all thalassemias.

TYPE:
Fellowships; Research grants. Clinical grants. Research, public and professional education, patient care and public information. Basic and clinical research and fellowships.

YEAR PROGRAM STARTED: 1954

PURPOSE:
To provide impetus to benefit the advancement of knowledge and the quality of care in Cooley's anemia and other thalassemias.

LEGAL BASIS:
Federal tax-exempt, nonprofit, voluntary health agency.

FINANCIAL DATA:
Amount of support per award: Fellowships: $32,500; Clinical grants: Up to $40,000.

NUMBER OF APPLICANTS MOST RECENT YEAR:
30.

APPLICATION INFORMATION:
Applications are available on the web site.
Duration: One year. Possibility for renewal for second year.
Deadline: First Monday in February.

PUBLICATIONS:
Lifeline Newsletter; screening material; educational pamphlets.

IRS IDENTIFICATION NUMBER: 11-1971539

OFFICERS:
Tony Viola, President

ADDRESS INQUIRIES TO:
Gina Cioffi, National Executive Director
(See address above.)

CROHN'S AND COLITIS FOUNDATION OF AMERICA, INC. [2412]
733 Third Avenue, Suite 510
New York, NY 10017
(646) 943-7505
(800) 932-2423
Fax: (212) 779-4098

E-MAIL ADDRESS:
grants@ccfa.org

WEB SITE ADDRESS:
www.ccfa.org

FOUNDED: 1967

AREAS OF INTEREST:
Research and education in inflammatory bowel disease (Crohn's disease and ulcerative colitis).

CONSULTING OR VOLUNTEER SERVICES:
Medical committees (consisting of physician volunteers) provide services in the areas of patient and professional education, research development, grants review, etc.

NAME(S) OF PROGRAMS:
- CCFA Career Development Award
- CCFA Research Fellowship Award
- CCFA Research Initiatives
- CCFA Senior Research Award
- CCFA Student Research Fellowship Awards

TYPE:
Awards/prizes; Conferences/seminars; Fellowships; Project/program grants; Research grants; Scholarships; Training grants; Visiting scholars. Senior Research Award provides funds to enable established investigators to generate sufficient data to become competitive for funds from other sources, such as the National Institutes of Health.

Research Fellowship Awards and Career Development Awards encourage the early developmental stages of individuals with potential for a career of independent basic and/or clinical investigation in IBD.

Student Research Fellowship Awards are available for undergraduate, medical or graduate students (not yet engaged in thesis research) in accredited North American institutions to conduct full-time research with a mentor investigating a subject relevant to IBD.

YEAR PROGRAM STARTED: 1967

PURPOSE:
To fund research leading to understanding of and ultimate cure for Crohn's disease and ulcerative colitis.

LEGAL BASIS:
Nonprofit, special-interest foundation.

ELIGIBILITY:
For Career Development Awards, candidates must have at least five years of relevant postdoctoral experience prior to the beginning date of the awards and not in excess of 10 years beyond the attainment of their Doctorate degrees.

For Research Fellowship Awards, candidates must have two years of relevant postdoctoral experience prior to the beginning date of the award.

For Research Training Awards, candidates must be sponsored by a public or private nonprofit institution or a government institution engaged in health care and health-related research within the U.S. and its possessions. Individuals who already are well established in the field are not considered eligible for these awards. Applicants must hold M.D. or Ph.D. degrees and be employed within the U.S. at the time of submission. Eligibility is not restricted by citizenship.

For Senior Research Award, applicants must be established researchers in the field of inflammatory bowel disease.

FINANCIAL DATA:
Amount of support per award: Career Development Award: $90,000 per year; Research Fellowship Award: $58,250 per year; Senior Research Award: $115,830 per year; Student Research Fellowship Award: $2,500.
Total amount of support: Approximately $16,000,000 annually.

COOPERATIVE FUNDING PROGRAMS:
NASPGHAN/CDHNF.

NUMBER OF APPLICANTS MOST RECENT YEAR:
249.

NUMBER OF AWARDS: Over 200.

REPRESENTATIVE AWARDS:
$5,396,724 to Subra Kugathasan, M.D., Emory University, Atlanta, GA, for "Risk stratification and identification of Immunogenetic markers of complicated disease course in pediatric Crohn's disease;" $2,715,000 to Jeffrey Gordon, M.D., Washington University School of Medicine, St. Louis, MO, for "CCFA Gut Microbiome Initiative."

APPLICATION INFORMATION:
Before submitting a Letter of Intent or Full Proposal, applicants are urged to view the online policies and instructions. After the Letter of Intent is submitted and approved, CCFA Research Grants Administration will send an e-mail to the applicant with a link to complete and submit a Full Proposal.
Duration: Senior Research Awards: One to three years.
Deadline: Student Research Fellowship Awards: March 15. Awards begin on or about June 15. Career Development Award,

Research Fellowship Award and Senior Research Award: January 14 for July 1 start date and July 1 for January 1 start date.

PUBLICATIONS:
Annual report; *Inflammatory Bowel Diseases; Foundation Focus;* brochures.

IRS IDENTIFICATION NUMBER: 13-6193105

STAFF:
Richard Geswell, President

FOUNDERS:
Henry D. Janowitz, M.D.
William D. Modell
Irwin M. Rosenthal

ADDRESS INQUIRIES TO:
Dorothy King
Grants Administrative Coordinator
(See address above.)

CYSTIC FIBROSIS FOUNDATION [2413]
6931 Arlington Road
Bethesda, MD 20814
(301) 951-4422
(800) 344-4823
Fax: (301) 951-6378; (301) 841-2605

E-MAIL ADDRESS:
grants@cff.org

WEB SITE ADDRESS:
www.cff.org

FOUNDED: 1955

AREAS OF INTEREST:
Research, care and education programs to benefit patients with cystic fibrosis.

NAME(S) OF PROGRAMS:
- CFF/NIH Unfunded Grants
- Clinical Research Grants
- Leroy Matthews Physician/Scientist Award
- Pilot and Feasibility Awards
- Research Grants
- Harry Shwachman Clinical Investigator Award
- Special Research Awards
- Therapeutics Development Awards

TYPE:
Fellowships; Research grants; Training grants. The CFF/NIH Unfunded Grants support excellent CF-related research projects that have been submitted to and approved by the National Institutes of Health (NIH) but cannot be supported by available NIH funds.

Clinical Research Grants offer support to clinical research projects directly related to cystic fibrosis treatment and care.

Leroy Matthews Physician/Scientist Award provides support for outstanding, newly trained pediatricians and internists (M.D. and M.D./Ph.D.) to complete subspecialty training, develop into independent investigators, and initiate a research program.

Pilot and Feasibility Awards are for developing and testing new hypotheses and/or new methods and to support promising new investigators as they establish themselves in research areas relevant to CF.

Research Grants are intended to encourage the development of new information that contributes to the understanding of the basic etiology and pathogenesis of cystic fibrosis.

The Harry Shwachman Award provides the opportunity for clinically-trained physicians to develop into independent biomedical research investigators who are actively involved in CF-related areas. It is also intended to facilitate the transition from postdoctoral training to a career in academic medicine.

Special Research Awards direct research efforts toward specific areas of CF-related research.

Therapeutics Development Awards provide funds to businesses that will develop commercial products to benefit individuals with CF. Structured as a matching grants program, funds will be awarded only if they are matched by the recipient.

YEAR PROGRAM STARTED: 1955

PURPOSE:
To encourage clinical research into the cause, care and treatment of cystic fibrosis; to train specialists for careers in academic medicine.

LEGAL BASIS:
501(c)(3) organization, incorporated as a nonprofit, tax-exempt organization.

ELIGIBILITY:
Contact the Foundation for specific eligibility details for the various grant programs.

FINANCIAL DATA:
Amount of support per award: CFF/NIH Unfunded Grants: $75,000 to $125,000 per year; Clinical Research Grants: Up to $80,000 per year (single-center) and up to $150,000 per year (multicenter); Leroy Matthews Physician/Scientist Award: $48,000 (stipend) plus $10,000 (research and development) for year one to $76,000 (stipend) plus $15,000 (research and development) for year six; Pilot and Feasibility Awards: Up to $40,000 per year; Research Grants: $90,000 per year; Harry Shwachman Clinical Investigator Award: Up to $76,000 per year plus $15,000 for supplies; Therapeutics Development Awards: Up to $200,000 per year for a maximum of two years for Component I and up to $750,000 per year for a maximum of two years for Component II.

APPLICATION INFORMATION:
Detailed information can be obtained from the CFF Grants and Contracts Office.
Duration: CFF/NIH Unfunded Grants: Up to two years (from CFF); Clinical Research Grants: Up to three years; Matthews Physician/Scientist Award: Up to six years; Pilot and Feasibility Awards: Up to two years; Research Grants: Two years with possible renewal for two additional years; Shwachman Clinical Investigator Award: Three years; Therapeutic Development Awards: Up to two years for both Components I and II.
Deadline: CFF/NIH Unfunded Grants and Therapeutics Development Awards reviewed on an ongoing basis; Clinical Research Grants: June 1 for letter of intent, first Wednesday in September for application for Fall deadline and December 1 for letter of intent, first Wednesday in March for application for Spring deadline; Matthews Physician/Scientist Award, Pilot and Feasibility Awards, and the Shwachman Clinical Investigator Award: First Wednesday in September for application; Research Grants: April 1 for letter of intent.

PUBLICATIONS:
Annual report; application form; guidelines.

STAFF:
Robert J. Beall, Ph.D., President and Chief Executive Officer
Rich Mattingly, Chief Operating Officer

ADDRESS INQUIRIES TO:
Grants and Contracts Manager
(See address above.)

JUVENILE DIABETES RESEARCH FOUNDATION INTERNATIONAL [2414]
26 Broadway
14th Floor
New York, NY 10004
(212) 785-9500
(800) 533-2873
Fax: (212) 785-9595

E-MAIL ADDRESS:
info@jdrf.org

WEB SITE ADDRESS:
www.jdrf.org

FOUNDED: 1970

AREAS OF INTEREST:
To support research into the causes, treatment, prevention and cure of diabetes and its complications.

NAME(S) OF PROGRAMS:
● **Regular Research Grant**

TYPE:
Project/program grants; Research grants. Support for a variety of needs, such as salaries for technical assistance, special equipment, animals and supplies for scientific investigations related to diabetes.

YEAR PROGRAM STARTED: 1973

PURPOSE:
To support scientific investigations of diabetes.

LEGAL BASIS:
Incorporated not-for-profit voluntary health agency.

ELIGIBILITY:
Grants are awarded to new or established researchers. Proposal must be for a scientific research project involving the cause, treatment, prevention, and/or cure of diabetes and its complications. Applicants must hold an M.D., D.M.D., D.V.M., Ph.D. or equivalent and have a full-time faculty position or equivalent at a college, university, medical school, company, or other research facility.

FINANCIAL DATA:
Salary support plus fringe benefits for the principal investigator may not exceed his or her percentage effort on the project multiplied by institutional base salary. Indirect costs (excluding equipment) may not exceed 10%. Funds may be used for salaries for technical assistant, special equipment, animals and supplies.
Amount of support per award: $110,000 per year for three years, including indirect cost.

APPLICATION INFORMATION:
Application forms are available from the address above. The current JDF or NIH application may be used; however, for the NIH the research plan must include two abstracts (one written in scientific language and one in lay language) and cannot exceed 10 pages. Applicants must submit a signed original with 15 copies and include information regarding all other sources of

support (current or pending) including title, abstract, annual total amount of grant, inclusive funding period and percentage effort of the applicant. In addition, applicants must include a detailed letter of intent outlining the rationale for the request, budgetary requirements, and curriculum vitae of the principal investigator. Applications from industry must also include the rationale of how the proposed device/technology will address an important issue in diabetes management or research and the potential to improve diabetes management or progress toward prevention or cure of diabetes and its complications.
Duration: One year with renewal by application for up to two additional years.
Deadline: Applications open May 1. Online applications due July 31, with review in November. Notification in January for start date of March 1.

PUBLICATIONS:
Annual report; policy statement; research appropriations sheet; *Countdown Magazine*.

ADDRESS INQUIRIES TO:
Director, Operations and Administration
(See address above.)

JUVENILE DIABETES RESEARCH FOUNDATION INTERNATIONAL [2415]
26 Broadway
14th Floor
New York, NY 10004
(212) 785-9500
(800) 533-2873
Fax: (212) 785-9595

E-MAIL ADDRESS:
info@jdrf.org

WEB SITE ADDRESS:
www.jdrf.org

FOUNDED: 1970

AREAS OF INTEREST:
To support research into the causes, treatment, prevention and cure of diabetes and its complications.

NAME(S) OF PROGRAMS:
● **Postdoctoral Fellowships**

TYPE:
Fellowships. Postdoctoral fellowships to attract qualified and promising scientists entering their professional career into fields of research in diabetes. The applicant is required to work with a sponsor who can provide a training environment most conducive to beginning a career in diabetes-relevant research. Fellowship research may be conducted at foreign and domestic, for-profit and nonprofit, public and private organizations such as universities, colleges, hospitals, laboratories, units of state and local governments, and eligible agencies of the federal government.

YEAR PROGRAM STARTED: 1973

PURPOSE:
To support advanced training in fields of research directly related to diabetes.

LEGAL BASIS:
Incorporated not-for-profit voluntary health agency.

ELIGIBILITY:
By the beginning of the period of support sought, the applicant must have a doctoral degree (M.D., D.M., D.V.M., Ph.D. or the

equivalent) for no more than five years before the fellowship and may not have a faculty appointment. Each applicant must be sponsored by a scientist who is affiliated full-time with an accredited institution and who agrees to supervise that individual's training. JDF welcomes applications from women and members of minority groups underrepresented in the sciences.

The applicant is responsible for selecting a research mentor and for making arrangements to work in this person's laboratory. The designated mentor must be the senior scientist who will directly supervise the proposed research.

FINANCIAL DATA:
The stipend is dependent on the number of years of relevant experience.
Amount of support per award: $39,264 to $54,180 per year, with a research allowance of $5,500 per year.

APPLICATION INFORMATION:
Application forms are available from the address above. Applicants must submit a signed original with 15 copies. The applicant must include three letters of reference assessing the scientific abilities and potential of the applicant and a statement of career goals with the relevance to diabetes-related research. The sponsor must outline a specific training program, confirm the space and facilities for the research project, provide information on all sources of grant support (current or pending, federal or nonfederal) and must include the title, amounts, funding periods and abstract pages of all current and pending support.
Duration: Three years.
Deadline: July 31. Notification in January for start date of March 1.

PUBLICATIONS:
Annual report; policy statement; research appropriations sheet; *Countdown Magazine.*

ADDRESS INQUIRIES TO:
Director, Operations and Administration (See address above.)

*SPECIAL STIPULATIONS:
Awardees will be required to attend an annual JDF two-day meeting to present the results of their work and produce a progress report at the end of each funding year. Awardees must spend at least 80% of time and effort on the research project during the period of the award.

JUVENILE DIABETES RESEARCH FOUNDATION INTERNATIONAL [2416]

26 Broadway
14th Floor
New York, NY 10004
(212) 785-9500
(800) 533-2873
Fax: (212) 785-9595

E-MAIL ADDRESS:
info@jdrf.org

WEB SITE ADDRESS:
www.jdrf.org

FOUNDED: 1970

AREAS OF INTEREST:
Prevention and treatment of type I diabetes and its complications.

NAME(S) OF PROGRAMS:
● **Career Development Awards**

TYPE:
Development grants; Research grants; Training grants. Grants are awarded to promising scientists entering their professional career in the diabetes research field. In the five-year term, awardees will focus their research efforts in a subject directly related to JDRF's research mission goals and position themselves to work at the leading edge of diabetes research.

YEAR PROGRAM STARTED: 1979

PURPOSE:
To attract qualified and promising scientists early in their faculty careers and to give them the opportunity to establish themselves in areas that reflect the JDRF research mission goals.

LEGAL BASIS:
Charitable foundation.

ELIGIBILITY:
The individuals must be in a relatively early stage of their career who have demonstrated superior scholarship and show the greatest promise for future achievement in research, including either clinically relevant research or basic research. Ordinarily, their first degree (M.D., Ph.D., D.M.D., D.V.D. or equivalent) will have been received at least three, but not more than seven, years before the award. The applicant must hold an academic position including assistant professor or equivalent at the time of the award. At the inception of the award, however, the applicant must be a faculty member in a university, health science center, or comparable institution with strong, well-established research and training programs for the chosen area of interest.

FINANCIAL DATA:
Indirect costs cannot exceed 10%.
Amount of support per award: $150,000 per year; up to $65,000 of this may be requested for research allowance which can include a technician, supplies, equipment and travel up to $2,000 per year.

APPLICATION INFORMATION:
Application forms are available from the address above. Applicants must submit a signed original with 15 copies and include three letters of reference assessing the candidate's scientific abilities, assurance from the university of an academic commitment to the applicant and the research project, all other sources of funding (current, federal and nonfederal), with the title, abstract, annual and total amount of support and inclusive funding periods of all current and pending grants.
Duration: One year. Renewable up to a maximum of four years pending satisfactory progress.
Deadline: Applications open May 1. Online applications due July 31, with review in November. Notification in January for start date of March 1.

PUBLICATIONS:
Annual report; policy statement; research appropriations sheet; *Countdown Magazine.*

ADDRESS INQUIRIES TO:
Director, Operations and Administration (See address above.)

THE KIDNEY FOUNDATION OF CANADA [2417]

5165 Sherbrooke Street West
Suite 300
Montreal QC H4A 1T6 Canada
(514) 369-4806
Fax: (514) 369-2472

E-MAIL ADDRESS:
research@kidney.ca

WEB SITE ADDRESS:
www.kidney.ca

FOUNDED: 1964

AREAS OF INTEREST:
Research that may further the current knowledge pertaining to the kidney and urinary tract.

NAME(S) OF PROGRAMS:
● **Biomedical Research Grant**

TYPE:
Research grants. Provides funds to defray the cost of research, including the purchase and maintenance of experimental animals, the purchase of materials, supplies and equipment and the payment of laboratory assistants.

YEAR PROGRAM STARTED: 1972

PURPOSE:
To acquire a greater understanding of kidney diseases and the importance of the role of the kidneys in the human body.

LEGAL BASIS:
Corporation.

ELIGIBILITY:
Applicants must be Canadian citizens or landed immigrants. Research must be conducted within Canada and funding is limited to individuals holding staff appointments at Canadian universities or other recognized Canadian academic institutions.

Grant applications for equipment only will not be considered.

GEOGRAPHIC RESTRICTIONS:
Canada.

FINANCIAL DATA:
Amount of support per award: Maximum $50,000 (CAN) per year.
Total amount of support: $100,000.

NUMBER OF APPLICANTS MOST RECENT YEAR: 72.

NUMBER OF AWARDS: 20.

APPLICATION INFORMATION:
Application information is available on the web site.
Duration: Up to three years. Grants run from July 1 to June 30.
Deadline: October 15.

ADDRESS INQUIRIES TO:
National Director of Research (See address above.)

THE KIDNEY FOUNDATION OF CANADA [2418]

5165 Sherbrooke Street West
Suite 300
Montreal QC H4A 1T6 Canada
(514) 369-4806
Fax: (514) 369-2472

E-MAIL ADDRESS:
research@kidney.ca

WEB SITE ADDRESS:
www.kidney.ca

FOUNDED: 1964

AREAS OF INTEREST:
Research that may further the current knowledge pertaining to the kidney and urinary tract.

NAME(S) OF PROGRAMS:
● **Allied Health Research Grant**

TYPE:
Research grants. Funds allocated to assist in defraying the cost of research, including the purchase and maintenance of experimental animals, the purchase of materials, supplies and equipment and the payment of laboratory assistants. Travel assistance is also available.

YEAR PROGRAM STARTED: 1972

PURPOSE:
To foster and encourage research relevant to clinical practice in the area of nephrology and urology by allied health professionals.

LEGAL BASIS:
Corporation.

ELIGIBILITY:
Open to Canadian citizens. The Foundation will consider only those applications which prove scientific excellence where there is clear, demonstrated relevance of the project and its outcomes to the mission of The Kidney Foundation and the primary investigator is an allied health professional (e.g., nurses, technicians, dieticians, social workers).

Funds are available for research conducted within Canada.

The majority of applicants/co-applicants must be allied health professionals.

Priority will be given to applications submitted where the primary investigation has a demonstrated commitment to nephrology, urology or organ donation.

Under no circumstance should the grant application exceed the amount of $50,000. An investigator may not hold more than $50,000 per year from The Kidney Foundation as an award from a single grant or from multiple grants where the applicant is listed as an investigator or as a co-investigator.

GEOGRAPHIC RESTRICTIONS:
Canada.

FINANCIAL DATA:
Amount of support per award: Up to $50,000 (CAN) per year.
Total amount of support: Varies.

APPLICATION INFORMATION:
Initial or renewal application must be made on the prescribed form and sent in 12 copies to The Kidney Foundation at the address above. Grant application must also include letters of intent to participate from collaborators who have a role in the research project. Additional documentation, in the future, may be requested from the applicant.
Duration: One year. Must reapply for renewal of second year. Grants run from July 1 to June 30.
Deadline: October 15.

ADDRESS INQUIRIES TO:
National Director of Research
(See address above.)

THE KIDNEY FOUNDATION OF CANADA [2419]
5165 Sherbrooke Street West
Suite 300
Montreal QC H4A 1T6 Canada
(514) 369-4806
Fax: (514) 369-2472

E-MAIL ADDRESS:
research@kidney.ca

WEB SITE ADDRESS:
www.kidney.ca

FOUNDED: 1964

AREAS OF INTEREST:
Research that may further the current knowledge pertaining to the kidney and urinary tract.

NAME(S) OF PROGRAMS:
● **Allied Health Doctoral Fellowship**

TYPE:
Fellowships. Designed to provide for full-time academic and research preparation at the doctoral level in Canada or abroad. The award is designed to encourage new students to enter doctoral programs, as well as support students currently enrolled in a program.

YEAR PROGRAM STARTED: 1991

PURPOSE:
To promote and enhance the development of nephrology/urology allied health investigators in Canada.

LEGAL BASIS:
Corporation.

ELIGIBILITY:
Open to nephrology/urology nurses and technicians, social workers, dietitians, transplant coordinators and other allied health professionals. Applicant must demonstrate commitment to the area of nephrology/urology with a minimum of two years direct clinic practice.

Applicant must intend to return to Canada, if studies are outside the country.

FINANCIAL DATA:
Amount of support per award: Up to $31,000 per year for fellowship, depending upon the applicant's qualifications.
Total amount of support: $56,000.

APPLICATION INFORMATION:
Applications must be made on the prescribed forms which are available from the National Office. The completed application must include a certified transcript of the applicant's postsecondary school academic records, a letter from the supervisor, dean or department chairperson outlining academic plan and possible research plans, a letter from the sponsoring institution confirming the acceptance of candidate by June 30 and two Assessment of Candidate forms from persons who can give an assessment of the applicant's ability.
Duration: One year. A second, third or fourth year may be obtained upon successful reapplication.
Deadline: March 15. Renewal possible.

PUBLICATIONS:
Guidelines; application form; annual report.

ADDRESS INQUIRIES TO:
Wim Wolfs
National Director of Research
(See address above.)

THE KIDNEY FOUNDATION OF CANADA [2420]
5165 Sherbrooke Street West
Suite 300
Montreal QC H4A 1T6 Canada
(514) 369-4806
Fax: (514) 369-2472

E-MAIL ADDRESS:
research@kidney.ca

WEB SITE ADDRESS:
www.kidney.ca

AREAS OF INTEREST:
Research into the incidence and cure of kidney and urinary tract disease, patient services and public education.

NAME(S) OF PROGRAMS:
● **Allied Health Scholarship**

TYPE:
Scholarships. To promote and enhance the development of nephrology/urology allied health investigators in Canada.

YEAR PROGRAM STARTED: 1991

PURPOSE:
To assist the student with a demonstrated interest in nephrology/urology in pursuing education at the Master's or doctoral level.

LEGAL BASIS:
Corporation.

ELIGIBILITY:
Open to nurses and technicians, social workers, dietitians, transplant coordinators, and other allied health professionals who demonstrate commitment to the area of nephrology, urology or organ donation. Applicants who demonstrate a minimum of two years direct clinical practice are eligible. Must have Canadian citizenship or landed immigrant status.

FINANCIAL DATA:
Amount of support per award: Up to $5,000 per year for full-time studies and $2,500 per year for part-time studies up to a maximum of $10,000 (CAN).

NUMBER OF AWARDS: Varies depending on funding.

APPLICATION INFORMATION:
Application information is available on the web site.
Duration: One year. Must reapply for second year of funding.
Deadline: March 15.

PUBLICATIONS:
Guidelines; application forms; annual report.

ADDRESS INQUIRIES TO:
Wim Wolfs
National Director of Research
(See address above.)

NATIONAL KIDNEY FOUNDATION [2421]
30 East 33rd Street
New York, NY 10016
(212) 889-2210
(800) 622-9010
Fax: (212) 779-0068

E-MAIL ADDRESS:
research@kidney.org

WEB SITE ADDRESS:
www.kidney.org

FOUNDED: 1950

AREAS OF INTEREST:
Function and diseases of the kidney.

NAME(S) OF PROGRAMS:
● **Research Fellowship Award**

TYPE:
Fellowships; Grants-in-aid; Research grants. Fellowships for research and training in the field of kidney function and disease. Current emphasis is on supporting research and training in academic nephrology on closely related fields.

YEAR PROGRAM STARTED: 1967

PURPOSE:
To support those aspects of kidney research and training which are not adequately financed by governmental agencies and to support training of individuals whose goal is a career in academic nephrology or related fields.

LEGAL BASIS:
Voluntary health agency.

ELIGIBILITY:
Applicants must have completed no more than 4.5 years of postdoctoral research training (after receipt of M.D., Ph.D., D.O., or equivalent degree) at the time of the activation of the award. For those applying for a second year (competitive renewal), applicants must have completed no more than 5.5 years of postdoctoral training. Individuals completing two years of training may be eligible for a third year of funding to gain additional training towards becoming an independent investigator, but that additional support will not be awarded to carry out the initial project proposal. Anyone who has ever held a faculty appointment at the level of assistant professor is ineligible.

FINANCIAL DATA:
Amount of support per award: $50,000 annual stipend for new awardees.
Total amount of support: Varies.

NUMBER OF AWARDS: 10 new research fellowships awarded each year.

APPLICATION INFORMATION:
Application available online.
Duration: Awards are made normally on an annual basis; however, fellows can reapply for a second year.
Deadline: First quarter of each calendar year.

OFFICERS:
Bill Cella, Chairman
Lynda Szczech, M.D., President

ADDRESS INQUIRIES TO:
Grant Coordinator
(See address above.)

NATIONAL KIDNEY FOUNDATION [2422]
30 East 33rd Street
New York, NY 10016
(212) 889-2210
(800) 622-9010
Fax: (212) 889-2038

E-MAIL ADDRESS:
research@kidney.org

WEB SITE ADDRESS:
www.kidney.org

AREAS OF INTEREST:
Improvement in the treatment and prevention of kidney disease.

NAME(S) OF PROGRAMS:
● **Young Investigator Grant Program**

TYPE:
Development grants; Project/program grants; Research grants; Seed money grants.

YEAR PROGRAM STARTED: 1987

PURPOSE:
To support research in the fields of nephrology, urology and related disciplines by individuals who have completed fellowship training and who hold junior faculty positions at university-affiliated medical centers in the U.S.

LEGAL BASIS:
Voluntary health agency.

ELIGIBILITY:
Applications will be considered from individuals who will have completed research training in nephrology or closely related fields prior to the start of the grant award and who intend to pursue research directly related to these areas. At the time funding begins (July 1), the applicant must hold a full-time appointment to a faculty position at a university or an equivalent position as a scientist on the staff of a research oriented institution, e.g., National Institutes of Health (NIH) or other research organization, in the U.S. Customarily, the appropriate faculty rank is that of Assistant Professor. (In some institutions a title other than Assistant Professor, e.g., Instructor, is used to designate junior faculty status; individuals at that rank in such institutions are eligible to apply for a Young Investigator Grant). Qualifications should be documented in the biosketch (maximum four pages).

Young Investigator Grants will be awarded to individuals no later than four years after initial appointment to a faculty (or equivalent) position or after appointment to a staff scientist (or equivalent) position in a research organization. Because of this policy, candidates who received a faculty appointment before July 1, 2009 would not be eligible for this award in this funding cycle. It is the responsibility of the applicant to demonstrate that he/she satisfies the eligibility requirements for a Young Investigator Grant. Eligibility rules will be strictly enforced. Anyone who may not be certain as to his/her eligibility should request an advisory opinion from NKF staff before submitting an application.

Young Investigator Grants are primarily intended to support research by individuals holding M.D. or Ph.D. degrees who are commencing careers on the faculty of medical schools or research institutions. In all cases, the applicant's research and career goals must be directed to the study of normal or abnormal kidney function or of diseases of the kidney and urinary tract. Only one investigator in an institution will be supported in any funding cycle by a Young Investigator Grant. Since the NKF research support program is an integral part of the Foundation's overall scientific mission, it is expected that candidates for support pursuant to this funding mechanism participate as dues-paying professional members of the National Kidney Foundation, Inc.

GEOGRAPHIC RESTRICTIONS:
United States.

NUMBER OF AWARDS: 5.

APPLICATION INFORMATION:
Application form, letter of commitment from the applicant's department and three letters of recommendation are required.

Duration: One year, with the opportunity to apply for a second year of funding.
Deadline: February 1.

PUBLICATIONS:
Program announcement.

STAFF:
Kerry Willis, Senior Vice President, Scientific Activities
Jessica Joseph, Senior Director, Professional Membership Programs

ADDRESS INQUIRIES TO:
Jessica Joseph, Senior Director Professional Membership Programs
(See address above.)

NATIONAL KIDNEY FOUNDATION [2423]
30 East 33rd Street
New York, NY 10016
(212) 889-2210
(800) 622-9010
Fax: (212) 889-2038

E-MAIL ADDRESS:
research@kidney.org

WEB SITE ADDRESS:
www.kidney.org

FOUNDED: 1993

AREAS OF INTEREST:
Function and diseases of the kidney.

NAME(S) OF PROGRAMS:
● **Satellite Dialysis Clinical Investigator Grant**

TYPE:
Research grants.

YEAR PROGRAM STARTED: 1993

PURPOSE:
To support investigators who have demonstrated outstanding clinical research potential to promote their continued success as independent investigators.

LEGAL BASIS:
Voluntary health agency.

ELIGIBILITY:
Applications will be considered from individuals who will have completed research training in nephrology, or closely related fields, prior to the start of the grant award and who intend to pursue research directly related to these areas. At the time funding begins, the applicant must hold a full-time appointment to a faculty position at a university or an equivalent position as a scientist on the staff of a research oriented institution, e.g., National Institutes of Health (NIH) or other research organization, in the U.S. Customarily, the appropriate faculty rank is that of Assistant Professor. (In some institutions a title other than Assistant Professor, e.g. Instructor, is used to designate junior faculty status; individuals at that rank in such institutions are eligible to apply for a Satellite Dialysis Clinical Investigator Grant.) Qualifications should be documented in the biosketch (maximum four pages).

GEOGRAPHIC RESTRICTIONS:
United States.

FINANCIAL DATA:
Total amount of support: $40,000.

NUMBER OF AWARDS: 1.

APPLICATION INFORMATION:
Applications will be reviewed by a committee designated by the National Kidney

Foundation. During the peer review process, the responsiveness of the individual application to the research agendas of the NKF will be one of the elements used to judge merit and assign ranking. Applicants will be asked on the face sheet of the application to provide a description of the applicability of the application to the research agenda of the NKF, with specific reference to any KDOQI Guideline upon which the research project impacts.

Duration: One year, with the opportunity for a second year of funding.

Deadline: February 1.

STAFF:
Kerry Willis, Senior Vice President, Scientific Activities
Jessica Joseph, Senior Director, Professional Membership Programs

ADDRESS INQUIRIES TO:
Research Program Manager
(See address above.)

Oncology

AMERICAN ASSOCIATION FOR CANCER RESEARCH   [2424]
615 Chestnut Street, 17th Floor
Philadelphia, PA 19106
(215) 440-9300
Fax: (267) 825-9550

E-MAIL ADDRESS:
grants@aacr.org

WEB SITE ADDRESS:
www.aacr.org

FOUNDED: 1907

AREAS OF INTEREST:
Cancer.

NAME(S) OF PROGRAMS:
- **Career Development Awards**
- **Innovator Awards in Cancer Research**
- **Research Grants and Fellowships**
- **Scholar-in-Training Awards**

TYPE:
Awards/prizes; Fellowships; Research grants; Travel grants. AACR Career Development Awards in Cancer Research support research by junior investigators. These awards, which include an annual stipend, provide important transitional support for direct research expenses as researchers move from the ranks of early career scientists to faculty status.

AACR Research Fellowships in Basic, Clinical and Translational Research foster cancer research throughout the world by scientists currently at the postdoctoral or clinical research fellow level.

AACR Scholar-in-Training Awards enhance the education and training of graduate students, medical students and residents, clinical fellows or equivalent, and postdoctoral fellows by facilitating their attendance at the Annual Meeting and Special Conferences of the American Association for Cancer Research. These awards are presented to scientists in training who are presenters of abstracts that have been highly rated by AACR.

Innovator Awards in Cancer Research are designed to foster innovation and collaboration in cancer research and support

independent investigators early in their careers. The awards provide the recipients with the recognition they need to further their careers and possibly leverage additional funding.

PURPOSE:
To facilitate communication and dissemination of knowledge among scientists and others dedicated to the cancer problem; to foster research in cancer and related biomedical sciences; to encourage presentation and discussion of new and important observations in the field; to foster public education, science education and training; to advance the understanding of cancer etiology, prevention, diagnosis and treatment throughout the world.

LEGAL BASIS:
Not-for-profit society.

ELIGIBILITY:
Grants are given to individuals. For some programs, applicants must be working at an academic institution in the U.S. No grants to religious organizations. AACR Associate Members and persons who are not yet members of AACR are eligible for awards.

Fellowship candidates must have completed a Ph.D., M.D., or other doctoral degree. Candidates must be working as a postdoctoral or clinical research fellow at an academic facility, teaching hospital, or research institution, and must be in their second, third, or fourth year of a cancer research fellowship at the beginning of the award year. Academic faculty holding the rank of adjunct professor, associate professor, assistant professor, or higher, graduate or medical students, medical residents, permanent national government employees, and employees of private industry are not eligible. Candidates must be nominated by a member of AACR and must be an AACR member or apply for membership by the time the fellowship application is submitted. AACR Associate Members may not serve as nominators.

Career Development Award candidates must be full-time, junior faculty at the time the grant term begins. Candidates must also have completed productive postdoctoral research and demonstrated independent, investigator-initiated research. Employees of a national government and employees of private industry are not eligible. Candidates must be nominated by a member of AACR and must be an AACR member or apply for membership by the time the application is submitted. AACR Associate Members may not serve as nominators.

FINANCIAL DATA:
Amount of support per award: Fellowships: $45,000 to $50,000 salary support per year; Career Development Awards: $50,000 to $75,000 per year for first five years for salary or direct research expenses.

Total amount of support: Varies.

NUMBER OF APPLICANTS MOST RECENT YEAR:
Over 250.

NUMBER OF AWARDS: Scholar-in-Training: Approximately 250 per year; Awards and Fellowships: Approximately 30 per year.

APPLICATION INFORMATION:
Application form is available online.
Duration: Fellowships: One to three years; Scholar-in-Training Awards: One year.

Deadline: Scholar-in-Training: November of each year for Annual Meeting Awards, with notification the following February; Fellowships and Awards: Fall of each year, with notification the following February.

PUBLICATIONS:
Cancer Research, scientific journal; *Clinical Cancer Research*, journal; *Cell Growth and Differentiation*, journal; *Cancer Epidemiology, Biomarkers and Prevention*, journal.

ADDRESS INQUIRIES TO:
Deborah L. Crabtree
(See address above.)

AMERICAN BRAIN TUMOR ASSOCIATION
8550 West Bryn Mawr Avenue
Suite 550
Chicago, IL 60031
(773) 577-8750
Fax: (773) 577-8738

E-MAIL ADDRESS:
info@abta.org

WEB SITE ADDRESS:
www.abta.org

TYPE:
Fellowships; Seed money grants; Training grants. Medical Student Summer Fellowships support a 10- to 12-week summer laboratory experience.

See entry 2454 for full listing.

AMERICAN CANCER SOCIETY, INC.   [2425]
250 Williams Street, N.W.
6th Floor
Atlanta, GA 30303-1002
(404) 329-7558
Fax: (404) 321-4669

E-MAIL ADDRESS:
grants@cancer.org

WEB SITE ADDRESS:
www.cancer.org/research

FOUNDED: 1946

AREAS OF INTEREST:
All forms of cancer and their cures.

NAME(S) OF PROGRAMS:
- **Postdoctoral Fellowship**

TYPE:
Fellowships.

YEAR PROGRAM STARTED: 1946

PURPOSE:
To speed the conquest of cancer by training and supporting personnel for cancer research.

LEGAL BASIS:
Nonprofit corporation.

ELIGIBILITY:
Applicants must be U.S. citizens or legal permanent residents. The latter must provide notarized evidence of their legal resident alien status. Applicants who hold doctoral degrees in appropriate disciplines are eligible to apply. Applicant shall have been awarded a doctoral degree prior to the activation of the grant.

GEOGRAPHIC RESTRICTIONS:
United States.

FINANCIAL DATA:
Amount of support per award: Award includes an annual stipend of $44,000 in the first year, $46,000 in the second and $48,000

in the third. Relocation travel expenses for fellow only and a fellowship allowance of up to $4,000 per year.

APPLICATION INFORMATION:
Official application materials are available on the Society's web site.

Duration: Up to three years.

Deadline: Deadlines for receipt of completed materials are April 1, for approved grants to be activated on or after January 1, and October 15, for approved grants to be activated on July 1.

ADDRESS INQUIRIES TO:
Shannon Mejri
Operations Systems Specialist
(See address above.)

AMERICAN CANCER SOCIETY, INC. [2426]
250 Williams Street, N.W.
6th Floor
Atlanta, GA 30303-1002
(404) 329-7558
Fax: (404) 321-4669

E-MAIL ADDRESS:
grants@cancer.org

WEB SITE ADDRESS:
www.cancer.org/research

FOUNDED: 1946

AREAS OF INTEREST:
Cancer and its cures.

NAME(S) OF PROGRAMS:
● **Institutional Research Grants**

TYPE:
Block grants. Grants for institutional cancer research projects. Support is available for integration of varied efforts in cancer research within the institution and preliminary testing of new and venturesome ideas for research on cancer by junior investigators without other national research support.

YEAR PROGRAM STARTED: 1957

PURPOSE:
To eliminate cancer as a major health problem by preventing cancer, saving lives and diminishing suffering from cancer through research, education, advocacy and service.

LEGAL BASIS:
Nonprofit corporation.

ELIGIBILITY:
Institutions of higher learning in the U.S. and its territories are eligible to apply for support of appropriate research to be conducted by qualified investigators.

GEOGRAPHIC RESTRICTIONS:
United States.

FINANCIAL DATA:
Amount of support per award: Average $90,000 per year.

APPLICATION INFORMATION:
Grant application materials become available January 1 and are accessible on the Society's web site.

Duration: One to three years. Renewable upon reapplication.

Deadline: April 1.

ADDRESS INQUIRIES TO:
Shannon Mejri
Operations Systems Specialist
(See address above.)

AMERICAN GASTROENTEROLOGICAL ASSOCIATION (AGA)
4930 Del Ray Avenue
Bethesda, MD 20814
(301) 222-4012
Fax: (301) 652-3890

E-MAIL ADDRESS:
awards@gastro.org

WEB SITE ADDRESS:
www.gastro.org/research/find-funding

TYPE:
Research grants. Recognition award for an established investigator working on novel approaches in gastric cancer, including the fields of gastric mucosal cell biology, regeneration and regulation of cell growth (not as they relate to peptic ulcer disease or repair), inflammation as precancerous lesions, genetics of gastric carcinoma, oncogenes in gastric epithelial malignancies, epidemiology of gastric cancer, etiology of gastric epithelial malignancies or clinical research in diagnosis or treatment of gastric carcinoma.

See entry 2404 for full listing.

AMERICAN INSTITUTE FOR CANCER RESEARCH [2427]
1759 R Street, N.W.
Washington, DC 20009
(202) 328-7744
Fax: (202) 328-7226

E-MAIL ADDRESS:
research@aicr.org

WEB SITE ADDRESS:
www.aicr.org

FOUNDED: 1982

AREAS OF INTEREST:
Food, nutrition, physical activity and the prevention and treatment of cancer; food, nutrition, physical activity and cancer survivorship.

NAME(S) OF PROGRAMS:
● **Investigator Initiated Grants (IIG)**

TYPE:
Research grants. The Investigator Initiated Research Grant program is open to researchers at not-for-profit universities, hospitals or research centers. The Institute encourages new research on dietary means of preventing and treating cancer, or improving the life of the cancer patient or survivor.

YEAR PROGRAM STARTED: 1983

PURPOSE:
To foster research on diet, nutrition, physical activity and cancer and educate the public about the results.

ELIGIBILITY:
Institutions: Research grants are awarded to nonprofit institutions in the Americas. Grant applications will not be accepted from agencies of the federal government or agencies supported entirely by the federal government of any country. Proof of nonprofit status of the institution must be submitted with the grant application.

Investigators: The Principal Investigator must have a Ph.D. or equivalent degree or M.D. degree and be a research staff or faculty member at a nonprofit academic or research institution at the minimum level of an assistant professor (or its equivalent) or higher. The Principal Investigator at an

institution in the U.S. must be a citizen of the U.S. or foreign national with a permanent residence visa that is valid for the duration of the grant award. In other countries, the Principal Investigator must meet the requirements of that country for permanent residency and employment.

GEOGRAPHIC RESTRICTIONS:
North, Central and South America and the Caribbean.

FINANCIAL DATA:
Amount of support per award: Up to $75,000 per year, plus 10% indirect costs.

Total amount of support: $165,000 to $247,500.

APPLICATION INFORMATION:
Online application is required. There are two stages to the application process. Letter of Intent is required before full application invitation.

Duration: One to three years.

PUBLICATIONS:
Grant application package; recipients list.

STAFF:
Susan Higginbotham, Ph.D., R.D., Director for Research

ADDRESS INQUIRIES TO:
Research Department
(See address above.)

ASSOCIATION FOR RESEARCH OF CHILDHOOD CANCER, INC. (AROCC) [2428]
P.O. Box 251
Buffalo, NY 14225-0251
(716) 681-4433

E-MAIL ADDRESS:
president@arocc.org

WEB SITE ADDRESS:
www.arocc.org

FOUNDED: 1971

AREAS OF INTEREST:
Pediatric cancer research and parent support.

TYPE:
Seed money grants. Pilot projects.

YEAR PROGRAM STARTED: 1971

PURPOSE:
To fund pediatric cancer research institutions in New York state to find better treatment, and eventually a cure, for the types of cancer that afflict children.

LEGAL BASIS:
Tax-exempt, not-for-profit corporation in New York state.

ELIGIBILITY:
Awarded to qualified investigators in pediatric cancer research.

FINANCIAL DATA:
Amount of support per award: Varies.

Total amount of support: Varies.

NUMBER OF APPLICANTS MOST RECENT YEAR:
30.

NUMBER OF AWARDS: 3 to 5 per year.

APPLICATION INFORMATION:
Application must be submitted on AROCC forms. All grants are evaluated by AROCC Medical Advisors.

Duration: One year average. Consideration for three years. Renewal is possible based on past progress supported by abstracts and publications.

Deadline: November 1. Announcement by June 30.

ADDRESS INQUIRIES TO:
Anne O'Donnell, President
(See address above.)

CANADIAN CANCER SOCIETY RESEARCH INSTITUTE   [2429]

55 St. Clair Avenue West
Suite 300
Toronto ON M4V 2Y7 Canada
(416) 961-7223
Fax: (416) 961-4189

E-MAIL ADDRESS:
ccsri@cancer.ca
research@cancer.ca

WEB SITE ADDRESS:
www.cancer.ca/research

FOUNDED: 1947

AREAS OF INTEREST:
Cancer research.

TYPE:
Research grants; Travel grants. Grants for support of clinical cancer research and basic research projects related to the problem of cancer.

PURPOSE:
To stimulate Canadian investigators in a very broad spectrum of cancer research, not limited to but including biological, chemical, physical, clinical and population health sciences.

LEGAL BASIS:
Registered charity.

ELIGIBILITY:
Applicants must be persons holding appointments at Canadian universities or other recognized Canadian institutions. Basic equipment and research facilities and necessary administrative services must be available at the institution concerned.

GEOGRAPHIC RESTRICTIONS:
Canada.

FINANCIAL DATA:
Grants may be used for the purchase and maintenance of animals, for expendable supplies and minor items of equipment and for payment of graduate students, postdoctoral fellows and technical and professional assistants, but do not include personal support for the grantee.
Amount of support per award: Varies.
Total amount of support: Approximately $38,000,000 (CAN) for fiscal year ended January 2013.

NUMBER OF AWARDS: 385 new and continuing grants/awards for the fiscal year ended January 2013.

APPLICATION INFORMATION:
Applications must be made via online application system available on Institute web site.
Duration: Up to five years.
Deadline: Varies.

PUBLICATIONS:
Research report/impact report.

BOARD OF DIRECTORS:
Marc Genereux, Chairperson

ADDRESS INQUIRIES TO:
Carol Bishop
Assistant Director, Research Operations
(See address above.)

CANCER RESEARCH INSTITUTE   [2430]

One Exchange Plaza
55 Broadway, Suite 1802
New York, NY 10006
(212) 688-7515
(800) 992-2623
Fax: (212) 832-9376

E-MAIL ADDRESS:
grants@cancerresearch.org

WEB SITE ADDRESS:
www.cancerresearch.org

FOUNDED: 1953

AREAS OF INTEREST:
Tumor immunology.

NAME(S) OF PROGRAMS:
● **Irvington Institute Fellowship Program of the Cancer Research Institute**

TYPE:
Fellowships; Research grants; Training grants.

YEAR PROGRAM STARTED: 1971

PURPOSE:
To offer postdoctoral fellowships to qualified individuals in the formative stages of their career who wish to receive training in cancer immunology.

LEGAL BASIS:
Private, nonprofit organization.

ELIGIBILITY:
Applicants must have a doctoral degree and must conduct research under a sponsor who holds a formal appointment at the sponsoring institution. There are no nationality restrictions. Work may be carried out in the U.S. or abroad at nonprofit institutions and medical centers. Fellows with five or more years of postdoctoral experience are ineligible.

FINANCIAL DATA:
Amount of support per award: $50,000 stipend for the first year, $53,000 for the second year, and $57,000 for the third year. An institutional allowance of $1,500 is provided for the host institution to cover laboratory supplies, scientific travel and health insurance on behalf of the fellow.
Total amount of support: $3,886,481 for fiscal year 2013.

NUMBER OF APPLICANTS MOST RECENT YEAR: 225 for the year 2013.

NUMBER OF AWARDS: 24 for the year 2013.

APPLICATION INFORMATION:
Paper applications will not be accepted. Applicants must complete an electronic application form to be submitted with the following attachments:
(1) scanned copy of paper application form with signatures of certifying officers;
(2) brief description of the applicant's background;
(3) list of other funding sources to which applications have been submitted;
(4) applicant's curriculum vitae and bibliography;
(5) brief summary of project with description of how the proposed research is relevant to cancer immunology;

(6) abstract of research in nontechnical English;
(7) concise research proposal, not to exceed six pages;
(8) letter of introduction from sponsor;
(9) sponsor's curriculum vitae, bibliography and current support and;
(10) letters of reference from two individuals acquainted with applicant's work.
Duration: Up to three years.
Deadline: April 1 and October 1. Notification eight to 10 weeks after the deadline.

PUBLICATIONS:
Annual report; application guidelines.

IRS IDENTIFICATION NUMBER: 13-1837442

STAFF:
Jill O'Donnell-Tormey, Executive Director
Lynne Harmer, Director of Grants Administration

ADDRESS INQUIRIES TO:
Denise Upton, Grants Administrator
(See address above.)

CANCER RESEARCH INSTITUTE   [2431]

55 Broadway, Suite 1802
New York, NY 10006
(212) 688-7515
Fax: (212) 832-9376

E-MAIL ADDRESS:
grants@cancerresearch.org

WEB SITE ADDRESS:
www.cancerresearch.org

FOUNDED: 1953

AREAS OF INTEREST:
Tumor immunology.

NAME(S) OF PROGRAMS:
● **Clinic and Laboratory Integration Program (CLIP)**

TYPE:
Awards/prizes; Research grants. This Program awards investigators at tenure-track assistant professor level or higher seeking to answer clinically relevant questions aimed at improving the effectiveness of cancer immunotherapies.

YEAR PROGRAM STARTED: 2011

PURPOSE:
To support qualified scientists who are working to explore clinically relevant questions aimed at improving the effectiveness of cancer immunotherapies; to support basic, preclinical and translational research, which will provide information that can be directly applied to optimizing cancer immunotherapy in the clinic.

ELIGIBILITY:
Investigators must be tenure-track assistant professors or higher when award activates. Eligible organizations must have IRS 501(c)(3) not-for-profit status. Grants are not made to religious organizations.

FINANCIAL DATA:
The award can be used at the recipient's discretion for salary, technical assistance, supplies and/or equipment.
Amount of support per award: Up to $100,000 per year for two years.

APPLICATION INFORMATION:
Letters of Intent are accepted November 1 annually. Candidates will be notified by

December 15 whether or not they have been invited to submit a full grant proposal. An application form needs to be completed.

Duration: Up to two years; grant is not renewable.

Deadline: Letters of Intent: November 1 annually. The full application is due February 1.

ADDRESS INQUIRIES TO:
Denise Upton, Grants Administrator
Cancer Research Institute
(See address above.)

CANCER RESEARCH INSTITUTE [2432]
55 Broadway, Suite 1802
New York, NY 10006
(212) 688-7515
Fax: (212) 832-9376

E-MAIL ADDRESS:
grants@cancerresearch.org

WEB SITE ADDRESS:
www.cancerresearch.org

FOUNDED: 1953

AREAS OF INTEREST:
Tumor immunology.

NAME(S) OF PROGRAMS:
● **Student Training and Research in Tumor Immunology (STaRT) Program**

TYPE:
Awards/prizes; Research grants; Training grants. The STaRT Program awards investigators at tenure-track assistant professor level or higher seeking to answer clinically relevant questions aimed at improving the effectiveness of cancer immunotherapies.

YEAR PROGRAM STARTED: 2011

PURPOSE:
To attract bright young minds to rewarding careers as cancer immunologists; to provide support for up to two years to graduate students conducting thesis research in the area of tumor immunology.

ELIGIBILITY:
Applicants must be pursuing research directly related to tumor immunology, be full-time graduate students engaged in thesis research as Ph.D. candidates, and will have successfully completed all of their host institution's requirements for advancement to candidacy by the time the award is activated. Applicants must conduct their CRI-funded research under the direct supervision of their thesis advisor, who holds a formal appointment at the host institution.

Eligible organizations have to have 501(c)(3) not-for-profit status. The Institute does not give grants to religious organizations.

FINANCIAL DATA:
The Institute does not permit deductions to cover administrative expenses from the stipend. Payments are made monthly in U.S. currency to the host institution.
Amount of support per award: Up to $30,000 of funding per year. The exact award amount is dictated by the host institution's annual stipend amount, but not to exceed $30,000.

APPLICATION INFORMATION:
An application form must be completed.
Duration: Up to two years; grant nonrenewable.

Deadline: Receipt of applications: March 1 annually. If the deadline falls on a weekend, applications will be due on the following Monday. Applicants will be notified of the review committee's decision by July 1, and awards will be activated September 1.

ADDRESS INQUIRIES TO:
Denise Upton, Grants Administrator
Cancer Research Institute
(See address above.)

*SPECIAL STIPULATIONS:
Students who have not yet chosen their thesis project and advisor, as well as those students in the fifth year or later of their Ph.D. program, should not apply.

CANCER RESEARCH SOCIETY [2433]
625 President Kennedy Avenue
Suite 402
Montreal QC H3A 3S5 Canada
(514) 861-9227
Fax: (514) 861-9220

E-MAIL ADDRESS:
grants@src-crs.ca

WEB SITE ADDRESS:
www.cancerresearchsociety.ca

FOUNDED: 1945

AREAS OF INTEREST:
Cancer research.

NAME(S) OF PROGRAMS:
● **Scholarship for the Next Generation of Scientists**

TYPE:
Fellowships; Research grants. One year of salary award as a postdoctoral fellow and two years of operating grants as a researcher associated with an accredited institution.

YEAR PROGRAM STARTED: 2013

PURPOSE:
To support the future generation of Canadian researchers in the field of cancer research.

LEGAL BASIS:
Nonprofit registered fund-raising corporation.

ELIGIBILITY:
Holders of a Ph.D. or a professional diploma (M.D., D.M.V. or other) obtained in September 2008 or later and undergoing an additional postdoctoral training since a minimum of two years, each one of these two years having been completed uninterrupted, with at least 75% of the time devoted to research.

The candidate must obtain an academic appointment in a Canadian university or accredited institution and must begin his or her functions between January 1, 2015 and March 1, 2016.

FINANCIAL DATA:
Amount of support per award: $40,000 for the first year and $60,000 for the second and third year.

NUMBER OF APPLICANTS MOST RECENT YEAR:
26 for the year 2013.

NUMBER OF AWARDS: 4 for the year 2013.

APPLICATION INFORMATION:
Application information is available on the web site.
Duration: Three years. No renewal possible.
Deadline: April 30.

ADDRESS INQUIRIES TO:
Josée-France Villemure, Ph.D., Scientific Advisor
(See address above.)

CANCER RESEARCH SOCIETY [2434]
625 President Kennedy Avenue
Suite 402
Montreal QC H3A 3S5 Canada
(514) 861-9227
Fax: (514) 861-9220

E-MAIL ADDRESS:
grants@src-crs.ca

WEB SITE ADDRESS:
www.cancerresearchsociety.ca

FOUNDED: 1945

AREAS OF INTEREST:
Cancer research.

NAME(S) OF PROGRAMS:
● **Grants for Cancer Research**

TYPE:
General operating grants.

YEAR PROGRAM STARTED: 1946

PURPOSE:
To find the cause, cure and prevention of cancer.

LEGAL BASIS:
Nonprofit registered fund-raising corporation.

ELIGIBILITY:
Any qualified researcher who is associated with an accredited institution may apply, provided the research is done in Canada.

GEOGRAPHIC RESTRICTIONS:
Canada.

FINANCIAL DATA:
Amount of support per award: $60,000 per year.

COOPERATIVE FUNDING PROGRAMS: Quebec Breast Cancer Foundation, Government of Quebec

NUMBER OF APPLICANTS MOST RECENT YEAR:
270 for the year 2013.

NUMBER OF AWARDS: 51 for the year 2013.

APPLICATION INFORMATION:
Application information is available on the web site.
Duration: Two years. Renewal possible.
Deadline: February 15 for research grants.

BOARD OF DIRECTORS:
Domenic Pilla, President
Mike G. Bouchard, L.L.B., MBA, Vice President
Nathalie Labelle, C.A., B.A.A., Treasurer
Micheline Bouchard, Secretary
Francois Castonguay
Benoit Durocher
Philippe P. Huneault
Heidi Lange, C.R.H.A.
Martin Langlais
Katia Marquier
Monique Mercier
Ivan Robert Nabi
Dr. Denis Soulières, M.D., M.Sc.
Martin Thibodeau

ADDRESS INQUIRIES TO:
Josée-France Villemure, Ph.D., Scientific Advisor
(See address above.)

CANCER RESEARCH UK [2435]
Research Funding
Angel Building
407 St. John Street
London EC1V 4AD England
44 020 7242 0200
44 020 3469 5452 (grants helpline)
Fax: 44 020 3469 6400

E-MAIL ADDRESS:
grants.helpline@cancer.org.uk

WEB SITE ADDRESS:
science.cancerresearchuk.org

FOUNDED: 2002

AREAS OF INTEREST:
Research into the causes, diagnosis, treatment and prevention of cancer.

TYPE:
Fellowships; Project/program grants; Research grants; Training grants. There are various grant programs for cancer research including clinical trials. Funding includes research groups, fellowships, programs and project grants.

YEAR PROGRAM STARTED: 2002

PURPOSE:
To carry out world-class research to improve understanding of cancer and find out how to prevent, diagnose and treat different kinds of cancer; to ensure that the findings are used to improve the lives of all cancer patients; to help people to understand cancer, the progress being made and the choices each person can make; to work in partnership with others to achieve the greatest impact in the fight against cancer.

LEGAL BASIS:
Charity (public-funded).

ELIGIBILITY:
Research should be conducted in the U.K. Awards are made to researchers in universities, medical schools and independent research organizations.

GEOGRAPHIC RESTRICTIONS:
United Kingdom.

FINANCIAL DATA:
Amount of support per award: Varies.
Matching fund requirements: Varies.

NUMBER OF APPLICANTS MOST RECENT YEAR:
Over 800.

NUMBER OF AWARDS: Over 1,100 projects supported.

APPLICATION INFORMATION:
Contact a member of Research Funding for a discussion prior to sending an application. Applications for funding must be made using the electronic Grants Management System (eGMS).
Duration: Two to six years (longer for clinical trials).
Deadline: Varies.

PUBLICATIONS:
Scientific Yearbook; Annual Review.

THE JANE COFFIN CHILDS MEMORIAL FUND FOR MEDICAL RESEARCH [2436]
333 Cedar Street
New Haven, CT 06510
(203) 785-4612
Fax: (203) 785-3301

E-MAIL ADDRESS:
jccfund@yale.edu

WEB SITE ADDRESS:
www.jccfund.org

FOUNDED: 1937

AREAS OF INTEREST:
Cancer research.

TYPE:
Fellowships. Postdoctoral fellowships for studies in the medical and related sciences bearing on cancer.

YEAR PROGRAM STARTED: 1944

PURPOSE:
To further research into the causes, origins and treatment of cancer.

LEGAL BASIS:
Private foundation.

ELIGIBILITY:
Applicants must be U.S. or foreign citizens holding the M.D. or Ph.D. degree in the proposed field of study (or the equivalent in training and experience) and have no more than one year postdoctoral experience. The prior sponsorship of the laboratory at which they promise to work must be obtained.

Awards to foreign nationals will be made only for work in the U.S., whereas fellowships to American citizens are tenable in the U.S. or any foreign country.

FINANCIAL DATA:
Amount of support per award: $50,000 annually. A grant of $2,000 per year to be applied toward the cost of research is usually made available to the sponsoring laboratory each year.
Total amount of support: $4,000,000.

NUMBER OF AWARDS: 25 to 30.

APPLICATION INFORMATION:
Official application materials are available online.
Duration: Two to three years.
Deadline: February 1 to be considered at late spring meetings.

IRS IDENTIFICATION NUMBER: 06-6034840

OFFICERS:
James E. Childs, Chairman
Bronwen Childs, Treasurer

STAFF:
Stephen Elledge, Science Director
Kim Roberts, Administrative Director

ADDRESS INQUIRIES TO:
Kim Roberts, Administrative Director
(See address above.)

RUTH ESTRIN GOLDBERG MEMORIAL FOR CANCER RESEARCH [2437]
653 Colonial Arms Road
Union, NJ 07083-7605
(908) 686-5508

E-MAIL ADDRESS:
goodfudgie@aol.com

FOUNDED: 1949

AREAS OF INTEREST:
Cancer research.

TYPE:
Development grants; General operating grants; Project/program grants; Research grants; Seed money grants.

YEAR PROGRAM STARTED: 1949

PURPOSE:
To raise funds to support cancer research.

LEGAL BASIS:
Nonprofit.

ELIGIBILITY:
Applicant must be affiliated with an accredited institution in New Jersey, New York or Pennsylvania.

GEOGRAPHIC RESTRICTIONS:
Eastern United States.

FINANCIAL DATA:
Amount of support per award: $10,000 to $15,000 average, if available.
Total amount of support: Average $10,000.

NUMBER OF APPLICANTS MOST RECENT YEAR:
10.

NUMBER OF AWARDS: 2.

APPLICATION INFORMATION:
Those interested should request an application form and copy of the Memorial's policy governing grants.
Duration: One year. Renewal possible upon reapplication the following year.
Deadline: April 30. Announcement June 1.

ADDRESS INQUIRIES TO:
Rhoda Goodman
(See address above.)

GREENBURG-MAY FOUNDATION [2438]
146 Central Park West
New York, NY 10023
(212) 451-3200

FOUNDED: 1947

AREAS OF INTEREST:
Medical research, Parkinson's disease, with primary focus on research in cancer and heart disease, the aged, and Jewish institutions.

TYPE:
Development grants; Research grants. Social services.

PURPOSE:
To improve health conditions and expedite cures in many diseases through research.

ELIGIBILITY:
Eligible organizations must be IRS 501(c)(3) tax-exempt and be located in Florida or New York. No funding to individuals.

GEOGRAPHIC RESTRICTIONS:
Florida and New York.

FINANCIAL DATA:
Amount of support per award: Varies depending on project.
Total amount of support: Varies.

APPLICATION INFORMATION:
Applicants must submit a copy of their tax-exempt determination letter. Contact the Foundation for further guidelines.

ADDRESS INQUIRIES TO:
Isabel May, President
(See address above.)

SUSAN G. KOMEN [2439]
5005 LBJ Freeway
Suite 250
Dallas, TX 75244
(972) 701-2050
(877) 465-6636
Fax: (972) 701-2121

E-MAIL ADDRESS:
helpdesk@komengrantsaccess.org

WEB SITE ADDRESS:
www.komen.org/grants

FOUNDED: 1982

AREAS OF INTEREST:
Breast cancer research.

CONSULTING OR VOLUNTEER SERVICES:
Through a Komen Affiliate; find a Komen Affiliate on the Organization's web site.

NAME(S) OF PROGRAMS:
- **Career Catalyst Research Grants**
- **Graduate Training in Disparities Research**
- **Postdoctoral Fellowship Grants**

TYPE:
Fellowships; Research grants; Training grants.

YEAR PROGRAM STARTED: 1982

PURPOSE:
To support breast cancer research and awareness.

LEGAL BASIS:
Texas nonprofit corporation.

ELIGIBILITY:
Varies with each award or grant.

FINANCIAL DATA:
Amount of support per award: $60,000 to $150,000 per year.
Total amount of support: Varies per program.

APPLICATION INFORMATION:
Application information is available on the web site.
Duration: Two to three years.
Deadline: Varies.

PUBLICATIONS:
Annual report.

IRS IDENTIFICATION NUMBER: 75-1835298

THE LADIES AUXILIARY TO THE VETERANS OF FOREIGN WARS [2440]

National Headquarters
406 West 34th Street, 10th Floor
Kansas City, MO 64111
(816) 561-8655
Fax: (816) 931-4753

E-MAIL ADDRESS:
info@ladiesauxvfw.org

WEB SITE ADDRESS:
www.ladiesauxvfw.org

AREAS OF INTEREST:
Cancer research.

NAME(S) OF PROGRAMS:
- **Postdoctoral Cancer Research Fellowship**

TYPE:
Fellowships; Research grants. A two-year fellowship for full-time cancer research.

YEAR PROGRAM STARTED: 1947

PURPOSE:
To support cancer research; to present an opportunity for researchers to devote two years, full-time, to making new discoveries about cancer.

LEGAL BASIS:
Nonprofit.

ELIGIBILITY:
U.S. universities, hospitals and other institutions are invited to nominate one individual who meets the criteria. Candidates

must:
(1) be U.S. citizens (the nominator does not have to be);
(2) be nominated by the person who will be supervising the lab in which the researcher will be working;
(3) be qualified in a specific cancer-related specialty and the proposed research project must be cancer-related;
(4) have earned a doctoral-level degree by July 1 of the year application is made; if candidate does not have the degree by the time of application, he or she must indicate the date expected on the application form no later than July 1 of the application year and;
(5) proposed research must be the principal professional responsibility of the recipient during the fellowship.

GEOGRAPHIC RESTRICTIONS:
United States.

FINANCIAL DATA:
The funds are to be used as a salary or stipend, which may cover fringe benefits. If the institution's normal postdoctoral salary is greater than $50,000 per year, it is acceptable for the institution to supplement the salary. If the normal salary is less than $50,000, the excess funds may be used for lab equipment or supplies. During the two-year term of this fellowship, the researcher may not receive other funding towards his or her salary except as just described. Funds must be used before the end of a 25-month period.
Amount of support per award: $100,000 ($50,000 per year for two years).
Total amount of support: $100,000.

NUMBER OF AWARDS: 1.

APPLICATION INFORMATION:
Applications will be reviewed by a panel of basic and clinical researchers in the oncology field. The application must include the following:
(1) completed Official Application Form for current year;
(2) NIH biographical sketch on candidate's training, experience, honors and list of candidate's published research;
(3) brief description of proposed research project including abstract, methods, procedures and significance;
(4) timeline for the project and expected results throughout study; specifically, the results anticipated to have been obtained after nine months of funding. This information will be used to review adequacy of progress;
(5) letter of recommendation from sponsor (and from co-mentor if another individual will contribute significantly to the training supervision);
(6) NIH biographical sketch on sponsor (and co-mentor, if applicable) and;
(7) brief description of lab funding available to support proposed project.
Items 2, 3 and 4 must not exceed 10 pages. (Excess will be viewed negatively by review panel.) Do not use type smaller than 11-point font.
Duration: Two years. Not renewable.
Deadline: Must be postmarked by March 1; no exceptions. The winner of the fellowship will be notified by June 1, and upon receipt of written acceptance $50,000 will be issued.

PUBLICATIONS:
Program announcement; application.

ADDRESS INQUIRIES TO:
Judy Millick, Administrator of Programs
Cancer Research Fellowship Program
(See address above.)

LEUKEMIA RESEARCH FOUNDATION [2441]

3520 Lake Avenue
Suite 202
Wilmette, IL 60091
(847) 424-0600
Fax: (847) 424-0606

E-MAIL ADDRESS:
info@lrfmail.org

WEB SITE ADDRESS:
www.leukemia-research.org

FOUNDED: 1946

AREAS OF INTEREST:
Curing leukemia, lymphoma and myelodysplastic syndromes.

NAME(S) OF PROGRAMS:
- **New Investigator Awards**

TYPE:
Research grants. The goal of the grant program is to support new investigators. It funds scientists and physicians around the world.

YEAR PROGRAM STARTED: 1946

PURPOSE:
To conquer leukemia, lymphoma and myelodysplastic syndromes by funding research into their causes and cures; to enrich the quality of life of those touched by these diseases.

ELIGIBILITY:
Preference will be given to applicants proposing new lines of investigation.

FINANCIAL DATA:
Amount of support per award: Up to $100,000.
Total amount of support: More than $1,000,000 annually.

NUMBER OF AWARDS: Varies.

APPLICATION INFORMATION:
Applications will only be accepted electronically and should be e-mailed to grants@lrfmail.org. All applicants will receive a receipt via e-mail when their application is received. Hard copies of grant applications will not be accepted.
Duration: One year. Funding cycle begins July 1.
Deadline: February.

IRS IDENTIFICATION NUMBER: 36-6102182

ADDRESS INQUIRIES TO:
Linda Kabot
Research Grants Administrator
(See address above.)

ONCOLOGY NURSING FOUNDATION [2442]

125 Enterprise Drive
Pittsburgh, PA 15275-1214
(412) 859-6298
Fax: (412) 859-6160

E-MAIL ADDRESS:
jbrown@ons.org

WEB SITE ADDRESS:
www.onsfoundation.org

FOUNDED: 1981

AREAS OF INTEREST:
Oncology nursing.

NAME(S) OF PROGRAMS:
- **Dissertation Research Grant**
- **ONF Foundation Research Grant Award**
- **Research Career Development Award**

TYPE:
Awards/prizes; Research grants. Dissertation Research Grant assists doctoral students with their dissertation.

YEAR PROGRAM STARTED: 1984

PURPOSE:
To support the professional development of oncology nurses around the world.

LEGAL BASIS:
National public, nonprofit, tax-exempt organization.

ELIGIBILITY:
An applicant must be a health professional actively involved in some aspect of cancer patient care, education or research. Membership in the Oncology Nursing Society is preferred but not required. Doctoral students are eligible. The Foundation does not fund completed projects or those nearing completion, tuition or conference registration fees, travel, the purchase of office equipment or institutional indirect costs.

FINANCIAL DATA:
Amount of support per award: Dissertation Research Grant: $5,000; ONF Foundation Research Grant Award: $25,000; Research Career Development Award: $20,000.
Total amount of support: $178,298 for the year 2013.

NUMBER OF APPLICANTS MOST RECENT YEAR: 25.

NUMBER OF AWARDS: Varies.

APPLICATION INFORMATION:
Letters of Intent and applications must be submitted online, including:
(1) an e-mail address;
(2) $25 application fee (make checks payable to the Oncology Nursing Foundation);
(3) if a resubmission, attach a cover letter explaining the revisions to the application;
(4) title page with all signatures;
(5) an IRB or animal welfare committee approval letter;
(6) 500-word abstract;
(7) an eight-page project narrative describing purpose and specific aims, significance, background and review of literature, research design, experimental variables, instruments, facilities and resources;
(8) reference list;
(9) timetable;
(10) statement of scientific integrity;
(11) letters of support;
(12) form documenting the signature of the thesis or dissertation chairperson;
(13) biographical sketches (two-page limit) and;
(14) itemized budgets and budget narratives.
Duration: Dissertation Research Grant and Research Grant Award: Two years; Research Career Development Award: One year.
Deadline: Dissertation Research Grant and Research Grant Award: August 15 for Letter of Intent and September 15 for Application. Notification by January 1; Research Career Development Award: June 1 for Letter of Intent and July 1 for Application.

PUBLICATIONS:
Program announcement; applications; guidelines; *Recognition of Achievement: Awards, Grants, Honors, Scholarships.*

ADDRESS INQUIRIES TO:
Jenny Brown, Grants Specialist
Oncology Nursing Society Research Team
(See address above.)

THE ELSA U. PARDEE FOUNDATION   [2443]
P.O. Box 2767
Midland, MI 48641-2767
(989) 832-3691
Fax: (989) 832-8842

WEB SITE ADDRESS:
www.pardeefoundation.org

FOUNDED: 1944

AREAS OF INTEREST:
Research for control and cure of cancer.

TYPE:
Research grants. Grants for research projects relating to the cure and control of cancer and for the treatment needs of cancer victims.

The Foundation supports activities in three major areas:
(1) innovative new cancer research projects;
(2) established, ongoing cancer programs and;
(3) Pardee Cancer Treatment Committees in six counties in central Michigan and one Texas county where the Dow Chemical Company has a presence. The Treatment Committees assist cancer victims with their treatment expenses.

PURPOSE:
To promote the control and cure of cancer.

LEGAL BASIS:
Private foundation.

ELIGIBILITY:
Grants are limited under the terms of the charter to the cure and control of cancer, and in general do not provide for building funds, equipment (except that used in a specific project), fellowships or fund-raising campaign contributions.

Priority is given to researchers at nonprofit institutions in the U.S. who are new to the field of cancer research, or to established research investigators examining new approaches to cancer cure.

FINANCIAL DATA:
The Foundation provides more than $3,733,000 annually to support research directed towards the detection, treatment and cure of cancer.
Amount of support per award: Grants vary in amount, depending upon the needs and nature of the request.

REPRESENTATIVE AWARDS:
$125,000 to University of Chicago for the study of non-invasive delivery of stem cells as therapeutic vehicles to the brain tumors; $93,750 to Florida State University for the study of phosphoprotein signatures of human triple-negative breast cancer; $138,431 to Michigan State University for the study of using bioinformatic methods to dissect tumor development and develop therapy.

APPLICATION INFORMATION:
Grant applications may be submitted online at the Foundation web site.
Duration: Typically one year.
Deadline: Grant applications are reviewed by the Medical Committee in April, August and November.

PUBLICATIONS:
Annual report; application guidelines.

PREVENT CANCER FOUNDATION   [2444]
1600 Duke Street, Suite 500
Alexandria, VA 22314
(703) 836-4412
Fax: (703) 836-4413

E-MAIL ADDRESS:
sarah.abou@preventcancer.org

WEB SITE ADDRESS:
www.preventcancer.org

FOUNDED: 1985

AREAS OF INTEREST:
Cancer prevention and cancer early detection.

TYPE:
Fellowships; Research grants. Grants/Fellowships are given for prevention and early detection of cancer through scientific research and education.

PURPOSE:
To support innovative projects in prevention and early detection of cancer through scientific research.

ELIGIBILITY:
Fellowships: Citizenship is unrestricted, but research must be conducted primarily in the U.S. Postdoctoral Fellows (graduate students who will have their doctoral degrees before the project start date) are eligible to apply. Individuals with academic or professional degrees (e.g., M.D., Phar.D., Ph.D.) who are conducting cancer prevention research under the guidance of a mentor are also eligible.

Grants: Citizenship is unrestricted, but research must be conducted primarily in the U.S. Researchers at the instructor or assistant professor level with relevant academic or professional degrees (e.g., M.D., Phar.D., Ph.D.) who are conducting cancer prevention research and researchers who are farther along in their careers and who are shifting their focus to cancer prevention are eligible to apply.

GEOGRAPHIC RESTRICTIONS:
United States.

FINANCIAL DATA:
Indirect costs will not be covered.
Amount of support per award: $40,000 per year.
Total amount of support: Varies.

APPLICATION INFORMATION:
Electronic submissions are required, along with the original sent by mail.
Duration: Two years.
Deadline: February 28 and September 14.

STAFF:
Pamela Nwoji, Manager

ADDRESS INQUIRIES TO:
Sarah Abou-El-Seoud, Coordinator
Research and Programs Administration
(See address above.)

PROSTATE CANCER RESEARCH AND EDUCATION FOUNDATION (PC-REF)   [2445]
6823 Deer Hollow Place
San Diego, CA 92120-1605
(619) 906-4700
Fax: (619) 794-2100

E-MAIL ADDRESS:
info@pcref.org

WEB SITE ADDRESS:
www.pcref.org

FOUNDED: 1997

AREAS OF INTEREST:
Prostate cancer.

TYPE:
Seed money grants. The Foundation provides seed money to deserving researchers to help them generate preliminary results that are needed to obtain major grants in the field of prostate cancer.

PURPOSE:
To promote medical research and treatment regarding prostate cancer.

ELIGIBILITY:
The Foundation concentrates on projects that will help prostate cancer patients sooner rather than later. Grants are not made to individuals.

FINANCIAL DATA:
The Foundation funds direct expenses only, not overhead expenses.
Amount of support per award: Varies.

APPLICATION INFORMATION:
Contact the Foundation.
Duration: Varies. Renewal possible.

IRS IDENTIFICATION NUMBER: 91-1863748

ADDRESS INQUIRIES TO:
Dr. Israel Barken
Founder and Medical Director
(See address above.)

DAMON RUNYON CANCER RESEARCH FOUNDATION [2446]
One Exchange Plaza
55 Broadway, Suite 302
New York, NY 10006-3720
(212) 455-0520
Fax: (212) 455-0529

E-MAIL ADDRESS:
awards@damonrunyon.org

WEB SITE ADDRESS:
www.damonrunyon.org

FOUNDED: 1946

AREAS OF INTEREST:
All theoretical and experimental research that is relevant to the study of cancer and the search for cancer causes, mechanisms, therapies and prevention.

NAME(S) OF PROGRAMS:
- **Damon Runyon Clinical Investigator Award**
- **Damon Runyon Dale F. Frey Award for Breakthrough Scientists**
- **Damon Runyon Fellowship Award**
- **Damon Runyon-Rachleff Innovation Award**
- **Damon Runyon-Sohn Pediatric Cancer Fellowship Award**

TYPE:
Fellowships; Project/program grants; Research grants. The Damon Runyon Clinical Investigator Award supports early career physician-scientists conducting patient-oriented research. The goal of this innovative program is to increase the number of physicians capable of moving seamlessly between the laboratory and the patient's bedside in search of breakthrough treatments.

Damon Runyon Dale F. Frey Award for Breakthrough Scientists provides additional funding to scientists completing a Damon Runyon Fellowship who are most likely to make paradigm-shifting breakthroughs. This funding is to accelerate their path to independence and their impact on cancer.

The Damon Runyon Fellowship Award supports the training of the brightest postdoctoral scientists as they embark upon their research careers. This funding enables them to be trained by established investigators in leading research laboratories across the country.

The Damon Runyon-Rachleff Innovation Award supports the next generation of exceptionally creative thinkers with high-risk/high-reward ideas that have the potential to significantly impact our understanding of and/or approaches to the prevention, diagnosis or treatment of cancer, but lack sufficient preliminary data to obtain traditional funding.

The Damon Runyon-Sohn Pediatric Cancer Fellowship Award provides funding to basic scientists and clinicians who conduct research with the potential to significantly impact the prevention, diagnosis, or treatment of one or more pediatric cancers.

YEAR PROGRAM STARTED: 1947

PURPOSE:
To advance cancer research through supporting the development of the most promising young talent in cancer research.

LEGAL BASIS:
501(c)(3) organization, classified as a publicly supported organization and not as a private foundation under Section 509(a)(1) of the IRS, incorporated in New York.

ELIGIBILITY:
Frey Award: Damon Runyon Fellows are eligible to apply in the third year of their Fellowship.

Clinical Investigator Award and Innovation Award: Institutional nominations are not required and there is no limit to the number of applications that can be received from a particular institution. Applicants (including non-U.S. citizens) must be conducting independent research at a U.S. research institution.

For the Fellowship Award, applicants must have completed one or more of the following degrees or its equivalent: M.D., M.D./Ph.D., Ph.D., D.D.S., D.V.M.

Level I Funding is for basic and physician scientist applicants who must have received their degrees within the year prior to the FAC meeting at which their applications are to be considered.

Level II Funding is for physician scientists (M.D.) and clinical scientists (M.D., M.D./Ph.D., D.D.S., D.V.M. or the equivalent) who have completed their residencies and clinical fellowship training, are board-eligible, and have not yet been appointed Assistant Professor (or equivalent).

The proposed investigation must be conducted at a university, hospital, or research institution. Foreign candidates may only apply to do research in the U.S.

Only candidates who are beginning their first full-time postdoctoral research fellowship are eligible.

FINANCIAL DATA:
Awards are made to institutions for the support of the Fellow under direct supervision of the Sponsor.
Amount of support per award: Clinical Investigator Awards: $150,000 per year. In addition, awardees may be eligible to retire up to $100,000 of their medical school debt.

Dale F. Frey Award: $100,000.

Fellowship Award: Level I stipend: $50,000 per year; Level II stipend: $60,000 per year.

Innovation Award: $150,000 per year.

A sum of $2,000 is awarded each year to the laboratory in which the Fellow is working, and can be used by the Fellow for his/her educational and scientific expenses. With a written request to the Foundation from the Fellow, the expense allowance may be used to defray the cost of health benefits. The Fellow determines how he/she would like to spend the money with approval from his/her mentor. It is not an allowance for institutional overhead, postdoctoral scholar registration fees or postdoctoral fellowship taxes. Institutions may not automatically deduct any fees from this allowance without the Fellow's approval.

Additionally, the Foundation also provides a Dependent Child Allowance of $1,000 per child per year. (There is no allowance for a spouse.) Eligible Fellows must provide a copy of the birth or adoption certificate for each child.
Total amount of support: Approximately $3,300,000 in Clinical Investigator Awards; approximately $4,900,000 in Fellowship Awards, and approximately $1,950,000 in Innovation Awards for fiscal year 2012.

NUMBER OF APPLICANTS MOST RECENT YEAR:
Clinical Investigator Awards: 58; Fellowship Awards: 359; Frey Awards: 17; Innovation Awards: 121; Sohn-Pedriatic Fellowship Awards: 27.

NUMBER OF AWARDS: Clinical Investigator Awards: 6 new, 16 renewals; Fellowship Awards: 41 new, 54 renewals; Frey Awards: 5 new, 4 renewals; Innovation Awards: 5 new, 7 renewals; Sohn-Pedriatic Fellowship Awards: 4 new, 3 renewals.

REPRESENTATIVE AWARDS:
Damon Runyon Clinical Investigator Award: Carey K. Anders, M.D., "mTOR inhibition in the treatment of HER2-positive breast cancer brain metastases," with Lisa A. Carey, M.D., and Charles M. Peron, Ph.D., University of North Carolina, Chapel Hill, NC; Damon Runyon Postdoctoral Fellowship: Douglas H. Phanstiel, Ph.D., "Exploring the regulatory role of long-range chromatin interactions," with Michael P. Snyder, Ph.D., Stanford University School of Medicine, Stanford, CA.

APPLICATION INFORMATION:
For Fellowship Awards, applicants must include:
(1) application cover sheet with all required signatures;
(2) the sponsor's biographical sketch in NIH format and a list of current funding - please limit the sponsor's bibliography to five publications that are most relevant to the proposed research;
(3) sponsor's letter describing training plan for the candidate, percentage of proposal written by the candidate and sponsor's track record of mentorship;
(4) the applicant's curriculum vitae, including a bibliography of all published works;
(5) a letter from the applicant describing his or her previous research and teaching experience - the letter must state that the applicant is committed to a career in cancer research and comment on the transformative impact of his/her graduate research on the field of study;
(6) the research proposal, which shall not exceed five pages of single-spaced 12-point type with at least one-half inch margins, should include a summary of the research proposed, a brief background to the proposed research, specific research objectives/aims, the method of approach for the proposed research concisely described, the significance of the proposed research to the Foundation's goals, the relevance of his or her own background and the background and previous work of the sponsor and any other investigators to the proposed research, a written statement testifying adequate safety precautions as well as appropriate board or committee approval for projects that involve any biohazards, a list of references including the full title of each work cited, although the references are not included in the five-page limit, and figures or tables appended or incorporated into the text (not to exceed two extra pages);
(7) a copy of the applicant's degree certificate;
(8) the Summary of Research Form, not to exceed one page - not stapled to the application;
(9) if available, up to three different reprints of the applicant's publications and;
(10) three reference letters from qualified individuals, other than the sponsor, who can evaluate the candidate's qualifications for the proposed research project and assess the candidate's potential for successful independent cancer research.

In addition to the above, applicants for the Damon Runyon-Sohn Fellowship must submit a statement indicating how the proposed research has the potential to significantly impact the prevention, diagnosis, or treatment of one or more pediatric cancers.
Duration: Clinical Investigator, Fellowship and Innovation Awards, and Damon Runyon-Sohn Fellowship: Three years. Frey Award: Up to two years.
Deadline: Clinical Investigator Award: February 18; Damon Runyon-Sohn Fellowship Award: March 17; Fellowship Award: March 17 and August 15 for consideration in May and November, respectively; Frey Award: July 15. Innovation Award: July 1.

PUBLICATIONS:
Annual report; award brochures.

BOARD OF DIRECTORS:
Alan M. Leventhal, Chairman

Leon G. Cooperman, Vice Chairman, Finance, and Treasurer
Michael L. Gordon, Vice Chairman, Board Development
David M. Livingston, M.D., Vice Chairman, Scientific Programs
Sanford W. Morhouse, Esq., Vice Chairman, Audit and Corporate Governance
David M. Beirne, Vice Chairman, Development and Communications
Steven J. Burakoff, M.D.
William L. Carroll, M.D.
Deborah J. Coleman
Gary E. Earlbaum
Thomas J. Fahey, Jr., M.D.
Buck French
Dale F. Frey
Elaine V. Fuchs, Ph.D.
Richard B. Gaynor, M.D.
Todd R. Golub, M.D.
Scott Greenstein
Steve Hayden
William W. Helman
Jay Ireland
Steven A. Kandarian
Noah Knauf
Ronald Levy, M.D.
David G. Marshall
John H. Myers
Richard J. O'Reilly, M.D.
Andrew S. Rachleff
Scott Ryles
Michael V. Seiden, M.D., Ph.D.
Karen D. Seitz
Samuel C. Silverstein, M.D.
Cynthia Sulzberger
Peter Van Camp

ADDRESS INQUIRIES TO:
Clare M. Cahill, Chief Administrative Officer
(See address above.)

THE SKIN CANCER FOUNDATION [2447]
149 Madison Avenue
Suite 901
New York, NY 10016
(212) 725-5176
Fax: (212) 725-5751

E-MAIL ADDRESS:
info@skincancer.org

WEB SITE ADDRESS:
www.skincancer.org

FOUNDED: 1979

AREAS OF INTEREST:
To promote skin cancer research.

NAME(S) OF PROGRAMS:
- **Melissa K. Bambino Memorial Award**
- **Dr. Alfred W. Kopf Research Grant Award**
- **Todd Nagel Memorial Award**
- **Dr. Marcia Robbins-Wilf Research Award**
- **Paul Silberberg Memorial Award**

TYPE:
Matching gifts; Project/program grants; Research grants.

YEAR PROGRAM STARTED: 1981

PURPOSE:
To reduce the incidence, morbidity, and mortality of skin cancer.

LEGAL BASIS:
Nonprofit foundation.

ELIGIBILITY:
Applications must be for research projects relevant to skin cancer which address, at the

basic science and clinical level, improved methods of prevention and detection of skin cancers.

GEOGRAPHIC RESTRICTIONS:
United States.

FINANCIAL DATA:
Amount of support per award: $10,000 to $25,000.

Total amount of support: $100,000 annually.

NUMBER OF APPLICANTS MOST RECENT YEAR:
39.

NUMBER OF AWARDS: 5 for the year 2013.

APPLICATION INFORMATION:
Application information is available on the web site.

Duration: One year.

OFFICERS:
Perry Robins, M.D., President
Rex A. Amonette, M.D., Senior Vice President
C. William Hanke, M.D., Senior Vice President
Deborah S. Sarnoff, M.D., Senior Vice President
Leonard H. Goldberg, M.D., Vice President
Elizabeth K. Hale, M.D., Vice President
Allan C. Halpern, M.D., Vice President
Maritza Perez, M.D., Vice President
Susan H. Weinkle, M.D., Vice President
Michael J. Cosgrove, Treasurer
Elizabeth Robins, Esq., Secretary
Bennet Weiner, Esq., General Counsel

EXECUTIVE DIRECTOR:
Mary Stine

ADDRESS INQUIRIES TO:
Mary Stine, Executive Director
(See address above.)

*SPECIAL STIPULATIONS:
E-mail applications are not accepted. Because the amounts of the grants are small, the Foundation does not fund overhead or indirect costs.

LADY TATA MEMORIAL TRUST [2448]
c/o Mr. J.D. Contractor
Tata Limited
18 Grosvenor Place
London SW1X 7HS England
(020) 7235 8281
Fax: (020) 7259 5996

E-MAIL ADDRESS:
tata@tata.co.uk

WEB SITE ADDRESS:
www.ladytatatrust.org

FOUNDED: 1933

AREAS OF INTEREST:
Leukemia research.

TYPE:
Fellowships; Research grants; Scholarships; Seed money grants. Annual awards for postgraduate scientists of any nationality to support programs of research likely to throw light on the nature of leukemia. One or more grants of a studentship for a student entering an M.Phil./Ph.D. program is available. The Trustees especially wish to encourage studies on the leukaemogenic agents and on the epidemiology, pathogenesis, immunology and genetic basis of leukemia. The work may be done in any country or in an institution where the candidate has been accepted.

YEAR PROGRAM STARTED: 1933

PURPOSE:
To support research in leukemia.

LEGAL BASIS:
Registered charity.

ELIGIBILITY:
Suitably qualified medical or science graduates of any nationality, who are accepted in the institution where the work is to be undertaken, may apply.

FINANCIAL DATA:
Stipends are paid in quarterly installments. Since amounts vary according to age, qualifications, experience and the scales appropriate to the institution where the applicant has been accepted, intending applicants should try to find out the range of salary that would be appropriate before they apply.
Amount of support per award: GBP 25,000 to 35,000 per annum.

NUMBER OF AWARDS: 13 for the academic year 2012-13.

APPLICATION INFORMATION:
Applications are only accepted online during the current year schedule.
Duration: All awards are tenable for one academic year, October to September. Awards for two years may be given if considered by the Trust to be in best interests of a particular project.
Deadline: March 15. Announcements June 18.

OFFICERS:
Prof. Daniel Catovsky, Chairman, Scientific Advisory Board
Prof. Barbara J. Bain, Secretary

ADDRESS INQUIRIES TO:
Professor D. Catovsky
c/o Mr. J.D. Contractor
(See address above.)

*SPECIAL STIPULATIONS:
Holders of awards are expected to submit half-yearly reports on their progress to the Scientific Advisory Committee and to acknowledge the support of the Trust in their publication.

UNION FOR INTERNATIONAL CANCER CONTROL (UICC) [2449]
62 route de Frontenex
1207 Geneva Switzerland
+41 22 809 1843
Fax: +41 22 809 1810

E-MAIL ADDRESS:
fellows@uicc.org

WEB SITE ADDRESS:
www.uicc.org

FOUNDED: 1933

AREAS OF INTEREST:
Cancer research, clinical oncology, oncology nursing and voluntary cancer societies.

NAME(S) OF PROGRAMS:
- **American Cancer Society International Fellowships for Beginning Investigators (ACSBI)**
- **Asia-Pacific Cancer Society Training Grants (APCASOT)**
- **International Cancer Technology Transfer Fellowships (ICRETT)**

- **Training Workshops**
- **Yamagiwa-Yoshida Memorial International Study Grants (YY)**

TYPE:
Fellowships. The UICC Fellowships Programme provides long-, medium- and short-term fellowships abroad to qualified investigators, clinicians, and nurses, who are actively engaged in cancer research, clinical oncology, or oncology nursing. Short-term scheme offers nonmedical training opportunities in the Asia-Pacific region.

YEAR PROGRAM STARTED: 1933

PURPOSE:
To enable qualified cancer investigators, doctors, nurses, cancer society staff or accredited volunteers to carry out specific research and clinical projects, or to obtain training in cancer society work in appropriate organizations abroad.

ELIGIBILITY:
Candidates must:
(1) possess appropriate professional qualifications and experience according to the specific fellowship applied for;
(2) be currently engaged in cancer research, clinical oncology practice, oncology nursing, or cancer society work;
(3) be on the staff payroll of a university, research laboratory or institute, hospital, oncology unit, or voluntary cancer society (or be accredited volunteers of such societies) to where they will return at the end of a fellowship and;
(4) have adequate fluency in a language that will permit effective communication at the host institute.
Candidates may submit application for only one fellowship scheme at a time. Applicants who have already obtained a UICC fellowship in the past may apply for further UICC awards only if they are members of the Association of UICC Fellows.

No distinction will be made among candidates on the basis of gender, ethnic origin, religious or political beliefs. Awards are made on the basis of scientific and expert evaluation of the application and the proposed work as set out by the candidate in the project description by reviewers of the highest international standing in their respective fields. Decisions are final and cannot be appealed.

Fellowships are conditional on Fellows returning to the home institutes at the end of the fellowship period. Awards are not granted for basic training courses, lectures, meetings, conferences, congresses or for visiting institutes. They cannot prolong or run concurrently with other awards and cannot be granted to candidates who are already physically present at the proposed host institute while their applications are under consideration. ICRETT Workshops and APCASOT may not be financially supplemented. Those programs terminated early must notify UICC immediately and appropriate funds be reimbursed. All awards require an end-of-the-project report in English, within one month at the end of the project.

FINANCIAL DATA:
Amount of support per award: ACSBI: $50,000 average; APCASOT: Up to $2,000 AUD; ICRETT: $3,400 average; Training Workshops: Maximum $15,000 for travel and stipend for three international faculty members; YY: $10,000 average.

NUMBER OF AWARDS: ACSBI: 6 to 8; APCASOT: 5 to 10; ICRETT: 120 to 150; Training Workshops: 10 to 20; YY: 14 to 16.

APPLICATION INFORMATION:
Applications and all supporting documentation for ACSBI, YY, ICRETT and APCASOT must be submitted in English. Applications may be submitted by fax or e-mail with originals also sent by airmail or courier service and will be acknowledged promptly. Candidates will be advised if items are missing. Those proposals that have undergone a review and selection process and were not approved for funding cannot be resubmitted. However, candidates are encouraged to submit new applications for new work programs.
Duration: ICRETT: One month; Training workshops: Three to five days; Fellowships and grants: Up to 12 months.
Deadline: ACSBI: November 1. APCASOT: Late September. ICRETT and Training Workshops: Applications accepted year-round. YY: January 15 and July 1.

ADDRESS INQUIRIES TO:
UICC Fellowships Department
(See address above.)

*SPECIAL STIPULATIONS:
UICC requires an end-of-the-project report in English within one month of the end of the project.

Rheumatology

ARTHRITIS FOUNDATION [2450]
1330 West Peachtree Street, N.W.
Suite 100
Atlanta, GA 30309
(404) 965-7537
Fax: (404) 872-9559

E-MAIL ADDRESS:
grantsupport@arthritis.org

WEB SITE ADDRESS:
www.arthritis.org

FOUNDED: 1948

AREAS OF INTEREST:
The cause, prevention and cure of arthritis, the nation's number one crippling disease.

NAME(S) OF PROGRAMS:
- **Innovative Research Grants**
- **Postdoctoral Fellowships**

TYPE:
Fellowships; Research grants; Training grants. Postdoctoral Fellowships are intended to encourage qualified physicians and scientists to embark on careers in research related to the understanding of arthritis and the rheumatic diseases.

YEAR PROGRAM STARTED: 1951

PURPOSE:
To improve lives through leadership in the prevention, control and cure of arthritis and related diseases; to create a world free of arthritis pain.

LEGAL BASIS:
Nonprofit organization.

ELIGIBILITY:
Qualified individuals holding an M.D., Ph.D., D.O., D.V.M., or equivalent degree from an accredited institution are eligible to apply.

GEOGRAPHIC RESTRICTIONS:
United States.

FINANCIAL DATA:
Fellowship provides salary support for the early years of the necessary training period. 75% of the time must be devoted to AF-funded project.

Amount of support per award: Innovative Research Grants: Up to $100,000 per year; Postdoctoral Fellowships: $50,000 annually, to be used as salary and fringe benefits.

APPLICATION INFORMATION:
Official application materials are available from the Foundation.

Duration: Two years.

OFFICERS:
Daniel T. McGowan, Chairperson
Dr. John Klippel, President

ADDRESS INQUIRIES TO:
Alicia Deleon, Grants Specialist
(See address above.)

THE ARTHRITIS SOCIETY [2451]
393 University Avenue, Suite 1700
Toronto ON M5G 1E6 Canada
(416) 979-3353
Fax: (416) 979-1149

E-MAIL ADDRESS:
info@arthritis.ca

WEB SITE ADDRESS:
www.arthritis.ca

FOUNDED: 1948

AREAS OF INTEREST:
Arthritis medical and scientific research.

NAME(S) OF PROGRAMS:
- **The Arthritis Society Clinical Fellowships in Rheumatology**
- **The Arthritis Society Clinician Teacher Award**
- **The Arthritis Society Consumer Activity Grants**
- **The Arthritis Society Investigator Award**
- **The Arthritis Society New Investigator Award**
- **The Arthritis Society Small Meeting Grants**
- **The Arthritis Society Strategic Operating Grants**

TYPE:
Fellowships; General operating grants; Research grants; Scholarships.

PURPOSE:
To search for the underlying causes and subsequent cures for arthritis; to promote the best possible care and treatment for people with arthritis.

LEGAL BASIS:
Registered charity.

ELIGIBILITY:
Applicants are restricted to Canadian citizens and permanent residents of Canada. Applicants for research grants must hold faculty appointments at Canadian medical schools. Specific requirements vary by program.

GEOGRAPHIC RESTRICTIONS:
Canada.

FINANCIAL DATA:
Amount of support per award: Varies.
Total amount of support: Varies.

APPLICATION INFORMATION:
Application information is available on the web site.

Duration: Varies by program.
Deadline: Varies by program.

PUBLICATIONS:
Annual report; regulations.

BOARD MEMBERS:
Ken Ready, Chairperson
Janet Yale, President and Chief Executive Officer
Dr. Brian Feldman, Chairman of the Medical Advisory Committee
Dr. Marc Pouliot, Chairman of Scientific Advisory Committee
Michael Whitcombe, Honourary Solicitor
Bruce Chislett, Director at Large
Chris Nelson, Director at Large
Kenneth Smith, Director at Large
Ronald Smith, Director at Large
David West, Director at Large

ADDRESS INQUIRIES TO:
Research and Career Development
(See address above.)

LUPUS FOUNDATION OF AMERICA, INC.
2000 L Street, N.W., Suite 410
Washington, DC 20036
(202) 349-1155
Fax: (202) 349-1156

WEB SITE ADDRESS:
www.lupus.org/rfa/finzifellowships

TYPE:
Research grants. Summer Fellowship.

See entry 2279 for full listing.

Neurology

ALZHEIMER'S ASSOCIATION, INC. [2452]
225 North Michigan Avenue
Suite 1700
Chicago, IL 60601-7633
(312) 335-5747
Fax: (866) 801-5503

E-MAIL ADDRESS:
mepps@alz.org
grantsapp@alz.org

WEB SITE ADDRESS:
www.alz.org

FOUNDED: 1980

AREAS OF INTEREST:
Basic and applied research relevant to Alzheimer's disease and related disorders.

NAME(S) OF PROGRAMS:
- **Everyday Technologies for Alzheimer Care (ETAC)**
- **Investigator-Initiated Research Grants**
- **New Investigator Research Grants**
- **The Zenith Fellows Award Program**

TYPE:
Fellowships; Research grants; Seed money grants. Reducing the duration of disability and shortening the period of dependency is one of the missions of the Ronald and Nancy Reagan Research Institute of the Alzheimer's Association. During the last few years, research on the behavioral, social, clinical and environmental aspects of Alzheimer's disease has been making impressive progress.

Everyday Technologies for Alzheimer Care (ETAC) is a program of research support.

Investigator-Initiated Research Grants concentrate on interventions for Alzheimer's disease.

New Investigator Research Grants fund investigators that are no more than 10 years past their doctoral degree. The funding will allow them to conduct preliminary research which will be the basis of later research grant applications to the National Institutes of Health or other funding agencies.

The Zenith Fellows Award is currently designed to provide major support for investigators who have made or who show promise of making significant contributions to Alzheimer's disease research.

YEAR PROGRAM STARTED: 1982

PURPOSE:
To target prevention of the devastating effects of Alzheimer's disease; to ensure effective treatments; to delay onset of Alzheimer's disabling symptoms.

LEGAL BASIS:
Private, voluntary health association.

ELIGIBILITY:
Public, private, domestic and foreign research laboratories, medical centers, hospitals and universities are eligible to apply, with the exception of state and federal government-appropriated laboratories and for-profit organizations, which are prohibited from serving as the applicant institution. However, state and federal government scientists can participate as collaborating scientists with research teams from other eligible applicant institutions. The award will be issued to the applicant institution, not to the investigator.

Each program has specific requirements. Therefore, contact the Association for additional information.

FINANCIAL DATA:
A maximum of 10% of expenses for overhead, not to exceed maximum funding level requested.

Amount of support per award: Everyday Technologies for Alzheimer Care (ETAC): Maximum $200,000; Investigator-Initiated Research Grants: Maximum $250,000; New Investigator Research Grants: Maximum $100,000; Zenith Fellows Award Program: Maximum $450,000.

NUMBER OF AWARDS: Everyday Technologies for Alzheimer Care (ETAC): 2; Investigator-Initiated Research Grants: 10; New Investigator Research Grants: 25; Zenith Fellows Award Program: 4.

APPLICATION INFORMATION:
Letter of Intent (LOI) must be submitted through the online application system and includes:
(1) name of the principal investigator;
(2) contact information for the principal investigator (complete mailing address, telephone number, fax number and e-mail address);
(3) institution(s) involved in the research proposal;
(4) title of the investigation;
(5) area of focus of the submission;
(6) grant competition for which applicant is applying and;
(7) brief rationale for the proposal.

An investigator may submit more than one application during the research grant competition, but each application must be a separate and distinct research proposal (i.e., non-overlapping specific aims).

Duration: Varies.

PUBLICATIONS:
Annual report; application guidelines.

ADDRESS INQUIRIES TO:
Mary Epps-Streeter
Pre-Award Grant Specialist
(See address above.)

ALZHEIMER'S ASSOCIATION, INC.   [2453]
225 North Michigan Avenue, Suite 1700
Chicago, IL 60601-7633
(312) 335-5747
Fax: (866) 801-5503

E-MAIL ADDRESS:
mepps@alz.org
grantsapp@alz.org

WEB SITE ADDRESS:
www.alz.org

FOUNDED: 1980

AREAS OF INTEREST:
Basic and applied research relevant to Alzheimer's disease and related disorders.

NAME(S) OF PROGRAMS:
- **Mentored New Investigator Research Grant to Promote Diversity (MNIRGD)**
- **New Investigator Research Grant to Promote Diversity (NIRGD)**
- **U.S.-U.K. Young Investigator Exchange Fellowship**

TYPE:
Fellowships; Research grants. Mentored New Investigator Research Grant to Promote Diversity (MNIRGD) funds mentored research conducted by underrepresented researchers who have earned their doctoral degrees within the last 10 years.

New Investigator Research Grant to Promote Diversity (NIRGD) funds new investigators from diverse backgrounds with intent to support early career development that will lay groundwork for future research grants.

U.S.-U.K. Young Investigator Exchange Fellowship aims to address important research questions as well as to help and encourage promising scientists as they establish their careers within Alzheimer's research internationally.

PURPOSE:
To target prevention of the devastating effects of Alzheimer's disease; to ensure effective treatments; to delay onset of Alzheimer's disabling symptoms.

LEGAL BASIS:
Private, voluntary health association.

ELIGIBILITY:
Mentored New Investigator Research Grant to Promote Diversity (MNIRGD) and New Investigator Research Grant to Promote Diversity (NIRGD): Applicants must be Assistant Professors or above at their respective institution. Eligibility is restricted to investigators who have less than 10 years of research experience after receipt of their terminal degree.

U.S.-U.K. Young Investigator Exchange Fellowship: Applicants must have less than 10 years of research experience after receipt of their terminal degree. Postdoctoral fellows are eligible to apply.

FINANCIAL DATA:
Amount of support per award: Mentored New Investigator Research Grant to Promote Diversity (MNIRGD): $170,000. New Investigator Research Grant to Promote Diversity (NIRGD): Up to $100,000. U.S.-U.K. Young Investigator Exchange Fellowship: U.S. - up to $300,000; U.K. - up to GBP 160,000.

APPLICATION INFORMATION:
Instructions can be found on the Association web site.
Duration: Mentored New Investigator Research Grant to Promote Diversity (MNIRGD): Up to three years. New Investigator Research Grant to Promote Diversity (NIRGD): Up to two years. U.S.-U.K. Young Investigator Exchange Fellowship: Up to three years.
Deadline: Varies.

ADDRESS INQUIRIES TO:
Mary Epps-Streeter
Pre-Award Grant Specialist
(See address above.)

AMERICAN BRAIN TUMOR ASSOCIATION   [2454]
8550 West Bryn Mawr Avenue
Suite 550
Chicago, IL 60031
(773) 577-8750
Fax: (773) 577-8738

E-MAIL ADDRESS:
info@abta.org

WEB SITE ADDRESS:
www.abta.org

AREAS OF INTEREST:
Brain tumor research.

NAME(S) OF PROGRAMS:
- **Basic Research Fellowship Awards**
- **Discovery Grants**
- **Medical Student Summer Fellowships**

TYPE:
Fellowships; Seed money grants; Training grants. Medical Student Summer Fellowships support a 10- to 12-week summer laboratory experience.

PURPOSE:
To encourage talented scientists early in their careers to enter, or remain in, the field of brain tumor research; to facilitate the development of potentially important research studies; to support innovative brain tumor research.

ELIGIBILITY:
Varies by grant mechanism.

GEOGRAPHIC RESTRICTIONS:
United States and Canada.

FINANCIAL DATA:
Amount of support per award: Discovery Grants: $50,000; Research Fellowships: $100,000; Medical Student Summer Fellowships: $3,000.

NUMBER OF AWARDS: Varies.

APPLICATION INFORMATION:
Contact the Organization for application procedures. Applications accepted by invitation only for Discovery Grants.

Duration: Discovery Grants: One year; Medical Student Summer Fellowships: 10 to 12 weeks over the summer; Research Fellowships: Two years.
Deadline: Discovery Grants: Letters of Intent due early fall. Research Fellowships: Applications should be submitted online in early January.

STAFF:
Alexandra Sierra, Research Program Coordinator

ADDRESS INQUIRIES TO:
Deneen Hesser, Research Director
Email: grants@abta.org

AMERICAN EPILEPSY SOCIETY (AES)   [2455]
342 North Main Street
West Hartford, CT 06117-2507
(860) 586-7505 ext. 572
Fax: (860) 586-7550

E-MAIL ADDRESS:
info@aesnet.org

WEB SITE ADDRESS:
www.aesnet.org
epilepsyresearchresource.org

FOUNDED: 1936

AREAS OF INTEREST:
Study and acquisition, dissemination and application of knowledge concerning epilepsy in all its phases including biological, clinical and social.

NAME(S) OF PROGRAMS:
- **The Grass Foundation - AES Young Investigator Travel Award**
- **Lennox and Lombroso Postdoctoral Research Fellowship**
- **Postdoctoral Research Fellowship**
- **Predoctoral Research Fellowship**
- **Research and Training Workshops**
- **Research Infrastructure Awards**
- **Research Initiative Fund Grants**
- **Seed Grants**
- **Susan S. Spencer Clinical Research Training Fellowship in Epilepsy**

TYPE:
Awards/prizes; Fellowships; Research grants; Seed money grants. The American Epilepsy Society is one of the oldest neurological professional organizations in the U.S. The Society, in partnership with other organizations, funds Research Grants and Fellowships that are awarded to individuals with a professional degree whose research impacts an aspect of the study of, and work toward the cure for, epilepsy. Some funding programs are for Society members only.

The Grass Foundation - AES Young Investigator Travel Award: This award recognizes and honors outstanding young investigators conducting research in basic or clinical neuroscience related to epilepsy; the Grass Foundation and the Society have combined resources to present this annual meeting poster travel award.

Lennox and Lombroso Postdoctoral Research Fellowship: This one-year fellowship, administered by the Epilepsy Foundation, is available to physicians or Ph.D. neuroscientists who desire postdoctoral research experience.

Postdoctoral Research Fellowship: This one-year fellowship, administered by the Epilepsy Foundation, is available to physicians or Ph.D. neuroscientists who desire postdoctoral research experience.

Predoctoral Research Fellowship: This one-year fellowship, administered by the Epilepsy Foundation, is offered to graduate students matriculating in a full-time doctoral (Ph.D.) program with an academic career focus, with dissertation research related to epilepsy.

Research and Training Workshops: The Society, through the Research and Training Committee, provides funding for targeted workshops, intended for clinical or scientific audiences and on specific collaborative topics in neuroscience.

Research Infrastructure Awards: This is a program for the Society's members that provides an opportunity to obtain support for nationwide or international networks of clinical or basic science researchers focused on understanding the causes, consequences and treatment of epilepsy.

Research Initiative Fund Grants: This is a funding mechanism for the Society's members that will provide seed support to encourage innovative, collaborative research in all disciplines (clinical, social, basic science, etc.) associated with the epilepsy field.

Seed Grants: This grant is to foster collaborative interactions between two or more established investigators to make future grants related to epilepsy more competitive for larger awards and to fuel multi-investigator projects.

Susan S. Spencer Clinical Research Training Fellowship in Epilepsy: A two-year fellowship, administered by the American Academy of Neurology, to support clinical research training in the field of epilepsy.

YEAR PROGRAM STARTED: 1970

PURPOSE:
To promote interdisciplinary communications, scientific investigation and exchange of clinical information about epilepsy; to improve the quality of life for people with epilepsy; to provide those engaged in research with information and assistance of potential benefit in advancing their work.

LEGAL BASIS:
501(c)(3) organization.

ELIGIBILITY:
Details for the different programs can be found online.

FINANCIAL DATA:
Amount of support per award: Varies by mechanism.
Total amount of support: Varies.

COOPERATIVE FUNDING PROGRAMS: The Society has formed alliances with other organizations that provide research funding, including the Grass Foundation, Epilepsy Foundation and other funding sources.

Susan S. Spencer Clinical Research Training Fellowship in Epilepsy is supported by the AAN Foundation, the American Epilepsy Society and the Epilepsy Foundation.

NUMBER OF APPLICANTS MOST RECENT YEAR: Varies.

NUMBER OF AWARDS: Varies.

APPLICATION INFORMATION:
Application information is available on the web site.
Duration: One to two years.
Deadline: Varies.

IRS IDENTIFICATION NUMBER: 04-6112600

STAFF:
Eileen M. Murray, MM, CAE, Executive Director
Cheryl-Ann Tubby, IOM, CPP, Assistant Executive Director

ADDRESS INQUIRIES TO:
Eileen M. Murray, MM, CAE
Executive Director
(See address above.)

AMERICAN PARKINSON DISEASE ASSOCIATION, INC. [2456]
135 Parkinson Avenue
Staten Island, NY 10305
(718) 981-8001
(800) 223-2732
Fax: (718) 981-4399

E-MAIL ADDRESS:
hgray@apdaparkinson.org

WEB SITE ADDRESS:
www.apdaparkinson.org

FOUNDED: 1961

AREAS OF INTEREST:
Parkinson's disease, medical neurology and neuropathology.

NAME(S) OF PROGRAMS:
● **Medical Student Summer Fellowships**

TYPE:
Fellowships. To assist investigators in establishing careers in the research of Parkinson's disease.

YEAR PROGRAM STARTED: 1965

PURPOSE:
To enable medical students to perform supervised laboratory or clinical research designed to clarify our understanding of Parkinson's disease, its nature, manifestations, etiology or treatment.

LEGAL BASIS:
Not-for-profit organization.

ELIGIBILITY:
Applicant should be a full-time medical student in good academic standing in an approved U.S. medical school. The proposed research project must be performed in an academic medical center or recognized research institute in the U.S. and be sponsored by a full-time faculty member or established institute scientist. The project must be part of the sponsor's ongoing research and be performed under the sponsor's direct supervision. Either laboratory or clinical research or a combination of both may be acceptable; however, merely reviewing literature or preparing reports will not be deemed acceptable.

GEOGRAPHIC RESTRICTIONS:
United States.

FINANCIAL DATA:
Amount of support per award: $4,000.

NUMBER OF AWARDS: Varies.

APPLICATION INFORMATION:
The medical student should provide a brief description of the proposed work, not to exceed three pages, containing the following elements:
(1) title of the research study;
(2) location of where the study will be performed (i.e., department or laboratory);
(3) identify sponsor (include mailing address,

phone number and e-mail address);
(4) background rationale including preliminary results of work completed by the sponsor;
(5) goals and objectives;
(6) investigative methods;
(7) data analysis method;
(8) significance of anticipated findings;
(9) institutional resources available and;
(10) description of study subjects (human or animal).

Application must be accompanied by a supporting letter from the sponsor, a letter of reference from another faculty member familiar with the student's previous academic performance, and a letter from the Dean's office assuring the student is in good academic standing.
Duration: Three months.
Deadline: January 31.

PUBLICATIONS:
Program announcement; guidelines.

ADDRESS INQUIRIES TO:
Heather Gray, Associate Director of Scientific and Medical Affairs
(See address above.)

THE AMYOTROPHIC LATERAL SCLEROSIS ASSOCIATION [2457]
National Office
27001 Agoura Road, Suite 250
Calabasas Hills, CA 91301-5104
(818) 880-9007
Fax: (818) 880-9006

E-MAIL ADDRESS:
researchgrants@alsa-national.org

WEB SITE ADDRESS:
www.alsa.org

FOUNDED: 1985

AREAS OF INTEREST:
Amyotrophic lateral sclerosis (ALS) programs include research grants, patient services, public education and awareness, local chapter development, and advocacy.

NAME(S) OF PROGRAMS:
● **Research Grant Program**

TYPE:
Awards/prizes; Conferences/seminars; Fellowships; Project/program grants; Research grants; Technical assistance; Research contracts. Grants, for a specified number of years, to neuroscientific researchers to pursue a project of relevance to Amyotrophic Lateral Sclerosis. Both basic and clinical research supported (including postdoctoral fellowships). The ALS Association forms partnerships on clinical trials.

YEAR PROGRAM STARTED: 1985

PURPOSE:
To find the cause and cure of amyotrophic lateral sclerosis; to support research vital to this goal.

LEGAL BASIS:
Nonprofit voluntary health agency under IRS 501(c)(3).

ELIGIBILITY:
Applicant should be a faculty member at a reputable scientific facility.

FINANCIAL DATA:
Amount of support per award: Multiyear grants: Maximum $80,000 per year; Starter

grants: Maximum $40,000 for 12-month period; Postdoctoral fellows: Maximum $40,000 per year for two years.
Total amount of support: Varies.

NUMBER OF APPLICANTS MOST RECENT YEAR: 650.

NUMBER OF AWARDS: 45.

REPRESENTATIVE AWARDS:
$120,000 to Joseph Beckman, Ph.D., University of Alabama at Birmingham; $80,000 to Laura Dugan, M.D., Massachusetts General Hospital; $35,000 to Charles Epstein, M.D., University of California at San Francisco.

APPLICATION INFORMATION:
Request an abstract form from the e-mail address above. Submit a one-page abstract, via e-mail, describing the proposed project. An application form will be sent with the invitation to submit, after review and interest in abstract.
Duration: Two to three years; longer if justifiable. Renewable on occasion. Some starter grants for 12 months.
Deadline: Information available upon request to the e-mail address above.

PUBLICATIONS:
Research ALS Today, newspaper; miscellaneous ALS information and patient care brochures; *ALS Journal News,* monthly.

IRS IDENTIFICATION NUMBER: 13-3271855

STAFF:
Lucie Bruijn, Ph.D., Chief Scientist

ADDRESS INQUIRIES TO:
Lucie Bruijn, Ph.D., Chief Scientist
(See address above.)

BENIGN ESSENTIAL BLEPHAROSPASM RESEARCH FOUNDATION INC.
637 North 7th Street
Suite 102
Beaumont, TX 77702
(409) 832-0788
Fax: (409) 832-0890

E-MAIL ADDRESS:
bebrf@blepharospasm.org

WEB SITE ADDRESS:
www.blepharospasm.org

TYPE:
Fellowships; Project/program grants; Research grants; Seed money grants. The Foundation offers research fellowships to support the training of exceptionally qualified physicians or scientists who wish to focus on blepharospasm with and without oromandibular dystonia.
See entry 2507 for full listing.

BRIGHT FOCUS FOUNDATION [2458]
22512 Gateway Center Drive
Clarksburg, MD 20871
(301) 948-3244
Fax: (301) 948-4403

E-MAIL ADDRESS:
researchgrants@brightfocus.org

WEB SITE ADDRESS:
www.brightfocus.org

FOUNDED: 1973

AREAS OF INTEREST:
Alzheimer's disease research.

NAME(S) OF PROGRAMS:
● **Alzheimer's Disease Research**

TYPE:
Research grants. Awards for basic research into the causes and treatment of age-related and degenerative diseases.

YEAR PROGRAM STARTED: 1985

PURPOSE:
To develop treatments, preventions and cures for Alzheimer's disease.

LEGAL BASIS:
Nonprofit foundation.

ELIGIBILITY:
Grants are awarded on the basis of the proposal's scientific merit and its relevance to understanding the disease studied. No funds for large equipment, institutional overhead costs, construction or building expenses.

FINANCIAL DATA:
Amount of support per award: Fellows: Up to $100,000; Standard award: Up to $250,000.
Total amount of support: Varies.

NUMBER OF AWARDS: 20 for fiscal year 2013.

APPLICATION INFORMATION:
Application information is available on the web site.
Duration: Three-year projects and two-year research fellowships.
Deadline: Contact the Foundation for exact dates.

PUBLICATIONS:
Annual report; clinical brochures; newsletters.

ADDRESS INQUIRIES TO:
Kara Summers, Program Officer
(See e-mail address above.)

CEREBRAL PALSY INTERNATIONAL RESEARCH FOUNDATION [2459]
445 Park Avenue
9th Floor
New York, NY 10022
(212) 836-4756
(917) 952-9900

E-MAIL ADDRESS:
christy.cravens@cpirf.org

WEB SITE ADDRESS:
www.cpirf.org

FOUNDED: 1955

NAME(S) OF PROGRAMS:
● **CPI Research Grants**

TYPE:
Research grants. Grants are awarded for pilot studies in areas which have a relationship to cerebral palsy. While most research in the central nervous system may be useful, the Foundation requires that research proposals define clear and direct relevance to cerebral palsy. Currently, high priority is assigned to prevention of prematurity, decrease of perinatal neurologic morbidity, prevention of central nervous system infections of the newborn and to medical, surgical and bioengineering methods that may improve the functioning of persons with cerebral palsy, addressing issues such as impaired mobility, impaired communication skills, swallowing, drooling and effects of aging on further diminution of function. However, any

proposal designed to prevent cerebral palsy or to improve its treatment and management will be considered.

YEAR PROGRAM STARTED: 1955

PURPOSE:
To support research pilot studies in areas of etiology, pathology, prevention and therapy bearing directly on cerebral palsy and the disabilities associated with it.

LEGAL BASIS:
Private foundation.

ELIGIBILITY:
Tax-exempt universities and other organizations are eligible to apply on behalf of qualified individuals.

FINANCIAL DATA:
Amount of support per award: Up to $50,000 for one year; total of $100,000 for two years including indirect costs not in excess of 10% of each budgetary item, except for equipment.
Total amount of support: Approximately $700,000 for fiscal year 2013.

NUMBER OF APPLICANTS MOST RECENT YEAR: 35.

NUMBER OF AWARDS: 7.

APPLICATION INFORMATION:
Application form required. The grant review process usually takes about three months.
Duration: Up to two years.
Deadline: March 1.

IRS IDENTIFICATION NUMBER: 13-6093337

STAFF:
Richard Ellenson, President and Chief Executive Officer
James A. Blackman, M.D., Medical Director
Christy Cravens, Administrative Director

ADDRESS INQUIRIES TO:
Christy Cravens
Administrative Director
(See address above.)

CUREPSP FOUNDATION FOR PSP/CBD AND RELATED BRAIN DISEASES [2460]
30 East Padonia Road
Suite 201
Timonium, MD 21093
(410) 785-7004
Fax: (410) 785-7009

E-MAIL ADDRESS:
bantum@curepsp.org

WEB SITE ADDRESS:
www.curepsp.org

FOUNDED: 1990

AREAS OF INTEREST:
Progressive supranuclear palsy and corticobasal degeneration.

TYPE:
Research grants.

YEAR PROGRAM STARTED: 1997

PURPOSE:
To provide support for basic and clinical research in progressive supranuclear palsy and corticobasal degeneration.

ELIGIBILITY:
Qualified investigators affiliated with appropriate institutions are eligible to apply. Applicants must have the approval of the institution where the research training will be conducted. Ph.D. or M.D. status is required.

FINANCIAL DATA:
There is a $8,000 maximum for durable equipment and $300 maximum for publication costs.
Amount of support per award: Varies.
Total amount of support: Varies.

NUMBER OF APPLICANTS MOST RECENT YEAR:
10.

NUMBER OF AWARDS: 4 to 5 per year.

APPLICATION INFORMATION:
Application information is available on the web site.
Duration: Varies.

ADDRESS INQUIRIES TO:
Lawrence I. Golbe, M.D.
Chairperson, Scientific Advisory Board and Director of Research
The Society for PSP
Department of Neurology
UMDNJ-Robert Wood Johnson
Medical School
97 Paterson Street
New Brunswick, NJ 08901
Tel: (732) 235-7729
Fax: (732) 235-7041
E-mail: golbe@umdnj.edu

DYSAUTONOMIA FOUNDATION, INC.   [2461]

315 West 39th Street
Suite 701
New York, NY 10018
(212) 279-1066
Fax: (212) 279-2066

E-MAIL ADDRESS:
info@famdys.org

WEB SITE ADDRESS:
www.familialdysautonomia.org

FOUNDED: 1951

AREAS OF INTEREST:
Familial dysautonomia.

CONSULTING OR VOLUNTEER SERVICES:
Dysautonomia Treatment and Evaluation Center at New York University Medical Center, 530 First Avenue, Suite 9Q, New York, NY 10016, under the direction of Felicia B. Axelrod, M.D.

NAME(S) OF PROGRAMS:
• **Dysautonomia Research Program**

TYPE:
Project/program grants; Research grants; Seed money grants. In addition to support for research and clinical study, the Foundation also provides financial support to the Dysautonomia Treatment and Evaluation Center at NYU and the Israeli FD Center in Tel Aviv.

YEAR PROGRAM STARTED: 1955

PURPOSE:
To fund research for treatment and/or cure for familial dysautonomia; to stimulate and promote medical research into familial dysautonomia (an inherited disease of the autonomic nervous system); to provide information to lay and medical public.

LEGAL BASIS:
Nonprofit, tax-exempt corporation.

ELIGIBILITY:
Researcher connected with a recognized medical and/or teaching institution may apply.

FINANCIAL DATA:
Amount of support per award: Varies, depending upon the needs and nature of the request.
Total amount of support: Varies.

NUMBER OF APPLICANTS MOST RECENT YEAR:
15.

NUMBER OF AWARDS: 6.

APPLICATION INFORMATION:
Application forms are supplied upon request. Researchers must check online to see if the Foundation is soliciting research application before submitting.
Duration: One year with option to apply for ongoing research and/or renewal. Renewal application (with progress report) is required each year.
Deadline: Contact the Foundation.

IRS IDENTIFICATION NUMBER: 13-6145280

STAFF:
David Brenner, Executive Director

DYSTONIA MEDICAL RESEARCH FOUNDATION   [2462]

One East Wacker Drive
Suite 2810
Chicago, IL 60601-1905
(312) 755-0198 ext. 107
Fax: (312) 803-0138

E-MAIL ADDRESS:
dystonia@dystonia-foundation.org

WEB SITE ADDRESS:
www.dystonia-foundation.org

FOUNDED: 1976

AREAS OF INTEREST:
Dystonia.

NAME(S) OF PROGRAMS:
• **Discretionary Grants**
• **Research Grants**

TYPE:
Fellowships; Project/program grants; Research grants. Research Grants to be used for hypothesis-driven dystonia-related research. Typically, studies focus on genetics, human brain tissue, anatomy and physiology of the basal ganglia and relevant brain circuitry.

YEAR PROGRAM STARTED: 1976

PURPOSE:
To fund research into the cause of, treatments and a cure for, dystonia.

LEGAL BASIS:
Private foundation.

ELIGIBILITY:
For all programs, all nonprofit institutions or organizations within the U.S., Canada and those foreign countries where supervision of grant administration is possible are eligible. For all investigations involving humans, approval by the institution's human subject protection committee is necessary. If research proposals involve human brain tissue, the Foundation will make every effort to obtain appropriate tissue from affected individuals and from controls. No support for medical care of dystonia patients, construction or alternations. Investigators must have M.D. or Ph.D. degrees.

FINANCIAL DATA:
Support cannot be used for indirect costs, new construction or renovation of existing facilities, consultant fees or travel costs unless specified in the original grant application.
Amount of support per award: Research Grants: Up to $75,000 per year; Two-Year Fellowships: Up to $50,000 per year.
Total amount of support: Varies.

APPLICATION INFORMATION:
Application form required for all programs. The principal investigator should submit a letter of recommendation with the proposal.
Duration: One or two years.

PUBLICATIONS:
Guidelines.

IRS IDENTIFICATION NUMBER: 95-3378526

ADDRESS INQUIRIES TO:
Janet Hieshetter, Executive Director
(See address above.)

EPILEPSY FOUNDATION OF AMERICA

8301 Professional Place East
Landover, MD 20785-8301
(301) 459-3700
(800) 332-1000
Fax: (301) 577-4941

E-MAIL ADDRESS:
grants@efa.org

WEB SITE ADDRESS:
www.epilepsyfoundation.org

TYPE:
Fellowships. Offers qualified individuals an opportunity to develop expertise in the area of epilepsy research relative to the health sciences through a three-month training experience with involvement in an epilepsy research project in either a clinical or laboratory setting.
See entry 1851 for full listing.

EPILEPSY FOUNDATION OF AMERICA

8301 Professional Place East
Landover, MD 20785-8301
(301) 459-3700
Fax: (301) 577-4941

E-MAIL ADDRESS:
grants@efa.org

WEB SITE ADDRESS:
www.epilepsyfoundation.org

TYPE:
Fellowships. Awards for postdoctoral study through a one-year training experience in the area of epilepsy research. Appropriate fields of study for applications in the behavioral sciences include sociology, social work, psychology, anthropology, nursing, political science and others relevant to epilepsy research or practice.
See entry 1852 for full listing.

EPILEPSY FOUNDATION OF AMERICA   [2463]

8301 Professional Place, Suite 200
Landover, MD 20785-2353
(800) 332-1000
Fax: (301) 577-4941

E-MAIL ADDRESS:
grants@efa.org
info@efa.org

WEB SITE ADDRESS:
www.epilepsyfoundation.org

FOUNDED: 1968

AREAS OF INTEREST:
Epilepsy research and training.

TYPE:
Research grants.

PURPOSE:
To support basic and clinical research in the biological and behavioral sciences that will advance the understanding, treatment and prevention of epilepsy.

LEGAL BASIS:
Private foundation.

ELIGIBILITY:
This program supports newly independent faculty members entering the field of epilepsy research. Postdoctoral fellows and established investigators (associate professor level or above) are ineligible.

GEOGRAPHIC RESTRICTIONS:
United States.

FINANCIAL DATA:
Amount of support per award: $50,000 per year.

NUMBER OF AWARDS: 8.

APPLICATION INFORMATION:
Application forms and guidelines can be obtained from the address above.
Duration: One year.

EPILEPSY FOUNDATION OF AMERICA [2464]
8301 Professional Place, Suite 200
Landover, MD 20785-2353
(800) 332-1000
Fax: (301) 577-4941

E-MAIL ADDRESS:
grants@efa.org
info@efa.org

WEB SITE ADDRESS:
www.epilepsyfoundation.org

FOUNDED: 1968

AREAS OF INTEREST:
Epilepsy research and training.

NAME(S) OF PROGRAMS:
• **Postdoctoral Research Fellowships**
• **Predoctoral Research Training Fellowships**
• **Research and Training Fellowships for Clinicians**

TYPE:
Fellowships. Awards offer qualified individuals the opportunity to develop expertise in clinical epilepsy research through a one-year clinical training experience and involvement in a clinical epilepsy research project. Research may be either basic or clinical, but there must be an equal emphasis on clinical training and clinical epileptology.

The Postdoctoral Research Fellowships are intended to develop academic physicians and scientists committed to research related to epilepsy. The program emphasizes individuals who will be trained in research in epilepsy rather than those who use epilepsy as a tool for research in other fields. Applications will be considered equally from individuals interested in acquiring experience either in basic laboratory research or in the conduct of human clinical studies.

The Predoctoral Research Training Fellowship proposes to support predoctoral students with dissertation research related to epilepsy, thus strengthening their interest in establishing epilepsy research as a career direction. Applications from all fields of epilepsy research, from basic to human, are encouraged.

The Research and Training Fellowships for Clinicians aim to develop academic clinicians to teach patient care of persons with epilepsy and advance knowledge about epilepsy through research. Applications will be considered equally from individuals interested in acquiring experience in the conduct of human clinical studies and who plan to study epilepsy as a human disorder. Research projects may be in the area of basic laboratory research or clinical research; however, there must be a substantial clinical training component of the program. Emphasis is placed on individuals who will be trained in research in epilepsy rather than use epilepsy as a tool in their research in other fields.

YEAR PROGRAM STARTED: 1981

LEGAL BASIS:
Private foundation.

GEOGRAPHIC RESTRICTIONS:
United States.

FINANCIAL DATA:
Amount of support per award: Postdoctoral Research Fellowships: $45,000 stipend; Predoctoral Research Training Fellowships: $20,000 stipend; Research and Training Fellowships for Clinicians: $50,000 stipend.

NUMBER OF APPLICANTS MOST RECENT YEAR: 125.

NUMBER OF AWARDS: 30.

APPLICATION INFORMATION:
Application forms and guidelines are available online.
Duration: One year.

THE GRASS FOUNDATION [2465]
P.O. Box 241458
Los Angeles, CA 90024
(424) 832-4188
Fax: (310) 986-2252

E-MAIL ADDRESS:
info@grassfoundation.org

WEB SITE ADDRESS:
www.grassfoundation.org

FOUNDED: 1955

AREAS OF INTEREST:
Research and education in neuroscience.

NAME(S) OF PROGRAMS:
• **Grass Fellowships in Neuroscience**

TYPE:
Fellowships; Research grants. Summer research support for independent research projects in neurobiology at the Marine Biological Laboratories, Woods Hole, MA.

YEAR PROGRAM STARTED: 1955

PURPOSE:
To encourage young investigators in the field of neurobiology.

LEGAL BASIS:
Private foundation.

ELIGIBILITY:
Applicants must be late predoctoral or early postdoctoral investigators who are qualified in neurobiological research. Preference will be given to applicants with no more than three years postdoctoral and with no prior research experience at MBL. Fellow must have proper visa.

FINANCIAL DATA:
The Grass Foundation pays traveling expenses, reasonable living expenses while at MBL and certain laboratory costs. There is a modest drawing account for personal expenses. Expenses of the spouse or domestic partner and dependent children are likewise paid.

APPLICATION INFORMATION:
Application materials may be obtained from the Foundation's web site.
Duration: 14 weeks.
Deadline: December 10. Announcement in January.

SELECTION COMMITTEE:
Catherine E. Carr, Ph.D.
Graeme W. Davis, Ph.D.
Bernice Grafstein, Ph.D.
Henry J. Grass, M.D.
Gregory L. Holmes, M.D.
Ronald R. Hoy, Ph.D.
Kamran Khodakhah, Ph.D.
George M. Langford, Ph.D.
Richard Larkin, C.P.A.
Jeff Lichtman, Ph.D.
Edwin McCleskey, Ph.D.
Felix E. Schweizer, Ph.D.
Amy R. Segal, Esq.
Janis C. Weeks, Ph.D.
Steven J. Zottoli, Ph.D.

ADDRESS INQUIRIES TO:
Executive Assistant
(See address above.)

HUNTINGTON'S DISEASE SOCIETY OF AMERICA, INC. [2466]
505 Eighth Avenue, Suite 902
New York, NY 10018
(212) 242-1968
Fax: (212) 239-3430

E-MAIL ADDRESS:
hdsainfo@hdsa.org

WEB SITE ADDRESS:
www.hdsa.org

FOUNDED: 1967

AREAS OF INTEREST:
Research into Huntington's disease.

NAME(S) OF PROGRAMS:
• **HD Human Biology Project**
• **Huntington's Disease Research**
• **Donald King Summer Research Fellowship**

TYPE:
Fellowships; Research grants.

YEAR PROGRAM STARTED: 1986

PURPOSE:
To support and stimulate research into the cause, prevention and treatment of Huntington's disease.

LEGAL BASIS:
Nonprofit, tax-exempt voluntary health agency.

FINANCIAL DATA:
Amount of support per award: Varies.
Total amount of support: Varies.

APPLICATION INFORMATION:
Application information is available on the web site.
Duration: One or two years. Nonrenewable.

Deadline: Letter of Intent must be received by May 23. Full application deadline is July 31.

PUBLICATIONS:
Annual report; application guidelines; *Toward a Cure*; *The Marker*.

IRS IDENTIFICATION NUMBER: 13-3349872

TRUSTEES:
Steven Seekins, Chairperson
Jang-Ho Cha, M.D., Ph.D., Chairperson-Elect
Larry Fisher, Treasurer
Theresa Hughes, Secretary
Donald L. Barr
Hugh DeLoayza
Samuel Frank, M.D.
Michelle Gray, Ph.D.
Steve Ireland
Barbara Jacobs
Arik Johnson, Psy.D.
Rob Millum
Arvind Sreedharan
Leon D. Tibben
Daniel S. Vandivort
Roger A. Vaughan

ADDRESS INQUIRIES TO:
George Yohrling, Director of Medical and Scientific Affairs
(See address above.)

THE MCKNIGHT ENDOWMENT FUND FOR NEUROSCIENCE   [2467]
The McKnight Foundation
710 South Second Street, Suite 400
Minneapolis, MN 55401
(612) 333-4220
Fax: (612) 332-3833

E-MAIL ADDRESS:
info@mcknight.org

WEB SITE ADDRESS:
www.neuroscience.mcknight.org

FOUNDED: 1986

AREAS OF INTEREST:
Neuroscience.

NAME(S) OF PROGRAMS:
● **McKnight Neuroscience Scholar Award**

TYPE:
Awards/prizes; Research grants.

PURPOSE:
To encourage neuroscientists in the early stages of their careers to focus on disorders of learning and memory.

LEGAL BASIS:
Nonprofit.

ELIGIBILITY:
Applicants must hold an M.D. and/or Ph.D. degree, have completed formal postdoctoral training and be in the early stages of an independent research career. Applicants should show evidence of a commitment to a continuing career in neuroscience and be in a tenured or tenure-track position.

GEOGRAPHIC RESTRICTIONS:
United States.

FINANCIAL DATA:
Awards are made to the sponsoring institution.
Amount of support per award: $75,000 per year.

NUMBER OF APPLICANTS MOST RECENT YEAR: 45.

NUMBER OF AWARDS: Up to 6 annually.

APPLICATION INFORMATION:
Application forms and guidelines are available September 15.
Duration: Three years.
Deadline: Early January. Announcement by mid-May.

OFFICER:
Kate Wolford, President

ADDRESS INQUIRIES TO:
Eileen Mahler, Program Manager
(See address above.)

MONTREAL NEUROLOGICAL INSTITUTE   [2468]
3801 University Street
Room 636
Montreal QC H3A 2B4 Canada
(514) 398-1903
(514) 398-5205
Fax: (514) 398-8248

E-MAIL ADDRESS:
viviane.poupon@mcgill.ca

WEB SITE ADDRESS:
www.mni.mcgill.ca

FOUNDED: 1934

AREAS OF INTEREST:
Neurology, neurosurgery and neuroscience.

NAME(S) OF PROGRAMS:
● **Jeanne Timmins Costello Fellowships**
● **Preston Robb Fellowship**

TYPE:
Exchange programs; Fellowships. Awards for research and study in the fields of clinical and basic neurosciences.

PURPOSE:
To provide the recipient with the experience of going from laboratory bench to the patient's bedside by exploiting the strengths of the Institute in basic and clinical science.

LEGAL BASIS:
University, research institute.

ELIGIBILITY:
For the Costello Fellowship, candidates must have an M.D. or Ph.D. degree. Those candidates with M.D. degrees will ordinarily have completed clinical studies in neurology or neurosurgery. Research themes at the MNI include neuroanatomy, neurochemistry, neurogenetics, molecular genetics, neuroimaging, neuroimmunology, epilepsy, neuromuscular disease, neuro-oncology, molecular and cellular biology and neuropsychology.

For the Robb Fellowship, candidates must have an M.D. degree with clinical studies in neurology or neurosurgery.

FINANCIAL DATA:
Amount of support per award: $40,000 per year.

NUMBER OF AWARDS: Jeanne Timmins Costello Fellowships: 4; Preston Robb Fellowship: 1.

APPLICATION INFORMATION:
Application form and guidelines are available online from August 1 to October 31.
Duration: One year. Renewal possible for one additional year.
Deadline: October 31.

PUBLICATIONS:
Annual report.

ADDRESS INQUIRIES TO:
Viviane Poupon
Associate Director, Scientific Affairs
(See address above.)

MULTIPLE SCLEROSIS SOCIETY OF CANADA   [2469]
175 Bloor Street East
Suite 700, North Tower
Toronto ON M4W 3R8 Canada
(416) 922-6065
Fax: (416) 922-7538

E-MAIL ADDRESS:
msresearchgrants@mssociety.ca

WEB SITE ADDRESS:
www.mssociety.ca

FOUNDED: 1948

AREAS OF INTEREST:
Neurology, immunology, virology, pathology and biochemistry.

NAME(S) OF PROGRAMS:
● **Research Studentship**

TYPE:
Research grants. Studentships offered at the Master's and Ph.D. levels.

PURPOSE:
To find the cause and cure of multiple sclerosis.

LEGAL BASIS:
Charitable organization.

ELIGIBILITY:
Applicant must be a Canadian citizen, landed immigrant, or person holding a Canadian student visa who is going to school at a recognized Canadian research institute, or a Canadian citizen or landed immigrant who is going to school at a recognized foreign research institute.

FINANCIAL DATA:
Amount of support per award: Master's: $18,000 (CAN) per year; Ph.D.: $20,000 (CAN) per year.
Total amount of support: Varies.

APPLICATION INFORMATION:
Applications are only accepted online.
Duration: One year beginning July 1. Renewal possible for up to three additional years.
Deadline: October 1. Announcement the following March 1.

ADDRESS INQUIRIES TO:
Research and Programs Department
(See e-mail address above.)

MULTIPLE SCLEROSIS SOCIETY OF CANADA   [2470]
175 Bloor Street East
Suite 700, North Tower
Toronto ON M4W 3R8 Canada
(416) 922-6065
Fax: (416) 922-7538

E-MAIL ADDRESS:
msresearchgrants@mssociety.ca

WEB SITE ADDRESS:
www.mssociety.ca

FOUNDED: 1948

AREAS OF INTEREST:
Neurology, immunology, virology, pathology and biochemistry.

NAME(S) OF PROGRAMS:
- **Biomedical Research Grants**
- **Clinical and Population Health Research Grants**

TYPE:
Research grants.

PURPOSE:
To find the cause and cure of multiple sclerosis.

LEGAL BASIS:
Charitable organization.

ELIGIBILITY:
Applicants must carry out research at a recognized Canadian research institute (e.g., university or hospital).

FINANCIAL DATA:
Amount of support per award: $10,000 to $100,000 (CAN) average per year.

Total amount of support: Varies.

APPLICATION INFORMATION:
Applications are only accepted online.

Duration: Up to three years, beginning April 1.

Deadline: October 1. Announcement the following March 1.

ADDRESS INQUIRIES TO:
Research and Programs Department
(See e-mail address above.)

MULTIPLE SCLEROSIS SOCIETY OF CANADA   [2471]

175 Bloor Street East
Suite 700, North Tower
Toronto ON M4W 3R8 Canada
(416) 922-6065
Fax: (416) 922-7538

E-MAIL ADDRESS:
msresearchgrants@mssociety.ca

WEB SITE ADDRESS:
www.mssociety.ca

FOUNDED: 1948

AREAS OF INTEREST:
Neurology, immunology, virology, pathology and biochemistry.

NAME(S) OF PROGRAMS:
- **Postdoctoral Fellowship**

TYPE:
Fellowships.

PURPOSE:
To find the cause and cure of multiple sclerosis.

LEGAL BASIS:
Charitable organization.

ELIGIBILITY:
Applicant must be a Canadian citizen, landed immigrant or person holding a Canadian student visa who is working at a recognized Canadian research institute, or a Canadian citizen or landed immigrant who is working at a recognized foreign research institute.

FINANCIAL DATA:
Amount of support per award: $39,000 (CAN) per year.

Total amount of support: Varies.

APPLICATION INFORMATION:
Applications are only accepted online.
Duration: One year beginning July 1. Renewal possible for an additional two years.
Deadline: October 1. Announcement the following March 1.

ADDRESS INQUIRIES TO:
Research and Programs Department
(See e-mail address above.)

MULTIPLE SCLEROSIS SOCIETY OF CANADA   [2472]

175 Bloor Street East
Suite 700, North Tower
Toronto ON M4W 3R8 Canada
(416) 922-6065
Fax: (416) 922-7538

E-MAIL ADDRESS:
msresearchgrants@mssociety.ca

WEB SITE ADDRESS:
www.mssociety.ca

FOUNDED: 1948

AREAS OF INTEREST:
Neurology, immunology, virology, pathology and biochemistry.

NAME(S) OF PROGRAMS:
- **Donald Paty Career Development Awards**

TYPE:
Training grants. Funding for the salary of an investigator starting his or her career as an independent researcher.

PURPOSE:
To find the cause and cure of multiple sclerosis.

LEGAL BASIS:
Charitable organization.

ELIGIBILITY:
Candidates must hold the award at a recognized Canadian research institute (e.g., university or hospital).

FINANCIAL DATA:
Amount of support per award: $50,000 (CAN) per year.

Total amount of support: Varies.

APPLICATION INFORMATION:
Applications are only accepted online.
Duration: Normally awarded for three years, beginning July 1.
Deadline: October 1. Announcement the following March 1.

ADDRESS INQUIRIES TO:
Research and Programs Department
(See e-mail address above.)

MUSCULAR DYSTROPHY ASSOCIATION   [2473]

3300 East Sunrise Drive
Tucson, AZ 85718
(520) 529-2000
Fax: (520) 529-5494

E-MAIL ADDRESS:
grants@mdausa.org

WEB SITE ADDRESS:
www.mdausa.org

FOUNDED: 1950

AREAS OF INTEREST:
Research into diseases of the neuromuscular system.

NAME(S) OF PROGRAMS:
- **Neuromuscular Disease Research**

TYPE:
Research grants; Training grants. Translational Research Grants. Basic scientific and clinical research grants are offered.

MDA supports research into diseases of the neuromuscular system to develop effective treatments for the muscular dystrophies and related diseases which include spinal muscular atrophy and other motor neuron diseases, inflammatory myopathies, metabolic myopathies, diseases of the neuromuscular junction, certain peripheral neuropathies and basic research increasing general knowledge in the neuromuscular field.

YEAR PROGRAM STARTED: 1950

PURPOSE:
To find the causes of, and treatments for, neuromuscular diseases.

LEGAL BASIS:
Nonprofit, voluntary health agency.

ELIGIBILITY:
An applicant must be a professional or faculty member at an appropriate educational, medical or research institution and be qualified to conduct and supervise a program of original research, have access to institutional resources necessary to conduct the proposed research project and hold a Doctor of Medicine, Doctor of Philosophy, Doctor of Science or equivalent degree.

Proposals from applicants outside the U.S. will be considered only for projects of highest priority to MDA and when, in addition to the applicant's having met the eligibility requirements noted above, one or more of the following conditions exist: the applicant's country of residence has inadequate sources of financial support for biomedical research, collaboration with an MDA-supported U.S. investigator is required to conduct the project, or an invitation to submit an application has been extended by MDA.

FINANCIAL DATA:
Funding levels for Primary Research Grants are unlimited. Overhead limited to a maximum of 10% of the total direct costs of the grant requested.

Amount of support per award: Development Grants: Up to $60,000 per year.

Total amount of support: Varies.

NUMBER OF APPLICANTS MOST RECENT YEAR: 600.

NUMBER OF AWARDS: Approximately 90.

APPLICATION INFORMATION:
Guidelines are available on the web site.

Duration: One, two or three years.

Deadline: For Neuromuscular Disease Research, applications must be requested by December 15 and submitted by January 15 for funding to commence the following August 1. Applications must be requested by June 15 and submitted by July 15 for funding to commence the following February 1.

STAFF:
Steven Derks, President and Chief Executive Officer
Valerie A. Cwik, M.D., Executive Vice President and Chief Medical and Scientific Officer
Pete Morgan, Executive Vice President and Chief Operations Officer
Julie Faber, Chief Financial Officer

ADDRESS INQUIRIES TO:
Research Department
(See address above.)

MYASTHENIA GRAVIS FOUNDATION OF AMERICA, INC. [2474]

355 Lexington Avenue
15th Floor
New York, NY 10017
(800) 541-5454
Fax: (212) 370-9047

E-MAIL ADDRESS:
mgfa@myasthenia.org

WEB SITE ADDRESS:
www.myasthenia.org

FOUNDED: 1952

AREAS OF INTEREST:
Myasthenia gravis and related neuromuscular conditions.

CONSULTING OR VOLUNTEER SERVICES:
Nationwide Chapter Network.

NAME(S) OF PROGRAMS:
● Nurses Research Fellowship

TYPE:
Fellowships; Research grants. Awards for research pertaining to problems faced by myasthenia gravis patients.

YEAR PROGRAM STARTED: 1988

PURPOSE:
To create an effective communications, service and human relations network for myasthenics, their families and friends; to educate both the lay and professional community about myasthenia gravis; to stimulate and support scientific inquiry, interchange and research in the quest for improved treatment techniques and a cure.

LEGAL BASIS:
Nonprofit corporate foundation.

ELIGIBILITY:
Candidates must be currently licensed as registered professional nurses. Fellowships are limited to U.S. or Canadian citizens or holders of bona fide permanent visas for training in U.S. institutions.

FINANCIAL DATA:
Amount of support per award: Up to $5,000.

NUMBER OF APPLICANTS MOST RECENT YEAR: 1.

NUMBER OF AWARDS: 1.

APPLICATION INFORMATION:
Candidates should submit four copies of cover letter stating that he or she is applying for the Nurses Research Fellowship, proposed budget, curriculum vitae, research proposal and letters of approval to conduct research by appropriate parties (i.e., institution, physicians and educational facilities).
Duration: One year.
Deadline: April 1.

PUBLICATIONS:
Guidelines.

IRS IDENTIFICATION NUMBER: 13-5672224

ADDRESS INQUIRIES TO:
Tor Holtan, Chief Executive Officer
(See address above.)

NATIONAL ATAXIA FOUNDATION [2475]

2600 Fernbrook Lane, Suite 119
Minneapolis, MN 55447
(763) 553-0020
Fax: (763) 553-0167

E-MAIL ADDRESS:
susan@ataxia.org

WEB SITE ADDRESS:
www.ataxia.org

FOUNDED: 1957

AREAS OF INTEREST:
Cause and treatment of ataxia.

NAME(S) OF PROGRAMS:
● National Ataxia Foundation Fellowship Award
● National Ataxia Foundation Pioneer SCA Translational Research Award
● National Ataxia Foundation Research Grant Program
● National Ataxia Foundation Young Investigator Award and Young Investigator Award for SCAs

TYPE:
Fellowships; Research grants; Seed money grants. Young investigator award.

YEAR PROGRAM STARTED: 1978

PURPOSE:
To support research into hereditary and sporadic ataxia, as well as treatment, services, and education of the disorder.

LEGAL BASIS:
Nonprofit 501(c)(3) organization.

ELIGIBILITY:
Individuals and organizations, including religious, can apply.

FINANCIAL DATA:
Amount of support per award: Fellowship Award: Up to $35,000; Pioneer SCA Translational Research Award: $100,000; Research Grant Program: Up to $30,000; Young Investigator Award: $35,000; Young Investigator Award for SCAs: $50,000.
Total amount of support: $1,000,000 for the fiscal year 2013.

NUMBER OF APPLICANTS MOST RECENT YEAR: 55.

NUMBER OF AWARDS: 24 for the year 2014.

APPLICATION INFORMATION:
Letter of Intent must be submitted one month prior to application deadlines.
Duration: Pioneer SCA Translational Award and Young Investigator Award: One year. Research Grant and Research Fellowship: One year. Renewals by reapplication each year for continuing support.
Deadline: Pioneer SCA Translational Award and Research Fellowship: September 15; Research Grant: August 15; Young Investigator: September 2.

PUBLICATIONS:
Annual report; application guidelines.

IRS IDENTIFICATION NUMBER: 41-0832903

ADDRESS INQUIRIES TO:
Susan Hagen, Patient Services Director
(See address above.)

NATIONAL HEADACHE FOUNDATION

820 North Orleans, Suite 411
Chicago, IL 60610-3132
(312) 274-2650
(888) 643-5552
Fax: (312) 640-9049

E-MAIL ADDRESS:
info@headaches.org

WEB SITE ADDRESS:
www.headaches.org

TYPE:
Research grants. Support for research in the field of headache and pain.

See entry 2368 for full listing.

NATIONAL INSTITUTE OF NEUROLOGICAL DISORDERS AND STROKE [2476]

Building 31, Room 8A34
9000 Rockville Pike
Bethesda, MD 20892
(301) 435-7726
Fax: (301) 402-6276

E-MAIL ADDRESS:
frushouk@ninds.nih.gov

WEB SITE ADDRESS:
www.ninds.nih.gov

FOUNDED: 1950

AREAS OF INTEREST:
Neurological disorders, including multiple sclerosis and amyotrophic lateral sclerosis, movement disorders, such as the dystonias and Tourette's syndrome and degenerative and dementing disorders such as Parkinson's, Huntington's and Alzheimer's diseases, stroke, spinal cord injury, neural regeneration and plasticity, coma, chronic pain, head injury, traumatic brain injury, peripheral nerve injury, tumors of the nervous system, brain edema and manipulative therapy, and convulsive, developmental and neuromuscular disorders.

NAME(S) OF PROGRAMS:
● NINDS Extramural Research Grants

TYPE:
Assistantships; Conferences/seminars; Fellowships; Project/program grants; Research grants; Training grants; Research contracts. Support for research, including neurological science basic research, which explores the fundamental structure and function of the brain and the nervous system, research to understand the causes and origins of pathological conditions of the nervous system with the goal of prevention of these disorders, research on the natural course of neurological disorders, research training in the basic neurological sciences and mechanisms associated with stroke and other cerebrovascular disorders, effects of trauma to the nervous system, neuroplasticity and regeneration and tumors of neural and sensory tissues.
Research may include:
(1) improved methods of disease prevention;
(2) new methods of diagnosis and treatment;
(3) clinical trials;
(4) drug development;
(5) development of neural prostheses for stroke and paraplegia;
(6) epidemiological research and;
(7) research training in the clinical sciences.

PURPOSE:
To support research on neurological diseases and stroke.

LEGAL BASIS:
PHS Act, Section 301, Section 431 and Section 433; Public Law 78-410, as amended; (42 U.S.C. 241), (42 U.S.C. 289C). PHS Act, Section 472; Public Law 78-410, as amended; (42 U.S.C. 289L-1).

ELIGIBILITY:
Research grants are available to any public or private nonprofit university, college, hospital, laboratory, or other institution, including state and local units of government, or to any individual. National Research Service Awards for the above areas may be made to individuals or to nonfederal public and private nonprofit institutions for the training of individuals at the pre- and postdoctoral levels.

FINANCIAL DATA:
Grants may be used for any usual research expenses including salaries, equipment supplies, travel to scientific meetings, patient care, publications, etc.
Amount of support per award: Approximately $380,000.
Total amount of support: $1.4 billion for extramural for the year 2012.

NUMBER OF AWARDS: Approximately 4,000 for fiscal year 2012.

APPLICATION INFORMATION:
Application forms may be requested from the Division of Research Grants, National Institutes of Health, Bethesda, MD 20892.
Duration: One to five years. Renewal applications may be submitted.
Deadline: November 1, March 1, and July 1. Awards are announced throughout the year.

ADDRESS INQUIRIES TO:
Director, Division of Extramural Activities NINDS, NIH MSC 9531
6001 Executive Boulevard
Rockville, MD 20892

NATIONAL MULTIPLE SCLEROSIS SOCIETY   [2477]
733 Third Avenue
New York, NY 10017-3288
(212) 476-0462
Fax: (212) 986-7981

E-MAIL ADDRESS:
jennifer.stark@nmss.org

WEB SITE ADDRESS:
www.nationalmssociety.org

FOUNDED: 1946

AREAS OF INTEREST:
Multiple sclerosis.

NAME(S) OF PROGRAMS:
- **Postdoctoral Fellowships Program in Multiple Sclerosis Research**

TYPE:
Fellowships. Postdoctoral fellowships for advanced training leading to an academic career involving clinical or fundamental research related to multiple sclerosis.

YEAR PROGRAM STARTED: 1955

PURPOSE:
To support investigators for whom further assistance may be critical in obtaining the training required for a research or academic career, or for whom the additional training will increase research or teaching potential in areas related to multiple sclerosis.

LEGAL BASIS:
Voluntary health agency, tax status 501(c)(3).

ELIGIBILITY:
Qualified investigators holding a doctoral-level degree in medicine or appropriate biological fields are eligible to apply. Candidates must select their own

training institutions and make all necessary arrangements for the conduct of proposed training or study program. Awards are based upon the applicant's professional status, training and experience.

FINANCIAL DATA:
Candidates must request all funds required.
Amount of support per award: Varies.

NUMBER OF APPLICANTS MOST RECENT YEAR:
47 for the year 2013.

NUMBER OF AWARDS: 13 for the year 2013.

APPLICATION INFORMATION:
Before submitting a proposal for fellowship support, the investigator may consult the Research Programs Department by phone or e-mail to determine whether the research plan is appropriate and relevant to the mission of the Society.
Duration: Up to three years.
Deadline: Mid-August.

OFFICERS OF THE BOARD:
Eli Rubenstein, Chairman
Cynthia Zagieboylo, President and Chief Executive Officer
Jim Cantalupo, Treasurer
Linda McAleer, Secretary

ADDRESS INQUIRIES TO:
Jennifer Stark, Ph.D.
Director of Research Training Programs
(See telephone and e-mail address above.)

NATIONAL MULTIPLE SCLEROSIS SOCIETY   [2478]
Research Programs
733 Third Avenue
New York, NY 10017-3288
(212) 986-3240
Fax: (212) 986-7981

E-MAIL ADDRESS:
research@nmss.org

WEB SITE ADDRESS:
www.nationalmssociety.org

FOUNDED: 1946

AREAS OF INTEREST:
Multiple sclerosis.

NAME(S) OF PROGRAMS:
- **National Multiple Sclerosis Society Research Grants Program**

TYPE:
Fellowships; Research grants; Training grants. Grants for fundamental or applied research in scientific areas pertinent to multiple sclerosis. Grants are available for clinical or nonclinical studies, providing they show a reasonable relevance to the Society's interests.

YEAR PROGRAM STARTED: 1947

PURPOSE:
To support research into the cause, prevention, alleviation and cure of multiple sclerosis.

LEGAL BASIS:
Voluntary health agency, tax status 501(c)(3).

ELIGIBILITY:
Qualified investigators affiliated with appropriate institutions are eligible to apply. Institutions are the official recipients of grants.

FINANCIAL DATA:
The principal investigator and the grantee institution will be advised of the exact

amount and duration of the grant award. Grant funds may be requested for professional and nonprofessional personnel, permanent equipment, consumable supplies, travel and other expenditures and indirect costs.
Amount of support per award: Varies.

NUMBER OF APPLICANTS MOST RECENT YEAR:
600 for the year 2013.

NUMBER OF AWARDS: 130 for the year 2013.

APPLICATION INFORMATION:
Before submitting a proposal for research support, investigators must submit pre-application online to determine whether the research plan is appropriate and relevant to the Society's goals.
Duration: Maximum of five years.
Deadline: August 1 and early February.

OFFICERS OF THE BOARD:
Eli Rubenstein, Chairman
Cynthia Zagieboylo, President and Chief Executive Officer
Jim Cantalupo, Treasurer
Linda McAleer, Secretary

ADDRESS INQUIRIES TO:
Bruce Bebo, Ph.D.
Associate Vice President of Discovery Research
Tel: (212) 476-0477
E-mail: bruce.bebo@nmss.org

NEUROSURGERY RESEARCH AND EDUCATION FOUNDATION   [2479]
5550 Meadowbrook Drive
Rolling Meadows, IL 60008
(847) 378-0500
(888) 566-AANS
Fax: (847) 378-0600

E-MAIL ADDRESS:
nref@aans.org

WEB SITE ADDRESS:
www.nref.org

FOUNDED: 1982

AREAS OF INTEREST:
Neurosurgery.

NAME(S) OF PROGRAMS:
- **Research Fellowships**
- **Young Clinician Investigator Award**

TYPE:
Awards/prizes; Fellowships; Research grants.

YEAR PROGRAM STARTED: 1983

PURPOSE:
To advance the neurosciences.

LEGAL BASIS:
Private foundation.

ELIGIBILITY:
Applicants for the Research Fellowship must be M.Ds. who have been accepted into or who are in an approved residency training program in neurological surgery in North America.

Applicants for the Young Clinician Investigator Award must be neurosurgeons who are full-time faculty in North American teaching institutions in the early years of their careers. Those who accept grants from other sources for the same project are ineligible.

GEOGRAPHIC RESTRICTIONS:
North America.

FINANCIAL DATA:
Amount of support per award: $40,000.

NUMBER OF APPLICANTS MOST RECENT YEAR:
75.

NUMBER OF AWARDS: 10 for the year 2013-14.

APPLICATION INFORMATION:
Applicants must provide a proposal, budget, a current curriculum vitae and three letters of reference. Electronic applications are accepted.
Duration: One year beginning July 1.
Deadline: Approximately October 31. Call for exact deadline. Announcement by end of March.

ADDRESS INQUIRIES TO:
See e-mail address above.

PARKINSON'S DISEASE FOUNDATION, INC.   [2480]
1359 Broadway, Suite 1509
New York, NY 10018
(212) 923-4700
(800) 457-6676
Fax: (212) 923-4778

E-MAIL ADDRESS:
vholt@pdf.org
grants@pdf.org

WEB SITE ADDRESS:
www.pdf.org

FOUNDED: 1957

AREAS OF INTEREST:
Basic and clinical research toward finding the cause and cure for Parkinson's disease.

CONSULTING OR VOLUNTEER SERVICES:
Information and referral service to Parkinson's disease patients and caregivers; counseling.

NAME(S) OF PROGRAMS:
- **Conference Awards**
- **PDF-PSG Mentored Clinical Research Award**

TYPE:
Conferences/seminars; Research grants.

ELIGIBILITY:
Conference Awards: Open to independent investigators, both nationally and internationally, possessing postdoctoral training or a medical degree (or the equivalent). The Award supports gatherings of experts in the field in order to address emerging clinical or basic science questions about Parkinson's. Award is not open to postdoctoral researchers or fellows.

PDF-PSG Mentored Clinical Research Award: Clinicians and scientists who are within five years of having completed formal training. Fellows may apply. Applicants must identify an appropriate mentor or mentors with extensive research experience. Either the applicant or the mentor must be a member of the PSG. An applicant may have co-mentors.

FINANCIAL DATA:
Amount of support per award: Conference Awards: Average award $10,000, with a maximum of $15,000. PDF-PSG Mentored Clinical Research Award: $75,000 per year.

COOPERATIVE FUNDING PROGRAMS: PDF-PSG Mentored Clinical Research Award is funded by a grant from the PDF to the Parkinson Study Group (PSG).

APPLICATION INFORMATION:
Conference Awards: Review program requirements and apply.

PDF-PSG Mentored Clinical Research Award: Review program overview and instructions, and apply directly to the PSG via e-mail to Roseanna.Battista@ctcc.rochester.edu.
Duration: Conference Awards: Up to one year. PDF-PSG Mentored Clinical Research Award: One year.
Deadline: Conference Awards: Proposals are due by 5 P.M. on November 1. PDF-PSG Mentored Clinical Research Award: March 23.

ADDRESS INQUIRIES TO:
Valerie Holt, Executive Assistant and Research Grants Administrator or James Beck, Ph.D., Research Director
(See address above.)

PARKINSON'S DISEASE FOUNDATION, INC.   [2481]
1359 Broadway, Suite 1509
New York, NY 10018
(212) 923-4700
Fax: (212) 923-4778

E-MAIL ADDRESS:
bvernaleo@pdf.org
grants@pdf.org

WEB SITE ADDRESS:
www.pdf.org

FOUNDED: 1957

AREAS OF INTEREST:
Basic and clinical research toward finding the cause and cure for Parkinson's disease.

CONSULTING OR VOLUNTEER SERVICES:
Information and referral service to Parkinson's disease patients and caregivers.

NAME(S) OF PROGRAMS:
- **International Research Grants Award**
- **Postdoctoral Fellowship**

TYPE:
Fellowships; Research grants.

YEAR PROGRAM STARTED: 1990

PURPOSE:
To help establish an independent laboratory research program in Parkinson's disease.

LEGAL BASIS:
Nonprofit organization.

FINANCIAL DATA:
The Postdoctoral Fellowship does not pay indirect or overhead costs and requires the grant recipient to account for all expenditures. The second year's funding is dependent upon submission of a satisfactory report covering the first year's work.
Amount of support per award: International Research Grants Award: Up to $75,000, plus 10% indirect expenses; Postdoctoral Fellowships: Up to $42,500 for basic science or up to $55,000 for clinical neurology, plus $5,000 research allowance.
Total amount of support: Approximately $1,000,000.

NUMBER OF APPLICANTS MOST RECENT YEAR:
200.

NUMBER OF AWARDS: 9.

APPLICATION INFORMATION:
Applications must be submitted online. Applicants for the Postdoctoral Fellowship must also submit the investigator's curriculum vitae, an outline of work to be undertaken and a detailed budget.

Duration: Fellowships: One year. Renewal competitively possible for up to two years for basic scientists or second year for clinical neurologists.
Deadline: Deadlines are posted on the Foundation web site.

PUBLICATIONS:
Annual reports; research reports; application guidelines.

ADDRESS INQUIRIES TO:
Research
(See address above.)

PARKINSON'S DISEASE FOUNDATION, INC.   [2482]
1359 Broadway, Suite 1509
New York, NY 10018
(212) 923-4700
(800) 457-6676
Fax: (212) 923-4778

E-MAIL ADDRESS:
bvernaleo@pdf.org
grants@pdf.org

WEB SITE ADDRESS:
www.pdf.org

FOUNDED: 1957

AREAS OF INTEREST:
Basic and clinical research toward finding the cause and cure for Parkinson's disease.

CONSULTING OR VOLUNTEER SERVICES:
Information and referral service to Parkinson's disease patients and caregivers; counseling.

NAME(S) OF PROGRAMS:
- **Summer Student Fellowship**

TYPE:
Fellowships. Supports medical students and undergraduates for study under the supervision of an established investigator.

YEAR PROGRAM STARTED: 2002

PURPOSE:
To seek the cause and cure of Parkinson's disease.

LEGAL BASIS:
Nonprofit organization.

ELIGIBILITY:
Undergraduate, graduate and medical students are eligible.

FINANCIAL DATA:
Amount of support per award: $4,000.
Total amount of support: $40,000.

NUMBER OF APPLICANTS MOST RECENT YEAR:
36.

NUMBER OF AWARDS: 15 for the year 2012.

APPLICATION INFORMATION:
Application information is available on the web site.
Duration: 10 weeks.
Deadline: Varies.

PUBLICATIONS:
Annual reports; research reports; application guidelines and forms.

BOARD OF DIRECTORS:
Howard D. Morgan, Chairman of the Board
Constance Woodruff Atwell, Ph.D., Vice Chairman
Robin Anthony Elliott, President
Stephen Ackerman, Treasurer
Isobel Robins Konecky, Secretary
Stanley Fahn, M.D., Scientific Director

DIRECTORS:
 Karen Elizabeth Burke, M.D., Ph.D.
 Margo Catsimatidis
 Peter Dorn
 George Pennington Egbert, III
 Richard D. Field
 Sara Belk Gambrell
 Stephanie Goldman-Pittel
 Arlene Levine
 Marshall Loeb
 Thomas A. Palizzi
 Timothy A. Pedley, M.D.
 Gregory Romero
 Lewis P. Rowland, M.D.
 Marie Schwartz
 Domna Stanton, Ph.D.
 Melvin S. Taub
 Martin Tuchman

ADDRESS INQUIRIES TO:
 Beth A. Vernaleo, Ph.D.
 Senior Manager, Research Programs or
 James Beck, Ph.D.
 Vice President, Scientific Affairs
 (See address above.)

TOURETTE SYNDROME ASSOCIATION, INC.   [2483]

42-40 Bell Boulevard
Suite 205
Bayside, NY 11361-2820
(718) 224-2999
Fax: (718) 279-9596

E-MAIL ADDRESS:
 ts@tsa-usa.org

WEB SITE ADDRESS:
 www.tsa-usa.org/research.html

FOUNDED: 1972

AREAS OF INTEREST:
 Education, research and services relating to
 Tourette Syndrome and relevant scientific
 fields, such as biochemistry, neuroanatomy,
 neurophysiology, genetics, molecular biology,
 epidemiology, psychiatry, psychology,
 neuropsychology, neurology, neuroimaging,
 neuropathology, pharmacology and/or animal
 models.

NAME(S) OF PROGRAMS:
 ● **Tourette Syndrome Research
   Fellowships**
 ● **Tourette Syndrome Research Grants**

TYPE:
 Fellowships; General operating grants;
 Research grants; Seed money grants;
 Technical assistance. Research grants
 available for Ph.D. and M.D. researchers in
 the following categories:
 (1) proposals in basic neuroscience
 specifically relevant to Tourette Syndrome
 and;
 (2) clinical studies related to the etiology,
 pathophysiology and treatment of Tourette
 Syndrome.

 Fellowships provide one-year postdoctoral
 training.

YEAR PROGRAM STARTED: 1984

PURPOSE:
 To support significant basic and clinical
 research in Tourette Syndrome.

LEGAL BASIS:
 Not-for-profit organization.

ELIGIBILITY:
 Open to Ph.D. and M.D. investigators from
 all areas of science who can contribute to the
 understanding of the genetics, pathogenesis,

pathophysiology and the treatment of
Tourette Syndrome. Investigators already
studying Tourette Syndrome and those
currently working in areas of science that can
be applied to the problems of Tourette
Syndrome are invited to apply.

FINANCIAL DATA:
 These designated award levels can include
 indirect costs no greater than 10%. However,
 the total grant award cannot exceed $75,000
 for a one-year research grant or $150,000 for
 a two-year award.

 Amount of support per award: Research
 grants: Up to $75,000 for one year or up to
 $150,000 for two years. Fellowships: Up to
 $40,000 for one year.

 Total amount of support: Varies.

NUMBER OF APPLICANTS MOST RECENT YEAR:
 36.

NUMBER OF AWARDS: 10.

REPRESENTATIVE AWARDS:
 $40,000 to Deanna Greene, Ph.D.,
 Washington University School of Medicine,
 St. Louis, MO, for "Pathophysiological
 Markers in the 'Pre-Tourette' Population;"
 $150,000 to Izhar Bar-Gad, Ilan University,
 Ramat-Gan, Israel, for "Interaction of the
 Dopaminergic and GABAergic Systems in
 the Formation of Tics."

APPLICATION INFORMATION:
 Application information is available on the
 web site.

 For preliminary screening, a preproposal is
 required. The approximate project funding
 level should be included. Inquirers will be
 informed as to whether to proceed with a full
 application.

 Duration: One or two years.

 Deadline: Preproposals are due in early
 September each year. Final proposals are due
 in November each year. Awards are
 announced in March.

PUBLICATIONS:
 Brochure.

OFFICERS:
 Michael Wolff, Chairperson
 Rovena Schirling, First Vice Chairperson
 Bruce Ochsman, Second Vice Chairperson
 Alice Kane, Third Vice Chairperson
 Cindy Kurtz, Fourth Vice Chairperson
 Frederick Cook, Finance Committee
 Chairperson
 Marcie Kirkpatrick, Secretary

ADVISORY BOARD:
 Tamara Hershey, Ph.D., Co-Chairperson
 Jonathan W. Mink, M.D., Ph.D.,
 Co-Chairperson
 Adam R. Aron, Ph.D.
 Erika Augustine, M.D.
 Nicole Calakos, M.D., Ph.D.
 Robert Chen, M.A., M.B.B. Chir
 Joseph Garner, Ph.D.
 Denise Head, Ph.D.
 Ellen Hess, Ph.D.
 Peggy Nopoulos, M.D.
 Laurie Ozelius, Ph.D.
 Rosalinda Roberts, Ph.D.
 Jeremiah Scharf, M.D., Ph.D.
 Tristram H. Smith, Ph.D.

ADDRESS INQUIRIES TO:
 Heather Cowley, Ph.D., Manager
 Medical and Scientific Programs
 (See address above.)

Nursing

AMERICAN ASSOCIATION FOR THE HISTORY OF NURSING, INC.   [2484]

10200 West 44th Avenue
Suite 304
Wheat Ridge, CO 80033
(303) 422-2685
Fax: (303) 422-8894

E-MAIL ADDRESS:
 dstumph@resourcenter.com

WEB SITE ADDRESS:
 www.aahn.org

FOUNDED: 1978

AREAS OF INTEREST:
 Nursing historical research.

NAME(S) OF PROGRAMS:
 ● **Competitive Student Research Award**
 ● **Postdoctoral Award to Honor the
   Nurse Cadet Corps**

TYPE:
 Awards/prizes; Research grants. Research
 awards.

PURPOSE:
 To encourage and support research in nursing
 history.

ELIGIBILITY:
 Competitive Student Research Award:
 Student must be an AAHN member enrolled
 in an accredited Master's or doctoral
 program. Proposals must focus on a
 significant question in the history of nursing
 and the research advisor will be doctorally
 prepared with scholarly activity in the field
 of nursing history and prior experience in
 guidance of research training.

 Postdoctoral Award: Applicant must be an
 AAHN member with a doctoral degree.
 Proposals will be judged for scholarly merit
 and significance to the field of nursing
 history.

FINANCIAL DATA:
 Amount of support per award: Competitive
 Student Research Award: $2,000;
 Postdoctoral Award: $3,000.

 Total amount of support: $5,000.

NUMBER OF APPLICANTS MOST RECENT YEAR: 8
to 12.

NUMBER OF AWARDS: 3.

APPLICATION INFORMATION:
 Contact the Association.

 Deadline: Spring.

ADDRESS INQUIRIES TO:
 David L. Stumph, IOM, CAE
 (See address above.)

THE AMERICAN LEGION NATIONAL HEADQUARTERS   [2485]

P.O. Box 1055
Indianapolis, IN 46206
(317) 630-1323
Fax: (317) 630-1369

E-MAIL ADDRESS:
 scholarships@legion.org

WEB SITE ADDRESS:
 www.legion.org

FOUNDED: 1919

NAME(S) OF PROGRAMS:
- **Eight and Forty Lung and Respiratory Disease Nursing Scholarship Fund**

TYPE:
Scholarships. Grants for registered nurses.

YEAR PROGRAM STARTED: 1957

PURPOSE:
To allow registered nurses to further their education at the graduate level in the area of pediatric lung and respiratory diseases.

ELIGIBILITY:
Applicant must be a registered nurse, in adequate health and a U.S. citizen. Applicant must also have freedom to pursue full-time employment, have qualities of leadership and be able to attend classes full- or part-time at an accredited school of nursing.

FINANCIAL DATA:
Amount of support per award: Up to $5,000.

NUMBER OF APPLICANTS MOST RECENT YEAR:
43.

APPLICATION INFORMATION:
Application forms may be obtained from the address above.
Duration: One school year.
Deadline: May 15. Announcement July 1.

PUBLICATIONS:
Brochure.

ADDRESS INQUIRIES TO:
Eight and Forty Scholarships
(See address above.)

AMERICAN NURSES FOUNDATION [2486]
8515 Georgia Avenue
Suite 400
Silver Spring, MD 20910
(301) 628-5227
Fax: (301) 628-5354

E-MAIL ADDRESS:
anf@ana.org

WEB SITE ADDRESS:
www.givetonursing.org

FOUNDED: 1955

AREAS OF INTEREST:
Nursing research.

NAME(S) OF PROGRAMS:
- **Nursing Research Grants**

TYPE:
Research grants.

YEAR PROGRAM STARTED: 1955

PURPOSE:
To support research conducted by nurse investigators.

LEGAL BASIS:
Not-for-profit corporation under Section 501(c)(3) of the Internal Revenue Code.

ELIGIBILITY:
Applicant must be an R.N. with a minimum of a Baccalaureate degree in nursing.

FINANCIAL DATA:
Total funding is dependent, in part, on the participation of external sponsors.
Amount of support per award: Varies.
Total amount of support: Varies.

NUMBER OF APPLICANTS MOST RECENT YEAR:
Varies.

NUMBER OF AWARDS: Varies.

APPLICATION INFORMATION:
The application packet is available online beginning February 1.
Duration: One year.
Deadline: May 1. Award announcement: August 31.

PUBLICATIONS:
Annual report; newsletter; research publications.

BOARD OF TRUSTEES:
Joyce Fitzpatrick, Chairperson
Timothy Porter-O'Grady, Vice Chairperson

ADDRESS INQUIRIES TO:
Kate Judge, Executive Director
(See address above.)

*PLEASE NOTE:
Some of the grants are restricted to a particular field of study.

ASSOCIATION OF WOMEN'S HEALTH, OBSTETRIC AND NEONATAL NURSES (AWHONN) [2487]
2000 L Street, N.W.
Suite 740
Washington, DC 20036
(202) 261-2400
Fax: (202) 728-0575

E-MAIL ADDRESS:
researchprograms@awhonn.org

WEB SITE ADDRESS:
www.awhonn.org

FOUNDED: 1969

AREAS OF INTEREST:
Women's health, obstetrics, neonatal nursing, newborns, nursing profession, advocacy, research and clinical resources for nurses.

NAME(S) OF PROGRAMS:
- **AWHONN Research Grants Program**

TYPE:
Research grants.

YEAR PROGRAM STARTED: 1993

PURPOSE:
To promote the advancement of nursing research among members.

ELIGIBILITY:
Applicant must be current member at the time of application and at time of selection and funding. Researchers who are currently principal investigators on a federally funded grant, or who have received an AWHONN-funded research grant within the past five years are ineligible to apply.

GEOGRAPHIC RESTRICTIONS:
United States.

FINANCIAL DATA:
Amount of support per award: $5,000 to $10,000.

NUMBER OF APPLICANTS MOST RECENT YEAR:
11 for the year 2012.

NUMBER OF AWARDS: 3 for the year 2012.

REPRESENTATIVE AWARDS:
Hill-Rom, Celeste Phillips Family-Centered Maternity Care Award; March of Dimes Margaret Comerford Freda "Saving Babies, Together®" Award; Every Woman, Every Baby Novice Researcher Award.

APPLICATION INFORMATION:
Application information is available on the web site.

Duration: One year.
Deadline: December 1.

PUBLICATIONS:
Journal of Obstetric, Gynecologic and Neonatal Nursing; Nursing for Women's Health.

ADDRESS INQUIRIES TO:
Research Programs
(See e-mail address above.)

THE CANADIAN LUNG ASSOCIATION (CLA) [2488]
1750 Courtwood Crescent
Suite 300
Ottawa ON K2C 2B5 Canada
(613) 569-6411 ext. 262
Fax: (613) 569-8860

E-MAIL ADDRESS:
research@lung.ca

WEB SITE ADDRESS:
www.lung.ca/crhp-pcsr/research-recherche_e.php

FOUNDED: 1977

AREAS OF INTEREST:
Respiratory health.

NAME(S) OF PROGRAMS:
- **The Canadian Respiratory Health Professionals Fellowships and Grants**

TYPE:
Fellowships; Research grants. Fellowships are offered to registered nurses pursuing postgraduate education with a major component of the program involving respiratory nursing practice, physiotherapists pursuing postgraduate training with respiratory research as the major component, and respiratory therapists pursuing postgraduate education with a major component of the program involving respiratory therapy practice.

Grants for research and feasibility studies are offered to registered nurses undertaking research investigations related to nursing management of patients with respiratory disease and symptoms. Grants are also offered to physiotherapists undertaking investigations related to management of patients with respiratory disease. Respiratory therapists undertaking research investigations related to the management of patients with respiratory disease and symptoms may also qualify.

PURPOSE:
To build research capacity in respiratory health; to support research excellence; to assist future researchers in their professional development in congruence with the mission of the Association; to increase the number of nurses with expertise in the clinical practice of respiratory nursing and as leaders in advancing knowledge, which will result in improved quality of care in respiratory nursing.

LEGAL BASIS:
Not-for-profit, incorporated.

ELIGIBILITY:
For Fellowships, an applicant must be a Canadian citizen or a permanent Canadian resident, a Registered Nurse, Registered Physiotherapist or Registered Respiratory Therapist, be enrolled or accepted for full-time studies in a graduate program at the Master's or Doctorate level and be a member of CRHP.

For Research Grants, the principal investigator must be a Canadian citizen or a permanent Canadian resident, a Registered Nurse, a Registered Physiotherapist or Registered Respiratory Therapist, hold an appointment in, or have an affiliation with, a health care agency, education institution, or other organization in Canada that can administer the funds in an approved manner and be a member of CRHP.

FINANCIAL DATA:
Amount of support per award: Varies.
Total amount of support: Varies.

NUMBER OF APPLICANTS MOST RECENT YEAR:
Approximately 12.

NUMBER OF AWARDS: Approximately 8 each year.

APPLICATION INFORMATION:
Application information is available on the web site.
Duration: One year.
Deadline: Contact the Foundation for exact dates.

PUBLICATIONS:
Brochure; newsletters.

OFFICERS:
Dr. Dina Brooks, Chairperson, CRHP Leadership Council
Mika Nonoyama, CRHP Research Committee Co-chair

ADDRESS INQUIRIES TO:
The Canadian Respiratory Health Professionals
c/o Michelle McEvoy
The Canadian Lung Association
(See address above.)

FOUNDATION FOR NEONATAL RESEARCH AND EDUCATION (FNRE) [2489]
East Holly Avenue
P.O. Box 56
Pitman, NJ 08071-0056
(856) 256-2343
Fax: (856) 589-7463

E-MAIL ADDRESS:
contact@fnre.com

WEB SITE ADDRESS:
ajj.com/fnre

FOUNDED: 1984

AREAS OF INTEREST:
Neonatal nursing.

TYPE:
Research grants; Scholarships.

YEAR PROGRAM STARTED: 1992

PURPOSE:
To support research and education in neonatal nursing.

LEGAL BASIS:
Nonprofit.

ELIGIBILITY:
Members of the FNRE Research Review Committee and the FNRE Board members are not eligible for research grants.

Applicant must be principal investigator of the project. If the principal investigator has limited research experience, it is expected that the application will reflect appropriate nursing research consultation.

GEOGRAPHIC RESTRICTIONS:
United States.

FINANCIAL DATA:
Amount of support per award: Varies.
Total amount of support: Varies.

NUMBER OF AWARDS: 1 to 2.

APPLICATION INFORMATION:
Applications must include the application form, budget, curriculum vitae/biographical sketch, abstract, a research plan, reference, appendices, IRB approval, and a conflict of interest disclosure.
Duration: One year. Extensions requested in writing may be granted.
Deadline: May 1. Award notifications will be mailed by September.

FOUNDATION OF THE NATIONAL STUDENT NURSES' ASSOCIATION, INC. [2490]
45 Main Street
Suite 606
Brooklyn, NY 11201-1075
(718) 210-0705
Fax: (718) 797-1186

E-MAIL ADDRESS:
lauren@nsna.org
nsna@nsna.org

WEB SITE ADDRESS:
www.nsna.org

FOUNDED: 1969

AREAS OF INTEREST:
Nursing education.

TYPE:
Scholarships. Scholarships based on academic achievement, financial need and involvement in nursing student organizations and community activities related to health care. Additional criteria may be required by some sponsors.

PURPOSE:
To provide aid to nursing students.

LEGAL BASIS:
501(c)(3) charitable foundation.

ELIGIBILITY:
Applicants must be U.S. citizens or students with an Alien Registration number. They must also be currently enrolled in state-approved schools of nursing or pre-nursing in Associate degree, Baccalaureate, diploma, generic Doctorate, and generic Master's programs. Funds are not available for graduate study unless it is for a first degree in nursing. Graduating high school seniors are not eligible. Monies are awarded in the spring to be used in the next academic year and summer school. Monies can only be used for nursing or pre-nursing in one of the above-mentioned programs. No monies can be used for graduate education unless leading to a first degree in nursing. If applicant is matriculating into a nursing program, letter of acceptance must accompany this application. Proof of enrollment will be required at time of award. Current Association Board of Directors and Association Nominating and Elections Committee members are not eligible.

FINANCIAL DATA:
Amount of support per award: Scholarships: $1,000 to $2,500.
Total amount of support: Over $125,000 annually in the general scholarship program.

NUMBER OF APPLICANTS MOST RECENT YEAR:
600.

NUMBER OF AWARDS: 200.

APPLICATION INFORMATION:
Applications can be completed online at the NSNA web site from August until the following January. Each completed application, when filed, must be accompanied by a $10 processing fee.

Applicants must submit a copy of their recent nursing school and college transcripts, or grade report. NSNA members must submit proof of their membership. Registered nurses in Baccalaureate programs and licensed practical/vocational nurses in programs leading to registered nurse licensure must submit a copy of their license to be considered for the Career Mobility Scholarships.
Duration: One year. Scholarships are awarded in the spring.
Deadline: January.

ADDRESS INQUIRIES TO:
Lauren Sperle
Scholarship Program Committee
(See address above.)

*PLEASE NOTE:
The scholarships are based on academic achievement, financial need, and involvement in nursing student organizations and community activities related to health care. Additional criteria may be required by some sponsors.

INDEPENDENCE FOUNDATION [2491]
Offices at the Bellevue
200 South Broad Street, Suite 1101
Philadelphia, PA 19102
(215) 985-4009
Fax: (215) 985-3989

E-MAIL ADDRESS:
ssherman@independencefoundation.org

WEB SITE ADDRESS:
www.independencefoundation.org

FOUNDED: 1932

AREAS OF INTEREST:
Community-based, nurse-managed health care, health promotion, family planning and comprehensive health care services where issues of quality, access and cost are taken into consideration; culture, arts and legal aid and assistance to the disadvantaged; visual and performing arts.

NAME(S) OF PROGRAMS:
- **Individual Artists Fellowship/Performing and Visual Arts**
- **New Theater Works Initiative**
- **Public Interest Law Fellowships**

TYPE:
Challenge/matching grants; Fellowships; General operating grants; Project/program grants.

YEAR PROGRAM STARTED: 1993

PURPOSE:
To encourage and support nursing; to have a valuable impact on the quality of health care services; to strengthen nursing education's focus on community-based care in both Philadelphia and surrounding Pennsylvania counties.

LEGAL BASIS:
Private foundation.

ELIGIBILITY:
No grants to individuals.

GEOGRAPHIC RESTRICTIONS:
Philadelphia and four surrounding counties of Bucks, Chester, Delaware and Montgomery.

FINANCIAL DATA:
Unaudited net assets of $70,000,000 for the year ended December 31, 2013.

Amount of support per award: Average: $3,000 to $10,000; Multiyear: Up to $100,000.

Total amount of support: $3,346,174 in unaudited grants for the year ended December 31, 2013.

Matching fund requirements: Match of contributions by individual new donors or increase in contributions by current individual donors (nongovernmental/nonfoundation funds).

NUMBER OF AWARDS: 128.

REPRESENTATIVE AWARDS:
Culture and the Arts: $5,000 to Headlong Dance Theater, Philadelphia, PA, for general operating support; Health and Human Services: $10,000 to Overbrook School for the Blind, Philadelphia, PA, for project support; Public Interest Law: $10,000 to Homeless Advocacy Project, Philadelphia, PA, for general operating support.

APPLICATION INFORMATION:
Each year the Foundation sends out RFP (Requests for Proposal) under the following categories: Nurse Managed Health Care Initiatives, Health and Human Services, Legal Aid Initiatives, Culture and Arts Initiatives, Public Interest Law Fellowship Program and Individual Artist Fellowship Program.

Contact the Foundation for the RFP packets and submission deadlines, or see web site.

Duration: Varies.

Deadline: Letters of Inquiry are accepted January 1 to January 31. Deadlines vary.

PUBLICATIONS:
Annual report; application guidelines.

IRS IDENTIFICATION NUMBER: 23-1352110

DIRECTORS AND OFFICERS:
Hon. Phyllis W. Beck, Chairperson
Susan E. Sherman, President and Chief Executive Officer
Andre Dennis, Esq., Vice President
Pedro A. Ramos, Esq., Director
Barton Silverman, Director
Andrea Mengel, Secretary

ADDRESS INQUIRIES TO:
Susan E. Sherman
President and Chief Executive Officer
(See address above.)

MYASTHENIA GRAVIS FOUNDATION OF AMERICA, INC.
355 Lexington Avenue
15th Floor
New York, NY 10017
(800) 541-5454
Fax: (212) 370-9047

E-MAIL ADDRESS:
mgfa@myasthenia.org

WEB SITE ADDRESS:
www.myasthenia.org

TYPE:
Fellowships; Research grants. Awards for research pertaining to problems faced by myasthenia gravis patients.

See entry 2474 for full listing.

NATIONAL BLACK NURSES ASSOCIATION, INC.   [2492]
8630 Fenton Street
Suite 330
Silver Spring, MD 20910
(301) 589-3200
Fax: (301) 589-3223

E-MAIL ADDRESS:
info@nbna.org

WEB SITE ADDRESS:
www.nbna.org

AREAS OF INTEREST:
HIV/AIDS, cardiovascular disease, women and children's health, cancer, substance abuse, diabetes, obesity, and violence in African American communities.

NAME(S) OF PROGRAMS:
● **Reverend Pauline L. Cole Scholarship**
● **Esther Colliflower/VITAS Scholarship**
● **Dr. Martha A. Dawson Genesis Nurse Leader Scholarship**
● **Maria Dudley Scholarship**
● **Martha R. Dudley Scholarship**
● **Sheila Haley Scholarship**
● **Rita E. Miller Scholarship**
● **NBNA Board of Directors Scholarship**
● **Margaret Pemberton Scholarship**
● **Della H. Raney Nursing Scholarship**
● **Dr. Lauranne Sams Scholarship**
● **United Health Foundation Scholarship**

TYPE:
Scholarships.

PURPOSE:
To advance nursing practice, improve health care for all Americans, particularly the unserved and the underserved, and shape health policy for the access and delivery of health care services.

LEGAL BASIS:
Nonprofit professional association.

ELIGIBILITY:
Awards are given primarily to African Americans enrolled at any level in a nursing program (AD, BSN or LPN/LVN). Applicant must be in good standing at the time of application and be a member of NBNA.

GEOGRAPHIC RESTRICTIONS:
United States.

FINANCIAL DATA:
Amount of support per award: $1,000 to $5,000.

NUMBER OF APPLICANTS MOST RECENT YEAR:
60.

NUMBER OF AWARDS: 25.

APPLICATION INFORMATION:
Applicant must submit completed scholarship application form. The following items (not to exceed 10 pages) must be included:
(1) two letters of recommendation; letters from the school of nursing and a nurse in the area will suffice for candidates who have no local chapter in the area;
(2) head shot photo; if not included, application will be deemed not ready;
(3) official transcript from school;
(4) one-page biographical sketch and;
(5) two-page statement on why applicant wants to become a nurse.

Duration: One year. Nonrenewable.

Deadline: April 15. Awards are presented at the July/August conference.

BOARD OF DIRECTORS:
Dr. Deidre Walton, President

ADDRESS INQUIRIES TO:
E-mail: millicent@nbna.org or
Scholarships Committee
(See address above.)

NATIONAL INSTITUTE OF NURSING RESEARCH   [2493]
31 Center Drive, Room 5B-10
Bethesda, MD 20892-2178
(301) 496-0207
Fax: (301) 480-4969

E-MAIL ADDRESS:
info@ninr.nih.gov

WEB SITE ADDRESS:
www.ninr.nih.gov

FOUNDED: 1986

AREAS OF INTEREST:
Health of individuals, families, communities and populations.

CONSULTING OR VOLUNTEER SERVICES:
For potential principal investigators.

NAME(S) OF PROGRAMS:
● **Career Development Grants**
● **Research Grants**
● **Research Training Grants**
● **Small Business Innovation Research Grants**

TYPE:
Fellowships; Project/program grants; Research grants; Training grants. Funds may be used for salaries, consultation, equipment, travel and other usual costs, subject to federal regulations applicable to the grant. Fellowships are for postdoctoral research training; predoctoral support is also available.

YEAR PROGRAM STARTED: 1986

PURPOSE:
To support nursing research, research training at pre- and postdoctoral levels, and research related to patient care, the promotion of health, the prevention of disease and the mitigation of the effects of acute and chronic illnesses and disabilities.

LEGAL BASIS:
Public Health Service Act, Sections 301, 483, 484, and 487, as amended by Public Law 99-158.

ELIGIBILITY:
Applicant may be a for-profit organization, a nonprofit organization, a public or private institution such as a university, college, hospital and laboratory, a unit of state government, a unit of local government, an eligible agency of the federal government, a foreign institution, a domestic institution, a faith-based or community-based organization, an Indian/Native American tribal government (federally recognized), an Indian/Native American tribal government (other than federally recognized), or an Indian/Native American tribally designated organization.

FINANCIAL DATA:
Amount of support per award: Varies based on type of grant and duration.

Total amount of support: Varies.

COOPERATIVE FUNDING PROGRAMS: Co-funding of research project grants with other NIH Institutes and Centers.

APPLICATION INFORMATION:
See web site for complete information.

Duration: Varies.

Deadline: Applications are accepted at any time for inclusion in one of the three annual review cycles (depending on the activity code).

PUBLICATIONS:
Investigators' publications.

STAFF:
Brian Albertini, Grants Manager

ADDRESS INQUIRIES TO:
Melissa Barrett, Communications Director
(See address above.)

NATIONAL SOCIETY DAUGHTERS OF THE AMERICAN REVOLUTION [2494]
1776 D Street, N.W.
Washington, DC 20006-5303
(202) 879-3292
Fax: (202) 879-3348

E-MAIL ADDRESS:
scholarships@dar.org

WEB SITE ADDRESS:
www.dar.org

FOUNDED: 1895

AREAS OF INTEREST:
Nursing.

NAME(S) OF PROGRAMS:
- **Madeline Pickett Cogswell Nursing Scholarship**
- **Caroline E. Holt Nursing Scholarship**

TYPE:
Scholarships. Awarded to students who are enrolled or currently attending an accredited school of nursing.

PURPOSE:
To provide ways and means to help students to attain higher education; to perpetuate the memory and spirit of men and women who achieved American Independence by acquisition and protection of historical spots and erection of monuments; to carry out injunction of Washington in his farewell address to the American people; to maintain institutions of American Freedom; to aid liberty.

LEGAL BASIS:
Incorporated historical society.

ELIGIBILITY:
Scholarships are awarded without regard to race, religion, sex or national origin. Candidates must be U.S. citizens and must attend an accredited college or university in the U.S. Awards are judged on the basis of academic excellence, commitment to field of study, as required, and financial need.

Applicants for the Cogswell Nursing Scholarship must be members, descendents of members or eligible for membership in NSDAR. DAR member number must be on the application.

No affiliation or relationship to DAR is required for qualification for the Holt Nursing Scholarship, but candidate must be sponsored by a local DAR Chapter.

GEOGRAPHIC RESTRICTIONS:
United States.

FINANCIAL DATA:
Amount of support per award: $1,000.
Total amount of support: Varies.

NUMBER OF AWARDS: Varies.

APPLICATION INFORMATION:
Application information is available online. The application package must be completed. All transcripts, letters of recommendation and other required documents must be in a single package.

Included with the application packet is the list of DAR State Scholarship Chairmen. All scholarship applicants are required to have a letter of sponsorship from a chapter. Individuals interested in obtaining a letter of sponsorship from a local chapter are encouraged to contact the DAR State Chairman.
Duration: One academic year. Nonrenewable.
Deadline: February 15.

PUBLICATIONS:
American Spirit, magazine.

ADDRESS INQUIRIES TO:
Office of the Reporter General
DAR Scholarship Committee
(See address above.)

*PLEASE NOTE:
Awards are placed on deposit with the college or university. Any unused portion shall be returned to the National Society.

NATIONAL SOCIETY DAUGHTERS OF THE AMERICAN REVOLUTION
1776 D Street, N.W.
Washington, DC 20006-5303
(202) 879-3292

WEB SITE ADDRESS:
www.dar.org

TYPE:
Scholarships.

See entry 2298 for full listing.

NURSES' EDUCATIONAL FUNDS, INC. [2495]
304 Park Avenue South, 11th Floor
New York, NY 10010
(212) 590-2443
Fax: (212) 590-2446

E-MAIL ADDRESS:
info@n-e-f.org

WEB SITE ADDRESS:
www.n-e-f.org

FOUNDED: 1912

AREAS OF INTEREST:
Graduate nursing studies.

TYPE:
Scholarships. Scholarships for registered nurses seeking Master's and Doctorate degrees in nursing.

YEAR PROGRAM STARTED: 1912

PURPOSE:
To increase the supply of nurses qualified for administrative, supervisory, teaching or research positions and clinical specialization in nursing.

LEGAL BASIS:
Private foundation.

ELIGIBILITY:
Registered nurses who are U.S. citizens, or who have officially declared intention of becoming citizens, are eligible to apply if they have been accepted into a Master's program, or applying to a Master's program of nursing education accredited by NLNAC

or CCNE, or enrolled full-time or part-time in a doctoral program in a field related to nursing. Applicants must be able to present proof of membership in a professional nursing association.

GEOGRAPHIC RESTRICTIONS:
United States.

FINANCIAL DATA:
Amount of support per award: Scholarships vary in amount, according to the funds available.
Total amount of support: Varies.

NUMBER OF APPLICANTS MOST RECENT YEAR:
50.

NUMBER OF AWARDS: Varies.

APPLICATION INFORMATION:
Official application materials are available upon request to the NEF or can be downloaded from the web site.
Duration: One academic year. Can reapply for one additional year.
Deadline: February 1.

BOARD OF DIRECTORS:
Susan Bowar-Ferres, Ph.D., R.N., President
Cynthia Sculco, R.N., Ed.D, Vice President
Joan Arnold, Ph.D., R.N., Treasurer
Rosanne Raso, M.S., R.N., Secretary
Allison Adams, B.A., B.S.
Thomas Adams, B.S., B.A.
Karen Ballard, M.A., R.N.
Vincent Batyr, C.P.A.
Hattie Bessent, Ed.D., R.N.
Kathleen Dirschel, Ph.D., R.N.
Aida Egues, D.N.P., R.N.
M. Louise Fitzpatrick, Ed.D., R.N.
Barbara R. Heller, Ed.D., R.N.
Margaret McClure, Ed.D., R.N.
Thelma Schorr, B.S.N., R.N.
Roy L. Simpson
Henry Spencer
Daniel M. Suarez, M.A., R.N.
Madeleine S. Sugimoto, M.Ed., R.N.
Kathryn Swintek
Judith Ann Vessey, Ph.D., R.N.
Jerelyn Peixoto Weiss, M.S., R.N.

ADDRESS INQUIRIES TO:
Maria Tantillo, Director of Development and Scholarship Coordinator
(See address above.)

REHABILITATION NURSING FOUNDATION (RNF) [2496]
8735 West Higgins Road
Suite 300
Chicago, IL 60631
(847) 375-4710
(800) 229-7530
Fax: (847) 375-6435

E-MAIL ADDRESS:
sfloutsakos@connect2amc.com

WEB SITE ADDRESS:
www.rehabnurse.org

FOUNDED: 1976

AREAS OF INTEREST:
Rehabilitation nursing.

NAME(S) OF PROGRAMS:
- **Evidence-based Practice (EBP) and Quality Improvement (QI) Project Grants**
- **RNF Fellow Research Grant**
- **RNF New Investigator Research Grant**
- **Sigma Theta Tau/RNF Research Grant**

TYPE:
Project/program grants; Research grants.

YEAR PROGRAM STARTED: 1988

PURPOSE:
To promote and advance professional rehabilitation nursing practice through education, advocacy, collaboration, and research to enhance the quality of life for those affected by disability and chronic illness.

ELIGIBILITY:
The principal investigator for the research project must be a registered nurse who is active in rehabilitation or who demonstrates interest in and significant contributions to rehabilitation nursing. Graduate student researchers are eligible for funding.

FINANCIAL DATA:
Amount of support per award: Evidence-based Practice (EBP) and Quality Improvement (QI) Fellow Grant: $2,500; EBP/QI New Investigator Award: $1,500; RNF Fellow Research Grant and RNF New Investigator Research Grant: $10,000; Sigma Theta Tau/RNF Research Grant: $4,500.

NUMBER OF APPLICANTS MOST RECENT YEAR: 8.

NUMBER OF AWARDS: RNF Fellow Research Grant: Up to 2; Others: 1 each.

APPLICATION INFORMATION:
Proposals must be typed and electronically submitted to the e-mail address above. All applicants must:
(1) complete a Summary Data Form;
(2) submit a typed, 250- to 350-word abstract defining the research or clinical problem, stating the significance of the research or EBP/QI project, and presenting the research or EBP/QI project methodology and plan for analysis;
(3) have the institution or agency named in the proposal complete the Administrative Approval Form to indicate acknowledgment and approval of the research or EBP/QI project;
(4) complete the Research Grant Checklist to verify inclusion of all required materials and include it as part of the application and;
(5) complete the Research Grant Contact Form regarding the contact person for the grant funding agreement and disbursement of funds should application be selected.

All forms and instructions can be downloaded from the web site.
Duration: Project must be completed within two years of initial funding.
Deadline: March 1.

ADDRESS INQUIRIES TO:
Susan Floutsakos, Manager
(See e-mail address above.)

SIGMA THETA TAU INTERNATIONAL [2497]

Honor Society of Nursing
550 West North Street
Indianapolis, IN 46202
(317) 634-8171 (Local)
(888) 634-7575 (U.S./Canada)
Fax: (317) 634-8188

E-MAIL ADDRESS:
research@stti.iupui.edu

WEB SITE ADDRESS:
www.nursingsociety.org

FOUNDED: 1922

AREAS OF INTEREST:
Nursing.

NAME(S) OF PROGRAMS:
- **Rosemary Berkel Crisp Research Award**
- **Doris Bloch Research Award**
- **Virginia Henderson Clinical Research Grant**
- **Small Grants**
- **Joan K. Stout, R.N., Research Grant**

TYPE:
Research grants.

YEAR PROGRAM STARTED: 1936

PURPOSE:
To encourage qualified nurses to contribute to the advancement of nursing through research.

LEGAL BASIS:
Incorporated.

ELIGIBILITY:
Applicants must meet the following requirements:
(1) be a registered nurse with a current license;
(2) hold a Master's or doctoral degree or be enrolled in a doctoral program;
(3) be ready to implement research project when funding is received and;
(4) complete the project within one year of funding.

For the Rosemary Berkel Crisp Research Award, applicant must be a member of Sigma Theta Tau International. Some preference will be given to applicants residing in Arkansas, Illinois, Kentucky, Missouri and Tennessee.

For the Virginia Henderson Clinical Research Grant, applicant must be a member of Sigma Theta Tau International and be actively involved in some aspect of health care delivery, education or research in a clinical setting.

FINANCIAL DATA:
Amount of support per award: $5,000 maximum.
Total amount of support: Varies.

NUMBER OF AWARDS: 10 to 15 Small Grants.

APPLICATION INFORMATION:
Application information is available on the web site.
Duration: For approved research time.
Deadline: Joan K. Stout, R.N., Research Grant: July 1. All others: December 1.

PUBLICATIONS:
Guidelines; applications.

ADDRESS INQUIRIES TO:
Grants Coordinator
(See address above.)

U.S. DEPARTMENT OF HEALTH AND HUMAN SERVICES [2498]

HRSA/BHPr, Division of Nursing
Parklawn Building, Room 9-89
5600 Fishers Lane
Rockville, MD 20857
(301) 443-5688
Fax: (301) 443-0791

WEB SITE ADDRESS:
www.bhpr.hrsa.gov/nursing

AREAS OF INTEREST:
Nursing education and practice.

TYPE:
Project/program grants; Training grants.

YEAR PROGRAM STARTED: 1965

PURPOSE:
To improve nursing practice and education through projects that increase the knowledge and skills of nursing personnel, enhance their effectiveness in primary care delivery, increase the number of qualified professional nurses and increase nursing workforce diversity.

LEGAL BASIS:
Amendment to Public Health Service Act, Title VIII, Section 820 by "The Health Professions Education Partnership Act of 1998" Public Law 105-392, Subtitle B.

ELIGIBILITY:
Eligible entities are schools of nursing, nursing centers, academic health centers, state or local governments, and other public or private nonprofit entities appropriate by the Secretary that submit an application in accordance with Section 802.

GEOGRAPHIC RESTRICTIONS:
United States.

FINANCIAL DATA:
Amount of support per award: Grants vary in amount, depending on the needs and nature of the project.
Total amount of support: Varies.

APPLICATION INFORMATION:
Contact the U.S. Department of Health and Human Services.
Duration: Varies according to project.

ADDRESS INQUIRIES TO:
Division of Nursing, BHPr/HRSA
Nursing Education Practice Quality and Retention Branch
(See address above.)

VIRGINIA DEPARTMENT OF HEALTH [2499]

Office of Minority Health and Health Equity
109 Governor Street, 10th Floor
Suite 1016-East
Richmond, VA 23219
(804) 864-7422
Fax: (804) 864-7440

E-MAIL ADDRESS:
incentiveprograms@vdh.virginia.gov

WEB SITE ADDRESS:
www.vdh.virginia.gov/healthpolicy

NAME(S) OF PROGRAMS:
- **Commonwealth of Virginia Nurse Educator Scholarship Program**
- **Mary Marshall Nursing Scholarship/Practical Nurse Program**
- **Mary Marshall Nursing Scholarship/Registered Nurse Program**
- **Nurse Practitioner/Nurse Midwife Scholarship Program**

TYPE:
Scholarships. Awarded to eligible students enrolled in undergraduate or graduate nursing programs at schools of nursing approved by the Virginia State Board of Nursing to assist with their professional education.

Undergraduate nursing programs are defined as those leading to a licensed practical nurse, an Associate degree, diploma, or Baccalaureate degree in nursing.

YEAR PROGRAM STARTED: 1950

PURPOSE:
To provide the citizens of the state with more skilled and greater nursing care coverage.

LEGAL BASIS:
Funding is appropriated by the General Assembly of Virginia under code 23-35.9-23-35.13; code 32.1-122.6-01; and Title 32.1, Chapter 6, 32.1-122.6-02.

ELIGIBILITY:
Criteria vary for the different scholarships. Because of the strict nature of these criteria, it is vital that the applicant contact the Department for full particulars.

GEOGRAPHIC RESTRICTIONS:
Virginia.

FINANCIAL DATA:
Amount of scholarships varies, depending upon amount appropriated by the General Assembly, amount collected by the Board of Nursing and the number of qualified applicants. There are strict conditions attached to these scholarships. (They are not outright gifts; require service in the Commonwealth of Virginia.)
Amount of support per award: Varies each year.

APPLICATION INFORMATION:
Applications are available online. Required data for application include most current transcript of grades (or last school attended if not currently enrolled), verification of need from the Financial Aid Officer and recommendation of the Director of the School of Nursing.
Duration: Each scholarship is awarded for a single year. Upon reapplication, scholarships may be awarded for succeeding years to a maximum of four years.

PUBLICATIONS:
Guidelines.

OFFICER:
Theresa Taylor, Director of the Division of Primary Care and Rural Health

ADDRESS INQUIRIES TO:
Nursing Scholarships
(See address above.)

Obstetrics and gynecology

CENTRAL ASSOCIATION OF OBSTETRICIANS AND GYNECOLOGISTS [2500]
15 North Main
Minot, ND 58703
(701) 838-8323
Fax: (701) 852-8733

E-MAIL ADDRESS:
rhickel@caog.org

WEB SITE ADDRESS:
www.caog.org

FOUNDED: 1929

AREAS OF INTEREST:
Obstetrics and gynecology, including investigative and/or clinical work.

NAME(S) OF PROGRAMS:
- **Annual Central Prize Award**
- **Central Poster Award**
- **Community Hospital Award**
- **FAR Research Network Award**
- **President's Certificate of Merit Award**
- **Young Investigator's Award**

TYPE:
Awards/prizes. The Annual Central Prize Award, President's Certificate of Merit Award and Central Poster Awards are presented annually for manuscripts demonstrating outstanding investigative or clinical work in the field of obstetrics and gynecology.

The Community Hospital Award is presented annually for clinical study or research in the field of obstetrics and gynecology to members located in community hospitals who are not full-time faculty in medical schools. Preference for this award will be given to papers concerning gynecologic endoscopy or any other diagnostic or therapeutic procedures which enhance the quality of care of gynecologic or obstetric patients.

The Young Investigator's Award is presented annually for clinical study or research in the field of obstetrics and gynecology to residents, fellows, and clinicians residing in the geographic confines of the Central Association.

YEAR PROGRAM STARTED: 1929

PURPOSE:
To encourage original work in obstetrics and gynecology.

LEGAL BASIS:
Nonprofit medical organization.

ELIGIBILITY:
Those eligible to compete are accredited physicians, teachers, research workers and medical students whose work was done within the geographic area of the Association.

For the Community Hospital Award, at least one author must be a member of the Central Association. Manuscripts must be written expressly for this competition and they must be original, not having been previously presented or published. Manuscripts will be considered for both the general program and the award unless the author specifically requests otherwise in writing.

GEOGRAPHIC RESTRICTIONS:
Alabama, Arizona, Arkansas, Colorado, Idaho, Illinois, Indiana, Iowa, Kansas, Kentucky, Louisiana, Michigan, Minnesota, Mississippi, Missouri, Montana, Nebraska, Nevada, New Mexico, North Dakota, Ohio, Oklahoma, South Dakota, Tennessee, Texas, Utah, West Virginia, Wisconsin and Wyoming.

FINANCIAL DATA:
Amount of support per award: Annual Central Prize Award: $2,000; Central Poster Award: $500 each; Community Hospital Award and FAR Research Network Award: $1,000; President's Certificate of Merit Award: $1,500; Young Investigator's Award: $750.

NUMBER OF APPLICANTS MOST RECENT YEAR:
50.

NUMBER OF AWARDS: Annual Central Prize Award, Community Hospital Award, FAR Research Network Award, President's Certificate of Merit, and Young Investigator's Award: 1 of each annually. Central Poster Award: 2 annually.

APPLICATION INFORMATION:
For consideration for these awards, an online abstract must be submitted. The abstract maximum length is 800 words.
Duration: One year. Nonrenewable.
Deadline: Mid-March each year. Award winners notified early May.

ADDRESS INQUIRIES TO:
Rochelle Hickel
(See address above.)

REPRODUCTIVE SCIENTIST DEVELOPMENT PROGRAM (RSDP) [2501]
Department of Obstetrics and Gynecology
Washington University, School of Medicine
BJC-IH, 10th Floor, Room 10631
425 South Euclid Avenue, Campus Box 8064
St. Louis, MO 63110
(314) 747-3598
Fax: (314) 747-0264

E-MAIL ADDRESS:
heflina@wudosis.wustl.edu

WEB SITE ADDRESS:
www.rsdp.wustl.edu/

FOUNDED: 1986

AREAS OF INTEREST:
Obstetric-gynecologic academic investigative careers in fundamental biomedical science.

NAME(S) OF PROGRAMS:
- **Reproductive Scientist Development Program**

TYPE:
Research grants. National career development program grant for full-time basic research under the mentorship of internationally recognized senior scientists.

YEAR PROGRAM STARTED: 1988

PURPOSE:
To train obstetrician-gynecologists committed to academic investigative careers in fundamental biomedical science.

ELIGIBILITY:
Candidates must be seeking a career in academic obstetrics and gynecology research and meet the following criteria:
(1) possess M.D. or D.O. degree;
(2) be a U.S. citizen, noncitizen national, verification as a permanent citizen at time of award;
(3) have completed a four-year internship and residency in obstetrics-gynecology approved by the Accreditation Council for Graduate Medical Education or the Royal College of Physicians and Surgeons of Canada and;
(4) submit a research proposal as part of application.

GEOGRAPHIC RESTRICTIONS:
United States.

FINANCIAL DATA:
Amount of support per award: Up to $125,000 for salary plus fringes and up to $25,000 for research support may be provided from NICHD funds for Phase I scholars.

Up to $100,000 for salary plus fringes and up to $25,000 for research support may be provided from NICHD funds for Phase II scholars. Phase II Scholars are also eligible to receive support from program sponsors of the RSDP Program. Award amounts vary.

NUMBER OF AWARDS: Up to 3 new positions are available each year.

APPLICATION INFORMATION:
Applicant must submit a Letter of Intent to the RSDP office indicating the name of the Department of Ob/Gyn sponsor, name and address of proposal scientific mentor, and a brief description of the research project. This will be reviewed by the Executive Committee for appropriateness, and feedback will be provided to potential applicants.
Duration: Two to five years of support is available.
Deadline: Letter of Intent: August 15. Application: October 1.

ADDRESS INQUIRIES TO:
Amanda Heflin, MBA
Project Administrator
(See address above.)

U.S. DEPARTMENT OF HEALTH AND HUMAN SERVICES   [2502]
Maternal and Child Health Bureau
Parklawn Building, Room 18-31
5600 Fishers Lane
Rockville, MD 20857
(301) 443-2204
Fax: (301) 443-9354

E-MAIL ADDRESS:
CallCenter@hrsa.gov (grants information)

WEB SITE ADDRESS:
www.mchb.hrsa.gov
www.hrsa.gov

FOUNDED: 1936

AREAS OF INTEREST:
Health of mothers and children.

NAME(S) OF PROGRAMS:
● **Maternal and Child Health Services Block Grant**

TYPE:
Block grants. The Title V Block Grant Program has as a general purpose the improvement of the health of all mothers and children in the nation. The Block Grant Program has three components: Formula Block Grants to 59 states and other political jurisdictions, Special Projects of Regional and National Significance (SPRANS), and Community Integrated Service Systems (CISS) Grants.

PURPOSE:
To improve the health of all mothers and children; to create federal-state partnerships to develop service systems in U.S. communities that can meet the critical challenges facing maternal and child health.

LEGAL BASIS:
Title V, Section 501, of the Social Security Act, as amended by Public Law 101-239.

ELIGIBILITY:
State health agencies.

GEOGRAPHIC RESTRICTIONS:
United States and its territories.

FINANCIAL DATA:
Amount of support per award: Grants vary in amount, depending upon the number of children at the poverty level in the state.
Total amount of support: Approximately $560,000,000.

Matching fund requirements: The Title V Block Grant Program requires that every four dollars of federal Title V money must be matched by at least three dollars of state and local money.

COOPERATIVE FUNDING PROGRAMS: NICHD, CDC, Department of Education, ADAMHA and other inter-agency agreements.

NUMBER OF AWARDS: 59.

APPLICATION INFORMATION:
Instructions available at grants.gov.
Duration: One to two years. Must reapply annually.
Deadline: July 15.

ADDRESS INQUIRIES TO:
Maternal and Child Health Bureau
(See address above.)

Ophthalmology and otolaryngology

THE ALCON FOUNDATION, INC.   [2503]
6201 South Freeway
Fort Worth, TX 76134-2099
(817) 293-0450

E-MAIL ADDRESS:
bettina.maunz@alcon.com

WEB SITE ADDRESS:
www.alcon.com

AREAS OF INTEREST:
Ophthalmology and vision care.

TYPE:
Project/program grants.

YEAR PROGRAM STARTED: 1962

PURPOSE:
To support programs designed to improve the quality of eye care and patient access to eye care, advance eye health education, research and awareness, and enhance and create sound communities where Alcon has a facility presence.

LEGAL BASIS:
Corporate foundation.

ELIGIBILITY:
Eligible organizations must be 501(c)(3) nonprofit entities. Grants are awarded for community activities of interest to Alcon employees in communities where Alcon has a facility. Generally, grants awarded outside of Alcon communities are for organizations with a national focus on eye care.

APPLICATION INFORMATION:
Only online application will be accepted.
Duration: One year.

ADDRESS INQUIRIES TO:
Bettina Maunz, Vice President, Global Head Communications
(See address above.)

AMERICAN ACADEMY OF OPTOMETRY   [2504]
2909 Fairgreen Street
Orlando, FL 32803
(321) 710-3937
Fax: (407) 893-9890

E-MAIL ADDRESS:
helenv@aaoptom.org

WEB SITE ADDRESS:
www.aaopt.org

FOUNDED: 1922

AREAS OF INTEREST:
Vision science and vision care.

NAME(S) OF PROGRAMS:
● **Julius F. Neumueller Award in Optics**

TYPE:
Awards/prizes.

YEAR PROGRAM STARTED: 1969

PURPOSE:
To advance optometric education in optics.

LEGAL BASIS:
Tax-exempt corporation.

ELIGIBILITY:
Applicant must be a student pursuing an O.D. degree in a school of optometry recognized by the AOA Council on Optometric Education.

GEOGRAPHIC RESTRICTIONS:
Primarily United States and Canada.

FINANCIAL DATA:
Amount of support per award: Approximately $750.
Total amount of support: Approximately $750 annually.

NUMBER OF APPLICANTS MOST RECENT YEAR: 10.

NUMBER OF AWARDS: 1.

APPLICATION INFORMATION:
Applicant must submit a paper, not to exceed 3,000 words, on Geometrical Optics, Physical Optics, Ophthalmic Optics or Optics of the Eye. Each school may submit two papers each year to the Chairman of the Awards Committee, which are judged by selected members of the American Academy of Optometry.
Duration: One-time award.
Deadline: April 2. Award announcement September 1.

ADDRESS INQUIRIES TO:
Helen Viksnins
Senior Director of Programs
(See address above.)

AMERICAN DIABETES ASSOCIATION
1701 North Beauregard Street
Alexandria, VA 22311
(703) 549-1500 ext. 2362
Fax: (703) 621-3759

E-MAIL ADDRESS:
grantquestions@diabetes.org

WEB SITE ADDRESS:
www.professional.diabetes.org/grants

TYPE:
Fellowships; Research grants; Training grants.

See entry 2403 for full listing.

AMERICAN OPTOMETRIC FOUNDATION   [2505]
2909 Fairgreen Street
Orlando, FL 32803
(321) 710-3936
Fax: (407) 893-9890

E-MAIL ADDRESS:
aof@aaoptom.org

WEB SITE ADDRESS:
www.aaopt.org/aof/programs

FOUNDED: 1947

AREAS OF INTEREST:
Optometric research and education.

NAME(S) OF PROGRAMS:
- **Award of Excellence**
- **J. Pat Cummings Fellowship**
- **William C. Ezell Fellowship**
- **Vistakon® Contact Lens Residency Award**
- **Vistakon® Pediatric Residency Award**

TYPE:
Awards/prizes; Fellowships; Project/program grants; Research grants; Scholarships. Scholarships for individuals pursuing an O.D. degree and fellowships for graduate students.

YEAR PROGRAM STARTED: 1952

PURPOSE:
To encourage teaching careers in optometry and to further vision research, both basic and clinical.

LEGAL BASIS:
IRS tax status 501(c)(3).

ELIGIBILITY:
Applicants must be postgraduate students (i.e., those who have received the Doctor of Optometry degree) and must be entering or continuing a full-time academic program toward the Master's or Ph.D. degree. They must also be planning on a career in teaching and/or research at an optometric school or college.

GEOGRAPHIC RESTRICTIONS:
Canada, Puerto Rico and United States.

FINANCIAL DATA:
Full fellowships are available in amounts of up to $8,000, plus travel grants to ARVO and American Academy of Optometry's annual meetings.
Amount of support per award: Varies.
Total amount of support: Varies.

NUMBER OF APPLICANTS MOST RECENT YEAR:
Ezell Fellowships: 46; Other awards: 30.

NUMBER OF AWARDS: 12.

APPLICATION INFORMATION:
Prospective applicants may obtain detailed information regarding application procedures from the optometric schools/colleges or the administrative offices of the AOF.
Duration: Fellowships are awarded for a period of one year and may be renewed two times. The maximum period of support for any one fellowship is three years.
Deadline: Varies.

PUBLICATIONS:
Application guidelines/criteria.

STAFF:
Lois Schoenbrun, C.A.E., FAAO, Executive Director, AAO
Greg Fulginiti, Development Director
Tracy Kitts, Coordinator for Administration of Programs

BOARD OF DIRECTORS AND OFFICERS:
Kathy Dumbleton, President
David Kirschen, President-Elect
Pete Kollbaum, Secretary-Treasurer
Catherine Amos
Judy Clay
Susan Eger
Wendy Harrison
Richard Madonna
Jason Nichols
Thomas Quinn
Jeffrey Walline
Karla Zadnik

AMERICAN SPEECH-LANGUAGE-HEARING FOUNDATION [2506]

2200 Research Boulevard
Rockville, MD 20850-3289
(301) 296-8703
Fax: (301) 296-8567

E-MAIL ADDRESS:
foundationprograms@asha.org

WEB SITE ADDRESS:
www.ashfoundation.org

FOUNDED: 1946

AREAS OF INTEREST:
Communication sciences and disorders.

NAME(S) OF PROGRAMS:
- **Clinical Research Grant**
- **Louis M. DiCarlo Award for Recent Clinical Achievement**
- **Graduate Student Scholarship for International/Minority Students**
- **Graduate Student Scholarship for Minority Students**
- **Graduate Student Scholarship for NSSLHA Members**
- **Graduate Student Scholarship for Students with a Disability**
- **Graduate Student Scholarships**
- **Frank R. Kleffner Clinical Career Award**
- **New Century Scholars Doctoral Scholarship**
- **New Century Scholars Research Grant**
- **New Investigators Research Grant**
- **Speech Science Research Grant**
- **Student Research Grant in Audiology**
- **Student Research Grant in Early Childhood Language Development**
- **Rolland J. Van Hattum Award for Contribution in the Schools**

TYPE:
Research grants; Scholarships. Clinical achievement awards. Clinical Research Grants are awarded to researchers to advance knowledge of the efficacy of treatment and assessment practices in communication sciences and disorders.

Louis M. DiCarlo Award for Clinical Achievement recognizes individuals demonstrating outstanding achievement in the advancement of knowledge in clinical practice within the past three years.

Graduate Student Scholarships are available to students demonstrating outstanding academic achievement in communication sciences and disorders. These include general scholarships, scholarships for students with disabilities, scholarships for international and minority students, and scholarships for NSSLHA members.

Frank R. Kleffner Clinical Career Award recognizes outstanding lifetime achievement in clinical science and practice.

New Century Scholars Doctoral Scholarships are available to students enrolled in a research doctoral program (Ph.D. or equivalent) in communication sciences and disorders.

New Century Scholars Research Grants are awarded to individuals committed to teacher-investigator careers in the university or college environment or in external research institutes or laboratories.

New Investigators Research Grants are awarded to new scientists to pursue research in audiology or speech-language pathology.

Speech Science Research Grants are awarded to new investigators to encourage research activities in the area of speech science.

Student Research Grant in Audiology supports a proposed one-year study to conduct research in audiology.

Student Research Grant in Early Childhood Language supports a proposed one-year study to conduct research in early childhood language development.

Rolland J. Van Hattum Award for Contribution in the Schools recognizes professionals demonstrating significant contribution to the delivery of audiology and/or speech pathology services in the schools.

YEAR PROGRAM STARTED: 1979

PURPOSE:
To further education in speech, language and hearing through the provision of financial assistance; to recognize and support research and similar endeavors which contribute to the advancement of knowledge and improvement of practice in serving children and adults with speech, language, or hearing disorders; to identify and facilitate new directions in the field of communication sciences and disorders through support of such vehicles as conferences, publications and other activities.

LEGAL BASIS:
501(c)(3) association.

FINANCIAL DATA:
Amount of support per award: Research Grants: $2,000 to $75,000, depending on grant type; Scholarships: $5,000 to $10,000.
Total amount of support: Varies.

NUMBER OF APPLICANTS MOST RECENT YEAR:
Approximately 300 for all programs.

NUMBER OF AWARDS: 40.

APPLICATION INFORMATION:
Guidelines are available from the ASH Foundation web site. Required documentation for scholarships includes application form, academic documentation, faculty recommendation committee report, and student essay. Research grant submissions require a research proposal.
Duration: One year. Nonrenewable.
Deadline: Usually April or May. Awards presented in November.

PUBLICATIONS:
Annual report; program and application guidelines; fact sheet.

IRS IDENTIFICATION NUMBER: 52-6055761

BOARD OF TRUSTEES:
Alex Johnson, President

ADDRESS INQUIRIES TO:
Program Administrator
(See address above.)

BENIGN ESSENTIAL BLEPHAROSPASM RESEARCH FOUNDATION INC. [2507]

637 North 7th Street
Suite 102
Beaumont, TX 77702
(409) 832-0788
Fax: (409) 832-0890

E-MAIL ADDRESS:
bebrf@blepharospasm.org

WEB SITE ADDRESS:
www.blepharospasm.org

FOUNDED: 1981

AREAS OF INTEREST:
Benign essential blepharospasm, Meige syndrome, hemifacial spasm and related disorders and infirmities of the facial musculature.

TYPE:
Fellowships; Project/program grants; Research grants; Seed money grants. The Foundation offers research fellowships to support the training of exceptionally qualified physicians or scientists who wish to focus on blepharospasm with and without oromandibular dystonia.

YEAR PROGRAM STARTED: 1985

PURPOSE:
To undertake, promote, develop and carry on the search for the cause and cure for benign essential blepharospasm and other related disorders and infirmities of the facial musculature.

LEGAL BASIS:
Foundation.

ELIGIBILITY:
For the Fellowship Program, physician applicants must be board certified or board eligible in neurology or ophthalmology, have completed a residency, and hold or be able to hold an unrestricted license to practice medicine in the U.S. Ph.Ds. should have completed their degree.

Research proposals must relate specifically to benign essential blepharospasm and Meige to include new treatments, pathophysiology and genetics, photophobia and dry eye.

FINANCIAL DATA:
Amount of support per award: Fellowships: Up to $75,000 per year; Grants: $10,000 to $150,000.
Total amount of support: $150,000.

NUMBER OF APPLICANTS MOST RECENT YEAR: 4 for the year 2013.

NUMBER OF AWARDS: 3 for the year 2012.

APPLICATION INFORMATION:
Application information is available on the web site or by sending an e-mail to the address above.
Duration: Fellowships: Two years. Grants: One to two years. Extensions have been granted.
Deadline: August 31.

PUBLICATIONS:
Program announcement; application guidelines; brochure.

IRS IDENTIFICATION NUMBER: 74-2193322

BOARD OF DIRECTORS:
Mary Lou Koster Thompson, President
Nilda Rendino, First Vice President
Linda Peterson, Second Vice President
Ed Dondzila, Treasurer
Emil Weaver, Assistant Treasurer
Mary Smith, Secretary

BRIGHT FOCUS FOUNDATION

22512 Gateway Center Drive
Clarksburg, MD 20871
(301) 948-3244
Fax: (301) 948-4403

E-MAIL ADDRESS:
researchgrants@brightfocus.org

WEB SITE ADDRESS:
www.brightfocus.org

TYPE:
Research grants.

See entry 1422 for full listing.

BRIGHT FOCUS FOUNDATION   [2508]

22512 Gateway Center Drive
Clarksburg, MD 20871
(301) 948-3244
Fax: (301) 948-4403

E-MAIL ADDRESS:
researchgrants@brightfocus.org

WEB SITE ADDRESS:
www.brightfocus.org

FOUNDED: 1978

AREAS OF INTEREST:
Glaucoma research.

NAME(S) OF PROGRAMS:
• **National Glaucoma Research Program**

TYPE:
Research grants. Support for basic research into the causes and potential treatments of glaucoma.

YEAR PROGRAM STARTED: 1978

PURPOSE:
To develop treatments, preventions and cures for glaucoma.

LEGAL BASIS:
Nonprofit foundation.

ELIGIBILITY:
Grants are awarded on the basis of the proposal's scientific merit and its relevance to understanding the disease studied. No funds for large equipment, institutional overhead costs, construction or building expenses.

FINANCIAL DATA:
Amount of support per award: Up to $50,000 per year.
Total amount of support: Varies.

NUMBER OF AWARDS: 7 for the year 2013.

APPLICATION INFORMATION:
Application information is available on the web site.
Duration: Up to two years.

PUBLICATIONS:
Annual report; newsletters; clinical brochures.

ADDRESS INQUIRIES TO:
Kara Summers, Program Officer
(See e-mail address above.)

CANADIAN NATIONAL INSTITUTE FOR THE BLIND   [2509]

1929 Bayview Avenue
Toronto ON M4G 3E8 Canada
(416) 486-2500 ext. 7622
Fax: (416) 480-7000

E-MAIL ADDRESS:
shampa.bose@cnib.ca

WEB SITE ADDRESS:
www.cnib.ca

FOUNDED: 1918

AREAS OF INTEREST:
Ophthalmic subspecialties and vision research.

NAME(S) OF PROGRAMS:
• **CNIB/Baker Grant**

TYPE:
Challenge/matching grants; Fellowships; Matching gifts; Research grants; Seed money grants; Training grants. Priority is given to a person assured of academic posting in Canada on completion of training.

YEAR PROGRAM STARTED: 1961

PURPOSE:
To promote research and vision health; to enhance independence for people with vision loss.

LEGAL BASIS:
Charitable organization.

ELIGIBILITY:
Graduate Canadian ophthalmologists and optometrists returning to a teaching position in Canada or to practice in underserved areas are eligible to apply. Travel costs will not be funded. If fellowship funding is received from any other source, the CNIB Fellowship must be declined or returned.

FINANCIAL DATA:
Amount of support per award: Fellowships: $30,000. Grants: $30,000 to $35,000.
Total amount of support: Varies.

NUMBER OF AWARDS: 3 fellowships and 6 research grants for 2012.

APPLICATION INFORMATION:
Applications must be submitted online.
Duration: One year. Applicants must reapply for additional or ongoing training assistance and must submit new references from the center in which they are presently doing their extra training.
Deadline: January 15. Grant payments will begin July 1 of the same year.

PUBLICATIONS:
Guidelines.

ADDRESS INQUIRIES TO:
Ms. Shampa Bose, Grants Administrator
(See address above.)

EYE BANK ASSOCIATION OF AMERICA   [2510]

1015 18th Street, N.W.
Suite 1010
Washington, DC 20036
(202) 775-4999
Fax: (202) 429-6036

E-MAIL ADDRESS:
info@restoresight.org

WEB SITE ADDRESS:
www.restoresight.org

FOUNDED: 1961

AREAS OF INTEREST:
Restoration of sight through eye banks.

NAME(S) OF PROGRAMS:
• **EBAA Research Grants**

TYPE:
Research grants.

PURPOSE:
To provide support for proposals specifically concerned with issues related to eye banking and corneal transplantation.

ELIGIBILITY:
Must be a physician, including corneal surgeon and other eye care specialist, basic scientist, including biomedical and social

scientists, or eye-bank technician, nurse, fellow, ophthalmology fellow or medical student that is supervised by a physician.

FINANCIAL DATA:
Amount of support per award: Generally $3,000 to $5,000.
Total amount of support: Varies.

NUMBER OF AWARDS: Varies.

APPLICATION INFORMATION:
Application form describing goals, background, methods and materials, and budgetary analysis must be completed. Applications should be typed and returned to the offices of the EBAA after approval by the appropriate eye bank or other nonprofit institution.

Applicants in training, eye-bank technicians, and nurses must submit a letter from the scientific supervisor regarding their capabilities of carrying out the proposed research study. Applicants who are not Paton Society members or who are not affiliated with an EBAA eye bank must submit a letter of support from a Paton Society member or the medical director of an EBAA eye bank; this letter must address the applicant's capabilities for carrying out the research and the available facilities. A curriculum vitae of the principal investigator and/or scientific supervisor should be enclosed.

Submit one original and 12 copies of the completed application. Faxed copies are not acceptable. Do not exceed the space allowed for describing the proposal or the application may be not considered for funding.
Duration: One year.
Deadline: Early March.

ADDRESS INQUIRIES TO:
Stacey Gardner
Manager, Education Programs
(See address above.)

FIGHT FOR SIGHT, INC.   [2511]
381 Park Avenue South
Suite 809
New York, NY 10016
(212) 679-6060
Fax: (212) 679-4466

E-MAIL ADDRESS:
janice@fightforsight.org

WEB SITE ADDRESS:
www.fightforsight.org

FOUNDED: 1946

AREAS OF INTEREST:
Ophthalmology and visual sciences.

NAME(S) OF PROGRAMS:
• **Research Awards Program**

TYPE:
Fellowships; Grants-in-aid; Research grants. Fight for Sight primarily supports new investigators, promoting the development of scientific findings and pilot studies necessary to successfully apply for more substantial federal and private funding such as that provided by the National Eye Institute and other divisions of the NIH.

YEAR PROGRAM STARTED: 1946

PURPOSE:
To support and inspire eye and vision research by funding promising young scientists early in their careers.

LEGAL BASIS:
501(c)(3) corporation.

ELIGIBILITY:
Summer Fellowships are open to undergraduate, graduate and medical students.

Postdoctoral Awards are offered to recent Ph.D., M.D., Dr.P.H., D.V.M., and O.D. graduates.

Grants-in-Aid are available for academic researchers within the first three years of their academic appointments.

GEOGRAPHIC RESTRICTIONS:
United States and Canada.

FINANCIAL DATA:
Funds are to be used to defray costs of equipment, consumable supplies and personnel (excluding applicant) for Postdoctoral Awards recipients.
Amount of support per award: Up to $22,500.
Total amount of support: Varies.

NUMBER OF APPLICANTS MOST RECENT YEAR: 90.

NUMBER OF AWARDS: 30.

APPLICATION INFORMATION:
Application guidelines are available on the web site.
Duration: One year; Summer Fellowships: Eight to 12 weeks.
Deadline: February 1. Start date between July 1 and September 1.

PUBLICATIONS:
Brochure.

ADDRESS INQUIRIES TO:
Janice Benson, Assistant Director
(See address above.)

FIGHT FOR SIGHT, INC.   [2512]
381 Park Avenue South
Suite 809
New York, NY 10016
(212) 679-6060
Fax: (212) 679-4466

E-MAIL ADDRESS:
janice@fightforsight.org

WEB SITE ADDRESS:
www.fightforsight.org

FOUNDED: 1946

AREAS OF INTEREST:
Ophthalmology and visual sciences.

NAME(S) OF PROGRAMS:
• **Fight for Sight Postdoctoral Fellowship**

TYPE:
Fellowships; Grants-in-aid; Research grants; Seed money grants. Stipend to support individuals with a Doctorate who are interested in academic careers involving basic or clinical research in ophthalmology or visual sciences.

YEAR PROGRAM STARTED: 1953

PURPOSE:
To assist research and treatment aimed at eliminating blinding eye diseases and sight impairment.

LEGAL BASIS:
501(c)(3) corporation.

ELIGIBILITY:
Physicians or scientists holding a Doctorate and who are interested in academic careers involving fundamental or clinical research in ophthalmology or its related sciences are

eligible to apply. If at the time of filing the applicant does not as yet have a Doctorate, it is required that a cover letter be submitted together with the application advising that the Doctorate will be conferred by the designated commencement date.

GEOGRAPHIC RESTRICTIONS:
United States and Canada.

FINANCIAL DATA:
Amount of support per award: Stipend up to $20,000.

NUMBER OF APPLICANTS MOST RECENT YEAR: 130.

NUMBER OF AWARDS: Approximately 15 to 20.

APPLICATION INFORMATION:
Applications are available online. Completed applications should include:
(1) application face pages and related information completed online and including information about the applicant, his or her education and training, institution and sponsor;
(2) a research proposal of no more than six single-spaced pages, not including references;
(3) letters of support from a sponsor, departmental chair, and a third reference. These letters should include an evaluation of the student, the role of the mentor in advising the applicant during the project, the training plan, any extracurricular training the student will receive and other information helpful to the committee in evaluating the mentor, the laboratory and the institutional resources in support of a FFS Postdoctoral Award. They should specifically address the suitability of the applicant's training, his or her academic achievements and, most importantly, his or her potential to develop into an independent eye and vision researcher and/or leader in academic ophthalmology;
(4) an NIH-style biosketch of the applicant and sponsor and;
(5) supplemental information, including relevant awards, previous research experience and academic or career goals.
Duration: One year.
Deadline: February 1. Start date is between July 1 and September 1.

PUBLICATIONS:
Brochure.

ADDRESS INQUIRIES TO:
Janice Benson, Assistant Director
(See address above.)

*SPECIAL STIPULATIONS:
Research work to be performed in the U.S. or Canada.

THE GLAUCOMA FOUNDATION   [2513]
80 Maiden Lane, Suite 700
New York, NY 10038-4778
(212) 285-0080
Fax: (212) 651-1888

E-MAIL ADDRESS:
info@glaucomafoundation.org

WEB SITE ADDRESS:
www.glaucomafoundation.org

FOUNDED: 1984

AREAS OF INTEREST:
Glaucoma.

TYPE:
Research grants.

PURPOSE:
To fund research to determine the causes of glaucoma; to improve methods of treatment, and ultimately to develop cures for the various kinds of glaucoma.

ELIGIBILITY:
Applicants must have a full-time faculty position or the equivalent. Applicant must also demonstrate the Principal Investigator's understanding of glaucoma or his or her collaboration with an investigator who has experience in glaucoma research. If collaboration is warranted, a letter of support from the glaucoma researcher must be included in the application.

FINANCIAL DATA:
Amount of support per award: $40,000.
Total amount of support: Varies.

NUMBER OF APPLICANTS MOST RECENT YEAR:
20.

APPLICATION INFORMATION:
Contact the Foundation for application information.
Duration: One year. Renewable.
Deadline: Varies.

GLAUCOMA RESEARCH FOUNDATION   [2514]

251 Post Street, Suite 600
San Francisco, CA 94108
(415) 986-3162
Fax: (415) 986-3763
E-MAIL ADDRESS:
research@glaucoma.org
WEB SITE ADDRESS:
www.glaucoma.org
FOUNDED: 1978

AREAS OF INTEREST:
Research and education pertaining to glaucoma.

NAME(S) OF PROGRAMS:
● **Shaffer Fund for Innovative Glaucoma Research**

TYPE:
Project/program grants; Research grants.

PURPOSE:
To protect the sight and independence of people with glaucoma through research and education; to provide funding for such research.

ELIGIBILITY:
Applicants must hold a graduate degree.

FINANCIAL DATA:
Amount of support per award: $15,000 to $40,000.

NUMBER OF APPLICANTS MOST RECENT YEAR:
35.

NUMBER OF AWARDS: 8.

APPLICATION INFORMATION:
Preliminary proposals are accepted annually between June 1 and July 31, when a link to the online application will be available on the GRF web site. A link to the full online grant application will be e-mailed to those whose preliminary proposals meet the required criteria.

Applications received by mail will not be reviewed or returned.
Duration: One year.
Deadline: Preliminary proposals: June 1 to July 31. Full grant application: September 1 to September 30.

IRS IDENTIFICATION NUMBER: 94-2495035

ADDRESS INQUIRIES TO:
Catalina San Agustin, Director of Operations
(See e-mail address above.)

HEARING HEALTH FOUNDATION   [2515]

363 Seventh Avenue, 10th Floor
New York, NY 10001-3904
(212) 257-6140
Fax: (212) 257-6139
E-MAIL ADDRESS:
grants@hearinghealthfoundation.org
WEB SITE ADDRESS:
www.hearinghealthfoundation.org
FOUNDED: 1958

AREAS OF INTEREST:
Research concerning the causes, treatment and prevention of hearing loss and related ear and balance disorders.

NAME(S) OF PROGRAMS:
● **Emerging Research Grants**
● **Hearing Restoration Project**

TYPE:
Research grants. Limited in amount and term, grants are awarded as seed funding in support of projects directed by new investigators or for promising new studies in areas of demonstrable basic science or clinical importance. It does include grant support for new research by established investigators.

Specifically, applications will be considered for research directed to any aspect of the ear; that is, investigation of the function, physiology, biochemistry, genetics, anatomy or pathology. Basic and applied research is welcome.

YEAR PROGRAM STARTED: 1958

PURPOSE:
To prevent and cure hearing loss through groundbreaking research.

LEGAL BASIS:
Nonprofit public voluntary organization.

ELIGIBILITY:
Applications are accepted from all U.S. institutions, including universities, hospitals and nonprofit tax-exempt institutions, public or private.

The HHF's Scientific Review Committee will consider the subject of the research, the quality of its design, its potential for significant advance in basic knowledge or clinical application, the available facilities and personnel at the institution in which the research will be carried out and the qualifications of the investigators.

In accepting a research grant, the institution and the principal investigator are responsible for using grant funds only for those purposes set forth in the application and approved in the HHF award letter.

GEOGRAPHIC RESTRICTIONS:
United States.

FINANCIAL DATA:
Grant funds may be budgeted and used for direct costs of carrying out approved projects, including equipment purchases and supplies. Grant funds may not be used for the salary of principal investigator or co-investigator, travel, living expenses, printing costs,

overhead costs exceeding 10% of project costs or public information/education programs.
Amount of support per award: Regardless of the indirect amount, the HHF award will not exceed $30,000.
Total amount of support: Varies.

NUMBER OF APPLICANTS MOST RECENT YEAR:
Approximately 25.

NUMBER OF AWARDS: 25 for the 2011 funding cycle.

APPLICATION INFORMATION:
New Project applications and Second-Year applications must be submitted using the current forms available on the web site.
Duration: One calendar year. Possible renewal for second-year grant support.
Deadline: December 1 for first-year applications. Principal investigators are notified in June.

PUBLICATIONS:
Hearing Health Magazine.

IRS IDENTIFICATION NUMBER: 13-1882107

STAFF:
Doug Olson, Director of Development
Tara Guastella, Program Administrator

ADDRESS INQUIRIES TO:
Program Administrator
(See address above.)

HEED OPHTHALMIC FOUNDATION   [2516]

Cleveland Clinic
9500 Euclid Avenue, i-13
Cleveland, OH 44195
(216) 444-2010
(216) 445-8145
Fax: (216) 444-8968; (216) 445-3676
E-MAIL ADDRESS:
sardelj@ccf.org
WEB SITE ADDRESS:
www.heed.org

AREAS OF INTEREST:
Diseases and surgery of the eye or research in opthalmology.

NAME(S) OF PROGRAMS:
● **Heed Fellowship**

TYPE:
Fellowships.

PURPOSE:
To provide assistance to men and women who desire to further their education or to conduct research in opthalmology.

ELIGIBILITY:
Open to U.S. citizens who are graduates of an institution approved by the AMA.

FINANCIAL DATA:
Amount of support per award: $10,000 for the year 2013.
Total amount of support: $170,000 for the year 2013.

NUMBER OF AWARDS: 17 for the year 2012.

APPLICATION INFORMATION:
Applicants are required to submit:
(1) a one-page statement setting forth the applicant's major ophthalmic interest, professional aims and objectives, and noting qualifications deserving of particular consideration;
(2) a letter of recommendation from the Chair of Ophthalmology who supervised residency training;

(3) a letter from the preceptor of the applicant's fellowship program describing the program, including a statement that a minimum of 20% of the fellowship will be spent in research;
(4) two additional letters of recommendation from physicians who have supervised the applicant;
(5) a letter of acceptance of the applicant at the institution where the fellowship is to be taken (this may be a copy of the applicant's match letter) and;
(6) a letter of recommendation from the Chairman of the department who has offered an academic appointment (optional).

Do not send curriculum vitae.

Facsimiles of application materials or letters of recommendation will not be accepted.

Duration: One year. Nonrenewable.

Deadline: January 15.

ADDRESS INQUIRIES TO:
Jane Sardelle
Heed Administrator
(See e-mail address above or admin1@heed.org)

THE MARFAN FOUNDATION [2517]
22 Manhasset Avenue
Port Washington, NY 11050
(516) 883-8712 ext. 117
Fax: (516) 883-8040

E-MAIL ADDRESS:
research@marfan.org

WEB SITE ADDRESS:
www.marfan.org

FOUNDED: 1981

AREAS OF INTEREST:
Education, support and research relating to Marfan syndrome.

NAME(S) OF PROGRAMS:
● **Early Investigator Grant Program**
● **Fellowship Grant Program**
● **The Marfan Foundation Faculty Grant Program**

TYPE:
Fellowships; Grants-in-aid; Project/program grants; Research grants. Basic and clinical research related to the Marfan syndrome and related connective tissue disorders. Areas include basic translational and clinical research in genetics, cardiology, ophthalmology and orthopaedic issues of the Marfan syndrome.

YEAR PROGRAM STARTED: 1986

PURPOSE:
To provide financial support for investigators, scientists and physicians studying any or all disciplines involved in Marfan syndrome research.

ELIGIBILITY:
The principal investigator must hold an M.D., D.O., Ph.D., Sc.D., D.D.S., D.V.M. or equivalent degree. The investigator must have proven ability to pursue independent research publications in peer-reviewed journals. Fellowships must be conducted in the U.S.

FINANCIAL DATA:
Amount of support per award: Early Investigator: $37,500; Faculty: $50,000; Fellowship: $50,000 to $75,000.
Total amount of support: Varies.

NUMBER OF APPLICANTS MOST RECENT YEAR: 30 for the year 2012.

NUMBER OF AWARDS: 3 Faculty and 1 Fellowship for the year 2012.

APPLICATION INFORMATION:
Application information is available on the web site.
Duration: Up to two years.
Deadline: Early Investigator and Fellowship: March 2; Faculty: April 27.

ADDRESS INQUIRIES TO:
Josephine Grima, Ph.D., Vice President Research and Legislative Affairs
(See address above.)

NATIONAL EYE INSTITUTE [2518]
National Institutes of Health
5635 Fishers Lane, Suite 1300
Bethesda, MD 20892
(301) 451-2020
Fax: (301) 402-0528

WEB SITE ADDRESS:
www.nei.nih.gov

FOUNDED: 1968

AREAS OF INTEREST:
Vision research, cooperative clinical trials for evaluation, diagnosis and therapy of ocular diseases, and epidemiologic and risk factor studies of ocular diseases.

NAME(S) OF PROGRAMS:
● **Cooperative Clinical Research Grants**
● **Small Business Innovation Research Awards**

TYPE:
Conferences/seminars; Fellowships; Research grants; Training grants. Research Project Grants support individual investigators whose work is aimed at discovering means of improving the prevention, diagnosis and treatment of blinding and disabling eye and vision disorders.

Small Business Innovation Research Awards aim to stimulate technological innovations, to use small business to meet federal research-development needs that may ultimately lead to commercial products or services and to foster and encourage participation by minority and disadvantaged persons in technological innovations.

Areas of study include vision research, retinal diseases, corneal diseases, cataract, glaucoma, low vision and blindness rehabilitation, visual impairment and its rehabilitation, strabismus, amblyopia and visual processing.

YEAR PROGRAM STARTED: 1968

PURPOSE:
To gain new knowledge about normal and abnormal functioning of the eye and visual system; to support research aimed at improving the prevention, diagnosis and treatment of eye disease and disorders of vision. These are essential for progress against the major causes of blindness and visual disability.

ELIGIBILITY:
Research grants are available to any public or private university, college, hospital, laboratory, or other institution, including state and local units of government and federal institutions; eligibility is no longer restricted to nonprofit organizations.

FINANCIAL DATA:
Amount of support per award: Grants vary in amount, depending upon the needs and nature of the request.

APPLICATION INFORMATION:
Those interested in applying are encouraged to contact the NEI staff prior to submitting applications.
Duration: Small Business Innovation Research Award: Six months to two years.
Deadline: Varies according to award.

IRS IDENTIFICATION NUMBER: 52-0858115

STAFF:
Paul Sieving, M.D., Director
Richard Fisher, Associate Director for Science Policy and Legislation

ADDRESS INQUIRIES TO:
Jerome Wujek, Ph.D.
Research Resources Officer
(See address above.)

NATIONAL EYE INSTITUTE [2519]
5635 Fishers Lane, Suite 1300
Bethesda, MD 20892
(301) 451-2020
Fax: (301) 496-9997

E-MAIL ADDRESS:
wwd@nei.nih.gov

WEB SITE ADDRESS:
www.nei.nih.gov

AREAS OF INTEREST:
Vision research, cooperative clinical trials for evaluation, diagnosis and therapy of ocular diseases, and epidemiologic and risk factor studies of ocular diseases.

NAME(S) OF PROGRAMS:
● **Center Core Grants**

TYPE:
Research grants; Research contracts.

PURPOSE:
To support centralized resources and facilities shared by investigators with existing NINDS-funded research projects; to enrich the effectiveness of ongoing research; to promote new research directions.

FINANCIAL DATA:
Amount of support per award: Applicants may request up to $500,000 per year in direct costs.
Matching fund requirements: Cost sharing is not required to be eligible for this program. However, it is strongly encouraged for applicant organizations to make appropriate and needed commitments to the Center in order to maximize the effectiveness and utility of the shared resources.

APPLICATION INFORMATION:
Contact NEI for details.
Duration: Maximum project period of five years.

ADDRESS INQUIRIES TO:
Ellen S. Liberman, Ph.D.
(See address above.)

NATIONAL INSTITUTES OF HEALTH [2520]
6705 Rockledge Drive, Suite 3516
Bethesda, MD 20892-7963
(301) 451-4225
Fax: (301) 480-0146

E-MAIL ADDRESS:
nihtrain@nih.gov

WEB SITE ADDRESS:
grants.nih.gov/training/nrsa.htm

NAME(S) OF PROGRAMS:
- **National Research Service Awards (NRSAs)**

TYPE:
Fellowships; Training grants. Support for research training.

LEGAL BASIS:
Government agency.

FINANCIAL DATA:
Amount of support per award: $22,476 stipend at predoctoral level and up to $55,272 at the postdoctoral level.

APPLICATION INFORMATION:
Application forms required. Contact the Institute.
Duration: Postdoctoral awards: One to three years. Predoctoral award: One to five years.
Deadline: April 8, August 8 and December 8.

ADDRESS INQUIRIES TO:
Extramural Outreach and Information Resources
(See address above.)

RESEARCH FUND OF THE AMERICAN OTOLOGICAL SOCIETY, INC. [2521]
1980 Warson Road
Springfield, IL 62074
(410) 955-7381
Fax: (410) 955-0035

E-MAIL ADDRESS:
jcarey@jhmi.edu
otosociety@yahoo.com

WEB SITE ADDRESS:
www.americanotologicalsociety.org/information.html

FOUNDED: 1868

AREAS OF INTEREST:
Otosclerosis, Meniere's disease and related ear disorders.

NAME(S) OF PROGRAMS:
- **AOS Clinician-Scientist Award**
- **Clinical Trial**
- **Research Grants**
- **Research Training Fellowship**

TYPE:
Fellowships; Research grants. AOS Clinician-Scientist Award: For salary support of a new clinician-scientist, at the assistant professor level, in order to facilitate development into an independent otologic investigator. Department chair guarantees at least 50% time commitment in research.

Clinical Trial: Study must be related to otosclerosis or Meniere's disease.

Research Grants: Should be related to otosclerosis or Meniere's disease.

Research Training Fellowship: For physicians only (residents and medical students), to support one to two years of full-time research conducted outside of residency training.

YEAR PROGRAM STARTED: 1926

PURPOSE:
To encourage research in otosclerosis, Meniere's disease and related ear disorders.

LEGAL BASIS:
Private foundation.

ELIGIBILITY:
Applicant must be a U.S. citizen or permanent U.S. resident, graduate of ACGME-approved otolaryngology residency program, and must hold or be approved for a full-time university faculty appointment. Preference will be given to candidates who are currently enrolled in or have completed a neurotology fellowship program. Research conducted during the Clinician-Scientist Award can be on any topic related to ear disorders.

Research must be conducted in U.S. or Canadian institutions.

GEOGRAPHIC RESTRICTIONS:
United States and Canada.

FINANCIAL DATA:
Amount of support per award: AOS Clinician-Scientist Award: Up to $80,000 for salary and research support; Clinical Trial: $66,000 maximum per year; Research Grants: $55,000 maximum per year; Research Training Fellowship: $35,000 stipend and $5,000 for supplies.

APPLICATION INFORMATION:
For the Clinical Trial and Research Grant Awards, a description of the relationship between the research study and otosclerosis or Meniere's disease is an integral part of the application. Applications for the Research Training Fellowship must be accompanied by sponsoring institution documentation stating that facilities and faculty are appropriate for requested research.

To obtain continued support, an application must be submitted annually along with a progress report.
Duration: AOS Clinician-Scientist Award: Up to three years. Renewable annually. Clinical Trial and Research Grants: Up to two years. Research Training Fellowship: One to two years.
Deadline: Postmarked by January 31.

STAFF:
John P. Carey, M.D., Executive Secretary

ADDRESS INQUIRIES TO:
John P. Carey, M.D., Executive Secretary
Johns Hopkins University School of Medicine
Department of Otolaryngology, Head and Neck Surgery
Baltimore, MD 21287-0910

Osteopathy

AMERICAN OSTEOPATHIC FOUNDATION [2522]
142 East Ontario Street, Suite 1450
Chicago, IL 60611-2864
(312) 202-8232
Fax: (312) 202-8216

E-MAIL ADDRESS:
vheck@aof.org

WEB SITE ADDRESS:
www.aof.org

FOUNDED: 1949

AREAS OF INTEREST:
Osteopathic medical education and research.

TYPE:
Awards/prizes; Scholarships. Grants.

PURPOSE:
To assist and encourage osteopathic medical students, researchers and physicians; to ensure the ideals of osteopathic medicine by initiating and supporting programs that enhance the profession, advance the quality of people's health, and recognize excellence in the areas of education and research.

LEGAL BASIS:
Private foundation.

ELIGIBILITY:
Specific requirements can be found on the Foundation web site.

FINANCIAL DATA:
Amount of support per award: Varies.
Total amount of support: Varies.

APPLICATION INFORMATION:
Applications or nomination forms are available January 1 on the Foundation web site.
Duration: Varies.
Deadline: Varies.

PUBLICATIONS:
Application; brochure.

ADDRESS INQUIRIES TO:
Vicki L. Heck, Director of Programs
(See address above.)

AMERICAN OSTEOPATHIC FOUNDATION
142 East Ontario Street, Suite 1450
Chicago, IL 60611
(312) 202-8232
(312) 202-8234
Fax: (312) 202-8216

E-MAIL ADDRESS:
vheck@aof.org

WEB SITE ADDRESS:
www.aof.org

TYPE:
Scholarships. Awarded annually to one rising last-year student at each of the accredited U.S. colleges of osteopathic medicine.

See entry 1661 for full listing.

FOUNDATION FOR OSTEOPATHIC EMERGENCY MEDICINE [2523]
142 East Ontario Street
Suite 1500
Chicago, IL 60611
(312) 587-1765
Fax: (312) 587-9951

E-MAIL ADDRESS:
swhitmer@foem.org

WEB SITE ADDRESS:
www.foem.org

FOUNDED: 1998

AREAS OF INTEREST:
Osteopathic emergency medicine.

NAME(S) OF PROGRAMS:
- **Investigator Grant**
- **David A. Kuchinski Memorial Research Grant**
- **Resident Research Grant**
- **Young Investigator Grant**

TYPE:
Awards/prizes; Research grants.

YEAR PROGRAM STARTED: 1998

PURPOSE:
To assist osteopathic emergency physicians in their research endeavors.

LEGAL BASIS:
501(c)(3).

ELIGIBILITY:
Grants are made to individuals or organizations that have tax-exempt status under Section 501(c)(3) of the Internal Revenue Code.

GEOGRAPHIC RESTRICTIONS:
United States.

FINANCIAL DATA:
Amount of support per award: Investigator Grant and Young Investigator Grant: $1,000 to $3,000; Kuchinski Memorial Research Grant: Varies; Resident Research Grant: $500 to $3,000.

Total amount of support: Varies.

NUMBER OF APPLICANTS MOST RECENT YEAR:
3.

NUMBER OF AWARDS: 1.

APPLICATION INFORMATION:
Contact the Foundation for application procedures.

Duration: One-time grants.

Deadline: July 1. Reviewed in April, July and October.

PUBLICATIONS:
Research Beacon.

ADDRESS INQUIRIES TO:
Stephanie Whitmer
Director of Development
(See address above.)

MAINE OSTEOPATHIC ASSOCIATION   [2524]
128 State Street
Augusta, ME 04330
(207) 623-1101
Fax: (207) 623-4228

E-MAIL ADDRESS:
info@mainedo.org

WEB SITE ADDRESS:
www.mainedo.org

FOUNDED: 1912

AREAS OF INTEREST:
Osteopathic medicine.

NAME(S) OF PROGRAMS:
● **Maine Osteopathic Association Scholarship**

TYPE:
Scholarships. The program is a tuition subsidy for eligible students who enroll in a qualifying medical school program.

LEGAL BASIS:
Nonprofit physician membership organization.

ELIGIBILITY:
Any Maine resident who will enroll in a participating accredited college of osteopathic medicine. School does not have to be located in Maine.

FINANCIAL DATA:
Amount of support per award: $1,000.

Total amount of support: Varies.

NUMBER OF AWARDS: Varies.

APPLICATION INFORMATION:
Contact the Association for an application form.

Duration: One year.

Deadline: June 1.

STAFF:
Angela Westhoff, Executive Director

ADDRESS INQUIRIES TO:
Angela Westhoff, Executive Director
(See address above.)

NEW JERSEY OSTEOPATHIC EDUCATION FOUNDATION   [2525]
One Distribution Way
Suite 201
Monmouth Junction, NJ 08852-3001
(732) 940-9000 ext. 303
Fax: (732) 940-8899

E-MAIL ADDRESS:
info@njosteo.com

WEB SITE ADDRESS:
www.njosteo.com

FOUNDED: 1901

AREAS OF INTEREST:
Osteopathic education.

TYPE:
Scholarships. For students pursuing osteopathic medical education. A first-year scholarship will be awarded to New Jersey residents accepted to the fall class of any approved college of osteopathic medicine.

YEAR PROGRAM STARTED: 1965

PURPOSE:
To provide the means to promote education in the field of osteopathic medicine.

LEGAL BASIS:
Not-for-profit corporation.

ELIGIBILITY:
Applicants must be residents of New Jersey having completed four years of pre-medical education and entering their first year in an osteopathic college. Applicants must have a 3.0 grade point average on a 4.0 scale or be in the upper 25% of his or her class. Selections are based on class standing, financial need, high motivation and professional promise. Students accepting scholarships must agree to become members of the New Jersey Association of Osteopathic Physicians and Surgeons and the American Osteopathic Association.

GEOGRAPHIC RESTRICTIONS:
New Jersey.

FINANCIAL DATA:
The scholarship sum will be paid directly to the college to cover part of the first year's tuition.

Amount of support per award: $4,000 to $7,000.

Total amount of support: $29,000.

NUMBER OF APPLICANTS MOST RECENT YEAR:
20.

NUMBER OF AWARDS: Approximately 7 each year.

APPLICATION INFORMATION:
To apply for a scholarship, qualified students must:
(1) submit a completed NJOEF scholarship application;
(2) provide four named references, at least one of whom is an osteopathic physician;
(3) provide four completed reference evaluation forms;
(4) supply MCAT scores with confirmation code;
(5) supply pre-med college transcripts directly from the college;
(6) compose an essay sharing his or her desire to become an osteopathic physician (why osteopathic medicine?) and;
(7) supply the prior year's tax return or that of the parent/guardian, if the student is claimed as a dependent.

Duration: One year.

Deadline: April 30.

IRS IDENTIFICATION NUMBER: 22-6088562

ADDRESS INQUIRIES TO:
Scholarship Program
(See address above.)

Pediatrics

ACADEMIC PEDIATRIC ASSOCIATION   [2526]
6728 Old McLean Village Drive
McLean, VA 22101
(703) 556-9222
Fax: (703) 556-8729

E-MAIL ADDRESS:
info@academicpeds.org

WEB SITE ADDRESS:
www.academicpeds.org

FOUNDED: 1960

AREAS OF INTEREST:
General pediatrics.

NAME(S) OF PROGRAMS:
● **Young Investigator Grant Program**

TYPE:
Project/program grants; Research grants.

YEAR PROGRAM STARTED: 1994

PURPOSE:
To provide financial support to teaching, research and health care delivery projects in general pediatrics.

ELIGIBILITY:
The principal investigator of any proposal submitted must be a member of the APA or have submitted an application for membership. Preference will be given to new investigators, including those in training. Preference will be given to proposals that have the potential of leading to projects of a larger or longer-term nature.

FINANCIAL DATA:
Amount of support per award: Up to $10,000.

NUMBER OF AWARDS: Varies.

APPLICATION INFORMATION:
Applicants must submit a two-page proposal. Only electronic submissions as an e-mail attachment are accepted. The proposals should contain a brief overview of the project including purpose, methods, evaluation and estimated budget. A curriculum vitae for the principal investigator must also be included with the proposal. Budget requests should not include overhead or salary for the principal investigator if they are full-time faculty. The review panel will identify those that warrant further elaboration. Re-submitted proposals can be no more than 10 pages in length including tables and appendices. They must

contain background, hypothesis, description of key personnel, detailed budget with justification and methods.

Duration: One year. Renewal possible.

ADDRESS INQUIRIES TO:
Connie Mackay
Young Investigator Grant
(See address above.)

AMERICAN ACADEMY OF PEDIATRICS   [2527]

141 Northwest Point Boulevard
Elk Grove Village, IL 60007
(847) 434-4000
(800) 433-9016 ext. 7134
Fax: (847) 434-8000

E-MAIL ADDRESS:
kvandenbrook@aap.org

WEB SITE ADDRESS:
www.aap.org/ypn

FOUNDED: 1930

AREAS OF INTEREST:
Pediatric training.

NAME(S) OF PROGRAMS:
• **American Academy of Pediatrics Residency Scholarships**

TYPE:
Residencies; Scholarships. Stipend for the support of pediatric residents.

YEAR PROGRAM STARTED: 1982

PURPOSE:
To enable young physicians to complete their pediatric training.

LEGAL BASIS:
Nonprofit organization.

ELIGIBILITY:
Applicant must have completed, or will have completed by July 1, a qualifying approved internship (PL-0) and have a definite commitment for a first-year pediatric residency (PL-1) accredited by the Residency Review Committee for Pediatrics. In addition, applicant must be a pediatric resident or chief resident (categorical pediatrics or combined-training program) in a training program and have made a definite commitment for another year of residency (not fellowship) in a U.S. or Canadian program accredited by the Residency Review Committee for Pediatrics, as well as have a substantial need for financial assistance.

GEOGRAPHIC RESTRICTIONS:
United States and Canada.

FINANCIAL DATA:
Amount of support per award: $1,000 to $5,000.
Total amount of support: Varies.

APPLICATION INFORMATION:
Official application materials are available upon request in December. Applications must be supported by a form from the Department Head or the Chief of Service or the Residency Program Director addressing the financial need, commitment to pediatrics and performance in the program.
Duration: One year. Possible renewals.
Deadline: Last day in February.

ADDRESS INQUIRIES TO:
Kimberley VandenBrook
Program Coordinator, Resident Initiatives
(See address above.)

CEREBRAL PALSY INTERNATIONAL RESEARCH FOUNDATION

445 Park Avenue
9th Floor
New York, NY 10022
(212) 836-4756
(917) 952-9900

E-MAIL ADDRESS:
christy.cravens@cpirf.org

WEB SITE ADDRESS:
www.cpirf.org

TYPE:
Research grants. Grants are awarded for pilot studies in areas which have a relationship to cerebral palsy. While most research in the central nervous system may be useful, the Foundation requires that research proposals define clear and direct relevance to cerebral palsy. Currently, high priority is assigned to prevention of prematurity, decrease of perinatal neurologic morbidity, prevention of central nervous system infections of the newborn and to medical, surgical and bioengineering methods that may improve the functioning of persons with cerebral palsy, addressing issues such as impaired mobility, impaired communication skills, swallowing, drooling and effects of aging on further diminution of function. However, any proposal designed to prevent cerebral palsy or to improve its treatment and management will be considered.

See entry 2459 for full listing.

DYSAUTONOMIA FOUNDATION, INC.

315 West 39th Street
Suite 701
New York, NY 10018
(212) 279-1066
Fax: (212) 279-2066

E-MAIL ADDRESS:
info@famdys.org

WEB SITE ADDRESS:
www.familialdysautonomia.org

TYPE:
Project/program grants; Research grants; Seed money grants. In addition to support for research and clinical study, the Foundation also provides financial support to the Dysautonomia Treatment and Evaluation Center at NYU and the Israeli FD Center in Tel Aviv.

See entry 2461 for full listing.

FIRST CANDLE/SIDS ALLIANCE   [2528]

2105 Laurel Bush Road
Suite 201
Bel Air, MD 21015
(443) 640-1049
Fax: (443) 640-1031

E-MAIL ADDRESS:
info@firstcandle.org

WEB SITE ADDRESS:
www.firstcandle.org

FOUNDED: 1962

AREAS OF INTEREST:
Medical research into the cause and prevention of Sudden Infant Death Syndrome, counseling and information projects which aid parents and educate the public about SIDS and SIDS-related issues and education of relevant professionals on SIDS and about care for infants at-risk.

CONSULTING OR VOLUNTEER SERVICES:
Local chapters provide voluntary peer support to parents and National Office provides consulting services in the management of specialized services, seminars to health professionals, review of SIDS medical research proposals and clearinghouse for literature and films on SIDS and related issues.

NAME(S) OF PROGRAMS:
• **Professional Research**

TYPE:
Conferences/seminars; Research grants. Professional medical research for SIDS, stillbirths and related issues.

YEAR PROGRAM STARTED: 1963

PURPOSE:
To promote infant health and survival during the prenatal period through two years of age by means of advocacy, education and research; to provide SIDS and other infant death bereavement services.

LEGAL BASIS:
Not-for-profit corporation.

ELIGIBILITY:
Applicant reviews are made on an individual basis by the First Candle/SIDS Alliance and the Alliance Medical and Scientific Advisory Council.

FINANCIAL DATA:
Amount of support per award: Grants vary in amount depending upon proposals.
Total amount of support: Varies.

NUMBER OF AWARDS: 6 per year average.

APPLICATION INFORMATION:
Letters soliciting Foundation interest prior to submission of proposals are welcome.

IRS IDENTIFICATION NUMBER: 52-1591162

ADDRESS INQUIRIES TO:
Chris Blake, Chief Executive Officer
(See address above.)

CHARLES H. HOOD FOUNDATION, INC.   [2529]

95 Berkeley Street, 2nd Floor
Boston, MA 02116
(617) 695-9439

WEB SITE ADDRESS:
www.tmfgrants.org/hood

FOUNDED: 1942

AREAS OF INTEREST:
Child health research.

NAME(S) OF PROGRAMS:
• **Child Health Research Awards Program**

TYPE:
Research grants. Medical research grants that are relevant to child health. Projects must be hypothesis-driven clinical, basic science, public health, health services research or epidemiology.

YEAR PROGRAM STARTED: 1942

PURPOSE:
To improve the health and quality of life for children through grant support of New England-based pediatric researchers.

LEGAL BASIS:
Private family foundation.

ELIGIBILITY:
Investigators working in tax-exempt academic, medical and research institutions in New England are eligible. Grants must have relevance to child health. Investigators must be within five years of their first faculty appointment. In addition to basic science research, grants are also given to researchers in public health, epidemiology, clinical research and health services research.

GEOGRAPHIC RESTRICTIONS:
New England.

FINANCIAL DATA:
Amount of support per award: $75,000 per year for two years (inclusive of 10% overhead).
Total amount of support: $1,500,000 over two years.

NUMBER OF APPLICANTS MOST RECENT YEAR:
68.

NUMBER OF AWARDS: 10 new grants for the year 2013.

REPRESENTATIVE AWARDS:
"Kisspeptin as a Novel Tool for the Evaluation of Delayed Puberty;" "The Effectiveness of Community Financing Approach in Improving Child Nutrition Status in Rwanda;" "Detecting and Correcting Errors During Cell Division;" "Prospective Study of Genomic Aberrations during Prenatal Gestation;" "The Impact of Genes and Experience on the Development of Brain Circuits."

APPLICATION INFORMATION:
Application guidelines, instructions and forms are available on the web site.
Duration: Two years.
Deadline: Spring and Fall for Child Health Research Grants. Funding begins on July 1 and January 1. Deadlines and guidelines change each cycle.

PUBLICATIONS:
Application guidelines; alumni directory; summaries of current and previous funded projects.

IRS IDENTIFICATION NUMBER: 04-3507847

OFFICERS:
Neil Smiley, President and Treasurer
John Parker, Jr., Vice President and Clerk
Raymond Considine, Secretary and Executive Director

TRUSTEES:
Jeffrey Boutwell, Ph.D.
Robert Boutwell
Barbara Bula
Brendon Bula

ADDRESS INQUIRIES TO:
E-mail: glockwood@hria.org

HUMAN GROWTH FOUNDATION [2530]
997 Glen Cove Avenue, Suite 5
Glen Head, NY 11545
(516) 671-4041
(800) 451-6434
Fax: (516) 671-4055

E-MAIL ADDRESS:
hgf1@hgfound.org

WEB SITE ADDRESS:
www.hgfound.org

FOUNDED: 1965

AREAS OF INTEREST:
Growth disorders and pediatrics.

NAME(S) OF PROGRAMS:
● **Small Grants for Research in Field of Short Stature**

TYPE:
Research grants.

YEAR PROGRAM STARTED: 1965

PURPOSE:
To help medical science better understand the process of growth and to help individuals with growth-related disorders, their families and health care professionals through education, research and advocacy.

ELIGIBILITY:
Applicants must be involved in research of the human growth process. Special consideration will be given to young investigators and to projects dealing with psychological, social, and educational aspects of dwarfism and its treatment and to new approaches to diagnosis and management, as well as clinical and basic research in the mechanisms of statural growth disorders of children including chondrodystrophies, genetic, or psychological causes.

FINANCIAL DATA:
Amount of support per award: $10,000 to $15,000.

NUMBER OF APPLICANTS MOST RECENT YEAR:
Over 40.

NUMBER OF AWARDS: Up to 3.

APPLICATION INFORMATION:
Application and guidelines are available from the Foundation. Applicants must first provide a Letter of Intent. Grant applications must be in NIH format.
Duration: One-time funding.
Deadline: Letter of Intent: May 15. Final application: September 1.

ADDRESS INQUIRIES TO:
Patricia D. Costa, Executive Director
(See address above.)

NATIONAL LEUKEMIA RESEARCH ASSOCIATION [2531]
585 Stewart Avenue
Suite LL-18
Garden City, NY 11530
(516) 222-1944
Fax: (516) 222-0457

E-MAIL ADDRESS:
info@childrensleukemia.org

WEB SITE ADDRESS:
www.childrensleukemia.org

FOUNDED: 1965

AREAS OF INTEREST:
Leukemia.

NAME(S) OF PROGRAMS:
● **Children's Leukemia Research Grants**

TYPE:
Research grants. Support for research efforts into the causes and cure of leukemia. Patient aid to families in need while meeting the expenses incurred in leukemia treatment.

YEAR PROGRAM STARTED: 1965

PURPOSE:
To work towards a cure for leukemia; to provide patient aid.

ELIGIBILITY:
Any doctor at the Ph.D. or M.D. level who is involved in research towards finding the causes and cure for leukemia may apply.

FINANCIAL DATA:
Amount of support per award: Up to $30,000 per year.

APPLICATION INFORMATION:
Application form required. Contact Association for other requirements.
Duration: One year. Renewal for a second year is considered if other funding for promising projects has not been obtained.
Deadline: June 30.

ADDRESS INQUIRIES TO:
Allan Weinberg, Executive Director
(See address above.)

SICKKIDS FOUNDATION
525 University Avenue, 14th Floor
Toronto ON M5G 2L3 Canada
(416) 813-6166 ext. 2354
(800) 661-1083
Fax: (416) 813-4912

E-MAIL ADDRESS:
national.grants@sickkidsfoundation.com

WEB SITE ADDRESS:
www.sickkidsfoundation.com/about-us/grants

TYPE:
Awards/prizes; Conferences/seminars; Project/program grants; Research grants. Community Conference Grants program brings together families with researchers and clinicians for medical presentations and family-oriented discussions. It helps ensure knowledge exchange with families so that they are able to access the most up-to-date information about their children's health.

New Investigator Research Grants program focus is to ensure that there continues to be well-trained researchers across the country working to address the most pressing childhood diseases and conditions.

See entry 1463 for full listing.

SOCIETY FOR PEDIATRIC DERMATOLOGY [2532]
8365 Keystone Crossing, Suite 107
Indianapolis, IN 46240
(317) 202-0224
Fax: (317) 205-9481

E-MAIL ADDRESS:
info@pedsderm.net

WEB SITE ADDRESS:
www.pedsderm.net

FOUNDED: 1975

AREAS OF INTEREST:
Pediatric dermatology.

NAME(S) OF PROGRAMS:
● **Pilot Project Award**
● **William Reston Research Award**

TYPE:
Research grants; Seed money grants. Research grants for investigators on the faculty and postdoctoral levels.

PURPOSE:
To foster research in pediatric dermatology.

LEGAL BASIS:
Medical society.

ELIGIBILITY:
Applicants must have completed training in pediatrics or dermatology and be active in

the investigation of pediatric dermatology. Importance of the project and feasibility within the timeframe available are selection criteria.

FINANCIAL DATA:
Amount of support per award: William Reston Research Award: Up to $20,000; Pilot Project Award: Up to $7,500.
Total amount of support: Varies.

NUMBER OF AWARDS: William Reston Research Award: 1; Pilot Project Award: 3.

APPLICATION INFORMATION:
Application form required. Notices also placed in various medical, dermatology and pediatrics publications.
Duration: One year.
Deadline: Mid-April. Notification about mid-May.

ADDRESS INQUIRIES TO:
Awards and Goals Committee
(See address above.)

THRASHER RESEARCH FUND   [2533]
68 South Main Street, Suite 400
Salt Lake City, UT 84101
(801) 240-4753
Fax: (801) 240-1625

E-MAIL ADDRESS:
martinezaf@thrasherresearch.org

WEB SITE ADDRESS:
www.thrasherresearch.org

FOUNDED: 1977

AREAS OF INTEREST:
Pediatric medical research, with emphasis on clinical/translational research with potential findings that would be clinically applicable in a short period of time in the prevention, diagnosis and/or treatment of pediatric medical problems.

TYPE:
Research grants. Grants for support of research that addresses problems in children's health in areas of critical illnesses that have been insufficiently researched or investigated. The Fund assumes that significant solutions to children's health problems remain undiscovered and invites a broad array of applications designed to remedy these deficiencies.

YEAR PROGRAM STARTED: 1977

PURPOSE:
To provide grants for pediatric medical research that addresses problems in children's health that are significant in terms of either magnitude or severity.

LEGAL BASIS:
Private organization.

ELIGIBILITY:
The Fund supports medical research that seeks to prevent or cure children's critical illnesses, injuries and disabilities. Projects should:
(1) be scientifically sound and culturally appropriate;
(2) document methods and practices that have sustainable benefits;
(3) have specific aims and a well-designed methodology and;
(4) evaluate the significance of impact on children's health.

Funding is limited to research. The Fund does not award grants for general operations, construction or renovation of buildings or facilities, nor does the Fund award grants for general donations, loans, student aid, scholarships, educational programs or support of other funds or institutions.

The Fund excludes research using human fetal tissue, stem cell research, or behavioral science research.

FINANCIAL DATA:
Financial support may be provided for supplies, minor equipment and technical personnel assistance related to a specific Fund-sponsored project. Principal investigators in need of salary support for a specific project may apply for 20% support, based on federal guidelines.
Amount of support per award: $25,000 to $500,000. Typically $100,000 to $300,000.
Total amount of support: Varies.

NUMBER OF APPLICANTS MOST RECENT YEAR:
100.

NUMBER OF AWARDS: 18.

APPLICATION INFORMATION:
Application guidelines are available on the Fund's web site. Potential applicants are encouraged to contact Fund staff prior to a formal submission to determine the potential fit of a project with current Fund interests.
Duration: Up to three years.

PUBLICATIONS:
Brochure; application information.

STAFF:
R. Justin Brown, M.P.H., President and Research Manager
Megan Duncan, M.P.H., Research Manager
Aaron V. Pontsler, M.S., MBA, Research Manager

U.S. DEPARTMENT OF HEALTH AND HUMAN SERVICES
Maternal and Child Health Bureau
Parklawn Building, Room 18-31
5600 Fishers Lane
Rockville, MD 20857
(301) 443-2204
Fax: (301) 443-9354

E-MAIL ADDRESS:
CallCenter@hrsa.gov (grants information)

WEB SITE ADDRESS:
www.mchb.hrsa.gov
www.hrsa.gov

TYPE:
Block grants. The Title V Block Grant Program has as a general purpose the improvement of the health of all mothers and children in the nation. The Block Grant Program has three components: Formula Block Grants to 59 states and other political jurisdictions, Special Projects of Regional and National Significance (SPRANS), and Community Integrated Service Systems (CISS) Grants.

See entry 2502 for full listing.

Pharmacology

AMERICAN ASSOCIATION OF COLLEGES OF PHARMACY   [2534]
1727 King Street, Floor 2
Alexandria, VA 22314
(703) 739-2330
Fax: (703) 836-8982

E-MAIL ADDRESS:
nia@aacp.org

WEB SITE ADDRESS:
www.aacp.org

FOUNDED: 1900

AREAS OF INTEREST:
Pharmaceutical education.

NAME(S) OF PROGRAMS:
• New Investigator Award

TYPE:
Research grants.

YEAR PROGRAM STARTED: 1985

PURPOSE:
To provide start-up funds for new faculty members to assist in establishing a research program; to assist new faculty in establishing themselves as independent investigators.

LEGAL BASIS:
Nonprofit foundation, tax-exempt under the IRS Code.

ELIGIBILITY:
Applicants must have earned terminal degrees in their disciplines (Pharm.D., Ph.D.), hold a regular full-time academic faculty appointment in a college or school of pharmacy, hold the rank of assistant professor, and be in the first to fifth year of their academic appointment. The applicant must be a current individual member of AACP. Only one application per investigator will be accepted for review.

A faculty member who has been a principle investigator on an AACP, NIA, NPFRAP or equivalent starter grant, on a professional (e.g., ACCP, ASHP, AAPS, PhRMA, etc.), organizational (e.g., American Heart or American Cancer) or federal grant (e.g., NIH, NSF, AHRQ, DOD, CDC, etc.) is not eligible to apply.

Intramural university or college/school start-up support may be used for supplementing the proposed research.

GEOGRAPHIC RESTRICTIONS:
United States.

FINANCIAL DATA:
No overhead allowed. In addition to grant monies, each award winner will receive $1,000 for required travel to the AACP Annual Meeting.
Amount of support per award: $10,000 maximum.

NUMBER OF APPLICANTS MOST RECENT YEAR:
113.

NUMBER OF AWARDS: Up to 18.

APPLICATION INFORMATION:
Application specifics are available on the AACP web site.
Duration: One year.
Deadline: Letter of Intent: Early August. Full Proposal: Early September.

PUBLICATIONS:
Program announcement.

OFFICERS:
Lucinda Maine, Executive Vice President and
Chief Executive Officer

ADDRESS INQUIRIES TO:
Vincent Lau, Vice President, Research and
Graduate Affairs
(See address above.)

AMERICAN FOUNDATION FOR PHARMACEUTICAL EDUCATION (AFPE)   [2535]
6076 Franconia Road, Suite C
Alexandria, VA 22310-1758
(703) 875-3095
Fax: (703) 875-3098

E-MAIL ADDRESS:
info@afpenet.org

WEB SITE ADDRESS:
www.afpenet.org

FOUNDED: 1942

AREAS OF INTEREST:
Pharmaceutical education.

NAME(S) OF PROGRAMS:
- **Phi Lambda Sigma-GlaxoSmithKline-AFPE First Year Graduate Scholarship**
- **Rho Chi-Schering Plough-AFPE First Year Graduate Scholarship**

TYPE:
Scholarships. Phi Lambda
Sigma-GlaxoSmithKline-AFPE First Year
Graduate Scholarship encourages outstanding
Phi Lambda Sigma members to pursue the
Ph.D. in a college of pharmacy graduate
program.

Rho Chi-Schering Plough-AFPE First Year
Graduate Scholarship encourages outstanding
Rho Chi Honor Society members to pursue
the Ph.D. in a college of pharmacy graduate
program.

YEAR PROGRAM STARTED: 1985

PURPOSE:
To encourage outstanding Rho Chi and Phi
Lambda Sigma members to continue their
education in a graduate program for the
Ph.D. in a college of pharmacy.

LEGAL BASIS:
Nonprofit foundation, tax-exempt under the
IRS Code.

ELIGIBILITY:
Phi Lambda Sigma-GlaxoSmithKline-AFPE
Scholarship: Applicants must be in the final
year of a pharmacy B.S. or Pharm.D.
program and be a member of Phi Lambda
Sigma. U.S. citizenship or permanent resident
status is required.

Rho Chi-Schering Plough-AFPE Scholarship:
An applicant must be a senior pharmacy
student enrolled in a dual-degree pathway
leading to a professional degree in pharmacy
and the Ph.D., or first-year graduate students,
entering a graduate Ph.D. program in an
accredited school or college of pharmacy as a
full-time student. Applicants must be in the
final year of professional studies or have
completed professional studies. U.S.
citizenship or permanent resident status is
required. Applicants must be members of the
Rho Chi Honor Society.

GEOGRAPHIC RESTRICTIONS:
United States.

FINANCIAL DATA:
Phi Lambda Sigma-GlaxoSmithKline-AFPE:
The scholarship may be used for any purpose
decided by the awardee and faculty sponsor
that will enable the student to have a
successful program, i.e., student stipend,
laboratory supplies, books, materials, travel,
etc., related to the program of graduate study.
None of the funds shall be used for indirect
costs by the institution. Funding will be
provided in two equal stipends on September
1 and February 1.
Amount of support per award: $7,500.
Total amount of support: $15,000.

NUMBER OF APPLICANTS MOST RECENT YEAR:
12.

NUMBER OF AWARDS: 1 of each.

APPLICATION INFORMATION:
For the Phi Lambda Sigma Award, the
following information should be sent to Mary
Euler, Executive Director of Phi Lambda
Sigma National Office, c/o University of
Charleston School of Pharmacy, 2300
MacCorkle, S.E., Charleston, WV 25304;
Tel: (304) 357-4860; E-mail:
exec.director@philambdasigma.org:
(1) letters of recommendation from two
college faculty members who are acquainted
with the student and his or her potential for
graduate study;
(2) name of the graduate school the student
plans to attend (if known);
(3) a one- to two-page statement by applicant
elaborating reasons for wishing to attend
graduate school;
(4) a list of special honors, awards and
accomplishments in high school and college
reflecting achievement and ability to succeed
in graduate school and;
(5) an official transcript of all collegiate
grades and copies of GRE, SAT and other
national achievement test scores.

For the Rho Chi Scholarship, application
forms are available from Rho Chi Faculty
Advisors or the Secretary of Rho Chi.
Required information should be sent to: The
Rho Chi Society National Office, UNC
School of Pharmacy, 3210 Kerr Hall, CB No.
7360, Chapel Hill, NC 27599-7360; Tel:
(919) 843-9001; E-mail: rhochi@unc.edu.
The packet should include the following:
(1) a completed application form;
(2) a one-page description of present
academic status including all previous
scholarships and fellowships and
memberships in professional, scientific,
scholastic and honor societies;
(3) a one-page account of involvement in
professional and extracurricular activities, list
of proposed expenses for the year; if married,
include spouse and family expenses; list all
sources and amounts of income;
(4) name of university to be attended and
planned field of study;
(5) graduate record examination scores;
(6) a one- to two-page statement describing
career goals;
(7) official transcripts from all colleges or
universities attended and;
(8) letters of reference from three individuals
who are directly familiar with the applicant
and can speak specifically to educational
achievements and capacity for graduate study.
Duration: One academic year.
Deadline: February 1. Notification by April
15.

PUBLICATIONS:
Program announcement.

OFFICERS:
Robert M. Bachman, President

ADDRESS INQUIRIES TO:
Sherri Hunter, Grants Manager
(See address above.)

AMERICAN FOUNDATION FOR PHARMACEUTICAL EDUCATION (AFPE)   [2536]
6076 Franconia Road, Suite C
Alexandria, VA 22310-1758
(703) 875-3095
Fax: (703) 875-3098

E-MAIL ADDRESS:
info@afpenet.org

WEB SITE ADDRESS:
www.afpenet.org

FOUNDED: 1942

AREAS OF INTEREST:
Pharmaceutical education.

NAME(S) OF PROGRAMS:
- **Kappa Epsilon-AFPE-Nellie Wakeman First Year Graduate Fellowship**

TYPE:
Fellowships.

PURPOSE:
To encourage an outstanding pharmacy
school graduate to pursue an advanced
degree in the pharmaceutical sciences.

ELIGIBILITY:
An applicant must be in the final year of a
pharmacy college B.S. or Pharm.D. program
or have completed a pharmacy degree.
Consideration is given to those who need
financial assistance to further their education
in pharmacy. At the time of application, the
Kappa Epsilon member must be in good
financial standing with the KE Fraternity and
planning to pursue a Doctor of Philosophy
(Ph.D.) degree, a Master's degree, or a
combined Residency/Master's degree
program at a U.S. college or school of
pharmacy. Applicants may apply annually
and receive up to three years of financial
support.

FINANCIAL DATA:
The funds may be used for any purpose
decided by the awardee and faculty sponsor
that will enable the student to have a
successful program, e.g., student stipend,
laboratory supplies, books, materials, travel
related to the program of study. None of the
funds shall be used for indirect costs by the
institution.
Amount of support per award: $7,500.
Total amount of support: $7,500.

NUMBER OF AWARDS: 1.

APPLICATION INFORMATION:
Applications can be downloaded from the
web site. Applications must include:
(1) a completed application form (application
and reference forms available from a Kappa
Epsilon faculty advisor or the Kappa Epsilon
Executive Office, Tel: (913) 262-2749);
(2) a letter of recommendation from the
faculty advisor and one other faculty member
familiar with the applicant (both faculty
members are to complete a letter of reference
form) and;
(3) official transcripts of all collegiate grades,
undergraduate and graduate.
Applications should be sent to the Kappa
Epsilon Executive Office: 7700 Shawnee
Mission Parkway, Suite 201, Overland Park,
KS 66202.

Duration: One year.

Deadline: All application materials must be received by February 1. Notification by March.

ADDRESS INQUIRIES TO:
Yona Mead, Grants Manager
(See address above.)

AMERICAN INSTITUTE OF THE HISTORY OF PHARMACY [2537]
University of Wisconsin School of Pharmacy
Rennebohm Hall
777 Highland Avenue
Madison, WI 53705-2222
(608) 262-5378

E-MAIL ADDRESS:
gia@aihp.org

WEB SITE ADDRESS:
www.aihp.org

AREAS OF INTEREST:
History of pharmacy.

NAME(S) OF PROGRAMS:
• **Fischelis Grants for Research in the History of American Pharmacy**
• **History of Pharmacy Thesis Research Grants-in-Aid**

TYPE:
Grants-in-aid; Research grants.

PURPOSE:
To contribute to the understanding of the development of civilization by fostering the creation, preservation and dissemination of knowledge concerning the history and related humanistic aspects of the pharmaceutical field.

ELIGIBILITY:
For grants-in-aid, applicants must be Ph.D. students in good standing at an institution of the U.S. Students need not be American citizens, nor does the research topic have to be related to American history. Thesis research must be clearly related to some aspect of pharmaceutical history or some other humanistic investigation that utilizes a pharmaco-historical approach.

For Fischelis Grants, applicants do not have to be U.S. citizens, but must attend American institutions.

FINANCIAL DATA:
Grants-in-Aid only cover direct costs of research attributable to supplies and other expenses that cannot be reimbursed by the degree-granting institution itself. These can include computer time and programming, obtaining a photocopy or microform of essential sources, travel and maintenance at a site away from the home university. Ineligible expenses include routine typing of the manuscript, living expenses at the home university, publication of research results or routine illustrations for the manuscript.

Amount of support per award: Fischelis Grants: Varies; Grants-in-Aid: Up to $2,500.

APPLICATION INFORMATION:
Application forms required for both programs. For Grants-in-Aid, application must be no longer than four pages and must include identifying information of the graduate student, educational background, faculty reference information, thesis topic and description, estimate of expenses, statement of other financial support applied for and other information considered important to the proper consideration of the application.

Deadline: February 1.

ADDRESS INQUIRIES TO:
Beth D. Fisher
Director of Curatorial Affairs
(See address above.)

AMERICAN SOCIETY OF REGIONAL ANESTHESIA AND PAIN MEDICINE   [2538]
239 4th Avenue, Suite 1714
Pittsburgh, PA 15222
(412) 471-2718
Fax: (412) 471-7503

E-MAIL ADDRESS:
asraassistant@kenes.com

WEB SITE ADDRESS:
www.asra.com

AREAS OF INTEREST:
Anesthesia and pain medicine.

NAME(S) OF PROGRAMS:
• **ASRA Carl Koller Memorial Research Grant**

TYPE:
Research grants.

PURPOSE:
To support research related to any aspect of regional anesthesia, acute and chronic pain medicine and their application to surgery, obstetrics and pain control; to encourage anesthesiologists and other researchers who are interested in the field.

ELIGIBILITY:
Applicant must be a member of the ASRA.

FINANCIAL DATA:
Amount of support per award: $500 to $50,000.

Total amount of support: Up to $75,000 biennially.

NUMBER OF APPLICANTS MOST RECENT YEAR:
17.

NUMBER OF AWARDS: 1.

APPLICATION INFORMATION:
The application, which must be written by the applicant, should be accompanied by a complete narrative research protocol. The research proposal must be concerned with an original idea or concept. The research must be carried out primarily by the applicant.

Deadline: September 1.

PHARMACEUTICAL RESEARCH AND MANUFACTURERS OF AMERICA FOUNDATION, INC.   [2539]
950 F Street, N.W.
Suite 300
Washington, DC 20004
(202) 572-7756
Fax: (202) 572-7799

E-MAIL ADDRESS:
foundation@phrma.org

WEB SITE ADDRESS:
www.phrmafoundation.org

AREAS OF INTEREST:
Pharmacology and clinical pharmacology.

NAME(S) OF PROGRAMS:
• **The Paul Calabresi Medical Student Research Fellowship**

TYPE:
Fellowships.

PURPOSE:
To generate interest in research careers in pharmacology, including clinical pharmacology, among medical and dental students.

ELIGIBILITY:
Candidates must be enrolled in a U.S. medical/dental school and have finished at least one year of the school curriculum. Must be U.S. citizen or permanent resident and have firm commitment from an accredited U.S. school.

GEOGRAPHIC RESTRICTIONS:
United States.

FINANCIAL DATA:
Amount of support per award: Maximum stipend $18,000.

NUMBER OF AWARDS: 2 budgeted.

APPLICATION INFORMATION:
Applications are to be submitted online by an accredited U.S. school. The following information will be requested on the application:
(1) registration information including basic contact information, as well as information on citizenship;
(2) an extended letter containing the candidate's name, personal data, education and training, a curriculum vitae, information regarding prior research experience, and a bibliography, if available. The name of the immediate supervisor of the student must be stated and their relation to the project indicated. The supervisor's curriculum vitae and bibliography are to be submitted in NIH format/PHS 398. Limit document to no more than three pages and;
(3) a description of the proposed research, including the background, aims, methods, significance and facilities available. Please type, single space, font size 12-point or larger and number pages. This portion should be five pages not including the bibliography. The candidate must state how the fellowship will assist them in making a choice on the type of career in pharmacology or clinical pharmacology they will pursue. This letter should outline the chronology of the student's medical/dental education indicating exactly where in the process from matriculation to graduation the fellowship falls. The candidate should list any other support they are receiving.

Duration: Three months to two years.

Deadline: February 1. Announcement May 15.

ADDRESS INQUIRIES TO:
The Paul Calabresi Medical
Student Research Fellowship
(See address above.)

*SPECIAL STIPULATIONS:
Commitment must be full-time. Student may undertake this investigative effort at their own school or another institution.

PHARMACEUTICAL RESEARCH AND MANUFACTURERS OF AMERICA FOUNDATION, INC.   [2540]
950 F Street, N.W.
Suite 300
Washington, DC 20004
(202) 572-7756
Fax: (202) 572-7799

E-MAIL ADDRESS:
foundation@phrma.org

WEB SITE ADDRESS:
www.phrmafoundation.org

FOUNDED: 1965

AREAS OF INTEREST:
Pharmaceutics.

NAME(S) OF PROGRAMS:
- **Postdoctoral Fellowships in Pharmaceutics**

TYPE:
Fellowships.

YEAR PROGRAM STARTED: 1992

PURPOSE:
To encourage more qualified graduates from Ph.D. programs in pharmaceutics to obtain postdoctoral research training in the area of pharmaceutics.

LEGAL BASIS:
501(c)(3) organization.

ELIGIBILITY:
Applicants must either hold a Ph.D. degree in a field of study logically or functionally related to the proposed postdoctoral activities or expect to receive such a degree before activating the fellowship. Suitable facilities for the necessary training and research must be available to the applicant. U.S. citizenship or permanent residency in the U.S. is required. Applicant must have firm commitment from an accredited U.S. university.

GEOGRAPHIC RESTRICTIONS:
United States.

FINANCIAL DATA:
The award is made to the institution on behalf of the Fellow. The program provides no other subsidies (travel, tuition, fringe benefit costs, etc.) and indirect costs are not paid to the institution.
Amount of support per award: Maximum $80,000 ($40,000 per year).

NUMBER OF APPLICANTS MOST RECENT YEAR:
10.

NUMBER OF AWARDS: 2 budgeted.

APPLICATION INFORMATION:
Applications are to be submitted online by an accredited U.S. school.
Duration: Two years.
Deadline: September 1 for awards beginning January through December of the following year. Announcement December 15.

PUBLICATIONS:
Brochure.

IRS IDENTIFICATION NUMBER: 52-6063009

BOARD OF DIRECTORS:
Elias A. Zerhouni, M.D., Chairman
John Castellani
Thomas O. Daniel, M.D.
G. Mikael Dolsten, M.D., Ph.D.
Glenn J. Gormley, M.D., Ph.D.
Jan M. Lundberg, Ph.D.
Michael Rosenblatt, M.D.
Moncef Slaoui, Ph.D.
Tadataka Yamada, M.D.

ADVISORY COMMITTEE:
Darrell R. Abernethy, M.D., Ph.D., Chairman
Terry L. Bowlin, Ph.D.
Jean Paul Gagnon, Ph.D.
Michael J. Hageman, Ph.D.
Michael N. Liebman, Ph.D.

ADDRESS INQUIRIES TO:
Postdoctoral Fellowships in Pharmaceutics (See address above.)

*SPECIAL STIPULATIONS:
The second year of this award is contingent upon a progress report approved by the Foundation and submission of a financial report.

PHARMACEUTICAL RESEARCH AND MANUFACTURERS OF AMERICA FOUNDATION, INC. [2541]

950 F Street, N.W.
Suite 300
Washington, DC 20004
(202) 572-7756
Fax: (202) 572-7799

E-MAIL ADDRESS:
foundation@phrma.org

WEB SITE ADDRESS:
www.phrmafoundation.org

FOUNDED: 1965

AREAS OF INTEREST:
Pharmaceutics.

NAME(S) OF PROGRAMS:
- **Predoctoral Fellowships in Pharmaceutics**

TYPE:
Fellowships. Support for full-time research for promising students in the field of pharmaceutics during their thesis research.

YEAR PROGRAM STARTED: 1987

PURPOSE:
To support promising students in the area of pharmaceutics during their thesis research.

LEGAL BASIS:
501(c)(3) organization.

ELIGIBILITY:
Applicants must be full-time, in-residence Ph.D. candidates in the field of pharmaceutics who are enrolled in schools of pharmacy and who expect to complete the requirements for the Ph.D. in two years or less from the time the fellowship begins. The program seeks to support advanced students who will have completed the bulk of their pre-thesis requirements (generally two years of study) and are starting their thesis research by the time the award is activated. Students just starting in graduate school should not apply. Applicants must be U.S. citizens or permanent residents and have a firm commitment from an accredited U.S. university.

GEOGRAPHIC RESTRICTIONS:
United States.

FINANCIAL DATA:
The award is made to the university on behalf of the Fellow and provides a stipend, payable monthly, which includes up to $1,000 for incidentals directly associated with the thesis research.
Amount of support per award: Maximum $40,000 ($20,000 per year), which includes up to $1,000 per year for expenses associated with thesis research.

NUMBER OF APPLICANTS MOST RECENT YEAR:
16.

NUMBER OF AWARDS: 7.

APPLICATION INFORMATION:
Applications are to be submitted on the Foundation web site.

Duration: Up to two years.
Deadline: September 1 for awards beginning January through August of the following year. Announcement December 15.

PUBLICATIONS:
Brochure.

IRS IDENTIFICATION NUMBER: 52-6063009

BOARD OF DIRECTORS:
Elias A. Zerhouni, M.D., Chairman
John Castellani
Thomas O. Daniel, M.D.
G. Mikael Dolsten, M.D., Ph.D.
Glenn J. Gormley, M.D., Ph.D.
Jan M. Lundberg, Ph.D.
Michael Rosenblatt, M.D.
Moncef Slaoui, Ph.D.
Tadataka Yamada, M.D.

ADVISORY COMMITTEE:
Darrell R. Abernethy, M.D., Ph.D., Chairman
Terry L. Bowlin, Ph.D.
Jean Paul Gagnon, Ph.D.
Michael J. Hageman, Ph.D.
Michael N. Liebman, Ph.D.

ADDRESS INQUIRIES TO:
See e-mail address above.

PHARMACEUTICAL RESEARCH AND MANUFACTURERS OF AMERICA FOUNDATION, INC. [2542]

950 F Street, N.W.
Suite 300
Washington, DC 20004
(202) 572-7756
Fax: (202) 572-7799

E-MAIL ADDRESS:
foundation@phrma.org

WEB SITE ADDRESS:
www.phrmafoundation.org

FOUNDED: 1965

AREAS OF INTEREST:
Pharmacology, clinical pharmacology, drug toxicology, pharmaceutics, informatics and health outcomes.

NAME(S) OF PROGRAMS:
- **Research Starter Grants in Adherence Improvement**
- **Research Starter Grants in Health Outcomes**
- **Research Starter Grants in Informatics**
- **Research Starter Grants in Pharmaceutics**
- **Research Starter Grants in Pharmacology/Toxicology**
- **Research Starter Grants in Translational Medicine**

TYPE:
Project/program grants; Research grants; Seed money grants. Starter grants to support research in the fields of pharmacology, clinical pharmacology, drug toxicology, pharmaceutics, informatics and health outcomes.

YEAR PROGRAM STARTED: 1972

PURPOSE:
To offer financial support to individuals beginning their independent research careers at the faculty level.

LEGAL BASIS:
501(c)(3) organization.

ELIGIBILITY:
Applicant must be a U.S. citizen or permanent resident. Those holding the

academic rank of instructor or assistant professor and investigators at the doctoral level with equivalent positions are eligible to apply, providing their proposed research is neither directly nor indirectly subsidized to any significant degree by an extramural support mechanism.

GEOGRAPHIC RESTRICTIONS:
United States.

FINANCIAL DATA:
Funds are generally unrestricted, to provide resources directly related to the proposed research. Funds may not be used as salary support for the applicant nor for indirect costs to the institution. No more than $1,000 per year may be used for travel to professional meetings.
Amount of support per award: $100,000.
Total amount of support: Varies.

APPLICATION INFORMATION:
Applications should be submitted on the Foundation web site.
Duration: One year.
Deadline: Adherence Improvement: October 1 for awards beginning January 1 of the following year; Health Outcomes and Translational: February 1 for awards beginning January 1 of the following year; Pharmaceutics, Pharmacology/Toxicology and Informatics: September 1 for awards beginning January 1 of the following year. Announcements December 15.

PUBLICATIONS:
Brochure.

IRS IDENTIFICATION NUMBER: 52-6063009

BOARD OF DIRECTORS:
Elias A. Zerhouni, M.D., Chairman
John Castellani
Thomas O. Daniel, M.D.
G. Mikael Dolsten, M.D., Ph.D.
Glenn J. Gormley, M.D., Ph.D.
Jan M. Lundberg, Ph.D.
Michael Rosenblatt, M.D.
Moncef Slaoui, Ph.D.
Tadataka Yamada, M.D.

ADVISORY COMMITTEE:
Darrell R. Abernethy, M.D., Ph.D., Chairman
Terry L. Bowlin, Ph.D.
Jean Paul Gagnon, Ph.D.
Michael J. Hageman, Ph.D.
Michael N. Liebman, Ph.D.

ADDRESS INQUIRIES TO:
See e-mail address above.

PHARMACEUTICAL RESEARCH AND MANUFACTURERS OF AMERICA FOUNDATION, INC.   [2543]
950 F Street, N.W.
Suite 300
Washington, DC 20004
(202) 572-7756
Fax: (202) 572-7799

E-MAIL ADDRESS:
foundation@phrma.org

WEB SITE ADDRESS:
www.phrmafoundation.org

FOUNDED: 1965

AREAS OF INTEREST:
Pharmacology or toxicology.

NAME(S) OF PROGRAMS:
● **Predoctoral Fellowships in Pharmacology/Toxicology**

TYPE:
Fellowships. Support for full-time research for promising students in the fields of pharmacology or toxicology during their thesis research.

YEAR PROGRAM STARTED: 1978

PURPOSE:
To support promising students during their thesis research.

LEGAL BASIS:
501(c)(3) organization.

ELIGIBILITY:
Applicants must be full-time, in-residence Ph.D. candidates in the fields of pharmacology or toxicology who are enrolled in schools of medicine, dentistry, or veterinary medicine and who expect to complete the requirements for the Ph.D. in two years or less from the time the fellowship begins. The program seeks to support advanced students who will have completed the bulk of their pre-thesis requirements (generally two years of study) and are starting their thesis research by the time the award is activated. Students just starting in graduate school should not apply. Applicant must be a U.S. citizen or a permanent resident and must have a firm commitment from an accredited U.S. university. One application per institution accepted.

GEOGRAPHIC RESTRICTIONS:
United States.

FINANCIAL DATA:
The award is made to the university on behalf of the Fellow and provides a stipend which includes up to $1,000 a year for incidentals directly associated with the thesis research.
Amount of support per award: Maximum $40,000 ($20,000 per year).

NUMBER OF APPLICANTS MOST RECENT YEAR:
53.

NUMBER OF AWARDS: Varies.

APPLICATION INFORMATION:
Applications should be submitted on the Foundation web site.
Duration: Up to two years.
Deadline: September 1 for awards beginning January through August of the following year. Announcement December 15.

PUBLICATIONS:
Brochure.

IRS IDENTIFICATION NUMBER: 52-6063009

BOARD OF DIRECTORS:
Elias A. Zerhouni, M.D., Chairman
John Castellani
Thomas O. Daniel, M.D.
G. Mikael Dolsten, M.D., Ph.D.
Glenn J. Gormley, M.D., Ph.D.
Jan M. Lundberg, Ph.D.
Michael Rosenblatt, M.D.
Moncef Slaoui, Ph.D.
Tadataka Yamada, M.D.

ADVISORY COMMITTEE:
Darrell R. Abernethy, M.D., Ph.D., Chairman
Terry L. Bowlin, Ph.D.
Jean Paul Gagnon, Ph.D.
Michael J. Hageman, Ph.D.
Michael N. Liebman, Ph.D.

ADDRESS INQUIRIES TO:
See e-mail address above.

PHI DELTA CHI PHARMACY FRATERNITY   [2544]
P.O. Box 320
Pinckney, MI 48169
(800) 732-1883

E-MAIL ADDRESS:
office@phideltachi.org

WEB SITE ADDRESS:
www.phideltachi.org

FOUNDED: 1883

AREAS OF INTEREST:
Leadership development and professional/service projects.

CONSULTING OR VOLUNTEER SERVICES:
Leadership development.

NAME(S) OF PROGRAMS:
● **Rand P. Hollenback Scholarship Program**

TYPE:
Scholarships.

YEAR PROGRAM STARTED: 1970

PURPOSE:
To improve scholarship within a Phi Delta Chi Chapter and/or School of Pharmacy.

LEGAL BASIS:
Professional fraternity.

ELIGIBILITY:
Phi Delta Chi membership required.

FINANCIAL DATA:
Amount of support per award: $100 to $150.
Total amount of support: $375.

NUMBER OF APPLICANTS MOST RECENT YEAR:
60.

NUMBER OF AWARDS: 3.

APPLICATION INFORMATION:
Selection is based on reports from Phi Delta Chi Chapters.
Duration: One-time award.
Deadline: May 31 of each year. Announcement in August of the following year.

PUBLICATIONS:
The Communicator.

OFFICERS:
Amy Valdez, President
Traci Thompson, Vice President for Alumni Affairs
Lexie Turner, Vice President for Collegiate Affairs
Ryan Costantino, Vice President for Communications
John Mondin, Vice President for Student Affairs
Kenny Walkup, Executive Director

ADDRESS INQUIRIES TO:
Kenny Walkup, Executive Director
(See address above.)

THE UNIVERSITY OF SYDNEY   [2545]
Scholarships Office
Level 5, Jane Foss Russell Building G02
The University of Sydney N.S.W. 2006
Australia
(02) 8627 8112
Fax: (02) 8627 8485

E-MAIL ADDRESS:
research.training@sydney.edu.au

WEB SITE ADDRESS:
www.sydney.edu.au/scholarships/research

FOUNDED: 1850

AREAS OF INTEREST:
Pharmacy.

NAME(S) OF PROGRAMS:
- **Elizabeth Wunsch Postgraduate Research Scholarship in Pharmacy**

TYPE:
Scholarships.

YEAR PROGRAM STARTED: 1982

PURPOSE:
To promote and encourage research work within the Faculty of Pharmacy at the University of Sydney.

LEGAL BASIS:
University.

ELIGIBILITY:
Open to graduates of the University of Sydney or any other university who are eligible to enroll in a higher degree in the Faculty of Pharmacy on a topic approved by the Head of the Department.

FINANCIAL DATA:
The scholarship does not cover tuition fees payable by international students.
Amount of support per award: $24,653 AUD per annum for the year 2013.

NUMBER OF AWARDS: 1 offered as vacancy occurs and funds are available.

APPLICATION INFORMATION:
Contact the University for guidelines.
Duration: Master's research degree: Two years; Ph.D. degree: Three years.

ADDRESS INQUIRIES TO:
Faculty of Pharmacy
The University of Sydney
N.S.W. 2006 Australia
Tel: (02) 9036 7243
Fax: (02) 9351 4391
E-mail: pharmacy.pg@sydney.edu.au

*PLEASE NOTE:
Very few awards are available and competition for them is extremely keen. They are awarded strictly on academic merit and only graduates with First Class Honours or equivalent qualifications (e.g., graduation magna cum laude) will be considered.

*SPECIAL STIPULATIONS:
Scholarships are tenable at the University of Sydney. Holder is required to enroll for a higher degree.

Physical medicine and rehabilitation

AMERICAN BURN ASSOCIATION [2546]

311 South Wacker Drive
Suite 4150
Chicago, IL 60606
(312) 642-9260
Fax: (312) 642-9130

E-MAIL ADDRESS:
info@ameriburn.org

WEB SITE ADDRESS:
www.ameriburn.org

AREAS OF INTEREST:
Thermal injury.

NAME(S) OF PROGRAMS:
- **International Education Exchange Program**
- **Cheryl Jordan Scholarship Fund**
- **Visiting Professor Program**

TYPE:
Exchange programs; Professorships; Travel grants.

PURPOSE:
To support efforts that address the problems of burn injuries and burn victims; to provide care and rehabilitation to burn patients, conduct burn-related research, educate burn team members, develop and implement burn injury prevention programs, fight fires and address the psychosocial needs of burn victims.

ELIGIBILITY:
Institutions of higher learning in the U.S. and its territories are eligible to apply for support of appropriate research to be conducted by qualified investigators.

GEOGRAPHIC RESTRICTIONS:
United States and Canada.

FINANCIAL DATA:
Amount of support per award: $1,500 to $2,000, depending on the award.

NUMBER OF AWARDS: 1 each annually.

APPLICATION INFORMATION:
Applicants must submit a brief letter outlining the purpose of the grant.

ADDRESS INQUIRIES TO:
John Krichbaum, Executive Director
(See address above.)

AMERICAN GERIATRICS SOCIETY [2547]

40 Fulton Street, 18th Floor
New York, NY 10038
(212) 308-1414
Fax: (212) 832-8646

E-MAIL ADDRESS:
info@americangeriatrics.org

WEB SITE ADDRESS:
www.americangeriatrics.org

AREAS OF INTEREST:
Problems of the aged.

NAME(S) OF PROGRAMS:
- **Clinical Student Research Award**
- **Clinician of the Year**
- **Edward Henderson Student Award**
- **Dennis W. Jahnigen Memorial Award**
- **Merck/AGS New Investigator Awards**
- **Nascher/Manning Award**
- **Outstanding Junior Clinical Education Manuscript**
- **Outstanding Junior Clinical Teacher of the Year**
- **Outstanding Junior Investigator of the Year**
- **Outstanding Junior Research Manuscript**
- **Outstanding Mid-Career Clinical Teacher of the Year**
- **Outstanding Scientific Achievement for Clinical Investigation Award**
- **Scientist-in-Training Research Award**

TYPE:
Awards/prizes. The AGS Student Research Award is presented to the student who submitted the most outstanding student abstract for the AGS Annual Meeting.

Clinician of the Year was established to recognize the great contributions of practitioners to the delivery of quality health care to older people, and the importance of the geriatrics clinician in our health care delivery system.

Edward Henderson Student Award is presented to a medical student interested in pursuing a career in geriatrics who has demonstrated excellence in the field.

Dennis W. Jahnigen Memorial Award is given annually to an AGS member who has provided leadership to train students in geriatrics and has contributed significantly to the progress of geriatrics education in health professions schools.

Merck/AGS New Investigator Awards are presented to individuals whose original research, as presented in a submitted abstract, reflects new and relevant research in geriatrics.

Nascher/Manning Award recognizes distinguished, lifelong achievement in clinical geriatrics, including medicine, psychiatry, and all other related disciplines.

Outstanding Scientific Achievement for Clinical Investigation Award recognizes outstanding achievement in clinical research addressing health care problems of older adults by an investigator who is actively involved in direct patient care.

PURPOSE:
To encourage and promote the field of geriatrics and to stress the importance of medical research in the field of aging; to recognize individuals whose outstanding work in geriatrics education, research and clinical practice contribute to the delivery of high-quality care for older people.

FINANCIAL DATA:
Amount of support per award: Clinical Student Research Award, Edward Henderson Student Award and Scientist-in-Training Research Award: $500; Clinician of the Year: $2,000; Dennis W. Jahnigen Memorial Award, Nascher/Manning Award and Outstanding Scientific Achievement for Clinical Investigation Award: travel expenses to attend the AGS meeting; Merck/AGS New Investigator Awards: $1,500.

APPLICATION INFORMATION:
Application is posted on the Society web site by mid-August.
Deadline: December 2, 2013.

ADDRESS INQUIRIES TO:
Dennise McAlpin, Manager of Professional Education and Special Projects
(See address above.)

AMERICAN KINESIOTHERAPY ASSOCIATION, INC. [2548]

118 College Drive, Box No. 5142
Hattiesburg, MS 39406
(800) 296-2582
Fax: (601) 266-4445

E-MAIL ADDRESS:
info@akta.org

WEB SITE ADDRESS:
www.akta.org

FOUNDED: 1946

AREAS OF INTEREST:
Kinesiotherapy, including adaptive physical education.

NAME(S) OF PROGRAMS:
- **AKTA Lou Montalvano Memorial Scholarship**

TYPE:
Scholarships. Award for students in AKTA-accredited kinesiotherapy programs.

PURPOSE:
To recognize academic excellence and career planning through funding for educational needs.

LEGAL BASIS:
Incorporated, nonprofit organization.

ELIGIBILITY:
Candidate must be currently enrolled in an AKTA-accredited kinesiotherapy program in a university and have definite intentions to pursue certification and a career in kinesiotherapy. Candidate must be a current member of the AKTA. Past AKTA scholarship winners are ineligible to apply for further AKTA scholarships.

FINANCIAL DATA:
Amount of support per award: $500.
Total amount of support: $500.

NUMBER OF AWARDS: 1 annually.

APPLICATION INFORMATION:
Application process includes college transcripts and three letters of recommendation. Further information is available from the Association.
Duration: One year.
Deadline: October 1.

ADDRESS INQUIRIES TO:
Melissa Ziegler, M.A., R.K.T.
Executive Director
(See e-mail address above.)

THE AMERICAN ORTHOPAEDIC SOCIETY FOR SPORTS MEDICINE (AOSSM)   [2549]

6300 North River Road
Suite 500
Rosemont, IL 60018
(877) 321-3500 (IL only)
(847) 292-4900
Fax: (847) 292-4905

E-MAIL ADDRESS:
bart@aossm.org

WEB SITE ADDRESS:
www.sportsmed.org

FOUNDED: 1972

AREAS OF INTEREST:
Sports medicine.

NAME(S) OF PROGRAMS:
- **AOSSM Young Investigator Grant**

TYPE:
Awards/prizes; Research grants. Grant is intended to encourage junior researchers.

PURPOSE:
To increase the knowledge of and improve the care of sports-related injuries and disease.

ELIGIBILITY:
Grants will be awarded to the principal investigators who fulfill the following criteria:
(1) has not received any peer-reviewed external funding nor any external funding greater than $15,000;
(2) must be an orthopaedic surgeon who has graduated from an approved residency program or is a resident currently in an approved program;

(3) must document and play the primary role in the proposed investigation and;
(4) must stay at the parent institution while completing the project.

FINANCIAL DATA:
Amount of support per award: $40,000 over a 24-month period.
Total amount of support: $40,000 annually.

NUMBER OF AWARDS: 1 or 2.

APPLICATION INFORMATION:
Online submission only.
Duration: Two years.
Deadline: Pre-review deadline: August 15. Final deadline: December 1.

ADDRESS INQUIRIES TO:
Barton J. Mann, Director of Research
(See address above.)

CHILDREN'S BRAIN TUMOR FOUNDATION

274 Madison Avenue
Suite 1004
New York, NY 10016
(212) 448-9494
Fax: (212) 448-1022

E-MAIL ADDRESS:
info@cbtf.org

WEB SITE ADDRESS:
www.cbtf.org

TYPE:
Research grants. Basic science research grants for pediatric brain and spinal cord tumors.

See entry 1113 for full listing.

FOUNDATION FOR PHYSICAL THERAPY, INC.   [2550]

1111 North Fairfax Street
Alexandria, VA 22314-1488
(703) 706-8505
(800) 875-1378 ext. 8505
Fax: (703) 706-8587

E-MAIL ADDRESS:
foundation@apta.org

WEB SITE ADDRESS:
foundation4pt.org

FOUNDED: 1979

AREAS OF INTEREST:
Physical therapy research, investigative studies that add to or refine the body of clinical knowledge on which physical therapy practice is based, and intervention projects involving therapeutic procedures and modalities.

TYPE:
Research grants.

YEAR PROGRAM STARTED: 1998

PURPOSE:
To add to or refine the body of clinical knowledge on which physical therapy practice is based and to evaluate patient interventions.

LEGAL BASIS:
Foundation.

ELIGIBILITY:
Awards are made to qualified physical therapists and physical therapist assistants or groups of investigators. Must be a U.S. citizen or permanent resident. Projects must be sponsored by a U.S. institution or

organization. No funds will be approved to finance cost overruns or deficits on existing projects or to finance projects already in progress.

GEOGRAPHIC RESTRICTIONS:
United States.

FINANCIAL DATA:
Amount of support per award: $40,000 per year.
Total amount of support: $120,000 for the year 2013.

NUMBER OF AWARDS: 3 for the year 2013.

APPLICATION INFORMATION:
Application guidelines and access to the online application system are available on the Foundation's web site.
Duration: One to two years.
Deadline: Proposals are due first week in August.

PUBLICATIONS:
Application guidelines.

IRS IDENTIFICATION NUMBER: 13-6161225

ADDRESS INQUIRIES TO:
Karen Chesbrough
Scientific Program Administrator
(See address above.)

FOUNDATION FOR PHYSICAL THERAPY, INC.   [2551]

1111 North Fairfax Street
Alexandria, VA 22314-1488
(800) 875-1378 ext. 8505
Fax: (703) 706-8587

E-MAIL ADDRESS:
info@foundation4pt.org

WEB SITE ADDRESS:
www.foundation4pt.org

FOUNDED: 1979

AREAS OF INTEREST:
Physical therapy.

NAME(S) OF PROGRAMS:
- **Doctoral Opportunities for Clinicians and Scholars (DOCS) I and II**
- **Florence P. Kendall Doctoral Scholarships**
- **New Investigator Fellowship Training Initiative (NIFTI)**

TYPE:
Fellowships; Scholarships. Fellowships for postdoctoral physical therapy research. Scholarships for physical therapists who intend to pursue physical therapy research as a career.

YEAR PROGRAM STARTED: 1979

PURPOSE:
To provide scholarships that support physical therapists who wish to continue their doctoral coursework and enter the dissertation phase; to provide fellowships that support developing researchers and improve their competitiveness in securing external funding for future research.

LEGAL BASIS:
Foundation.

ELIGIBILITY:
Must be U.S. citizen or permanent resident. Scholarship applicants must be physical therapists or physical therapist assistants pursuing a doctoral degree in physical therapy or a related field with a research

focus related to the clinical practice of physical therapy. Applicants must demonstrate a commitment to research.

Fellowship applicants must be physical therapists or physical therapist assistants who have completed Doctorate, or the professional education degree in physical therapy for those already holding a post-professional doctoral degree in the last five years.

One year of teaching is expected for each year of support.

FINANCIAL DATA:
Amount of support per award: Maximum of $15,000 for scholarships; $78,000 for fellowships.

Total amount of support: PODS I Scholarships: $7,500 annually for a maximum of three years (must reapply each year); PODS II Scholarships: Up to $15,000 annually for a maximum of two years (must reapply each year); Florence P. Kendall Doctoral Scholarships: $5,000; Fellowships: A two-year award totaling $78,000.

NUMBER OF APPLICANTS MOST RECENT YEAR: 75 for the year 2013.

NUMBER OF AWARDS: 15 scholarships for the year 2013.

APPLICATION INFORMATION:
Applicants must check the online eligibility guidelines, review the application instructions, then submit the online application.
Duration: Scholarships: One year; Fellowships: Two years.
Deadline: Mid-January for Program of Doctoral Studies (PODS) Scholarships and New Investigator Fellowship Training Initiative (NIFTI) Fellowships; Mid-August for Florence P. Kendall Doctoral Scholarships.

IRS IDENTIFICATION NUMBER: 13-6161225

ADDRESS INQUIRIES TO:
Karen Chesbrough
Scientific Program Administrator
(See address above.)

INTERNATIONAL ORDER OF ALHAMBRA [2552]
4200 Leeds Avenue
Baltimore, MD 21229-5496
(410) 227-4545
Fax: (941) 486-8833

E-MAIL ADDRESS:
reid003@verizon.net

WEB SITE ADDRESS:
www.orderalhambra.org

FOUNDED: 1904

AREAS OF INTEREST:
Scholarships for those interested in teaching special education.

NAME(S) OF PROGRAMS:
● **Scholarship and Charity Fund**

TYPE:
Grants-in-aid; Scholarships.

YEAR PROGRAM STARTED: 1970

PURPOSE:
To further education in the field of the intellectually disabled.

LEGAL BASIS:
A nonprofit 501(c)(3) fraternal organization of Catholic men and women dedicated to assisting intellectually disabled persons.

ELIGIBILITY:
Applicant should be entering the junior or senior year of college or postgraduate study. Applicants must be majoring in special education, which involves the mentally, physically or emotionally handicapped person, and must be eligible to teach special education upon graduation.

GEOGRAPHIC RESTRICTIONS:
United States and Canada.

FINANCIAL DATA:
Amount of support per award: $1,000 per semester.

NUMBER OF AWARDS: 70 per year.

APPLICATION INFORMATION:
Students may only apply for one semester per application. Call (800) 478-2946 for further information.
Duration: One semester. Renewable by reapplication.

ADDRESS INQUIRIES TO:
Roger Reid, Executive Director
(See address above.)

RUTH JACKSON ORTHOPAEDIC SOCIETY [2553]
6300 North River Road
Suite 727
Rosemont, IL 60018
(847) 698-1626
Fax: (847) 823-0536

E-MAIL ADDRESS:
rjos@aaos.org

WEB SITE ADDRESS:
www.rjos.org

FOUNDED: 1983

AREAS OF INTEREST:
Orthopaedic surgery, musculoskeletal health and osteoporosis.

NAME(S) OF PROGRAMS:
● **Jacquelin Perry, MD Resident Research Award**
● **RJOS Traveling Fellowships**

TYPE:
Awards/prizes; Conferences/seminars; Research grants; Travel grants.

PURPOSE:
To encourage, promote and advance the science and medical art and practice of orthopaedic surgery amongst women; to promote women's musculoskeletal health through scientific, educational and charitable activities.

ELIGIBILITY:
Resident Research Award: Applicant must be a current resident in an accredited orthopaedic surgical residency and must be the primary investigator. Clinical and basic research projects are eligible.

RJOS Traveling Fellowships: Applicant must be a member of RJOS.

FINANCIAL DATA:
Amount of support per award: Jacquelin Perry, MD Resident Research Award: $2,000; RJOS Traveling Fellowships: Up to $6,000.

NUMBER OF AWARDS: Typically one each, annually.

APPLICATION INFORMATION:
Contact the Society for guidelines.
Deadline: October 1.

PUBLICATIONS:
Newsletter.

IRS IDENTIFICATION NUMBER: 52-1398991

ADDRESS INQUIRIES TO:
Susan Koshy, Society Manager
(See address above.)

NATIONAL AMBUCS, INC. [2554]
4285 Regency Drive
Greensboro, NC 27410
(336) 852-0052
Fax: (336) 852-6830

E-MAIL ADDRESS:
scholars@ambucs.org

WEB SITE ADDRESS:
www.ambucs.org

FOUNDED: 1948

AREAS OF INTEREST:
Physical therapy, occupational therapy, speech-language pathology and hearing audiology.

NAME(S) OF PROGRAMS:
● **AMBUCS Scholars-Scholarships for Therapists**

TYPE:
Scholarships. AMBUCS Scholars is the largest private single source of educational grants for therapists in America. The goal of this program is to provide financial assistance to needy students studying therapy, which in return places trained individuals in the therapy community to help people with disabilities.

YEAR PROGRAM STARTED: 1955

PURPOSE:
To financially assist students studying for qualification in one of the therapy professions.

LEGAL BASIS:
Private nonprofit association.

ELIGIBILITY:
Applicant must be a citizen of the U.S., document financial need, document good scholastic standing and be accepted at the junior or senior undergraduate or graduate level in an accredited program by the appropriate health therapy profession authority in occupational therapy, physical therapy, speech-language pathology or hearing audiology.

GEOGRAPHIC RESTRICTIONS:
United States.

FINANCIAL DATA:
Amount of support per award: $500 to $1,500, plus one two-year scholarship (awarded annually) of $6,000.

Total amount of support: $167,150 for the year 2013.

COOPERATIVE FUNDING PROGRAMS: Funding for this scholarship program is provided entirely by individual AMBUCS chapters and private donations.

NUMBER OF APPLICANTS MOST RECENT YEAR: 1,267 for the year 2011.

NUMBER OF AWARDS: Approximately 200 scholarships each year.

APPLICATION INFORMATION:
Applications must be submitted electronically. If the student is being sponsored by a local chapter, the student should give the local chapter a copy of the

completed application, along with the most current IRS Form 1040, a narrative statement, and enrollment certification.

Duration: One academic year.

Deadline: Applications accepted from mid-January to April 15 only.

ADDRESS INQUIRIES TO:
Janice Blankenship
AMBUCS Scholarship Coordinator
AMBUCS Resource Center
P.O. Box 5127
High Point, NC 27262
E-mail: ambucs@ambucs.org

NATIONAL ASSOCIATION OF HEALTH SERVICES EXECUTIVES (NAHSE)   [2555]
NAHSE National Office
1050 Connecticut Avenue, N.W.
10th Floor
Washington, DC 20036
(202) 772-1030
Fax: (202) 772-1072

E-MAIL ADDRESS:
nahsehq@nahse.org

WEB SITE ADDRESS:
www.nahse.org

AREAS OF INTEREST:
Health care.

TYPE:
Scholarships.

PURPOSE:
To promote the advancement and development of Black health care leaders and elevate the quality of health care services rendered to minority and underserved communities.

ELIGIBILITY:
Applicant must:
(1) be either enrolled or accepted in an accredited college or university program, pursuing a B.S., M.S. or Doctorate degree, majoring in computer science, management of information technology or information management, or provide proof of intent to pursue a major in one of the above areas of study;
(2) be able to demonstrate financial need;
(3) be an active NAHSE member;
(4) have a minimum academic grade point average of 3.0 or above on a scale of 4.0 and;
(5) submit a position paper examining new information and technology trends and their effects on health care.

To retain the scholarship for the second year, the recipient must maintain a 3.0 grade point average and produce a position paper on new technologies and present the position paper to an FCG or NAHSE panel.

FINANCIAL DATA:
Amount of support per award: $2,500.
Total amount of support: $7,500.

NUMBER OF APPLICANTS MOST RECENT YEAR:
12.

NUMBER OF AWARDS: 3.

APPLICATION INFORMATION:
Contact the Association for guidelines.
Duration: One year.
Deadline: July 1.

ADDRESS INQUIRIES TO:
Beverly Glover, Manager
(See address above.)

NATIONAL SOCIETY DAUGHTERS OF THE AMERICAN REVOLUTION [2556]
1776 D Street, N.W.
Washington, DC 20006-5303
(202) 879-3292
Fax: (202) 879-3348

E-MAIL ADDRESS:
scholarships@dar.org

WEB SITE ADDRESS:
www.dar.org

FOUNDED: 1895

AREAS OF INTEREST:
Occupational and physical therapy.

NAME(S) OF PROGRAMS:
● **Occupational/Physical Therapy Scholarship**

TYPE:
Scholarships. Awarded to students who are in financial need and have been accepted or are attending an accredited school of occupational or physical therapy (including art, music, or physical therapy).

PURPOSE:
To provide ways and means to aid students in attaining higher education.

LEGAL BASIS:
Incorporated historical society.

ELIGIBILITY:
Scholarships are awarded without regard to race, religion, sex or national origin. Candidates must be U.S. citizens and must be enrolled in an accredited school of occupational or physical therapy in the U.S. No affiliation or relationship to DAR is required for qualification, but candidate must be sponsored by a local DAR Chapter.

Candidate must be majoring in occupational therapy or physical therapy and must be in financial need.

Awards are judged on the basis of academic excellence, commitment to field of study, as required, and need.

GEOGRAPHIC RESTRICTIONS:
United States.

FINANCIAL DATA:
Amount of support per award: $1,000.
Total amount of support: Varies.

NUMBER OF AWARDS: Varies.

APPLICATION INFORMATION:
Application information is available online. All scholarship applicants are required to have a letter of sponsorship from a chapter. Individuals interested in obtaining a letter of sponsorship from a local chapter are encouraged to contact the DAR State Chairman. A letter of acceptance into the occupational therapy program or the transcript stating the applicant is in the occupational therapy program must be included with the application.

Duration: One-time scholarship.
Deadline: February 15.

PUBLICATIONS:
American Spirit, magazine.

ADDRESS INQUIRIES TO:
Office of the Reporter General
DAR Scholarship Committee
(See address above.)

PHYSIOTHERAPY FOUNDATION OF CANADA   [2557]
955 Green Valley Crescent
Suite 270
Ottawa ON K2C 3V4 Canada
(613) 686-1818
(888) 285-4136
Fax: (613) 564-1577

E-MAIL ADDRESS:
foundation@physiotherapy.ca

WEB SITE ADDRESS:
www.physiotherapyfoundation.ca

FOUNDED: 1982

AREAS OF INTEREST:
Canadian research and scholarship in physiotherapy.

NAME(S) OF PROGRAMS:
● **Alberta Research Award**
● **Constance Beattie Memorial Fund Bursary Program**
● **Alun Morgan Memorial Research Fund in Orthopaedic Physiotherapy**
● **PFC Research Grants**
● **B.E. Schnurr Memorial Fund Research Grant**
● **Ann Collins Whitmore Memorial Fund Awards**
● **Ann Collins Whitmore Memorial Fund Student Awards Competition**

TYPE:
Fellowships; Research grants; Scholarships. Beattie Memorial Fund Bursary Program is to provide support for continuing education courses that are relevant to applicants' career goals.

Alun Morgan Memorial Research Fund provides support for physiotherapy research projects that deal with the management of musculoskeletal problems in Canada.

PFC Research Grants seek to encourage the development of new technology and treatment methods, develop methods for the prevention and early recognition of physical disabilities, evaluate the effectiveness and efficiency of both new and existing treatment methods, and encourage epidemiological studies on the incidence and prevalence of physical disabilities.

Schnurr Memorial Fund Research Grant and Alberta Research Award provide for physiotherapy research projects, with special encouragement made for projects from Alberta.

Ann Collins Whitmore Memorial Fund Awards are for physiotherapists enrolled in a Ph.D. or Master's program.

Ann Collins Whitmore Memorial Fund Student Awards Competition is designed to encourage young researchers and is open to students pursuing a Baccalaureate degree in physiotherapy at one of the accredited university programs in Canada.

YEAR PROGRAM STARTED: 1983

PURPOSE:
To develop the science of physiotherapy and expand knowledge and skills of individual physiotherapists.

LEGAL BASIS:
Public foundation.

GEOGRAPHIC RESTRICTIONS:
Canada.

FINANCIAL DATA:
Amount of support per award: Beattie Memorial Fund Bursary Program: Up to $1,500 for two recipients (up to $750 each); Morgan Memorial Research Fund and Schnurr Memorial Fund Research Grant: Up to $5,000; PFC Research Grants: $2,500; Whitmore Memorial Fund: Up to $4,000.

Total amount of support: $1,300,000 since inception.

NUMBER OF APPLICANTS MOST RECENT YEAR: 15.

NUMBER OF AWARDS: 15.

APPLICATION INFORMATION:
Applicant must use authorized application form.

Duration: One year. Renewal possible with reapplication.

GOVERNING BOARD:
Rob Werstine, President

ADDRESS INQUIRIES TO:
Rosalby Kelly, Fund-raising Coordinator
(See address above.)

PVA RESEARCH FOUNDATION   [2558]
801 Eighteenth Street, N.W.
Washington, DC 20006
(202) 416-7651
Fax: (202) 416-7641

E-MAIL ADDRESS:
foundations@pva.org

WEB SITE ADDRESS:
www.pva.org

FOUNDED: 1976

AREAS OF INTEREST:
Basic and applied research in spinal cord injury and diseases.

NAME(S) OF PROGRAMS:
● **Spinal Cord Injury Research Grants and Fellowships**

TYPE:
Awards/prizes; Conferences/seminars; Demonstration grants; Development grants; Fellowships; Project/program grants; Research grants; Seed money grants. The PVA Research Foundation funds research projects and fellowships relevant to spinal cord injury and diseases, in addition to sponsoring basic research that will increase scientific knowledge leading to a cure for spinal cord injury. The Foundation also funds research that deals with applied medical, psychological and technological areas of importance to persons with spinal cord injury or disease.

YEAR PROGRAM STARTED: 1976

PURPOSE:
To promote research to find better treatments and cures for paralysis; to support efforts to improve the quality of life of individuals with spinal cord dysfunction until cures are found.

LEGAL BASIS:
Tax-exempt corporation under Sections 170(c) and 501(c)(3) of the Internal Revenue Code. Incorporated in the District of Columbia as a nonprofit organization.

ELIGIBILITY:
New faculty and fellows in a field related to spinal cord injury or diseases may submit a proposal for consideration. Postdoctoral fellowship proposals are considered for

funding. Grants are based on the proposal submitted. Funding consideration on proposals submitted to the Foundation must pass a merit and relevance review by a Scientific Advisory Board and independent peer reviewers.

GEOGRAPHIC RESTRICTIONS:
United States and Canada.

FINANCIAL DATA:
Fringe benefits limited to 40%. Indirect cost limited to eight percent.

Amount of support per award: Fellowships: Maximum $50,000 per year; Basic science, clinical, design development: Maximum $75,000 per year.

NUMBER OF APPLICANTS MOST RECENT YEAR: 70.

NUMBER OF AWARDS: 13.

APPLICATION INFORMATION:
All application submissions must be made at the Foundation web site.

Completed application includes the following components:
(1) title page not exceeding 75 characters;
(2) applicant/principal investigator;
(3) institution and contacts;
(4) letters of reference (required for fellowships; optional for others);
(5) abstract;
(6) organization assurances;
(7) proposal narrative (20-page maximum, including references) and supporting documents (including biosketches and budget) and;
(8) signature page(s).

Specific instructions for completing each component are included with the templates for each component. All applicants must use templates as appropriate for their application to ensure uniformity of presentation for reviewers.

Duration: One to two years.

Deadline: September 1.

PUBLICATIONS:
Annual report; application guidelines.

IRS IDENTIFICATION NUMBER: 52-1064398

DIRECTORS AND OFFICERS:
Bill Lawson, Chairman and President
Peter Axelson, M.S., M.E.
John C. Bollinger
Rory Cooper, Ph.D.
Kenneth Clark Curley, M.D.
Donald F. Eastmead, M.D.
Ivenhoe T. Richey, II

ADDRESS INQUIRIES TO:
Marietta Jimmerson
Grants Portfolio Manager
(See address above.)

CHRISTOPHER AND DANA REEVE FOUNDATION   [2559]
636 Morris Turnpike, Suite 3A
Short Hills, NJ 07078
(973) 379-2690
(800) 225-0292
Fax: (973) 912-9433

E-MAIL ADDRESS:
qol@christopherreeve.org

WEB SITE ADDRESS:
www.paralysis.org
www.christopherreeve.org

FOUNDED: 1982

AREAS OF INTEREST:
Improving the quality of life for individuals living with paralysis, as well as their families.

NAME(S) OF PROGRAMS:
● **Quality of Life Grants**

TYPE:
Project/program grants. Provide funding to organizations nationwide that help improve opportunities, access and day-to-day quality of life for individuals with paralysis. The program recognizes the unique and numerous needs of these individuals and the importance of providing services that enable them to participate in all areas of life. The awards fulfill a variety of needs for recipient organizations.

YEAR PROGRAM STARTED: 1999

PURPOSE:
To support exemplary organizations that provide valuable services to individuals with paralysis and their quality of life and health.

LEGAL BASIS:
Not-for-profit organization.

ELIGIBILITY:
Quality of Life Grants are awarded to 501(c)(3) organizations, as well as community parks, schools, veterans hospitals, tribal entities, etc.

GEOGRAPHIC RESTRICTIONS:
Support for programs outside of the United States is currently limited.

FINANCIAL DATA:
Amount of support per award: Up to $25,000. Partial grants may be awarded.

Matching fund requirements: Matching funds are not required. However, it is beneficial to seek funding from additional sources.

COOPERATIVE FUNDING PROGRAMS: Quality of Life Grants are currently funded through a cooperative agreement with the Centers for Disease Control and Prevention.

NUMBER OF APPLICANTS MOST RECENT YEAR: Approximately 620.

NUMBER OF AWARDS: 200.

REPRESENTATIVE AWARDS:
$5,000 to help support program of aquatic therapy sessions for community members with paralysis.

APPLICATION INFORMATION:
All applications must be submitted online through the Reeve Foundation web site. Potential applicants may call to discuss proposed project if unsure of relevance to Foundation's funding goals.

Duration: One year.

Deadline: March 1 and September 1. Grants awarded in June and January.

PUBLICATIONS:
Guidelines; application form; final report form; People First; Language Guide; A Quick Guide to Establishing Evaluation Indicators.

IRS IDENTIFICATION NUMBER: 22-2939536

ADDRESS INQUIRIES TO:
Donna Valente, Director
Tel: (973) 467-8270 ext. 7211
E-mail: dvalente@christopherreeve.org

*SPECIAL STIPULATIONS:
Prior grant recipients must wait two grant cycles upon receiving grant to reapply for funding.

SOCIETY OF CRITICAL CARE
MEDICINE   [2560]
500 Midway Drive
Mount Prospect, IL 60056
(847) 827-6869
Fax: (847) 493-6441

E-MAIL ADDRESS:
splenner@sccm.org

WEB SITE ADDRESS:
www.sccm.org

AREAS OF INTEREST:
Critical care medicine.

NAME(S) OF PROGRAMS:
● Vision Grant

TYPE:
Research grants. Recipients receive financial
rewards, prestige and recognition within the
field of critical care medicine.

PURPOSE:
To promote excellence in critical care
teaching and research for the improved care
of the critically ill and injured.

ELIGIBILITY:
SCCM membership is required for research
grants. Entries are judged by a committee
with expertise in the field.

FINANCIAL DATA:
Amount of support per award: $50,000.
Total amount of support: $50,000.

NUMBER OF AWARDS: 1.

APPLICATION INFORMATION:
Contact the Society for guidelines.

ADDRESS INQUIRIES TO:
Sharon Plenner, Education Specialist
(See e-mail address above.)

U.S. DEPARTMENT OF
EDUCATION   [2561]
400 Maryland Avenue, S.W.
Room PCP-5052
Washington, DC 20202-2800
(202) 245-6768

E-MAIL ADDRESS:
mark.snyderman@ed.gov

WEB SITE ADDRESS:
www.ed.gov

FOUNDED: 1978

AREAS OF INTEREST:
Priorities are established annually for certain
programs.

NAME(S) OF PROGRAMS:
● Assistive Technology Programs
● Rehabilitation Service Program

TYPE:
Project/program grants. Project grants
(contracts) are awarded for American Indians
vocational rehabilitation services, projects
with industry, migrant and seasonal farm
workers and recreational programs. Grants
must substantially contribute to solution of
vocational rehabilitation problems common to
special groups of individuals with significant
disabilities. For example, projects to prepare
disabled individuals for gainful employment
in the competitive labor market and payment
to cover cost of establishing programs to
expand or improve rehabilitation services for
individuals with disabilities.

YEAR PROGRAM STARTED: 1978

PURPOSE:
To provide funds to state vocational
rehabilitation agencies and public nonprofit
organizations for projects and demonstrations
which hold promise of expanding and
otherwise improving services to individuals
with disabilities.

LEGAL BASIS:
Rehabilitation Act of 1973, Public Law
93-112, as amended by Public Law 98-221,
Sections 121, 303(a)(1), 304, 305 and 611,
29 U.S.C. 701 and Public Law 99-506.

ELIGIBILITY:
Requirements vary according to program.
Full information is available on the
Department of Education web site.

FINANCIAL DATA:
Amount of support per award: Grants vary in
amount depending on type of program.
Matching fund requirements: 20% for
Projects with Industry and 10% for Migratory
Worker and Indian Programs.

APPLICATION INFORMATION:
Guidelines are available online.
Duration: Most programs fund five-year
projects.
Deadline: Varies.

Psychiatry, psychology,
mental health

AMERICAN ACADEMY OF
CHILD AND ADOLESCENT
PSYCHIATRY   [2562]
3615 Wisconsin Avenue, N.W.
Washington, DC 20016-3007
(202) 966-7300 ext. 117
Fax: (202) 966-5894

E-MAIL ADDRESS:
arutter@aacap.org

WEB SITE ADDRESS:
www.aacap.org

FOUNDED: 1953

AREAS OF INTEREST:
Child and adolescent psychiatry.

NAME(S) OF PROGRAMS:
● Robinson-Cunningham Award
● Jeanne Spurlock Research Fellowship
  in Substance Abuse and Addiction for
  Minority Medical Students

TYPE:
Awards/prizes; Conferences/seminars;
Fellowships; Research grants; Travel grants.
The Robinson-Cunningham Award recognizes
a paper on some aspect of child and
adolescent psychiatry started during residency
and completed within three years of
graduation. Preference will be given to
independent work. If the research is done as
part of a collaborative team, the resident or
recently trained child and adolescent
psychiatrist should be the first author or
principal investigator. The selected author
will be invited to attend the AACAP Annual
Meeting.

Jeanne Spurlock Research Fellowship in
Substance Abuse and Addiction for Minority
Medical Students Program, supported by the
National Institute on Drug Abuse (NIDA),
includes a fellowship for work during the

summer with a child and adolescent
psychiatrist research-mentor, plus four days
at the AACAP Annual Meeting.

YEAR PROGRAM STARTED: 1994

PURPOSE:
To increase the number of minority child and
adolescent psychiatrists trained in research.

LEGAL BASIS:
Nonprofit organization.

GEOGRAPHIC RESTRICTIONS:
United States.

FINANCIAL DATA:
Amount of support per award:
Robinson-Cunningham Award: $200
honorarium, plus certificate; Jeanne Spurlock
Research Fellowship: $4,000 per award.
Total amount of support: Varies.

NUMBER OF APPLICANTS MOST RECENT YEAR:
11.

NUMBER OF AWARDS: Robinson-Cunningham
Award: 1; Jeanne Spurlock Research
Fellowship: Up to 3.

APPLICATION INFORMATION:
Contact the Academy for guidelines.
Duration: Eight to 12 weeks.
Deadline: Varies.

PUBLICATIONS:
Program announcement; *Research Notes*,
newsletter.

ADDRESS INQUIRIES TO:
Ashley Rutter
Training and Education Manager
(See address above.)

AMERICAN GROUP
PSYCHOTHERAPY
ASSOCIATION, INC.   [2563]
25 East 21st Street, 6th Floor
New York, NY 10010
(212) 477-2677
Fax: (212) 979-6627

E-MAIL ADDRESS:
dfeirman@agpa.org

WEB SITE ADDRESS:
www.agpa.org

FOUNDED: 1942

AREAS OF INTEREST:
Group psychotherapy.

CONSULTING OR VOLUNTEER SERVICES:
Volunteer Program provided at Annual
Conferences for local students. Specific
duties are required in lieu of payment for
events at Annual Conferences.

NAME(S) OF PROGRAMS:
● The Anne Alonso Scholarship
● Donald T. Brown Memorial
  Scholarship
● The Barry Bukatman, M.D. Memorial
  AGPA Scholarship
● Josephine M. Cunningham-Tervalon
  Scholarship
● Durkin/Glatzer Scholarship
● The Howard and Barbara Goldstein
  Scholarship
● Ruth Hochberg Scholarship
● International Scholarship
● Susanne Jensen Scholarship
● Saul Scheidlinger Scholarship
● Mary M. Tanenbaum Scholarship
● The Wilkenfeld Psychiatric Resident
  Scholarship

TYPE:
Scholarships; Travel grants; Visiting scholars. Special rates for students in addition to the volunteer program.

PURPOSE:
To enable professionals and other interested people to attend these professional meetings who would not otherwise be able to do so due to lack of funds.

LEGAL BASIS:
Incorporated, nonprofit, professional association.

ELIGIBILITY:
Financial need and proximity to location of annual meetings are considered.

For the Durkin-Glatzer Scholarship, applicants must be women entering or re-entering the field of group psychotherapy.

Josephine M. Cunningham Scholarship is for minority women.

Susanne Jensen Scholarship is for a foreign-born woman working or training in the U.S. as a group psychotherapist.

FINANCIAL DATA:
Amount of support per award: Tuition for Annual Meeting and travel stipend for Alonso Scholarship, Cunningham Scholarship, Durkin-Glatzer Scholarship, Hochberg Scholarship, and Wilkenfeld Scholarship.
Total amount of support: $8,000 to $25,000.

NUMBER OF AWARDS: 1 of each award or program.

APPLICATION INFORMATION:
Current application guidelines are available on the Association's web site.
Duration: Two days for the Institute; three days for Conference.
Deadline: November 1.

PUBLICATIONS:
International Journal of Group Psychotherapy; The Group Circle, newsletter.

EXECUTIVE COMMITTEE:
Lisa Mahon, Chairman

ADDRESS INQUIRIES TO:
Diane Feirman, CAE
Public Affairs Director
(See address above.)

AMERICAN PSYCHIATRIC FOUNDATION   [2564]
1000 Wilson Boulevard, Suite 1825
Arlington, VA 22209-3901
(703) 907-8622
(800) 852-1390

E-MAIL ADDRESS:
eguerra@psych.org

WEB SITE ADDRESS:
www.psychfoundation.org
www.psych.org

AREAS OF INTEREST:
Psychiatric research.

NAME(S) OF PROGRAMS:
● **Kempf Fund Award for Research Development in Psychobiological Psychiatry**

TYPE:
Awards/prizes; Research grants. The Award supports the research-career development of a young research psychiatrist working in a

mentor-trainee relationship with the award winner on further research in the field of schizophrenia.

PURPOSE:
To recognize a senior researcher who has made a significant contribution to research on the causes and treatment of schizophrenia as both a researcher and a mentor.

ELIGIBILITY:
Applicants must be American Psychiatric Association members. Detailed guidelines are available from the Association. Contact the Association's Research Training Programs Office to obtain a copy of the printed announcement.

GEOGRAPHIC RESTRICTIONS:
Applicants must be citizens of the United States or Canada.

FINANCIAL DATA:
Amount of support per award: $1,500 award to the senior researcher, and $20,000 for support of the research-career development of a young research psychiatrist working in a mentor-trainee relationship with the award winner on further research in this field.

APPLICATION INFORMATION:
Application information is available on the web site. Completed application materials required may be submitted online via a PDF format or by regular mail to: APA/Kempf Fund Award; American Psychiatric Association; at the address above.
Duration: One year; nonrenewable.
Deadline: Postmarked by October 15.

ADDRESS INQUIRIES TO:
Ernesto Guerra
Director of Research Training
(See e-mail address above.)

AMERICAN PSYCHIATRIC FOUNDATION   [2565]
1000 Wilson Boulevard, Suite 1825
Arlington, VA 22209
(703) 907-8622
(800) 852-1390

E-MAIL ADDRESS:
eguerra@psych.org

WEB SITE ADDRESS:
www.psychfoundation.org
www.psych.org

AREAS OF INTEREST:
Psychiatric research.

NAME(S) OF PROGRAMS:
● **APF-Merck & Co. Early Academic Career Research Award**

TYPE:
Research grants. Awards are made to candidates who have completed a psychiatry residency, at least one year of a psychiatry research fellowship, and are seeking to make a commitment to a research career with the end goal of successfully transitioning to that of an independent investigator.

PURPOSE:
To help support the research of a junior faculty member with an interest in schizophrenia research.

ELIGIBILITY:
Candidates should be American Psychiatric Association members. Eligible candidates will be trained psychiatrists with an M.D., M.D./Ph.D. or D.O. degree who have completed residency training in general

psychiatry or child psychiatry in the U.S. or Canada, have also completed at least one year of a psychiatry research fellowship but are not three or more years postfellowship completion, and do not currently hold an academic rank higher than Assistant Professor. Individuals who have obtained K-awards or are considered an Independent Principal Investigator on R-01 or R-21 research grants from NIH are not eligible.

GEOGRAPHIC RESTRICTIONS:
Citizens or permanent residents of the United States or Canada.

FINANCIAL DATA:
Stipend will be paid to the institution for disbursement to the fellow. The institution must agree not to deduct indirect costs from this award, but may augment this award for further salary support for the faculty member.
Amount of support per award: Stipend of $45,000; award can be used to either support the candidate's salary or expenses related to his or her research program.

APPLICATION INFORMATION:
Application information is available on the web site.
Duration: One year; nonrenewable.
Deadline: October 15.

*SPECIAL STIPULATIONS:
Applications will not be accepted from previous winners of American Psychiatric Association-administered fellowships or awards. This rule will not apply to persons who have been selected for the Resident Research Award or NIH-funded fellowships and research training experiences.

AMERICAN PSYCHOLOGICAL ASSOCIATION
Minority Fellowship Program/APA
750 First Street, N.E.
Washington, DC 20002-4242
(202) 336-6127
Fax: (202) 336-6012

E-MAIL ADDRESS:
mfp@apa.org

WEB SITE ADDRESS:
www.apa.org/pi/mfp

TYPE:
Fellowships. Geared to those pursuing careers in substance abuse treatment and prevention as practitioners and as researchers specializing in the delivery of mental health services to ethnic minority populations.
See entry 974 for full listing.

AMERICAN PSYCHOLOGICAL ASSOCIATION   [2566]
Government Relations Office
Public Interest Directorate
750 First Street, N.E.
Washington, DC 20002-4242
(202) 336-5935
Fax: (202) 336-6063

E-MAIL ADDRESS:
mhaskell-hoehl@apa.org

WEB SITE ADDRESS:
www.apa.org/about/gr/fellows

FOUNDED: 1892

AREAS OF INTEREST:
Professional organization to advance psychology as a science and profession and as a means of promoting health, education and human welfare.

NAME(S) OF PROGRAMS:
● **APA Congressional Fellowship Program**

TYPE:
Fellowships. Program provides trained scientists and practitioners an opportunity for enhanced understanding of and involvement in the federal policymaking process by serving as congressional staff in Washington, DC.

YEAR PROGRAM STARTED: 1974

PURPOSE:
To provide an opportunity for psychologists to participate in the policymaking process.

LEGAL BASIS:
Nonprofit professional organization.

ELIGIBILITY:
Doctoral degree in psychology and APA membership required. Two years of postdoctoral experience is preferred. Individuals with sabbatical funds are eligible. Must be U.S. citizen and willing to relocate to Washington, DC.

GEOGRAPHIC RESTRICTIONS:
United States.

FINANCIAL DATA:
Amount of support per award: For the year 2015-16: $75,000 to $90,000, depending on years of postdoctoral experience. Up to $3,750 is allocated per Fellow for relocation to the Washington, DC area and for travel expenses during the year. Additional funds may be available for health insurance.
Total amount of support: Varies.

COOPERATIVE FUNDING PROGRAMS: Fellowship is sponsored by the APA in cooperation with the American Association for the Advancement of Science and with funds from the ASA Goldman Fellowship.

NUMBER OF AWARDS: Up to 2.

APPLICATION INFORMATION:
Completed online application form, curriculum vitae, three letters of reference and a statement of interest are required.
Duration: September through August. Nonrenewable.
Deadline: Early January. Announcement in March.

STAFF:
Micah Haskell-Hoehl, Program Administrator

ADDRESS INQUIRIES TO:
Micah Haskell-Hoehl, Program Administrator
APA Congressional Fellowship Program
(See telephone number and e-mail address above.)

AMERICAN PSYCHOLOGICAL ASSOCIATION   [2567]
Minority Fellowship Program/APA
750 First Street, N.E.
Washington, DC 20002-4242
(202) 336-6127
Fax: (202) 336-6012

E-MAIL ADDRESS:
mfp@apa.org

WEB SITE ADDRESS:
www.apa.org/pi/mfp

FOUNDED: 1892

AREAS OF INTEREST:
Psychology.

NAME(S) OF PROGRAMS:
● **MFP Mental Health and Substance Abuse Services Fellowship**

TYPE:
Fellowships. Fellowship is geared to those pursuing careers as practitioners and as researchers specializing in the delivery of mental health services to ethnic minority populations. Students specializing in clinical, school and counseling psychology are encouraged to apply.

YEAR PROGRAM STARTED: 1974

PURPOSE:
To provide financial support, professional development activities, and guidance to promising doctoral students and postdoctoral trainees with the goal of moving them toward high achievement in areas related to ethnic minority behavioral health research or services.

LEGAL BASIS:
Nonprofit.

ELIGIBILITY:
Applicants must:
(1) be citizens, noncitizen nationals, or permanent residents of the U.S.;
(2) be enrolled full-time in a doctoral degree program in psychology (Ph.D. or Psy.D.); Mental Health Services applicants must be enrolled in an APA-accredited program and;
(3) have a strong commitment to a career in ethnic minority behavioral health services or policy.

African-Americans, Alaskan Natives, Asian Americans, Latino/Hispanic, Native Americans and Pacific Islanders are especially encouraged to apply.

Person receiving Fellowship from MFP cannot be the recipient of federal funds.

FINANCIAL DATA:
Amount of support per award: Follows NRSA guidelines.

COOPERATIVE FUNDING PROGRAMS: Funding for services training is made available through the Substance Abuse and Mental Health Services Administration allocations.

NUMBER OF APPLICANTS MOST RECENT YEAR: 198.

NUMBER OF AWARDS: 10 to 15.

APPLICATION INFORMATION:
Applications are available October 1 to January 15. Guidelines are available online.
Duration: One academic year. Renewable for up to two additional years.
Deadline: January 15. Announcement by April.

PUBLICATIONS:
Program brochure.

ADDRESS INQUIRIES TO:
Minority Fellowship Program
(See telephone and e-mail address above.)

AMERICAN PSYCHOSOMATIC SOCIETY   [2568]
6728 Old McLean Village Drive
McLean, VA 22101
(703) 556-9222
Fax: (703) 556-8729

E-MAIL ADDRESS:
info@psychosomatic.org

WEB SITE ADDRESS:
www.psychosomatic.org

FOUNDED: 1942

AREAS OF INTEREST:
Psychosomatic medicine.

NAME(S) OF PROGRAMS:
● **Herbert Weiner Early Career Award for Contributions to Psychosomatic Society**

TYPE:
Awards/prizes.

PURPOSE:
To support individuals who show substantial promise in continuing study in psychosomatic medicine.

LEGAL BASIS:
Not-for-profit organization.

ELIGIBILITY:
Nominees must be fewer than 10 years past their final academic degree and must be members of the American Psychosomatic Society.

FINANCIAL DATA:
Amount of support per award: $1,000, plaque and an opportunity to present the research for which the award was given during the annual meeting of the Society.

NUMBER OF APPLICANTS MOST RECENT YEAR: 5.

NUMBER OF AWARDS: 1.

APPLICATION INFORMATION:
Nominations must include a 500- to 1,000-word justification for the nomination, an updated curriculum vitae and reprints of the two to six publications of the work for which the nomination is being made. Two- to three-page proposal of the project and a copy of the curriculum vitae are due June 1 of each year.
Duration: One-time award.
Deadline: December 1.

PUBLICATIONS:
Award announcement.

IRS IDENTIFICATION NUMBER: 11-1866747

ADDRESS INQUIRIES TO:
Award Committee
(See address above.)

ANNA-MONIKA FOUNDATION   [2569]
Kieshecker Weg 240
D-40468 Duesseldorf Germany
49 211 437187 13
Fax: 49 211 437187 23

E-MAIL ADDRESS:
m.bommers@gospax.com

WEB SITE ADDRESS:
www.anna-monika-stiftung.com

FOUNDED: 1965

AREAS OF INTEREST:
Biochemistry, neurophysiology, neuropathology, psychopharmacology, psychiatry, depression and psychosomatic illnesses.

NAME(S) OF PROGRAMS:
● **The Anna-Monika Foundation Prize**

TYPE:
Awards/prizes. Prizes for research papers investigating the biological substrate and functional disturbances of depression. Prize-winning lectures will be published in *Pharmacopsychiatry*.

YEAR PROGRAM STARTED: 1966

PURPOSE:
To support international pioneering research in the area of depression research.

LEGAL BASIS:
Private foundation, authorized by the state of Nordrhein-Westfalen, Germany.

ELIGIBILITY:
As far as possible, the papers describing the studies should feature information about the recent advances and the knowledge that should be helpful in promoting treatment and open new paths of scientific progress in depression. Papers published in the last two years in an international scientific peer-reviewed journal may be submitted. Papers may be written in German, French or English.

FINANCIAL DATA:
Total amount of support: EUR 25,000.

NUMBER OF AWARDS: Maximum of 3 biennially in odd-numbered years.

APPLICATION INFORMATION:
A maximum of three publications (in sets of four copies) plus a short summary (approximately 600 words) emphasizing the relevance and importance of the research are required. Papers may be written in English and should be submitted to the Executive Board only by e-mail.
Deadline: March 31.

ADDRESS INQUIRIES TO:
Michael Bommers, Managing Director
(See address above.)

ANXIETY AND DEPRESSION ASSOCIATION OF AMERICA [2570]
8701 Georgia Avenue, Suite 412
Silver Spring, MD 20910
(240) 485-1001
Fax: (240) 485-1035

E-MAIL ADDRESS:
information@adaa.org

WEB SITE ADDRESS:
www.adaa.org

FOUNDED: 1980

AREAS OF INTEREST:
Anxiety, depression and related disorders.

NAME(S) OF PROGRAMS:
● **Junior Faculty Research Grants**

TYPE:
Conferences/seminars; Project/program grants; Research grants; Seed money grants; Travel grants.

YEAR PROGRAM STARTED: 1999

PURPOSE:
To promote the prevention and cure of anxiety disorders and depression and to improve the lives of all people who suffer from them; to increase the pool of independent investigators with interest and expertise in anxiety disorders research.

LEGAL BASIS:
Nonprofit association.

FINANCIAL DATA:
Total amount of support: $8,750.

NUMBER OF AWARDS: 15 for the year 2012.

APPLICATION INFORMATION:
Visit the Association web site in the early fall to see a description of the award and the application details.

PUBLICATIONS:
Guidelines.

ADDRESS INQUIRIES TO:
Sarah Gerfen, Business Manager
(See address above.)

THE ARC OF THE UNITED STATES [2571]
1825 K Street, N.W.
Suite 1200
Washington, DC 20006
(202) 534-3727
Fax: (202) 534-3731

E-MAIL ADDRESS:
williams@thearc.org

WEB SITE ADDRESS:
www.thearc.org

FOUNDED: 1950

AREAS OF INTEREST:
Prevention or improvement of mental retardation/developmental disabilities.

NAME(S) OF PROGRAMS:
● **Research Matters! Award**

TYPE:
Awards/prizes. Rewards an individual (or individuals) who has contributed in significant ways to research that enhances the well-being of persons with intellectual and developmental disabilities and their families, or that prevents such conditions and/or related effects.

PURPOSE:
To prevent or improve mental retardation.

ELIGIBILITY:
Selection is based on the importance of the research discovery to people with intellectual and developmental disabilities and their families, its practical significance and impact for people with disabilities, its relationship to research topics identified as priorities in the *National Goals and Research for People with Intellectual and Developmental Disabilities* report of 2006, and the history of work in the specified research area over a number of years that leads to a significant research conclusion.

FINANCIAL DATA:
Amount of support per award: $1,000.

ADDRESS INQUIRIES TO:
Ann Cameron Williams
Chief Research and Innovation Officer
(See address above.)

ASSOCIATION FOR APPLIED PSYCHOPHYSIOLOGY AND BIOFEEDBACK [2572]
10200 West 44th Avenue
Suite 304
Wheat Ridge, CO 80033-2840
(303) 422-8436
Fax: (303) 422-8894

E-MAIL ADDRESS:
aapb@resourcecenter.com

WEB SITE ADDRESS:
www.aapb.org

FOUNDED: 1969

AREAS OF INTEREST:
Biofeedback and psychophysiology.

NAME(S) OF PROGRAMS:
● **Student Travel Scholarship Program**

TYPE:
Travel grants.

PURPOSE:
To advance the development, dissemination and utilization of knowledge about applied psychophysiology and biofeedback to improve health and the quality of life through research, education and practice.

ELIGIBILITY:
Must be a full-time student pursuing a professional or doctoral degree in a health-related field.

FINANCIAL DATA:
Amount of support per award: $400.
Total amount of support: Varies.

NUMBER OF AWARDS: Varies.

APPLICATION INFORMATION:
Contact the Organization for application procedures.
Deadline: October 1 for presentation. January 1 for scholarship application.

ASSOCIATION FOR BEHAVIORAL AND COGNITIVE THERAPIES [2573]
305 Seventh Avenue
16th Floor
New York, NY 10001
(212) 647-1890
Fax: (212) 647-1865

E-MAIL ADDRESS:
mjeimer@abct.org

WEB SITE ADDRESS:
www.abct.org

AREAS OF INTEREST:
Behavior therapy and cognitive behavior therapy.

NAME(S) OF PROGRAMS:
● **Virginia Roswell Dissertation Award**

TYPE:
Awards/prizes.

PURPOSE:
To explore the application of behavioral and cognitive sciences to understanding human behavior, developing interventions to enhance the human condition, and promoting the appropriate utilization of these interventions.

ELIGIBILITY:
Applicant must be an AABT student member who has already had their dissertation proposal approved and be investigating an area of direct relevance to behavior therapy or cognitive behavior therapy.

FINANCIAL DATA:
Amount of support per award: $1,000.

NUMBER OF AWARDS: 1.

APPLICATION INFORMATION:
All candidates must be nominated. Contact the Organization for nomination procedures.
Deadline: March 1.

ADDRESS INQUIRIES TO:
M.J. Eimer, Executive Director
(See address above.)

ASSOCIATION FOR BEHAVIORAL AND COGNITIVE THERAPIES [2574]
305 Seventh Avenue
16th Floor
New York, NY 10001
(212) 647-1890
Fax: (212) 647-1865

E-MAIL ADDRESS:
mjeimer@abct.org

WEB SITE ADDRESS:
www.abct.org

AREAS OF INTEREST:
Behavior therapy and cognitive sciences.

NAME(S) OF PROGRAMS:
- **President's New Researcher Award**

TYPE:
Awards/prizes.

PURPOSE:
To explore the application of behavioral and cognitive sciences to understanding human behavior, developing interventions to enhance the human condition, and promoting the appropriate utilization of these interventions.

ELIGIBILITY:
Must be authored by an individual with five years or less post-training experience and have been published in the last two years or currently in press.

FINANCIAL DATA:
Amount of support per award: $500.

APPLICATION INFORMATION:
Contact the Organization for application procedures.
Deadline: August 6.

ADDRESS INQUIRIES TO:
M.J. Eimer, Executive Director
(See address above.)

AUTISM SPEAKS

1060 State Road, 2nd Floor
Princeton, NJ 08540
(609) 228-7313
Fax: (609) 430-9163

E-MAIL ADDRESS:
jnew@autismspeaks.org

WEB SITE ADDRESS:
www.autismspeaks.org

TYPE:
Fellowships; Project/program grants; Research grants. Research grants that are in line with Autism Speaks research priorities.

See entry 2242 for full listing.

BRAIN & BEHAVIOR RESEARCH FOUNDATION [2575]

90 Park Avenue, 16th Floor
New York, NY 10016
(800) 829-8289
Fax: (646) 681-4891

E-MAIL ADDRESS:
grants@bbrfoundation.org

WEB SITE ADDRESS:
www.bbrfoundation.org

FOUNDED: 1987

AREAS OF INTEREST:
Mental health, brain and behavior disorders.

NAME(S) OF PROGRAMS:
- **Distinguished Investigator Grant**
- **Independent Investigator Grant**
- **Young Investigator Grant**

TYPE:
Research grants. Distinguished Investigator Grant supports senior investigators (professor or equivalent level) who maintain a laboratory and who propose an innovative and new direction in their research with a one-year grant to encourage pursuit of innovative projects in schizophrenia, affective disorders, or other serious mental illnesses.

Independent Investigator Grant is intended for the scientist at the academic level of associate professor or equivalent, who has won national competitive support as a principal investigator. Assistant professors who have NIH R01s and equivalent are also eligible. The program is intended to facilitate innovative research opportunities.

Young Investigator Grant enables promising investigators to either extend their research fellowship training or to begin careers as independent research faculty.

PURPOSE:
To raise and distribute funds for scientific research into the causes, cures, treatments and prevention of severe psychiatric brain disorders.

LEGAL BASIS:
Private, not-for-profit organization.

ELIGIBILITY:
Applicant must hold a doctoral-level degree and be affiliated with a university or research institution. For the Distinguished Investigator Grant, applicant must be a full professor (or professional equivalent) who maintains a laboratory. For the Independent Investigator Grant, applicant must be at associate professor level with national competitive support as a principal investigator. Assistant professors who have NIH R01s and equivalent are also eligible. For the Young Investigator Grant, applicant must be advanced postdoctoral fellow through assistant professor (or equivalent) to either extend research fellowship training or to begin career as independent research faculty. Basic and/or clinical investigators are supported, but research must be relevant to schizophrenia, major affective disorders or other serious mental illnesses.

FINANCIAL DATA:
Amount of support per award: Distinguished Investigator: Up to $100,000 for one year; Independent Investigator: $50,000 per year for two years; Young Investigator: Up to $30,000 per year for up to two years.

NUMBER OF APPLICANTS MOST RECENT YEAR:
Distinguished Investigator: 225 for the year 2012; Independent Investigator: 487 for the year 2012; Young Investigator: 1,030 for the year 2013.

NUMBER OF AWARDS: Distinguished Investigator: 15 for the year 2011; Independent Investigator: 42; Young Investigator: 202 for the year 2012.

APPLICATION INFORMATION:
Guidelines are available on the Foundation web site.
Duration: Distinguished Investigator Grant: One-year, one-time award; Independent Investigator Grant: Two-year, one-time award; Young Investigator Grant: One or two years. May not apply more than twice for initial grant and more than once for second grant.
Deadline: Varies.

IRS IDENTIFICATION NUMBER: 31-1020010

STAFF:
Jeff Borenstein, President and Chief Executive Officer
Lou Innamorato, Vice President, Finance and Chief Financial Officer
Laura Wells, Vice President, Marketing and Communications
Faith Rothblatt, Vice President of Development
Abbey Chakalis, Director of Special Events
Marissa Martonyi, Associate Director of Design and Production
Josh Okun, Associate Director of Web Services and Online Marketing
Sho Tin Chen, Manager, Research Grants
Nieves Ortiz, Manager of Donor-based Management
Laura Terio, C.S.W., Outreach Manager
John Bayat, Senior Accountant
Mike Kirsic, Senior Accountant
Grace Nagaur, Senior Associate, Research Grants

ADDRESS INQUIRIES TO:
Grants Management
(See address above.)

JAMES MCKEEN CATTELL FUND [2576]

Duke University
Genome Sciences Research Building II, 3rd floor
572 Research Drive, Box 91050
Durham, NC 27708
(919) 660-5713
(919) 660-5638
Fax: (919) 660-5726

E-MAIL ADDRESS:
williams@psych.duke.edu

WEB SITE ADDRESS:
www.cattell.duke.edu

FOUNDED: 1941

NAME(S) OF PROGRAMS:
- **James McKeen Cattell Fund Sabbatical Fellowships for Psychologists**

TYPE:
Fellowships. The fellowship provides funds to supplement the regular sabbatical allowance provided by the recipients' home institutions.

YEAR PROGRAM STARTED: 1942

PURPOSE:
To promote scientific research and the dissemination of knowledge with the object of obtaining results beneficial to the development of the science of psychology.

LEGAL BASIS:
Tax-exempt foundation.

ELIGIBILITY:
The awards are available to psychologists who are faculty members at colleges and universities in the U.S. and Canada and are eligible, according to the regulations of their own institutions, for a sabbatical leave or its equivalent.

GEOGRAPHIC RESTRICTIONS:
United States and Canada.

FINANCIAL DATA:
Amount of support per award: Up to $40,000.
Total amount of support: Varies.

NUMBER OF APPLICANTS MOST RECENT YEAR:
Approximately 35.

NUMBER OF AWARDS: 1 to 6 per year.

APPLICATION INFORMATION:
Fellowship application is available at the Fund web site.
Duration: One academic year.
Deadline: December 15.

ADDRESS INQUIRIES TO:
Dr. Christina L. Williams
Secretary-Treasurer
(See address above.)

COUNCIL ON SOCIAL WORK EDUCATION

1701 Duke Street, Suite 200
Alexandria, VA 22314-3457
(703) 683-8080
Fax: (703) 683-8099

E-MAIL ADDRESS:
gmeeks@cswe.org

WEB SITE ADDRESS:
www.cswe.org/mfp

TYPE:
Fellowships. Awards for minority doctoral-level studies in social work, specializing in mental health and substance abuse-related education, research, policy and practice.

See entry 986 for full listing.

DEPARTMENT OF VETERANS AFFAIRS [2577]

Associated Health Education (10A2D)
Office of Academic Affiliations
810 Vermont Avenue, N.W.
Washington, DC 20420
(202) 461-9493
Fax: (202) 461-9855

E-MAIL ADDRESS:
kenneth.jones6@va.gov

WEB SITE ADDRESS:
www.psychologytraining.va.gov

FOUNDED: 1946

NAME(S) OF PROGRAMS:
• **VA Psychology Training Program**

TYPE:
Fellowships; Internships. Stipends for internship and postdoctoral training in clinical or counseling psychology. Provides one year of supervised training in the skills and techniques of these specialty areas. Participants have no obligation to remain with the VA after completion of training.

YEAR PROGRAM STARTED: 1946

PURPOSE:
To provide a source of highly qualified psychologists who are interested in the direct delivery of professional services in federal, state, and community facilities; to provide internship training to students enrolled in doctoral programs in clinical or counseling psychology from those schools accredited by the American Psychological Association; to provide postdoctoral fellowships to graduates of clinical or counseling psychology doctoral programs and internships that are accredited by the American Psychological Association.

LEGAL BASIS:
Federal agency.

ELIGIBILITY:
Applicant must be a U.S. citizen. Prospective intern must be enrolled in an academic graduate program leading to the doctoral degree in clinical or counseling psychology from an APA-accredited program. Prospective postdoctoral fellow must have completed a doctoral program and internship in clinical or counseling psychology accredited by the APA.

FINANCIAL DATA:
Amount of support per award: Stipend of $23,974 and up for full-time interns, $42,239 and up for full-time postdoctoral fellows for the first year and $44,522 and up for full-time postdoctoral fellows for the second year, including benefits.
Total amount of support: Varies.

NUMBER OF AWARDS: 598 intern positions at 115 sites and 349 postdoctoral fellow positions at 71 sites for academic year 2014-15.

APPLICATION INFORMATION:
Interested persons should contact the Director of Psychology Training at the VA Medical Center they are interested in.
Duration: One year. Occasionally two years for postdoctoral fellowships.
Deadline: November.

ADDRESS INQUIRIES TO:
Chief of Psychology Service or
Director of Psychology Training
at a local VA Medical Center

ALBERT ELLIS INSTITUTE [2578]

145 East 32nd Street, 9th Floor
New York, NY 10016
(212) 535-0822
Fax: (212) 249-3582

E-MAIL ADDRESS:
krisdoyle@albertellis.org

WEB SITE ADDRESS:
www.albertellis.org

FOUNDED: 1968

AREAS OF INTEREST:
Psychotherapy.

CONSULTING OR VOLUNTEER SERVICES:
Work-study positions offered.

NAME(S) OF PROGRAMS:
• **Postgraduate Clinical Fellowship Training Program at the Albert Ellis Institute**

TYPE:
Conferences/seminars; Fellowships; Internships; Work-study programs. Postdoctoral fellowships and internships in cognitive behavior therapy for a comprehensive program, featuring intensive supervision of individual and group clients seen at the Institute's clinic, seminars and workshops.

YEAR PROGRAM STARTED: 1969

PURPOSE:
To train professionals in cognitive behavioral and Rational Emotive Behavior Therapy.

LEGAL BASIS:
Not-for-profit organization.

ELIGIBILITY:
Applicant must have a Ph.D. in psychology, M.D., M.S.W. or R.N. and be eligible for New York state certification or license in the field.

NUMBER OF APPLICANTS MOST RECENT YEAR:
30.

NUMBER OF AWARDS: 6 for the academic year 2011.

APPLICATION INFORMATION:
Application form required. On a separate page, state the reasons for wishing to enter the Fellowship Training Program, future plans in psychology, and curriculum vitae. Personal interviews are necessary.
Duration: One to two years.
Deadline: February 15.

ADDRESS INQUIRIES TO:
Dr. Kristene Doyle, Director
(See address above.)

*PLEASE NOTE:
Training takes place in New York City.

FONDATION DES ETATS-UNIS

15, boulevard Jourdan
75014 Paris France
(33 1) 53 80 68 87
Fax: (33 1) 53 80 68 99

E-MAIL ADDRESS:
culture@feusa.org

WEB SITE ADDRESS:
www.feusa.org
www.harriet-hale-woolley.com

TYPE:
Awards/prizes; Development grants; Scholarships. Bequeathed to the Fondation des Etats-Unis, Cite Internationale Universitaire de Paris in the early 1930s, the Harriet Hale Woolley Scholarship is awarded annually to a select number of exceptional American artists and musicians who plan to pursue their studies in Paris.

A scholarship is also available to French, Swiss and American medical postgraduates specializing in psychiatry with an internship in a Parisian hospital.

See entry 449 for full listing.

INTERNATIONAL OCD FOUNDATION [2579]

18 Tremont Street, Suite 903
Boston, MA 02108
(617) 973-5801
Fax: (617) 973-5803

E-MAIL ADDRESS:
info@ocfoundation.org

WEB SITE ADDRESS:
www.ocfoundation.org

FOUNDED: 1986

AREAS OF INTEREST:
Obsessive-compulsive disorders and obsessive compulsive spectrum disorder.

NAME(S) OF PROGRAMS:
• **Annual Conference**
• **Behavior Therapy Training Institute (BTTI)**
• **Research Awards**

TYPE:
Awards/prizes; Conferences/seminars; Research grants.

YEAR PROGRAM STARTED: 1986

PURPOSE:
To disseminate information and to fund research for the ultimate causes and cures for obsessive-compulsive disorders.

ELIGIBILITY:
Investigators whose research focuses on the nature, causes and treatment of OCD and related disorders are eligible to apply. Senior

investigators may also ask for grant funding for projects that would provide pilot data for future larger-scale federal grant applications.

FINANCIAL DATA:
Awards do not cover indirect or travel costs.
Amount of support per award: Varies.
Total amount of support: Varies.

NUMBER OF APPLICANTS MOST RECENT YEAR: 50.

NUMBER OF AWARDS: 5.

APPLICATION INFORMATION:
Applicants should request application guidelines from the Foundation.
Duration: One to two years.
Deadline: January.

PUBLICATIONS:
OCD Newsletter.

IRS IDENTIFICATION NUMBER: 22-2894564

STAFF:
Jeff Szymanski, Ph.D., Executive Director
Marissa Keegan, Program Director

ADDRESS INQUIRIES TO:
Grace Riley, Administrative Assistant
(See address above.)

THE KLINGENSTEIN THIRD GENERATION FOUNDATION   [2580]
125 Park Avenue
Suite 1700
New York, NY 10017-5529
(212) 492-6179
Fax: (212) 492-7007

E-MAIL ADDRESS:
sally@ktgf.org
info@ktgf.org

WEB SITE ADDRESS:
www.ktgf.org

FOUNDED: 1993

AREAS OF INTEREST:
Child and adolescent depression and ADHD.

TYPE:
Fellowships; Research grants. The Foundation funds research and other programs related to childhood and adolescent ADHD and depression. All funding is directed towards two research fellowship programs and the medical student training program. The Foundation does not accept general applications for project or research funding.

YEAR PROGRAM STARTED: 1993

PURPOSE:
To address the need for further research in pediatric ADHD and pediatric depression, and the need to cultivate more child and adolescent psychiatrists and psychologists.

LEGAL BASIS:
Family foundation.

ELIGIBILITY:
The Foundation is prohibited from making grants to political action groups and from lobbying the government, and makes no grants to individuals.

FINANCIAL DATA:
Amount of support per award: $30,000 per year.

NUMBER OF AWARDS: Up to 4.

APPLICATION INFORMATION:
Applications must be submitted online.

Duration: Two years.
Deadline: January.

BOARD OF TRUSTEES:
Andrew D. Klingenstein, President
Susan Klingenstein, Vice President
Thomas D. Klingenstein, Treasurer
Nancy K. Simpkins, Secretary
Sally Klingenstein Martell, Executive Director
Kathy Klingenstein
Amy Pollinger

ADVISORY COMMITTEE:
Thomas F. Anders, M.D.
William R. Beardslee, M.D.
David Brent, M.D.
Kiki Chang, M.D.
Heidi B. Fordi
Anne Glowinski, M.D.
Jeffrey H. Newcorn, M.D.

*PLEASE NOTE:
The Foundation does not accept unsolicited applications.

DELLA MARTIN FOUNDATION   [2581]
333 South Hope Street
43rd Floor
Los Angeles, CA 90071
(213) 617-4143
Fax: (213) 620-1398

FOUNDED: 1975

AREAS OF INTEREST:
Mental health research.

TYPE:
Endowments; Fellowships. Foundation has endowed four university chairs for mental health research.

YEAR PROGRAM STARTED: 1975

PURPOSE:
To promote research into causes of and cures for mental illness.

LEGAL BASIS:
Nonprofit foundation.

ELIGIBILITY:
For southern California tax-exempt organizations only. No grants are made to individuals.

GEOGRAPHIC RESTRICTIONS:
Southern California.

FINANCIAL DATA:
Amount of support per award: Varies.
Total amount of support: $250,000 annually.
Matching fund requirements: Generally 1:1.

NUMBER OF APPLICANTS MOST RECENT YEAR: 20.

NUMBER OF AWARDS: 1 annually.

REPRESENTATIVE AWARDS:
$250,000 to University of California, Irvine to establish postgraduate research fellowship.

APPLICATION INFORMATION:
Send brief letter to the Foundation describing grant request.

IRS IDENTIFICATION NUMBER: 23-7444954

TRUSTEES:
Laurence K. Gould, Jr.
James A. Lonergan
Allen W. Mathias, Jr., M.D.
Nancy B. Reimann
Jane H. Roney
Eileen D. Sheppard
Philip A. Swan

ADDRESS INQUIRIES TO:
Laurence K. Gould, Jr., Trustee
(See address above.)

NATIONAL INSTITUTE OF MENTAL HEALTH   [2582]
6001 Executive Boulevard, Room 6160
Bethesda, MD 20892
(301) 443-5047
Fax: (301) 443-9474

E-MAIL ADDRESS:
waldeckt@mail.nih.gov

WEB SITE ADDRESS:
www.nimh.nih.gov

FOUNDED: 1948

AREAS OF INTEREST:
Basic neuroscience, genetics, basic behavioral science aimed at understanding mental disorders, research training, resource and technology development and drug discovery; translational research on the mechanisms of adult psychopathology and the development of novel treatment approaches for adult mental disorders; integrated research and research training that translates knowledge from basic/behavioral science into a better understanding of pediatric psychopathology and the development of novel treatment and prevention strategies; research on mechanisms and interventions on the interrelationship of physical and mental health; mental health research on AIDS that includes studies that range from the molecular and cellular basis of HIV/AIDS CNS infection to the domestic and international dissemination of effective preventative interventions; research that evaluates the effectiveness of treatment and preventive mental health interventions and mental health services research.

TYPE:
Development grants; Fellowships; Project/program grants; Research grants; Training grants; Research contracts.

YEAR PROGRAM STARTED: 1948

PURPOSE:
To support innovative science that will profoundly transform the diagnosis, treatment and prevention of mental disorders, paving the way for a cure; to reduce the burden of mental illness and behavioral disorders through research on mind, brain and behavior.

LEGAL BASIS:
Government agency.

ELIGIBILITY:
Public, private, profit or nonprofit agencies, including state and local government agencies, eligible Federal agencies, universities, colleges, hospitals, and academic or research institutions may apply for research grants. SBIR grants can be awarded only to domestic small businesses, and STTR grants can be awarded only to domestic small businesses which partner with a research institution in cooperative research and development.

An applicant for individual predoctoral fellowship support must be enrolled in a research doctoral degree program by the proposed activation date of the fellowship. A postdoctoral applicant must have received a Ph.D., Psy.D., M.D., D.D.S., Sc.D., D.N.S.,

D.O., D.S.W., or equivalent degree from an accredited institution to be eligible for an individual postdoctoral fellowship.

All research training awards are made to appropriate domestic research centers, medical schools, departments of psychiatry, nonmedical academic departments, psychiatric hospitals or hospitals with psychiatric services, community mental health centers, and biomedical research institutes on behalf of individuals who need the opportunity to realize research potential. Except for the NIH Pathway to Independence Award, the individuals must be citizens or nationals of the U.S. or have been lawfully admitted for permanent residence. NIH Pathway to Independence Award is open to both U.S. citizens and non-U.S. citizens. Individuals must qualify by scholastic degree and previous training and/or experience.

FINANCIAL DATA:
Amount of support per award: Grants and awards vary in amount, depending upon the program and type of funding mechanism.

Total amount of support: Varies.

NUMBER OF AWARDS: Approximately 3,063 for the year 2013.

APPLICATION INFORMATION:
Application materials are available on NIMH web site. Prospective applicants should contact NIMH staff prior to submission to ensure the area of research that they investigate is within NIMH priorities.

Duration: Varies, with project periods ranging one to five years. Funding commitments are made annually.

Deadline: Contact the headquarters or regional office, as appropriate, for application deadlines.

ADDRESS INQUIRIES TO:
Dr. Tracy Waldeck
Division of Extramural Activities
(See address above.)

NATIONAL INSTITUTE OF MENTAL HEALTH

Division of Adult Translational Research and Treatment Development (DATR)
6001 Executive Boulevard, Room 7111, MSC 9632
Bethesda, MD 20892-9632
(301) 443-3648

E-MAIL ADDRESS:
ftuma@nih.gov

WEB SITE ADDRESS:
www.nimh.nih.
gov/about/organization/datr/index.shtml

TYPE:
Fellowships; Internships; Project/program grants; Research grants; Technical assistance; Training grants; Visiting scholars; Research contracts.

See entry 1865 for full listing.

NATIONAL SCIENCE FOUNDATION [2583]

Directorate for Social Behavorial and Economic Sciences
4201 Wilson Boulevard, Room 995
Arlington, VA 22230
(703) 292-7277
Fax: (703) 292-9083

E-MAIL ADDRESS:
sdickers@nsf.gov

WEB SITE ADDRESS:
www.nsf.gov

FOUNDED: 1950

AREAS OF INTEREST:
Social behavior and social development.

NAME(S) OF PROGRAMS:
● **Social Psychology Program**

TYPE:
Project/program grants; Research grants; Training grants; Travel grants; Visiting scholars. Support for laboratory and field research in all areas of human social behavior including social cognition, attitude formation and change, and social influence. The Program includes research on social, personality and emotional development in children and adults. Research to improve the conceptual and methodological base of social and developmental psychology is encouraged.

YEAR PROGRAM STARTED: 1972

PURPOSE:
To initiate and support scientific research and programs to strengthen research potential.

LEGAL BASIS:
National Science Foundation Act of 1950.

ELIGIBILITY:
Applicants may be colleges and universities on behalf of their staff members, nonprofit, nonacademic research institutions, such as independent museums, observatories, research laboratories, stock centers and similar organizations, private profit organizations, in exceptional circumstances, rarely, foreign institutions utilizing U.S. currency and, under special circumstances, unaffiliated U.S. scientists.

GEOGRAPHIC RESTRICTIONS:
United States.

FINANCIAL DATA:
Support may cover salaries, research assistantships, staff benefits if a direct cost, permanent equipment, travel, publication costs, computer costs and certain other direct and indirect costs.

Amount of support per award: Average $95,000 to $150,000 per year.

NUMBER OF APPLICANTS MOST RECENT YEAR: Approximately 2,000.

NUMBER OF AWARDS: 50.

APPLICATION INFORMATION:
A proposal should include title and description of proposed research, information about the institution, principal investigator and business administrator, desired effective date of grant, duration of support, endorsement, facilities, personnel, current support and pending applications and budget.

Duration: Research grants may be awarded for periods of up to five years. Most grants are for two or three years.

Deadline: Target dates are January 15 and July 15.

STAFF:
Sally Dickerson, Program Director

ADDRESS INQUIRIES TO:
Sally Dickerson, Program Director
(See address above.)

NATIONAL SCIENCE FOUNDATION [2584]

Division of Behavioral and Cognitive Sciences
4201 Wilson Boulevard, Room 995N
Arlington, VA 22230
(703) 292-7238
Fax: (703) 292-9068

WEB SITE ADDRESS:
www.nsf.gov

FOUNDED: 1950

NAME(S) OF PROGRAMS:
● **Perception, Action & Cognition Program**

TYPE:
Research grants. Supports research on perception, action and cognition. Emphasis is on research strongly grounded in theory. Research topics include vision, audition, haptics, attention, memory, reasoning, written and spoken discourse, motor control, and developmental issues in all topic areas. The program encompasses a wide range of theoretical perspectives such as symbolic computation, connectionism, ecological, nonlinear dynamics, complex systems, and a variety of methodologies including both experimental studies and modeling. Research involving acquired or developmental deficits is appropriate if the results speak to basic issues of cognition, perception or action.

YEAR PROGRAM STARTED: 1976

PURPOSE:
To initiate and support scientific research and programs to strengthen research potential.

LEGAL BASIS:
National Science Foundation Act of 1950.

ELIGIBILITY:
Requirements vary according to program. Applicants should consult web site for current programs.

GEOGRAPHIC RESTRICTIONS:
United States.

FINANCIAL DATA:
Amount of support per award: Approximately $120,000 per year.

Total amount of support: Varies.

APPLICATION INFORMATION:
Application should be submitted by FastLane or through Foundation's web site. Standard grant proposal guidelines apply.

Duration: 12 to 60 months, depending on the scientific merit and requirements of the project, and the type of program.

STAFF:
Betty Tuller, Director

ADDRESS INQUIRIES TO:
Betty Tuller, Director
(See address above.)

PARAPSYCHOLOGY FOUNDATION, INC. [2585]

P.O. Box 1562
New York, NY 10021
(212) 628-1550
Fax: (212) 628-1559

E-MAIL ADDRESS:
info@parapsychology.org

WEB SITE ADDRESS:
www.parapsychology.org

AREAS OF INTEREST:
Parapsychology.

NAME(S) OF PROGRAMS:
● **Eileen J. Garrett Scholarship**

TYPE:
Scholarships. Assists students attending an accredited college or university in pursuing the academic study of the science of parapsychology.

PURPOSE:
To promote research in parapsychology.

ELIGIBILITY:
Open to nationals of any country.

FINANCIAL DATA:
Amount of support per award: $3,000.

NUMBER OF AWARDS: 1.

APPLICATION INFORMATION:
Applicants must submit samples of writings on the subject with an application form from the Foundation. Letters of reference from three individuals who are familiar with the applicant's work and/or studies in parapsychology are required.
Duration: One year.
Deadline: July 15. Notification on August 1.

PARAPSYCHOLOGY FOUNDATION, INC. [2586]
P.O. Box 1562
New York, NY 10021
(212) 628-1550
Fax: (212) 628-1559

E-MAIL ADDRESS:
office@parapsychology.org

WEB SITE ADDRESS:
www.parapsychology.org

AREAS OF INTEREST:
Parapsychology and psychic phenomena.

NAME(S) OF PROGRAMS:
• **Frances P. Bolton Fellowship**

TYPE:
Fellowships.

PURPOSE:
To further write up and polish the data amassed during the preparation of a doctoral dissertation/thesis.

ELIGIBILITY:
Awarded to a person who obtained their Ph.D. on the basis of a dissertation/thesis which dealt with some aspect of parapsychological phenomena.

FINANCIAL DATA:
Amount of support per award: $3,000.

APPLICATION INFORMATION:
Applications must be accompanied by a copy of the doctoral dissertation/thesis.
Deadline: February 15. Award notification March 1.

ADDRESS INQUIRIES TO:
Lisette Coly, Executive Director
(See address above.)

PARAPSYCHOLOGY FOUNDATION, INC. [2587]
P.O. Box 1562
New York, NY 10021
(212) 628-1550
Fax: (212) 628-1559

E-MAIL ADDRESS:
office@parapsychology.org

WEB SITE ADDRESS:
www.parapsychology.org

AREAS OF INTEREST:
Parapsychology and psychic phenomena.

NAME(S) OF PROGRAMS:
• **Charles T. and Judith A. Tart Student Incentive Award**

TYPE:
Awards/prizes. Incentive award for research proposal.

YEAR PROGRAM STARTED: 2001

ELIGIBILITY:
Student must demonstrate a strong commitment to work within parapsychology. Open to undergraduate, graduate and postgraduate students who have in mind a specific research proposal which may be experimental, experiential, clinical, historical, survey- or questionnaire-based, archival, bibliographic, literary or any other type of investigation a student may propose.

FINANCIAL DATA:
Amount of support per award: $500.

APPLICATION INFORMATION:
Application must be in English and should be accompanied by two letters of reference, a one- to two-page description of the project that includes purpose, method, materials and duration of the project, and a one-page budget.
Deadline: November 15. Award notification on or around December 1.

ADDRESS INQUIRIES TO:
Lisette Coly, Executive Director
(See address above.)

PARAPSYCHOLOGY FOUNDATION, INC. [2588]
P.O. Box 1562
New York, NY 10021
(212) 628-1550
Fax: (212) 628-1559

E-MAIL ADDRESS:
office@parapsychology.org

WEB SITE ADDRESS:
www.parapsychology.org

AREAS OF INTEREST:
Parapsychology and psychic phenomena.

NAME(S) OF PROGRAMS:
• **Robert R. Coly Prize**

TYPE:
Awards/prizes. Essay competition.

YEAR PROGRAM STARTED: 2004

PURPOSE:
To understand the complexities of parapsychology and help conceptualize its future.

ELIGIBILITY:
Incoming and current undergraduate college and university students who have sufficient interest in the field, even if they are not in a parapsychology degree program.

FINANCIAL DATA:
Amount of support per award: $1,000.

APPLICATION INFORMATION:
Application must be in English and include the following:
(1) copy of high school/college transcript;
(2) letters of recommendation (English only) from individuals who know their abilities and interest in parapsychology and;
(3) 1,000- to 1,500-word essay, written in English, addressing the topic "The Challenge of Parapsychology."
Deadline: November 15. Award notification on or around December 1.

ADDRESS INQUIRIES TO:
Lisette Coly, Executive Director
(See address above.)

PSI CHI, THE INTERNATIONAL HONOR SOCIETY IN PSYCHOLOGY [2589]
825 Vine Street
Chattanooga, TN 37403
(423) 756-2044
Fax: (877) 774-2443

E-MAIL ADDRESS:
awards@psichi.org

WEB SITE ADDRESS:
www.psichi.org

FOUNDED: 1929

AREAS OF INTEREST:
Psychology.

CONSULTING OR VOLUNTEER SERVICES:
Honor society for psychology majors.

NAME(S) OF PROGRAMS:
• **Psi Chi/APA Edwin B. Newman Graduate Research Award**

TYPE:
Awards/prizes.

PURPOSE:
To give recognition to a graduate student for research in the field of psychology.

LEGAL BASIS:
Honor society.

ELIGIBILITY:
Psi Chi membership not required. The submitter of a research paper must:
(1) be a graduate student at the time the research was carried out and submitted for publication and/or presentation;
(2) be the primary and first author and;
(3) have presented the results of the research at a state, regional or national psychology convention, or have been published in a psychology journal.

FINANCIAL DATA:
Amount of support per award: Up to $1,000 in travel expenses to attend the APA (American Psychological Association) National Convention, plus a three-year membership in APA.

NUMBER OF APPLICANTS MOST RECENT YEAR:
7.

NUMBER OF AWARDS: 1.

APPLICATION INFORMATION:
Submit online at the web site, under the Awards/Grants section. The link to submissions is available at least one month prior to the submission deadline.
Duration: One-time award.
Deadline: February 1.

PUBLICATIONS:
Eye on Psi Chi, magazine; *Journal of Undergraduate Research.*

ADDRESS INQUIRIES TO:
Jennifer Baldwin, Director of Awards/Grants
(See address above.)

SCOTTISH RITE CHARITABLE FOUNDATION OF CANADA [2590]
4 Queen Street South
Hamilton ON L8P 3R3 Canada
(905) 522-0033
Fax: (905) 522-3716

E-MAIL ADDRESS:
grantsandawards@srcf.ca
info@srcf.ca

WEB SITE ADDRESS:
www.srcf.ca

FOUNDED: 1970

AREAS OF INTEREST:
Biomedical research into intellectual
impairment.

NAME(S) OF PROGRAMS:
● **Scottish Rite Charitable Foundation
Major Research Grants**

TYPE:
Research grants. SRCFC grants support
biomedical research into intellectual
impairment focused on:
(1) the causes and eventual cure of
intellectual impairment, such as autism and
Down syndrome, especially as it affects
children;
(2) the causes and eventual cure of
Alzheimer's Disease and;
(3) research into other forms of intellectual
impairment.

The focus should be on the causes and cure
of the disease as opposed to the active
treatment or palliative care.

YEAR PROGRAM STARTED: 1970

PURPOSE:
To provide financial support to researchers
studying developmental disabilities.

LEGAL BASIS:
Nonprofit.

ELIGIBILITY:
The following criteria apply:
(1) applications are invited from researchers
who hold, or have a firm offer of, at least a
three-year academic appointment at a
Canadian university or similar appointment at
a Canadian research hospital;
(2) applicant must be a Canadian citizen or a
permanent resident of Canada;
(3) special consideration will be given to
applicants who have received their doctoral
degree within the past five years;
(4) research projects must be endorsed by the
research services department or equivalent of
the university, hospital or research institute
and;
(5) research must be carried out within
Canada.

GEOGRAPHIC RESTRICTIONS:
Canada.

FINANCIAL DATA:
Amount of support per award: Up to $35,000
per year.

NUMBER OF AWARDS: Approximately 10 new
and renewals per year.

APPLICATION INFORMATION:
The research proposals submitted should be
accompanied by an explanation of the
relationship of the research to the areas of
priority, a proposed budget, published papers
of the applicant relevant to the proposed
research and the time lines of the research.
Applications should be submitted to the
Chair of the Awards Committee at the
address above.
Duration: One, two or three years. Renewal
contingent on a progress report of the work
and research results.
Deadline: April 30 each year.

OFFICERS:
C. Robert Townshend, President

ADDRESS INQUIRIES TO:
The Awards Committee
(See address above.)

SOCIETY OF BIOLOGICAL
PSYCHIATRY   [2591]
Mayo Clinic - Jacksonville
Research-Birdsall 310
4500 San Pablo Road
Jacksonville, FL 32224
(904) 953-2842
Fax: (904) 953-7117

E-MAIL ADDRESS:
maggie@sobp.org

WEB SITE ADDRESS:
www.sobp.org

FOUNDED: 1945

AREAS OF INTEREST:
Biological psychiatry,
neuropsychopharmacology and clinical
neuroscience.

NAME(S) OF PROGRAMS:
● **A.E. Bennett Research Awards**

TYPE:
Awards/prizes. Awards for recent,
unpublished research papers in the field of
biological psychiatry.

YEAR PROGRAM STARTED: 1958

PURPOSE:
To promote research in biological psychiatry.

LEGAL BASIS:
Nonprofit foundation.

ELIGIBILITY:
Applicants must be qualified investigators
with appropriate interests. Preference is given
to investigators 35 years of age or less who
have not been engaged in research for greater
than 10 years following award of their
terminal degree or the end of formal
clinical/fellowship training, whichever is
later. Membership in the Society is not
required.

FINANCIAL DATA:
Amount of support per award: $5,000 each
for the best clinical paper and the best basic
science paper submitted.

NUMBER OF AWARDS: 1 or 2 each year.

APPLICATION INFORMATION:
Applications are submitted electronically.
Duration: One year.
Deadline: Manuscripts must be received by
January 14.

OFFICERS:
Scott L. Rauch, President
Elliott Richelson, M.D., Treasurer
Trey Sunderland, Executive Secretary

STAFF:
Maggie Peterson, MBA, Executive Director

ADDRESS INQUIRIES TO:
Maggie Peterson, MBA, Executive Director
(See address and e-mail above.)

SOCIETY OF BIOLOGICAL
PSYCHIATRY   [2592]
Mayo Clinic - Jacksonville
Research-Birdsall 310
4500 San Pablo Road
Jacksonville, FL 32224
(904) 953-2842
Fax: (904) 953-7117

E-MAIL ADDRESS:
maggie@sobp.org

WEB SITE ADDRESS:
www.sobp.org

FOUNDED: 1945

AREAS OF INTEREST:
Biological psychiatry,
neuropsychopharmacology and clinical
neuroscience.

NAME(S) OF PROGRAMS:
● **Ziskind-Somerfeld Research Award**

TYPE:
Awards/prizes. Award for recent,
unsubmitted, unpublished research paper in
the field of biological psychiatry.

YEAR PROGRAM STARTED: 1991

PURPOSE:
To stimulate investigations in biological
psychiatry by senior investigators.

LEGAL BASIS:
Nonprofit.

ELIGIBILITY:
Candidates must be at least 35 years of age
at time of submission, must continue to be
actively involved in the area of research
described in the submission and must be a
member in good standing of the Society of
Biological Psychiatry.

FINANCIAL DATA:
Amount of support per award: $5,000.
Total amount of support: $5,000 annually.

NUMBER OF APPLICANTS MOST RECENT YEAR:
5.

NUMBER OF AWARDS: 1 each year.

APPLICATION INFORMATION:
No application submission is required for the
award. The Society provides a list of the top
15 articles to the Ziskind-Somerfeld Award
Committee to review and make a final award
selection.
Duration: One-time award.
Deadline: Announcement in May.

ADDRESS INQUIRIES TO:
Maggie Peterson, Executive Director
(See address above.)

SUBSTANCE ABUSE AND
MENTAL HEALTH SERVICES
ADMINISTRATION, DISASTER
TECHNICAL ASSISTANCE
CENTER   [2593]
One Choke Cherry, Room 6-1101
Rockville, MD 20857
(800) 308-3515
Fax: (240) 276-1890

WEB SITE ADDRESS:
www.samhsa.gov/dtac

AREAS OF INTEREST:
Emergency mental health and crisis
counseling.

NAME(S) OF PROGRAMS:
● **Crisis Counseling Assistance and
Training Program**

TYPE:
Project/program grants. Grants to address the
various dimensions of mental health crises
affecting victims of presidentially declared
major disasters. Support is available for
development of training models and other
psychological material for the delivery of
crisis intervention services/outreach.

YEAR PROGRAM STARTED: 1974

PURPOSE:
   To provide supplemental support to victims
   of major disasters and their families in
   emergency mental health and crisis
   intervention.

LEGAL BASIS:
   Section 416 of The Robert T. Stafford
   Disaster Relief and Emergency Assistance
   Act (Public Law 100-707).

ELIGIBILITY:
   Must be presidentially declared major
   disaster. U.S. territories and federally
   recognized tribes are also eligible.

FINANCIAL DATA:
   Amount of support per award: Grants given
   according to justifiable need. Amounts vary
   in accordance with existing resources in
   stricken community.

   Total amount of support: Varies.

COOPERATIVE FUNDING PROGRAMS: Program
   funding is supplemental when existing
   programs are inadequate to meet the needs of
   the community.

APPLICATION INFORMATION:
   Contact the organization for guidelines.

   Duration: Nine months; renewal possible
   upon approval of CMHS and SAMHSA.
   Extension of grant possible in limited
   circumstances.

   Deadline: 60 days following the disaster.

ADDRESS INQUIRIES TO:
   Nikki Bellamy, Project Officer
   SAMHSA/CMHS

VAN AMERINGEN FOUNDATION, INC. [2594]

509 Madison Avenue
Room 2010
New York, NY 10022
(212) 758-6221
Fax: (212) 688-2105

E-MAIL ADDRESS:
   info@vanamfound.org

WEB SITE ADDRESS:
   www.vanamfound.org

FOUNDED: 1950

AREAS OF INTEREST:
   Mental illness and mental health.

TYPE:
   Demonstration grants; General operating
   grants; Project/program grants; Research
   grants; Seed money grants. Grants for
   projects and activities in areas of social
   welfare, with particular emphasis on mental
   health.

YEAR PROGRAM STARTED: 1950

PURPOSE:
   To promote mental health through preventive
   medicine, research, treatment and
   rehabilitation.

LEGAL BASIS:
   Private foundation.

ELIGIBILITY:
   Tax-exempt organizations with appropriate
   interests are eligible. No grants are made to
   individuals.

GEOGRAPHIC RESTRICTIONS:
   Metropolitan New York area and
   Philadelphia.

FINANCIAL DATA:
   Amount of support per award: Up to
   $50,000, according to the needs and nature of
   the project.
   Total amount of support: Approximately
   $4,000,000 for the year 2012.

NUMBER OF APPLICANTS MOST RECENT YEAR:
   520.

NUMBER OF AWARDS: 89.

APPLICATION INFORMATION:
   No formal application forms are required.
   Proposals may be submitted in the form of a
   short descriptive letter, enclosing such
   pertinent background as tax status
   documentation and the organization's annual
   reports and financial statements. Proposals
   may be submitted to the president at the
   address above.

   Deadline: Notification by December 1 for
   March Board meeting, April 1 for June
   meeting and July 1 for November meeting.

PUBLICATIONS:
   Annual report; guidelines.

DIRECTORS:
   Henry van Ameringen, President and
   Treasurer
   George Rowe, Jr., Vice President and
   Secretary
   Judith Beck
   Alexandra Herzan
   Christina K. Kind
   Kenneth A. Kind
   Patricia Kind
   Valerie Kind-Rubin
   Andrew Kindfuller
   Laura K. McKenna
   Clarence Sundram

ADDRESS INQUIRIES TO:
   Henry van Ameringen, President
   (See address above.)

TECHNOLOGY AND INDUSTRY

Technology and industry

AIR & WASTE MANAGEMENT ASSOCIATION (A&WMA)   [2595]

One Gateway Center, 3rd Floor
420 Fort Duquesne Boulevard
Pittsburgh, PA 15222
(412) 904-6006
Fax: (412) 232-3450

E-MAIL ADDRESS:
sglyptis@awma.org

WEB SITE ADDRESS:
www.awma.org

FOUNDED: 1907

AREAS OF INTEREST:
Air quality, waste management and/or
environmental management/policy/law.

NAME(S) OF PROGRAMS:
● **Scholarship Endowment Trust Fund**

TYPE:
Scholarships.

PURPOSE:
To provide monies for students with interest
in the area of air quality, waste management
and/or environmental management/policy/law.

ELIGIBILITY:
Must be a full-time graduate student pursuing
studies in the area of air quality, waste
management and/or environmental
management/policy/law.

FINANCIAL DATA:
Amount of support per award: $2,000 to
$7,500.
Total amount of support: Approximately
$26,000 annually.

NUMBER OF APPLICANTS MOST RECENT YEAR:
50.

NUMBER OF AWARDS: Approximately 10.

APPLICATION INFORMATION:
Applications must be completed online.
Duration: One year. Renewal possible by
reapplying.
Deadline: December 1.

ADDRESS INQUIRIES TO:
Stephanie Glyptis, Director of Education
(See address above.)

AIR TRAFFIC CONTROL ASSOCIATION (ATCA)   [2596]

1101 King Street, Suite 300
Alexandria, VA 22314
(703) 299-2430 ext. 314
Fax: (703) 299-2437

E-MAIL ADDRESS:
tim.wagner@atca.org

WEB SITE ADDRESS:
www.atca.org

FOUNDED: 1956

AREAS OF INTEREST:
Air traffic control and aviation.

TYPE:
Scholarships. Scholarships to promising
young men and women enrolled in programs
leading to careers in aviation or air traffic
control and scholarships for dependents of air
traffic controllers pursuing a degree.

PURPOSE:
To promote careers in air traffic control or
aviation disciplines.

LEGAL BASIS:
Private, 501(c)(3) charity.

FINANCIAL DATA:
Amount of support per award: $2,000 to
$8,000.
Total amount of support: Varies.

NUMBER OF APPLICANTS MOST RECENT YEAR:
300.

NUMBER OF AWARDS: 8 to 12.

APPLICATION INFORMATION:
Contact the Association.
Duration: One year.
Deadline: May 1.

ADDRESS INQUIRIES TO:
Tim Wagner, Membership Manager
(See address above.)

AMERICAN GROUND WATER TRUST   [2597]

50 Pleasant Street, Suite 2
Concord, NH 03301-4073
(603) 228-5444
Fax: (603) 228-6557

E-MAIL ADDRESS:
trustinfo@agwt.org

WEB SITE ADDRESS:
www.agwt.org

FOUNDED: 1986

AREAS OF INTEREST:
Groundwater education, sustainable
management and protection.

NAME(S) OF PROGRAMS:
● **AMTROL Scholarship**
● **Baroid Scholarship**
● **Thomas M. Stetson Scholarship**

TYPE:
Awards/prizes; Scholarships.

YEAR PROGRAM STARTED: 1986

PURPOSE:
To provide education outreach to inform the
public about the optimal utilization and
protection of groundwater for the benefit of
mankind.

LEGAL BASIS:
501(c)(3) nonprofit organization.

ELIGIBILITY:
Applicants must be U.S. citizens, apply
during their senior year in high school, and
be enrolled the following year in an
undergraduate program relevant to the
groundwater industry.

GEOGRAPHIC RESTRICTIONS:
United States.

FINANCIAL DATA:
Amount of support per award: $1,000 to
$2,000.

NUMBER OF APPLICANTS MOST RECENT YEAR:
40.

NUMBER OF AWARDS: 3.

APPLICATION INFORMATION:
Applicant must submit only one application
to be considered for all scholarships.
Completed application form must be
countersigned by a teacher at the applicant's
high school and accompanied by two letters
of recommendation. A 500-word essay and a
300-word description of the applicant's high
school groundwater project and/or practical
environmental work experience must

accompany the application. Documentary
evidence of scholastic achievements and
references will be requested from finalists.
Duration: One academic year.
Deadline: June 1. The Trust will write to all
applicants (successful and unsuccessful) at
the end of August.

IRS IDENTIFICATION NUMBER: 23-7244958

STAFF:
Andrew W. Stone, Executive Director
Garret W. Graaskamp, Director of Programs

ADDRESS INQUIRIES TO:
Andrew W. Stone, Executive Director
(See address above.)

AMERICAN SOCIETY FOR ENOLOGY AND VITICULTURE

1784 Picasso Avenue, Suite D
Davis, CA 95618-0551
(530) 753-3142
Fax: (530) 753-3318

E-MAIL ADDRESS:
society@asev.org

WEB SITE ADDRESS:
www.asev.org

TYPE:
Scholarships. Awards for undergraduate or
graduate students enrolled in enology or
viticulture or in a curriculum which
emphasizes a science basic to the wine and
grape industry and who intend to pursue a
career in research for the wine or grape
industry after graduation from college or
university.

See entry 2115 for full listing.

THE AMERICAN SOCIETY FOR NONDESTRUCTIVE TESTING, INC.   [2598]

1711 Arlingate Lane
Columbus, OH 43228-0518
(614) 274-6003
(800) 222-2768
Fax: (614) 274-6899

E-MAIL ADDRESS:
mthomas@asnt.org

WEB SITE ADDRESS:
www.asnt.org

FOUNDED: 1941

AREAS OF INTEREST:
Nondestructive testing.

NAME(S) OF PROGRAMS:
● **ASNT Fellowship Award**

TYPE:
Fellowships. Nondestructive evaluation and
testing (NDE/NDT) is the science of
examining components and systems in a
manner that does not impair their further
usefulness. NDE/NDT is a complex,
multidisciplinary field offering exciting career
opportunities. Current areas for applying new
and advanced nondestructive testing
technology include power plant life
extension, aging aircraft and deteriorating
civil engineering structures.

YEAR PROGRAM STARTED: 1981

PURPOSE:
To advance the examination of objects with
technology that does not affect the object's
future usefulness; to identify up to three
ABET-accredited educational institutions that
may receive one of the awards for NDT
postgraduate research.

LEGAL BASIS:
Nonprofit organization.

ELIGIBILITY:
ABET-accredited academic institutions with graduate educational research programs are invited to submit proposals. Proposals are evaluated based on their soundness of approach, value of potential contribution, potential for successful completion, qualifications of potential student recipient, qualifications of advisor, adequacy of program of study, adequacy of facilities, and qualifications of faculty members.

FINANCIAL DATA:
Amount of support per award: $20,000.
Total amount of support: Up to $100,000.

NUMBER OF AWARDS: Up to 5 per year.

APPLICATION INFORMATION:
The proposal, with all support materials, should not exceed 20 one-sided sheets. It must include a title page, table of contents, research proposal, program of study, research facilities, budget, research advisor, and recipient. The educational facility must submit a written report on the completed study within 24 months of the program's initiation. This report must be in a format suitable for publication in the Society's technical journal, *Materials Evaluation.* In addition, the postgraduate student must present his findings at an ASNT national conference. No more than one proposal per faculty member.
Duration: One year.
Deadline: October 15.

ADDRESS INQUIRIES TO:
Michelle Thomas
ASNT Administrative Assistant
ASNT Headquarters
(See address above.)

APICS EDUCATIONAL AND RESEARCH FOUNDATION, INC.   [2599]
8430 West Bryn Mawr Avenue
Suite 1000
Chicago, IL 60631-3439
(800) 444-2742 (customer service)
(773) 867-1777
Fax: (773) 639-3115

E-MAIL ADDRESS:
jstults@apics.org

WEB SITE ADDRESS:
www.apics.org/education/erfoundation

FOUNDED: 1965

AREAS OF INTEREST:
Applied resource management, manufacturing, service industries, production and inventory management.

NAME(S) OF PROGRAMS:
● **George and Marion Plossl Doctoral Dissertation Competition**

TYPE:
Awards/prizes; Conferences/seminars; Fellowships; Project/program grants; Research grants. Plossl Doctoral Dissertation Competition is in the area of business management.

Grants are also available at the postdoctoral, academic-practitioner level in the field of business.

YEAR PROGRAM STARTED: 1965

PURPOSE:
To further develop the APICS body of knowledge; to develop professional efficiency in production and inventory management.

LEGAL BASIS:
Tax-exempt 501(c)(3) organization.

ELIGIBILITY:
The Plossl Doctoral Dissertation Competition is for doctoral students.

The program is a competition, not a scholarship. Applicants must be currently matriculated students in a business program. High school students are not eligible.

FINANCIAL DATA:
Amount of support per award: $2,500.
Total amount of support: $2,500 annually.

NUMBER OF APPLICANTS MOST RECENT YEAR:
8.

NUMBER OF AWARDS: 1.

APPLICATION INFORMATION:
Application must include:
(1) project planning description;
(2) planned progress report dates;
(3) total itemized expenses;
(4) planned method for publication or presentation and;
(5) qualifications of applicant.
Deadline: June 1.

PUBLICATIONS:
Guidelines.

STAFF:
John Stults, Director of Corporate Partnerships

ADDRESS INQUIRIES TO:
John Stults
Director of Corporate Partnerships
(See address above.)

AWS FOUNDATION, INC.   [2600]
8669 Doral Boulevard
Suite 130
Doral, FL 33166
(305) 443-9353
Fax: (305) 443-7559

E-MAIL ADDRESS:
vpinsky@aws.org

WEB SITE ADDRESS:
www.aws.org

FOUNDED: 1989

AREAS OF INTEREST:
Welding and materials joining.

NAME(S) OF PROGRAMS:
● **Howard E. and Wilma J. Adkins Memorial Scholarship**
● **Airgas-Jerry Baker Scholarship**
● **Airgas-Terry Jarvis Memorial Scholarship**
● **Arsham Amirikian Engineering Scholarship**
● **D. Fred and Marian L. Bovie Scholarship**
● **John C. Lincoln Memorial Scholarship**
● **Matsuo Bridge Company, Ltd. of Japan Scholarship**

TYPE:
Scholarships. Howard E. and Wilma J. Adkins Memorial Scholarship is awarded to a full-time college junior or senior pursuing a minimum four-year degree in welding engineering or welding engineering technology.

Airgas-Jerry Baker Scholarship is awarded to a full-time college undergraduate pursuing a minimum four-year degree in welding engineering or welding engineering technology; however, priority will be given to welding engineering students.

Airgas-Terry Jarvis Memorial Scholarship is awarded to a full-time college undergraduate pursuing a minimum four-year degree in welding engineering or welding engineering technology; however, priority will be given to welding engineering students.

Arsham Amirikian Engineering Scholarship is awarded to a college undergraduate pursuing a minimum four-year degree in civil engineering or welding engineering.

D. Fred and Marian L. Bovie Scholarship is awarded to a full-time college undergraduate pursuing a minimum four-year degree in welding engineering at The Ohio State University.

John C. Lincoln Memorial Scholarship is awarded to a college undergraduate pursuing a minimum four-year degree in welding engineering or welding engineering technology. Priority will be given to welding engineering students.

Matsuo Bridge Company Ltd. of Japan Scholarship is for a college junior, senior, or graduate student pursuing a minimum four-year degree in civil engineering, welding engineering, welding engineering technology or a related discipline.

PURPOSE:
To promote education in welding engineering.

ELIGIBILITY:
Howard E. and Wilma J. Adkins Memorial Scholarship: U.S. citizens with a 3.2 grade point average in engineering, scientific and technical subjects, with a 2.8 overall grade point average.

Airgas-Jerry Baker Scholarship and Airgas-Terry Jarvis Memorial Scholarship: U.S. or Canadian citizens/residents who maintain a minimum overall grade point average of 2.8 with a 3.0 in engineering courses. Essay required: "Why I want to pursue a career with an industrial gas or welding equipment distributor?"

Arsham Amirikian Engineering Scholarship: Applicant must be a U.S. citizen or resident and have a minimum 3.0 overall grade point average.

D. Fred and Marian L. Bovie Scholarship: U.S. citizen or resident welding engineering student at The Ohio State University with a 3.0 overall grade point average. Electrical engineering students at The Ohio State University may be considered if there is no qualified welding engineering applicant at The Ohio State University.

John C. Lincoln Memorial Scholarship: U.S. citizen or resident with a 2.5 overall grade point average.

Matsuo Bridge Company Ltd. of Japan Scholarship: Applicant must be a U.S. citizen with a 3.0 overall grade point average; preference given to students from California, Oregon, Texas and Washington.

GEOGRAPHIC RESTRICTIONS:
United States and Canada.

FINANCIAL DATA:
Amount of support per award: Howard E. and Wilma J. Adkins Memorial Scholarship,

Airgas-Jerry Baker Scholarship, Airgas-Terry Jarvis Memorial Scholarship, Arsham Amirikian Engineering Scholarship and Matsuo Scholarship: $2,500; D. Fred and Marian L. Bovie Scholarship: $3,000; John C. Lincoln Memorial Scholarship: $3,500.

APPLICATION INFORMATION:
Contact the Foundation.

Duration: Howard E. and Wilma J. Adkins Memorial Scholarship: One year; may reapply for second year. All others, one year and renewable up to three years.

Deadline: February 15.

ADDRESS INQUIRIES TO:
Vicki L. Pinsky, Manager
(See address above.)

AWS FOUNDATION, INC.   [2601]

8669 Doral Boulevard
Suite 130
Doral, FL 33166
(305) 443-9353
Fax: (305) 443-7559

E-MAIL ADDRESS:
vpinsky@aws.org

WEB SITE ADDRESS:
www.aws.org

FOUNDED: 1989

AREAS OF INTEREST:
Welding and materials joining.

NAME(S) OF PROGRAMS:
- **Jack R. Barckhoff Welding Management Scholarship**
- **Edward J. Brady Memorial Scholarship**
- **William A. and Ann M. Brothers Scholarship**
- **Don and Shirley Hastings Scholarship**
- **Donald F. Hastings Scholarship**
- **William B. Howell Memorial Scholarship**
- **Miller Electric Mfg. Co. Scholarship**

TYPE:
Scholarships. Jack R. Barckhoff Welding Management Scholarship is awarded to a college junior pursuing a minimum four-year degree in welding engineering at The Ohio State University. Applicants will be expected to enroll and complete the two-hour course in Total Welding Management at The Ohio State University. Applicants must also complete an essay on how they see their role once they have graduated in improving the world of welding and the welding industry in the U.S., and how they will use their education to improve the U.S. competitive position in welding and manufacturing.

Edward J. Brady Memorial Scholarship is awarded to a college undergraduate pursuing a minimum four-year degree in welding engineering or welding engineering technology. Priority will be given to welding engineering students.

William A. and Ann M. Brothers Scholarship is awarded to a full-time college undergraduate pursuing a minimum four-year degree in welding or a related program.

Don and Shirley Hastings Scholarship is awarded to a college undergraduate pursuing a minimum four-year degree in welding engineering or welding engineering technology. Priority will be given to welding engineering students.

Donald F. Hastings Scholarship is awarded to a college undergraduate pursuing a minimum four-year degree in welding engineering or welding engineering technology. Priority will be given to welding engineering students.

William B. Howell Memorial Scholarship is awarded to a full-time college undergraduate pursuing a minimum four-year degree in a welding program at an accredited university.

Miller Electric Mfg. Co. Scholarship is awarded to a senior in a four-year Bachelor's program in welding engineering or welding engineering technology. Priority is given to Ferris State University.

PURPOSE:
To promote education in welding engineering.

ELIGIBILITY:
For all scholarships, applicants must be U.S. citizens/residents and have a minimum 2.5 grade point average.

Jack R. Barckhoff Welding Management Scholarship: Applicant must attend The Ohio State University.

William A. and Ann M. Brothers Scholarship: Priority will be given to those individuals residing or attending school in the state of Ohio.

Don and Shirley Hastings Scholarship: Priority will be given to those individuals who reside or attend school in the states of California, Iowa or Ohio.

Donald F. Hastings Scholarship: Priority will be given to those individuals who reside or attend school in California or Ohio.

William B. Howell Memorial Scholarship: Priority will be given to those individuals who reside or attend school in Florida, Michigan or Ohio.

Miller Electric Mfg. Co. Scholarship: Priority will be given to individuals attending Ferris State University.

GEOGRAPHIC RESTRICTIONS:
United States.

FINANCIAL DATA:
Amount of support per award: Jack R. Barckhoff Welding Management Scholarship, Edward J. Brady Memorial Scholarship, Don and Shirley Hastings Scholarship, Donald F. Hastings Scholarship and William B. Howell Memorial Scholarship: $2,500; William A. and Ann M. Brothers Scholarship: $3,500; Miller Electric Mfg. Co. Scholarship: $3,000.

NUMBER OF AWARDS: Jack R. Barckhoff Welding Management Scholarship and Miller Electric Mfg. Co. Scholarship: 2 of each.

APPLICATION INFORMATION:
Detailed information is available on the web site.

Duration: Jack R. Barckhoff Welding Management Scholarship: One year, with up to two years of scholarship support by reapplication; Edward J. Brady Memorial Scholarship, William A. and Ann M. Brothers Scholarship, Don and Shirley Hastings Scholarship, Donald F. Hastings Scholarship and William B. Howell Memorial Scholarship: One year, with up to four years of scholarship support by reapplication.

Deadline: February 15.

ADDRESS INQUIRIES TO:
Vicki L. Pinsky, Manager
(See address above.)

AWS FOUNDATION, INC.   [2602]

8669 Doral Boulevard
Suite 130
Doral, FL 33166
(305) 443-9353
Fax: (305) 443-7559

E-MAIL ADDRESS:
vpinsky@aws.org

WEB SITE ADDRESS:
www.aws.org

FOUNDED: 1989

AREAS OF INTEREST:
Welding and materials joining.

NAME(S) OF PROGRAMS:
- **Past Presidents Scholarship**
- **Robert L. Peaslee-Detroit Brazing and Soldering Scholarship**
- **Praxair International Scholarship**
- **James A. Turner, Jr. Memorial Scholarship**

TYPE:
Scholarships. Past Presidents Scholarship is for a student in a four-year program in welding engineering, welding engineering technology, or an engineering program with an emphasis on welding, or a graduate student pursuing a Master's or Doctorate in engineering and/or management.

Robert L. Peaslee-Detroit Brazing and Soldering Scholarship is for a college junior or senior pursuing a minimum four-year degree, or a graduate student, in welding engineering, welding engineering technology, or materials joining science with an emphasis on brazing or soldering applications.

Praxair International Scholarship is for a full-time college student pursuing a minimum four-year degree in welding engineering or welding engineering technology; however, priority will be given to welding engineering students. Applicant must demonstrate leadership abilities through clubs, organizations, extracurricular academic activities, community involvement, etc.

James A. Turner, Jr. Memorial Scholarship is for a student pursuing a Bachelor's degree in business that will lead to a management career in welding store operations or welding distributorship.

PURPOSE:
To promote education in welding engineering.

ELIGIBILITY:
Past Presidents Scholarship: Applicant must be a U.S. citizen and write a 300- to 500-word essay on their career aspirations. Applicant must have demonstrated leadership qualities, i.e., community involvement, AWS Section or other professional society participation, industry leadership, and be an AWS member.

Robert L. Peaslee-Detroit Brazing and Soldering Scholarship: Applicant may be a citizen of any country and plan to attend a university in the U.S. or Canada; U.S. citizens will receive priority. Minimum grade point average of 3.0 in engineering courses.

Praxair International Scholarship: Applicant must be a U.S. or Canadian citizen with a minimum overall grade point average of 2.5.

James A. Turner, Jr. Memorial Scholarship: Applicant must be employed at least 10 hours per week at a welding store operation or welding distributorship.

GEOGRAPHIC RESTRICTIONS:
United States.

FINANCIAL DATA:
Amount of support per award: Robert L. Peaslee-Detroit Brazing and Soldering Scholarship and Praxair International Scholarship: $2,500. James A. Turner, Jr. Memorial Scholarship: $3,500.

APPLICATION INFORMATION:
Past Presidents Scholarship: One or more recommendation letters must come from community members, local AWS Section Officers, and/or AWS District Director, attesting to leadership capability; one or more recommendation letters must come from faculty (if a student), or from employer (if employed).

Robert L. Peaslee-Detroit Brazing and Soldering Scholarship: Personal statement must include at least one paragraph on applicant's interest in brazing or soldering, any courses taken in related subjects, and any other information that would help the Selection Committee in selecting a recipient. Also, include a description of applicant's impressions of any experience he or she has had involving soldering or brazing.

Duration: Robert L. Peaslee-Detroit Brazing and Soldering Scholarship: Maximum of two years per award; Praxair International Scholarship and James A. Turner, Jr. Memorial Scholarship: Award recipients may reapply with a maximum of four years per award.

Deadline: February 15.

ADDRESS INQUIRIES TO:
Vicki L. Pinsky, Manager
(See address above.)

AWS FOUNDATION, INC. [2603]
8669 Doral Boulevard, Suite 130
Doral, FL 33166
(305) 443-9353 ext. 212
(800) 443-9353 ext. 212
Fax: (305) 443-7559

E-MAIL ADDRESS:
vpinsky@aws.org

WEB SITE ADDRESS:
www.aws.org/rwma

FOUNDED: 1935

AREAS OF INTEREST:
Resistance welding processes.

NAME(S) OF PROGRAMS:
● **Resistance Welding Manufacturing Alliance Scholarship**

TYPE:
Scholarships.

YEAR PROGRAM STARTED: 2005

PURPOSE:
To encourage the highest standards of ethics in the resistance welding industry; to encourage education pertaining to the resistance welding processes.

ELIGIBILITY:
Applicant must:
(1) be a junior-level student in a four-year program and working towards a degree in welding engineering or welding engineering technology;
(2) have a minimum 3.0 overall grade point average and;
(3) be a U.S. or Canadian citizen and plan to attend an academic institution in the U.S. or Canada.

FINANCIAL DATA:
Awards are for tuition and fees only and will be paid directly to the academic institution.
Amount of support per award: $2,500.
Total amount of support: $2,500.

NUMBER OF AWARDS: 1.

APPLICATION INFORMATION:
Candidates must submit the following:
(1) a completed application form;
(2) an essay of 500 words or less about why the student wishes to become involved in the resistance welding industry;
(3) a letter of recommendation from an academic advisor or faculty member using the RWMA Scholarship Recommendation form;
(4) a second letter of recommendation from another party, such as an employer, using the RWMA Scholarship Recommendation form and;
(5) a personal statement.
Duration: One year. Renewal possible; must reapply.
Deadline: February 15.

ADDRESS INQUIRIES TO:
Vicki L. Pinsky, Manager
(See address above.)

CHARLES BABBAGE INSTITUTE [2604]
University of Minnesota
211 Elmer L. Anderson Library
222 21st Avenue South
Minneapolis, MN 55455
(612) 624-5050

E-MAIL ADDRESS:
cbi@umn.edu

WEB SITE ADDRESS:
www.cbi.umn.edu

FOUNDED: 1978

AREAS OF INTEREST:
History of computers and information technology.

NAME(S) OF PROGRAMS:
● **The Adelle and Erwin Tomash Fellowship in the History of Information Technology**

TYPE:
Fellowships.

YEAR PROGRAM STARTED: 1978

PURPOSE:
To advance the professional development of historians of information technology.

LEGAL BASIS:
University and research association.

ELIGIBILITY:
Open to graduate students whose dissertation addresses some aspect of the history of computers and information technology. Topics may be chosen from the technical history of hardware or software, economic or business aspects of the information technology industry or other topics in the social, institutional or legal history of computing. Theses that consider technical issues in their socio-economic context are especially encouraged.

Priority will be given to students who have completed all requirements for the doctoral degree except the research and writing of the dissertation.

The fellowship may be held at the home academic institution, the Babbage Institute or any other location where there are appropriate research facilities.

FINANCIAL DATA:
Amount of support per award: $14,000 stipend.
Total amount of support: $14,000.

NUMBER OF APPLICANTS MOST RECENT YEAR:
5.

NUMBER OF AWARDS: 1.

APPLICATION INFORMATION:
Applicants should send biographical data and a research plan. The plan should contain a statement and justification of the research problem, a discussion of procedure for research and writing, information on availability of research materials and evidence of faculty support for the project. Applicants should arrange for three letters of reference and certified transcripts of college credits to be sent directly to the Institute. There is no special application form. A one-page flyer describing the fellowship is available.
Duration: One academic year.
Deadline: January 15.

PUBLICATIONS:
Newsletter.

ADDRESS INQUIRIES TO:
Jeffrey Yost, Associate Director
Charles Babbage Institute
(See address above.)

COIN-OP CARES CHARITABLE AND EDUCATION FOUNDATION [2605]
c/o Amusement & Music Operators Association
600 Spring Hill Ring Road, Suite 111
West Dundee, IL 60118
(847) 428-7699
(800) 937-2662
Fax: (847) 428-7719

E-MAIL ADDRESS:
amoa@amoa.com

WEB SITE ADDRESS:
www.amoa.com

FOUNDED: 1948

AREAS OF INTEREST:
Higher education.

NAME(S) OF PROGRAMS:
● **Wayne E. Hesch Memorial Scholarships**

TYPE:
Scholarships. Designed to provide financial support to students who are, or plan or hope to be, engaged in the profession.

PURPOSE:
To provide leadership for the amusement, music, entertainment and vending industry; to protect and promote the industry interests.

ELIGIBILITY:
Open to individuals in need of financial assistance who are attending or plan to attend an institution of higher education and have a 3.0 grade point average on a 4.0 scale.

FINANCIAL DATA:
Amount of support per award: $1,000 each.
Total amount of support: $48,000 annually.

APPLICATION INFORMATION:
Contact the Foundation.
Duration: One year.

Deadline: January 15. Selection in late March. Announcement in April.

ADDRESS INQUIRIES TO:
Maggie Kapinos, Program Coordinator
(See address above.)

EARLY AMERICAN INDUSTRIES ASSOCIATION, INC. [2606]
P.O. Box 524
Hebron, MD 21830-0524
(410) 749-1965

E-MAIL ADDRESS:
eaia1933@verizon.net

WEB SITE ADDRESS:
www.eaiainfo.org

FOUNDED: 1933

AREAS OF INTEREST:
To encourage study and better understanding of early American industries in the home, shop, on the farm and the sea; to discover, identify, classify, preserve and exhibit obsolete tools, implements and mechanical devices used in early America, craft practices, and industrial technology.

NAME(S) OF PROGRAMS:
● **Research Grants Program**

TYPE:
Research grants. These are not scholarship or internship grants.

YEAR PROGRAM STARTED: 1977

PURPOSE:
To preserve and present historic trades, crafts and tools, and to interpret their impact on the present generation.

LEGAL BASIS:
Nonprofit corporation.

ELIGIBILITY:
Applicants may be sponsored by an institution or engaged in self-directed projects. Projects must relate to the purposes of the Association. Grants can supplement existing aid. These are not scholarship, fellowship or internship funds. A grant may not be used to pay for salaries, historical artifacts, software or equipment in whole or in part.

GEOGRAPHIC RESTRICTIONS:
United States.

FINANCIAL DATA:
A project report including a statement of expenditures must be filed by recipients.
Amount of support per award: Up to $2,000.

NUMBER OF APPLICANTS MOST RECENT YEAR: 8.

NUMBER OF AWARDS: 2.

APPLICATION INFORMATION:
Application is available online, and must be completed and mailed to the above address.
Duration: One year. Nonrenewable.
Deadline: March 15 annually. Announcements in April annually.

PUBLICATIONS:
The Chronicle, quarterly journal; *Shavings,* newsletter for members; application guidelines; E.A.I.A. brochure.

OFFICERS:
John H. Verrill, Executive Director

ADDRESS INQUIRIES TO:
John H. Verrill, Executive Director
(See address above.)

FEDERAL HIGHWAY ADMINISTRATION [2607]
Technology Partnerships Program
1310 North Courthouse Road, Suite 300
Arlington, VA 22201
(703) 235-0536
Fax: (703) 235-0593

E-MAIL ADDRESS:
fawn.thompson@dot.gov

WEB SITE ADDRESS:
www.fhwa.dot.gov/ugp

AREAS OF INTEREST:
Transportation-related disciplines.

NAME(S) OF PROGRAMS:
● **Dwight David Eisenhower Transportation Fellowship Program**

TYPE:
Fellowships; Internships; Research grants. Dwight David Eisenhower Transportation Fellowship Program's objectives are to attract the nation's brightest minds to the field of transportation, to enhance the careers of transportation professionals by encouraging them to seek advanced degrees, and to retain top talent in the transportation industry of the U.S. This Program encompasses all areas of transportation. The Program has seven award categories:
(1) Eisenhower Graduate (GRAD) Fellowships enable students to pursue Master's degrees or Doctorates in transportation-related fields at the university of their choice;
(2) Eisenhower Grants for Research (GRF) Fellowships acquaint undergraduate and graduate students with transportation research, development and technology-transfer activities at the U.S. Department of Transportation facilities;
(3) Eisenhower Historically Black Colleges and Universities (HBCU) Fellowships provide HBCU students with additional opportunities to enter careers in transportation. The Fellowships also serve as a feeder for other Eisenhower fellowships;
(4) Eisenhower Hispanic Serving Institutions (HSI) Fellowships provide HSI students with additional opportunities to enter careers in transportation. The Fellowships also serve as a feeder for other Eisenhower fellowships;
(5) Eisenhower Tribal College Fellowships (TC) identify transportation-related activities and provide student fellowship opportunities at tribal colleges. The Fellowships also serve as a feeder for other Eisenhower fellowships;
(6) Eisenhower Intern Fellowships (EIF);
(7) Eisenhower People with Disabilities (PWD) Fellowships and;
(8) Eisenhower Community College Fellowship.

YEAR PROGRAM STARTED: 1983

PURPOSE:
To attract the nation's brightest minds to the field of transportation; to enhance the careers of transportation professionals by encouraging them to seek advanced degrees; to retain top talent in the transportation industry of the U.S.

LEGAL BASIS:
Government agency.

ELIGIBILITY:
Applicants must be enrolled in transportation-related disciplines (e.g., engineering, computer science, physics, transportation planning) at accredited universities.

GEOGRAPHIC RESTRICTIONS:
United States.

FINANCIAL DATA:
Award may include an allowance for tuition, stipend and travel expenses for the student to attend the annual Transportation Research Board (TRB) conference held in Washington, DC every January.
Amount of support per award: $1,500 to $40,000.
Total amount of support: $2,200,000 per year.

NUMBER OF AWARDS: Approximately 200 per year.

APPLICATION INFORMATION:
Undergraduate applicants must submit applications through their faculty advisors and be nominated for awards by their respective universities. Graduate applicants must apply to the Arlington, VA office. Further information is available from the Administration.
Duration: Minimum three months during the summer. Maximum three years of funding, with five years to complete the course.
Deadline: Varies.

PUBLICATIONS:
Application guidelines; brochures.

ADDRESS INQUIRIES TO:
Fawn Thompson, Program Manager
(See address above.)

FOUNDATION FOR TECHNOLOGY AND ENGINEERING EDUCATION
1914 Association Drive
Suite 201
Reston, VA 20191-1539
(703) 860-2100
Fax: (703) 860-0353

E-MAIL ADDRESS:
iteea@iteea.org

WEB SITE ADDRESS:
www.iteea.org

TYPE:
Scholarships. The scholarship is for an undergraduate student majoring in technology and engineering education teacher preparation.

See entry 1689 for full listing.

FOUNDATION FOR TECHNOLOGY AND ENGINEERING EDUCATION
1914 Association Drive
Suite 201
Reston, VA 20191-1539
(703) 860-2100
Fax: (703) 860-0353

E-MAIL ADDRESS:
iteea@iteea.org

WEB SITE ADDRESS:
www.iteea.org

TYPE:
Grants-in-aid.

See entry 1545 for full listing.

FOUNDATION FOR TECHNOLOGY AND ENGINEERING EDUCATION

1914 Association Drive
Suite 201
Reston, VA 20191-1539
(703) 860-2100
Fax: (703) 860-0353

E-MAIL ADDRESS:
iteea@iteea.org

WEB SITE ADDRESS:
www.iteea.org

TYPE:
Scholarships.

See entry 1546 for full listing.

FOUNDATION FOR TECHNOLOGY AND ENGINEERING EDUCATION

1914 Association Drive
Suite 201
Reston, VA 20191-1539
(703) 860-2100
Fax: (703) 860-0353

E-MAIL ADDRESS:
iteea@iteea.org

WEB SITE ADDRESS:
www.iteea.org

TYPE:
Scholarships.

See entry 1690 for full listing.

THE FOUNDATION OF FLEXOGRAPHIC TECHNICAL ASSOCIATION   [2608]

3920 Veterans Memorial Highway, Suite 9
Bohemia, NY 11716
(631) 737-6020
Fax: (631) 737-6813

E-MAIL ADDRESS:
srubin@flexography.org

WEB SITE ADDRESS:
www.flexography.org

FOUNDED: 1958

AREAS OF INTEREST:
Flexographic printing.

NAME(S) OF PROGRAMS:
● **Flexographic Technical Association Scholarship**

TYPE:
Scholarships.

PURPOSE:
To support education in the study of flexography.

ELIGIBILITY:
Must be enrolled in a qualified school offering a study of flexography. Must have grade point average of 3.0 or better.

FINANCIAL DATA:
Amount of support per award: $3,000 per year.
Total amount of support: Varies.

NUMBER OF AWARDS: Varies.

APPLICATION INFORMATION:
Contact the Organization for application procedures.
Duration: One year. Renewable upon reapplication.

Deadline: Usually March of each year.

ADDRESS INQUIRIES TO:
Shelley Rubin
Manager, Educational Services
(See address above.)

GREAT MINDS IN STEM   [2609]

602 Monterey Pass Road
Monterey Park, CA 91754
(323) 262-0997
Fax: (323) 262-0946

E-MAIL ADDRESS:
info@greatmindsinstem.org

WEB SITE ADDRESS:
www.greatmindsinstem.org

AREAS OF INTEREST:
Science, technology, computer science, engineering and math.

NAME(S) OF PROGRAMS:
● **HENAAC Scholars Program**

TYPE:
Scholarships.

YEAR PROGRAM STARTED: 2000

PURPOSE:
To provide undergraduate and graduate scholarships to students majoring in science, technology, computer science, engineering and math.

ELIGIBILITY:
Applicants must be of Hispanic origin and/or must significantly participate in and promote organizations and activities in the Hispanic community. Applicants must be enrolled in an undergraduate or graduate engineering or science program at a college or university and must be planning to pursue a career in either area. Selection is based on academic standing, financial need, career potential and character.

GEOGRAPHIC RESTRICTIONS:
United States.

FINANCIAL DATA:
Amount of support per award: $500 to $10,000.
Total amount of support: Varies.

NUMBER OF APPLICANTS MOST RECENT YEAR:
584.

NUMBER OF AWARDS: 85 for the year 2012.

APPLICATION INFORMATION:
Application form required. If requesting an application in writing, send a self-addressed, stamped envelope. Absolutely no faxes will be accepted.
Duration: One academic year. Renewal possible.
Deadline: April 30.

ADDRESS INQUIRIES TO:
HENAAC Scholars Program
(See address above.)

HIMSS FOUNDATION

33 West Monroe Street, Suite 1700
Chicago, IL 60603-5616
(312) 915-9277
(312) 664-4467
Fax: (312) 664-6143

E-MAIL ADDRESS:
scholarship@himss.org

WEB SITE ADDRESS:
www.himss.org

TYPE:
Awards/prizes; Conferences/seminars; Fellowships; Internships; Research grants; Scholarships.

See entry 2269 for full listing.

IEEE

IEEE History Center
Rutgers University
39 Union Street
New Brunswick, NJ 08901-8538
(732) 562-5468
Fax: (732) 932-1193

E-MAIL ADDRESS:
ieee-history@ieee.org

WEB SITE ADDRESS:
www.ieee.org/history_center

TYPE:
Fellowships; Internships. Fellowship in the History of Electrical and Computing Technology: Award for one year of full-time doctoral or postdoctoral work in the history of electrical engineering and technology at a college or university of recognized standing.
Internship in Electrical History: Two-month internship for graduate research.

See entry 599 for full listing.

INSTITUTE OF FOOD TECHNOLOGISTS FOUNDATION   [2610]

1025 Connecticut Avenue, N.W.
Suite 503
Washington, DC 20036
(312) 604-0284
Fax: (312) 416-7919

E-MAIL ADDRESS:
feedingtomorrow@ift.org

WEB SITE ADDRESS:
www.ift.org/scholarships

FOUNDED: 1939

AREAS OF INTEREST:
Food science and technology.

NAME(S) OF PROGRAMS:
● **Freshman Scholarships**
● **Graduate Scholarships**
● **Undergraduate Scholarships**

TYPE:
Scholarships. Freshman Scholarships and Undergraduate Scholarships encourage undergraduate enrollment in food science and technology. Graduate Scholarships support advanced study in the field of food science and technology.

YEAR PROGRAM STARTED: 1950

PURPOSE:
To encourage and support outstanding research in food science/technology including such areas as food packaging, flavor chemistry, new food ingredients and products; to recognize scholastic achievement.

LEGAL BASIS:
Nonprofit 501(c)(3) foundation.

ELIGIBILITY:
Freshman scholarships are awarded to high school seniors entering college for the first time. Applicant must be a current high school senior and accepted into an IFT-approved undergraduate food science program, have at least a 3.0 cumulative grade point average, and become an IFT student member.

Graduate scholarships are awarded to outstanding M.S. and Ph.D. students pursuing research and education in the field of food science and technology. Student applicants must be pursuing a graduate with an emphasis in food science and related disciplines. They must be able to understand and appreciate the impact of their research on the global food supply. Research in such disciplines as genetics, horticulture, nutrition, microbiology, biochemistry, engineering, chemistry, etc. are not eligible unless it is directly related to the student's research program in food science, except as otherwise noted. The school of enrollment can be any educational institution conducting fundamental investigations for the advancement of food science and food technology, unless there are stated exceptions of scholarship criteria for sponsored scholarships. Applicant must be enrolled as a full-time M.S. or Ph.D. student, have at least a 3.0 cumulative grade point average, and be a student member of IFT at the time of application.

Undergraduate scholarships are awarded to sophomore, junior, and senior students enrolled as a full-time student pursuing an undergraduate degree in an IFT-approved undergraduate food science program, have at least a 3.0 cumulative grade point average, and be a student member of IFT at the time of application.

FINANCIAL DATA:
Amount of support per award: $1,000 to $5,000.
Total amount of support: Varies.

COOPERATIVE FUNDING PROGRAMS: The scholarships are sponsored by Feeding Tomorrow donors.

NUMBER OF APPLICANTS MOST RECENT YEAR: Approximately 300.

NUMBER OF AWARDS: 75.

APPLICATION INFORMATION:
Applications are available on the Institute's web site.
Duration: One year.
Deadline: Varies.

ADDRESS INQUIRIES TO:
Jamie Larkins, Development Coordinator
(See address and e-mail above.)

THE INTERNATIONAL EXECUTIVE HOUSEKEEPERS ASSOCIATION [2611]

1001 Eastwind Drive
Suite 301
Westerville, OH 43081-3361
(614) 895-7166
Fax: (614) 895-1248

E-MAIL ADDRESS:
excel@ieha.org

WEB SITE ADDRESS:
www.ieha.org

FOUNDED: 1930

AREAS OF INTEREST:
Directors of housekeeping, environmental service and facilities management, and training.

NAME(S) OF PROGRAMS:
● **330-Hour Self Study Program**

TYPE:
Scholarships.

YEAR PROGRAM STARTED: 1960

PURPOSE:
To provide a professional organization for executive housekeepers, directors of environmental services, managers within the housekeeping or custodial activities, and suppliers of custodial goods and services.

ELIGIBILITY:
Must be a member or have a family member that is a member of IEHA and be working towards any degree program at a university or college, in a certification program or engaged in self-study.

FINANCIAL DATA:
Amount of support per award: $800 to $1,500 per year.
Total amount of support: Varies.

NUMBER OF APPLICANTS MOST RECENT YEAR: 14.

NUMBER OF AWARDS: Approximately 10.

APPLICATION INFORMATION:
Application may be requested from the e-mail address above.
Duration: One year.
Deadline: Must be postmarked by January 10.

ADDRESS INQUIRIES TO:
Beth Risinger, Chief Executive Officer
(See address above.)

INTERNATIONAL FOOD SERVICE EXECUTIVES ASSOCIATION, INC. (IFSEA) [2612]

4955 Miller Street, Suite 107
Wheat Ridge, CO 80033
(800) 893-5499

E-MAIL ADDRESS:
HQ@ifsea.com

WEB SITE ADDRESS:
www.ifsea.com

FOUNDED: 1901

AREAS OF INTEREST:
Food service field.

NAME(S) OF PROGRAMS:
● **Kae Debrent Hodges Fund**
● **Worthy Goal Scholarship**

TYPE:
Scholarships. Tuition scholarships.

YEAR PROGRAM STARTED: 1939

PURPOSE:
To give needed assistance to qualified young people in furthering their careers in the food service field.

LEGAL BASIS:
Nonprofit.

ELIGIBILITY:
Students must be enrolled as or accepted as a full-time student in a food service-related major at a two- or four-year college/university.

GEOGRAPHIC RESTRICTIONS:
United States.

FINANCIAL DATA:
Amount of support per award: $250 to $1,500.

APPLICATION INFORMATION:
Scholarship application is available at the Association web site.

Duration: One year. Renewable.
Deadline: February 1.

MICROSCOPY SOCIETY OF AMERICA [2613]

12100 Sunset Hills Road
Suite 130
Reston, VA 20190
(703) 234-4115
(800) 538-3672
Fax: (703) 435-4390

E-MAIL ADDRESS:
associationmanagement@microscopy.org

WEB SITE ADDRESS:
www.microscopy.org

FOUNDED: 1942

AREAS OF INTEREST:
Microscopy.

NAME(S) OF PROGRAMS:
● **MSA Awards for Microscopists in Developing Countries**

TYPE:
Awards/prizes; Conferences/seminars. Awards to encourage attendance at the MSA Annual Meeting by microscopists working in developing countries who will travel to the meeting. Several awards include free full registration and attendance to the proceedings.

PURPOSE:
To encourage microscopists who work in developing countries to attend the Microscopy Society of America's meeting.

LEGAL BASIS:
Nonprofit society.

ELIGIBILITY:
Applicants must be traveling from the developing country to the nation to the meeting and not be on extended visits to the U.S. Preference will be given to applicants who submit papers for presentation at the meeting.

FINANCIAL DATA:
Amount of support per award: Average $295.
Total amount of support: Varies.

NUMBER OF APPLICANTS MOST RECENT YEAR: 2 to 3.

NUMBER OF AWARDS: Up to 10.

APPLICATION INFORMATION:
Applications consist of a completed Advance Registration Form. If payment is included, it will be assumed applicant will attend the meeting even if application is denied. If payment is not included, it will be assumed applicant will be unable to attend the meeting if no award is granted and the submitted paper, if any, will be withdrawn.

A letter outlining the circumstances of the applicant and stating the reasons for requesting the award should also be included.
Duration: One-time award for attendance.
Deadline: February 15. Announcement March 31.

PUBLICATIONS:
Proceedings.

ADDRESS INQUIRIES TO:
Liz Kasabian, Managing Director
Scholarships and Award Inquiry
(See address above.)

PRINT AND GRAPHICS SCHOLARSHIP FOUNDATION   [2614]

200 Deer Run Road
Sewickley, PA 15143
(412) 259-1740
(800) 910-4283
Fax: (412) 741-2311

E-MAIL ADDRESS:
pgsf@printing.org

WEB SITE ADDRESS:
www.printing.org/pgsf

FOUNDED: 1956

AREAS OF INTEREST:
Graphic communications and graphic arts;
printing technology and management.

NAME(S) OF PROGRAMS:
● **PGSF Undergraduate Awards**

TYPE:
Scholarships. Awarded to students who plan
to major and have a career in graphic
communications, printing technology, printing
management or publishing.

YEAR PROGRAM STARTED: 1956

PURPOSE:
To encourage eligible students to enter the
field of graphic communications in the
printing and publishing industries.

LEGAL BASIS:
Nonprofit foundation.

ELIGIBILITY:
Applicants must be high school seniors who
will graduate in January or June of current
year or high school graduates. Grants are
usually restricted to colleges and universities
offering two-year and four-year degree
programs recognized by the graphic
communications industry. A limited number
of awards also are available for students
already enrolled in two-year or four-year
college programs and for sons and daughters
of employees of scholarship sponsors.
Financial need is not a criterion for selection.

Applicant must be a full-time student and
must have and maintain a 3.0 grade point
average or higher.

GEOGRAPHIC RESTRICTIONS:
United States.

FINANCIAL DATA:
Awards are paid directly to colleges for
payment of tuition, fees and other charges.
Amount of support per award: $500 to
$5,000.

NUMBER OF APPLICANTS MOST RECENT YEAR:
600.

NUMBER OF AWARDS: Approximately 180
four-year scholarships annually.

APPLICATION INFORMATION:
Applications and letters of recommendation
must be submitted online.
Duration: Renewable for up to four years
(unless otherwise specified).
Deadline: April 1. Decisions are announced
in July or August.

PUBLICATIONS:
Annual reports; newsletter; career brochures.

IRS IDENTIFICATION NUMBER: 25-1668339

ADDRESS INQUIRIES TO:
Bernadine Eckert
Scholarship Administrator
(See address above.)

*SPECIAL STIPULATIONS:
Candidates must be pursuing a career in
graphic communications or printing and must
maintain a 3.0 grade point average.

PRINT AND GRAPHICS SCHOLARSHIP FOUNDATION   [2615]

200 Deer Run Road
Sewickley, PA 15143
(412) 259-1740
(800) 910-4283
Fax: (412) 741-2311

E-MAIL ADDRESS:
pgsf@printing.org

WEB SITE ADDRESS:
www.printing.org/pgsf

FOUNDED: 1956

AREAS OF INTEREST:
Graphic communications, printing
technology, printing management and
publishing.

TYPE:
Fellowships. For advanced study relating to
the printing, publishing and packaging
industries. Support is provided for research
and study in engineering, chemistry, physics,
mathematics, industrial education or such
business technology areas as systems
analysis, operations research and marketing
research, provided the area of study has
potential application in the printing,
publishing and packaging industries.

YEAR PROGRAM STARTED: 1956

PURPOSE:
To strengthen the print and graphics industry
through scholarship assistance.

LEGAL BASIS:
Nonprofit organization.

ELIGIBILITY:
Applicants must be students who plan to
major and have a career in graphic
communications, printing technology, printing
management or publishing. Must have and
maintain a 3.0 grade point average or higher,
submit two recommendations, and be a
full-time student.

FINANCIAL DATA:
Amount of support per award: $1,000 to
$3,000.

NUMBER OF AWARDS: Varies.

APPLICATION INFORMATION:
Contact the Foundation.
Duration: One academic year. Renewable.
Deadline: February 15.

ADDRESS INQUIRIES TO:
Bernadine Eckert, Administrator
(See address above.)

SOCIETY OF MANUFACTURING ENGINEERS EDUCATION FOUNDATION (SMEEF)   [2616]

P.O. Box 930
Dearborn, MI 48121-0930
(313) 425-3300
Fax: (313) 425-3411

E-MAIL ADDRESS:
foundation@sme.org

WEB SITE ADDRESS:
www.smeef.org

FOUNDED: 1932

AREAS OF INTEREST:
Manufacturing and industrial engineering
technology, machining technology, robotics,
automated systems and technology.

NAME(S) OF PROGRAMS:
● **Connie and Robert T. Gunter Scholarship**
● **Clinton J. Helton Manufacturing Scholarship**
● **Kalamazoo Chapter No. 116-Roscoe Douglas Scholarship**
● **Lucille B. Kaufman Women's Scholarship**
● **E. Wayne Kay Scholarships**
● **St. Louis Chapter No. 17 Scholarship**
● **Myrtle and Earl Walker Scholarship**
● **William E. Weisel Scholarship**

TYPE:
Scholarships. Support for full- or part-time
students seeking careers in manufacturing or
industrial engineering technology or closely
related fields.

YEAR PROGRAM STARTED: 1982

LEGAL BASIS:
Professional society.

ELIGIBILITY:
Applicants must reside in the U.S. or
Canada, be a full- or part-time student
pursuing a degree in manufacturing
engineering, manufacturing engineering
technology, or a closely related engineering
field of study, and must attend an accredited
institution in the U.S. or Canada. Applicants
must have a minimum 2.5 grade point
average.

GEOGRAPHIC RESTRICTIONS:
United States and Canada.

FINANCIAL DATA:
Amount of support per award: Varies
according to scholarship.
Total amount of support: Over $60,000.

APPLICATION INFORMATION:
Application must be completed online.
Duration: One year. Students may reapply
for undergraduate scholarships.
Deadline: February 1. Announcements in
May and June.

PUBLICATIONS:
Program announcement.

BOARD OF DIRECTORS:
Brian A. Ruestow, President
Kathy Burnham, Vice President
Peter Mackie, Treasurer
Edward M. Swallow, Assistant Treasurer
Ashok Agrawal
David Bozeman
Barbara Fossum
Elizabeth Kautzmann
Lazaro Lopez
Dr. Irving Pressley McPhail
Julian Pate
Ted Peachee
Pamela J. Ruschau
Mike Sayen
Mike Schmidt
Sue Shimoyama
William Taylor
Peter Zierhut

ADDRESS INQUIRIES TO:
Kathy Carter, Program Officer
(See address above.)

TRANSPORTATION ASSOCIATION OF CANADA FOUNDATION [2617]

2323 St. Laurent Boulevard
Ottawa ON K1G 4J8 Canada
(613) 736-1350
Fax: (613) 736-1395

E-MAIL ADDRESS:
foundation@tac-atc.ca

WEB SITE ADDRESS:
www.tac-foundation.ca

FOUNDED: 2003

AREAS OF INTEREST:
Transportation.

NAME(S) OF PROGRAMS:
● **TAC Foundation Scholarships and Bursaries**

TYPE:
Scholarships. Awards are provided for the study of road and transportation sciences, such as highway engineering, transport economics and administration.

YEAR PROGRAM STARTED: 2004

PURPOSE:
To encourage studies by Canadians in the field of transportation.

LEGAL BASIS:
Foundation.

ELIGIBILITY:
Applicants must be Canadian citizens or permanent residents in Canada who are enrolled in a university or college and pursuing studies full-time in some aspect of transportation.

FINANCIAL DATA:
Amount of support per award: $1,000 to $10,000.

Total amount of support: Over $140,000 annually.

NUMBER OF APPLICANTS MOST RECENT YEAR:
Approximately 125.

NUMBER OF AWARDS: 46 for the year 2012.

APPLICATION INFORMATION:
Contact the Foundation.
Duration: One year. Winners may reapply.
Deadline: Second week of February.

ADDRESS INQUIRIES TO:
Executive Director
(See address above.)

THE UNIVERSITY OF CALGARY

Faculty of Graduate Studies
MacKimmie Library Tower, Room 213
2500 University Drive, N.W.
Calgary AB T2N 1N4 Canada
(403) 220-4938
Fax: (403) 289-7635

E-MAIL ADDRESS:
gsaward@ucalgary.ca

WEB SITE ADDRESS:
www.grad.ucalgary.ca

TYPE:
Awards/prizes; Scholarships. Graduate scholarship for study in all areas relevant to the petroleum industry. Tenable at The University of Calgary. Award endowed through a bequest of the late Corinne Patteson.

See entry 1782 for full listing.

Aeronautics and astronautics

AIRCRAFT ELECTRONICS ASSOCIATION (AEA) [2618]

3570 N.E. Ralph Powell Road
Lee's Summit, MO 64064
(816) 347-8400
Fax: (816) 347-8405

E-MAIL ADDRESS:
info@aea.net

WEB SITE ADDRESS:
www.aea.net/scholarship

AREAS OF INTEREST:
Avionics and aircraft electronics.

NAME(S) OF PROGRAMS:
● **Aircell Scholarship**
● **David Arver Memorial Scholarship**
● **Dutch and Ginger Arver Scholarship**
● **Johnny Davis Memorial Scholarship**
● **Duncan Aviation Scholarship**
● **Field Aviation Company Scholarship**
● **Garmin - Jerry Smith Memorial Scholarship**
● **Garmin Scholarship**
● **Lowell Gaylor Memorial Scholarship**
● **Leon Harris/Les Nichols Memorial Scholarship**
● **L-3 Avionics Systems Scholarship**
● **Mid-Continent Instrument Scholarship**
● **Rockwell Collins Scholarship**
● **Lee Tarbox Memorial Scholarship**
● **Universal Avionics Systems Corporation Scholarship**

TYPE:
Scholarships.

PURPOSE:
To provide funding for students seeking higher education in the fields of avionics and aircraft electronics.

LEGAL BASIS:
Nonprofit.

ELIGIBILITY:
Applicants for the Mid-Continent Instruments Scholarship and the Lowell Gaylor Memorial Scholarship can be anyone who plans to or is enrolled in an avionics program in an accredited U.S. or Canadian school.

Applicants for the Leon Harris/Les Nichols Memorial Scholarship may not be currently enrolled in the avionics program at Spartan.

Applicants for the Field Aviation Company Scholarship must attend an accredited vocational school located in Canada.

Applicants for Lee Tarbox Memorial, Garmin Scholarship, Johnny Davis Memorial and the Garmin-Jerry Smith Memorial Scholarships must be high school or vocational/technical school/college students who plan to or are attending an accredited vocational or technical school in an avionics or aviation-related program.

The Scholarships are not available to obtain pilot licenses.

GEOGRAPHIC RESTRICTIONS:
North America.

FINANCIAL DATA:
Amount of support per award: $1,000 to $30,000, depending on award.

Total amount of support: Varies.

NUMBER OF APPLICANTS MOST RECENT YEAR:
400.

NUMBER OF AWARDS: 15.

APPLICATION INFORMATION:
Contact the Association.
Duration: One year.
Deadline: Approximately April 1.

ADDRESS INQUIRIES TO:
Educational Foundation
(See address above.)

THE AMERICAN HISTORICAL ASSOCIATION

400 A Street, S.E.
Washington, DC 20003
(202) 544-2422
Fax: (202) 544-8307

E-MAIL ADDRESS:
awards@historians.org

WEB SITE ADDRESS:
www.historians.org

TYPE:
Fellowships. The Association annually funds at least one fellow for a period of six to nine months, to undertake a proposed research project related to aerospace history. The Fellowship is supported by the National Aeronautics and Space Administration (NASA).

See entry 580 for full listing.

AMERICAN INSTITUTE OF AERONAUTICS AND ASTRONAUTICS [2619]

1801 Alexander Bell Drive
Suite 500
Reston, VA 20191
(703) 264-7500
Fax: (703) 264-7551

E-MAIL ADDRESS:
rachela@aiaa.org

WEB SITE ADDRESS:
www.aiaa.org

FOUNDED: 1977

AREAS OF INTEREST:
Arts, sciences, and technology of aeronautics and astronautics.

NAME(S) OF PROGRAMS:
● **American Institute of Aeronautics and Astronautics Undergraduate Scholarship Program**

TYPE:
Scholarships. Program presents yearly scholarship awards to college sophomores, college juniors and college seniors. Graduate awards are also offered.

YEAR PROGRAM STARTED: 1977

PURPOSE:
To encourage original research; to further dissemination of new knowledge; to foster the professional development of those engaged in scientific and engineering activities; to improve public understanding of the profession and its contributions; to foster education in engineering and science; to promote communication among engineers and scientists and with other professional groups; to stimulate outstanding professional accomplishments.

ELIGIBILITY:
The AIAA requirements are as follows:
(1) applicant must be a student member to

apply;

(2) applicant's scholastic plan shall be such as to provide entry into some field of science or engineering encompassed by the technical activities of AIAA;

(3) applicant shall be enrolled in an accredited college or university in the U.S.;

(4) applicant shall not have or subsequently receive any other scholarship award which combined with the AIAA award would provide a stipend greater than the tuition plus direct educational expenses (such as books, lab fees, room, board, etc.) estimated by the educational institute he or she plans to attend;

(5) sophomore and junior students who receive one of these awards are eligible to reapply for these awards (until completion of their senior year) provided they maintain a 3.3 (B+) grade point average on a scale of 4.0. Continuation, however, is not automatic. Students must reapply each year;

(6) financial background will not be a factor for eligibility;

(7) student must have a college grade point average of at least a 3.3 on a 4.0 scale and;

(8) student must have completed one semester or quarter of full-time academic college work.

FINANCIAL DATA:
Amount of support per award: Up to $2,500.
Total amount of support: Varies.

NUMBER OF APPLICANTS MOST RECENT YEAR: 60.

NUMBER OF AWARDS: 11.

APPLICATION INFORMATION:
Form and guidelines are available on the web site.
Duration: One year.
Deadline: Applications must be received by January 31.

ADDRESS INQUIRIES TO:
Rachel Andino, Student and Young Professionals Coordinator
(See address above.)

AMERICAN METEOROLOGICAL SOCIETY [2620]
45 Beacon Street
Boston, MA 02108-3693
(617) 226-3907
Fax: (617) 742-8718

E-MAIL ADDRESS:
dfernandez@ametsoc.org

WEB SITE ADDRESS:
www.ametsoc.org

FOUNDED: 1919

AREAS OF INTEREST:
Meteorology, atmospheric, hydrologic and oceanic sciences.

NAME(S) OF PROGRAMS:
- **AMS Freshman Undergraduate Scholarship Program**
- **AMS Graduate Fellowship in the History of Science**
- **AMS Graduate Fellowships**
- **AMS/Industry Minority Scholarship**
- **AMS Named Scholarships**
- **The Father James B. Macelwane Annual Awards in Meteorology**

TYPE:
Fellowships; Scholarships. AMS Freshman Undergraduate Scholarship Program awards funding to high school seniors entering their freshman year of undergraduate study in the fall.

AMS Graduate Fellowship in the History of Science is awarded to a student wishing to complete a dissertation on the history of the atmospheric and related oceanic or hydrologic sciences.

AMS Graduate Fellowships are designed to attract students entering their first year of graduate study in the fall who wish to pursue advanced degrees in the atmospheric and related oceanic and hydrologic sciences.

AMS/Industry Minority Scholarships award funding to high school minority students who have been traditionally underrepresented in the sciences, especially Hispanic, Native American and Black/African American students.

AMS Named Scholarships are directed to students entering their final year of undergraduate study in the fall.

The Father James B. Macelwane Annual Awards in Meteorology are intended to stimulate interest in meteorology among college students through the submission of original student papers concerned with some phase of the atmospheric sciences. The student must be enrolled as an undergraduate at the time the paper was written.

YEAR PROGRAM STARTED: 1965

PURPOSE:
To stimulate interest in meteorology among college students and to recognize academic excellence and achievement; to stimulate careers in atmospheric and related oceanic and hydrologic sciences.

LEGAL BASIS:
Nonprofit organization.

ELIGIBILITY:
Candidates must be U.S. citizens or hold permanent resident status.

AMS encourages applications from women, minorities and disabled students who are traditionally underrepresented in the atmospheric and related oceanic and hydrologic sciences.

AMS Freshman Undergraduate Scholarship Program makes awards on the basis of academic excellence.

AMS Graduate Fellowship in the History of Science: Candidate must be a graduate student in good standing who proposes to complete a dissertation on the history of the atmospheric, or related oceanic or hydrologic sciences.

AMS Graduate Fellowships: Applicants must be entering their first year of graduate study in the fall pursuing an advanced degree in the atmospheric and related oceanic and hydrologic sciences. Prospective candidates from the fields of chemistry, computer sciences, engineering, environmental sciences, mathematics or physics who intend to pursue careers in the atmospheric or related oceanic or hydrologic sciences are also encouraged to apply.

AMS/Industry Minority Scholarships: Funding to high school minority students who have been traditionally underrepresented in the sciences, especially Hispanic, Native American and Black/African American students. Minority students must be entering their freshman year of undergraduate study in the fall at a four-year U.S. accredited institution, and must plan to pursue a career in the atmospheric or related oceanic or hydrologic sciences.

AMS Named Scholarships: Candidates must be entering their final undergraduate year in the fall and majoring in the atmospheric or related oceanic or hydrologic sciences and/or must show clear intent to make atmospheric or related sciences their career.

Father James B. Macelwane Annual Awards in Meteorology: Student must be enrolled as an undergraduate at the time the paper is written. No more than two students from any one institution may enter papers in any one contest.

GEOGRAPHIC RESTRICTIONS:
United States.

FINANCIAL DATA:
Amount of support per award: AMS Freshman Undergraduate Scholarship Program: $2,500 per year (freshman and sophomore years); AMS Graduate Fellowship in the History of Science: $15,000 stipend; AMS Graduate Fellowships: $24,000 stipend; AMS/Industry Minority Scholarships: $3,000 per year (freshman and sophomore years); AMS Named Scholarships: Varies; Father James B. Macelwane Annual Awards in Meteorology: $1,000 stipend and partial travel support to the AMS Annual Meeting.
Total amount of support: Varies.

NUMBER OF APPLICANTS MOST RECENT YEAR: 340.

NUMBER OF AWARDS: 55.

APPLICATION INFORMATION:
Those interested should apply online at the Society's web site. When writing for an application package, specify which application is being requested, and what year of academic study applicant will be entering in the fall. Submit a complete application form, written letters of reference and official transcripts.
Duration: AMS Freshman Undergraduate Scholarship Program: Up to two years; AMS Graduate History of Science Fellowship: One year; AMS/Industry Minority: Two years; AMS/Industry/Government Graduate Fellowships: Nine months.
Deadline: Graduate Fellowship: January 16, 2015. Father James B. Macelwane: Mid-June 2015. All other programs: February 13, 2015.

PUBLICATIONS:
Program announcement.

OFFICERS:
Dr. Keith L. Seitter, Executive Director

ADDRESS INQUIRIES TO:
Donna Fernandez, Development and Student Programs Manager
(See address/phone/e-mail above) or

Stephanie Armstrong
Director of Development
Tel: (617) 226-3906 or 3907
E-mail: armstrong@ametsoc.org

*SPECIAL STIPULATIONS:
Applicants must review program requirements before applying.

AVIATION DISTRIBUTORS AND MANUFACTURERS ASSOCIATION (ADMA) [2621]
100 North 20th Street, Suite 400
Philadelphia, PA 19103
(215) 564-3484
Fax: (215) 564-2175

E-MAIL ADDRESS:
adma@fernley.com

WEB SITE ADDRESS:
www.adma.org

FOUNDED: 1943

AREAS OF INTEREST:
Aviation and pilot education, mechanics and maintenance.

NAME(S) OF PROGRAMS:
- **ADMA Scholarship Programs**

TYPE:
Scholarships.

ELIGIBILITY:
Applicant must be one of following:
(1) third- or fourth-year B.S. candidate with Aviation Management major, emphasis in General Aviation, Airway Science Management, Aviation Maintenance or Airway Science Maintenance Management;
(2) third- or fourth-year B.S. candidate with major in Professional Pilot with any of the following emphases: General Aviation, Flight Engineer, Airway Science A/C Systems Management or;
(3) second-year student in A/P education program (two-year accredited aviation technical school).

Applicant must also have 3.0 grade point average or higher.

GEOGRAPHIC RESTRICTIONS:
United States.

FINANCIAL DATA:
Amount of support per award: $3,000.
Total amount of support: $12,000.

NUMBER OF AWARDS: 4.

APPLICATION INFORMATION:
Detailed information is available from the Association.
Duration: One year. Renewable by reapplication.

ADDRESS INQUIRIES TO:
Kristen Olszewski, Executive Director
(See address above.)

AVIATION INSURANCE ASSOCIATION (AIA) [2622]

7200 West 75th Street
Overland Park, KS 66204
(913) 627-9632
Fax: (913) 381-2515

E-MAIL ADDRESS:
mandie@aiaweb.org

WEB SITE ADDRESS:
www.aiaweb.org

AREAS OF INTEREST:
Aviation insurance.

NAME(S) OF PROGRAMS:
- **AIA Scholarship**

TYPE:
Scholarships.

PURPOSE:
To help students with an interest in aviation insurance to continue on to higher education.

LEGAL BASIS:
Nonprofit association.

ELIGIBILITY:
Applicants must:
(1) be currently enrolled in an accredited undergraduate or graduate degree program;
(2) currently be an intern or recently

completed an internship program within a facet of the aviation insurance industry;
(3) have completed at least 45 college credits and;
(4) have a minimum 2.5 grade point average on a 4.0 scale.

FINANCIAL DATA:
Amount of support per award: $2,500.

NUMBER OF AWARDS: 4.

APPLICATION INFORMATION:
Applicants must submit five sets of the following documents to be considered a scholarship candidate:
(1) completed AIA Scholarship application;
(2) letter describing activities, indicating leadership qualities, goals, rolls and reason for applying;
(3) at least one letter of recommendation from an employer or instructor;
(4) latest transcript(s) from all universities and colleges attended and;
(5) any FAA certificates.
Duration: One-time award.
Deadline: February 28.

ADDRESS INQUIRIES TO:
Mandie Bannwarth, Executive Director
(See address above.)

MCDONNELL CENTER FOR THE SPACE SCIENCES [2623]

Washington University, Campus Box 1105
One Brookings Drive
St. Louis, MO 63130-4899
(314) 935-5332

E-MAIL ADDRESS:
trecia@physics.wustl.edu

WEB SITE ADDRESS:
mcss.wustl.edu

FOUNDED: 1974

AREAS OF INTEREST:
Space sciences.

NAME(S) OF PROGRAMS:
- **McDonnell Astronaut Fellowships**
- **McDonnell Graduate Fellowships**

TYPE:
Fellowships. These fellowships are funded by a gift from the McDonnell Douglas Foundation to Washington University and provide tuition remission plus stipend for graduate students interested in pursuing research in the space sciences who are enrolled in the Washington University Departments of Physics or Earth and Planetary Sciences.

PURPOSE:
To support graduate students in the space sciences.

LEGAL BASIS:
University.

ELIGIBILITY:
All applicants for admission to graduate school in physics or earth and planetary sciences are considered for the McDonnell Graduate Fellowships if they are interested in pursuing research in the space sciences and note it on their application forms; only U.S. citizens are considered for the McDonnell Astronaut Fellowships.

GEOGRAPHIC RESTRICTIONS:
United States.

FINANCIAL DATA:
Amount of support per award: Varies.

Total amount of support: Varies.

APPLICATION INFORMATION:
Application materials for the individual graduate school programs may be obtained at the web site.
Duration: Three years.
Deadline: January 15. Announcement by April 1.

ADDRESS INQUIRIES TO:
Ramanath Cowsik, Director
(See address above.)

NATIONAL BUSINESS AVIATION ASSOCIATION [2624]

1200 G Street, N.W.
Suite 1100
Washington, DC 20005
(202) 783-9000
Fax: (202) 331-8364

E-MAIL ADDRESS:
info@nbaa.org
scholarships@nbaa.org

WEB SITE ADDRESS:
www.nbaa.org/scholarships

AREAS OF INTEREST:
Aviation.

NAME(S) OF PROGRAMS:
- **William M. Fanning Maintenance Scholarship**
- **Flight Attendant Scholarship**
- **International Operators Scholarship**

TYPE:
Scholarships. The William M. Fanning Maintenance Scholarship is for those who are pursuing careers as maintenance technicians.

The Flight Attendant Scholarship is dedicated to promoting education and training as a means to increase professionalism for business aviation flight attendants.

The International Operators Scholarship is dedicated to promoting education and training to increase safety and professionalism.

PURPOSE:
To help students continue their education in aviation and advance in that field.

LEGAL BASIS:
Nonprofit association.

ELIGIBILITY:
Contact the Association for details.

GEOGRAPHIC RESTRICTIONS:
United States.

FINANCIAL DATA:
Amount of support per award: Fanning Maintenance Scholarship: $2,500; International Operators Scholarship: $5,000.

Total amount of support: Varies.

NUMBER OF AWARDS: Fanning Maintenance Scholarship: 2.

APPLICATION INFORMATION:
Applications are available at the Association web site.
Duration: One-time award.
Deadline: Fanning Maintenance Scholarship: July 30; Flight Attendant Scholarship: March 31; International Operators Scholarship: November 30.

STAFF:
Jay Evans, Director, Professional Development

ADDRESS INQUIRIES TO:
E-mail: info@nbaa.org

*PLEASE NOTE:
Awards will be made to U.S. citizens without regard to sex, race, religion or national origin.

NATIONAL BUSINESS AVIATION ASSOCIATION [2625]
1200 G Street, N.W.
Suite 1100
Washington, DC 20005
(202) 783-9000
Fax: (202) 331-8364

E-MAIL ADDRESS:
info@nbaa.org

WEB SITE ADDRESS:
www.nbaa.org/scholarships

AREAS OF INTEREST:
Aviation and business aviation.

NAME(S) OF PROGRAMS:
● **Lawrence Ginocchio Scholarship**
● **Schedulers & Dispatchers Scholarship**
● **UAA Janice K. Barden Scholarship**

TYPE:
Scholarships. Janice K. Barden Scholarship is presented to undergraduates who are studying aviation-related curricula.

Lawrence Ginocchio Scholarship honors individuals whose strength of character inspired a high standard. Applicants must be students at NBAA/UAA Member programs.

PURPOSE:
To help students continue their education in aviation and advance in that field.

LEGAL BASIS:
Nonprofit association.

ELIGIBILITY:
Contact the Association for details.

FINANCIAL DATA:
Amount of support per award: Janice K. Barden Scholarship: $1,000; Lawrence Ginocchio Scholarship: $4,500.

Total amount of support: Janice K. Barden Scholarship: $5,000; Lawrence Ginocchio Scholarship: $22,500.

NUMBER OF AWARDS: Janice K. Barden and Lawrence Ginocchio Scholarships: 5 each.

APPLICATION INFORMATION:
Contact the Association for guidelines.
Deadline: Varies.

STAFF:
Jay Evans, Director, Professional Development

ADDRESS INQUIRIES TO:
Jay Evans
Director, Professional Development
(See address above.)
E-mail: jevans@nbaa.org

NATIONAL BUSINESS AVIATION ASSOCIATION [2626]
1200 18th Street, N.W.
Suite 400
Washington, DC 20036-2527
(202) 783-9000
(202) 783-9250
Fax: (202) 331-8364

E-MAIL ADDRESS:
info@nbaa.org

WEB SITE ADDRESS:
www.nbaa.org/scholarships

AREAS OF INTEREST:
Aviation.

NAME(S) OF PROGRAMS:
● **Donald A. Baldwin Sr. Business Aviation Management Scholarship**

TYPE:
Scholarships. Promotes professional development in business aviation.

YEAR PROGRAM STARTED: 2007

PURPOSE:
To benefit individuals seeking to become NBAA-Certified Aviation Managers (CAMs).

FINANCIAL DATA:
Amount of support per award: $1,225 per recipient.

APPLICATION INFORMATION:
Applicants must submit their resume, a 250-word essay explaining their plans for a career in business aviation, two letters of recommendation in support, and meet minimum qualifications to take the CAM exam.

ADDRESS INQUIRIES TO:
Jay Evans, Director, Professional Development
(See address above.)

RTCA [2627]
1150 18th Street, N.W.
Suite 910
Washington, DC 20036
(202) 330-0654
Fax: (202) 833-9434

E-MAIL ADDRESS:
hmoses@rtca.org

WEB SITE ADDRESS:
www.rtca.org

FOUNDED: 1935

AREAS OF INTEREST:
Aviation electronics, telecommunications, and other closely allied fields such as determination of common operational requirements, state-of-the-art developments and applications, other problems associated with air traffic control, navigation, communications, and efficient utilization of airports and airspace.

NAME(S) OF PROGRAMS:
● **The William E. Jackson Award**

TYPE:
Awards/prizes. Award for a paper by an outstanding graduate student in aviation electronics or telecommunications, in memory of William E. Jackson, an outstanding pioneer in the development and implementation of the present airways, air traffic control, and aviation communication systems.

YEAR PROGRAM STARTED: 1975

PURPOSE:
To honor an outstanding graduate student in aviation electronics or telecommunications.

LEGAL BASIS:
Nonprofit, 501(c)(3) organization.

ELIGIBILITY:
Open to any graduate student earning a degree in the field of aviation electronics or telecommunication systems. There are no restrictions as to race, creed, color, religious affiliation, national origin or citizenship. The sole basis for selection will be the written report, which must be in English.

FINANCIAL DATA:
The recipient will travel at the expense of RTCA to the location of the award presentation. Complimentary registration for any RTCA business meeting taking place concurrently is also awarded.
Amount of support per award: $4,000.

NUMBER OF APPLICANTS MOST RECENT YEAR:
10.

NUMBER OF AWARDS: 1.

APPLICATION INFORMATION:
Submissions must be in the form of a thesis, project report, or paper in a technical journal. The work must have been completed no earlier than three years before the submission deadline and only those in English and without publication restrictions will be considered. Joint authors may submit if both or all qualify as students and candidates for undergraduate or graduate degrees in this field. Joint authors would share the award. Additionally, candidates must submit two copies (one paper and one electronic) of a one- to two-page summary of the written material, a biographical sketch of the candidate, and a letter of endorsement from the candidate's instructor, professor, or departmental head. Submit material to the address above.
Deadline: September 30.

OFFICERS:
Harold E. Moses, Program Director

ADDRESS INQUIRIES TO:
William E. Jackson Award Committee
(See address above.)

SMITHSONIAN NATIONAL AIR AND SPACE MUSEUM [2628]
Smithsonian Institution
Independence Avenue at Sixth Street, S.W.
Room 3313, MRC 312
Washington, DC 20013-7012
(202) 633-2648
Fax: (202) 786-2447

E-MAIL ADDRESS:
nasm-fellowships@si.edu

WEB SITE ADDRESS:
www.nasm.si.edu

FOUNDED: 1946

AREAS OF INTEREST:
Aeronautics.

NAME(S) OF PROGRAMS:
● **Guggenheim Fellowship**
● **Charles A. Lindbergh Chair in Aerospace History**
● **Postdoctoral Earth and Planetary Sciences Fellowship**
● **A. Verville Fellowship**

TYPE:
Fellowships. The Guggenheim Fellowship is a competitive three- to 12-month in-residence fellowship for pre- or postdoctoral research in aviation and space history.

The Charles A. Lindbergh Chair in Aerospace History is a competitive 12-month fellowship.

Postdoctoral Earth and Planetary Sciences Fellowship supports scientific research in the area of earth and planetary sciences. Scientists in the Center for Earth and Planetary Studies concentrate on geologic and geophysical research of the earth and other terrestrial planets, using remote sensing data obtained from earth-orbiting and interplanetary spacecraft. Research also focuses on global environmental change.

The A. Verville Fellowship is a competitive nine- to 12-month in-residence fellowship intended for analysis of major trends, developments, and accomplishments in the history of aviation or space studies.

All candidates are encouraged to pursue programs of research and writing that support publication of works that are scholarly in tone and substance, and/or addressed to an audience with broad interests. Each fellow will work closely with staff members who share similar interests.

PURPOSE:
To promote research into, and writing about, the history of aviation and space flight.

ELIGIBILITY:
All applicants must be able to write and converse fluently in English. Additional information is available online.

Guggenheim Fellowship: Predoctoral applicants should have completed preliminary course work and examinations and be engaged in dissertation research. Postdoctoral applicants should have received their Ph.D. within the past seven years.

Lindbergh Chair in Aerospace History: Open to senior scholars with distinguished records of publication who are at work on, or anticipate being at work on, books in aerospace history.

Verville Fellowship: Open to interested candidates with demonstrated skills in research and writing. Publishing experience should demonstrate either a mid-level academic record of accomplishment or proven ability to engage in a reliable manner broader audiences. An advanced degree in history or a related field is preferred but not a requirement.

FINANCIAL DATA:
Amount of support per award: Guggenheim Fellowship: Annual stipend of $30,000 for predoctoral candidates and $45,000 for postdoctoral candidates. Lindbergh Chair in Aerospace History: Support is available for replacement of salary and benefits up to a maximum of $100,000 a year. Postdoctoral Earth and Planetary Sciences Fellowship: Stipends are compatible with National Research Council postdoctoral fellowships in the applicant's field. Verville Fellowship: Annual stipend of $55,000 (for a 12-month fellowship tenure), with limited additional funds for travel and miscellaneous expenses.

NUMBER OF AWARDS: 1 each.

APPLICATION INFORMATION:
Instructions and forms for each program are available on the web site.
Duration: Guggenheim Fellowship: three to 12 months; Lindbergh Chair in Aerospace History: typically for an academic year (September through August); Postdoctoral Earth and Planetary Sciences Fellowship: appointments can be made for one or more years; Verville Fellowship: nine to 12 months.
Deadline: Guggenheim and Verville Fellowships and Lindbergh Chair: January 15. Lindbergh deadline is January 15 of the year preceding the award of this fellowship.

PUBLICATIONS:
Brochure; application package.

ADDRESS INQUIRIES TO:
Collette Williams, Fellowship Program Coordinator
(See e-mail address above.)

Postdoctoral Earth and Planetary Sciences Fellowship: Rose Aiello
Center for Earth and Planetary Studies
National Air and Space Museum
Washington, DC 20560
E-mail: aiellor@si.edu

*PLEASE NOTE:
Applicants are restricted to applying for a single National Air and Space Museum fellowship grant at a time. Proposals must reflect that the research to be undertaken is intended for publication in peer-reviewed books and journals.

SMITHSONIAN NATIONAL AIR AND SPACE MUSEUM [2629]
601 Independence Avenue, S.W.
Washington, DC 20560
(202) 633-2540
Fax: (202) 633-8928

E-MAIL ADDRESS:
banksscottm@si.edu

WEB SITE ADDRESS:
airandspace.si.edu

FOUNDED: 1946

AREAS OF INTEREST:
Aeronautics.

NAME(S) OF PROGRAMS:
● **Summer Internship Program**

TYPE:
Internships. Full-time interns work 40 hours per week from approximately the first week in June until the second week in August.

PURPOSE:
To give interns a firsthand opportunity to learn about the historic artifacts and archival materials housed in the Museum and to study the scientific and technological advances they represent.

ELIGIBILITY:
Applicant must be a high school graduate and be enrolled in a degree-granting undergraduate or graduate program at an accredited college or university. Applicant is expected to have a strong academic record.

International applicants must have the appropriate J-1 visa.

Applicants from outside the United States are welcome.

FINANCIAL DATA:
Interns are responsible for locating and securing lodging.
Amount of support per award: $5,500.

APPLICATION INFORMATION:
Application information is available on the web site. Visit the Smithsonian Online Academic Appointment System (SOLAA) web site to apply.
Duration: 10 weeks during the summer; nonrenewable.
Deadline: Applications are accepted from January 15 to February 15 during the calendar year of the internship. Interns are notified of the status of their application by April 1.

*SPECIAL STIPULATIONS:
A commitment of 10 weeks during the summer is required.

VERTICAL FLIGHT FOUNDATION [2630]
217 North Washington Street
Alexandria, VA 22314
(703) 684-6777
Fax: (703) 739-9279

E-MAIL ADDRESS:
staff@vtol.org

WEB SITE ADDRESS:
www.vtol.org

FOUNDED: 1967

AREAS OF INTEREST:
Support of scientific and educational activities related to VTOL (Vertical Take-Off and Landing) flight.

NAME(S) OF PROGRAMS:
● **Vertical Flight Foundation Engineering Scholarships**

TYPE:
Awards/prizes; Scholarships. Annual scholarships to undergraduate senior, Master's or Ph.D. students interested in pursuing careers in some technical aspect of helicopter or vertical flight engineering.

YEAR PROGRAM STARTED: 1967

PURPOSE:
To acquire the best technical experts for the vertical flight industry.

LEGAL BASIS:
Independent, charitable trust.

ELIGIBILITY:
The VFF scholarships will be awarded to undergraduate senior, Master's and Ph.D. students studying for a career in the helicopter or vertical flight industry.

The scholarships are merit-based and are awarded in two categories: undergraduate and graduate. Individuals will be eligible once for one of the final two years of undergraduate studies and once for a year of graduate study. Applicants must be in school through the full academic year following receipt of the scholarship. To be eligible for a scholarship, an applicant must be a full-time student at an accredited school of engineering.

Applicants need not be members of the American Helicopter Society.

FINANCIAL DATA:
Amount of support per award: $1,000 to $5,000.
Total amount of support: $50,000 for the year 2012.

NUMBER OF APPLICANTS MOST RECENT YEAR: 63.

NUMBER OF AWARDS: 21.

APPLICATION INFORMATION:
Detailed instructions are available at the web site. Applicants can also download a copy of the application form.
Duration: One academic year.
Deadline: February 1. Notification by April 15.

PUBLICATIONS:
Applications.

IRS IDENTIFICATION NUMBER: 23-6428319

ADDRESS INQUIRIES TO:
Holly Cafferelli, Student Liaison
(See address above.)

Engineering

ADSC: THE INTERNATIONAL ASSOCIATION OF FOUNDATION DRILLING [2631]

8445 Freeport Parkway
Suite 325
Irving, TX 75063
(469) 359-6000
Fax: (469) 359-6007

E-MAIL ADDRESS:
adsc@adsc-iafd.com

WEB SITE ADDRESS:
www.adsc-iafd.com

FOUNDED: 1972

AREAS OF INTEREST:
Civil, geotechnical and structural engineering.

TYPE:
Scholarships.

PURPOSE:
To promote the foundation drilling and anchored earth retention industry.

ELIGIBILITY:
Must be a graduate student studying civil engineering.

GEOGRAPHIC RESTRICTIONS:
United States or Canada.

FINANCIAL DATA:
Amount of support per award: Maximum $3,000; $1,500 per semester. Part-time scholarship program: Maximum $3,000; $500 per semester.
Total amount of support: Approximately $42,000 annually.

NUMBER OF AWARDS: Minimum of 14 per year.

APPLICATION INFORMATION:
Applicants must submit a brief letter outlining personal goals, two letters of recommendation and a copy of their transcript with application. Further information and application may be obtained from the Association.
Duration: One year.
Deadline: Contact the Association for deadline.

ADDRESS INQUIRIES TO:
Yolanda Maloney, Executive Assistant
(See address above.)

AGC EDUCATION AND RESEARCH FOUNDATION [2632]

2300 Wilson Boulevard, Suite 300
Arlington, VA 22201
(703) 837-5342
Fax: (703) 837-5451

E-MAIL ADDRESS:
patricianm@agc.org

WEB SITE ADDRESS:
www.agcfoundation.org

FOUNDED: 1968

AREAS OF INTEREST:
Construction and civic interest in improving the quality of educational programs for students specifically in the area of construction and construction research.

NAME(S) OF PROGRAMS:
- **James L. Allhands Essay Competition**
- **Graduate Scholarship Program**
- **Outstanding Educator Award**
- **Undergraduate Scholarship Program**

TYPE:
Scholarships. Scholarships for students in civil engineering, construction management or construction-related programs.

YEAR PROGRAM STARTED: 1968

PURPOSE:
To improve the science of construction through the funding of scholarships and construction research projects.

LEGAL BASIS:
501(c)(3).

ELIGIBILITY:
James L. Allhands Essay Competition is for seniors only.

Undergraduate scholarships are available to college sophomores and juniors enrolled or planning to enroll in a full-time, four- or five-year ABET or ACCE-accredited construction or civil engineering program. High school seniors and college freshman are not eligible.

Graduate awards are available to college seniors enrolled in an undergraduate construction or civil engineering degree program, or others possessing an undergraduate degree in construction or civil engineering. The applicant must be enrolled, or planning to enroll, in a graduate-level construction or civil engineering degree program as a full-time student. All candidates must be U.S. citizens or permanent U.S. residents.

GEOGRAPHIC RESTRICTIONS:
United States.

FINANCIAL DATA:
Amount of support per award: Allhands Essay Competition: First Prize $1,000 and an expense-paid trip to the AGC Convention; Graduate Scholarships: Up to $7,500; Outstanding Educator Award: $5,000 scholarship and an expense-paid trip to the AGC Convention, plus two $2,500 scholarships for students of the educator; Undergraduate Scholarships: $2,500 per year renewable to a maximum of $7,500.
Total amount of support: $400,000 for all programs.

NUMBER OF APPLICANTS MOST RECENT YEAR: 400.

NUMBER OF AWARDS: Over 100 scholarships are awarded each year.

APPLICATION INFORMATION:
Application is posted online after July 1. Online link: scholarship.agc.org.
Duration: Varies.
Deadline: November 1.

IRS IDENTIFICATION NUMBER: 52-6083465

BOARD OF DIRECTORS:
John F. Kelly, III, President
Norman J. Walton, Vice President
Robert L. Bowen, Treasurer
Monique T. Valentine, Secretary
Russell F. Agosta
Thomas J. Burleson
Dan K. Fordice, III
Jorge Fuentes
Martin J. Garza
Maria Guy
B. Scott Holloway
Harry L. Mashburn
Rebecca Mirsky
Barry Paceley
Shannon Sapp
John Schaufelberger
Leonard P. Toenjes

Stephen C. VanderBloemen
Eric Wilson

ADDRESS INQUIRIES TO:
Melinda Patrician, Director
(See address above.)

AMERICAN CHEMICAL SOCIETY

1155 16th Street, N.W.
Washington, DC 20036-4800
(202) 872-6283
Fax: (202) 776-8008

E-MAIL ADDRESS:
awards@acs.org

WEB SITE ADDRESS:
www.acs.org/awards

TYPE:
Awards/prizes.

See entry 2061 for full listing.

AMERICAN INSTITUTE OF CHEMICAL ENGINEERS (AICHE) [2633]

120 Wall Street, Floor 23
New York, NY 10005-4020
(646) 495-1384
Fax: (646) 495-1503

E-MAIL ADDRESS:
awards@aiche.org

WEB SITE ADDRESS:
www.aiche.org

FOUNDED: 1908

AREAS OF INTEREST:
Chemical engineering.

NAME(S) OF PROGRAMS:
- **Minority Scholarship Awards for College Students**

TYPE:
Scholarships.

YEAR PROGRAM STARTED: 1994

PURPOSE:
To encourage minority undergraduate study of chemical engineering.

LEGAL BASIS:
Nonprofit.

ELIGIBILITY:
Nominations are accepted from AIChE student chapters or chemical engineering clubs. Nominees must be AIChE national student members at the time of nomination, undergraduates in chemical engineering during the academic year, and members of a disadvantaged minority group that is underrepresented in chemical engineering. Chapters may nominate a student who will complete the chemical engineering Baccalaureate degree requirements in mid-year, but such nominees, if successful, will receive prorated awards. The selection of winners will be based on the nominee's academic record, participation in AIChE student and professional activities, career objectives, and financial need.

GEOGRAPHIC RESTRICTIONS:
United States.

FINANCIAL DATA:
Amount of support per award: $1,000.

NUMBER OF AWARDS: 10.

APPLICATION INFORMATION:
Contact the Institute.

ENGINEERING**937**/

Duration: One-time award. No students may apply again.

Deadline: July 1.

PUBLICATIONS:
AIChExtra; awards nomination form.

AMERICAN NUCLEAR SOCIETY (ANS) [2634]
555 North Kensington Avenue
LaGrange Park, IL 60526
(708) 352-6611
Fax: (708) 352-0499

E-MAIL ADDRESS:
outreach@ans.org

WEB SITE ADDRESS:
www.ans.org

FOUNDED: 1954

AREAS OF INTEREST:
Nuclear science, nuclear engineering or nuclear-related field.

NAME(S) OF PROGRAMS:
- **Delayed Education for Women Scholarship**
- **John and Muriel Landis Scholarships**

TYPE:
Scholarships. Delayed Education for Women Scholarship is designed for women in a nuclear-related field whose formal studies have been delayed or interrupted for at least one year.

Landis Scholarships are administered by the ANS NEED Committee, and are awarded to undergraduate and graduate students who have greater-than-average financial need.

PURPOSE:
To encourage mature women whose formal studies in the field of nuclear science, nuclear engineering, or a nuclear-related field have been delayed or interrupted for at least one year; to provide financial aid to students with greater-than-average need.

ELIGIBILITY:
Delayed Education for Women Scholarship: Applicants must have experienced a minimum of a one-year delay or interruption of their undergraduate studies and must be entering a four-year curriculum. Those at graduate level of education can also apply. Applicants must also have proven academic ability as well as demonstrated financial need. An applicant must be a U.S. citizen or possess a permanent resident visa, be enrolled in a U.S. college or university, and must be sponsored by an ANS local section, division, student branch, committee or organization member. More than one applicant can be sponsored by any of these organizations. Those applying must be enrolled in a course of study relating to a degree in nuclear science or nuclear engineering in a U.S. institution. Applicants must be mature women whose undergraduate studies in nuclear science, nuclear engineering, or a nuclear-related field have been delayed.

Landis Scholarships: Applicants must be undergraduates or graduates who are U.S. citizens or permanent residents. The student must be enrolled in a course of study relating to a degree in nuclear science or nuclear engineering in a U.S. institution. The applicant also must have greater-than-average financial need. Consideration is given to conditions or experiences that render the student disadvantaged (poor high school/undergraduate preparation, etc.). Qualified high school seniors are eligible to apply for this scholarship.

GEOGRAPHIC RESTRICTIONS:
United States.

FINANCIAL DATA:
Scholarship funds may be used by the student to defray any bona fide education costs including tuition, books, room and board.

Amount of support per award: $5,000.

COOPERATIVE FUNDING PROGRAMS: Delayed Education for Women Scholarship: Sponsored jointly by the NEED and Professional Women in the ANS Committees.

NUMBER OF AWARDS: Delayed Education for Women Scholarship: 1; Landis Scholarships: Up to 8.

APPLICATION INFORMATION:
Separate applications are required. Forms can be downloaded from the web site.

Duration: One year. Nonrenewable.

Deadline: February 1.

ADDRESS INQUIRIES TO:
Scholarship Coordinator
(See address above.)

AMERICAN NUCLEAR SOCIETY (ANS) [2635]
555 North Kensington Avenue
LaGrange Park, IL 60526
(708) 352-6611
Fax: (708) 352-0499

E-MAIL ADDRESS:
outreach@ans.org

WEB SITE ADDRESS:
www.ans.org

FOUNDED: 1954

AREAS OF INTEREST:
Nuclear science, nuclear engineering or nuclear-related fields.

NAME(S) OF PROGRAMS:
- **Decommissioning and Environmental Sciences (DESD) Scholarship**

TYPE:
Scholarships. For an undergraduate student in the engineering or science discipline that is associated with either decommissioning/decontamination of nuclear facilities, management/characterization of nuclear waste or restoration of the environment.

ELIGIBILITY:
Applicant must be at junior or senior undergraduate level and must be a U.S. citizen or permanent resident. He or she must be enrolled in a course of study relating to a degree in nuclear science or nuclear engineering in a U.S. institution. Additional criteria to be met include:
(1) the student must be enrolled in a curriculum of engineering or science that is associated either with decommissioning/decontamination of nuclear facilities, management/characterization of nuclear waste, restoration of the environment, or nuclear engineering;
(2) the scholarship is limited to U.S. citizens who are enrolled in U.S. schools;
(3) the student will join the American Nuclear Society (ANS);
(4) the student will designate the ANS DDR Division as one of his or her professional divisions and;
(5) he or she will commit to provide student support to the ANS DDR Division at the next ANS meeting after receipt of the scholarship award. (DDR will provide funding for the student's travel to the ANS meeting, including student registration, reasonable transportation, food and lodging.)

FINANCIAL DATA:
Scholarship funds may be used by the student to defray any bona fide education costs including tuition, books, room and board.

Amount of support per award: $3,000.

NUMBER OF AWARDS: 1 annually.

APPLICATION INFORMATION:
Applicant must submit a brief description of long- and short-term professional objectives. Scholarship application, transcript, letter of recommendation and three confidential reference forms must all be mailed together as a complete packet to ANS Headquarters, to the attention of Scholarship Coordinator. If all of the above forms are not included in the same packet, it will be considered an incomplete application. An incomplete packet could delay the scholarship application process. Please send a self-addressed, stamped envelope for a mail request.

Applicants must include the current year in school, the college or university he or she will be attending and the intended major.

Duration: One year. Nonrenewable.

Deadline: February 1.

ADDRESS INQUIRIES TO:
Scholarship Coordinator
(See address above.)

AMERICAN NUCLEAR SOCIETY (ANS) [2636]
555 North Kensington Avenue
LaGrange Park, IL 60526
(708) 352-6611
Fax: (708) 352-0499

E-MAIL ADDRESS:
outreach@ans.org

WEB SITE ADDRESS:
www.ans.org

FOUNDED: 1954

AREAS OF INTEREST:
Nuclear science, nuclear engineering or nuclear-related field.

NAME(S) OF PROGRAMS:
- **Raymond DiSalvo Scholarship**
- **Robert T. Liner Scholarship**
- **Operations and Power Division Scholarship**
- **Charles (Tommy) Thomas Memorial Scholarship**

TYPE:
Scholarships. Award for a full-time undergraduate student in a program leading to a degree in nuclear science or nuclear engineering at an accredited institution in the U.S.

ELIGIBILITY:
Applicant must be a U.S. citizen or possess a permanent resident visa.

Academic accomplishments must be substantiated by transcript. Applicants must be sponsored by an ANS local section, division, student branch, committee or organization member.

Charles (Tommy) Thomas Memorial Scholarship: Undergraduate of at least junior-year status pursuing a degree in a discipline preparing them for a career dealing with the environmental aspects of nuclear science or nuclear engineering.

GEOGRAPHIC RESTRICTIONS:
United States.

FINANCIAL DATA:
Scholarship funds may be used by the student to defray any bona fide education costs including tuition, fees, books, room and board.
Amount of support per award: Raymond DiSalvo and Robert T. Liner Scholarships: $2,000; Operations and Power Division Scholarship: $2,500; Charles (Tommy) Thomas Memorial Scholarship: $3,000.

NUMBER OF AWARDS: 1 each.

APPLICATION INFORMATION:
Scholarship application, transcript, letter of recommendation and three confidential reference forms must all be mailed together as a complete packet to ANS Headquarters, to the attention of Scholarship Coordinator. Application should be mailed at least seven days prior to the deadline. If all of the above forms are not included in the same packet, it will be considered an incomplete application. An incomplete packet could delay the scholarship application process.

Additionally, a brief essay is required for the Thomas Memorial Scholarship describing how the applicant perceives environmental science- and engineering-related topics fitting into the nuclear field and how he or she plans to contribute to the field during the course of their professional career.

Duration: One year. Nonrenewable.

Deadline: February 1.

ADDRESS INQUIRIES TO:
Scholarship Coordinator
(See address above.)

AMERICAN NUCLEAR SOCIETY (ANS)

555 North Kensington Avenue
LaGrange Park, IL 60526
(708) 352-6611
Fax: (708) 352-0499

E-MAIL ADDRESS:
outreach@ans.org

WEB SITE ADDRESS:
www.ans.org

TYPE:
Scholarships. Scholarship award to recognize one outstanding undergraduate student or one graduate student pursuing a career in radioanalytical chemistry or analytical applications of nuclear science.

See entry 2062 for full listing.

AMERICAN NUCLEAR SOCIETY (ANS) [2637]

555 North Kensington Avenue
LaGrange Park, IL 60526
(708) 352-6611
Fax: (708) 352-0499

E-MAIL ADDRESS:
outreach@ans.org

WEB SITE ADDRESS:
www.ans.org

FOUNDED: 1954

AREAS OF INTEREST:
Nuclear science, nuclear engineering or nuclear-related fields.

NAME(S) OF PROGRAMS:
- **ANS Undergraduate Scholarships**
- **Joseph R. Dietrich Memorial Scholarship**
- **Alan F. Henry/Paul A. Greebler Memorial Graduate Scholarship**
- **John R. Lamarsh Memorial Scholarship**

TYPE:
Scholarships.

ELIGIBILITY:
U.S. and non-U.S. applicants must be ANS student members enrolled in and attending an accredited institution in the U.S. Applicants must have completed a minimum of two complete academic years in a four-year nuclear engineering program and must be U.S. citizens or possess a permanent resident visa. Academic accomplishments must be substantiated by transcript. Applicant must be sponsored by an ANS local section, division, student branch, committee or organization member.

ANS Undergraduate Scholarships and Lamarsh Memorial Scholarship are open to full-time undergraduate students in a program leading to a degree in nuclear science or nuclear engineering at an accredited institution in the U.S.

Joseph R. Dietrich Scholarship is open to a full-time graduate student in a program leading to a degree in nuclear science or nuclear engineering at an accredited institution in the U.S.

Henry/Greebler Scholarship is open to a full-time graduate student of a North American university engaged in Master's or Ph.D. research in the area of nuclear reactor physics or radiation transport. Students of all nationalities are eligible.

FINANCIAL DATA:
Scholarship funds may be used by the student to defray any bona fide education costs including tuition, fees, room and board.
Amount of support per award: ANS Undergraduate, Joseph R. Dietrich Memorial and John R. Lamarsh Memorial Scholarships: $2,000; Alan F. Henry/Paul A. Greebler Memorial Graduate Scholarship: $3,500.

NUMBER OF AWARDS: ANS Undergraduate Scholarships: Up to 21; Dietrich, Greebler and Lamarsh Memorial Scholarships: 1 each.

APPLICATION INFORMATION:
Applications are available on the web site or from the ANS headquarters. Please send a self-addressed, stamped envelope for a mail request. Applicants must include the current year in school, the college or university he or she will be attending and the intended major.

Duration: One year. Nonrenewable.

Deadline: February 1.

ADDRESS INQUIRIES TO:
Scholarship Coordinator
(See address above.)

AMERICAN NUCLEAR SOCIETY (ANS) [2638]

555 North Kensington Avenue
LaGrange Park, IL 60526
(708) 352-6611
Fax: (708) 352-0499

E-MAIL ADDRESS:
outreach@ans.org

WEB SITE ADDRESS:
www.ans.org

FOUNDED: 1954

AREAS OF INTEREST:
Nuclear science, nuclear engineering or nuclear-related field.

NAME(S) OF PROGRAMS:
- **Angelo F. Bisesti Memorial Scholarship**
- **Robert G. Lacy Memorial Scholarship**

TYPE:
Scholarships. Scholarship awards for undergraduate students who have completed two or more years in a course of study leading to a degree in nuclear science, nuclear engineering or a nuclear-related field.

PURPOSE:
To support higher education in the nuclear science field.

ELIGIBILITY:
An applicant must be a U.S. citizen or possess a permanent resident visa, be enrolled in a U.S. college or university, and must be sponsored by an ANS local section, division, student branch, committee or organization member. More than one applicant can be sponsored by any of these organizations.

FINANCIAL DATA:
Amount of support per award: $2,000.

NUMBER OF AWARDS: 1 each.

APPLICATION INFORMATION:
Scholarship application, transcript, letter of recommendation and three confidential reference forms must all be mailed together as a complete packet to ANS Headquarters, to the attention of Scholarship Coordinator. Application should be mailed at least seven days prior to the deadline. If all of the above forms are not included in the same packet, it will be considered an incomplete application. An incomplete packet could delay the scholarship application process. Please send a self-addressed, stamped envelope for a mail request.

Applicants must include the current year in school, the college or university he or she will be attending, and the intended major.

Duration: One year. Nonrenewable.

Deadline: February 1.

ADDRESS INQUIRIES TO:
Scholarship Coordinator
(See address above.)

AMERICAN NUCLEAR SOCIETY (ANS) [2639]

555 North Kensington Avenue
LaGrange Park, IL 60526
(708) 352-6611
Fax: (708) 352-0499

E-MAIL ADDRESS:
outreach@ans.org

WEB SITE ADDRESS:
www.ans.org

FOUNDED: 1954

AREAS OF INTEREST:
Nuclear science, nuclear engineering or nuclear-related field.

NAME(S) OF PROGRAMS:
- **ANS Graduate Scholarships**

- **Everitt P. Blizard Scholarship**
- **Robert A. Dannels Memorial Graduate Scholarship**
- **Verne R. Dapp Memorial Scholarship**
- **Walter Meyer Scholarship**
- **James F. Schumar Scholarship**

TYPE:
Scholarships. Blizard Scholarship is for students pursuing graduate studies in the field of radiation protection and shielding.

Dapp and Meyer Scholarships are for full-time graduate students in a program leading to an advanced degree in nuclear science or nuclear engineering. The Dapp is awarded in odd-numbered years. The Meyer is awarded in even-numbered years.

Schumar Scholarship is for a student pursuing graduate studies in materials science and technology for nuclear applications.

PURPOSE:
To support higher education in the field of nuclear science.

ELIGIBILITY:
An applicant must be a U.S. citizen or possess a permanent resident visa, be enrolled in a U.S. university and must be sponsored by an ANS local section, division, student branch, committee or organization member. More than one applicant can be sponsored by any of these organizations.

The Dannels Scholarship is for a graduate-level course of study leading toward a degree in mathematics and computation. Only U.S. citizens or persons possessing a permanent resident visa are eligible. Nomination of handicapped persons is encouraged.

The Dapp Scholarship is awarded on the graduate level toward a degree in nuclear engineering at an accredited institution in the U.S. The nominee must be an ANS Student Section member. Only U.S. citizens or persons possessing a permanent resident visa are eligible.

GEOGRAPHIC RESTRICTIONS:
United States.

FINANCIAL DATA:
Scholarship funds may be used to defray any bona fide education costs including tuition, books, room and board.

Amount of support per award: Blizard, Dapp, Meyer, Schumar and ANS Graduate Scholarships: $3,000 each; Dannels Scholarship: $3,500.

NUMBER OF AWARDS: Blizard, Dannels, Dapp, Meyer and Schumar: 1 each; ANS Graduate Scholarships: Up to 29.

APPLICATION INFORMATION:
Scholarship application, transcript, letter of recommendation and three confidential reference forms must all be mailed together as a complete packet to ANS Headquarters, to the attention of Scholarship Coordinator. Application should be mailed at least seven days prior to the deadline. If all of the above forms are not included in the same packet, it will be considered an incomplete application. An incomplete packet could delay the scholarship application process. Please send a self-addressed, stamped envelope for a mail request.

Applicants must include the current year in school, the college or university he or she will be attending, and the intended major.

Duration: One year. Nonrenewable.

Deadline: February 1.

ADDRESS INQUIRIES TO:
Scholarship Coordinator
(See address above.)

AMERICAN NUCLEAR SOCIETY (ANS) [2640]
555 North Kensington Avenue
LaGrange Park, IL 60526
(708) 352-6611
Fax: (708) 352-0499

E-MAIL ADDRESS:
outreach@ans.org

WEB SITE ADDRESS:
www.ans.org

FOUNDED: 1954

AREAS OF INTEREST:
Nuclear science, nuclear engineering and nuclear-related field.

NAME(S) OF PROGRAMS:
- **Pittsburgh Local Section Scholarship**

TYPE:
Scholarships. Two Pittsburgh Local Section Scholarships: one for a graduate student (studying nuclear science and technology) and one for an undergraduate student (studying nuclear science and technology) who either have some affiliation with western Pennsylvania or who attend school at a nearby university within the region.

PURPOSE:
To support higher education in nuclear science.

ELIGIBILITY:
An applicant must be a U.S. citizen or possess a permanent resident visa, be enrolled in a U.S. college or university, and must be sponsored by an ANS local section, division, student branch, committee or organization member. More than one applicant can be sponsored by any of these organizations.

GEOGRAPHIC RESTRICTIONS:
Western Pennsylvania.

FINANCIAL DATA:
Scholarship funds may be used to defray any bona fide education costs including tuition, books, room and board.

Amount of support per award:
Undergraduate: $2,000; Graduate: $3,500.

NUMBER OF AWARDS: Undergraduate and Graduate: 1 each.

APPLICATION INFORMATION:
Scholarship application, transcript, letter of recommendation and three confidential reference forms must all be mailed together as a complete packet to ANS Headquarters, to the attention of Scholarship Coordinator. Application should be mailed at least seven days prior to the deadline. If all of the above forms are not included in the same packet, it will be considered an incomplete application. An incomplete packet could delay the scholarship application process. Please send a self-addressed, stamped envelope for a mail request.

Applicants must include the current year in school, the college or university he or she will be attending, and the intended major.

Duration: One year. Nonrenewable.

Deadline: February 1.

ADDRESS INQUIRIES TO:
Scholarship Coordinator
(See address above.)

AMERICAN PUBLIC POWER ASSOCIATION (APPA) [2641]
1875 Connecticut Avenue, N.W.
Suite 1200
Washington, DC 20009-5715
(202) 467-2900
Fax: (202) 467-2910

E-MAIL ADDRESS:
deed@publicpower.org

WEB SITE ADDRESS:
www.publicpower.org/deed

FOUNDED: 1980

AREAS OF INTEREST:
Engineering, mathematics and computer science.

NAME(S) OF PROGRAMS:
- **DEED Scholarship**

TYPE:
Demonstration grants; Development grants; Internships; Research grants; Scholarships.

YEAR PROGRAM STARTED: 1980

PURPOSE:
To promote the involvement of students studying in energy-related disciplines in the public power industry; to provide host utilities with technical assistance.

ELIGIBILITY:
Open to students conducting research on a project approved by the sponsoring utility who will then submit a final report on the project, describing the activities, cost, bibliography, achievements, problems, results and recommendations. Applicants will not be discriminated against on the basis of sex, race, religion, national origin or citizenship.

FINANCIAL DATA:
Amount of support per award: $4,000.
Total amount of support: Up to $40,000 per year.

NUMBER OF APPLICANTS MOST RECENT YEAR:
20.

NUMBER OF AWARDS: 10.

APPLICATION INFORMATION:
Applications must be sent from a DEED member utility and must be dated on the last page by an authorized individual at the utility.
Deadline: February 15 and October 15.

ADDRESS INQUIRIES TO:
Monica Stowe, DEED Assistant
(See address above.)

AMERICAN SOCIETY FOR ENGINEERING EDUCATION [2642]
1818 N Street, N.W., Suite 600
Washington, DC 20036
(202) 649-3834

E-MAIL ADDRESS:
sffp@asee.org

WEB SITE ADDRESS:
sffp.asee.org

AREAS OF INTEREST:
Science, engineering and mathematics.

NAME(S) OF PROGRAMS:
- **USAF Summer Faculty Fellowship Program**

TYPE:
Fellowships. Research fellowship.

PURPOSE:
To complement research efforts and build critical links between Air Force scientists and counterparts in the academic community.

ELIGIBILITY:
Must be a full-time faculty member of an accredited Baccalaureate-granting U.S. college, university or technical institution, and have earned a Ph.D. in science or engineering. No other employment or remuneration is permitted during the period of the award, eight to 12 weeks from May through August.

GEOGRAPHIC RESTRICTIONS:
United States.

FINANCIAL DATA:
Amount of support per award: Assistant Professor: $1,300 per week; Associate Professor: $1,500 per week; Full Professor: $1,700 per week.
Total amount of support: Varies.

NUMBER OF APPLICANTS MOST RECENT YEAR: 265.

NUMBER OF AWARDS: Up to 100.

APPLICATION INFORMATION:
Each applicant must get approval to apply to a program from the Advisor before uploading his or her proposal. Application opens September 1. Applications, curriculum vitae and references must be submitted electronically.
Duration: One summer.
Deadline: Late November.

ADDRESS INQUIRIES TO:
Melanie Suydam, Program Manager
(See address above.)

AMERICAN SOCIETY FOR ENGINEERING EDUCATION [2643]

1818 N Street, N.W., Suite 600
Washington, DC 20036-2479
(202) 331-3500
Fax: (202) 265-8504

E-MAIL ADDRESS:
projects@asee.org

WEB SITE ADDRESS:
www.asee.org

FOUNDED: 1893

AREAS OF INTEREST:
Engineering education programs and scientific research in government and industry.

NAME(S) OF PROGRAMS:
- **Department of Defense National Defense Science and Engineering Graduate Fellowship Program (NDSEG)**
- **Summer Research Opportunity Program**

TYPE:
Awards/prizes; Fellowships; Professorships; Research grants; Visiting scholars.

YEAR PROGRAM STARTED: 1964

ELIGIBILITY:
The Department of Defense National Defense Science and Engineering Graduate Fellowship Program is for students at or near the beginning of their graduate study in science or engineering. Applicants must be citizens or nationals of the U.S.

FINANCIAL DATA:
Amount of support per award: Varies.
Total amount of support: Varies.

NUMBER OF AWARDS: NDSEG: 200 annually.

AMERICAN SOCIETY FOR ENGINEERING EDUCATION [2644]

1818 N Street, N.W., Suite 600
Washington, DC 20036
(202) 350-5763
Fax: (202) 265-8504

E-MAIL ADDRESS:
postdocs@asee.org

WEB SITE ADDRESS:
www.asee.org/nrl

FOUNDED: 1893

AREAS OF INTEREST:
Engineering education programs, scientific research in government, industry and the military.

NAME(S) OF PROGRAMS:
- **Naval Research Laboratory (NRL) Postdoctoral Fellowship Program**

TYPE:
Fellowships. Offered at Naval research and development centers and laboratories. NRL is charged with developing technologies that will support Naval Forces in meeting future operational needs. Scientists and fellows working at NRL pursue research on subjects including, but not limited to, processing, biomedicine, logistics, command control and intelligence, training and oceanography.

YEAR PROGRAM STARTED: 2002

PURPOSE:
To significantly increase the involvement of creative and highly trained scientists and engineers from academia and industry in scientific and technical areas of interest and relevance to the Navy.

LEGAL BASIS:
Special interest society.

ELIGIBILITY:
Applicants must be U.S. citizens and permanent residents and must be eligible for a Department of Defense security clearance of "Secret." In most cases, participants will be permitted to do research pending completion of the security clearance. All appointments are contingent upon fellows obtaining the appropriate level of security clearance. Prior to appointment, participants must present evidence of having received the Ph.D., Sc.D. or other earned research doctoral degree recognized in U.S. as equivalent to the Ph.D. within seven years of the date of application or must present acceptable evidence of having completed all formal academic requirements for one of these degrees. No support to applicants who received prior postdoctoral appointment under any program at the same Navy laboratory. No appointments or denials based on grounds of race, creed, color, national origin, age or sex.

GEOGRAPHIC RESTRICTIONS:
United States.

FINANCIAL DATA:
Awards include stipend, insurance, relocation expenses and travel.
Amount of support per award: $74,000.
Total amount of support: Varies.

NUMBER OF AWARDS: Approximately 40 new appointments each year.

APPLICATION INFORMATION:
Applicants should contact the research facility of interest to develop a suitable research proposal. Proposals developed closely with the proposed host facility stand the greatest chance of success in the selection process. A proposal should be no more than 10 pages, be concise, and address a problem of mutual interest to the applicant and Navy research facility.
Duration: One year. Renewable for a second and third year with satisfactory performance and availability of funds.

PUBLICATIONS:
Program announcement.

STAFF:
Shannon Koonce, Program Manager

ADDRESS INQUIRIES TO:
NRL Postdoctoral Program
Contracts/Grants Office
(See address above.)

THE AMERICAN SOCIETY FOR NONDESTRUCTIVE TESTING, INC.

1711 Arlingate Lane
Columbus, OH 43228
(614) 274-6003
(800) 222-2768
Fax: (614) 274-6899

E-MAIL ADDRESS:
mthomas@asnt.org

WEB SITE ADDRESS:
www.asnt.org

TYPE:
Scholarships.

See entry 1662 for full listing.

AMERICAN SOCIETY OF CIVIL ENGINEERS [2645]

1801 Alexander Bell Drive
Reston, VA 20191-4400
(703) 295-6300 ext. 6382
(800) 548-2723
Fax: (703) 295-6144

E-MAIL ADDRESS:
awards@asce.org

WEB SITE ADDRESS:
www.asce.org

FOUNDED: 1852

AREAS OF INTEREST:
Civil engineering.

NAME(S) OF PROGRAMS:
- **O.H. Ammann Research Fellowship in Structural Engineering**
- **CI Construction Engineering Scholarship and Student Prizes**
- **Lawrence W. and Francis W. Cox Scholarship**
- **Trent R. Dames and William W. Moore Fellowship**
- **Eugene C. Figg, Jr. Civil Engineering Scholarship**
- **Freeman Fellowship**
- **Jack E. Leisch Memorial National Graduate Fellowship**
- **John Lenard Civil Engineering Scholarship**

- **Robert B.B. and Josephine N. Moorman Scholarship**
- **J. Waldo Smith Hydraulic Fellowship**
- **Samuel Fletcher Tapman ASCE Student Chapter Scholarship**
- **Arthur S. Tuttle Memorial Scholarship**
- **Y.C. Yang Civil Engineering Scholarship**

TYPE:
Fellowships; Grants-in-aid; Research grants; Scholarships. Scholarships, fellowships and grants for research; undergraduate and graduate studies in civil engineering fields from ASCE endowments, operation or other funds.

Fellowships and scholarships are awarded annually.

YEAR PROGRAM STARTED: 1924

PURPOSE:
To aid and encourage education, research and studies in civil engineering.

LEGAL BASIS:
Nonprofit professional organization.

ELIGIBILITY:
Qualified engineers or engineering undergraduate or graduate students with appropriate interests are eligible to apply. Undergraduate students must be enrolled at an ABET-accredited university, be a member of an ASCE student chapter and also be a national student member. (A list of schools that have student chapters is available from the address above.)

FINANCIAL DATA:
Amount of support per award: $2,000 to $10,000.

APPLICATION INFORMATION:
Application forms are available at www.asce.org/Student-Organizations/Scholarships-and-Fellowships/Scholarships—Fellowships/.

PUBLICATIONS:
Scholarships/Fellowships brochure.

OFFICERS:
Pat Natale, Executive Director

ADDRESS INQUIRIES TO:
See e-mail address above.

THE AMERICAN SOCIETY OF MECHANICAL ENGINEERS AUXILIARY, INC.   [2646]
2 Park Avenue, MS-RB
New York, NY 10016-5990
(212) 591-7650
Fax: (212) 591-7739

E-MAIL ADDRESS:
bigleyr@asme.org

WEB SITE ADDRESS:
go.asme.org/scholarships

FOUNDED: 1923

AREAS OF INTEREST:
Mechanical engineering students.

NAME(S) OF PROGRAMS:
- **ASME/ASME Auxiliary Clarke Scholarship**
- **ASME/ASME Auxiliary FIRST Clarke Scholarship**
- **Allen J. Baldwin Scholarship**
- **Berna Lou Cartwright Scholarship**
- **Sylvia W. Farny Scholarship**
- **Agnes Malakate Kezios Scholarship**
- **Elisabeth M. and Winchell M. Parsons Scholarship**

- **Rice-Cullimore Scholarship**
- **Marjorie Roy Rothermel Scholarship**
- **Charles B. Scharp Scholarship**
- **Student Loan Fund**

TYPE:
Scholarships. ASME/ASME Auxiliary Clarke Scholarship is for incoming freshman enrolling in a mechanical engineering program.

ASME/ASME Auxiliary FIRST Clarke Scholarship is for high school seniors participating on a FIRST team.

Baldwin, Cartwright, Farny, Kezios and Scharp Scholarships are for undergraduate students in mechanical engineering.

Parsons and Rothermel Scholarships are for graduate students with a degree in mechanical engineering, to be used to pursue a Master's degree in mechanical engineering.

Rice-Cullimore Scholarship is for foreign students at the graduate level.

Student Loan Fund is for juniors, seniors or graduate students enrolled as degree candidates in good standing.

YEAR PROGRAM STARTED: 1924

PURPOSE:
To give financial assistance to mechanical engineering students.

LEGAL BASIS:
Incorporated organization.

ELIGIBILITY:
Applicants must be U.S. citizens, enrolled in a degree program in a school with accredited mechanical engineering curriculum and members of the ASME for scholarships and student loans. Applicants must be foreign students, selected in their home country, who meet the requirements of the sponsor in their home country who holds a contract with the International Institute of Education for the Rice-Cullimore Scholarship.

FINANCIAL DATA:
Amount of support per award: ASME/ASME Auxiliary FIRST Clarke Scholarship: $5,000. All other Scholarships: $2,000; Student Loans: $5,000 maximum.
Total amount of support: Varies.

NUMBER OF APPLICANTS MOST RECENT YEAR:
Undergraduate Scholarships: 15; Rothermel: 1.

NUMBER OF AWARDS: Undergraduate Scholarships: 9; Rothermel: 1.

APPLICATION INFORMATION:
Contact the Society.
Duration: One year. Nonrenewable.
Deadline: Contact the Auxiliary for individual scholarship deadlines and notification dates.

PUBLICATIONS:
Application guidelines; scholarship forms; applications.

OFFICERS:
Kay Simmons, President
Benetta Cook, Executive Vice President
Julie Kulik, Vice President, Members-at-Large
Stella Seiders, Treasurer
Margaret Holdredge, Student Loan Fund Treasurer
Ella Baldwin-Viereck, Recording Secretary
Vatsala Menon, Corresponding Secretary

ADDRESS INQUIRIES TO:
RuthAnn Bigley, Coordinator, Governance
(See address above.)

AMERICAN SOCIETY OF NAVAL ENGINEERS (ASNE)   [2647]
1452 Duke Street
Alexandria, VA 22314-3458
(703) 836-6727
Fax: (703) 836-7491

E-MAIL ADDRESS:
jpierce@navalengineers.org

WEB SITE ADDRESS:
www.navalengineers.org

FOUNDED: 1888

AREAS OF INTEREST:
Naval Engineering includes all arts and sciences as applied in the research, development, design, construction, operation, maintenance and logistic support of surface and sub-surface ships and marine craft, naval maritime auxiliaries, aviation and space systems, combat systems, command control, electronics and ordnance systems, ocean structures and associated shore facilities, which are used by naval and other military forces and civilian maritime organizations for the defense and well-being of the Nation.

CONSULTING OR VOLUNTEER SERVICES:
Volunteer Services.

NAME(S) OF PROGRAMS:
- **ASNE Scholarship Program**

TYPE:
Scholarships. Stipend for tuition, fees and expenses to follow a full-time or co-op program of study that applies to naval engineering, such as naval architecture, marine engineering, ocean engineering, mechanical engineering, structural engineering, electrical engineering, electronic engineering and the physical sciences, as well as other programs leading to careers with civilian and military maritime organizations supporting and developing work and life at sea.

YEAR PROGRAM STARTED: 1979

PURPOSE:
To encourage college students to enter the field of naval engineering; to support naval engineers seeking advanced education in the field.

LEGAL BASIS:
Nonprofit professional society.

ELIGIBILITY:
Support will be limited to the last year of undergraduate education or one year of graduate education in an accredited college or university. Candidates must be U.S. citizens and must have demonstrated or expressed a genuine interest in a career in naval engineering. Graduate students must be members of ASNE or SNAME and may apply at time of application.

Selection criteria will be based on academic record, work history, professional promise and interest in naval engineering, extracurricular activities, recommendations of college faculty, employers and other character references. Demonstrated financial need is not a requirement, but it may be taken into consideration by the Scholarship Committee.

A scholarship will not be awarded to a doctoral candidate or to a person already having an advanced degree.

GEOGRAPHIC RESTRICTIONS:
United States.

FINANCIAL DATA:
The award will be in the form of a check for the first academic period payable jointly to the awardee and the college or university that the student will attend. Transcripts showing satisfactory performance constitute the basis for further awards for subsequent academic periods.
Amount of support per award: Undergraduate: $3,000; Graduate: $4,000.

NUMBER OF AWARDS: Varies.

APPLICATION INFORMATION:
Application information is available on the Society's web site.
Duration: One year.
Deadline: February 28. Notification by early May.

PUBLICATIONS:
Naval Engineers Journal.

IRS IDENTIFICATION NUMBER: 53-0229465

OFFICERS:
Capt. Dennis K. Kruse, USN (Ret.), Executive Director

ADDRESS INQUIRIES TO:
ASNE Scholarship Committee
(See address above.)

AMERICAN SOCIETY OF SAFETY ENGINEERS [2648]

1800 East Oakton Street
Des Plaines, IL 60018-2187
(847) 699-2929
Fax: (847) 296-9221

E-MAIL ADDRESS:
customerservice@asse.org

WEB SITE ADDRESS:
www.asse.org

FOUNDED: 1911

AREAS OF INTEREST:
Occupational safety and health.

NAME(S) OF PROGRAMS:
● **Edgar Monsanto Queeny Safety Professional of the Year Award**

TYPE:
Awards/prizes. Cash honorarium to Society-selected award winners from Monsanto Co.

YEAR PROGRAM STARTED: 1980

PURPOSE:
To recognize exemplary achievements in Safety, Health and Environmental (SHE) Education.

LEGAL BASIS:
Not-for-profit professional society.

ELIGIBILITY:
Nominee must be a professional member or member of the Society, and not have received this award within the past five years. U.S. members must be active, dues-paying members of a chapter. Nominee cannot be running opposed for national ASSE Executive Committee office or currently serving on the national Technical and Professional Recognition Committee.

FINANCIAL DATA:
Amount of support per award: $1,500 honorarium.

NUMBER OF APPLICANTS MOST RECENT YEAR:
9.

NUMBER OF AWARDS: 1 each year.

APPLICATION INFORMATION:
Nominations must be submitted in writing to the ASSE Technical and Professional Recognition Committee Chairman, postmarked no later than November 1, to be considered that same year. Individual members, chapters, regions, practice specialty, councils or the Society Board of Directors may submit them. Must be accompanied by a letter of endorsement from the nominating colleague (Chapter, Regional Operating Committees, Practice Specialty, Councils or the Society Board of Directors), as well as the immediate employment supervisor, a single-page resume, plus a petition listing the nominee's achievements. Submit seven copies.
Deadline: November 1. Award announcement in early March.

ADDRESS INQUIRIES TO:
Dennis Hudson
Director, Professional Affairs
(See address above.)

ASHRAE [2649]

1791 Tullie Circle, N.E.
Atlanta, GA 30329
(404) 636-8400

E-MAIL ADDRESS:
mvaughn@ashrae.org

WEB SITE ADDRESS:
www.ashrae.org

FOUNDED: 1894

AREAS OF INTEREST:
Engineering, environmental technology, technical assistance, public health and conservation.

CONSULTING OR VOLUNTEER SERVICES:
Cooperative research with government agencies and other organizations by supplying ASHRAE expertise, usually in the form of an advisory committee.

NAME(S) OF PROGRAMS:
● **ASHRAE Research Grants**

TYPE:
Research contracts. Institutional grants for basic research and technical studies concerned with the arts and sciences of heating, refrigeration, air conditioning and ventilation.

YEAR PROGRAM STARTED: 1912

PURPOSE:
To increase the amount and accuracy of fundamental information in the fields of heating, refrigeration, air conditioning/ventilation and related areas and to make this information available.

LEGAL BASIS:
Organization exempt under 501(c)(3) of the Internal Revenue Code.

ELIGIBILITY:
Accredited institutions of higher learning may apply with appropriate proposals.

FINANCIAL DATA:
Amount of support per award: $5,000 to $250,000 per year.
Total amount of support: $2,500,000 to $3,000,000 annually.

NUMBER OF APPLICANTS MOST RECENT YEAR:
60.

NUMBER OF AWARDS: Approximately 20 grants annually.

APPLICATION INFORMATION:
Applications take the form of a proposal. Detailed information concerning its preparation is available upon request to the Manager of Research at the address above.
Duration: Up to three years, with the possibility of extension.
Deadline: Applications may be submitted throughout the year. Proposals are generally acted upon only in January and June.

ADDRESS INQUIRIES TO:
Michael R. Vaughn, Manager of Research and Technical Services
(See address above.)

ASHRAE [2650]

1791 Tullie Circle, N.E.
Atlanta, GA 30329
(404) 636-8400

E-MAIL ADDRESS:
mvaughn@ashrae.org

WEB SITE ADDRESS:
www.ashrae.org

FOUNDED: 1894

AREAS OF INTEREST:
Engineering, environmental technology, technical assistance, public health and conservation.

NAME(S) OF PROGRAMS:
● **ASHRAE Graduate Student Grant-in-Aid Program**

TYPE:
Grants-in-aid. Support for projects of original research concerned with the arts and sciences of heating, refrigeration, air-conditioning/ventilation and related areas.

YEAR PROGRAM STARTED: 1968

PURPOSE:
To stimulate interest in the areas of heating, refrigeration, air-conditioning and ventilation through the encouragement of original research in these fields.

LEGAL BASIS:
Organization exempt under 501(c)(3) of the Internal Revenue Code.

ELIGIBILITY:
Qualified graduate engineering students capable of carrying out appropriate and scholarly research are eligible to apply.

FINANCIAL DATA:
Amount of support per award: $10,000 with the opportunity to earn an additional $1,500 honorarium for presentation of an authored research paper at an ASHRAE meeting.
Total amount of support: Approximately $200,000 annually.

NUMBER OF APPLICANTS MOST RECENT YEAR:
60.

NUMBER OF AWARDS: Approximately 20 per year.

APPLICATION INFORMATION:
Prospective applicants should complete the official Grant-in-Aid application containing the following:
(1) significance of proposed research;
(2) outline or plan of procedure;
(3) approximate budget and extent to which the applicant's institution will support the work;
(4) plans for seeking other funds for this or related work;

(5) anticipated plans for publication of research results;
(6) student's name and qualifications;
(7) faculty advisor's and institution's qualifications to do the work and;
(8) copy of official transcripts.

Duration: Grants are usually awarded for a maximum period of one year. Students who have previously received grants may not reapply; one grant per student.

Deadline: Applications should be submitted by or before December 15, for consideration at review meeting held in January.

OFFICERS:
Tom Phoenix, President
David Underwood, President-Elect
Jeff Littleton, Executive Vice President and Secretary

ADDRESS INQUIRIES TO:
Michael R. Vaughn, Manager of Research and Technical Services
(See address above.)

ASM MATERIALS EDUCATION FOUNDATION
9639 Kinsman Road
Materials Park, OH 44073-0002
(440) 338-5151 ext. 5533
(800) 336-5152 ext. 5533
Fax: (440) 338-4634

E-MAIL ADDRESS:
jeane.deatherage@asminternational.org

WEB SITE ADDRESS:
www.asmfoundation.org

TYPE:
Scholarships.

See entry 2677 for full listing.

CANADIAN SOCIETY FOR CHEMICAL ENGINEERING   [2651]
130 Slater Street
Suite 550
Ottawa ON K1P 6E2 Canada
(613) 232-6252 ext. 223
Fax: (613) 232-5862

E-MAIL ADDRESS:
awards@cheminst.ca

WEB SITE ADDRESS:
www.cheminst.ca/awards

FOUNDED: 1945

AREAS OF INTEREST:
Chemical engineering.

NAME(S) OF PROGRAMS:
• **The CSChE Chemical Engineering Local Section Scholarships**
• **SNC-LAVALIN Plant Design Competition**

TYPE:
Scholarships. The CSChE Chemical Engineering Local Section Scholarships are offered to undergraduate students in chemical engineering about to enter the final year of studies at a Canadian university and will be made for leadership qualities and demonstrated contributions to the Canadian Society for Chemical Engineering, such as participation in student chapters. Two scholarships will be given annually.

The SNC-LAVALIN Plant Design Competition is offered to students enrolled in undergraduate chemical engineering programs at Canadian universities.

PURPOSE:
To promote undergraduate study in chemical engineering and provide financial support for that study.

LEGAL BASIS:
Special interest society.

ELIGIBILITY:
Applicants for the CSChE Chemical Engineering Local Section Scholarships must be members of the Canadian Society for Chemical Engineering.

Applicants for the SNC-LAVALIN Plant Design Competition must be individuals and groups of undergraduate students registered in chemical engineering programs in Canadian universities during the current academic year. To minimize the number of projects to be judged, each chemical engineering department may submit no more than two entries.

GEOGRAPHIC RESTRICTIONS:
Canada.

FINANCIAL DATA:
Amount of support per award: Chemical Engineering Local Section: $2,000; SNC-LAVALIN Plant Design Competition: $1,000 to the team with the best design.

NUMBER OF AWARDS: Local Section Scholarships: 2; SNC-LAVALIN Plant Design Competition: 1.

APPLICATION INFORMATION:
For the scholarships, applications should contain evidence of academic standing, description of work to be undertaken, letters of reference, and evidence of contributions to the Society.

Entries for the SNC-LAVALIN Plant Design Competition should contain copies of the following:
(1) a short summary, including a simplified flowsheet of the process;
(2) a copy of the final report submitted to the university at the end of the project;
(3) a list of students who performed the work, with their permanent addresses and phone numbers;
(4) the name of the collaborating organization and the engineers who assisted the students and;
(5) a brief description of the assistance provided by that organization.

The entry should be accompanied by a letter from the head of the department of chemical engineering indicating that the information is not confidential and that the summary may be published in *Canadian Chemical News.*

Deadline: Local Section Scholarships: April 30; SNC-LAVALIN Competition: May 30.

PUBLICATIONS:
Announcement.

ADDRESS INQUIRIES TO:
Gale Thirlwall, Awards Manager
(See address above.)

GEORGE WASHINGTON UNIVERSITY   [2652]
Department of Electrical and Computer Engineering
801 22nd Street, N.W., Room 607
Washington, DC 20052
(202) 994-6083
Fax: (202) 994-9380

E-MAIL ADDRESS:
zaghloul@gwu.edu

WEB SITE ADDRESS:
www.ece.seas.gwu.edu

FOUNDED: 1821

AREAS OF INTEREST:
Electrical engineering, computer engineering, biomedical engineering, and telecommunications.

NAME(S) OF PROGRAMS:
• **Graduate Teaching Assistantships**

TYPE:
Assistantships. Merit-based awards for graduate studies at George Washington University.

PURPOSE:
To attract high-quality graduate students.

LEGAL BASIS:
University.

ELIGIBILITY:
Usually for currently enrolled students. Some fellowships are limited to U.S. citizens. Must have a grade point average of 3.5 on a possible scale of 4.0 and have taken the Graduate Record Examination.

GEOGRAPHIC RESTRICTIONS:
United States.

FINANCIAL DATA:
Amount of support per award: Varies.
Total amount of support: Varies.

APPLICATION INFORMATION:
Graduate students should submit an application for admission to the School of Engineering and Applied Science.
Duration: One academic year. Must reapply for additional funding.

ADDRESS INQUIRIES TO:
Dr. Mona Zaghloul, Chairperson
(See address above.)

GREAT MINDS IN STEM
602 Monterey Pass Road
Monterey Park, CA 91754
(323) 262-0997
Fax: (323) 262-0946

E-MAIL ADDRESS:
info@greatmindsinstem.org

WEB SITE ADDRESS:
www.greatmindsinstem.org

TYPE:
Scholarships.

See entry 2609 for full listing.

INSTITUTE OF INDUSTRIAL ENGINEERS (IIE)   [2653]
3577 Parkway Lane, Suite 200
Norcross, GA 30092
(770) 449-0461
Fax: (770) 441-3295

E-MAIL ADDRESS:
bcameron@iienet.org

WEB SITE ADDRESS:
www.iienet.org

FOUNDED: 1948

AREAS OF INTEREST:
The design, improvement and installation of integrated systems of people, material, information, equipment and energy, incorporating specialized knowledge and skills from the mathematical, physical and social sciences, together with the principles

and methods of engineering analysis and design to specify, predict and evaluate the results to be obtained from such systems.

NAME(S) OF PROGRAMS:
- **CIE Undergraduate Scholarship**
- **John S.W. Fargher Scholarship**
- **C.B. Gambrell Undergraduate Scholarship**
- **Dwight D. Garden Scholarship**
- **Gilbreth Memorial Fellowship**
- **IIE Council of Fellows Undergraduate Scholarship**
- **John L. Imhoff Scholarship**
- **Harold and Inge Marcus Scholarship**
- **Marvin Mundel Memorial Scholarship**
- **Presidents Scholarship**
- **A.O. Putnam Memorial Scholarship**
- **E.J. Sierleja Memorial Fellowship**
- **Society for Health Systems Scholarship**
- **United Parcel Service Scholarship for Female Students**
- **United Parcel Service Scholarship for Minority Students**
- **Lisa Zaken Award of Excellence**

TYPE:
Fellowships; Scholarships. The Institute supports the advancement of engineering education and research through scholarships and fellowships to recognize and support these types of endeavors.

PURPOSE:
To recognize academic excellence and campus leadership.

LEGAL BASIS:
Nonprofit, international professional membership society.

ELIGIBILITY:
Candidates must be active Institute members enrolled full-time in graduate or undergraduate industrial engineering programs. The nominee's scholastic ability, character, leadership, service, and financial need are all considered.

Membership is not required for the Imhoff Scholarship.

FINANCIAL DATA:
Amount of support per award: Varies per award.

APPLICATION INFORMATION:
Students may not apply directly for scholarships. They must be nominated by their department head or faculty advisor. Nominations must be mailed to the Institute. Call for nominations are sent out at the beginning of each school year in the fall.
Deadline: December 1 (postmark).

STAFF:
Don Greene, Executive Director

ADDRESS INQUIRIES TO:
Bonnie Cameron
Headquarters Operations Administrator
(See address above.)

THE JAMES F. LINCOLN ARC WELDING FOUNDATION [2654]

22801 St. Clair Avenue
Cleveland, OH 44117
(216) 481-8100
Fax: (216) 486-6476

E-MAIL ADDRESS:
innovate@lincolnelectric.com

WEB SITE ADDRESS:
www.lincolnelectric.com
www.jflf.org

FOUNDED: 1936

AREAS OF INTEREST:
Engineering, welded design and fabrication.

NAME(S) OF PROGRAMS:
- **Awards for Achievement in Arc Welded Design, Engineering and Fabrication: College Division**

TYPE:
Awards/prizes. Awards to recognize and reward achievement by engineering and technology students (graduate and undergraduate) in solving design, engineering or fabricating problems involving the knowledge or application of arc welding.

YEAR PROGRAM STARTED: 1956

PURPOSE:
To recognize outstanding work in the welding design and fabrication field.

LEGAL BASIS:
Private corporate foundation.

ELIGIBILITY:
Graduate or undergraduate students enrolled in college or university programs leading to a Bachelor's, Master's or doctoral degree may submit papers completed within a one-year period, ending June 30 of the year of the contest. Papers should represent students' work on design, engineering or fabrication problems relating to any type of building, bridge or other generally stationary structure, any type of machine, product or mechanical apparatus or arc welding research, testing, procedure or process development.

Students to participate in the Undergraduate Division must be enrolled in a four-year or longer curriculum leading to a Bachelor's degree. Students to participate in the Graduate Division must be enrolled in a graduate program leading to a Master's or Doctorate degree. Qualified students may apply individually or jointly in groups of not more than five. Undergraduate students compete for 17 awards, and graduate students compete for 12 awards.

GEOGRAPHIC RESTRICTIONS:
United States.

FINANCIAL DATA:
Amount of support per award: $50 to $1,000.
Total amount of support: Varies.

NUMBER OF AWARDS: Varies.

APPLICATION INFORMATION:
Official application materials are available upon request to the Secretary. Any number of entries may be submitted from one school, but no student may participate in more than one entry.
Duration: One year.
Deadline: June 30.

TRUSTEES:
Duane Miller

EXECUTIVE STAFF:
Leslie Brown, President
Carl Peters, Executive Director
Lori Hurley, Secretary

ADDRESS INQUIRIES TO:
Lori Hurley, Secretary
(See address above.)

LOS ALAMOS NATIONAL LABORATORY

P.O. Box 1663
MS-P125
Los Alamos, NM 87545
(505) 664-6947 ext. 05004
Fax: (505) 606-5901

E-MAIL ADDRESS:
hrstaffing-postdocs@lanl.gov

WEB SITE ADDRESS:
www.lanl.gov/science/postdocs

TYPE:
Fellowships. The Distinguished Postdoctoral Fellowships provide the opportunity for the recipients to collaborate with LANL scientists and engineers on staff-initiated research. Candidates for these awards must display extraordinary ability in scientific research and show clear and definite promise of becoming outstanding leaders in the research they pursue.

See entry 1826 for full listing.

NATIONAL ACTION COUNCIL FOR MINORITIES IN ENGINEERING, INC. (NACME)

440 Hamilton Avenue
Suite 302
White Plains, NY 10601-1813
(914) 539-4010 ext. 222
Fax: (914) 539-4032

E-MAIL ADDRESS:
scholars@nacme.org

WEB SITE ADDRESS:
www.nacme.org

TYPE:
Block grants; Endowments; Fellowships; Scholarships. NACME encourages students to consider engineering as a career and to pursue the requisite preparation in mathematics and science. It motivates high school students and channels them to engineering schools and provides scholarship support and leadership development seminars to its university scholars. The retention of minority students in engineering is a priority issue for NACME.

See entry 1000 for full listing.

THE NATIONAL GEM CONSORTIUM

1430 Duke Street
Alexandria, VA 22314
(703) 562-3646
Fax: (202) 207-2518

E-MAIL ADDRESS:
info@gemfellowship.org

WEB SITE ADDRESS:
www.gemfellowship.org

TYPE:
Internships; Matching gifts; Project/program grants; Scholarships. All-expense fellowship for graduate study (tuition and stipend) and paid summer work experience in a scientific or engineering environment.

See entry 1003 for full listing.

NATIONAL RESEARCH COUNCIL OF CANADA
1200 Montreal Road, Building M-55
Room 369A
Ottawa ON K1A 0R6 Canada
(613) 949-4655
Fax: (613) 990-1286

E-MAIL ADDRESS:
info@nrc-cnrc.gc.ca
racoordinator.hrb@nrc-cnrc.gc.ca

WEB SITE ADDRESS:
careers-carrieres.nrc-cnrc.gc.ca
www.nrc-cnrc.gc.ca

TYPE:
Assistantships. Research Associates will be appointed to the staff of the National Research Council on a term basis and will be offered salaries and benefits currently available to members of the continuing staff.

See entry 1831 for full listing.

NATIONAL SCIENCE FOUNDATION [2655]
Directorate for Engineering
Office of Assistant Director
4201 Wilson Boulevard, Room 505
Arlington, VA 22230
(703) 292-8300
(703) 292-8301
Fax: (703) 292-9013

WEB SITE ADDRESS:
www.nsf.gov

FOUNDED: 1950

AREAS OF INTEREST:
Chemical, biochemical and thermal engineering, mechanics, structures and materials engineering, electrical, communications and systems engineering, design, manufacturing and computer engineering, emerging engineering systems, cross-disciplinary research, engineering research centers, civil and environment engineering, earthquake engineering and small business innovation research.

NAME(S) OF PROGRAMS:
● **Directorate for Engineering Grants Program**

TYPE:
Assistantships; Conferences/seminars; Fellowships; Internships; Project/program grants; Research grants; Travel grants; Visiting scholars.

YEAR PROGRAM STARTED: 1984

PURPOSE:
To strengthen U.S. engineering education and research; to focus on areas relevant to national problems by supporting research across the entire range of engineering disciplines and by identifying areas where results are expected to have timely applications.

LEGAL BASIS:
Government agency.

ELIGIBILITY:
Proposals may be submitted by colleges, universities, profit and nonprofit organizations and by state, local or regional governments. Industry, state and local governments and other organizations are eligible to participate. Joint proposals are encouraged.

NSF does not make loans or grants to develop or promote any business venture, technical assistance, pilot plant efforts, research requiring security classification, the development of products for commercial marketing or market research for a particular product or invention.

GEOGRAPHIC RESTRICTIONS:
United States and its territories.

FINANCIAL DATA:
Amount of support per award: $2,000 to $5,000,000. Average $63,000.
Total amount of support: Varies.

APPLICATION INFORMATION:
Informal inquiry to the Directorate for Engineering may be made to determine whether or not a potential project would qualify for support.
Duration: One to five years. Average is approximately 30 months.
Deadline: Varies. Approximately six to eight months are required for consideration of formal proposals.

PUBLICATIONS:
Grants for Research and Education in Science and Engineering; Guide to Programs.

STAFF:
Dr. Cora Marrett, Deputy Director
Pramod Khargonekar, Assistant Director, Engineering

ADDRESS INQUIRIES TO:
Directorate for Engineering
(See address above.)

NATIONAL SOCIETY OF PROFESSIONAL SURVEYORS (NSPS) [2656]
5119 Pegasus Court
Suite Q
Frederick, MD 21704
(240) 439-4615 ext. 106
Fax: (240) 439-4952

E-MAIL ADDRESS:
curtis.sumner@nsps.us.com

WEB SITE ADDRESS:
www.nsps.us.com

AREAS OF INTEREST:
Surveying.

NAME(S) OF PROGRAMS:
● **The Schonstedt Scholarship in Surveying**

TYPE:
Scholarships. For students enrolled in four-year degree programs in surveying or in closely related degree programs such as geomatics or surveying engineering.

PURPOSE:
To encourage and recognize students committed to a career in surveying.

LEGAL BASIS:
Nonprofit educational organization.

ELIGIBILITY:
The Schonstedt Scholarship is for students enrolled in four-year degree programs in surveying or in closely related degree programs such as geomatics or surveying engineering. Preference will be given to applicants with junior or senior standing.

GEOGRAPHIC RESTRICTIONS:
United States, Canada and South America.

FINANCIAL DATA:
Amount of support per award: $1,500.
Total amount of support: $1,500 annually.

COOPERATIVE FUNDING PROGRAMS: Scholarship is made possible by a donation from the Schonstedt Instrument Company of Kearneysville, WV.

NUMBER OF APPLICANTS MOST RECENT YEAR: 15.

NUMBER OF AWARDS: 1 annually.

APPLICATION INFORMATION:
Required documentation includes:
(1) a completed application form;
(2) proof of membership in NSPS (this will be checked);
(3) a brief yet complete statement indicating educational objectives, future plans of study or research, professional activities and financial need;
(4) at least three letters of recommendation (at least two from faculty members familiar with the student's work) and;
(5) a complete original official transcript through May of the year prior to when the award will be presented (the others may be copies).

Do not send applications by fax or e-mail. Include one set of original transcripts. Mail all documents in one package. In addition, send unofficial transcripts for the fall semester when available.
Duration: One academic year.
Deadline: Varies.

ADDRESS INQUIRIES TO:
Curtis Sumner, Executive Director
(See address above.)

NATIONAL SOCIETY OF PROFESSIONAL SURVEYORS (NSPS) [2657]
5119 Pegasus Court
Suite Q
Frederick, MD 21704
(240) 439-4615 ext. 106
Fax: (240) 439-4952

E-MAIL ADDRESS:
curtis.sumner@nsps.us.com

WEB SITE ADDRESS:
www.nsps.us.com

FOUNDED: 1941

AREAS OF INTEREST:
Surveying and surveying technology.

NAME(S) OF PROGRAMS:
● **The Berntsen International Scholarship in Surveying**
● **The Berntsen International Scholarship in Surveying Technology**

TYPE:
Scholarships. Berntsen International Scholarship in Surveying: Annual scholarship award for undergraduate study in four-year degree programs in surveying or in closely related degree programs such as geomatics or surveying engineering.

Berntsen International Scholarship in Surveying Technology: For students enrolled in two-year degree programs in surveying technology.

PURPOSE:
To provide financial assistance to students pursuing two- or four-year degree programs in surveying, surveying technology or closely related fields.

LEGAL BASIS:
Nonprofit, educational organization.

ELIGIBILITY:
The Berntsen International Scholarship in Surveying: Student applicants must be enrolled in four-year degree programs in surveying or in closely related degree programs such as geomatics or surveying engineering.

The Berntsen International Scholarship in Surveying Technology: Student applicants must be enrolled in two-year degree programs in surveying technology.

GEOGRAPHIC RESTRICTIONS:
United States.

FINANCIAL DATA:
Amount of support per award: Berntsen International Scholarship in Surveying: $2,000; Berntsen International Scholarship in Surveying Technology: $1,000.

COOPERATIVE FUNDING PROGRAMS:
Scholarships are made possible by Berntsen International, Inc., of Madison, WI.

NUMBER OF APPLICANTS MOST RECENT YEAR:
15.

NUMBER OF AWARDS: 1 each annually.

APPLICATION INFORMATION:
Required documentation includes:
(1) a completed application form;
(2) proof of membership in NSPS (this will be checked);
(3) a brief yet complete statement indicating educational objectives, future plans of study or research, professional activities and financial need;
(4) at least three letters of recommendation (at least two from faculty members familiar with the student's work) and;
(5) a complete original official transcript through May of the year prior to when the award will be presented (the others may be copies).

Do not send applications by fax or e-mail. Include one set of original transcripts. Mail all documents in one package. In addition, send unofficial transcripts for the fall semester when available.

Duration: One academic year.

Deadline: Varies.

ADDRESS INQUIRIES TO:
Curtis Sumner, Executive Director
(See address above.)

NATIONAL SOCIETY OF PROFESSIONAL SURVEYORS (NSPS)   [2658]
5119 Pegasus Court
Suite 2
Frederick, MD 21704
(240) 439-4615 ext. 106
Fax: (240) 439-4952

E-MAIL ADDRESS:
curtis.sumner@nsps.us.com

WEB SITE ADDRESS:
www.nsps.us.com

FOUNDED: 1941

AREAS OF INTEREST:
Surveying.

NAME(S) OF PROGRAMS:
• **NSPS Board of Governors Scholarship**
• **The NSPS Scholarships**

TYPE:
Scholarships.

PURPOSE:
To recognize outstanding surveying students; to encourage qualified candidates to pursue an undergraduate degree in surveying.

LEGAL BASIS:
Nonprofit foundation.

ELIGIBILITY:
NSPS Board of Governors Scholarship applicants must be enrolled in studies in surveying or in closely related degree programs and entering their junior year of study in a four-year degree program of their choice (either full- or part-time) and must have maintained a minimum 3.0 grade point average.

The NSPS Scholarships are awarded to students enrolled in four-year degree programs in surveying or in closely related degree programs such as geomatics or surveying engineering. The Scholarships are intended to recognize outstanding students enrolled full-time in undergraduate surveying programs.

GEOGRAPHIC RESTRICTIONS:
United States.

FINANCIAL DATA:
Amount of support per award: $1,000.
Total amount of support: $3,000 annually.

NUMBER OF AWARDS: NSPS Board of Governors Scholarship: 1; The NSPS Scholarships: 2.

APPLICATION INFORMATION:
Applicants must submit (in the following order):
(1) a completed application form;
(2) proof of membership in NSPS (this will be checked);
(3) a brief yet complete statement indicating educational objectives, future plans of study or research, professional activities and financial need;
(4) at least three letters of recommendation (at least two from faculty members familiar with the student's work) and;
(5) a complete original official transcript through May of the year prior to when the award will be presented (the others may be copies).

Do not send applications by fax or e-mail. Include one set of original transcripts. Mail all documents in one package. In addition, send unofficial transcripts for the fall semester when available.

Duration: One academic year.

Deadline: Varies.

ADDRESS INQUIRIES TO:
Curtis Sumner, Executive Director
(See address above.)

NATIONAL SOCIETY OF PROFESSIONAL SURVEYORS (NSPS) AMERICAN ASSOCIATION FOR GEODETIC SURVEYING (AAGS)   [2659]
5119 Pegasus Court
Suite Q
Frederick, MD 21704
(240) 439-4615 ext. 106
Fax: (240) 439-4952

E-MAIL ADDRESS:
curtis.sumner@nsps.us.com

WEB SITE ADDRESS:
www.aagsmo.org

FOUNDED: 1941

AREAS OF INTEREST:
Geodetic surveying.

NAME(S) OF PROGRAMS:
• **American Association for Geodetic Surveying Graduate Fellowship Award**

TYPE:
Fellowships. Annual fellowship award to support graduate study in a program with a significant focus on geodetic surveying or geodesy at a school of the recipient's choice.

PURPOSE:
To recognize outstanding graduate students committed to the pursuit of knowledge in geodetic surveying, thus enhancing the ability of the profession to better serve the needs of society.

LEGAL BASIS:
Nonprofit educational organization.

ELIGIBILITY:
Nominees must be members of the National Society of Professional Surveyors and should be enrolled in or accepted by a graduate program with a significant focus on geodetic surveying or geodesy. Preference will be given to applicants having at least two years of employment experience in the surveying profession.

GEOGRAPHIC RESTRICTIONS:
United States, Canada and South America.

FINANCIAL DATA:
Amount of support per award: $2,000 and an appropriate citation to be presented at the annual meeting.

Total amount of support: $2,000 annually.

COOPERATIVE FUNDING PROGRAMS: Provided by the American Association for Geodetic Surveying and administered by NSPS Foundation.

NUMBER OF AWARDS: 1 annually.

APPLICATION INFORMATION:
Required documentation includes:
(1) a completed application form;
(2) proof of membership in NSPS (this will be checked);
(3) a brief yet complete statement indicating educational objectives, future plans of study or research, professional activities and financial need;
(4) at least three letters of recommendation (at least two from faculty members familiar with the student's work) and;
(5) a complete original official transcript through May of the year prior to when the award will be presented (the others may be copies).

Do not send applications by fax or e-mail. Include one set of original transcripts. Mail all documents in one package. In addition, send unofficial transcripts for the fall semester when available.

Duration: One academic year.

Deadline: Varies.

PUBLICATIONS:
Surveying and Land Information Science Journal.

ADDRESS INQUIRIES TO:
Curtis Sumner, Executive Director
(See address above.)

NATIONAL SOCIETY OF PROFESSIONAL SURVEYORS (NSPS) AMERICAN ASSOCIATION FOR GEODETIC SURVEYING (AAGS) [2660]

5119 Pegasus Court
Suite Q
Frederick, MD 21704
(240) 439-4615 ext. 106
Fax: (240) 439-4952

E-MAIL ADDRESS:
curtis.sumner@nsps.us.com

WEB SITE ADDRESS:
www.aagsmo.org

AREAS OF INTEREST:
Geodetic surveying.

NAME(S) OF PROGRAMS:
● **AAGS Joseph F. Dracup Scholarship Award**

TYPE:
Scholarships. The award is intended for students enrolled in four-year degree programs in surveying or in closely related degree programs.

PURPOSE:
To promote study in the surveying and mapping professions.

LEGAL BASIS:
Nonprofit educational organization.

ELIGIBILITY:
Nominees must be members of the National Society of Professional Surveyors. Student applicants must be enrolled in four-year degree programs in surveying or in closely related degree programs such as geomatics or surveying engineering. Preference will be given to applicants from programs with a significant focus on geodetic surveying.

GEOGRAPHIC RESTRICTIONS:
United States, Canada and South America.

FINANCIAL DATA:
Amount of support per award: $2,000 and an appropriate citation to be presented at the annual meeting.
Total amount of support: $2,000 annually.

COOPERATIVE FUNDING PROGRAMS: Provided by the American Association for Geodetic Surveying and administered by NSPS.

NUMBER OF APPLICANTS MOST RECENT YEAR:
15.

NUMBER OF AWARDS: 1 annually.

APPLICATION INFORMATION:
Required documentation includes:
(1) a completed application form;
(2) proof of membership in NSPS (this will be checked);
(3) a brief yet complete statement indicating educational objectives, future plans of study or research, professional activities and financial need;
(4) at least three letters of recommendation (at least two from faculty members familiar with the student's work) and;
(5) a complete original official transcript through May of the year prior to when the award will be presented (the others may be copies).

Do not send applications by fax or e-mail. Include one set of original transcripts. Mail all documents in one package. In addition, send unofficial transcripts for the fall semester when available.

Duration: One academic year.

PUBLICATIONS:
Surveying and Land Information Science Journal.

ADDRESS INQUIRIES TO:
Curtis Sumner, Executive Director
(See address above.)

OAK RIDGE INSTITUTE FOR SCIENCE AND EDUCATION [2661]

P.O. Box 117
Oak Ridge, TN 37831-0117
(865) 574-7798
Fax: (865) 576-1609

E-MAIL ADDRESS:
ruth.keller@orau.org
science.education@orau.org

WEB SITE ADDRESS:
orise.orau.gov/sep/catalog.htm
see.orau.org

FOUNDED: 1946

AREAS OF INTEREST:
Energy-related disciplines and technologies.

NAME(S) OF PROGRAMS:
● **Professional Internship Program**

TYPE:
Internships. Full- and part-time appointments are available for a period of three to 12 months. Assignments afford students the opportunity to apply and practice theories and methods learned in the classroom. Program participants are assigned individual projects that relate to their academic majors, career goals, and the ongoing research and development missions of the facility. They make recommendations or reports regarding their findings or solutions to a staff member of the facility who provides guidance and advice, serves as their research advisor, and reviews their findings.

YEAR PROGRAM STARTED: 1950

PURPOSE:
To provide hands-on research training for students seeking Associate, Baccalaureate, or graduate degrees in appropriate disciplines relating to science and engineering education, training and management systems, energy and environment systems.

LEGAL BASIS:
Government agency.

ELIGIBILITY:
Applicants must be U.S. citizens or permanent residents, at least 18 years of age, and have a cumulative grade point average of 2.5 or higher. Appointments are tenable at Department of Energy national laboratories, as well as other federal agencies with research facilities located across the country.

GEOGRAPHIC RESTRICTIONS:
United States.

FINANCIAL DATA:
Amount of support per award: $384 to $850 per week.
Total amount of support: Varies.

NUMBER OF APPLICANTS MOST RECENT YEAR:
350.

NUMBER OF AWARDS: 102.

APPLICATION INFORMATION:
Contact ORISE for general information and application guidelines.
Duration: Three to 18 months continuously. Renewals possible.

Deadline: February 15, June 1 and October 1.

PUBLICATIONS:
Program announcement; ORISE Resource Guide.

ADDRESS INQUIRIES TO:
Craig Layman
Science and Engineering Education, MS 36
(See address above.)

PRECAST/PRESTRESSED CONCRETE INSTITUTE [2662]

200 West Adams Street
Suite 2100
Chicago, IL 60606
(312) 786-0300
Fax: (312) 621-1114

E-MAIL ADDRESS:
rbecker@pci.org

WEB SITE ADDRESS:
www.pci.org

AREAS OF INTEREST:
Research, design and construction of buildings, bridges and other structures using precast/prestressed concrete.

NAME(S) OF PROGRAMS:
● **Daniel P. Jenny Research Fellowships**

TYPE:
Fellowships.

YEAR PROGRAM STARTED: 1972

PURPOSE:
To support graduate students in civil engineering interested in research related to precast and prestressed concrete.

LEGAL BASIS:
Nonprofit trade association.

ELIGIBILITY:
Student applicants must be graduate students in civil engineering interested in research related to precast/prestressed concrete and enrolled in a U.S., Canadian or Mexican university. Religious organizations are ineligible.

GEOGRAPHIC RESTRICTIONS:
United States, Canada and Mexico.

FINANCIAL DATA:
Amount of support per award: $20,000.

NUMBER OF AWARDS: Up to 5.

APPLICATION INFORMATION:
Contact the Institute for application.
Duration: One to two years.
Deadline: Proposals are solicited in December. Deadline generally mid-February. Decision by end of April, with announcement in May for following academic year.

ADDRESS INQUIRIES TO:
Roger Becker, Managing Director
Research and Development
(See address above.)

THE SOCIETY OF NAVAL ARCHITECTS AND MARINE ENGINEERS [2663]

99 Canal Center Plaza, Suite 310
Alexandria, VA 22314
(703) 997-6709
Fax: (703) 997-6702

E-MAIL ADDRESS:
bgreer@sname.org

WEB SITE ADDRESS:
www.sname.org

FOUNDED: 1893

AREAS OF INTEREST:
Naval architecture, marine engineering, ocean engineering or marine industry-related fields.

NAME(S) OF PROGRAMS:
- **Graduate Scholarships**
- **Undergraduate Scholarships**

TYPE:
Scholarships. The Society annually awards both graduate and undergraduate scholarships to encourage study in naval architecture, marine engineering, ocean engineering or marine industry-related fields.

Graduate Scholarships are made for one year of study leading to a Master's in naval architecture, marine engineering, ocean engineering or in fields directly related to the marine industry.

Undergraduate Scholarships are administered by schools offering undergraduate programs on grants given to the schools.

YEAR PROGRAM STARTED: 1933

PURPOSE:
To encourage young men and women to enter the fields of naval architecture, marine engineering, ocean engineering or marine industry-related fields as a career by aiding them to pursue courses of study in these specialties and to provide the incentive and attractions for such a career.

LEGAL BASIS:
Technical Society.

ELIGIBILITY:
Society scholarships are based soley on merit, not financial need.

Graduate Scholarships: Open to U.S., Canadian, or international applicants. Awards are made for one year of study leading to a Master's degree in naval architecture, marine engineering, ocean engineering or in fields directly related to the marine industry. Society membership is required one year prior to application submission deadline. Applicants must not receive their Master's prior to October 1 of the year in which they are applying for their scholarship. Graduate scholarships are awarded to an individual only once. Non-U.S. or Canadian citizens must plan to study in U.S. or Canadian schools. Generally, applicants are not expected to receive their Master's Degree prior to April 15 of the academic year in which graduate study is undertaken.

Undergraduate Scholarships: Open to citizens of the U.S. and Canada, or study must be toward a degree in naval architecture, marine engineering or ocean engineering. The applicant must be entering his or her junior or senior year and must be a member in the Society for at least four months prior to the application submittal deadline. Scholarship awardees may repeat as an undergraduate recipient and subsequently apply for a graduate scholarship.

FINANCIAL DATA:
Amount of support per award: Graduate Scholarships: Up to $12,000 per year; Undergraduate Scholarships: Varies.

Total amount of support: Varies.

NUMBER OF AWARDS: Graduate Scholarships: At least 8 annually.

APPLICATION INFORMATION:
Graduate Scholarships: Application may be downloaded from the Society web site or may be obtained by written request to the attention of the Chairperson, Scholarships Committee, at the address above. Applicants are required to provide GRE scores regardless of graduate school admission requirements. Application and supporting data are sent to the Scholarships Committee.

Undergraduate Scholarships: Requests are made directly to schools. The schools present their nominations in biographical form for each applicant and include a statement from the student indicating his or her career goals and why he or she is interested in the marine field. Selection of the recipients is made by the colleges in accordance with their established procedures.

Duration: Graduate Scholarships: One year. No renewals. Undergraduate Scholarships: One year. Awardee may repeat as an undergraduate recipient and subsequently apply for a Graduate Scholarship.

Deadline: Graduate Scholarships: Application prior to February 1; supporting data by February 15. Graduate Scholarships selected in April.

Undergraduate Scholarships: Application prior to June 1; supporting data by June 15. Nominations are presented to the Society's Scholarships Committee annually for approval in July.

SCHOLARSHIP COMMITTEE:
Dr. Walter MacLean, Chairman

ADDRESS INQUIRIES TO:
Brittany Greer, Scholarships Coordinator
(See address above.)

SOCIETY OF WOMEN ENGINEERS
203 North La Salle Street
Suite 1675
Chicago, IL 60601
(312) 596-5223
Fax: (312) 596-5252

E-MAIL ADDRESS:
scholarships@swe.org

WEB SITE ADDRESS:
www.swe.org/scholarships

TYPE:
Awards/prizes; Conferences/seminars; Scholarships. Support for undergraduate and graduate engineering studies including women who have been out of the engineering job market for a minimum of two years and who will return to school for an engineering program.

See entry 1096 for full listing.

THE TAU BETA PI ASSOCIATION, INC.   [2664]
508 Dougherty Engineering Building
1512 Middle Drive
Knoxville, TN 37996-2215
(865) 546-4578
Fax: (865) 546-4579

E-MAIL ADDRESS:
tbp@tbp.org

WEB SITE ADDRESS:
www.tbp.org

FOUNDED: 1885

AREAS OF INTEREST:
Engineering.

NAME(S) OF PROGRAMS:
- **Raymond A. and Ina C. Best Fellowship for MBA**
- **Graduate Fellowship in Engineering**
- **Tau Beta Pi Undergraduate Scholarship**

TYPE:
Fellowships; Scholarships. The Fellowship awards are for one academic year of study in engineering for qualified graduate students.

The scholarships are awarded for senior year of full-time undergraduate study.

YEAR PROGRAM STARTED: 1928

PURPOSE:
To support the advancement of engineering education and the profession.

LEGAL BASIS:
Corporation.

ELIGIBILITY:
Candidate must be a member of Tau Beta Pi.

FINANCIAL DATA:
Fellows having other graduate study financial aid that is in excess of tuition may be awarded Tau Beta Pi Fellowships without stipend. Persons supported by a salary from industry, government or other sources may not be entitled to the stipend.

Amount of support per award: Fellowships: $50,000; Scholarships: $2,000.

Total amount of support: $450,000 to $700,000 per year.

NUMBER OF APPLICANTS MOST RECENT YEAR: 593.

NUMBER OF AWARDS: 40 fellowships and 200 scholarships for the year 2012-13.

APPLICATION INFORMATION:
Application forms are available November 1 for the following academic year.

Duration: One academic year. Fellowships and scholarships are not renewable.

Deadline: Fellowships: February 1 postmark. Scholarships: April 1 postmark.

PUBLICATIONS:
The Bent of Tau Beta Pi, quarterly magazine.

IRS IDENTIFICATION NUMBER: 62-0479545

OFFICERS:
Curtis D. Gomulinski, Executive Director
D. Stephen Pierre, P.E., Director of Fellowships

EXECUTIVE COUNCIL:
J.P. Blackford, President
Solange C. Dao, Vice President
Susan Holl, Councillor
George Morales, Councillor
Alan Passman, Councillor
Norman Pih, Councillor

ADDRESS INQUIRIES TO:
Curtis D. Gomulinski, Executive Director
(See address above.)

U.S. DEPARTMENT OF ENERGY   [2665]
3610 Collins Ferry Road
P.O. Box 880
Morgantown, WV 26507-0880
(412) 386-7406

E-MAIL ADDRESS:
vito.cedro@netl.doe.gov

WEB SITE ADDRESS:
www.grants.gov

FOUNDED: 1979

AREAS OF INTEREST:
Materials development to support direct power extraction and low-cost distributed sensing of fossil energy power systems.

NAME(S) OF PROGRAMS:
• **University Coal Research Program**

TYPE:
Assistantships; Project/program grants; Research grants.

YEAR PROGRAM STARTED: 1980

PURPOSE:
To foster the highest quality fundamental research on coal at the university level; to ensure the continued training of researchers in the areas of fossil energy.

LEGAL BASIS:
Government agency.

ELIGIBILITY:
Open to U.S. colleges and universities only.

GEOGRAPHIC RESTRICTIONS:
United States.

FINANCIAL DATA:
Amount of support per award: Maximum DOE funding for grant applications submitted by one or two universities is up to $400,000 for a 36-month performance period.
Total amount of support: Approximately $2,100,000 for the year 2014.
Matching fund requirements: No matching fund requirements; however, cost-sharing and/or industrial collaboration is encouraged.

APPLICATION INFORMATION:
Contact the U.S. Department of Energy.
Duration: Up to 36 months. No renewals.
Deadline: Early February.

ADDRESS INQUIRIES TO:
Vito Cedro, Program Manager
University Coal Research Program
U.S. Department of Energy
626 Cochrans Mill Road
P.O. Box 10940
Pittsburgh, PA 15236

U.S. SOCIETY ON DAMS   [2666]
1616 17th Street, Suite 483
Denver, CO 80202
(303) 628-5430
Fax: (303) 628-5431

E-MAIL ADDRESS:
stephens@ussdams.org

WEB SITE ADDRESS:
www.ussdams.org

AREAS OF INTEREST:
Dams and water resources.

NAME(S) OF PROGRAMS:
• **USSD Scholarship**

TYPE:
Scholarships.

PURPOSE:
To advance the technology of dam engineering, construction, operation, maintenance and dam safety; to foster socially and environmentally responsible water resources projects; to promote awareness of the role of dams in the beneficial and sustainable development of the nation's water resources.

ELIGIBILITY:
Open to U.S. college or university graduate students whose research studies have a potential for developing practical solutions to design and construction problems. Applicants must be U.S. citizens enrolled in U.S. academic institutions which have programs related to dams.

GEOGRAPHIC RESTRICTIONS:
United States.

FINANCIAL DATA:
Amount of support per award: $10,000; two finalists receive $1,000.
Total amount of support: $12,000 for the year 2011.

APPLICATION INFORMATION:
Applicants must submit a proposal describing a specific research topic. The proposed research work should be original and innovative. The proposed research can be part of an ongoing research project. Applicants are encouraged to submit proposals in topics that are related to their graduate research work. The application package must include the application form, a description of the proposed research work, an official set of academic transcripts and two letters of recommendation, one of which must be from the applicant's academic advisor.

ADDRESS INQUIRIES TO:
Dr. Enrique E. Matheu
U.S. Department of Homeland Security
3700 Massachusetts Avenue, N.W.
Washington, DC 20016
Tel: (703) 235-5638
E-mail: enrique.matheu@dhs.gov

THE UNIVERSITY OF SYDNEY   [2667]
Scholarships Office
Level 5, Jane Foss Russell Building G02
The University of Sydney N.S.W. 2006
Australia
(02) 8627 8112
Fax: (02) 8627 8485

E-MAIL ADDRESS:
research.training@sydney.edu.au

WEB SITE ADDRESS:
www.sydney.edu.au/scholarships/research

FOUNDED: 1850

AREAS OF INTEREST:
Civil and mining engineering, electrical engineering, mechanical and mechatronic engineering.

NAME(S) OF PROGRAMS:
• **Civil and Mining Engineering Foundation Scholarship**
• **William John Padbury Scholarship**
• **Norman I. Price Scholarship in Electrical Engineering**
• **Peter Nicol Russell Postgraduate Scholarship in Mechanical and Mechatronic Engineering**
• **William Girling Watson Travelling Scholarship**

TYPE:
Scholarships. Awarded for research leading to a higher degree. Tenable at the University of Sydney.

PURPOSE:
To promote and encourage research and study in various fields of engineering.

LEGAL BASIS:
University.

ELIGIBILITY:
Open to graduates of the University of Sydney or to any other person eligible for admission to full-time candidature for a higher degree by research in the Faculty of Engineering and Information Technologies at the University of Sydney.

FINANCIAL DATA:
This scholarship does not cover tuition fees payable by international students.
Amount of support per award: Varies.

NUMBER OF AWARDS: 1 offered as vacancy occurs.

APPLICATION INFORMATION:
Contact the University.
Duration: One year. May be renewed for a second year in the case of a Master's degree, and for a third year for a Ph.D.

ADDRESS INQUIRIES TO:
Faculty of Engineering and Information Technologies
The University of Sydney
N.S.W. 2006 Australia
Tel: (02) 9351 8719
Fax: (02) 9351 7082
E-mail: engineering.postgraduate@sydney.edu.au

THE UNIVERSITY OF SYDNEY
Scholarships Office
Level 5, Jane Foss Russell Building G02
The University of Sydney N.S.W. 2006
Australia
(02) 8627 8112
Fax: (02) 8627 8485

E-MAIL ADDRESS:
research.training@sydney.edu.au

WEB SITE ADDRESS:
www.sydney.edu.au/scholarships/research

TYPE:
Scholarships. Awarded for research leading to a higher degree. Tenable at the University of Sydney.

See entry 2131 for full listing.

Home economics and nutrition

THE ACADEMY OF NUTRITION AND DIETETIC FOUNDATION   [2668]
120 South Riverside Plaza, 20th Floor
Chicago, IL 60606
(312) 899-4773
Fax: (312) 899-4796

WEB SITE ADDRESS:
www.eatright.org/foundation

FOUNDED: 1966

AREAS OF INTEREST:
Food, nutrition, dietetics and food service management.

TYPE:
Awards/prizes; Fellowships; Grants-in-aid; Research grants; Scholarships.

YEAR PROGRAM STARTED: 1966

PURPOSE:
To further progress in the educational and scientific advancement of dietetics.

LEGAL BASIS:
Public, not-for-profit foundation.

ELIGIBILITY:
Applicant must be a member of the Academy to qualify for its scholarships and (in general) for its awards as well.

GEOGRAPHIC RESTRICTIONS:
Primarily United States.

FINANCIAL DATA:
Amount of support per award: Scholarships: $500 to $10,000.

Total amount of support: Over $942,000.

COOPERATIVE FUNDING PROGRAMS:
Collaborative Consumer Research Program.

NUMBER OF APPLICANTS MOST RECENT YEAR:
1,000.

NUMBER OF AWARDS: 200.

APPLICATION INFORMATION:
One common application form is used for all scholarships. Scholarship applications are available online to Academy members.

Awards applications are available online.
Deadline: Scholarships: February 15. Announcement in June; Awards and Fellowships: February 1; Grants: April 1.

PUBLICATIONS:
Annual report.

IRS IDENTIFICATION NUMBER: 36-6150906

ADDRESS INQUIRIES TO:
Martha Ontizeros
(See telephone number above.)

AMERICAN ASSOCIATION OF FAMILY AND CONSUMER SCIENCES (AAFCS)

400 North Columbus Street
Suite 202
Alexandria, VA 22314-2752
(703) 706-4600
(800) 424-8080
Fax: (703) 706-4663

E-MAIL ADDRESS:
rayona@aafcs.org

WEB SITE ADDRESS:
www.aafcs.org/awards/index.asp

TYPE:
Fellowships. AAFCS awards fellowships to individuals who have exhibited the potential to make contributions to the family and consumer sciences profession.

See entry 956 for full listing.

AMERICAN ASSOCIATION OF FAMILY AND CONSUMER SCIENCES (AAFCS)   [2669]

400 North Columbus Street
Suite 202
Alexandria, VA 22314-2752
(703) 706-4600
(800) 424-8080
Fax: (703) 706-4663

E-MAIL ADDRESS:
awards@aafcs.org

WEB SITE ADDRESS:
www.aafcs.org

FOUNDED: 1909

AREAS OF INTEREST:
Family and consumer sciences.

NAME(S) OF PROGRAMS:
● **National Teacher of the Year Award**

TYPE:
Awards/prizes. Recognizes exemplary teachers who utilize cutting-edge methods, techniques and activities to provide the stimulus for and give visibility to family and consumer sciences elementary and secondary education.

YEAR PROGRAM STARTED: 1972

PURPOSE:
To provide leadership and support for professionals whose work assists individuals, families and communities in making informed decisions about their well-being, relationships and resources to achieve optimal quality of life.

LEGAL BASIS:
501(c)(3) nonprofit charity.

ELIGIBILITY:
National-level competitors for this award must have been chosen as an Affiliate Teacher of the Year (through competitions run at the affiliate level); each affiliate may enter no more than one Affiliate Teacher of the Year into the national competition per year and the nomination must be submitted by the Affiliate President. An Affiliate Teacher of the Year who is eligible for the National Teacher of the Year Award:
(1) is employed as a full-time family and consumer sciences teacher of grades kindergarten through 12 at the time the nomination is submitted;
(2) is an AAFCS member at the time of nomination and for at least three consecutive years prior to nomination and;
(3) created and runs a family and consumer sciences program that focuses on one of the following five program areas: (a) career awareness/job skill training; (b) consumer education/family finance; (c) creative dimensions/alternative program designs; (d) family life/personal and social development and; (e) nutrition education/diet and health.

Members of the AAFCS Board of Directors, Awards and Recognition Committee, and Development Committee are not eligible for nomination during their terms of office. AAFCS staff members are not eligible for nomination during their periods of employment with the Association.

Award recipient must attend the AAFCS Annual Conference & Expo for presentation and recognition.

FINANCIAL DATA:
Amount of support per award: A commemorative plaque and a $2,500 award, plus up to $1,000 of support for one year of AAFCS membership and participation in the AAFCS Annual Conference & Expo.

NUMBER OF AWARDS: Up to 3 merit finalists, from whom 1 National Teacher of the Year is selected.

APPLICATION INFORMATION:
Detailed guidelines and instructions are available from the Association.

ADDRESS INQUIRIES TO:
See e-mail address above.

CENTER FOR SCIENCE IN THE PUBLIC INTEREST   [2670]

1220 L Street, N.W.
Suite 300
Washington, DC 20005
(202) 332-9110
Fax: (202) 265-4954

E-MAIL ADDRESS:
coday@cspinet.org

WEB SITE ADDRESS:
www.cspinet.org

FOUNDED: 1971

AREAS OF INTEREST:
Consumer advocacy on nutrition, diet and health, and food safety.

NAME(S) OF PROGRAMS:
● **Public Interest Internships**

TYPE:
Internships. Stipends allow interns to work on specific projects under the direction of a Project Director or the Executive Director.

YEAR PROGRAM STARTED: 1978

PURPOSE:
To provide interns with direct, practical experience; to provide the Center with extra assistance.

LEGAL BASIS:
501(c)(3).

ELIGIBILITY:
Students in undergraduate, graduate, law and medical schools are eligible to apply. Requirements vary depending on specific internship applied for.

Must work out of the Washington, DC office.

FINANCIAL DATA:
Amount of support per award: Undergraduate interns are paid an hourly wage of $8.25 per hour and graduate students $9.25 per hour.
Total amount of support: Varies.

NUMBER OF APPLICANTS MOST RECENT YEAR:
250.

NUMBER OF AWARDS: Varies.

APPLICATION INFORMATION:
Cover letter should indicate preferred dates. Application materials should include the following:
(1) cover letter indicating issues of interest, future plans, and the dates that applicant is available;
(2) resume (experience with advocacy groups is not required, but would be advantageous);
(3) writing sample (a popularly written piece is preferred over a technical report);
(4) two letters of recommendation from instructors or employers that address applicant's academic/work ability and character and;
(5) official transcript of courses with grades.
Duration: 10 weeks. Renewal possible.
Deadline: Applicants are advised to follow the application guidelines and apply as soon as possible. Applications are taken on a rolling basis until all positions have been filled.

PUBLICATIONS:
Status report; general brochure; publications list; *Nutrition Action Healthletter.*

OFFICERS:
Michael F. Jacobson, Ph.D., Chief Executive Officer

ADDRESS INQUIRIES TO:
Colleen O'Day, Human Resources Director
(See address above.)

DAIRY RESEARCH INSTITUTE - NATIONAL DAIRY COUNCIL [2671]

10255 West Higgins Road
Suite 900
Rosemont, IL 60018-5616
(847) 803-2000
Fax: (847) 803-2077

E-MAIL ADDRESS:
chris.cifelli@rosedmi.com

WEB SITE ADDRESS:
www.driresearchsubmission.com

FOUNDED: 1915

AREAS OF INTEREST:
Independent research to aid in the ongoing discovery of information about dairy foods' important role in a healthy lifestyle. This research provides insights to industry for new dairy product innovation.

NAME(S) OF PROGRAMS:
• **Nutrition Research Program**

TYPE:
Research contracts. The National Dairy Council is the nutrition research, education and communications arm of Dairy Management Inc. On behalf of U.S. dairy farmers, the National Dairy Council provides science-based nutrition information to, and in collaboration with, a variety of stakeholders committed to fostering a healthier society, including health professionals, educators, school nutrition directors, academia, industry, consumers and media. The National Dairy Council comprises a staff of nutrition science researchers, registered dietitians and communications experts dedicated to educating the public on the health benefits of consuming milk and milk products throughout a person's lifespan.

YEAR PROGRAM STARTED: 1941

PURPOSE:
To disseminate nutrition programs, materials and research to support government recommendations for improved nutrition for Americans, including consumption of at least three servings of nutrient-rich low-fat or fat-free milk and milk products a day, in partnership with its network of state and regional dairy councils.

LEGAL BASIS:
Nonprofit educational-scientific institution under IRS 501(c)(3).

ELIGIBILITY:
Qualified investigators associated with accredited institutions of higher learning are eligible for support. Applicants must hold a Ph.D., M.D., D.D.S., D.V.M. or other degree, with experience demonstrating ability to conduct the proposed research.

Funds are not available for alteration of facilities or purchase of permanent equipment.

FINANCIAL DATA:
Amount of support per award: Administered research contracts vary in amount, depending upon the needs and nature of the request.
Total amount of support: Varies.

COOPERATIVE FUNDING PROGRAMS: If research interests of additional organizations coincide, cooperative projects are preferred to enhance efficiency of funds utilized and to benefit the researcher through a broader base of support.

NUMBER OF APPLICANTS MOST RECENT YEAR:
75 preproposals; approximately 25 selected for full proposal submission.

APPLICATION INFORMATION:
The National Dairy Council invites submission of two-page preproposals in the beginning of each calendar year, typically early February. Applications which meet the needs of the research program, which are stated in the guidelines for preproposal submission, will be reviewed. Approximately two to three weeks following the submission deadline, all applicants will receive notice of the outcome of this screening process. Applicants whose preproposals generated interest will receive further information and materials for submission of a detailed full research application to the program. Full proposals will be due approximately six to eight weeks later. All full proposals will be peer-reviewed for scientific merit by the Nutrition Research Scientific Advisory Committee, which is comprised of expert scientists from academia, government and industry. For information on the research program and research topics of interest in the next solicitation, please send a letter requesting the information and a self-addressed label to the address above or contact the NDC research office.
Duration: Projects supported on a yearly basis for up to three years.
Deadline: Preproposal: Typically first half of the year. Full proposal: Three months after preproposal deadline.

PUBLICATIONS:
Guidelines for application and administration.

ADMINISTRATION:
Christopher J. Cifelli, Ph.D., Director, Nutrition Research

ADDRESS INQUIRIES TO:
Christopher J. Cifelli, Ph.D.
Director, Nutrition Research
(See address above.)

DIETITIANS OF CANADA [2672]

480 University Avenue
Suite 604
Toronto ON M5G 1V2 Canada
(416) 596-0857
Fax: (416) 596-0603

E-MAIL ADDRESS:
isla.horvath@cfdr.ca

WEB SITE ADDRESS:
www.dietitians.ca

FOUNDED: 1935

AREAS OF INTEREST:
Dietetics and nutrition.

NAME(S) OF PROGRAMS:
• **Graduate Awards in Dietetics**
• **Research Grants in Dietetics**
• **Undergraduate Awards in Dietetics**

TYPE:
Awards/prizes; Research grants.

YEAR PROGRAM STARTED: 1966

PURPOSE:
To encourage members in graduate studies; to promote and support dietetic research.

LEGAL BASIS:
Incorporated under Canada Corporations Act.

ELIGIBILITY:
For Graduate Awards, applicants must be DC members registered in a graduate program in dietetics.

For the Research Awards, applicants must be practicing dietitians who are delivering direct or indirect client/patient public care or service. One of the investigators must be a DC member.

For Undergraduate Awards, applicants must be enrolled in final year of Bachelor's degree program and student member of DC.

GEOGRAPHIC RESTRICTIONS:
Canada.

FINANCIAL DATA:
Amount of support per award: Research Grants: $5,000 maximum small grants; $5,000 to $20,000 large grants. Undergraduate and Graduate Awards: $2,500.
Total amount of support: Varies.

APPLICATION INFORMATION:
Completed application form, statement of purpose for graduate study, academic transcript, and four recommendations are required.
Duration: One year. Large grants: One to two years.
Deadline: Research Grant Proposals: Letter of Intent, mid-September; Full Proposal, March 1. Student Awards: February 1; announcement in July.

PUBLICATIONS:
Canadian Journal of Dietetic Practice and Research (Revue Canadienne de la Pratique et de la Recherche en Dietetique).

ADDRESS INQUIRIES TO:
CFDR Research Grants:
E-mail: info@cfdr.ca

Student Awards:
E-mail:centralinfo@dietitians.ca

FOOD AND DRUG LAW INSTITUTE (FDLI)

1155 15th Street, N.W., Suite 800
Washington, DC 20005-2706
(202) 371-1420
Fax: (202) 371-0649

E-MAIL ADDRESS:
comments@fdli.org

WEB SITE ADDRESS:
www.fdli.org/resources/academics/h-thomas-austern-memorial-writing-competition

TYPE:
Awards/prizes. The subject matter of the competition is an in-depth analysis of a current issue relevant to the food and drug field, including a relevant case law, legislative history and other authorities, particularly where the U.S. Food and Drug Administration is involved.

There are two categories of prizes:
(1) papers of 40 pages or less (including appendices and footnotes) and;
(2) papers of more than 40 pages, but less than 101 pages.

See entry 1975 for full listing.

ILLINOIS RESTAURANT ASSOCIATION EDUCATIONAL FOUNDATION

33 West Monroe, Suite 250
Chicago, IL 60603
(312) 787-4000
Fax: (312) 845-1956

WEB SITE ADDRESS:
www.illinoisrestaurants.org

TYPE:
Scholarships.

See entry 1698 for full listing.

INTERNATIONAL ASSOCIATION FOR FOOD PROTECTION [2673]

6200 Aurora Avenue
Suite 200W
Des Moines, IA 50322
(515) 276-3344
(800) 369-6337
Fax: (515) 276-8655

E-MAIL ADDRESS:
info@foodprotection.org

WEB SITE ADDRESS:
www.foodprotection.org

FOUNDED: 1911

AREAS OF INTEREST:
Food science and research.

NAME(S) OF PROGRAMS:
- **Harold Barnum Industry Award**
- **Food Safety Innovation Award**
- **Harry Haverland Citation Award**
- **International Service Award**
- **Elmer Marth Educator Award**
- **Sanitarian Award**
- **State or Local Health or State Agricultural Department Employees Travel Award**
- **Student Travel Scholarship Award**
- **Maurice Weber Laboratorian Award**

TYPE:
Awards/prizes; Travel grants. Cash awards and plaques to outstanding members.

YEAR PROGRAM STARTED: 1973

PURPOSE:
To recognize and reward outstanding member contributions in the specified award area.

LEGAL BASIS:
Nonprofit, incorporated professional association.

ELIGIBILITY:
Nominees must be members of the International Association for Food Protection.

FINANCIAL DATA:
Amount of support per award: $1,500 to $2,500 and plaque or travel expense paid.

NUMBER OF AWARDS: 1 of each award annually.

IRS IDENTIFICATION NUMBER: 35-0894354

OFFICERS:
Don Schaffner, President
Donald Zink, President-Elect
Alejandro Mazzotta, Vice President
Linda Harris, Secretary

ADDRESS INQUIRIES TO:
David W. Tharp, Executive Director
(See address above.)

KAPPA OMICRON NU HONOR SOCIETY [2674]

4990 Northwind Drive
Suite 140
East Lansing, MI 48823-5031
(517) 351-8335
Fax: (517) 351-8336

E-MAIL ADDRESS:
dmitstifer@kon.org

WEB SITE ADDRESS:
www.kon.org

FOUNDED: 1912

AREAS OF INTEREST:
Home economics, family and consumer sciences, and human sciences.

NAME(S) OF PROGRAMS:
- **Marjorie M. Brown Dissertation Fellowship**
- **Ruth E. Hawthorne Research Grant**
- **Kappa Omicron Phi/Hettie Margaret Anthony Fellowship**
- **LeaderShape Institute Award**
- **Eileen C. Maddex Fellowship**
- **National Alumni Chapter Fellowship**
- **National Alumni Chapter Grant**
- **National Scholar Program**
- **New Initiatives Grant**
- **Omicron Nu Master's Fellowship**
- **Omicron Nu Research Fellowship**
- **Betty Jeanne Root Fellowship**
- **Undergraduate Research**

TYPE:
Fellowships; Project/program grants; Research grants; Scholarships. Awarded to members for graduate or postgraduate study and research in human sciences or one of its specializations at colleges or universities with strong research programs and supporting disciplines for the chosen major or topic.

YEAR PROGRAM STARTED: 1969

PURPOSE:
To promote research and graduate study in human sciences by recognizing and encouraging scholastic excellence.

LEGAL BASIS:
Nonprofit corporation, 501(c)(3) status.

ELIGIBILITY:
Applicant must be a member of Kappa Omicron Nu who has demonstrated scholarship, research and leadership potential.

FINANCIAL DATA:
Amount of support per award: $150 to $10,000 per year.
Total amount of support: $40,000 for the year 2013.

NUMBER OF APPLICANTS MOST RECENT YEAR:
6.

NUMBER OF AWARDS: Doctoral Fellowships: 4; Master's Fellowships: 3; Scholar Grants: 50; Marjorie M. Brown Dissertation Fellowship, Ruth E. Hawthorne Research Grant, Leadership Award, Kappa Omicron Phi/Hettie Margaret Anthony Fellowship, National Alumni Chapter Grant, New Initiatives Grant and Betty Jeanne Root Fellowship: 1 per award or fellowship.

APPLICATION INFORMATION:
Contact the Society.
Duration: One academic year. Nonrenewable.
Deadline: Research and Project Grants: February 15; announcement April 15. Doctoral Fellowships: January 15; announcement April 1. Master's Fellowships: April 1; announcement May 15.

PUBLICATIONS:
Brochure.

IRS IDENTIFICATION NUMBER: 38-1245233

BOARD OF DIRECTORS:
Kathleen O'Rourke, Chairperson
Kendra Brandes, First Vice Chairperson
Bridgett Clinton, Second Vice Chairperson
Joni Roh, Chairperson-Elect
Bonita Manson, Secretary

EXECUTIVE DIRECTOR:
Dr. Dorothy I. Mitstifer

ADDRESS INQUIRIES TO:
Dr. Dorothy I. Mitstifer, Executive Director
(See address above.)

NATIONAL CATTLEMAN'S BEEF ASSOCIATION [2675]

9110 East Nichols Avenue
Centennial, CO 80112-3450
(830) 569-0046
Fax: (303) 770-6921

E-MAIL ADDRESS:
smcneill@beef.org

WEB SITE ADDRESS:
www.beefresearch.org

FOUNDED: 1922

AREAS OF INTEREST:
Human nutrition, the relationship between nutrients in beef and health (including amino acids, vitamins and minerals), diet and health.

NAME(S) OF PROGRAMS:
- **Nutrition Research**

TYPE:
Grants-in-aid; Research grants; Research contracts. Research contracts and grants-in-aid for experimental projects in the areas of:
(1) beef as part of a balanced diet;
(2) parity studies;
(3) health benefits of beef lipids and;
(4) contribution of beef nutrients to total diet.

Proposals solicited via specific RFPs (request for proposals).

YEAR PROGRAM STARTED: 1923

PURPOSE:
To gain further knowledge of the value of beef in our diets; to develop research technology that can be applied to the areas noted above.

LEGAL BASIS:
Professional, nonprofit association.

ELIGIBILITY:
Open to qualified institutions (including universities, medical centers, nonprofit organizations and/or contract research laboratories) with appropriate interests.

GEOGRAPHIC RESTRICTIONS:
Primarily United States.

FINANCIAL DATA:
Amount of support per award: $20,000 to $50,000 for one year to $200,000 to $400,000 for multiyear awards. Most are $50,000 to $100,000.
Total amount of support: Varies.

COOPERATIVE FUNDING PROGRAMS:
Occasionally federally funded programs are under way that can be facilitated with other funds to expand the scope of the work.

APPLICATION INFORMATION:
Official application materials are available upon request to NCBA at the address above, after it has been established that the proposal would be of mutual interest.
Duration: Support is provided for one to three years depending upon the project.
Deadline: Varies for RFPs.

PUBLICATIONS:
Annual research report.

OFFICERS AND STAFF:
Mandy Carr, Ph.D., Executive Director, Beef Safety Research
Shalene McNeill, Ph.D., Executive Director, Nutrition Research

ADDRESS INQUIRIES TO:
Shalene McNeill, Ph.D.
Executive Director, Nutrition Research
(See address above.)

THE NATIONAL RESTAURANT ASSOCIATION EDUCATIONAL FOUNDATION [2676]
175 West Jackson Boulevard
Suite 1500
Chicago, IL 60604-2702
(800) 765-2122 ext. 6744
Fax: (312) 566-9733

E-MAIL ADDRESS:
scholars@nraef.org

WEB SITE ADDRESS:
www.nraef.org/scholarships

FOUNDED: 1987

AREAS OF INTEREST:
Foodservice education and training.

NAME(S) OF PROGRAMS:
• **National Restaurant Association Educational Foundation (NRAE) Scholarship Program**

TYPE:
Scholarships. Provides scholarships for students who are pursuing an education and career in the foodservice industry.

YEAR PROGRAM STARTED: 1987

PURPOSE:
To encourage and support students pursuing an education and career in the foodservice industry.

LEGAL BASIS:
Not-for-profit organization.

ELIGIBILITY:
All applicants must be:
(1) U.S. citizen or permanent resident alien;
(2) accepted and/or enrolled in a foodservice-related postsecondary program and;
(3) submit a completed application packet postmarked by the deadline date.

GEOGRAPHIC RESTRICTIONS:
United States and its territories.

FINANCIAL DATA:
Amount of support per award: Undergraduate Scholarships: $2,500.

NUMBER OF AWARDS: Approximately 400.

APPLICATION INFORMATION:
Contact the Association.
Duration: Varies depending upon the award.

PUBLICATIONS:
Awards brochure.

ADDRESS INQUIRIES TO:
Scholarships
(See address above.)

SHARE OUR STRENGTH
1030 15th Street, NW, Suite 1100 W
Suite 700
Washington, DC 20005
(202) 393-2925
(800) 969-4767
Fax: (202) 347-5868

E-MAIL ADDRESS:
grants@strength.org

WEB SITE ADDRESS:
www.strength.org

TYPE:
Project/program grants. Grants are focused on increasing participation in the federal nutrition programs, including summer meals, after-school meals, SNAP, WIC, school breakfast, and on nutrition education.

See entry 1508 for full listing.

USDA FOOD AND NUTRITION SERVICE
Child Nutrition Division
3101 Park Center Drive, Room 640
Alexandria, VA 22302
(703) 305-2590
Fax: (703) 305-2879

WEB SITE ADDRESS:
www.fns.usda.gov/cnd

TYPE:
Formula grants; Grants-in-aid; Project/program grants. Reimbursement for the support of food service in schools, child and adult care institutions to improve nutrition.

The Child and Adult Care Food Program helps child care facilities and institutions serve nutritious meals and snacks to preschool and school-age children. To participate, facilities and institutions must be licensed or approved to provide child care services. They must also meet certain other eligibility requirements. The program operates in nonresidential day care centers, settlement houses, outside-school-hours care centers, family day care homes, institutions providing day care for handicapped children and others. Participating facilities and institutions get cash assistance, USDA-donated foods and technical guidance. In child care centers, the amount of cash assistance varies according to the family size and income of children served. In day care homes, the amount of cash assistance is based on a food service payment rate. Similar benefits are also now available to adult day care centers which serve functionally impaired adults or persons 60 years of age or older.

The National School Lunch Program makes well-planned nutritious meals available to school children. Any public or nonprofit private schools of high school grade or under and licensed public or nonprofit private residential child care institutions are eligible to participate in the National School Lunch and School Breakfast Programs. Schools that participate are required to provide free and reduced-price meals to children unable to pay the full price. Eligibility is based on application information submitted by a parent or guardian. The household income limit for free lunches is set at or below 130% of the federal poverty level and for reduced price lunches household income must be above 130% or at or below 185% of the federal poverty level. Children from households not eligible for free or reduced-price meals must pay the school's full price charge for lunch. Cash and donated commodities are provided to participating schools and institutions according to the number of meals served.

The School Breakfast Program makes nutritious breakfasts available to school children under the same eligibility guidelines and general requirements as the National School Lunch Program.

The Special Milk Program for Children makes it possible for all children attending a participating school or institution to purchase milk at a reduced price or receive it free, if they are eligible. Reimbursement is provided for each half-pint of milk served under the program. Schools and institutions that participate in other federal child nutrition programs authorized under the National School Lunch Act or the Child Nutrition Act of 1966 may not participate in the Special Milk Program for Children, except for split-session kindergarten programs conducted in schools in which the children do not have access to the other meal program.

The Summer Food Service Program for Children helps communities serve meals to needy children when school is not in session. The program is sponsored by public or private nonprofit school food authorities or local, municipal, county or state governments. Public or private nonprofit residential camps, other private nonprofit organizations, colleges and universities which participate in the National Youth Sports Program also may be sponsors. The program operates in areas in which at least 50% of the children meet the income criteria for free and reduced-price school meals. USDA reimburses sponsors for operating costs of food services up to a specified maximum rate for each meal served. In addition, sponsors receive some reimbursement for planning, operating and supervising expenses.

See entry 1154 for full listing.

Mining and metallurgy

ASM MATERIALS EDUCATION FOUNDATION [2677]
9639 Kinsman Road
Materials Park, OH 44073-0002
(440) 338-5151 ext. 5533
(800) 336-5152 ext. 5533
Fax: (440) 338-4634

E-MAIL ADDRESS:
jeane.deatherage@asminternational.org

WEB SITE ADDRESS:
www.asmfoundation.org

FOUNDED: 1913

AREAS OF INTEREST:
Materials science and engineering in related fields such as metallurgy, metallurgical engineering, polymeric engineering, ceramic engineering, advanced composites engineering and engineering of electronic materials.

NAME(S) OF PROGRAMS:
• **ASM Outstanding Scholars**
• **Edward J. Dulis Scholarship**
• **William & Mary Dyrkacz Scholarships**
• **John M. Haniak Scholarship**
• **Ladish Co. Foundation Scholarships**
• **George A. Roberts Scholarship**
• **Lucille & Charles A. Wert Scholarship**
• **William Park Woodside Founder's Scholarship**

TYPE:
Scholarships.

YEAR PROGRAM STARTED: 1953

PURPOSE:
To encourage and support capable students with interest and potential in the field of metallurgy and materials science.

LEGAL BASIS:
501(c)(3) educational charity.

ELIGIBILITY:
Applicant must be a student member of ASM International and have an intended or declared major in metallurgy/materials science engineering. Applicants majoring in related science or engineering disciplines will be considered if they demonstrate a strong academic emphasis and interest in materials science. Applicant must also be at the sophomore level or above. Open to U.S. and international students.

G.A. Roberts and W.P. Woodside Scholarship candidates must have a junior or senior standing in the fall at a North American university, have proof of financial need, and must be a citizen of the U.S., Canada or Mexico and attending school in one of these countries. University must have an accredited science and engineering program leading to a Bachelor's degree.

Applicants are eligible for ASM Scholar or ASM Outstanding Scholar award a total of two times.

Criteria for selection include the student's academic achievement, interest in the field, and personal qualities. Financial need is not a factor, except for the G.A. Roberts and W.P. Woodside Scholarships.

GEOGRAPHIC RESTRICTIONS:
United States.

FINANCIAL DATA:
Amount of support per award: Up to $10,000.

NUMBER OF AWARDS: 37 scholarships are awarded annually through the ASM International Foundation.

APPLICATION INFORMATION:
Completed scholarship application (Part One), two letters of recommendation, transcript of college academic records, a photograph, and an individual statement that is no longer than two typewritten pages are required. For G.A. Roberts and W.P. Woodside Scholarships only, applicants should complete Part Two of the application form, including a personal statement and a financial aid officer contact, along with previous requirements.

Duration: Ladish Co. Foundation Scholarship: Up to two years; All others: One academic year.

Deadline: Application and materials must be sent by May 1. Award winners will be notified by mail by July 15.

IRS IDENTIFICATION NUMBER: 34-6541397

OFFICERS:
Charles R. Hayes, Executive Director and Secretary

ADDRESS INQUIRIES TO:
ASM Foundation Undergraduate Scholarship Program
(See e-mail address above.)

*SPECIAL STIPULATIONS:
Must have completed one year of undergraduate work.

INSTITUTE OF MATERIALS, MINERALS AND MINING   [2678]
The Boilerhouse
Springfield Business Park
Caunt Road
Grantham Lincs NG31 7FZ England
44 (0) 1476 513886
Fax: 44 (0) 1476 513899

E-MAIL ADDRESS:
graham.woodrow@iom3.org

WEB SITE ADDRESS:
www.iom3.org

FOUNDED: 1892

AREAS OF INTEREST:
Mining and metallurgy.

NAME(S) OF PROGRAMS:
- **Centenary Scholarship**
- **Stanley Elmore Fellowship Fund**
- **G. Vernon Hobson Bequest**
- **Mining Club Award**
- **Edgar Pam Fellowship**
- **The Tom Seaman Travelling Scholarship**
- **Bosworth Smith Trust Fund**

TYPE:
Awards/prizes; Fellowships; Research grants; Scholarships; Training grants; Travel grants. The Centenary Scholarship is restricted to first- or second-year undergraduates in student membership of the Institute and will be awarded for projects, visits, etc., in furtherance of applicants' career development.

Stanley Elmore Fellowship Fund offers fellowships (normally two for one year) applicable at a U.K. university for research into all branches of extractive metallurgy and mineral processing and, in special cases, for expenditure related to such research.

The G. Vernon Hobson Bequest awards are given for the advancement of teaching and practice of geology as applied to mining. One or more awards may be made for travel, research or other objects in accordance with the terms of the Bequest.

The Mining Club Award will be offered to British subjects 21 to 35 years of age who are actively engaged (in full- or part-time postgraduate study or in employment) in the minerals industry, as defined by the Institute, for travel purposes (for example, to study mineral industry operations in the U.K. or overseas, to present a paper at an international minerals industry conference or to assist the applicant in attending a full-time course of study related to the minerals industry outside the U.K.), or for any other similar purpose that may be regarded as being within the spirit of the award.

The Edgar Pam Fellowship is awarded for postgraduate study in subjects within the Institute's fields of interest, which range from exploration geology to extractive metallurgy. Those eligible for the award are young graduates, domiciled in Australia, Canada, New Zealand, South Africa and the U.K., who wish to undertake advanced study or research in the U.K.

The Tom Seaman Travelling Scholarship is awarded annually to a member, not older than 35 years of age, who is training or has been trained for a career in mining and/or related technologies. The scholarship shall be to assist the study for an aspect of engineering in the minerals industry, with the intention of advancing the associated standards or techniques.

The Bosworth Smith Trust Fund is given for the assistance of postgraduate research in metal mining, non-ferrous extraction metallurgy or mineral dressing. Applications will be considered for grants towards working expenses, the cost of visits to mines and plants in connection with such research, and purchase of apparatus.

ELIGIBILITY:
Applicants should note that, in general, preference will be given to members of the Institution (student membership is required for the Centenary Scholarship). Recipients of the awards will be required to submit summary reports of the ways in which such awards have been used for publication.

In judging the applications received for each award, the Institute will take into account academic excellence and scholarship. The application must, therefore, specify academic ability. Candidates merely seeking assistance for financial hardship will not be considered.

Applicants for awards must ensure that the particular fund from which support is being sought is relevant to their field(s) of interest. Applications not in accordance with the specified terms and conditions of the various funds, those which are received after the deadline, and those for which the appropriate letters of support have not been received by that date will not be submitted to the awards committee.

FINANCIAL DATA:
Amount of support per award: Centenary Scholarship: GBP 500; Stanley Elmore Fellowship Fund: Up to GBP 14,000 distributed between one or two awardees; G. Vernon Hobson Bequest: Up to GBP 1,300; Mining Club Award: Up to GBP 1,500; Edgar Pam Fellowship: Maximum GBP 2,000; Tom Seaman Travelling Scholarship: Up to GBP 5,500; Bosworth Smith Trust Fund: Approximately GBP 5,000 in grants.

APPLICATION INFORMATION:
Application form required. Applications not in accordance with the specified terms and conditions of the various funds, those which are received after the closing date each year, and those for which the appropriate levels of support have not been received by that date, will not be accepted for consideration.

Deadline: April 6.

PUBLICATIONS:
Guidelines.

ADDRESS INQUIRIES TO:
Dr. G.J.M. Woodrow
Deputy Chief Executive
(See address above.)

INTERNATIONAL CENTRE FOR DIFFRACTION DATA   [2679]
12 Campus Boulevard
Newtown Square, PA 19073-3273
(610) 325-9814
Fax: (610) 325-9823

E-MAIL ADDRESS:
info@icdd.com

WEB SITE ADDRESS:
www.icdd.com

AREAS OF INTEREST:
The science of crystallography.

NAME(S) OF PROGRAMS:
- **The Ludo Frevel Crystallography Scholarship Award**

TYPE:
Scholarships.

PURPOSE:
To encourage promising graduate students to pursue crystallographically oriented research.

ELIGIBILITY:
Applicant should be a graduate student seeking a degree with major interest in crystallography, crystal structure analysis, crystal morphology, modulated structures, correlation of atomic structures with physical properties, systematic classification of crystal structures, phase identification and materials characterization. There are no restrictions on country, race, age or sex. Students with a graduation date prior to July 1 of the award year are not eligible.

Funds are not to be used for travel.

FINANCIAL DATA:
The scholarship stipend is to be used by the graduate student to help defray tuition and laboratory fees. A portion of the stipend may be applied to registration fees to accredited scientific meetings related to crystallography. *Amount of support per award:* $2,500.

NUMBER OF APPLICANTS MOST RECENT YEAR: 45.

NUMBER OF AWARDS: 13.

APPLICATION INFORMATION:
The following information must be prepared in advance of applying online:
(1) a description of the candidate's proposed research (limit two pages), including purpose and rationale for the research, proposed methodology to be used in the study, and references and/or descriptions of the scientific background for the proposed research and; (2) a curriculum vitae, including educational preparation (institutions, dates, degrees obtained and in progress, and particularly pertinent coursework), awards/honors received, any research publications and/or presentations given, any work experience (dates, employers, positions), and professional activities and memberships.
Duration: One year. Renewals possible. Renewal applications will be considered on a competitive basis in conjunction with all applications that have been submitted up to the closing date.

Deadline: October 22.

ADDRESS INQUIRIES TO:
Eileen Jennings, Education Coordinator
(See address above.)

MINERALOGICAL ASSOCIATION OF CANADA [2680]
490, rue de la Couronne
Quebec QC G1K 9A9 Canada
(418) 653-0333
Fax: (418) 653-0777

E-MAIL ADDRESS:
office@mineralogicalassociation.ca

WEB SITE ADDRESS:
www.mineralogicalassociation.ca

FOUNDED: 1955

AREAS OF INTEREST:
Mineralogy.

NAME(S) OF PROGRAMS:
- **Leonard G. Berry Medal**
- **Hawley Medal**
- **MAC Foundation Scholarship**
- **MAC Student Travel/Research Grants**
- **Peacock Medal**
- **Pinch Medal**
- **Undergraduate Awards**
- **Young Scientist Award**

TYPE:
Awards/prizes; Grants-in-aid; Research grants; Scholarships; Travel grants.

PURPOSE:
To promote and advance the knowledge of mineralogy and the allied disciplines of crystallography, petrology, geochemistry and mineral deposits.

LEGAL BASIS:
Nonprofit scientific and charitable organization.

ELIGIBILITY:
The Leonard G. Berry Medal is awarded for distinguished service to the Mineralogical Association of Canada.

The Hawley Medal is presented to the author(s) of what is judged to be the best paper published in the preceding year's volume of *The Canadian Mineralogist*.

The MAC Foundation Scholarship is awarded to a graduate student involved in an M.Sc. or Ph.D. thesis program in the fields of mineralogy, crystallography, petrology, geochemistry or mineral deposits.

The MAC Student Travel/Research Grants are given to assist honours undergraduate and graduate students in the mineral sciences.

The Peacock Medal is awarded annually for excellence in research to a scientist who has made outstanding contributions to the mineralogical sciences in Canada.

The Pinch Medal is awarded every other year to recognize major and sustained contributions to the advancement of mineralogy by members of the collector-dealer community.

Undergraduate Awards are given to university students in mineralogy. The Association presents a MAC publication to the top student in the introductory mineralogy course at each Canadian university.

The Young Scientist Award is given to a young scientist who has made a significant international research contribution in a promising start to a scientific career.

FINANCIAL DATA:
Amount of support per award: Varies depending on award.
Total amount of support: $22,000.

NUMBER OF APPLICANTS MOST RECENT YEAR:
MAC Travel/Research Grants: 20.

NUMBER OF AWARDS: Varies.

APPLICATION INFORMATION:
Contact the Association.
Duration: Varies.
Deadline: Varies.

PUBLICATIONS:
The Canadian Mineralogist.

STAFF:
Lee A. Groat, Editor
Robert F. Martin, Editor

ADDRESS INQUIRIES TO:
Johanne Caron, Executive Coordinator
(See address above.)

Indexes

Entry Listing by Chapter

MULTIPLE SPECIAL PURPOSE: 1-343

HUMANITIES (GENERAL): 344-408
Architecture: 409-425
Arts (multiple disciplines): 426-523
  Performing arts: 524-540
  Fine arts: 541-575
History: 576-650
Languages: 651-664
Literature: 665-707
Museums and libraries: 708-744
Music: 745-798
Religion and theology: 799-827

**INTERNATIONAL AFFAIRS AND AREA
  STUDIES: 828-866**
International studies and research abroad: 867-954
Programs for foreign scholars: 955-965
Technical assistance and cooperative research:
  966-968

SPECIAL POPULATIONS: 969-1023
African-American: 1024-1035
Native American: 1036-1062
Spanish-speaking: 1063-1069
Women: 1070-1105

**URBAN AND REGIONAL AFFAIRS:
  1106-1514**
Children and youth: 1106-1156
Community development and services: 1157-1407
Crime prevention: 1408-1414
Public health: 1415-1471
Social welfare: 1472-1514

EDUCATION: 1515-1804
Educational projects and research (general):
  1515-1599
Elementary and secondary education: 1600-1612
Higher education projects and research: 1613-1649
Scholar aid programs (all disciplines): 1650-1804

**SCIENCES (MULTIPLE DISCIPLINES):
  1805-1846**

SOCIAL SCIENCES (GENERAL): 1847-1887
Business and economics: 1888-1919
Communications: 1920-1964
Labor: 1965-1969
Law: 1970-1986
Political science: 1987-2019
Sociology and anthropology: 2020-2030

**PHYSICAL SCIENCES (GENERAL):
  2031-2045**
Astronomy and aerospace science: 2046-2059
Chemistry: 2060-2070
Earth sciences: 2071-2090
Mathematics: 2091-2098
Physics: 2099-2104

LIFE SCIENCES (GENERAL): 2105-2111
Agriculture, land resources, rural development:
  2112-2134
Biology: 2135-2162
Environment: 2163-2213
Medicine (multiple disciplines): 2214-2334
Allergy, immunology, infectious diseases: 2335-2339
Dentistry: 2340-2353
Internal medicine: 2354-2371
  Cardiovascular and pulmonary: 2372-2401
  Metabolism, gastroenterology, nephrology:
    2402-2423
  Oncology: 2424-2449
  Rheumatology: 2450-2451
Neurology: 2452-2483
Nursing: 2484-2499
Obstetrics and gynecology: 2500-2502
Ophthalmology and otolaryngology: 2503-2521
Osteopathy: 2522-2525
Pediatrics: 2526-2533
Pharmacology: 2534-2545
Physical medicine and rehabilitation: 2546-2561
Psychiatry, psychology, mental health: 2562-2594

TECHNOLOGY AND INDUSTRY: 2595-2617
Aeronautics and astronautics: 2618-2630
Engineering: 2631-2667
Home economics and nutrition: 2668-2676
Mining and metallurgy: 2677-2680

Subject Index

A

Academic Medicine. *See* Medicine, Academic

Accessibility: 2559

Accounting: 1520, 1627, 1658, 1724, 1888, 1889, 1890, 1896, 1897; *see also* Business; Financial Management

Acoustics: 2039; *see also* Noise

Acquired Immunodeficiency Syndrome (AIDS): 177, 313, 470, 1008, 1273, 1432, 1812, 2326, 2369

Acting. *See* Theatre

Actuarial Science: 2091, 2092, 2097, 2098; *see also* Insurance

Addictions: 2267

Administration. *See* Arts Administration; Business Administration; Educational Administration; Health Administration; Library Administration; Management; Museum Administration; Public Administration

Adolescence. *See* Child Welfare and Health; Youth Adoption; Children, Adoption and Foster Care

Adult Education. *See* Education, Adult

Advertising: 593, 990, 1894, 1904, 1922; *see also* Business; Public Relations

Aerodynamics: 2644

Aeronautics: 1843, 2618, 2619, 2621, 2622, 2624, 2625, 2627, 2628, 2630

Aerospace Sciences: 2038, 2039, 2056, 2058, 2059, 2175, 2618, 2621, 2622, 2624, 2625, 2627, 2628; *see also* Engineering; Sciences; Technology, Aerospace

Aerospace Sciences, History: 580, 1839, 2629

Africa: 184, 407, 901, 907, 933, 934, 1538, 2025, 2213; *see also* History, African; Literature, African; also specific nations

Africa, Research and Study in: 901

African-American Studies. *See* Minority Studies; Race Relations; also any discipline that may be given African-American emphasis

African Americans: 399, 407, 603, 728, 1018, 1024, 1029, 1032, 1236, 1404, 2492; *see also* America; Inner-City; Minority Studies; Race Relations; Urban Affairs; also any discipline that may be given African American emphasis or be of concern to African Americans

African Americans, Eligibility of: 970, 973, 974, 975, 986, 990, 1000, 1003, 1005, 1020, 1024, 1025, 1026, 1027, 1030, 1031, 1033, 1034, 1288, 1542, 1571, 1616, 1725, 1892, 1988, 2091, 2139, 2140, 2151, 2296, 2567, 2607; *see also* Minority Group Members, Eligibility of

African Countries, Nationals of: 1979; *see also* Foreign Nationals, Eligibility of

Aged: 28, 31, 58, 73, 92, 155, 158, 172, 176, 178, 195, 197, 202, 203, 216, 223, 228, 250, 264, 275, 289, 295, 296, 301, 307, 319, 998, 1009, 1131, 1167, 1170, 1174, 1192, 1218, 1256, 1258, 1274, 1279, 1286, 1292, 1323, 1324, 1360, 1364, 1377, 1419, 1426, 1434, 1437, 1450, 1452, 1466, 1473, 1476, 1480, 1486, 1500, 1505, 2128, 2216, 2222, 2225, 2226, 2227, 2254, 2322, 2334, 2458, 2547; *see also* Geriatrics and Gerontology

Agricultural Cooperatives. *See* Cooperatives, Rural and Consumer

Agricultural Economics: 2118, 2120, 2124, 2126, 2206

Agricultural Sciences: 64, 79, 154, 158, 837, 919, 1820, 2124, 2131, 2187, 2194, 2206, 2671; *see also* Animal Sciences; Food Technology; Nutrition

Agricultural Sciences, Education: 200, 576, 1202, 1945, 2113, 2115, 2119, 2124, 2125, 2132, 2134

Agricultural Sciences, Research and Study Abroad: 850, 2069, 2116, 2130, 2132

Agrodiversity: 64

Agroecology: 64

Air Pollution: 1435, 2175, 2187, 2595; *see also* Environmental Studies

Alabama: 233, 427, 708, 1187, 1238, 1257, 1600, 1650, 1651, 1652, 1806

Alaska: 241, 428, 1008, 2030, 2165

Alaskan Natives. *See* American Indians and Alaskan Natives

Alcohol Abuse and Alcoholism: 1416, 1454, 1465; *see also* Behavioral Sciences; Medicine

Allergy: 2335, 2338; *see also* Immunology

Alpine Area: 2167

Alzheimer's Disease: 27, 2216, 2438, 2452, 2453, 2458, 2476, 2590

America: 763, 1953, 2012, 2091, 2114; *see also* Economics; History, American; Literature, American; Minority Studies; Political Science

American Indian and Alaskan Native Community Development: 1048, 1049, 1050, 1056, 1058, 1387, 1576; *see also* Minority Community and Institutional Development; Minority-Owned Businesses; Small Business Development

American Indians and Alaskan Natives: 391, 727, 728, 1012, 1018, 1040, 1051, 1057, 1061, 1062, 1722, 1723; *see also* Minority Studies; Race Relations; also any discipline that may be given American Indian emphasis or be of concern to American Indians

American Indians and Alaskan Natives, Eligibility of: 394, 970, 973, 974, 975, 986, 987, 1000, 1003, 1005, 1020, 1036, 1037, 1038, 1039, 1041, 1042, 1043, 1044, 1045, 1046, 1047, 1048, 1050, 1051, 1053, 1054, 1055, 1058, 1059, 1060, 1062, 1576, 1595, 1616, 1774, 1892, 1988, 2091, 2139, 2140, 2151, 2290, 2296, 2567, 2607; *see also* Minority-Group Members, Eligibility of

American Indians and Alaskan Natives, Employment: 1048, 1055, 1967; *see also* Equal Employment Opportunity; Labor

Amyotrophic Lateral Sclerosis (ALS): 2457, 2473, 2476

Anatomy: 2483

Anesthesiology: 2258, 2272, 2289

Animal Cruelty: 85, 197, 202, 240, 1378, 1384, 1823, 1886, 2109, 2239

Animal Sciences: 201, 1265, 1807, 1820, 1858, 2043, 2106, 2109, 2111, 2124, 2136, 2158, 2238, 2265; *see also* Veterinary Sciences

Animal Welfare: 18, 42, 291, 998, 1012, 1404, 2183

Antarctica: 1834

Anthropology: 362, 383, 402, 403, 444, 643, 835, 837, 869, 894, 1754, 1801, 1809, 1810, 1839, 1855, 1856, 2020, 2021, 2023, 2024, 2025, 2026, 2027, 2028, 2029, 2081, 2137, 2142; *see also* Behavioral Sciences; History; Sociology

Anthropology, Research and Study Abroad: 906, 2030

Applied Sciences: 4, 939, 1454

Appraisal: 1891

Apprenticeships. *See* In-Service Training Projects

Aquatic Ecology. *See* Ecology, Aquatic

Arboriculture: 2129; *see also* Forestry

Archaeology: 348, 350, 630, 631, 837, 886, 1093, 1801, 1817, 2020, 2022, 2026, 2081

Archaeology, Research and Study Abroad: 351, 352, 353, 355, 374, 432, 830, 868, 870, 883, 885, 887, 888, 889, 890, 893, 894, 895, 901, 913, 1618, 1665

Architecture: 225, 371, 404, 408, 409, 410, 411, 413, 414, 415, 416, 417, 419, 422, 423, 424, 439, 460, 468, 474, 482, 488, 512, 574, 615, 621, 949, 1022, 1071, 1801, 1802; *see also* Arts; Landscape Design; Urban and Regional Planning

Architecture, Research and Study Abroad: 344, 351, 413, 421, 422, 425, 574, 890

Arctic: 1619, 1835, 2167

Area Studies: 403, 647, 648, 662, 663, 664, 828, 832, 851, 853, 854, 858, 859, 862, 863, 879, 897, 926, 927, 942, 943, 944, 1644, 1710, 1855; *see also* Africa; America; Asia; Atlantic Community; Canada; Europe; Geography; Latin and South America; Mediterranean Area; Middle East; NATO Member Countries; Orient; Pacific Area; Slavic and East Europe; also specific states, U.S. regions, or nations

Argentina: 1700

Arizona: 20, 128, 132, 433, 545, 742, 1038, 1045, 1171

Arkansas: 76, 187, 475, 1172, 1275

Armaments: 2644; *see also* Defense Projects and Research; International Security; National Security

Armed Services Personnel and Dependents, Eligibility of: 1682, 1728; *see also* Veterans, Eligibility or; Veterans' Children and Dependents, Eligibility of

Arms Control: 57, 833, 857, 865

Art Criticism: 559; *see also* Literary Criticism

Art Galleries: 470, 480, 567; *see also* Exhibitions; Museums

Art History: 210, 344, 345, 348, 355, 367, 371, 373, 383, 397, 402, 403, 404, 408, 432, 444, 480, 489, 514, 542, 549, 552, 554, 556, 559, 573, 869, 890, 949, 1796, 1801, 1839

Art Therapy: 2556

Arthritis. *See* Rheumatology and Rheumatic Diseases

Arts: 1, 2, 3, 5, 6, 7, 8, 11, 12, 13, 16, 17, 18, 19, 23, 29, 30, 31, 33, 39, 40, 41, 46, 49, 51, 52, 53, 54, 58, 64, 66, 67, 68, 73, 74, 78, 82, 84, 85, 86, 89, 90, 93, 95, 99, 100, 101, 104, 110, 111, 119, 121, 125, 127, 128, 130, 132, 133, 134, 136, 140, 145, 149, 151, 152, 153, 154, 161, 164, 171, 172, 176, 180, 185, 190, 191, 193, 195, 197, 199, 203, 205, 207, 211, 216, 217, 222, 226, 228, 232, 233, 234, 235, 236, 237, 241, 242, 248, 250, 254, 255, 258, 259, 264, 265, 270, 272, 277, 281, 287, 291, 292, 293, 294, 307, 309, 310, 312, 313, 315, 317, 321, 323, 329, 333, 335, 336, 338, 339, 341, 366, 377, 406, 419, 427, 428, 429, 431, 433, 434, 435, 436, 437, 438, 440, 445, 446, 447, 448, 450, 452, 453, 456, 458, 459, 460, 461, 462, 463, 464, 465, 466, 468, 469, 470, 471, 472, 474, 475, 476, 477, 478, 479, 480, 481, 482, 483, 485, 486, 487, 488, 490, 491, 492, 493, 494, 495, 497, 498, 499, 501, 502, 503, 504, 505, 506, 511, 512, 513, 516, 517, 518, 522, 523, 536, 564, 567, 575, 594, 644, 705, 725, 763, 915, 948, 980, 998, 1012, 1086, 1087, 1094, 1111, 1121, 1139, 1155, 1158, 1160, 1162, 1163, 1164, 1170, 1173, 1176, 1178, 1191, 1196, 1199, 1200, 1201, 1206, 1207, 1209, 1213,

1215, 1216, 1217, 1218, 1220, 1221, 1223, 1225, 1229, 1230, 1232, 1233, 1234, 1235, 1238, 1239, 1240, 1241, 1242, 1243, 1249, 1251, 1252, 1253, 1256, 1259, 1260, 1261, 1264, 1265, 1267, 1269, 1270, 1273, 1274, 1276, 1277, 1278, 1283, 1284, 1285, 1286, 1287, 1288, 1293, 1294, 1297, 1298, 1299, 1302, 1303, 1306, 1308, 1310, 1315, 1320, 1322, 1323, 1332, 1340, 1341, 1348, 1349, 1350, 1354, 1355, 1361, 1364, 1365, 1368, 1369, 1370, 1371, 1375, 1377, 1378, 1381, 1382, 1385, 1387, 1388, 1390, 1398, 1400, 1403, 1406, 1426, 1432, 1495, 1500, 1506, 1507, 1528, 1532, 1550, 1563, 1610, 1632, 1640, 1836, 1905, 2003, 2030, 2270, 2491, 2559; see also Crafts; Creative Arts; Cultural Affairs; Cultural Events, Community; Fine Arts; Humanities; Performing Arts; also specific arts
Arts Administration: 492, 532
Arts, Construction and Facilities Projects: 196, 480; see also Construction and Facilities Projects
Arts, Consulting Services: 427, 428, 433, 445, 447, 448, 453, 459, 461, 463, 465, 471, 474, 475, 482, 483, 490, 491, 494, 501, 503, 511, 516, 518, 783, 795
Arts, Education: 239, 258, 296, 311, 329, 433, 437, 446, 448, 449, 451, 456, 461, 465, 467, 472, 480, 481, 483, 486, 488, 492, 495, 497, 500, 503, 507, 518, 520, 551, 555, 574, 575, 653, 916, 1026, 1202, 1231, 1258, 1272, 1317, 1524, 1922; see also specific arts
Arts, In-Service Training Programs: 556
Arts, Publication: 419, 470, 489; see also Publication Prizes, History and Humanities
Arts, Research and Study Abroad: 344, 449, 542, 554, 569, 573, 574, 832, 883, 893, 898, 906, 1703; see also specific arts
Arts, Workshops and Residencies: 406, 428, 433, 437, 443, 459, 471, 477, 481, 483, 490, 496, 510, 511, 519, 520, 521, 523, 532, 534, 558, 566; see also specific art forms
Asia: 131, 434, 452, 845, 846, 875, 898, 907, 920, 933, 934, 2213; see also History, Asian; Languages, Asian; Orient; Southeast Asia; also specific nations
Asian-Americans: 1018, 1021; see also Minority Studies; Race Relations; also any discipline that may be given Asian- American emphasis
Asian-Americans, Eligibility of: 533, 974, 975, 986, 1020, 1667, 1988, 2567; see also Minority-Group Members, Eligibility of
Asian Nationals, Eligibility of: 1979
Asian Nations, Research and Study in: 210
Asthma: 2391, 2488
Astronautics: 2619, 2623
Astronomy: 1816, 1832, 2041, 2046, 2047, 2048, 2049, 2050, 2051, 2054, 2055, 2056, 2057, 2058, 2081, 2099, 2108; see also Physical Sciences
Astrophysics: 1829, 2037, 2047, 2053, 2054, 2055, 2056, 2057, 2058, 2137, 2628, 2644
At-Risk Youth: 1150
Athletics: 1104; see also Physical Education; Sports
Atmospheric Sciences: 968, 1829, 1834, 1835, 2038, 2040, 2082, 2175, 2620; see also Earth Sciences
Atomic Energy. See Nuclear Sciences
Audiology: 2506; see also Deafness and Hearing Impairments; Speech Impairments and Communicative Disorders
Australia: 354, 505, 539, 700, 950, 965, 1700, 2069, 2131, 2132, 2210, 2333, 2545, 2667
Australia, Eligibility of Nationals of: 2667; see also Foreign Nationals, Eligibility of
Austria: 832, 899, 942, 1700
Austrian-American Relations: 832, 899
Autism: 71, 2242
Autobiography: 354
Aviation: 2002, 2596, 2618, 2621, 2622, 2624, 2625, 2626, 2627, 2628, 2629; see also Aerospace Sciences

B

Ballet. See Dance; Performing Arts
Bands: 748; see also Music
Bangladesh: 876
Basic, Clinical and Translational Biomedical Research 2279, 2326
Behavioral Sciences: 1588, 1854, 1908, 2261, 2562, 2570, 2574, 2582; see also Anthropology; Psychology; Social Sciences; Sociology
Behavioral Sciences, Education: 1005, 1802, 2292, 2293
Behavioral Sciences, Research: 221, 966, 1452, 1453, 1454, 1615, 1640, 1834, 1853, 1857, 1865, 1887, 2021, 2022, 2160, 2292, 2293, 2353, 2463, 2464, 2576, 2581, 2583
Belgium: 787, 900
Bibliographic Research: 345, 382, 718, 724; see also Libraries and Librarianship; Writers and Writing
Biochemical Engineering: 2147

Biochemistry: 953, 1786, 1825, 2039, 2063, 2064, 2065, 2066, 2143, 2157, 2175, 2261, 2288, 2413; see also Biological Sciences; Chemistry
Biodiversity: 64
Bioethics: 2107; see also Medical Ethics
Biography: 354, 587, 635, 684, 802
Biological Pollution: 2182
Biological Psychiatry: 2591, 2592
Biological Sciences: 4, 128, 221, 284, 919, 937, 948, 1003, 1806, 1817, 1820, 1828, 1834, 1835, 1839, 1842, 1853, 1865, 2032, 2039, 2064, 2067, 2081, 2136, 2137, 2142, 2143, 2147, 2148, 2149, 2152, 2157, 2158, 2174, 2189, 2201, 2289, 2324, 2325, 2591, 2592, 2613; see also Chemistry; Life Sciences; Medicine; Sciences; also specific biological sciences
Biological Sciences, Education: 1005, 1786, 1801, 1802, 1816, 2111, 2139, 2140, 2148, 2159, 2271, 2359, 2530
Biological Sciences, Research and Study: 1523, 1805, 1826, 2060, 2108, 2135, 2137, 2144, 2145, 2147, 2150, 2151, 2152, 2153, 2160, 2338
Biological Sciences, Research and Study Abroad: 953, 2147
Biomedical Engineering: 968, 2652
Biomedical Sciences and Research: 278, 284, 966, 1004, 1452, 1453, 1615, 1640, 1801, 1802, 1812, 1825, 1836, 1845, 2032, 2067, 2136, 2139, 2140, 2146, 2147, 2149, 2222, 2244, 2252, 2271, 2276, 2289, 2290, 2292, 2293, 2295, 2307, 2324, 2325, 2326, 2353, 2369, 2417, 2458, 2463, 2464, 2501, 2518, 2519, 2533, 2590; see also Medical Research; Medicine
Biophysics: 974, 2039, 2157, 2261; see also Biological Sciences; Physical Sciences
Biotechnology: 2352, 2378, 2644
Birth Control. See Family Planning; Population Studies
Birth Defects: 2242, 2278, 2282, 2283, 2284, 2530; see also Genetics; Handicapped; Mental Retardation
Black Community Development: 1335; see also Minority Community and Institutional Development
Blacks. See African Americans
Blacksmithing: 457
Blind, Assistance for: 971, 1002, 1106, 1656; see also Handicapped
Blindness. See Ophthalmology; Visual Disorders
Blood. See Hematology
Blood Banks: 2396
Botany: 2081, 2135, 2138, 2142, 2155, 2158, 2178, 2179, 2180; see also Ecology; Plant Physiology and Pathology
Broadcast Media: 1001, 1100, 1750, 1920, 1924, 1934, 1935, 1938, 1943, 1944, 1945, 1947, 1949, 1954, 1958; see also Communications; Radio and Television; Telecommunications
Building Projects. See Construction and Facilities Projects
Bulgaria: 880
Business: 555, 1006, 1627, 1645, 1692, 1893, 1904, 1906, 1908, 1927, 1975; see also Accounting; Economics; Finance; Labor; Management; Small Business Development
Business Administration: 837, 912, 1006, 1071, 1801, 1802, 1892, 1902, 1912, 1913, 1915, 1917, 2536; see also Management
Business Development Assistance: 2118; see also Small Business Development
Business, Education: 200, 271, 990, 1033, 1045, 1047, 1627, 1645, 1734, 1787, 1897, 1902, 1905, 1910, 1918, 1919, 2599
Business, History: 593, 603, 644
Business, International: 843, 910, 911, 1915, 1916
Business, Publication: 1942
Byzantine Studies: 367, 886, 893; see also Archaeology; Classical Studies; History

C

California: 7, 24, 62, 87, 110, 133, 139, 154, 159, 171, 195, 247, 253, 256, 257, 260, 287, 291, 332, 437, 498, 549, 568, 633, 655, 656, 717, 796, 998, 1020, 1038, 1045, 1070, 1083, 1117, 1140, 1174, 1192, 1261, 1280, 1303, 1306, 1308, 1353, 1370, 1371, 1376, 1394, 1423, 1424, 1440, 1442, 1448, 1456, 1479, 1500, 1547, 1560, 1633, 1639, 1653, 1670, 1671, 1672, 1684, 1697, 1705, 1797, 1798, 1918, 1990, 1991, 1992, 1993, 2186, 2305
Canada: 198, 442, 964, 977, 1077, 1295, 1420, 1460, 1463, 1471, 1619, 1628, 1668, 1673, 1674, 1776, 1777, 1782, 1783, 1784, 1785, 1786, 1787, 1788, 1789, 1790, 1791, 1792, 1831, 1836, 1873, 1912, 1913, 1937, 1963, 1972, 1986, 2030, 2177, 2215, 2245, 2249, 2252, 2417, 2418, 2433, 2434, 2470, 2472, 2557, 2590, 2610, 2616
Canadians, Eligibility of: 151, 352, 353, 355, 438, 533, 543, 577, 597, 670, 676, 680, 710, 713, 720, 744, 761, 804, 844, 881, 885, 902, 903, 919, 949, 1304, 1628, 1673, 1674, 1702, 1706, 1707, 1778, 1779, 1780, 1781, 1783, 1785, 1788, 1831, 1848, 1871, 1872, 1873, 1874, 1875, 1876, 1927, 1929, 1934, 1937, 1963, 1971, 2065, 2141, 2155, 2247,

2248, 2250, 2251, 2267, 2361, 2362, 2391, 2393, 2394, 2395, 2409, 2410, 2419, 2420, 2429, 2451, 2468, 2469, 2471, 2474, 2488, 2576, 2617, 2618, 2651, 2663, 2677

Cancer: 2261, 2326, 2352, 2359, 2424, 2430, 2435, 2439, 2440, 2442, 2447, 2454

Cancer Research: 106, 221, 301, 2149, 2255, 2263, 2288, 2322, 2359, 2364, 2365, 2366, 2404, 2424, 2426, 2427, 2429, 2430, 2431, 2432, 2433, 2434, 2435, 2436, 2437, 2438, 2439, 2440, 2441, 2442, 2443, 2444, 2445, 2446, 2447, 2448, 2449; see also Medical Research

Cancer Research Training: 330, 2149, 2424, 2425, 2428, 2439, 2440, 2444, 2446, 2449

Cancer Support Services: 71

Cancer Therapy and Treatment: 2322, 2424, 2428, 2436, 2443; see also Rehabilitation

Capacity Building: 1279

Cardiology and Cardiovascular Diseases: 301, 2322, 2326, 2372, 2373, 2374, 2375, 2376, 2377, 2378, 2379, 2380, 2381, 2382, 2383, 2384, 2389, 2390, 2392, 2393, 2394, 2397, 2400, 2401, 2438, 2517; see also Stroke; Vascular Diseases

Cardiovascular Research Training: 2372, 2374, 2375, 2376, 2377, 2378, 2379, 2380, 2381, 2382, 2383, 2393, 2394, 2395, 2400, 2401, 2403

Career Counseling: 1965, 2397

Caribbean: 151, 184, 584, 856, 963

Cartography: 584, 1834

Cartoons: 402

Catholicism: 81, 322, 589, 590, 630, 801, 802, 803, 804, 816, 822, 824, 995, 1476, 1708

Cell Biology: 2147, 2261, 2421, 2518, 2519; see also Biological Sciences

Ceramics: 430, 457, 528; see also Crafts; Creative Arts

Cerebral Palsy: 2459

Cerebrovascular Diseases: 2395; see also Birth Defects; Medical Research

Chemical Engineering: 1808, 2061, 2063, 2064, 2131, 2633, 2651, 2655

Chemistry: 4, 968, 1818, 1819, 1820, 1829, 1832, 1842, 1843, 2031, 2041, 2042, 2060, 2061, 2063, 2065, 2070, 2201, 2661; see also Biological Sciences; Physical Sciences; also specific chemical sciences

Chemistry, Education: 209, 1801, 1816, 2031, 2062, 2066, 2067, 2068

Chemistry, Research and Study: 1826, 2031, 2060, 2061, 2063, 2065, 2067, 2108, 2175, 2615

Chemistry, Research and Study Abroad: 953, 2069

Chicanos. See Spanish-Speaking Americans

Chicanos, Eligibility of: 986, 1005, 1892; see also Minority-Group Members, Eligibility of

Child Abuse: 40, 107, 135, 202, 319, 1114, 1122, 1486, 1886

Child Care. See Preschool Education and Care

Child Development and Behavior: 79, 142, 296, 1127, 1141, 1144, 1150, 1151, 1190, 1360, 1450, 1531, 1640, 1923, 2580; see also Behavioral Sciences

Child Psychology: 1137

Child Welfare and Health: 16, 39, 40, 52, 108, 112, 137, 156, 175, 212, 240, 291, 297, 301, 319, 338, 372, 817, 825, 1070, 1090, 1099, 1113, 1114, 1117, 1118, 1122, 1128, 1131, 1133, 1134, 1135, 1140, 1141, 1142, 1146, 1147, 1149, 1150, 1151, 1153, 1154, 1172, 1257, 1345, 1350, 1397, 1427, 1429, 1446, 1462, 1463, 1474, 1483, 1509, 1659, 1886, 2267, 2502, 2529, 2533, 2562; see also Pediatrics; Social Welfare

Childhood Obesity: 2275

Children: 27, 31, 40, 74, 134, 153, 154, 158, 172, 190, 197, 203, 216, 224, 244, 253, 264, 265, 289, 295, 313, 329, 330, 332, 998, 1023, 1024, 1029, 1094, 1099, 1106, 1110, 1111, 1112, 1117, 1122, 1123, 1125, 1126, 1132, 1134, 1135, 1137, 1140, 1141, 1143, 1145, 1146, 1147, 1150, 1153, 1156, 1171, 1174, 1201, 1207, 1213, 1217, 1218, 1242, 1273, 1277, 1292, 1303, 1323, 1326, 1356, 1377, 1381, 1382, 1389, 1423, 1446, 1479, 1486, 1489, 1500, 1531, 1547, 1587, 1603, 1629, 1675, 2428, 2531, 2532; see also Child Welfare and Health; Education, Elementary; Education, Secondary; Preschool Education and Care; Social Welfare; Youth

Children, Adoption and Foster Care: 234, 1138, 1147, 1153, 1169, 1207, 1544

Children, Handicapped. See Handicapped Children

Children's Literature: 672, 673, 686, 697, 702, 704, 743; see also Writers and Writing

Chile: 1700

China: 542, 1700, 2197

Choir: 765; see also Music

Choreography: 532, 536; see also Dance; Performing Arts

Christianity: 88, 369, 802, 809, 819, 1255, 1563, 1566; see also Catholicism; Protestantism; Religion

Church Facilities and Construction. See Construction and Facilities Projects; Religious Institutions

Church History. See Religion, History

Cinema. See Film

Citizen Action Legislation: 282, 1198

Citizenship: 193, 1659

City and Regional Planning. See Urban and Regional Planning

Civic Affairs: 1, 8, 21, 38, 40, 45, 55, 60, 62, 66, 75, 77, 81, 83, 100, 113, 115, 121, 126, 130, 133, 134, 146, 147, 148, 176, 193, 209, 218, 219, 226, 235, 242, 246, 249, 251, 257, 262, 268, 271, 272, 274, 289, 299, 310, 313, 315, 320, 325, 335, 338, 431, 458, 814, 1029, 1094, 1112, 1133, 1158, 1186, 1199, 1214, 1215, 1223, 1224, 1225, 1239, 1252, 1254, 1259, 1278, 1280, 1294, 1297, 1298, 1308, 1309, 1314, 1322, 1324, 1329, 1341, 1349, 1357, 1365, 1369, 1370, 1379, 1386, 1387, 1405, 1511, 1528, 1548, 1610, 2172; see also Community Development; Community Services; Urban Affairs

Civil Liberties: 112, 1280, 1432, 1472, 1491, 1847, 1936; see also Human Rights

Classical Studies: 348, 356, 362, 368, 383, 403, 561, 679, 932, 1093, 1618; see also Archaeology; History; Humanities; Languages, Classical; Literature, Classical

Classical Studies, Overseas: 344, 351, 353, 355, 366, 374, 432, 885, 886, 890

Climatology: 1817, 2082, 2175, 2190, 2192; see also Atmospheric Sciences; Earth Sciences; Environmental Studies; Meteorology

Clinical Laboratory Science: 1811, 1844, 2457; see also Medical Technology

Clinical Medicine: 2272, 2539

Clinical Psychology: 2332; see also Psychology

Clinical Research: 2261, 2282, 2344, 2376, 2377, 2378, 2379, 2380, 2381, 2382, 2383, 2407, 2449, 2517

Clinics. See Health Care Facilities; Sciences, Equipment and Facilities

Coal: 1813, 1814, 2665; see also Mineral Sciences; Technology, Mining

Cognitive Processes. See Learning Process and Memory

Collective Bargaining. See Labor, Management Relations

College Teaching, Career Preparation: 644, 1020, 1542, 1801, 1899; see also Education, Teacher Preparation

Colorado: 92, 115, 118, 165, 187, 258, 440, 502, 545, 1034, 1038, 1045, 1116, 1325, 1427, 1449, 1486, 1489, 1847, 2183

Commerce. See Business

Commercial Design: 417, 1922; see also Creative Arts; Design

Commercial Growth: 2069

Communications: 186, 384, 467, 541, 837, 843, 906, 912, 1198, 1613, 1904, 1922, 1934, 1938, 1940, 1943, 1948, 1950, 1963, 1964, 1997, 2002, 2003, 2010, 2644, 2670; see also Broadcast Media; Educational Media; Film; Information Sciences; Journalism; Print Media; Publications; Radio and Television; Technology, Communications; Telecommunications

Communications Media, Internships: 1920, 1939

Communications Science: 1411, 1963, 2506

Communicative Disorders. See Speech Impairments and Communicative Disorders

Community Centers: 1300

Community Colleges. See Junior Colleges

Community Development: 2, 6, 12, 17, 18, 19, 20, 26, 30, 31, 34, 41, 47, 49, 59, 67, 70, 73, 74, 75, 76, 77, 78, 79, 82, 85, 96, 100, 104, 111, 113, 119, 125, 137, 143, 148, 150, 153, 164, 166, 171, 182, 192, 206, 211, 217, 219, 230, 231, 232, 234, 235, 236, 242, 244, 245, 249, 251, 259, 262, 265, 276, 283, 287, 294, 300, 302, 310, 311, 312, 313, 318, 326, 337, 339, 343, 372, 415, 436, 440, 460, 466, 850, 1024, 1058, 1061, 1074, 1075, 1092, 1120, 1157, 1159, 1162, 1163, 1164, 1166, 1168, 1170, 1173, 1175, 1176, 1180, 1182, 1183, 1184, 1186, 1187, 1195, 1201, 1203, 1204, 1206, 1208, 1209, 1213, 1214, 1215, 1216, 1217, 1220, 1221, 1225, 1226, 1227, 1229, 1232, 1233, 1237, 1238, 1241, 1242, 1245, 1246, 1247, 1249, 1251, 1254, 1255, 1256, 1262, 1263, 1264, 1273, 1275, 1277, 1281, 1283, 1284, 1285, 1286, 1287, 1288, 1289, 1290, 1291, 1293, 1295, 1296, 1298, 1300, 1302, 1303, 1319, 1320, 1321, 1322, 1323, 1324, 1326, 1327, 1328, 1330, 1333, 1336, 1345, 1346, 1347, 1348, 1349, 1351, 1352, 1353, 1354, 1359, 1362, 1364, 1365, 1366, 1367, 1370, 1375, 1376, 1377, 1381, 1383, 1385, 1387, 1388, 1390, 1392, 1395, 1396, 1399, 1403, 1404, 1405, 1406, 1407, 1457, 1485, 1490, 1500, 1507, 1511, 1522, 1532, 1535, 1548, 1585, 1610, 1815, 2118, 2126, 2190, 2275; see also Business; Civic Affairs; Cultural Events, Community; Environmental Studies; Housing; Inner-City; Poverty Programs; Small Business Development; Social Welfare; Urban Affairs; Urban and Regional Planning

Community Development, Consulting Services: 1349

Community Economic Development: 279

Community Education: 1052, 1061, 1185, 1202, 1255, 1271, 1333, 1358, 2528

Community Funds: 89, 124, 130, 147, 168, 252, 303, 340, 1157, 1182, 1192, 1205, 1219, 1268, 1285, 1324, 1329, 1331, 1337, 1342, 1349, 1373, 1393, 1436, 1613; see also Relief Organizations

Community Government: 285, 1207, 1994; see also Government

Community Health and Welfare. *See* Health; Health Care Facilities; Public Health; Social Welfare

Community Leadership: 128, 1159, 1333, 1363, 1405

Community Organization: 148, 268, 727, 728, 1075, 1212, 1222, 1472, 1481

Community Services: 36, 45, 51, 54, 55, 56, 75, 105, 109, 112, 115, 126, 135, 150, 153, 185, 195, 198, 208, 228, 233, 247, 257, 271, 272, 274, 277, 285, 288, 292, 297, 318, 321, 324, 325, 328, 332, 815, 878, 1058, 1157, 1161, 1172, 1173, 1179, 1181, 1183, 1190, 1192, 1201, 1210, 1214, 1215, 1227, 1228, 1237, 1243, 1245, 1250, 1263, 1265, 1266, 1270, 1273, 1281, 1284, 1286, 1290, 1291, 1294, 1295, 1296, 1306, 1309, 1320, 1324, 1327, 1333, 1334, 1344, 1349, 1350, 1351, 1371, 1372, 1373, 1376, 1382, 1389, 1398, 1399, 1404, 1405, 1440, 1442, 1476, 1486, 1495, 1585, 1692, 1709; *see also* specific services

Comparative Education. *See* Education, Comparative

Compensatory Education. *See* Equal Educational Opportunity

Composition. *See* Music, Composition.

Computer Analysis and Modeling: 2665

Computer Engineering: 2604, 2652

Computer Sciences: 4, 953, 989, 1039, 1047, 1071, 1084, 1096, 1409, 1813, 1814, 1826, 1832, 1887, 2095, 2108, 2609, 2627, 2641, 2655, 2661; *see also* Information Sciences; Mathematics; Operations Research

Concrete: 2662; *see also* Engineering; Technology

Conferences: 483, 1571, 2028, 2094, 2157, 2158, 2280, 2563, 2572; *see also* International Projects and Seminars; Seminars; Travel Grants, Seminar Attendance; Workshops; also specific disciplines

Conflict Resolution: 844, 1169; *see also* International Security

Connecticut: 6, 363, 446, 534, 691, 721, 1177, 1216

Conservation: 2, 53, 61, 122, 124, 135, 196, 215, 230, 232, 238, 244, 248, 258, 259, 282, 323, 340, 517, 725, 1239, 1326, 1366, 1533, 1535, 1813, 1814, 1830, 1869, 1918, 2045, 2111, 2123, 2141, 2148, 2164, 2165, 2171, 2172, 2174, 2176, 2177, 2179, 2180, 2183, 2190, 2191, 2192, 2195, 2196, 2198, 2202, 2204, 2210, 2212, 2213, 2665; *see also* Ecology; Energy Resources and Utilization; Environmental Studies; Life Sciences

Conservation, Art Objects: 549, 552, 557, 573, 725, 732

Construction: 212, 1300, 2632; *see also* Engineering

Construction and Facilities Projects: 61, 115, 196, 212, 306, 1129, 1243, 1282, 1300, 1392, 1649, 2632, 2662; *see also* Equipment Grants; also specific fields of interest

Consulting Services: 463, 733, 961, 1510, 2649; *see also* Counseling and Guidance; Technical Assistance; also specific fields of interest

Consumer Action: 1973, 1975

Consumer Affairs: 1898, 1973, 2670

Consumer Information and Education: 1417; *see also* Business

Continuing Education. *See* Education, Continuing

Cooley's Anemia: 2411; *see also* Hematology

Cooperatives, Rural and Consumer: 200

Corrective Therapy: 2548; *see also* Rehabilitation

Cost Engineering. *See* Engineering; Finance

Costa Rica: 1700

Counseling and Guidance: 1146, 1356; *see also* Career Counseling; Consulting Services; Education, Counseling and Guidance; Family Services; Mental and Emotional Health; Psychology; Social Work

Crafts: 426, 441, 453, 457, 461, 474, 486, 492, 513, 514; *see also* Ceramics; Creative Arts; Folk Arts; Mosaics; Printmaking; Weaving

Crafts, Research and Study Abroad: 543

Creative Arts: 151, 346, 427, 429, 438, 439, 440, 445, 446, 448, 453, 457, 486, 495, 506, 512, 564, 1051, 1608, 1789; *see also* Arts; Crafts; Fine Arts; Performing Arts; Visual Arts; Writers and Writing; also related disciplines

Creative Arts, Workshops and Residencies: 455, 496, 510

Crime Prevention: 28, 67, 1217, 1286, 1408, 1409, 1410, 1414, 1502, 1865; *see also* Juvenile Delinquency; Law Enforcement

Criminal Justice: 2, 273, 1409, 1410, 1411, 1938, 1990; *see also* Justice

Criminal Rehabilitation: 1408, 1410, 1499

Criminology: 1394, 1408; *see also* Law Enforcement

Crippled. *See* Handicapped; Rehabilitation

Cross-Cultural Studies: 867; *see also* Cultural Affairs

Cross-Disciplinary Study. *See* Interdisciplinary Research and Study

Cubans, Eligibility of: 439, 986, 1892; *see also* Foreign Nationals, Eligibility of

Culinary Arts: 2612; *see also* Restaurant Management and Food Service

Cultural Affairs: 1, 2, 8, 13, 17, 18, 22, 28, 29, 30, 31, 36, 38, 48, 50, 56, 61, 62, 64, 66, 69, 72, 75, 79, 81, 85, 86, 90, 97, 100, 101, 104, 110, 113, 116, 117, 118, 119, 124, 126, 128, 129, 130, 132, 133, 138, 144, 146, 147, 163, 168, 171, 176, 179, 187, 188, 192, 193, 194, 200, 204, 209, 226, 229, 232, 241, 242, 245, 247, 248, 249, 257, 265, 268, 271, 272, 274, 276, 284, 287, 289, 296, 297, 302, 315, 316, 318, 327, 331, 335, 338, 339, 343, 431, 435, 474, 480, 502, 592, 611, 644, 675, 725, 843, 845, 846, 856, 910, 943, 998, 1029, 1061, 1121, 1148, 1158, 1160,

1162, 1171, 1173, 1174, 1175, 1177, 1178, 1179, 1181, 1191, 1199, 1200, 1206, 1207, 1216, 1221, 1223, 1225, 1230, 1233, 1235, 1241, 1251, 1252, 1253, 1256, 1266, 1269, 1270, 1276, 1277, 1284, 1285, 1286, 1287, 1294, 1297, 1298, 1302, 1303, 1311, 1315, 1322, 1323, 1328, 1338, 1345, 1354, 1357, 1362, 1364, 1368, 1369, 1371, 1375, 1377, 1378, 1385, 1390, 1395, 1398, 1404, 1405, 1426, 1601, 1609, 1742, 1905, 2491; *see also* Fine Arts; International Relations and International Affairs; Performing Arts; also specific arts

Cultural Events, Community: 19, 45, 109, 122, 134, 164, 179, 211, 228, 235, 237, 244, 259, 260, 292, 299, 308, 335, 337, 341, 427, 428, 436, 437, 442, 445, 446, 447, 448, 453, 456, 460, 465, 469, 471, 472, 475, 483, 485, 490, 491, 492, 493, 494, 495, 497, 500, 501, 503, 504, 511, 512, 516, 518, 523, 814, 832, 1061, 1111, 1146, 1176, 1185, 1208, 1210, 1214, 1216, 1225, 1236, 1279, 1288, 1308, 1310, 1318, 1340, 1349, 1361, 1401, 1565, 1610, 2117; *see also* Community Development

Cultural Exchange Programs: 434, 439, 836, 853, 866, 867, 872, 876, 884, 896, 898, 911, 918, 920, 924, 936, 1596, 1617, 1624; *see also* International Study and Research Programs

Cultural Studies: 63, 672, 832

Curriculum Development: 656, 836, 852, 865, 944, 1552, 1583, 1644, 1915, 1916, 2280; *see also* Education and entries beginning with Education and Educational; Humanities, Curriculum Development; Instructional Materials; Sciences, Curriculum Development

Cystic Fibrosis: 2361, 2362, 2413; *see also* Metabolism and Metabolic Disorders

Cytology: 2157, 2252

D

Dairy Sciences. *See* Agricultural Sciences; Animal Sciences

Dance: 442, 446, 448, 453, 460, 461, 464, 467, 474, 481, 484, 486, 488, 490, 500, 513, 523, 525, 526, 527, 529, 531, 532, 536, 538, 539, 777, 779, 955; *see also* Choreography; Performing Arts

Data Processing. *See* Computer Sciences; Information Sciences

Day Care Service. *See* Preschool Education and Care

Deaf, Educational Support for: 981; *see also* Education, Special

Deafness and Hearing Impairments: 981, 2515, 2521; *see also* Audiology; Handicapped; Otology; Rehabilitation; Speech Impairments and Communicative Disorders

Decorative Arts: 406, 412, 420, 423, 473, 479, 489, 562; *see also* Fine Arts

Defense Projects and Research: 2644; *see also* Military Sciences; National Security; Technology, Strategic and Tactical

Delaware: 445

Democracy: 179, 279, 1280

Demography. *See* Population Studies

Demonstration Projects. *See* specific disciplines

Denmark: 884; *see also* Scandinavia

Dental Administration. *See* Health Administration

Dental Assisting: 2230, 2347

Dental Education: 2340, 2346, 2348, 2349; *see also* Medical Education and Training

Dental Hygiene: 2342, 2343, 2344, 2345, 2348, 2350

Dental Research: 2341, 2342, 2343, 2344, 2345, 2350

Dentistry: 334, 2346, 2351, 2352

Dentistry, Education: 2332, 2340, 2346, 2349; *see also* Medical Education and Training

Dentistry, Preventive: 1437, 2351, 2352

Dermatology: 2220, 2255, 2324, 2325, 2327, 2336, 2447, 2532

Desert Research. *See* Environmental Studies

Design: 412, 461, 467, 1922, 2654; *see also* Commercial Design; Creative Arts; Decorative Arts; Fine Arts; Industrial Design; Interior Design; Landscape Design

Developing Nations: 850, 856, 1082, 2173; *see also* International Relations and International Affairs; also specific nations

Developing Nations, Economic Growth: 129, 850, 1082; *see also* Economics, International

Developing Nations, Education: 850, 1082, 2027

Developing Nations, Health and Nutrition: 850; *see also* Food Technology; Health; Nutrition

Developing Nations, Resource Development: 850, 2173; *see also* Resource Development and Management

Development Grants. *See* specific areas of interest

Developmental Disabilities: 71, 1017, 1391, 2571

Diabetes: 2268, 2326, 2403, 2409, 2414, 2415, 2416, 2438; *see also* Metabolism and Metabolic Disorders

Diagnosis of Illness. *See* Medicine, Diagnostic

Dietetics: 2427, 2612, 2668, 2670, 2672; *see also* Nutrition

Digestive Diseases: 2404, 2405, 2406, 2407, 2408, 2423

Disabilities: 92, 2559

Disabled. *See* Handicapped

Disadvantaged: 103, 129, 134, 137, 152, 174, 178, 200, 244, 275, 305, 307, 998, 1046, 1115, 1132, 1138, 1139, 1141, 1151, 1198, 1258, 1325, 1361, 1396, 1423, 1544, 1547, 1579, 1643, 1730, 1923, 2231, 2635; *see also* Equal Economic Opportunity; Equal Educational Opportunity; Equal Employment Opportunity; Inner-City; Minority-Group Members; Poverty Programs

Disaster. *See* Emergency Grants; Emergency Measures Research

District of Columbia: 54, 187, 447, 1059, 1115, 1123, 1327, 1980, 2013, 2331

Divorce. *See* Family Life

Domestic Violence: 122, 135, 328, 1083, 1090, 1114, 1443, 1475, 1486, 1660, 1854, 1865, 2231; *see also* Behaviorial Sciences; Sexual Abuse

Drama: 404, 524, 653, 689, 955, 1926; *see also* Playwrights; Theatre; Writers and Writing

Drama, Theatre: 526, 530, 535, 540, 696; *see also* Playwrights; Theatre

Drop-Out Prevention: 1502

Drug Abuse: 1083, 1343, 1443, 1573, 1574; *see also* Narcotics; Rehabilitation

Drugs. *See* Pharmacy and Pharmacology

Dysautonomia: 2461

E

Early Childhood Education: 219, 1145, 1360, 1502, 1601, 1611, 1795; *see also* Preschool Education and Care

Earth Sciences: 968, 1801, 1806, 1810, 1816, 1817, 1821, 1826, 1832, 1834, 1836, 1839, 1843, 2040, 2071, 2072, 2080, 2082, 2086, 2090, 2110, 2137, 2175; *see also* Atmospheric Sciences; Geology; Oceanography; Petroleum Sciences

Earthquake: 2175

East European Studies. *See* Slavic and East Europe

Eastern States: 160, 263, 331, 530, 691, 1697, 2045, 2254; *see also* states by name

Ecological Restoration: 2182

Ecology: 90, 939, 1806, 1816, 1817, 1835, 2081, 2111, 2123, 2148, 2151, 2158, 2160, 2163, 2169, 2173, 2181, 2184, 2188, 2192, 2195, 2201, 2206, 2207, 2208, 2209; *see also* Biological Sciences; Botany; Conservation; Environmental Studies

Ecology, Aquatic: 1575, 1830, 1835, 2083, 2084, 2141, 2158, 2177, 2188, 2193, 2211; *see also* Marine Biology

Economic Education: 1901

Economic Growth and Development: 20, 29, 48, 60, 74, 75, 114, 125, 132, 137, 150, 152, 172, 179, 180, 184, 207, 231, 234, 239, 340, 341, 431, 850, 856, 1012, 1061, 1082, 1171, 1186, 1198, 1208, 1215, 1216, 1230, 1233, 1247, 1272, 1285, 1294, 1302, 1303, 1309, 1310, 1315, 1324, 1326, 1329, 1330, 1335, 1350, 1371, 1379, 1387, 1390, 1404, 1474, 1483, 1490, 1502, 1635, 1737, 1903, 1906, 1936; *see also* Developing Nations, Economic Growth

Economic History: 593, 644, 1895, 2002

Economic Justice: 141

Economic Policy: 21, 1198, 1867, 1868, 1996; *see also* Policy Analysis

Economics: 298, 311, 580, 592, 835, 837, 845, 856, 869, 1061, 1212, 1492, 1629, 1774, 1777, 1855, 1856, 1868, 1901, 1908, 1927, 2097, 2098, 2197; *see also* Appraisal; Business; Finance; Labor, Economics; Management; Social Sciences

Economics, Education: 1562, 1627, 1745, 1792, 1801, 1866, 1891, 1905, 1906, 1910, 1915

Economics, International: 843, 844, 853, 906, 951, 1706

Economics, Research: 948, 968, 1895, 1915, 1965, 1997

Economics, Teaching: 1915

Ecuador: 1700

Education: 2, 3, 4, 5, 6, 7, 8, 9, 11, 13, 18, 19, 22, 23, 24, 27, 28, 29, 30, 31, 33, 34, 36, 38, 40, 41, 42, 44, 45, 46, 47, 48, 49, 51, 52, 53, 54, 58, 59, 60, 61, 62, 66, 67, 68, 71, 72, 74, 75, 77, 78, 81, 83, 84, 85, 86, 87, 91, 92, 93, 95, 96, 97, 100, 102, 103, 104, 105, 110, 111, 113, 114, 115, 116, 118, 119, 121, 122, 124, 127, 128, 129, 132, 133, 136, 137, 138, 139, 140, 142, 143, 144, 145, 148, 149, 152, 153, 154, 156, 157, 158, 159, 160, 161, 163, 164, 165, 167, 172, 177, 179, 180, 184, 185, 187, 190, 191, 192, 194, 195, 203, 204, 205, 206, 207, 211, 214, 215, 216, 217, 222, 223, 224, 225, 226, 228, 232, 233, 234, 235, 236, 238, 239, 240, 241, 244, 245, 246, 247, 248, 249, 250, 251, 253, 255, 258, 259, 260, 265, 266, 267, 268, 269, 270, 271, 272, 274, 275, 277, 278, 281, 283, 287, 288, 289, 290, 292, 294, 295, 297, 299, 303, 304, 305, 307, 309, 310, 312, 313, 315, 316, 320, 321, 323, 326, 328, 335, 336, 337, 338, 339, 341, 369, 371, 420, 431, 437, 446, 451, 458, 466, 492, 538, 585, 657, 674, 709, 710, 740, 814, 823, 829, 837, 850, 856, 906, 983, 987, 993, 995, 998, 1012, 1015, 1016, 1029, 1062, 1083, 1099, 1110, 1111, 1115, 1117, 1118, 1119, 1120, 1122, 1124, 1126, 1129, 1130, 1131, 1134, 1143, 1144, 1145, 1147, 1155, 1156, 1158, 1160, 1162,

1163, 1164, 1165, 1166, 1167, 1168, 1173, 1174, 1175, 1178, 1179, 1181, 1182, 1188, 1189, 1190, 1193, 1194, 1195, 1196, 1197, 1198, 1199, 1200, 1201, 1206, 1208, 1209, 1210, 1213, 1215, 1216, 1220, 1223, 1224, 1225, 1229, 1230, 1232, 1233, 1234, 1235, 1236, 1238, 1239, 1240, 1241, 1242, 1243, 1244, 1246, 1249, 1250, 1251, 1252, 1253, 1256, 1258, 1259, 1260, 1261, 1264, 1265, 1266, 1267, 1269, 1270, 1273, 1274, 1275, 1276, 1277, 1278, 1280, 1281, 1282, 1283, 1284, 1285, 1287, 1288, 1289, 1291, 1293, 1294, 1297, 1298, 1299, 1308, 1309, 1310, 1311, 1314, 1315, 1317, 1318, 1320, 1322, 1323, 1324, 1326, 1327, 1328, 1329, 1332, 1338, 1339, 1340, 1342, 1344, 1345, 1348, 1349, 1350, 1354, 1356, 1357, 1360, 1362, 1363, 1364, 1365, 1366, 1369, 1372, 1375, 1376, 1377, 1378, 1379, 1381, 1385, 1386, 1388, 1390, 1395, 1396, 1398, 1400, 1401, 1403, 1404, 1420, 1426, 1461, 1465, 1470, 1474, 1477, 1479, 1483, 1493, 1496, 1501, 1511, 1515, 1516, 1517, 1518, 1519, 1524, 1527, 1528, 1529, 1531, 1532, 1533, 1535, 1536, 1537, 1545, 1546, 1548, 1550, 1551, 1552, 1554, 1558, 1560, 1561, 1567, 1578, 1581, 1585, 1586, 1587, 1592, 1600, 1601, 1604, 1610, 1611, 1613, 1626, 1630, 1642, 1649, 1659, 1668, 1689, 1690, 1692, 1708, 1716, 1732, 1735, 1755, 1756, 1797, 1801, 1815, 1856, 1905, 1906, 1907, 1965, 2089, 2096, 2148, 2160, 2190, 2201, 2270, 2298, 2311, 2490, 2676; *see also* Consumer Information and Education; Curriculum Development; entries beginning with Education and Educational; Equal Educational Opportunity; Faculty, Study and Research Programs; Instructional Materials; International Study and Research Programs; Medical Education and Training; Nursing Education; Preschool Education and Care; Reading; Teaching, Outside U.S.; also specific professions and areas of study

Education, Adult: 1397, 1594, 1650, 1735, 1894, 1967; *see also* Education, Continuing

Education, Alternative Modes: 1126, 1648

Education, Comparative: 954

Education, Continuing: 1085, 1607, 2190; *see also* Education, Adult

Education, Counseling and Guidance: 1560, 1643

Education, Developing Nations. *See* Developing Nations, Education

Education, Elementary: 170, 329, 1057, 1126, 1136, 1149, 1187, 1283, 1313, 1380, 1502, 1545, 1546, 1549, 1578, 1583, 1593, 1595, 1601, 1602, 1604, 1608, 1621, 1626, 1675, 1690

Education, Elementary and Secondary, Construction and Facilities Projects: 300, 1402, 1822; *see also* Construction and Facilities Projects

Education, Government Policy and Legislation. *See* Education, Policy-Making

Education, Higher, Aid Programs for Undergraduate and Graduate Students in All Disciplines: 16, 77, 98, 181, 208, 296, 301, 302, 407, 411, 420, 467, 506, 655, 698, 741, 796, 905, 928, 929, 931, 950, 956, 963, 965, 971, 972, 976, 977, 981, 985, 987, 988, 992, 993, 996, 1000, 1002, 1006, 1007, 1011, 1028, 1030, 1033, 1034, 1035, 1036, 1037, 1038, 1041, 1042, 1043, 1044, 1046, 1047, 1050, 1051, 1054, 1060, 1062, 1063, 1065, 1067, 1068, 1069, 1073, 1076, 1077, 1080, 1085, 1097, 1098, 1121, 1138, 1225, 1246, 1254, 1266, 1299, 1431, 1520, 1527, 1530, 1534, 1541, 1542, 1544, 1545, 1546, 1580, 1584, 1590, 1614, 1616, 1621, 1638, 1645, 1647, 1650, 1651, 1652, 1653, 1655, 1656, 1658, 1659, 1662, 1663, 1664, 1666, 1668, 1670, 1671, 1674, 1676, 1677, 1678, 1679, 1680, 1681, 1682, 1683, 1684, 1685, 1686, 1687, 1688, 1689, 1690, 1691, 1692, 1693, 1694, 1695, 1696, 1698, 1699, 1700, 1703, 1704, 1705, 1706, 1707, 1708, 1709, 1711, 1712, 1713, 1714, 1716, 1717, 1718, 1719, 1720, 1721, 1722, 1723, 1726, 1727, 1728, 1729, 1730, 1731, 1732, 1733, 1734, 1735, 1736, 1737, 1738, 1739, 1740, 1741, 1742, 1743, 1746, 1748, 1749, 1751, 1752, 1753, 1755, 1757, 1758, 1759, 1760, 1761, 1762, 1763, 1764, 1765, 1766, 1767, 1768, 1769, 1770, 1771, 1772, 1773, 1774, 1775, 1776, 1778, 1779, 1780, 1781, 1782, 1783, 1785, 1788, 1790, 1793, 1794, 1796, 1799, 1800, 1802, 1803, 1804, 1822, 1888, 1889, 1890, 1896, 1919, 1922, 1963, 2004, 2019, 2033, 2034, 2062, 2124, 2168, 2186, 2190, 2203, 2285, 2338, 2346, 2359, 2490, 2525, 2537, 2551, 2555, 2596, 2597, 2605, 2609, 2611, 2613, 2616, 2618, 2622, 2623, 2624, 2625, 2631, 2634, 2635, 2636, 2637, 2638, 2640, 2647, 2653, 2658; *see also* specific disciplines

Education, Higher, Aid Programs for Undergraduate and Graduate Students in Surveying and Geomatics: 2656

Education, Higher, Aid Programs for Undergraduate Students in All Disciplines of Surveying: 2657

Education, Higher, Construction and Facilities Projects: 115, 119, 196, 209, 212, 261, 300, 306, 1649; *see also* Construction and Facilities Projects

Education, Higher, Research, Project, and General Support: 1, 10, 20, 43, 50, 56, 57, 68, 82, 88, 89, 94, 108, 109, 117, 120, 126, 130, 146, 147, 164, 166, 176, 188, 206, 209, 218, 229, 242, 254, 257, 261, 262, 280, 291, 300, 306, 308, 314, 317, 327, 330, 332, 340, 365, 467, 644, 649, 650, 752, 786, 823, 827, 834, 863, 875, 916, 987, 1004, 1031, 1035, 1072, 1078, 1108, 1109, 1142, 1157, 1176, 1177, 1187, 1203, 1268, 1279, 1291, 1380, 1401, 1527, 1536, 1541, 1545, 1546, 1551,

1563, 1566, 1577, 1593, 1599, 1620, 1621, 1623, 1625, 1626, 1629, 1630, 1631, 1632, 1633, 1634, 1635, 1636, 1637, 1644, 1648, 1689, 1690, 1702, 1806, 1827, 1850, 1855, 1896, 1897, 1926, 1990, 1991, 1992, 1993, 2067, 2073, 2075, 2254, 2296, 2536, 2627, 2639, 2640, 2645

Education, Independent Schools: 823, 1035, 1374, 1582, 1605, 1668; *see also* Education, Secondary

Education, Learning Process. *See* Learning Process and Memory

Education, Legal. *See* Law, Education

Education, Loan Funds: 735, 739, 963, 1371, 1529, 1652, 1684, 1699, 1799, 2646

Education, Medical. *See* Medical Education and Training; Nursing Education

Education, Methods: 152, 1130, 1552, 1593, 1607, 1634; *see also* specific subjects of instruction

Education, Musical. *See* Music, Education

Education, Physical. *See* Physical Education

Education, Policy-Making: 5, 46, 1126, 1130, 1552, 1593; *see also* Policy Analysis

Education, Preschool. *See* Preschool Education and Care

Education, Private Institutions: 50, 94, 289, 302, 807, 1342, 1543, 1668, 1676, 1760, 2254; *see also* Education, Higher, Research, Project, and General Support; Education, Secondary

Education, Professional. *See* specific professions

Education, Programs for Undergraduate and Graduate Students in the Field of Geodetic Surveying: 2659

Education, Publication. *See* Publication Prizes, Education

Education Reform: 57, 1291, 1583, 1634, 1996

Education, Religious. *See* Religious Education

Education, Secondary: 94, 99, 105, 109, 120, 166, 170, 222, 329, 381, 1047, 1057, 1123, 1126, 1130, 1141, 1279, 1380, 1401, 1545, 1546, 1549, 1577, 1578, 1579, 1583, 1589, 1593, 1594, 1595, 1602, 1603, 1604, 1605, 1608, 1609, 1612, 1621, 1626, 1643, 1675, 1690, 1957; *see also* Education, Elementary and Secondary, Construction and Facilities Projects

Education, Special: 296, 949, 977, 1023, 1128, 1133, 1557, 1594, 1643, 1656, 1659, 1708, 2552; *see also* specific handicaps

Education, STEM 1548

Education, Teacher Preparation: 507, 663, 866, 943, 958, 1045, 1047, 1126, 1136, 1527, 1537, 1545, 1546, 1577, 1592, 1597, 1638, 1644, 1659, 1672, 1689, 1690, 1708, 1719, 1770, 1802, 1899; *see also* College Teaching, Career Preparation; Faculty, Study and Research Programs; Language Teachers, Study and Research Abroad

Education, Technical: 60, 936, 1000, 1033, 1610, 1670, 1712, 1732, 1734, 2294, 2596, 2597, 2653

Education, Vocational: 38, 217, 936, 993, 1055, 1117, 1291, 1527, 1555, 1564, 1594, 1610, 1670, 1705, 1712, 1752, 1991, 1993, 2600, 2601, 2602, 2603; *see also* Industrial Arts and Education; specific fields

Education, Work-Study: 1003, 1773, 1800

Educational Administration: 1552, 1593, 1624

Educational Exchange Programs: 836, 867, 900, 906, 918, 925, 932, 936, 954, 1596, 1617, 1624, 1648; *see also* International Study and Research Programs

Educational Measurement: 1539, 1540

Educational Media: 711, 713, 734, 1607, 1923; *see also* Curriculum Development; Education, Methods; Instructional Materials

Educational Research: 152, 210, 413, 948, 1074, 1130, 1521, 1539, 1540, 1552, 1562, 1567, 1588, 1593, 1607, 1915, 2117, 2294, 2333, 2573

Egypt: 879; *see also* Africa; Middle East

Elderly. *See* Aged

Electrical Engineering: 2652, 2667

Electrochemistry: 1818, 1819

Electron Microscopy: 1828, 2613

Electronics: 1842, 2627; *see also* Engineering; Physical Sciences

Embryology: 1816; *see also* Biological Sciences; Life Sciences

Emergency Financial Assistance: 460, 550, 690, 1504

Emergency Grants: 1476, 1504, 2206, 2593

Emergency Measures Research: 2593

Emergency Medical Services. *See* Medical and Health Services

Emotional Health. *See* Mental and Emotional Health

Employment and Training. *See* Labor, Employment and Training

Endocrinology: 2361, 2403; *see also* Biological Sciences; Metabolism and Metabolic Disorders

Energy Resources and Utilization: 256, 968, 1180, 1208, 1366, 1585, 2038, 2172, 2175, 2176, 2185, 2198, 2634, 2635, 2636, 2637, 2638, 2639, 2661, 2665; *see also* Coal; Conservation; Engineering; Forest and Range Resources; Mineral Sciences; Petroleum Sciences; Resource Development and Management; Solar Energy and Solar Research; Technology; Water Resources

Engineering: 170, 298, 910, 911, 930, 1013, 1014, 1630, 1692, 1824, 1831, 1836, 1842, 1843, 1920, 2059, 2061, 2096, 2175, 2609, 2619, 2627, 2632, 2633, 2641, 2642, 2643, 2644, 2645, 2647, 2648, 2649, 2651, 2653, 2654, 2655, 2662, 2677; *see also* Aerospace Sciences; Nuclear Sciences; Ocean Engineering; Sciences; Technology

Engineering, Education: 170, 209, 262, 959, 989, 1000, 1003, 1005, 1038, 1039, 1045, 1047, 1071, 1076, 1084, 1096, 1124, 1519, 1537, 1607, 1630, 1662, 1725, 1792, 1801, 1802, 1840, 2044, 2609, 2615, 2616, 2631, 2632, 2634, 2635, 2636, 2637, 2638, 2639, 2645, 2646, 2652, 2653, 2661, 2663, 2664, 2667, 2677

Engineering, Research and Development 930, 1813, 1814, 1826, 2175, 2604, 2644, 2651

Engineering, Research and Study: 1020, 1798, 2108, 2642, 2661

Engineering, Research and Study Abroad: 904, 930, 2667

England: 408, 419, 704, 904, 905, 929, 945, 946, 947, 948, 1700, 1706, 2178, 2435

England, Eligibility Limited to Residents of: 958, 2069

English-American Relations: 402

English as a Second Language: 653

Enology. *See* Viticulture and Enology

Entomology: 1809, 2120, 2137, 2142, 2144, 2145; *see also* Biological Sciences

Entrepreneurship: 71, 162

Environment: 9, 54, 56, 64, 80, 91, 101, 157, 218, 244, 260, 266, 272, 279, 341, 343, 998, 1178, 1191, 1206, 1221, 1269, 1345, 1389, 1400, 1404

Environmental Conservation: 18, 84, 99, 107, 119, 131, 845, 846, 1815; *see also* Conservation; Resource Development and Management

Environmental Design. *See* Design; Industrial Design; Landscape Design

Environmental Education: 296, 1202, 1252, 1519, 1589

Environmental Engineering: 79, 2197, 2203

Environmental Health: 284, 1092, 1243, 1425, 1449, 1451, 1495, 1565, 2153, 2185, 2188, 2338

Environmental Law: 1793, 1974, 2211

Environmental Pollution: 1387, 1396, 1435, 1547, 2088, 2163, 2173, 2188, 2192, 2193, 2195, 2197, 2206, 2207, 2208, 2211; *see also* Air Pollution; Sanitation; Solid Waste Management; Wastewater Management; Water Pollution

Environmental Science: 79, 837, 894, 1836, 2108, 2148, 2151

Environmental Studies: 2, 8, 13, 19, 51, 67, 82, 100, 152, 159, 164, 243, 256, 282, 287, 311, 337, 466, 845, 1003, 1094, 1162, 1170, 1197, 1216, 1251, 1261, 1265, 1273, 1280, 1283, 1292, 1320, 1332, 1366, 1370, 1371, 1379, 1385, 1420, 1479, 1774, 1830, 1835, 1842, 1843, 1928, 1996, 2083, 2084, 2085, 2087, 2088, 2114, 2123, 2158, 2163, 2167, 2174, 2175, 2177, 2181, 2183, 2184, 2187, 2188, 2189, 2190, 2191, 2198, 2201, 2203, 2206, 2211, 2212, 2595, 2597, 2661; *see also* Conservation; Ecology; Engineering; Resource Development and Management; Water Resources

Environmental Technology: 422, 968, 1813, 1814, 2088, 2188, 2207, 2208, 2211, 2655

Environmental Toxicology: 2067, 2163, 2211

Epidemiology: 2242, 2254, 2261, 2352, 2448

Epilepsy: 1851, 1852, 2323, 2455, 2463, 2464; *see also* Neuromuscular Disorders

Equal Economic Opportunity: 102, 326, 1090, 1497, 1847; *see also* Social Welfare

Equal Educational Opportunity 45, 79, 102, 122, 152, 298, 992, 1038, 1046, 1048, 1198, 1583, 1639, 1643, 1670; *see also* Education; Race Relations; Social Welfare

Equal Employment Opportunity: 282, 1198, 1967; *see also* Labor

Equal Rights. *See* Human Rights

Equipment Grants: 61, 115, 196, 212, 306, 1243, 1838, 2157, 2645; *see also* Construction and Facilities Projects; specific fields of interest

Ethics: 22, 1282, 1804, 1833, 2107; *see also* Human Values; Legal Ethics; Medical Ethics

Ethnology: 345, 383, 403, 456, 1021, 1040, 2030, 2208; *see also* Anthropology; Sociology

Eurasia and East Europe 854, 933, 934

Europe: 543, 912, 920, 942; *see also* Area Studies; History, European; Languages; Literature; Slavic and East Europe; Social Sciences; also specific nations

European Integration: 835

Evolution: 2020, 2158

Exchange Programs. *See* Cultural Exchange Programs; Educational Exchange Programs; International Projects and Seminars; International Study and Research Programs; Scientific Exchange Programs

Exhibitions: 437, 450, 471, 503, 2606; *see also* Cultural Events, Community; Museums; also specific disciplines

Experimental and Pilot Programs. *See* specific disciplines

Exploration and Field Research: 1817, 1821, 1834, 2080, 2081, 2110, 2160, 2167, 2193

F

Faculty Development: 852
Faculty, Study and Research Programs: 151, 378, 380, 381, 385, 386, 387, 389, 390, 391, 400, 651, 1597, 1605, 1632, 1902, 1904, 2153, 2404, 2405, 2407, 2534, 2576, 2643; *see also* Education, Teacher Preparation
Faculty, Study and Research Programs Abroad: 932, 943, 944, 1596; *see also* specific disciplines
Families in Crisis: 1099, 1141, 1153
Family Development: 5, 46, 134, 154, 825, 1360, 1389, 1560
Family Life: 46, 134, 135, 138, 156, 250, 253, 265, 982, 1090, 1123, 1200, 1213, 1281, 1303, 1337, 1396, 1476, 1498, 1505, 2669, 2674
Family Planning: 1070, 1207, 1513, 2194, 2491; *see also* Genetics; Population Studies; Reproduction Research; Social Sciences; Social Welfare
Family Practice. *See* Medicine, Family Practice
Family Services: 52, 80, 112, 140, 153, 258, 1145, 1147, 1261, 1308, 1350, 1425, 1476, 1483, 1502, 1513; *see also* Social Services
Fashion: 444, 1768
Fats and Proteins. *See* Biological Sciences; Food Technology; Nutrition
Fiction: 665, 667, 674, 683, 684, 686, 689, 692, 693, 698, 701, 703; *see also* Literature; Manuscript Prizes, Poetry and Fiction; Publication Prizes, Creative Writing; Writers and Writing
Field Research. *See* Exploration and Field Research
Film: 346, 418, 442, 453, 460, 462, 464, 468, 474, 481, 496, 514, 541, 955, 1100, 1536, 1962; *see also* Creative Arts
Film, Directing: 462, 536, 1100
Filmmaking: 498, 522
Finance: 80, 843, 1907, 1908, 1911, 1918, 1942, 2010, 2097, 2098; *see also* Business; Economics
Financial Assistance. *See* Emergency Financial Assistance
Financial Counseling: 2670
Financial Management: 21, 1888, 1889, 1890; *see also* Accounting
Fine Arts: 44, 122, 325, 419, 428, 433, 438, 446, 469, 470, 471, 483, 491, 493, 495, 500, 502, 512, 518, 523, 541, 545, 546, 547, 556, 560, 561, 563, 564, 567, 575, 1051, 1313, 1479, 1801; *see also* Arts; Creative Arts; Decorative Arts; Design; Graphic Arts; Humanities; Painting; Photography; Sculpture
Fine Arts, Publication: 419, 470, 489, 559; *see also* Publication Prizes, History and Humanities
Fine Arts, Research and Study: 362, 408, 423, 555, 558, 559, 560, 561, 568, 574, 1051, 1802
Fine Arts, Research and Study Abroad: 344, 374, 449, 543, 569, 574
Fine Arts, Workshops and Residencies: 548, 558, 559
Finland: 884, 954; *see also* Scandinavia
Fire Control: 1271, 2035
Fire Department Administration: 1316, 1701
Fire Prevention and Research: 1271, 1701, 2035, 2546
Fish and Game Management: 1575, 1830, 2141, 2177, 2193; *see also* Animal Sciences; Conservation; Ecology, Aquatic; Marine Biology; Wildlife
Fitness. *See* Physical Fitness
Fitness: 2559
Flemish Studies. *See* Arts; Europe; History, European
Floriculture: 2114, 2120; *see also* Botany; Horticulture
Florida: 52, 110, 234, 264, 448, 740, 1009, 1028, 1067, 1139, 1224, 1437, 1441, 1459, 1507, 1543, 1608, 1681, 1687, 1688, 1763, 1764, 2438
Folk Arts: 437, 440, 448, 453, 456, 459, 461, 467, 483, 486, 488, 490, 492, 497, 500, 503, 513, 518, 523, 1087; *see also* Crafts; Creative Arts
Folk Studies. *See* Ethnology
Folklore: 832
Food Service. *See* Restaurant Management and Food Service
Food Technology: 156, 184, 1808, 1820, 2402, 2610, 2673; *see also* Nutrition
Foreign Faculty Study Programs: 961; *see also* Foreign Nationals, Eligibility of; Travel Grants, Foreign Faculty and Researchers; also specific nations
Foreign Languages. *See* Languages
Foreign Nationals, Eligibility of: 14, 15, 349, 400, 405, 408, 409, 452, 554, 584, 587, 675, 745, 753, 771, 774, 782, 787, 788, 845, 846, 856, 864, 868, 870, 881, 895, 913, 917, 949, 950, 955, 956, 957, 959, 961, 962, 963, 964, 965, 1004, 1085, 1408, 1455, 1710, 1825, 1839, 1869, 1937, 1976, 1977, 2026, 2027, 2036, 2039, 2046, 2058, 2146, 2149, 2150, 2436, 2446, 2448, 2512, 2646; *see also* Foreign Faculty Study Programs; Travel Grants, Foreign Faculty and Researchers; Travel Grants, Foreign Students; Women, Foreign Nationals, Eligibility of; also specific nations
Foreign Policy Studies: 21, 840, 841, 842, 1998
Forest and Range Resources: 2123, 2179, 2206; *see also* Conservation; Ecology; Environmental Studies; Resource Development and Management

Forestry: 225, 919, 1387, 2123, 2129
Forestry, Education: 2127
France: 409, 449, 634, 902, 935, 939, 1624, 1700
Franco-American Relations: 634, 909
Fraternal Organizations, Eligibility Limited to Members of: 1696, 2664, 2672
Freedom: 1491, 1513, 1959, 2000
Freshwater: 2182

G

Gardens. *See* Horticulture; Landscape Design
Gas: 2071; *see also* Petroleum Sciences
Gastroenterology: 2404, 2405, 2406, 2407, 2408, 2412, 2413
Gay and Lesbian Issues: 234, 978, 979, 980, 982, 984, 985, 991, 993, 1008, 1012, 1090, 1273, 1387, 1432, 1490; *see also* Acquired Immunodeficiency Syndrome (AIDS); Minority Affairs
Genetics: 201, 1422, 2107, 2149, 2157, 2158, 2242, 2261, 2278, 2282, 2283, 2284, 2288, 2289, 2361, 2413, 2462, 2466, 2473, 2483, 2508, 2517, 2518, 2582; *see also* Biological Sciences; Birth Defects; Medical Research; Reproduction Research
Genocide Studies: 643
Geochemistry: 2042, 2086
Geodesy: 2086, 2660; *see also* Earth Sciences; Engineering; Mathematics
Geographic Information Systems/Land Information Systems 2033, 2034, 2660
Geography: 835, 845, 1821, 1843, 1861, 2073, 2074, 2075, 2076, 2081, 2175; *see also* Area Studies; Earth Sciences; Social Sciences
Geology: 4, 1792, 1834, 1835, 2071, 2072, 2077, 2080, 2081, 2086, 2087, 2142, 2525; *see also* Earth Sciences; Mineral Sciences
Geophysics: 1792, 1816, 1826, 1834, 1835, 1843, 2047, 2072, 2086, 2087, 2089, 2175; *see also* Earth Sciences; Physical Sciences; Physics
Georgia: 246, 323, 338, 453, 722, 1193, 1214, 1219, 1257, 1600
Geospatial Sciences: 2033
Geriatrics and Gerontology: 155, 1425, 1452, 1473, 2216, 2222, 2225, 2226, 2227, 2268, 2547; *see also* Aged
Germany: 592, 643, 654, 872, 912, 916, 917, 954, 1615, 1624, 1657, 1700
Gerontology. *See* Geriatrics and Gerontology
Glaciology: 1834, 1835; *see also* Earth Sciences; Geology
Government: 57, 129, 152, 186, 282, 843, 1145, 1207, 1866, 1868, 1949, 1990, 1991, 1992, 1993, 1996, 1997, 1998, 2000, 2006, 2010, 2012, 2017, 2018, 2019; *see also* Community Government; Political Science; Public Administration
Government, Internships: 1027, 1059, 1064, 1987, 1994, 2005, 2008, 2009, 2011, 2013, 2016, 2192, 2566
Graphic Arts: 457, 555, 1922; *see also* Arts; Creative Arts; Design; Fine Arts; Visual Arts
Graphic Communications: 2614, 2615
Great Britain. *See* England; Ireland; Scotland
Greece: 351, 353, 355, 432, 885, 886, 887, 888, 889, 890, 891, 892, 893, 894, 972, 988
Greece, Eligibility Limited to Descendants of: 972, 988, 1080
Growth Factor Research: 2331
Guidance. *See* Counseling and Guidance
Gynecology. *See* Obstetrics and Gynecology

H

Handicapped: 87, 89, 158, 172, 197, 218, 250, 289, 307, 313, 326, 977, 989, 994, 1002, 1106, 1131, 1222, 1265, 1298, 1325, 1391, 1426, 1429, 1431, 1489, 1525, 1606, 1735, 1920, 2186, 2399, 2558, 2559, 2561, 2639; *see also* Education, Special; Occupational Therapy; Rehabilitation; also specific handicapping conditions
Handicapped Children: 1023, 1128, 1133, 1139, 1489, 1606, 2502
Hawaii: 59, 456, 727, 728, 845, 846, 1298, 1601, 2186
Health: 6, 7, 22, 28, 29, 33, 34, 36, 38, 49, 54, 56, 58, 61, 62, 66, 75, 78, 81, 85, 90, 93, 111, 116, 118, 120, 122, 125, 140, 145, 147, 149, 150, 154, 156, 157, 161, 163, 164, 165, 172, 175, 176, 185, 187, 190, 191, 202, 205, 215, 220, 222, 226, 232, 233, 236, 242, 244, 245, 249, 250, 251, 253, 262, 263, 264, 268, 274, 277, 281, 288, 295, 307, 310, 312, 313, 314, 321, 327, 332, 335, 336, 337, 338, 436, 644, 814, 817, 850, 998, 1016, 1024, 1094, 1112, 1113, 1118, 1125, 1131, 1144, 1160, 1163, 1173, 1179, 1180, 1185, 1188, 1192, 1198, 1201, 1206, 1208, 1216, 1217, 1220, 1223, 1224, 1230, 1231, 1234, 1235, 1236, 1238, 1239, 1241, 1243, 1244, 1265, 1266, 1267, 1269, 1278, 1280, 1307, 1312, 1314, 1315, 1320, 1322, 1328, 1336, 1344, 1349, 1361, 1363, 1364, 1369, 1378, 1380, 1385, 1388, 1402, 1403, 1420, 1422, 1427, 1428, 1429, 1430, 1432, 1433, 1434, 1435, 1436, 1441, 1443, 1444, 1448, 1450, 1451, 1458, 1459, 1462, 1464, 1469, 1500, 1502, 1509,

1514, 1535, 1581, 1613, 1629, 1637, 2231, 2254, 2270, 2276, 2297, 2308, 2314, 2351, 2418, 2542, 2670; *see also* Medicine; Public Health; Social Welfare; entries beginning with Health

Health Administration: 110, 155, 1045, 1431, 1440, 2314, 2522

Health Agencies: 113, 164, 1171, 2266

Health Agencies, Construction and Facilities Projects: 115, 196, 2314; *see also* Construction and Facilities Projects; Health; Hospitals, Construction and Facilities Projects

Health and Human Services: 2, 8, 29, 30, 44, 48, 49, 52, 53, 56, 67, 79, 84, 100, 121, 133, 152, 164, 171, 207, 234, 241, 272, 287, 296, 299, 312, 339, 431, 458, 466, 538, 817, 1012, 1117, 1123, 1140, 1177, 1199, 1200, 1225, 1233, 1239, 1249, 1251, 1252, 1256, 1260, 1272, 1273, 1284, 1287, 1293, 1294, 1297, 1314, 1322, 1340, 1365, 1370, 1371, 1375, 1398, 1400, 1470, 1479, 1486, 1501, 1511, 1528, 1548, 1601, 1815

Health and Medical Research. *See* Medical Research

Health and Well-Being: 18, 132, 184, 266, 1139, 1140, 1176, 1275, 1438, 1439, 1533, 2559

Health Care: 32, 35, 50, 68, 69, 73, 94, 98, 128, 130, 136, 138, 144, 155, 166, 171, 177, 194, 203, 220, 223, 227, 228, 238, 257, 275, 286, 291, 299, 313, 316, 325, 328, 330, 333, 372, 458, 466, 829, 983, 1017, 1070, 1081, 1088, 1117, 1140, 1143, 1155, 1158, 1162, 1167, 1170, 1174, 1182, 1192, 1194, 1213, 1222, 1240, 1277, 1308, 1310, 1311, 1317, 1327, 1337, 1348, 1350, 1355, 1360, 1386, 1419, 1421, 1423, 1424, 1426, 1427, 1428, 1430, 1432, 1433, 1437, 1440, 1441, 1442, 1443, 1444, 1448, 1456, 1457, 1458, 1459, 1461, 1464, 1466, 1469, 1478, 1483, 1484, 1503, 1509, 1514, 1610, 1641, 1654, 1774, 2107, 2117, 2269, 2275, 2277, 2280, 2484, 2491, 2560; *see also* Medical and Health Services

Health Care Facilities: 167, 196, 209, 261, 275, 299, 338, 410, 1133, 1400, 1424, 1444, 1458, 1461, 1466, 1467, 1469, 2322

Health Care Practitioners. *See* Medical and Health Practitioners

Health Journalism. *See* Journalism, Medical and Health; Publication Prizes, Medical and Health Sciences

Health Policy Research: 1025, 1360, 1418, 1424, 1427, 1954, 2324, 2325

Health Sciences: 968, 1430, 1455, 1581, 1615, 1748, 1806, 2105, 2189, 2246, 2249, 2379

Health Sciences, Education: 1, 227, 1132, 1442, 1459, 1460, 1471, 1553, 1734, 1760, 2247, 2248, 2280, 2294, 2391, 2488; *see also* Medical Education and Training

Health Services. *See* Medical and Health Services

Healthy Eating: 1437

Hearing Defects. *See* Deafness and Hearing Impairments

Heart Disease. *See* Cardiology and Cardiovascular Diseases

Heating: 2649, 2650

Hebrew Studies. *See* Judaism

Helicopter. *See* Aeronautics; Aviation

Hematology: 2149, 2235, 2236, 2245, 2252, 2263, 2288, 2354, 2369, 2396, 2411, 2448, 2531

Hemophilia: 2288

Hepatology: 2250, 2251, 2405, 2410

Herpetology: 1809

High School Seniors, Scholarships and Financial Aid: 429, 1045, 1063, 1108, 1109, 1383, 1598, 1663, 1676, 1678, 1682, 1683, 1713, 1736, 1737, 1738, 1743, 1746, 1769, 1772, 1840; *see also* Education, Higher, Aid Programs for Undergraduate and Graduate Students in All Disciplines; Education, Loan Funds

Higher Education. *See* Education, Higher, Research, Project, and General Support

Hispanics: 973, 974, 986, 990, 1003, 1006, 1063, 1064, 1065, 1066, 1067, 1068, 1288, 1395, 1892, 1981, 1982, 1985, 2091, 2139, 2140, 2151, 2349, 2567; *see also* Spanish-Speaking Americans

Histology: 2363

Historic Preservation and Restoration: 61, 69, 86, 109, 111, 183, 245, 259, 265, 302, 376, 409, 412, 416, 420, 441, 615, 616, 617, 621, 725, 1094, 1160, 1239, 1284, 1293, 1322, 2190, 2204

Historic Site Administration: 183, 616, 617, 644, 645; *see also* Museum Administration

History: 25, 56, 186, 350, 355, 357, 368, 371, 402, 403, 404, 446, 466, 578, 581, 585, 586, 592, 597, 599, 605, 607, 608, 609, 616, 629, 631, 634, 646, 679, 835, 844, 869, 1040, 1078, 1332, 1507, 1632, 1777, 1801, 1856, 1998, 2604; *see also* Area Studies, also area studies by name; Classical Studies; Ethnology; Humanities; Labor, History; Law, History; Medicine, History; Medieval Studies; Military History; Political History; Religion, History; Renaissance Studies; Sciences, History; Social History; Social Sciences; Technology, History; Theatre, History; also specific disciplines which lend themselves to an historical approach

History, African: 399, 578, 901

History, American: 346, 371, 373, 389, 393, 576, 577, 578, 579, 587, 592, 593, 594, 595, 602, 603, 604, 606, 612, 613, 614, 615, 616, 618, 619, 620, 622, 624, 631, 633, 635, 636, 637, 644, 647, 648, 1839, 1866, 1995, 1997, 1998, 1999, 2001, 2017

History, American–Colonial: 345, 395, 584, 612, 624, 625, 626

History, American–Contemporary: 2006, 2018

History, Asian: 578

History, Canadian: 578, 634, 1836

History, English: 373, 396, 408, 479, 578

History, European: 396, 397, 577, 578, 593, 598, 643, 832, 889, 926, 927, 942, 1093

History, Latin American: 578, 584, 587

History, Publication: 489, 577, 578, 583, 587, 595, 597, 601, 610, 612, 613, 622, 627, 1526, 2537; *see also* Publication Prizes, History and Humanities

History, Research and Study: 349, 356, 362, 367, 370, 373, 383, 387, 389, 392, 393, 395, 396, 399, 579, 580, 581, 584, 586, 591, 593, 598, 618, 620, 623, 625, 626, 628, 629, 631, 637, 639, 640, 641, 642, 644, 645, 647, 1093, 1706, 1745, 2001

History, Research and Study Abroad: 351, 374, 432, 600, 634, 643, 868, 883, 885, 890, 892, 893, 895, 899, 901, 949, 1706

History, Teaching Methods: 645

Home Economics: 956, 2669, 2674; *see also* Food Technology; Housing; Nutrition; Technology

Homelessness: 195, 1222, 1300, 1306, 1329, 1486; *see also* Disadvantaged; Poverty Programs; Urban Affairs

Horticulture: 1697, 2112, 2114, 2119, 2121, 2122, 2129, 2134, 2138, 2178, 2180; *see also* Arboriculture; Botany; Floriculture

Hospice: 1434

Hospital Administration. *See* Health Administration

Hospitality: 1766

Hospitality Management: 1571

Hospitals: 1, 43, 89, 108, 109, 223, 237, 264, 280, 289, 304, 331, 340, 1181, 1188, 1257, 1266, 1424, 1426, 1429, 1466, 2266, 2285, 2314, 2322; *see also* Health Care Facilities; Medical and Health Services; Medicine

Hospitals, Construction and Facilities Projects: 196, 261, 300, 306, 1279, 2314; *see also* Construction and Facilities Projects

Hotel Management: 2611

Housing and Shelter: 112, 122, 172, 232, 250, 621, 1121, 1184, 1185, 1192, 1198, 1236, 1269, 1292, 1300, 1301, 1327, 1330, 1356, 1366, 1390, 1392, 1466, 1481, 1487, 1585, 1936, 2128; *see also* Community Development; Homelessness; Poverty Programs; Social Welfare; Urban Affairs; Urban and Regional Planning

Human Relations: 147; *see also* Race Relations

Human Resources: 1817; *see also* Labor

Human Rights: 80, 129, 141, 173, 213, 354, 865, 949, 983, 1030, 1052, 1198, 1472, 1491, 1513, 1812, 1873, 1936

Human Sciences: 2674

Human Values: 142, 1130, 1552, 1804, 1833, 1870, 2583; *see also* Ethics

Humanities: 7, 14, 15, 23, 54, 115, 130, 149, 172, 191, 205, 220, 232, 254, 281, 283, 292, 364, 365, 368, 376, 378, 379, 384, 401, 403, 404, 594, 643, 915, 939, 1053, 1168, 1194, 1265, 1349, 1370, 1379, 1500, 1528, 1615, 1669, 1754, 1836, 1850, 1872, 1876, 1947, 1964, 2003, 2010; *see also* Arts; Social Sciences; specific disciplines

Humanities, Curriculum Development 363, 507

Humanities, International Cooperative Programs: 853

Humanities, Publication, Exhibition, and Public Information Projects: 363, 375, 384, 472, 1380, 1848; *see also* Publication Prizes, History and Humanities

Humanities, Related to Other Disciplines: 347, 365, 405, 1817, 1833

Humanities, Research and Study: 345, 347, 358, 359, 360, 361, 362, 365, 370, 373, 377, 378, 380, 381, 382, 383, 385, 386, 387, 388, 389, 390, 391, 392, 393, 394, 395, 396, 397, 398, 399, 400, 405, 406, 582, 584, 598, 623, 828, 858, 1005, 1053, 1669, 1791, 1802, 1804, 1817, 1871, 1872, 1873, 1874, 1875, 1876, 1964, 2023

Humanities, Research and Study Abroad 354, 366, 374, 859, 868, 870, 873, 880, 881, 883, 893, 895, 906, 908, 913, 940, 1628, 1673

Humanities, Teaching Methods: 1130

Humanities, Workshops and Seminars: 348, 365, 381, 391

Humor: 680

Hunger: 195, 200, 326, 1174, 1221, 1307, 1314, 1482, 1492, 1493, 1508; *see also* Disadvantaged; Poverty Programs, Social Welfare

Huntington's Disease: 2466, 2476; *see also* Neuromuscular Disorders

Hydrology: 2086, 2184, 2620

I

Iberia: 655; *see also* Europe; specific nations

Iceland: 884

Ichthyology: 1809, 2142

Idaho: 168, 241, 459, 1008, 1510, 2169

Illinois: 1, 35, 71, 101, 102, 106, 119, 122, 136, 268, 277, 296, 319, 327, 460, 815, 1009, 1181, 1182, 1206, 1307, 1338, 1698, 1711, 1822, 1849, 2185

Illustration: 240, 508, 697, 702; *see also* Graphic Arts

Immigrant Resettlement: 1376, 1622

Immigration Studies. *See* Ethnology

Immunology: 177, 301, 996, 2039, 2157, 2252, 2324, 2325, 2335, 2337, 2338, 2352, 2408, 2430, 2431, 2432, 2448; *see also* Microbiology

In-Service Training Projects: 713, 856, 912, 990, 1813, 1894, 1932, 1939, 1956, 1968, 2191, 2578, 2668; *see also* specific disciplines

India: 652, 877, 903, 941, 1624, 1642, 1700

Indiana: 29, 206, 461, 726, 1233, 1251, 1307, 1393, 1699, 1849, 2119

Industrial Arts and Education: 2614, 2615, 2653; *see also* Education, Technical; Education, Vocational

Industrial Development: 2606

Industrial Relations: 1706

Industry and Industrial Research: 1900, 1966, 2063, 2067, 2069; *see also* Technology, Industrial

Infectious Diseases: 2339, 2533; *see also* Immunology; Microbiology

Information Sciences: 235, 713, 714, 715, 716, 729, 734, 837, 1409, 1888, 1889, 1923, 2269, 2604; *see also* Communications; Computer Sciences; Educational Media; Libraries and Librarianship

Inner-City: 31, 136, 305, 1130, 1149, 1150, 1300, 1356; *see also* Community Development; Urban Affairs

Instructional Materials: 866, 1607; *see also* Communications; Curriculum Development; Education; Educational Media

Instrumentation, Biomedical: 2295

Insurance: 1899, 2091; *see also* Business; Finance

Interdisciplinary Research and Study: 360, 845, 846, 1817, 1833, 2101; *see also* Humanities, Related to Other Disciplines; Medicine, Related to Other Disciplines; Sciences, Related to Other Disciplines

Interior Design: 412, 479

Internal Medicine. *See* Medicine, Internal

International Development: 24, 848, 856, 949, 951, 1304, 1305, 1495; *see also* Developing Nations

International Education. *See* Education, Comparative

International Exchange. *See* Cultural Exchange Programs; Educational Exchange Programs; International Study and Research Programs

International Law. *See* Law, International

International Market. *See* Trade

International Migration: 1622

International Projects and Seminars: 943, 1624, 1648, 1915, 2028, 2029; *see also* Humanities, International Cooperative Programs; Medicine, International Cooperative Programs; Scientific Research and Development, International Cooperative Programs; Social Sciences, International Cooperative Programs

International Relations and International Affairs: 57, 80, 129, 135, 173, 643, 662, 664, 831, 833, 836, 837, 838, 839, 840, 841, 842, 844, 845, 846, 847, 848, 849, 851, 853, 855, 856, 857, 860, 862, 863, 864, 865, 932, 936, 942, 943, 944, 949, 1022, 1085, 1494, 1497, 1644, 1706, 1745, 1794, 1931, 1978, 1997, 2014, 2015; *see also* Area Studies; Economics, International: Environment, International; Law, International; Political Science, International; Social Sciences; also specific nations and disciplines of international concern

International Security: 57, 841, 842, 1868

International Study and Research Programs: 344, 354, 405, 652, 731, 835, 843, 848, 849, 852, 854, 856, 858, 859, 861, 863, 866, 867, 869, 871, 873, 874, 875, 876, 877, 878, 879, 884, 885, 898, 899, 900, 901, 902, 903, 904, 905, 906, 907, 908, 909, 910, 911, 912, 914, 916, 918, 919, 920, 921, 922, 923, 926, 927, 928, 929, 931, 933, 934, 936, 938, 940, 941, 942, 943, 944, 945, 946, 947, 948, 949, 950, 952, 953, 954, 968, 1085, 1304, 1305, 1592, 1605, 1622, 1623, 1628, 1648, 1673, 1700, 1706, 1915, 1971, 1972, 2046, 2069, 2110, 2132, 2166, 2178, 2545, 2667; *see also* specific disciplines, research and study abroad

International Travel: 832, 856, 877, 943; *see also* Travel Grants, Foreign Faculty and Researchers

Internships. *See* In-Service Training Projects

Interracial Cooperation. *See* Race Relations

Inventory. *See* Materials Handling

Iowa: 463, 1009, 1134, 1166, 1284, 1307, 1625

Ireland: 675, 851, 1700

Islam: 870; *see also* Religion

Israel: 195, 278, 823, 826, 829, 868, 914, 953, 955, 968, 983, 997, 1016, 1123, 1308, 1628, 2130

Italian-American Relations: 577, 601, 1015

Italy: 344, 351, 366, 554, 573, 577, 600, 745, 940, 952, 1015, 1700, 1720

Italy, Eligibility Limited to Descendants of: 1015, 1681, 1720, 1742

J

Japan: 452, 852, 858, 921, 922, 930, 954, 966, 1624, 1700; *see also* Orient

Japanese-American Relations: 838, 853, 860, 866, 924, 2005

Japanese Studies: 838, 852, 924, 1703

Jazz: 481, 527, 528, 532; *see also* Music

Jewish Life: 27, 90, 145, 203, 598, 643, 647, 648, 649, 650, 820, 823, 826, 878, 983, 997, 1016, 1123, 1211, 1280, 1360, 1559, 1711; *see also* Judaism

Job Preparedness: 97, 132, 207, 319, 341, 1116, 1184, 1361, 1519; *see also* Labor, Employment and Training

Journalism: 63, 104, 149, 186, 219, 225, 681, 843, 912, 1667, 1750, 1763, 1926, 1929, 1931, 1933, 1936, 1937, 1938, 1940, 1941, 1942, 1945, 1950, 1951, 1952, 1953, 1954, 1955, 1957, 1960, 1964, 2000, 2002; *see also* Communications; News Reporting: Public Relations; Publications; Writers and Writing

Journalism, Education: 37, 193, 1001, 1551, 1750, 1930, 1932, 1935, 1937, 1948, 1949, 1951, 1954, 1956, 1958, 1962, 1964

Journalism, Internships: 1920, 1927, 1932, 1939, 1956, 1987, 2010

Journalism, Medical and Health: 1660, 1939

Journalism, Religious: 1019, 1961

Journalism, Scientific: 1920, 1921, 1930, 1946, 2099

Judaism: 27, 145, 195, 278, 647, 648, 676, 677, 818, 820, 823, 826, 923, 1010, 1211, 1308, 1372, 1432, 1511, 1705; *see also* Religion

Judicial Administration: 1408, 1990

Judicial Reform: 1412

Junior Colleges: 823; *see also* Education; Education, Higher, Research, Project, and General Support

Justice: 91, 129, 141, 178, 205, 244, 1198, 1212, 1241, 1327, 1409, 1490, 1491, 1492, 1951; *see also* Criminal Justice; Judicial Reform; Juvenile Justice; Law; Law Enforcement

Juvenile Delinquency: 1410, 1412, 1413; *see also* Children; Youth

Juvenile Justice: 273, 1394, 1412, 1413, 1509

K

Kansas: 187, 475, 1038, 1045, 1095, 1195, 1288, 1446, 1514

Kentucky: 166, 465, 602, 1009, 1086, 1276, 2119, 2211

Korea: 840, 902, 1624

L

Labor: 21, 25, 251, 1281, 1936, 1948, 1966, 1969; *see also* American Indians and Alaskan Natives, Employment; Business; Business Development Assistance; Economics; Equal Employment Opportunity; Industrial Development; Management; Women, Employment

Labor, Economics: 1345, 1903

Labor, Employment and Training: 5, 45, 46, 112, 136, 143, 179, 195, 231, 250, 305, 313, 316, 319, 969, 1116, 1269, 1281, 1330, 1815, 1965, 1967, 1968, 1969

Labor, History: 593, 644, 647

Labor, Management Relations: 1968

Labor, Manpower Research: 1969

Labor, Unemployment: 1210, 1969

Land Use Management: 258, 1287, 1376, 1869, 2118

Landmark Preservation. *See* Historic Preservation and Restoration

Landscape Design: 344, 367, 416, 1022, 2166, 2178, 2186; *see also* Architecture

Language Teachers, Study and Research Abroad: 656, 920, 925, 943, 944; *see also* Faculty, Study and Research Programs Abroad; International Study and Research Programs

Languages: 403, 512, 585, 648, 657, 1592, 1595, 1916, 2030; *see also* Esperanto; Humanities; Linguistics; Translation

Languages, Asian: 652, 852, 853, 1801

Languages, Classical: 356, 651, 885, 1093

Languages, Germanic: 654, 657, 743, 832, 916, 942, 1801

Languages, Latin and Romance: 573, 651, 656, 657, 743, 1093, 1972

Languages, Mid- and Near-Eastern: 882

Languages, Modern: 362, 661, 1801

Languages, Publication Projects: 658; *see also* Translation; Writers and Writing

Languages, Research and Study: 362, 648, 658, 659, 662, 664, 933, 934, 1093, 1592

Languages, Research and Study Abroad: 374, 652, 656, 663, 843, 882, 910, 911, 920, 924, 926, 933, 934, 935, 942, 943, 949

Languages, Semitic: 25

Languages, Slavic: 657, 743, 920

Laser Physics: 2037

Latin and South America: 184, 862, 933, 934, 943, 1937, 2213; *see also* Area Studies; History; Languages; Literature; also specific nations

Latin and South American Nationals, Eligibility of: 151, 578, 961, 963, 1929, 1937, 1979, 2296

Law: 383, 643, 837, 869, 915, 948, 1669, 1745, 1793, 1794, 1865, 1970, 1973, 1975, 1983, 2010, 2017; *see also* Citizen Action Legislation; Civic Affairs; Community Services; Crime Prevention; Environmental Law; Judicial Reform; Justice; Juvenile Delinquency; Maritime Law; Public Administration; Race Relations

Law, Criminal. *See* Criminal Justice

Law, Education: 709, 970, 1030, 1071, 1628, 1673, 1793, 1971, 1972, 1980, 1981, 1982, 1984, 1985, 1986

Law Enforcement: 1409, 1411

Law, History: 396, 578, 891, 1673, 1970

Law, International: 21, 843, 865, 906, 912, 951, 1706, 1976, 1977, 1978, 1979

Law, Internships: 1980

Law Library: 709, 710, 1984; *see also* Library Science, Education; Library Services and Collection Utilization

Law, Preventive: 1973, 1975

Law, Publication: 1974

Leadership Development: 41, 128, 184, 206, 230, 298, 549, 1000, 1025, 1029, 1105, 1254, 1363, 1396, 1446, 1458, 1509, 1522, 1552, 1583, 1587, 1692, 2004, 2005, 2544, 2605; *see also* Community Leadership

Learning Disabilities: 1122, 1557, 1568, 1569, 1570; *see also* Education, Special

Learning Process and Memory: 221, 659, 1588, 1593, 2467, 2584; *see also* Behavioral Sciences; Education

Legal Ethics: 1971

Legal Research: 1970, 1971

Legal Services: 122, 1394, 2491

Leukemia: 2263, 2441, 2448, 2531; *see also* Cancer; Hematology

Libraries and Librarianship: 12, 61, 82, 109, 186, 197, 235, 267, 291, 366, 375, 382, 586, 711, 712, 714, 717, 719, 720, 727, 728, 730, 734, 740, 1188; *see also* Art Galleries; Educational Media; Information Sciences; Law Library; Medical Library; Museums; Scientific Library

Libraries and Librarianship, Elementary and Secondary School: 711, 712, 723, 1188

Library Acquisitions: 719, 734, 852

Library Administration: 186, 644, 733; *see also* Management

Library Construction and Facilities: 10, 733, 1188; *see also* Construction and Facilities Projects

Library Science, Continuing Education: 716, 721, 733, 735

Library Science, Education: 585, 708, 709, 710, 713, 714, 715, 716, 717, 720, 722, 723, 726, 729, 735, 736, 737, 739, 741, 742, 744, 837, 962, 999, 1616

Library Science, Research: 366, 714, 715, 716

Library Services and Collection Utilization: 719, 727, 728, 730, 733, 734, 740, 1188

Life Sciences: 377, 968, 1003, 1832, 1842; *see also* Biological Sciences; Medicine; Sciences; also specific life sciences

Life Sciences, Research and Study: 1813, 1814, 2067, 2110

Lifelong Learning. *See* Education, Adult

Lighting Research: 2186

Linguistics: 659, 837, 883, 901, 1040, 1539, 1540, 2026, 2030; *see also* Languages

Literacy: 22, 52, 97, 104, 190, 291, 295, 326, 734, 1128, 1139, 1258, 1280, 1352, 1361, 1495, 1549, 1551, 1556, 1610, 1660, 1905

Literary Criticism: 672, 673, 694; *see also* Writers and Writing

Literature: 3, 25, 240, 357, 403, 404, 439, 440, 445, 446, 448, 453, 460, 461, 464, 465, 467, 474, 477, 479, 482, 486, 488, 490, 503, 512, 513, 523, 584, 585, 630, 643, 657, 658, 661, 681, 684, 685, 687, 688, 705, 755, 869, 1632, 1926; *see also* Languages; Publications; Reading; Writers and Writing

Literature, African: 684

Literature, American: 267, 345, 346, 371, 373, 671, 688

Literature, Asian: 684

Literature, Classical: 356, 679, 885, 1093; *see also* Classical Studies

Literature, Comparative: 402, 1801

Literature, English: 267, 373, 408, 698, 1789

Literature, European: 832, 926, 927, 1093

Literature, Publication Projects: 472, 1208; *see also* Manuscript Prizes; Publication Prizes

Literature, Research and Study: 362, 373, 383, 669, 672, 673, 704, 1093

Literature, Research and Study Abroad: 344, 374, 883, 899, 935, 949

Liver: 2250, 2251, 2405, 2410; *see also* Metabolism and Metabolic Disorders

Loan Funds: 617; *see also* Education, Loan Funds

Louisiana: 49, 184, 436, 467, 594, 595, 1275, 1292, 1407, 1599

Lunar Science: 2052; *see also* Aerospace Sciences

Lung. *See* Respiratory and Pulmonary Diseases

Lutheranism: 817, 1525

M

Magazines: 472, 1920, 1921, 1936, 1942, 1955; *see also* News Reporting; Publications

Maine: 51, 205, 240, 469, 691, 1131, 1332, 1483, 1492, 1903, 2524

Mammalogy: 1809, 2142

Management: 4, 298, 1792; *see also* Arts Administration; Business Administration; Educational Administration; Hotel Management; Labor; Library Administration; Museum Administration; Restaurant Management and Food Service

Management, Education: 1006, 1645, 1787, 1892, 1893, 1897

Manpower. *See* Labor

Manufacturing and Distribution: 1966

Manuscript Completion: 697; *see also* Writers and Writing; specific disciplines

Manuscript Prizes, Medical and Health Sciences: 730, 2500, 2591, 2592

Manuscript Prizes, Nonfiction: 601, 619, 622, 624, 629, 635, 636, 661, 689, 705, 715, 724, 801, 803, 813

Manuscript Prizes, Poetry and Fiction: 665, 667, 681, 682, 689, 695, 699, 701, 706

Manuscript Prizes, Sciences: 2591, 2592, 2627, 2654

Marine Biology: 2087, 2141, 2169, 2193, 2196, 2201

Marine Policy. *See* Ocean Management and Marine Policy

Marine Resource Conservation: 59

Marine Sciences: 1575, 1809, 1817, 1830, 1832, 1835, 2078, 2083, 2084, 2087, 2177, 2193, 2213, 2647; *see also* Oceanography; Sciences

Marketing: 1893, 1894, 1904, 1934; *see also* Advertising; Business; Public Relations

Maryland: 31, 194, 208, 435, 471, 699, 1111, 1115, 1226, 1281, 1317, 1361, 1609, 1714, 2205

Mass Communications. *See* Broadcast Media; Communications; Journalism; Print Media

Mass Spectrometry: 2032

Massachusetts: 36, 53, 69, 112, 249, 263, 276, 305, 342, 375, 421, 472, 605, 606, 607, 608, 609, 691, 1075, 1106, 1129, 1131, 1178, 1185, 1243, 1267, 1290, 1311, 1381, 1382, 1383, 1410, 1461, 1466, 1483, 1487, 1505, 1512, 1551, 1585, 1715, 1716, 2326

Materials Handling: 2599

Materials Science: 901, 968, 1816, 1826, 1832, 1843, 2044, 2108, 2665, 2677, 2678

Maternal Health Care: 175, 2502; *see also* Health; Medical and Health Services

Mathematics: 4, 170, 298, 1013, 1014, 1124, 1581, 1824, 1832, 1842, 1843, 1920, 2042, 2093, 2094, 2095, 2096, 2609, 2641, 2642; *see also* Computer Sciences; Sciences; Statistics

Mathematics, Education: 170, 1005, 1039, 1047, 1071, 1076, 1126, 1376, 1519, 1581, 1602, 1607, 1801, 1802, 1840, 2091, 2092, 2096, 2097, 2615

Mathematics, Research and Study: 1020, 1813, 1814, 1826, 2092, 2098, 2108, 2642

Mathematics, Research and Study Abroad: 904, 953, 968

Measurement Sciences: 2037, 2665

Mechanical Arts. *See* Industrial Arts and Education

Media. *See* Communications; also specific media forms

Media Arts: 438, 440, 445, 448, 460, 461, 462, 465, 467, 513, 1087, 1924, 1957, 1962; *see also* Arts

Medical Administration. *See* Health Administration

Medical and Health Practitioners: 35, 1081, 1417, 1427, 1433, 1654, 2221, 2419, 2420, 2498, 2522; *see also* Medical and Health Services; Midwifery; Nursing

Medical and Health Services: 1, 17, 50, 51, 58, 155, 177, 178, 239, 258, 260, 267, 301, 308, 1012, 1225, 1360, 1374, 1417, 1421, 1448, 1462, 1463, 1467, 1468, 1469, 1471, 1478, 1506, 1509, 1514, 1572, 1654, 1701, 2229, 2275, 2314, 2322, 2324, 2325, 2493, 2533, 2555, 2582; *see also* Health Care Facilities; Hospitals

Medical Conference, Symposia, and Workshops: 1654, 1660, 2335

Medical Costs: 1417, 1421, 1468, 1654, 1660, 2275, 2531

Medical Education and Training: 155, 175, 177, 289, 331, 372, 1045, 1071, 1081, 1098, 1132, 1430, 1450, 1458, 1463, 1659, 1660, 1661, 1715, 1799, 1802, 1840, 2225, 2227, 2230, 2236, 2253, 2266, 2280, 2281, 2286, 2291, 2292, 2294, 2296, 2298, 2314, 2332, 2338, 2339, 2386, 2388, 2389, 2425, 2450, 2483, 2522, 2524, 2525, 2527, 2557, 2582; *see also* Midwifery; Nursing Education; specific diseases and areas of medicine by name

Medical Education and Training, Armed Services: 2332

Medical Education and Training, Outside of U.S.: 1563, 1784, 2246, 2247, 2248, 2250, 2251, 2333, 2449

Medical Ethics: 2107; *see also* Bioethics

Medical Facilities, Construction Grants 2334; *see also* Construction and Facilities Projects; Hospitals, Construction and Facilities Projects

Medical Journalism. *See* Journalism, Medical and Health

Medical Library: 729, 730, 962, 999; *see also* Library Science, Education; Library Services and Collection Utilization

Medical Research: 68, 85, 93, 105, 106, 107, 212, 221, 239, 251, 264, 288, 291, 294, 301, 330, 331, 372, 586, 1106, 1279, 1298, 1368, 1422, 1428, 1442, 1456, 1460, 1463, 1529, 1621, 1841, 1843, 1845, 2039, 2108, 2146, 2156, 2179, 2214, 2215, 2217, 2218, 2219, 2220, 2222, 2223, 2225, 2226, 2227, 2232, 2235, 2237, 2240, 2241, 2243, 2244, 2255, 2256, 2260, 2262, 2264, 2271, 2272, 2273, 2274, 2276, 2278, 2282, 2283, 2284, 2285, 2287, 2289, 2292, 2293, 2297, 2299, 2300, 2301, 2302, 2303, 2304, 2305, 2306, 2308, 2310, 2311, 2313, 2315, 2322, 2323, 2324, 2325, 2327, 2331, 2334, 2337, 2339, 2353, 2354, 2356, 2363, 2367, 2368, 2385, 2386, 2387, 2388, 2396, 2398, 2399, 2401, 2402, 2403, 2407, 2408, 2409, 2412, 2414, 2416, 2417, 2418, 2419, 2420, 2422, 2423, 2427, 2430, 2438, 2439, 2440, 2441, 2442, 2446, 2447, 2454, 2456, 2457, 2458, 2460, 2461, 2462, 2466, 2473, 2483, 2505, 2508, 2509, 2510, 2514, 2515, 2518, 2519, 2526, 2530, 2531, 2532, 2533, 2538, 2541, 2542, 2543, 2549, 2558, 2568, 2575; *see also* diseases and areas of medicine by name

Medical Research, Outside U.S.: 930, 948, 966, 1615, 1657, 2146, 2215, 2249, 2252, 2267, 2333, 2410, 2436

Medical Research, Supplies and Equipment: 2295, 2426, 2429, 2515; *see also* Sciences, Equipment and Facilities

Medical Technology: 807, 1417, 1660, 2230, 2234, 2329, 2330, 2389, 2526, 2533; *see also* Dental Laboratory Technology

Medicine: 5, 7, 46, 89, 124, 128, 192, 204, 247, 277, 284, 314, 334, 335, 337, 449, 915, 937, 1182, 1421, 1465, 1528, 1574, 2229, 2257, 2258, 2265, 2270, 2271, 2273, 2276, 2278, 2280, 2291, 2300, 2301, 2302, 2311, 2313, 2324, 2325, 2334, 2338, 2368, 2457, 2459, 2475, 2481, 2490, 2526, 2537, 2553, 2568; *see also* Biomedical Sciences and Research; Health; Hospitals; Surgery; also diseases and areas of medicine by name

Medicine, Academic: 1657, 1660, 2224, 2244, 2310, 2386, 2388, 2413, 2501

Medicine, Diagnostic: 181, 2231, 2330, 2389, 2446

Medicine, Experimental: 2039

Medicine, Family Practice: 2221, 2266

Medicine, History: 586, 1081, 2537; *see also* Sciences, History

Medicine, Internal: 2367, 2368, 2412

Medicine, International Cooperative Programs: 1615, 2281

Medicine, Organ Transplant: 2419

Medicine, Preventive: 177, 1437, 2225, 2226, 2227, 2260, 2427, 2446, 2533

Medicine, Public Information Projects: 177, 1417, 1463, 2334, 2533; *see also* Community Education

Medicine, Publication: 2252, 2291, 2568; *see also* Journalism, Medical and Health; Manuscript Prizes, Medical and Health Sciences; Publication Prizes, Medical and Health Sciences

Medicine, Related to Other Disciplines: 2334, 2390, 2549

Medieval Studies: 357, 610, 630, 893; *see also* History; Humanities; Literature

Mediterranean Area: 352

Memory. *See* Learning Process and Memory

Mental and Emotional Health: 31, 226, 244, 330, 817, 986, 1171, 1371, 1386, 1388, 1425, 1442, 1488, 1639, 1865, 2562, 2564, 2565, 2569, 2571, 2575, 2579, 2580, 2581, 2582, 2594

Mental Health Services: 95, 280, 974, 983, 1327, 1360, 1433, 1509, 1514, 2267, 2582, 2593, 2594; *see also* Medical and Health Services

Mental Retardation: 326, 1106, 1391, 2552, 2571, 2590

Metabolism and Metabolic Disorders: 2157, 2282, 2283, 2284, 2361, 2409, 2422, 2423

Metallurgy: 1818, 1819, 1842, 1843, 2677, 2678, 2679, 2680; *see also* Materials Sciences; Physical Sciences; Technology, Mining

Meteorology: 1834, 1835, 2081, 2620; *see also* Atmospheric Sciences; Climatology

Mexican-Americans. *See* Spanish-Speaking Americans

Mexicans, Eligibility of: 834, 970, 2677

Mexico: 141, 834, 902, 1265, 2030, 2610

Michigan: 75, 150, 184, 222, 297, 321, 336, 377, 474, 995, 1009, 1088, 1125, 1161, 1162, 1194, 1220, 1246, 1277, 1289, 1299, 1302, 1309, 1310, 1328, 1348, 1388, 1403, 1554, 2119

Microbiology: 1786, 2039, 2139, 2140, 2151, 2152, 2261, 2288, 2338, 2352; *see also* Biological Sciences

Middle East: 868, 870, 895, 907, 913, 933, 934; *see also* Area Studies; History; Languages; Literature; Social Sciences; also specific nations

Midwestern States: 109, 179, 1009, 2500; *see also* states by name

Military History: 578, 631, 638, 639, 640, 641, 642; *see also* History

Military Sciences: 2644; *see also* Defense Projects and Research

Mineral Sciences: 2079, 2680; *see also* Geology; Materials Sciences; Sciences

Minimal Brain Dysfunction. *See* Learning Disabilities

Mining. *See* Technology, Mining

Minnesota: 38, 97, 200, 215, 228, 317, 330, 450, 464, 696, 733, 1101, 1102, 1166, 1167, 1168, 1186, 1191, 1200, 1259, 1264, 1282, 1344, 1354, 1359, 1390, 1429, 1495

Minority Affairs: 120, 152, 172, 216, 316, 331, 978, 979, 982, 1192, 1487, 1494, 1574, 1610, 1727, 2296, 2633; *see also* Equal Educational Opportunity; Equal Employment Opportunity; Poverty Programs; Race Relations; Social Welfare; Urban Affairs; also specific minority groups

Minority Community and Institutional Development: 122, 1396, 1454, 1538; *see also* Community Development

Minority-Group Members, Eligibility of: 411, 710, 713, 717, 752, 811, 970, 973, 974, 975, 981, 982, 986, 990, 992, 999, 1000, 1003, 1004, 1005, 1011, 1013, 1014, 1019, 1020, 1022, 1026, 1028, 1064, 1065, 1066, 1067, 1431, 1520, 1539, 1540, 1616, 1658, 1670, 1797, 1816, 1892, 1902, 1920, 1983, 1988, 2091, 2139, 2140, 2151, 2186, 2280, 2289, 2290, 2296, 2506, 2522, 2567, 2607, 2653; *see also* specific minority groups

Minority-Owned Businesses: 1049; *see also* Business Development Assistance

Minority Studies: 391, 399, 407, 1018, 1021, 1061, 1538, 1849; *see also* American Indians and Alaskan Natives; Asian-Americans; Blacks; Spanish-Speaking Americans; specific minority groups

Mississippi: 49, 76, 184, 1275, 1552

Missouri: 50, 117, 153, 187, 475, 1009, 1095, 1143, 1144, 1241, 1288, 1357, 1717, 1718

Molecular Biology: 221, 1786, 2151, 2157, 2261, 2421, 2454, 2457, 2518, 2519

Molecular Physics: 2037, 2057, 2101

Money and Banking. *See* Banking

Montana: 241, 1008, 1331, 1398, 1510, 2169

Morocco: 1700

Morphology: 2537

Mortuary Education. *See* Funeral Service; Thanatology

Motion Pictures. *See* Film

Multidisciplinary Studies. *See* Interdisciplinary Research and Study

Multiple Sclerosis: 2469, 2470, 2471, 2472, 2476, 2477, 2478; *see also* Neuromuscular Disorders

Muscular Atrophy: 2525

Muscular Dystrophy: 2473

Museology: 725

Museum Administration: 631, 644, 645, 731; *see also* Historic Site Administration

Museum Education: 562, 611, 643, 731, 738, 1051

Museums: 43, 82, 93, 101, 122, 197, 229, 260, 423, 444, 446, 453, 470, 488, 500, 513, 549, 556, 643, 725, 727, 728; *see also* Cultural Affairs; Historic Preservation and Restoration; Libraries and Librarianship

Museums, Acquisitions: 470

Museums, Collection Utilization and Maintenance: 470, 552, 725, 727, 728

Music: 3, 89, 122, 133, 253, 277, 340, 433, 442, 446, 448, 453, 460, 461, 464, 467, 474, 481, 484, 486, 488, 490, 500, 512, 513, 515, 523, 527, 574, 749, 760, 763, 768, 773, 775, 781, 784, 832, 916, 955, 1087, 1313, 1748, 2030; *see also* Choir; Opera; Performing Arts

Music, Competitions: 528, 746, 747, 748, 750, 751, 753, 754, 761, 762, 769, 770, 771, 772, 774, 776, 777, 780, 781, 782, 784, 785, 787, 789, 790, 791, 795, 797, 798

Music, Composition: 344, 439, 468, 477, 484, 486, 510, 522, 745, 746, 747, 748, 749, 754, 757, 762, 763, 767, 769, 776, 777, 778, 779, 783, 784, 785, 790, 1926

Music, Conducting: 745, 749, 763

Music, Education: 507, 528, 745, 752, 755, 759, 764, 765, 769, 770, 777, 779, 781, 786, 787, 788, 793, 794, 796, 797, 1801

Music, Festivals: 757, 778

Music, History: 649, 650, 768

Music, Instrumentalists: 745, 753, 755, 756, 758, 759, 761, 766, 769, 770, 771, 774, 777, 782, 787, 791, 794, 795, 796, 797

Music, Lyricists and Vocalists: 745, 753, 763, 773, 777, 780, 787, 789, 792, 796; *see also* Choir; Opera

Music, Publication: 751

Music, Research and Study Abroad: 449, 574, 745, 765

Music, Therapy: 779, 2556

Music, Workshops and Residencies: 443, 477, 496, 510, 756, 778, 781

Myasthenia Gravis: 2473, 2474

Mycology: 2155; *see also* Botany

N

National Security: 933, 934, 1084, 1868; *see also* Defense Projects and Research
Native American Art 484
Native Americans. *See* American Indians and Alaskan Natives
NATO Member Countries: 967
Natural History: 2191
Natural Resources: 23, 79, 134, 173, 200, 1277, 1387, 1388, 2182, 2183, 2197, 2198, 2208, 2597; *see also* Conservation; Energy Resources and Utilization; Environmental Studies; Forest and Range Resources; Land Use Management; Mineral Sciences; Petroleum Studies; Resource Development and Management; Water Resources
Natural Sciences: 15, 64, 241, 908, 930, 937, 1013, 1014, 1619, 1805, 1817, 1920, 1921, 2045, 2135, 2201; *see also* Physical Sciences; Sciences
Natural Sciences, Education: 1045, 2108
Near East: 879, 923; *see also* Area Studies; History; Languages; Literature; Social Sciences; also specific nations
Nebraska: 84, 237, 252, 257, 475, 482, 1405
Neonatology: 2487
Nephrology: 2228, 2229, 2355, 2356, 2357, 2358, 2417, 2418, 2419, 2420, 2421, 2422, 2423
Netherlands: 1700
Neurobiology: 2151, 2161, 2352, 2466, 2575
Neurological Research: 2326, 2360, 2370, 2371, 2452, 2453, 2455, 2456, 2459, 2462, 2466, 2468, 2470, 2472, 2474, 2475, 2476
Neurological Research Training: 2464, 2469, 2471, 2477, 2480, 2482
Neurology: 2242, 2331, 2368, 2454, 2457, 2458, 2460, 2461, 2462, 2481, 2483, 2507
Neuromuscular Disorders: 2463, 2466, 2473, 2474, 2475, 2476, 2477, 2478, 2480, 2481, 2482, 2483; *see also* specific diseases
Neurophysiology: 2480, 2482
Neuropsychiatry: 2592
Neurosciences: 221, 974, 1452, 2042, 2216, 2254, 2259, 2261, 2326, 2331, 2454, 2455, 2456, 2460, 2462, 2465, 2466, 2467, 2481, 2518, 2519, 2570, 2575, 2582, 2592
Neurosurgery: 2273, 2454, 2468, 2479; *see also* Surgery
Nevada: 275, 483, 498, 1560
New England States. *See* Eastern States; also states by name
New Hampshire: 485, 691, 735, 1131, 1179, 1483
New Jersey: 32, 46, 167, 175, 265, 486, 534, 616, 617, 618, 619, 620, 736, 1024, 1145, 1150, 1166, 1351, 1396, 1693, 1694, 1695, 1728, 1729, 1730, 2525
New Mexico: 92, 184, 187, 545, 703, 737, 1012, 1038, 1045, 1265, 1337, 2305
New York: 5, 46, 65, 109, 167, 178, 182, 244, 278, 286, 302, 384, 464, 487, 488, 489, 534, 544, 621, 622, 997, 1119, 1129, 1215, 1222, 1244, 1258, 1266, 1279, 1386, 1441, 1612, 1647, 1677, 1731, 1732, 1733, 1734, 1737, 1761, 1762, 1894, 2008, 2009, 2010, 2011, 2184, 2194, 2428, 2438
New Zealand: 903, 1700
News Reporting: 1750, 1920, 1925, 1927, 1928, 1931, 1935, 1936, 1941, 1952, 1953, 1954, 1956, 1960; *see also* Journalism
Newspaper: 382, 1920, 1921, 1925, 1932, 1936, 1941, 1942, 1953, 1955, 1956; *see also* Communications; Journalism; Publications
Nonfiction: 666, 667, 689, 694, 703, 1936; *see also* Journalism; Literature; Manuscript Prizes, Nonfiction; Publication Prizes; Writers and Writing; also specific disciplines
Nonprofit Organizations. *See* areas of interest to nonprofit organizations
North Carolina: 79, 108, 110, 127, 183, 248, 285, 490, 739, 1136, 1228, 1404, 1503, 1532, 1581, 1591, 1600, 1638, 1736
North Dakota: 491, 1054, 1186
Norway: 884, 932, 949, 1617; *see also* Scandinavia
Novel: 692; *see also* Publication Prizes, Creative Writing; Writers and Writing
Nuclear Medicine: 2328, 2329
Nuclear Proliferation: 841, 842, 857; *see also* Arms Control
Nuclear Sciences: 1813, 1814, 2062, 2101, 2634, 2635, 2636, 2637, 2638, 2639; *see also* Energy Resources and Utilization; Engineering; Physical Sciences; Radiology and Radiation Sciences; Sciences
Numismatics: 348, 581, 582
Nurse-Midwifery. *See* Midwifery
Nursery Schools. *See* Preschool Education and Care
Nursing: 1427, 1553, 2442, 2449, 2484, 2489, 2490, 2492; *see also* Hospitals; Medicine
Nursing Education: 289, 1641, 1732, 1743, 2298, 2442, 2484, 2485, 2488, 2490, 2491, 2492, 2494, 2495, 2498, 2499; *see also* Medical Education and Training
Nursing Research: 2442, 2474, 2484, 2486, 2487, 2488, 2489, 2493, 2496, 2497

Nutrition: 184, 225, 250, 850, 956, 1120, 1154, 1307, 1437, 1508, 1820, 1920, 1975, 2187, 2351, 2361, 2402, 2406, 2533, 2668, 2669, 2671, 2672; *see also* Agricultural Sciences; Dietetics; Food Technology; Home Economics; Medicine
Nutrition Research: 2402, 2427, 2670, 2671, 2675

O

OAS Member Countries: 856
Obstetrics and Gynecology: 2244, 2459, 2487, 2500, 2501
Occupational Safety and Health: 132, 146, 1090, 2107, 2648; *see also* Health; Industry and Industrial Research
Occupational Therapy: 334, 2554, 2556; *see also* Handicapped; Health; Rehabilitation
Ocean Engineering: 1830, 1846, 2083, 2084, 2647, 2663
Ocean Management and Marine Policy: 1830, 2083, 2084, 2196; *see also* Environmental Studies
Oceanography: 968, 1829, 1830, 1834, 1843, 1846, 2038, 2042, 2081, 2083, 2084, 2087, 2193, 2196, 2620, 2644; *see also* Earth Sciences; Physical Sciences
Ohio: 70, 77, 124, 126, 146, 152, 169, 209, 242, 246, 492, 1148, 1158, 1208, 1210, 1211, 1237, 1276, 1285, 1342, 1355, 1379, 1388, 1401, 1450, 1604, 1739, 1740, 2109, 2119, 2314
Oklahoma: 187, 288, 431, 475, 493, 545, 1038, 1045, 1341, 1637
Oncology. *See* Cancer
Opera: 486, 526, 528, 539, 765, 779, 780, 789, 792, 798; *see also* Music; Performing Arts
Ophthalmology: 1422, 2507, 2508, 2509, 2511, 2512, 2514, 2516, 2518, 2519, 2520; *see also* Visual Disorders
Optics: 2037, 2503, 2509
Optometry: 334, 2332, 2503, 2504, 2505, 2509, 2513, 2516
Oregon: 62, 72, 232, 241, 494, 1008, 1183, 1196, 1345, 1494, 1510, 2169
Organ Transplant. *See* Medicine, Organ Transplant
Ornithology: 1809, 2142, 2162, 2179; *see also* Zoology
Orphanages. *See* Children, Adoption and Foster Care
Orthopaedics. *See* Podiatry and Orthopaedics
Osteopathic Medicine: 334, 1661, 2266, 2522, 2523, 2524, 2525
Otology: 2521

P

Pacific Area: 845, 846, 2449; *see also* Area Studies; History; Languages; Literature; also specific nations
Pacific Islanders, Eligibility of: 975, 1005, 1058, 1595, 1616, 2139, 2140
Pain: 1137, 2368; *see also* Neurology
Painting: 439, 468, 474, 478, 498, 505, 506, 514, 543, 551, 555, 559, 567, 572, 731, 955; *see also* Arts; Creative Arts; Fine Arts
Painting, Workshops and Residencies: 344, 510, 522, 548, 570
Pakistan: 828
Paleobiology: 1839, 2158
Paleontology: 1809, 1810, 2020, 2081, 2086, 2137, 2142; *see also* Geology
Paralysis: 2559
Parapsychology: 2585, 2586, 2587, 2588
Parasitology: 2039, 2151
Parkinson's Disease: 2260, 2456, 2476, 2480, 2481, 2482
Parks and Recreation. *See* Recreation
Pathology: 2285, 2410, 2421; *see also* Cytopathology: related sciences
Pathology, Plant. *See* Plant Physiology and Pathology
Peace. *See* International Relations and International Affairs
Pediatric Nursing: 2485
Pediatrics: 1462, 2244, 2255, 2386, 2459, 2487, 2526, 2527, 2528, 2529, 2530, 2531, 2532; *see also* Child Welfare and Health
Peer Monitoring: 2559
Pennsylvania: 103, 125, 156, 192, 223, 265, 271, 300, 301, 340, 495, 1023, 1033, 1146, 1155, 1190, 1205, 1270, 1273, 1293, 1326, 1349, 1350, 1373, 1743, 1753, 2119, 2286, 2311, 2491, 2640
Penology. *See* Correctional Institutions and Procedures
Performing Arts: 43, 89, 107, 159, 166, 172, 215, 229, 253, 260, 286, 346, 366, 427, 428, 433, 434, 437, 438, 440, 442, 445, 446, 448, 449, 450, 453, 456, 465, 467, 469, 471, 472, 475, 481, 482, 483, 484, 485, 486, 490, 491, 492, 493, 494, 495, 496, 498, 500, 502, 503, 511, 512, 518, 523, 526, 527, 538, 564, 749, 750, 755, 758, 764, 765, 766, 767, 772, 776, 780, 788, 791, 792, 797, 798, 1026, 1087, 1180, 1313, 1536, 1666, 1692; *see also* Arts; Cultural Affairs; Dance; Music; Theatre
Performing Arts, Research and Study Abroad: 898
Performing Arts, Workshops and Residencies: 537
Periodontology: 2344, 2351
Pesticides: 2207

Petroleum Sciences: 1782, 2031, 2071, 2090, 2208; *see also* Earth Sciences

Pharmacy and Pharmacology: 334, 1003, 2216, 2229, 2261, 2271, 2289, 2308, 2309, 2421, 2483, 2534, 2537, 2539, 2540, 2541, 2542, 2543; *see also* Morphology

Pharmacy and Pharmacology, Education: 1, 1614, 2535, 2536, 2539, 2544, 2545

Philanthropy: 134, 184, 192, 206, 252, 263, 293, 342, 632, 829, 1131, 1149, 1172, 1173, 1209, 1212, 1214, 1221, 1233, 1238, 1257, 1274, 1276, 1367, 1482, 1554, 1591, 1742, 2239

Philology. *See* Linguistics

Philosophy: 314, 368, 403, 404, 630, 643, 679, 705, 893, 1744, 1801; *see also* Humanities; Political Philosophy

Philosophy, Classical. *See* Classical Studies

Philosophy, Renaissance. *See* Renaissance Studies

Philosophy, Research and Study: 362, 383

Philosophy, Research and Study Abroad: 374

Photogrammetry: 2033, 2034; *see also* Photography; Surveying

Photography: 429, 453, 468, 470, 481, 498, 506, 510, 514, 522, 528, 544, 553, 555, 570, 571, 573, 1955; *see also* Creative Arts; Fine Arts; Visual Arts

Physical Education: 1447, 2548

Physical Fitness: 1447, 2427

Physical Sciences: 15, 298, 377, 937, 1806, 1817, 1828, 1834, 1842, 2058, 2101, 2326, 2613, 2661; *see also* Chemistry; Materials Sciences; Natural Sciences; Nuclear Sciences; Physics; also specific physical sciences

Physical Sciences, Education: 1005, 1045, 1084, 1802, 1816, 2036, 2100

Physical Sciences, Research and Study: 1020, 1813, 1814, 1836, 2037, 2039, 2041, 2101

Physical Sciences, Research and Study Abroad: 953, 1615, 2036

Physical Therapy: 334, 2550, 2551, 2554, 2556, 2557; *see also* Rehabilitation

Physics: 953, 968, 1757, 1801, 1816, 1826, 1829, 1832, 1834, 1835, 1842, 1843, 2041, 2042, 2058, 2099, 2102, 2103, 2104, 2108, 2175, 2201, 2615, 2661; *see also* Mathematics; Nuclear Sciences; Physical Sciences

Physiology: 201, 1825, 2039, 2151, 2157, 2160, 2261, 2289, 2331, 2421; *see also* Biological Sciences; related sciences

Physiotherapy: 2488

Planetology: 2052, 2058

Plant Physiology and Pathology: 1816, 2120, 2151; *see also* Botany

Plastic Surgery: 2217, 2218, 2219, 2220, 2273, 2312

Playwrights: 468, 496, 530, 533, 534, 535, 536, 537, 540, 696; *see also* Drama; Literature; Theatre; Writers and Writing

Podiatry and Orthopaedics: 334, 1023, 2288, 2300, 2301, 2302, 2517, 2549, 2553

Poetry: 479, 498, 522, 653, 667, 669, 674, 681, 682, 684, 685, 687, 688, 689, 695, 698, 703, 706, 707; *see also* Literature; Manuscript Prizes, Poetry and Fiction; Publication Prizes, Creative Writing; Writers and Writing

Poetry, Publication Support: 681, 682

Poetry, Translation: 660, 665, 669, 687

Poland: 925, 926, 927, 928

Poland, Eligibility Limited to Descendants of: 1655, 1710

Police. *See* Law Enforcement

Policy Analysis: 866, 1540, 1868, 1870

Political History: 345, 592, 1777, 1995, 1998, 1999, 2001, 2002, 2018

Political Philosophy: 368, 383, 403, 2001, 2012; *see also* Political Science

Political Science: 4, 80, 157, 198, 604, 643, 835, 837, 844, 869, 1777, 1855, 1856, 1949, 1988, 1989, 1996, 1998, 2000, 2002, 2007, 2015, 2017, 2030; *see also* Area Studies; Government; International Relations and International Affairs; Social Sciences

Political Science, Education: 1091, 1103, 1745, 1801, 1866, 1891, 1988, 1989

Political Science, International: 831, 843, 845, 847, 932, 951, 1706, 1998, 2007

Political Science, Internships: 1027, 1059, 1064, 1987, 1991, 1993, 2003, 2005, 2010, 2011, 2013

Political Science, Research 1989, 2001

Political Science, Research and Study Abroad: 906, 949

Pollution. *See* Air Pollution; Environmental Pollution; Water Pollution

Population Planning: 80, 258, 850, 2107, 2183

Population Studies: 43, 80, 159, 845, 846, 2107, 2212, 2244; *see also* Developing Nations, Population Studies; Family Planning; Social Sciences; Sociology

Portugal: 655, 656, 830; *see also* Iberia

Poverty Programs: 26, 129, 152, 179, 222, 228, 249, 290, 296, 829, 994, 1052, 1083, 1118, 1131, 1146, 1174, 1198, 1208, 1248, 1300, 1325, 1356, 1363, 1461, 1464, 1466, 1482, 1485, 1487, 1494, 1501, 1508,

1849, 1967; *see also* Community Development; Equal Educational Opportunity; Equal Employment Opportunity; Minority Affairs; Race Relations; Social Welfare

Pre-Collegiate Education: 279

Presbyterianism: 821, 1749

Preschool Education and Care: 87, 142, 1118, 1126, 1145, 1150, 1151, 1401, 1531, 1601; *see also* Child Welfare and Health

Press: 1954, 1959

Preterm Birth and Preterm Birth Prevention: 2283

Primary Care: 1437

Print Media: 467, 1926, 1943, 1954; *see also* Communications; Journalism; Magazines; Newspaper; Publications

Printing and Publishing Industry: 468, 670, 1534, 2608, 2614, 2615

Printmaking: 439, 498, 514, 551, 567, 626, 2608; *see also* Crafts

Production Planning: 2206, 2599

Professional Development: 1006, 1556, 1766, 1909

Prosthetics. *See* Orthotics and Prosthetics

Protestantism: 88, 214, 810, 812, 813

Psychiatry: 449, 1182, 2288, 2298, 2483, 2562, 2564, 2565, 2569, 2570, 2575, 2579, 2581, 2582, 2591, 2592; *see also* Mental and Emotional Health; Psychology

Psychical Manifestations: 2586, 2587, 2588

Psychology: 4, 362, 402, 906, 968, 1182, 1539, 1540, 1832, 1855, 1879, 1880, 1881, 1882, 1883, 1885, 2015, 2030, 2261, 2483, 2566, 2568, 2570, 2572, 2573, 2574, 2575, 2576, 2579, 2589; *see also* Behavioral Sciences; Child Psychology; Mental and Emotional Health; Psychiatry; Social Psychology; Social Sciences

Psychology, Education: 1801, 2567, 2577

Psychology, Experimental: 1887

Psychology, Internships: 2577

Psychology, Organizational: 1887

Psychology, Research and Study: 1857, 1879, 1880, 1881, 1882, 1883, 1885

Psychotherapy: 2563, 2578

Public Administration: 26, 225, 1103, 2002, 2009, 2010, 2013, 2016, 2017; *see also* Government; Law Enforcement; Political Science

Public Affairs: 8, 45, 99, 114, 191, 196, 231, 232, 335, 843, 1022, 1074, 1105, 1528, 1646, 1898, 2006, 2015; *see also* Civic Affairs

Public Art 484, 492

Public Assistance: 1494, 1532

Public Broadcasting: 94

Public Health: 225, 292, 837, 845, 850, 974, 1025, 1256, 1266, 1303, 1325, 1358, 1423, 1425, 1441, 1446, 1448, 1450, 1451, 1458, 1660, 1812, 2184, 2207, 2208, 2215, 2376, 2377, 2378, 2379, 2380, 2381, 2382, 2383, 2546, 2572; *see also* Environmental Studies; Health; entries beginning with Medical and Medicine; Social Welfare

Public Information Programs: 45, 865, 1515, 1516, 1517, 1518, 1868, 1930; *see also* Communications; Community Education; Cultural Events, Community; Humanities, Publication, Exhibition, and Public Information Projects; Medicine, Public Information Projects; Sciences, Public Information and Citizen Involvement Projects; Publication Prizes, Public Information

Public Policy: 130, 173, 405, 843, 912, 1066, 1145, 1180, 1196, 1406, 1450, 1485, 1774, 1850, 1954, 1996, 2014, 2015, 2017, 2566

Public Policy Research: 120, 188, 847, 1103, 2184, 2198

Public Service: 173, 333, 997, 1030, 1415, 2005, 2019; *see also* Public Administration; Social Services

Public Welfare. *See* Social Welfare

Publication Assistance: 267, 622, 624, 670, 695, 852, 1074, 1665, 1848, 2606; *see also* specific fields

Publication Prizes, Creative Writing: 674, 676, 677, 678, 680, 681, 683, 685, 686, 688, 691, 692, 699, 700, 707, 1926

Publication Prizes, Education: 1557

Publication Prizes, History and Humanities: 452, 489, 577, 578, 583, 587, 595, 596, 597, 610, 619, 627, 661, 666, 675, 676, 677, 678, 694, 700, 804, 825, 1936, 1938, 1940, 2018, 2024

Publication Prizes, Medical and Health Sciences: 2222, 2568

Publication Prizes, Public Information: 1925, 1928, 1929, 1942

Publication Prizes, Sciences: 597, 694, 1921, 2025, 2063, 2099

Publication Prizes, Social Sciences: 2024

Publications: 830, 1526, 1926, 1938; *see also* Fiction; Journalism; Literature; Magazines; Manuscript Completion; Manuscript Prizes; Newspaper; Novel; Playwrights; Poetry; Translation; Writers and Writing; also specific fields

Publishing Industry. *See* Printing and Publishing Industry

Puerto Rican Community Development. *See* Minority Community and Institutional Development; Minority-Owned Businesses; Small Business Development

Puerto Ricans. *See* Spanish-Speaking Americans; also any discipline that may be given Puerto Rican emphasis

Puerto Ricans, Eligibility of: 970, 986, 1005, 1892; *see also* Minority-Group Members, Eligibility of
Pulmonary Diseases. *See* Respiratory and Pulmonary Diseases
Purchasing: 1900

R

Race Relations: 26, 122, 983, 1024, 1092, 1130, 1215, 1285, 1497, 1849, 1867, 1936, 2633; *see also* Equal Educational Opportunity; Equal Employment Opportunity; Human Relations; Minority Affairs; Poverty Programs; Social Welfare
Racial Equity: 184
Radio and Television: 453, 653, 955, 1920, 1921, 1924, 1936, 1938, 1943, 1944, 1945, 1947, 1958; *see also* Broadcast Media; Communications; Educational Media; Social Sciences; Technology, Communications; Telecommunications
Radiology and Radiation Sciences: 2039, 2233, 2259, 2316, 2317, 2318, 2319, 2320, 2321; *see also* Medicine; Nuclear Sciences; Physical Sciences
Range Resources. *See* Forest and Range Resources
Rape. *See* Sexual Abuse
Reading: 363, 1047, 1556, 1557, 2584; *see also* Education and entries beginning with Education or Educational
Real Estate: 1891; *see also* Appraisal; Business; Finance
Recreation: 4, 29, 125, 197, 291, 312, 1029, 1107, 1144, 1173, 1236, 1280, 1287, 1310, 1318, 1325, 1336, 1371, 1385, 1403, 1404, 1447, 1474, 1565, 2183, 2191; *see also* Athletics; Community Development; Sports; Urban and Regional Planning
Refrigeration: 2649, 2650
Regional Planning. *See* Urban and Regional Planning
Rehabilitation: 5, 46, 1132, 2256, 2399, 2459, 2496, 2546, 2548, 2551, 2553, 2558, 2559; *see also* Corrective Therapy; Education, Special; Handicapped; Narcotics; Occupational Therapy; Physical Therapy; Vocational Rehabilitation
Relief Organizations: 829, 1192, 1268; *see also* Community Funds; Community Services; Emergency Grants
Religion: 3, 40, 47, 49, 72, 83, 111, 139, 157, 161, 191, 205, 206, 214, 245, 250, 294, 314, 362, 383, 403, 643, 799, 800, 805, 806, 807, 817, 822, 824, 825, 826, 827, 1010, 1112, 1181, 1193, 1211, 1260, 1266, 1399, 1430, 1465, 1721, 1804, 2003, 2030; *see also* Catholicism; Christianity; Islam; Journalism, Religious; Judaism; Lutheranism; Protestantism
Religion, Comparative: 809
Religion, History: 589, 590, 801, 802, 803, 804, 806, 813, 818
Religion - Interfaith 1222
Religion, Research and Study Abroad: 799, 898, 923, 1666
Religious Denominations, Eligibility Limited to Members of: 812, 813, 814, 819, 821, 822, 826, 1211, 1476, 1748, 1749
Religious Education: 94, 210, 217, 322, 806, 808, 809, 811, 812, 817, 819, 820, 821, 1010, 1430, 1563, 1748
Religious Institutions: 108, 109, 191, 275, 277, 322, 807, 822, 998; *see also* Construction and Facilities Projects
Remote Sensing: 2033, 2034, 2175
Renaissance Studies: 357, 366, 370, 386, 392, 396, 952; *see also* Arts; History; Literature; Philosophy
Renal Diseases. *See* Nephrology
Reproduction Research: 1825, 2149, 2283, 2284, 2501; *see also* Biological Sciences; Family Planning; Genetics; Medicine; Population Studies
Research: 14, 130, 151, 213, 378, 508, 632, 851, 852, 908, 920, 937, 984, 1357, 1435, 1614, 1660, 1902, 2020, 2058, 2063, 2074, 2082, 2129, 2216, 2242, 2257, 2283, 2284, 2297, 2326, 2334, 2396, 2517, 2520, 2598; *see also* Educational Research; Medical Research; Scientific Research and Development; Technological Research; also specific fields of interest
Research Training: 1455, 1597, 1871, 1874, 1875, 2037, 2218, 2391, 2406, 2415, 2419, 2420, 2520, 2540, 2564, 2565; *see also* specific disciplines
Residential Artist or Scholar Programs: 344, 345, 349, 359, 361, 367, 383, 388, 399, 405, 437, 443, 455, 459, 477, 496, 510, 558, 559, 584, 625, 809, 868, 952, 1754, 1839, 2023, 2166; *see also* specific disciplines
Resource Development and Management: 99, 115, 845, 862, 1817, 1830, 2123, 2190, 2192, 2193, 2198, 2202; *see also* Developing Nations, Resource Development; Energy Resources and Utilization; Environmental Studies; also specific resources
Respiratory and Pulmonary Diseases: 1449, 2261, 2338, 2385, 2386, 2387, 2388, 2391, 2392, 2398, 2488
Respiratory and Pulmonary Diseases, Research Training: 2338, 2386, 2388, 2485, 2488

Restaurant Management and Food Service: 1154, 1698, 1909, 2612, 2668, 2676
Restoration. *See* Historic Preservation and Restoration
Rheumatology and Rheumatic Diseases: 330, 2241, 2324, 2325, 2450, 2451
Rhode Island: 61, 280, 316, 376, 497, 691, 2016
Rockefeller Organizations: 632
Rural Development: 184, 1130, 1337, 1380, 1394, 1727, 1869, 2128, 2133; *see also* Agricultural Sciences; Cooperatives, Rural and Consumer; Sociology; Urban and Regional Planning
Russia: 843, 854, 902, 920; *see also* other former republics of the U.S.S.R.
Russian Studies. *See* Slavic and East Europe

S

Sabbatical. *See* Faculty, Study and Research Programs
Safety. *See* Occupational Safety and Health; Social Welfare; Traffic Engineering and Safety
Safety: 1336, 2670
Salivary Research: 2331
Sanitation: 2673; *see also* Engineering; Environmental Pollution; Health; Solid Waste Management, Wastewater Management
Scandinavia: 543, 884; *see also* Europe; specific nations
Schools. *See* entries beginning with Education and Educational
Science, Communications: 1930, 1943
Science, Technology, Engineering and Mathematics Education: 147, 1033, 1832
Sciences: 3, 8, 11, 12, 25, 47, 49, 60, 72, 204, 227, 238, 247, 255, 293, 309, 314, 377, 466, 597, 906, 915, 1124, 1222, 1433, 1454, 1528, 1581, 1640, 1808, 1824, 1825, 1827, 1831, 2082, 2096, 2108, 2642, 2643; *see also* specific sciences
Sciences, Conferences and Symposia: 1833, 1842, 2157, 2158
Sciences, Curriculum Development and Teaching Methods: 1607, 2280
Sciences, Education: 17, 170, 240, 258, 262, 271, 989, 1038, 1039, 1045, 1047, 1076, 1126, 1433, 1519, 1581, 1602, 1607, 1612, 1746, 1798, 1822, 1837, 1840, 1930, 2033, 2034, 2057, 2062, 2089, 2096, 2139, 2140, 2187, 2271, 2609, 2634, 2635, 2636, 2637, 2638, 2639; *see also* specific sciences
Sciences, Equipment and Facilities: 10, 2157, 2158, 2645; *see also* specific sciences
Sciences, Ethics: 1833; *see also* Bioethics; Medical Ethics
Sciences, History: 349, 373, 580, 596, 597, 1832, 1839, 2537, 2604, 2628
Sciences, In-Service Programs: 1817, 1846, 1920, 2566, 2643
Sciences, Public Information and Citizen Involvement Projects: 472, 1607, 1943; *see also* Community Education
Sciences, Publication Projects: 1921, 1930, 1946, 2167, 2339; *see also* Journalism, Scientific; Manuscript Prizes, Sciences; Publication Prizes, Sciences
Sciences, Related to Other Disciplines: 1554, 1833, 1920, 1930, 2010
Sciences, Research and Study Abroad: 904, 917, 940, 948, 953, 968
Scientific Exchange Programs: 917, 1657, 2052, 2178
Scientific Research and Development: 14, 15, 28, 212, 318, 768, 953, 995, 1276, 1416, 1445, 1453, 1460, 1575, 1614, 1621, 1806, 1811, 1820, 1821, 1823, 1825, 1826, 1829, 1831, 1833, 1834, 1836, 1838, 1841, 1842, 1843, 2032, 2033, 2034, 2038, 2042, 2052, 2055, 2056, 2083, 2084, 2085, 2115, 2157, 2209, 2215, 2289, 2339, 2417, 2418, 2433, 2434, 2483, 2590, 2649, 2650, 2655; *see also* specific scientific disciplines
Scientific Research and Development, International Cooperative Programs: 401, 966, 967, 968, 2046
Scotland: 374, 937, 938, 2178
Scotland, Eligibility Limited to Descendants of: 938
Sculpture: 351, 439, 468, 474, 478, 498, 499, 506, 514, 522, 551, 555, 559, 567, 955; *see also* Arts; Creative Arts; Fine Arts; Humanities
Sculpture, Workshops and Residencies: 344, 510, 548, 570
Secondary Education. *See* Education, Secondary
Seismology. *See* Earth Sciences
Semantics. *See* Linguistics
Seminars: 348, 428, 433, 523, 1624, 2157, 2158; *see also* Conferences; International Projects and Seminars; Teacher Seminars and Workshops; Travel Grants, Seminar Attendance; Workshops; also specific disciplines
Sensory Function: 2331
Sex Role Stereotyping: 984, 1494, 1849; *see also* Family Life; Women's Rights
Sexual Abuse: 1090, 1865
Skin Diseases. *See* Dermatology
Slavic and East Europe: 647, 648, 657, 854, 920, 933, 934; *see also* Area Studies; History; Languages; Literature; also specific nations

Small Business Development: 97, 1049, 1454, 2518; *see also* Business Development Assistance

Social Change and Development: 129, 145, 156, 825, 850, 982, 1086, 1092, 1186, 1198, 1247, 1465, 1472, 1485, 1492, 1494, 1497, 1510, 1847, 1951, 2117, 2583

Social History: 404, 593, 603, 611, 643, 1839, 2018

Social Justice and Equity: 279, 1394, 1406

Social Psychology: 968, 1877, 1878, 1884, 2583, 2589; *see also* Behavioral Sciences

Social Sciences: 11, 14, 225, 347, 585, 915, 937, 939, 1103, 1182, 1619, 1631, 1669, 1748, 1754, 1806, 1829, 1833, 1849, 1850, 1853, 1854, 1855, 1872, 1876, 1879, 1880, 1881, 1882, 1883, 1885, 1920, 2030; *see also* social sciences by name

Social Sciences, Education: 1005, 1053, 1802, 1806, 1850, 1861, 1862, 1863, 1864

Social Sciences, Publication: 1848, 1879, 1885

Social Sciences, Research and Study: 401, 405, 828, 858, 864, 865, 970, 1127, 1452, 1453, 1498, 1669, 1777, 1802, 1804, 1836, 1851, 1852, 1857, 1859, 1860, 1861, 1862, 1863, 1864, 1867, 1870, 1871, 1872, 1873, 1874, 1875, 1876, 1877, 1878, 1879, 1880, 1881, 1882, 1883, 1884, 1885, 1887, 1970, 2026, 2107, 2463

Social Sciences, Research and Study Abroad: 859, 860, 862, 873, 880, 881, 906, 908, 942, 948

Social Sciences, Teaching: 1859, 1860

Social Services: 5, 8, 17, 22, 24, 25, 28, 29, 30, 31, 33, 35, 40, 46, 51, 52, 53, 58, 60, 61, 62, 69, 74, 75, 81, 93, 97, 103, 111, 112, 113, 117, 119, 123, 125, 127, 136, 138, 146, 150, 160, 167, 169, 172, 176, 180, 189, 196, 199, 200, 207, 209, 216, 220, 226, 228, 233, 235, 245, 248, 251, 257, 260, 263, 265, 268, 281, 283, 292, 304, 307, 309, 313, 317, 318, 325, 338, 369, 371, 377, 644, 814, 817, 998, 1032, 1099, 1111, 1123, 1145, 1158, 1162, 1166, 1173, 1175, 1181, 1191, 1192, 1196, 1197, 1208, 1215, 1224, 1231, 1232, 1234, 1238, 1240, 1241, 1244, 1249, 1250, 1251, 1257, 1258, 1259, 1266, 1267, 1274, 1278, 1280, 1283, 1286, 1291, 1298, 1308, 1310, 1313, 1314, 1326, 1344, 1348, 1354, 1355, 1356, 1369, 1370, 1372, 1386, 1388, 1401, 1404, 1451, 1457, 1461, 1469, 1470, 1474, 1483, 1495, 1500, 1503, 1506, 1507, 1585, 1610, 1629, 1748; *see also* Community Funds; Community Services

Social Welfare: 1, 11, 16, 17, 23, 38, 67, 78, 79, 82, 83, 84, 92, 95, 102, 103, 115, 116, 118, 122, 124, 132, 133, 135, 145, 149, 154, 157, 161, 163, 169, 171, 185, 193, 194, 215, 222, 232, 236, 237, 242, 244, 245, 246, 249, 250, 259, 262, 270, 274, 275, 281, 289, 290, 297, 301, 305, 312, 322, 326, 327, 331, 333, 451, 815, 825, 826, 1016, 1024, 1032, 1058, 1111, 1117, 1131, 1155, 1160, 1168, 1179, 1184, 1185, 1192, 1195, 1198, 1199, 1206, 1210, 1217, 1223, 1225, 1235, 1236, 1239, 1243, 1249, 1256, 1266, 1269, 1277, 1279, 1281, 1284, 1285, 1286, 1289, 1292, 1296, 1303, 1311, 1313, 1315, 1322, 1338, 1339, 1350, 1356, 1363, 1365, 1368, 1376, 1377, 1378, 1380, 1385, 1399, 1402, 1423, 1469, 1475, 1477, 1479, 1486, 1487, 1496, 1497, 1501, 1504, 1506, 1508, 1510, 1512, 1586, 1610, 1870, 1936, 1949, 2594; *see also* Aged; Child Welfare and Health; Health; Human Relations; Minority Affairs; Poverty Programs

Social Welfare, Publication: 1950

Social Work: 225, 837, 2578; *see also* Social Services

Social Work, Education: 986, 1801, 1802

Sociology: 4, 362, 402, 643, 835, 837, 968, 1843, 1855, 1856, 1879, 1885; *see also* Behavioral Sciences; Social Sciences

Sociology, Education: 975, 1745

Solar Energy and Solar Research: 2053; *see also* Atmospheric Sciences; Energy Resources and Utilization; Physical Sciences

Solid State Sciences. *See* Physical Sciences; Sciences

South Africa: 1700

South Carolina: 101, 108, 1209, 1374, 1759

South Dakota: 501

Southern States: 211, 308; *see also* states by name

Space Sciences. *See* Aerospace Sciences

Spain: 1700; *see also* Iberia

Spanish-Speaking Americans: 975, 1000, 1001, 1005, 1018, 1020, 1063, 1064, 1065, 1066, 1067, 1068, 1069, 1988; *see also* Minority-Group Members, Eligibility of; Minority Studies; Race Relations; also any discipline that may be given Spanish-Speaking American emphasis or be of concern to Spanish-Speaking Americans

Special Education. *See* Education, Special

Speech Impairments and Communicative Disorders: 653, 2506

Speech, Language and Hearing Therapy: 2506, 2554; *see also* Rehabilitation

Sports: 324, 954, 1104, 1107, 1282, 1336, 1385, 1447, 2559; *see also* Recreation

Sri Lanka: 873, 874

Staffing Grants. *See* specific disciplines

State Agencies, Eligibility of. *See* areas of interest to state agencies

Statistics: 4, 1539, 1540, 2092, 2097, 2098; *see also* Actuarial Science; Insurance; Mathematics

Stroke: 2376, 2377, 2378, 2379, 2380, 2381, 2382, 2383, 2384, 2400, 2476; *see also* Cardiology and Cardiovascular Diseases

Student Aid Programs. *See* Education, Higher, Aid Programs for Undergraduate and Graduate Students in All Disciplines; also specific disciplines

Substance Abuse: 2, 92, 172, 244, 974, 1389, 1660; *see also* Alcohol Abuse and Alcoholism

Sudden Infant Death Syndrome: 2528; *see also* Medical Research; Pediatrics

Suicide: 1515, 1516, 1517, 1518

Surgery: 2220, 2312, 2516; *see also* Neurosurgery; Plastic Surgery; also diseases and areas of medicine by name

Surveying: 2033, 2034, 2658; *see also* Engineering; Mathematics

Sustainability: 112, 328, 1206

Sweden: 401, 861, 884, 896, 897, 1617; *see also* Scandinavia

Switzerland: 848, 902

Systematic Biology: 2154

Systems Science: 1887, 2615, 2655; *see also* Computer Sciences; Mathematics

T

Taxonomy: 2154

Teacher Education. *See* Education, Teacher Preparation

Teacher Seminars and Workshops: 381, 865, 1596; *see also* Faculty, Study and Research Programs; specific disciplines

Teaching, Outside U.S.: 654, 916, 917, 925, 1596; *see also* Language Teachers, Study and Research Abroad; also specific nations

Technical Assistance: 428, 433, 463, 491, 523, 920, 1212, 1217; *see also* Consulting Services

Technical Education. *See* Education, Technical

Technological Research: 1546, 2598, 2607

Technology: 12, 127, 193, 271, 284, 1096, 1124, 1369, 1454, 1537, 1545, 1546, 1610, 1689, 1690, 1692, 1824, 1833, 1966, 2064, 2609, 2613, 2616, 2662; *see also* Dental Laboratory Technology; Engineering; Industrial Arts and Education; Medical Technology; Sciences

Technology, Aerospace: 2627, 2628

Technology, Communications: 328, 1943, 1958

Technology, History: 349, 593, 599, 644, 1839, 2606

Technology, Industrial: 1966, 2207, 2208, 2614, 2615, 2616, 2653; *see also* Industry and Industrial Research

Technology, Maritime: 2647

Technology, Mining: 2667, 2678, 2679, 2680

Teen Pregnancy: 127, 1024, 1164, 1425, 1443, 1486; *see also* Family Life

Telecommunications: 1750, 2627; *see also* Broadcast Media; Communications; Radio and Television

Television. *See* Radio and Television

Tennessee: 22, 76, 211, 214, 308, 503, 1227, 1272, 1278, 1765

Texas: 89, 163, 164, 185, 187, 189, 209, 226, 281, 319, 320, 475, 504, 509, 545, 546, 547, 636, 637, 741, 994, 1173, 1223, 1242, 1249, 1262, 1265, 1321, 1347, 1367, 1368, 1384, 1389, 1397, 1528, 1746, 2070, 2183, 2349

Textiles: 444

Thanatology: 2107

Theatre: 404, 441, 442, 446, 448, 453, 460, 461, 464, 467, 468, 481, 484, 486, 488, 490, 500, 513, 523, 527, 530, 536, 537, 538, 540, 653, 746; *see also* Drama; Performing Arts; Playwrights

Theatre, Actors and Acting: 528, 536

Theatre Arts, Education: 507, 532, 536

Theatre, Consulting Services: 696

Theatre, Criticism: 526

Theatre, History: 526

Theatrical Design: 536

Theology: 314, 679, 799, 800, 807, 810, 811, 827, 948; *see also* Religion

Therapy. *See* Corrective Therapy; Music Therapy; Occupational Therapy; Physical Therapy; Psychotherapy; Rehabilitation; Speech, Language, and Hearing Therapy

Tourism: 856, 2204

Toxicology: 2067, 2151, 2153, 2207, 2208, 2211, 2261, 2309, 2541, 2542, 2543

Trade: 856, 1916; *see also* International Market; International Relations and International Affairs

Traffic Engineering and Safety: 959, 1415, 1475, 2596, 2607, 2617; *see also* Transportation

Translation: 660, 665, 743; *see also* Languages; Poetry, Translation; Writers and Writing

Transportation: 31, 1376, 1475, 1914, 2176, 2596, 2607, 2617; *see also* Traffic Engineering and Safety

Travel and Tourism: 1766

Travel Grants, Domestic: 508, 539, 547, 589, 590, 702, 713, 1104, 1212, 1806, 1955, 1998, 2335

Travel Grants, Foreign Students: 352, 2667

Travel Grants, Outside U.S.: 351, 409, 547, 569, 1097, 1104, 1869, 1955, 2281

Travel Grants, Seminar Attendance: 1828, 2563, 2613; *see also* Seminars

Tropics: 2179

Tuberculosis: 1449, 2391, 2399, 2488

Turkey: 881, 882, 883, 1700

U

Ukraine: 724

Underdeveloped Nations. *See* Developing Nations

Unemployment. *See* Labor, Unemployment

Union of Soviet Socialist Republics. *See* Baltics; Russia; Ukraine; other former republics of the U.S.S.R.

United Funds: 45, 113, 119, 146, 176, 200, 209, 228, 261, 327, 644

United Kingdom: 903, 960, 2435; *see also* England; Ireland; Scotland; Wales

United Nations: 856

Urban Affairs: 45, 122, 129, 130, 277, 278, 280, 1279, 1306, 1319, 1388, 1392, 1487, 1585, 1849, 1994; *see also* Civic Affairs; Community Development; Community Services; Inner-City; Social Welfare

Urban Affairs, Research and Study Abroad: 1165

Urban and Regional Planning: 37, 42, 409, 416, 417, 837, 912, 973, 1165, 1215, 1392, 1396, 1774, 1855, 1869, 2129, 2183; *see also* Architecture; Community Development; Environmental Studies; Rural Development

Urban History: 413

Urology: 2338, 2417, 2418, 2419, 2420, 2422

Utah: 92, 294, 1886

V

Vacuum Science: 2036, 2100; *see also* Physical Sciences

Values. *See* Human Values

Vascular Diseases: 2397, 2400; *see also* Cardiology and Cardiovascular Diseases

Venereal Disease. *See* Infectious Diseases

Ventilation: 2649, 2650

Vermont: 131, 511, 691, 1131, 1150, 1386, 1799

Veterans' Children and Dependents, Eligibility of: 1659, 1663, 1664, 1729, 1732, 1739, 1756, 1771

Veterans, Eligibility of: 18, 219, 1371, 1664, 1727, 1728

Veterinary Sciences: 334, 2106, 2109, 2131, 2136, 2238, 2239, 2265, 2338; *see also* Animal Sciences; Medicine

Video Arts: 418, 442, 464, 528, 571, 1536, 1962; *see also* Broadcast Media; Communications; Film; Radio and Television; Telecommunications

Violence. *See* Behavioral Sciences

Virgin Islands: 512

Virginia: 513, 514, 1115, 1166, 1296, 1399, 1443, 1496, 1506, 1760, 2211, 2499

Virology: 2261; *see also* Biomedical Sciences and Research; Immunology; Microbiology

Vision Impaired, Eligibility of: 2509

Visual Arts: 215, 260, 344, 402, 427, 428, 433, 434, 437, 438, 440, 441, 442, 445, 446, 448, 450, 453, 454, 460, 461, 464, 465, 467, 468, 469, 470, 471, 472, 473, 475, 481, 482, 483, 486, 488, 490, 493, 494, 495, 503, 511, 512, 513, 514, 518, 523, 528, 544, 545, 546, 547, 549, 550, 553, 565, 566, 570, 573, 980, 1026, 1051, 1087, 1089, 1692, 1747, 1922; *see also* Fine Arts

Visual Arts, Research and Study Abroad: 898

Visual Arts, Workshops and Residencies: 443, 477, 496, 510, 522, 548

Visual Disorders: 2503, 2505, 2507, 2509, 2511, 2512, 2514, 2516, 2517, 2518, 2519, 2520; *see also* Ophthalmology; Optometry

Viticulture and Enology: 2115; *see also* Agricultural Sciences

Vocational Education. *See* Education, Vocational

Vocational Rehabilitation: 969, 1656, 1851, 2561; *see also* Occupational Therapy; Rehabilitation

Volunteer Service: 5, 46, 195, 925, 1189, 1248, 1480, 1709, 2190

Volunteerism: 184, 326, 1105

W

War. *See* International Security

Washington: 62, 241, 245, 292, 993, 1008, 1183, 1313, 1363, 1470, 1510, 1603, 1800, 2169, 2200

Wastewater Management: 2133, 2206, 2208; *see also* Environmental Pollution; Sanitation

Water Pollution: 2175, 2187, 2206, 2211; *see also* Environmental Pollution

Water Resources: 200, 1533, 2133, 2168, 2171, 2177, 2182, 2186, 2202, 2206, 2210, 2597, 2666; *see also* Environmental Studies; Resource Development and Management

Water Sports. *See* Sports

Weapons. *See* Armaments; Defense Projects and Research

Weather Modification: 2175; *see also* Climatology; Meteorology

Weaving: 457; *see also* Crafts; Creative Arts

Welfare. *See* Social Welfare

West Virginia: 516, 1276, 1803, 2119, 2211

Wildlife: 164, 291, 1426, 1809, 1817, 1918, 2111, 2177, 2183, 2191, 2206; *see also* Conservation; Fish and Game Management

Wisconsin: 27, 259, 518, 646, 1009, 1166, 1167, 1168, 1175, 1186, 1259, 1263, 1286, 1291, 1323, 1474, 1659

Women, Education of: 210, 390, 1033, 1052, 1053, 1077, 1081, 1082, 1095, 1097, 1098, 1099, 1101, 1102, 1352, 2072, 2346, 2634

Women, Eligibility of: 390, 583, 588, 812, 988, 992, 1002, 1020, 1053, 1070, 1071, 1072, 1073, 1074, 1075, 1076, 1078, 1080, 1081, 1082, 1084, 1085, 1087, 1088, 1089, 1091, 1092, 1093, 1096, 1097, 1098, 1100, 1104, 1105, 1682, 1756, 1802, 1816, 1836, 1837, 1919, 1920, 2047, 2059, 2072, 2186, 2231, 2346, 2653

Women, Employment: 282, 1079, 1081, 1088, 1090, 1095, 1099, 1101, 1102, 1967, 2231; *see also* Equal Employment Opportunity

Women, Foreign Nationals, Eligibility of: 957, 964, 1085

Women's Health: 1280, 2487

Women's Issues: 93, 103, 120, 122, 123, 140, 141, 172, 190, 313, 316, 1052, 1070, 1075, 1079, 1082, 1086, 1090, 1092, 1099, 1101, 1102, 1105, 1220, 1273, 1280, 1352, 1387, 1395, 1404, 1425, 1513

Women's Rights: 141, 178, 282, 1070, 1075, 1079, 1082, 1083, 1090, 1095, 1105, 1192, 1494

Women's Studies: 390, 585, 588, 1053, 1078, 1079, 1081

Work. *See* Labor

Workers' Rights: 273

Workforce Development 2, 27, 112, 162, 343, 1184, 1292, 1459, 1815

Workshops: 483, 2157, 2158; *see also* Conferences; International Projects and Seminars; Seminars; Teacher Seminars and Workshops; also any discipline that lends itself to a workshop approach

World Affairs. *See* Area Studies; International Relations and International Affairs

Writers and Writing: 139, 346, 429, 457, 468, 481, 498, 508, 522, 524, 535, 634, 658, 666, 667, 668, 670, 674, 680, 681, 683, 684, 685, 686, 687, 688, 689, 690, 692, 693, 694, 698, 700, 701, 702, 703, 801, 803, 804, 805, 825, 869, 1087, 1640, 1921, 1927, 1930, 1935, 1940, 1941, 1946, 2000, 2076; *see also* Art Criticism; Biography; Children's Literature; Drama; Fiction; Journalism; Literary Criticism; Literature; Magazines; Manuscript Completion; Manuscript Prizes; News Reporting; Newspaper; Nonfiction; Novel; Playwrights; Poetry; Publication Prizes; Translation; also specific subjects

Writers and Writing, Publication Support: 686, 697, 1301, 1930, 2373; *see also* specific subjects

Writers and Writing, Subsistence Aid: 671

Writers and Writing, Workshops and Residencies: 443, 477, 496, 509, 510, 548, 668, 696, 703

Wyoming: 92, 523, 1510

Y

Youth: 13, 27, 28, 29, 31, 36, 45, 58, 61, 62, 67, 85, 93, 102, 121, 124, 125, 133, 140, 153, 154, 158, 165, 169, 172, 174, 177, 178, 184, 191, 195, 199, 207, 216, 239, 244, 249, 253, 258, 260, 263, 264, 265, 276, 297, 307, 309, 313, 316, 323, 329, 332, 440, 485, 826, 954, 982, 998, 1029, 1088, 1110, 1112, 1115, 1116, 1123, 1127, 1129, 1130, 1132, 1137, 1138, 1139, 1140, 1143, 1145, 1146, 1147, 1148, 1150, 1152, 1156, 1164, 1167, 1170, 1172, 1192, 1194, 1200, 1201, 1213, 1216, 1217, 1220, 1232, 1236, 1251, 1253, 1256, 1264, 1266, 1267, 1273, 1274, 1277, 1281, 1282, 1288, 1292, 1297, 1303, 1309, 1312, 1318, 1323, 1326, 1336, 1354, 1356, 1357, 1363, 1364, 1381, 1382, 1398,

1401, 1414, 1426, 1443, 1446, 1462, 1475, 1486, 1490, 1500, 1502, 1509, 1519, 1524, 1544, 1547, 1549, 1585, 1610, 1611, 1675, 2190, 2267; *see also* Children; Community Development; Social Welfare

Youth Agencies: 174, 176, 191, 209, 237, 247, 261, 280, 291, 331, 340, 644, 1119, 1129, 1135, 1147, 1150, 1152, 1171, 1279, 1513

Youth Development: 41, 53, 65, 68, 74, 78, 92, 122, 147, 156, 169, 198, 223, 230, 244, 245, 250, 312, 319, 1029, 1094, 1118, 1121, 1124, 1126, 1127, 1141, 1144, 1166, 1176, 1222, 1261, 1269, 1282, 1286, 1325, 1361, 1377, 1387, 1396, 1547, 1560, 1585, 1589, 1608, 1621, 1737, 1923, 2562

Z

Zoology: 1810, 2081, 2135, 2136, 2142, 2148, 2261; *see also* Animal Sciences; Biological Sciences

Organization and Program Index

The Organization and Program Index alphabetically lists grant programs in upper-lower case and funding organizations in upper case. In addition, programs also are listed following the organizations which sponsor them.

A

A-T CHILDREN'S PROJECT
  A-T Postdoctoral Fellowship Award: 2214
  A-T Research Grant Program: 2214
A-T Postdoctoral Fellowship Award: 2214
A-T Research Grant Program: 2214
A-dec Scholarship: 2349
A.G.B.U. Scholarship Program: 1666
A.R.S. Lazarian Graduate Scholarship: 976
A.R.S. Undergraduate Scholarship: 976
A.S.P.E.N. RHOADS RESEARCH FOUNDATION: 2402
AA&MDSIF Research Grant Program: 2240
AAA FOUNDATION FOR TRAFFIC SAFETY: 1415
AAAS Kavli Science Journalism Awards: 1921
AACC Van Slyke Foundation Critical and Point-of-Care Testing Research Grant: 1844
AADR/Johnson & Johnson Healthcare Products Hatton Competition: 2342
AAED Esthetic Dentistry Research Grants: 2340
AAG Dissertation Research Grants: 2075
AAG Globe Book Award for Public Understanding of Geography: 2076
AAG-IGIF Graduate Research Awards: 2073
AAG-IGIF Student Paper Awards: 2073
AAG-IGIF Student Travel Grants: 2073
AAG Meridian Book Award for the Outstanding Scholarly Work in Geography: 2076
AAG Research Grant: 2074
AAGS Joseph F. Dracup Scholarship Award: 2660
AAPG Foundation Grants-in-Aid: 2071
AAS American Society for Eighteenth Century Studies Fellowship: 345
AAS Fellowship for Creative and Performing Artists and Writers: 346
AAS National Endowment for the Humanities Fellowships: 345
AAS-Northeast Modern Language Association Fellowship: 345
AASL Collaborative School Library Award: 711
AASL Frances Henne Award: 711
AASL Innovative Reading Grant: 711
AASL National School Library Program of the Year Award: 711
AAUW Educational Foundation International Fellowships: 957
ABBOTT FUND
  General Grant Program: 1
ABC-CLIO Leadership Grant: 711
ABC News Videosource Award: 462
Abe Fellowship Program: 860
ABEL FOUNDATION: 1157
ABELARD FOUNDATION-EAST (THE): 1472
ABELL FOUNDATION, INC. (THE): 2
ABF Fellowships in Law and Social Science: 1970
ABLE TRUST (THE)
  Organization Grant Program: 969
  Special Projects Program: 969
  Strategic Employment Grant Program: 969
ABMRF/THE FOUNDATION FOR ALCOHOL RESEARCH: 1416
ABNEY FOUNDATION (THE): 3
Abramowicz (The Dina) Emerging Scholar Fellowship: 650
Abrams (Charles) Scholarship Program: 1165
Abstract Achievement Award: 2354
Academic Achievement Graduate Assistantships: 992
Academic Career Awards (K07): 1453
ACADEMIC PEDIATRIC ASSOCIATION
  Young Investigator Grant Program: 2526
Academic Program Fellowship Competition: 880
Academic Studies: 856
ACADEMY FOUNDATION OF THE ACADEMY OF MOTION PICTURE ARTS AND SCIENCES
  Academy Nicholl Fellowships in Screenwriting (The): 524
  Student Academy Awards Competition: 541
Academy Nicholl Fellowships in Screenwriting (The): 524

ACADEMY OF NATURAL SCIENCES OF PHILADELPHIA (THE)
  Gallagher (John J. and Anna H.) Fellowship: 1805
  Jessup Fellowship: 2135
  McHenry Fellowship: 2135
ACADEMY OF NUTRITION AND DIETETIC FOUNDATION (THE): 2668
Acadia Graduate Awards: 4
ACADIA UNIVERSITY
  Acadia Graduate Awards: 4
ACC Young Investigators Awards Competition: 2373
ACCADEMIA MUSICALE CHIGIANA
  Scholarships for Summer Music Courses: 745
Access Camps: 150
Access Missouri Financial Assistance Program: 1718
Access Reimbursement Grants: 494
Access to Better Learning and Education Grant Program (ABLE): 1687
Access to College and Career Education (ACE) Program: 1033
Access to Health Care-System Change and Advocacy: 1514
Accessible Faith: 1009
ACCF/Merck Research Fellowships in Cardiovascular Disease: 2372
ACCF/William F. Keating, Esq. Endowment Award for Hypertension and Peripheral Vascular Disease: 2374
ACCP/Alfred Soffer Research Award: 2392
ACCP Young Investigator Award: 2392
ACF General Grants: 2165
ACGG EDUCATION FOUNDATION
  Gunsmithing Student Scholarships: 426
  Trinidad State Gunsmithing Scholarship: 426
ACHA Graduate Student Summer Research Grant: 801
ACHA Junior Faculty Grant: 801
ACHELIS FOUNDATION (THE): 5
Acheson (Edward Goodrich) Award: 1819
ACLS Fellowship: 347
ACOR-CAORC Fellowship: 870
ACOR-CAORC Postgraduate Fellowships: 870
ACORN FOUNDATION: 2163
ACPC Scholarship, Summer Studies in Poland: 1655
Active Trails: 2190
Actuarial Diversity Scholarship: 2091
ACTUARIAL FOUNDATION (THE)
  Actuarial Diversity Scholarship: 2091
ACTUARIAL FOUNDATION (THE)
  Actuary of Tomorrow - Stuart A. Robertson Memorial Scholarship: 2092
Actuary of Tomorrow - Stuart A. Robertson Memorial Scholarship: 2092
ADAMS (EMMA J.) MEMORIAL FUND, INC.: 1473
Adams (The Herbert Baxter) Prize: 578
Adams (John and Abigail) Arts Program for Cultural Economic Development: 472
ADC National Scholarships: 1922
ADCO FOUNDATION: 1613
ADHA Institute Dental Hygiene Scholarships: 2348
Adkins (Howard E. and Wilma J.) Memorial Scholarship: 2600
Adler Fellowships: 789
ADMA Scholarship Programs: 2621
ADSC: THE INTERNATIONAL ASSOCIATION OF FOUNDATION DRILLING: 2631
Adult Literacy Transition Grants: 295
Advanced Fellowships: 890
Advanced Language Program in India: 652
Advanced Seminar Program: 2023
Advanced Technological Education (ATE): 1607
Aetna Foundation/NMF Healthcare Leadership Program: 2296
AETNA FOUNDATION, INC.
  National Grants: 6
  Regional Grants: 6
AFAR Research Grants: 2227
Affiliate Councils Award for Meritorious Service: 1498
Affiliated Fellowships: 1779
Affiliated Writer Program: 696
Affordable Health Insurance: 1478
AFPE Predoctoral Fellowships in the Pharmaceutical Sciences: 1614
African-American and African Studies Fellowships: 407
African American Community Fund: 1236
African American Endowment Fund (The): 1170
AFRICAN AMERICAN FUND OF NEW JERSEY: 1024
African American Graduate Fellowship: 1762
African American Male Mentoring Initiative (AAMMI): 1033
African-American Scholarship Fund (Star Supporter): 808
African American Unity Fund: 252

African Rift Valley: 64
AFS Cultural Studies Program: 867
AFS Faces of America Diversity Scholarship Program: 867
AFS Gap Year Program: 867
AFS INTERCULTURAL PROGRAMS/USA
    AFS Cultural Studies Program: 867
    AFS Faces of America Diversity Scholarship Program: 867
    AFS Gap Year Program: 867
    AFS Language Studies Program: 867
    AFS Semester Program: 867
    AFS Summer Home Stay Program: 867
    AFS Volunteer Development Program: 867
    AFS Year Program: 867
AFS Language Studies Program: 867
AFS Semester Program: 867
AFS Summer Home Stay Program: 867
AFS Volunteer Development Program: 867
AFS Year Program: 867
After School Grants: 1354
Ag Broadcast Scholarships: 1945
AGA R. Robert and Sally D. Funderburg Research Award in Gastric
    Cancer: 2404
AGA Research Scholar Award: 2405
AGA Student Research Fellowship Award: 2406
Agan (Tessie) Award Competition: 1301
AGC EDUCATION AND RESEARCH FOUNDATION
    Allhands (James L.) Essay Competition: 2632
    Graduate Scholarship Program: 2632
    Outstanding Educator Award: 2632
    Undergraduate Scholarship Program: 2632
AGENCY FOR HEALTHCARE RESEARCH AND QUALITY (AHRQ)
    AHRQ Research Grants: 1417
Aging and Health Program: 155
Aging Research: 1452
AGRICULTURAL HISTORY SOCIETY
    Edwards (Everett E.) Awards in Agricultural History: 576
    Fite (Gilbert C.) Dissertation Award: 576
    Rasmussen (Wayne D.) Award: 576
    Saloutos (Theodore) Book Award: 576
Agriscience Awards: 1477
Ahmanson and Getty Postdoctoral Fellowships: 360
AHMANSON FOUNDATION (THE): 7
Ahmanson Research Fellowships for the Study of Medieval and
    Renaissance Books and Manuscripts: 357
AHRQ Research Grants: 1417
AIA Arthur N. Tuttle, Jr. Graduate Fellowship in Health Facility Planning
    and Design: 410
AIA Publication Subvention Program (The): 1665
AIA Scholarship: 2622
AIA/F Diversity Advancement Scholarship: 411
AICPA Accountemps Student Scholarship: 1888
AICPA Fellowship for Minority Doctoral Students: 1658
AICPA Foundation Two-Year Transfer Scholarship: 1889
AICPA Scholarship for Minority Accounting Students: 1520
AIDS: 2352
AIHS Catalyst Opportunities: 2215
AIHS Collaborative Research and Innovation Opportunities: 2215
AIHS Conference Grants: 2215
AIHS HYRS Program: 2215
AIHS Industry Partnered Translational Fund: 2215
AIHS Sustainability Funding Opportunity: 2215
AIHS Training and Early Career Development Programs: 2215
AIIS Fellowships: 877
AINA Grants-in-Aid: 1619
AIPS Post Doctoral Fellowship: 828
AIPS Pre-Doctoral Fellowship: 828
AIR & WASTE MANAGEMENT ASSOCIATION (A&WMA)
    Scholarship Endowment Trust Fund: 2595
AIR TRAFFIC CONTROL ASSOCIATION (ATCA): 2596
Aircell Scholarship: 2618
AIRCRAFT ELECTRONICS ASSOCIATION (AEA)
    Aircell Scholarship: 2618
    Arver (David) Memorial Scholarship: 2618
    Arver (Dutch and Ginger) Scholarship: 2618
    Davis (Johnny) Memorial Scholarship: 2618
    Duncan Aviation Scholarship: 2618
    Field Aviation Company Scholarship: 2618
    Garmin - Jerry Smith Memorial Scholarship: 2618
    Garmin Scholarship: 2618
    Gaylor (Lowell) Memorial Scholarship: 2618

    Harris (Leon)/Les Nichols Memorial Scholarship: 2618
    L-3 Avionics Systems Scholarship: 2618
    Mid-Continent Instrument Scholarship: 2618
    Rockwell Collins Scholarship: 2618
    Tarbox (Lee) Memorial Scholarship: 2618
    Universal Avionics Systems Corporation Scholarship: 2618
Airgas-Jerry Baker Scholarship: 2600
Airgas-Terry Jarvis Memorial Scholarship: 2600
AISES Google Scholarship: 1039
AISLS Dissertation Planning Grant: 874
AISLS Fellowship Program: 873
Akehurst (Carville M.) Memorial Scholarship: 1697
AKRON COMMUNITY FOUNDATION: 1158
AKTA Lou Montalvano Memorial Scholarship: 2548
ALA Awards: 713
ALA/Century Scholarship: 1616
ALABAMA ACADEMY OF SCIENCE, INC.
    Gorgas Scholarship: 1806
    Mason Science Teaching Fellowships: 1806
    Student Research Grants: 1806
    Student Travel Awards: 1806
ALABAMA COMMISSION ON HIGHER EDUCATION
    Alabama National Guard Educational Assistance Program: 1651
    Alabama Student Assistance Program: 1652
    Alabama Student Grant Program: 1652
    Senior Adult Scholarship Program: 1650
ALABAMA LIBRARY ASSOCIATION SCHOLARSHIP LOAN FUND,
INC.
    Scholarships in Library Science: 708
Alabama National Guard Educational Assistance Program: 1651
ALABAMA POWER FOUNDATION, INC.
    Educational Grant Program: 8
    Gateway Grant: 8
    Good Roots Grant: 8
ALABAMA STATE COUNCIL ON THE ARTS
    Art and Cultural Facilities: 427
    Arts-in-Education: 427
    Community Arts Development: 427
    Folk Arts: 427
    Literary Art: 427
    Performing Arts: 427
    Visual Arts and Crafts: 427
Alabama Student Assistance Program: 1652
Alabama Student Grant Program: 1652
ALASKA CONSERVATION FOUNDATION
    ACF General Grants: 2165
    Alaska Native Fund: 2165
    Rapid Response Grant: 2164
Alaska Native Fund: 2165
ALASKA STATE COUNCIL ON THE ARTS: 428
Alberta Cancer Grants Program: 2215
ALBERTA INNOVATES - HEALTH SOLUTIONS
    AIHS Catalyst Opportunities: 2215
    AIHS Collaborative Research and Innovation Opportunities: 2215
    AIHS Conference Grants: 2215
    AIHS HYRS Program: 2215
    AIHS Industry Partnered Translational Fund: 2215
    AIHS Sustainability Funding Opportunity: 2215
    AIHS Training and Early Career Development Programs: 2215
    Alberta Cancer Grants Program: 2215
    Campus Alberta/AIHS Translational Health Chairs: 2215
    Knowledge Exchange Grants: 2215
    Knowledge-to-Action Grant: 2215
    Partnership for Research and Innovation in the Health System (PRIHS):
    2215
Alberta Research Award: 2557
ALBION COMMUNITY FOUNDATION: 1159
ALBRIGHT INSTITUTE OF ARCHAEOLOGICAL RESEARCH (AIAR)
    Fellowships at the Albright Institute of Archaeological Research in
    Jerusalem: 868
Albright-Wirth Grants Program: 2190
ALBUQUERQUE COMMUNITY FOUNDATION: 1160
ALCOA FOUNDATION: 9
ALCON FOUNDATION, INC. (THE): 2503
ALDEN (GEORGE I.) TRUST: 10
ALDEN (THE JOHN W.) TRUST: 1106
ALEXANDER (JUDD S.) FOUNDATION: 1474
Alexander (Paula J.) Memorial Scholarship (Undergraduate): 1080
Alfa Fellowship Program: 843
ALGER REGIONAL COMMUNITY FOUNDATION: 1161
ALISE Research Awards: 714

ALISE/ProQuest Methodology Paper Competition: 715
ALLEGAN COUNTY COMMUNITY FOUNDATION: 1162
ALLEGHENY FOUNDATION: 11
Allen (Frances C.) Fellowships: 1053
ALLEN (THE PAUL G.) FAMILY FOUNDATION
    Arts and Culture: 12
    Asset Building: 12
    Basic Needs: 12
    Education: 12
    Libraries: 12
    Science and Technology: 12
ALLENDE (THE ISABEL) FOUNDATION
    Esperanza Grants: 1070
    Paula Scholarships: 1653
Allhands (James L.) Essay Competition: 2632
ALLIANCE FOR YOUNG ARTISTS & WRITERS (THE)
    Scholastic Art and Writing Awards (The): 429
Allied Health Doctoral Fellowship: 2419
Allied Health Research Grant: 2418
Allied Health Scholarship: 2420
Allport (Gordon) Intergroup Relations Prize: 1877
ALLSTATE FOUNDATION (THE): 1475
Allyson (June) Award: 2105
Alonso (The Anne) Scholarship: 2563
Alpha-1 Foundation/CHEST Foundation Clinical Research Award in
    COPD and Alpha-1 Antitrypsin (AAT) Deficiency: 2392
ALSC/Bound-to-Stay-Bound Books Scholarship: 1616
ALSC/Frederic G. Melcher Scholarship: 1616
Altenhofen (Robert E.) Memorial Scholarship: 2033
ALTERNATIVES RESEARCH AND DEVELOPMENT FOUNDATION
    Alternatives Research Grant Program: 1807
    Cave (William and Eleanor) Award: 1807
Alternatives Research Grant Program: 1807
ALTMAN FOUNDATION: 1163
ALTRIA GROUP, INC.: 13
Alumni Grant: 481
ALZHEIMER'S ASSOCIATION, INC.
    Everyday Technologies for Alzheimer Care (ETAC): 2452
    Investigator-Initiated Research Grants: 2452
    Mentored New Investigator Research Grant to Promote Diversity
    (MNIRGD): 2453
    New Investigator Research Grant to Promote Diversity (NIRGD): 2453
    New Investigator Research Grants: 2452
    U.S.-U.K. Young Investigator Exchange Fellowship: 2453
    Zenith Fellows Award Program (The): 2452
Alzheimer's Disease Research: 2458
ALZHEIMER'S DRUG DISCOVERY FOUNDATION
    Novel Approaches to Drug Discovery in Alzheimer's Disease: 2216
AMARILLO AREA FOUNDATION: 1164
Amateur Achievement Award: 2051
AMBUCS Scholars-Scholarships for Therapists: 2554
AMERICA-ISRAEL CULTURAL FOUNDATION
    Scholarship Program for Israelis: 955
America's Best Idea: 2190
AMERICAN ACADEMY IN BERLIN (THE)
    Berlin Prize Fellowship: 869
AMERICAN ACADEMY IN ROME
    Rome Prize Fellowships: 344
    Rome Prize Fellowship in Landscape Architecture (The): 2166
AMERICAN ACADEMY OF ALLERGY ASTHMA & IMMUNOLOGY
    Travel Grant Awards: 2335
AMERICAN ACADEMY OF ARTS AND LETTERS
    Rodgers (The Richard) Awards: 746
AMERICAN ACADEMY OF CHILD AND ADOLESCENT
    PSYCHIATRY
    Robinson-Cunningham Award: 2562
    Spurlock (Jeanne) Research Fellowship in Substance Abuse and
    Addiction for Minority Medical Students: 2562
AMERICAN ACADEMY OF ESTHETIC DENTISTRY (THE)
    AAED Esthetic Dentistry Research Grants: 2340
AMERICAN ACADEMY OF FACIAL PLASTIC AND
    RECONSTRUCTIVE SURGERY (AAFPRS)
    Bernstein (Leslie) Investigator Development Grant: 2218
    Bernstein (Leslie) Research Grant: 2219
    Bernstein (Leslie) Resident Research Grants: 2217
    Community Service Award: 2220
    Dickinson (John) Teacher of the Year Award: 2220
    Gillies (Sir Harold Delf) Award: 2220
    Rafaty (F. Mark) Memorial Award: 2220
    Residency Travel Award: 2220
    Roe (John Orlando) Award: 2220

    Shuster (Ben) Memorial Award: 2220
    Tresley (Ira) Research Award: 2220
    Wright (William K.) Award: 2220
AMERICAN ACADEMY OF FAMILY PHYSICIANS FOUNDATION
    Joint Grant Awards Program: 2221
    Pfizer Teacher Development Award: 2221
AMERICAN ACADEMY OF IMPLANT DENTISTRY (AAID)
    FOUNDATION
    Humanitarian Project Support: 2341
    Research Award: 2341
    Student Research Grant: 2341
AMERICAN ACADEMY OF OPTOMETRY
    Neumueller (Julius F.) Award in Optics: 2504
AMERICAN ACADEMY OF PEDIATRICS
    American Academy of Pediatrics Residency Scholarships: 2527
American Academy of Pediatrics Residency Scholarships: 2527
AMERICAN ACADEMY OF RELIGION
    Collaborative Research Grants: 799
    Individual Research Grants: 799
    International Dissertation Research Grant: 799
    Regional Development Grants: 800
AMERICAN ACCORDION MUSICOLOGICAL SOCIETY
    Annual Symposium and Festival: 747
AMERICAN AGING ASSOCIATION
    Glenn (Paul) Award: 2222
    Nicolai (Walter) Award in Biomedical Gerontology: 2222
AMERICAN ALPINE CLUB
    McNeill-Nott Climbing Award: 2167
    Mountain Fellowship: 2167
    Research Grants: 2167
    Spitzer (Lyman) Cutting Edge Climbing Award: 2167
AMERICAN ANTIQUARIAN SOCIETY (AAS)
    AAS American Society for Eighteenth Century Studies Fellowship: 345
    AAS Fellowship for Creative and Performing Artists and Writers: 346
    AAS National Endowment for the Humanities Fellowships: 345
    AAS-Northeast Modern Language Association Fellowship: 345
    American Historical Print Collectors Fellowship: 345
    Botein (Stephen) Fellowships: 345
    Drawn to Art Fellowship (The): 345
    Lapides (Linda F. and Julian L.) Fellowship: 345
    Last (Jay and Deborah) Fellowship: 345
    Legacy Fellowship (The): 345
    Packer (Barbara) Fellowship: 345
    Peterson (Kate B. and Hall J.) Fellowships: 345
    Reese Fellowship (The): 345
    Schiller (Justin G.) Fellowship: 345
    Tracy (Joyce A.) Fellowship: 345
AMERICAN ARCHITECTURAL FOUNDATION
    Hunt (The Richard Morris) Fellowship: 409
American Art Program: 210
AMERICAN ASSOCIATION FOR CANCER RESEARCH
    Career Development Awards: 2424
    Innovator Awards in Cancer Research: 2424
    Research Grants and Fellowships: 2424
    Scholar-in-Training Awards: 2424
AMERICAN ASSOCIATION FOR DENTAL RESEARCH
    AADR/Johnson & Johnson Healthcare Products Hatton Competition:
    2342
    Clark (William B.) Fellowship in Clinical Research: 2344
    Gies (William J.) Award: 2345
    Student Research Fellowships: 2343
American Association for Geodetic Surveying Graduate Fellowship
    Award: 2659
AMERICAN ASSOCIATION FOR HAND SURGERY: 2223
AMERICAN ASSOCIATION FOR THE ADVANCEMENT OF
    SCIENCE
    AAAS Kavli Science Journalism Awards: 1921
    Mass Media Science and Engineering Fellows Program: 1920
AMERICAN ASSOCIATION FOR THE HISTORY OF NURSING, INC.
    Competitive Student Research Award: 2484
    Postdoctoral Award to Honor the Nurse Cadet Corps: 2484
AMERICAN ASSOCIATION OF COLLEGES OF PHARMACY
    New Investigator Award: 2534
AMERICAN ASSOCIATION OF FAMILY AND CONSUMER
    SCIENCES (AAFCS)
    National and International Fellowships: 956
    National Teacher of the Year Award: 2669
AMERICAN ASSOCIATION OF LAW LIBRARIES
    Library Degree for Law School Graduates: 709
    Library Degree for Non-Law School Graduates: 709

Library School Graduates Attending Law School: 709
Library School Graduates Seeking a Non-Law Degree: 709
Strait (George A.) Minority Stipend Scholarship Endowment: 710
AMERICAN ASSOCIATION OF PETROLEUM GEOLOGISTS
FOUNDATION
    AAPG Foundation Grants-in-Aid: 2071
AMERICAN ASSOCIATION OF SCHOOL LIBRARIANS
    AASL Collaborative School Library Award: 711
    AASL Frances Henne Award: 711
    AASL Innovative Reading Grant: 711
    AASL National School Library Program of the Year Award: 711
    ABC-CLIO Leadership Grant: 711
    Distinguished Service Award: 712
AMERICAN ASSOCIATION OF UNIVERSITY WOMEN
    Selected Professions Fellowships: 1071
AMERICAN ASSOCIATION OF UNIVERSITY WOMEN
EDUCATIONAL FOUNDATION
    AAUW Educational Foundation International Fellowships: 957
    American Fellowships: 1072
    Career Development Grants: 1073
    Community Action Grants: 1074
AMERICAN ASSOCIATION OF WOMEN DENTISTS
    Colgate Research Scholarship: 2346
    Procter & Gamble Research Award for Postdoctoral Students: 2346
    Smiles for Success Program: 2346
AMERICAN ASSOCIATION OF ZOO KEEPERS
    Zoo Keeper Grants in Zoology: 2136
AMERICAN ASTRONOMICAL SOCIETY
    Chrétien International Research Grant: 2046
    Pierce (Newton Lacy) Prize in Astronomy: 2047
AMERICAN BANDMASTERS ASSOCIATION (THE)
    Sousa/Ostwald Award: 748
AMERICAN BAR FOUNDATION
    ABF Fellowships in Law and Social Science: 1970
    Summer Research Diversity Fellowships in Law and Social Science for
    Undergraduate Students: 970
AMERICAN BRAIN TUMOR ASSOCIATION
    Basic Research Fellowship Awards: 2454
    Discovery Grants: 2454
    Medical Student Summer Fellowships: 2454
AMERICAN BURN ASSOCIATION
    International Education Exchange Program: 2546
    Jordan (Cheryl) Scholarship Fund: 2546
    Visiting Professor Program: 2546
American Cancer Society International Fellowships for Beginning
    Investigators (ACSBI): 2449
AMERICAN CANCER SOCIETY, INC.
    Institutional Research Grants: 2426
    Postdoctoral Fellowship: 2425
AMERICAN CATHOLIC HISTORICAL ASSOCIATION
    ACHA Graduate Student Summer Research Grant: 801
    ACHA Junior Faculty Grant: 801
    Ellis (John Tracy) Dissertation Award: 801
    Graduate Student Travel Grant: 801
    Guilday (The Peter) Prize: 803
    Koenig (The Msgr. Harry C.) Award for Catholic Biography: 802
    Marraro (The Howard R.) Prize: 577
    Shea (The John Gilmary) Prize: 804
AMERICAN CENTER OF ORIENTAL RESEARCH
    ACOR-CAORC Fellowship: 870
    ACOR-CAORC Postgraduate Fellowships: 870
    Bikai (Pierre and Patricia) Fellowship: 870
    de Vries (Bert and Sally) Fellowship: 870
    Groot (Jennifer C.) Fellowships in the Archaeology of Jordan: 870
    Harrell Family Fellowship: 870
    MacDonald/Sampson Fellowship: 870
    National Endowment for the Humanities (NEH) Fellowship: 870
    Sauer (James A.) Fellowship: 870
AMERICAN CERAMIC SOCIETY (THE)
    Graduate Student Poster Contest: 430
    Outstanding Educator Award: 430
    Student Speaking Contest: 430
    Undergraduate Student Poster Contest: 430
AMERICAN CHEMICAL SOCIETY
    Murphree (E.V.) Award in Industrial and Engineering Chemistry: 2061
    Nakanishi Prize: 2060
    Petroleum Research Fund (The): 2031
AMERICAN CHESTNUT FOUNDATION (THE): 2112
AMERICAN CLASSICAL LEAGUE (THE)
    McKinlay Scholarship: 651

AMERICAN COLLEGE OF CARDIOLOGY
    ACC Young Investigators Awards Competition: 2373
    ACCF/Merck Research Fellowships in Cardiovascular Disease: 2372
    ACCF/William F. Keating, Esq. Endowment Award for Hypertension
    and Peripheral Vascular Disease: 2374
    ISCTR-ACCF Cardiovascular Translational Research Scholarship: 2375
AMERICAN COLLEGE OF LEGAL MEDICINE
    American College of Legal Medicine's Student Writing Competition in
    Law, Medicine and Bioethics: 2224
American College of Legal Medicine's Student Writing Competition in
    Law, Medicine and Bioethics: 2224
AMERICAN COLLEGE OF MEDICAL PRACTICE EXECUTIVES:
    1654
AMERICAN CONSERVATORY OF MUSIC
    Heim (Leo) Presidential Scholarships: 749
AMERICAN COUNCIL FOR POLISH CULTURE (ACPC)
    ACPC Scholarship, Summer Studies in Poland: 1655
    Pulaski Scholarships for Advanced Studies: 1655
    Skalny (Louis and Nellie) Scholarships for Polish Studies: 1655
AMERICAN COUNCIL OF LEARNED SOCIETIES
    ACLS Fellowship: 347
AMERICAN COUNCIL OF THE BLIND
    American Council of the Blind Scholarships: 1656
American Council of the Blind Scholarships: 1656
AMERICAN DANCE FESTIVAL
    Tuition Scholarships: 525
AMERICAN DENTAL ASSISTANTS ASSOCIATION
    Southard (Juliette A.)/Oral-B Laboratories Scholarship Program: 2347
AMERICAN DENTAL HYGIENISTS' ASSOCIATION INSTITUTE FOR
ORAL HEALTH
    ADHA Institute Dental Hygiene Scholarships: 2348
AMERICAN DIABETES ASSOCIATION
    Basic Science Award: 2403
    Career Development Award: 2403
    Clinical Research and Epidemiological Award: 2403
    Clinical Scholars Award: 2403
    Clinical Scientist Training Award: 2403
    Distinguished Clinical Scientist Award: 2403
    Innovation Award: 2403
    Junior Faculty Award: 2403
    Mentor-Based Postdoctoral Fellowship Program: 2403
    Mentor-Based Postdoctoral Minority Fellowship: 2403
    Translational Research Award: 2403
AMERICAN EPILEPSY SOCIETY (AES)
    Grass Foundation (The) - AES Young Investigator Travel Award: 2455
    Lennox and Lombroso Postdoctoral Research Fellowship: 2455
    Postdoctoral Research Fellowship: 2455
    Predoctoral Research Fellowship: 2455
    Research and Training Workshops: 2455
    Research Infrastructure Awards: 2455
    Research Initiative Fund Grants: 2455
    Seed Grants: 2455
    Spencer (Susan S.) Clinical Research Training Fellowship in Epilepsy:
    2455
AMERICAN FARM BUREAU FOUNDATION FOR AGRICULTURE
    White-Reinhardt Fund for Education: 2113
AMERICAN FEDERATION FOR AGING RESEARCH (AFAR)
    AFAR Research Grants: 2227
    Beeson (Paul) Career Development Awards in Aging Research Program:
    2227
    Gilbert (Rosalinde and Arthur) Foundation/AFAR New Investigator
    Awards in Alzheimer's Disease: 2225
    Glenn/AFAR Breakthroughs in Gerontology Awards: 2227
    Glenn/AFAR Scholarships for Research in the Biology of Aging: 2226
    Martin (Julie) Mid-Career Awards in Aging Research: 2225
    Medical Student Training in Aging Research Program (MSTAR): 2227
American Fellowships: 1072
AMERICAN FIDELITY FOUNDATION: 431
AMERICAN FLORAL ENDOWMENT: 2114
AMERICAN FOUNDATION FOR PHARMACEUTICAL EDUCATION
(AFPE)
    AFPE Predoctoral Fellowships in the Pharmaceutical Sciences: 1614
    Kappa Epsilon-AFPE-Nellie Wakeman First Year Graduate Fellowship:
    2536
    Phi Lambda Sigma-GlaxoSmithKline-AFPE First Year Graduate
    Scholarship: 2535
    Rho Chi-Schering Plough-AFPE First Year Graduate Scholarship: 2535
AMERICAN FOUNDATION FOR SUICIDE PREVENTION (THE)
    Distinguished Investigator Award: 1517
    Pilot Grant: 1515

Postdoctoral Research Fellowships: 1516
Standard Research Grants: 1518
Young Investigator Grants: 1518
AMERICAN FOUNDATION FOR THE BLIND, INC.
Anderson (Gladys C.) Memorial Scholarship: 971
Carsel (The Karen D.) Memorial Scholarship: 971
Delta Gamma Foundation Florence Margaret Harvey Memorial
Scholarship (The): 971
Dillman (The Rudolph) Memorial Scholarship: 971
Gillette (The R.L.) Scholarship: 971
Ruckes (The Paul and Ellen) Scholarship: 971
AMERICAN FRIENDS OF THE ALEXANDER VON HUMBOLDT
FOUNDATION
German Chancellor Fellowship: 872
Humboldt Research Awards for Foreign Scholars: 1657
Humboldt Research Fellowship for Experienced Researchers: 871
Humboldt Research Fellowship for Postdoctoral Researchers: 1615
AMERICAN GASTROENTEROLOGICAL ASSOCIATION (AGA)
AGA R. Robert and Sally D. Funderburg Research Award in Gastric
Cancer: 2404
AGA Research Scholar Award: 2405
AGA Student Research Fellowship Award: 2406
Elsevier Pilot Research Award: 2407
AMERICAN GEOSCIENCES INSTITUTE (AGI) (THE)
Wallace (Harriet Evelyn) Scholarship: 2072
AMERICAN GERIATRICS SOCIETY
Clinical Student Research Award: 2547
Clinician of the Year: 2547
Henderson (Edward) Student Award: 2547
Jahnigen (Dennis W.) Memorial Award: 2547
Merck/AGS New Investigator Awards: 2547
Nascher/Manning Award: 2547
Outstanding Junior Clinical Education Manuscript: 2547
Outstanding Junior Clinical Teacher of the Year: 2547
Outstanding Junior Investigator of the Year: 2547
Outstanding Junior Research Manuscript: 2547
Outstanding Mid-Career Clinical Teacher of the Year: 2547
Outstanding Scientific Achievement for Clinical Investigation Award:
2547
Scientist-in-Training Research Award: 2547
AMERICAN GROUND WATER TRUST
AMTROL Scholarship: 2597
Baroid Scholarship: 2597
Stetson (Thomas M.) Scholarship: 2597
AMERICAN GROUP PSYCHOTHERAPY ASSOCIATION, INC.
Alonso (The Anne) Scholarship: 2563
Brown (Donald T.) Memorial Scholarship: 2563
Bukatman (The Barry), M.D. Memorial AGPA Scholarship: 2563
Cunningham-Tervalon (Josephine M.) Scholarship: 2563
Durkin/Glatzer Scholarship: 2563
Goldstein (The Howard and Barbara) Scholarship: 2563
Hochberg (Ruth) Scholarship: 2563
International Scholarship: 2563
Jensen (Susanne) Scholarship: 2563
Scheidlinger (Saul) Scholarship: 2563
Tanenbaum (Mary M.) Scholarship: 2563
Wilkenfeld Psychiatric Resident Scholarship (The): 2563
AMERICAN HEART ASSOCIATION
Beginning Grant-in-Aid: 2378
Grant-in-Aid Program: 2381
Great Rivers Affiliate Student Undergraduate Research Fellowship:
2380
Greater Southeast Affiliate Health Sciences Fellowship Program: 2379
National Clinical Research Program: 2384
National Established Investigator Award: 2383
National Innovative Research Grant: 2382
National Scientist Development Grant: 2384
Postdoctoral Fellowship: 2376
Predoctoral Fellowship: 2377
AMERICAN HELLENIC EDUCATIONAL PROGRESSIVE
ASSOCIATION (THE): 972
AMERICAN HISTORICAL ASSOCIATION (THE)
Adams (The Herbert Baxter) Prize: 578
Beer (The George Louis) Prize: 578
Bentley (The Jerry) Prize: 578
Beveridge (The Albert J.) Award: 578
Beveridge (The Albert J.) Grant: 578
Birdsall (The Paul) Prize: 578
Breasted (The James Henry) Prize: 578
Corey (The Albert B.) Prize in Canadian-American Relations: 578
Dunning (The John H.) Prize in United States History: 578

Fairbank (The John K.) Prize in East Asian History: 578
Feis (The Herbert) Award: 578
Fellowship in Aerospace History: 580
Forkosch (The Morris D.) Prize: 578
Gershoy (The Leo) Award: 578
Haring (The Clarence H.) Prize: 578
Jameson (J. Franklin) Award: 578
Jameson (The J. Franklin) Fellowship: 579
Katz (The Friedrich) Prize: 578
Kelly (The Joan) Memorial Prize in Women's History: 578
Klein (Martin A.) Prize in African History: 578
Kraus (Michael) Research Grant: 578
Leland (The Waldo G.) Prize: 578
Littleton-Griswold Grant: 578
Littleton-Griswold Prize in American Law and Society (The): 578
Major (The J. Russell) Prize: 578
Marraro (The Helen and Howard R.) Prize in Italian History: 578
Mosse (The George L.) Prize: 578
O'Connor (The John E.) Film Award: 578
Premio Del Rey (The): 578
Rawley (The James A.) Prize in Atlantic History: 578
Richards (John F.) Prize in South Asian History: 578
Robinson (The James Harvey) Prize: 578
Schmitt (Bernadotte) Grant: 578
Wesley-Logan Prize (The): 578
American Historical Print Collectors Fellowship: 345
AMERICAN HONDA FOUNDATION: 1519
AMERICAN INDIAN COLLEGE FUND
Full Circle Scholarship Program: 1036
TCU Scholarship Program: 1036
American Indian Endowed Scholarship Program: 1062
AMERICAN INDIAN GRADUATE CENTER
Fellowships for American Indians or Alaskan Natives: 1037
American Indian Scholarship: 1722
AMERICAN INDIAN SCIENCE AND ENGINEERING SOCIETY
(AISES)
AISES Google Scholarship: 1039
Anderson (A.T.) Memorial Scholarship: 1038
AMERICAN INSTITUTE FOR CANCER RESEARCH
Investigator Initiated Grants (IIG): 2427
AMERICAN INSTITUTE FOR SRI LANKAN STUDIES (AISLS)
AISLS Dissertation Planning Grant: 874
AISLS Fellowship Program: 873
AMERICAN INSTITUTE FOR YEMENI STUDIES
General Fellowship Program: 875
AMERICAN INSTITUTE OF AERONAUTICS AND ASTRONAUTICS
American Institute of Aeronautics and Astronautics Undergraduate
Scholarship Program: 2619
American Institute of Aeronautics and Astronautics Undergraduate
Scholarship Program: 2619
AMERICAN INSTITUTE OF ARCHITECTS (THE)
AIA Arthur N. Tuttle, Jr. Graduate Fellowship in Health Facility
Planning and Design: 410
AIA/F Diversity Advancement Scholarship: 411
AMERICAN INSTITUTE OF BANGLADESH STUDIES
Junior Fellowship: 876
Pre-Dissertation Fellowships: 876
Seminar, Workshop and Conference Support: 876
Senior Fellowship: 876
Undergraduate Research Initiative: 876
AMERICAN INSTITUTE OF CERTIFIED PUBLIC ACCOUNTANTS
(AICPA)
AICPA Accountemps Student Scholarship: 1888
AICPA Fellowship for Minority Doctoral Students: 1658
AICPA Foundation Two-Year Transfer Scholarship: 1889
AICPA Scholarship for Minority Accounting Students: 1520
Carey (John L.) Scholarship: 1890
AMERICAN INSTITUTE OF CHEMICAL ENGINEERS (AICHE)
Food, Pharmaceutical and Bioengineering Division Award in Chemical
Engineering: 1808
Minority Scholarship Awards for College Students: 2633
AMERICAN INSTITUTE OF INDIAN STUDIES
Advanced Language Program in India: 652
AIIS Fellowships: 877
AMERICAN INSTITUTE OF PAKISTAN STUDIES
AIPS Post Doctoral Fellowship: 828
AIPS Pre-Doctoral Fellowship: 828
AMERICAN INSTITUTE OF PHYSICS
American Institute of Physics Science Writing Award in Physics and
Astronomy: 2099

American Institute of Physics Science Writing Award in Physics and
 Astronomy: 2099
AMERICAN INSTITUTE OF THE HISTORY OF PHARMACY
  Fischelis Grants for Research in the History of American Pharmacy:
  2537
  History of Pharmacy Thesis Research Grants-in-Aid: 2537
American Jewish Archives Fellowship Program (The): 818
AMERICAN JEWISH JOINT DISTRIBUTION COMMITTEE (THE)
  Goldman (The Ralph I.) Fellowship: 878
AMERICAN KIDNEY FUND
  Clinical Scientist in Nephrology (CSN): 2228
  Patient Services Grants: Safety Net Grant Program: 2229
AMERICAN KINESIOTHERAPY ASSOCIATION, INC.
  AKTA Lou Montalvano Memorial Scholarship: 2548
American Legion Auxiliary Badger Girls State Scholarships: 1659
AMERICAN LEGION AUXILIARY - DEPARTMENT OF WISCONSIN
  American Legion Auxiliary Badger Girls State Scholarships: 1659
  American Legion Auxiliary National Scholarships: 1659
  Child Welfare Scholarship: 1659
  Health Careers Scholarships: 1659
  Knox (Eileen) Memorial Scholarship: 1659
  Kuehl (Harry and Shirley) Foundation Scholarship: 1659
  Lewis (H.S. and Angeline) Scholarships: 1659
  Merit and Memorial Scholarships: 1659
  State President's Scholarships: 1659
  Van Deuren (Della) Scholarships: 1659
American Legion Auxiliary National Scholarships: 1659
AMERICAN LEGION NATIONAL HEADQUARTERS (THE)
  Eight and Forty Lung and Respiratory Disease Nursing Scholarship
  Fund: 2485
AMERICAN LIBRARY ASSOCIATION (ALA)
  ALA Awards: 713
  ALA/Century Scholarship: 1616
  ALSC/Bound-to-Stay-Bound Books Scholarship: 1616
  ALSC/Frederic G. Melcher Scholarship: 1616
  Clift (David H.) Scholarship: 1616
  Drewes (Tom and Roberta) Scholarship: 1616
  Gaver (Mary V.) Scholarship: 1616
  Hornback (Miriam L.) Scholarship: 1616
  Hoy (Christopher J.)/ERT Scholarship: 1616
  Leisner (Tony B.) Scholarship: 1616
  LITA/Christian Larew Memorial Scholarship: 1616
  LITA/LSSI Minority Scholarship: 1616
  LITA/OCLC Minority Scholarship: 1616
  Lyman (Peter) Memorial/SAGE Scholarships: 1616
  Marks (Cicely Phippen) Scholarship: 1616
  Spectrum Initiative Scholarship Program: 1616
AMERICAN LUNG ASSOCIATION
  Biomedical Research Grants: 2387
  Dalsemer Research Grant: 2385
  Lung Health Dissertation Grant: 2388
  Senior Research Training Fellowships: 2386
AMERICAN MATHEMATICAL SOCIETY
  American Mathematical Society Centennial Fellowship: 2093
American Mathematical Society Centennial Fellowship: 2093
AMERICAN MATTHAY ASSOCIATION
  Wells (Clara) Scholarships for Piano Study: 750
AMERICAN MEDICAL ASSOCIATION FOUNDATION
  Excellence in Medicine: 1660
  Giambalvo (Joan F.) Memorial Scholarship: 1660
  Health Literacy Initiative: 1660
  Healthy Communities/Healthy America: 1660
  Healthy Living Grant Program: 1660
  Minority Scholars Award: 1660
  Physicians of Tomorrow Scholarship: 1660
  Scholars Fund: 1660
  Seed Grant Research Program: 1660
  Wilson (Arthur N.), M.D. Scholarship: 1660
AMERICAN MEDICAL TECHNOLOGISTS
  AMT Student Scholarships: 2230
AMERICAN MEDICAL WOMEN'S ASSOCIATION, INC.
  American Women's Hospitals Service (AWHS): 2231
AMERICAN METEOROLOGICAL SOCIETY
  AMS Freshman Undergraduate Scholarship Program: 2620
  AMS Graduate Fellowship in the History of Science: 2620
  AMS Graduate Fellowships: 2620
  AMS Named Scholarships: 2620
  AMS/Industry Minority Scholarship: 2620
  Macelwane (The Father James B.) Annual Awards in Meteorology:
  2620

AMERICAN MUSEUM OF NATURAL HISTORY (THE)
  Collection Study Grants: 1809
  Graduate Student Fellowship Program: 2137
  Lerner-Gray Grants for Marine Research: 1809
  Postdoctoral Research Fellowship Program: 1810
  Roosevelt (Theodore) Memorial Grants: 1809
AMERICAN MUSICOLOGICAL SOCIETY
  Brett (The Philip) Award: 751
  Brown (Howard Mayer) Fellowship: 752
  Einstein (The Alfred) Award: 751
  Greenberg (Noah) Award: 751
  Hampson (Thomas) Award: 751
  Johnson (Alvin H.) AMS 50 Dissertation Fellowships: 752
  Kinkeldey (The Otto) Award: 751
  Lockwood (Lewis) Award: 751
  Music in American Culture Award: 751
  Palisca (Claude V.) Award: 751
  Pisk (Paul A.) Prize: 751
  Slim (H. Colin) Award: 751
  Solie (Ruth A.) Award: 751
  Stevenson (Robert M.) Award: 751
AMERICAN NUCLEAR SOCIETY (ANS)
  ANS Graduate Scholarships: 2639
  ANS Undergraduate Scholarships: 2637
  Bisesti (Angelo F.) Memorial Scholarship: 2638
  Blizard (Everitt P.) Scholarship: 2639
  Dannels (Robert A.) Memorial Graduate Scholarship: 2639
  Dapp (Verne R.) Memorial Scholarship: 2639
  Decommissioning and Environmental Sciences (DESD) Scholarship:
  2635
  Delayed Education for Women Scholarship: 2634
  Dietrich (Joseph R.) Memorial Scholarship: 2637
  DiSalvo (Raymond) Scholarship: 2636
  Henry (Alan F.)/Paul A. Greebler Memorial Graduate Scholarship: 2637
  Lacy (Robert G.) Memorial Scholarship: 2638
  Lamarsh (John R.) Memorial Scholarship: 2637
  Landis (John and Muriel) Scholarships: 2634
  Liner (Robert T.) Scholarship: 2636
  Meyer (Walter) Scholarship: 2639
  Operations and Power Division Scholarship: 2636
  Pittsburgh Local Section Scholarship: 2640
  Schumar (James F.) Scholarship: 2639
  Thomas (Charles Tommy) Memorial Scholarship: 2636
  Vogt (James R.) Radiochemistry Scholarship: 2062
AMERICAN NUMISMATIC SOCIETY (THE)
  Groves (The Donald) Fund: 582
  Newman (The Eric P.) Graduate Summer Seminar: 348
  Schwartz (Frances M.) Fellowship: 581
AMERICAN NURSES FOUNDATION
  Nursing Research Grants: 2486
AMERICAN OIL CHEMISTS SOCIETY
  Chang (Stephen S.) Award: 2063
  Schroepfer Medal Award: 2063
  Supelco AOCS Research Award: 2063
AMERICAN OPTOMETRIC FOUNDATION
  Award of Excellence: 2505
  Cummings (J. Pat) Fellowship: 2505
  Ezell (William C.) Fellowship: 2505
  Vistakon® Contact Lens Residency Award: 2505
  Vistakon® Pediatric Residency Award: 2505
AMERICAN ORCHID SOCIETY
  American Orchid Society Grants for Orchid Research: 2138
American Orchid Society Grants for Orchid Research: 2138
AMERICAN ORIENTAL SOCIETY
  Hackney (Louise Wallace) Fellowship: 542
AMERICAN ORTHOPAEDIC SOCIETY FOR SPORTS MEDICINE
  (AOSSM) (THE)
  AOSSM Young Investigator Grant: 2549
AMERICAN OSTEOPATHIC FOUNDATION: 2522
  McCaughan Heritage Scholarship: 1661
American Overseas Research Centers (AORC) Program: 863
AMERICAN PARKINSON DISEASE ASSOCIATION, INC.
  Medical Student Summer Fellowships: 2456
AMERICAN PHILOSOPHICAL SOCIETY
  Franklin Research Grants: 14
  Lewis and Clark Fund for Exploration and Field Research (The): 15
  Library Resident Research Fellowships (The): 349
  Phillips Fund Grants for Native American Research: 1040
AMERICAN PLANNING ASSOCIATION
  Abrams (Charles) Scholarship Program: 1165
  McManus (Judith) Fellowship: 973

AMERICAN POLITICAL SCIENCE ASSOCIATION
  APSA Minority Fellows Program: 1988
  Congressional Fellowship Program: 1987
  Small Research Grant Program: 1989
AMERICAN PORPHYRIA FOUNDATION (THE): 2232
AMERICAN PSYCHIATRIC FOUNDATION
  APF-Merck & Co. Early Academic Career Research Award: 2565
  Kempf Fund Award for Research Development in Psychobiological Psychiatry: 2564
AMERICAN PSYCHOLOGICAL ASSOCIATION
  APA Congressional Fellowship Program: 2566
  Mental Health and Substance Abuse Services Fellowship: 974
  MFP Mental Health and Substance Abuse Services Fellowship: 2567
AMERICAN PSYCHOSOMATIC SOCIETY
  Weiner (Herbert) Early Career Award for Contributions to Psychosomatic Society: 2568
AMERICAN PUBLIC POWER ASSOCIATION (APPA)
  DEED Scholarship: 2641
AMERICAN RESEARCH CENTER IN EGYPT, INC.
  Fellowships for Research in Egypt: 879
AMERICAN RESEARCH CENTER IN SOFIA (ARCS) - U.S. OFFICE
  Academic Program Fellowship Competition: 880
AMERICAN RESEARCH INSTITUTE IN TURKEY, INC.
  ARIT Fellowship Program: 881
  Bogazici University Summer Language Program for Intensive Advanced Turkish Language Study: 882
  NEH Fellowships for Research in Turkey: 883
AMERICAN ROENTGEN RAY SOCIETY
  ARRS Annual Scholarship Program: 2233
AMERICAN-SCANDINAVIAN FOUNDATION (THE)
  American-Scandinavian Foundation Translation Prize: 665
  ASF Awards for Study in Scandinavia: 884
  Visiting Lectureships: 1617
American-Scandinavian Foundation Translation Prize: 665
AMERICAN SCHLAFHORST FOUNDATION: 16
AMERICAN SCHOOL OF CLASSICAL STUDIES AT ATHENS (THE)
  Advanced Fellowships: 890
  Bikakis (The Harry) Fellowship: 891
  CAORC Multi-Country Research Fellowships: 432
  Cotsen Traveling Fellowship for Research in Greece: 892
  Frantz (M. Alison) Fellowship in Post-Classical Studies at the Gennadius Library: 886
  Hirsch (The Jacob) Fellowship in Archaeology: 886
  Kress Publication Fellowships: 888
  Medieval Greek Summer Session at the Gennadius Library: 893
  National Endowment for the Humanities Fellowships: 885
  Papaioannou (The George) Fellowship: 889
  Robinson (Henry S.) Corinth Research Fellowship: 887
  Wiener Laboratory Fellowships: 894
  Wiener Laboratory Research Associateships: 894
  Wiener Laboratory Travel Grants: 894
AMERICAN SCHOOLS OF ORIENTAL RESEARCH (ASOR)
  Harris Grants: 895
  Heritage Fellowships: 895
  Mesopotamian Fellowship: 895
  Platt Fellowships: 895
AMERICAN SOCIETY FOR CLINICAL PATHOLOGY
  ASCP Scholarships: 2234
American Society for Eighteenth-Century Studies Fellowships: 623
AMERICAN SOCIETY FOR ENGINEERING EDUCATION
  Department of Defense National Defense Science and Engineering Graduate Fellowship Program (NDSEG): 2643
  Naval Research Laboratory (NRL) Postdoctoral Fellowship Program: 2644
  Summer Research Opportunity Program: 2643
  USAF Summer Faculty Fellowship Program: 2642
AMERICAN SOCIETY FOR ENOLOGY AND VITICULTURE: 2115
AMERICAN SOCIETY FOR HEALTHCARE RISK MANAGEMENT: 1418
AMERICAN SOCIETY FOR MASS SPECTROMETRY
  ASMS Research Awards in Mass Spectrometry: 2032
AMERICAN SOCIETY FOR MICROBIOLOGY
  ASM Robert D. Watkins Graduate Research Fellowships: 2140
  ASM/CDC Postdoctoral Research Fellowship Program: 2139
  Undergraduate Research Capstone Program: 2139
AMERICAN SOCIETY FOR NONDESTRUCTIVE TESTING, INC. (THE)
  ASNT Faculty Grant Award: 1521
  ASNT Fellowship Award: 2598
  Engineering Undergraduate Award: 1662
  Oliver (Robert B.) Scholarship: 1662

AMERICAN SOCIETY FOR THEATRE RESEARCH (ASTR)
  ASTR Collaborative Research Award (The): 526
  Biennial Sally Banes Publication Prize: 526
  Brockett (Oscar G.) Essay Prize: 526
  Cambridge University Press Prize: 526
  Chinoy Dissertation Research Fellowships: 526
  Co-sponsored Events Awards: 526
  Cohen (Selma Jeanne) Conference Presentation Award: 526
  Distinguished Scholar Award: 526
  Grants for Researchers with Heavy Teaching Loads: 526
  Hewitt (Barnard) Award: 526
  Hill (Errol) Award: 526
  Kahan (Gerald) Scholar's Prize: 526
  Keller (David) Travel Grants: 526
  Marshall (Thomas F.) Graduate Student Awards: 526
  McNamara (Brooks) Publishing Subvention: 526
  Research Fellowships: 526
  Targeted Research Areas Grants: 526
AMERICAN SOCIETY OF CIVIL ENGINEERS
  Ammann (O.H.) Research Fellowship in Structural Engineering: 2645
  CI Construction Engineering Scholarship and Student Prizes: 2645
  Cox (Lawrence W. and Francis W.) Scholarship: 2645
  Dames (Trent R.) and William W. Moore Fellowship: 2645
  Figg (Eugene C., Jr.) Civil Engineering Scholarship: 2645
  Freeman Fellowship: 2645
  Leisch (Jack E.) Memorial National Graduate Fellowship: 2645
  Lenard (John) Civil Engineering Scholarship: 2645
  Moorman (Robert B.B. and Josephine N.) Scholarship: 2645
  Smith (J. Waldo) Hydraulic Fellowship: 2645
  Tapman (Samuel Fletcher) ASCE Student Chapter Scholarship: 2645
  Tuttle (Arthur S.) Memorial Scholarship: 2645
  Yang (Y.C.) Civil Engineering Scholarship: 2645
AMERICAN SOCIETY OF COMPOSERS, AUTHORS AND PUBLISHERS (ASCAP)
  ASCAP Deems Taylor Awards: 666
AMERICAN SOCIETY OF ECHOCARDIOGRAPHY EDUCATION AND RESEARCH FOUNDATION (ASE)
  Waggoner (The Alan D.) Student Scholarship Award: 2389
AMERICAN SOCIETY OF ECHOCARDIOGRAPHY EDUCATION AND RESEARCH FOUNDATION (ASE FOUNDATION)
  ASE Foundation Research Awards: 2390
AMERICAN SOCIETY OF HEMATOLOGY
  Abstract Achievement Award: 2354
  Fellow Scholar Award: 2235
  Junior Faculty Scholar Award: 2235
  Outstanding Abstract Achievement Award: 2354
  Trainee Research Award Program: 2236
AMERICAN SOCIETY OF HYPERTENSION: 2237
AMERICAN SOCIETY OF INTERIOR DESIGNERS EDUCATIONAL FOUNDATION
  ASID Foundation Legacy Scholarship for Graduate Students: 412
  ASID Foundation Legacy Scholarship for Undergraduates: 412
  Eno (Irene Winifred) Grant: 412
  Polsky (Joel) Academic Achievement Award: 412
  Polsky (Joel) Prize: 412
AMERICAN SOCIETY OF MECHANICAL ENGINEERS AUXILIARY, INC. (THE)
  ASME/ASME Auxiliary Clarke Scholarship: 2646
  ASME/ASME Auxiliary FIRST Clarke Scholarship: 2646
  Baldwin (Allen J.) Scholarship: 2646
  Cartwright (Berna Lou) Scholarship: 2646
  Farny (Sylvia W.) Scholarship: 2646
  Kezios (Agnes Malakate) Scholarship: 2646
  Parsons (Elisabeth M. and Winchell M.) Scholarship: 2646
  Rice-Cullimore Scholarship: 2646
  Rothermel (Marjorie Roy) Scholarship: 2646
  Scharp (Charles B.) Scholarship: 2646
  Student Loan Fund: 2646
AMERICAN SOCIETY OF NAVAL ENGINEERS (ASNE)
  ASNE Scholarship Program: 2647
AMERICAN SOCIETY OF NEPHROLOGY
  ASN Research Fellowships: 2358
AMERICAN SOCIETY OF NEPHROLOGY
  ASN Student Scholar Grant: 2357
  Gottschalk (Carl W.) Research Scholar Grant: 2356
  Merrill (John) Grant in Transplantation: 2356
  Scherbenske (The M. James) Grant: 2355
  Siegel (Norman) Research Scholar Grant: 2356
AMERICAN SOCIETY OF REGIONAL ANESTHESIA AND PAIN MEDICINE
  ASRA Carl Koller Memorial Research Grant: 2538

AMERICAN SOCIETY OF SAFETY ENGINEERS
  Queeny (Edgar Monsanto) Safety Professional of the Year Award: 2648
AMERICAN SOCIOLOGICAL ASSOCIATION
  Minority Fellowship Program: 975
AMERICAN SPEECH-LANGUAGE-HEARING FOUNDATION
  Clinical Research Grant: 2506
  DiCarlo (Louis M.) Award for Recent Clinical Achievement: 2506
  Graduate Student Scholarship for International/Minority Students: 2506
  Graduate Student Scholarship for Minority Students: 2506
  Graduate Student Scholarship for NSSLHA Members: 2506
  Graduate Student Scholarship for Students with a Disability: 2506
  Graduate Student Scholarships: 2506
  Kleffner (Frank R.) Clinical Career Award: 2506
  New Century Scholars Doctoral Scholarship: 2506
  New Century Scholars Research Grant: 2506
  New Investigators Research Grant: 2506
  Speech Science Research Grant: 2506
  Student Research Grant in Audiology: 2506
  Student Research Grant in Early Childhood Language Development:
  2506
  Van Hattum (Rolland J.) Award for Contribution in the Schools: 2506
AMERICAN SWEDISH INSTITUTE (THE)
  Lorénzen (Lilly) Scholarship: 896
  Malmberg Scholarship for Study in Sweden (The): 897
AMERICAN TINNITUS ASSOCIATION (ATA)
  ATA Student Research Grant Program: 1811
  ATA Tinnitus Research Grant Program: 1811
AMERICAN UROGYNECOLOGIC FOUNDATION
  Allyson (June) Award: 2105
AMERICAN VACUUM SOCIETY (AVS)
  Graduate Research Awards: 2100
  Varian (Russell and Sigurd) Award: 2100
  Whetten (Nellie Yeoh) Award: 2100
AMERICAN VETERINARY MEDICAL ASSOCIATION
  AVMA Fellowship: 2238
AMERICAN WATER RESOURCES ASSOCIATION
  Herbert (Richard A.) Memorial Educational Fund: 2168
American Women's Hospitals Service (AWHS): 2231
Americans Overseas Summer, Semester and Year Programs: 954
AmeriCorps VISTA: 1248
AMES (THE KATHRYN) FOUNDATION: 829
AMFAR, THE FOUNDATION FOR AIDS RESEARCH
  GMT Initiative Grants: 1812
  Krim (Mathilde) Fellowships in Basic Biomedical Research: 1812
  Research Grants: 1812
AMGEN FOUNDATION, INC.: 17
Amirikian (Arsham) Engineering Scholarship: 2600
Ammann (O.H.) Research Fellowship in Structural Engineering: 2645
AMS Freshman Undergraduate Scholarship Program: 2620
AMS Graduate Fellowship in the History of Science: 2620
AMS Graduate Fellowships: 2620
AMS Named Scholarships: 2620
AMS/Industry Minority Scholarship: 2620
AMT Student Scholarships: 2230
AMTROL Scholarship: 2597
AMVETS
  AMVETS National Scholarship Program: Entering College Freshman
  Scholarship: 1663
  AMVETS National Scholarship Program: JROTC Scholarship: 1663
  AMVETS/University of Phoenix Scholarship: 1664
AMVETS National Scholarship Program: Entering College Freshman
  Scholarship: 1663
AMVETS National Scholarship Program: JROTC Scholarship: 1663
AMVETS/University of Phoenix Scholarship: 1664
AMY FOUNDATION (THE)
  Amy Writing Awards: 805
Amy Writing Awards: 805
AMYOTROPHIC LATERAL SCLEROSIS ASSOCIATION (THE)
  Research Grant Program: 2457
ANDERSEN CORPORATE FOUNDATION (THE): 1166
ANDERSEN (FRED C. AND KATHERINE B.) FOUNDATION: 1167
ANDERSEN (HUGH J.) FOUNDATION: 1168
Andersen (Hugh J.) Scholarship: 2296
Anderson (A.T.) Memorial Scholarship: 1038
Anderson (Gladys C.) Memorial Scholarship: 971
Andrew W. Mellon Foundation Fellowship: 398
ANDRUS FAMILY FUND
  Community Reconciliation: 1169
  Foster Care to Independence: 1169
Anesthesiology Teaching Recognition Awards: 2272
ANIMAL ASSISTANCE FOUNDATION: 2239

Animal Protection Program: 1384
ANN ARBOR AREA COMMUNITY FOUNDATION
  African American Endowment Fund (The): 1170
  Botsford Bach (The Anna) Fund: 1170
  Community Foundation of Plymouth: 1170
  General Grantmaking: 1170
  Youth Council: 1170
  Ypsilanti Area Community Fund (The): 1170
ANNA-MONIKA FOUNDATION
  Anna-Monika Foundation Prize (The): 2569
Anna-Monika Foundation Prize (The): 2569
ANNENBERG FOUNDATION (THE): 18
  Annenberg Graduate Fellowship Program: 1797
Annual Awards for Voice: 773
Annual Central Prize Award: 2500
Annual Composition Contest: 784
Annual Conference: 2579
Annual International Juried Award Exhibition: 567
Annual Loren L. Zachary National Vocal Competition for Young Opera
  Singers: 798
Annual Symposium and Festival: 747
ANRF Arthritis Research Grants: 2241
ANS Graduate Scholarships: 2639
ANS Undergraduate Scholarships: 2637
Anson (Abraham) Memorial Scholarship: 2034
ANXIETY AND DEPRESSION ASSOCIATION OF AMERICA
  Junior Faculty Research Grants: 2570
AOS Clinician-Scientist Award: 2521
AOSSM Young Investigator Grant: 2549
APA Congressional Fellowship Program: 2566
APF-Merck & Co. Early Academic Career Research Award: 2565
APICS EDUCATIONAL AND RESEARCH FOUNDATION, INC.
  Plossl (George and Marion) Doctoral Dissertation Competition: 2599
APLASTIC ANEMIA AND MDS INTERNATIONAL FOUNDATION
  AA&MDSIF Research Grant Program: 2240
Appalachian Scholarship: 739
Applegate/Jackson Parks Future Teacher Scholarship: 1719
Applied Materials Corporate Philanthropy Program: 19
Applied Materials Excellence in the Arts: 500
APPLIED MATERIALS, INC.
  Applied Materials Corporate Philanthropy Program: 19
  Applied Social Issues Internship Program (The): 1880
APPRAISAL INSTITUTE EDUCATION TRUST
  Appraisal Institute Education Trust Scholarship: 1891
Appraisal Institute Education Trust Scholarship: 1891
Apprenticeships: 485
APS CORPORATE GIVING PROGRAM: 20
APSA Minority Fellows Program: 1988
Arboriculture Education Grant: 2129
ARC OF THE UNITED STATES (THE)
  Research Matters! Award: 2571
ARCA FOUNDATION (THE): 21
ARCHAEOLOGICAL INSTITUTE OF AMERICA
  AIA Publication Subvention Program (The): 1665
  Archaeology of Portugal Fellowship (The): 830
  Colburn (Anna C. and Oliver C.) Fellowship: 353
  James (Olivia) Traveling Fellowship: 351
  Kress (Samuel H.) Grants for Research and Publication in Classical Art
  and Architecture: 1665
  Pomerance (Harriet and Leon) Fellowship: 352
  Waldbaum (Jane C.) Archaeological Field School Scholarship: 350
  Woodruff (Helen M.) Fellowship of the AIA and the American
  Academy in Rome: 1618
Archaeology of Portugal Fellowship (The): 830
Archaeology Program: 2022
Archaeometry Program: 2022
Archbold (John Dana) Fellowships: 932
ARCHITECTURAL LEAGUE OF NEW YORK
  League Prize for Young Architects and Designers (The): 414
  Norden (Deborah J.) Fund: 413
ARCHSTONE FOUNDATION: 1419
ARCTIC INSTITUTE OF NORTH AMERICA
  AINA Grants-in-Aid: 1619
Arctic Research Program: 1835
Arcus (Margaret E.) Outstanding Family Life Educator Award: 1498
ARD INTERNATIONAL MUSIC COMPETITION
  Music Competition: 753
ARGONNE NATIONAL LABORATORY
  Laboratory-Graduate Program: 1814
  Science Undergraduate Laboratory Internships: 1813
  Thesis Parts Program: 1814

ARIT Fellowship Program: 881
Arizona Center for Civic Leadership: 128
ARIZONA COMMISSION ON THE ARTS: 433
ARIZONA COMMUNITY FOUNDATION
    Arizona Economic Success: 1171
    Communities for All Ages: 1171
Arizona Economic Success: 1171
ARIZONA STATE UNIVERSITY
    ASU Leadership Scholarship Program: 1522
Arkans (Rick) Eagle Scout Scholarship: 1721
ARKANSAS COMMUNITY FOUNDATION: 1172
Armed Forces Interest Group: 1353
ARMENIAN GENERAL BENEVOLENT UNION
    A.G.B.U. Scholarship Program: 1666
    Fellowship for U.S.-Based Study: 1666
    International Scholarships: 1666
    Performing Arts Fellowship: 1666
    Religious Studies Fellowship: 1666
ARMENIAN RELIEF SOCIETY OF EASTERN U.S.A., INC.
    A.R.S. Lazarían Graduate Scholarship: 976
    A.R.S. Undergraduate Scholarship: 976
ARRS Annual Scholarship Program: 2233
Art Administration Interns: 544
Art and Change Grant: 1087
Art and Cultural Facilities: 427
Art Awards: 498
ART DIRECTORS CLUB, INC.
    ADC National Scholarships: 1922
Art Education (Low-residency/online MA): 555
Art History Fellowships in Florence: 554
Art-in-Education Artists' Book Residency Grant: 520
Art Meets Activism: 1086
Art Projects Grants: 523
ARTHRITIS FOUNDATION
    Innovative Research Grants: 2450
    Postdoctoral Fellowships: 2450
Arthritis Grants: 330
ARTHRITIS NATIONAL RESEARCH FOUNDATION (ANRF)
    ANRF Arthritis Research Grants: 2241
ARTHRITIS SOCIETY (THE)
    Arthritis Society Clinical Fellowships in Rheumatology (The): 2451
    Arthritis Society Clinician Teacher Award (The): 2451
    Arthritis Society Consumer Activity Grants (The): 2451
    Arthritis Society Investigator Award (The): 2451
    Arthritis Society New Investigator Award (The): 2451
    Arthritis Society Small Meeting Grants (The): 2451
    Arthritis Society Strategic Operating Grants (The): 2451
Arthritis Society Clinical Fellowships in Rheumatology (The): 2451
Arthritis Society Clinician Teacher Award (The): 2451
Arthritis Society Consumer Activity Grants (The): 2451
Arthritis Society Investigator Award (The): 2451
Arthritis Society New Investigator Award (The): 2451
Arthritis Society Small Meeting Grants (The): 2451
Arthritis Society Strategic Operating Grants (The): 2451
Artist Development Grants: 511
Artist Enrichment: 1086
Artist Entrepreneurial Workshops: 485
Artist Fellowship Program: 447
Artist Fellowships: 472, 490
Artist Grants: 501
Artist in Residence: 485
Artist Laureates: 500
Artist Residencies: 443
Artist Residency Program: 468
Artist Services: 485
Artist Services Program: 483
Artist-in-Schools & Communities: 501
Artists Across Wyoming Grants: 523
Artists in Education: 471
Artists in Schools: 437, 511
Artists-in-the-Schools Grants Program: 507
Artists with Disabilities Access: 492
Artists' Book Residency Grants: 519
Artists' Fellowships: 487
Artists-in-Schools/Communities Grants: 482
Arts: 1192, 1242
Arts Access: 492
Arts Access Grant (AAG): 497
Arts and Audiences: 490
Arts and Culture: 12, 90, 133, 257, 1270

Arts and Entertainment Districts Program: 471
Arts and Humanities Grants: 469
Arts Build Communities: 494
Arts Catalyze Placemaking: 446
Arts Education Grants: 523
Arts Education Program: 447
Arts Education Programs: 465
Arts Education Projects: 459
Arts for Young People: 329
Arts Fund: 1214
Arts in Communities: 471
Arts in Education: 445, 485
Arts in Education Grants: 490
Arts in Health Care Project Grants: 485
Arts Learning: 469
Arts Learning Grants: 494
Arts Learning Program: 483
Arts Learning Projects: 482
Arts Learning: Artist Express: 492
Arts Learning: Artist in Residence/Artists: 492
Arts Learning: Artist in Residence/Sponsors: 492
Arts Learning: Arts Partnership: 492
Arts Management Internship: 796
ARTS MIDWEST
    Arts Midwest Conference: 527
    Arts Midwest Touring Fund: 527
Arts Midwest Conference: 527
Arts Midwest Touring Fund: 527
Arts Organization Challenge Grants: 501
Arts Organization Grants: 495
Arts Organizations: 465
Arts Organizations Grants: 445
Arts Partnership Grants: 511
Arts Program: 107, 193, 1495
Arts Project Grants: 482, 486
Arts Recognition Grants: 494
Arts Resources and Artists Programs: 463
Arts Services Grants: 494
Arts, Culture and Humanities: 1355
Arts-in-Education: 427
Arts-in-Education/Artists in Residence: 491
Arts-in-Education/STE[A]M: 491
Arts-in-Education/Teacher Incentive: 491
ArtsConnect: 476
ArtsEverywhere Fund: 1236
Arver (David) Memorial Scholarship: 2618
Arver (Dutch and Ginger) Scholarship: 2618
ASCAP Deems Taylor Awards: 666
ASCAP FOUNDATION (THE)
    Young (The Morton Gould) Composer Awards: 754
ASCP Scholarships: 2234
ASE Foundation Research Awards: 2390
ASECS/Clark Library Fellowships: 359
ASF Awards for Study in Scandinavia: 884
ASHBURN INSTITUTE INC.
    Frank Educational Fund: 831
ASHRAE
    ASHRAE Graduate Student Grant-in-Aid Program: 2650
    ASHRAE Research Grants: 2649
ASHRAE Graduate Student Grant-in-Aid Program: 2650
ASHRAE Research Grants: 2649
Asia-Pacific Cancer Society Training Grants (APCASOT): 2449
Asia Pacific Leadership Program Fellowship: 846
ASIAN AMERICAN JOURNALISTS ASSOCIATION
    Broadcast News Grant: 1667
    Chen (Stanford) Grant: 1667
    Chin (Vincent) Scholarships: 1667
    Woo (William) Print & Online News Grant: 1667
ASIAN CULTURAL COUNCIL: 434
    Asian Cultural Council Fellowships: 898
Asian Cultural Council Fellowships: 898
ASID Foundation Legacy Scholarship for Graduate Students: 412
ASID Foundation Legacy Scholarship for Undergraduates: 412
Askin (Lady Mollie Isabelle) Ballet Scholarship: 539
Askin (Sir Robert William) Operatic Scholarship: 539
ASLA Council of Fellows Scholarship: 2186
ASM MATERIALS EDUCATION FOUNDATION
    ASM Outstanding Scholars: 2677
    Dulis (Edward J.) Scholarship: 2677
    Dyrkacz (William & Mary) Scholarships: 2677
    Haniak (John M.) Scholarship: 2677

Ladish Co. Foundation Scholarships: 2677
Roberts (George A.) Scholarship: 2677
Wert (Lucille & Charles A.) Scholarship: 2677
Woodside (William Park) Founder's Scholarship: 2677
ASM Outstanding Scholars: 2677
ASM Robert D. Watkins Graduate Research Fellowships: 2140
ASM/CDC Postdoctoral Research Fellowship Program: 2139
ASME/ASME Auxiliary Clarke Scholarship: 2646
ASME/ASME Auxiliary FIRST Clarke Scholarship: 2646
ASMS Research Awards in Mass Spectrometry: 2032
ASN Research Fellowships: 2358
ASN Student Scholar Grant: 2357
ASNE Scholarship Program: 2647
ASNT Faculty Grant Award: 1521
ASNT Fellowship Award: 2598
ASPRS - THE IMAGING AND GEOSPATIAL INFORMATION
   SOCIETY
   Altenhofen (Robert E.) Memorial Scholarship: 2033
   Anson (Abraham) Memorial Scholarship: 2034
   BAE Systems Award: 2034
   Behrens (John O.) Institute for Land Information (ILI) Memorial
   Scholarship: 2034
   Colwell (Robert N.) Memorial Fellowship: 2034
   DigitalGlobe Foundation Award: 2033
   ERDAS Internship: 2033
   Fischer (William A.) Memorial Scholarship: 2033
   Moffitt (Francis H.) Memorial Scholarship: 2034
   Osborn (The Kenneth J.) Memorial Scholarship: 2034
   Ta Liang Memorial Award: 2033
   Wolf (Paul R.) Memorial Scholarship: 2033
   Z/I Imaging Scholarship: 2033
ASRA Carl Koller Memorial Research Grant: 2538
Assembly Session Internships: 2008
Asset Building: 12
ASSISI FOUNDATION OF MEMPHIS INC.: 22
Assisting Women's Groups Globally: 1082
Assistive Technology Programs: 2561
ASSOCIATION FOR APPLIED PSYCHOPHYSIOLOGY AND
   BIOFEEDBACK
   Student Travel Scholarship Program: 2572
ASSOCIATION FOR BEHAVIORAL AND COGNITIVE THERAPIES
   President's New Researcher Award: 2574
   Roswell (Virginia) Dissertation Award: 2573
ASSOCIATION FOR LIBRARY AND INFORMATION SCIENCE
   EDUCATION
   ALISE Research Awards: 714
   ALISE/ProQuest Methodology Paper Competition: 715
   Garfield (The Eugene)/ALISE Doctoral Dissertation Competition: 715
   Wynar (Bohdan S.) Research Paper Competition: 715
ASSOCIATION FOR RESEARCH OF CHILDHOOD CANCER, INC.
   (AROCC): 2428
ASSOCIATION OF AMERICAN GEOGRAPHERS (THE)
   AAG Dissertation Research Grants: 2075
   AAG Globe Book Award for Public Understanding of Geography: 2076
   AAG Meridian Book Award for the Outstanding Scholarly Work in
   Geography: 2076
   AAG Research Grant: 2074
   AAG-IGIF Graduate Research Awards: 2073
   AAG-IGIF Student Paper Awards: 2073
   AAG-IGIF Student Travel Grants: 2073
ASSOCIATION OF UNIVERSITIES AND COLLEGES OF CANADA
   Howe (C.D.) Scholarships: 1668
   Mattinson Scholarship Program for Students with Disabilities: 977
ASSOCIATION OF WOMEN'S HEALTH, OBSTETRIC AND
   NEONATAL NURSES (AWHONN)
   AWHONN Research Grants Program: 2487
ASSOCIATION OF WRITERS & WRITING PROGRAMS (THE)
   AWP Award Series in Creative Nonfiction: 667
   AWP Award Series in the Novel: 667
   Hall (Donald) Prize in Poetry: 667
   Paley (Grace) Prize in Short Fiction: 667
ASSOCIATION ON AMERICAN INDIAN AFFAIRS
   Graduate Scholarships: 1042
   Risling (David) Emergency Aid Scholarships: 1041
   Slagle (Allogan) Memorial Scholarship: 1044
   Undergraduate Scholarships: 1043
Assumption Program of Loans for Education (APLE): 1672
ASTR Collaborative Research Award (The): 526

ASTRAEA LESBIAN FOUNDATION FOR JUSTICE
   Global Arts Fund: 980
   International Fund: 978
   U.S. General Fund: 979
ASTRONOMICAL SOCIETY OF THE PACIFIC
   Amateur Achievement Award: 2051
   Brennan (Thomas) Award for Outstanding Contributions to the Teaching
   of Astronomy in Grades 9-12: 2050
   Klumpke-Roberts Award: 2049
   Las Cumbres Amateur Outreach Award: 2051
   Muhlmann (Maria and Eric) Award: 2048
Astronomy and Astrophysics Research Grants: 2055
ASU Leadership Scholarship Program: 1522
ATA Student Research Grant Program: 1811
ATA Tinnitus Research Grant Program: 1811
ATHWIN FOUNDATION: 23
ATKINSON FOUNDATION: 24
Atkinson Scholarship Program (The): 1383
ATLANTIC SALMON FEDERATION
   Olin Fellowships: 2141
ATLANTIC SCHOOL OF THEOLOGY
   Betts (The Evelyn Hilchie) Memorial Fellowship: 806
ATRAN FOUNDATION, INC.: 25
Austern (H. Thomas) Memorial Writing Competition-Food and Drug Law:
   1975
AUSTIN COMMUNITY FOUNDATION FOR THE CAPITAL AREA
   (THE): 1173
AUSTRALIAN NATIONAL UNIVERSITY (THE)
   Visiting Fellowships: 354
Australian Postgraduate Awards (APA): 950
AUSTRIAN CULTURAL FORUM: 899
AUSTRO-AMERICAN ASSOCIATION OF BOSTON: 832
AUTISM SPEAKS
   Family Services Community Grants: 2242
   Meixner Translational Postdoctoral Fellowships: 2242
   Weatherstone Predoctoral Fellowships: 2242
   Wright (Suzanne & Bob) Trailblazer: 2242
AUTRY FOUNDATION: 1174
AVIATION DISTRIBUTORS AND MANUFACTURERS ASSOCIATION
   (ADMA)
   ADMA Scholarship Programs: 2621
AVIATION INSURANCE ASSOCIATION (AIA)
   AIA Scholarship: 2622
AVMA Fellowship: 2238
Award for Excellence and Achievement in Hospital Librarianship: 730
Award for Global Understanding: 1863
Award in Gender Studies (The): 1836
Award of Excellence: 2505
Award Program for Summer Music Festivals and Music Centers: 778
Awards for Achievement in Arc Welded Design, Engineering and
   Fabrication: College Division: 2654
Awards for Outstanding Teaching and Mentoring: 1879
Awards to Scholarly Publications Program: 1848
AWHONN Research Grants Program: 2487
AWP Award Series in Creative Nonfiction: 667
AWP Award Series in the Novel: 667
AWS FOUNDATION, INC.
   Adkins (Howard E. and Wilma J.) Memorial Scholarship: 2600
   Airgas-Jerry Baker Scholarship: 2600
   Airgas-Terry Jarvis Memorial Scholarship: 2600
   Amirikian (Arsham) Engineering Scholarship: 2600
   Barckhoff (Jack R.) Welding Management Scholarship: 2601
   Bovie (D. Fred and Marian L.) Scholarship: 2600
   Brady (Edward J.) Memorial Scholarship: 2601
   Brothers (William A. and Ann M.) Scholarship: 2601
   Hastings (Don and Shirley) Scholarship: 2601
   Hastings (Donald F.) Scholarship: 2601
   Howell (William B.) Memorial Scholarship: 2601
   Lincoln (John C.) Memorial Scholarship: 2600
   Matsuo Bridge Company, Ltd. of Japan Scholarship: 2600
   Miller Electric Mfg. Co. Scholarship: 2601
   Past Presidents Scholarship: 2602
   Peaslee (Robert L.)-Detroit Brazing and Soldering Scholarship: 2602
   Praxair International Scholarship: 2602
   Resistance Welding Manufacturing Alliance Scholarship: 2603
   Turner (James A., Jr.) Memorial Scholarship: 2602
AXE-HOUGHTON FOUNDATION: 653

B

B.A.E.F. Fellowships for Study in Belgium: 900
BABBAGE (CHARLES) INSTITUTE
    Tomash (The Adelle and Erwin) Fellowship in the History of
        Information Technology: 2604
BABCOCK (MARY REYNOLDS) FOUNDATION
    Moving People and Places Out of Poverty: 26
Bache-Renshaw Fellowship: 2004
Bachelor of Music Degree Program: 764
Backus Award: 2155
Baden-Wuerttemberg-STIPENDIUM Work Immersion Study Program: 910
BADER (HELEN) FOUNDATION, INC.: 27
BADGER METER FOUNDATION, INC.: 1175
BAE Systems Award: 2034
Bahlsen (Bettina) Memorial Graduate Scholarship: 1786
BAKER (R.C.) FOUNDATION: 28
BAKER (THE WILLIAM G., JR.) MEMORIAL FUND: 435
Baldwin (Allen J.) Scholarship: 2646
Baldwin (Birgit) Fellowship: 610
Baldwin (Donald A. Sr.) Business Aviation Management Scholarship:
    2626
BALL BROTHERS FOUNDATION: 29
BALL (GEORGE AND FRANCES) FOUNDATION: 30
BALTIMORE COMMUNITY FOUNDATION: 31
Bambino (Melissa K.) Memorial Award: 2447
Bancroft Award (The): 1836
Bancroft Prizes: 587
BANFF CENTRE (THE): 528
Banting (Frederick) and Charles Best Canada Graduate
    Scholarship-Doctoral Awards: 2247
Banting Postdoctoral Fellowships: 1876
BARAGA COUNTY COMMUNITY FOUNDATION: 1176
Barckhoff (Jack R.) Welding Management Scholarship: 2601
BARD (C.R.) FOUNDATION: 32
BARNES GROUP FOUNDATION: 1177
Barnes Scholarship: 1764
Barnum (Harold) Industry Award: 2673
Baroid Scholarship: 2597
Barr (David S.) Award: 1951
BARR FOUNDATION: 1178
BARRA FOUNDATION: 33
Barrett (Anne Louise) Fellowship: 1097
BASEBALL TOMORROW FUND: 1107
Baseball Writers of America Scholarship: 1750
Basic Needs: 12
Basic Research Challenge Program: 1843
Basic Research Fellowship Awards: 2454
Basic Science Award: 2403
Basic Support Grants: 482
Basic, Clinical and Translational Research Grant Programs: 2279
Basilone Postgraduate Scholarship: 1775
BAT CONSERVATION INTERNATIONAL
    BCI Student Scholarship: 1523
BATON ROUGE AREA FOUNDATION: 436
Batten Disease Research Grant: 2243
BATTEN DISEASE SUPPORT AND RESEARCH ASSOCIATION
    Batten Disease Research Grant: 2243
BATTLE CREEK COMMUNITY FOUNDATION: 34
BAXTER INTERNATIONAL FOUNDATION (THE): 35
BAY AND PAUL FOUNDATIONS (THE): 1524
Bay Area Grants Program: 287
BAYER USA FOUNDATION: 1815
Bayliss (John) Scholarship Fund: 1924
BAYRD (ADELAIDE BREED) FOUNDATION: 36
BCI Student Scholarship: 1523
BEAN (NORWIN S. AND ELIZABETH N.) FOUNDATION: 1179
Beard Scholarship: 722
Beattie (Catherine) Fellowship: 2180
Beattie (Catherine H.) Fellowship for Conservation Horticulture: 2116
Beattie (Constance) Memorial Fund Bursary Program: 2557
Beckett (Dr. Joyce) Scholarship: 1032
Beer (The George Louis) Prize: 578
Beeson (Paul) Career Development Awards in Aging Research Program:
    2227
Beginning Grant-in-Aid: 2378
Begun Scholarship: 717
Behavior Therapy Training Institute (BTTI): 2579
Behavioral Sciences Postdoctoral Fellowship: 1852
Behavioral Sciences Student Fellowships: 1851
Behavioral/Social Science Research: 2352

Behrens (John O.) Institute for Land Information (ILI) Memorial
    Scholarship: 2034
Beldecos (Helen J.), Past Grand President, Scholarship (Undergraduate):
    1080
BELGIAN AMERICAN EDUCATIONAL FOUNDATION, INC.
    B.A.E.F. Fellowships for Study in Belgium: 900
BELK FOUNDATION (THE): 1600
Belkin (Alice) Memorial Scholarship: 1794
BELL (ALEXANDER GRAHAM) ASSOCIATION FOR THE DEAF
    AND HARD OF HEARING
    Bell (Alexander Graham) College Scholarship Awards: 981
Bell (Alexander Graham) College Scholarship Awards: 981
BELL (MAX) FOUNDATION: 1420
BELO FOUNDATION (THE): 37
BEMIS COMPANY FOUNDATION
    Bemis Scholarship Program: 38
    Educational Gift Matching: 38
    FoodShare Program: 38
    Nonprofit Gift Matching Program: 38
    United Way Program: 38
Bemis Scholarship Program: 38
BEN & JERRY'S FOUNDATION: 982
Bene (John G.) Fellowship in Community Forestry: Trees and People:
    2123
BENIGN ESSENTIAL BLEPHAROSPASM RESEARCH FOUNDATION
    INC.: 2507
Bennett (A.E.) Research Awards: 2591
Bentley Cropping Systems Fellowship (The): 919
Bentley (The Jerry) Prize: 578
BENTON FOUNDATION
    Media Policy and Public Service Media: 1923
Berardo (Felix) Mentoring Award: 1498
BERGER (H.N. AND FRANCES C.) FOUNDATION: 39
Berger (Mike) Award: 1925
Berkel Crisp (Rosemary) Research Award: 2497
BERKS COUNTY COMMUNITY FOUNDATION
    Boyertown Area Grantmaking: 1180
    Governor Mifflin Area Grantmaking: 1180
    Metropolitan Edison Energy Fund: 1180
BERKSHIRE CONFERENCE OF WOMEN HISTORIANS: 583
Berkshire Conference of Women Historians Graduate Student Fellowship:
    588
Berlin Prize Fellowship: 869
Bernard (Jessie) Outstanding Contribution to Feminist Scholarship Paper:
    1498
Bernard (Jessie) Outstanding Research Proposal: 1498
BERNSEN (THE GRACE AND FRANKLIN) FOUNDATION: 40
Bernstein (Leslie) Investigator Development Grant: 2218
Bernstein (Leslie) Research Grant: 2219
Bernstein (Leslie) Resident Research Grants: 2217
Berntsen International Scholarship in Surveying (The): 2657
Berntsen International Scholarship in Surveying Technology (The): 2657
BERRIEN COMMUNITY FOUNDATION: 41
Berry (Leonard G.) Medal: 2680
Berryman (Clifford K. and James T.) Award for Editorial Cartoons: 1949
BERWIND CORPORATION: 42
Best (Charles H.) Research Fund: 2409
Best (Raymond A. and Ina C.) Fellowship for MBA: 2664
BETA PHI MU
    Garfield (Eugene) Doctoral Dissertation Fellowship: 716
    Lancour (Harold) Scholarship for Foreign Study: 716
    Reed (Sarah Rebecca) Scholarship: 716
    Sessa (Frank B.) Scholarship for Continuing Education of a Beta Phi
        Mu Member: 716
    Woolls (Blanche E.) Scholarship for School Media Service: 716
BETHESDA LUTHERAN COMMUNITIES, INC.
    Developmental Disabilities Scholastic Achievement Scholarships: 1525
Bethune (Mary McLeod) Scholarship Program (MMB): 1687
Betts (The Evelyn Hilchie) Memorial Fellowship: 806
Beveridge (The Albert J.) Award: 578
Beveridge (The Albert J.) Grant: 578
BIBLIOGRAPHICAL SOCIETY OF AMERICA
    BSA Fellowship Program: 1526
Biennial Dissertation Competition: 780
Biennial Promising Playwright Award: 530
Biennial Sally Banes Publication Prize: 526
Biennium Grants Program: 456
Biestock (N.S.) Fellowship: 1958
Big Five Graduate Scholarship (The): 1080
Big Yellow School Bus (The): 472

Bigelow (Timothy) and Palmer W. Bigelow, Jr. Scholarship: 1697
Biggane (James L.) Fellowship in Finance: 2010
Bikai (Pierre and Patricia) Fellowship: 870
Bikakis (The Harry) Fellowship: 891
BING FUND: 43
BINGHAM (THE WILLIAM) FOUNDATION: 44
Bingham (Worth) Prize for Investigative Journalism: 1952
Binnie (Ruth) Fellowship: 1077
Biomedical Research Grant: 2417
Biomedical Research Grants: 2387, 2470
Biotechnology/Regenerative Medicine: 2352
Birdsall (The Paul) Prize: 578
Bisesti (Angelo F.) Memorial Scholarship: 2638
Black Philanthropy Grants: 1404
Blahd (Mitzi & William, M.D.) Pilot Research Grant: 2328
BLAIR (WILLIAM) AND COMPANY FOUNDATION: 1181
BLAUSTEIN (JACOB AND HILDA) FOUNDATION: 983
Blinder (Richard) Award: 416
Blizard (Everitt P.) Scholarship: 2639
Bloch (Doris) Research Award: 2497
Block (Jeanne Humphrey) Dissertation Award: 1857
Blood Diseases and Resources Research: 2369
BLOWITZ-RIDGEWAY FOUNDATION: 1182
BLUE MOUNTAIN COMMUNITY FOUNDATION: 1183
BLUESCOPE FOUNDATION NORTH AMERICA (THE): 45
Blum (Stella) Research Grant: 444
BNSF RAILWAY FOUNDATION
	Hispanic American Scholarship Program: 1063
	Native American Scholarship Program: 1045
BNY MELLON FOUNDATION OF SOUTHWESTERN
	PENNSYLVANIA (THE): 1184
Board Grants: 2280
Boardroom Awards: 1894
BODMAN FOUNDATION (THE): 46
Bogazici University Summer Language Program for Intensive Advanced
	Turkish Language Study: 882
Bolton (Frances P.) Fellowship: 2586
Bombardier (Joseph-Armand) Canada Graduate Scholarships Program -
	Master's Scholarships: 1874
Bone (The Roger C.) Advances in End-of-Life Care Award: 2392
Bonner Scholarship: 1254
BONNEVILLE ENVIRONMENTAL FOUNDATION
	Model Watershed Program: 2169
	Renewable Energy Program: 2169
Book Award: 835
BOOTH-BRICKER FUND (THE): 47
Boren Fellowships: 934
Boren Scholarships: 933
Bosch (The Robert) Foundation Fellowship Program: 912
BOSTON FOUNDATION: 1185
BOSTON WOMEN'S FUND: 1075
Botein (Stephen) Fellowships: 345
Bothmer Fellowship (The): 561
Botsford Bach (The Anna) Fund: 1170
Boulton (Maxwell) Q.C. Fellowship: 1984
Bovie (D. Fred and Marian L.) Scholarship: 2600
Bowers (Margaret Freeman) Fellowship: 1097
BOY SCOUTS OF AMERICA, NATIONAL EAGLE SCOUT
	ASSOCIATION (THE)
	Cooke (Mabel and Lawrence S.) Scholarship: 1109
	Hall/McElwain Merit Scholarships: 1108
	National Eagle Scout Scholarship Fund: 1109
	STEM Scholarship: 1109
	United Health Foundation Scholarship: 1109
Boyertown Area Grantmaking: 1180
Bradley (Ed) Scholarship: 1958
Bradley Fellowship Program: 1669
BRADLEY (THE LYNDE AND HARRY) FOUNDATION, INC.
	Bradley Fellowship Program: 1669
	Bradley-Alavi Student Fellowship: 2328
	Brady (Edward J.) Memorial Scholarship: 2601
BRAIN & BEHAVIOR RESEARCH FOUNDATION
	Distinguished Investigator Grant: 2575
	Independent Investigator Grant: 2575
	Young Investigator Grant: 2575
Brain Research Tumor Grant: 1113
BRAINERD FOUNDATION
	Grassroots Fund Grants: 2170
	Opportunity Fund Grants: 2170
BRANDON UNIVERSITY: 755

Brandt (John) Memorial Scholarship Fund: 201
Bray (Jeanne E.) Memorial Scholarship: 1738
BREAD LOAF WRITERS' CONFERENCE
	Fellowship and Scholarship Program for Writers: 668
Breasted (The James Henry) Prize: 578
BREMER (OTTO) FOUNDATION: 1186
Brennan (Thomas) Award for Outstanding Contributions to the Teaching
	of Astronomy in Grades 9-12: 2050
BRETT FAMILY FOUNDATION
	Social Justice Grant Program: 1847
Brett (The Philip) Award: 751
BRIGHAM AND WOMEN'S HOSPITAL
	Deland Fellowship Program in Health Care and Society: 1421
BRIGHT FOCUS FOUNDATION
	Alzheimer's Disease Research: 2458
	Macular Degeneration Research Program: 1422
	National Glaucoma Research Program: 2508
Bright (Norman and Marion) Memorial Award: 2064
British Federation Crosby Hall Fellowship: 1085
BRITISH INSTITUTE IN EASTERN AFRICA (THE)
	Minor Research Grant Program: 901
British Marshall Scholarships: 948
British Morehead-Cain Scholarship to the University of North Carolina at
	Chapel Hill (The): 958
BROAD (THE ELI AND EDYTHE) FOUNDATION
	Broad Medical Research Program: 2408
Broad Medical Research Program: 2408
BROADCAST EDUCATION ASSOCIATION
	Bayliss (John) Scholarship Fund: 1924
	Eaton (Richard) Foundation Award: 1924
	Patterson (Walter S.) Scholarship: 1924
	Tanger (Alexander M.) Scholarship: 1924
	Two Year/Community College BEA Award: 1924
	Voron (Abe) Scholarship: 1924
	Wasilewski (Vincent T.) Scholarship: 1924
Broadcast News Grant: 1667
BROCK (THE HARRY B. AND JANE H.) FOUNDATION: 1187
Brockett (Oscar G.) Essay Prize: 526
Brodman (Estelle) Award for Academic Medical Librarian of the Year:
	730
BROOKHAVEN WOMEN IN SCIENCE
	Chasman (Renate W.) Scholarship for Women: 1076
BROOKS (GLADYS) FOUNDATION: 1188
Brooks (Thornton H.) Award: 1228
Brothers (William A. and Ann M.) Scholarship: 2601
Broun (Heywood) Award: 1950
Broward Advisors for Continuing Education (BRACE) Scholarship Fund:
	1527
BROWARD EDUCATION FOUNDATION, INC. (THE)
	Broward Advisors for Continuing Education (BRACE) Scholarship
	Fund: 1527
	Florida Prepaid College Tuition Program (The): 1527
	Impact Teacher Grants: 1527
	Tools for Schools Broward: 1527
Brown (Donald T.) Memorial Scholarship: 2563
BROWN FOUNDATION, INC. (THE): 1528
Brown (Howard Mayer) Fellowship: 752
BROWN (JAMES GRAHAM) FOUNDATION, INC.: 48
BROWN (THE JOE W. AND DOROTHY DORSETT) FOUNDATION:
	49
BROWN (JOHN CARTER) LIBRARY
	Brown (The John Carter) Library Research Fellowships: 584
Brown (The John Carter) Library Research Fellowships: 584
Brown (John Nicholas) Prize: 610
Brown (Marjorie M.) Dissertation Fellowship: 2674
Brown (Selena Danette) Book Scholarship: 1032
BROWN SHOE COMPANY, INC. CHARITABLE TRUST: 50
Bruce (W.B.) European Fine Art Scholarship: 543
BRUCEBO FINE ART SCHOLARSHIP FOUNDATION
	Bruce (W.B.) European Fine Art Scholarship: 543
	Brucebo Fine Art Summer Residency Scholarship: 543
Brucebo Fine Art Summer Residency Scholarship: 543
Brunswick Employee Sons and Daughters Scholarship: 1189
BRUNSWICK FOUNDATION, INC.
	Brunswick Employee Sons and Daughters Scholarship: 1189
	Dollars for Doers Volunteer Program: 1189
BRUNSWICK PUBLIC FOUNDATION: 2171
BSA Fellowship Program: 1526
BUHL FOUNDATION (THE): 1190
Build Your Dollars Grant: 1586

BUILDING AND FIRE RESEARCH LABORATORY
Fire Research Grants Program: 2035
Building Cultural Diversity: 492
Building Healthy Communities Initiative: 1423
Bukatman (The Barry), M.D. Memorial AGPA Scholarship: 2563
BULLITT FOUNDATION (THE)
Ecosystem Services: 2172
Energy Industry and Technology: 2172
Leadership and Civic Engagement: 2172
Urban Ecology: 2172
Bullock (Dorothy Dann) Music Therapy Award: 779
BUREAU OF INDIAN EDUCATION
Higher Education Grant Program for American Indians: 1046
Burgess (Ernest W.) Award: 1498
BURNHAM (THE MARGARET E.) CHARITABLE TRUST: 51
BURNS (FRITZ B.) FOUNDATION: 1529
BURROUGHS WELLCOME FUND
Career Awards at the Scientific Interface: 2244
Career Awards for Medical Scientists: 2244
Institutional Program Unifying Population and Laboratory Based
Sciences: 2244
Investigators in the Pathogenesis of Infectious Disease: 2244
Preterm Birth Initiative: 2244
BUSH (EDYTH) CHARITABLE FOUNDATION, INC.: 52
Bush (Laura) 21st Century Librarian Program: 728
Business Achievement Awards: 1692
Business and International Education Program: 1915
Business Reporting Interns, Sophomore and Junior Students: 1932
BUSINESS SOLUTIONS ASSOCIATION EDUCATIONAL
FOUNDATION
Business Solutions Association Educational Foundation Scholarships:
1530
Business Solutions Association Educational Foundation Scholarships:
1530
BUTLER (PATRICK AND AIMEE) FAMILY FOUNDATION: 1191
BYNNER (THE WITTER) FOUNDATION FOR POETRY, INC.: 669

C

Cabell (Harry H.) Scholarship Program: 1753
CABOT FAMILY CHARITABLE TRUST: 53
Cabot (Maria Moors) Prizes: 1929
Cadogan Fine Arts Scholarships: 568
CAESAR'S ENTERTAINMENT CORPORATION: 1620
CAFRITZ (THE MORRIS AND GWENDOLYN) FOUNDATION: 54
Cairns (The A.T.J.) Memorial Scholarship: 1789
Cal Grants A, B and C: 1670
Calabresi (The Paul) Medical Student Research Fellowship: 2539
CALDER (THE LOUIS) FOUNDATION: 1110
Caldwell (J.E.R.) Centennial Scholarship: 420
CALIFORNIA ACADEMY OF SCIENCES
Summer Systematics Institute: 2142
CALIFORNIA ARTS COUNCIL
Artists in Schools: 437
Creating Places of Vitality: 437
State-Local Partnership Program in the Arts: 437
Statewide Service Networks in the Arts: 437
CALIFORNIA COMMUNITY FOUNDATION
Arts: 1192
Civic Engagement: 1192
Education: 1192
Health Care: 1192
Housing and Economic Development: 1192
Human Development: 1192
Scholarships: 1192
California Community Service-Learning Program: 2296
CALIFORNIA ENDOWMENT (THE)
Building Healthy Communities Initiative: 1423
CALIFORNIA HEALTHCARE FOUNDATION: 1424
CALIFORNIA LIBRARY ASSOCIATION
Begun Scholarship: 717
CLA Scholarship for Minority Students in Memory of Edna Yelland:
717
Reference Service Press Fellowship: 717
California Regions Grant Program: 200
California Senate Fellows Program: 1991
CALIFORNIA STUDENT AID COMMISSION
Assumption Program of Loans for Education (APLE): 1672
Cal Grants A, B and C: 1670
Law Enforcement Personnel Dependents' Grant Program (LEPD): 1671

CALIFORNIA WELLNESS FOUNDATION (THE): 1425
CALLAWAY FOUNDATION, INC.: 1193
CAMBRIDGE UNIVERSITY LIBRARY
Munby Fellowship in Bibliography (The): 718
Cambridge University Press Prize: 526
Camp Erin: 1137
Camp Mariposa: 1137
CAMPBELL FOUNDATION, INC.: 1111
CAMPBELL SOUP FOUNDATION
Campbell Summer Program: 55
Dollars for Doers Fund: 55
Campbell Summer Program: 55
Campus Alberta/AIHS Translational Health Chairs: 2215
Campus Ecology Fellowships: 2192
CAMS Scholarship Program: 2253
CANADA COUNCIL FOR THE ARTS
Grants to Professional Canadian Artists and Arts Organizations: 438
Writing and Publishing Section Grants: 670
Canada Graduate Scholarships Master's Awards: 2246
CANADIAN BAR ASSOCIATION (THE)
Viscount Bennett Fellowship: 1971
CANADIAN BLOOD SERVICES
Canadian Blood Services Trainee Awards Graduate Fellowship
Program: 2245
Canadian Blood Services Trainee Awards Postdoctoral Fellowship: 2245
Canadian Blood Services Trainee Awards Graduate Fellowship Program:
2245
Canadian Blood Services Trainee Awards Postdoctoral Fellowship: 2245
CANADIAN BUREAU FOR INTERNATIONAL EDUCATION (CBIE)
Commonwealth Scholarship Plan: 903
Foreign Government Awards: 902
CANADIAN CANCER SOCIETY RESEARCH INSTITUTE: 2429
CANADIAN DIABETES ASSOCIATION
Best (Charles H.) Research Fund: 2409
CANADIAN FEDERATION FOR THE HUMANITIES AND SOCIAL
SCIENCES
Awards to Scholarly Publications Program: 1848
CANADIAN FEDERATION OF UNIVERSITY WOMEN
Binnie (Ruth) Fellowship: 1077
Canadian Home Economics Association (CHEA) Fellowship: 1077
CFUW Beverly Jackson Fellowship: 1077
CFUW Bourse Georgette Lemoyne: 1077
CFUW Dr. Alice E. Wilson Awards: 1077
CFUW Dr. Margaret McWilliams Pre-Doctoral Fellowship: 1077
CFUW Elizabeth Massey Award: 1077
CFUW Margaret Dale Philp Award: 1077
CFUW Memorial Fellowship: 1077
CFUW 1989 Ecole Polytechnique Commemorative Awards: 1077
CANADIAN FRIENDS OF THE HEBREW UNIVERSITY: 1673
Canadian Home Economics Association (CHEA) Fellowship: 1077
CANADIAN INSTITUTE FOR ADVANCED LEGAL STUDIES
French Language Scholarship: 1972
Martin (The Right Honourable Paul, Sr.) Scholarship: 1972
CANADIAN INSTITUTE IN GREECE/L'INSTITUT CANADIEN EN
GRECE
Elizabeth Alfoldi-Rosenbaum Fellowship: 355
Leipen (Franz and Neda) Fellowship: 355
Thompson (Homer and Dorothy) Fellowship: 355
CANADIAN INSTITUTE OF UKRAINIAN STUDIES
Darcovich (The Helen) Memorial Doctoral Fellowship: 585
Dorosh (Marusia and Michael) Master's Fellowship: 585
Neporany Doctoral Fellowship: 585
Research Grants: 585
CANADIAN INSTITUTES OF HEALTH RESEARCH (CIHR)
Banting (Frederick) and Charles Best Canada Graduate
Scholarship-Doctoral Awards: 2247
Canada Graduate Scholarships Master's Awards: 2246
Doctoral Research Award: 2248
Fellowship Program: 2249
CANADIAN LIBRARY ASSOCIATION/ASSOCIATION CANADIENNE
DES BIBLIOTHEQUES
CLA/ACB Dafoe Scholarship: 720
Library Research and Development Grants: 719
Wilson (The H.W.) Scholarship: 720
CANADIAN LIVER FOUNDATION
Canadian Liver Foundation Graduate Studentships: 2250
Canadian Liver Foundation Operating Grant: 2410
Summer Studentships: 2251
Canadian Liver Foundation Graduate Studentships: 2250
Canadian Liver Foundation Operating Grant: 2410

CANADIAN LUNG ASSOCIATION (CLA) (THE)
  Canadian Respiratory Health Professionals Fellowships and Grants
  (The): 2488
  Canadian Thoracic Society Fellowship: 2391
  Canadian Thoracic Society Studentship: 2391
CANADIAN MERIT SCHOLARSHIP FOUNDATION
  Loran Awards: 1674
CANADIAN NATIONAL INSTITUTE FOR THE BLIND
  CNIB/Baker Grant: 2509
Canadian Natural Resources Limited Graduate Scholarship: 1792
Canadian Respiratory Health Professionals Fellowships and Grants (The):
  2488
CANADIAN SOCIETY FOR CHEMICAL ENGINEERING
  CSChE Chemical Engineering Local Section Scholarships (The): 2651
  SNC-LAVALIN Plant Design Competition: 2651
CANADIAN SOCIETY FOR CHEMICAL TECHNOLOGY
  Bright (Norman and Marion) Memorial Award: 2064
CANADIAN SOCIETY FOR CHEMISTRY
  CCUCC Chemistry Doctoral Award: 2065
CANADIAN SOCIETY FOR MEDICAL LABORATORY SCIENCE:
  2252
Canadian Thoracic Society Fellowship: 2391
Canadian Thoracic Society Studentship: 2391
CANCER FEDERATION, INC.: 2359
Cancer Grants: 330
CANCER RESEARCH INSTITUTE
  Clinic and Laboratory Integration Program (CLIP): 2431
  Irvington Institute Fellowship Program of the Cancer Research Institute:
  2430
  Student Training and Research in Tumor Immunology (STaRT)
  Program: 2432
CANCER RESEARCH SOCIETY
  Grants for Cancer Research: 2434
  Scholarship for the Next Generation of Scientists: 2433
CANCER RESEARCH UK: 2435
CANNON FOUNDATION, INC. (THE): 56
CAORC Multi-Country Research Fellowships: 432
Capacity Building: 332
Capacity Building Grants: 494, 523, 1245
Capacity-Building Grant Initiative: 1222
Capezio Dance Award: 529
CAPEZIO/BALLET MAKERS DANCE FOUNDATION, INC.
  Capezio Dance Award: 529
  Grants Program: 529
Capital Beginnings: 1273
Capital Grants: 1308
CAPITAL REGION COMMUNITY FOUNDATION: 1194
Capital Support: 332
Capitol Art Travel Subsidies: 493
Capitol Complex Exhibition Program: 448
CAPITOL FEDERAL FOUNDATION: 1195
Capitol Hill Issues Briefings: 1949
Career Awards at the Scientific Interface: 2244
Career Awards for Medical Scientists: 2244
Career Catalyst Research Grants: 2439
Career Development Award: 2147, 2403
Career Development Awards: 2416, 2424
Career Development Grants: 1073, 2301, 2493
Career Development Program: 2364
Career Enhancement Award for Stem Cell Research (K18): 1453
Career Journalism Scholarship: 1763
Career Opportunity Grants: 494
Carey (John L.) Scholarship: 1890
Carlson (Axel W.) Award: 1204
CARNEGIE CORPORATION OF NEW YORK: 57
CARNEGIE FUND FOR AUTHORS: 671
CARNEGIE INSTITUTION OF WASHINGTON
  Predoctoral and Postdoctoral Fellowships at the Carnegie Institution:
  1816
CARPENTER FOUNDATION (THE): 1196
Carsel (The Karen D.) Memorial Scholarship: 971
CARSON SCHOLARS FUND, INC. (THE)
  Carson Scholarships: 1675
Carson Scholarships: 1675
CARTER (AMON G.) FOUNDATION: 58
Cartwright (Berna Lou) Scholarship: 2646
CARVEL (THOMAS AND AGNES) FOUNDATION: 1112
CARVER (ROY J.) CHARITABLE TRUST: 1621
Cary New Music Performance Fund: 783
Casey Family Scholars: 1544

Casey (James E.) Scholarship Program: 326
Cash Grant: 1716
CASTLE (HAROLD K.L.) FOUNDATION: 59
CASTLE (SAMUEL N. AND MARY) FOUNDATION: 1601
CATCHING THE DREAM
  Math and Science Teaching (MAST): 1047
  MESBEC (Math, Engineering, Science, Business, Education and
  Computers) Program: 1047
  Native American Leadership in Education (NALE) Program: 1047
  Reading Award Program (RAP): 1047
  Tribal Business Management (TBM) Program: 1047
CATERPILLAR CORPORATE GIVING PROGRAM: 1197
CATHOLIC CAMPAIGN FOR HUMAN DEVELOPMENT
  Community Development Grant: 1198
  Economic Development Grant: 1198
  Strategic National Grant: 1198
CATHOLIC CHARITIES USA: 1476
CATTELL (JAMES MCKEEN) FUND
  Cattell (James McKeen) Fund Sabbatical Fellowships for Psychologists:
  2576
Cattell (James McKeen) Fund Sabbatical Fellowships for Psychologists:
  2576
Cave (William and Eleanor) Award: 1807
CAYL INSTITUTE (THE)
  Early Educators Fellowship Initiative: 1531
CBC Spouses Cheerios Brand Health Initiative Scholarship: 1027
CBC Spouses Education Scholarship Fund: 1027
CBCF Congressional Fellows Program (The): 1027
CBCF Congressional Internship Program (The): 1027
CBCS Performing Arts Scholarship: 1026
CBCS Visual Arts Scholarship: 1026
CCED Grant: 469
CCFA Career Development Award: 2412
CCFA Research Fellowship Award: 2412
CCFA Research Initiatives: 2412
CCFA Senior Research Award: 2412
CCFA Student Research Fellowship Awards: 2412
CCUCC Chemistry Doctoral Award: 2065
CEMALA FOUNDATION: 1532
Centenary Scholarship: 2678
Center Core Grants: 2519
CENTER FOR CALIFORNIA STUDIES, CAPITAL FELLOWS
  PROGRAMS
  California Senate Fellows Program: 1991
  Executive Fellowship Program: 1992
  Judicial Administration Fellowship Program: 1990
  Unruh (Jesse M.) Assembly Fellowship Program: 1993
CENTER FOR COMPARATIVE IMMIGRATION STUDIES AT THE
  UNIVERSITY OF CALIFORNIA-SAN DIEGO
  Visiting Research Fellowship Program: 1622
CENTER FOR HELLENIC STUDIES: 356
CENTER FOR INTERNATIONAL SECURITY AND COOPERATION
  (CISAC)
  Cybersecurity and International Security Fellowship: 833
  Law and International Security Fellowship: 833
  MacArthur Foundation Nuclear Security Fellowship (The): 833
  Natural Sciences or Engineering International Security Fellowship: 833
  Perry (The William J.) Fellowship in International Security: 833
  Social Sciences or Humanities International Security Fellowship: 833
  Stanton Nuclear Security Fellowship (The): 833
CENTER FOR LESBIAN AND GAY STUDIES (THE)
  Duberman (The Martin) Fellowship: 984
CENTER FOR MEDIEVAL AND RENAISSANCE STUDIES
  Ahmanson Research Fellowships for the Study of Medieval and
  Renaissance Books and Manuscripts: 357
  CMRS Travel Grants: 357
  Research Assistantships in Medieval and Renaissance Studies: 357
  Romani (The George T. and Margaret W.) Fellowship: 357
  Summer Fellowships in Medieval and Renaissance Studies: 357
  White (Lynn and Maude) Fellowship: 357
Center for Nonprofit Excellence: 1267
Center for Nonprofit Excellence (CNE): 1269
CENTER FOR PHOTOGRAPHY AT WOODSTOCK (THE)
  Art Administration Interns: 544
  Photographers' Fund (The): 544
  Woodstock A-I-R: 544
  Workshop Interns: 544
CENTER FOR PLANT CONSERVATION
  Beattie (Catherine H.) Fellowship for Conservation Horticulture: 2116
CENTER FOR SCIENCE IN THE PUBLIC INTEREST
  Public Interest Internships: 2670

CENTER FOR 17TH AND 18TH CENTURY STUDIES
  Ahmanson and Getty Postdoctoral Fellowships: 360
  ASECS/Clark Library Fellowships: 359
  Clark Predoctoral Fellowships: 358
  Short-Term Research Fellowships: 361
CENTER FOR THE HUMANITIES
  Mellon (Andrew W.) Postdoctoral Fellowship: 362
CENTER FOR U.S. - MEXICAN STUDIES, UNIVERSITY OF
  CALIFORNIA, SAN DIEGO
  USMEX Visiting Scholars Program: 834
Center Stage: 484
Centers for International Business Education Program: 1916
Central Asia: 64
CENTRAL ASSOCIATION OF OBSTETRICIANS AND
  GYNECOLOGISTS
  Annual Central Prize Award: 2500
  Central Poster Award: 2500
  Community Hospital Award: 2500
  FAR Research Network Award: 2500
  President's Certificate of Merit Award: 2500
  Young Investigator's Award: 2500
CENTRAL INDIANA COMMUNITY FOUNDATION: 1199
CENTRAL MAINE POWER COMPANY
  Central Maine Power Company Corporate Contributions Program: 60
Central Maine Power Company Corporate Contributions Program: 60
CENTRAL MINNESOTA COMMUNITY FOUNDATION: 1200
CENTRAL NEW YORK COMMUNITY FOUNDATION: 1201
Central Poster Award: 2500
Centre for Studies and Research in International Law and International
  Relations: 1978
CEREBRAL PALSY INTERNATIONAL RESEARCH FOUNDATION
  CPI Research Grants: 2459
CFF/NIH Unfunded Grants: 2413
CFUW Beverly Jackson Fellowship: 1077
CFUW Bourse Georgette Lemoyne: 1077
CFUW Dr. Alice E. Wilson Awards: 1077
CFUW Dr. Margaret McWilliams Pre-Doctoral Fellowship: 1077
CFUW Elizabeth Massey Award: 1077
CFUW Margaret Dale Philp Award: 1077
CFUW Memorial Fellowship: 1077
CFUW 1989 Ecole Polytechnique Commemorative Awards: 1077
CFUW/A. Vibert Douglas Fellowship: 1085
CH FOUNDATION (THE): 2117
Chall (Jeanne S.) Research Fellowship: 1557
CHAMBER MUSIC AMERICA
  Chamber Music America Classical Commissioning Program: 757
  Residency Partnership Program: 756
Chamber Music America Classical Commissioning Program: 757
Chamber Music Series (CMS): 797
Chamber Opera Competition: 780
CHAMPLIN FOUNDATIONS (THE): 61
Chancellor's Graduate Fellowship Program at Washington University in
  St. Louis (The): 1801
Chang (Stephen S.) Award: 2063
CHAPIN (HARRY) FOUNDATION: 1202
Charitable Giving Program (The): 272
CHARLESTON AREA CHARITABLE FOUNDATION: 1203
Chasman (Renate W.) Scholarship for Women: 1076
Chateaubriand Fellowships Program: 939
Chatham (The Anne S.) Fellowship in Medicinal Botany: 2179
CHATHAM UNIVERSITY
  Chatham University Merit Scholarship Programs (The): 1676
Chatham University Merit Scholarship Programs (The): 1676
CHATLOS FOUNDATION, INC. (THE): 807
Chaudhuri (Nupur) First Article Prize: 588
Chautauqua Institution Scholarships (The): 958
CHAUTAUQUA REGION COMMUNITY FOUNDATION (THE)
  Carlson (Axel W.) Award: 1204
  Hamilton (John D.) Community Service Award: 1204
Chavez/Eastman/Marshall Dissertation Fellowships: 987
CHCI Congressional Internship: 1064
CHCI Graduate Fellowship Program: 1066
CHCI Public Policy Fellowship: 1066
CHCI Scholarship Fund: 1065
Chen (Stanford) Grant: 1667
CHENEY (BEN B.) FOUNDATION: 62
CHEROKEE NATION
  College Resource Center: 1048
Chesapeake Bay Fisheries Research Program: 1575

CHEST FOUNDATION (THE)
  ACCP/Alfred Soffer Research Award: 2392
  ACCP Young Investigator Award: 2392
  Alpha-1 Foundation/CHEST Foundation Clinical Research Award in
    COPD and Alpha-1 Antitrypsin (AAT) Deficiency: 2392
  Bone (The Roger C.) Advances in End-of-Life Care Award: 2392
  CHEST Foundation Clinical Research Award in Pulmonary Arterial
    Hypertension (The): 2392
  CHEST Foundation Clinical Research Award in Women's Health (The):
    2392
  Clinical Research Trainee Awards: 2392
  Distinguished Scholar Awards in Respiratory Health, Critical Care and
    Thrombosis: 2392
  Humanitarian Project Development Grants: 2392
  Humanitarian Recognition Awards: 2392
  OneBreath Clinical Research Award for Lung Cancer (The): 2392
CHEST Foundation Clinical Research Award in Pulmonary Arterial
  Hypertension (The): 2392
CHEST Foundation Clinical Research Award in Women's Health (The):
  2392
CHESTER COUNTY COMMUNITY FOUNDATION: 1205
CHICAGO BOARD OF TRADE FOUNDATION: 1426
CHICAGO COMMUNITY TRUST (THE): 1206
CHICAGO TRIBUNE FOUNDATION: 63
Child Abuse Prevention and Treatment Act (CAPTA) Research and
  Demonstration Grants: 1114
Child Abuse Prevention Program: 107
Child and Adult Care Food Program (The): 1154
Child Development and Behavior Branch (CDBB): 1462
Child Health Recognition Awards: 1581
Child Health Research Awards Program: 2529
Child Language Doctoral Program: 1795
Child Welfare: 1147
Child Welfare Scholarship: 1659
Children and Education: 1242
CHILDREN'S BRAIN TUMOR FOUNDATION
  Brain Research Tumor Grant: 1113
CHILDREN'S BUREAU
  Child Abuse Prevention and Treatment Act (CAPTA) Research and
    Demonstration Grants: 1114
Children's Leukemia Research Grants: 2531
CHILDREN'S LITERATURE ASSOCIATION
  ChLA Beiter Graduate Student Research Grants: 673
  ChLA Diversity Research Grant: 672
  ChLA Faculty Research Grants: 673
Children's Medical Health Grants: 330
Children's Mental Health: 1354
CHILDREN'S TUMOR FOUNDATION
  Drug Discovery Initiative Award: 2360
  NF Clinic Network (CTF-NFCN): 2360
  Young Investigator Awards: 2360
Children, Families and Communities: 258
Children, Youth and Families Program: 1383
CHILDS (THE JANE COFFIN) MEMORIAL FUND FOR MEDICAL
  RESEARCH: 2436
Chin (Vincent) Scholarships: 1667
Chinard (The Gilbert) Prize: 634
CHINESE AMERICAN MEDICAL SOCIETY
  CAMS Scholarship Program: 2253
  Medical Student Summer Research Fellowship: 2253
Chinoy Dissertation Research Fellowships: 526
ChLA Beiter Graduate Student Research Grants: 673
ChLA Diversity Research Grant: 672
ChLA Faculty Research Grants: 673
CHOPIN FOUNDATION OF THE U.S.
  Scholarship Program for Young Pianists: 758
Chopin Piano Competition: 770
Chrétien International Research Grant: 2046
CHRISTENSEN FUND (THE)
  African Rift Valley: 64
  Central Asia: 64
  Global: 64
  Melanesia: 64
  San Francisco-Bay Area: 64
  Southwest U.S. and Northern Mexico: 64
CHRISTIAN CHURCH (DISCIPLES OF CHRIST)
  African-American Scholarship Fund (Star Supporter): 808
  Disciple Chaplains' Scholarship Fund: 808
  Kagiwada (David Tamotsu) Memorial Fund: 808
  Michael (Edwin G. & Lauretta M.) Scholarship for Minister's Spouses:
    808

Philputt (James M.) Memorial Loan Fund: 808
Rowley/Wolfe Ministerial Education Scholarship: 808
Schutze (Katherine J.) Memorial Scholarship for Women Seminary
  Students: 808
Churchill Scholarship: 904
CHURCHILL (WINSTON) FOUNDATION OF THE UNITED STATES
  Churchill Scholarship: 904
CI Construction Engineering Scholarship and Student Prizes: 2645
CIE Undergraduate Scholarship: 2653
Cintas Fellowships in the Arts: 439
CINTAS FOUNDATION
  Cintas Fellowships in the Arts: 439
CIRES Visiting Fellowship Program in Environmental Sciences: 2175
City Arts Projects: 447
City Life Grant: 182
CITY OF NEW YORK
  New York City Urban Fellows Program: 1994
City Ventures Fund: 621
Civic Engagement: 1192
Civic Orchestra Lesson Scholarship Stipends: 759
CIVIC ORCHESTRA OF CHICAGO
  Civic Orchestra Lesson Scholarship Stipends: 759
Civic Program: 219
Civic, Community, and Environment: 257
Civil and Mining Engineering Foundation Scholarship: 2667
CIVIL JUSTICE FOUNDATION: 1973
CLA Scholarship for Minority Students in Memory of Edna Yelland: 717
CLA/ACB Dafoe Scholarship: 720
CLAIBORNE (LIZ) ART ORTENBERG FOUNDATION: 2173
CLARK (EDNA MCCONNELL) FOUNDATION
  Youth Development Fund: 65
CLARK FOUNDATION (THE)
  Clark Foundation Scholarship Program: 1677
Clark Foundation Scholarship Program: 1677
Clark (Michele) Fellowship: 1958
Clark Predoctoral Fellowships: 358
CLARK (ROBERT STERLING) FOUNDATION: 1207
Clark (William B.) Fellowship in Clinical Research: 2344
Classroom and Community Grants: 1541
Clay Postdoctoral Fellowship: 2057
CLEVELAND FOUNDATION (THE): 1208
CLEVELAND INSTITUTE OF MUSIC
  Cleveland Institute of Music Scholarships: 760
Cleveland Institute of Music Scholarships: 760
Cleven (The Nels Andrew N.) Founder's Paper Prize Awards: 629
CLIFFS FOUNDATION (THE): 66
Clift (David H.) Scholarship: 1616
Climate and Global Change Program: 2082
Clinic and Laboratory Integration Program (CLIP): 2431
Clinic Incentive Grants: 2362
Clinical and Population Health Research Grants: 2470
Clinical Investigator - Career Development Awards: 2367
Clinical Neuroscience Research: 2254
Clinical Research and Epidemiological Award: 2403
Clinical Research Grant: 2506
Clinical Research Grants: 2413
Clinical Research in Pulmonary Fibrosis Program: 2315
Clinical Research Trainee Awards: 2392
Clinical Research/Clinical Trials: 2352
Clinical Scholars Award: 2403
Clinical Scientist in Nephrology (CSN): 2228
Clinical Scientist Training Award: 2403
Clinical Seed Grants: 2303
Clinical Student Research Award: 2547
Clinical Traveling Fellowship: 2299
Clinical Trial: 2521
Clinician of the Year: 2547
Closing the Achievement Gap: 265
CMRS Travel Grants: 357
CNIB/Baker Grant: 2509
Co-sponsored Events Awards: 526
COASTAL BEND COMMUNITY FOUNDATION: 67
COASTAL COMMUNITY FOUNDATION OF SOUTH CAROLINA:
  1209
Coastal Conservation Research Program: 2160
Coca-Cola Centennial Scholarship Fund: 1227
COCA-COLA FOUNDATION, INC. (THE): 1533
COCA-COLA SCHOLARS FOUNDATION
  Coca-Cola Scholars Program: 1678
Coca-Cola Scholars Program: 1678

COCKRELL FOUNDATION (THE): 68
CODMAN (THE OGDEN) TRUST: 69
CODRINGTON (THE GEORGE W.) CHARITABLE FOUNDATION: 70
Cogeco Inc. Graduate Scholarship: 1963
Cogswell (Madeline Pickett) Nursing Scholarship: 2494
Cohen (Morton N.) Award: 658
Cohen (Selma Jeanne) Conference Presentation Award: 526
Cohn (The Victor) Prize for Excellence in Medical Science Reporting:
  1930
COIN-OP CARES CHARITABLE AND EDUCATION FOUNDATION
  Hesch (Wayne E.) Memorial Scholarships: 2605
COLAGE
  Dubin (Lee) Memorial Scholarship: 985
Colburn (Anna C. and Oliver C.) Fellowship: 353
Cole (Arthur H.) Grants-in-Aid: 1895
Cole (Paul) Technologist Scholarships: 2329
Cole (Reverend Pauline L.) Scholarship: 2492
COLEMAN FOUNDATION, INC. (THE): 71
Colgate Oral Health Research Award: 2350
Colgate-Palmolive Scholarship: 2349
Colgate Research Scholarship: 2346
Collaboration for Innovation: 1583
Collaborative Activity Awards: 221
Collaborative Initiatives: 90
Collaborative Research Grants: 799
Collection Study Grants: 1809
College Intern Program: 1052
COLLEGE OF PHYSICIANS OF PHILADELPHIA
  Wood Institute Travel Grants: 586
College Resource Center: 1048
College Scholarship Fund: 737
College Scholarship Program: 1680
College Scholarships: 301
COLLEGEVILLE INSTITUTE FOR ECUMENICAL AND CULTURAL
  RESEARCH
  Hoyt Fellowship: 809
  McDonnell (Kilian) Fellowship: 809
  Pastoral Fellowship: 809
  Post-Doctoral Fellowship: 809
  Resident Scholars Program: 809
  Seminars on Vocation: 809
  Summer Writing Workshops: 809
Collegiate Inventors Competition: 1824
Collegiate Opera Scenes Competition: 780
Colliflower (Esther)/VITAS Scholarship: 2492
COLLINS FOUNDATION (THE): 72
COLONIAL PLAYERS, INC. THEATER-IN-THE-ROUND
  Biennial Promising Playwright Award: 530
Colorado Creates: 440
COLORADO CREATIVE INDUSTRIES
  Colorado Creates: 440
  Creative Districts: 440
  Jumpstart: 440
  Start Schools: 440
Colorado Program: 141
COLORADO TRUST (THE)
  Community-based Participatory Grantmaking: 1427
  Health Equity Advocacy: 1427
  Health Equity Learning Series: 1427
COLUMBIA JOURNALISM SCHOOL
  Berger (Mike) Award: 1925
COLUMBIA UNIVERSITY
  Bancroft Prizes: 587
  Horwitz (The Louisa Gross) Prize: 2143
  Knight-Bagehot Fellowship in Economics and Business Journalism:
    1927
  Oakes (John B.) Award: 1928
  Pulitzer Fellowships: 1926
  Pulitzer Prizes: 1926
COLUMBIA UNIVERSITY GRADUATE SCHOOL OF JOURNALISM
  Cabot (Maria Moors) Prizes: 1929
Columbus (Christopher) Awards: 1477
COLUMBUS (CHRISTOPHER) FELLOWSHIP FOUNDATION
  Agriscience Awards: 1477
  Columbus (Christopher) Awards: 1477
  Homeland Security Award: 1477
  Life Sciences Awards: 1477

COLUMBUS FOUNDATION (THE)
Community Improvement Project: 1210
Fund for Financial Innovation: 1210
Fund for Innovative Operations: 1210
Fund for Targeted Needs: 1210
COLUMBUS JEWISH FOUNDATION: 1211
Colwell (Robert N.) Memorial Fellowship: 2034
Coly (Robert R.) Prize: 2588
Commission on a High Performance Health System: 1478
COMMON COUNSEL FOUNDATION: 1212
Common Good: 1214
COMMONWEAL FOUNDATION, INC.: 1115
COMMONWEALTH FUND (THE)
Affordable Health Insurance: 1478
Commission on a High Performance Health System: 1478
Health System Quality and Efficiency: 1478
International Program in Health Policy and Innovation: 1478
Patient-Centered Coordinated Care Program: 1478
Payment and System Reform: 1478
Commonwealth of Virginia Nurse Educator Scholarship Program: 2499
Commonwealth Scholarship Plan: 903
Communities for All Ages: 1171
COMMUNITIES FOUNDATION OF TEXAS, INC.
Community Impact Grants: 73
Donor-Advised Grants: 73
Communities Program: 193, 219
Community: 1242
Community Action Funds: 1329
Community Action Grants: 1074
Community and Business Project Grants: 1898
Community Arts: 465
Community Arts Access: 491
Community Arts Development: 427, 471, 483
Community Arts Grant: 447
Community Arts Partners Grants: 523
Community Arts Reach Program: 507
Community Based Organizations Grants: 445
Community Betterment: 1120
Community Building Grants: 1303
Community Capital Projects: 134
Community Collaborative Grants: 1858
Community Concerns: 1270
Community Conference Grants Program: 1463
Community Connection Employee Volunteer Gift Program: 209
Community Development: 1275
Community Development Block Grant Program: Entitlement Communities
Program: 1392
Community Development Grant: 1198
Community Education: 228
COMMUNITY FOUNDATION (THE)
Gray (Garland and Agnes Taylor) Foundation: 1213
Jenkins Foundation: Improving the Health of Greater Richmond (The):
1213
Medarva Foundation Fund: 1213
R.E.B. Awards for Teaching Excellence: 1213
Sheltering Arms Fund: 1213
Strengthening Families - Strengthening Communities: 74
COMMUNITY FOUNDATION FOR GREATER ATLANTA, INC.
Arts Fund: 1214
Common Good: 1214
Grants to Green: 1214
Neighborhood Fund: 1214
COMMUNITY FOUNDATION FOR GREATER BUFFALO: 1215
COMMUNITY FOUNDATION FOR GREATER NEW HAVEN (THE):
1216
COMMUNITY FOUNDATION FOR MONTEREY COUNTY (THE)
Community Impact Program: 1217
Neighborhood Grants Program: 1217
COMMUNITY FOUNDATION FOR NORTHEAST FLORIDA (THE):
1218
COMMUNITY FOUNDATION FOR NORTHEAST GEORGIA: 1219
COMMUNITY FOUNDATION FOR NORTHEAST MICHIGAN: 1220
COMMUNITY FOUNDATION FOR PALM BEACH AND MARTIN
COUNTIES: 1221
COMMUNITY FOUNDATION FOR SOUTHEAST MICHIGAN: 75
COMMUNITY FOUNDATION FOR THE GREATER CAPITAL
REGION (THE)
Capacity-Building Grant Initiative: 1222
Regular Competitive Grants: 1222
Rubin (Lou) and Ike Cohen Memorial Scholarship: 1534

Community Foundation Grants: 1225
COMMUNITY FOUNDATION OF ABILENE: 1223
COMMUNITY FOUNDATION OF COLLIER COUNTY
Daphne Vocational Fund (The): 1224
Deifik (Joel A.) Memorial Scholarship Fund: 1224
Diano-Tougas Memorial Scholarship Fund: 1224
Edwards (Dorothy) Vocational Scholarship Fund: 1224
Jones (Judy B. and David M.) Scholarship Fund: 1224
Kelly (Ashley) Memorial Scholarship Fund: 1224
Meli (John and Edith) Scholarship Fund: 1224
Prothero (Louise) Leadership Fund - Women's Club: 1224
Schneeberger (Jimmy) Scholarship Fund: 1224
Thomas (Raymond D. and Sara) Fund: 1224
COMMUNITY FOUNDATION OF EASTERN CONNECTICUT
Community Foundation Grants: 1225
Community Foundation Scholarship Awards: 1225
Norwich Women and Girls Fund: 1225
Norwich Youth Fund: 1225
Windham Women and Girls Fund: 1225
Women and Girls Fund: 1225
COMMUNITY FOUNDATION OF FREDERICK COUNTY, MD, INC.
(THE): 1226
COMMUNITY FOUNDATION OF GREATER CHATTANOOGA, INC.
(THE)
Coca-Cola Centennial Scholarship Fund: 1227
Together We Can Scholarship Fund: 1227
COMMUNITY FOUNDATION OF GREATER GREENSBORO
Brooks (Thornton H.) Award: 1228
Community Service Award: 1228
Humphrey (Hugh) Award: 1228
COMMUNITY FOUNDATION OF GREATER MEMPHIS
Nonprofit Capacity Building Grants: 76
Scholarship Funds: 76
COMMUNITY FOUNDATION OF GREATER ROCHESTER: 1229
COMMUNITY FOUNDATION OF HERKIMER & ONEIDA
COUNTIES, INC. (THE): 1230
COMMUNITY FOUNDATION OF JACKSON HOLE: 1231
COMMUNITY FOUNDATION OF LORAIN COUNTY (THE): 1232
COMMUNITY FOUNDATION OF LOUISVILLE, INC. (THE): 441
COMMUNITY FOUNDATION OF MOUNT VERNON & KNOX
COUNTY (THE): 77
COMMUNITY FOUNDATION OF MUNCIE AND DELAWARE
COUNTY, INC. (THE): 1233
COMMUNITY FOUNDATION OF NORTH CENTRAL WISCONSIN:
1234
COMMUNITY FOUNDATION OF NORTHEAST ALABAMA: 1235
Community Foundation of Plymouth: 1170
COMMUNITY FOUNDATION OF SAINT JOSEPH COUNTY
African American Community Fund: 1236
ArtsEverywhere Fund: 1236
Leighton Award for Nonprofit Excellence: 1236
Milton (Robert P. and Clara I.) Fund for Senior Housing: 1236
Special Project Challenge Grant: 1236
COMMUNITY FOUNDATION OF SHELBY COUNTY (THE): 1237
COMMUNITY FOUNDATION OF SOUTH ALABAMA (THE): 1238
COMMUNITY FOUNDATION OF THE EASTERN SHORE
Community Needs Grants: 1239
Excellence in Education Program: 1239
Henson (Richard A.) Award of Excellence: 1239
Morris (Frank H.) Humanitarian Award: 1239
Nonprofit Support Program: 1239
Small Grants Program: 1239
COMMUNITY FOUNDATION OF THE FOX RIVER VALLEY: 1240
COMMUNITY FOUNDATION OF THE HOLLAND/ZEELAND AREA
(THE): 78
COMMUNITY FOUNDATION OF THE LOWCOUNTRY, INC.: 1535
COMMUNITY FOUNDATION OF THE OZARKS: 1241
COMMUNITY FOUNDATION OF THE TEXAS HILL COUNTRY
Arts: 1242
Children and Education: 1242
Community: 1242
Designated and Donor Advised Funds: 1242
Healers: 1242
Pass Through Grants: 1242
COMMUNITY FOUNDATION OF THE VERDUGOS: 1479
COMMUNITY FOUNDATION OF WESTERN MASSACHUSETTS
(CFWM): 1243
COMMUNITY FOUNDATION OF WESTERN NORTH CAROLINA
(THE) : 79
Community Foundation Scholarship Awards: 1225

COMMUNITY FOUNDATIONS OF THE HUDSON VALLEY
  Community Response Grants of Dutchess County: 1244
  Community Response Grants of Ulster County: 1244
  Fund for Excellence in Education Grants: 1244
Community Fund: 1393
Community Grantmaking Program: 292
Community Grants: 1128, 1404
Community Grants Program: 130, 200, 234, 1345
Community Health Grants: 228
Community Hospital Award: 2500
Community Impact Grants: 73
Community Impact Grants Program: 1300
Community Impact Program: 1217
Community Improvement Project: 1210
Community Leadership Awards: 1370
Community Needs Grants: 1239
Community Reconciliation: 1169
Community Response Grants: 1303
Community Response Grants of Dutchess County: 1244
Community Response Grants of Ulster County: 1244
Community Service Award: 1228, 1692, 2220
Community-based Participatory Grantmaking: 1427
Competition for Orchestral Compositions: 762
Competitive Student Research Award: 2484
COMPTON FOUNDATION, INC.: 80
Computational Science: 2352
CONCORDIA UNIVERSITY
  Concordia University Graduate Fellowships: 1679
Concordia University Graduate Fellowships: 1679
CONCOURS OSM STANDARD LIFE
  OSM Standard Life Competition: 761
Conference and Convening Program: 1509
Conference and Workshop Grants: 2028
Conference Awards: 2480
CONFERENCE BOARD OF THE MATHEMATICAL SCIENCES
  NSF-CBMS Regional Conferences in the Mathematical Sciences: 2094
Conference Grants: 2352
Congress-Bundestag Youth Exchange Program: 954
Congress-Bundestag Youth Exchange for Young Professionals: 911
CONGRESSIONAL BLACK CAUCUS FOUNDATION, INC.
  CBC Spouses Cheerios Brand Health Initiative Scholarship: 1027
  CBC Spouses Education Scholarship Fund: 1027
  CBCF Congressional Fellows Program (The): 1027
  CBCF Congressional Internship Program (The): 1027
  CBCS Performing Arts Scholarship: 1026
  CBCS Visual Arts Scholarship: 1026
  Stokes (The Louis) Urban Health Policy Fellows Program: 1025
Congressional Fellowship Program: 1987
Congressional Fellowships on Women and Public Policy: 1103
CONGRESSIONAL HISPANIC CAUCUS INSTITUTE
  CHCI Congressional Internship: 1064
  CHCI Graduate Fellowship Program: 1066
  CHCI Public Policy Fellowship: 1066
  CHCI Scholarship Fund: 1065
Congressional Internships: 1059
Congressional Research Grants: 1995
Conklin (Edwin G.) Medal: 2159
Connecticut Center for the Book: 363
CONNECTICUT COMMUNITY FOUNDATION
  Capacity Building Grants: 1245
  Nonprofit Assistance Initiative: 1245
  Program Grants: 1245
  Training Programs: 1245
CONNECTICUT HUMANITIES
  Connecticut Center for the Book: 363
  Connecticut Humanities Fund: 363
  Humanities Resource Center: 363
Connecticut Humanities Fund: 363
CONNECTICUT LIBRARY ASSOCIATION
  Connecticut Library Association's Program for Educational Grants: 721
Connecticut Library Association's Program for Educational Grants: 721
CONNELLY FOUNDATION (THE): 81
CONSEIL DES ARTS DE MONTREAL
  Programme de tournees: 442
  Programme General: 442
CONSERVATION AND RESEARCH FOUNDATION
  Research and Conservation Grants: 2174
Conservation and Science: 258
Conservation Assessment Program: 725, 727
Conservation Internships: 2191

Consortium Fellowship: 1892
CONSORTIUM FOR GRADUATE STUDY IN MANAGEMENT (THE)
  Consortium Fellowship: 1892
  Fellowships for Minorities in Management: 1892
CONSORTIUM OF COLLEGE AND UNIVERSITY MEDIA CENTERS
  Rieck (Donald A.) Research Grant: 1536
CONSUMERS ENERGY FOUNDATION
  Volunteer Investment Program: 82
Consumption: 2212
Contemplative Practice: 90
CONTEMPORARY MUSIC FESTIVAL
  Competition for Orchestral Compositions: 762
Continuing Education Grants: 737
Continuing Education Scholarships: 1541
Continuing Legal Education Scholarship Program: 1974
COOK FAMILY FOUNDATION: 1246
COOKE (JACK KENT) FOUNDATION
  College Scholarship Program: 1680
  Dissertation Fellowship Award: 1680
  Graduate Arts Award: 1680
  Undergraduate Transfer Scholarship: 1680
  Young Scholars Program: 1680
Cooke (Mabel and Lawrence S.) Scholarship: 1109
COOKE (V.V.) FOUNDATION: 83
COOLEY'S ANEMIA FOUNDATION, INC.: 2411
COOPER FOUNDATION: 84
Cooper (James Fenimore) Prize: 635
Cooperative Clinical Research Grants: 2518
COOPERATIVE DEVELOPMENT FOUNDATION: 1247
COOPERATIVE INSTITUTE FOR RESEARCH IN ENVIRONMENTAL SCIENCES (CIRES)
  CIRES Visiting Fellowship Program in Environmental Sciences: 2175
Cooperative Research Program Grants: 2083
Cooperstown Graduate Program (The): 738
COORDINATING COUNCIL FOR WOMEN IN HISTORY, INC. (THE)
  Berkshire Conference of Women Historians Graduate Student Fellowship: 588
  Chaudhuri (Nupur) First Article Prize: 588
  National History Day Prize in Women's History, Junior Division: 588
  Prelinger (Catherine) Award: 1078
  Wells (Ida B.) Graduate Student Fellowship: 588
COORS (ADOLPH) FOUNDATION: 1116
COPLAND (AARON) FUND FOR MUSIC, INC.
  Performing Ensembles Program: 763
  Recording Program: 763
  Supplemental Program: 763
CORBIN (THE MARY S. AND DAVID C.) FOUNDATION: 85
Core Support: 332
Core Writer Program: 696
Corey (The Albert B.) Prize in Canadian-American Relations: 578
CORNELL UNIVERSITY
  Mellon Postdoctoral Fellowships: 364
  Society for the Humanities Fellowships: 365
Corporate Contributions Program: 102, 114
Corporate Giving Program: 119
Corporate Scholarship Program: 954
CORPORATION FOR NATIONAL AND COMMUNITY SERVICE
  AmeriCorps VISTA: 1248
  Foster Grandparent Program: 1480
  Retired and Senior Volunteer Program (RSVP): 1480
  Senior Companion Program: 1480
CORPORATION OF YADDO (THE)
  Artist Residencies: 443
CORPUS CHRISTI COLLEGE
  Postgraduate Research at the University of Cambridge: 905
Costello (Jeanne Timmins) Fellowships: 2468
COSTUME SOCIETY OF AMERICA (THE)
  Blum (Stella) Research Grant: 444
  CSA Travel Research Grant: 444
  Filene (Adele) Travel Award: 444
Cotsen Traveling Fellowship for Research in Greece: 892
Cottone Postgraduate Scholarship (Medical Only): 1775
Cottrell Scholar Awards: 2041
COUNCIL FOR EUROPEAN STUDIES AT COLUMBIA UNIVERSITY
  Book Award: 835
  Council for European Studies Pre-Dissertation Research Fellowships: 835
  First Article Prize in Humanities and Social Sciences: 835
  Mellon-CES Dissertation Completion Fellowship in European Studies: 835
Council for European Studies Pre-Dissertation Research Fellowships: 835

COUNCIL FOR INTERNATIONAL EXCHANGE OF SCHOLARS (CIES)
Fulbright Distinguished Chairs: 1623
Fulbright International Education Administrators Program: 1624
Fulbright Scholar Program: 906
Fulbright Scholar-in-Residence Program: 836
Fulbright Specialist Program: 837
Middle East, North Africa and Regional Research Programs and Country Grants: 907
COUNCIL FOR THE ADVANCEMENT OF SCIENCE WRITING, INC.
Cohn (The Victor) Prize for Excellence in Medical Science Reporting: 1930
Taylor (Rennie)/Alton Blakeslee Fellowships for Graduate Study in Science Writing: 1930
COUNCIL OF AMERICAN OVERSEAS RESEARCH CENTERS (CAORC)
Multi-Country Research Fellowship Program: 908
COUNCIL ON FOREIGN RELATIONS
International Affairs Fellowship (IAF): 839
International Affairs Fellowship in Japan (IAF-J): 838
International Affairs Fellowship in Nuclear Security (IAF-NS): 841
International Affairs Fellowship in South Korea (IAF-SK): 840
Murrow (Edward R.) Press Fellowship: 1931
Stanton Nuclear Security Fellowship Program (SNSF): 842
COUNCIL ON SOCIAL WORK EDUCATION
Mental Health and Substance Abuse Fellowship Program (The): 986
COUNCIL ON TECHNOLOGY AND ENGINEERING TEACHER EDUCATION (CTETE)
Engineering and Technology Education: 1537
COVINGTON (MARION STEDMAN) FOUNDATION: 86
COWELL (S.H.) FOUNDATION: 87
Cowen (Walker) Memorial Prize: 705
COWLES (GARDNER AND FLORENCE CALL) FOUNDATION: 1625
Cox (The Eugene L.) Fellowship: 1097
Cox (Lawrence W. and Francis W.) Scholarship: 2645
CPI Research Grants: 2459
Craigie (Peter C.) Memorial Scholarship: 1791
CRAIL-JOHNSON FOUNDATION (THE): 1117
Creating Places of Vitality: 437
Creation & Presentation: 518
Creation Grants: 511
Creative Communities: 265, 518
Creative Districts: 440
Criminal Justice: 273
Criminal Justice Program: 1499
Crisis Counseling Assistance and Training Program: 2593
Critical Response Grants: 1494
CROHN'S AND COLITIS FOUNDATION OF AMERICA, INC.
CCFA Career Development Award: 2412
CCFA Research Fellowship Award: 2412
CCFA Research Initiatives: 2412
CCFA Senior Research Award: 2412
CCFA Student Research Fellowship Awards: 2412
Cross-Disciplinary Fellowships: 2147
CROSSROADS FUND: 1849
CROWELL (HENRY P. AND SUSAN C.) TRUST: 88
CSA Travel Research Grant: 444
CSChE Chemical Engineering Local Section Scholarships (The): 2651
CULLEN FOUNDATION (THE): 89
CULLEN TRUST FOR HEALTH CARE (THE): 1428
Cullis (Winifred) Grant: 1085
Cultural Anthropology Program: 2021
Cultural Conservation: 485
Cultural Facilities Grants: 511
Cultural Facilities Program: 447, 448
Cultural Investment Portfolio: 472
Cultural Routes Grants: 511
CULTURAL SERVICES OF THE FRENCH EMBASSY
Partner University Fund: 909
Cultural Tourism Grants: 494
CULTURAL VISTAS
Alfa Fellowship Program: 843
Baden-Wuerttemberg-STIPENDIUM Work Immersion Study Program: 910
Bosch (The Robert) Foundation Fellowship Program: 912
Congress-Bundestag Youth Exchange for Young Professionals: 911
Culture Lab: 939
Cummings (J. Pat) Fellowship: 2505
CUMMINGS (THE NATHAN) FOUNDATION, INC.
Arts and Culture: 90
Collaborative Initiatives: 90
Contemplative Practice: 90
Ecological Innovation: 90
Health: 90
Jewish Life and Values: 90
CUMMINS FOUNDATION (THE): 91
Cunningham Memorial International Fellowship: 962
Cunningham-Tervalon (Josephine M.) Scholarship: 2563
CUREPSP FOUNDATION FOR PSP/CBD AND RELATED BRAIN DISEASES: 2460
CURTIS INSTITUTE OF MUSIC (THE)
Bachelor of Music Degree Program: 764
Diploma Program: 764
Master of Music in Opera: 764
CUSHWA CENTER FOR THE STUDY OF AMERICAN CATHOLICISM
Hibernian Research Award: 589
Research Travel Grants: 590
Cutting Edge Grants: 1308
Cybersecurity and International Security Fellowship: 833
CYPRUS AMERICAN ARCHAEOLOGICAL RESEARCH INSTITUTE
O'Donovan (The Anita Cecil) Fellowship: 913
Parks (The Danielle) Memorial Fellowship: 913
Swiny (The Helena Wylde) and Stuart Swiny Fellowship: 913
CYSTIC FIBROSIS CANADA: 2361
Clinic Incentive Grants: 2362
CYSTIC FIBROSIS FOUNDATION
CFF/NIH Unfunded Grants: 2413
Clinical Research Grants: 2413
Matthews (Leroy) Physician/Scientist Award: 2413
Pilot and Feasibility Awards: 2413
Research Grants: 2413
Shwachman (Harry) Clinical Investigator Award: 2413
Special Research Awards: 2413
Therapeutics Development Awards: 2413
Czaplewski Fellowship Award: 1498

D

DAAD Emigre Memorial German Internship Program (EMGIP-Bundestag): 916
DAAD German Studies Summer Seminar: 916
DAAD Intensive Language Grant: 916
DAAD Research Grant: 916
DAAD Research Internships in Science and Engineering (RISE): 916
DAAD Research Visit for Faculty: 916
DAAD RISE Pro: 916
DAAD Study Scholarship: 916
DAAD Undergraduate Scholarship: 916
DAAD University Summer Language Grant: 916
DAAD Visiting Professorship: 916
DAFOE (J.W.) FOUNDATION: 844
DAIRY RESEARCH INSTITUTE - NATIONAL DAIRY COUNCIL
Nutrition Research Program: 2671
Dale (Chester) Fellowships: 559
DALLAS FOUNDATION (THE): 1249
DALLAS MUSEUM OF ART
DeGolyer (Clare Hart) Memorial Fund: 545
Dozier (Otis and Velma Davis) Travel Grant: 547
Kimbrough (Arch and Anne Giles) Fund: 546
DALLAS WOMEN'S FOUNDATION: 1079
Dalsemer Research Grant: 2385
Dames (Trent R.) and William W. Moore Fellowship: 2645
DANA FOUNDATION (THE)
Clinical Neuroscience Research: 2254
Mahoney (David) Neuro-Imaging Program: 2254
DANIELS FUND
Daniels Fund Grants Program: 92
Daniels Fund Scholarship Program: 92
Daniels Fund Grants Program: 92
Daniels Fund Scholarship Program: 92
Daniels (Mitch) Early Graduation Scholarship: 1699
Dannels (Robert A.) Memorial Graduate Scholarship: 2639
Daphne Vocational Fund (The): 1224
Dapp (Verne R.) Memorial Scholarship: 2639
Darbaker (Leasure K.) Prize in Botany: 2209
Darcovich (The Helen) Memorial Doctoral Fellowship: 585
DARLING (HUGH AND HAZEL) FOUNDATION: 1626
Darling (Louise) Medal for Distinguished Achievement in Collection Development in the Health Sciences: 730
DARRIN (MARGARET A.) FOUNDATION, INC.: 93

DARTMOUTH COLLEGE
  Chavez/Eastman/Marshall Dissertation Fellowships: 987
DAUGHTERS OF ITALY LODGE #2825
  Daughters of Italy Lodge #2825 Scholarship: 1681
Daughters of Italy Lodge #2825 Scholarship: 1681
DAUGHTERS OF PENELOPE FOUNDATION, INC.
  Alexander (Paula J.) Memorial Scholarship (Undergraduate): 1080
  Beldecos (Helen J.), Past Grand President, Scholarship (Undergraduate):
  1080
  Big Five Graduate Scholarship (The): 1080
  Daughters of Penelope National Scholarship Awards: 988
  Daughters of Penelope Past Grand Presidents Memorial Scholarship
  (Undergraduate): 1080
  Daughters of Penelope Past Grand Presidents Undergraduate
  Scholarship: 1080
  Daughters of Penelope - St. Basil's Academy: 1080
  Eos #1 Mother Lodge Chapter Scholarship (Undergraduate): 1080
  Hologgitas (Joanne V.) Ph.D., Past Grand President, Scholarship
  (Undergraduate): 1080
  Hopewell Agave Chapter #224 Scholarship (Undergraduate): 1080
  Kottis Family Scholarship (Undergraduate): 1080
  Quincey (Dorothy Lillian) Memorial Graduate Scholarship: 1080
  Sonenfeld (Alexandra Apostolides) Memorial Undergraduate
  Scholarship: 1080
  Stefanadis (Sonja B.) Graduate Student Scholarship: 1080
  Thorndyke (Barbara Edith Quincey) Memorial Undergraduate
  Scholarship: 1080
  Verges (Mary M.), Past Grand President, Scholarship (Undergraduate):
  1080
  Zervoulias (The Sotiri) & Lea Soupata Scholarship (St. Basil's
  Academy): 1080
Daughters of Penelope National Scholarship Awards: 988
Daughters of Penelope Past Grand Presidents Memorial Scholarship
  (Undergraduate): 1080
Daughters of Penelope Past Grand Presidents Undergraduate Scholarship:
  1080
Daughters of Penelope - St. Basil's Academy: 1080
DAUGHTERS OF THE CINCINNATI
  Daughters of the Cincinnati Scholarship Program: 1682
Daughters of the Cincinnati Scholarship Program: 1682
Davie & Yadkin County Program (The): 1136
Davies (William H.) Medical Research Scholarships: 1784
Davini (William C.) Scholarship: 1775
DAVIS (THE ARTHUR VINING) FOUNDATIONS: 94
DAVIS (EDWIN W. AND CATHERINE M.) FOUNDATION: 95
DAVIS (IRENE E. AND GEORGE A.) FOUNDATION: 1250
Davis (Johnny) Memorial Scholarship: 2618
DAVIS (THE LADY) FELLOWSHIP TRUST
  Postdoctoral Researchers Fellowship: 914
  Visiting Professorships Fellowship: 914
DAVIS (SHELBY CULLOM) CENTER FOR HISTORICAL STUDIES:
  591
Davis (Watson) and Helen Miles Davis Prize: 597
Dawson (Dr. Martha A.) Genesis Nurse Leader Scholarship: 2492
de Nora (Vittorio) Award: 1819
de Vries (Bert and Sally) Fellowship: 870
DEARBORN COMMUNITY FOUNDATION, INC.: 1251
DEBRA International Research Grants: 2336
Debut Concerto Competition: 796
Debut Orchestra: 796
DECA: 1893
Decentralized Arts Funding Program: 467
Decommissioning and Environmental Sciences (DESD) Scholarship: 2635
DEED Scholarship: 2641
Deer Creek Fund Grants: 168
DEERE (JOHN) FOUNDATION: 96
Defense of Academic Freedom Award: 1862
DeGolyer (Clare Hart) Memorial Fund: 545
Deifik (Joel A.) Memorial Scholarship Fund: 1224
Deines (Ginger and Fred) Canada Scholarships: 1914
Deines (Ginger and Fred) Mexico Scholarships: 1914
Deland Fellowship Program in Health Care and Society: 1421
DELAWARE COUNTY FOUNDATION
  Designated Funds: 1252
  Donor Advised Funds: 1252
  Field of Interest Funds: 1252
  Organizational Endowment Funds: 1252
  Scholarship Funds: 1252
  Special Project Funds: 1252
  Unrestricted Funds: 1252

DELAWARE DIVISION OF THE ARTS
  Arts in Education: 445
  Arts Organizations Grants: 445
  Community Based Organizations Grants: 445
  Gallery Program: 445
  Individual Artist Fellowships: 445
  Opportunity Grants: 445
Delayed Education for Women Scholarship: 2634
DELL (MICHAEL AND SUSAN) FOUNDATION: 1118
  Dell Scholars Program: 1683
DELL (ROGER L. AND AGNES C.) CHARITABLE TRUST: 1253
Dell Scholars Program: 1683
DELMAS (GLADYS KRIEBLE) FOUNDATION
  Humanities Program: 366
  Performing Arts Program: 366
  Research Library Program: 366
  Venetian Research Program: 366
DELOITTE FOUNDATION: 1627
Delta Gamma Foundation Florence Margaret Harvey Memorial
  Scholarship (The): 971
DELUXE CORPORATION FOUNDATION: 97
Democracy, Rights and Justice Program: 129
Dent (Albert W.) Graduate Student Scholarship: 1431
Department of Defense National Defense Science and Engineering
  Graduate Fellowship Program (NDSEG): 2643
DEPARTMENT OF ECONOMIC AND COMMUNITY
  DEVELOPMENT/CONNECTICUT OFFICE OF THE ARTS
  Arts Catalyze Placemaking: 446
DEPARTMENT OF VETERANS AFFAIRS
  VA Psychology Training Program: 2577
Departmental Grants: 2070
DEPAUW UNIVERSITY KEY CLUB INTERNATIONAL
  BONNER/WRIGHT SCHOLARSHIP
  Bonner Scholarship: 1254
  Wright (John Ellis) Award: 1254
Dependent Children Scholarship Program: 1765
DERMATOLOGY FOUNDATION: 2255
Designated and Donor Advised Funds: 1242
Designated Beneficiary Funds: 1329
Designated Funds: 1252
Developmental Biology-SDB Lifetime Achievement Award: 2159
Developmental Disabilities Scholastic Achievement Scholarships: 1525
DEVOS (RICHARD AND HELEN) FOUNDATION: 1255
Diano-Tougas Memorial Scholarship Fund: 1224
DiCarlo (Louis M.) Award for Recent Clinical Achievement: 2506
DICKINSON AREA COMMUNITY FOUNDATION: 1256
Dickinson (John) Teacher of the Year Award: 2220
DICKSON FOUNDATION: 98
DIETITIANS OF CANADA
  Graduate Awards in Dietetics: 2672
  Research Grants in Dietetics: 2672
  Undergraduate Awards in Dietetics: 2672
Dietrich (Joseph R.) Memorial Scholarship: 2637
DigitalGlobe Foundation Award: 2033
Dillman (The Rudolph) Memorial Scholarship: 971
DiMattio Celli Undergraduate Study Abroad Program: 1775
Dingman (The Archibald Waynne) Memorial Graduate Scholarship: 1782
Diploma Program: 764
Direct Grants Program: 1366
DIRECT MARKETING CLUB OF NEW YORK (DMCNY) (THE)
  Boardroom Awards: 1894
  Silver Apple Award Scholarships: 1894
Directorate for Engineering Grants Program: 2655
Directory of Teaching Artists: 459
DIRKSEN CONGRESSIONAL CENTER (THE)
  Congressional Research Grants: 1995
DiSalvo (Raymond) Scholarship: 2636
Disaster Response and Humanitarian Relief: 235
Disciple Chaplains' Scholarship Fund: 808
Discover New Jersey History License Plate Fund for Heritage Tourism:
  616
Discovery Grants: 2454
Discovery Research K-12 (DR K12): 1607
Discretionary Grant Process: 1368
Discretionary Grant Programs: 1153
Discretionary Grants: 182, 2462
Dissertation Fellowship Award: 1680
Dissertation Fellowships: 406
Dissertation Fellowships in Marine Corps History: 641
Dissertation Research Grant: 2442
Dissertation Year Fellowships: 638, 2018

Distinguished Clinical Scientist Award: 2403
Distinguished Investigator Award: 1517
Distinguished Investigator Grant: 2575
Distinguished Scholar Award: 526
Distinguished Scholar Awards in Respiratory Health, Critical Care and Thrombosis: 2392
Distinguished Service Award: 712
DISTRICT OF COLUMBIA COMMISSION ON THE ARTS AND HUMANITIES
    Artist Fellowship Program: 447
    Arts Education Program: 447
    City Arts Projects: 447
    Community Arts Grant: 447
    Cultural Facilities Program: 447
    East of the River Arts Initiative: 447
    Public Art Building Communities: 447
    UPSTART Program: 447
Diversity-Promoting Institutions Drug Abuse Research Program: 1574
Division of Arts Programs: 503
Division of Biomedical Technology, Bioinformatics, and Computational Biology: 2289
Division of Cell Biology and Biophysics: 2289
Division of Communications, Information & Technology: 503
Division of Environmental Biology: 2158
Division of Genetics and Developmental Biology: 2289
Division of Molecular and Cellular Biosciences Programs: 2157
Division of Pharmacology, Physiology, and Biological Chemistry: 2289
Division of Training, Workforce Development, and Diversity: 2289
DIXON FOUNDATION (THE): 1257
DJ & T FOUNDATION: 2106
Dobie Paisano Fellowship Program (The): 509
Doctor (John) Best Education Poster Award: 2159
Doctoral and Postdoctoral Fellowships: 592
Doctoral Awards: 1871
Doctoral Dissertation Research Improvement Grants (DDRIG): 659
Doctoral Fellowship: 852
Doctoral Opportunities for Clinicians and Scholars (DOCS) I and II: 2551
Doctoral Program in Chemistry: 2066
Doctoral Research Award: 2248
Doctoral Scholarships in International Law: 1976
Documenting Endangered Languages (DEL): 659
DODGE (THE CLEVELAND H.) FOUNDATION, INC.: 1119
DODGE (GERALDINE R.) FOUNDATION: 99
Doe (Janet) Lectureship: 730
Dollars-for-Doers: 138
Dollars for Doers Fund: 55
Dollars for Doers Program: 200
Dollars for Doers Volunteer Program: 1189
Domestic Biodiversity: 2212
Domestic Public Policy Program: 1868
DOMINION FOUNDATION: 100
DONNELLEY (GAYLORD AND DOROTHY) FOUNDATION: 101
DONNELLEY (R.R.)
    Corporate Contributions Program: 102
DONNER CANADIAN FOUNDATION: 1996
Donor Advised Funds: 1252
Donor-Advised Funds: 1329
Donor-Advised Grants: 73
Dorosh (Marusia and Michael) Master's Fellowship: 585
Dorroh (Marion) Memorial Scholarship: 737
Douglass Foundation Fellowship in American Art (The): 473
DOUGLASS (FREDERICK) INSTITUTE FOR AFRICAN AND AFRICAN-AMERICAN STUDIES
    FDI Postdoctoral Fellowship: 1538
    FDI Predoctoral Dissertation Fellowship: 1538
DOUTY FOUNDATION (THE): 103
DOW JONES FOUNDATION: 104
DOW JONES NEWS FUND (THE)
    Business Reporting Interns, Sophomore and Junior Students: 1932
    Editing Intern Program for College Juniors, Seniors and Graduate Students: 1932
Dozier (Otis and Velma Davis) Travel Grant: 547
Drawn to Art Fellowship (The): 345
Drewes (Tom and Roberta) Scholarship: 1616
DREXEL UNIVERSITY COLLEGE OF MEDICINE
    Gloeckner (M. Louise), M.D., Summer Research Fellowship: 1081
DREYFUS (THE JEAN AND LOUIS) FOUNDATION, INC.: 1258
Driscoll (Alfred E.) Dissertation Prize: 619
DROWN (JOSEPH) FOUNDATION: 105
Drug Addiction Treatment Program (The): 1343

Drug Discovery Initiative Award: 2360
du Pont (Henry Belin) Dissertation Fellowship in Business, Technology, and Society: 593
du Pont (Henry Belin) Fellowships: 593
Duberman (The Martin) Fellowship: 984
Dubin (Lee) Memorial Scholarship: 985
DUCHOSSOIS FAMILY FOUNDATION (THE): 106
Dudley (Maria) Scholarship: 2492
Dudley (Martha R.) Scholarship: 2492
DUKE (DORIS) CHARITABLE FOUNDATION
    Arts Program: 107
    Child Abuse Prevention Program: 107
    Environment Program: 107
    Medical Research Program: 107
DUKE ENDOWMENT (THE): 108
DULA (THE CALEB C. AND JULIA W.) EDUCATIONAL AND CHARITABLE FOUNDATION: 109
Duling (John) Grant: 2129
Dulis (Edward J.) Scholarship: 2677
DULUTH SUPERIOR AREA COMMUNITY FOUNDATION: 1259
DUMBARTON OAKS
    Fellowships and Project Grants in Byzantine Studies, Pre-Columbian Studies and Garden and Landscape Studies: 367
Duncan Aviation Scholarship: 2618
DUNCAN (THE JOHN G.) TRUST: 1260
Dunlap (Joseph R.) Memorial Fellowship: 479
Dunning (The John H.) Prize in United States History: 578
DUNSPAUGH DALTON FOUNDATION: 110
DUPONT (JESSIE BALL) FUND: 111
DUPONT PIONEER
    Community Betterment: 1120
    Food Security: 1120
    Science Education: 1120
DUQUESNE UNIVERSITY, DEPARTMENT OF PHILOSOPHY
    Duquesne University Graduate Assistantship: 368
Duquesne University Graduate Assistantship: 368
Durkin/Glatzer Scholarship: 2563
Dyrkacz (William & Mary) Scholarships: 2677
DYSAUTONOMIA FOUNDATION, INC.
    Dysautonomia Research Program: 2461
Dysautonomia Research Program: 2461
DYSTONIA MEDICAL RESEARCH FOUNDATION
    Discretionary Grants: 2462
    Research Grants: 2462
DYSTROPHIC EPIDERMOLYSIS BULLOSA RESEARCH ASSOCIATION OF AMERICA, INC. (DEBRA)
    DEBRA International Research Grants: 2336

E

Eagle Staff Fund (The): 1049
Earhart (Amelia) Fellowship: 2059
EARHART FOUNDATION
    Fellowship Research Grants: 1850
    Grants to Organizations: 1850
EARLY AMERICAN INDUSTRIES ASSOCIATION, INC.
    Research Grants Program: 2606
Early Career Research Grants: 1969
Early Childhood Development Program (The): 1136
Early Educators Fellowship Initiative: 1531
Early Investigator Grant Program: 2517
Early Modern Studies: 370
Early Postdoctoral Research Fellowship Program in Biomedical Sciences: 1845
EARN Indiana (State Work Study): 1699
Earthwatch Education Awards: 1817
Earthwatch Funding for Field Research: 1817
EARTHWATCH INSTITUTE
    Earthwatch Education Awards: 1817
    Earthwatch Funding for Field Research: 1817
EAST BAY COMMUNITY FOUNDATION (THE): 1261
East of the River Arts Initiative: 447
EAST TENNESSEE FOUNDATION: 1121
EAST TEXAS COMMUNITIES FOUNDATION: 1262
EAST-WEST CENTER (THE)
    Asia Pacific Leadership Program Fellowship: 846
    East-West Center Graduate Degree Fellowship: 845
East-West Center Graduate Degree Fellowship: 845
EASTERN BANK CHARITABLE FOUNDATION: 112
Eastman School of Music Graduate Awards: 765

EASTMAN SCHOOL OF MUSIC OF THE UNIVERSITY OF
    ROCHESTER
    Eastman School of Music Graduate Awards: 765
EATON CHARITABLE FUND: 113
Eaton (Richard) Foundation Award: 1924
EAU CLAIRE COMMUNITY FOUNDATION: 1263
EBAA Research Grants: 2510
Ebell/Flint Scholarship: 1684
EBELL OF LOS ANGELES (THE)
    Ebell/Flint Scholarship: 1684
ECA Alumni Small Grants Program: 920
ECF Fellowship Partners Program: 810
ECOLAB FOUNDATION: 1264
Ecological Innovation: 90
Economic Development Grant: 1198
ECONOMIC HISTORY ASSOCIATION
    Cole (Arthur H.) Grants-in-Aid: 1895
Economic Justice: 1090
Economic Justice for Women: 282
Economic Opportunity and Assets Program: 129
Ecosystem Services: 2172
ECS Summer Fellowships: 1818
EDDY (EDWIN H.) FAMILY FOUNDATION: 2256
Edell (Norman) Scholarship: 1559
EDISON INTERNATIONAL
    Corporate Contributions Program: 114
    Employee Matching Gifts Program: 114
Editing Intern Program for College Juniors, Seniors and Graduate
    Students: 1932
EDSA Minority Scholarship: 2186
Education: 12, 159, 257, 1192, 1275, 1355
Education Achievement Awards: 1692
Education and Learning: 1495
Education Opportunity Program: 992
Education Program: 219
Education Research: 1593
Education Scholar Grant: 2318
Education, Creativity and Free Expression Program: 129
Educational and Scholastic Advancement Programs: 1910
Educational Environments: 827
EDUCATIONAL FOUNDATION FOR WOMEN IN ACCOUNTING
    (THE)
    Laurels Fund: 1896
    McDonald (Michelle L.) Scholarship: 1896
    Moss Adams LLP Scholarship: 1896
    Seattle ASWA Chapter Scholarship: 1896
    Women in Need Scholarship: 1896
    Women in Transition Scholarship: 1896
Educational Gift Matching: 38
Educational Grant Program: 8, 656, 811, 1586
Educational Loans & Grants Program: 1705
Educational Programme Grants: 419
EDUCATIONAL TESTING SERVICE
    ETS Postdoctoral Fellowship Award Program: 1539
    Summer Internship Program for Graduate Students: 1540
Educational Trust Scholarships: 1708
Edwards (Dorothy) Vocational Scholarship Fund: 1224
Edwards (Everett E.) Awards in Agricultural History: 576
EDWARDS (RAY) MEMORIAL TRUST: 1429
Eight and Forty Lung and Respiratory Disease Nursing Scholarship Fund:
    2485
Einstein (The Alfred) Award: 751
Eisenhower (Dwight David) Transportation Fellowship Program: 2607
EISENHOWER FOUNDATION (THE)
    Travel Grants: 1997
EISENHOWER INSTITUTE (THE)
    Eisenhower Institute Scholarship Programs: 847
Eisenhower Institute Scholarship Programs: 847
EISNER FOUNDATION (THE): 1122
EL PASO COMMUNITY FOUNDATION: 1265
EL POMAR FOUNDATION
    Fellowship Program: 115
    Grants Program: 115
ELECTROCHEMICAL SOCIETY (THE)
    Acheson (Edward Goodrich) Award: 1819
    de Nora (Vittorio) Award: 1819
    ECS Summer Fellowships: 1818
    Linford (Henry B.) Award for Distinguished Teaching: 1819
    Moore (Gordon E.) Medal for Outstanding Achievement in Solid State
        Science and Technology: 1819

    Olin Palladium Award: 1819
    Tobias (Charles W.) Young Investigator Award: 1819
    Wagner (Carl) Memorial Award: 1819
Eliot (Ida and George) Prize: 730
Elizabeth Alfoldi-Rosenbaum Fellowship: 355
Elkin/Tri-County Grants: 1404
Elliott (Van Courtlandt) Prize: 610
ELLIS (ALBERT) INSTITUTE
    Postgraduate Clinical Fellowship Training Program at the Albert Ellis
        Institute: 2578
Ellis (Bill) Teacher Preparation Award: 1568
Ellis (John Tracy) Dissertation Award: 801
ELLSWORTH (RUTH H. AND WARREN A.) FOUNDATION: 116
Elmore (Stanley) Fellowship Fund: 2678
Elsevier Pilot Research Award: 2407
Emergency Assistance Program: 550
Emergency Conservation Program (ECP): 2206
Emergency Loans: 617
EMERGENCY MEDICINE FOUNDATION: 2257
Emergency Scholarship Fund: 2296
Emerging Artists: 1354
Emerging Leaders Fellowships: 2192
Emerging Research Grants: 2515
EMERSON: 117
EMERSON (FRED L.) FOUNDATION, INC.: 1266
Emerson (Ralph Waldo) Award: 694
Employee Giving and Volunteer Programs: 235
Employee Matching Gifts: 138
Employee Matching Gifts Program: 114
Encouraging Civic Progress: 134
Ending Violence: 1090
Endowment Funds of Southwest Iowa: 252
Energy Fellowship Program: 2038
ENERGY FOUNDATION (THE): 2176
Energy Industry and Technology: 2172
Enforcing the Underage Drinking Laws Program: 1414
Engineering and Technology Education: 1537
Engineering Undergraduate Award: 1662
Engineering/Technology Achievement Awards: 1692
ENGLAND (LOIS & RICHARD) FAMILY FOUNDATION: 1123
ENGLISH-SPEAKING UNION (THE)
    British Morehead-Cain Scholarship to the University of North Carolina
        at Chapel Hill (The): 958
    Chautauqua Institution Scholarships (The): 958
    Lindemann Trust Fellowships (The): 958
    Page (Walter Hines) Scholarships: 958
Enhancing the Lives of Children and Their Families: 134
Eno (Irene Winifred) Grant: 412
ENTERPRISE COMMUNITY PARTNERS
    MetLife Foundation Awards for Excellence in Affordable Housing:
        1481
    Rose Architectural Fellowship: 415
Enterprise Journalism Fellowships: 1750
ENTOMOLOGICAL FOUNDATION (THE)
    LaFage (Jeffery P.) Graduate Student Research Award: 2145
    Richardson (Henry and Sylvia) Research Grant: 2144
Entrepreneurship @ Work: SOURCE: 162
Entry Track: 459
Environment: 133, 159, 282
Environment Program: 107
Environment Program Grant: 182
Environmental and Natural Resources Management Program: 173
Environmental Grant Program: 2195
Environmental Health Sciences Research and Training Grants: 2189
ENVIRONMENTAL LAW INSTITUTE
    Continuing Legal Education Scholarship Program: 1974
Environmental Program (The): 1383
Eos #1 Mother Lodge Chapter Scholarship (Undergraduate): 1080
Epidemiology/Population Research: 2352
EPILEPSY FOUNDATION OF AMERICA: 2463
    Behavioral Sciences Postdoctoral Fellowship: 1852
    Behavioral Sciences Student Fellowships: 1851
    Health Sciences Student Fellowships: 1851
    Postdoctoral Research Fellowships: 2464
    Predoctoral Research Training Fellowships: 2464
    Research and Training Fellowships for Clinicians: 2464
EPISCOPAL CHURCH FOUNDATION
    ECF Fellowship Partners Program: 810
ERDAS Internship: 2033
ERION FOUNDATION: 118
ERNST & YOUNG FOUNDATION: 1897

Escue (Walter H.) Memorial Scholarship: 741
Esperanza Grants: 1070
ESSEX COUNTY COMMUNITY FOUNDATION
    Center for Nonprofit Excellence: 1267
    Essex County Youth-at-Risk: 1267
    First Jobs: 1267
    Greater Lawrence Summer Fund: 1267
    Hunger Project (The): 1267
    Institute for Trustees: 1267
    Women's Fund of Essex County (The): 1267
Essex County Youth-at-Risk: 1267
Ethnic Studies Fellowships: 1021
ETS Postdoctoral Fellowship Award Program: 1539
Eurasia/South Asia Teaching Excellence and Achievement Program
    (TEA): 920
Europe and Global Challenges: 401
EVANGELICAL LUTHERAN CHURCH IN AMERICA
    Educational Grant Program: 811
Event Grants: 1438
Everest (D.C.) Fellowship: 646
Everyday Technologies for Alzheimer Care (ETAC): 2452
Evidence-based Practice (EBP) and Quality Improvement (QI) Project
    Grants: 2496
Excellence in Education Program: 1239
Excellence in Medicine: 1660
Executive Fellowship Program: 1992
EXELON CORPORATION
    Corporate Giving Program: 119
Exemplary Research in Social Studies: 1859
Exhibitions Abroad Support Program: 1703
Expanding Opportunities for Participation in the Arts: 512
Expeditions: 484
Exploring Program: 1564
Express Grants: 1371
External Faculty Fellowships: 400
External Programme: 1979
EXXON MOBIL CORPORATION: 120
EYE BANK ASSOCIATION OF AMERICA
    EBAA Research Grants: 2510
EZ (Empowerment Zone) Consulting Grants: 621
Ezell (William C.) Fellowship: 2505

F

FACES Grant: 451
Faculty of Law Graduate Scholarship: 1793
Faculty Practices and Vocation: 827
FAER Health Services Research Grant: 2258
FAER Mentored Research Training Grant: 2258
FAER Research Education Grant: 2258
FAER Research Fellowship Grant: 2258
FAIR OAKS FOUNDATION: 1268
Fairbank (The John K.) Prize in East Asian History: 578
Fairchild (The Sherman) Foundation Fellowships: 557
FAIRFIELD COUNTY COMMUNITY FOUNDATION
    Center for Nonprofit Excellence (CNE): 1269
Fall/Spring Study Abroad: 573
Family Services Community Grants: 2242
Fanning (William M.) Maintenance Scholarship: 2624
FAR Research Network Award: 2500
Fargher (John S.W.) Scholarship: 2653
FARGO-MOORHEAD AREA FOUNDATION: 121
FARM AID: 2118
Farm Kids for College Scholarships: 2125
Farny (Sylvia W.) Scholarship: 2646
Farrar (Marjorie M. and Lancelot L.) Awards: 634
FASSE-IA International Understanding Grants: 1864
FATS AND PROTEINS RESEARCH FOUNDATION, INC.: 1820
FCS Scholarship Fund: 1544
FDI Postdoctoral Fellowship: 1538
FDI Predoctoral Dissertation Fellowship: 1538
Feddie Award (The): 1949
FEDERAL HIGHWAY ADMINISTRATION
    Eisenhower (Dwight David) Transportation Fellowship Program: 2607
Federal Supplemental Educational Opportunity Grant (FSEOG): 1769
Federal Work-Study: 1773
FEDERATION OF AMERICAN CONSUMERS AND TRAVELERS
    Classroom and Community Grants: 1541
    Community and Business Project Grants: 1898
    Continuing Education Scholarships: 1541

Federico II Scholarship: 600
FEEA SCHOLARSHIP PROGRAM
    Scholarship Program: 1685
FEINSTEIN FOUNDATION (THE)
    Feinstein $1 Million Giveaway to Fight Hunger: 1482
Feinstein $1 Million Giveaway to Fight Hunger: 1482
Feis (The Herbert) Award: 578
Feitelson (Dina) Research Award: 1557
Felder Fund for Art and Action: 1492
Felix (Robert) Memorial Scholarship: 2129
Fellow Scholar Award: 2235
Fellowship and Scholarship Program for Writers: 668
Fellowship for U.S.-Based Study: 1666
Fellowship Grant Program: 2517
Fellowship in Aerospace History: 580
Fellowship in American Jewish Studies: 647
Fellowship in Baltic Jewish Studies: 649
Fellowship in East European Jewish Literature and Arts: 648
Fellowship in East European Jewish Studies: 650
Fellowship in Polish Jewish Studies: 649
Fellowship of the Flanders House: 915
Fellowship Program: 115, 930, 2249
Fellowship Program at the Woodrow Wilson International Center for
    Scholars: 405
Fellowship Program for Journalists: 1955
Fellowship Research Grants: 1850, 2268
Fellowships: 380, 459
Fellowships and Project Grants in Byzantine Studies, Pre-Columbian
    Studies and Garden and Landscape Studies: 367
Fellowships at the Albright Institute of Archaeological Research in
    Jerusalem: 868
Fellowships for American Indians or Alaskan Natives: 1037
Fellowships for Independent Study on the Italian Renaissance: 952
Fellowships for Minorities in Management: 1892
Fellowships for Research in Egypt: 879
Fellowships in Art Conservation: 552
FELS (SAMUEL S.) FUND
    Arts and Culture: 1270
    Community Concerns: 1270
    Public Education: 1270
Feynman (Richard P.) Postdoctoral Fellowship in Theory and Computing:
    1826
Field Aviation Company Scholarship: 2618
FIELD FOUNDATION OF ILLINOIS: 122
Field Grants: 1336
Field of Interest Funds: 1252, 1329
Field of Interest Grant Program: 1303
Fielding (Carole) Student Grants: 1962
FIELDSTONE FOUNDATION (THE): 369
FIFTH & PACIFIC FOUNDATION: 123
Figg (Eugene C., Jr.) Civil Engineering Scholarship: 2645
Fight for Sight Postdoctoral Fellowship: 2512
FIGHT FOR SIGHT, INC.
    Fight for Sight Postdoctoral Fellowship: 2512
    Research Awards Program: 2511
Filene (Adele) Travel Award: 444
Financial Aid for Education of Black Residents of Colorado: 1034
Financial Aid for Study at The Graduate Institute of International and
    Development Studies: 848
Financial Grants of Support: 1282
FINANCIAL SERVICE CENTERS OF AMERICA, INC.
    FiSCA National Scholarship Program: 1686
FINE ARTS WORK CENTER IN PROVINCETOWN
    Visual Arts Fellowship: 548
    Writing Fellowship: 548
Finland-U.S. Senate Youth Exchange Program: 954
Finzi (Gina) Memorial Student Summer Fellowship Program: 2279
Fire Research Grants Program: 2035
FIREMAN'S FUND INSURANCE COMPANY
    Heritage Program: 1271
FIRMAN FUND: 124
First Article Prize in Humanities and Social Sciences: 835
FIRST CANDLE/SIDS ALLIANCE
    Professional Research: 2528
FIRST COMMUNITY FOUNDATION PARTNERSHIP OF
    PENNSYLVANIA
    Smith (The Ralph and Josephine) Fund for Northumberland County:
    125
    Waldron (The Margaret) Memorial Fund: 125
    Williamsport-Lycoming Community Fund (The): 125

First Generation Matching Grant Program (FGMG): 1687
FIRST HORIZON NATIONAL CORPORATION: 1272
First Jobs: 1267
FIRST NATIONS DEVELOPMENT INSTITUTE
    Eagle Staff Fund (The): 1049
FIRSTENERGY
    STEM Grants Program: 1602
FIRSTENERGY FOUNDATION: 126
FiSCA National Scholarship Program: 1686
Fischelis Grants for Research in the History of American Pharmacy: 2537
Fischer (William A.) Memorial Scholarship: 2033
FISHAMERICA FOUNDATION
    Fisheries Conservation and Research Projects: 2177
Fishbein (Morris) Fellowship in Medical Editing: 1939
FISHER (AVERY) ARTIST PROGRAM
    Fisher (The Avery) Career Grants: 766
    Fisher (The Avery) Prize: 766
Fisher (The Avery) Career Grants: 766
Fisher (The Avery) Prize: 766
Fisher (Joseph L.) Dissertation Fellowships: 2197
Fisher (Professor Elizabeth F.) Fellowship: 1097
Fisheries Conservation and Research Projects: 2177
FITCH (THE JAMES MARSTON) CHARITABLE FOUNDATION
    Blinder (Richard) Award: 416
    Mid-Career Grant: 416
Fite (Gilbert C.) Dissertation Award: 576
FLANDERS HOUSE
    Fellowship of the Flanders House: 915
Flavelle Medal (The): 1836
Fleishman-Hillard, Inc. Scholarship: 1750
Fleming (Charlie) Scholarship: 1007
Fleming (Patricia) Visiting Fellowship in Bibliography and Book History:
    744
FLETCHER (A.J.) FOUNDATION: 127
Flexit: 401
Flexographic Technical Association Scholarship: 2608
Flight Attendant Scholarship: 2624
FLINN FOUNDATION (THE)
    Arizona Center for Civic Leadership: 128
    Flinn Scholars Program: 128
Flinn Scholars Program: 128
Florida Bright Futures Scholarship Program: 1688
Florida Cultural Endowment Program: 448
FLORIDA DEPARTMENT OF EDUCATION
    Access to Better Learning and Education Grant Program (ABLE): 1687
    Bethune (Mary McLeod) Scholarship Program (MMB): 1687
    First Generation Matching Grant Program (FGMG): 1687
    Florida Bright Futures Scholarship Program: 1688
    Florida Resident Access Grant (FRAG): 1687
    Florida Student Assistance Grant Program (FSAG): 1687
    Florida Work Experience Program (FWEP): 1687
    Marti (Jose) Scholarship Challenge Grant Fund: 1067
    Rosewood Family Scholarship Program: 1028
    Scholarships for Children and Spouses of Deceased or Disabled
    Veterans (CSDDV): 1687
FLORIDA DEPARTMENT OF STATE, DIVISION OF CULTURAL
AFFAIRS
    Capitol Complex Exhibition Program: 448
    Cultural Facilities Program: 448
    Florida Cultural Endowment Program: 448
    Florida Individual Artist Fellowship Program: 448
    General Program Support Grants Program: 448
    Specific Cultural Projects Grants Program: 448
    State Touring Program: 448
FLORIDA EDUCATION FUND
    McKnight Doctoral Fellowship: 1542
Florida Individual Artist Fellowship Program: 448
Florida Prepaid College Tuition Program (The): 1527
Florida Resident Access Grant (FRAG): 1687
FLORIDA STATE UNIVERSITY FOUNDATION: 1543
Florida Student Assistance Grant Program (FSAG): 1687
Florida Work Experience Program (FWEP): 1687
Focus Area Grants: CLL/SLL: 2367
Focus Area Grants: DLBCL: 2367
Focus Area Grants: Follicular Lymphoma Research Grants: 2367
Focus Area Grants: Mantle Cell Lymphoma Correlative Grants: 2367
Fogarty International Research Collaboration Award (FIRCA): 2146
FOGARTY (JOHN E.) INTERNATIONAL CENTER
    Fogarty International Research Collaboration Award (FIRCA): 2146

FOLGER INSTITUTE (THE)
    Early Modern Studies: 370
Folk Arts: 427
Folk Arts Apprenticeship Program: 518
Folk Arts Apprenticeships: 486
Folklife Program: 483
FONDATION DES ETATS-UNIS
    Woolley (Harriet Hale) Scholarships: 449
FOOD AND DRUG LAW INSTITUTE (FDLI)
    Austern (H. Thomas) Memorial Writing Competition-Food and Drug
    Law: 1975
Food Safety Innovation Award: 2673
Food Security: 1120
Food, Clothing and Shelter: 301
Food, Pharmaceutical and Bioengineering Division Award in Chemical
    Engineering: 1808
FoodShare Program: 38
Forbes Fellowship: 452
Ford (Allegra) Scholarship: 1569
Ford (Anne) Scholarship: 1569
FORD FOUNDATION (THE)
    Democracy, Rights and Justice Program: 129
    Economic Opportunity and Assets Program: 129
    Education, Creativity and Free Expression Program: 129
Ford Foundation Fellowship Program: 1005
FORD (GERALD R.) PRESIDENTIAL LIBRARY
    Ford (Gerald R.) Scholar Award (Dissertation Award) in Honor of
    Robert M. Teeter: 1999
    Research Travel Grant Program: 1998
Ford (Gerald R.) Scholar Award (Dissertation Award) in Honor of Robert
    M. Teeter: 1999
FORD MOTOR COMPANY FUND & COMMUNITY SERVICES
    Community Grants Program: 130
Ford Motor Scholarship: 1001
FORECAST PUBLIC ARTWORKS
    Jerome Planning Grant for Arts: 450
    Jerome Project Grant for Emerging Artists: 450
    McKnight Professional Development Grant for Mid-Career Artists: 450
    McKnight Project Grant for Mid-Career Artists: 450
    MN Regional Grant Program: 450
Foreign Government Awards: 902
Foreign Language and Area Studies Fellowships: 662
Foreman (George) Tribute to Lyndon B. Johnson: 1958
Forest Fungal Ecology Award: 2155
Forkosch (The Morris D.) Prize: 578
Foster Care to Independence: 1169
FOSTER CARE TO SUCCESS
    Casey Family Scholars: 1544
    FCS Scholarship Fund: 1544
Foster Grandparent Program: 1480
Fostering Economic Self-Sufficiency: 1330
FOUNDATION FOR ANESTHESIA EDUCATION AND RESEARCH
    FAER Health Services Research Grant: 2258
    FAER Mentored Research Training Grant: 2258
    FAER Research Education Grant: 2258
    FAER Research Fellowship Grant: 2258
FOUNDATION FOR ENHANCING COMMUNITIES (THE)
    Capital Beginnings: 1273
    Women's Fund: 1273
FOUNDATION FOR NEONATAL RESEARCH AND EDUCATION
(FNRE): 2489
FOUNDATION FOR OSTEOPATHIC EMERGENCY MEDICINE
    Investigator Grant: 2523
    Kuchinski (David A.) Memorial Research Grant: 2523
    Resident Research Grant: 2523
    Young Investigator Grant: 2523
FOUNDATION FOR PHYSICAL THERAPY, INC.: 2550
    Doctoral Opportunities for Clinicians and Scholars (DOCS) I and II:
    2551
    Kendall (Florence P.) Doctoral Scholarships: 2551
    New Investigator Fellowship Training Initiative (NIFTI): 2551
FOUNDATION FOR SCIENCE AND DISABILITY: 989
FOUNDATION FOR SPIRITUALITY AND MEDICINE (THE): 1430
FOUNDATION FOR TECHNOLOGY AND ENGINEERING
EDUCATION
    FTEE Undergraduate Scholarship: 1689
    Litherland/FTEE Scholarship Undergraduate Major in Technology and
    Engineering Education: 1690
    Maley/FTEE Scholarship Technology and Engineering Teacher

Professional Development: 1546
Pittsco/Hearlihy/FTEE Grant Excellence in Teaching Technology and Engineering: 1545
FOUNDATION FOR THE CAROLINAS: 1274
FOUNDATION FOR THE MID SOUTH
Community Development: 1275
Education: 1275
Health & Wellness: 1275
Wealth Building: 1275
FOUNDATION FOR THE TRI-STATE COMMUNITY, INC.
21st Century Endowment Fund: 1276
Foundation Initiative Grants: 290
FOUNDATION OF FLEXOGRAPHIC TECHNICAL ASSOCIATION (THE)
Flexographic Technical Association Scholarship: 2608
FOUNDATION OF THE AMERICAN COLLEGE OF HEALTHCARE EXECUTIVES (THE)
Dent (Albert W.) Graduate Student Scholarship: 1431
McGaw (Foster G.) Graduate Student Scholarship: 1431
FOUNDATION OF THE AMERICAN SOCIETY OF NEURORADIOLOGY (THE): 2259
FOUNDATION OF THE NATIONAL STUDENT NURSES' ASSOCIATION, INC.: 2490
4A'S
Multicultural Advertising Intern Program: 990
Four Year Doctoral Fellowships: 1780
Fox (The Dixon Ryan) Manuscript Prize of the New York State Historical Association: 622
FOX (THE MICHAEL J.) FOUNDATION FOR PARKINSON'S RESEARCH: 2260
Framing Hope Program: 1300
FRANCIS (THE PARKER B.) FELLOWSHIP PROGRAM: 2261
Frank Educational Fund: 831
Franklin (Benjamin) Travel Grant for Undergraduate Students: 939
Franklin (Miles) Literary Award: 700
Franklin Research Grants: 14
Frantz (M. Alison) Fellowship in Post-Classical Studies at the Gennadius Library: 886
FRAXA Grants and Fellowships: 2262
FRAXA RESEARCH FOUNDATION
FRAXA Grants and Fellowships: 2262
FREEDOM ALLIANCE
Freedom Alliance Scholarship Fund: 1691
Freedom Alliance Scholarship Fund: 1691
FREEMAN (CARL M.) FOUNDATION
FACES Grant: 451
Freeman (Don) Memorial Grant-in-Aid: 697
Freeman Fellowship: 2645
FREEMAN FOUNDATION: 131
FREEPORT-MCMORAN COPPER AND GOLD FOUNDATION
Matching Gifts Program: 132
Social Investment Program: 132
FREER GALLERY OF ART AND ARTHUR M. SACKLER GALLERY
Forbes Fellowship: 452
Lee (The J.S.) Memorial Fellowship: 452
Smithsonian Fellowship: 452
van Biema (Anne) Fellowship: 452
FREMONT AREA COMMUNITY FOUNDATION (THE): 1277
French Language Scholarship: 1972
French-American Jazz Exchange: 476
Freshman Scholarships: 2610
FRESNO REGIONAL FOUNDATION
Arts and Culture: 133
Environment: 133
High Impact: 133
Human Services: 133
Teen Pregnancy Prevention Initiative: 133
Youth Grants: 133
Frevel (The Ludo) Crystallography Scholarship Award: 2679
FREY FOUNDATION
Community Capital Projects: 134
Encouraging Civic Progress: 134
Enhancing the Lives of Children and Their Families: 134
Nurturing Community Arts: 134
Protecting the Environment: 134
Strengthening Philanthropy: 134
FRIENDS OF JOSE CARRERAS INTERNATIONAL LEUKEMIA FOUNDATION
Research Fellowships: 2263

FRIST FOUNDATION (THE)
Frist Foundation Awards of Achievement (The): 1278
Frist Foundation Technology Grants Program (The): 1278
Frist Foundation Awards of Achievement (The): 1278
Frist Foundation Technology Grants Program (The): 1278
FROMM MUSIC FOUNDATION AT HARVARD: 767
Frontiers in Anesthesia Research Award: 2272
FROST FOUNDATION, LTD. (THE): 135
FRY (LLOYD A.) FOUNDATION: 136
FSH SOCIETY, INC.: 2264
FTEE Undergraduate Scholarship: 1689
Fuertes (Louis Agassiz) Award: 2162
Fulbright - University of Manchester Award: 948
Fulbright Distinguished Chairs: 1623
Fulbright-Hays Faculty Research Abroad Program: 944
Fulbright-Hays Group Projects Abroad Program: 943
Fulbright International Education Administrators Program: 1624
Fulbright Scholar Program: 906
Fulbright Scholar-in-Residence Program: 836
Fulbright Specialist Program: 837
Fulbright Teacher Exchange Program: 1596
Fulbright-Hays Doctoral Dissertation Research Abroad: 663
Full Circle Scholarship Program: 1036
FULLER (H.B.) COMPANY FOUNDATION: 1124
FUND FOR AMERICAN STUDIES (THE)
Novak (The Robert) Journalism Fellowship Program: 2000
Fund for Change: 1490
Fund for Excellence in Education Grants: 1244
Fund for Financial Innovation: 1210
Fund for Innovative Operations: 1210
FUND FOR INVESTIGATIVE JOURNALISM: 1933
Fund for Omaha: 252
Fund for Targeted Needs: 1210
Fund for the Arts: 484
Fund for Women and Girls (The): 1351
Funding and Arts in Education Programs: 463
Furthermore Grant: 182
Future Faces of Physics Awards: 2103
Future Latino Leaders Law Camp: 1982
Futuro Latino Fund: 252

G

Gallagher (John J. and Anna H.) Fellowship: 1805
Gallatin Fellowships: 951
Gallery Program: 445
GAMBLE FOUNDATION (THE): 1547
Gambrell (C.B.) Undergraduate Scholarship: 2653
GANNETT FOUNDATION: 137
Gannett Foundation Scholarship: 1001
GARDEN CLUB OF AMERICA (THE)
Beattie (Catherine) Fellowship: 2180
Chatham (The Anne S.) Fellowship in Medicinal Botany: 2179
Garden Club of America Awards in Tropical Botany: 2179
GCA Award in Coastal Wetland Studies (The): 2180
GCA Awards for Summer Environmental Studies: 2181
GCA Interchange Fellowship in Horticulture and Martin McLaren Scholarship: 2178
Grosscup (Katharine M.) Scholarships: 2119
Marks (The Loy McCandless) Scholarship in Tropical Ornamental Horticulture: 2180
Peacock (The Frances M.) Scholarship for Native Bird Habitat: 2179
Garden Club of America Awards in Tropical Botany: 2179
Garden (Dwight D.) Scholarship: 2653
Garden State Historic Preservation Trust Fund (GSHPTF): 616
Garfield (Eugene) Doctoral Dissertation Fellowship: 716
Garfield (The Eugene)/ALISE Doctoral Dissertation Competition: 715
Garmin - Jerry Smith Memorial Scholarship: 2618
Garmin Scholarship: 2618
Garrett (Eileen J.) Scholarship: 2585
Garvin (Mildred Barry) Prize: 619
Gates Millennium Scholars Program: 1068
Gateway Grant: 8
GATX CORPORATION
Dollars-for-Doers: 138
Employee Matching Gifts: 138
Gaul (Harvey) Music Composition Contest: 785
Gauss (Christian) Award: 694
Gaver (Mary V.) Scholarship: 1616

Gaylor (Lowell) Memorial Scholarship: 2618
GCA Award in Coastal Wetland Studies (The): 2180
GCA Awards for Summer Environmental Studies: 2181
GCA Interchange Fellowship in Horticulture and Martin McLaren
   Scholarship: 2178
GE/NMF International Medical Scholars Program: 2296
GE-NMF Primary Care Leadership Program (PCLP): 2296
GE-Reagan Foundation Scholarship Program: 1751
Geach (Portia) Memorial Award: 505
GEFFEN (THE DAVID) FOUNDATION: 1432
GEICO Life Scholarship: 1692
Geiger Memorial Internship: 633
Geisman (Michael) Fellowships: 2303
GELLERT (CARL) AND CELIA BERTA GELLERT FOUNDATION
   (THE): 139
GELLERT (THE FRED) FAMILY FOUNDATION: 140
GEM M.S. Engineering Fellowship (The): 1003
GEM Ph.D. Engineering Fellowship (The): 1003
GEM Ph.D. Science Fellowship (The): 1003
GENERAL BOARD OF HIGHER EDUCATION AND MINISTRY, THE
   UNITED METHODIST CHURCH
   Harkness (Georgia) Scholarships: 812
General College Scholarship Program: 1068
GENERAL COMMISSION ON ARCHIVES AND HISTORY OF THE
   UNITED METHODIST CHURCH
   Ness (John Harrison) Memorial Award: 813
General Community Grants: 1308
General Fellowship Program: 875
General Grant Program: 1
General Grantmaking: 1170
General Operating Support Grants: 486, 618
General Program Support Grants: 486
General Program Support Grants Program: 448
General Project Grants: 485
GENERAL SERVICE FOUNDATION
   Colorado Program: 141
   Human Rights and Economic Justice: 141
   Reproductive Justice: 141
Genetic Studies: 2352
Gentile (Major Don S.) Scholarship: 1775
Geography Grants: 168
GEOLOGICAL SOCIETY OF AMERICA, INC. (THE)
   GSA Research Grants: 2077
GEORGE FOUNDATION (THE): 142
GEORGE WASHINGTON UNIVERSITY
   Graduate Teaching Assistantships: 2652
GEORGETOWN UNIVERSITY
   Doctoral Program in Chemistry: 2066
GEORGIA COUNCIL FOR THE ARTS
   Georgia Masterpieces: 453
   Literary Events Grants: 453
   Poet Laureate: 453
   Poetry Out Loud: 453
   State Art Collection: 453
GEORGIA LIBRARY ASSOCIATION
   Beard Scholarship: 722
   Hubbard Scholarship: 722
Georgia Masterpieces: 453
GEORGIA-PACIFIC FOUNDATION: 143
GERBER FOUNDATION (THE): 1125
GERMAN ACADEMIC EXCHANGE SERVICE
   DAAD Emigre Memorial German Internship Program
   (EMGIP-Bundestag): 916
   DAAD German Studies Summer Seminar: 916
   DAAD Intensive Language Grant: 916
   DAAD Research Grant: 916
   DAAD Research Internships in Science and Engineering (RISE): 916
   DAAD Research Visit for Faculty: 916
   DAAD RISE Pro: 916
   DAAD Study Scholarship: 916
   DAAD Undergraduate Scholarship: 916
   DAAD University Summer Language Grant: 916
   DAAD Visiting Professorship: 916
German Chancellor Fellowship: 872
GERMAN HISTORICAL INSTITUTE
   Doctoral and Postdoctoral Fellowships: 592
Gershoy (The Leo) Award: 578
GETTY (J. PAUL) TRUST, GETTY FOUNDATION: 549
GHEENS FOUNDATION: 144
Giambalvo (Joan F.) Memorial Scholarship: 1660

Gies (William J.) Award: 2345
GIFFORD (THE ROSAMOND) CHARITABLE CORPORATION: 1279
Gifted Young Pianists Concerto Competition: 772
Gilbert Grants: 1716
Gilbert (Rosalinde and Arthur) Foundation/AFAR New Investigator
   Awards in Alzheimer's Disease: 2225
Gilbreth Memorial Fellowship: 2653
GILL FOUNDATION
   Gill Foundation General Fund: 991
Gill Foundation General Fund: 991
Gillette (The R.L.) Scholarship: 971
Gillies (Sir Harold Delf) Award: 2220
Ginocchio (Lawrence) Scholarship: 2625
girlsBEST: 1102
GLAUCOMA FOUNDATION (THE): 2513
GLAUCOMA RESEARCH FOUNDATION
   Shaffer Fund for Innovative Glaucoma Research: 2514
GLAXOSMITHKLINE: 1433
GLBT Community Projects Fund: 234
Glenn (Paul) Award: 2222
Glenn/AFAR Breakthroughs in Gerontology Awards: 2227
Glenn/AFAR Scholarships for Research in the Biology of Aging: 2226
Global: 64
Global Arts Fund: 980
Global Development and Population: 159
GLOBAL FUND FOR WOMEN
   Assisting Women's Groups Globally: 1082
Global Ph.D. Fellowship: 1797
Global Philanthropy Program: 305
Global Undergraduate Exchange Program in Eurasia and Central Asia
   (UGRAD): 920
GLOECKNER (THE FRED C.) FOUNDATION, INC.: 2120
Gloeckner (M. Louise), M.D., Summer Research Fellowship: 1081
GMT Initiative Grants: 1812
Gold Fund for Health: 1440
GOLDBERG (RUTH ESTRIN) MEMORIAL FOR CANCER
   RESEARCH: 2437
Golden Key Graduate Scholarship Award (The): 1692
GOLDEN KEY INTERNATIONAL HONOUR SOCIETY, INC.
   Business Achievement Awards: 1692
   Community Service Award: 1692
   Education Achievement Awards: 1692
   Engineering/Technology Achievement Awards: 1692
   GEICO Life Scholarship: 1692
   Golden Key Graduate Scholarship Award (The): 1692
   Golden Key Research Grants: 1692
   Literary Achievement Awards: 1692
   Student Leader Award (Regional and International): 1692
   Study Abroad Scholarships: 1692
   Visual and Performing Arts Achievement Awards: 1692
Golden Key Research Grants: 1692
GOLDMAN (HERMAN) FOUNDATION: 145
GOLDMAN (LISA AND DOUGLAS) FUND: 1280
Goldman (The Ralph I.) Fellowship: 878
Goldmark (Ruth Ingersoll) Fellowship: 1097
GOLDSEKER FOUNDATION: 1281
Goldstein (The Howard and Barbara) Scholarship: 2563
Good Companies @ Work Program: 162
Good Neighborhood: 297
Good Opportunities: 297
Good Roots Grant: 8
Good Schools: 297
GOODRICH FOUNDATION (THE): 1548
GOODYEAR TIRE & RUBBER COMPANY (THE): 146
Gorgas Scholarship: 1806
GOTTLIEB (ADOLPH AND ESTHER) FOUNDATION, INC.
   Emergency Assistance Program: 550
   Individual Support Program: 550
Gottlieb (Murray) Prize: 730
Gottschalk (Carl W.) Research Scholar Grant: 2356
Governor Mifflin Area Grantmaking: 1180
Governor's Arts Awards: 483
GRABLE FOUNDATION (THE): 1126
GRACE (W. R.) FOUNDATION, INC.: 147
GRACO FOUNDATION (THE)
   Financial Grants of Support: 1282
Grad Lab: 1003
Graduate and Faculty Development Program: 1003
Graduate Arts Award: 1680
Graduate Awards in Dietetics: 2672

GRADUATE EDUCATION OPPORTUNITY PROGRAM
 Academic Achievement Graduate Assistantships: 992
 Education Opportunity Program: 992
 University Distinguished Fellowships: 992
 University Enrichment Fellowships: 992
Graduate Faculty Council Scholarship: 1790
Graduate Fellowship in Engineering: 2664
GRADUATE INSTITUTE OF INTERNATIONAL AND
 DEVELOPMENT STUDIES
 Financial Aid for Study at The Graduate Institute of International and
 Development Studies: 848
Graduate Nursing Loan-Forgiveness Program: 1765
Graduate Program in Creative Writing: 698
Graduate Research Awards: 2100
Graduate Research Scholarships: 1766
Graduate Scholarship Program: 2632
Graduate Scholarships: 1042, 2610, 2663
Graduate School Scholarships for Study in Italy: 940
Graduate Student Essay Prize: 661
Graduate Student Fellowship Program: 2130, 2137
Graduate Student Initiative: 1781
Graduate Student Network: 1559
Graduate Student Poster Contest: 430
Graduate Student Scholarship for International/Minority Students: 2506
Graduate Student Scholarship for Minority Students: 2506
Graduate Student Scholarship for NSSLHA Members: 2506
Graduate Student Scholarship for Students with a Disability: 2506
Graduate Student Scholarships: 2506
Graduate Student Travel Grant: 801
Graduate Teaching Assistantships: 2652
Graduate Training in Disparities Research: 2439
GRAHAM FOUNDATION FOR ADVANCED STUDIES IN THE FINE
 ARTS
 Manny (Carter) Award: 417
 Production and Presentation Grants: 417
 Research and Development Grants: 417
GRAHAM HOLDINGS COMPANY: 148
Graham II Performing Group Scholarship: 531
GRAHAM (MARTHA) SCHOOL OF CONTEMPORARY DANCE, INC.
 Graham II Performing Group Scholarship: 531
 Independent Program: 531
 Professional Trainee Program: 531
 Summer Intensive: 531
 Teens Program: 531
 Third Year Post Certificate Program: 531
 Winter Intensive: 531
GRAHAM (PHILIP L.) FUND: 149
Grambs (Jean Dresden) Distinguished Career in Social Studies: 1859
GRAMMY FOUNDATION (THE): 768
GRAND HAVEN AREA COMMUNITY FOUNDATION: 1283
GRAND RAPIDS COMMUNITY FOUNDATION
 Access Camps: 150
Grant for the Enhancement of Geographic Literacy: 1861
Grant-in-Aid: 2393
Grant Incentives for Volunteerism by PPG Employees and Retirees
 (GIVE): 271
Grant (Kenneth E.) Research Scholarship: 2202
Grant Program: 274
Grant (William T.) Distinguished Fellows: 1127
GRANT (THE WILLIAM T.) FOUNDATION
 Grant (William T.) Distinguished Fellows: 1127
 Grant (William T.) Scholars Program: 1127
 Investigator Initiated Grants: 1127
 Youth Service Improvement Grants Program: 1127
Grant (William T.) Scholars Program: 1127
Grant-in-Aid Program: 2381
Grantee Workshops: 1410
Grants: 866
Grants for Cancer Research: 2434
Grants for Change: 1492
Grants for Literacy Projects in Countries with Developing Economies:
 1556
Grants for Nonprofit Organizations: 342
Grants for Organizations: 471
Grants for Research in Broadcasting: 1944
Grants for Researchers with Heavy Teaching Loads: 526
Grants for Visual Artists: 454
Grants in Herpetology: 2043
Grants Program: 115, 483, 529, 1009, 1582
Grants to Green: 1214

Grants to Organizations: 1850
Grants to Organizations Grants: 523
Grants to Professional Canadian Artists and Arts Organizations: 438
Grants-in-Aid for Research at the Rockefeller Archive Center: 632
Grants-in-Aid of Research: 1838
Grants-to-Educators Program: 1604
Grass Fellowships in Neuroscience: 2465
GRASS FOUNDATION (THE)
 Grass Fellowships in Neuroscience: 2465
Grass Foundation (The) - AES Young Investigator Travel Award: 2455
Grasso (Ella) Literary Scholarship: 1775
Grassroots Arts Program: 490
Grassroots Fund Grants: 2170
Grassroots Grants: 232
GRAVES (NANCY) FOUNDATION
 Grants for Visual Artists: 454
Gray (Charles Montgomery) Fellowship: 396
Gray (Garland and Agnes Taylor) Foundation: 1213
GRAYSON-JOCKEY CLUB RESEARCH FOUNDATION (THE): 2265
GREAT BAY FOUNDATION (THE): 1483
GREAT LAKES COLLEGES ASSOCIATION NEW WRITERS
 AWARDS
 New Writers Awards: 674
GREAT LAKES PROTECTION FUND
 Great Lakes Protection Fund: 2182
Great Lakes Protection Fund: 2182
GREAT MINDS IN STEM
 HENAAC Scholars Program: 2609
Great Rivers Affiliate Student Undergraduate Research Fellowship: 2380
GREATER CEDAR RAPIDS COMMUNITY FOUNDATION (THE)
 Nonprofit Network: 1284
 Youth Power: 1284
GREATER CINCINNATI FOUNDATION (THE): 1285
GREATER GREEN BAY COMMUNITY FOUNDATION: 1286
GREATER KANAWHA VALLEY FOUNDATION (THE): 1287
GREATER KANSAS CITY COMMUNITY FOUNDATION AND
 AFFILIATED TRUSTS (THE): 1288
GREATER LANSING FOUNDATION (THE)
 Greater Lansing Foundation General Fund (The): 1289
Greater Lansing Foundation General Fund (The): 1289
Greater Lawrence Summer Fund: 1267
GREATER LOWELL COMMUNITY FOUNDATION: 1290
Greater Mercer Grants: 1351
GREATER MILWAUKEE FOUNDATION: 1291
GREATER NEW ORLEANS FOUNDATION (THE): 1292
Greater Southeast Affiliate Health Sciences Fellowship Program: 2379
Greco (Bishop Charles P.) Graduate Fellowships: 1708
Greenberg (Noah) Award: 751
GREENBURG-MAY FOUNDATION: 2438
Greenfield (Albert M.) Foundation Dissertation Fellowships: 603
Greenfield (Vivian) Education Award: 741
GREENSHIELDS (THE ELIZABETH) FOUNDATION
 Greenshields (The Elizabeth) Foundation Grants: 551
Greenshields (The Elizabeth) Foundation Grants: 551
Greer (Violet D.) Grant Awards: 1029
Griswold (Enid Hall) Memorial Scholarship: 1866
Gritton (Henry Bertie and Florence Mabel) Postgraduate Research
 Scholarships/Fellowships: 2069
Grizzly Creek Ranch Camp and Conference Center: 1509
Groot (Jennifer C.) Fellowships in the Archaeology of Jordan: 870
Gross (The Barry R.) Memorial Award: 1636
Grosscup (Katharine M.) Scholarships: 2119
Groves (The Donald) Fund: 582
GRUNDY FOUNDATION (THE): 1293
GSA Research Grants: 2077
GSBA SCHOLARSHIP FUND
 GSBA Scholarships: 993
GSBA Scholarships: 993
Guggenheim Fellowship: 2628
Guggenheim Fellowships: 151
GUGGENHEIM (THE HARRY FRANK) FOUNDATION
 Guggenheim (The Harry Frank) Foundation Dissertation Fellowship:
 1854
 Guggenheim (The Harry Frank) Foundation Research Grant: 1853
Guggenheim (The Harry Frank) Foundation Dissertation Fellowship: 1854
Guggenheim (The Harry Frank) Foundation Research Grant: 1853
GUGGENHEIM (JOHN SIMON) MEMORIAL FOUNDATION
 Guggenheim Fellowships: 151
Guilday (The Peter) Prize: 803

GUITAR FOUNDATION OF AMERICA
   International Concert Artists Competition: 769
   International Youth Competition: 769
GULF COAST COMMUNITY FOUNDATION : 1294
GUND (THE GEORGE) FOUNDATION: 152
Gunsmithing Student Scholarships: 426
Gunter (Connie and Robert T.) Scholarship: 2616
Guynn Family Book Scholarship: 1032
GWATHMEY MEMORIAL TRUST (THE): 371

H

Hackney (Louise Wallace) Fellowship: 542
HAFIF FAMILY FOUNDATION (THE): 1083
Hagley Exploratory Research Grant: 593
HAGLEY MUSEUM AND LIBRARY
   du Pont (Henry Belin) Dissertation Fellowship in Business, Technology,
      and Society: 593
   du Pont (Henry Belin) Fellowships: 593
   Hagley Exploratory Research Grant: 593
HAGUE ACADEMY OF INTERNATIONAL LAW (THE)
   Centre for Studies and Research in International Law and International
      Relations: 1978
   Doctoral Scholarships in International Law: 1976
   External Programme: 1979
   Hague Academy of International Law Summer Courses: 1977
Hague Academy of International Law Summer Courses: 1977
Hague (The George) Memorial Travel Award: 2068
HALBERT CENTRE FOR CANADIAN STUDIES
   Halbert Centre for Canadian Studies Visiting Appointment: 1628
Halbert Centre for Canadian Studies Visiting Appointment: 1628
Haley (Sheila) Scholarship: 2492
Hall (Donald) Prize in Poetry: 667
HALL FAMILY FOUNDATION: 153
Hall (George A.)/Harold Mayfield Award: 2162
Hall/McElwain Merit Scholarships: 1108
HALLETT CHARITABLE TRUSTS (THE): 1629
HALLIBURTON FOUNDATION, INC.: 1630
HAMBIDGE
   Hambidge Residency Program Fellowships: 455
Hambidge Residency Program Fellowships: 455
Hamburger (Viktor) Outstanding Educator Prize: 2159
HAMILTON COMMUNITY FOUNDATION: 1295
HAMILTON FAMILY FOUNDATION: 1549
Hamilton (John D.) Community Service Award: 1204
HAMMILL (THE DONALD D.) FOUNDATION
   Organizational Grants: 994
Hammond (Dr. George P.) Paper Prize: 629
HAMNER INSTITUTES FOR HEALTH SCIENCES (THE)
   Postdoctoral Fellowship at The Hamner Institutes for Health Sciences:
      2067
Hampson (Thomas) Award: 751
HAMPTON ROADS COMMUNITY FOUNDATION (THE): 1296
HANCOCK COUNTY COMMUNITY FOUNDATION: 1297
HANCOCK (RUTH) SCHOLARSHIP FOUNDATION
   Hancock (Ruth) Scholarships: 1934
Hancock (Ruth) Scholarships: 1934
Haniak (John M.) Scholarship: 2677
HANNAFORD CHARITABLE FOUNDATION: 1550
HARBUS FOUNDATION: 1551
HARDEN FOUNDATION: 154
HARDIN (THE PHIL) FOUNDATION: 1552
Haring (The Clarence H.) Prize: 578
Harkness (Georgia) Scholarships: 812
Harper Fund Award: 661
Harrell Family Fellowship: 870
Harris Grants: 895
Harris (Leon)/Les Nichols Memorial Scholarship: 2618
HARTFORD (THE JOHN A.) FOUNDATION, INC.
   Aging and Health Program: 155
HARTFORD PUBLIC LIBRARY
   Hewins (The Caroline M.) Scholarship: 723
HARVARD TRAVELLERS CLUB, PERMANENT FUND: 1821
HARVARD UKRAINIAN RESEARCH INSTITUTE
   Shklar (Eugene and Daymel) Fellowships in Ukrainian Studies: 724
Harvey Fellows Program: 1566
HASBRO CHILDREN'S FUND
   Community Grants: 1128
Haskins Medal: 610

HASTINGS CENTER (THE)
   Visiting Scholars Program: 2107
Hastings (Don and Shirley) Scholarship: 2601
Hastings (Donald F.) Scholarship: 2601
Haverland (Harry) Citation Award: 2673
Hawaii Chapter David T. Woolsey Scholarship: 2186
HAWAII COMMUNITY FOUNDATION: 1298
HAWAII STATE FOUNDATION ON CULTURE AND THE ARTS
   Biennium Grants Program: 456
Hawley Medal: 2680
Hawthorne (Ruth E.) Research Grant: 2674
HAYDEN (CHARLES) FOUNDATION: 1129
HAYNES (THE JOHN RANDOLPH) AND DORA HAYNES
   FOUNDATION: 1631
HAYSTACK MOUNTAIN SCHOOL OF CRAFTS: 457
HAZEN (EDWARD W.) FOUNDATION
   Public Education Grants: 1130
   Youth Organizing Grants: 1130
Hazen (Joseph H.) Education Prize: 597
HBA-DC Foundation Fellowship (The): 1980
HCR MANOR CARE FOUNDATION: 1434
HD Human Biology Project: 2466
Head Start: 1151
Healers: 1242
Health: 90
Health and Human Services: 257
Health & Wellness: 1275
Health and Wellness Grant: 1365
Health Care: 1192
Health Care Division: 1503
Health Care Improvement Grant Program: 1469
Health Careers Scholarships: 1659
Health Center Program (The): 1467
HEALTH EFFECTS INSTITUTE (HEI)
   Health Effects of Air Pollution: 1435
   Rosenblith (Walter A.) New Investigator Award: 1435
Health Effects of Air Pollution: 1435
Health Equity Advocacy: 1427
Health Equity Learning Series: 1427
HEALTH FOUNDATION OF GREATER INDIANAPOLIS (THE): 1484
   Indiana AIDS Fund: 1436
HEALTH FOUNDATION OF SOUTH FLORIDA: 1437
Health Leadership Program: 1509
Health Literacy Initiative: 1660
Health Literacy Research: 2352
Health Partnership Grants: 1439
HEALTH RESOURCES AND SERVICES ADMINISTRATION: 2266
   Scholarships for Disadvantaged Students: 1553
Health Sciences Student Fellowships: 1851
Health System Quality and Efficiency: 1478
HEALTH TRUST (THE)
   Event Grants: 1438
   Health Partnership Grants: 1439
HEALTHCARE FOUNDATION FOR ORANGE COUNTY (THE)
   Gold Fund for Health: 1440
   Healthy Orange County: 1440
   Partners for Health: 1440
Healthy Communities/Healthy America: 1660
Healthy Congregations Program: 1514
Healthy Living Grant Program: 1660
HEALTHY MINDS CANADA
   HMC Partnership Awards - Children's Mental Health: 2267
   Open Minds Across Canada: 2267
   Youth Summit: 2267
Healthy Nutrition and Physical Activity for Young Children: 1514
Healthy Orange County: 1440
Healthy Sacramento Coalition: 1509
HEARING HEALTH FOUNDATION
   Emerging Research Grants: 2515
   Hearing Restoration Project: 2515
Hearing Restoration Project: 2515
HEARST (WILLIAM RANDOLPH) FOUNDATION
   Journalism Awards Program: 1935
Hearst (William Randolph) Foundation Fellowship: 611
HEART AND STROKE FOUNDATION OF CANADA
   Grant-in-Aid: 2393
   New Investigator: 2394
   Research Fellowship: 2395
HeartRescue: 228
Heed Fellowship: 2516

HEED OPHTHALMIC FOUNDATION
   Heed Fellowship: 2516
Heim (Leo) Presidential Scholarships: 749
HEINRICH HERTZ-STIFTUNG: 917
Heinz (Elgin) Award: 866
HEINZ (H.J.) COMPANY FOUNDATION: 156
Helton (Clinton J.) Manufacturing Scholarship: 2616
HENAAC Scholars Program: 2609
Henderson (Edward) Student Award: 2547
HENDERSON FOUNDATION: 157
Henderson (Virginia) Clinical Research Grant: 2497
Henry (Alan F.)/Paul A. Greebler Memorial Graduate Scholarship: 2637
Henson (Richard A.) Award of Excellence: 1239
HERB SOCIETY OF AMERICA, INC. (THE): 2121
Herbert (Richard A.) Memorial Educational Fund: 2168
Heritage Fellowships: 895
HERITAGE FOUNDATION (THE)/B. KENNETH SIMON CENTER
   FOR AMERICAN STUDIES
   Research Fellowship in American Studies: 2001
HERITAGE PRESERVATION
   Conservation Assessment Program: 725
Heritage Program: 1271
HERSHEY (THE JACOB AND TERESE) FOUNDATION : 2183
Hesch (Wayne E.) Memorial Scholarships: 2605
HESS (WILLIAM G. AND MYRTLE E.) CHARITABLE TRUST: 995,
1554
HEUERMANN (B. KEITH & NORMA F.) FOUNDATION: 158
Hewins (The Caroline M.) Scholarship: 723
Hewitt (Barnard) Award: 526
HEWLETT (THE WILLIAM AND FLORA) FOUNDATION
   Education: 159
   Environment: 159
   Global Development and Population: 159
   Performing Arts: 159
   Philanthropy: 159
Hibernian Research Award: 589
Higgins (Colin) Youth Courage Awards: 1387
HIGGINSON (CORINA) TRUST: 160
High Impact: 133
High School Research Fellowship (The): 2153
High School Scholarships: 1766
Higher Education Grant Program for American Indians: 1046
HIGHER EDUCATION STUDENT ASSISTANCE AUTHORITY (THE)
   Law Enforcement Officer Memorial Scholarship: 1695
   New Jersey Student Tuition Assistance Reward Scholarship: 1695
   New Jersey Student Tuition Assistance Reward Scholarship II: 1695
   New Jersey World Trade Center Scholarship: 1695
   Survivor Tuition Benefits Program: 1694
   Tuition Aid Grant (TAG): 1693
Hill (Errol) Award: 526
Hill (Reuben) Award: 1498
HILLBLOM (THE LARRY L.) FOUNDATION, INC.
   Fellowship Research Grants: 2268
   Start-Up Research Grants: 2268
Hillman Prizes in Journalism: 1936
HILLMAN (THE SIDNEY) FOUNDATION, INC.
   Hillman Prizes in Journalism: 1936
   Sidney Awards: 1936
HILLSDALE COUNTY COMMUNITY FOUNDATION: 1299
HILLSDALE FUND INC.: 161
HIMSS FOUNDATION
   HIMSS Foundation Scholarship Program: 2269
HIMSS Foundation Scholarship Program: 2269
Hirsch (The Jacob) Fellowship in Archaeology: 886
Hispanic American Scholarship Program: 1063
HISPANIC BAR ASSOCIATION OF D.C. FOUNDATION (THE)
   HBA-DC Foundation Fellowship (The): 1980
HISPANIC DENTAL ASSOCIATION FOUNDATION
   A-dec Scholarship: 2349
   Colgate-Palmolive Scholarship: 2349
   Procter & Gamble Scholarship: 2349
   Villarreal (Dr. Juan D.) Scholarship: 2349
HISPANIC NATIONAL BAR FOUNDATION
   Future Latino Leaders Law Camp: 1982
   HNBF Princeton Review Duard Bradshaw Memorial Scholarship: 1981
HISPANIC SCHOLARSHIP FUND
   Gates Millennium Scholars Program: 1068
   General College Scholarship Program: 1068
HISTIOCYTOSIS ASSOCIATION
   Research Grant Program: 2363

HISTORIC NEW ORLEANS COLLECTION (THE)
   Williams (Kemper and Leila) Prize in Louisiana History: 595
   Woest (The Dianne) Fellowship in the Arts and Humanities: 594
Historic Preservation Grant: 182
Historic Properties Fund: 621
History of Pharmacy Thesis Research Grants-in-Aid: 2537
HISTORY OF SCIENCE SOCIETY
   Davis (Watson) and Helen Miles Davis Prize: 597
   Hazen (Joseph H.) Education Prize: 597
   Levinson (Suzanne J.) Prize: 597
   Pfizer Prize: 597
   Price (Derek)/Rod Webster Prize: 596
   Reingold (Nathan) Prize: 597
   Rossiter (Margaret W.) History of Women in Science Prize: 597
   Sarton Medal: 597
HITACHI FOUNDATION (THE)
   Entrepreneurship @ Work: SOURCE: 162
   Good Companies @ Work Program: 162
HMC Partnership Awards - Children's Mental Health: 2267
HNBF Princeton Review Duard Bradshaw Memorial Scholarship: 1981
HOBLITZELLE FOUNDATION: 163
Hobson (G. Vernon) Bequest: 2678
Hochberg (Ruth) Scholarship: 2563
Hodges (Kae Debrent) Fund: 2612
Hoey (Fred) Scholarship: 784
Hoffberger School of Painting (MFA): 555
HOFFMAN (MAXIMILIAN E. & MARION O.) FOUNDATION, INC.:
2270
HOLLAND & KNIGHT CHARITABLE FOUNDATION, INC.
   Young Native Writers Essay Contest: 1050
   Holocaust Remembrance Project: 598
Hollenback (Rand P.) Scholarship Program: 2544
Hollinshead (Marilyn) Fellowship: 508
Holocaust Remembrance Project: 598
Hologgitas (Joanne V.) Ph.D., Past Grand President, Scholarship
   (Undergraduate): 1080
Holt (Caroline E.) Nursing Scholarship: 2494
HOME DEPOT FOUNDATION (THE)
   Community Impact Grants Program: 1300
   Framing Hope Program: 1300
   Sustainable Community Development Program: 1300
   Team Depot: 1300
Homeland Security Award: 1477
HONIG (VICTOR AND LORRAINE) FUND: 1485
HONOR SOCIETY OF PHI KAPPA PHI (THE)
   Phi Kappa Phi Fellowship (The): 1696
HOOD (CHARLES H.) FOUNDATION, INC.
   Child Health Research Awards Program: 2529
Hook (The Sidney) Memorial Award: 1636
Hooper Memorial Scholarship: 1914
HOOVER (HERBERT) PRESIDENTIAL LIBRARY ASSOCIATION,
INC.
   Hoover (Herbert) Presidential Travel Grant Program: 2002
Hoover (Herbert) Presidential Travel Grant Program: 2002
Hopewell Agave Chapter #224 Scholarship (Undergraduate): 1080
Hopscotch House Artist Retreat Center: 1086
HORIZONS FOUNDATION
   Horizons Foundation Scholarship Program: 1084
Horizons Foundation Scholarship Program: 1084
Hornback (Miriam L.) Scholarship: 1616
HOROWITZ FOUNDATION FOR SOCIAL POLICY (THE): 1855
HORTICULTURAL RESEARCH INSTITUTE, INC.
   Akehurst (Carville M.) Memorial Scholarship: 1697
   Bigelow (Timothy) and Palmer W. Bigelow, Jr. Scholarship: 1697
   HRI Competitive Grants Program: 2122
   Muggets Scholarship: 1697
   Spring Meadow Nursery Scholarship: 1697
Horton Fellowship: 562
Horton-Hallowell Fellowship: 1097
Horwitz (The Louisa Gross) Prize: 2143
Housing and Economic Development: 1192
HOUSING EDUCATION AND RESEARCH ASSOCIATION (HERA)
   Agan (Tessie) Award Competition: 1301
HOUSTON ENDOWMENT INC.: 164
HOWARD (THE GEORGE A. AND ELIZA GARDNER)
   FOUNDATION: 1632
Howard (Peggy) Fellowship in Economics: 1097
Howe (C.D.) Scholarships: 1668
Howell (William B.) Memorial Scholarship: 2601
Hoy (Christopher J.)/ERT Scholarship: 1616
Hoyt Fellowship: 809

HRI Competitive Grants Program: 2122
Hubbard Scholarship: 722
Hubble Fellowship Program: 2058
HUDSON RIVER FOUNDATION (THE)
    Hudson River Fund: 2184
    Hudson River Improvement Fund: 2184
    New York City Environmental Fund: 2184
Hudson River Fund: 2184
Hudson River Improvement Fund: 2184
HUDSON-WEBBER FOUNDATION: 1302
HUEBNER (THE S.S.) FOUNDATION FOR INSURANCE
    EDUCATION: 1899
HUGHES (HOWARD) MEDICAL INSTITUTE
    Medical Research Fellows Program: 2271
HUGHES (MABEL Y.) CHARITABLE TRUST: 165
HUGOTON FOUNDATION: 1441
Human Development: 1192
HUMAN FRONTIER SCIENCE PROGRAM ORGANIZATION
    Career Development Award: 2147
    Cross-Disciplinary Fellowships: 2147
    Long-Term Fellowships: 2147
    Program Grants: 2147
    Young Investigator Grants: 2147
HUMAN GROWTH FOUNDATION
    Small Grants for Research in Field of Short Stature: 2530
Human Rights and Economic Justice: 141
Human Rights Program: 173
Human Service - Other: 1355
Human Service Health: 1355
Human Services: 133
HUMANA FOUNDATION (THE): 166
Humane Studies Fellowships: 2003
Humanitarian Project Development Grants: 2392
Humanitarian Project Support: 2341
Humanitarian Recognition Awards: 2392
Humanities Program: 366
Humanities Resource Center: 363
HUMBOLDT AREA FOUNDATION
    Community Building Grants: 1303
    Community Response Grants: 1303
    Field of Interest Grant Program: 1303
    Summer Youth Program: 1303
Humboldt Research Awards for Foreign Scholars: 1657
Humboldt Research Fellowship for Experienced Researchers: 871
Humboldt Research Fellowship for Postdoctoral Researchers: 1615
Humphrey (Hugh) Award: 1228
Hunger Project (The): 1267
Hunt (The Richard Morris) Fellowship: 409
HUNTER (A.V.) TRUST, INC.: 1486
Hunter (Amy Louise) Fellowship: 646
HUNTINGTON FOUNDATION, INC. (THE): 372
HUNTINGTON (HENRY E.) LIBRARY AND ART GALLERY
    Research Awards at the Huntington Library and Art Gallery: 373
Huntington's Disease Research: 2466
HUNTINGTON'S DISEASE SOCIETY OF AMERICA, INC.
    HD Human Biology Project: 2466
    Huntington's Disease Research: 2466
    King (Donald) Summer Research Fellowship: 2466
Hursky Fellowship: 1762
HUSTON (THE STEWART) CHARITABLE TRUST: 814
HUTCHINSON COMMUNITY FOUNDATION: 458
HYAMS FOUNDATION (THE): 1487
HYDE AND WATSON FOUNDATION (THE): 167

I

IACI Visiting Fellowship in Irish Studies at NUI-G: 675
IACI/NUI-G: 851
IAIA Merit Scholarship: 1051
IAIA Tuition Scholarship: 1051
IAICDV Annual Scholarship: 1555
IAPA Scholarship Fund: 1937
IARS Mentored Research Awards: 2272
IASA Memorial Fellowship: 601
IBM Herman Goldstine Memorial Postdoctoral Fellowship for Research in
    Mathematical and Computer Sciences: 2095
IBM THOMAS J. WATSON RESEARCH CENTER
    IBM Herman Goldstine Memorial Postdoctoral Fellowship for Research
    in Mathematical and Computer Sciences: 2095
ICS Scholarship: 2273

IDA/David L. Wolper Student Documentary Achievement Award: 462
IDAHO COMMISSION ON THE ARTS
    Arts Education Projects: 459
    Directory of Teaching Artists: 459
    Entry Track: 459
    Fellowships: 459
    Public Programs in the Arts: 459
    Quick Fund$: 459
    Traditional Arts Apprenticeship Program: 459
    Tumblewords: 459
    Writer-in-Residence Program: 459
IDAHO COMMUNITY FOUNDATION
    Deer Creek Fund Grants: 168
    Geography Grants: 168
    IFFT Fund Grants: 168
    Northern, Eastern and Southwestern Region Competitive Grants: 168
    Shelton (Perc H.) and Gladys A. Pospisil Shelton Foundation Advised
        Fund Grants: 168
IDDINGS BENEVOLENT TRUST: 169
IDRC Doctoral Research Awards (IDRA): 1304
IDRC Research Awards: 1305
IEEE
    IEEE Fellowship in the History of Electrical and Computing
        Technology: 599
    Internship in Electrical History: 599
IEEE Fellowship in the History of Electrical and Computing Technology:
    599
IES Abroad Boren and Gilman Scholarship Support Grants (The): 1700
IES Abroad Merit-Based Scholarships: 1700
IFFT Fund Grants: 168
IFUW Recognition Award: 1085
IIE Council of Fellows Undergraduate Scholarship: 2653
ILLINOIS ARTS COUNCIL: 460
ILLINOIS CLEAN ENERGY COMMUNITY FOUNDATION: 2185
ILLINOIS RESTAURANT ASSOCIATION EDUCATIONAL
    FOUNDATION
    IRA Educational Foundation Scholarship Program: 1698
ILLINOIS STATE ACADEMY OF SCIENCE
    Scientific Research Grants/Proposal Writing Contest: 1822
Imagine America Adult Skills Education Program (ASEP): 1965
IMAGINE AMERICA FOUNDATION
    Imagine America Adult Skills Education Program (ASEP): 1965
    Imagine America High School Scholarship Program: 1965
    Imagine America LDRSHIP Award: 1965
    Imagine America Military Award Program (MAP): 1965
    Imagine America Promise Scholarship Program: 1965
Imagine America High School Scholarship Program: 1965
Imagine America LDRSHIP Award: 1965
Imagine America Military Award Program (MAP): 1965
Imagine America Promise Scholarship Program: 1965
Imhoff (John L.) Scholarship: 2653
IMMANUEL BIBLE FOUNDATION: 815
IMMUNE DEFICIENCY FOUNDATION: 996
    U.S. Immunodeficiency Network: 2337
Impact Award: 204
Impact Teacher Grants: 1527
INDEPENDENCE FOUNDATION
    Individual Artists Fellowship/Performing and Visual Arts: 2491
    New Theater Works Initiative: 2491
    Public Interest Law Fellowships: 2491
Independent Grant Awards: 1029
Independent Investigator Grant: 2575
Independent Program: 531
Independent Scientist Awards (K02): 1453
India Studies Fellowship Competition: 941
Indian Education-Formula Grants to Local Education Agencies (LEAs):
    1057
Indian Employment Assistance: 1055
Indiana AIDS Fund: 1436
INDIANA ARTS COMMISSION: 461
INDIANA COMMISSION FOR HIGHER EDUCATION, DIVISION OF
    STUDENT FINANCIAL AID
    Daniels (Mitch) Early Graduation Scholarship: 1699
    EARN Indiana (State Work Study): 1699
    Minority Teacher Scholarship: 1699
    National Guard Grant: 1699
    O'Bannon (The Frank) Grant: 1699
    Student Teaching Stipend for High-Needs Fields: 1699
    Student Teaching Stipend for Minorities: 1699
    21st Century Scholars Program: 1699

INDIANA LIBRARY FEDERATION
  Schlundt (The Esther) Fund: 726
  Weller (The Sue Marsh) Fund: 726
Individual Advanced Research Opportunities (IARO): 920
Individual Artist Awards: 471
Individual Artist Fellowship: 469
Individual Artist Fellowships: 445, 482
Individual Artist Grants and Services: Traditional Arts Apprenticeships: 492
Individual Artist Professional Development Grants: 523
Individual Artist Support Grants: 1089
Individual Artists: 465
Individual Artists Fellowship Grants: 494
Individual Artists Fellowship/Performing and Visual Arts: 2491
Individual Artists Fellowships: 491
Individual NRSA Postdoctoral Fellowships (F-32): 2351
Individual NRSA Senior Fellowship Award (F-33): 2353
Individual Research Grants: 799, 2026
Individual Support Program: 550
Informal Science Education (ISE) (AISL): 1607
Innovation Award: 2403
Innovative Research Grants: 2450
Innovative Teaching Award: 1878
Innovative Technology Experiences for Students and Teachers (ITEST): 1607
Innovator Awards in Cancer Research: 2424
INSTITUTE FOR ADVANCED STUDIES IN THE HUMANITIES (THE)
  Visiting Research Fellowships: 374
INSTITUTE FOR ADVANCED STUDY
  School of Social Science Fellowships: 1856
INSTITUTE FOR HUMANE STUDIES (IHS)
  Humane Studies Fellowships: 2003
  Koch (Charles G.) Summer Fellowship: 2003
INSTITUTE FOR QUANTITATIVE SOCIAL SCIENCE, HARVARD UNIVERSITY
  Block (Jeanne Humphrey) Dissertation Award: 1857
INSTITUTE FOR SUPPLY MANAGEMENT
  ISM Dissertation Research Grant - Phase 1 (Doctoral): 1900
INSTITUTE FOR THE INTERNATIONAL EDUCATION OF STUDENTS (IES)
  IES Abroad Boren and Gilman Scholarship Support Grants (The): 1700
  IES Abroad Merit-Based Scholarships: 1700
Institute for Trustees: 1267
Institute of American Cultures Fellowship Program: 1069
Institute of American Cultures Grant: 1061
INSTITUTE OF AMERICAN INDIAN ARTS (IAIA)
  IAIA Merit Scholarship: 1051
  IAIA Tuition Scholarship: 1051
INSTITUTE OF CURRENT WORLD AFFAIRS: 849
INSTITUTE OF FOOD TECHNOLOGISTS FOUNDATION
  Freshman Scholarships: 2610
  Graduate Scholarships: 2610
  Undergraduate Scholarships: 2610
INSTITUTE OF INDUSTRIAL ENGINEERS (IIE)
  CIE Undergraduate Scholarship: 2653
  Fargher (John S.W.) Scholarship: 2653
  Gambrell (C.B.) Undergraduate Scholarship: 2653
  Garden (Dwight D.) Scholarship: 2653
  Gilbreth Memorial Fellowship: 2653
  IIE Council of Fellows Undergraduate Scholarship: 2653
  Imhoff (John L.) Scholarship: 2653
  Marcus (Harold and Inge) Scholarship: 2653
  Mundel (Marvin) Memorial Scholarship: 2653
  Presidents Scholarship: 2653
  Putnam (A.O.) Memorial Scholarship: 2653
  Sierleja (E.J.) Memorial Fellowship: 2653
  Society for Health Systems Scholarship: 2653
  United Parcel Service Scholarship for Female Students: 2653
  United Parcel Service Scholarship for Minority Students: 2653
  Zaken (Lisa) Award of Excellence: 2653
INSTITUTE OF INTERNATIONAL EDUCATION
  Padagogischer Austauschdienst Teaching Assistantships: 654
  U.S. Department of State Fulbright U.S. Student Program: 918
INSTITUTE OF MATERIALS, MINERALS AND MINING
  Centenary Scholarship: 2678
  Elmore (Stanley) Fellowship Fund: 2678
  Hobson (G. Vernon) Bequest: 2678
  Mining Club Award: 2678

  Pam (Edgar) Fellowship: 2678
  Seaman (The Tom) Travelling Scholarship: 2678
  Smith (Bosworth) Trust Fund: 2678
INSTITUTE OF MUSEUM AND LIBRARY SERVICES
  Bush (Laura) 21st Century Librarian Program: 728
  Conservation Assessment Program: 727
  Museum Assessment Program: 727
  Museum Grants for African American History and Culture: 728
  Museums for America: 728
  National Leadership Grants: 727
  National Medal for Museum and Library Services: 727
  Native American Library Services: Basic Grants: 727
  Native American Library Services: Enhancement Grants: 728
  Native American/Native Hawaiian Museum Services Program: 728
  Native Hawaiian Library Services Grant: 727
  Sparks! Ignition Grants for Libraries: 727
  Sparks! Ignition Grants for Museums: 727
Institutional Accountability and Individual Liberty: 282
Institutional Program Unifying Population and Laboratory Based Sciences: 2244
Institutional Project Support Program for Japanese Studies: 852
Institutional Research Grants: 2426
Institutional Support: 491
INTEL FOUNDATION: 170
Intel Science Talent Search: 1840
INTER AMERICAN PRESS ASSOCIATION (IAPA)
  IAPA Scholarship Fund: 1937
Inter-American Music Awards: 790
INTERCOLLEGIATE STUDIES INSTITUTE (THE)
  Bache-Renshaw Fellowship: 2004
  Salvatori Fellowship: 2004
  Weaver (Richard M.) Fellowship: 2004
  Western Civilization Fellowship: 2004
Intern Program at Jacob's Pillow (The): 532
International: 1495
International Affairs Education Program: 173
International Affairs Fellowship (IAF): 839
International Affairs Fellowship in Japan (IAF-J): 838
International Affairs Fellowship in Nuclear Security (IAF-NS): 841
International Affairs Fellowship in South Korea (IAF-SK): 840
INTERNATIONAL ANESTHESIA RESEARCH SOCIETY (IARS)
  Anesthesiology Teaching Recognition Awards: 2272
  Frontiers in Anesthesia Research Award: 2272
  IARS Mentored Research Awards: 2272
INTERNATIONAL ASSOCIATION FOR DENTAL RESEARCH
  Colgate Oral Health Research Award: 2350
INTERNATIONAL ASSOCIATION FOR FOOD PROTECTION
  Barnum (Harold) Industry Award: 2673
  Food Safety Innovation Award: 2673
  Haverland (Harry) Citation Award: 2673
  International Service Award: 2673
  Marth (Elmer) Educator Award: 2673
  Sanitarian Award: 2673
  State or Local Health or State Agricultural Department Employees Travel Award: 2673
  Student Travel Scholarship Award: 2673
  Weber (Maurice) Laboratorian Award: 2673
International Association of Fire Chiefs Foundation Scholarship Program: 1701
INTERNATIONAL ASSOCIATION OF FIRE CHIEFS FOUNDATION, INC.
  International Association of Fire Chiefs Foundation Scholarship Program: 1701
INTERNATIONAL ASSOCIATION OF ICE CREAM DISTRIBUTORS AND VENDORS
  IAICDV Annual Scholarship: 1555
International Biodiversity: 2212
International Cancer Technology Transfer Fellowships (ICRETT): 2449
INTERNATIONAL CENTRE FOR COMPARATIVE CRIMINOLOGY
  Research Fieldwork: 1408
INTERNATIONAL CENTRE FOR DIFFRACTION DATA
  Frevel (The Ludo) Crystallography Scholarship Award: 2679
International Collaborative Research Grants: 2029
INTERNATIONAL COLLEGE OF SURGEONS
  ICS Scholarship: 2273
International Concert Artists Competition: 769
INTERNATIONAL CRANE FOUNDATION, INC.: 2148
INTERNATIONAL DEVELOPMENT RESEARCH CENTRE (IDRC)
  Bene (John G.) Fellowship in Community Forestry: Trees and People: 2123

References in index are to entry numbers.

Bentley Cropping Systems Fellowship (The): 919
IDRC Doctoral Research Awards (IDRA): 1304
IDRC Research Awards: 1305
International Dissertation Research Fellowship Program (IDRF): 859
International Dissertation Research Grant: 799
International Doctoral Scholarship for Studies Specializing in Jewish
   Fields: 820
INTERNATIONAL DOCUMENTARY ASSOCIATION
   ABC News Videosource Award: 462
   IDA/David L. Wolper Student Documentary Achievement Award: 462
   Lorentz (Pare) Award: 462
International Education Exchange Program: 2546
INTERNATIONAL EXECUTIVE HOUSEKEEPERS ASSOCIATION
   (THE)
   330-Hour Self Study Program: 2611
INTERNATIONAL FEDERATION OF UNIVERSITY WOMEN
   British Federation Crosby Hall Fellowship: 1085
   CFUW/A. Vibert Douglas Fellowship: 1085
   Cullis (Winifred) Grant: 1085
   IFUW Recognition Award: 1085
   Leet (Dorothy) Grant: 1085
   MacLean (Ida Smedley) Fellowship: 1085
   NZFGW Daphne Purves Grant: 1085
International Fellowship in Jewish Studies and Jewish Culture: 820
INTERNATIONAL FOOD SERVICE EXECUTIVES ASSOCIATION,
   INC. (IFSEA)
   Hodges (Kae Debrent) Fund: 2612
   Worthy Goal Scholarship: 2612
INTERNATIONAL FOUNDATION (THE): 850
INTERNATIONAL FOUNDATION FOR ETHICAL RESEARCH, INC.:
   1823
International Fund: 978
International Health: 2352
International Leaders in Education Program (ILEP): 920
INTERNATIONAL MYELOMA FOUNDATION (IMF)
   Novis (Brian D.) Research Grants: 2274
INTERNATIONAL OCD FOUNDATION
   Annual Conference: 2579
   Behavior Therapy Training Institute (BTTI): 2579
   Research Awards: 2579
International Operators Scholarship: 2624
INTERNATIONAL ORDER OF ALHAMBRA
   Scholarship and Charity Fund: 2552
International Postgraduate Research Scholarships (IPRS): 950
International Program in Health Policy and Innovation: 1478
INTERNATIONAL READING ASSOCIATION
   Chall (Jeanne S.) Research Fellowship: 1557
   Feitelson (Dina) Research Award: 1557
   Grants for Literacy Projects in Countries with Developing Economies:
   1556
   IRA Jerry Johns Outstanding Teacher Educator in Reading Award: 1556
   IRA Regie Routman Teacher Recognition Grant: 1556
   Knight (Elva) Research Grant: 1557
   National Affiliate Conference Grants: 1556
   Outstanding Dissertation of the Year Award: 1557
   Robinson (Helen M.) Grant: 1557
   Stahl (Steven A.) Research Grant: 1557
   Teacher as Researcher Grant: 1557
INTERNATIONAL RESEARCH & EXCHANGES BOARD (IREX)
   ECA Alumni Small Grants Program: 920
   Eurasia/South Asia Teaching Excellence and Achievement Program
   (TEA): 920
   Global Undergraduate Exchange Program in Eurasia and Central Asia
   (UGRAD): 920
   Individual Advanced Research Opportunities (IARO): 920
   International Leaders in Education Program (ILEP): 920
   Muskie (Edmund S.) Graduate Fellowship Program: 920
   Short-Term Travel Grants: 920
International Research and Studies Grant Program: 1592
International Research Grants Award: 2481
INTERNATIONAL ROAD FEDERATION
   IRF Fellowship Program: 959
International Scholarship: 2563
International Scholarships: 1666
International Security and Foreign Policy Program: 1868
International Semester and Year Programs: 954
International Service Award: 2673
International Summer Program (Summer Campus Strobl/St.
   Wolfgang/Austria): 942

INTERNATIONAL UNION FOR VACUUM SCIENCE, TECHNIQUE
   AND APPLICATIONS (IUVSTA)
   Welch (M.W.) International Scholarship: 2036
INTERNATIONAL WOMEN'S FISHING ASSOCIATION
   SCHOLARSHIP TRUST
   IWFA Scholarship Trust: 2078
International Youth Competition: 769
Internship in Electrical History: 599
Internship Program: 784
Interpretive Fellowships: 552
INVENT NOW
   Collegiate Inventors Competition: 1824
INVESTED
   InvestED School Fund Program: 1603
InvestED School Fund Program: 1603
INVESTIGATIVE REPORTERS AND EDITORS
   Investigative Reporters and Editors Contest: 1938
Investigative Reporters and Editors Contest: 1938
Investigator Grant: 2523
Investigator Initiated Grants: 1127
Investigator Initiated Grants (IIG): 2427
Investigator-Initiated Research Grants: 2452
Investigators in the Pathogenesis of Infectious Disease: 2244
Investment Management Services: 1329
Investments in Arts and Culture (AIC): 497
IODE
   War Memorial Scholarships: 1702
IOWA ARTS COUNCIL
   Arts Resources and Artists Programs: 463
   Funding and Arts in Education Programs: 463
   Technical Assistance and Community Development Programs: 463
Iowa Short Fiction Award (The): 701
IRA Educational Foundation Scholarship Program: 1698
IRA Jerry Johns Outstanding Teacher Educator in Reading Award: 1556
IRA Regie Routman Teacher Recognition Grant: 1556
Iraq and Afghanistan Service Grant: 1771
IRF Fellowship Program: 959
IRISH AMERICAN CULTURAL INSTITUTE
   IACI Visiting Fellowship in Irish Studies at NUI-G: 675
   IACI/NUI-G: 851
IRMAS (AUDREY AND SYDNEY) CHARITABLE FOUNDATION:
   1306
IRVINE HEALTH FOUNDATION: 1442
Irvington Institute Fellowship Program of the Cancer Research Institute:
   2430
ISCTR-ACCF Cardiovascular Translational Research Scholarship: 2375
ISM Dissertation Research Grant - Phase 1 (Doctoral): 1900
Israel Grants: 1308
ISTITUTO ITALIANO PER GLI STUDI STORICI
   Federico II Scholarship: 600
   Scholarships Istituto italiano per gli studi storici for Graduate Students
   and Young Postdocs, Italian and Foreign: 600
ITALIAN AMERICAN STUDIES ASSOCIATION
   IASA Memorial Fellowship: 601
ITTLESON FOUNDATION, INC.: 1488
IWFA Scholarship Trust: 2078

J

JACK AND JILL OF AMERICA FOUNDATION (THE)
   Greer (Violet D.) Grant Awards: 1029
   Independent Grant Awards: 1029
   Robinson (Jacqueline) Regional Competition Grant Awards: 1029
JACKSON (ANN) FAMILY FOUNDATION: 171
JACKSON FOUNDATION (THE): 172
JACKSON (HENRY M.) FOUNDATION
   Environmental and Natural Resources Management Program: 173
   Human Rights Program: 173
   International Affairs Education Program: 173
   Public Service Program: 173
JACKSON LABORATORY (THE)
   Postdoctoral Program at the Jackson Laboratory: 2149
JACKSON (RUTH) ORTHOPAEDIC SOCIETY
   Perry (Jacquelin), MD Resident Research Award: 2553
   RJOS Traveling Fellowships: 2553
Jackson (The William E.) Award: 2627
JACKSONVILLE JAGUARS FOUNDATION: 174
JACL National Scholarship and Awards Program: 1704

JACOB'S PILLOW DANCE FESTIVAL, INC.
  Intern Program at Jacob's Pillow (The): 532
  School at Jacob's Pillow (The): 532
Jacobs Research Funds Small Grants Program: 2030
Jacques (Harry and Laura) Bursary: 2090
Jahnigen (Dennis W.) Memorial Award: 2547
James (Olivia) Traveling Fellowship: 351
Jameson (J. Franklin) Award: 578
Jameson (The J. Franklin) Fellowship: 579
Jamestown Prize: 624
Jane's Fellowship Program: 1363
Janeway (Ray C.) Scholarship: 741
Jansky Fellowships at the NRAO: 2054
JAPAN FOUNDATION (THE)
  Doctoral Fellowship: 852
  Institutional Project Support Program for Japanese Studies: 852
  JFNY Grant for Japanese Studies: 852
  JFNY Grant Program - Arts and Culture: 852
  Performing Arts Japan Program: 852
  Research Fellowship: 852
  Short-Term Research Fellowship: 852
  Support Program for Translation and Publication on Japan: 852
JAPAN FOUNDATION, LOS ANGELES (THE)
  Exhibitions Abroad Support Program: 1703
  Program for the Donation of Japanese Language Teaching Materials (for the United States): 1703
  Translation and Publication Support Program: 1703
JAPAN INFORMATION CENTER
  Japanese Government (Monbukagakusho) Scholarships for Japanese Studies: 921
  Japanese Government (Monbukagakusho) Scholarships for Research Students: 922
Japan Society for the Promotion of Science Postdoctoral Research Fellowships (Extramural): 966
JAPAN-U.S. FRIENDSHIP COMMISSION: 853
Japan-U.S. Senate Youth Exchange Program: 954
JAPANESE AMERICAN CITIZENS LEAGUE (JACL) (THE)
  JACL National Scholarship and Awards Program: 1704
  Masaoka (Mike M.) Fellowship Fund Congressional Program: 2005
  Schaar (Ruby Yoshino) Playwright Award: 533
Japanese Government (Monbukagakusho) Scholarships for Japanese Studies: 921
Japanese Government (Monbukagakusho) Scholarships for Research Students: 922
Jazz Touring Network: 476
JEFFRESS (THOMAS F. AND KATE MILLER) MEMORIAL TRUST
  Jeffress Trust Awards Program in Interdisciplinary Research: 2108
Jeffress Trust Awards Program in Interdisciplinary Research: 2108
JELLISON BENEVOLENT SOCIETY: 1558
JENKINS FOUNDATION (THE): 1443
Jenkins Foundation: Improving the Health of Greater Richmond (The): 1213
JENNINGS (MARTHA HOLDEN) FOUNDATION
  Grants-to-Educators Program: 1604
  Open Grants: 1604
Jenny (Daniel P.) Research Fellowships: 2662
Jensen (Susanne) Scholarship: 2563
Jensen (The Walter J.) Fellowship for French Language, Literature and Culture: 935
Jerome Fellowships: 696
JEROME FOUNDATION, INC.: 464
Jerome Planning Grant for Arts: 450
Jerome Project Grant for Emerging Artists: 450
Jessup Fellowship: 2135
JEWEL-OSCO: 1307
JEWISH BOOK COUNCIL
  National Jewish Book Award-American Jewish Studies: 676
  National Jewish Book Award-Anthologies and Collections: 676
  National Jewish Book Award-Biography, Autobiography and Memoir: 676
  National Jewish Book Award-Children's and Young Adult Literature: 676
  National Jewish Book Award-Contemporary Jewish Life: 676
  National Jewish Book Award-Education and Jewish Identity: 676
  National Jewish Book Award-Fiction: 676
  National Jewish Book Award-History: 676
  National Jewish Book Award-Holocaust: 676
  National Jewish Book Award-Illustrated Children's Book: 676
  National Jewish Book Award-Modern Jewish Thought and Experience: 676
  National Jewish Book Award-Outstanding Debut Fiction: 676

  National Jewish Book Award-Poetry: 676
  National Jewish Book Award-Scholarship: 676
  National Jewish Book Award-Sephardic Culture: 676
  National Jewish Book Award-Visual Arts: 676
  National Jewish Book Award-Women's Studies: 676
  National Jewish Book Award-Writing Based on Archival Materials: 676
  Rohr (Sami) Prize for Jewish Literature: 677
JEWISH COMMUNAL SERVICE ASSOCIATION OF NORTH AMERICA
  Edell (Norman) Scholarship: 1559
  Graduate Student Network: 1559
  Local Groups Network: 1559
  Mandelkorn Distinguished Service Award: 1559
  Professional Development Programs: 1559
  Young Professional Award: 1559
JEWISH COMMUNITY FOUNDATION OF LOS ANGELES
  Capital Grants: 1308
  Cutting Edge Grants: 1308
  General Community Grants: 1308
  Israel Grants: 1308
JEWISH FAMILY AND CHILDREN'S SERVICES
  Educational Loans & Grants Program: 1705
JEWISH HEALTHCARE FOUNDATION OF PITTSBURGH (THE): 1444
Jewish Life and Values: 90
Jewson (Ruth) Award: 1498
JFNY Grant for Japanese Studies: 852
JFNY Grant Program - Arts and Culture: 852
JILA
  Postdoctoral Research Associateships: 2037
  Visiting Fellowships: 2037
JOHNS HOPKINS CENTER FOR ALTERNATIVES TO ANIMAL TESTING (THE): 1445
Johns (Hyland) Grant: 2129
Johnson (Alvin H.) AMS 50 Dissertation Fellowships: 752
JOHNSON & JOHNSON FAMILY OF COMPANIES: 175
JOHNSON CONTROLS FOUNDATION: 176
Johnson (Lyndon B.) School of Public Affairs: 1646
JOHNSON (THE LYNDON BAINES) FOUNDATION
  Middleton Fellowship in Presidential Studies: 2006
  Moody Research Grants: 2006
Johnson (Magic) Foundation HIV/AIDS Grant: 177
JOHNSON (MAGIC) FOUNDATION, INC.
  Johnson (Magic) Foundation HIV/AIDS Grant: 177
  Michaels (Taylor) Scholarship: 177
JOHNSON (ROBERT WOOD) FOUNDATION: 2275
JOHNSON (WALTER S.) FOUNDATION: 1560
Joint Grant Awards Program: 2221
JONES (DAISY MARQUIS) FOUNDATION: 178
JONES (THE FLETCHER) FOUNDATION: 1633
Jones (Judy B. and David M.) Scholarship Fund: 1224
Jordan (Cheryl) Scholarship Fund: 2546
JOSLYN (THE CARL W. AND CARRIE MAE) CHARITABLE TRUST: 1489
JOURNAL OF THE AMERICAN MEDICAL ASSOCIATION
  Fishbein (Morris) Fellowship in Medical Editing: 1939
Journalism Awards Program: 1935
Journalism Foundation Scholarships: 1750
Journalism Program: 193, 219
JOYCE FOUNDATION (THE): 179
JPMORGAN CHASE FOUNDATION (THE): 180
Judaic and Related Studies Postdoctoral Fellowships: 923
Judicial Administration Fellowship Program: 1990
Jumpstart: 440
Junior Faculty Award: 2403
Junior Faculty Research Grants: 2570
Junior Faculty Scholar Award: 2235
Junior Fellowship: 876
Junior Fellowships: 419
Junior Ranger Program (The): 2190
JUVENILE DIABETES RESEARCH FOUNDATION INTERNATIONAL
  Career Development Awards: 2416
  Postdoctoral Fellowships: 2415
  Regular Research Grant: 2414
Juvenile Justice: 273
Juvenile Justice and Delinquency Prevention Allocation to States: 1413
Juvenile Justice and Delinquency Prevention Program: 1412

K

Kabis (Dorothy) Internship: 1091
Kagiwada (David Tamotsu) Memorial Fund: 808
Kahan (Gerald) Scholar's Prize: 526
Kalamazoo Chapter No. 116-Roscoe Douglas Scholarship: 2616
KALAMAZOO COMMUNITY FOUNDATION: 1309
Kanawha and Ohio River Valleys Program: 2211
KANSAS HEALTH FOUNDATION
  Recognition Grants: 1446
KANTOR (ALICE AND JULIUS) CHARITABLE TRUST: 181
KANTZLER FOUNDATION (THE): 1310
KAPLAN (THE J.M.) FUND, INC.
  City Life Grant: 182
  Discretionary Grants: 182
  Environment Program Grant: 182
  Furthermore Grant: 182
  Historic Preservation Grant: 182
  Migrations Grant: 182
Kaplan-Goodkind Memorial Scholarship Fund: 793
Kappa Epsilon-AFPE-Nellie Wakeman First Year Graduate Fellowship: 2536
KAPPA OMICRON NU HONOR SOCIETY
  Brown (Marjorie M.) Dissertation Fellowship: 2674
  Hawthorne (Ruth E.) Research Grant: 2674
  Kappa Omicron Phi/Hettie Margaret Anthony Fellowship: 2674
  LeaderShape Institute Award: 2674
  Maddex (Eileen C.) Fellowship: 2674
  National Alumni Chapter Fellowship: 2674
  National Alumni Chapter Grant: 2674
  National Scholar Program: 2674
  New Initiatives Grant: 2674
  Omicron Nu Master's Fellowship: 2674
  Omicron Nu Research Fellowship: 2674
  Root (Betty Jeanne) Fellowship: 2674
  Undergraduate Research: 2674
Kappa Omicron Phi/Hettie Margaret Anthony Fellowship: 2674
KAPPA TAU ALPHA
  Mott (Frank Luther) KTA Research/Book Award: 1940
Katz (The Friedrich) Prize: 578
KATZ (HERBERT D.) CENTER FOR ADVANCED JUDAIC STUDIES
  Judaic and Related Studies Postdoctoral Fellowships: 923
Kaufman (Lucille B.) Women's Scholarship: 2616
Kay (E. Wayne) Scholarships: 2616
KAZANJIAN (THE CALVIN K.) ECONOMICS FOUNDATION, INC.: 1901
KCC-JEE High School Essay Contest (The): 924
Keats (Ezra Jack) Children's Literature Research Fellowship Program: 704
Keats (Ezra Jack)/Janina Domanska Research Fellowship: 743
Keats (Ezra Jack)/Kerlan Collection Memorial Fellowship: 702
KELLENBERGER (MAY GORDON LATHAM) HISTORICAL FOUNDATION: 183
Keller (David) Travel Grants: 526
KELLEY (EDWARD BANGS) & ELZA KELLEY FOUNDATION, INC.: 1311
KELLOGG (W.K.) FOUNDATION: 184
Kelly (Ashley) Memorial Scholarship Fund: 1224
Kelly (Barbara Mandigo) Peace Poetry Awards: 855
Kelly (The Joan) Memorial Prize in Women's History: 578
Kempf Fund Award for Research Development in Psychobiological Psychiatry: 2564
KEMPNER (HARRIS AND ELIZA) FUND
  Matching Gifts Program: 185
  Primary Grant Program: 185
  Program Related Investments: 185
KENAN (WILLIAM R., JR.) CHARITABLE TRUST: 1561
Kendall (Florence P.) Doctoral Scholarships: 2551
KENNEDY (JOHN F.) PRESIDENTIAL LIBRARY
  Kennedy Library Archival Internships: 186
Kennedy Library Archival Internships: 186
KENNEDY MEMORIAL TRUST (THE)
  Kennedy Scholarships: 960
Kennedy (Robert F.) Book Award: 678
KENNEDY (ROBERT F.) CENTER FOR JUSTICE AND HUMAN RIGHTS
  Kennedy (Robert F.) Book Award: 678
  Kennedy (Robert F.) Journalism Award: 678
Kennedy (Robert F.) Journalism Award: 678
Kennedy Scholarships: 960

KENTUCKY ARTS COUNCIL
  Arts Education Programs: 465
  Arts Organizations: 465
  Community Arts: 465
  Individual Artists: 465
KENTUCKY FOUNDATION FOR WOMEN
  Art Meets Activism: 1086
  Artist Enrichment: 1086
  Hopscotch House Artist Retreat Center: 1086
KENTUCKY HISTORICAL SOCIETY
  Scholarly Research Fellowship Program: 602
KERR FOUNDATION, INC. (THE): 187
KERR (GRAYCE B.) FUND, INC.: 188
Kestnbaum (Robert) Research Program: 1904
KEWEENAW COMMUNITY FOUNDATION: 1312
Kezios (Agnes Malakate) Scholarship: 2646
Kidder (The Louise) Early Career Award: 1883
KIDNEY FOUNDATION OF CANADA (THE)
  Allied Health Doctoral Fellowship: 2419
  Allied Health Research Grant: 2418
  Allied Health Scholarship: 2420
  Biomedical Research Grant: 2417
Kids Do Matter (KDM): 1572
Killam (Izaak Walton) Memorial Postdoctoral Fellowship: 1776
Killam (Izaak Walton) Memorial Postdoctoral Research Fellowships: 1778
Killam (Izaak Walton) Predoctoral Scholarships: 1785
KIMBERLY-CLARK FOUNDATION, INC.: 189
Kimbrough (Arch and Anne Giles) Fund: 546
Kimmel (Jack) International Grant: 2129
King (Donald) Summer Research Fellowship: 2466
King (The Mackenzie) Open Scholarship: 1707
KING (MACKENZIE) SCHOLARSHIP TRUST
  King (The Mackenzie) Open Scholarship: 1707
  King (The Mackenzie) Traveling Scholarships: 1706
King (The Mackenzie) Traveling Scholarships: 1706
KING (STEPHEN AND TABITHA) FOUNDATION: 190
King (Steven G.) Play Environments Scholarship: 2186
Kinkeldey (The Otto) Award: 751
Kinley (Kate Neal) Memorial Fellowship: 574
KIRBY (F.M.) FOUNDATION, INC.: 191
Kirschstein (Ruth L.) National Research Service Awards (NRSA) for Individual Postdoctoral Fellows (Parent F32): 2292
Kirschstein (Ruth L.) National Research Service Awards (NRSA) for Individual Senior Fellows (Parent F33): 2294
KITSAP COMMUNITY FOUNDATION: 1313
Klausman (Jane M.) Women in Business Scholarships: 1919
KLEBERG (ROBERT J., JR.) AND HELEN C. KLEBERG FOUNDATION: 2276
Kleffner (Frank R.) Clinical Career Award: 2506
Klein (Martin A.) Prize in African History: 578
Kligman (Albert M.) Fellowship Fund Award: 2327
Kline Foundation Grants: 192
KLINE (JOSIAH W. AND BESSIE H.) FOUNDATION, INC.
  Kline Foundation Grants: 192
Klineberg (Otto) Intercultural and International Relations Award: 2015
KLINGENSTEIN CENTER FOR INDEPENDENT SCHOOL LEADERSHIP
  Klingenstein Heads Program: 1605
  Klingenstein Summer Institute: 1605
  Master's Degree in Educational Leadership: 1605
Klingenstein Heads Program: 1605
Klingenstein Summer Institute: 1605
KLINGENSTEIN THIRD GENERATION FOUNDATION (THE): 2580
Klumpke-Roberts Award: 2049
Knight-Bagehot Fellowship in Economics and Business Journalism: 1927
Knight (Elva) Research Grant: 1557
KNIGHT (JOHN S. AND JAMES L.) FOUNDATION
  Arts Program: 193
  Communities Program: 193
  Journalism Program: 193
  National Program: 193
Knight Science Journalism Fellowships: 1943
Knight-Wallace Fellows: 1964
KNIGHTS OF COLUMBUS
  Educational Trust Scholarships: 1708
  Greco (Bishop Charles P.) Graduate Fellowships: 1708
  McDevitt (John W.) Fourth Degree Scholarships: 1708
  Pro Deo and Pro Patria Scholarships: 1708
KNIGHTS OF COLUMBUS VATICAN FILM LIBRARY AT ST. LOUIS UNIVERSITY
  Vatican Film Library Mellon Fellowship: 679

KNOTT (MARION I. AND HENRY J.) FOUNDATION, INC.: 194
Knowledge Exchange Grants: 2215
Knowledge-to-Action Grant: 2215
Knox (Eileen) Memorial Scholarship: 1659
KOBE COLLEGE CORPORATION-JAPAN EDUCATION EXCHANGE
    KCC-JEE High School Essay Contest (The): 924
KOCH (CHARLES G.) CHARITABLE FOUNDATION: 1562
Koch (Charles G.) Summer Fellowship: 2003
KOCH FOUNDATION, INC.: 816
Koenig (The Msgr. Harry C.) Award for Catholic Biography: 802
Kohl's Cares® Scholarship Program: 1709
KOHL'S CORPORATION
    Kohl's Cares® Scholarship Program: 1709
KOMEN (SUSAN G.)
    Career Catalyst Research Grants: 2439
    Graduate Training in Disparities Research: 2439
    Postdoctoral Fellowship Grants: 2439
Kopf (Dr. Alfred W.) Research Grant Award: 2447
Koren (The William, Jr.) Prize: 634
KORET FOUNDATION: 195
Kosciuszko Foundation Graduate Studies and Research in Poland (The): 928
Kosciuszko Foundation Tuition Scholarship (The): 1710
Kosciuszko Foundation Year Abroad Program (The): 927
KOSCIUSZKO FOUNDATION, INC. (THE)
    Chopin Piano Competition: 770
    Kosciuszko Foundation Graduate Studies and Research in Poland (The): 928
    Kosciuszko Foundation Tuition Scholarship (The): 1710
    Kosciuszko Foundation Year Abroad Program (The): 927
    Summer Study Abroad Programs: 926
    Teaching English in Poland: 925
Kottis Family Scholarship (Undergraduate): 1080
Kovacs (Katherine Singer) Prize: 657
KPMG FOUNDATION
    KPMG Professorships: 1902
    Minority Accounting Doctoral Scholarships: 1902
    PhD Project (The): 1902
KPMG Professorships: 1902
Kraft (Henry Phillip) Memorial Fund-Environmental Grants: 1320
Kraus (Michael) Research Grant: 578
KRESGE FOUNDATION (THE): 196
Kress Publication Fellowships: 888
KRESS (SAMUEL H.) FOUNDATION
    Fellowships in Art Conservation: 552
    Interpretive Fellowships: 552
    Research Fellowships in Art History: 552
Kress (Samuel H.) Grants for Research and Publication in Classical Art and Architecture: 1665
Krim (Mathilde) Fellowships in Basic Biomedical Research: 1812
KROGER COMPANY FOUNDATION (THE): 1314
KRONKOSKY (ALBERT AND BESSIE MAE) CHARITABLE FOUNDATION
    Precious Minds, New Connections: 197
Krutilla (John V.) Research Stipend: 2199
Kuchinski (David A.) Memorial Research Grant: 2523
Kuehl (Harry and Shirley) Foundation Scholarship: 1659
Kummerow (Glenn) Memorial Scholarship: 1945
Kun Scholarship Fund: 793
KVAMME (THE JEAN AND E. FLOYD) FOUNDATION: 1563

L

L-3 Avionics Systems Scholarship: 2618
Labatt (John) Limited Scholarship: 1787
Laboratory-Graduate Program: 1814
Lacy (Robert G.) Memorial Scholarship: 2638
LADIES AUXILIARY TO THE VETERANS OF FOREIGN WARS (THE)
    Postdoctoral Cancer Research Fellowship: 2440
Ladish Co. Foundation Scholarships: 2677
LA84 FOUNDATION: 1447
LaFage (Jeffery P.) Graduate Student Research Award: 2145
LAIDLAW FOUNDATION
    Youth-led Community Change (YLCC): 198
Lalor Foundation Postdoctoral Fellowship Program (The): 1825
LALOR FOUNDATION, INC. (THE)
    Lalor Foundation Postdoctoral Fellowship Program (The): 1825
Lamarsh (John R.) Memorial Scholarship: 2637
LAMB FOUNDATION: 199

Lancour (Harold) Scholarship for Foreign Study: 716
LAND O'LAKES FOUNDATION
    Brandt (John) Memorial Scholarship Fund: 201
    California Regions Grant Program: 200
    Community Grants Program: 200
    Dollars for Doers Program: 200
    Matching Gifts to Education Program: 200
    Member Co-op Match Program: 200
    Mid-Atlantic Grant Program: 200
Landis (John and Muriel) Scholarships: 2634
LANDSCAPE ARCHITECTURE FOUNDATION
    ASLA Council of Fellows Scholarship: 2186
    EDSA Minority Scholarship: 2186
    Hawaii Chapter David T. Woolsey Scholarship: 2186
    King (Steven G.) Play Environments Scholarship: 2186
    Landscape Forms Design for People Scholarship: 2186
    Olmsted Scholars Program: 2186
    Paul (Courtland) Scholarship: 2186
    Peridian International/Rae L. Price, FASLA Scholarship: 2186
    Rain Bird Intelligent Use of Water Scholarship: 2186
    Thomas (Douglas Dockery) Fellowship in Garden History and Design: 2186
Landscape Forms Design for People Scholarship: 2186
LANGELOTH (THE JACOB AND VALERIA) FOUNDATION: 2277
Lapides (Linda F. and Julian L.) Fellowship: 345
Lapidus-OIEAHC Fellowship: 626
Las Cumbres Amateur Outreach Award: 2051
Laskin (Bora) National Fellowship in Human Rights Research: 1873
LASPAU: ACADEMIC AND PROFESSIONAL PROGRAMS FOR THE AMERICAS: 961
Last (Jay and Deborah) Fellowship: 345
Latin American-Caribbean Scholarships: 2159
LATKIN (HERBERT AND GERTRUDE) CHARITABLE FOUNDATION: 202
Laurels Fund: 1896
LAURIE (THE BLANCHE AND IRVING) FOUNDATION: 203
Law and International Security Fellowship: 833
Law Enforcement Officer Memorial Scholarship: 1695
Law Enforcement Personnel Dependents' Grant Program (LEPD): 1671
LAWRENCE COUNTY COMMUNITY FOUNDATION: 1315
LDF Earl Warren Legal Training Program: 1030
LDF Herbert Lehman Education Fund Scholarship Program: 1030
LEACOCK (STEPHEN) ASSOCIATION
    Leacock (Stephen) Memorial Medal for Humour: 680
Leacock (Stephen) Memorial Medal for Humour: 680
LeaderShape Institute Award: 2674
Leadership and Civic Engagement: 2172
League Prize for Young Architects and Designers (The): 414
Leakey Foundation Grants: 2020
LEAKEY (L.S.B.) FOUNDATION
    Leakey Foundation Grants: 2020
LEARNING FOR LIFE
    Exploring Program: 1564
LEARY FIREFIGHTERS FOUNDATION (THE)
    Lucey (The Jeremiah) Grant Program: 1316
Lee (The J.S.) Memorial Fellowship: 452
LEEDS INTERNATIONAL PIANOFORTE COMPETITION (THE)
    Leeds International Pianoforte Competition: 771
Leeds International Pianoforte Competition: 771
Leeds International Research Scholarship: 947
Leet (Dorothy) Grant: 1085
LEEWAY FOUNDATION (THE)
    Art and Change Grant: 1087
    Leeway Transformation Award: 1087
Leeway Transformation Award: 1087
LEF FOUNDATION (THE)
    Moving Image Fund: 418
Legacy Fellowship (The): 345
LEHIGH VALLEY COMMUNITY FOUNDATION: 466
Lehman (Jane Bagley) Awards for Excellence in Public Advocacy: 1387
LEHRMAN (JACOB AND CHARLOTTE) FOUNDATION, INC.
    Impact Award: 204
LEIDY (THE JOHN J.) FOUNDATION: 1317
Leighton Award for Nonprofit Excellence: 1236
Leipen (Franz and Neda) Fellowship: 355
Leisch (Jack E.) Memorial National Graduate Fellowship: 2645
Leisner (Tony B.) Scholarship: 1616
Leland (The Waldo G.) Prize: 578
Lenard (John) Civil Engineering Scholarship: 2645
Lennox and Lombroso Postdoctoral Research Fellowship: 2455

Lerner-Gray Grants for Marine Research: 1809
LES CHENEAUX COMMUNITY FOUNDATION (THE): 1318
LESCHETIZKY ASSOCIATION, INC. (THE)
    Gifted Young Pianists Concerto Competition: 772
LEUKEMIA & LYMPHOMA SOCIETY (THE)
    Career Development Program: 2364
    Lichtman (Marshall A.) Specialized Center of Research Program: 2366
    Translational Research Program: 2365
LEUKEMIA RESEARCH FOUNDATION
    New Investigator Awards: 2441
Leviant (Fenia and Yaakov) Memorial Prize in Yiddish Studies: 657
LEVIE (MARCUS AND THERESA) EDUCATION FUND: 1711
Levinson (Suzanne J.) Prize: 597
Lewis and Clark Fund for Exploration and Field Research (The): 15
Lewis (H.S. and Angeline) Scholarships: 1659
Lewis (Lloyd) Fellowship in American History: 389
LIBERTY HILL FOUNDATION
    Fund for Change: 1490
    Marks (Wally) Leadership Institute for Change: 1490
    Queer Youth Fund: 1490
LIBRA FOUNDATION: 205
LIBRA FUTURE FUND
    Libra Future Fund Young Adult Grant Program: 1903
Libra Future Fund Young Adult Grant Program: 1903
Libraries: 12
Library Accessibility and Improvement Grants: 733
LIBRARY COMPANY OF PHILADELPHIA
    Greenfield (Albert M.) Foundation Dissertation Fellowships: 603
    NEH Postdoctoral Fellowships: 603
    Program in African-American History: 603
    Program in Early American Economy and Society: 603
    Research Fellowships in American History and Culture: 603
Library Degree for Law School Graduates: 709
Library Degree for Non-Law School Graduates: 709
Library Research and Development Grants: 719
Library Resident Research Fellowships (The): 349
Library School Graduates Attending Law School: 709
Library School Graduates Seeking a Non-Law Degree: 709
Library Services and Technology Act: 740
Library Services and Technology Act Competitive Grants: 733
Lichtman (Marshall A.) Specialized Center of Research Program: 2366
LIEDERKRANZ FOUNDATION, INC.
    Annual Awards for Voice: 773
Life Sciences Awards: 1477
LIFE SCIENCES RESEARCH FOUNDATION (LSRF)
    Three-Year Postdoctoral Fellowships: 2150
Lifesaving Awards: 1858
LIGHT WORK
    Light Work Artist-in-Residence Program: 553
Light Work Artist-in-Residence Program: 553
LILLY ENDOWMENT INC.: 206
LINCOLN FINANCIAL FOUNDATION: 207
LINCOLN (THE JAMES F.) ARC WELDING FOUNDATION
    Awards for Achievement in Arc Welded Design, Engineering and
      Fabrication: College Division: 2654
Lincoln (John C.) Memorial Scholarship: 2600
Lindbergh (Charles A.) Chair in Aerospace History: 2628
Lindemann Trust Fellowships (The): 958
LINDSAY (THE AGNES M.) TRUST: 1131
Liner (Robert T.) Scholarship: 2636
Linford (Henry B.) Award for Distinguished Teaching: 1819
Linguistics Program: 659
LINK FOUNDATION
    Energy Fellowship Program: 2038
    Oceanography Engineering Fellowship Program: 2038
    Simulation Fellowship Program: 2038
Lipman (David) Scholarship at the Missouri School of Journalism: 1750
LITA/Christian Larew Memorial Scholarship: 1616
LITA/LSSI Minority Scholarship: 1616
LITA/OCLC Minority Scholarship: 1616
Literary Achievement Awards: 1692
Literary Art: 427
Literary Arts Fellowships: 523
Literary Events Grants: 453
Litherland/FTEE Scholarship Undergraduate Major in Technology and
    Engineering Education: 1690
LITTAUER (THE LUCIUS N.) FOUNDATION, INC.: 997
Littleton-Griswold Grant: 578
Littleton-Griswold Prize in American Law and Society (The): 578
LIUU Fund-Progressive Social Change Grants: 1320

Living Legacy Jazz Award: 476
LIVINGSTON AWARDS
    Livingston Awards for Young Journalists: 1941
Livingston Awards for Young Journalists: 1941
LIVINGSTON MEMORIAL FOUNDATION
    Operational Program Grants: 1448
    Special Project Grants: 1448
LOATS FOUNDATION, INC. (THE): 208
Local Arts Grants: 500
Local Cultural Council Program: 472
Local Groups Network: 1559
LOCAL INITIATIVES SUPPORT CORPORATION: 1319
Lockwood (Lewis) Award: 751
LOEB (THE GERALD) AWARDS: 1942
Logan (The George and Jessie) Scholarship: 1945
Londin (Larrie) Scholarship: 784
LONG ISLAND COMMUNITY FOUNDATION
    Kraft (Henry Phillip) Memorial Fund-Environmental Grants: 1320
    LIUU Fund-Progressive Social Change Grants: 1320
Long-Term Fellowships: 2147
Long-Term Research Fellowship: 608
Long-Term Residencies: 486
LONG-THIBAUD-CRESPIN COMPETITION: 774
LONGHI (THE ROBERTO) FOUNDATION FOR THE STUDY OF THE
    HISTORY OF ART
    Art History Fellowships in Florence: 554
Loran Awards: 1674
Lorentz (Pare) Award: 462
Lorénzen (Lilly) Scholarship: 896
Loring (Suzanne and Caleb) Research Fellowship: 606
LOS ALAMOS NATIONAL LABORATORY
    Feynman (Richard P.) Postdoctoral Fellowship in Theory and
      Computing: 1826
    Oppenheimer (J. Robert) Postdoctoral Fellowship: 1826
    Reines (Frederick) Postdoctoral Fellowship in Experimental Sciences:
      1826
LOUISIANA DIVISION OF THE ARTS, DEPARTMENT OF
    CULTURE, RECREATION AND TOURISM
    Decentralized Arts Funding Program: 467
    Statewide Arts Grants Programs: 467
LOVELACE RESPIRATORY RESEARCH INSTITUTE
    Postdoctoral Training Program: 2338
LOWE SYNDROME ASSOCIATION
    McSpadden (The Leland) Memorial Fund for Medical and Scientific
      Research: 2278
Lowell (James Russell) Prize: 657
Loxton (F.H.) Postgraduate Studentships: 2131
LUBBOCK AREA FOUNDATION, INC.
    Mini Grant for Teachers Program: 1321
LUBRIZOL FOUNDATION (THE)
    Community Connection Employee Volunteer Gift Program: 209
    Matching Gift Program: 209
Luce (Clare Boothe) Program: 210
Luce Foundation Theology Program: 210
LUCE (THE HENRY) FOUNDATION, INC.
    American Art Program: 210
    Luce (Clare Boothe) Program: 210
    Luce Foundation Theology Program: 210
    Luce (Henry III) Fellows in Theology: 210
    Luce Scholars Program: 210
Luce (Henry III) Fellows in Theology: 210
Luce Scholars Program: 210
Lucey (The Jeremiah) Grant Program: 1316
LUMINA FOUNDATION: 1634
Lumsden-Kouvel (The Audrey) Fellowship: 386
LUNAR AND PLANETARY INSTITUTE
    Lunar Exploration Summer Intern Program: 2052
Lunar Exploration Summer Intern Program: 2052
Lung Diseases Research: 2398
Lung Health Dissertation Grant: 2388
LUPUS FOUNDATION OF AMERICA, INC.
    Basic, Clinical and Translational Research Grant Programs: 2279
    Finzi (Gina) Memorial Student Summer Fellowship Program: 2279
Luso-American Education: 655
LUSO-AMERICAN EDUCATION FOUNDATION
    Educational Grant Program: 656
    Luso-American Education: 655
LUTHERAN FOUNDATION OF ST. LOUIS: 817
Lydic (Denny) Scholarship: 1914
Lyman (Peter) Memorial/SAGE Scholarships: 1616

LYMPHOMA RESEARCH FOUNDATION
    Clinical Investigator - Career Development Awards: 2367
    Focus Area Grants: CLL/SLL: 2367
    Focus Area Grants: DLBCL: 2367
    Focus Area Grants: Follicular Lymphoma Research Grants: 2367
    Focus Area Grants: Mantle Cell Lymphoma Correlative Grants: 2367
    Postdoctoral Fellowships: 2367
LYNDHURST FOUNDATION: 211

M

M & M AREA COMMUNITY FOUNDATION: 1322
M.F.A. Teaching Assistantships: 575
MA in Critical Studies: 555
MA Social Design: 555
MABEE (THE J.E. AND L.E.) FOUNDATION, INC.: 212
MAC Foundation Scholarship: 2680
MAC Program Scholarship Fund: 1397
MAC Student Travel/Research Grants: 2680
MacArthur Fellows Program: 213
MacArthur Foundation Nuclear Security Fellowship (The): 833
MACARTHUR (JOHN D. AND CATHERINE T.) FOUNDATION
    MacArthur Fellows Program: 213
MACARTHUR (RODERICK) FOUNDATION: 1491
MACDONALD (THE DR. JOHN T.) FOUNDATION, INC.: 1132
MacDonald/Sampson Fellowship: 870
MACDOWELL COLONY (THE)
    Artist Residency Program: 468
Macelwane (The Father James B.) Annual Awards in Meteorology: 2620
MacGregor (Irene and Daisy) Memorial Scholarship: 2298
MacLean (Ida Smedley) Fellowship: 1085
MACLELLAN FOUNDATION, INC. (THE): 214
Macular Degeneration Research Program: 1422
Macy Faculty Scholars: 2280
MACY (JOSIAH JR.) FOUNDATION
    Board Grants: 2280
    Macy Faculty Scholars: 2280
    President's Grants: 2280
Maddex (Eileen C.) Fellowship: 2674
MADDIE'S FUND
    Community Collaborative Grants: 1858
    Lifesaving Awards: 1858
    Medical Equipment Grants: 1858
    Shelter Medicine Programs: 1858
MADISON COMMUNITY FOUNDATION: 1323
Madison (James) Fellowships: 604
MADISON (JAMES) MEMORIAL FELLOWSHIP FOUNDATION
    Madison (James) Fellowships: 604
Maguire (Richard C.) Scholarship: 631
Mahoney (David) Neuro-Imaging Program: 2254
MAINE ARTS COMMISSION
    Arts and Humanities Grants: 469
    Arts Learning: 469
    CCED Grant: 469
    Individual Artist Fellowship: 469
    Morrison (Jane) Film Fund: 469
    Partnership Grant: 469
    Project Grant for Artists: 469
    Project Grant for Organizations: 469
    Traditional Arts Apprenticeship: 469
    Traditional Arts Fellowship: 469
MAINE INITIATIVES
    Felder Fund for Art and Action: 1492
    Grants for Change: 1492
    Public Life Program: 1492
    Rapid Response "Lightning" Grants: 1492
MAINE OSTEOPATHIC ASSOCIATION
    Maine Osteopathic Association Scholarship: 2524
Maine Osteopathic Association Scholarship: 2524
Major Grant Support: 493
Major Grants: 384
Major (The J. Russell) Prize: 578
MALDEF Law School Scholarship: 1985
Maley/FTEE Scholarship Technology and Engineering Teacher
    Professional Development: 1546
Malmberg Scholarship for Study in Sweden (The): 897
Mandelkorn Distinguished Service Award: 1559
Mankin (Richard Claude) Scholarship: 2210
Manny (Carter) Award: 417
Manufacturing Extension Partnership: 1966

Many Voices Fellowships: 696
MAP INTERNATIONAL
    MAP International Medical Fellowship: 2281
MAP International Medical Fellowship: 2281
MAPPLETHORPE (ROBERT) FOUNDATION, INC.
    Photography Program: 470
MARBROOK FOUNDATION: 215
MARCH OF DIMES FOUNDATION
    O'Connor (Basil) Starter Scholar Research Award: 2284
    Prematurity Research Initiative (PRI): 2283
    Research Grants Program: 2282
Marcus (Harold and Inge) Scholarship: 2653
MARCUS (JACOB RADER) CENTER OF THE AMERICAN JEWISH
    ARCHIVES
    American Jewish Archives Fellowship Program (The): 818
MARDAG FOUNDATION: 216
MARFAN FOUNDATION (THE)
    Early Investigator Grant Program: 2517
    Fellowship Grant Program: 2517
    Marfan Foundation Faculty Grant Program (The): 2517
Marfan Foundation Faculty Grant Program (The): 2517
MARIETTA COMMUNITY FOUNDATION: 1324
MARIN COMMUNITY FOUNDATION: 217
MARINE BIOLOGICAL LABORATORY
    Marine Biological Laboratory Research Awards: 2151
Marine Biological Laboratory Research Awards: 2151
Marine Corps Historical Program Research Grants: 640
MARINE CORPS SCHOLARSHIP FOUNDATION, INC.: 1712
Marine Fisheries Initiative Grants: 2083
Maritime Education: 301
MARKETING EDGE
    Kestnbaum (Robert) Research Program: 1904
    Marketing EDGE Leadership Development Program: 1904
    Marketing EDGE Scholarship Program: 1904
    Shankar-Spiegel Award for the Best Dissertation Proposal in
        Direct/Interactive Marketing: 1904
Marketing EDGE Leadership Development Program: 1904
Marketing EDGE Scholarship Program: 1904
Marks (Cicely Phippen) Scholarship: 1616
Marks (The Loy McCandless) Scholarship in Tropical Ornamental
    Horticulture: 2180
Marks (Wally) Leadership Institute for Change: 1490
Marraro (The Helen and Howard R.) Prize in Italian History: 578
Marraro (The Howard R.) Prize: 577
Marraro (Howard R.) Prize: 657
MARRIOTT INTERNATIONAL, INC.: 218
MARSHALL AID COMMEMORATION COMMISSION
    Marshall Scholarships: 929
MARSHALL COMMUNITY FOUNDATION: 1565
Marshall (Mary) Nursing Scholarship/Practical Nurse Program: 2499
Marshall (Mary) Nursing Scholarship/Registered Nurse Program: 2499
Marshall Scholarships: 929
Marshall (Thomas F.) Graduate Student Awards: 526
MARSHALL (THURGOOD) COLLEGE FUND
    TMCF Scholarships: 1713
    Williams (The Sidney B., Jr.) Intellectual Property Law Scholarship:
        1983
Marth (Elmer) Educator Award: 2673
Marti (Jose) Scholarship Challenge Grant Fund: 1067
Martin-Baker Research Awards: 2155
MARTIN (DELLA) FOUNDATION: 2581
Martin (Julie) Mid-Career Awards in Aging Research: 2225
Martin (The Right Honourable Paul, Sr.) Scholarship: 1972
Marvin (Frances Crawford) American Indian Scholarship: 1723
Maryland Folklife Program: 471
MARYLAND HIGHER EDUCATION COMMISSION
    Maryland State Scholarships: 1714
MARYLAND INSTITUTE COLLEGE OF ART
    Art Education (Low-residency/online MA): 555
    Hoffberger School of Painting (MFA): 555
    MA in Critical Studies: 555
    MA Social Design: 555
    Master of Arts in Community Arts: 555
    Master of Arts in Teaching: 555
    MBA/MA: 555
    MFA Community Arts: 555
    MFA Curatorial Practice: 555
    MFA Illustration Practice: 555
    MFA in Graphic Design: 555
    Mt. Royal School of Art (MFA): 555
    MPS in Art and Design: 555

MPS in Information Visualization: 555
   Photographic and Electronic Media (MFA): 555
   Post-Baccalaureate Program: 555
   Rinehart School of Sculpture (MFA): 555
   Studio Art (Low-residency MFA): 555
MARYLAND STATE ARTS COUNCIL
   Artists in Education: 471
   Arts and Entertainment Districts Program: 471
   Arts in Communities: 471
   Community Arts Development: 471
   Grants for Organizations: 471
   Individual Artist Awards: 471
   Maryland Folklife Program: 471
   Public Art Program: 471
Maryland State Scholarships: 1714
Masaoka (Mike M.) Fellowship Fund Congressional Program: 2005
Mason Science Teaching Fellowships: 1806
MASS HUMANITIES
   Project Grants: 375
   Reading and Discussion Grants: 375
   Research Inventory Grants: 375
   Scholar in Residence Grants: 375
Mass Media Science and Engineering Fellows Program: 1920
MASSACHUSETTS CULTURAL COUNCIL
   Adams (John and Abigail) Arts Program for Cultural Economic
     Development: 472
   Artist Fellowships: 472
   Big Yellow School Bus (The): 472
   Cultural Investment Portfolio: 472
   Local Cultural Council Program: 472
   Massachusetts Cultural Facilities Fund: 472
   STARS Residencies: 472
   Traditional Arts Apprenticeship: 472
   YouthReach Initiative: 472
Massachusetts Cultural Facilities Fund: 472
MASSACHUSETTS HISTORICAL SOCIETY (THE)
   Long-Term Research Fellowship: 608
   Loring (Suzanne and Caleb) Research Fellowship: 606
   New England Regional Fellowship Consortium: 609
   Short-Term Research Fellowship: 607
   Swensrud Teacher Fellowships at MHS: 605
MASSACHUSETTS INSTITUTE OF TECHNOLOGY
   Knight Science Journalism Fellowships: 1943
Massachusetts Medical Society International Health Studies Grant
   Program: 1715
MASSACHUSETTS MEDICAL SOCIETY (MMS)
   Massachusetts Medical Society International Health Studies Grant
     Program: 1715
   Massachusetts Medical Society (MMS) Scholars Program: 1715
   MMS Medical Information Technology Awards: 1715
   MMS Student Section Community Service Grants: 1715
Massachusetts Medical Society (MMS) Scholars Program: 1715
MASSACHUSETTS OFFICE OF STUDENT FINANCIAL ASSISTANCE
   Cash Grant: 1716
   Gilbert Grants: 1716
   MASSGrants: 1716
MASSERINI (MAURICE J.) CHARITABLE TRUST: 998
MASSGrants: 1716
Master of Arts in Community Arts: 555
Master of Arts in Teaching: 555
Master of Music in Opera: 764
Master's Awards: 1874
Master's Degree in Educational Leadership: 1605
Master's Program in Material Science and Engineering: 2044
Master's Thesis Fellowships in Marine Corps History: 642
Matching Gift Program: 209, 274
Matching Gifts Program: 132, 185, 271
Matching Gifts to Education Program: 200
Maternal and Child Health Services Block Grant: 2502
Math and Science Teaching (MAST): 1047
MATSUMAE INTERNATIONAL FOUNDATION (THE)
   Fellowship Program: 930
Matsuo Bridge Company, Ltd. of Japan Scholarship: 2600
Matthews (Leroy) Physician/Scientist Award: 2413
Mattinson Scholarship Program for Students with Disabilities: 977
Maury Award (The): 2068
Mayo (Clara) Grants: 1881
MAYO CLINIC
   Surgical Pathology Fellowships: 2285
Mayr (Ernst) Grants in Animal Systematics: 2154
MAYTAG (FREDA)-GRACE CRAWFORD TRUST: 1449

MAZON: A JEWISH RESPONSE TO HUNGER: 1493
Mazza (Theodore) Scholarship: 1775
MBA/MA: 555
McAdoo (John L. and Harriet P.) Award: 1498
McAuliffe (Christa) Reach for the Stars Award: 1860
McAuliffe (Christa) Scholarship Program: 1765
MCBEAN (ALLETTA MORRIS) CHARITABLE TRUST: 376
McCaughan Heritage Scholarship: 1661
MCCAULEY (LUTHER T.) CHARITABLE TRUST: 1325
McConnell Foundation Fund (The): 1375
MCCORMICK FOUNDATION
   Civic Program: 219
   Communities Program: 219
   Education Program: 219
   Journalism Program: 219
   Veterans Program: 219
McCormick (Richard P.) Prize for Scholarly Publication: 619
McDermid (The Honourable N.D.) Graduate Scholarship in Law: 1986
McDevitt (John W.) Fourth Degree Scholarships: 1708
MCDONALD (J.M.) FOUNDATION, INC.: 220
McDonald (Michelle L.) Scholarship: 1896
MCDONALD (RONALD) HOUSE CHARITIES: 1133
McDonnell Astronaut Fellowships: 2623
MCDONNELL CENTER FOR THE SPACE SCIENCES
   McDonnell Astronaut Fellowships: 2623
   McDonnell Graduate Fellowships: 2623
McDonnell Graduate Fellowships: 2623
MCDONNELL (JAMES S.) FOUNDATION
   Collaborative Activity Awards: 221
   Postdoctoral Fellowship Awards in Studying Complex Systems: 221
   Scholar Awards: 221
   21st Century Research Awards: 221
McDonnell (Kilian) Fellowship: 809
MCDOWELL (VERNE CATT) CORPORATION
   McDowell (Verne Catt) Scholarship: 819
McDowell (Verne Catt) Scholarship: 819
MCELROY (R.J.) TRUST: 1134
McGaw (Foster G.) Graduate Student Scholarship: 1431
MCGILL UNIVERSITY
   Boulton (Maxwell) Q.C. Fellowship: 1984
MCGRAW HILL FINANCIAL: 1905
MCGREGOR FUND: 222
McHenry Fellowship: 2135
MCJ AMELIOR FOUNDATION (THE): 1135
MCKENZIE RIVER GATHERING FOUNDATION
   Critical Response Grants: 1494
   Public Interest Grants (General Fund): 1494
   Travel Grants: 1494
McKinlay Scholarship: 651
McKinley Research Fund: 2209
McKnight Advancement Grants: 696
McKnight Doctoral Fellowship: 1542
MCKNIGHT ENDOWMENT FUND FOR NEUROSCIENCE (THE)
   McKnight Neuroscience Scholar Award: 2467
MCKNIGHT FOUNDATION (THE)
   Arts Program: 1495
   Education and Learning: 1495
   International: 1495
   Midwest Climate and Energy: 1495
   Mississippi River: 1495
   Neuroscience: 1495
   Region and Communities: 1495
   Research and Applied Sciences: 1495
McKnight National Residency and Commission: 696
McKnight Neuroscience Scholar Award: 2467
McKnight Professional Development Grant for Mid-Career Artists: 450
McKnight Project Grant for Mid-Career Artists: 450
McKnight Theater Artist Fellowships: 696
McLaughlin Medal (The): 1836
MCLEAN CONTRIBUTIONSHIP (THE): 223
McLendon Scholarship: 739
McManus (Judith) Fellowship: 973
MCMICKING (THE JOSEPH R.) FOUNDATION: 224
McNair Graduate Fellowship: 1762
McNamara (Brooks) Publishing Subvention: 526
MCNAMARA (THE MARGARET) MEMORIAL FUND (MMMF): 225
McNeil Medal (The): 1836
McNeill-Nott Climbing Award: 2167
McSpadden (The Leland) Memorial Fund for Medical and Scientific
   Research: 2278

McWherter (Ned) Scholars Program: 1765
MEADOWS FOUNDATION, INC.: 226
MEASEY (BENJAMIN AND MARY SIDDONS) FOUNDATION
  Medical Education Grants: 2286
MEBANE CHARITABLE FOUNDATION, INC.
  Davie & Yadkin County Program (The): 1136
  Early Childhood Development Program (The): 1136
  Teacher Training and Professional Development Program (The): 1136
Medarva Foundation Fund: 1213
Media Policy and Public Service Media: 1923
Medicaid: 1468
Medical Education Grants: 2286
Medical Equipment Grants: 1858
MEDICAL LIBRARY ASSOCIATION
  Award for Excellence and Achievement in Hospital Librarianship: 730
  Brodman (Estelle) Award for Academic Medical Librarian of the Year: 730
  Cunningham Memorial International Fellowship: 962
  Darling (Louise) Medal for Distinguished Achievement in Collection Development in the Health Sciences: 730
  Doe (Janet) Lectureship: 730
  Eliot (Ida and George) Prize: 730
  Gottlieb (Murray) Prize: 730
  MLA Continuing Education Grants: 227
  MLA Scholarship: 729
  MLA Scholarship for Minority Students: 999
  Noyes (Marcia C.) Award: 730
  Rittenhouse Award: 730
  Rogers (Frank Bradway) Information Advancement Award: 730
  Thomson Reuters/MLA Doctoral Fellowship: 729
Medical Research: 301
Medical Research Fellows Program: 2271
Medical Research Program: 107
Medical Scientist Training Program: 2291
Medical Student Summer Fellowships: 2454, 2456
Medical Student Summer Research Fellowship: 2253
Medical Student Training in Aging Research Program (MSTAR): 2227
MEDIEVAL ACADEMY OF AMERICA (THE)
  Baldwin (Birgit) Fellowship: 610
  Brown (John Nicholas) Prize: 610
  Elliott (Van Courtlandt) Prize: 610
  Haskins Medal: 610
  Schallek Fellowship: 610
Medieval Greek Summer Session at the Gennadius Library: 893
MEDTRONIC FOUNDATION
  Community Education: 228
  Community Health Grants: 228
  HeartRescue: 228
  Patient Link: 228
  Strengthening Health Systems: 228
Meixner Translational Postdoctoral Fellowships: 2242
Melanesia: 64
Melcher (Frederic G.) Book Award: 825
Meli (John and Edith) Scholarship Fund: 1224
Mellon (Andrew W.) Conservation Fellowship: 732
Mellon (Andrew W.) Fellowships: 558
MELLON (THE ANDREW W.) FOUNDATION: 229
Mellon (Andrew W.) Postdoctoral Fellowship: 362
Mellon (Andrew W.) Postdoctoral Fellowships in the Humanities: 403
Mellon-CES Dissertation Completion Fellowship in European Studies: 835
MELLON (THE PAUL) CENTRE FOR STUDIES IN BRITISH ART
  Educational Programme Grants: 419
  Junior Fellowships: 419
  Mellon (Paul) Centre Rome Fellowship: 419
  Postdoctoral Fellowships: 419
  Research Support Grants: 419
  Senior Fellowships: 419
Mellon (Paul) Centre Rome Fellowship: 419
Mellon Postdoctoral Fellowships: 364, 630
MELLON (RICHARD KING) FOUNDATION: 1326
Mellon Visiting Fellowships: 952
Meloid (Emma) and Algood Tuition Scholarship (Undergraduate): 1032
Member Co-op Match Program: 200
Member's First Book Award: 627
Member's Subsequent Book Award: 627
MEMORIAL FOUNDATION FOR JEWISH CULTURE
  International Doctoral Scholarship for Studies Specializing in Jewish Fields: 820
  International Fellowship in Jewish Studies and Jewish Culture: 820
Mental Health and Substance Abuse Fellowship Program (The): 986
Mental Health and Substance Abuse Services Fellowship: 974

Mental Health for Young Children: 1514
Mentor-Based Postdoctoral Fellowship Program: 2403
Mentor-Based Postdoctoral Minority Fellowship: 2403
Mentor Student Travel Awards: 2155
Mentored Clinical Scientist Research Career Development Award (Parent K08): 2293
Mentored New Investigator Research Grant to Promote Diversity (MNIRGD): 2453
Mentored Patient-Oriented Research Career Development Award (K23): 1453
Mentored Quantitative Research Career Development Award (K25): 1453
Mentoring and Leadership Development Program: 1011
MERCK FAMILY FUND: 230
Merck/AGS New Investigator Awards: 2547
Merit and Memorial Scholarships: 1659
Merola Opera Program: 789
Merrill (John) Grant in Transplantation: 2356
MESBEC (Math, Engineering, Science, Business, Education and Computers) Program: 1047
Mesopotamian Fellowship: 895
Metcalf (The Larry) Exemplary Dissertation Award: 1859
METLIFE FOUNDATION: 231
MetLife Foundation Awards for Excellence in Affordable Housing: 1481
Metropolitan Edison Energy Fund: 1180
METROPOLITAN MUSEUM OF ART (THE): 556
  Bothmer Fellowship (The): 561
  Dale (Chester) Fellowships: 559
  Douglass Foundation Fellowship in American Art (The): 473
  Fairchild (The Sherman) Foundation Fellowships: 557
  Mellon (Andrew W.) Conservation Fellowship: 732
  Mellon (Andrew W.) Fellowships: 558
  Mills (J. Clawson) Scholarships: 560
  Rousseau (Theodore) Fellowships: 731
Meudt (The Edna) Memorial Award & The Florence Kahn Memorial Award: 681
MEXICAN AMERICAN LEGAL DEFENSE AND EDUCATIONAL FUND
  MALDEF Law School Scholarship: 1985
MEYER (EUGENE AND AGNES E.) FOUNDATION: 1327
MEYER MEMORIAL TRUST
  Grassroots Grants: 232
  Responsive Grants: 232
MEYER (ROBERT R.) FOUNDATION: 233
Meyer (Walter) Scholarship: 2639
MFA Community Arts: 555
MFA Curatorial Practice: 555
MFA Grant Program: 478
MFA Illustration Practice: 555
MFA in Graphic Design: 555
MFA in Photography: 573
MFA in Studio Art (Painting or Drawing): 573
MFP Mental Health and Substance Abuse Services Fellowship: 2567
MIAMI FOUNDATION (THE)
  Community Grants Program: 234
  GLBT Community Projects Fund: 234
  Safe Passage: Youth Transitioning from Foster Care: 234
Michael (Edwin G. & Lauretta M.) Scholarship for Minister's Spouses: 808
Michaels (Taylor) Scholarship: 177
MICHIGAN COUNCIL FOR ARTS AND CULTURAL AFFAIRS
  Program for Operational and Projects Support: 474
  School Bus Grants: 474
MICHIGAN GATEWAY COMMUNITY FOUNDATION: 1328
MICHIGAN SOCIETY OF FELLOWS
  Postdoctoral Fellowships in the Humanities and the Arts, Sciences and Professions: 377
MICHIGAN STATE UNIVERSITY
  MSU Study Abroad Scholarships: 931
MICHIGAN WOMEN'S FOUNDATION
  Young Women for Change: 1088
MICRON TECHNOLOGY FOUNDATION, INC.: 2096
MICROSCOPY SOCIETY OF AMERICA
  MSA Awards for Microscopists in Developing Countries: 2613
  MSA Presidential Student Awards: 1828
  MSA Professional Technical Staff Awards: 2152
  Undergraduate Research Scholarship Program: 1827
MICROSOFT CORPORATION
  Disaster Response and Humanitarian Relief: 235
  Employee Giving and Volunteer Programs: 235
  Microsoft Grants and Programs in Puget Sound: 235

References in index are to entry numbers.

Microsoft Unlimited Potential-Community Technology Skills Program: 235
  Nongovernmental Organization Capacity Building: 235
  Software Donations: 235
Microsoft Grants and Programs in Puget Sound: 235
Microsoft Unlimited Potential-Community Technology Skills Program: 235
MID-AMERICA ARTS ALLIANCE
  Regional Touring Program: 475
  Touring Exhibits through ExhibitsUSA: 475
MID ATLANTIC ARTS FOUNDATION
  ArtsConnect: 476
  French-American Jazz Exchange: 476
  Jazz Touring Network: 476
  Living Legacy Jazz Award: 476
  Mid Atlantic Creative Fellowships: 476
  Mid Atlantic Folk Arts Outreach Program: 476
  Mid Atlantic Tours: 476
  On Screen/In Person: 476
  Pennsylvania Performing Arts on Tour: 476
  Southern Exposure: 476
  Special Presenter Initiatives: 476
  USArtists International: 476
Mid Atlantic Creative Fellowships: 476
Mid Atlantic Folk Arts Outreach Program: 476
Mid-Atlantic Grant Program: 200
Mid Atlantic Tours: 476
Mid-Career Grant: 416
Mid-Continent Instrument Scholarship: 2618
MID-NEBRASKA COMMUNITY FOUNDATION, INC.: 236
Midcareer Investigator Award in Patient-Oriented Research (K24): 1453
Middle East, North Africa and Regional Research Programs and Country Grants: 907
Middleton Fellowship in Presidential Studies: 2006
Midwest Climate and Energy: 1495
Miele (Alphonse A.) Scholarship: 1775
Migrations Grant: 182
Mildenberger (Kenneth W.) Prize: 658
Military Service Recognition Scholarship (MSRS): 1732
MILLARD (ADAH K.) CHARITABLE TRUST: 237
MILLAY COLONY FOR THE ARTS, INC. (THE): 477
Miller Electric Mfg. Co. Scholarship: 2601
Miller (Paul) Washington Reporting Fellowship: 1949
Miller (Rita E.) Scholarship: 2492
MILLIPORE CORPORATE GIVING PROGRAM: 238
Mills (J. Clawson) Scholarships: 560
Milton (Robert P. and Clara I.) Fund for Senior Housing: 1236
Mimmotte (Jacque I.) Fellowship: 1958
MINERALOGICAL ASSOCIATION OF CANADA
  Berry (Leonard G.) Medal: 2680
  Hawley Medal: 2680
  MAC Foundation Scholarship: 2680
  MAC Student Travel/Research Grants: 2680
  Peacock Medal: 2680
  Pinch Medal: 2680
  Undergraduate Awards: 2680
  Young Scientist Award: 2680
MINERALOGICAL SOCIETY OF AMERICA (THE)
  Research Grant in Crystallography, Mineral Physics or Chemistry and Mineralogy: 2079
  Student Research Grant in Mineralogy and Petrology: 2079
Mini Grant for Teachers Program: 1321
Mini Grants: 482
Minigrants: 620
Mining Club Award: 2678
MINNEAPOLIS FOUNDATION (THE)
  Community Action Funds: 1329
  Designated Beneficiary Funds: 1329
  Donor-Advised Funds: 1329
  Field of Interest Funds: 1329
  Investment Management Services: 1329
  Nonprofit Assistance Fund: 1329
  Robins, Kaplan, Miller and Ciresi Foundation for Children: 1329
MINNESOTA DEPARTMENT OF EDUCATION
  Library Accessibility and Improvement Grants: 733
  Library Services and Technology Act Competitive Grants: 733
  Multi-Type Library Cooperation Aid: 733
  Regional Library Telecommunications Aid: 733
  Regional Public Libraries Systems Support: 733
Minor Research Grant Program: 901
Minority Accounting Doctoral Scholarships: 1902

Minority Biomedical Research Support Awards: 2290
Minority Fellowship Program: 975
Minority Health and Health Disparities International Research Training Grant (MIRT): 1004
Minority Ph.D. Program: 1013
Minority Scholars Award: 1660
Minority Scholarship Awards for College Students: 2633
Minority Teacher Scholarship: 1699
Minority Teaching Fellows Program: 1765
Mississippi River: 1495
MISSOURI DEPARTMENT OF HIGHER EDUCATION
  Access Missouri Financial Assistance Program: 1718
  Missouri Higher Education Academic Scholarship Program ("Bright Flight"): 1717
Missouri Higher Education Academic Scholarship Program ("Bright Flight"): 1717
Missouri Professional Communicators Scholarships: 1750
MITCHELL (JOAN) FOUNDATION
  MFA Grant Program: 478
  Painters and Sculptors Grant Program: 478
Mitchell (Kathleen) Award: 539
MITSUBISHI ELECTRIC AMERICA FOUNDATION: 1606
Mizuho Community Involvement Grants Program: 1330
Mizuho Matching Gifts Program: 1330
MIZUHO USA FOUNDATION, INC.
  Fostering Economic Self-Sufficiency: 1330
  Mizuho Community Involvement Grants Program: 1330
  Mizuho Matching Gifts Program: 1330
  Promoting Economic Development: 1330
  Strengthening Affordable Housing: 1330
MLA Continuing Education Grants: 227
MLA Prize for a Distinguished Bibliography: 657
MLA Prize for a First Book: 657
MLA Prize in United States Latina and Latino and Chicana and Chicano Literary and Cultural Studies: 657
MLA Scholarship: 729
MLA Scholarship for Minority Students: 999
MMS Medical Information Technology Awards: 1715
MMS Student Section Community Service Grants: 1715
MN Regional Grant Program: 450
Model Watershed Program: 2169
MODERN LANGUAGE ASSOCIATION OF AMERICA
  Cohen (Morton N.) Award: 658
  Kovacs (Katherine Singer) Prize: 657
  Leviant (Fenia and Yaakov) Memorial Prize in Yiddish Studies: 657
  Lowell (James Russell) Prize: 657
  Marraro (Howard R.) Prize: 657
  Mildenberger (Kenneth W.) Prize: 658
  MLA Prize for a Distinguished Bibliography: 657
  MLA Prize for a First Book: 657
  MLA Prize in United States Latina and Latino and Chicana and Chicano Literary and Cultural Studies: 657
  Modern Language Association Prize for a Scholarly Edition: 658
  Modern Language Association Prize for Independent Scholars: 658
  Roth (Lois) Award for a Translation of a Literary Work: 657
  Scaglione (Aldo and Jeanne) Prize for a Translation of a Literary Work: 657
  Scaglione (Aldo and Jeanne) Prize for a Translation of a Scholarly Study of Literature: 657
  Scaglione (Aldo and Jeanne) Prize for Comparative Literary Studies: 657
  Scaglione (Aldo and Jeanne) Prize for French and Francophone Studies: 657
  Scaglione (Aldo and Jeanne) Prize for Italian Studies: 657
  Scaglione (Aldo and Jeanne) Prize for Slavic Studies: 657
  Scaglione (Aldo and Jeanne) Prize for Studies in Germanic Languages and Literatures: 657
  Scaglione (Aldo and Jeanne) Publication Award for a Manuscript in Italian Literary Studies: 657
  Scarborough (William Sanders) Prize: 657
  Shaughnessy (Mina P.) Prize: 658
Modern Language Association Prize for a Scholarly Edition: 658
Modern Language Association Prize for Independent Scholars: 658
Moe (Henry Allen) Prize: 489
Moffett (Edna V.) Fellowship: 1097
Moffitt (Francis H.) Memorial Scholarship: 2034
MoGro: 1012
Monash/Scott Medical Student Scholarship Program: 2296
MONEY FOR WOMEN/BARBARA DEMING MEMORIAL FUND, INC.
  Individual Artist Support Grants: 1089

MONROE-BROWN FOUNDATION: 1635
MONSANTO FUND: 2187
MONTANA COMMUNITY FOUNDATION
  Social Justice Montana: 1331
  Women's Foundation of Montana: 1331
Monticello College Foundation Fellowship for Women: 390
MONTREAL NEUROLOGICAL INSTITUTE
  Costello (Jeanne Timmins) Fellowships: 2468
  Robb (Preston) Fellowship: 2468
MOODY FOUNDATION (THE): 239
Moody Research Grants: 2006
Moon (Bill) Scholarships: 1726
Moore (Gordon E.) Medal for Outstanding Achievement in Solid State
  Science and Technology: 1819
Moorman (Robert B.B. and Josephine N.) Scholarship: 2645
Morgan (Alun) Memorial Research Fund in Orthopaedic Physiotherapy:
  2557
MORGAN (THE BURTON D.) FOUNDATION: 1906
MORGAN (MARIETTA MCNEILL) AND SAMUEL TATE MORGAN,
  JR. FOUNDATION: 1496
Morgan (Thomas S.) Scholarship: 628
Morris (Frank H.) Humanitarian Award: 1239
Morris (William) Society Award: 479
MORRIS (WILLIAM) SOCIETY IN THE U.S.
  Dunlap (Joseph R.) Memorial Fellowship: 479
  Morris (William) Society Award: 479
Morrison (Jane) Film Fund: 469
Morrow (Mary)/Edna Richards Scholarship Fund: 1638
MORTON-KELLY CHARITABLE TRUST (THE): 1332
Moss Adams LLP Scholarship: 1896
Mosse (The George L.) Prize: 578
MOTT (CHARLES STEWART) FOUNDATION: 1333
Mott (Frank Luther) KTA Research/Book Award: 1940
MOUNT DESERT ISLAND BIOLOGICAL LABORATORY
  High School Research Fellowship (The): 2153
  Summer Research Fellowships for Undergraduate Faculty and Students:
  2153
  Towle (David W.) Fellowship: 2153
Mt. Royal School of Art (MFA): 555
MT. SINAI HEALTH CARE FOUNDATION: 1450
MOUNT VERNON HOTEL MUSEUM & GARDEN
  Hearst (William Randolph) Foundation Fellowship: 611
Mountain Fellowship: 2167
Moving Image Fund: 418
Moving People and Places Out of Poverty: 26
MOYER FOUNDATION (THE)
  Camp Erin: 1137
  Camp Mariposa: 1137
MPS in Art and Design: 555
MPS in Information Visualization: 555
MS. FOUNDATION FOR WOMEN
  Economic Justice: 1090
  Ending Violence: 1090
  Women's Health: 1090
MSA Awards for Microscopists in Developing Countries: 2613
MSA Graduate Fellowship: 2155
MSA Presidential Student Awards: 1828
MSA Professional Technical Staff Awards: 2152
MSU Study Abroad Scholarships: 931
Muggets Scholarship: 1697
Muhlmann (Maria and Eric) Award: 2048
MULFORD (THE CLARENCE E.) TRUST: 240
Multi-Country Research Fellowship Program: 908
Multi-Type Library Cooperation Aid: 733
Multicultural Academic Opportunity Graduate Student Scholars Program:
  1022
Multicultural Advertising Intern Program: 990
MULTIPLE SCLEROSIS SOCIETY OF CANADA
  Biomedical Research Grants: 2470
  Clinical and Population Health Research Grants: 2470
  Paty (Donald) Career Development Awards: 2472
  Postdoctoral Fellowship: 2471
  Research Studentship: 2469
Munby Fellowship in Bibliography (The): 718
Mundel (Marvin) Memorial Scholarship: 2653
MURDOCK (M.J.) CHARITABLE TRUST: 241
Murphree (E.V.) Award in Industrial and Engineering Chemistry: 2061
Murphy Fine Arts Fellowships: 568
Murrow (Edward R.) Press Fellowship: 1931

MUSCULAR DYSTROPHY ASSOCIATION
  Neuromuscular Disease Research: 2473
Museum Assessment Program: 727
Museum Grants for African American History and Culture: 728
MUSEUM OF COMPARATIVE ZOOLOGY
  Mayr (Ernst) Grants in Animal Systematics: 2154
MUSEUM OF EARLY SOUTHERN DECORATIVE ARTS (MESDA)
  Horton Fellowship: 562
Museums for America: 728
Music Alive: 783
Music Competition: 753
Music Director: 796
Music Education Grant: 1365
Music in American Culture Award: 751
Music Mentors Program: 796
Music 360 Degrees: 796
Muskie (Edmund S.) Graduate Fellowship Program: 920
MUSKINGUM COUNTY COMMUNITY FOUNDATION
  Scholarship Central: 1334
  Zanesville Prize for Contemporary Ceramics: 1334
MUSTARD SEED FOUNDATION (THE)
  Harvey Fellows Program: 1566
MUSTE (A.J.) MEMORIAL INSTITUTE: 1497
MYASTHENIA GRAVIS FOUNDATION OF AMERICA, INC.
  Nurses Research Fellowship: 2474
MYCOLOGICAL SOCIETY OF AMERICA
  Backus Award: 2155
  Forest Fungal Ecology Award: 2155
  Martin-Baker Research Awards: 2155
  Mentor Student Travel Awards: 2155
  MSA Graduate Fellowship: 2155
  NAMA Memorial Graduate Fellowship: 2155
  Rippon (John W.) Research Award: 2155
  Rogerson (Clark T.) Research Award: 2155
  Smith (Alexander H. and Helen V.) Research Fund: 2155

N

NAACP LEGAL DEFENSE AND EDUCATIONAL FUND, INC. (THE)
  LDF Earl Warren Legal Training Program: 1030
  LDF Herbert Lehman Education Fund Scholarship Program: 1030
NACB Scholarship Fund: 1576
NACME Pre-Engineering Student Scholarship: 1000
NAFEO Internship Program: 1031
Nagel (Todd) Memorial Award: 2447
NAHJ General Scholarships (Ruben Salazar Fund): 1001
NAKAMICHI (E.) FOUNDATION: 775
Nakanishi Prize: 2060
NAMA Memorial Graduate Fellowship: 2155
NAMTA COUNCIL FOR ART ADVOCACY: 563
NANSEN FUND, INC. (THE)
  Archbold (John Dana) Fellowships: 932
NANTUCKET HISTORICAL ASSOCIATION
  Verney (E. Geoffrey and Elizabeth Thayer) Fellowship: 612
Nascher/Manning Award: 2547
NASDAQ OMX GROUP EDUCATIONAL FOUNDATION, INC. (THE):
  1907
NATIONAL ACADEMY OF EDUCATION (THE)
  National Academy of Education/Spencer Dissertation Fellowship: 1567
  National Academy of Education/Spencer Postdoctoral Fellowship: 1567
National Academy of Education/Spencer Dissertation Fellowship: 1567
National Academy of Education/Spencer Postdoctoral Fellowship: 1567
NATIONAL ACTION COUNCIL FOR MINORITIES IN
  ENGINEERING, INC. (NACME)
  NACME Pre-Engineering Student Scholarship: 1000
National Affiliate Conference Grants: 1556
NATIONAL ALOPECIA AREATA FOUNDATION: 2156
National Alumni Chapter Fellowship: 2674
National Alumni Chapter Grant: 2674
National Alzheimer's Council (NAC): 1572
NATIONAL AMBUCS, INC.
  AMBUCS Scholars-Scholarships for Therapists: 2554
National and International Fellowships: 956
National Apprenticeship System: 1968
NATIONAL ASSOCIATION FOR EQUAL OPPORTUNITY IN HIGHER
  EDUCATION (NAFEO)
  NAFEO Internship Program: 1031
NATIONAL ASSOCIATION OF BLACK SOCIAL WORKERS (THE)
  Beckett (Dr. Joyce) Scholarship: 1032
  Brown (Selena Danette) Book Scholarship: 1032

Guynn Family Book Scholarship: 1032
Meloid (Emma) and Algood Tuition Scholarship (Undergraduate): 1032
Williams (Cenie Jomo) Tuition Scholarship: 1032
NATIONAL ASSOCIATION OF BROADCASTERS
Grants for Research in Broadcasting: 1944
NATIONAL ASSOCIATION OF COMPOSERS, USA (NACUSA)
Young Composers' Competition: 776
NATIONAL ASSOCIATION OF FARM BROADCASTING
FOUNDATION
Ag Broadcast Scholarships: 1945
Kummerow (Glenn) Memorial Scholarship: 1945
Logan (The George and Jessie) Scholarship: 1945
NATIONAL ASSOCIATION OF GEOSCIENCE TEACHERS
Stout (Dottie) Professional Development Grants: 2080
Summer Field Course Scholarship: 2080
NATIONAL ASSOCIATION OF HEALTH SERVICES EXECUTIVES
(NAHSE): 2555
NATIONAL ASSOCIATION OF HISPANIC JOURNALISTS
Ford Motor Scholarship: 1001
Gannett Foundation Scholarship: 1001
NAHJ General Scholarships (Ruben Salazar Fund): 1001
NBC Fellowship: 1001
News Corporation Scholarship: 1001
O'Brien (Soledad) Scholarship: 1001
PepsiCo Scholarships/Internship: 1001
Rivera (Geraldo) Scholarship: 1001
Salinas (Maria Elena) Scholarship: 1001
NATIONAL ASSOCIATION OF SCHOLARS
Gross (The Barry R.) Memorial Award: 1636
Hook (The Sidney) Memorial Award: 1636
Shaw (The Peter) Memorial Award: 1636
NATIONAL ASSOCIATION OF SCIENCE WRITERS, INC.
Science in Society Awards: 1946
NATIONAL ATAXIA FOUNDATION
National Ataxia Foundation Fellowship Award: 2475
National Ataxia Foundation Pioneer SCA Translational Research
Award: 2475
National Ataxia Foundation Research Grant Program: 2475
National Ataxia Foundation Young Investigator Award and Young
Investigator Award for SCAs: 2475
National Ataxia Foundation Fellowship Award: 2475
National Ataxia Foundation Pioneer SCA Translational Research Award:
2475
National Ataxia Foundation Research Grant Program: 2475
National Ataxia Foundation Young Investigator Award and Young
Investigator Award for SCAs: 2475
NATIONAL BLACK MBA ASSOCIATION
NBMBAA Graduate Scholarship Program: 1335
NATIONAL BLACK NURSES ASSOCIATION, INC.
Cole (Reverend Pauline L.) Scholarship: 2492
Colliflower (Esther)/VITAS Scholarship: 2492
Dawson (Dr. Martha A.) Genesis Nurse Leader Scholarship: 2492
Dudley (Maria) Scholarship: 2492
Dudley (Martha R.) Scholarship: 2492
Haley (Sheila) Scholarship: 2492
Miller (Rita E.) Scholarship: 2492
NBNA Board of Directors Scholarship: 2492
Pemberton (Margaret) Scholarship: 2492
Raney (Della H.) Nursing Scholarship: 2492
Sams (Dr. Lauranne) Scholarship: 2492
United Health Foundation Scholarship: 2492
NATIONAL BLOOD FOUNDATION
Scientific Research Grants Program: 2396
National Book Fund (NBF): 1352
NATIONAL BRAIN TUMOR SOCIETY
NBTF Brain Tumor Research Grants: 2287
NATIONAL BUSINESS AVIATION ASSOCIATION
Baldwin (Donald A. Sr.) Business Aviation Management Scholarship:
2626
Fanning (William M.) Maintenance Scholarship: 2624
Flight Attendant Scholarship: 2624
Ginocchio (Lawrence) Scholarship: 2625
International Operators Scholarship: 2624
Schedulers & Dispatchers Scholarship: 2625
UAA Janice K. Barden Scholarship: 2625
NATIONAL CATTLEMAN'S BEEF ASSOCIATION
Nutrition Research: 2675
NATIONAL CENTER FOR ATMOSPHERIC RESEARCH
Newkirk Graduate Research Assistantships: 2053
Postdoctoral Fellowships at NCAR: 1829

NATIONAL CENTER FOR LEARNING DISABILITIES
Ellis (Bill) Teacher Preparation Award: 1568
Ford (Allegra) Scholarship: 1569
Ford (Anne) Scholarship: 1569
Rozelle (Pete and Carrie) Award: 1570
National Clinical Research Program: 2384
NATIONAL COALITION OF BLACK MEETING PLANNERS
(NCBMP): 1571
NATIONAL COUNCIL FOR EURASIAN AND EAST EUROPEAN
RESEARCH (THE): 854
NATIONAL COUNCIL FOR THE SOCIAL STUDIES
Award for Global Understanding: 1863
Defense of Academic Freedom Award: 1862
Exemplary Research in Social Studies: 1859
FASSE-IA International Understanding Grants: 1864
Grambs (Jean Dresden) Distinguished Career in Social Studies: 1859
Grant for the Enhancement of Geographic Literacy: 1861
McAuliffe (Christa) Reach for the Stars Award: 1860
Metcalf (The Larry) Exemplary Dissertation Award: 1859
Outstanding Social Studies Teacher of the Year Awards: 1859
Woodson (Carter G.) Book Awards: 1859
NATIONAL COUNCIL ON FAMILY RELATIONS
Affiliate Councils Award for Meritorious Service: 1498
Arcus (Margaret E.) Outstanding Family Life Educator Award: 1498
Berardo (Felix) Mentoring Award: 1498
Bernard (Jessie) Outstanding Contribution to Feminist Scholarship
Paper: 1498
Bernard (Jessie) Outstanding Research Proposal: 1498
Burgess (Ernest W.) Award: 1498
Czaplewski Fellowship Award: 1498
Hill (Reuben) Award: 1498
Jewson (Ruth) Award: 1498
McAdoo (John L. and Harriet P.) Award: 1498
NCFR Student Award: 1498
Osborne (Ernest G.) Award: 1498
Peters (Marie) Award: 1498
Straus (Anselm) Award for Qualitative Family Research: 1498
Trost (Jan) Award: 1498
Winter (Cindy) Award: 1498
NATIONAL DAIRY SHRINE
National Dairy Shrine Student Recognition Program: 2124
NDS Graduate Production Award: 2124
NDS Progressive Dairy Producers Awards: 2124
NDS/Core Scholarship: 2124
NDS/DMI Milk Marketing Scholarships: 2124
NDS/Iager Scholarship: 2124
NDS/Kildee Scholarships: 2124
NDS/Klussendorf Scholarship: 2124
NDS/McCullough Scholarships: 2124
NDS/McKown Scholarship: 2124
National Dairy Shrine Student Recognition Program: 2124
National Dance Project: 484
National Eagle Scout Scholarship Fund: 1109
NATIONAL EMERGENCY MEDICINE ASSOCIATION
Kids Do Matter (KDM): 1572
National Alzheimer's Council (NAC): 1572
National Heart Council (NHC): 1572
National Stroke Council (NSC): 1572
NATIONAL ENDOWMENT FOR DEMOCRACY
National Endowment for Democracy Grants: 2007
National Endowment for Democracy Grants: 2007
NATIONAL ENDOWMENT FOR FINANCIAL EDUCATION (NEFE)
NEFE Fellows Program: 1908
NEFE Grants Program: 1908
National Endowment for Plastic Surgery: 2312
NATIONAL ENDOWMENT FOR THE ARTS: 480
NATIONAL ENDOWMENT FOR THE HUMANITIES
Fellowships: 380
Office of Challenge Grants: 379
Preservation and Access: 382
Public Programs: 1947
Research Program: 378
Seminars and Institutes Program: 381
Summer Stipends: 380
National Endowment for the Humanities Fellowships: 387, 885
National Endowment for the Humanities (NEH) Fellowship: 870
National Established Investigator Award: 2383
NATIONAL EYE INSTITUTE
Center Core Grants: 2519
Cooperative Clinical Research Grants: 2518
Small Business Innovation Research Awards: 2518

NATIONAL FARMER'S ORGANIZATION
Farm Kids for College Scholarships: 2125
NATIONAL FEDERATION OF MUSIC CLUBS
Award Program for Summer Music Festivals and Music Centers: 778
Bullock (Dorothy Dann) Music Therapy Award: 779
NFMC Competitions and Awards: 777
NATIONAL FEDERATION OF REPUBLICAN WOMEN
Kabis (Dorothy) Internship: 1091
National Pathfinders Scholarship: 1091
Rendel (Betty) Scholarship: 1091
NATIONAL FEDERATION OF STATE POETRY SOCIETIES, INC.
Meudt (The Edna) Memorial Award & The Florence Kahn Memorial Award: 681
NFSPS College University Level Poetry Competition Awards: 681
NATIONAL FEDERATION OF THE BLIND
National Federation of the Blind Scholarship Program: 1002
National Federation of the Blind Scholarship Program: 1002
NATIONAL FISH AND WILDLIFE FOUNDATION: 2188
NATIONAL FOOTBALL LEAGUE FOUNDATION
Field Grants: 1336
Player Foundation Grants: 1336
Pro Bowl Grants: 1336
Youth Football Grants: 1336
NATIONAL FOSTER PARENT ASSOCIATION
NFPA Scholarship: 1138
NATIONAL FOUNDATION FOR ADVANCEMENT IN THE ARTS
Alumni Grant: 481
YoungArts Miami: 481
YoungArts New York: 481
YoungArts Week: 481
NATIONAL FOUNDATION FOR INFECTIOUS DISEASES
NFID Advanced Vaccinology Course Travel Grants: 2339
NFID Traveling Professorship in Rural Areas: 2339
NATIONAL GEM CONSORTIUM (THE)
GEM M.S. Engineering Fellowship (The): 1003
GEM Ph.D. Engineering Fellowship (The): 1003
GEM Ph.D. Science Fellowship (The): 1003
Grad Lab: 1003
Graduate and Faculty Development Program: 1003
NATIONAL GEOGRAPHIC SOCIETY
National Geographic Society Committee for Research and Exploration: 2081
National Geographic Society Committee for Research and Exploration: 2081
National Glaucoma Research Program: 2508
National Grants: 6
National Guard Grant: 1699
NATIONAL HEADACHE FOUNDATION: 2368
NATIONAL HEALTH SERVICE CORPS (NHSC)
National Health Service Corps Scholarship Program: 1451
National Health Service Corps Scholarship Program: 1451
National Heart Council (NHC): 1572
NATIONAL HEART, LUNG AND BLOOD INSTITUTE (NHLBI): 2397
Blood Diseases and Resources Research: 2369
Lung Diseases Research: 2398
NATIONAL HEMOPHILIA FOUNDATION (THE)
Pool (Judith Graham) Postdoctoral Research Fellowships in Bleeding Disorders: 2288
NATIONAL HISTORICAL PUBLICATIONS AND RECORDS COMMISSION: 613
National History Day Prize in Women's History, Junior Division: 588
NATIONAL HOME LIBRARY FOUNDATION: 734
NATIONAL HUMANITIES CENTER
National Humanities Center Fellowships: 383
National Humanities Center Fellowships: 383
National Innovative Research Grant: 2382
NATIONAL INSTITUTE FOR LABOR RELATIONS RESEARCH
Applegate/Jackson Parks Future Teacher Scholarship: 1719
Ruggles (The William B.) Journalist Scholarship: 1948
NATIONAL INSTITUTE OF DENTAL AND CRANIOFACIAL RESEARCH (NIDCR)
AIDS: 2352
Behavioral/Social Science Research: 2352
Biotechnology/Regenerative Medicine: 2352
Clinical Research/Clinical Trials: 2352
Computational Science: 2352
Conference Grants: 2352
Epidemiology/Population Research: 2352
Genetic Studies: 2352
Health Literacy Research: 2352
Individual NRSA Postdoctoral Fellowships (F-32): 2351

Individual NRSA Senior Fellowship Award (F-33): 2353
International Health: 2352
Neurobiology/Pain: 2352
Oral Cancer: 2352
Oral Health Disparities Research: 2352
Teeth and Bone: 2352
Women's Health: 2352
NATIONAL INSTITUTE OF ENVIRONMENTAL HEALTH SCIENCES
Environmental Health Sciences Research and Training Grants: 2189
NATIONAL INSTITUTE OF GENERAL MEDICAL SCIENCES
Division of Biomedical Technology, Bioinformatics, and Computational Biology: 2289
Division of Cell Biology and Biophysics: 2289
Division of Genetics and Developmental Biology: 2289
Division of Pharmacology, Physiology, and Biological Chemistry: 2289
Division of Training, Workforce Development, and Diversity: 2289
Medical Scientist Training Program: 2291
Minority Biomedical Research Support Awards: 2290
NATIONAL INSTITUTE OF JUSTICE, U.S. DEPARTMENT OF JUSTICE
Research Grants: 1409
NATIONAL INSTITUTE OF MENTAL HEALTH: 2582
Research Training and Career Development Program: 1865
Traumatic Stress Research Program: 1865
NATIONAL INSTITUTE OF NEUROLOGICAL DISORDERS AND STROKE
NINDS Extramural Research Grants: 2476
NATIONAL INSTITUTE OF NURSING RESEARCH
Career Development Grants: 2493
Research Grants: 2493
Research Training Grants: 2493
Small Business Innovation Research Grants: 2493
NATIONAL INSTITUTE OF STANDARDS AND TECHNOLOGY
Manufacturing Extension Partnership: 1966
NATIONAL INSTITUTE ON AGING
Aging Research: 1452
NATIONAL INSTITUTE ON ALCOHOL ABUSE AND ALCOHOLISM
Academic Career Awards (K07): 1453
Career Enhancement Award for Stem Cell Research (K18): 1453
Independent Scientist Awards (K02): 1453
Mentored Patient-Oriented Research Career Development Award (K23): 1453
Mentored Quantitative Research Career Development Award (K25): 1453
Midcareer Investigator Award in Patient-Oriented Research (K24): 1453
NIH Pathway to Independence Award (K99/R00): 1453
Scientist Development Awards for Mentored Clinical (K08): 1453
Scientist Development Awards for Mentored Research (K01): 1453
Small Business Innovation Research Program: 1454
NATIONAL INSTITUTE ON DRUG ABUSE: 1573
Diversity-Promoting Institutions Drug Abuse Research Program: 1574
NATIONAL INSTITUTE ON MINORITY HEALTH AND HEALTH DISPARITIES
Minority Health and Health Disparities International Research Training Grant (MIRT): 1004
NATIONAL INSTITUTES OF HEALTH
Japan Society for the Promotion of Science Postdoctoral Research Fellowships (Extramural): 966
Kirschstein (Ruth L.) National Research Service Awards (NRSA) for Individual Postdoctoral Fellows (Parent F32): 2292
Kirschstein (Ruth L.) National Research Service Awards (NRSA) for Individual Senior Fellows (Parent F33): 2294
Mentored Clinical Scientist Research Career Development Award (Parent K08): 2293
National Research Service Awards (NRSAs): 2520
NIH Visiting Program (The): 1455
Shared Instrumentation Grant Program: 2295
National Issues Programs: 1949
NATIONAL ITALIAN AMERICAN FOUNDATION (THE)
NIAF Scholarship Program: 1720
National Jewish Book Award-American Jewish Studies: 676
National Jewish Book Award-Anthologies and Collections: 676
National Jewish Book Award-Biography, Autobiography and Memoir: 676
National Jewish Book Award-Children's and Young Adult Literature: 676
National Jewish Book Award-Contemporary Jewish Life: 676
National Jewish Book Award-Education and Jewish Identity: 676
National Jewish Book Award-Fiction: 676
National Jewish Book Award-History: 676
National Jewish Book Award-Holocaust: 676
National Jewish Book Award-Illustrated Children's Book: 676

National Jewish Book Award-Modern Jewish Thought and Experience: 676
National Jewish Book Award-Outstanding Debut Fiction: 676
National Jewish Book Award-Poetry: 676
National Jewish Book Award-Scholarship: 676
National Jewish Book Award-Sephardic Culture: 676
National Jewish Book Award-Visual Arts: 676
National Jewish Book Award-Women's Studies: 676
National Jewish Book Award-Writing Based on Archival Materials: 676
NATIONAL JEWISH COMMITTEE ON SCOUTING
  Arkans (Rick) Eagle Scout Scholarship: 1721
  Vernon (Chester M.) Memorial Eagle Scout Scholarship: 1721
  Weil (Frank L.) Memorial Eagle Scout Scholarship: 1721
NATIONAL KIDNEY FOUNDATION
  Research Fellowship Award: 2421
  Satellite Dialysis Clinical Investigator Grant: 2423
  Young Investigator Grant Program: 2422
National Leadership Grant Competition: 1015
National Leadership Grants: 727
NATIONAL LEUKEMIA RESEARCH ASSOCIATION
  Children's Leukemia Research Grants: 2531
National Medal for Museum and Library Services: 727
NATIONAL MEDICAL FELLOWSHIPS, INC.
  Aetna Foundation/NMF Healthcare Leadership Program: 2296
  Andersen (Hugh J.) Scholarship: 2296
  California Community Service-Learning Program: 2296
  Emergency Scholarship Fund: 2296
  GE/NMF International Medical Scholars Program: 2296
  GE-NMF Primary Care Leadership Program (PCLP): 2296
  Monash/Scott Medical Student Scholarship Program: 2296
  United Health Foundation/Diverse Medical Scholars Program: 2296
National Merit Scholarships: 271
NATIONAL MOLE DAY FOUNDATION
  Hague (The George) Memorial Travel Award: 2068
  Maury Award (The): 2068
  National Mole of the Year Award (MOTY): 2068
National Mole of the Year Award (MOTY): 2068
NATIONAL MULTIPLE SCLEROSIS SOCIETY
  National Multiple Sclerosis Society Research Grants Program: 2478
  Postdoctoral Fellowships Program in Multiple Sclerosis Research: 2477
National Multiple Sclerosis Society Research Grants Program: 2478
NATIONAL OCEANIC AND ATMOSPHERIC ADMINISTRATION
  Chesapeake Bay Fisheries Research Program: 1575
  Climate and Global Change Program: 2082
  Cooperative Research Program Grants: 2083
  Marine Fisheries Initiative Grants: 2083
  National Sea Grant College Program: 1830
  Ocean Exploration and Research Program: 2084
  Research in Remote Sensing of the Earth and Environment Grants: 2085
NATIONAL OPERA ASSOCIATION, INC.
  Biennial Dissertation Competition: 780
  Chamber Opera Competition: 780
  Collegiate Opera Scenes Competition: 780
  Opera Production Competition: 780
  Sacred in Opera: 780
  Scholarly Paper Competition: 780
  Student and Artist Vocal Auditions: 780
NATIONAL ORCHESTRAL INSTITUTE: 781
NATIONAL ORGANIZATION FOR RARE DISORDERS (THE)
  Restricted Research Program: 2297
NATIONAL PARK FOUNDATION
  Active Trails: 2190
  Albright-Wirth Grants Program: 2190
  America's Best Idea: 2190
  Junior Ranger Program (The): 2190
  Parks Climate Challenge: 2190
  Parks Stewards Program: 2190
  Transportation Scholars: 2190
  Yount (Harry) National Park Ranger Award: 2190
National Pathfinders Scholarship: 1091
NATIONAL POETRY SERIES (THE)
  National Poetry Series Open Competition: 682
National Poetry Series Open Competition: 682
NATIONAL PRESS FOUNDATION
  Berryman (Clifford K. and James T.) Award for Editorial Cartoons: 1949
  Capitol Hill Issues Briefings: 1949
  Feddie Award (The): 1949

Miller (Paul) Washington Reporting Fellowship: 1949
National Issues Programs: 1949
Stokes (Thomas L.) Award: 1949
National Professional Development Program: 1595
National Program: 193
NATIONAL RADIO ASTRONOMY OBSERVATORY
  Jansky Fellowships at the NRAO: 2054
National Research Council Graduate, Postdoctoral and Senior Research Associateship Programs: 2039
National Research Council Laboratories Research Associateships Program: 1831
NATIONAL RESEARCH COUNCIL OF CANADA
  National Research Council Laboratories Research Associateships Program: 1831
NATIONAL RESEARCH COUNCIL OF THE NATIONAL ACADEMIES
  Ford Foundation Fellowship Program: 1005
  National Research Council Graduate, Postdoctoral and Senior Research Associateship Programs: 2039
National Research Service Awards (NRSAs): 2520
National Resource Centers (NRC) Program: 664
NATIONAL RESTAURANT ASSOCIATION EDUCATIONAL FOUNDATION (THE)
  National Restaurant Association Educational Foundation (NRAE) Scholarship Program: 2676
  Professional Development for Educators Scholarship: 1909
National Restaurant Association Educational Foundation (NRAE) Scholarship Program: 2676
National Scholar Program: 2674
National School Lunch Program (The): 1154
NATIONAL SCIENCE FOUNDATION: 2040, 2086
  Advanced Technological Education (ATE): 1607
  Archaeology Program: 2022
  Archaeometry Program: 2022
  Arctic Research Program: 1835
  Astronomy and Astrophysics Research Grants: 2055
  Cultural Anthropology Program: 2021
  Directorate for Engineering Grants Program: 2655
  Discovery Research K-12 (DR K12): 1607
  Division of Environmental Biology: 2158
  Division of Molecular and Cellular Biosciences Programs: 2157
  Doctoral Dissertation Research Improvement Grants (DDRIG): 659
  Documenting Endangered Languages (DEL): 659
  Informal Science Education (ISE) (AISL): 1607
  Innovative Technology Experiences for Students and Teachers (ITEST): 1607
  Linguistics Program: 659
  NSF Graduate Research Fellowship Program: 1832
  Ocean Section: 2087
  Perception, Action & Cognition Program: 2584
  Physics Research Grants: 2101
  Research and Evaluation on Education in Science and Engineering (REESE): 1607
  Science, Technology and Society: 1833
  Social Psychology Program: 2583
  U.S. Antarctic Research Program: 1834
National Scientist Development Grant: 2384
National Sea Grant College Program: 1830
NATIONAL SECURITY EDUCATION PROGRAM
  Boren Fellowships: 934
  Boren Scholarships: 933
NATIONAL SOCIETY DAUGHTERS OF THE AMERICAN REVOLUTION
  American Indian Scholarship: 1722
  Caldwell (J.E.R.) Centennial Scholarship: 420
  Cogswell (Madeline Pickett) Nursing Scholarship: 2494
  Griswold (Enid Hall) Memorial Scholarship: 1866
  Holt (Caroline E.) Nursing Scholarship: 2494
  MacGregor (Irene and Daisy) Memorial Scholarship: 2298
  Marvin (Frances Crawford) American Indian Scholarship: 1723
  Occupational/Physical Therapy Scholarship: 2556
  Pittenger (Dr. Aura-Lee A. and James Hobbs) American History Scholarship: 614
NATIONAL SOCIETY OF ACCOUNTANTS SCHOLARSHIP FOUNDATION
  Stearman (The Stanley H.) Award: 1724
NATIONAL SOCIETY OF BLACK ENGINEERS: 1725
NATIONAL SOCIETY OF HISPANIC MBAS (NSHMBA)
  NSHMBA Scholarship Program: 1006
NATIONAL SOCIETY OF PROFESSIONAL SURVEYORS (NSPS)
  Berntsen International Scholarship in Surveying (The): 2657
  Berntsen International Scholarship in Surveying Technology (The):

2657
NSPS Board of Governors Scholarship: 2658
NSPS Scholarships (The): 2658
Schonstedt Scholarship in Surveying (The): 2656
NATIONAL SOCIETY OF PROFESSIONAL SURVEYORS (NSPS)
AMERICAN ASSOCIATION FOR GEODETIC SURVEYING (AAGS)
AAGS Joseph F. Dracup Scholarship Award: 2660
American Association for Geodetic Surveying Graduate Fellowship
Award: 2659
National Stroke Council (NSC): 1572
NATIONAL TAXIDERMISTS ASSOCIATION
Fleming (Charlie) Scholarship: 1007
National Teacher of the Year Award: 2669
National Theater Pilot: 484
NATIONAL TRUST FOR HISTORIC PRESERVATION
National Trust Preservation Funds (NTPF): 615
National Trust Preservation Funds (NTPF): 615
NATIONAL WILDLIFE FEDERATION
Campus Ecology Fellowships: 2192
Conservation Internships: 2191
Emerging Leaders Fellowships: 2192
NATIONWIDE INSURANCE FOUNDATION: 242
Native American and Alaska Native Children in School Program: 1595
NATIVE AMERICAN COMMUNITY BOARD (NACB)
College Intern Program: 1052
NACB Scholarship Fund: 1576
Native American Leadership in Education (NALE) Program: 1047
Native American Library Services: Basic Grants: 727
Native American Library Services: Enhancement Grants: 728
Native American Programs: 1058
Native American Scholarship Program: 1045
Native American/Native Hawaiian Museum Services Program: 728
Native Hawaiian Library Services Grant: 727
NATSO FOUNDATION
Moon (Bill) Scholarships: 1726
Natural Sciences or Engineering International Security Fellowship: 833
NAUMBURG (THE WALTER W.) FOUNDATION, INC.: 782
Naval Research Laboratory (NRL) Postdoctoral Fellowship Program: 2644
Navy Health Professions Scholarship Program (HPSP): 2332
NBC Fellowship: 1001
NBCC Foundation Military Scholarship: 1727
NBCC Foundation Minority Scholarships: 1727
NBCC Foundation Rural Scholarship: 1727
NBCC FOUNDATION, INC.
NBCC Foundation Military Scholarship: 1727
NBCC Foundation Minority Scholarships: 1727
NBCC Foundation Rural Scholarship: 1727
NBCC Minority Fellowships: 1727
NBCC Minority Fellowships: 1727
NBMBAA Graduate Scholarship Program: 1335
NBNA Board of Directors Scholarship: 2492
NBTF Brain Tumor Research Grants: 2287
NCFR Student Award: 1498
NDS Graduate Production Award: 2124
NDS Progressive Dairy Producers Awards: 2124
NDS/Core Scholarship: 2124
NDS/DMI Milk Marketing Scholarships: 2124
NDS/Iager Scholarship: 2124
NDS/Kildee Scholarships: 2124
NDS/Klussendorf Scholarship: 2124
NDS/McCullough Scholarships: 2124
NDS/McKown Scholarship: 2124
NEA FOUNDATION (THE): 1577
NEA Foundation Learning and Leadership Grants: 1578
NEA Foundation Student Achievement Grants: 1578
NEA Foundation Learning and Leadership Grants: 1578
NEA Foundation Student Achievement Grants: 1578
NEBRASKA ARTS COUNCIL
Artists-in-Schools/Communities Grants: 482
Arts Learning Projects: 482
Arts Project Grants: 482
Basic Support Grants: 482
Individual Artist Fellowships: 482
Mini Grants: 482
Nebraska Touring Program: 482
School Bus for the Arts Grants: 482
Nebraska Touring Program: 482
NEED
Access to College and Career Education (ACE) Program: 1033
African American Male Mentoring Initiative (AAMMI): 1033

Science Technology Engineering & Math (STEM) Female Mentoring
Program: 1033
Unmet NEED Grants and Scholarships: 1033
NEFE Fellows Program: 1908
NEFE Grants Program: 1908
NEH Fellowships: 406
NEH Fellowships for Research in Turkey: 883
NEH Postdoctoral Fellowships: 603
Neighbor to Neighbor: 326
Neighborhood Fund: 1214
Neighborhood Grants Program: 1217
NELA Annual Scholarship Contest: 2127
NELLIE MAE EDUCATION FOUNDATION: 1579
Neporany Doctoral Fellowship: 585
Ness (John Harrison) Memorial Award: 813
Neumueller (Julius F.) Award in Optics: 2504
NEURO-DEVELOPMENTAL TREATMENT ASSOCIATION: 2370
Neurobiology/Pain: 2352
Neuromuscular Disease Research: 2473
NEUROPATHY ASSOCIATION (THE): 2371
Neuroscience: 1495
NEUROSURGERY RESEARCH AND EDUCATION FOUNDATION
Research Fellowships: 2479
Young Clinician Investigator Award: 2479
NEVADA ARTS COUNCIL
Artist Services Program: 483
Arts Learning Program: 483
Community Arts Development: 483
Folklife Program: 483
Governor's Arts Awards: 483
Grants Program: 483
Nevins (Allan) Prize: 635
New Century Scholars Doctoral Scholarship: 2506
New Century Scholars Research Grant: 2506
NEW DRAMATISTS: 534
NEW ENGLAND BIOLABS FOUNDATION: 243
NEW ENGLAND FOUNDATION FOR THE ARTS
Center Stage: 484
Expeditions: 484
Fund for the Arts: 484
National Dance Project: 484
National Theater Pilot: 484
New England States Touring Program: 484
Presenter Travel Fund: 484
New England Regional Fellowship Consortium: 609
New England States Touring Program: 484
NEW HAMPSHIRE LIBRARY ASSOCIATION
Norris (Rosalie) Scholarship: 735
Winchell (F. Mabel) Loan Fund: 735
NEW HAMPSHIRE STATE COUNCIL ON THE ARTS
Apprenticeships: 485
Artist Entrepreneurial Workshops: 485
Artist in Residence: 485
Artist Services: 485
Arts in Education: 485
Arts in Health Care Project Grants: 485
Cultural Conservation: 485
General Project Grants: 485
Operating Grants: 485
Percent for Art: 485
Public Value Partnerships: 485
Traditional Arts Apprenticeship: 485
Youth Arts Project Grants: 485
New Initiatives Grant: 2674
New Investigator: 2394
New Investigator Award: 2534
New Investigator Awards: 2441
New Investigator Fellowship Training Initiative (NIFTI): 2551
New Investigator Research Grant to Promote Diversity (NIRGD): 2453
New Investigator Research Grants: 1463, 2452
New Investigators Research Grant: 2506
NEW JERSEY DEPARTMENT OF MILITARY AND VETERANS
AFFAIRS
Prisoner of War/Missing in Action (POW/MIA) Program: 1729
Veterans Tuition Credit Program (VTCP): 1728
New Jersey Educational Opportunity Fund (EOF) Program (The): 1730
NEW JERSEY HISTORIC TRUST
Discover New Jersey History License Plate Fund for Heritage Tourism:
616
Emergency Loans: 617
Garden State Historic Preservation Trust Fund (GSHPTF): 616

NEW JERSEY HISTORICAL COMMISSION
  Driscoll (Alfred E.) Dissertation Prize: 619
  Garvin (Mildred Barry) Prize: 619
  General Operating Support Grants: 618
  McCormick (Richard P.) Prize for Scholarly Publication: 619
  Minigrants: 620
  Project Grants: 620
NEW JERSEY LIBRARY ASSOCIATION
  Scholarships for Study in Library Service: 736
New Jersey Network of Superintendents: 1583
NEW JERSEY OFFICE OF THE SECRETARY OF HIGHER
  EDUCATION
  New Jersey Educational Opportunity Fund (EOF) Program (The): 1730
NEW JERSEY OSTEOPATHIC EDUCATION FOUNDATION: 2525
NEW JERSEY STATE COUNCIL ON THE ARTS
  Arts Project Grants: 486
  Folk Arts Apprenticeships: 486
  General Operating Support Grants: 486
  General Program Support Grants: 486
  Long-Term Residencies: 486
  Short-Term Residencies/Arts Education: 486
  Special Project Grants: 486
New Jersey Student Tuition Assistance Reward Scholarship: 1695
New Jersey Student Tuition Assistance Reward Scholarship II: 1695
New Jersey World Trade Center Scholarship: 1695
New Mexico Community AIDS Partnership Initiative (NMCAP): 1337
NEW MEXICO COMMUNITY FOUNDATION
  New Mexico Community AIDS Partnership Initiative (NMCAP): 1337
NEW MEXICO LIBRARY ASSOCIATION
  College Scholarship Fund: 737
  Continuing Education Grants: 737
  Dorroh (Marion) Memorial Scholarship: 737
NEW MUSIC USA
  Cary New Music Performance Fund: 783
  Music Alive: 783
  New Music USA Project Grants: 783
New Music USA Project Grants: 783
New Plays on Campus: 696
New Theater Works Initiative: 2491
New Writers Awards: 674
New York City Environmental Fund: 2184
New York City Urban Fellows Program: 1994
NEW YORK COMMUNITY TRUST (THE): 244
NEW YORK COUNCIL FOR THE HUMANITIES
  Major Grants: 384
  Reading and Discussion Grants: 384
  Speakers in the Humanities Program: 384
NEW YORK FOUNDATION FOR THE ARTS
  Artists' Fellowships: 487
NEW YORK LANDMARKS CONSERVANCY
  City Ventures Fund: 621
  EZ (Empowerment Zone) Consulting Grants: 621
  Historic Properties Fund: 621
  Sacred Sites Program: 621
  Technical Services Program: 621
NEW YORK SEA GRANT INSTITUTE: 2193
NEW YORK STATE ASSEMBLY INTERN COMMITTEE: 2009
  Assembly Session Internships: 2008
NEW YORK STATE COUNCIL ON THE ARTS: 488
NEW YORK STATE EDUCATION DEPARTMENT
  Regents Physician Loan Forgiveness Award Program: 1731
  Scholarships for Academic Excellence: 1731
NEW YORK STATE HIGHER EDUCATION SERVICES
  CORPORATION
  Military Service Recognition Scholarship (MSRS): 1732
  New York State Tuition Assistance Program (TAP): 1734
  NYS Aid for Part-Time Study (APTS): 1733
  NYS Memorial Scholarships: 1732
NEW YORK STATE HISTORICAL ASSOCIATION
  Cooperstown Graduate Program (The): 738
  Fox (The Dixon Ryan) Manuscript Prize of the New York State
    Historical Association: 622
  Moe (Henry Allen) Prize: 489
NEW YORK STATE SENATE
  Biggane (James L.) Fellowship in Finance: 2010
  New York State Senate Legislative Fellows Program: 2010
  Roth (Richard J.) Journalism Fellowship: 2010
  Undergraduate Session Assistants Program: 2011
  Wiebe (Richard A.) Public Service Fellowship: 2010
New York State Senate Legislative Fellows Program: 2010
New York State Tuition Assistance Program (TAP): 1734

Newberry Consortium in American Indian Studies Faculty Fellowship:
  391
NEWBERRY LIBRARY (THE)
  Allen (Frances C.) Fellowships: 1053
  American Society for Eighteenth-Century Studies Fellowships: 623
  Andrew W. Mellon Foundation Fellowship: 398
  Gray (Charles Montgomery) Fellowship: 396
  Lewis (Lloyd) Fellowship in American History: 389
  Lumsden-Kouvel (The Audrey) Fellowship: 386
  Monticello College Foundation Fellowship for Women: 390
  National Endowment for the Humanities Fellowships: 387
  Newberry Consortium in American Indian Studies Faculty Fellowship:
    391
  Newberry Library - Jack Miller Center Fellowship: 393
  Newberry Library - Kress Foundation Fellowship: 397
  Newberry Library Short-Term Fellowships: 385
  Power (Susan Kelly) and Helen Hornbeck Tanner Fellowship: 394
  Sixteenth Century Society and Conference (SCSC) Fellowship: 392
  Society of Mayflower Descendants in the State of Illinois Fellowship:
    395
  Weinberg (Arthur and Lila) Fellowship for Independent Scholars: 388
Newberry Library - Jack Miller Center Fellowship: 393
Newberry Library - Kress Foundation Fellowship: 397
Newberry Library Short-Term Fellowships: 385
Newcombe (Charlotte W.) Doctoral Dissertation Fellowships: 1804
NEWCOMBE (THE CHARLOTTE W.) FOUNDATION
  Newcombe Fellowships: 1735
  Newcombe Scholarships for Mature Women: 1735
  Newcombe Scholarships for Students with Disabilities: 1735
  Special Scholarship Endowment Grants: 1735
Newcombe Fellowships: 1735
Newcombe Scholarships for Mature Women: 1735
Newcombe Scholarships for Students with Disabilities: 1735
Newkirk Graduate Research Assistantships: 2053
Newman (The Eric P.) Graduate Summer Seminar: 348
News Corporation Scholarship: 1001
NEWSPAPER GUILD-CWA (THE)
  Barr (David S.) Award: 1951
  Broun (Heywood) Award: 1950
NF Clinic Network (CTF-NFCN): 2360
NFID Advanced Vaccinology Course Travel Grants: 2339
NFID Traveling Professorship in Rural Areas: 2339
NFMC Competitions and Awards: 777
NFPA Scholarship: 1138
NFSPS College University Level Poetry Competition Awards: 681
NIAF Scholarship Program: 1720
Nicolai (Walter) Award in Biomedical Gerontology: 2222
NICSA
  NICSA/William T. Blackwell Scholarship Fund (The): 1580
NICSA/William T. Blackwell Scholarship Fund (The): 1580
Nieman Fellowships in Journalism: 1954
NIEMAN FOUNDATION FOR JOURNALISM AT HARVARD
  Bingham (Worth) Prize for Investigative Journalism: 1952
  Nieman Fellowships in Journalism: 1954
  Taylor Family Award for Fairness in Newspapers: 1953
Nigogosian (Aram and Rose) Fund: 793
NIH Pathway to Independence Award (K99/R00): 1453
NIH Visiting Program (The): 1455
NINDS Extramural Research Grants: 2476
NM Health Equity Partnership: 1012
No Kid Hungry: 1508
NOBLE (SAMUEL ROBERTS) FOUNDATION, INC.: 1637
Non-SDB Education Activities Grant: 2159
Non-SDB Meeting Grants: 2159
Nongovernmental Organization Capacity Building: 235
Nonprofit Assistance Fund: 1329
Nonprofit Assistance Initiative: 1245
Nonprofit Capacity Building Grants: 76
Nonprofit Gift Matching Program: 38
Nonprofit Network: 1284
Nonprofit Support Program: 1239
NORCLIFFE FOUNDATION (THE): 245
Norden (Deborah J.) Fund: 413
NORDSON CORPORATION FOUNDATION (THE)
  Time and Talent: 246
NORRIS (KENNETH T. AND EILEEN L.) FOUNDATION: 247
Norris (Rosalie) Scholarship: 735
North American Foundation Awards: 948

NORTH AMERICAN SPINE SOCIETY (NASS)
  Clinical Traveling Fellowship: 2299
  Research Grant: 2299
  Research Traveling Fellowship: 2299
  Young Investigator Grants: 2299
NORTH ATLANTIC TREATY ORGANIZATION
  Science for Peace and Security (SPS) Programme: 967
NORTH CAROLINA ARTS COUNCIL
  Artist Fellowships: 490
  Arts and Audiences: 490
  Arts in Education Grants: 490
  Grassroots Arts Program: 490
  Regional Artist Project Grants: 490
  State Arts Resources: 490
  Statewide Service Organizations: 490
NORTH CAROLINA ASSOCIATION OF EDUCATORS
  Morrow (Mary)/Edna Richards Scholarship Fund: 1638
NORTH CAROLINA COMMUNITY FOUNDATION: 248
NORTH CAROLINA GLAXOSMITHKLINE FOUNDATION
  Child Health Recognition Awards: 1581
  Ribbon of Hope: 1581
  Traditional Grants: 1581
  Women in Science Scholars Program: 1581
NORTH CAROLINA LIBRARY ASSOCIATION
  Appalachian Scholarship: 739
  McLendon Scholarship: 739
  Query-Long Scholarship (The): 739
NORTH CAROLINA STATE EDUCATION ASSISTANCE
  AUTHORITY/COLLEGE FOUNDATION OF NORTH CAROLINA:
  1736
NORTH DAKOTA COUNCIL ON THE ARTS
  Arts-in-Education/Artists in Residence: 491
  Arts-in-Education/STE[A]M: 491
  Arts-in-Education/Teacher Incentive: 491
  Community Arts Access: 491
  Individual Artists Fellowships: 491
  Institutional Support: 491
  Presenter Support: 491
  Professional Development: 491
  Special Projects: 491
  Traditional Arts Apprenticeships: 491
North Dakota Indian Scholarship Program: 1054
NORTH DAKOTA STATE BOARD FOR INDIAN SCHOLARSHIPS
  North Dakota Indian Scholarship Program: 1054
NORTHEAST AGRICULTURAL EDUCATION FOUNDATION: 2126
NORTHEASTERN LOGGERS' ASSOCIATION, INC.
  NELA Annual Scholarship Contest: 2127
NORTHERN CHAUTAUQUA COMMUNITY FOUNDATION: 1737
Northern Trust Company Charitable Trust (The): 1338
NORTHERN TRUST CORPORATION
  Northern Trust Company Charitable Trust (The): 1338
  Northern Trust Matching Gift Program (The): 1338
  Volunteer Grants Program: 1338
Northern Trust Matching Gift Program (The): 1338
Northern, Eastern and Southwestern Region Competitive Grants: 168
NORTHWEST MINNESOTA FOUNDATION (THE): 1339
NORTHWESTERN MUTUAL FOUNDATION (THE): 1340
Norwich Women and Girls Fund: 1225
Norwich Youth Fund: 1225
Notley (Grant) Memorial Postdoctoral Fellowship: 1777
Novak (The Robert) Journalism Fellowship Program: 2000
Novel Approaches to Drug Discovery in Alzheimer's Disease: 2216
Novis (Brian D.) Research Grants: 2274
NOYES (JESSIE SMITH) FOUNDATION: 2194
Noyes (Marcia C.) Award: 730
NRA FOUNDATION, INC. (THE)
  Bray (Jeanne E.) Memorial Scholarship: 1738
NSF-CBMS Regional Conferences in the Mathematical Sciences: 2094
NSF Graduate Research Fellowship Program: 1832
NSHMBA Scholarship Program: 1006
NSPS Board of Governors Scholarship: 2658
NSPS Scholarships (The): 2658
NSTAR FOUNDATION: 249
NUCLEAR AGE PEACE FOUNDATION
  Kelly (Barbara Mandigo) Peace Poetry Awards: 855
Nurse Practitioner/Nurse Midwife Scholarship Program: 2499
Nurses Research Fellowship: 2474
NURSES' EDUCATIONAL FUNDS, INC.: 2495
Nursing Research Grants: 2486
Nurturing Community Arts: 134
Nutrition Research: 2675

Nutrition Research Program: 2671
NYS Aid for Part-Time Study (APTS): 1733
NYS Memorial Scholarships: 1732
NZFGW Daphne Purves Grant: 1085

O

O'Bannon (The Frank) Grant: 1699
O'Brien (Soledad) Scholarship: 1001
O'Connor (Basil) Starter Scholar Research Award: 2284
O'Connor (The John E.) Film Award: 578
O'Donovan (The Anita Cecil) Fellowship: 913
O'NEILL (WILLIAM J. AND DOROTHY K.) FOUNDATION: 250
OAK GROVE SCHOOL FOUNDATION
  Grants Program: 1582
  Tuition Assistance: 1582
OAK RIDGE INSTITUTE FOR SCIENCE AND EDUCATION
  Professional Internship Program: 2661
Oakes (John B.) Award: 1928
Obstetric and Pediatric Pharmacology and Therapeutics Branch (OPPTB):
  1462
Occupational/Physical Therapy Scholarship: 2556
Ocean Exploration and Research Program: 2084
Ocean Section: 2087
Oceanography Engineering Fellowship Program: 2038
Office of Challenge Grants: 379
OFFICE OF INDIAN ENERGY AND ECONOMIC DEVELOPMENT
  Indian Employment Assistance: 1055
  Public Law 102-477: 1055
OHF Research Grant: 2304
Ohio Artists on Tour: 492
OHIO ARTS COUNCIL
  Artists with Disabilities Access: 492
  Arts Access: 492
  Arts Learning: Artist Express: 492
  Arts Learning: Artist in Residence/Artists: 492
  Arts Learning: Artist in Residence/Sponsors: 492
  Arts Learning: Arts Partnership: 492
  Building Cultural Diversity: 492
  Individual Artist Grants and Services: Traditional Arts Apprenticeships:
  492
  Ohio Artists on Tour: 492
  Ohio Heritage Fellowship Awards: 492
  Project Support: 492
  Sustainability: 492
OHIO BOARD OF REGENTS
  Ohio College Opportunity Grant Program (OCOG): 1740
  Ohio War Orphans Scholarship: 1739
Ohio Chapter ISA Education Grant: 2129
Ohio College Opportunity Grant Program (OCOG): 1740
Ohio Heritage Fellowship Awards: 492
OHIO NATIONAL GUARD SCHOLARSHIP PROGRAM: 1741
Ohio War Orphans Scholarship: 1739
OISHEI (THE JOHN R.) FOUNDATION: 251
OKLAHOMA ARTS COUNCIL
  Capitol Art Travel Subsidies: 493
  Major Grant Support: 493
  Organizational Support: 493
  Small Grant Support: 493
  Small Grant Support for Schools: 493
OKLAHOMA CITY COMMUNITY FOUNDATION, INC.: 1341
Oldfield (Vada and Barney) Fellowship for National Security Reporting:
  1958
Olin Fellowships: 2141
Olin (Mr. and Mrs. Spencer T.) Fellowships for Women: 1802
Olin Palladium Award: 1819
Oliver (Robert B.) Scholarship: 1662
Olmsted Scholars Program: 2186
OMAHA COMMUNITY FOUNDATION
  African American Unity Fund: 252
  Endowment Funds of Southwest Iowa: 252
  Fund for Omaha: 252
  Futuro Latino Fund: 252
  Youth in Philanthropy: 252
Omicron Nu Master's Fellowship: 2674
Omicron Nu Research Fellowship: 2674
OMNOVA SOLUTIONS FOUNDATION: 1342

OMOHUNDRO INSTITUTE OF EARLY AMERICAN HISTORY AND
CULTURE
Jamestown Prize: 624
Lapidus-OIEAHC Fellowship: 626
Omohundro Institute Postdoctoral Fellowship: 625
Omohundro Institute Postdoctoral Fellowship: 625
On Screen/In Person: 476
ONCOLOGY NURSING FOUNDATION
Dissertation Research Grant: 2442
ONF Foundation Research Grant Award: 2442
Research Career Development Award: 2442
OneBreath Clinical Research Award for Lung Cancer (The): 2392
ONF Foundation Research Grant Award: 2442
Open Grants: 1604
OPEN MEADOWS FOUNDATION: 1092
Open Minds Across Canada: 2267
OPEN SOCIETY INSTITUTE - BALTIMORE
Criminal Justice Program: 1499
Drug Addiction Treatment Program (The): 1343
Opera Production Competition: 780
Operating Funds: 283
Operating Grants: 485
Operating Support Grants: 494, 511, 523
Operation We Care: 1504
Operational Program Grants: 1448
Operations and Power Division Scholarship: 2636
Oppenheimer (J. Robert) Postdoctoral Fellowship: 1826
Opportunity Fund Grants: 2170
Opportunity Grants: 445, 1371
Oral Cancer: 2352
Oral Health Disparities Research: 2352
ORANGE COUNTY COMMUNITY FOUNDATION: 253
ORDEAN FOUNDATION (THE): 1344
ORDER SONS OF ITALY IN AMERICA, GRAND LODGE OF
FLORIDA: 1742
OREF Clinical Research Award: 2300
OREGON ARTS COMMISSION
Access Reimbursement Grants: 494
Arts Build Communities: 494
Arts Learning Grants: 494
Arts Recognition Grants: 494
Arts Services Grants: 494
Capacity Building Grants: 494
Career Opportunity Grants: 494
Cultural Tourism Grants: 494
Individual Artists Fellowship Grants: 494
Operating Support Grants: 494
Oregon Media Arts Fellowship: 494
OREGON COMMUNITY FOUNDATION (THE)
Community Grants Program: 1345
Oregon Media Arts Fellowship: 494
Organization Grant Program: 969
ORGANIZATION OF AMERICAN STATES
Academic Studies: 856
Professional Development: 856
Rowe (The Leo S.) Pan American Fund: 963
Organizational Capacity Building: 1009
Organizational Endowment Funds: 1252
Organizational Grants: 994
Organizational Support: 493
ORLANDO MAGIC YOUTH FUND
Orlando Magic Youth Fund, a McCormick Foundation Fund: 1139
Orlando Magic Youth Fund, a McCormick Foundation Fund: 1139
ORTHOPAEDIC RESEARCH AND EDUCATION FOUNDATION
Career Development Grants: 2301
OREF Clinical Research Award: 2300
Resident Clinician-Scientist Training Grant: 2302
Osborn (The Kenneth J.) Memorial Scholarship: 2034
Osborne (Ernest G.) Award: 1498
OSHER (THE BERNARD) FOUNDATION: 254
OSM Standard Life Competition: 761
OSTEOGENESIS IMPERFECTA FOUNDATION
Clinical Seed Grants: 2303
Geisman (Michael) Fellowships: 2303
Seed Grants: 2303
OUTER BANKS COMMUNITY FOUNDATION: 1346
Outstanding Abstract Achievement Award: 2354
Outstanding Dissertation of the Year Award: 1557
Outstanding Educator Award: 430, 2632
Outstanding Junior Clinical Education Manuscript: 2547

Outstanding Junior Clinical Teacher of the Year: 2547
Outstanding Junior Investigator of the Year: 2547
Outstanding Junior Research Manuscript: 2547
Outstanding Mid-Career Clinical Teacher of the Year: 2547
Outstanding Scientific Achievement for Clinical Investigation Award: 2547
Outstanding Social Studies Teacher of the Year Awards: 1859
OXALOSIS AND HYPEROXALURIA FOUNDATION
OHF Research Grant: 2304
OXNARD FOUNDATION: 2305

P

P.E.O. International Peace Scholarships: 964
P.E.O. SISTERHOOD
P.E.O. International Peace Scholarships: 964
PACCAR FOUNDATION: 255
PACIFIC FOUNDATION SERVICES: 1639
PACIFIC GAS AND ELECTRIC COMPANY: 256
PACIFIC LIFE FOUNDATION
Arts and Culture: 257
Civic, Community, and Environment: 257
Education: 257
Health and Human Services: 257
PACKARD (THE DAVID AND LUCILE) FOUNDATION
Children, Families and Communities: 258
Conservation and Science: 258
Population and Reproductive Health: 258
PACKARD (LUCILE) FOUNDATION FOR CHILDREN'S HEALTH:
1140
Packer (Barbara) Fellowship: 345
Padagogischer Austauschdienst Teaching Assistantships: 654
Padbury (William John) Scholarship: 2667
Page (Walter Hines) Scholarships: 958
Painters and Sculptors Grant Program: 478
Paley (Grace) Prize in Short Fiction: 667
Palisca (Claude V.) Award: 751
Palmer (Alice Freeman) Fellowship: 1097
Pam (Edgar) Fellowship: 2678
Panasonic Foundation Partnership Program for School Reform: 1583
PANASONIC FOUNDATION, INC.
Collaboration for Innovation: 1583
New Jersey Network of Superintendents: 1583
Panasonic Foundation Partnership Program for School Reform: 1583
Panowski (Mildred and Albert) Playwriting Award: 537
Papaioannou (The George) Fellowship: 889
Pape Research Fund: 2209
PARAPSYCHOLOGY FOUNDATION, INC.
Garrett (Eileen J.) Scholarship: 2585
Bolton (Frances P.) Fellowship: 2586
Coly (Robert R.) Prize: 2588
Tart (Charles T. and Judith A.) Student Incentive Award: 2587
PARDEE (THE ELSA U.) FOUNDATION: 2443
PARENTS WITHOUT PARTNERS
Parents Without Partners International Scholarship: 1584
Parents Without Partners International Scholarship: 1584
PARK BANK FOUNDATION, INC.: 259
PARKER FOUNDATION (THE): 260
PARKER HANNIFIN CORPORATION FOUNDATION: 261
PARKINSON'S DISEASE FOUNDATION, INC.
Conference Awards: 2480
International Research Grants Award: 2481
PDF-PSG Mentored Clinical Research Award: 2480
Postdoctoral Fellowship: 2481
Summer Student Fellowship: 2482
Parkman (Francis) Prize: 635
Parks Climate Challenge: 2190
Parks (The Danielle) Memorial Fellowship: 913
Parks Stewards Program: 2190
Parrish (William P.) Scholarship: 628
Parsons (Elisabeth M. and Winchell M.) Scholarship: 2646
PARSONS (THE RALPH M.) FOUNDATION: 262
Partner University Fund: 909
Partners for Health: 1440
Partnership for Research and Innovation in the Health System (PRIHS):
2215
Partnership Grant: 469
PASADENA COMMUNITY FOUNDATION: 1500
PASIC International Scholarship: 784
PASIC Scholarships: 784
Pass Through Grants: 1242

Past Presidents Scholarship: 2602
Pastoral Fellowship: 809
PATAGONIA INC.
    Environmental Grant Program: 2195
Patient-Centered Coordinated Care Program: 1478
Patient Link: 228
Patient Services Grants: Safety Net Grant Program: 2229
PATRON SAINTS FOUNDATION (THE): 1456
PATTERSON (THE ALICIA) FOUNDATION
    Fellowship Program for Journalists: 1955
Patterson (Walter S.) Scholarship: 1924
Paty (Donald) Career Development Awards: 2472
Paul (Courtland) Scholarship: 2186
Paula Scholarships: 1653
Pawlett (Thomas Lawrance) Scholarship: 2132
Payment and System Reform: 1478
PDEF Mickey Williams Technologist Minority Student Scholarships: 2329
PDF-PSG Mentored Clinical Research Award: 2480
PEABODY (AMELIA) CHARITABLE FUND: 263
PEACOCK FOUNDATION, INC.: 264
Peacock (The Frances M.) Scholarship for Native Bird Habitat: 2179
Peacock Medal: 2680
Peaslee (Robert L.)-Detroit Brazing and Soldering Scholarship: 2602
Pediatric Growth and Nutrition Branch (PGNB): 1462
Pell Grant: 1772
Pemberton (Margaret) Scholarship: 2492
PEN AMERICAN CENTER
    PEN Award for Poetry in Translation: 687
    PEN Open Book Award: 684
    PEN Prison Writing Program: 689
    PEN Translation Prize: 660
    PEN Writers' Fund: 690
    PEN/Joyce Osterweil Award for Poetry: 685
    PEN/Laura Pels Foundation Awards for Drama: 535
    PEN/Phyllis Naylor Working Writer Fellowship: 686
    PEN/Robert W. Bingham Prize: 683
    PEN/Voelcker Award for Poetry: 688
PEN Award for Poetry in Translation: 687
PEN/Hemingway Award for Debut Fiction: 692
PEN NEW ENGLAND
    PEN/Hemingway Award for Debut Fiction: 692
    PEN New England Awards: 691
PEN New England Awards: 691
PEN Open Book Award: 684
PEN Prison Writing Program: 689
PEN Translation Prize: 660
PEN Writers' Fund: 690
PEN/Faulkner Award for Fiction: 693
PEN/FAULKNER FOUNDATION
    PEN/Faulkner Award for Fiction: 693
PEN/Joyce Osterweil Award for Poetry: 685
PEN/Laura Pels Foundation Awards for Drama: 535
PEN/Phyllis Naylor Working Writer Fellowship: 686
PEN/Robert W. Bingham Prize: 683
PEN/Voelcker Award for Poetry: 688
PENN (THE WILLIAM) FOUNDATION
    Closing the Achievement Gap: 265
    Creative Communities: 265
    Watershed Protection: 265
PENNSYLVANIA COUNCIL ON THE ARTS
    Arts Organization Grants: 495
PENNSYLVANIA HIGHER EDUCATION ASSISTANCE AGENCY
    Pennsylvania State Grant Program: 1743
Pennsylvania Performing Arts on Tour: 476
Pennsylvania State Grant Program: 1743
Pepler (George) International Award: 1869
PEPSICO FOUNDATION: 266
PepsiCo Scholarships/Internship: 1001
Percent for Art: 485
Perception, Action & Cognition Program: 2584
PERCUSSIVE ARTS SOCIETY
    Annual Composition Contest: 784
    Hoey (Fred) Scholarship: 784
    Internship Program: 784
    Londin (Larrie) Scholarship: 784
    PASIC International Scholarship: 784
    PASIC Scholarships: 784
    Yamaha Terry Gibbs Scholarship: 784
    Zildjian (Armand) Scholarship: 784
    Zildjian Family Opportunity Fund: 784

Performance Scholarships in Music for Students in Bachelor and Master
    of Music Programs: 788
Performing Arts: 159, 286, 427
Performing Arts Fellowship: 1666
Performing Arts Fellowships: 523
Performing Arts Japan Program: 852
Performing Arts Program: 366
Performing Ensembles Program: 763
Peridian International/Rae L. Price, FASLA Scholarship: 2186
PERMIAN BASIN AREA FOUNDATION: 1347
Perry (Jacquelin), MD Resident Research Award: 2553
Perry (The William J.) Fellowship in International Security: 833
Perryman (The Leonard M.) Communications Scholarship for Ethnic
    Minority Students: 1019
Pesticide Enforcement Cooperative Agreements: 2207
Peters (Marie) Award: 1498
Peterson (Kate B. and Hall J.) Fellowships: 345
PETOSKEY-HARBOR SPRINGS AREA COMMUNITY FOUNDATION:
    1348
Petroleum Research Fund (The): 2031
PEW FELLOWS PROGRAM IN MARINE CONSERVATION: 2196
PEW FELLOWSHIPS AT THE PEW CENTER FOR ARTS &
    HERITAGE: 564
PFC Research Grants: 2557
Pfizer Prize: 597
Pfizer Teacher Development Award: 2221
PFORZHEIMER (THE CARL AND LILY) FOUNDATION, INC.: 267
PGSF Undergraduate Awards: 2614
Ph.D. Program in Material Science and Engineering: 2044
PHARMACEUTICAL RESEARCH AND MANUFACTURERS OF
    AMERICA FOUNDATION, INC.
    Calabresi (The Paul) Medical Student Research Fellowship: 2539
    Postdoctoral Fellowship in Health Outcomes: 2310
    Postdoctoral Fellowship in Pharmacology/Toxicology: 2309
    Postdoctoral Fellowships in Informatics: 2307
    Postdoctoral Fellowships in Pharmaceutics: 2540
    Predoctoral Fellowships in Health Outcomes: 2306
    Predoctoral Fellowships in Pharmaceutics: 2541
    Predoctoral Fellowships in Pharmacology/Toxicology: 2543
    Research Starter Grants in Adherence Improvement: 2542
    Research Starter Grants in Health Outcomes: 2542
    Research Starter Grants in Informatics: 2542
    Research Starter Grants in Pharmaceutics: 2542
    Research Starter Grants in Pharmacology/Toxicology: 2542
    Research Starter Grants in Translational Medicine: 2542
    Sabbatical Fellowships in Health Outcomes: 2308
    Sabbatical Fellowships in Informatics: 2308
    Sabbatical Fellowships in Pharmaceutics: 2308
    Sabbatical Fellowships in Pharmacology/Toxicology: 2308
PhD Project (The): 1902
PHI ALPHA THETA HISTORY HONOR SOCIETY
    Cleven (The Nels Andrew N.) Founder's Paper Prize Awards: 629
    Hammond (Dr. George P.) Paper Prize: 629
    Member's First Book Award: 627
    Member's Subsequent Book Award: 627
    Morgan (Thomas S.) Scholarship: 628
    Parrish (William P.) Scholarship: 628
    Phi Alpha Theta Scholarship: 628
    Pine (John) Memorial Award: 628
    Tunstall (Graydon A., Jr.) Scholarship: 628
    Turner (Dr. Lynn W.) Paper Prize: 629
    Zimmerman (A.F.) Scholarship: 628
Phi Alpha Theta Scholarship: 628
Phi Beta Kappa Award in Science: 694
PHI BETA KAPPA SOCIETY (THE)
    Emerson (Ralph Waldo) Award: 694
    Gauss (Christian) Award: 694
    Jensen (The Walter J.) Fellowship for French Language, Literature and
        Culture: 935
    Phi Beta Kappa Award in Science: 694
    Romanell-Phi Beta Kappa Professorship in Philosophy (The): 1744
    Sibley (Mary Isabel) Fellowship: 1093
PHI CHI THETA EDUCATIONAL FOUNDATION
    Educational and Scholastic Advancement Programs: 1910
PHI DELTA CHI PHARMACY FRATERNITY
    Hollenback (Rand P.) Scholarship Program: 2544
Phi Kappa Phi Fellowship (The): 1696
Phi Lambda Sigma-GlaxoSmithKline-AFPE First Year Graduate
    Scholarship: 2535
PHILADELPHIA FOUNDATION (THE): 1349
Philanthropy: 159

PHILLIPS (DR. AND MRS. ARTHUR WILLIAM) CHARITABLE
   TRUST: 2311
Phillips Fund Grants for Native American Research: 1040
PHILLIPS (JAY AND ROSE) FAMILY FOUNDATION OF
   MINNESOTA: 1501
Philputt (James M.) Memorial Loan Fund: 808
Photographers' Fund (The): 544
Photographic and Electronic Media (MFA): 555
Photography Program: 470
Physicians of Tomorrow Scholarship: 1660
Physics Research Grants: 2101
PHYSIOTHERAPY FOUNDATION OF CANADA
   Alberta Research Award: 2557
   Beattie (Constance) Memorial Fund Bursary Program: 2557
   Morgan (Alun) Memorial Research Fund in Orthopaedic Physiotherapy:
      2557
   PFC Research Grants: 2557
   Schnurr (B.E.) Memorial Fund Research Grant: 2557
   Whitmore (Ann Collins) Memorial Fund Awards: 2557
   Whitmore (Ann Collins) Memorial Fund Student Awards Competition:
      2557
Pi Gamma Mu Scholarships: 1745
PI GAMMA MU, INTERNATIONAL HONOR SOCIETY IN SOCIAL
   SCIENCE
   Pi Gamma Mu Scholarships: 1745
PICK (THE ALBERT, JR.) FUND: 268
PIEDMONT HEALTH FOUNDATION: 1457
PIERCE (THE HAROLD WHITWORTH) CHARITABLE TRUST: 269
Pierce (The Lorne) Medal: 1836
Pierce (Newton Lacy) Prize in Astronomy: 2047
Pilot and Feasibility Awards: 2413
Pilot Grant: 1515
Pilot Project Award: 2532
Pilot Research Grant: 2312
Pinch Medal: 2680
Pine (John) Memorial Award: 628
PINKERTON FOUNDATION (THE): 1141
Pinkney (The David) Prize: 634
PIPER FUND: 2012
PIPER (MINNIE STEVENS) FOUNDATION
   Piper Professor Program: 1746
   Piper Scholar Program: 1746
   Student Loan Program: 1746
Piper Professor Program: 1746
Piper Scholar Program: 1746
Pisk (Paul A.) Prize: 751
PITT POETRY SERIES
   Starrett (Agnes Lynch) Poetry Prize: 695
Pittenger (Dr. Aura-Lee A. and James Hobbs) American History
   Scholarship: 614
PITTSBURGH FOUNDATION (THE): 1350
Pittsburgh Local Section Scholarship: 2640
PITTSBURGH NEW MUSIC ENSEMBLE, INC. (THE)
   Gaul (Harvey) Music Composition Contest: 785
Pittsco/Hearlihy/FTEE Grant Excellence in Teaching Technology and
   Engineering: 1545
Pizzigati (Antonio) Prize for Software in the Public Interest: 1387
PLANNING AND VISUAL EDUCATION PARTNERSHIP (THE): 1747
PLASTIC SURGERY FOUNDATION (PSF)
   National Endowment for Plastic Surgery: 2312
   Pilot Research Grant: 2312
   Research Fellowship: 2312
Platt Fellowships: 895
Player Foundation Grants: 1336
PLAYWRIGHTS' CENTER (THE)
   Affiliated Writer Program: 696
   Core Writer Program: 696
   Jerome Fellowships: 696
   Many Voices Fellowships: 696
   McKnight Advancement Grants: 696
   McKnight National Residency and Commission: 696
   McKnight Theater Artist Fellowships: 696
   New Plays on Campus: 696
Plossl (George and Marion) Doctoral Dissertation Competition: 2599
PLOUGH FOUNDATION: 1502
Poet Laureate: 453
Poetry Out Loud: 453
POLLOCK-KRASNER FOUNDATION, INC. (THE): 565
Polsky (Joel) Academic Achievement Award: 412
Polsky (Joel) Prize: 412

Pomerance (Harriet and Leon) Fellowship: 352
PONTIFICAL INSTITUTE OF MEDIAEVAL STUDIES
   Mellon Postdoctoral Fellowships: 630
POOL (THE DOROTHY RIDER) HEALTH CARE TRUST: 1458
Pool (Judith Graham) Postdoctoral Research Fellowships in Bleeding
   Disorders: 2288
Poor and Needy Division: 1503
Population: 2212
Population and Reproductive Health: 258
PORTER (IRWIN ANDREW) FOUNDATION: 270
Post Baccalaureate Certificate Programs: 573
Post-Baccalaureate Program: 555
Post-Doctoral Fellowship: 809
POST-POLIO HEALTH INTERNATIONAL
   Research Fund (The): 2313
Postdoctoral Award to Honor the Nurse Cadet Corps: 2484
Postdoctoral Cancer Research Fellowship: 2440
Postdoctoral Earth and Planetary Sciences Fellowship: 2628
Postdoctoral Fellowship: 2376, 2425, 2471, 2481
Postdoctoral Fellowship at The Hamner Institutes for Health Sciences:
   2067
Postdoctoral Fellowship Awards in Studying Complex Systems: 221
Postdoctoral Fellowship Grants: 2439
Postdoctoral Fellowship in Health Outcomes: 2310
Postdoctoral Fellowship in Pharmacology/Toxicology: 2309
Postdoctoral Fellowships: 419, 2367, 2415, 2450
Postdoctoral Fellowships at NCAR: 1829
Postdoctoral Fellowships in Informatics: 2307
Postdoctoral Fellowships in Pharmaceutics: 2540
Postdoctoral Fellowships in the Humanities and the Arts, Sciences and
   Professions: 377
Postdoctoral Fellowships Program at the Weizmann Institute of Science:
   953
Postdoctoral Fellowships Program in Multiple Sclerosis Research: 2477
Postdoctoral Program at the Jackson Laboratory: 2149
Postdoctoral Research Associateships: 2037
Postdoctoral Research Fellowship: 2455
Postdoctoral Research Fellowship Program: 1810
Postdoctoral Research Fellowships: 1516, 2464
Postdoctoral Researchers Fellowship: 914
Postdoctoral Training Program: 2338
Postgraduate Clinical Fellowship Training Program at the Albert Ellis
   Institute: 2578
Postgraduate Research at the University of Cambridge: 905
Postgraduate Research Scholarships: 945
POTTS MEMORIAL FOUNDATION (THE): 2399
POVERTY & RACE RESEARCH ACTION COUNCIL: 1867
Power (Susan Kelly) and Helen Hornbeck Tanner Fellowship: 394
PPG CARE Fund: 271
PPG INDUSTRIES FOUNDATION
   Grant Incentives for Volunteerism by PPG Employees and Retirees
      (GIVE): 271
   Matching Gifts Program: 271
   National Merit Scholarships: 271
   PPG CARE Fund: 271
   Public Education Leadership Community Grants (PELC): 271
Prato (Lou and Carole) Sports Reporting Scholarship: 1958
Praxair International Scholarship: 2602
Pre-Dissertation Fellowships: 876
PRECAST/PRESTRESSED CONCRETE INSTITUTE
   Jenny (Daniel P.) Research Fellowships: 2662
Precious Minds, New Connections: 197
Predoctoral and Postdoctoral Fellowships at the Carnegie Institution: 1816
Predoctoral Fellowship: 2377
Predoctoral Fellowships in Health Outcomes: 2306
Predoctoral Fellowships in Pharmaceutics: 2541
Predoctoral Fellowships in Pharmacology/Toxicology: 2543
Predoctoral Research Fellowship: 2455
Predoctoral Research Fellowships: 2056
Predoctoral Research Training Fellowships: 2464
Prelinger (Catherine) Award: 1078
Prematurity Research Initiative (PRI): 2283
Premio Del Rey (The): 578
PRENTISS (THE ELISABETH SEVERANCE) FOUNDATION: 2314
PRESBYTERIAN CHURCH (U.S.A.)
   Presbyterian Study Grants: 821
   Robinson (Samuel) Essay Contest: 1749
   Student Opportunity Scholarship: 1748
Presbyterian Study Grants: 821
Presenter Support: 491
Presenter Travel Fund: 484

Preservation and Access: 382
President's Certificate of Merit Award: 2500
PRESIDENT'S COMMISSION ON WHITE HOUSE FELLOWSHIPS
  White House Fellowships: 2013
President's Doctoral Scholar Award: 948
President's Grants: 2280
President's New Researcher Award: 2574
President's Scholarships (The): 1958
Presidents Scholarship: 2653
Presidio La Bahia Award: 637
Press Club Media and Internship Scholarships: 1750
PRESS CLUB OF METROPOLITAN ST. LOUIS AND JOURNALISM
  FOUNDATION OF METROPOLITAN ST. LOUIS (THE)
  Baseball Writers of America Scholarship: 1750
  Enterprise Journalism Fellowships: 1750
  Fleishman-Hillard, Inc. Scholarship: 1750
  Journalism Foundation Scholarships: 1750
  Lipman (David) Scholarship at the Missouri School of Journalism: 1750
  Missouri Professional Communicators Scholarships: 1750
  Press Club Media and Internship Scholarships: 1750
  Press Club of Metropolitan St. Louis Scholarships: 1750
  St. Louis Public Library Media Archives: 1750
  Times Newspapers and Webster University Journalism Scholarships:
    1750
Press Club of Metropolitan St. Louis Scholarships: 1750
PRESSER FOUNDATION
  Presser Undergraduate Scholar Award: 786
Presser Undergraduate Scholar Award: 786
Preterm Birth Initiative: 2244
PREVENT CANCER FOUNDATION: 2444
Preyer (Kathryn Conway) Fellowship: 1097
Price (Derek)/Rod Webster Prize: 596
Price (Norman I.) Scholarship in Electrical Engineering: 2667
PRIDE FOUNDATION: 1008
Primary Grant Program: 185
Princess Grace Awards: 536
PRINCESS GRACE FOUNDATION-USA
  Princess Grace Awards: 536
PRINCETON AREA COMMUNITY FOUNDATION
  Fund for Women and Girls (The): 1351
  Greater Mercer Grants: 1351
PRINCIPAL FINANCIAL GROUP FOUNDATION INC.
  Charitable Giving Program (The): 272
Principal Pipeline Initiative: 329
Principal Supervisor Initiative: 329
PRINT AND GRAPHICS SCHOLARSHIP FOUNDATION: 2615
  PGSF Undergraduate Awards: 2614
Prisoner of War/Missing in Action (POW/MIA) Program: 1729
PRITCHETT TRUST: 1142
Pro Bowl Grants: 1336
Pro Deo and Pro Patria Scholarships: 1708
Pro Futura: 401
Procter & Gamble Research Award for Postdoctoral Students: 2346
Procter & Gamble Scholarship: 2349
Production and Presentation Grants: 417
Professional Development: 491, 501, 856
Professional Development for Educators Scholarship: 1909
Professional Development Programs: 1559
Professional Development Scholarship Program: 1766
Professional Fellowship Program: 514
Professional Internship Program: 2661
Professional Research: 2528
Professional Student Exchange Program (PSEP): 334
Professional Trainee Program: 531
Professional Training: 2201
Program for Operational and Projects Support: 474
Program for the Donation of Japanese Language Teaching Materials (for
  the United States): 1703
Program Grants: 1245, 2147
Program in African-American History: 603
Program in Early American Economy and Society: 603
Program Related Investments: 185
Program Support: 332
Program Support Grants: 507
Program/Project Support: 283
Programme de tournees: 442
Programme General: 442
Project Grant for Artists: 469
Project Grant for Organizations: 469
Project Grants: 375, 501, 511, 620

Project Support: 492
Projects of National Significance for Persons with Developmental
  Disabilities: 1391
PROLITERACY WORLDWIDE
  National Book Fund (NBF): 1352
Promoting Economic Development: 1330
Promoting Safe and Stable Families: 1153
PROSTATE CANCER RESEARCH AND EDUCATION FOUNDATION
  (PC-REF): 2445
Protecting the Environment: 134
Prothero (Louise) Leadership Fund - Women's Club: 1224
Provost's Ph.D. Fellowship Program: 1797
Psi Chi/APA Edwin B. Newman Graduate Research Award: 2589
PSI CHI, THE INTERNATIONAL HONOR SOCIETY IN
  PSYCHOLOGY
  Psi Chi/APA Edwin B. Newman Graduate Research Award: 2589
Public Art Building Communities: 447
Public Art Program: 471
Public Education: 1147, 1270
Public Education Grants: 1130
Public Education Leadership Community Grants (PELC): 271
Public Interest Grants (General Fund): 1494
Public Interest Internships: 2670
Public Interest Law Fellowships: 2491
Public Law 102-477: 1055
Public Life Program: 1492
Public Programs: 1947
Public Programs in the Arts: 459
Public Service Program: 173
Public Value Partnerships: 485
PUBLIC WELFARE FOUNDATION, INC.
  Criminal Justice: 273
  Juvenile Justice: 273
  Workers' Rights: 273
Pulaski Scholarships for Advanced Studies: 1655
Pulitzer Fellowships: 1926
Pulitzer Prizes: 1926
PULLIAM JOURNALISM FELLOWSHIP: 1956
PULMONARY FIBROSIS FOUNDATION
  Clinical Research in Pulmonary Fibrosis Program: 2315
Putnam (A.O.) Memorial Scholarship: 2653
PVA RESEARCH FOUNDATION
  Spinal Cord Injury Research Grants and Fellowships: 2558

Q

QUAKER CHEMICAL FOUNDATION (THE)
  Grant Program: 274
  Matching Gift Program: 274
  Scholarship Program: 274
Quality of Life Grants: 2559
QUANTUM FOUNDATION: 1459
QUEEN ELISABETH INTERNATIONAL MUSIC COMPETITION OF
  BELGIUM (THE): 787
Queen Elizabeth II Graduate Scholarships: 1783
Queeny (Edgar Monsanto) Safety Professional of the Year Award: 2648
Queer Youth Fund: 1490
Query-Long Scholarship (The): 739
Quick Fund$: 459
QUILL AND SCROLL FOUNDATION: 1957
Quincey (Dorothy Lillian) Memorial Graduate Scholarship: 1080

R

R.E.B. Awards for Teaching Excellence: 1213
Radcliffe Institute Fellowship Program: 1640
RADCLIFFE INSTITUTE FOR ADVANCED STUDY, HARVARD
  UNIVERSITY
  Radcliffe Institute Fellowship Program: 1640
Radiant Peace Education Awards: 1608
RADIANT PEACE FOUNDATION INTERNATIONAL, INC. (THE)
  Radiant Peace Education Awards: 1608
RADIO TELEVISION DIGITAL NEWS FOUNDATION
  Biestock (N.S.) Fellowship: 1958
  Bradley (Ed) Scholarship: 1958
  Clark (Michele) Fellowship: 1958
  Foreman (George) Tribute to Lyndon B. Johnson: 1958
  Mimmotte (Jacque I.) Fellowship: 1958
  Oldfield (Vada and Barney) Fellowship for National Security Reporting:

1958
  Prato (Lou and Carole) Sports Reporting Scholarship: 1958
  President's Scholarships (The): 1958
  Reynolds (Mike) Journalism Scholarship: 1958
  Schecter (Abe) Graduate Scholarship: 1958
  Simpson (Carole) Scholarship: 1958
  Wilson (Pete) Scholarship: 1958
RADIOLOGICAL SOCIETY OF NORTH AMERICA RESEARCH AND
  EDUCATION FOUNDATION
  Education Scholar Grant: 2318
  Research Medical Student Grant: 2317
  Research Resident/Fellow Grant: 2321
  Research Seed Grant: 2316
  RSNA Research Scholar Grant: 2320
  RSNA/AUR/APDR/SCARD Radiology Education Research
  Development Grant: 2319
Rafaty (F. Mark) Memorial Award: 2220
RAGDALE FOUNDATION
  Residencies at Ragdale Foundation: 496
Rain Bird Intelligent Use of Water Scholarship: 2186
RANCHO SANTA FE FOUNDATION
  Armed Forces Interest Group: 1353
  Rancho Santa Fe Women's Fund: 1353
Rancho Santa Fe Women's Fund: 1353
Randolph (Jennings) Fellowship Programs for International Peace: 864
Raney (Della H.) Nursing Scholarship: 2492
Rapid Response Grant: 2164
Rapid Response "Lightning" Grants: 1492
RASKOB FOUNDATION FOR CATHOLIC ACTIVITIES: 822
RASMUSSEN (V. KANN) FOUNDATION: 2088
Rasmussen (Wayne D.) Award: 576
Rawley (The James A.) Prize in Atlantic History: 578
RBC FOUNDATION - U.S.A.
  After School Grants: 1354
  Children's Mental Health: 1354
  Emerging Artists: 1354
Reading and Discussion Grants: 375, 384
Reading Award Program (RAP): 1047
REAGAN (RONALD) PRESIDENTIAL FOUNDATION
  GE-Reagan Foundation Scholarship Program: 1751
Recognition Grants: 1446
Recording Program: 763
Redding Rancheria Community Fund: 1375
REDFIELD (THE NELL J.) FOUNDATION: 275
REEBOK FOUNDATION (THE): 276
Reed (Sarah Rebecca) Scholarship: 716
Reese Fellowship (The): 345
REEVE (CHRISTOPHER AND DANA) FOUNDATION
  Quality of Life Grants: 2559
Reference Service Press Fellowship: 717
REGENSTEIN FOUNDATION (THE): 277
Regents Physician Loan Forgiveness Award Program: 1731
Region and Communities: 1495
Regional Artist Grants: 507
Regional Artist Project Grants: 490
Regional Development Grants: 800
Regional Grants: 6
Regional Library Telecommunications Aid: 733
Regional Public Libraries Systems Support: 733
Regional Touring Program: 475
Regular Competitive Grants: 1222
Regular Research Grant: 2414
REHABILITATION NURSING FOUNDATION (RNF)
  Evidence-based Practice (EBP) and Quality Improvement (QI) Project
  Grants: 2496
  RNF Fellow Research Grant: 2496
  RNF New Investigator Research Grant: 2496
  Sigma Theta Tau/RNF Research Grant: 2496
Rehabilitation Service Program: 2561
REINBERGER FOUNDATION (THE)
  Arts, Culture and Humanities: 1355
  Education: 1355
  Human Service - Other: 1355
  Human Service Health: 1355
Reines (Frederick) Postdoctoral Fellowship in Experimental Sciences:
  1826
Reingold (Nathan) Prize: 597
Religious Studies Fellowship: 1666
Rendel (Betty) Scholarship: 1091
Renewable Energy Program: 2169

REPLOGLE (LUTHER I.) FOUNDATION: 1356
REPORTERS COMMITTEE FOR FREEDOM OF THE PRESS
  Reporters Committee Legal Fellowship (The): 1959
Reporters Committee Legal Fellowship (The): 1959
Reproductive Justice: 141
Reproductive Scientist Development Program: 2501
REPRODUCTIVE SCIENTIST DEVELOPMENT PROGRAM (RSDP)
  Reproductive Scientist Development Program: 2501
Research and Applied Sciences: 1495
Research and Conservation Grants: 2174
Research and Development Grants: 417
Research and Evaluation on Education in Science and Engineering
  (REESE): 1607
Research and Training Fellowships for Clinicians: 2464
Research and Training Workshops: 2455
Research Assistantships in Medieval and Renaissance Studies: 357
Research Award: 2341
Research Awards: 2579
Research Awards at the Huntington Library and Art Gallery: 373
Research Awards Program: 2511
Research Career Development Award: 2442
RESEARCH CORPORATION FOR SCIENCE ADVANCEMENT
  Cottrell Scholar Awards: 2041
  Scialog: Solar Energy Conversion: 2041
  Single Investigator Cottrell College Science Awards: 2041
Research Fellowship: 852, 2312, 2395
Research Fellowship Award: 2421
Research Fellowship in American Studies: 2001
Research Fellowship Program: 2213
Research Fellowships: 526, 2263, 2479
Research Fellowships in American History and Culture: 603
Research Fellowships in Art History: 552
Research Fieldwork: 1408
Research Fund (The): 2313
RESEARCH FUND OF THE AMERICAN OTOLOGICAL SOCIETY,
  INC.
  AOS Clinician-Scientist Award: 2521
  Clinical Trial: 2521
  Research Grants: 2521
  Research Training Fellowship: 2521
Research Grant: 2018, 2299
Research Grant in Crystallography, Mineral Physics or Chemistry and
  Mineralogy: 2079
Research Grant Program: 1588, 2363, 2457
Research Grants: 585, 1409, 1812, 2070, 2167, 2413, 2462, 2493, 2521
Research Grants and Fellowships: 2424
Research Grants in Dietetics: 2672
Research Grants Program: 2282, 2606
Research in Remote Sensing of the Earth and Environment Grants: 2085
Research Infrastructure Awards: 2455
Research Initiative Fund Grants: 2455
Research Inventory Grants: 375
Research Library Program: 366
RESEARCH MANITOBA: 1460
Research Matters! Award: 2571
Research Medical Student Grant: 2317
Research Program: 378
Research Resident/Fellow Grant: 2321
Research Seed Grant: 2316
Research Starter Grants in Adherence Improvement: 2542
Research Starter Grants in Health Outcomes: 2542
Research Starter Grants in Informatics: 2542
Research Starter Grants in Pharmaceutics: 2542
Research Starter Grants in Pharmacology/Toxicology: 2542
Research Starter Grants in Translational Medicine: 2542
Research Studentship: 2469
Research Support Grants: 419
Research Training and Career Development Program: 1865
Research Training Fellowship: 2521
Research Training Grants: 2493
Research Travel Award: 634
Research Travel Grant Program: 1998
Research Travel Grants: 590
Research Traveling Fellowship: 2299
Residencies at Ragdale Foundation: 496
Residency Partnership Program: 756
Residency Travel Award: 2220
Resident Clinician-Scientist Training Grant: 2302
Resident Research Grant: 2523
Resident Scholar Fellowships: 2023
Resident Scholars Program: 809

Resistance Welding Manufacturing Alliance Scholarship: 2603
RESOURCES FOR THE FUTURE
  Fisher (Joseph L.) Dissertation Fellowships: 2197
  Krutilla (John V.) Research Stipend: 2199
  Spofford (The Walter O., Jr.) Memorial Internship: 2197
  White (Gilbert F.) Postdoctoral Fellowship Program: 2198
Responsive Grants: 232, 295
Responsive Grants Program: 1509
Reston (William) Research Award: 2532
Restricted Research Program: 2297
Retired and Senior Volunteer Program (RSVP): 1480
RETIREMENT RESEARCH FOUNDATION (THE)
  Accessible Faith: 1009
  Grants Program: 1009
  Organizational Capacity Building: 1009
REVSON (THE CHARLES H.) FOUNDATION: 278
Rey (H.A. and Margret) Translation Fellowship: 743
REYNOLDS (J.B.) FOUNDATION: 1357
REYNOLDS (KATE B.) CHARITABLE TRUST
  Health Care Division: 1503
  Poor and Needy Division: 1503
Reynolds (Mike) Journalism Scholarship: 1958
REYNOLDS (Z. SMITH) FOUNDATION, INC.: 279
RGK FOUNDATION: 1358
Rho Chi-Schering Plough-AFPE First Year Graduate Scholarship: 2535
RHODE ISLAND FOUNDATION/RHODE ISLAND COMMUNITY
  FOUNDATION (THE): 280
RHODE ISLAND STATE COUNCIL ON THE ARTS
  Arts Access Grant (AAG): 497
  Investments in Arts and Culture (AIC): 497
RIBA Research Trusts Awards: 422
Ribbon of Hope: 1581
Rice-Cullimore Scholarship: 2646
Richards (John F.) Prize in South Asian History: 578
Richardson (Henry and Sylvia) Research Grant: 2144
RICHARDSON (SID) MEMORIAL FUND: 1752
RICHARDSON (SID W.) FOUNDATION: 281
RICHARDSON (SMITH) FOUNDATION, INC.
  Domestic Public Policy Program: 1868
  International Security and Foreign Policy Program: 1868
Ridgway (General and Mrs. Matthew B.) Research Grant: 639
Rieck (Donald A.) Research Grant: 1536
RIGHTEOUS PERSONS FOUNDATION: 1010
RILEY (THE MABEL LOUISE) FOUNDATION : 1585
Rinehart School of Sculpture (MFA): 555
RIPPEL (FANNIE E.) FOUNDATION: 2322
Rippon (John W.) Research Award: 2155
Risling (David) Emergency Aid Scholarships: 1041
Rittenhouse Award: 730
Rivera (Geraldo) Scholarship: 1001
RJOS Traveling Fellowships: 2553
RNF Fellow Research Grant: 2496
RNF New Investigator Research Grant: 2496
Robb (Preston) Fellowship: 2468
Robbins-Wilf (Dr. Marcia) Research Award: 2447
ROBERTS (FOREST) THEATRE
  Panowski (Mildred and Albert) Playwriting Award: 537
Roberts (George A.) Scholarship: 2677
Roberts (Summerfield G.) Award: 636
Robins, Kaplan, Miller and Ciresi Foundation for Children: 1329
Robinson (Helen M.) Grant: 1557
Robinson (Henry S.) Corinth Research Fellowship: 887
ROBINSON (JACKIE) FOUNDATION
  Mentoring and Leadership Development Program: 1011
Robinson (Jacqueline) Regional Competition Grant Awards: 1029
Robinson (The James Harvey) Prize: 578
Robinson (Samuel) Essay Contest: 1749
Robinson-Cunningham Award: 2562
ROCHESTER AREA COMMUNITY FOUNDATION: 1094
ROCHESTER AREA FOUNDATION: 1359
ROCK ISLAND ARSENAL MUSEUM
  Maguire (Richard C.) Scholarship: 631
ROCKEFELLER ARCHIVE CENTER
  Grants-in-Aid for Research at the Rockefeller Archive Center: 632
ROCKEFELLER FAMILY FUND
  Economic Justice for Women: 282
  Environment: 282
  Institutional Accountability and Individual Liberty: 282
Rockwell Collins Scholarship: 2618

ROCKWELL FUND, INC.
  Operating Funds: 283
  Program/Project Support: 283
Rodgers (The Richard) Awards: 746
Roe (John Orlando) Award: 2220
Rogers (Frank Bradway) Information Advancement Award: 730
Rogerson (Clark T.) Research Award: 2155
Rohr (Sami) Prize for Jewish Literature: 677
Roizen & Anesthesia Research Foundation New Investigator Grant: 2401
Rolex Awards for Enterprise Program: 284
ROLEX SA
  Rolex Awards for Enterprise Program: 284
Romanell-Phi Beta Kappa Professorship in Philosophy (The): 1744
Romani (The George T. and Margaret W.) Fellowship: 357
Romanowski (The Miroslaw) Medal: 1836
Rome Prize Fellowship in Landscape Architecture (The): 2166
Rome Prize Fellowships: 344
Roosevelt (Theodore) Memorial Grants: 1809
Root (Betty Jeanne) Fellowship: 2674
Root2Fruit: 1012
Rose Architectural Fellowship: 415
ROSE COMMUNITY FOUNDATION: 1360
Rose Hills Foundation Summer Science and Engineering Fellowships: 1798
Rose Hills Ph.D. Fellowship: 1797
ROSENBERG (HENRY AND RUTH BLAUSTEIN) FOUNDATION: 1361
Rosenblith (Walter A.) New Investigator Award: 1435
Rosewood Family Scholarship Program: 1028
ROSS FOUNDATION: 1362
Rossiter (Margaret W.) History of Women in Science Prize: 597
ROSWELL ARTIST-IN-RESIDENCE PROGRAM: 566
Roswell (Virginia) Dissertation Award: 2573
ROTARY CLUB OF BRYN MAWR (THE)
  Cabell (Harry H.) Scholarship Program: 1753
ROTARY FOUNDATION OF ROTARY INTERNATIONAL (THE)
  Rotary Peace Fellowships: 936
Rotary Peace Fellowships: 936
Rotch Travelling Scholarship: 421
ROTCH TRAVELLING SCHOLARSHIP IN ARCHITECTURE
  Rotch Travelling Scholarship: 421
  Rotch Travelling Studio: 421
Rotch Travelling Studio: 421
Roth (Lois) Award for a Translation of a Literary Work: 657
Roth (Richard J.) Journalism Fellowship: 2010
Rothermel (Marjorie Roy) Scholarship: 2646
Rousseau (Theodore) Fellowships: 731
Rowe (The Leo S.) Pan American Fund: 963
Rowley/Wolfe Ministerial Education Scholarship: 808
ROYAL INSTITUTE OF BRITISH ARCHITECTS
  RIBA Research Trusts Awards: 422
ROYAL SOCIETY OF CANADA (THE)
  Award in Gender Studies (The): 1836
  Bancroft Award (The): 1836
  Flavelle Medal (The): 1836
  McLaughlin Medal (The): 1836
  McNeil Medal (The): 1836
  Pierce (The Lorne) Medal (The): 1836
  Romanowski (The Miroslaw) Medal: 1836
  Rutherford Memorial Medals (The): 1836
  Tyrrell (The J.B.) Historical Medal: 1836
  Wilson (The Alice) Award: 1836
ROYAL SOCIETY OF EDINBURGH (THE)
  Royal Society of Edinburgh Scottish Government Personal Research Fellowships: 937
Royal Society of Edinburgh Scottish Government Personal Research Fellowships: 937
ROYAL TOWN PLANNING INSTITUTE (THE)
  Pepler (George) International Award: 1869
Rozelle (Pete and Carrie) Award: 1570
RSNA Research Scholar Grant: 2320
RSNA/AUR/APDR/SCARD Radiology Education Research Development Grant: 2319
RTCA
  Jackson (The William E.) Award: 2627
Rubin (Lou) and Ike Cohen Memorial Scholarship: 1534
Ruckes (The Paul and Ellen) Scholarship: 971
Ruggles (The William B.) Journalist Scholarship: 1948
Runaway and Homeless Youth (RHY) Programs: 1152
RUNNING STRONG FOR AMERICAN INDIAN YOUTH: 1056

RUNYON (DAMON) CANCER RESEARCH FOUNDATION
    Runyon (Damon) Clinical Investigator Award: 2446
    Runyon (Damon) Dale F. Frey Award for Breakthrough Scientists: 2446
    Runyon (Damon) Fellowship Award: 2446
    Runyon (Damon)-Rachleff Innovation Award: 2446
    Runyon (Damon)-Sohn Pediatric Cancer Fellowship Award: 2446
Runyon (Damon) Clinical Investigator Award: 2446
Runyon (Damon) Dale F. Frey Award for Breakthrough Scientists: 2446
Runyon (Damon) Fellowship Award: 2446
Runyon (Damon)-Rachleff Innovation Award: 2446
Runyon (Damon)-Sohn Pediatric Cancer Fellowship Award: 2446
Rural Housing Grants (Section 504): 2128
RURAL HOUSING SERVICE
    Rural Housing Grants (Section 504): 2128
RURITAN NATIONAL FOUNDATION
    Build Your Dollars Grant: 1586
    Educational Grant Program: 1586
    Operation We Care: 1504
RUSSELL FAMILY FOUNDATION (THE): 2200
    Jane's Fellowship Program: 1363
RUSSELL (JOSEPHINE G.) TRUST: 1461
Russell (Peter Nicol) Postgraduate Scholarship in Mechanical and
    Mechatronic Engineering: 2667
Rutherford Memorial Medals (The): 1836

S

Sabbatical Fellowships in Health Outcomes: 2308
Sabbatical Fellowships in Informatics: 2308
Sabbatical Fellowships in Pharmaceutics: 2308
Sabbatical Fellowships in Pharmacology/Toxicology: 2308
SACHS FOUNDATION
    Financial Aid for Education of Black Residents of Colorado: 1034
Sacramento Region Health Care Partnership: 1509
Sacred in Opera: 780
Sacred Sites Program: 621
Safe Passage: Youth Transitioning from Foster Care: 234
SAGE (RUSSELL) FOUNDATION: 1870
SAGES Program (The): 1882
SAGINAW COMMUNITY FOUNDATION: 1364
SAIGH FOUNDATION (THE): 1143
SAILORS' SNUG HARBOR OF BOSTON: 1505
ST. ANDREW'S SOCIETY OF THE STATE OF NEW YORK
    Scholarship Program for Graduate Study in Scotland: 938
ST. CROIX VALLEY FOUNDATION
    Health and Wellness Grant: 1365
    Music Education Grant: 1365
    Valley Arts Initiative Grant: 1365
SAINT-GOBAIN CORPORATION FOUNDATION
    Direct Grants Program: 1366
St. Louis Chapter No. 17 Scholarship: 2616
ST. LOUIS RAMS FOUNDATION: 1144
Salinas (Maria Elena) Scholarship: 1001
SALISBURY COMMUNITY FOUNDATION: 285
Saloutos (Theodore) Book Award: 576
Salvatori Fellowship: 2004
SAMLA Studies Award: 661
Sams (Dr. Lauranne) Scholarship: 2492
SAMUELS (THE FAN FOX AND LESLIE R.) FOUNDATION, INC.
    Performing Arts: 286
SAN ANGELO AREA FOUNDATION: 1367
SAN ANTONIO AREA FOUNDATION
    Discretionary Grant Process: 1368
SAN DIEGO ART INSTITUTE
    Annual International Juried Award Exhibition: 567
    Southern California Regional Juried Award: 567
    Youth Art: 567
SAN DIEGO FOUNDATION (THE): 1369
San Francisco-Bay Area: 64
SAN FRANCISCO CONSERVATORY OF MUSIC
    Performance Scholarships in Music for Students in Bachelor and Master
    of Music Programs: 788
SAN FRANCISCO FOUNDATION (THE)
    Art Awards: 498
    Bay Area Grants Program: 287
    Cadogan Fine Arts Scholarships: 568
    Community Leadership Awards: 1370
    Murphy Fine Arts Fellowships: 568

SAN FRANCISCO OPERA CENTER
    Adler Fellowships: 789
    Merola Opera Program: 789
    Schwabacher Debut Recitals: 789
Sanitarian Award: 2673
SANTA BARBARA FOUNDATION
    Express Grants: 1371
    Opportunity Grants: 1371
SANTA BARBARA MISSION ARCHIVE-LIBRARY
    Geiger Memorial Internship: 633
SANTA FE COMMUNITY FOUNDATION
    MoGro: 1012
    NM Health Equity Partnership: 1012
    Root2Fruit: 1012
SAR Prize: 661
SARKEYS FOUNDATION: 288
SARNOFF CARDIOVASCULAR RESEARCH FOUNDATION (THE)
    Sarnoff Fellowship Program: 2400
    Sarnoff Scholar Fellow-to-Faculty Transition Award: 2400
Sarnoff Fellowship Program: 2400
Sarnoff Scholar Fellow-to-Faculty Transition Award: 2400
Sarton Medal: 597
Satellite Dialysis Clinical Investigator Grant: 2423
Sauer (James A.) Fellowship: 870
SAVOY FOUNDATION: 2323
SCA Starter Grants: 2401
SCA-IARS Mid-Career Grant: 2401
SCAC (FRENCH CULTURAL AND EDUCATIONAL OFFICE)
    Chateaubriand Fellowships Program: 939
    Culture Lab: 939
    Franklin (Benjamin) Travel Grant for Undergraduate Students: 939
    Teacher Training in France: 939
    Teaching Assistant Program in France: 939
Scaglione (Aldo and Jeanne) Prize for a Translation of a Literary Work:
    657
Scaglione (Aldo and Jeanne) Prize for a Translation of a Scholarly Study
    of Literature: 657
Scaglione (Aldo and Jeanne) Prize for Comparative Literary Studies: 657
Scaglione (Aldo and Jeanne) Prize for French and Francophone Studies:
    657
Scaglione (Aldo and Jeanne) Prize for Italian Studies: 657
Scaglione (Aldo and Jeanne) Prize for Slavic Studies: 657
Scaglione (Aldo and Jeanne) Prize for Studies in Germanic Languages
    and Literatures: 657
Scaglione (Aldo and Jeanne) Publication Award for a Manuscript in
    Italian Literary Studies: 657
SCAIFE (SARAH) FOUNDATION, INC.: 2014
Scarborough (William Sanders) Prize: 657
Schaar (Ruby Yoshino) Playwright Award: 533
Schallek Fellowship: 610
Scharp (Charles B.) Scholarship: 2646
Schecter (Abe) Graduate Scholarship: 1958
Schedulers & Dispatchers Scholarship: 2625
Scheidlinger (Saul) Scholarship: 2563
Scherbenske (The M. James) Grant: 2355
Schiller (Justin G.) Fellowship: 345
Schimke (Mary McEwen) Scholarship: 1098
Schizophrenia Grants: 330
Schlundt (The Esther) Fund: 726
Schmitt (Bernadotte) Grant: 578
Schneeberger (Jimmy) Scholarship Fund: 1224
Schnurr (B.E.) Memorial Fund Research Grant: 2557
Scholar Awards: 221
Scholar in Residence Grants: 375
Scholar's Award: 2018
Scholar-in-Training Awards: 2424
Scholarly Paper Competition: 780
Scholarly Research Fellowship Program: 602
Scholars Fund: 1660
Scholars-in-Residence: 399
Scholarship and Charity Fund: 2552
Scholarship Central: 1334
Scholarship Endowment Trust Fund: 2595
Scholarship for the Next Generation of Scientists: 2433
Scholarship Funds: 76, 1252
Scholarship Program: 274, 330, 796, 1685
Scholarship Program for Graduate Study in Scotland: 938
Scholarship Program for Israelis: 955
Scholarship Program for Young Pianists: 758
Scholarships: 1192
Scholarships for Academic Excellence: 1731

Scholarships for Children and Spouses of Deceased or Disabled Veterans (CSDDV): 1687
Scholarships for Disadvantaged Students: 1553
Scholarships for Study in Library Service: 736
Scholarships for Summer Music Courses: 745
Scholarships in Library Science: 708
Scholarships Istituto italiano per gli studi storici for Graduate Students and Young Postdocs, Italian and Foreign: 600
Scholastic Art and Writing Awards (The): 429
SCHOLL (DR.) FOUNDATION: 289
SCHOMBURG CENTER FOR RESEARCH IN BLACK CULTURE (THE)
    Scholars-in-Residence: 399
Schonstedt Scholarship in Surveying (The): 2656
School at Jacob's Pillow (The): 532
School Breakfast Program (The): 1154
School Bus for the Arts Grants: 482
School Bus Grants: 474
SCHOOL FOR ADVANCED RESEARCH
    Advanced Seminar Program: 2023
    Resident Scholar Fellowships: 2023
    Staley (J.I.) Prize: 2024
    Summer Scholar Fellowships: 1754
School of Social Science Fellowships: 1856
SCHOOL OF THE MUSEUM OF FINE ARTS, BOSTON
    Traveling Fellowship Award: 569
Schork (Kurt) Awards in International Journalism: 1960
SCHORK (KURT) MEMORIAL FUND
    Schork (Kurt) Awards in International Journalism: 1960
SCHOTT FOUNDATION FOR PUBLIC EDUCATION (THE): 1587
Schroepfer Medal Award: 2063
SCHUMANN FUND FOR NEW JERSEY (THE): 1145
Schumar (James F.) Scholarship: 2639
SCHUSTERMAN (CHARLES AND LYNN) FAMILY FOUNDATION: 1372
Schutze (Katherine J.) Memorial Scholarship for Women Seminary Students: 808
SCHWAB (CHARLES AND HELEN) FOUNDATION
    Foundation Initiative Grants: 290
SCHWAB (CHARLES) FOUNDATION
    Schwab Moneywise^^99: 1911
    Schwab Moneywise^^99: 1911
    Schwabacher Debut Recitals: 789
Schwartz (Frances M.) Fellowship: 581
Scialog: Solar Energy Conversion: 2041
Science and Technology: 12
Science Education: 1120
Science for Peace and Security (SPS) Programme: 967
Science in Society Awards: 1946
Science Technology Engineering & Math (STEM) Female Mentoring Program: 1033
Science Undergraduate Laboratory Internships: 1813
Science, Technology and Society: 1833
Scientific Research Grants Program: 2396
Scientific Research Grants/Proposal Writing Contest: 1822
Scientist Development Awards for Mentored Clinical (K08): 1453
Scientist Development Awards for Mentored Research (K01): 1453
Scientist-in-Training Research Award: 2547
SCLERODERMA FOUNDATION
    Scleroderma Foundation Multi-Center Collaborative Research Grant: 2325
    Scleroderma Foundation Research Grants: 2324
Scleroderma Foundation Multi-Center Collaborative Research Grant: 2325
Scleroderma Foundation Research Grants: 2324
ScotiaMcLeod Scholarship: 1787
SCOTT (KENNETH A.) CHARITABLE TRUST: 2109
Scottish Rite Charitable Foundation Major Research Grants: 2590
SCOTTISH RITE CHARITABLE FOUNDATION OF CANADA
    Scottish Rite Charitable Foundation Major Research Grants: 2590
SCOVILLE (HERBERT, JR.) PEACE FELLOWSHIP
    Scoville Jr. (Herbert) Peace Fellowship Program: 857
Scoville Jr. (Herbert) Peace Fellowship Program: 857
SCRANTON AREA FOUNDATION: 1373
SCRIPPS (THE ELLEN BROWNING) FOUNDATION: 291
Scudder (Vida Dutton) Fellowship: 1097
SCUOLA NORMALE SUPERIORE
    Graduate School Scholarships for Study in Italy: 940
SDB Boot Camp for New Faculty: 2159
SDB Travel Awards: 2159
SDE Fellowship Program: 1837

Seaman (The Tom) Travelling Scholarship: 2678
Seattle ASWA Chapter Scholarship: 1896
SEATTLE FOUNDATION (THE)
    Community Grantmaking Program: 292
SEAVER INSTITUTE (THE): 293
SEAY (GEORGE J. AND EFFIE L.) MEMORIAL TRUST: 1506
Seed Grant Research Program: 1660
Seed Grants: 2303, 2455
SEG Scholarship Program: 2089
SEGAL (THE GEORGE AND HELEN) FOUNDATION: 499
SELBY (WILLIAM G. AND MARIE) FOUNDATION: 1507
Selected Professions Fellowships: 1071
SELF FAMILY FOUNDATION (THE): 1374
Seminar, Workshop and Conference Support: 876
Seminars and Institutes Program: 381
Seminars on Vocation: 809
Senior Adult Scholarship Program: 1650
Senior Companion Program: 1480
Senior Fellowship: 876
Senior Fellowships: 419
Senior Research Fellowship Program: 2130
Senior Research Training Fellowships: 2386
Sessa (Frank B.) Scholarship for Continuing Education of a Beta Phi Mu Member: 716
SEYBERT FOUNDATION (THE): 1146
SFU Graduate Fellowships: 1913
SFU Teaching Assistantships: 1912
Shackford (M.A. Cartland) Medical Fellowship: 1098
Shaffer Fund for Innovative Glaucoma Research: 2514
Shankar-Spiegel Award for the Best Dissertation Proposal in Direct/Interactive Marketing: 1904
SHARE OUR STRENGTH
    No Kid Hungry: 1508
Shared Instrumentation Grant Program: 2295
SHASTA REGIONAL COMMUNITY FOUNDATION
    McConnell Foundation Fund (The): 1375
    Redding Rancheria Community Fund: 1375
SHASTRI INDO-CANADIAN INSTITUTE (SICI)
    India Studies Fellowship Competition: 941
Shaughnessy (Mina P.) Prize: 658
Shaw Foundation Grants: 1410
SHAW (GARDINER HOWLAND) FOUNDATION
    Grantee Workshops: 1410
    Shaw Foundation Grants: 1410
Shaw (Harriet A.) Fellowship: 1097
Shaw (The Peter) Memorial Award: 1636
Shea (The John Gilmary) Prize: 804
Shelter Medicine Programs: 1858
Sheltering Arms Fund: 1213
Shelton (Perc H.) and Gladys A. Pospisil Shelton Foundation Advised Fund Grants: 168
SHERIDAN (THOMAS B. AND ELIZABETH M.) FOUNDATION: 1609
Shklar (Eugene and Daymel) Fellowships in Ukrainian Studies: 724
Short-Term Research Fellowships: 361
Short-Term Residencies/Arts Education: 486
Short-Term Research Fellowship: 607, 852
Short-Term Travel Grants: 920
SHRIVER (EUNICE KENNEDY) NATIONAL INSTITUTE OF CHILD HEALTH AND HUMAN DEVELOPMENT
    Child Development and Behavior Branch (CDBB): 1462
    Obstetric and Pediatric Pharmacology and Therapeutics Branch (OPPTB): 1462
    Pediatric Growth and Nutrition Branch (PGNB): 1462
SHUBERT FOUNDATION, INC. (THE): 538
Shuster (Ben) Memorial Award: 2220
Shwachman (Harry) Clinical Investigator Award: 2413
Sibley (Mary Isabel) Fellowship: 1093
SICKKIDS FOUNDATION
    Community Conference Grants Program: 1463
    New Investigator Research Grants: 1463
Sidney Awards: 1936
Siegel (Norman) Research Scholar Grant: 2356
Sierleja (E.J.) Memorial Fellowship: 2653
SIERRA HEALTH FOUNDATION
    Conference and Convening Program: 1509
    Grizzly Creek Ranch Camp and Conference Center: 1509
    Health Leadership Program: 1509
    Healthy Sacramento Coalition: 1509
    Responsive Grants Program: 1509
    Sacramento Region Health Care Partnership: 1509
    Youth Pathways to Health: 1509

SIGMA ALPHA IOTA PHILANTHROPIES, INC.
  Inter-American Music Awards: 790
SIGMA DELTA EPSILON/GRADUATE WOMEN IN SCIENCE
  SDE Fellowship Program: 1837
Sigma Pi Sigma Undergraduate Research Awards: 2102
SIGMA THETA TAU INTERNATIONAL
  Berkel Crisp (Rosemary) Research Award: 2497
  Bloch (Doris) Research Award: 2497
  Henderson (Virginia) Clinical Research Grant: 2497
  Small Grants: 2497
  Stout (Joan K.), R.N., Research Grant: 2497
Sigma Theta Tau/RNF Research Grant: 2496
SIGMA XI: THE SCIENTIFIC RESEARCH SOCIETY
  Grants-in-Aid of Research: 1838
Silberberg (Paul) Memorial Award: 2447
SILICON VALLEY COMMUNITY FOUNDATION: 1376
SILICON VALLEY CREATES
  Applied Materials Excellence in the Arts: 500
  Artist Laureates: 500
  Local Arts Grants: 500
Silver Apple Award Scholarships: 1894
SIMMONS FAMILY FOUNDATION: 294
Simmons (The John) Short Fiction Award: 701
SIMON FRASER UNIVERSITY
  SFU Graduate Fellowships: 1913
  SFU Teaching Assistantships: 1912
Simpson (Carole) Scholarship: 1958
SIMS (J. MARION) FOUNDATION
  Adult Literacy Transition Grants: 295
  Responsive Grants: 295
  Teachers' Pet Grants: 295
Simulation Fellowship Program: 2038
Single Investigator Cottrell College Science Awards: 2041
SIRAGUSA FOUNDATION (THE): 296
SISTERS OF ST. JOSEPH HEALTHCARE FOUNDATION: 1464
Sixteenth Century Society and Conference (SCSC) Fellowship: 392
Skalny (Louis and Nellie) Scholarships for Polish Studies: 1655
SKELLY (GERTRUDE E.) CHARITABLE FOUNDATION: 1641
SKILLBUILDERS FUND: 1095
SKILLMAN FOUNDATION (THE)
  Good Neighborhood: 297
  Good Opportunities: 297
  Good Schools: 297
SKIN CANCER FOUNDATION (THE)
  Bambino (Melissa K.) Memorial Award: 2447
  Kopf (Dr. Alfred W.) Research Grant Award: 2447
  Nagel (Todd) Memorial Award: 2447
  Robbins-Wilf (Dr. Marcia) Research Award: 2447
  Silberberg (Paul) Memorial Award: 2447
SKOWHEGAN SCHOOL OF PAINTING AND SCULPTURE: 570
SLADEN (THE PERCY) MEMORIAL FUND
  Sladen (Percy) Memorial Fund Grants: 2110
Sladen (Percy) Memorial Fund Grants: 2110
Slagle (Allogan) Memorial Scholarship: 1044
Slim (H. Colin) Award: 751
SLOAN (ALFRED P.) FOUNDATION: 298
  Minority Ph.D. Program: 1013
  Sloan Indigenous Graduate Partnership: 1014
  Sloan Research Fellowships: 2042
Sloan Indigenous Graduate Partnership: 1014
Sloan Research Fellowships: 2042
Small Business Innovation Research Awards: 2518
Small Business Innovation Research Grants: 2493
Small Business Innovation Research Program: 1454
Small Grant Program: 332
Small Grant Support: 493
Small Grant Support for Schools: 493
Small Grants: 2497
Small Grants for Research in Field of Short Stature: 2530
Small Grants Program: 1239
Small Research Grant Program: 1989
Smiles for Success Program: 2346
SMITH (A.O.) FOUNDATION: 299
Smith (Alexander H. and Helen V.) Research Fund: 2155
Smith (Alice E.) Fellowship: 646
Smith (Bosworth) Trust Fund: 2678
SMITH (THE ETHEL SERGEANT CLARK) MEMORIAL FUND: 300
SMITH FAMILY AWARDS PROGRAM FOR EXCELLENCE IN
  BIOMEDICAL RESEARCH: 2326
Smith (George D.) Scholarship Program: 326

SMITH (HORACE) FUND: 1755
Smith (J. Waldo) Hydraulic Fellowship: 2645
Smith (The Ralph and Josephine) Fund for Northumberland County: 125
Smith (W. Eugene) Grant in Humanistic Photography: 571
SMITH (W. EUGENE) MEMORIAL FUND
  Smith (W. Eugene) Grant in Humanistic Photography: 571
SMITH (THE W.W.) CHARITABLE TRUST
  College Scholarships: 301
  Food, Clothing and Shelter: 301
  Maritime Education: 301
  Medical Research: 301
SMITHERS (THE CHRISTOPHER D.) FOUNDATION, INC.: 1465
SMITHSONIAN ASTROPHYSICAL OBSERVATORY
  Clay Postdoctoral Fellowship: 2057
  Predoctoral Research Fellowships: 2056
SMITHSONIAN ENVIRONMENTAL RESEARCH CENTER
  Professional Training: 2201
Smithsonian Fellowship: 452
Smithsonian Graduate Student Fellowships: 1839
SMITHSONIAN INSTITUTION
  Smithsonian Graduate Student Fellowships: 1839
  Smithsonian Postdoctoral Fellowships: 1839
  Smithsonian Predoctoral Fellowships: 1839
  Smithsonian Senior Fellowships: 1839
SMITHSONIAN NATIONAL AIR AND SPACE MUSEUM
  Guggenheim Fellowship: 2628
  Lindbergh (Charles A.) Chair in Aerospace History: 2628
  Postdoctoral Earth and Planetary Sciences Fellowship: 2628
  Summer Internship Program: 2629
  Verville (A.) Fellowship: 2628
Smithsonian Postdoctoral Fellowships: 1839
Smithsonian Predoctoral Fellowships: 1839
Smithsonian Senior Fellowships: 1839
Smyth (Craig Hugh) Visiting Fellowships: 952
SNC-LAVALIN Plant Design Competition: 2651
SNOW (THE JOHN BEN) FOUNDATION, INC.: 302
SOANE (SIR JOHN) MUSEUM FOUNDATION
  Soane (Sir John) Museum Foundation Traveling Fellowship: 423
Soane (Sir John) Museum Foundation Traveling Fellowship: 423
Social Change Fund: 1101
Social Investment Program: 132
Social Issues Dissertation Award (The): 1885
SOCIAL JUSTICE FUND NORTHWEST: 1510
Social Justice Grant Program: 1847
Social Justice Montana: 1331
Social Psychology Program: 2583
SOCIAL SCIENCE RESEARCH COUNCIL
  Abe Fellowship Program: 860
  International Dissertation Research Fellowship Program (IDRF): 859
  SSRC/JSPS Long-Term Fellowship: 858
  SSRC/JSPS Short-Term Fellowship: 858
SOCIAL SCIENCES AND HUMANITIES RESEARCH COUNCIL OF
  CANADA
  Banting Postdoctoral Fellowships: 1876
  Bombardier (Joseph-Armand) Canada Graduate Scholarships Program -
    Master's Scholarships: 1874
  Doctoral Awards: 1871
  Laskin (Bora) National Fellowship in Human Rights Research: 1873
  Master's Awards: 1874
  SSHRC Postdoctoral Fellowships: 1872
  Vanier Canada Graduate Scholarships (CGS): 1875
Social Sciences or Humanities International Security Fellowship: 833
SOCIETY FOR DEVELOPMENTAL BIOLOGY
  Conklin (Edwin G.) Medal: 2159
  Developmental Biology-SDB Lifetime Achievement Award: 2159
  Doctor (John) Best Education Poster Award: 2159
  Hamburger (Viktor) Outstanding Educator Prize: 2159
  Latin American-Caribbean Scholarships: 2159
  Non-SDB Education Activities Grant: 2159
  Non-SDB Meeting Grants: 2159
  SDB Boot Camp for New Faculty: 2159
  SDB Travel Awards: 2159
  Teaching Faculty Travel Grants: 2159
SOCIETY FOR FRENCH HISTORICAL STUDIES
  Chinard (The Gilbert) Prize: 634
  Farrar (Marjorie M. and Lancelot L.) Awards: 634
  Koren (The William, Jr.) Prize: 634
  Pinkney (The David) Prize: 634
  Research Travel Award: 634
  Wolf (John B. and Theta H.) Travel Fellowship: 634
Society for Health Systems Scholarship: 2653

SOCIETY FOR INVESTIGATIVE DERMATOLOGY (THE)
  Kligman (Albert M.) Fellowship Fund Award: 2327
SOCIETY FOR PEDIATRIC DERMATOLOGY
  Pilot Project Award: 2532
  Reston (William) Research Award: 2532
SOCIETY FOR SCIENCE AND THE PUBLIC
  Intel Science Talent Search: 1840
Society for the Humanities Fellowships: 365
SOCIETY FOR THE PSYCHOLOGICAL STUDY OF SOCIAL ISSUES
  (SPSSI) (THE)
  Allport (Gordon) Intergroup Relations Prize: 1877
  Applied Social Issues Internship Program (The): 1880
  Awards for Outstanding Teaching and Mentoring: 1879
  Innovative Teaching Award: 1878
  Kidder (The Louise) Early Career Award: 1883
  Klineberg (Otto) Intercultural and International Relations Award: 2015
  Mayo (Clara) Grants: 1881
  SAGES Program (The): 1882
  Social Issues Dissertation Award (The): 1885
  SPSSI Grants-in-Aid: 1884
SOCIETY FOR THE SCIENTIFIC STUDY OF SEXUALITY (THE)
  Student Research Grants: 1841
SOCIETY FOR THE STUDY OF AMPHIBIANS AND REPTILES
  Grants in Herpetology: 2043
Society of Actuaries Educational Institution Grant: 2098
SOCIETY OF ACTUARIES (SOA)
  Society of Actuaries Educational Institution Grant: 2098
  Society of Actuaries' James C. Hickman Scholar Doctoral Stipend
    Program: 2097
Society of Actuaries' James C. Hickman Scholar Doctoral Stipend
  Program: 2097
SOCIETY OF AMERICAN HISTORIANS, INC. (THE)
  Cooper (James Fenimore) Prize: 635
  Nevins (Allan) Prize: 635
  Parkman (Francis) Prize: 635
SOCIETY OF ARCHITECTURAL HISTORIANS
  Tompkins (Sally Kress) Fellowship: 424
SOCIETY OF BIOLOGICAL PSYCHIATRY
  Bennett (A.E.) Research Awards: 2591
  Ziskind-Somerfeld Research Award: 2592
SOCIETY OF CARDIOVASCULAR ANESTHESIOLOGISTS
  Roizen & Anesthesia Research Foundation New Investigator Grant:
    2401
  SCA Starter Grants: 2401
  SCA-IARS Mid-Career Grant: 2401
SOCIETY OF CHILDREN'S BOOK WRITERS AND ILLUSTRATORS
  Freeman (Don) Memorial Grant-in-Aid: 697
  Work-In-Progress Grants: 697
SOCIETY OF CRITICAL CARE MEDICINE
  Vision Grant: 2560
SOCIETY OF DAUGHTERS OF THE U.S. ARMY
  Society of Daughters of the United States Army Scholarships: 1756
Society of Daughters of the United States Army Scholarships: 1756
SOCIETY OF EXPLORATION GEOPHYSICISTS
  SEG Scholarship Program: 2089
SOCIETY OF MANUFACTURING ENGINEERS EDUCATION
  FOUNDATION (SMEEF)
  Gunter (Connie and Robert T.) Scholarship: 2616
  Helton (Clinton J.) Manufacturing Scholarship: 2616
  Kalamazoo Chapter No. 116-Roscoe Douglas Scholarship: 2616
  Kaufman (Lucille B.) Women's Scholarship: 2616
  Kay (E. Wayne) Scholarships: 2616
  St. Louis Chapter No. 17 Scholarship: 2616
  Walker (Myrtle and Earl) Scholarship: 2616
  Weisel (William E.) Scholarship: 2616
Society of Mayflower Descendants in the State of Illinois Fellowship: 395
SOCIETY OF NAVAL ARCHITECTS AND MARINE ENGINEERS
  (THE)
  Graduate Scholarships: 2663
  Undergraduate Scholarships: 2663
SOCIETY OF NUCLEAR MEDICINE AND MOLECULAR IMAGING
  (SNMMI)
  Blahd (Mitzi & William, M.D.) Pilot Research Grant: 2328
  Bradley-Alavi Student Fellowship: 2328
  Cole (Paul) Technologist Scholarships: 2329
  PDEF Mickey Williams Technologist Minority Student Scholarships:
    2329

SOCIETY OF PHYSICS STUDENTS
  Future Faces of Physics Awards: 2103
  Sigma Pi Sigma Undergraduate Research Awards: 2102
  Society of Physics Students Leadership Scholarship: 1757
  White (Marsh W.) Awards: 2104
Society of Physics Students Leadership Scholarship: 1757
SOCIETY OF RADIOLOGISTS IN ULTRASOUND: 2330
SOCIETY OF WOMEN ENGINEERS
  Society of Women Engineers Scholarship Program: 1096
Society of Women Engineers Scholarship Program: 1096
Software Donations: 235
SOIL AND WATER CONSERVATION SOCIETY
  Grant (Kenneth E.) Research Scholarship: 2202
Solie (Ruth A.) Award: 751
SOMMERHOCHSCHULE-UNIVERSITY OF VIENNA
  International Summer Program (Summer Campus Strobl/St.
    Wolfgang/Austria): 942
Sonenfeld (Alexandra Apostolides) Memorial Undergraduate Scholarship:
  1080
SONS OF ITALY FOUNDATION
  National Leadership Grant Competition: 1015
SONS OF THE REPUBLIC OF TEXAS (THE)
  Presidio La Bahia Award: 637
  Roberts (Summerfield G.) Award: 636
SONY USA FOUNDATION, INC.: 1610
SOROS (THE PAUL & DAISY) FELLOWSHIPS FOR NEW
  AMERICANS : 1758
SOSLAND FOUNDATION (THE): 1016
Sousa/Ostwald Award: 748
SOUTH ATLANTIC MODERN LANGUAGE ASSOCIATION
  Graduate Student Essay Prize: 661
  Harper Fund Award: 661
  SAMLA Studies Award: 661
  SAR Prize: 661
SOUTH CAROLINA HIGHER EDUCATION TUITION GRANTS
  COMMISSION
  South Carolina Tuition Grants Program: 1759
South Carolina Tuition Grants Program: 1759
SOUTH DAKOTA ARTS COUNCIL
  Artist Grants: 501
  Artist-in-Schools & Communities: 501
  Arts Organization Challenge Grants: 501
  Professional Development: 501
  Project Grants: 501
  Technical Assistance: 501
  Touring Arts: 501
Southard (Juliette A.)/Oral-B Laboratories Scholarship Program: 2347
Southern California Regional Juried Award: 567
Southern Exposure: 476
SOUTHFIELD COMMUNITY FOUNDATION (THE): 1377
SOUTHWEST FLORIDA COMMUNITY FOUNDATION: 1378
Southwest U.S. and Northern Mexico: 64
SOWERS CLUB OF NEBRASKA FOUNDATION: 303
SPACE TELESCOPE SCIENCE INSTITUTE
  Hubble Fellowship Program: 2058
Sparks! Ignition Grants for Libraries: 727
Sparks! Ignition Grants for Museums: 727
Speakers in the Humanities Program: 384
SPECIAL HOPE FOUNDATION (THE): 1017
Special Milk Program for Children (The): 1154
Special Presenter Initiatives: 476
Special Project Challenge Grant: 1236
Special Project Funds: 1252
Special Project Grants: 486, 1448
Special Projects: 491
Special Projects Program: 969
Special Research Awards: 2413
Special Scholarship Endowment Grants: 1735
Specific Cultural Projects Grants Program: 448
Spectrum Initiative Scholarship Program: 1616
Speech Science Research Grant: 2506
SPENCER FOUNDATION
  Research Grant Program: 1588
Spencer (Susan S.) Clinical Research Training Fellowship in Epilepsy:
  2455
Spinal Cord Injury Research Grants and Fellowships: 2558
Spitzer (Lyman) Cutting Edge Climbing Award: 2167
Spofford (The Walter O., Jr.) Memorial Internship: 2197
SPRAGUE (SETH) EDUCATIONAL AND CHARITABLE
  FOUNDATION: 304

Spring Meadow Nursery Scholarship: 1697
SPSSI Grants-in-Aid: 1884
Spurlock (Jeanne) Research Fellowship in Substance Abuse and Addiction
  for Minority Medical Students: 2562
SSHRC Postdoctoral Fellowships: 1872
SSRC/JSPS Long-Term Fellowship: 858
SSRC/JSPS Short-Term Fellowship: 858
St. Louis Public Library Media Archives: 1750
STACEY (THE JOHN F. AND ANNA LEE) SCHOLARSHIP FUND:
  572
Stahl (Steven A.) Research Grant: 1557
Staley (J.I.) Prize: 2024
Standard Research Grants: 1518
Stanfield and D'Orlando Art Scholarship: 506
STANFORD HUMANITIES CENTER
  External Faculty Fellowships: 400
Stanley Drama Award: 540
Stanton Nuclear Security Fellowship (The): 833
Stanton Nuclear Security Fellowship Program (SNSF): 842
STARK COMMUNITY FOUNDATION: 1379
Starrett (Agnes Lynch) Poetry Prize: 695
STARS Residencies: 472
Start Schools: 440
Start-Up Research Grants: 2268
State & Tribal Grant Programs: 1153
State Art Collection: 453
State Arts Resources: 490
State Community Development Block Grant Program: 1392
STATE COUNCIL OF HIGHER EDUCATION FOR VIRGINIA
  Virginia Tuition Assistance Grant Program (TAGP): 1760
State Formula Grants: 1153
State Government Intern Program (Spring Semester Program): 2016
State Intern Summer Program: 2016
State Justice Statistics for Statistical Analysis Centers: 1411
STATE LIBRARY AND ARCHIVES OF FLORIDA
  Library Services and Technology Act: 740
STATE OF RHODE ISLAND
  State Government Intern Program (Spring Semester Program): 2016
  State Intern Summer Program: 2016
State or Local Health or State Agricultural Department Employees Travel
  Award: 2673
State President's Scholarships: 1659
STATE STREET FOUNDATION (THE)
  Global Philanthropy Program: 305
State Touring Program: 448
State-Local Partnership Program in the Arts: 437
Statewide Arts Grants Programs: 467
Statewide Service Networks in the Arts: 437
Statewide Service Organizations: 490
STAUFFER (JOHN) CHARITABLE TRUST: 306
Stearman (The Stanley H.) Award: 1724
STEARNS (ARTEMAS W.) TRUST: 1466
Steedman (James Harrison) Memorial Fellowship in Architecture: 425
STEELCASE FOUNDATION: 307
STEELE-REESE FOUNDATION (THE): 1380
Stefanadis (Sonja B.) Graduate Student Scholarship: 1080
STEINER (DAVID AND SYLVIA) CHARITABLE TRUST: 823
STEM Doctoral Fellowships: 1762
STEM Grants Program: 1602
STEM Scholarship: 1109
STERN (IRVIN) FOUNDATION: 1511
Stetson (Thomas M.) Scholarship: 2597
STEVENS (THE ABBOT AND DOROTHY H.) FOUNDATION: 1381
Stevens (Mary Elvira) Traveling Fellowship: 1097
STEVENS (THE NATHANIEL AND ELIZABETH P.) FOUNDATION:
  1382
Stevenson (Robert M.) Award: 751
Stewart (E. Lyman) Fellowship: 645
Stewart (Paul A.) Award: 2162
STIFTELSEN RIKSBANKENS JUBILEUMSFOND
  Europe and Global Challenges: 401
  Flexit: 401
  Pro Futura: 401
STODDARD CHARITABLE TRUST (THE): 1512
STOKELY (THE WILLIAM B., JR.) FOUNDATION: 308
Stokes County Grants: 1404
Stokes (The Louis) Urban Health Policy Fellows Program: 1025
Stokes (Thomas L.) Award: 1949
STONE (H. CHASE) TRUST: 502
STONE (W. CLEMENT & JESSIE V.) FOUNDATION: 1611

Stoody-West Fellowship (The): 1961
Stout (Dottie) Professional Development Grants: 2080
Stout (Joan K.), R.N., Research Grant: 2497
Strait (George A.) Minority Stipend Scholarship Endowment: 710
Strategic Employment Grant Program: 969
Strategic National Grant: 1198
Straus (Anselm) Award for Qualitative Family Research: 1498
Strengthening Affordable Housing: 1330
Strengthening Families - Strengthening Communities: 74
Strengthening Health Systems: 228
Strengthening Philanthropy: 134
Strong Local Economy: 311
Strong (Walter Mersh) Scholarship: 965
STUART FOUNDATION
  Child Welfare: 1147
  Public Education: 1147
Student Academy Awards Competition: 541
Student Aid Grants, Scholarship, and Loans: 1404
Student and Artist Vocal Auditions: 780
Student Fellowship Program: 514
Student Leader Award (Regional and International): 1692
Student Loan Fund: 2646
Student Loan Program: 1746
Student Opportunity Scholarship: 1748
Student Research Fellowships: 2343
Student Research Grant: 2341
Student Research Grant in Audiology: 2506
Student Research Grant in Early Childhood Language Development: 2506
Student Research Grant in Mineralogy and Petrology: 2079
Student Research Grants: 1806, 1841
Student Speaking Contest: 430
Student Teaching Stipend for High-Needs Fields: 1699
Student Teaching Stipend for Minorities: 1699
Student Training and Research in Tumor Immunology (STaRT) Program:
  2432
Student Travel Awards: 1806, 2162
Student Travel Scholarship Award: 2673
Student Travel Scholarship Program: 2572
Studio Art (Low-residency MFA): 555
STUDIO ARTS CENTERS INTERNATIONAL (SACI)
  Fall/Spring Study Abroad: 573
  MFA in Photography: 573
  MFA in Studio Art (Painting or Drawing): 573
  Post Baccalaureate Certificate Programs: 573
Studio Residency: 521
Study Abroad Scholarships: 1692
STURGIS (ROY AND CHRISTINE) CHARITABLE AND
  EDUCATIONAL TRUST: 309
SUBARU OF AMERICA FOUNDATION, INC.: 1589
SUBCOMMITTEE ON THE HOME MISSIONS: 824
SUBSTANCE ABUSE AND MENTAL HEALTH SERVICES
  ADMINISTRATION, DISASTER TECHNICAL ASSISTANCE
  CENTER
  Crisis Counseling Assistance and Training Program: 2593
SUDBURY FOUNDATION
  Atkinson Scholarship Program (The): 1383
  Children, Youth and Families Program: 1383
  Environmental Program (The): 1383
  Sudbury Program (The): 1383
Sudbury Program (The): 1383
Summer Fellowships in Medieval and Renaissance Studies: 357
Summer Field Course Scholarship: 2080
Summer Food Service Program for Children (The): 1154
Summer Intensive: 531
Summer Internship Program: 2629
Summer Internship Program for Graduate Students: 1540
Summer Learning District Demonstration Project: 329
Summer Research Diversity Fellowships in Law and Social Science for
  Undergraduate Students: 970
Summer Research Fellowships for Undergraduate Faculty and Students:
  2153
Summer Research Opportunity Program: 2643
Summer Scholar Fellowships: 1754
Summer Stipends: 380
Summer Student Fellowship: 2482
Summer Student Fellowship Program in Oceanography: 1846
Summer Studentships: 2251
Summer Study Abroad Programs: 926
Summer Systematics Institute: 2142
Summer Writing Workshops: 809
Summer Youth Program: 1303

SUMMERLEE FOUNDATION (THE)
  Animal Protection Program: 1384
  Texas History: 1384
SUMMIT FOUNDATION (THE): 1385
SUMNERS (HATTON W.) FOUNDATION: 2017
SUNNEN FOUNDATION: 1513
SUNTRUST FOUNDATION: 310
Supelco AOCS Research Award: 2063
Superfund State and Indian Tribe Core Program Cooperative Agreements: 2208
Superfund State, Political Subdivision, and Indian Tribe Site-Specific Cooperative Agreements: 2208
Supplemental Program: 763
Support Program for Translation and Publication on Japan: 852
SURDNA FOUNDATION INC.
  Strong Local Economy: 311
  Sustainable Environment: 311
  Thriving Cultures: 311
Surgical Pathology Fellowships: 2285
Survivor Tuition Benefits Program: 1694
Sustainability: 492
Sustainable Community Development Program: 1300
Sustainable Environment: 311
Swann Foundation Fellowship: 402
SWANN FOUNDATION FOR CARICATURE AND CARTOON
  Swann Foundation Fellowship: 402
SWANSON (DR. W.C.) FAMILY FOUNDATION, INC.: 1886
SWEA Scholarship in Literature, Language and Area Studies: 861
SWEDISH WOMEN'S EDUCATIONAL ASSOCIATION INC.
  SWEA Scholarship in Literature, Language and Area Studies: 861
Swensrud Teacher Fellowships at MHS: 605
Swiny (The Helena Wylde) and Stuart Swiny Fellowship: 913
Switzer Environmental Fellowship Program: 2203
SWITZER (THE ROBERT & PATRICIA) FOUNDATION
  Switzer Environmental Fellowship Program: 2203
Sydney Medical School Postgraduate Research Scholarships: 2333
SYMPHONY OF THE MOUNTAINS
  Vaughn (Elizabeth Harper) Concerto Competition: 791
SYRACUSE UNIVERSITY
  African American Graduate Fellowship: 1762
  Graduate Program in Creative Writing: 698
  Hursky Fellowship: 1762
  McNair Graduate Fellowship: 1762
  STEM Doctoral Fellowships: 1762
  Syracuse University Fellowship: 1762
  Syracuse University Graduate Assistantships: 1761
Syracuse University Fellowship: 1762
Syracuse University Graduate Assistantships: 1761

T

Ta Liang Memorial Award: 2033
TAC Foundation Scholarships and Bursaries: 2617
TAHOE TRUCKEE COMMUNITY FOUNDATION: 312
TAILHOOK EDUCATIONAL FOUNDATION
  Tailhook Educational Foundation Scholarship Award: 1590
Tailhook Educational Foundation Scholarship Award: 1590
TAIT (THE FRANK M.) FOUNDATION: 1148
TALBOT (THE AMAURY) FUND
  Talbot (Amaury) Prize for African Anthropology: 2025
Talbot (Amaury) Prize for African Anthropology: 2025
TAMPA BAY TIMES FUND, INC.
  Barnes Scholarship: 1764
  Career Journalism Scholarship: 1763
Tanenbaum (Mary M.) Scholarship: 2563
Tanger (Alexander M.) Scholarship: 1924
Taos Summer Writers' Conference: 703
TAPER (S. MARK) FOUNDATION: 313
Tapman (Samuel Fletcher) ASCE Student Chapter Scholarship: 2645
TARAKNATH DAS FOUNDATION: 1642
Tarbox (Lee) Memorial Scholarship: 2618
Targeted Research Areas Grants: 526
Tart (Charles T. and Judith A.) Student Incentive Award: 2587
TASTE AND SMELL CLINIC
  Taste and Smell Disorders Internship Program: 2331
Taste and Smell Disorders Internship Program: 2331
TATA (LADY) MEMORIAL TRUST: 2448

TAU BETA PI ASSOCIATION, INC. (THE)
  Best (Raymond A. and Ina C.) Fellowship for MBA: 2664
  Graduate Fellowship in Engineering: 2664
  Tau Beta Pi Undergraduate Scholarship: 2664
Tau Beta Pi Undergraduate Scholarship: 2664
Taylor Family Award for Fairness in Newspapers: 1953
Taylor (Rennie)/Alton Blakeslee Fellowships for Graduate Study in Science Writing: 1930
TCA Grant Programs: 504
TCU Scholarship Program: 1036
Teacher as Researcher Grant: 1557
Teacher Education Assistance for College and Higher Education (TEACH) Grant: 1770
Teacher Grants: 1404
Teacher Training and Professional Development Program (The): 1136
Teacher Training in France: 939
Teachers' Pet Grants: 295
Teaching and Learning Resources: 827
Teaching Assistant Program in France: 939
Teaching English in Poland: 925
Teaching Faculty Travel Grants: 2159
Team Depot: 1300
TEAMMATES FOR KIDS FOUNDATION: 1149
Technical Assistance: 501
Technical Assistance and Community Development Programs: 463
Technical Services Program: 621
Teen Pregnancy Prevention Initiative: 133
Teens Program: 531
Teeth and Bone: 2352
TEMPLETON (JOHN) FOUNDATION: 314
Temporary Assistance for Needy Families (TANF): 1967
TENNESSEE ARTS COMMISSION
  Division of Arts Programs: 503
  Division of Communications, Information & Technology: 503
Tennessee Education Lottery Scholarship Program: 1765
Tennessee Math & Science Teachers Loan Forgiveness Program: 1765
Tennessee Student Assistance Award: 1765
TENNESSEE STUDENT ASSISTANCE CORPORATION
  Dependent Children Scholarship Program: 1765
  Graduate Nursing Loan-Forgiveness Program: 1765
  McAuliffe (Christa) Scholarship Program: 1765
  McWherter (Ned) Scholars Program: 1765
  Minority Teaching Fellows Program: 1765
  Tennessee Education Lottery Scholarship Program: 1765
  Tennessee Math & Science Teachers Loan Forgiveness Program: 1765
  Tennessee Student Assistance Award: 1765
  Tennessee Teaching Scholars Program: 1765
Tennessee Teaching Scholars Program: 1765
Tenth Gate Prize: 707
Tetley and Lupton Scholarships for International Students: 946
TEXAS COMMISSION ON THE ARTS
  TCA Grant Programs: 504
Texas History: 1384
TEXAS INSTRUMENTS FOUNDATION: 315
TEXAS LIBRARY ASSOCIATION
  Escue (Walter H.) Memorial Scholarship: 741
  Greenfield (Vivian) Education Award: 741
  Janeway (Ray C.) Scholarship: 741
  TLA Summer School Scholarship: 741
  Van Dusen-Tobin-Kaiser Scholarship: 741
Texas Transportation Scholarship: 1914
TEXTRON CHARITABLE TRUST: 316
Therapeutics Development Awards: 2413
Thesis Parts Program: 1814
Third Year Post Certificate Program: 531
Thomas (Charles Tommy) Memorial Scholarship: 2636
Thomas (Douglas Dockery) Fellowship in Garden History and Design: 2186
Thomas (Raymond D. and Sara) Fund: 1224
Thompson (Homer and Dorothy) Fellowship: 355
THOMPSON (THOMAS) TRUST: 1386
Thomson Reuters/MLA Doctoral Fellowship: 729
Thorndyke (Barbara Edith Quincey) Memorial Undergraduate Scholarship: 1080
Thornett (Christian Rowe) Scholarship: 2132
THRASHER RESEARCH FUND: 2533
330-Hour Self Study Program: 2611
3M FOUNDATION, INC.: 317
Three-Year Postdoctoral Fellowships: 2150
Thriving Cultures: 311
Thurburn (Alexander Hugh) Scholarship: 2132

TIDES FOUNDATION
  Higgins (Colin) Youth Courage Awards: 1387
  Lehman (Jane Bagley) Awards for Excellence in Public Advocacy: 1387
  Pizzigati (Antonio) Prize for Software in the Public Interest: 1387
Time and Talent: 246
Times Newspapers and Webster University Journalism Scholarships: 1750
Tinker Field Research Grants: 862
TINKER FOUNDATION INC.
  Tinker Field Research Grants: 862
TLA Summer School Scholarship: 741
TMCF Scholarships: 1713
Tobias (Charles W.) Young Investigator Award: 1819
Together We Can Scholarship Fund: 1227
TOLEDO COMMUNITY FOUNDATION: 1388
Tomash (The Adelle and Erwin) Fellowship in the History of Information
  Technology: 2604
TOMFOHRDE (JOHN H. AND H. NAOMI) FOUNDATION: 318
Tompkins (Sally Kress) Fellowship: 424
Tools for Schools Broward: 1527
TOPFER FAMILY FOUNDATION: 319
Torraco (Bernard and Carolyn) Nursing Scholarships: 1775
Torraco (Louise) Memorial Scholarship for a Doctorate in Science: 1775
Torraco (Ralph J.) Doctoral Scholarship for Music Study: 1775
Torraco (Ralph J.) Doctoral Scholarship for the Study of Ancient
  Mediterranean History/Archaeology: 1775
TOSHIBA AMERICA FOUNDATION: 1612
TOTAL PETROCHEMICALS & REFINING USA FOUNDATION: 320
TOURETTE SYNDROME ASSOCIATION, INC.
  Tourette Syndrome Research Fellowships: 2483
  Tourette Syndrome Research Grants: 2483
Tourette Syndrome Research Fellowships: 2483
Tourette Syndrome Research Grants: 2483
Touring Arts: 501
Touring Exhibits through ExhibitsUSA: 475
TOURISM CARES
  Graduate Research Scholarships: 1766
  High School Scholarships: 1766
  Professional Development Scholarship Program: 1766
  Undergraduate or Graduate Scholarships: 1766
  Worldwide Grant Program: 2204
Towle (David W.) Fellowship: 2153
TOWN CREEK FOUNDATION, INC.: 2205
TOWSLEY (THE HARRY A. AND MARGARET D.) FOUNDATION:
  321
TOWSON UNIVERSITY
  Towson University Prize for Literature: 699
Towson University Prize for Literature: 699
Tracy (Joyce A.) Fellowship: 345
Traditional Arts Apprenticeship: 469, 472, 485
Traditional Arts Apprenticeship Program: 459
Traditional Arts Apprenticeships: 491
Traditional Arts Fellowship: 469
Traditional Grants: 1581
Trainee Research Award Program: 2236
Training Programs: 1245
Training Workshops: 2449
Translation and Publication Support Program: 1703
Translational Research Award: 2403
Translational Research Program: 2365
TRANSPORTATION ASSOCIATION OF CANADA FOUNDATION
  TAC Foundation Scholarships and Bursaries: 2617
TRANSPORTATION CLUBS INTERNATIONAL SCHOLARSHIPS
  Deines (Ginger and Fred) Canada Scholarships: 1914
  Deines (Ginger and Fred) Mexico Scholarships: 1914
  Hooper Memorial Scholarship: 1914
  Lydic (Denny) Scholarship: 1914
  Texas Transportation Scholarship: 1914
  Warfield (Alice Glaisyer) Memorial Scholarship: 1914
  Woods (Charlotte) Memorial Scholarship: 1914
Transportation Scholars: 2190
Traumatic Stress Research Program: 1865
Travel & Training Fund: 1104
Travel Grant Awards: 2335
Travel Grants: 1494, 1997
Traveling Fellowship Award: 569
TREE RESEARCH & EDUCATION ENDOWMENT FUND
  Arboriculture Education Grant: 2129
  Duling (John) Grant: 2129
  Felix (Robert) Memorial Scholarship: 2129
  Johns (Hyland) Grant: 2129

  Kimmel (Jack) International Grant: 2129
  Ohio Chapter ISA Education Grant: 2129
  Wright (John) Memorial Scholarship: 2129
Tresley (Ira) Research Award: 2220
TRIANGLE COMMUNITY FOUNDATION: 1591
Tribal Business Management (TBM) Program: 1047
Trinidad State Gunsmithing Scholarship: 426
Trost (Jan) Award: 1498
TRULL FOUNDATION (THE): 1389
Truman (Harry S.) Book Award: 2018
TRUMAN (HARRY S.) LIBRARY INSTITUTE
  Dissertation Year Fellowships: 2018
  Research Grant: 2018
  Scholar's Award: 2018
  Truman (Harry S.) Book Award: 2018
TRUMAN (THE HARRY S.) SCHOLARSHIP FOUNDATION
  Truman (Harry S.) Scholarship Program: 2019
Truman (Harry S.) Scholarship Program: 2019
TRUST COMPANY (THE)
  Askin (Lady Mollie Isabelle) Ballet Scholarship: 539
  Askin (Sir Robert William) Operatic Scholarship: 539
  Franklin (Miles) Literary Award: 700
  Geach (Portia) Memorial Award: 505
  Mitchell (Kathleen) Award: 539
TRUST FUNDS INCORPORATED: 322
Tucker (Richard) Award: 792
Tucker (Richard) Career Grants: 792
TUCKER (THE RICHARD) MUSIC FOUNDATION, INC.
  Tucker (Richard) Award: 792
  Tucker (Richard) Career Grants: 792
  Tucker (Sara) Study Grants: 792
Tucker (Sara) Study Grants: 792
Tuition Aid Grant (TAG): 1693
Tuition Assistance: 1582
Tuition Scholarships: 525
TULL CHARITABLE FOUNDATION, INC.: 323
Tumblewords: 459
Tunstall (Graydon A., Jr.) Scholarship: 628
Turner (Dr. Lynn W.) Paper Prize: 629
Turner (James A., Jr.) Memorial Scholarship: 2602
TURRELL FUND: 1150
TUSCHMAN FOUNDATION (THE): 324
TUSKEGEE UNIVERSITY
  Master's Program in Material Science and Engineering: 2044
  Ph.D. Program in Material Science and Engineering: 2044
Tuttle (Arthur S.) Memorial Scholarship: 2645
21st Century Endowment Fund: 1276
21st Century Research Awards: 221
21st Century Scholars Program: 1699
TWO TEN FOOTWEAR FOUNDATION
  Two Ten Footwear Foundation College Scholarship Program: 1767
  Two Ten Footwear Foundation Design Scholarship Program: 1768
Two Ten Footwear Foundation College Scholarship Program: 1767
Two Ten Footwear Foundation Design Scholarship Program: 1768
Two Year/Community College BEA Award: 1924
Tyler (Maria Opasnov) '52 Scholarship: 1097
Tyrrell (The J.B.) Historical Medal: 1836
Tyson (Sarah Bradley) Memorial Fellowship: 2134

U

U.S. Antarctic Research Program: 1834
U.S. ARMY CENTER OF MILITARY HISTORY
  Dissertation Year Fellowships: 638
U.S. ARMY MILITARY HISTORY INSTITUTE
  Ridgway (General and Mrs. Matthew B.) Research Grant: 639
U.S. ARMY RESEARCH INSTITUTE FOR BEHAVIORAL AND
  SOCIAL SCIENCES: 1887
U.S. ARMY RESEARCH OFFICE: 1842
U.S. BANCORP FOUNDATION: 1390
U.S. DEPARTMENT OF AGRICULTURE
  Emergency Conservation Program (ECP): 2206
U.S. DEPARTMENT OF EDUCATION: 1594
  American Overseas Research Centers (AORC) Program: 863
  Assistive Technology Programs: 2561
  Business and International Education Program: 1915
  Centers for International Business Education Program: 1916
  Education Research: 1593
  Federal Supplemental Educational Opportunity Grant (FSEOG): 1769
  Federal Work-Study: 1773

Foreign Language and Area Studies Fellowships: 662
Fulbright-Hays Faculty Research Abroad Program: 944
Fulbright-Hays Group Projects Abroad Program: 943
Fulbright-Hays Doctoral Dissertation Research Abroad: 663
Indian Education-Formula Grants to Local Education Agencies (LEAs): 1057
International Research and Studies Grant Program: 1592
Iraq and Afghanistan Service Grant: 1771
National Professional Development Program: 1595
National Resource Centers (NRC) Program: 664
Native American and Alaska Native Children in School Program: 1595
Pell Grant: 1772
Rehabilitation Service Program: 2561
Teacher Education Assistance for College and Higher Education (TEACH) Grant: 1770
Undergraduate International Studies and Foreign Language Program: 1644
Upward Bound: 1643
U.S. DEPARTMENT OF ENERGY
University Coal Research Program: 2665
U.S. DEPARTMENT OF HEALTH AND HUMAN SERVICES: 2498
Discretionary Grant Programs: 1153
Head Start: 1151
Health Center Program (The): 1467
Maternal and Child Health Services Block Grant: 2502
Medicaid: 1468
Native American Programs: 1058
Projects of National Significance for Persons with Developmental Disabilities: 1391
Promoting Safe and Stable Families: 1153
Runaway and Homeless Youth (RHY) Programs: 1152
State & Tribal Grant Programs: 1153
State Formula Grants: 1153
U.S. DEPARTMENT OF HEALTH AND HUMAN SERVICES/ADMINISTRATION FOR CHILDREN AND FAMILIES/OFFICE OF FAMILY ASSISTANCE
Temporary Assistance for Needy Families (TANF): 1967
U.S. DEPARTMENT OF HOUSING AND URBAN DEVELOPMENT
Community Development Block Grant Program: Entitlement Communities Program: 1392
State Community Development Block Grant Program: 1392
U.S. DEPARTMENT OF JUSTICE
Enforcing the Underage Drinking Laws Program: 1414
Juvenile Justice and Delinquency Prevention Allocation to States: 1413
Juvenile Justice and Delinquency Prevention Program: 1412
State Justice Statistics for Statistical Analysis Centers: 1411
U.S. DEPARTMENT OF LABOR
National Apprenticeship System: 1968
U.S. Department of State Fulbright U.S. Student Program: 918
U.S. DEPARTMENT OF STATE, FULBRIGHT TEACHER EXCHANGE PROGRAM
Fulbright Teacher Exchange Program: 1596
U.S. DEPARTMENT OF THE NAVY
Basic Research Challenge Program: 1843
Navy Health Professions Scholarship Program (HPSP): 2332
University Research Initiative: 1843
Young Investigator Program: 1843
U.S. ENVIRONMENTAL PROTECTION AGENCY
Pesticide Enforcement Cooperative Agreements: 2207
Superfund State and Indian Tribe Core Program Cooperative Agreements: 2208
Superfund State, Political Subdivision, and Indian Tribe Site-Specific Cooperative Agreements: 2208
U.S. General Fund: 979
U.S. Immunodeficiency Network: 2337
U.S. INSTITUTE OF PEACE
Randolph (Jennings) Fellowship Programs for International Peace: 864
U.S. Institute of Peace Grant Program: 865
U.S. Institute of Peace Grant Program: 865
U.S.-ISRAEL BINATIONAL AGRICULTURE RESEARCH AND DEVELOPMENT FUND (BARD)
Graduate Student Fellowship Program: 2130
Senior Research Fellowship Program: 2130
Vaadia-BARD Postdoctoral Fellowship Program: 2130
U.S.-ISRAEL BINATIONAL SCIENCE FOUNDATION (BSF): 968
U.S. MARINE CORPS
Dissertation Fellowships in Marine Corps History: 641
Marine Corps Historical Program Research Grants: 640
Master's Thesis Fellowships in Marine Corps History: 642
U.S. SOCIETY ON DAMS
USSD Scholarship: 2666

U.S.-Japan Leadership Program: 866
U.S.-U.K. Young Investigator Exchange Fellowship: 2453
UAA Janice K. Barden Scholarship: 2625
UCLA CHICANO STUDIES RESEARCH CENTER
Institute of American Cultures Fellowship Program: 1069
UCLA IAC Visiting Scholar/Researcher Program in Ethnic Studies: 1018
UCLA INSTITUTE OF AMERICAN CULTURES (IAC)
UCLA IAC Visiting Scholar/Researcher Program in Ethnic Studies: 1018
UDALL (THE MORRIS K.) AND STEWART L. UDALL FOUNDATION
Congressional Internships: 1059
Udall Scholarship: 1774
Udall Scholarship: 1774
Undergraduate Awards: 2680
Undergraduate Awards in Dietetics: 2672
Undergraduate International Studies and Foreign Language Program: 1644
Undergraduate or Graduate Scholarships: 1766
Undergraduate Research: 2674
Undergraduate Research Capstone Program: 2139
Undergraduate Research Initiative: 876
Undergraduate Research Scholarship Program: 1827
Undergraduate Scholarship Program: 2632
Undergraduate Scholarships: 1043, 2610, 2663
Undergraduate Session Assistants Program: 2011
Undergraduate Student Poster Contest: 430
Undergraduate Transfer Scholarship: 1680
UNICO NATIONAL, INC.
Basilone Postgraduate Scholarship: 1775
Cottone Postgraduate Scholarship (Medical Only): 1775
Davini (William C.) Scholarship: 1775
DiMattio Celli Undergraduate Study Abroad Program: 1775
Gentile (Major Don S.) Scholarship: 1775
Grasso (Ella) Literary Scholarship: 1775
Mazza (Theodore) Scholarship: 1775
Miele (Alphonse A.) Scholarship: 1775
Torraco (Bernard and Carolyn) Nursing Scholarships: 1775
Torraco (Louise) Memorial Scholarship for a Doctorate in Science: 1775
Torraco (Ralph J.) Doctoral Scholarship for Music Study: 1775
Torraco (Ralph J.) Doctoral Scholarship for the Study of Ancient Mediterranean History/Archaeology: 1775
UNION FOR INTERNATIONAL CANCER CONTROL (UICC)
American Cancer Society International Fellowships for Beginning Investigators (ACSBI): 2449
Asia-Pacific Cancer Society Training Grants (APCASOT): 2449
International Cancer Technology Transfer Fellowships (ICRETT): 2449
Training Workshops: 2449
Yamagiwa-Yoshida Memorial International Study Grants (YY): 2449
UNION PACIFIC FOUNDATION: 325
UNITARIAN UNIVERSALIST ASSOCIATION OF CONGREGATIONS
Melcher (Frederic G.) Book Award: 825
Stanfield and D'Orlando Art Scholarship: 506
UNITED ARTS COUNCIL OF RALEIGH AND WAKE COUNTY, INC.
Artists-in-the-Schools Grants Program: 507
Community Arts Reach Program: 507
Program Support Grants: 507
Regional Artist Grants: 507
United Health Foundation/Diverse Medical Scholars Program: 2296
United Health Foundation Scholarship: 1109, 2492
UNITED HOSPITAL FUND OF NEW YORK
Health Care Improvement Grant Program: 1469
UNITED JEWISH APPEAL-FEDERATION OF JEWISH PHILANTHROPIES OF NEW YORK: 826
UNITED METHODIST COMMUNICATIONS
Perryman (The Leonard M.) Communications Scholarship for Ethnic Minority Students: 1019
Stoody-West Fellowship (The): 1961
UNITED METHODIST HEALTH MINISTRY FUND
Access to Health Care-System Change and Advocacy: 1514
Healthy Congregations Program: 1514
Healthy Nutrition and Physical Activity for Young Children: 1514
Mental Health for Young Children: 1514
UNITED NEGRO COLLEGE FUND: 1035
United Parcel Service Scholarship for Female Students: 2653
United Parcel Service Scholarship for Minority Students: 2653
UNITED SOUTH AND EASTERN TRIBES, INC.: 1060
UNITED STATES HOLOCAUST MEMORIAL MUSEUM, CENTER FOR ADVANCED HOLOCAUST STUDIES
Visiting Scholar Program: 643

UNITED STATES-JAPAN FOUNDATION
    Grants: 866
    Heinz (Elgin) Award: 866
    U.S.-Japan Leadership Program: 866
United Way Program: 38
UNITY FOUNDATION OF LAPORTE COUNTY (THE)
    Community Fund: 1393
Universal Avionics Systems Corporation Scholarship: 2618
University Coal Research Program: 2665
University Distinguished Fellowships: 992
University Enrichment Fellowships: 992
UNIVERSITY FILM AND VIDEO ASSOCIATION
    Fielding (Carole) Student Grants: 1962
UNIVERSITY OF ALBERTA
    Killam (Izaak Walton) Memorial Postdoctoral Fellowship: 1776
    Notley (Grant) Memorial Postdoctoral Fellowship: 1777
UNIVERSITY OF ARIZONA SCHOOL OF INFORMATION
    RESOURCES AND LIBRARY SCIENCE: 742
UNIVERSITY OF BRISTOL
    Postgraduate Research Scholarships: 945
UNIVERSITY OF BRITISH COLUMBIA (THE)
    Affiliated Fellowships: 1779
    Four Year Doctoral Fellowships: 1780
    Graduate Student Initiative: 1781
    Killam (Izaak Walton) Memorial Postdoctoral Research Fellowships:
    1778
UNIVERSITY OF CALGARY (THE)
    Bahlsen (Bettina) Memorial Graduate Scholarship: 1786
    Cairns (The A.T.J.) Memorial Scholarship: 1789
    Canadian Natural Resources Limited Graduate Scholarship: 1792
    Cogeco Inc. Graduate Scholarship: 1963
    Craigie (Peter C.) Memorial Scholarship: 1791
    Davies (William H.) Medical Research Scholarships: 1784
    Dingman (The Archibald Waynne) Memorial Graduate Scholarship:
    1782
    Faculty of Law Graduate Scholarship: 1793
    Graduate Faculty Council Scholarship: 1790
    Jacques (Harry and Laura) Bursary: 2090
    Killam (Izaak Walton) Predoctoral Scholarships: 1785
    Labatt (John) Limited Scholarship: 1787
    McDermid (The Honourable N.D.) Graduate Scholarship in Law: 1986
    Queen Elizabeth II Graduate Scholarships: 1783
    ScotiaMcLeod Scholarship: 1787
    University of Calgary Silver Anniversary Graduate Fellowships (The):
    1788
    Willson (Robert A.) Doctoral Management Scholarship: 1645
University of Calgary Silver Anniversary Graduate Fellowships (The):
    1788
UNIVERSITY OF CALIFORNIA
    University of California President's Postdoctoral Fellowship Program:
    1020
University of California President's Postdoctoral Fellowship Program:
    1020
UNIVERSITY OF CALIFORNIA, LOS ANGELES
    Belkin (Alice) Memorial Scholarship: 1794
    Ethnic Studies Fellowships: 1021
    Institute of American Cultures Grant: 1061
UNIVERSITY OF DELAWARE-HAGLEY GRADUATE PROGRAM
    (THE): 644
UNIVERSITY OF DELAWARE, DEPARTMENT OF HISTORY
    Stewart (E. Lyman) Fellowship: 645
UNIVERSITY OF ILLINOIS AT URBANA-CHAMPAIGN
    Kinley (Kate Neal) Memorial Fellowship: 574
UNIVERSITY OF IOWA (THE)
    Iowa Short Fiction Award (The): 701
    Simmons (The John) Short Fiction Award: 701
UNIVERSITY OF KANSAS CHILD LANGUAGE DOCTORAL
    PROGRAM
    Child Language Doctoral Program: 1795
UNIVERSITY OF LEEDS
    Leeds International Research Scholarship: 947
    Tetley and Lupton Scholarships for International Students: 946
UNIVERSITY OF MANCHESTER (THE)
    British Marshall Scholarships: 948
    Fulbright - University of Manchester Award: 948
    North American Foundation Awards: 948
    President's Doctoral Scholar Award: 948
UNIVERSITY OF MANITOBA
    University of Manitoba Graduate Fellowships: 1597
University of Manitoba Graduate Fellowships: 1597

UNIVERSITY OF MICHIGAN
    Knight-Wallace Fellows: 1964
UNIVERSITY OF MINNESOTA
    Hollinshead (Marilyn) Fellowship: 508
    Keats (Ezra Jack)/Kerlan Collection Memorial Fellowship: 702
UNIVERSITY OF NEBRASKA AT OMAHA
    UNO Graduate Assistantships: 1917
UNIVERSITY OF NEW MEXICO
    Taos Summer Writers' Conference: 703
UNIVERSITY OF OSLO INTERNATIONAL SUMMER SCHOOL: 949
UNIVERSITY OF PENNSYLVANIA, PENN HUMANITIES FORUM
    Mellon (Andrew W.) Postdoctoral Fellowships in the Humanities: 403
UNIVERSITY OF PITTSBURGH
    Darbaker (Leasure K.) Prize in Botany: 2209
    McKinley Research Fund: 2209
    Pape Research Fund: 2209
UNIVERSITY OF SOUTHERN CALIFORNIA: 1796
    Annenberg Graduate Fellowship Program: 1797
    Global Ph.D. Fellowship: 1797
    Provost's Ph.D. Fellowship Program: 1797
    Rose Hills Foundation Summer Science and Engineering Fellowships:
    1798
    Rose Hills Ph.D. Fellowship: 1797
UNIVERSITY OF SOUTHERN CALIFORNIA ROSKI SCHOOL OF
    ART AND DESIGN
    M.F.A. Teaching Assistantships: 575
UNIVERSITY OF SOUTHERN MISSISSIPPI (THE)
    Keats (Ezra Jack) Children's Literature Research Fellowship Program:
    704
    Keats (Ezra Jack)/Janina Domanska Research Fellowship: 743
    Rey (H.A. and Margret) Translation Fellowship: 743
UNIVERSITY OF SYDNEY (THE)
    Australian Postgraduate Awards (APA): 950
    Civil and Mining Engineering Foundation Scholarship: 2667
    Gritton (Henry Bertie and Florence Mabel) Postgraduate Research
    Scholarships/Fellowships: 2069
    International Postgraduate Research Scholarships (IPRS): 950
    Loxton (F.H.) Postgraduate Studentships: 2131
    Mankin (Richard Claude) Scholarship: 2210
    Padbury (William John) Scholarship: 2667
    Pawlett (Thomas Lawrance) Scholarship: 2132
    Price (Norman I.) Scholarship in Electrical Engineering: 2667
    Russell (Peter Nicol) Postgraduate Scholarship in Mechanical and
    Mechatronic Engineering: 2667
    Strong (Walter Mersh) Scholarship: 965
    Sydney Medical School Postgraduate Research Scholarships: 2333
    Thornett (Christian Rowe) Scholarship: 2132
    Thurburn (Alexander Hugh) Scholarship: 2132
    Watson (William Girling) Travelling Scholarship: 2667
    Wunsch (Elizabeth) Postgraduate Research Scholarship in Pharmacy:
    2545
UNIVERSITY OF TEXAS AT AUSTIN
    Johnson (Lyndon B.) School of Public Affairs: 1646
UNIVERSITY OF TEXAS AT AUSTIN (THE) AND THE TEXAS
    INSTITUTE OF LETTERS
    Dobie Paisano Fellowship Program (The): 509
UNIVERSITY OF TORONTO
    Fleming (Patricia) Visiting Fellowship in Bibliography and Book
    History: 744
UNIVERSITY OF VIRGINIA
    Gallatin Fellowships: 951
UNIVERSITY OF VIRGINIA PRESS
    Cowen (Walker) Memorial Prize: 705
University Research Initiative: 1843
Unmet NEED Grants and Scholarships: 1033
UNO Graduate Assistantships: 1917
Unrestricted Funds: 1252
Unruh (Jesse M.) Assembly Fellowship Program: 1993
UPJOHN (W.E.) INSTITUTE FOR EMPLOYMENT RESEARCH
    Early Career Research Grants: 1969
UPS FOUNDATION (THE)
    Casey (James E.) Scholarship Program: 326
    Neighbor to Neighbor: 326
    Smith (George D.) Scholarship Program: 326
UPSTART Program: 447
Upward Bound: 1643
Urban Ecology: 2172
USAF Summer Faculty Fellowship Program: 2642
USArtists International: 476

References in index are to entry numbers.

USDA FOOD AND NUTRITION SERVICE
  Child and Adult Care Food Program (The): 1154
  National School Lunch Program (The): 1154
  School Breakfast Program (The): 1154
  Special Milk Program for Children (The): 1154
  Summer Food Service Program for Children (The): 1154
USDA - RURAL UTILITIES SERVICE
  Water and Waste Disposal Systems for Rural Communities: 2133
USG FOUNDATION, INC.: 327
USMEX Visiting Scholars Program: 834
USSD Scholarship: 2666

V

VA Psychology Training Program: 2577
Vaadia-BARD Postdoctoral Fellowship Program: 2130
Valley Arts Initiative Grant: 1365
VALLEY FOUNDATION (THE): 2334
VAN AMERINGEN FOUNDATION, INC.: 2594
van Biema (Anne) Fellowship: 452
Van Deuren (Della) Scholarships: 1659
Van Dusen-Tobin-Kaiser Scholarship: 741
Van Hattum (Rolland J.) Award for Contribution in the Schools: 2506
VAN LOEBENSELS/REMBEROCK FOUNDATION: 1394
VAN SLYKE FOUNDATION (THE)
  AACC Van Slyke Foundation Critical and Point-of-Care Testing
    Research Grant: 1844
Vanier Canada Graduate Scholarships (CGS): 1875
Varian (Russell and Sigurd) Award: 2100
Vatican Film Library Mellon Fellowship: 679
Vaughn (Elizabeth Harper) Concerto Competition: 791
VCCA (VIRGINIA CENTER FOR THE CREATIVE ARTS): 510
Venetian Research Program: 366
VENTURA COUNTY COMMUNITY FOUNDATION: 1395
Verges (Mary M.), Past Grand President, Scholarship (Undergraduate):
  1080
VERIZON FOUNDATION: 328
VERMONT ARTS COUNCIL
  Artist Development Grants: 511
  Artists in Schools: 511
  Arts Partnership Grants: 511
  Creation Grants: 511
  Cultural Facilities Grants: 511
  Cultural Routes Grants: 511
  Operating Support Grants: 511
  Project Grants: 511
Vermont Incentive Grants and Scholarships: 1799
Vermont Outreach Programs: 1799
VERMONT STUDENT ASSISTANCE CORPORATION
  Vermont Incentive Grants and Scholarships: 1799
  Vermont Outreach Programs: 1799
Verney (E. Geoffrey and Elizabeth Thayer) Fellowship: 612
Vernon (Chester M.) Memorial Eagle Scout Scholarship: 1721
VERTICAL FLIGHT FOUNDATION
  Vertical Flight Foundation Engineering Scholarships: 2630
Vertical Flight Foundation Engineering Scholarships: 2630
Verville (A.) Fellowship: 2628
Veterans Program: 219
Veterans Tuition Credit Program (VTCP): 1728
Victim Assistance Grants: 1404
VICTORIA FOUNDATION, INC.: 1396
VIETNOW NATIONAL: 1598
VILLA I TATTI: THE HARVARD UNIVERSITY CENTER FOR
  ITALIAN RENAISSANCE STUDIES
  Fellowships for Independent Study on the Italian Renaissance: 952
  Mellon Visiting Fellowships: 952
  Smyth (Craig Hugh) Visiting Fellowships: 952
Villarreal (Dr. Juan D.) Scholarship: 2349
VIOLIN SOCIETY OF AMERICA (THE)
  Kaplan-Goodkind Memorial Scholarship Fund: 793
  Kun Scholarship Fund: 793
  Nigogosian (Aram and Rose) Fund: 793
VIRGIN ISLANDS COUNCIL ON THE ARTS
  Expanding Opportunities for Participation in the Arts: 512
VIRGINIA COMMISSION FOR THE ARTS: 513
VIRGINIA DEPARTMENT OF HEALTH
  Commonwealth of Virginia Nurse Educator Scholarship Program: 2499
  Marshall (Mary) Nursing Scholarship/Practical Nurse Program: 2499
  Marshall (Mary) Nursing Scholarship/Registered Nurse Program: 2499
  Nurse Practitioner/Nurse Midwife Scholarship Program: 2499

VIRGINIA ENVIRONMENTAL ENDOWMENT
  Kanawha and Ohio River Valleys Program: 2211
  Virginia Program: 2211
VIRGINIA MUSEUM OF FINE ARTS
  Professional Fellowship Program: 514
  Student Fellowship Program: 514
VIRGINIA POLYTECHNIC INSTITUTE AND STATE UNIVERSITY
  Multicultural Academic Opportunity Graduate Student Scholars
    Program: 1022
Virginia Program: 2211
Virginia Tuition Assistance Grant Program (TAGP): 1760
Viscount Bennett Fellowship: 1971
Vision Grant: 2560
Visiting Fellowships: 354, 2037
Visiting Lectureships: 1617
Visiting Professor Program: 2546
Visiting Professorships Fellowship: 914
Visiting Research Fellowship Program: 404, 1622
Visiting Research Fellowships: 374
Visiting Scholar Awards: 408
Visiting Scholar Program: 643
Visiting Scholars Program: 2107
Vistakon® Contact Lens Residency Award: 2505
Vistakon® Pediatric Residency Award: 2505
Visual and Performing Arts Achievement Awards: 1692
Visual Arts and Crafts: 427
Visual Arts Fellowship: 548
Visual Arts Fellowships: 523
Vogt (James R.) Radiochemistry Scholarship: 2062
Volunteer Grants Program: 1338
Volunteer Investment Program: 82
Voron (Abe) Scholarship: 1924

W

WABASH CENTER FOR TEACHING AND LEARNING IN
  THEOLOGY AND RELIGION (THE)
  Educational Environments: 827
  Faculty Practices and Vocation: 827
  Teaching and Learning Resources: 827
WACO FOUNDATION (THE)
  MAC Program Scholarship Fund: 1397
Wadsworth International Fellowships: 2027
Waggoner (The Alan D.) Student Scholarship Award: 2389
Wagner (Carl) Memorial Award: 1819
WAGNER COLLEGE
  Stanley Drama Award: 540
Waldbaum (Jane C.) Archaeological Field School Scholarship: 350
Waldron (The Margaret) Memorial Fund: 125
Walker (Myrtle and Earl) Scholarship: 2616
WALLACE FOUNDATION (THE)
  Arts for Young People: 329
  Principal Pipeline Initiative: 329
  Principal Supervisor Initiative: 329
  Summer Learning District Demonstration Project: 329
Wallace (Harriet Evelyn) Scholarship: 2072
WALPOLE (LEWIS) LIBRARY
  Visiting Research Fellowship Program: 404
War Memorial Scholarships: 1702
Warfield (Alice Glaisyer) Memorial Scholarship: 1914
WASHINGTON (DENNIS & PHYLLIS) FOUNDATION: 1398
WASHINGTON FORREST FOUNDATION: 1399
WASHINGTON HIGHER EDUCATION COORDINATING BOARD
  American Indian Endowed Scholarship Program: 1062
Washington Prize (The): 706
Washington State Need Grant Program: 1800
Washington State Work-Study Program: 1800
WASHINGTON STUDENT ACHIEVEMENT COUNCIL
  Washington State Need Grant Program: 1800
  Washington State Work-Study Program: 1800
WASHINGTON UNIVERSITY
  Chancellor's Graduate Fellowship Program at Washington University in
    St. Louis (The): 1801
  Olin (Mr. and Mrs. Spencer T.) Fellowships for Women: 1802
  Steedman (James Harrison) Memorial Fellowship in Architecture: 425
WASIE FOUNDATION (THE)
  Arthritis Grants: 330
  Cancer Grants: 330

Children's Medical Health Grants: 330
Schizophrenia Grants: 330
Scholarship Program: 330
Wasilewski (Vincent T.) Scholarship: 1924
Water and Waste Disposal Systems for Rural Communities: 2133
Watershed Protection: 265
WATSON (JEANNETTE K.) FELLOWSHIP: 1647
WATSON (THOMAS J.) FELLOWSHIP PROGRAM: 1648
Watson (William Girling) Travelling Scholarship: 2667
Wealth Building: 1275
Weatherstone Predoctoral Fellowships: 2242
Weaver (Richard M.) Fellowship: 2004
Weber (Maurice) Laboratorian Award: 2673
WEBSTER (EDWIN S.) FOUNDATION: 331
WEEDEN FOUNDATION
   Consumption: 2212
   Domestic Biodiversity: 2212
   International Biodiversity: 2212
   Population: 2212
WEGE FOUNDATION: 1400
WEHR (TODD) FOUNDATION: 1649
Weil (Frank L.) Memorial Eagle Scout Scholarship: 1721
WEILL (KURT) FOUNDATION FOR MUSIC: 515
Weinberg (Arthur and Lila) Fellowship for Independent Scholars: 388
Weiner (Herbert) Early Career Award for Contributions to Psychosomatic
   Society: 2568
WEINGART FOUNDATION
   Capacity Building: 332
   Capital Support: 332
   Core Support: 332
   Program Support: 332
   Small Grant Program: 332
Weisel (William E.) Scholarship: 2616
WEIZMANN INSTITUTE OF SCIENCE
   Postdoctoral Fellowships Program at the Weizmann Institute of Science:
   953
Welch (M.W.) International Scholarship: 2036
WELCH (THE ROBERT A.) FOUNDATION
   Departmental Grants: 2070
   Research Grants: 2070
   Welch Summer Scholar Program: 2070
Welch Summer Scholar Program: 2070
WELDER (ROB AND BESSIE) WILDLIFE FOUNDATION: 2111
Weller (The Sue Marsh) Fund: 726
WELLESLEY COLLEGE
   Barrett (Anne Louise) Fellowship: 1097
   Bowers (Margaret Freeman) Fellowship: 1097
   Cox (The Eugene L.) Fellowship: 1097
   Fisher (Professor Elizabeth F.) Fellowship: 1097
   Goldmark (Ruth Ingersoll) Fellowship: 1097
   Horton-Hallowell Fellowship: 1097
   Howard (Peggy) Fellowship in Economics: 1097
   Moffett (Edna V.) Fellowship: 1097
   Palmer (Alice Freeman) Fellowship: 1097
   Preyer (Kathryn Conway) Fellowship: 1097
   Schimke (Mary McEwen) Scholarship: 1098
   Scudder (Vida Dutton) Fellowship: 1097
   Shackford (M.A. Cartland) Medical Fellowship: 1098
   Shaw (Harriet A.) Fellowship: 1097
   Stevens (Mary Elvira) Traveling Fellowship: 1097
   Tyler (Maria Opasnov) '52 Scholarship: 1097
   Wood (Sarah Perry) Medical Fellowship: 1097
   Workman (Fanny Bullock) Fellowship: 1097
Wells (Clara) Scholarships for Piano Study: 750
WELLS (FRANKLIN H. AND RUTH L.) FOUNDATION: 1155
Wells (Ida B.) Graduate Student Fellowship: 588
WENNER-GREN FOUNDATION FOR ANTHROPOLOGICAL
   RESEARCH, INC.
   Conference and Workshop Grants: 2028
   Individual Research Grants: 2026
   International Collaborative Research Grants: 2029
   Wadsworth International Fellowships: 2027
   Wenner-Gren Symposium Program: 2028
Wenner-Gren Symposium Program: 2028
Wert (Lucille & Charles A.) Scholarship: 2677
Wesley-Logan Prize (The): 578
WEST (HERMAN O.) FOUNDATION: 333
WEST VIRGINIA DIVISION OF CULTURE AND HISTORY: 516
West Virginia Higher Education Grant Program: 1803
WEST VIRGINIA HIGHER EDUCATION POLICY COMMISSION
   West Virginia Higher Education Grant Program: 1803

Western Civilization Fellowship: 2004
WESTERN INTERSTATE COMMISSION FOR HIGHER EDUCATION
   Professional Student Exchange Program (PSEP): 334
WETLANDS INSTITUTE (THE)
   Coastal Conservation Research Program: 2160
WHARTON (WILLIAM P.) TRUST: 2045
WHATCOM MUSEUM
   Jacobs Research Funds Small Grants Program: 2030
Whetten (Nellie Yeoh) Award: 2100
WHITAKER FOUNDATION: 517
White (Gilbert F.) Postdoctoral Fellowship Program: 2198
White House Fellowships: 2013
White (Lynn and Maude) Fellowship: 357
White (Marsh W.) Awards: 2104
WHITE (THOMAS H.) FOUNDATION: 1401
White-Reinhardt Fund for Education: 2113
WHITEHALL FOUNDATION, INC.: 2161
WHITEHEAD (JOSEPH B.) FOUNDATION: 1156
WHITEHORSE FOUNDATION (THE): 1470
Whitmore (Ann Collins) Memorial Fund Awards: 2557
Whitmore (Ann Collins) Memorial Fund Student Awards Competition:
   2557
WHITNEY (THE HELEN HAY) FOUNDATION
   Early Postdoctoral Research Fellowship Program in Biomedical
   Sciences: 1845
WHO (WOMEN HELPING OTHERS FOUNDATION) (THE): 1099
WICHITA COMMUNITY FOUNDATION: 1402
WICKES (HARVEY RANDALL) FOUNDATION: 1403
WIDENER MEMORIAL FOUNDATION IN AID OF HANDICAPPED
   CHILDREN: 1023
Wiebe (Richard A.) Public Service Fellowship: 2010
WIEGAND (E. L.) FOUNDATION: 335
Wiener Laboratory Fellowships: 894
Wiener Laboratory Research Associateships: 894
Wiener Laboratory Travel Grants: 894
WILDLIFE CONSERVATION SOCIETY (THE)
   Research Fellowship Program: 2213
Wilkenfeld Psychiatric Resident Scholarship (The): 2563
Williams (Cenie Jomo) Tuition Scholarship: 1032
Williams (Kemper and Leila) Prize in Louisiana History: 595
Williams (The Sidney B., Jr.) Intellectual Property Law Scholarship: 1983
Williamsport-Lycoming Community Fund (The): 125
Willson (Robert A.) Doctoral Management Scholarship: 1645
Wilson (Alexander) Student Presentation Award: 2162
Wilson (The Alice) Award: 1836
Wilson (Arthur N.), M.D. Scholarship: 1660
Wilson (The H.W.) Scholarship: 720
WILSON (MATILDA R.) FUND: 336
WILSON ORNITHOLOGICAL SOCIETY
   Fuertes (Louis Agassiz) Award: 2162
   Hall (George A.)/Harold Mayfield Award: 2162
   Stewart (Paul A.) Award: 2162
   Student Travel Awards: 2162
   Wilson (Alexander) Student Presentation Award: 2162
Wilson (Pete) Scholarship: 1958
WILSON (WOODROW) INTERNATIONAL CENTER FOR SCHOLARS
   Fellowship Program at the Woodrow Wilson International Center for
   Scholars: 405
WILSON (THE WOODROW) NATIONAL FELLOWSHIP
   FOUNDATION
   Newcombe (Charlotte W.) Doctoral Dissertation Fellowships: 1804
Winchell (F. Mabel) Loan Fund: 735
Windham Women and Girls Fund: 1225
WINSTON-SALEM FOUNDATION (THE)
   Black Philanthropy Grants: 1404
   Community Grants: 1404
   Elkin/Tri-County Grants: 1404
   Stokes County Grants: 1404
   Student Aid Grants, Scholarship, and Loans: 1404
   Teacher Grants: 1404
   Victim Assistance Grants: 1404
   Women's Fund Grants: 1404
   Youth Philanthropy Grants: 1404
Winter (Cindy) Award: 1498
Winter Intensive: 531
Winterthur Fellowships: 406
WINTERTHUR MUSEUM, GARDEN & LIBRARY
   Dissertation Fellowships: 406
   NEH Fellowships: 406
   Winterthur Fellowships: 406

WISCONSIN ARTS BOARD
 Creation & Presentation: 518
 Creative Communities: 518
 Folk Arts Apprenticeship Program: 518
 Wisconsin Regranting Program: 518
WISCONSIN HISTORICAL SOCIETY PRESS
 Everest (D.C.) Fellowship: 646
 Hunter (Amy Louise) Fellowship: 646
 Smith (Alice E.) Fellowship: 646
Wisconsin Regranting Program: 518
WITTER (THE DEAN) FOUNDATION: 1918
Woest (The Dianne) Fellowship in the Arts and Humanities: 594
Wolf (John B. and Theta H.) Travel Fellowship: 634
Wolf (Paul R.) Memorial Scholarship: 2033
WOLFE ASSOCIATES, INC.: 337
WOMAN'S NATIONAL FARM & GARDEN ASSOCIATION, INC.
 Tyson (Sarah Bradley) Memorial Fellowship: 2134
Women and Girls Fund: 1225
WOMEN IN FILM
 Women in Film Foundation Film Finishing Fund: 1100
Women in Film Foundation Film Finishing Fund: 1100
Women in Need Scholarship: 1896
Women in Science Scholars Program: 1581
Women in Transition Scholarship: 1896
WOMEN'S FOUNDATION OF MINNESOTA
 girlsBEST: 1102
 Social Change Fund: 1101
Women's Foundation of Montana: 1331
Women's Fund: 1273
Women's Fund Grants: 1404
Women's Fund of Essex County (The): 1267
Women's Health: 1090, 2352
WOMEN'S POLICY, INC. (WPI)
 Congressional Fellowships on Women and Public Policy: 1103
WOMEN'S SPORTS FOUNDATION
 Travel & Training Fund: 1104
WOMEN'S STUDIO WORKSHOP (WSW)
 Art-in-Education Artists' Book Residency Grant: 520
 Artists' Book Residency Grants: 519
 Studio Residency: 521
Woo (William) Print & Online News Grant: 1667
Wood Institute Travel Grants: 586
Wood (Sarah Perry) Medical Fellowship: 1097
Woodruff (Helen M.) Fellowship of the AIA and the American Academy
 in Rome: 1618
WOODRUFF (THE ROBERT W.) FOUNDATION: 338
WOODS CHARITABLE FUND, INC.: 1405
Woods (Charlotte) Memorial Scholarship: 1914
WOODS FUND OF CHICAGO: 1406
WOODS HOLE OCEANOGRAPHIC INSTITUTION
 Summer Student Fellowship Program in Oceanography: 1846
Woodside (William Park) Founder's Scholarship: 2677
Woodson (Carter G.) Book Awards: 1859
WOODSON (CARTER G.) INSTITUTE FOR AFRICAN-AMERICAN
 AND AFRICAN STUDIES
 African-American and African Studies Fellowships: 407
Woodstock A-I-R: 544
WOODWARD'S (MR. AND MRS. P.A.) FOUNDATION: 1471
WOOLF (WILLIAM C.) FOUNDATION: 1407
Woolley (Harriet Hale) Scholarships: 449
Woolls (Blanche E.) Scholarship for School Media Service: 716
WORD WORKS, INC. (THE)
 Tenth Gate Prize: 707
 Washington Prize (The): 706
Work-In-Progress Grants: 697
Workers' Rights: 273
Workman (Fanny Bullock) Fellowship: 1097
Workmen's Circle (The)/Dr. Emanuel Patt Visiting Professorship: 650
Workshop Interns: 544
WORLD PIANO COMPETITION (THE)
 World Piano Competition: 794
World Piano Competition: 794
Worldwide Grant Program: 2204
Worthy Goal Scholarship: 2612
Wright (John Ellis) Award: 1254
Wright (John) Memorial Scholarship: 2129
Wright (Suzanne & Bob) Trailblazer: 2242
Wright (William K.) Award: 2220
Writer-in-Residence Program: 459
Writing and Publishing Section Grants: 670

Writing Fellowship: 548
Wunsch (Elizabeth) Postgraduate Research Scholarship in Pharmacy: 2545
WURLITZER (THE HELENE) FOUNDATION OF NEW MEXICO: 522
WYMAN-GORDON FOUNDATION: 339
Wynar (Bohdan S.) Research Paper Competition: 715
WYOMING ARTS COUNCIL
 Art Projects Grants: 523
 Artists Across Wyoming Grants: 523
 Arts Education Grants: 523
 Capacity Building Grants: 523
 Community Arts Partners Grants: 523
 Grants to Organizations Grants: 523
 Individual Artist Professional Development Grants: 523
 Literary Arts Fellowships: 523
 Operating Support Grants: 523
 Performing Arts Fellowships: 523
 Visual Arts Fellowships: 523
WYOMISSING FOUNDATION (THE): 340

X

XCEL ENERGY FOUNDATION: 341
XERIC FOUNDATION
 Grants for Nonprofit Organizations: 342
XEROX FOUNDATION (THE): 343

Y

YALE CENTER FOR BRITISH ART
 Visiting Scholar Awards: 408
Yamagiwa-Yoshida Memorial International Study Grants (YY): 2449
Yamaha Terry Gibbs Scholarship: 784
Yang (Y.C.) Civil Engineering Scholarship: 2645
YIVO INSTITUTE FOR JEWISH RESEARCH
 Abramowicz (The Dina) Emerging Scholar Fellowship: 650
 Fellowship in American Jewish Studies: 647
 Fellowship in Baltic Jewish Studies: 649
 Fellowship in East European Jewish Literature and Arts: 648
 Fellowship in East European Jewish Studies: 650
 Fellowship in Polish Jewish Studies: 649
 Workmen's Circle (The)/Dr. Emanuel Patt Visiting Professorship: 650
Young Clinician Investigator Award: 2479
Young Composers' Competition: 776
Young Concert Artists International Auditions: 795
YOUNG CONCERT ARTISTS, INC.
 Young Concert Artists International Auditions: 795
Young Investigator Awards: 2360
Young Investigator Grant: 2523, 2575
Young Investigator Grant Program: 2422, 2526
Young Investigator Grants: 1518, 2147, 2299
Young Investigator Program: 1843
Young Investigator's Award: 2500
Young (The Morton Gould) Composer Awards: 754
YOUNG MUSICIANS FOUNDATION (YMF)
 Arts Management Internship: 796
 Chamber Music Series (CMS): 797
 Debut Concerto Competition: 796
 Debut Orchestra: 796
 Music Director: 796
 Music Mentors Program: 796
 Music 360 Degrees: 796
 Scholarship Program: 796
Young Native Writers Essay Contest: 1050
Young Professional Award: 1559
Young Scholars Program: 1680
Young Scientist Award: 2680
Young Women for Change: 1088
Young Women in Public Affairs Awards: 1105
YoungArts Miami: 481
YoungArts New York: 481
YoungArts Week: 481
Yount (Harry) National Park Ranger Award: 2190
Youth Art: 567
Youth Arts Project Grants: 485
Youth Council: 1170
Youth Development Fund: 65
Youth Football Grants: 1336

YOUTH FOR UNDERSTANDING USA
    Americans Overseas Summer, Semester and Year Programs: 954
    Congress-Bundestag Youth Exchange Program: 954
    Corporate Scholarship Program: 954
    Finland-U.S. Senate Youth Exchange Program: 954
    International Semester and Year Programs: 954
    Japan-U.S. Senate Youth Exchange Program: 954
Youth Grants: 133
Youth in Philanthropy: 252
Youth Organizing Grants: 1130
Youth Pathways to Health: 1509
Youth Philanthropy Grants: 1404
Youth Power: 1284
Youth Service Improvement Grants Program: 1127
Youth Summit: 2267
Youth-led Community Change (YLCC): 198
YouthReach Initiative: 472
Ypsilanti Area Community Fund (The): 1170

Z

Z/I Imaging Scholarship: 2033
ZACHARY (THE LOREN L.) SOCIETY FOR THE PERFORMING
    ARTS
    Annual Loren L. Zachary National Vocal Competition for Young Opera
    Singers: 798
Zaken (Lisa) Award of Excellence: 2653
Zanesville Prize for Contemporary Ceramics: 1334
Zenith Fellows Award Program (The): 2452
Zervoulias (The Sotiri) & Lea Soupata Scholarship (St. Basil's Academy):
    1080
ZIGLER (FRED B. AND RUTH B.) FOUNDATION: 1599
Zildjian (Armand) Scholarship: 784
Zildjian Family Opportunity Fund: 784
Zimmerman (A.F.) Scholarship: 628
Ziskind-Somerfeld Research Award: 2592
ZONTA INTERNATIONAL FOUNDATION
    Earhart (Amelia) Fellowship: 2059
    Klausman (Jane M.) Women in Business Scholarships: 1919
    Young Women in Public Affairs Awards: 1105
Zoo Keeper Grants in Zoology: 2136

Geographical Index

UNITED STATES

Alabama

Alabama Academy of Science, Inc.: 1806
Alabama Commission on Higher Education: 1650, 1651, 1652
Alabama Library Association Scholarship Loan Fund, Inc.: 708
Alabama Power Foundation, Inc.: 8
Alabama State Council on the Arts: 427
Brock (The Harry B. and Jane H.) Foundation: 1187
Community Foundation of Northeast Alabama: 1235
Community Foundation of South Alabama (The): 1238
Dixon Foundation (The): 1257
Meyer (Robert R.) Foundation: 233
Tuskegee University: 2044

Alaska

Alaska Conservation Foundation: 2164, 2165
Alaska State Council on the Arts: 428

Arizona

American Association of Zoo Keepers: 2136
American Matthay Association: 750
APS Corporate Giving Program: 20
Arizona Commission on the Arts: 433
Arizona Community Foundation: 1171
Arizona State University: 1522
Economic History Association: 1895
Flinn Foundation (The): 128
Freeport-McMoRan Copper and Gold Foundation: 132
Institute for Supply Management: 1900
Muscular Dystrophy Association: 2473
Research Corporation for Science Advancement: 2041
Udall (The Morris K.) and Stewart L. Udall Foundation: 1059, 1774
University of Arizona School of Information Resources and Library Science: 742

Arkansas

Arkansas Community Foundation: 1172
Ross Foundation: 1362

California

Academy Foundation of the Academy of Motion Picture Arts and Sciences: 524, 541
Acorn Foundation: 2163
Ahmanson Foundation (The): 7
Allende (The Isabel) Foundation: 1070, 1653
American Honda Foundation: 1519
American Society for Enology and Viticulture: 2115
Amgen Foundation, Inc.: 17
Amyotrophic Lateral Sclerosis Association (The): 2457
Annenberg Foundation (The): 18
Applied Materials, Inc.: 19
Archstone Foundation: 1419
Arthritis National Research Foundation (ANRF): 2241
Asian American Journalists Association: 1667
Astronomical Society of the Pacific: 2048, 2049, 2050, 2051
Atkinson Foundation: 24
Autry Foundation: 1174
Baker (R.C.) Foundation: 28
Berger (H.N. and Frances C.) Foundation: 39
Bing Fund: 43
Broad (The Eli and Edythe) Foundation : 2408
Burns (Fritz B.) Foundation: 1529
California Academy of Sciences: 2142
California Arts Council: 437
California Community Foundation: 1192
California Endowment (The): 1423
California Healthcare Foundation: 1424
California Library Association: 717
California Student Aid Commission: 1670, 1671, 1672
California Wellness Foundation (The): 1425
Cancer Federation, Inc.: 2359

Center for California Studies, Capital Fellows Programs: 1990, 1991, 1992, 1993
Center for Comparative Immigration Studies at the University of California-San Diego: 1622
Center for International Security and Cooperation (CISAC): 833
Center for Medieval and Renaissance Studies: 357
Center for 17th and 18th Century Studies: 358, 359, 360, 361
Center for U.S. - Mexican Studies, University of California, San Diego: 834
Christensen Fund (The): 64
Common Counsel Foundation: 1212
Community Foundation for Monterey County (The): 1217
Community Foundation of the Verdugos: 1479
Compton Foundation, Inc.: 80
Cowell (S.H.) Foundation: 87
Crail-Johnson Foundation (The): 1117
Darling (Hugh and Hazel) Foundation: 1626
DJ & T Foundation: 2106
Drown (Joseph) Foundation: 105
East Bay Community Foundation (The): 1261
Ebell of Los Angeles (The): 1684
Edison International: 114
Eisner Foundation (The): 1122
Energy Foundation (The): 2176
Fieldstone Foundation (The): 369
Fireman's Fund Insurance Company: 1271
Fresno Regional Foundation: 133
Gamble Foundation (The): 1547
Geffen (The David) Foundation: 1432
Gellert (Carl) and Celia Berta Gellert Foundation (The): 139
Gellert (The Fred) Family Foundation: 140
Getty (J. Paul) Trust, Getty Foundation: 549
Glaucoma Research Foundation: 2514
Global Fund for Women: 1082
Goldman (Lisa and Douglas) Fund: 1280
GRAMMY Foundation (The): 768
Grass Foundation (The): 2465
Great Minds in STEM: 2609
Hafif Family Foundation (The): 1083
Harden Foundation: 154
Haynes (The John Randolph) and Dora Haynes Foundation: 1631
Health Trust (The): 1438, 1439
HealthCare Foundation for Orange County (The): 1440
Hearst (William Randolph) Foundation: 1935
Hewlett (The William and Flora) Foundation: 159
Hillblom (The Larry L.) Foundation, Inc.: 2268
Hispanic Scholarship Fund: 1068
Honig (Victor and Lorraine) Fund: 1485
Humboldt Area Foundation: 1303
Huntington (Henry E.) Library and Art Gallery: 373
International Anesthesia Research Society (IARS): 2272
International Documentary Association: 462
International Myeloma Foundation (IMF): 2274
Irmas (Audrey and Sydney) Charitable Foundation: 1306
Irvine Health Foundation: 1442
Italian American Studies Association: 601
Jackson (Ann) Family Foundation: 171
Japan Foundation, Los Angeles (The): 1703
Japanese American Citizens League (JACL) (The): 1704
Jewish Community Foundation of Los Angeles: 1308
Jewish Family and Children's Services: 1705
Johnson (Magic) Foundation, Inc.: 177
Johnson (Walter S.) Foundation: 1560
Jones (The Fletcher) Foundation: 1633
Kantor (Alice and Julius) Charitable Trust: 181
Koret Foundation: 195
Kvamme (The Jean and E. Floyd) Foundation: 1563
LA84 Foundation: 1447
Latkin (Herbert and Gertrude) Charitable Foundation: 202
Leakey (L.S.B.) Foundation: 2020
Liberty Hill Foundation: 1490
Livingston Memorial Foundation: 1448
Loeb (The Gerald) Awards: 1942
Luso-American Education Foundation: 655, 656
Maddie's Fund: 1858
Marin Community Foundation: 217
Martin (Della) Foundation: 2581
Masserini (Maurice J.) Charitable Trust: 998
MAZON: A Jewish Response to Hunger: 1493
McBean (Alletta Morris) Charitable Trust: 376

McMicking (The Joseph R.) Foundation: 224
Mexican American Legal Defense and Educational Fund: 1985
Nakamichi (E.) Foundation: 775
National Alopecia Areata Foundation: 2156
National Association of Composers, USA (NACUSA): 776
National Association of Science Writers, Inc.: 1946
Neuro-Developmental Treatment Association: 2370
Norris (Kenneth T. and Eileen L.) Foundation: 247
Nuclear Age Peace Foundation: 855
Orange County Community Foundation: 253
Osher (The Bernard) Foundation: 254
Oxnard Foundation: 2305
Pacific Foundation Services: 1639
Pacific Gas and Electric Company: 256
Pacific Life Foundation: 257
Packard (The David and Lucile) Foundation: 258
Packard (Lucile) Foundation for Children's Health: 1140
Parker Foundation (The): 260
Parsons (The Ralph M.) Foundation: 262
Pasadena Community Foundation: 1500
Patagonia Inc.: 2195
Patron Saints Foundation (The): 1456
Prostate Cancer Research and Education Foundation (PC-REF): 2445
Rancho Santa Fe Foundation: 1353
Reagan (Ronald) Presidential Foundation: 1751
Righteous Persons Foundation: 1010
San Diego Art Institute: 567
San Diego Foundation (The): 1369
San Francisco Conservatory of Music: 788
San Francisco Foundation (The): 1370, 287, 498, 568
San Francisco Opera Center: 789
Santa Barbara Foundation: 1371
Santa Barbara Mission Archive-Library: 633
Schwab (Charles and Helen) Foundation: 290
Schwab (Charles) Foundation: 1911
Scripps (The Ellen Browning) Foundation: 291
Seaver Institute (The): 293
Shasta Regional Community Foundation: 1375
Sierra Health Foundation: 1509
Silicon Valley Community Foundation: 1376
Silicon Valley Creates: 500
Sisters of St. Joseph Healthcare Foundation: 1464
Society of Children's Book Writers and Illustrators: 697
Special Hope Foundation (The): 1017
Stanford Humanities Center: 400
Stauffer (John) Charitable Trust: 306
Stuart Foundation: 1147
Tahoe Truckee Community Foundation: 312
Tailhook Educational Foundation: 1590
Taper (S. Mark) Foundation: 313
Tides Foundation: 1387
Trust Funds Incorporated: 322
UCLA Chicano Studies Research Center: 1069
UCLA Institute of American Cultures (IAC): 1018
University of California: 1020
University of California, Los Angeles: 1021, 1061, 1794
University of Southern California: 1796, 1797, 1798
University of Southern California Roski School of Art and Design: 575
Valley Foundation (The): 2334
van LoebenSels/RembeRock Foundation: 1394
Ventura County Community Foundation: 1395
Weingart Foundation: 332
Witter (The Dean) Foundation: 1918
Women In Film: 1100
Young Musicians Foundation (YMF): 796, 797
Zachary (The Loren L.) Society for the Performing Arts: 798

Colorado

American Alpine Club: 2167
American Association for the History of Nursing, Inc.: 2484
American College of Medical Practice Executives: 1654
American Indian College Fund: 1036
American Society for Theatre Research (ASTR): 526
Animal Assistance Foundation: 2239
Association for Applied Psychophysiology and Biofeedback: 2572
Brett Family Foundation: 1847
Colorado Creative Industries: 440
Colorado Trust (The): 1427

Cooperative Institute for Research in Environmental Sciences (CIRES): 2175
Coors (Adolph) Foundation: 1116
Crowell (Henry P. and Susan C.) Trust: 88
Daniels Fund: 92
Duncan (The John G.) Trust: 1260
El Pomar Foundation: 115
Erion Foundation: 118
FEEA Scholarship Program: 1685
First Nations Development Institute: 1049
General Service Foundation: 141
Geological Society of America, Inc. (The): 2077
Gill Foundation: 991
Hughes (Mabel Y.) Charitable Trust: 165
Hunter (A.V.) Trust, Inc.: 1486
International Food Service Executives Association, Inc. (IFSEA): 2612
JILA: 2037
Maytag (Freda)-Grace Crawford Trust: 1449
McCauley (Luther T.) Charitable Trust: 1325
McDonald (J.M.) Foundation, Inc.: 220
National Cattleman's Beef Association: 2675
National Center for Atmospheric Research: 1829, 2053
National Endowment for Financial Education (NEFE): 1908
Rose Community Foundation: 1360
Sachs Foundation: 1034
Stone (H. Chase) Trust: 502
Summit Foundation (The): 1385
Teammates for Kids Foundation: 1149
U.S. Society on Dams: 2666
Western Interstate Commission For Higher Education: 334

Connecticut

Aetna Foundation, Inc.: 6
American Epilepsy Society (AES): 2455
Axe-Houghton Foundation: 653
Barnes Group Foundation: 1177
Belgian American Educational Foundation, Inc.: 900
Calder (The Louis) Foundation: 1110
Center for the Humanities: 362
Childs (The Jane Coffin) Memorial Fund for Medical Research: 2436
Community Foundation for Greater New Haven (The): 1216
Community Foundation of Eastern Connecticut: 1225
Connecticut Community Foundation: 1245
Connecticut Humanities: 363
Connecticut Library Association: 721
Deloitte Foundation: 1627
Department of Economic and Community Development/Connecticut Office of the Arts: 446
Fairfield County Community Foundation: 1269
Hartford Public Library: 723
Hoffman (Maximilian E. & Marion O.) Foundation, Inc.: 2270
Knights of Columbus: 1708
National Organization for Rare Disorders (The): 2297
Richardson (Smith) Foundation, Inc.: 1868
Walpole (Lewis) Library: 404
Xerox Foundation (The): 343
Yale Center for British Art: 408

Delaware

Delaware Division of the Arts: 445
Freeman (Carl M.) Foundation: 451
Hagley Museum and Library: 593
Intercollegiate Studies Institute (The): 2004
International Reading Association: 1556, 1557
Raskob Foundation for Catholic Activities: 822
University of Delaware-Hagley Graduate Program (The): 644
University of Delaware, Department of History: 645
Winterthur Museum, Garden & Library: 406

District of Columbia

AAA Foundation for Traffic Safety: 1415
American Academy of Child and Adolescent Psychiatry: 2562
American Aging Association: 2222
American Architectural Foundation: 409
American Association for the Advancement of Science: 1920, 1921
American Astronomical Society: 2046, 2047
American Chemical Society: 2031, 2060, 2061
American College of Cardiology: 2372, 2373, 2374, 2375

1045

American Farm Bureau Foundation for Agriculture: 2113
American Friends of the Alexander von Humboldt Foundation: 1615, 1657, 871, 872
American Hellenic Educational Progressive Association (The): 972
American Historical Association (The): 578, 579, 580
American Institute for Cancer Research: 2427
American Institute of Architects (The): 410, 411
American Political Science Association: 1987, 1988, 1989
American Psychological Association: 2566, 2567, 974
American Public Power Association (APPA): 2641
American Society for Engineering Education: 2642, 2643, 2644
American Society for Microbiology: 2139, 2140
American Society of Hematology: 2235, 2236, 2354
American Society of Interior Designers Educational Foundation: 412
American Society of Nephrology: 2358
American Society of Nephrology : 2355, 2356, 2357
American Sociological Association: 975
American Urogynecologic Foundation: 2105
American Veterinary Medical Association: 2238
ARC of the United States (The): 2571
Arca Foundation (The): 21
Association of American Geographers (The): 2074, 2075, 2076, 2073
Association of Women's Health, Obstetric and Neonatal Nurses (AWHONN): 2487
Bell (Alexander Graham) Association for the Deaf and Hard of Hearing: 981
Benton Foundation: 1923
Broadcast Education Association: 1924
Bureau of Indian Education: 1046
Cafritz (The Morris and Gwendolyn) Foundation: 54
Carnegie Institution of Washington: 1816
Catholic Campaign for Human Development: 1198
Center for Hellenic Studies: 356
Center for Science in the Public Interest: 2670
Children's Bureau: 1114
Civil Justice Foundation: 1973
Conference Board of the Mathematical Sciences: 2094
Congressional Black Caucus Foundation, Inc.: 1025, 1026, 1027
Congressional Hispanic Caucus Institute: 1064, 1065, 1066
Cooperative Development Foundation: 1247
Corporation for National and Community Service: 1248, 1480
Council for International Exchange of Scholars (CIES): 1623, 1624, 836, 837, 906, 907
Council of American Overseas Research Centers (CAORC): 908
Daughters of Penelope Foundation, Inc.: 1080, 988
Department of Veterans Affairs: 2577
District of Columbia Commission on the Arts and Humanities: 447
Dumbarton Oaks: 367
Eisenhower Institute (The): 847
Environmental Law Institute: 1974
Eye Bank Association of America: 2510
Folger Institute (The): 370
Food and Drug Law Institute (FDLI): 1975
Freer Gallery of Art and Arthur M. Sackler Gallery: 452
Fund for American Studies (The): 2000
Fund for Investigative Journalism: 1933
George Washington University: 2652
Georgetown University: 2066
German Historical Institute: 592
Graham Holdings Company: 148
Graham (Philip L.) Fund: 149
Heritage Foundation (The)/B. Kenneth Simon Center for American Studies: 2001
Heritage Preservation: 725
Hispanic Bar Association of D.C. Foundation (The): 1980
Hispanic Dental Association Foundation: 2349
Hispanic National Bar Foundation: 1981, 1982
Hitachi Foundation (The): 162
Horticultural Research Institute, Inc.: 1697
Institute of Current World Affairs: 849
Institute of Food Technologists Foundation: 2610
Institute of Museum and Library Services: 727, 728
International Research & Exchanges Board (IREX): 920
Jack and Jill of America Foundation (The): 1029
Japan-U.S. Friendship Commission: 853
Japanese American Citizens League (JACL) (The): 2005
Kennedy (Robert F.) Center for Justice and Human Rights: 678
Landscape Architecture Foundation: 2186
Lehrman (Jacob and Charlotte) Foundation, Inc.: 204
Lupus Foundation of America, Inc.: 2279

Marshall (Thurgood) College Fund: 1983
McNamara (The Margaret) Memorial Fund (MMMF): 225
Meyer (Eugene and Agnes E.) Foundation: 1327
Morris (William) Society in the U.S.: 479
National Academy of Education (The): 1567
National Association for Equal Opportunity in Higher Education (NAFEO): 1031
National Association of Black Social Workers (The): 1032
National Association of Broadcasters: 1944
National Association of Health Services Executives (NAHSE): 2555
National Association of Hispanic Journalists: 1001
National Business Aviation Association: 2624, 2625, 2626
National Council for Eurasian and East European Research (The): 854
National Endowment for Democracy: 2007
National Endowment for the Arts: 480
National Endowment for the Humanities: 1947, 378, 379, 380, 381, 382
National Fish and Wildlife Foundation: 2188
National Geographic Society: 2081
National Historical Publications and Records Commission: 613
National Institute of Justice, U.S. Department of Justice: 1409
National Italian American Foundation (The): 1720
National Park Foundation: 2190
National Press Foundation: 1949
National Research Council of the National Academies: 1005, 2039
National Security Education Program: 933, 934
National Society Daughters of the American Revolution: 1722, 1723, 1866, 2298, 2494, 2556, 420, 614
National Trust for Historic Preservation: 615
NEA Foundation (The): 1577, 1578
Newspaper Guild-CWA (The): 1950, 1951
Office of Indian Energy and Economic Development: 1055
Organization of American States: 856, 963
Patterson (The Alicia) Foundation: 1955
PEN/Faulkner Foundation: 693
Pew Fellows Program in Marine Conservation: 2196
Pharmaceutical Research and Manufacturers of America Foundation, Inc.: 2306, 2307, 2308, 2309, 2310, 2539, 2540, 2541, 2542, 2543
Phi Beta Kappa Society (The): 1093, 1744, 694, 935
Poverty & Race Research Action Council: 1867
President's Commission on White House Fellowships: 2013
Public Welfare Foundation, Inc.: 273
PVA Research Foundation: 2558
Radio Television Digital News Foundation: 1958
Replogle (Luther I.) Foundation: 1356
Resources for the Future: 2197, 2198, 2199
RTCA: 2627
Rural Housing Service: 2128
SCAC (French Cultural and Educational Office): 939
Schork (Kurt) Memorial Fund: 1960
Scoville (Herbert, Jr.) Peace Fellowship: 857
Share Our Strength: 1508
Smithsonian Institution: 1839
Smithsonian National Air and Space Museum: 2628, 2629
Society for Science and the Public: 1840
Society for the Psychological Study of Social Issues (SPSSI) (The): 1877, 1878, 1879, 1880, 1881, 1882, 1883, 1884, 1885, 2015
Sons of Italy Foundation: 1015
Subcommittee on the Home Missions: 824
Swann Foundation for Caricature and Cartoon: 402
Taste and Smell Clinic: 2331
Truman (The Harry S.) Scholarship Foundation: 2019
U.S. Army Center of Military History: 638
U.S. Department of Agriculture: 2206
U.S. Department of Education: 1057, 1592, 1593, 1594, 1595, 1643, 1644, 1769, 1770, 1771, 1772, 1773, 1915, 1916, 2561, 662, 663, 664, 863, 943, 944
U.S. Department of Health and Human Services: 1058, 1151, 1152, 1153, 1391
U.S. Department of Health and Human Services/Administration for Children and Families/Office of Family Assistance: 1967
U.S. Department of Housing and Urban Development: 1392
U.S. Department of Justice: 1411, 1412, 1413, 1414
U.S. Department of Labor: 1968
U.S. Department of State, Fulbright Teacher Exchange Program: 1596
U.S. Environmental Protection Agency: 2207, 2208
U.S. Institute of Peace: 864, 865
United Negro College Fund: 1035
United States Holocaust Memorial Museum, Center for Advanced Holocaust Studies: 643
USDA - Rural Utilities Service: 2133
Van Slyke Foundation (The): 1844

Wilson (Woodrow) International Center for Scholars: 405
Women's Policy, Inc. (WPI): 1103
Word Works, Inc. (The): 706, 707

Florida

A-T Children's Project: 2214
Able Trust (The): 969
American Academy of Optometry: 2504
American Optometric Foundation: 2505
American Orchid Society: 2138
AWS Foundation, Inc.: 2600, 2601, 2602, 2603
Broward Education Foundation, Inc. (The): 1527
Bush (Edyth) Charitable Foundation, Inc.: 52
Chatlos Foundation, Inc. (The): 807
Chopin Foundation of the U.S.: 758
Cintas Foundation: 439
Community Foundation for Northeast Florida (The): 1218
Community Foundation for Palm Beach and Martin Counties: 1221
Community Foundation of Collier County: 1224
Daughters of Italy Lodge #2825: 1681
Davis (The Arthur Vining) Foundations: 94
Dunspaugh Dalton Foundation: 110
duPont (Jessie Ball) Fund: 111
Florida Department of Education: 1028, 1067, 1687, 1688
Florida Department of State, Division of Cultural Affairs: 448
Florida Education Fund: 1542
Florida State University Foundation: 1543
Foundation for Science and Disability: 989
Gulf Coast Community Foundation : 1294
Health Foundation of South Florida: 1437
Holland & Knight Charitable Foundation, Inc.: 1050, 598
Inter American Press Association (IAPA): 1937
International Women's Fishing Association Scholarship Trust: 2078
Jacksonville Jaguars Foundation: 174
Knight (John S. and James L.) Foundation: 193
Koch Foundation, Inc.: 816
Macdonald (The Dr. John T.) Foundation, Inc.: 1132
Miami Foundation (The): 234
National Foundation for Advancement in the Arts: 481
National Oceanic and Atmospheric Administration: 2083
Order Sons of Italy in America, Grand Lodge of Florida: 1742
Orlando Magic Youth Fund: 1139
Peacock Foundation, Inc.: 264
Phi Alpha Theta History Honor Society: 627, 628, 629
Planning and Visual Education Partnership (The): 1747
Quantum Foundation: 1459
Radiant Peace Foundation International, Inc. (The): 1608
Selby (William G. and Marie) Foundation: 1507
Skelly (Gertrude E.) Charitable Foundation: 1641
Society of Biological Psychiatry: 2591, 2592
Southwest Florida Community Foundation: 1378
State Library and Archives of Florida: 740
Swedish Women's Educational Association Inc.: 861
Tampa Bay Times Fund, Inc.: 1763, 1764
Violin Society of America (The): 793
Whitehall Foundation, Inc.: 2161

Georgia

American Academy of Religion: 799, 800
American Cancer Society, Inc.: 2425, 2426
Arthritis Foundation: 2450
ASHRAE: 2649, 2650
Callaway Foundation, Inc.: 1193
Coca-Cola Foundation, Inc. (The): 1533
Coca-Cola Scholars Foundation: 1678
Community Foundation for Greater Atlanta, Inc.: 1214
Community Foundation for Northeast Georgia: 1219
Georgia Council for the Arts: 453
Georgia Library Association: 722
Georgia-Pacific Foundation: 143
Golden Key International Honour Society, Inc.: 1692
Hambidge: 455
Home Depot Foundation (The): 1300
Huebner (The S.S.) Foundation for Insurance Education: 1899
Institute of Industrial Engineers (IIE): 2653
MAP International: 2281
South Atlantic Modern Language Association: 661
Tull Charitable Foundation, Inc.: 323

UPS Foundation (The): 326
Whitehead (Joseph B.) Foundation: 1156
Woodruff (The Robert W.) Foundation: 338

Hawaii

Castle (Harold K.L.) Foundation: 59
Castle (Samuel N. and Mary) Foundation: 1601
East-West Center (The): 845, 846
Hawaii Community Foundation: 1298
Hawaii State Foundation on Culture and the Arts: 456

Idaho

Idaho Commission on the Arts: 459
Idaho Community Foundation: 168
Micron Technology Foundation, Inc.: 2096

Illinois

Abbott Fund: 1
Academy of Nutrition and Dietetic Foundation (The): 2668
Actuarial Foundation (The) : 2091
Actuarial Foundation (The): 2092
Allstate Foundation (The): 1475
Alzheimer's Association, Inc.: 2452, 2453
American Academy of Esthetic Dentistry (The): 2340
American Academy of Implant Dentistry (AAID) Foundation: 2341
American Academy of Pediatrics: 2527
American Association of Law Libraries: 709, 710
American Association of School Librarians: 711, 712
American Association of Women Dentists: 2346
American Bar Foundation: 1970, 970
American Brain Tumor Association: 2454
American Burn Association: 2546
American College of Legal Medicine: 2224
American Dental Assistants Association: 2347
American Dental Hygienists' Association Institute for Oral Health: 2348
American Institute of Indian Studies: 652, 877
American Library Association (ALA): 1616, 713
American Medical Association Foundation: 1660
American Medical Technologists: 2230
American Nuclear Society (ANS): 2062, 2634, 2635, 2636, 2637, 2638, 2639, 2640
American Oil Chemists Society: 2063
American Orthopaedic Society for Sports Medicine (AOSSM) (The): 2549
American Osteopathic Foundation: 1661, 2522
American Planning Association: 1165, 973
American Society for Clinical Pathology: 2234
American Society for Healthcare Risk Management: 1418
American Society of Safety Engineers: 2648
APICS Educational and Research Foundation, Inc.: 2599
Appraisal Institute Education Trust: 1891
Argonne National Laboratory: 1813, 1814
Association for Library and Information Science Education: 714, 715
Baxter International Foundation (The): 35
Blair (William) and Company Foundation: 1181
Blowitz-Ridgeway Foundation: 1182
Brunswick Foundation, Inc.: 1189
Brunswick Public Foundation: 2171
Caterpillar Corporate Giving Program: 1197
Charleston Area Charitable Foundation: 1203
CHEST Foundation (The): 2392
Chicago Board of Trade Foundation: 1426
Chicago Community Trust (The): 1206
Chicago Tribune Foundation: 63
Children's Literature Association: 672, 673
Civic Orchestra of Chicago: 759
Coin-Op Cares Charitable and Education Foundation: 2605
Coleman Foundation, Inc. (The): 71
Community Foundation of the Fox River Valley: 1240
Coordinating Council for Women in History, Inc. (The): 1078, 588
Crossroads Fund: 1849
Dairy Research Institute - National Dairy Council: 2671
Deere (John) Foundation: 96
Dermatology Foundation: 2255
Dirksen Congressional Center (The): 1995
Donnelley (Gaylord and Dorothy) Foundation: 101
Donnelley (R.R.): 102
Duchossois Family Foundation (The): 106
Dystonia Medical Research Foundation: 2462

Evangelical Lutheran Church in America: 811
Exelon Corporation: 119
Federation of American Consumers and Travelers: 1541, 1898
Field Foundation of Illinois: 122
Foundation for Osteopathic Emergency Medicine: 2523
Foundation of the American College of Healthcare Executives (The): 1431
Foundation of the American Society of Neuroradiology (The): 2259
Fry (Lloyd A.) Foundation: 136
GATX Corporation: 138
Graham Foundation for Advanced Studies in the Fine Arts: 417
Great Lakes Protection Fund: 2182
HIMSS Foundation: 2269
Illinois Arts Council: 460
Illinois Clean Energy Community Foundation: 2185
Illinois Restaurant Association Educational Foundation: 1698
Illinois State Academy of Science: 1822
Immanuel Bible Foundation: 815
Institute for the International Education of Students (IES): 1700
International College of Surgeons: 2273
International Foundation for Ethical Research, Inc.: 1823
Jackson (Ruth) Orthopaedic Society: 2553
Jewel-OSCO: 1307
Journal of the American Medical Association: 1939
Joyce Foundation (The): 179
Kobe College Corporation-Japan Education Exchange: 924
Leukemia Research Foundation: 2441
Levie (Marcus and Theresa) Education Fund: 1711
MacArthur (John D. and Catherine T.) Foundation: 213
MacArthur (Roderick) Foundation: 1491
McCormick Foundation: 219
McDonald (Ronald) House Charities: 1133
Medical Library Association: 227, 729, 730, 962, 999
Millard (Adah K.) Charitable Trust: 237
National Black MBA Association: 1335
National Headache Foundation: 2368
National Restaurant Association Educational Foundation (The): 1909, 2676
Neurosurgery Research and Education Foundation: 2479
Newberry Library (The): 1053, 385, 386, 387, 388, 389, 390, 391, 392, 393, 394, 395, 396, 397, 398, 623
North American Spine Society (NASS): 2299
Northern Trust Corporation: 1338
Orthopaedic Research and Education Foundation: 2300, 2301, 2302
Pick (The Albert, Jr.) Fund: 268
Plastic Surgery Foundation (PSF): 2312
Precast/Prestressed Concrete Institute: 2662
Pulmonary Fibrosis Foundation: 2315
Radiological Society of North America Research and Education Foundation: 2316, 2317, 2318, 2319, 2320, 2321
Ragdale Foundation: 496
Regenstein Foundation (The): 277
Rehabilitation Nursing Foundation (RNF): 2496
Research Fund of the American Otological Society, Inc.: 2521
Retirement Research Foundation (The): 1009
Rock Island Arsenal Museum: 631
Rotary Foundation of Rotary International (The): 936
Scholl (Dr.) Foundation: 289
Siragusa Foundation (The): 296
Society of Actuaries (SOA): 2097, 2098
Society of Architectural Historians: 424
Society of Critical Care Medicine: 2560
Society of Women Engineers: 1096
Spencer Foundation: 1588
Stern (Irvin) Foundation: 1511
Stone (W. Clement & Jessie V.) Foundation: 1611
Tree Research & Education Endowment Fund: 2129
University Film and Video Association: 1962
University of Illinois at Urbana-Champaign: 574
USG Foundation, Inc.: 327
VietNow National: 1598
Woods Fund of Chicago: 1406
Zonta International Foundation: 1105, 1919, 2059

Indiana

American Conservatory of Music: 749
American Legion National Headquarters (The): 2485
Ball Brothers Foundation: 29
Ball (George and Frances) Foundation: 30
Central Indiana Community Foundation: 1199

Christian Church (Disciples of Christ): 808
Community Foundation of Muncie and Delaware County, Inc. (The): 1233
Community Foundation of Saint Joseph County: 1236
Consortium of College and University Media Centers: 1536
Contemporary Music Festival: 762
Cummins Foundation (The): 91
Cushwa Center for the Study of American Catholicism: 589, 590
Dearborn Community Foundation, Inc.: 1251
DePauw University Key Club International Bonner/Wright Scholarship: 1254
Hancock County Community Foundation: 1297
Health Foundation of Greater Indianapolis (The): 1436, 1484
History of Science Society: 596, 597
Indiana Arts Commission: 461
Indiana Commission for Higher Education, Division of Student Financial Aid: 1699
Indiana Library Federation: 726
Lawrence County Community Foundation: 1315
Lilly Endowment Inc.: 206
Lincoln Financial Foundation: 207
Lumina Foundation: 1634
National Federation of Music Clubs: 777, 778, 779
Percussive Arts Society: 784
Pulliam Journalism Fellowship: 1956
Sigma Theta Tau International: 2497
Society for Pediatric Dermatology: 2532
Unity Foundation of LaPorte County (The): 1393
Wabash Center for Teaching and Learning in Theology and Religion (The): 827

Iowa

American Association of University Women: 1071
American Association of University Women Educational Foundation: 1072, 1073, 1074, 957
Carver (Roy J.) Charitable Trust: 1621
Cowles (Gardner and Florence Call) Foundation: 1625
DuPont Pioneer: 1120
Greater Cedar Rapids Community Foundation (The): 1284
Hoover (Herbert) Presidential Library Association, Inc.: 2002
International Association for Food Protection: 2673
Iowa Arts Council: 463
McElroy (R.J.) Trust: 1134
National Farmer's Organization: 2125
P.E.O. Sisterhood: 964
Principal Financial Group Foundation Inc.: 272
Quill and Scroll Foundation: 1957
Soil and Water Conservation Society: 2202
University of Iowa (The): 701

Kansas

American Academy of Family Physicians Foundation: 2221
Aviation Insurance Association (AIA): 2622
Capitol Federal Foundation: 1195
Eisenhower Foundation (The): 1997
Hutchinson Community Foundation: 458
Jellison Benevolent Society: 1558
Kansas Health Foundation: 1446
Mycological Society of America: 2155
Pi Gamma Mu, International Honor Society in Social Science: 1745
Pritchett Trust: 1142
SkillBuilders Fund: 1095
United Methodist Health Ministry Fund: 1514
University of Kansas Child Language Doctoral Program: 1795
Wichita Community Foundation: 1402

Kentucky

Brown (James Graham) Foundation, Inc.: 48
Community Foundation of Louisville, Inc. (The): 441
Cooke (V.V.) Foundation: 83
Foundation for the Tri-State Community, Inc.: 1276
Gheens Foundation: 144
Grayson-Jockey Club Research Foundation (The): 2265
Humana Foundation (The): 166
Kentucky Arts Council: 465
Kentucky Foundation for Women: 1086
Kentucky Historical Society: 602
Presbyterian Church (U.S.A.): 1748, 1749, 821

Louisiana

Baton Rouge Area Foundation: 436
Booth-Bricker Fund (The): 47
Brown (The Joe W. and Dorothy Dorsett) Foundation: 49
Greater New Orleans Foundation (The): 1292
Historic New Orleans Collection (The): 594, 595
Honor Society of Phi Kappa Phi (The): 1696
Louisiana Division of the Arts, Department of Culture, Recreation and
    Tourism: 467
National Taxidermists Association: 1007
Woolf (William C.) Foundation: 1407
Zigler (Fred B. and Ruth B.) Foundation: 1599

Maine

American Musicological Society: 751, 752
Berkshire Conference of Women Historians: 583
Burnham (The Margaret E.) Charitable Trust: 51
Central Maine Power Company: 60
Great Bay Foundation (The): 1483
Hannaford Charitable Foundation: 1550
Haystack Mountain School of Crafts: 457
Jackson Laboratory (The): 2149
King (Stephen and Tabitha) Foundation: 190
Libra Foundation: 205
Libra Future Fund: 1903
Maine Arts Commission: 469
Maine Initiatives: 1492
Maine Osteopathic Association: 2524
Morton-Kelly Charitable Trust (The): 1332
Mount Desert Island Biological Laboratory: 2153
Mulford (The Clarence E.) Trust: 240
Oak Grove School Foundation: 1582
Switzer (The Robert & Patricia) Foundation: 2203

Maryland

A.S.P.E.N. Rhoads Research Foundation: 2402
Abell Foundation, Inc. (The): 2
ABMRF/The Foundation for Alcohol Research: 1416
Agency for Healthcare Research and Quality (AHRQ): 1417
American Gastroenterological Association (AGA): 2404, 2405, 2406, 2407
American Institute of Physics: 2099
American Kidney Fund: 2228, 2229
American Nurses Foundation: 2486
American Speech-Language-Hearing Foundation: 2506
Ames (The Kathryn) Foundation: 829
AMVETS: 1663, 1664
Anxiety and Depression Association of America: 2570
Aplastic Anemia and MDS International Foundation: 2240
ASPRS - The Imaging and Geospatial Information Society: 2033, 2034
Association on American Indian Affairs: 1041, 1042, 1043, 1044
Baker (The William G., Jr.) Memorial Fund: 435
Baltimore Community Foundation: 31
Blaustein (Jacob and Hilda) Foundation: 983
Bright Focus Foundation: 1422, 2458, 2508
Building and Fire Research Laboratory: 2035
Business Solutions Association Educational Foundation: 1530
Campbell Foundation, Inc.: 1111
Carson Scholars Fund, Inc. (The): 1675
Colonial Players, Inc. Theater-in-the-Round: 530
Commonweal Foundation, Inc.: 1115
Community Foundation of Frederick County, MD, Inc. (The): 1226
Community Foundation of the Eastern Shore: 1239
CurePSP Foundation for PSP/CBD and Related Brain Diseases: 2460
Cystic Fibrosis Foundation: 2413
Early American Industries Association, Inc.: 2606
England (Lois & Richard) Family Foundation: 1123
Enterprise Community Partners: 415
Epilepsy Foundation of America: 1851, 1852, 2463, 2464
First Candle/SIDS Alliance: 2528
Fogarty (John E.) International Center: 2146
Foundation for Spirituality and Medicine (The): 1430
Goldseker Foundation: 1281
Grace (W. R.) Foundation, Inc.: 147
Health Resources and Services Administration: 1553, 2266
Higginson (Corina) Trust: 160
Hughes (Howard) Medical Institute: 2271
Immune Deficiency Foundation: 2337, 996
International Association of Ice Cream Distributors and Vendors: 1555

International Order of Alhambra: 2552
Johns Hopkins Center for Alternatives to Animal Testing (The): 1445
Kerr (Grayce B.) Fund, Inc.: 188
Knott (Marion I. and Henry J.) Foundation, Inc.: 194
Leidy (The John J.) Foundation: 1317
Loats Foundation, Inc. (The): 208
Marriott International, Inc.: 218
Maryland Higher Education Commission: 1714
Maryland Institute College of Art: 555
Maryland State Arts Council: 471
Mid Atlantic Arts Foundation: 476
NASDAQ OMX Group Educational Foundation, Inc. (The): 1907
National Black Nurses Association, Inc.: 2492
National Blood Foundation: 2396
National Coalition of Black Meeting Planners (NCBMP): 1571
National Council for the Social Studies: 1859, 1860, 1861, 1862, 1863,
    1864
National Emergency Medicine Association: 1572
National Eye Institute: 2518, 2519
National Federation of the Blind: 1002
National Foundation for Infectious Diseases: 2339
National Health Service Corps (NHSC): 1451
National Heart, Lung and Blood Institute (NHLBI): 2369, 2397, 2398
National Home Library Foundation: 734
National Institute of Dental and Craniofacial Research (NIDCR): 2351,
    2352, 2353
National Institute of General Medical Sciences: 2289, 2290, 2291
National Institute of Mental Health: 1865, 2582
National Institute of Neurological Disorders and Stroke: 2476
National Institute of Nursing Research: 2493
National Institute of Standards and Technology: 1966
National Institute on Aging: 1452
National Institute on Alcohol Abuse and Alcoholism: 1453, 1454
National Institute on Drug Abuse: 1573, 1574
National Institute on Minority Health and Health Disparities: 1004
National Institutes of Health: 1455, 2292, 2293, 2294, 2295, 2520, 966
National Oceanic and Atmospheric Administration: 1575, 1830, 2082,
    2084, 2085
National Orchestral Institute: 781
National Society of Professional Surveyors (NSPS): 2656, 2657, 2658
National Society of Professional Surveyors (NSPS) American Association
    for Geodetic Surveying (AAGS): 2659, 2660
Open Society Institute - Baltimore: 1343, 1499
Osteogenesis Imperfecta Foundation: 2303
Rosenberg (Henry and Ruth Blaustein) Foundation: 1361
Sheridan (Thomas B. and Elizabeth M.) Foundation: 1609
Shriver (Eunice Kennedy) National Institute of Child Health and Human
    Development: 1462
Smithsonian Environmental Research Center: 2201
Society for Developmental Biology: 2159
Society of Physics Students: 1757, 2102, 2103, 2104
Space Telescope Science Institute: 2058
Substance Abuse and Mental Health Services Administration, Disaster
    Technical Assistance Center: 2593
Town Creek Foundation, Inc.: 2205
Towson University: 699
U.S. Department of Health and Human Services: 1467, 1468, 2498, 2502
U.S. Department of the Navy: 2332
Youth For Understanding USA: 954

Massachusetts

Abelard Foundation-East (The): 1472
Alden (George I.) Trust: 10
Alden (The John W.) Trust: 1106
American Antiquarian Society (AAS): 345, 346
American Association for Hand Surgery: 2223
American Center of Oriental Research: 870
American Institute for Sri Lankan Studies (AISLS): 873, 874
American Institute for Yemeni Studies: 875
American Meteorological Society: 2620
American Schools of Oriental Research (ASOR): 895
Archaeological Institute of America: 1618, 1665, 350, 351, 352, 353, 830
Armenian Relief Society of Eastern U.S.A., Inc.: 976
Austro-American Association of Boston: 832
Barr Foundation: 1178
Bayrd (Adelaide Breed) Foundation: 36
Boston Foundation: 1185
Boston Women's Fund: 1075
Brigham and Women's Hospital: 1421
Cabot Family Charitable Trust: 53

CAYL Institute (The): 1531
Codman (The Ogden) Trust: 69
Community Foundation of Western Massachusetts (CFWM): 1243
Cyprus American Archaeological Research Institute: 913
Davis (Irene E. and George A.) Foundation: 1250
Earthwatch Institute: 1817
Eastern Bank Charitable Foundation: 112
Ellsworth (Ruth H. and Warren A.) Foundation: 116
Essex County Community Foundation: 1267
Farm Aid: 2118
Fine Arts Work Center in Provincetown: 548
FRAXA Research Foundation: 2262
Fromm Music Foundation at Harvard: 767
FSH Society, Inc.: 2264
Greater Lowell Community Foundation: 1290
Harbus Foundation: 1551
Harvard Travellers Club, Permanent Fund: 1821
Harvard Ukrainian Research Institute: 724
Health Effects Institute (HEI): 1435
Henderson Foundation: 157
Hood (Charles H.) Foundation, Inc.: 2529
Hyams Foundation (The): 1487
Institute for Quantitative Social Science, Harvard University: 1857
International OCD Foundation: 2579
Jacob's Pillow Dance Festival, Inc.: 532
Kelley (Edward Bangs) & Elza Kelley Foundation, Inc.: 1311
Kennedy (John F.) Presidential Library: 186
Lalor Foundation, Inc. (The): 1825
LASPAU: Academic and Professional Programs for the Americas: 961
LEF Foundation (The): 418
Marine Biological Laboratory: 2151
Mass Humanities: 375
Massachusetts Cultural Council: 472
Massachusetts Historical Society (The): 605, 606, 607, 608, 609
Massachusetts Institute of Technology: 1943
Massachusetts Medical Society (MMS): 1715
Massachusetts Office of Student Financial Assistance: 1716
Medieval Academy of America (The): 610
Merck Family Fund: 230
Millipore Corporate Giving Program: 238
Museum of Comparative Zoology: 2154
Nantucket Historical Association: 612
National Brain Tumor Society: 2287
Nellie Mae Education Foundation: 1579
New England Biolabs Foundation: 243
New England Foundation for the Arts: 484
Nieman Foundation for Journalism at Harvard: 1952, 1953, 1954
NSTAR Foundation: 249
Peabody (Amelia) Charitable Fund: 263
PEN New England: 691, 692
Pierce (The Harold Whitworth) Charitable Trust: 269
Piper Fund: 2012
Radcliffe Institute for Advanced Study, Harvard University: 1640
Reebok Foundation (The): 276
Riley (The Mabel Louise) Foundation : 1585
Rotch Travelling Scholarship in Architecture: 421
Russell (Josephine G.) Trust: 1461
Sailors' Snug Harbor of Boston: 1505
School of the Museum of Fine Arts, Boston: 569
Schott Foundation for Public Education (The): 1587
Scleroderma Foundation: 2324, 2325
Shaw (Gardiner Howland) Foundation: 1410
Smith Family Awards Program for Excellence in Biomedical Research: 2326
Smith (Horace) Fund: 1755
Smithsonian Astrophysical Observatory: 2056, 2057
State Street Foundation (The): 305
Stearns (Artemas W.) Trust: 1466
Stevens (The Abbot and Dorothy H.) Foundation: 1381
Stevens (The Nathaniel and Elizabeth P.) Foundation: 1382
Stoddard Charitable Trust (The): 1512
Sudbury Foundation: 1383
Thompson (Thomas) Trust: 1386
Tomfohrde (John H. and H. Naomi) Foundation: 318
Tourism Cares: 1766, 2204
Two Ten Footwear Foundation: 1767, 1768
Unitarian Universalist Association of Congregations: 506, 825
Webster (Edwin S.) Foundation: 331
Wellesley College: 1097, 1098
Wharton (William P.) Trust: 2045

Woods Hole Oceanographic Institution: 1846
Wyman-Gordon Foundation: 339
Xeric Foundation: 342

Michigan

Albion Community Foundation: 1159
Alger Regional Community Foundation: 1161
Allegan County Community Foundation: 1162
American Oriental Society: 542
Amy Foundation (The): 805
Ann Arbor Area Community Foundation: 1170
Baraga County Community Foundation: 1176
Battle Creek Community Foundation: 34
Berrien Community Foundation: 41
Capital Region Community Foundation: 1194
Community Foundation for Northeast Michigan: 1220
Community Foundation for Southeast Michigan: 75
Community Foundation of Greater Rochester: 1229
Community Foundation of the Holland/Zeeland Area (The): 78
Consumers Energy Foundation: 82
Cook Family Foundation: 1246
DeVos (Richard and Helen) Foundation: 1255
Dickinson Area Community Foundation: 1256
Earhart Foundation: 1850
Ford (Gerald R.) Presidential Library: 1998, 1999
Ford Motor Company Fund & Community Services: 130
Fremont Area Community Foundation (The): 1277
Frey Foundation: 134
Gerber Foundation (The): 1125
Graduate Education Opportunity Program: 992
Grand Haven Area Community Foundation: 1283
Grand Rapids Community Foundation: 150
Great Lakes Colleges Association New Writers Awards: 674
Greater Lansing Foundation (The): 1289
Hess (William G. and Myrtle E.) Charitable Trust: 1554, 995
Hillsdale County Community Foundation: 1299
Hudson-Webber Foundation: 1302
Kalamazoo Community Foundation: 1309
Kantzler Foundation (The): 1310
Kappa Omicron Nu Honor Society: 2674
Kellogg (W.K.) Foundation: 184
Keweenaw Community Foundation: 1312
Kresge Foundation (The): 196
Les Cheneaux Community Foundation (The): 1318
Livingston Awards: 1941
M & M Area Community Foundation: 1322
Marshall Community Foundation: 1565
McGregor Fund: 222
Michigan Council for Arts and Cultural Affairs: 474
Michigan Gateway Community Foundation: 1328
Michigan Society of Fellows: 377
Michigan State University: 931
Michigan Women's Foundation: 1088
Monroe-Brown Foundation: 1635
Mott (Charles Stewart) Foundation: 1333
National Mole Day Foundation: 2068
Pardee (The Elsa U.) Foundation: 2443
Petoskey-Harbor Springs Area Community Foundation: 1348
Phi Delta Chi Pharmacy Fraternity: 2544
Roberts (Forest) Theatre: 537
Saginaw Community Foundation: 1364
Skillman Foundation (The): 297
Society of Manufacturing Engineers Education Foundation (SMEEF): 2616
Southfield Community Foundation (The): 1377
Steelcase Foundation: 307
Towsley (The Harry A. and Margaret D.) Foundation: 321
University of Michigan: 1964
Upjohn (W.E.) Institute for Employment Research: 1969
Wege Foundation: 1400
Wickes (Harvey Randall) Foundation: 1403
Wilson (Matilda R.) Fund: 336
Wilson Ornithological Society: 2162

Minnesota

American Swedish Institute (The): 896, 897
Andersen Corporate Foundation (The): 1166
Andersen (Fred C. and Katherine B.) Foundation: 1167
Andersen (Hugh J.) Foundation: 1168

Arts Midwest: 527
Athwin Foundation: 23
Babbage (Charles) Institute: 2604
Bremer (Otto) Foundation: 1186
Butler (Patrick and Aimee) Family Foundation: 1191
Central Minnesota Community Foundation: 1200
Collegeville Institute for Ecumenical and Cultural Research: 809
Davis (Edwin W. and Catherine M.) Foundation: 95
Dell (Roger L. and Agnes C.) Charitable Trust: 1253
Deluxe Corporation Foundation: 97
Duluth Superior Area Community Foundation: 1259
Ecolab Foundation: 1264
Eddy (Edwin H.) Family Foundation: 2256
Edwards (Ray) Memorial Trust: 1429
Forecast Public Artworks: 450
Foundation for Anesthesia Education and Research: 2258
Fuller (H.B.) Company Foundation: 1124
Hallett Charitable Trusts (The): 1629
Jerome Foundation, Inc.: 464
Land O'Lakes Foundation: 200, 201
Marbrook Foundation: 215
Mardag Foundation: 216
Mayo Clinic: 2285
McKnight Endowment Fund for Neuroscience (The): 2467
McKnight Foundation (The): 1495
Medtronic Foundation: 228
Minneapolis Foundation (The): 1329
Minnesota Department of Education: 733
National Association of Geoscience Teachers: 2080
National Ataxia Foundation: 2475
National Council on Family Relations: 1498
National Foster Parent Association: 1138
Northwest Minnesota Foundation (The): 1339
Ordean Foundation (The): 1344
Phillips (Jay and Rose) Family Foundation of Minnesota: 1501
Playwrights' Center (The): 696
Porter (Irwin Andrew) Foundation: 270
RBC Foundation - U.S.A.: 1354
Rochester Area Foundation: 1359
Sigma Delta Epsilon/Graduate Women in Science: 1837
3M Foundation, Inc.: 317
U.S. Bancorp Foundation: 1390
University of Minnesota: 508, 702
University of Oslo International Summer School: 949
Wasie Foundation (The): 330
Women's Foundation of Minnesota: 1101, 1102
Xcel Energy Foundation: 341

Mississippi

Agricultural History Society: 576
American Kinesiotherapy Association, Inc.: 2548
Foundation for the Mid South: 1275
Hardin (The Phil) Foundation: 1552
University of Southern Mississippi (The): 704, 743

Missouri

Aircraft Electronics Association (AEA): 2618
BlueScope Foundation North America (The): 45
Brown Shoe Company, Inc. Charitable Trust: 50
Center for Plant Conservation: 2116
Community Foundation of the Ozarks: 1241
Consortium for Graduate Study in Management (The): 1892
Dula (The Caleb C. and Julia W.) Educational and Charitable Foundation: 109
Emerson: 117
Greater Kansas City Community Foundation and Affiliated Trusts (The): 1288
Hall Family Foundation: 153
Investigative Reporters and Editors: 1938
Kappa Tau Alpha: 1940
Knights of Columbus Vatican Film Library at St. Louis University: 679
Ladies Auxiliary to the Veterans of Foreign Wars (The): 2440
Lutheran Foundation of St. Louis: 817
McDonnell Center for the Space Sciences: 2623
McDonnell (James S.) Foundation: 221
Mid-America Arts Alliance: 475
Missouri Department of Higher Education: 1717, 1718
Monsanto Fund: 2187

National Association of Farm Broadcasting Foundation: 1945
Post-Polio Health International: 2313
Press Club of Metropolitan St. Louis and Journalism Foundation of Metropolitan St. Louis (The): 1750
Reproductive Scientist Development Program (RSDP): 2501
Reynolds (J.B.) Foundation: 1357
Saigh Foundation (The): 1143
St. Louis Rams Foundation: 1144
Sosland Foundation (The): 1016
Sunnen Foundation: 1513
Truman (Harry S.) Library Institute: 2018
Washington University: 1801, 1802, 425
Whitaker Foundation: 517

Montana

Housing Education and Research Association (HERA): 1301
Montana Community Foundation: 1331
Washington (Dennis & Phyllis) Foundation: 1398

Nebraska

Abel Foundation: 1157
Cooper Foundation: 84
Heuermann (B. Keith & Norma F.) Foundation: 158
Mid-Nebraska Community Foundation, Inc.: 236
Nebraska Arts Council: 482
Omaha Community Foundation: 252
Sowers Club of Nebraska Foundation: 303
Union Pacific Foundation: 325
University of Nebraska at Omaha : 1917
Woods Charitable Fund, Inc.: 1405

Nevada

Caesar's Entertainment Corporation: 1620
Nevada Arts Council: 483
Redfield (The Nell J.) Foundation: 275
Wiegand (E. L.) Foundation: 335

New Hampshire

American Ground Water Trust: 2597
Bean (Norwin S. and Elizabeth N.) Foundation: 1179
Dartmouth College: 987
Lindsay (The Agnes M.) Trust: 1131
MacDowell Colony (The): 468
Money for Women/Barbara Deming Memorial Fund, Inc.: 1089
New Hampshire Library Association: 735
New Hampshire State Council on the Arts: 485

New Jersey

African American Fund of New Jersey: 1024
American Accordion Musicological Society: 747
American School of Classical Studies at Athens (The): 432, 885, 886, 887, 888, 889, 890, 891, 892, 893, 894
Atran Foundation, Inc.: 25
Autism Speaks: 2242
Bard (C.R.) Foundation: 32
Campbell Soup Foundation: 55
Capezio/Ballet Makers Dance Foundation, Inc.: 529
Costume Society of America (The): 444
Darrin (Margaret A.) Foundation, Inc.: 93
Davis (Shelby Cullom) Center for Historical Studies: 591
Dodge (Geraldine R.) Foundation: 99
Dow Jones News Fund (The): 1932
Educational Testing Service: 1539, 1540
Electrochemical Society (The): 1818, 1819
Ernst & Young Foundation: 1897
Financial Service Centers of America, Inc.: 1686
Foundation for Neonatal Research and Education (FNRE): 2489
General Commission on Archives and History of The United Methodist Church: 813
Goldberg (Ruth Estrin) Memorial for Cancer Research: 2437
Higher Education Student Assistance Authority (The): 1693, 1694, 1695
Histiocytosis Association : 2363
Horowitz Foundation for Social Policy (The): 1855
Hyde and Watson Foundation (The): 167
IEEE: 599
Institute for Advanced Study: 1856

International Foundation (The): 850
Irish American Cultural Institute: 675, 851
Japanese American Citizens League (JACL) (The): 533
Johnson & Johnson Family of Companies: 175
Johnson (Robert Wood) Foundation: 2275
Kirby (F.M.) Foundation, Inc.: 191
KPMG Foundation: 1902
Laurie (The Blanche and Irving) Foundation: 203
Life Sciences Research Foundation (LSRF): 2150
MCJ Amelior Foundation (The): 1135
National Poetry Series (The): 682
New Jersey Department of Military and Veterans Affairs: 1728, 1729
New Jersey Historic Trust: 616, 617
New Jersey Historical Commission: 618, 619, 620
New Jersey Library Association: 736
New Jersey Office of the Secretary of Higher Education: 1730
New Jersey Osteopathic Education Foundation: 2525
New Jersey State Council on the Arts: 486
Newcombe (The Charlotte W.) Foundation: 1735
Panasonic Foundation, Inc.: 1583
Princeton Area Community Foundation: 1351
Reeve (Christopher and Dana) Foundation : 2559
Rippel (Fannie E.) Foundation: 2322
Schumann Fund for New Jersey (The): 1145
Segal (The George and Helen) Foundation: 499
Steiner (David and Sylvia) Charitable Trust: 823
Subaru of America Foundation, Inc.: 1589
Turrell Fund: 1150
UNICO National, Inc.: 1775
Verizon Foundation: 328
Victoria Foundation, Inc.: 1396
Wetlands Institute (The): 2160
Wilson (The Woodrow) National Fellowship Foundation: 1804

New Mexico

Albuquerque Community Foundation: 1160
American Indian Graduate Center: 1037
American Indian Science and Engineering Society (AISES): 1038, 1039
American Society for Mass Spectrometry: 2032
Bynner (The Witter) Foundation for Poetry, Inc.: 669
Catching the Dream: 1047
Frost Foundation, Ltd. (The): 135
Institute of American Indian Arts (IAIA): 1051
Los Alamos National Laboratory: 1826
Lovelace Respiratory Research Institute: 2338
New Mexico Community Foundation: 1337
New Mexico Library Association: 737
Roswell Artist-in-Residence Program: 566
Santa Fe Community Foundation: 1012
School for Advanced Research: 1754, 2023, 2024
University of New Mexico: 703
Wurlitzer (The Helene) Foundation of New Mexico: 522

New York

Achelis Foundation (The): 5
Adams (Emma J.) Memorial Fund, Inc.: 1473
AFS Intercultural Programs/USA: 867
Alliance for Young Artists & Writers (The): 429
Altman Foundation: 1163
Alzheimer's Drug Discovery Foundation: 2216
America-Israel Cultural Foundation: 955
American Academy in Rome: 344, 2166
American Academy of Arts and Letters: 746
American Catholic Historical Association: 577, 801, 802, 803, 804
American Council of Learned Societies: 347
American Federation for Aging Research (AFAR): 2225, 2226, 2227
American Foundation for Suicide Prevention (The): 1515, 1516, 1517, 1518
American Geriatrics Society: 2547
American Group Psychotherapy Association, Inc.: 2563
American Institute of Chemical Engineers (AIChE): 1808, 2633
American Jewish Joint Distribution Committee (The) : 878
American Lung Association: 2385, 2386, 2387, 2388
American Museum of Natural History (The): 1809, 1810, 2137
American Numismatic Society (The): 348, 581, 582
American Parkinson Disease Association, Inc.: 2456
American Research Center in Sofia (ARCS) - U.S. Office: 880
American-Scandinavian Foundation (The): 1617, 665, 884
American Society of Composers, Authors and Publishers (ASCAP): 666

American Society of Hypertension: 2237
American Society of Mechanical Engineers Auxiliary, Inc. (The): 2646
American Vacuum Society (AVS): 2100
amfAR, The Foundation for AIDS Research: 1812
Andrus Family Fund: 1169
Architectural League of New York: 413, 414
Armenian General Benevolent Union: 1666
Art Directors Club, Inc.: 1922
ASCAP Foundation (The): 754
Asian Cultural Council: 434, 898
Association for Behavioral and Cognitive Therapies: 2573, 2574
Association for Research of Childhood Cancer, Inc. (AROCC): 2428
Astraea Lesbian Foundation for Justice: 978, 979, 980
Austrian Cultural Forum: 899
Baseball Tomorrow Fund: 1107
Bay and Paul Foundations (The): 1524
Bibliographical Society of America: 1526
Bodman Foundation (The): 46
Brain & Behavior Research Foundation: 2575
Brookhaven Women in Science: 1076
Brooks (Gladys) Foundation: 1188
Cancer Research Institute: 2430, 2431, 2432
Carnegie Corporation of New York: 57
Carnegie Fund for Authors: 671
Carvel (Thomas and Agnes) Foundation: 1112
Center for Lesbian and Gay Studies (The): 984
Center for Photography at Woodstock (The): 544
Central New York Community Foundation: 1201
Cerebral Palsy International Research Foundation: 2459
Chamber Music America: 756, 757
Chapin (Harry) Foundation: 1202
Chautauqua Region Community Foundation (The): 1204
Children's Brain Tumor Foundation: 1113
Children's Tumor Foundation: 2360
Chinese American Medical Society: 2253
Churchill (Winston) Foundation of the United States: 904
City of New York: 1994
Claiborne (Liz) Art Ortenberg Foundation: 2173
Clark (Edna McConnell) Foundation: 65
Clark Foundation (The): 1677
Clark (Robert Sterling) Foundation: 1207
Columbia Journalism School: 1925
Columbia University: 1926, 1927, 1928, 2143, 587
Columbia University Graduate School of Journalism: 1929
Columbus (Christopher) Fellowship Foundation: 1477
Commonwealth Fund (The): 1478
Community Foundation for Greater Buffalo: 1215
Community Foundation for the Greater Capital Region (The): 1222, 1534
Community Foundation of Herkimer & Oneida Counties, Inc. (The): 1230
Community Foundations of the Hudson Valley : 1244
Cooley's Anemia Foundation, Inc.: 2411
Copland (Aaron) Fund for Music, Inc.: 763
Cornell University: 364, 365
Corporation of Yaddo (The): 443
Council for European Studies at Columbia University: 835
Council on Foreign Relations: 1931, 838, 839, 840, 841, 842
Crohn's and Colitis Foundation of America, Inc.: 2412
Cultural Services of the French Embassy: 909
Cultural Vistas: 843, 910, 911, 912
Cummings (The Nathan) Foundation, Inc.: 90
Dana Foundation (The): 2254
Daughters of the Cincinnati: 1682
Delmas (Gladys Krieble) Foundation: 366
Direct Marketing Club of New York (DMCNY) (The): 1894
Dodge (The Cleveland H.) Foundation, Inc.: 1119
Douglass (Frederick) Institute for African and African-American Studies: 1538
Dow Jones Foundation: 104
Dreyfus (The Jean and Louis) Foundation, Inc.: 1258
Duke (Doris) Charitable Foundation: 107
Dysautonomia Foundation, Inc.: 2461
Dystrophic Epidermolysis Bullosa Research Association of America, Inc. (debra): 2336
Eastman School of Music of the University of Rochester: 765
Ellis (Albert) Institute: 2578
Emerson (Fred L.) Foundation, Inc.: 1266
Enterprise Community Partners: 1481
Episcopal Church Foundation: 810
Fifth & Pacific Foundation: 123
Fight For Sight, Inc.: 2511, 2512

Fisher (Avery) Artist Program: 766
Fitch (The James Marston) Charitable Foundation: 416
Flanders House: 915
Ford Foundation (The): 129
Foundation of Flexographic Technical Association (The): 2608
Foundation of the National Student Nurses' Association, Inc.: 2490
4A's: 990
Fox (The Michael J.) Foundation for Parkinson's Research: 2260
Freeman Foundation: 131
Garden Club of America (The): 2119, 2178, 2179, 2180, 2181
German Academic Exchange Service: 916
Gifford (The Rosamond) Charitable Corporation: 1279
Glaucoma Foundation (The): 2513
Gloeckner (The Fred C.) Foundation, Inc.: 2120
Goldman (Herman) Foundation: 145
Gottlieb (Adolph and Esther) Foundation, Inc.: 550
Graham (Martha) School of Contemporary Dance, Inc.: 531
Grant (The William T.) Foundation: 1127
Graves (Nancy) Foundation: 454
Greenburg-May Foundation: 2438
Guggenheim (The Harry Frank) Foundation: 1853, 1854
Guggenheim (John Simon) Memorial Foundation: 151
Hartford (The John A.) Foundation, Inc.: 155
Hastings Center (The): 2107
Hayden (Charles) Foundation: 1129
Hazen (Edward W.) Foundation: 1130
Hearing Health Foundation: 2515
Hillman (The Sidney) Foundation, Inc.: 1936
Hudson River Foundation (The): 2184
Hugoton Foundation: 1441
Human Growth Foundation: 2530
Huntington's Disease Society of America, Inc.: 2466
IBM Thomas J. Watson Research Center: 2095
Institute of International Education: 654, 918
Ittleson Foundation, Inc.: 1488
Japan Foundation (The): 852
Japan Information Center: 921, 922
Jewish Book Council: 676, 677
Jewish Communal Service Association of North America: 1559
Jones (Daisy Marquis) Foundation: 178
JPMorgan Chase Foundation (The): 180
Juvenile Diabetes Research Foundation International: 2414, 2415, 2416
Kaplan (The J.M.) Fund, Inc.: 182
Klingenstein Center for Independent School Leadership: 1605
Klingenstein Third Generation Foundation (The): 2580
Kosciuszko Foundation, Inc. (The): 1710, 770, 925, 926, 927, 928
Kress (Samuel H.) Foundation: 552
Langeloth (The Jacob and Valeria) Foundation: 2277
Leary Firefighters Foundation (The): 1316
Leschetizky Association, Inc. (The): 772
Leukemia & Lymphoma Society (The): 2364, 2365, 2366
Liederkranz Foundation, Inc.: 773
Light Work: 553
Link Foundation: 2038
Littauer (The Lucius N.) Foundation, Inc.: 997
Local Initiatives Support Corporation: 1319
Long Island Community Foundation: 1320
Luce (The Henry) Foundation, Inc.: 210
Lymphoma Research Foundation: 2367
Macy (Josiah Jr.) Foundation: 2280
Mapplethorpe (Robert) Foundation, Inc.: 470
March of Dimes Foundation: 2282, 2283, 2284
Marfan Foundation (The): 2517
Marketing EDGE: 1904
McGraw Hill Financial: 1905
Mellon (The Andrew W.) Foundation: 229
Memorial Foundation for Jewish Culture: 820
MetLife Foundation: 231
Metropolitan Museum of Art (The): 473, 556, 557, 558, 559, 560, 561, 731, 732
Millay Colony for the Arts, Inc. (The): 477
Mitchell (Joan) Foundation: 478
Mizuho USA Foundation, Inc.: 1330
Modern Language Association of America: 657, 658
Mount Vernon Hotel Museum & Garden: 611
Ms. Foundation for Women: 1090
Muste (A.J.) Memorial Institute: 1497
Myasthenia Gravis Foundation of America, Inc.: 2474
NAACP Legal Defense and Educational Fund, Inc. (The) : 1030

National Action Council for Minorities in Engineering, Inc. (NACME): 1000
National Association of Scholars: 1636
National Center for Learning Disabilities: 1568, 1569, 1570
National Football League Foundation: 1336
National Hemophilia Foundation (The): 2288
National Kidney Foundation: 2421, 2422, 2423
National Leukemia Research Association: 2531
National Medical Fellowships, Inc.: 2296
National Multiple Sclerosis Society: 2477, 2478
Naumburg (The Walter W.) Foundation, Inc.: 782
Neuropathy Association (The): 2371
New Dramatists: 534
New Music USA: 783
New York Community Trust (The): 244
New York Council for the Humanities: 384
New York Foundation for the Arts: 487
New York Landmarks Conservancy: 621
New York Sea Grant Institute: 2193
New York State Assembly Intern Committee: 2008, 2009
New York State Council on the Arts: 488
New York State Education Department: 1731
New York State Higher Education Services Corporation: 1732, 1733, 1734
New York State Historical Association: 489, 622, 738
New York State Senate: 2010, 2011
Northeast Agricultural Education Foundation: 2126
Northeastern Loggers' Association, Inc.: 2127
Northern Chautauqua Community Foundation: 1737
Noyes (Jessie Smith) Foundation: 2194
Nurses' Educational Funds, Inc.: 2495
Oishei (The John R.) Foundation: 251
Open Meadows Foundation: 1092
Oxalosis and Hyperoxaluria Foundation: 2304
Parapsychology Foundation, Inc.: 2585, 2586, 2587, 2588
Parkinson's Disease Foundation, Inc.: 2480, 2481, 2482
PEN American Center: 535, 660, 683, 684, 685, 686, 687, 688, 689, 690
PepsiCo Foundation: 266
Pforzheimer (The Carl and Lily) Foundation, Inc.: 267
Pinkerton Foundation (The): 1141
Pollock-Krasner Foundation, Inc. (The): 565
Potts Memorial Foundation (The): 2399
Princess Grace Foundation-USA: 536
ProLiteracy Worldwide: 1352
Rasmussen (V. Kann) Foundation: 2088
Revson (The Charles H.) Foundation: 278
Robinson (Jackie) Foundation: 1011
Rochester Area Community Foundation: 1094
Rockefeller Archive Center: 632
Rockefeller Family Fund: 282
Rolex SA: 284
Runyon (Damon) Cancer Research Foundation: 2446
Sage (Russell) Foundation: 1870
St. Andrew's Society of the State of New York: 938
Samuels (The Fan Fox and Leslie R.) Foundation, Inc.: 286
Schomburg Center for Research in Black Culture (The): 399
Shubert Foundation, Inc. (The): 538
Skin Cancer Foundation (The): 2447
Skowhegan School of Painting and Sculpture: 570
Sloan (Alfred P.) Foundation: 1013, 1014, 2042, 298
Smith (W. Eugene) Memorial Fund: 571
Smithers (The Christopher D.) Foundation, Inc.: 1465
Snow (The John Ben) Foundation, Inc.: 302
Soane (Sir John) Museum Foundation: 423
Social Science Research Council: 858, 859, 860
Society of American Historians, Inc. (The): 635
Sony USA Foundation, Inc.: 1610
Soros (The Paul & Daisy) Fellowships for New Americans : 1758
Sprague (Seth) Educational and Charitable Foundation: 304
Steele-Reese Foundation (The): 1380
Surdna Foundation Inc.: 311
Syracuse University: 1761, 1762, 698
Taraknath DAS Foundation: 1642
Tinker Foundation Inc. : 862
Toshiba America Foundation: 1612
Tourette Syndrome Association, Inc.: 2483
Tucker (The Richard) Music Foundation, Inc.: 792
United Hospital Fund of New York: 1469
United Jewish Appeal-Federation of Jewish Philanthropies of New York: 826
United States-Japan Foundation: 866

References in index are to entry numbers.

van Ameringen Foundation, Inc.: 2594
Wagner College: 540
Wallace Foundation (The): 329
Watson (Jeannette K.) Fellowship: 1647
Watson (Thomas J.) Fellowship Program: 1648
Weeden Foundation: 2212
Weill (Kurt) Foundation for Music: 515
Wenner-Gren Foundation for Anthropological Research, Inc.: 2026, 2027, 2028, 2029
Whitney (The Helen Hay) Foundation: 1845
Wildlife Conservation Society (The): 2213
Women's Sports Foundation: 1104
Women's Studio Workshop (WSW): 519, 520, 521
YIVO Institute for Jewish Research: 647, 648, 649, 650
Young Concert Artists, Inc.: 795

North Carolina

American Chestnut Foundation (The): 2112
American Dance Festival: 525
American Institute of Certified Public Accountants (AICPA): 1520, 1658, 1888, 1889, 1890
American Schlafhorst Foundation: 16
American Society of Echocardiography Education and Research Foundation (ASE): 2389
American Society of Echocardiography Education and Research Foundation (ASE Foundation): 2390
Babcock (Mary Reynolds) Foundation: 26
Belk Foundation (The): 1600
Burroughs Wellcome Fund: 2244
Cannon Foundation, Inc. (The): 56
Cattell (James McKeen) Fund: 2576
Cemala Foundation: 1532
Community Foundation of Greater Greensboro: 1228
Community Foundation of Western North Carolina (The) : 79
Covington (Marion Stedman) Foundation: 86
Dickson Foundation: 98
Duke Endowment (The): 108
Fletcher (A.J.) Foundation: 127
Foundation for the Carolinas: 1274
GlaxoSmithKline: 1433
Goodrich Foundation (The): 1548
Hamner Institutes for Health Sciences (The): 2067
Hillsdale Fund Inc.: 161
Kellenberger (May Gordon Latham) Historical Foundation: 183
Kenan (William R., Jr.) Charitable Trust: 1561
Mebane Charitable Foundation, Inc.: 1136
Museum of Early Southern Decorative Arts (MESDA): 562
NAMTA Council for Art Advocacy: 563
National AMBUCS, Inc.: 2554
National Humanities Center: 383
National Institute of Environmental Health Sciences: 2189
NBCC Foundation, Inc.: 1727
North Carolina Arts Council: 490
North Carolina Association of Educators: 1638
North Carolina Community Foundation: 248
North Carolina GlaxoSmithKline Foundation: 1581
North Carolina Library Association: 739
North Carolina State Education Assistance Authority/College Foundation of North Carolina: 1736
Outer Banks Community Foundation: 1346
Reynolds (Kate B.) Charitable Trust: 1503
Reynolds (Z. Smith) Foundation, Inc.: 279
Salisbury Community Foundation: 285
Sigma Alpha Iota Philanthropies, Inc.: 790
Sigma Xi: The Scientific Research Society: 1838
Triangle Community Foundation: 1591
U.S. Army Research Office: 1842
United Arts Council of Raleigh and Wake County, Inc.: 507
Winston-Salem Foundation (The): 1404

North Dakota

Central Association of Obstetricians and Gynecologists: 2500
Fargo-Moorhead Area Foundation: 121
North Dakota Council on the Arts: 491
North Dakota State Board for Indian Scholarships: 1054

Ohio

Akron Community Foundation: 1158
American Ceramic Society (The): 430
American Classical League (The): 651
American Society for Nondestructive Testing, Inc. (The): 1521, 1662, 2598
ASM Materials Education Foundation: 2677
Batten Disease Support and Research Association: 2243
Bingham (The William) Foundation: 44
Cleveland Foundation (The): 1208
Cleveland Institute of Music: 760
Cliffs Foundation (The): 66
Codrington (The George W.) Charitable Foundation: 70
Columbus Foundation (The): 1210
Columbus Jewish Foundation: 1211
Community Foundation of Lorain County (The): 1232
Community Foundation of Mount Vernon & Knox County (The): 77
Community Foundation of Shelby County (The): 1237
Corbin (The Mary S. and David C.) Foundation: 85
Delaware County Foundation: 1252
Eaton Charitable Fund: 113
Educational Foundation for Women in Accounting (The): 1896
Firman Fund: 124
FirstEnergy: 1602
FirstEnergy Foundation: 126
Goodyear Tire & Rubber Company (The): 146
Greater Cincinnati Foundation (The): 1285
Gund (The George) Foundation: 152
HCR Manor Care Foundation: 1434
Heed Ophthalmic Foundation: 2516
Herb Society of America, Inc. (The): 2121
Horticultural Research Institute, Inc.: 2122
Iddings Benevolent Trust: 169
International Executive Housekeepers Association (The): 2611
Invent Now: 1824
Jennings (Martha Holden) Foundation: 1604
Kroger Company Foundation (The): 1314
Lincoln (The James F.) Arc Welding Foundation: 2654
Lubrizol Foundation (The): 209
Marcus (Jacob Rader) Center of the American Jewish Archives: 818
Marietta Community Foundation: 1324
Morgan (The Burton D.) Foundation: 1906
Mt. Sinai Health Care Foundation: 1450
Muskingum County Community Foundation: 1334
Nationwide Insurance Foundation: 242
Nordson Corporation Foundation (The): 246
O'Neill (William J. and Dorothy K.) Foundation: 250
Ohio Arts Council: 492
Ohio Board of Regents: 1739, 1740
Ohio National Guard Scholarship Program: 1741
OMNOVA Solutions Foundation: 1342
Parents Without Partners: 1584
Parker Hannifin Corporation Foundation: 261
Prentiss (The Elisabeth Severance) Foundation: 2314
Reinberger Foundation (The): 1355
Scott (Kenneth A.) Charitable Trust: 2109
Society for Investigative Dermatology (The): 2327
Stark Community Foundation: 1379
Tait (The Frank M.) Foundation: 1148
Toledo Community Foundation: 1388
White (Thomas H.) Foundation: 1401
Wolfe Associates, Inc.: 337
Woman's National Farm & Garden Association, Inc.: 2134
World Piano Competition (The): 794

Oklahoma

American Association of Petroleum Geologists Foundation: 2071
American Fidelity Foundation: 431
Bernsen (The Grace and Franklin) Foundation: 40
Cherokee Nation : 1048
Kerr Foundation, Inc. (The): 187
Mabee (The J.E. and L.E.) Foundation, Inc.: 212
Noble (Samuel Roberts) Foundation, Inc.: 1637
Oklahoma Arts Council: 493
Oklahoma City Community Foundation, Inc.: 1341
Sarkeys Foundation: 288
Schusterman (Charles and Lynn) Family Foundation: 1372
Society of Exploration Geophysicists: 2089
Stacey (The John F. and Anna Lee) Scholarship Fund: 572

Oregon

American Tinnitus Association (ATA): 1811
Bonneville Environmental Foundation: 2169
Carpenter Foundation (The): 1196
Collins Foundation (The): 72
Intel Foundation: 170
Jackson Foundation (The): 172
Lamb Foundation: 199
McDowell (Verne Catt) Corporation: 819
McKenzie River Gathering Foundation: 1494
Meyer Memorial Trust: 232
National Federation of State Poetry Societies, Inc.: 681
Oregon Arts Commission: 494
Oregon Community Foundation (The): 1345

Pennsylvania

Academy of Natural Sciences of Philadelphia (The): 1805, 2135
ADCO Foundation: 1613
Air & Waste Management Association (A&WMA): 2595
Alcoa Foundation: 9
Allegheny Foundation: 11
Alternatives Research and Development Foundation: 1807
American Association for Cancer Research: 2424
American Council for Polish Culture (ACPC): 1655
American Philosophical Society: 1040, 14, 15, 349
American Research Institute in Turkey, Inc.: 881, 882, 883
American Society of Regional Anesthesia and Pain Medicine: 2538
Aviation Distributors and Manufacturers Association (ADMA): 2621
Barra Foundation: 33
Bayer USA Foundation: 1815
Berks County Community Foundation: 1180
Berwind Corporation: 42
Beta Phi Mu: 716
BNY Mellon Foundation of Southwestern Pennsylvania (The): 1184
Buhl Foundation (The): 1190
Chatham University: 1676
Chester County Community Foundation: 1205
College of Physicians of Philadelphia: 586
Connelly Foundation (The): 81
Curtis Institute of Music (The): 764
Douty Foundation (The): 103
Drexel University College of Medicine: 1081
Duquesne University, Department of Philosophy: 368
Fair Oaks Foundation: 1268
Fels (Samuel S.) Fund: 1270
First Community Foundation Partnership of Pennsylvania: 125
Foundation for Enhancing Communities (The): 1273
Grable Foundation (The): 1126
Grundy Foundation (The): 1293
Hamilton Family Foundation: 1549
Heinz (H.J.) Company Foundation: 156
Huston (The Stewart) Charitable Trust: 814
Independence Foundation: 2491
International Centre for Diffraction Data: 2679
Jewish Healthcare Foundation of Pittsburgh (The): 1444
Katz (Herbert D.) Center for Advanced Judaic Studies: 923
Kazanjian (The Calvin K.) Economics Foundation, Inc.: 1901
Kline (Josiah W. and Bessie H.) Foundation, Inc.: 192
Leeway Foundation (The): 1087
Lehigh Valley Community Foundation: 466
Library Company of Philadelphia: 603
McLean Contributionship (The): 223
Measey (Benjamin and Mary Siddons) Foundation: 2286
Mellon (Richard King) Foundation: 1326
Moyer Foundation (The): 1137
NEED: 1033
Oncology Nursing Foundation: 2442
Penn (The William) Foundation: 265
Pennsylvania Council on the Arts: 495
Pennsylvania Higher Education Assistance Agency: 1743
Pew Fellowships at the Pew Center for Arts & Heritage: 564
Philadelphia Foundation (The): 1349
Phillips (Dr. and Mrs. Arthur William) Charitable Trust: 2311
Pitt Poetry Series: 695
Pittsburgh Foundation (The): 1350
Pittsburgh New Music Ensemble, Inc. (The): 785
Pool (The Dorothy Rider) Health Care Trust: 1458
PPG Industries Foundation: 271
Presser Foundation: 786

Print and Graphics Scholarship Foundation: 2614, 2615
Quaker Chemical Foundation (The): 274
Rotary Club of Bryn Mawr (The): 1753
Saint-Gobain Corporation Foundation: 1366
Scaife (Sarah) Foundation, Inc.: 2014
Scranton Area Foundation: 1373
Seybert Foundation (The): 1146
Smith (The Ethel Sergeant Clark) Memorial Fund: 300
Smith (The W.W.) Charitable Trust: 301
Society for the Scientific Study of Sexuality (The): 1841
Templeton (John) Foundation: 314
U.S. Army Military History Institute: 639
University of Pennsylvania, Penn Humanities Forum: 403
University of Pittsburgh: 2209
Wells (Franklin H. and Ruth L.) Foundation: 1155
West (Herman O.) Foundation: 333
Widener Memorial Foundation in Aid of Handicapped Children: 1023
Wyomissing Foundation (The): 340

Rhode Island

Albright Institute of Archaeological Research (AIAR): 868
American Mathematical Society: 2093
Brown (John Carter) Library: 584
Champlin Foundations (The): 61
Feinstein Foundation (The): 1482
Hasbro Children's Fund: 1128
Howard (The George A. and Eliza Gardner) Foundation: 1632
Rhode Island Foundation/Rhode Island Community Foundation (The): 280
Rhode Island State Council on the Arts: 497
State of Rhode Island: 2016
Textron Charitable Trust: 316

South Carolina

Abney Foundation (The): 3
Ashburn Institute Inc.: 831
Coastal Community Foundation of South Carolina: 1209
Community Foundation of the Lowcountry, Inc.: 1535
Piedmont Health Foundation: 1457
Self Family Foundation (The): 1374
Sims (J. Marion) Foundation: 295
South Carolina Higher Education Tuition Grants Commission: 1759

South Dakota

Graco Foundation (The): 1282
Native American Community Board (NACB): 1052, 1576
South Dakota Arts Council: 501

Tennessee

Assisi Foundation of Memphis Inc.: 22
Community Foundation of Greater Chattanooga, Inc. (The): 1227
Community Foundation of Greater Memphis: 76
East Tennessee Foundation: 1121
First Horizon National Corporation: 1272
Frist Foundation (The): 1278
General Board of Higher Education and Ministry, The United Methodist Church: 812
Lyndhurst Foundation: 211
Maclellan Foundation, Inc. (The): 214
Oak Ridge Institute for Science and Education: 2661
Plough Foundation: 1502
Psi Chi, The International Honor Society in Psychology: 2589
Stokely (The William B., Jr.) Foundation: 308
Symphony of the Mountains: 791
Tau Beta Pi Association, Inc. (The): 2664
Tennessee Arts Commission: 503
Tennessee Student Assistance Corporation: 1765
United Methodist Communications: 1019, 1961
United South and Eastern Tribes, Inc.: 1060

Texas

ADSC: The International Association of Foundation Drilling: 2631
Alcon Foundation, Inc. (The): 2503
Amarillo Area Foundation: 1164
American Bandmasters Association (The): 748
American Heart Association: 2376, 2377, 2378, 2379, 2380, 2381, 2382, 2383, 2384

American Porphyria Foundation (The): 2232
American Research Center in Egypt, Inc.: 879
Austin Community Foundation for the Capital Area (The): 1173
Bat Conservation International: 1523
Belo Foundation (The): 37
Benign Essential Blepharospasm Research Foundation Inc.: 2507
BNSF Railway Foundation: 1045, 1063
Boy Scouts of America, National Eagle Scout Association (The): 1108, 1109
Brown Foundation, Inc. (The): 1528
Carter (Amon G.) Foundation: 58
CH Foundation (The): 2117
Coastal Bend Community Foundation: 67
Cockrell Foundation (The): 68
Communities Foundation of Texas, Inc.: 73
Community Foundation of Abilene: 1223
Community Foundation of the Texas Hill Country: 1242
Cullen Foundation (The): 89
Cullen Trust for Health Care (The): 1428
Dallas Foundation (The): 1249
Dallas Museum of Art: 545, 546, 547
Dallas Women's Foundation: 1079
Dell (Michael and Susan) Foundation: 1118, 1683
East Texas Communities Foundation: 1262
El Paso Community Foundation: 1265
Emergency Medicine Foundation: 2257
Exxon Mobil Corporation: 120
George Foundation (The): 142
Guitar Foundation of America: 769
Halliburton Foundation, Inc.: 1630
Hammill (The Donald D.) Foundation: 994
Hershey (The Jacob and Terese) Foundation : 2183
Hoblitzelle Foundation: 163
Houston Endowment Inc.: 164
Johnson (The Lyndon Baines) Foundation: 2006
Joslyn (The Carl W. and Carrie Mae) Charitable Trust: 1489
Kempner (Harris and Eliza) Fund: 185
Kimberly-Clark Foundation, Inc.: 189
Kleberg (Robert J., Jr.) and Helen C. Kleberg Foundation: 2276
Komen (Susan G.): 2439
Kronkosky (Albert and Bessie Mae) Charitable Foundation: 197
Learning for Life: 1564
Lowe Syndrome Association: 2278
Lubbock Area Foundation, Inc.: 1321
Lunar and Planetary Institute: 2052
Marshall (Thurgood) College Fund: 1713
Meadows Foundation, Inc.: 226
Moody Foundation (The): 239
Nansen Fund, Inc. (The): 932
National Jewish Committee on Scouting: 1721
National Opera Association, Inc.: 780
National Society of Hispanic MBAs (NSHMBA): 1006
Permian Basin Area Foundation: 1347
Phi Chi Theta Educational Foundation: 1910
Piper (Minnie Stevens) Foundation: 1746
RGK Foundation: 1358
Richardson (Sid) Memorial Fund: 1752
Richardson (Sid W.) Foundation: 281
Rockwell Fund, Inc.: 283
San Angelo Area Foundation: 1367
San Antonio Area Foundation: 1368
Sons of the Republic of Texas (The): 636, 637
Sturgis (Roy and Christine) Charitable and Educational Trust: 309
Summerlee Foundation (The): 1384
Sumners (Hatton W.) Foundation: 2017
Texas Commission on the Arts: 504
Texas Instruments Foundation: 315
Texas Library Association: 741
Topfer Family Foundation: 319
Total Petrochemicals & Refining USA Foundation: 320
Transportation Clubs International Scholarships: 1914
Trull Foundation (The): 1389
Tuschman Foundation (The): 324
University of Texas at Austin: 1646
University of Texas at Austin (The) and The Texas Institute of Letters: 509
Waco Foundation (The): 1397
Welch (The Robert A.) Foundation: 2070
Welder (Rob and Bessie) Wildlife Foundation: 2111
WHO (Women Helping Others Foundation) (The): 1099

Utah

Council on Technology and Engineering Teacher Education (CTETE): 1537
Simmons Family Foundation: 294
Swanson (Dr. W.C.) Family Foundation, Inc.: 1886
Thrasher Research Fund: 2533

Vermont

Ben & Jerry's Foundation: 982
Bread Loaf Writers' Conference: 668
Conservation and Research Foundation: 2174
Society for French Historical Studies: 634
Vermont Arts Council: 511
Vermont Student Assistance Corporation: 1799

Virgin Islands

Virgin Islands Council on the Arts: 512

Virginia

Academic Pediatric Association: 2526
AGC Education and Research Foundation: 2632
Air Traffic Control Association (ATCA): 2596
Altria Group, Inc.: 13
American Academy of Facial Plastic and Reconstructive Surgery (AAFPRS): 2217, 2218, 2219, 2220
American Association for Dental Research: 2342, 2343, 2344, 2345
American Association of Colleges of Pharmacy: 2534
American Association of Family and Consumer Sciences (AAFCS): 2669, 956
American Council of the Blind: 1656
American Diabetes Association: 2403
American Floral Endowment: 2114
American Foundation for Pharmaceutical Education (AFPE): 1614, 2535, 2536
American Geosciences Institute (AGI) (The): 2072
American Institute of Aeronautics and Astronautics: 2619
American Medical Women's Association, Inc.: 2231
American Psychiatric Foundation: 2564, 2565
American Psychosomatic Society: 2568
American Roentgen Ray Society: 2233
American Society of Civil Engineers: 2645
American Society of Naval Engineers (ASNE): 2647
American Water Resources Association: 2168
Association of Writers & Writing Programs (The): 667
Catholic Charities USA: 1476
Community Foundation (The): 1213, 74
Cooke (Jack Kent) Foundation: 1680
Council on Social Work Education: 986
DECA: 1893
Dominion Foundation: 100
Fats and Proteins Research Foundation, Inc.: 1820
Federal Highway Administration: 2607
FishAmerica Foundation: 2177
Foster Care to Success: 1544
Foundation for Physical Therapy, Inc.: 2550, 2551
Foundation for Technology and Engineering Education: 1545, 1546, 1689, 1690
Freedom Alliance: 1691
Gannett Foundation: 137
Gwathmey Memorial Trust (The): 371
Hampton Roads Community Foundation (The): 1296
Horizons Foundation: 1084
Imagine America Foundation: 1965
Institute for Humane Studies (IHS): 2003
International Association for Dental Research: 2350
International Association of Fire Chiefs Foundation, Inc.: 1701
International Road Federation: 959
Jeffress (Thomas F. and Kate Miller) Memorial Trust: 2108
Jenkins Foundation (The): 1443
Koch (Charles G.) Charitable Foundation: 1562
Madison (James) Memorial Fellowship Foundation: 604
Marine Corps Scholarship Foundation, Inc.: 1712
Microscopy Society of America: 1827, 1828, 2152, 2613
Mineralogical Society of America (The): 2079
Mitsubishi Electric America Foundation: 1606

Morgan (Marietta McNeill) and Samuel Tate Morgan, Jr. Foundation: 1496
Mustard Seed Foundation (The): 1566
National Federation of Republican Women: 1091
National GEM Consortium (The): 1003
National Institute for Labor Relations Research: 1719, 1948
National Radio Astronomy Observatory: 2054
National Science Foundation: 1607, 1832, 1833, 1834, 1835, 2021, 2022, 2040, 2055, 2086, 2087, 2101, 2157, 2158, 2583, 2584, 2655, 659
National Society of Accountants Scholarship Foundation: 1724
National Society of Black Engineers: 1725
National Wildlife Federation: 2191, 2192
NATSO Foundation: 1726
NICSA: 1580
NRA Foundation, Inc. (The): 1738
Omohundro Institute of Early American History and Culture: 624, 625, 626
Prevent Cancer Foundation: 2444
Reporters Committee for Freedom of the Press: 1959
Running Strong for American Indian Youth: 1056
Ruritan National Foundation: 1504, 1586
Sarnoff Cardiovascular Research Foundation (The): 2400
Seay (George J. and Effie L.) Memorial Trust: 1506
Society of Cardiovascular Anesthesiologists: 2401
Society of Daughters of the U.S. Army: 1756
Society of Naval Architects and Marine Engineers (The): 2663
Society of Nuclear Medicine and Molecular Imaging (SNMMI): 2328, 2329
Society of Radiologists in Ultrasound: 2330
State Council of Higher Education for Virginia: 1760
SunTrust Foundation: 310
U.S. Army Research Institute for Behavioral and Social Sciences: 1887
U.S. Department of the Navy: 1843
U.S. Marine Corps: 640, 641, 642
University of Virginia: 951
University of Virginia Press: 705
USDA Food and Nutrition Service: 1154
VCCA (Virginia Center for the Creative Arts): 510
Vertical Flight Foundation: 2630
Virginia Commission for the Arts: 513
Virginia Department of Health: 2499
Virginia Environmental Endowment: 2211
Virginia Museum of Fine Arts: 514
Virginia Polytechnic Institute and State University: 1022
Washington Forrest Foundation: 1399
Woodson (Carter G.) Institute for African-American and African Studies: 407

Washington

Allen (The Paul G.) Family Foundation: 12
Blue Mountain Community Foundation: 1183
Brainerd Foundation: 2170
Bullitt Foundation (The): 2172
Cheney (Ben B.) Foundation: 62
COLAGE : 985
Francis (The Parker B.) Fellowship Program: 2261
Friends of Jose Carreras International Leukemia Foundation: 2263
GSBA Scholarship Fund: 993
InvestED: 1603
Jackson (Henry M.) Foundation: 173
Kitsap Community Foundation: 1313
Microsoft Corporation: 235
Murdock (M.J.) Charitable Trust: 241
Norcliffe Foundation (The): 245
PACCAR Foundation: 255
Pride Foundation: 1008
Russell Family Foundation (The): 1363, 2200
Seattle Foundation (The): 292
Social Justice Fund Northwest: 1510
Washington Higher Education Coordinating Board: 1062
Washington Student Achievement Council: 1800
Whatcom Museum: 2030
Whitehorse Foundation (The): 1470

West Virginia

American Foundation for the Blind, Inc.: 971
Council for the Advancement of Science Writing, Inc.: 1930
Greater Kanawha Valley Foundation (The): 1287

Huntington Foundation, Inc. (The): 372
U.S. Department of Energy: 2665
West Virginia Division of Culture and History: 516
West Virginia Higher Education Policy Commission: 1803

Wisconsin

Alexander (Judd S.) Foundation: 1474
American Academy of Allergy Asthma & Immunology: 2335
American Institute of Bangladesh Studies: 876
American Institute of Pakistan Studies: 828
American Institute of the History of Pharmacy: 2537
American Legion Auxiliary - Department of Wisconsin: 1659
Bader (Helen) Foundation, Inc.: 27
Badger Meter Foundation, Inc.: 1175
Bemis Company Foundation: 38
Bethesda Lutheran Communities, Inc.: 1525
Bradley (The Lynde and Harry) Foundation, Inc.: 1669
Community Foundation of North Central Wisconsin: 1234
Eau Claire Community Foundation: 1263
Entomological Foundation (The): 2144, 2145
Greater Green Bay Community Foundation: 1286
Greater Milwaukee Foundation: 1291
International Crane Foundation, Inc.: 2148
Johnson Controls Foundation: 176
Kohl's Corporation: 1709
Madison Community Foundation: 1323
National Dairy Shrine: 2124
Northwestern Mutual Foundation (The): 1340
Park Bank Foundation, Inc.: 259
St. Croix Valley Foundation: 1365
Smith (A.O.) Foundation: 299
Society for the Study of Amphibians and Reptiles: 2043
Wehr (Todd) Foundation: 1649
Wisconsin Arts Board: 518
Wisconsin Historical Society Press: 646

Wyoming

ACGG Education Foundation: 426
Community Foundation of Jackson Hole: 1231
Wyoming Arts Council: 523

FOREIGN COUNTRIES

Australia

Australian National University (The): 354
Trust Company (The): 505, 539, 700
University of Sydney (The): 2069, 2131, 2132, 2210, 2333, 2545, 2667, 950, 965

Austria

Sommerhochschule-University of Vienna : 942

Belgium

North Atlantic Treaty Organization: 967
Queen Elisabeth International Music Competition of Belgium (The): 787

Canada

Acadia University: 4
Alberta Innovates - Health Solutions: 2215
Arctic Institute of North America: 1619
Arthritis Society (The): 2451
Association of Universities and Colleges of Canada: 1668, 977
Atlantic Salmon Federation: 2141
Atlantic School of Theology: 806
Banff Centre (The): 528
Bell (Max) Foundation: 1420
Brandon University: 755
Brucebo Fine Art Scholarship Foundation: 543
Canada Council for the Arts: 438, 670
Canadian Bar Association (The): 1971
Canadian Blood Services: 2245
Canadian Bureau for International Education (CBIE): 902, 903
Canadian Cancer Society Research Institute: 2429
Canadian Diabetes Association: 2409
Canadian Federation for the Humanities and Social Sciences: 1848

Canadian Federation of University Women: 1077
Canadian Friends of the Hebrew University: 1673
Canadian Institute for Advanced Legal Studies: 1972
Canadian Institute in Greece/L'Institut Canadien en Grèce: 355
Canadian Institute of Ukrainian Studies: 585
Canadian Institutes of Health Research (CIHR): 2246, 2247, 2248, 2249
Canadian Library Association/Association canadienne des bibliotheques: 719, 720
Canadian Liver Foundation: 2250, 2251, 2410
Canadian Lung Association (CLA) (The): 2391, 2488
Canadian Merit Scholarship Foundation: 1674
Canadian National Institute for the Blind: 2509
Canadian Society for Chemical Engineering: 2651
Canadian Society for Chemical Technology: 2064
Canadian Society for Chemistry: 2065
Canadian Society for Medical Laboratory Science: 2252
Cancer Research Society: 2433, 2434
Concordia University: 1679
Concours OSM Standard Life: 761
Conseil des Arts de Montreal: 442
Cystic Fibrosis Canada: 2361, 2362
Dafoe (J.W.) Foundation: 844
Dietitians of Canada: 2672
Donner Canadian Foundation: 1996
Greenshields (The Elizabeth) Foundation: 551
Halbert Centre for Canadian Studies: 1628
Hamilton Community Foundation: 1295
Hancock (Ruth) Scholarship Foundation: 1934
Healthy Minds Canada: 2267
Heart and Stroke Foundation of Canada: 2393, 2394, 2395
International Centre for Comparative Criminology: 1408
International Development Research Centre (IDRC): 1304, 1305, 2123, 919
IODE: 1702
Kidney Foundation of Canada (The): 2417, 2418, 2419, 2420
King (Mackenzie) Scholarship Trust: 1706, 1707
Laidlaw Foundation: 198
Leacock (Stephen) Association: 680
McGill University: 1984
Mineralogical Association of Canada: 2680
Montreal Neurological Institute: 2468
Multiple Sclerosis Society of Canada: 2469, 2470, 2471, 2472
National Research Council of Canada: 1831
Physiotherapy Foundation of Canada: 2557
Pontifical Institute of Mediaeval Studies: 630
Research Manitoba: 1460
Royal Society of Canada (The): 1836
Savoy Foundation: 2323
Scottish Rite Charitable Foundation of Canada: 2590
Shastri Indo-Canadian Institute (SICI): 941
SickKids Foundation: 1463
Simon Fraser University: 1912, 1913
Social Sciences and Humanities Research Council of Canada: 1871, 1872, 1873, 1874, 1875, 1876
Transportation Association of Canada Foundation: 2617
University of Alberta: 1776, 1777
University of British Columbia (The): 1778, 1779, 1780, 1781
University of Calgary (The): 1645, 1782, 1783, 1784, 1785, 1786, 1787, 1788, 1789, 1790, 1791, 1792, 1793, 1963, 1986, 2090
University of Manitoba: 1597
University of Toronto: 744
Woodward's (Mr. and Mrs. P.A.) Foundation: 1471

England

Cambridge University Library: 718
Cancer Research UK: 2435
Corpus Christi College: 905
English-Speaking Union (The): 958
Institute of Materials, Minerals and Mining: 2678

International Union for Vacuum Science, Technique and Applications (IUVSTA): 2036
Kennedy Memorial Trust (The): 960
Leeds International Pianoforte Competition (The): 771
Marshall Aid Commemoration Commission: 929
Mellon (The Paul) Centre for Studies in British Art: 419
Royal Institute of British Architects: 422
Royal Town Planning Institute (The): 1869
Sladen (The Percy) Memorial Fund: 2110
Talbot (The Amaury) Fund: 2025
Tata (Lady) Memorial Trust: 2448
University of Bristol: 945
University of Leeds: 946, 947
University of Manchester (The): 948

France

Fondation des Etats-Unis: 449
Human Frontier Science Program Organization: 2147
Long-Thibaud-Crespin Competition: 774

Germany

American Academy in Berlin (The): 869
Anna-Monika Foundation: 2569
ARD International Music Competition: 753
Heinrich Hertz-Stiftung: 917

Israel

Davis (The Lady) Fellowship Trust: 914
U.S.-Israel Binational Agriculture Research and Development Fund (BARD): 2130
U.S.-Israel Binational Science Foundation (BSF): 968
Weizmann Institute of Science: 953

Italy

Accademia Musicale Chigiana: 745
Istituto Italiano per gli Studi Storici: 600
Longhi (The Roberto) Foundation for the Study of the History of Art: 554
Scuola Normale Superiore: 940
Studio Arts Centers International (SACI): 573
Villa I Tatti: The Harvard University Center for Italian Renaissance Studies: 952

Japan

Matsumae International Foundation (The): 930

Kenya

British Institute in Eastern Africa (The): 901

The Netherlands

Hague Academy of International Law (The): 1976, 1977, 1978, 1979

Scotland

Institute for Advanced Studies in the Humanities (The): 374
Royal Society of Edinburgh (The): 937

Sweden

Stiftelsen Riksbankens Jubileumsfond: 401

Switzerland

Graduate Institute of International and Development Studies: 848
International Federation of University Women: 1085
Union for International Cancer Control (UICC): 2449

Personnel Index

A

Aase, Craig: 273
Abara, Obinna I., Esq.: 1146
Abbott, David T.: 152
Abdullah, Sylvia: 278
Abeles, Max: 230
Abendshein, Nancy: 1528
Abernethy, Darrell R., M.D., Ph.D.: 2306, 2310, 2540, 2541, 2542, 2543
Abernethy, Samuel F.: 938
Abeywardena, Palitha: 274
Abrams, Sheila M.: 1469
Abramson, Rosina: 647, 648
Abregu, Martin: 129
Acker, David: 832
Ackerman, Stephen: 2482
Acuff, A. Marshall, Jr.: 1333
Adams, Aileen: 332
Adams, Allan B.: 1486
Adams, Allison, B.A., B.S.: 2495
Adams, J. Welborn: 1374
Adams, Jean: 1101, 1329
Adams, Jeanna: 1712
Adams, Jerry: 1172
Adams, Larry S.: 2311
Adams, Robert M.: 1735
Adams, Thomas, B.S., B.A.: 2495
Adamski, Janet: 1745
Adamson, Rebecca: 1524
Addams, Cynthia G.: 72
Addison, Garrik: 239
Adkinson, Kimberly M.: 1020
Adolphe, Marie: 1904
Adrain, Lorne: 280
Adwan, Teresa B.: 288
Agger, David: 254
Aghdami, Farhad: 74, 1213
Agosta, Russell F.: 2632
Agrawal, Ashok: 2616
Aguado, Lynn: 931
Ahart, Edward: 2322
Ahlgrim, Judy: 283
Ahlstrom, Theresa: 1902
Aiello, Leslie C., Dr.: 2026, 2027, 2028, 2029
Ainsworth, Maryan: 900
Aitken, Wylie: 437
Akimoto, Miki: 1106
Akin, Hugh C.: 2017
Akman, Larry: 1123
Akman, Nonie: 1123
Ako, Roen: 993
Albanese, Licia: 798
Alberding, Ellen S.: 179, 2190
Albertini, Brian: 2493
Alcock, Charles R.: 2056, 2057
Alcorn, Gregory M.: 285
Alden, A.F. Drew: 1216
Alderman, Ellen Hartwell: 417
Aldrich, Hope: 434
Alenier, Karren L.: 706
Alesson, Tami: 531
Alexander, Bruce K.: 1486
Alexander, Cindy: 1752
Alexander, Daniel, QC: 960
Alexander, Michael: 437
Alexander, W. Robert: 1486
Alexander, W.R.: 165
Alexander-Minter, Rae: 783
Alfonso-Jones, Sol Marie: 1320
Ali, Fred J.: 332
Allan, Karen C.: 1196
Allen, Cynthia: 1816
Allen, Danielle S.: 229, 1926
Allen, John H.: 155

Allen, LaRue: 531
Allen, Lisa: 185
Allen, Tonya: 297
Allen, W. James: 2443
Allen, William C.: 332
Alley, Sherri: 1121
Allgor, Catherine: 373
Allison, Twyla: 1079
Allstrom, Peter: 531
Alongi, Carl M.: 1160
Alpers, Ann: 87
Alpert, Arthur: 185
Alsup, Afrika: 1741
Alvarado, Gil: 1509
Alvarez, Frank: 1396
Alvarez, Jose B.: 179
Amar, Michele: 1648
Amato, Paul R.: 1498
Amel, Kate: 1531
Ames, Aubin Z.: 1145
Amonette, Rex A., M.D.: 2447
Amoroso, Henry: 1396
Amos, Catherine: 2505
Amsden, D.M.: 317
Amundson, Dana: 220
Anaya, Nena: 1051
Anchia, Raphael M.: 163
Anders, Thomas F., M.D.: 2580
Anderson, Carol: 2018
Anderson, Debbie: 1353
Anderson, Derek: 938
Anderson, Gerard: 222
Anderson, Jeff: 1345
Anderson, Jennifer A.: 97
Anderson, Johanna: 1600
Anderson, John T.: 179
Anderson, Loren J., Dr.: 1700
Anderson, Melanie K.: 1384
Anderson, Rob: 1803
Anderson, Stefan S.: 30
Anderson, Tammy: 1010
Anderson, William, FAICP: 1165
Andrews, Robert: 1129
Andrews, Valerie: 584
Anema, Arielle: 690
Angeles, Fatima: 1425
Angelica, Robert E.: 1150
Angell, Janice K.: 216
Angelson, Lynn: 653
Anglin, Dale Robinson: 1735
Anlyan, William G., M.D.: 108
Annen, Lesly: 1079
Anstine, Mary K.: 1486
Antonatos, Julia: 101
Appenteng, Kofi: 129
Apt, Adam: 597
Aquila, Allan: 993
Aragon, Andrea: 115
Aranda, Olivia O.: 24
Aranda, Peter: 1892
Arbuthnott, John, Sir: 937
Archetti, Kathleen: 1583
Ardali, Azade: 278
Ardisana, Lizabeth: 297, 1333
Arkwright, Jill: 1473
Armienta, Angelo: 745
Armor, David J.: 1855
Arndt, Randall: 1211
Arnet, Heather: 1090
Arnold, Claire: 323
Arnold, Craig: 113
Arnold, Isaac, Jr.: 89
Arnold, Joan, Ph.D., R.N.: 2495
Arnold, Lisa: 12
Arnold, Nancy: 1320
Aron, Adam R., Ph.D.: 2483
Arwade, Jennifer: 1130
Asam, Claire L., Dr.: 59
Asante, Abena K.: 1503
Ashe, Dan: 2188

Asher, Frederick: 652, 877
Asher, James: 1935
Atkins, Maria: 2220
Atkinson, Jean S.: 24
Atkinson, Susan R.: 24
Atterbury, Alan: 2018
Atwell, Constance Woodruff, Ph.D.: 2482
Au, Carlton K.C.: 59
Auchincloss, Andrew: 1488
Auerbach, Elise: 652, 877
Auerbach, Meg, Esq.: 1215
Augustine, Erika, M.D.: 2483
Augusto, Carl R.: 971
Aupperle, Tammy B.: 156
Austin, Kenneth W.: 329
Austin, Susan Davenport: 468
Austin, Terry: 748
Avedisian, James R.: 24
Averill, Terry: 530
Avery, Caroline D.: 1358
Awad, Aida: 2080
Ax, Emanuel: 766
Axelson, Peter, M.S., M.E.: 2558
Aylierff, Lindsey: 1358
Aymer, Albert J.D., Dr.: 285
Azuara, Katherine: 35

B

Babbio, Lawrence T., Jr.: 329
Babcock, Bruce: 26
Baca, Rita E.: 504
Baccante, Richard: 2099
Bachman, Robert M.: 2535
Bachner, David: 954
Backus, Lisa: 87
Badal, Sharon: 1316
Bader, Daniel J.: 27
Bader, David M.: 27
Bader, Linda C.: 27
Badger, Tony: 960
Bagley, Nancy R.: 21, 279
Bagley, Nicole: 21
Bailey, John: 524
Bailey, Tammy: 1283
Bain, Barbara J., Prof.: 2448
Baker, Barbara W.: 1278
Baker, Beverly: 233
Baker, Tracy: 1125
Bakker, Annette: 2360
Baldwin, Kittredge A., Dr.: 59, 1601
Baldwin-Viereck, Ella: 2646
Bales, John F.: 223
Baliles, Robin D.: 2211
Ball, Charles: 29
Ball, Deborah Loewenberg: 1588
Ball, Frank E.: 29
Ballard, Karen, M.A., R.N.: 2495
Balson, Annissa: 1935
Bamattre, William R.: 262
Bame, Tracy: 132
Bandier, Martin: 666
Bane, Marylou: 1491
Bank, Ray: 31
Barbeau, Alain: 2323
Barbee, Amy: 2006
Barbee, Millie: 183
Barclay, Gillian R., D.D.S., Dr.P.H.: 6
Bard, Karen: 1160
Bardes, Judith L.: 103
Barillaro, Laura: 2265
Bark, Dennis L.: 1850
Barker, Peter: 1633
Barlow, David: 1147
Barlow, David S.: 1425
Barlow, Toby: 1302
Barnes, Ronald R.: 247
Barnet, William, III: 108
Barnett, Mary Jo: 794
Barnhart, Cynthia: 298

Barnhill, Taddy: 1358
Barnholt, Ned: 258
Baron, Jason: 162
Barr, Donald L.: 2466
Barr, Gwin: 285
Barr, Robin A., D.Phil.: 1452
Barra, Frank N.: 191
Barra, John A.: 1995
Barrett, David: 1935
Barrick, Julie: 1637
Barritt, Dan: 1603
Barron, Laura: 203
Bartlett, Terri L.: 1904
Base, Elizabeth: 288
Basham, Arthur A., M.D.: 2334
Baskin, Tobias, Dr.: 2174
Basom, Rita: 523
Bass, Edward P.: 281
Bass, Lee M.: 281
Bass, Sid R.: 281
Bates, George P.: 1821
Battey, Jayne: 1376
Battle, LaVeeda: 26
Battles, Charon: 495
Batyr, Vincent, C.P.A.: 2495
Baucum, Kaili: 1583
Bauer, Douglas: 1677
Bauer, Laurie: 1166
Baumann, Marsha: 1389
Baumgart, Melissa: 1215
Bay, Frederick: 1524
Bayat, John: 2575
Beall, J.H.: 706
Beall, Robert J., Ph.D.: 2413
Beals, Dan: 1353
Bean, Bruce W.: 23
Bean, Glen: 23
Bean, Mary F.: 23
Beardslee, William R., M.D.: 2580
Becerra, M. Isabel: 1425
Becht, Colleen: 1215
Bechtle, Nancy: 290
Beck, Judith: 2594
Beck, Norman E.: 30
Beck, Phyllis W., Hon.: 2491
Beck, Randell: 1926
Becker, Jack: 450
Bednarowski, Mary: 809
Beeson, Joel T.: 1503
Begier, Mary: 456
Behr, Gregg S.: 1126
Beinecke, Candace K.: 329
Beinecke, Frederick W.: 552
Beirne, David M.: 2446
Bekavac, Nancy: 293
Belden, Ted: 1172
Belisle, Helene: 2241
Bell, Hilton: 595
Bell, John, Dr.: 288
Bell, Judy: 115
Bell, Phebe: 312
Bell, R. Terry: 283
Bell, Samuel P.: 1633
Bell-Rose, Stephanie: 193, 273
Bellis, Richard: 666
Bellot, Dario: 1146
Bellsey, Lisa, Esq.: 2284
Beltran-del Olmo, Magdalena: 1425
Bendheim, Jack: 647, 648
Benedict, James: 28
Benglis, Lynda: 550
Bennack, Frank A., Jr.: 1935
Bennett, James T.: 1855
Bennett, Robert M.: 251
Bennett, Sharon: 2341
Bennici, Aldo: 745
Bennyhoff, George R.: 333
Benoliel, Peter: 383
Benson, Elizabeth Reiter: 1285
Benson, Martha L.: 1384

Bentley, Marie C.: 139
Bercovici, Nancy: 1330
Berge, Anne-Brith: 932
Bergman, Charles C.: 565
Bergman, Marilyn: 666, 754
Bergstrom, Christopher: 446
Berlin, Charles: 997
Berlin, Ira, Dr.: 2026
Berliner, James: 1192
Berman, Amy J.: 155
Berman, Richard A.: 1469
Bernard, Andre: 151
Bernard, Lewis: 229
Berners-Lee, Tim: 129
Bernhardt, Kenneth L.: 1214
Bernstein, Charles: 754
Bernstein, Charlie: 1492
Bernstein, Jed: 766
Bernstein, Jeffrey L.: 1995
Bernstein, Joshua: 1327
Bernstein, Richard: 298
Berry, Chad: 26
Berry, Donald C., Jr.: 220
Berry, Mike: 1227
Berry, Thomas W.: 167
Bertino, Joseph R., M.D.: 2367
Bertolini, Mark T.: 6
Bertolini, Mary: 2134
Bessant, Catherine P.: 1274
Bessent, Hattie, Ed.D., R.N.: 2495
Betancourt, Jennifer: 1647
Beumer, Robert E.: 817
Beveridge, Piper Neal: 279
Beyerstein, Lindsay: 1936
Bezahler, Lori: 1130
Bhagat, Vandna Wendy: 734
Bianchini, Thomas J.: 191
Bias, Val: 2288
Biber, David D.: 206
Biddiscombe, Raymond J.: 1210
Bienstock, Caroline: 666
Billiard, Thomas D.: 257
Bilski, Berthald: 997
Bilski, Mark A.: 997
Biltekoff, James: 1215
Binger, Anne: 1495
Binger, Erika: 1495
Birckmayer, Ann: 182
Bird, Peter F., Jr.: 1278
Birkholz, Patty: 2182
Birnbaum, Benjamin: 375
Birnbaum, Michael: 1469
Birshan, Michael: 929
Bischoff, Winfried F.W., Sir: 1905
Bishop, Aaron: 1391
Bishop, Leah M.: 1308
Bishop, Timothy R.: 72
Bisognano, Maureen: 1478
Bither, Philip: 464
Bitterman, Mary G.F.: 254
Bjorkman, Jenny, Dr.: 401
Black, Caroline: 565
Black, Janice R.: 1273
Black, Lynne: 150
Black, Roslyn: 1207
Black, Sherry Salway: 162
Blackburn, Sharon L.: 233
Blackford, J.P.: 2664
Blackman, James A., M.D.: 2459
Blake, Pier A.H.: 1029
Blakely, Carolyn: 1172
Blalock, Becky: 1214
Blanchard, Ashley: 1090
Blankenship, Terry, Ph.D.: 2111
Blau, Robert: 1926
Blausey, Bill: 113
Blazevich, David: 254
Bleier, Edward: 2254
Blevins, Kerrie: 1191
Block, Judith S.: 122

Blomquist, Goran: 401
Bloodworth, Carolyn A.: 82
Bloomfield, Doug: 246
Bluemle, Lewis W.: 81
Blum, Deborah: 1930
Blumenthal, Amy: 531
Blumenthal, David: 1478
Blumenthal, David, M.D.: 1478, 2280
Blumenthal, Jabe: 2172
Boas, Suzanne E.: 1214
Bobby, Ted: 156
Bobolts, Joyce: 134
Bodel, John, Prof.: 1632
Boesch, Donald: 2205
Bogen, Andrew E.: 332
Bogucki, Kim: 993
Bolliger, Ralph: 72
Bollinger, John C.: 2558
Bollinger, Lee C.: 1926
Bolster, Jane: 746
Bomberger, Carolyn: 816
Bomberger, Dorothy C.: 816
Bomberger, Matthew A.: 816
Bomberger, Michelle H.: 816
Bomberger, Rachel A.: 816
Bomberger, William A.: 816
Bond, Katharine: 100
Bonde-Henriksen, Nils: 1821
Bonneau, Christiane: 442
Bonnici, Laurie: 714, 715
Bonta, Diana M., Dr.P.H., R.N.: 1419, 1425
Boo, Katherine: 1926
Borenstein, Jeff: 2575
Borges, Francisco L.: 193
Born, Daniel: 1811
Bornancin, M. Janet: 2129
Bornick, Sue: 1263
Boshak, Toby E.: 536
Boskoff, Susan: 483
Bosman, Cal: 1283
Bost, Glenn, II: 271
Boswell, Kenya: 1184
Bosworth, Wendy Reed: 1291
Bouchard, Micheline: 2434
Bouchard, Mike G., L.L.B., MBA: 2434
Boufford, Jo Ivey, M.D.: 1469
Bouge, Rejane: 442
Boughton, Lori: 2182
Boulpaep, Emile L., Dr.: 900
Boulton, Lyndie M.: 2115
Bouricius, Pleun: 375
Boutwell, Jeffrey, Ph.D.: 2529
Boutwell, Robert: 2529
Bouwman, Laurie G.: 2443
Bowar-Ferres, Susan, Ph.D., R.N.: 2495
Bowdich, Julia B.: 1160
Bowen, Cindy: 961
Bowen, Edward L.: 2265
Bowen, Robert L.: 2632
Bower, Angela: 1274
Bowlin, Terry L., Ph.D.: 2306, 2310, 2540, 2541, 2542, 2543
Bowren, Randy: 993
Boyce, Judith: 2183
Boyce, Phillip R.: 2334
Boyd, Kathleen S., Dr.: 285
Boykins, Ayanna: 252
Boyle, Alan: 1930
Bozeman, David: 2616
Brabander, Cynthia: 113
Bracey, John: 474
Bracken, Frank A.: 30
Bracken, Thomas C.: 30
Bracken, William: 29
Brackett, Leanna: 1121
Bradley, Frank: 53
Bradley, James, Dr.: 1806
Bradley, John F., Sr.: 306
Brady, Amber: 1739
Brady, Maureen: 1089
Brandes, Kendra: 2674

References in index are to entry numbers.

Brannen, Elizabeth: 1562
Brasel, Susan S.: 1513
Brasier, Anne: 185
Braun, Andrew G., Sc.D.: 1825
Braun, Robert, Dr.: 2149
Braun, Theresa C.: 2099
Bravo, Teresa: 1059
Bray, Helen: 55
Bray, Marge: 1344
Breen, John: 1954
Brelsford, Jonathan: 1350
Bremner, Elizabeth: 1090
Brennan, Bob: 1460
Brennan, James C., Esq.: 2286
Brenner, David: 2461
Brent, David, M.D.: 2580
Breslauer, Gerald: 1010
Bresso, Gineen: 330
Breul, Jonathan D.: 1855
Brewer, Michael: 179
Brewer, Michael F.: 54
Brewer, Thomas: 262
Brewster, Sharon: 1127
Bricker, Diane R.: 300
Briggs, Robert W.: 193
Brisson, Katie G.: 75
Brister, Rachael: 993
Britt, Deirdre: 27
Britt, Kenneth F.: 1214
Britt, Wayman P.: 150
Brobeck, Carol: 370
Brock, Charlie: 1227
Brock, Dale W.: 504
Brodhead, Richard H.: 229
Broidy, Steven D.: 332
Bronars, Edward J., USMC, Lt Gen: 1691
Bronk, Deborah: 2087
Brooks, Conley, Jr.: 215
Brooks, Deborah W.: 2260
Brooks, Dina, Dr.: 2488
Brooks, Kelli: 1902
Brooks, Markell: 215
Brooks, Minna: 215
Brooks, Sarah: 215
Brooks, Stephen B.: 215
Brost, Gary: 1215
Brothers, M. Elizabeth: 1465
Broughton, Bruce: 666, 754
Brower, Susan: 1536
Brown, Andrew: 1327
Brown, Angela: 1487
Brown, Carlyle: 464
Brown, Charlotte: 1172
Brown, Christie: 1214
Brown, Denise: 1087
Brown, Francis K., II: 36
Brown, Gloria: 1376
Brown, Jackie Lett, Mrs.: 794
Brown, Jayna: 400
Brown, Kathleen: 2182
Brown, Leslie: 2654
Brown, Marcia E.: 155
Brown, Matthew: 1562
Brown, Meghan Binger: 1495
Brown, Michael, Dr.: 2023, 2024
Brown, Peter P.: 1410
Brown, R. Justin, M.P.H.: 2533
Brown, Robert L.: 1214
Brown, Robert W., M.D.: 58
Brown, Rod: 2172
Brown, Sherilyn: 497
Brown, Timothy: 101
Brown-Graham, Anita: 279
Browne, Janet: 597
Brownlee, Susan H.: 1126
Bruce, Peter W.: 1291
Bruer, John T., Dr.: 221
Bruijn, Lucie, Ph.D.: 2457
Bruininks, Robert: 1495
Brunner, James E.: 82

Bryan, Darrell: 1603
Bryan, Trish: 794
Bryant, Douglas E.: 1358
Bryant, Patricia A.: 504
Bryant, Ruth D.: 251
Brynteson, Susan: 443
Bryson, Louise Henry: 1192
Bucco, Diana A.: 1190
Buchanan, Millie: 2194
Buchanan, Robert J.: 1471
Buchholz, Andrew: 474
Buchholz, Carolyn: 363
Buckmaster, Raleigh D., Dr.: 1134
Buckner, Ellen B., Dr.: 1806
Budnik, Shaun: 1627
Buford, Calvin D.: 1285
Bugdanowitz, Sheila: 1360
Buitrago, Kerrie: 565
Bula, Barbara: 2529
Bula, Brendon: 2529
Bull, George: 217
Bullitt, Harriet: 2172
Bulthuis, Dave: 2177
Bumpus, R. Leroy: 77
Bunce, Valerie: 854
Bunch, Charles E.: 271
Bundy, Emory: 1603
Bunting, Josiah, III: 1853, 1854
Burakoff, Steven J., M.D.: 2446
Burchinal, Margaret R.: 1127
Burden, Alex: 2018
Burdick, Amy: 993
Burdick, Christopher: 1825
Burdick, Lalor: 1825
Burgess, Karen E.: 357
Burget, Mark: 2176
Burke, Charles R., Jr.: 1126
Burke, Jennifer: 1327
Burke, Karen Elizabeth, M.D., Ph.D.: 2482
Burke, Kevin: 298
Burke, Kimberly: 2011
Burke, Patricia Grable: 1126
Burke, Sheila P., R.N.: 1478
Burke, Sheryl A.: 6
Burke, Steven E.: 1126
Burleson, Thomas J.: 2632
Burnett, Jason: 258
Burnett, Nancy Packard: 258
Burnham, Kathy: 2616
Burnham, Patricia R.: 1502
Burns, Brian, Dr.: 1806
Burns, Jennifer, Dr.: 1676
Burns, Kristen: 1126
Burns, Richard R., Jr.: 36
Buron, Ashley: 2237
Burrows, David D.: 904
Burton, Angus M.: 302
Burton, Maggie L.: 1661
Bury, David: 1524
Busby, Sarah: 285
Bush, Val: 12
Buthman, Mark A.: 189
Butler, Brigid M.: 1191
Butler, Dixon M.: 2211
Butler, Frederick K.: 280
Butler, John K.: 1191
Butler, John M.: 82
Butler, Karen A.: 2280
Butler, Katherine: 1191
Butler, Patricia M.: 1191
Butler, Patrick: 1191
Butler, Paul S.: 1191
Butler, Peter M.: 1191
Butler, Sandra K.: 1191
Butler, Tim: 1995
Butler-McIntyre, Cynthia: 1477
Byerly, Stacy S.: 308
Byers, William: 1211
Byrd, Edward R.: 257
Byrd, Robert: 464

Byrne, Dana W.: 66
Byrnes, Brian: 1012
Byrnes, William H.: 191
Bzdak, Michael J.: 175

C

Cable, Nancy J., Dr.: 94
Cabot, John G.L.: 53
Cacciatore, Mark: 55
Cafritz, Anthony W.: 54
Cafritz, Calvin: 54
Cafritz, Elliot S.: 54
Cafritz, Jane Lipton: 54
Cahill, Nick: 881, 882, 883
Cahillane, Mary: 1700
Cahn, Tita: 754
Calakos, Nicole, M.D., Ph.D.: 2483
Calder, Peter D.: 1110
Caldwell, Joseph: 522
Caldwell, Nanci: 669
Caldwell, Stacy: 312
Callahan, Eugene J.: 1502
Calonge, Ned, M.D.: 1427
Camarena, Gene: 1068
Camp, Patsy White: 503
Campbell, Alice J.: 35
Campbell, Bert L.: 89
Campbell, C. David: 222
Campbell, Davis: 1147
Campbell, Dennis M., Ph.D.: 108
Campbell, E. Wallace: 1471
Campbell, George, Jr., Ph.D.: 2280
Campbell, Jan: 1371
Campbell, John D.: 2322
Campbell, Lebrena Fulp: 3
Campbell, Mary Schmidt: 298
Campbell, Michael: 1090
Campbell, Michael L.: 2188
Campbell, Paul, III: 1227
Campbell-Zopf, Mary: 492
Cannon, William C.: 183
Cantalupo, Jim: 2477, 2478
Cantini, Armin: 185
Capell, Sandra E.: 1589
Capobianco, Tito: 798
Carabine, Angela: 182
Cardenas, Gilberto: 461
Cardiff, Christopher: 1562
Cardinale, Ruth: 1513
Carey, Ashley: 2152
Carey, John P., M.D.: 2521
Carlson, Maria: 854
Carlson, Richard: 1816
Carmichael, Daniel P.: 206
Carmola, Jack: 1548
Caro, Robert A.: 151
Carpenter, Kirk: 2018
Carr, Catherine E., Ph.D.: 2465
Carr, Mandy, Ph.D.: 2675
Carrico, John D.: 850
Carrigan, Laura C.: 53
Carrington, John E., Rev.: 1469
Carroll, John H.: 60
Carroll, William L., M.D.: 2446
Carson, Carrie: 993
Carson, Emmett D., Ph.D.: 1376
Carson, Gale Jones: 503
Carter, Don E.: 1932
Carter, Lynn: 884
Carter, Prudence L.: 1127
Carter, Ron, Ph.D.: 1274
Carullo, Julie: 1759
Carwell, Peter H.: 792
Case, Peter Gill: 282
Cash, Michelle: 1351
Casiano, Kimberly: 1068
Casini, Marlene A.: 1252
Cass, Cynthia A.: 226

Cassin, Carolyn J.: 1088
Castellani, John: 2306, 2540, 2541, 2542, 2543
Castillo, Ernesto: 1405
Castillo, Gloria: 122
Castle, Alfred L.: 1601
Castleberry-Singleton, Candi: 1033
Castles, John W.: 241
Castonguay, Francois: 2434
Castor, Bruce L., Esq.: 1023
Castria, Mary E.: 2275
Castro, Ricardo: 129
Catalla, Ted: 1460
Catanese, Lynn: 593
Catello, Elli, Dr.: 600
Cathey, Shay Wyrick: 1099
Catovsky, Daniel, Prof.: 2448
Catron, Fletcher: 669
Catsimatidis, Margo: 2482
Cella, Bill: 2421
Cemar, Cindy: 274
Certo, Matthew W.: 52
Cesario, Thomas C., M.D.: 1442
Cha, Jang-Ho, M.D., Ph.D.: 2466
Chabon, Michael: 468
Chadwick, Douglas: 2173
Chakalis, Abbey: 2575
Chalutz, Edo: 2130
Chamberlin, Katie: 230
Chamberlin, Nathaniel: 230
Champer, Jeanne M.: 221
Chan, John, M.D.: 2399
Chandler, Carol, Esq.: 1825
Chandler, Mark: 1817
Chang, Kiki, M.D.: 2580
Chang, Lan Samantha: 701
Chanin, Anthony: 1308
Chano, Junichi: 852
Chapin, Charles M., III: 1396
Chapin, Ted: 548
Chapin, Theodore: 783
Chapman, Daniel H.: 226
Chapman, Philip: 1469
Chapoton, John E.: 54
Charlson, Kim: 1656
Chase, Donna: 503
Chasin, Alexandra: 282
Chatlos, Janet A.: 807
Chatlos, William J.: 807
Chatlos, William J., III: 807
Chavers, Dean, Dr.: 1047
Chen, Ida: 1270
Chen, Milton: 1583
Chen, Robert, M.A., M.B.B. Chir: 2483
Chen, Sho Tin: 2575
Cheney, Amy: 1285
Cheng, Eva: 155
Chernin, Louise: 993
Chernin, Rachel: 993
Chidsey, Molly: 1510
Child, Desmond: 666
Childs, Alfred: 2284
Childs, Bronwen: 2436
Childs, James E.: 2436
Childs, Melinda: 450
Chiloyan, Vart: 976
Chislett, Bruce: 2451
Chitnis, Parag R., Dr.: 2157
Choi, William C.: 1192
Chopus, Kelly: 1548
Chow, Leonard: 456
Christ, Donald C.: 376
Christensen, Clay: 288
Christensen, Katie: 523
Christian, Mary: 262
Christian, Ronald C., Esq.: 1285
Christie, Elizabeth W.: 1150
Christopherson, Elizabeth: 2322
Christovich, William K., Mrs.: 595
Chu, Benjamin K., M.D.: 1478
Chu, Clara: 714, 715

Chubb, Percy, III: 1396
Chubb, Sally: 1396
Chubb-Sauvayre, Sara: 1396
Chumley, Brenda: 1288
Churchill, John: 694, 1093
Ciavolella, Massimo: 357
Cicatello, Anthony: 1145
Cifelli, Christopher J., Ph.D.: 2671
Cipollone, Kristin: 1215
Cisneros, Bob: 2136
Clabaugh, Sue: 1536
Clack, Mary, Prof.: 1632
Clancy, Michael, M.D.: 1023
Clapp, Katherine: 2262
Clark, Andrew M., Dr.: 2038
Clark, Benic M., III: 211
Clark, H. Lawrence: 65
Clark, James McConnell, Jr.: 65
Clark, Jane Forbes: 1677
Clark, Jessica: 1848
Clark, Kristen: 156
Clark, Nate: 96
Clark, Sashya: 1510
Clark, Sondra: 1024
Clasen, Robert: 440
Classen, Julia: 1101
Clausen, Alf: 666, 754
Clausman, Linette: 1238
Clay, Judy: 2505
Claybourn, Colleen: 1389
Clayton, Valerie: 1270
Clegg, Jackie: 273
Clemons, G. Scott: 2041
Cleveland, Rose Ann: 54
Cliatt, Cass: 2026
Clifford, Linda M.: 250
Cline, J. Michael: 2188
Clinton, Bridgett: 2674
Clodfelter, Daniel G.: 279
Clore, Dale Ann: 1558
Co, Eric: 59
Coatsworth, John H.: 862
Cobb, Sara B.: 206
Coble, Christopher L.: 206
Coburn, Barry: 666
Coburn, Jeff: 961
Cochems, Beth: 565
Cochrane, Eugene W., Jr.: 108
Cockrell, David A.: 68
Cockrell, Ernest D.: 68
Cockrell, Ernest H.: 68
Cockrell, Janet S.: 68
Cody, George: 1816
Coen, Beverly: 246
Coene, Luc: 900
Cogswell, Wilton, III: 1034
Cohen, Audra: 531
Cohen, Jeremy: 666
Cohen, Martin: 149
Cohn, Diane: 1932
Cola, Marianne: 1350
Colburn, Michael J., Col.: 748
Colby, David, Ph.D.: 2275
Cole, Elizabeth, Ph.D.: 864
Colello, Joan: 1141
Coleman, Beverly: 1270
Coleman, Deborah J.: 2446
Coleman, Leonard S., Jr.: 1145
Coleman, Michelle: 459
Coleman, Morton: 1350
Coleman, Morton, M.D.: 2367
Coliton, Susan: 12
Coll, Steve: 1926
Collard, Yvette: 1246
Collier, Christina: 1358
Collier, Michael: 668
Collins, Gail: 1926
Collins, J. Barclay, II: 1469
Collins, James E.: 10
Collins, Maribeth W.: 72

Collins, Michael H.: 1384
Collins, Truman W., Jr.: 72
Colombo, Marie: 297
Colvard, Karen: 1853, 1854
Colvin, Theresa: 471
Comber, Neil: 1285
Combs, Kathleen: 714, 715
Compton, Vanessa: 80
Compton, W. Danforth: 80
Conarroe, Joel: 151
Condon, Tom: 2367
Condra, Rhea: 503
Condrat, Paul: 1603
Conley, Cort: 459
Conlin, Mark J.: 343
Conn, Lance: 2188
Conner, Stephanie B.: 503
Connolly-Keesler, Eileen: 1224
Conomikes, John G.: 1935
Considine, Raymond: 2529
Considine, William H.: 193
Constantine, Betsy: 1215
Constantine, Mark: 111
Conti, Florence M.: 251
Conti, Rena: 417
Conway, Jennifer: 403
Conway, William: 2173
Cook, Benetta: 2646
Cook, Errol M.: 2367
Cook, Frederick: 2483
Cook, Kathleen D.: 1179
Cook, Nancy: 1820
Cook, Phyllis: 254
Cook, Sara D.: 285
Cook, Thomas: 1691
Cook, Wallace L.: 2254
Cooke, Terry: 1295
Coolidge, Calvin: 1691
Cooper, Alan W.: 476
Cooper, Kelli: 1160
Cooper, Peter T.: 1227
Cooper, Rory, Ph.D.: 2558
Cooper-Basch, Irene: 1396
Cooperman, Leon G.: 2446
Cope, Lanis: 503
Cope, Lewis: 1930
Coppola, Christopher: 437
Corbet, Aaron: 1945
Corbin, Hunter W.: 167
Corbo, Mike: 1606
Cordova, Robert: 1491
Correa, Jennifer: 1141
Corro, Maruja: 1030
Corsello, Dan: 1394
Corty, Julie: 1101
Cosgrove, Michael J.: 2447
Costantino, Ryan: 2544
Cotton, Richard: 1469
Coudreaut, Terese: 193
Coughlin, Becky: 169
Council, LaVerne H., D.B.A.: 2284
Courtice, Lisa S., Ph.D.: 1210
Cousler-Emig, Julie: 1146
Covington, J.S., Dr.: 1552
Cowal, Kirsten: 862
Cowal, Sally Grooms: 862
Cowen, Sonia: 1054
Cox, Benita B.: 155
Cox, C. Richard: 1146
Coye, Molly J., M.D.: 6
Cozad, Kent: 1812
Craig, Charles, Hon.: 1024
Craig, Debbie F.: 232
Craig, John E., Jr.: 1478
Craig, Richard, Dr.: 2120
Craig-Meyer, Jeffrey A.: 817
Crain, John W.: 1384
Cramer, Ann W.: 1214
Crandall, William: 24
Crane, Christopher: 119
Crane, Marjorie Knight: 193

Crane, Peter, Sir: 101
Crane, Robert: 2176
Crary, Horace I., Jr.: 5, 46
Cravens, Christy: 2459
Craver, Theodore: 114
Craveri, Piero: 600
Crawford, Alva Jean: 1285
Crawford, Carl: 1344
Crawford, Crystal D.: 1425
Crawford, James: 1700
Crawford, Teresa J.: 134
Creager, Angela: 597
Creason, Kennard: 1283
Cresci, Andrew A.: 139
Creswell, Tom: 1283
Criswell, Pamela: 220
Crochet, Marcel: 900
Crocker, Joe D.: 1503
Croft, Edward S., III: 1214
Croft, Thomas D.: 1285
Cron, Marie-Michele: 442
Cronenwett, Linda, Ph.D., R.N.: 2280
Cronin, Dennis: 28
Crosby, David: 1495
Cross, Beverly: 1130
Crossgrove, William C., Prof.: 1632
Crothers, Chris: 111
Cruden, John: 1974
Cruickshanks, Elizabeth: 514
Crumpacker, Caroline: 477
Cruse, Rebecca: 501
Crutchfield, James N.: 193
Cuddy, Amy: 1196
Cuellar Rojas, Adrianna: 226
Cullar, Catherine: 2225, 2226, 2227
Cullen, Mark: 1471
Cullen, Matthew P.: 1302
Cullen, Meredith T.: 89
Culliton, Barbara J.: 1930
Culman, Sita: 2
Culp, Stephen A.: 211
Cummings, Kathleen Sprows: 589, 590
Cunningham, Helen: 1270
Cureton, Sara R.: 619
Curley, John J.: 155
Curley, Kenneth Clark, M.D.: 2558
Curley, Walter J.P., Jr.: 5, 46
Curran, Carol Cockrell: 68
Curran, Richard B.: 68
Currie, Jan: 1460
Currin, Katherine: 211
Curry, Elizabeth R.: 167
Curry, Ravenel B., III: 108
Curtis, Elizabeth H.: 24
Curtis, Mary E.: 1855
Curtiss, David: 2071
Cushing, Margaret J.: 862
Cusic, Anne, Dr.: 1806
Cwik, Valerie A., M.D.: 2473
Cyr, Susan, Esq.: 1457

D

D'Amato, Catherine: 1185
D'Amico, Julia: 282
D'Angelo, Leah: 282
D'Arcy, Stephen R.: 1302
D'Avila, Luiz Felipe: 961
D'Elia, Lorraine: 139
D'Olier, H. Mitchell: 59
Daggett, Brian, M.D.: 2399
Daggett, Christopher J.: 99, 1145
Dajani, Virginia: 746
Dalio, Ray: 2188
Dallas, Stephanie: 993
Dalton, Marla: 2339
Dalton, Sharon C., MBA: 6
Daly, Charles U.: 179
Daly, James J.: 1188

Daly, Mary W.C.: 280
Dammrich, Thomas: 2177
Dana, Charles A.: 155
Dana, Charles A., III: 2254
Daniel, Clifton Truman: 2018
Daniel, Thomas O., M.D.: 2306, 2540, 2541,
    2542, 2543
Daniels, Dianne J.: 1524
Daniels, John W., Jr.: 1291
Daniszewski, John: 1926
Dankenbring, James R.: 817
Dankers, Paul: 1330
Dann-Messier, Brenda, Hon.: 853
Danner, Michael D., Dr.: 1995
Dannhaeuser, Cherlyn: 807
Danziger, Sheldon: 1870
Dao, Solange C.: 2664
Dardess, Margaret B.: 1581
Darling, Linda: 881, 882, 883
Darling-Hammond, Linda: 329
Daucher, Lynn: 1419
Daudet, Yves, Prof.: 1977, 1978, 1979
Daudon, Maud: 2172
Daugherty, Barbara: 2212
Daughtery, Margery: 2120
Daughtry, Deborah K.: 80
Daum, Paul L.: 2120
Daut, Shannon: 428
David, Justine: 1215
Davidow, Jeffrey: 961
Davidson, Betsy: 182
Davidson, Bradford: 182
Davidson, Gretchen D.: 216
Davidson, Gwen: 435
Davidson, Marty: 1552
Davidson, Matthew: 182
Davidson, Peter: 182
Davidson, Suzanne Schwartz: 653
Davis, Chastity: 1338
Davis, Dee: 26
Davis, Frank: 56
Davis, Graeme W., Ph.D.: 2465
Davis, J.H. Dow: 94
Davis, Jonathan P.: 94
Davis, Leigh Evans: 1296
Davis, Leroy: 111
Davis, Martha: 993
Davis, Maynard K.: 94
Davis, Scott: 1054
Davis, Shelly A.: 268
Davis, Stephanie L.: 1469
Davis, Tamara: 94
Davison, H.: 1488
Day, Betty: 1532
Day, Martha: 1145
Dayton, Eric: 282
Dayton, John: 163
de Caprariis, Giulio: 600
de Groote, Jacques: 900
de Hoyos, Debora: 1700
De Luca, Victor: 2194
De Maio, Stephen: 798
de Souza Briggs, Xavier: 129
de Vega, Sonia Marie De Leon: 1192
Deacon, Bob, Prof.: 929
Dean, Victoria Seaver: 293
Deaver, Carolyn J.: 54
DeBartolo, Lisa: 1189, 2171
DeBerry, Valerie: 1215
DeBevoise, Jane: 434
deBuys, William: 2173
Decaro Bonella, Melina: 600
Decherd, Robert W.: 37
Dedecker, Clotilde Perez-Bode: 1215
Deen, R.B., Jr.: 1552
DeFrantz, Anita L.: 1447
Degnan, Peter: 265
Dehli, Joyce: 1926
Deibele, Theresa: 232
Dekker, Hans: 167

Dela Cruz-Viesca, Melany: 1021
Delage, Joane: 2249
DeLano, Mike: 1606
DeLoach, Harris E., Jr.: 108
DeLoayza, Hugh: 2466
DeLucia, Michael S.: 1131
DeMain, John: 798
Demopoulos, Harry B.: 107
Demyan, Kirk C.: 1273
Dendas, Ronald C., M.S.: 1458
Dendy, Richard: 929
Dennis, Andre, Esq.: 2491
Denyer, Mary C.: 929
DePillis, Mark S., Esq.: 1023
Derks, Steven: 2473
Des Landes, Claude: 442
DeSantis, Daniel: 133
DeShazo, Nikki, Hon.: 1384
DeShazo, Peter: 961
Desmond, Amy B.: 536
Deverman, Christopher: 1995
Devine, Michael J.: 2018
Devonish, Carrolle Perry: 103
Dew, Patti: 1291
Diachun, Elizabeth: 1215
Diamonstein-Spielvogel, Barbaralee, Dr.: 488
Diaz, Junot: 1926
DiCarlo, Mary: 2129
DiChiera, Cristina: 497
Dick, Stacy: 278
Dick, Sylvia Looney: 323
Dickerson, Sally: 2583
Dickson, Mary: 2190
Dicovitsky, Gary: 850
DiCroce, Deborah M.: 1296
DiDomenico, Rebecca: 80
Diefenderfer, Jeannie: 1090
Dieffenbach, Ann: 2289
Dien, Laurie: 1141
Diethrick, June C.: 1204
Dietz, Philip E.L., Jr.: 2205
Digges, Ryan: 993
Dillingham, John A.: 2018
Dillon, Diane: 385, 387, 388, 392, 393, 394,
    395, 396, 397, 398, 623, 1053
DiMichele, Donna, M.D.: 2369
Dinges, Stan: 303
Dinkel, John F., Jr.: 1179
Dinovitz, Dino: 1935
Dion, Ernest E.: 1131
Dirschel, Kathleen, Ph.D., R.N.: 2495
Dishman, J. Dallas, Ph.D.: 1432
DiSilvestro, Anthony: 55
DiTrapani, Joseph: 1015
Divelbiss, Terry L.: 77
Diver, Colin: 273
Divola, Julie: 1394
Dixon, Edith R.: 1023
Dixon, George W.: 1023
Do, Megan: 1510
Doane, Craig: 2221
Dodd, Julie: 1957
Dodson, David: 26, 273
Dodson, Richard: 793
Doerfler, Ron: 1935
Doerr, John: 2177
Doggett, W.B.: 113
Dohrer, Kim: 1886
Dolan, Paul: 1207
Doligez, Philippe: 320
Doll, Francisco J.: 155
Dolsten, G. Mikael, M.D., Ph.D.: 2306, 2540,
    2541, 2542, 2543
Donahey, Robert W.: 250
Donaldson, M.S., Esq.: 2286
Donaldson, Phil: 1166
Dondzila, Ed: 2507
Donley, Shannon: 2182
Donlon, Marcia: 1448
Donnelley, Ceara: 101

Donnelley, Laura: 101
Donnelley, Shawn M.: 101
Donnelley, Vivian: 101
Donnelly, Edward J.: 1350
Donovan, Thomas J.: 1179
Doore, Daniel P.: 2334
Doppstadt, Eric: 129
Dorhout, Peter K.: 2041
Dorn, Holbrook: 1528
Dorn, Peter: 2482
Dotson, Alphonse A.: 504
Doughty, Heather: 495
Dowell, Gregory C.: 226
Dowling, Patrick, Dr.: 1192
Downey, Stephen S.: 1661
Doyle, Jennifer: 1273
Drake, Barbara E.: 1995
Drake, Jamie: 244
Drake, Michael V., M.D.: 1478
Driscoll, Matthew: 2182
Droth, Martina: 408
Drowota, Frank F., III: 1278
Drushel, William H., Jr.: 89
du Monceau, Diego: 900
Dubester, Ilana: 279
DuCharme, Elaine: 993
Duchossois, Kimberly: 106
Duckmann, Stephanie: 29
Dudderar, Frederick: 2182
Duff, Stephen M.: 489, 622
Duffy, Stephen C.: 2220
Duggan, Ervin S.: 734
Dumbleton, Kathy: 2505
Dunajcik, Karl A.: 817
Dunbar, William: 1327
Duncan, Angus: 2169
Duncan, Megan, M.P.H.: 2533
Dunham, Linda: 1133
Dunlap, Jamie: 495
Dunlap, William: 1179
Dunn, Eileen: 1737
Dunn, John M.: 1969
Dunn, Kathryn: 1291
Dunn, Mary Amber: 1121
Dunn, Michael, Ed.D.: 1603
Dunn, Peter A.: 1201
Dunn, Robert P.: 2018
Dunstan, Christopher T.: 251
Duong, Melissa: 1272
Dupont, Benoit: 1408
Durand, Cassandra: 1247
Durkan, James: 296
Durocher, Benoit: 2434
Dvorak, Elizabeth: 52
Dvorak, Jack: 1957
Dyer, Barbara: 162
Dykstra, Craig R.: 206
Dylla, H. Frederick: 2099
Dziuban, Bob: 2152

E

Eakes, Martin: 129
Earl, Anthony S.: 179
Earlbaum, Gary E.: 2446
Easter, Colette R.: 1278
Eastmead, Donald F., M.D.: 2558
Eaton, Brenda: 1420
Ebel, William E.: 1160
Eberhart, Cornelia M.: 216
Eberle, John G.: 1201
Ebie, Bill: 522
Eckenrode, Beth: 156
Eckert, Ross: 1215
Edelson, Richard L., M.D.: 2255
Eder, Robert: 2182
Edgerley, Sandra M.: 1185
Edmonds, Ana: 1351
Edwards, Carl T.: 3

Edwards, Ollie: 2220
Effron, Cheryl Cohen: 278
Egbert, George Pennington, III: 2482
Egbert, Marcia: 152
Eger, Susan: 2505
Egginton, Everett: 961
Egner, David O.: 1302
Egues, Aida, D.N.P., R.N.: 2495
Eichert, Jerome: 794
Einhorn, Peggi: 2275
Eisenberg, D.D.: 1502
Eisenson, Michael R.: 1185
Eisiminger, Terri L.: 458
El-Antably, Camilla: 523
El-Porter, Fatima E.: 2220
Elcan, Patricia Frist: 1278
Elderidge, Rev. Joseph: 21
Eldridge, Mary Elizabeth: 1172
Eliasson, Hugh: 1460
Elledge, Amy: 2182
Elledge, Stephen: 2436
Ellenson, Richard: 2459
Ellerbrook, Karen: 461
Elliott, Robin Anthony: 2482
Elliott, Virginia: 1514
Ellis, David W., III: 1285
Ellis, Donald: 622
Ellis, Eve: 1090
Ellis, Maria de Jong: 881, 882, 883
Ellwein, Charles E.: 87
Elmendorf, Michael: 2182
Elorza, Jorge O.: 280
Elston, Jan: 1121
Elton, David, Dr.: 1420
Embrey, Lauren: 1090
Embry, Robert C., Jr.: 2
Emerson, Alice F.: 65
Emrick, John: 232
Eng, Phoebe: 1090
Eng, Torbjorn, Dr.: 401
Engel, William V.: 167
Engelberg, Stephen: 1926
England, Cathy: 1123
England, Diana: 1123
England, Lois: 1123
England, Rick: 1123
Englander, Peter, Dr.: 960
Engleman, Thomas E.: 1932
English, James F.: 403
Enright, William G.: 206
Enriquez, Mary Schneider: 53
Ensign, Katie: 111
Ensor, Robert P.: 817
Enszer, Julie R.: 1089
Enzerra, D.J.: 209
Ephgrave, Samantha: 1637
Epstein, Deena M.: 152
Erickson, Ceil: 292, 1470
Erickson, Jon D., Dr.: 2174
Erickson, Patricia, Dr.: 2174
Ernster, Mark: 794
Escamilla, James: 1309
Escobar, Patrick: 1447
Escobedo, Marcus R.: 155
Eshed, Yuval, Prof.: 953
Eskridge, Carl: 1405
Esposito, Richard: 1465
Esterline, Bruce H.: 226
Estes, Jane M.: 94
Estrin, Eliot: 141
Estrin, Mary Lloyd: 141
Estrin, Robert L.: 141
Estrin, Zoe: 141
Eurich, Juliet A.: 31
Evans, C. Lawrence: 1995
Evans, Eric, Ph.D.: 1003
Evans, Jay: 2624, 2625
Evans, Linda P.: 226
Evans, Scott: 1127
Evans, Susie S.: 2018

Evarts, William M., Jr.: 1469
Evelyn, Douglas E., Dr.: 489, 622
Everett, Joe: 1344
Eveslage, Thomas: 1957
Ewing, Lakweshia: 1227
Ewing, Stephen E.: 297

F

Faber, Julie: 2473
Fagiano, Rachel: 862
Fahey, Thomas J., Jr., M.D.: 2446
Fahn, Stanley, M.D.: 2482
Falahee, William: 182
Falk, Thomas J.: 189
Falls, Amy C.: 129
Famiglietti, Armanda: 90
Fanton, Jonathan: 434
Faraci, John V., Jr.: 2188
Farber, Jeff: 195
Farley, Katherine: 229
Farmer, W. Paul, FAICP: 1165
Farrell, Betty L.: 80
Farrell, Michael: 851
Farren, David: 101
Farrenkopf, Tina: 1038
Farrow, Jackson: 1172
Farzan, Dorienne: 376
Fath, Linda C.: 1285
Fattah, Chaka, Rep.: 1027
Fauci, Anthony S.: 107
Fauquher, Ronald K.: 30
Fawcett, Daniel W.: 69, 1386
Featherman, Sandra: 1270
Feiler, William R.: 1308
Feinman, Abby L.T.: 1308
Feinstein, Alan Shawn: 1482
Feinstein, Karen Wolk, Ph.D.: 1444
Feldman, Brian, Dr.: 2451
Fellows, Glenn: 1160
Fenza, D.W.: 667
Ferrell, Lynne J.: 134
Ferrero, Dave: 12
Ferriby, Robin D.: 75
Ferris, Mindy: 1196
Fey, Grace: 1185, 1585
Fick, John: 1536
Ficklin, Linda: 483
Field, Christopher: 1816
Field, Marshall, V: 122
Field, Richard D.: 2482
Fields, Charles: 1130
Fields, Curtland E.: 1150
Fields-Taylor, Joetta: 63
Fiene, Michael: 303
Fike, Nancy: 1603
Filemyr, Ann, Dr.: 1051
Finch, Mat D., Dr.: 1473
Finckel, David: 766
Findlay, Keith: 844
Finear, David R.: 257
Fineberg, Harvey: 159
Fineberg, Harvey, M.D., Ph.D.: 2280
Finn, Hayley: 696
Finnell, Michael: 954
Fionda, Andrea: 2277
Fiorella, Jillian: 1215
Firman, Royal, III: 124
Firman, Stephanie: 124
Fischer, Alison: 25
Fischer, Diane: 25
Fischer, Robert E.: 2367
Fish, Marion Hancock: 302
Fisher, Brannon: 29
Fisher, Diane L.: 285
Fisher, Elliott: 2322
Fisher, J. Steven: 285
Fisher, James A.: 29
Fisher, Jud: 29

References in index are to entry numbers.

Fisher, Larry: 2466
Fisher, Pamela: 1932
Fisher, Richard: 2518
Fisher, Robert: 1902
Fiske, Brian: 2260
Fister, Christopher L.: 1285
Fitton, Chana: 2322
Fitts, Hatty Walker: 548
Fitzgerald, David, Prof.: 1622
FitzGerald, Karen: 1327
Fitzgerald, Melody: 1327
Fitzpatrick, Jack: 139
Fitzpatrick, James A., Jr.: 904
Fitzpatrick, Joyce: 2486
Fitzpatrick, M. Louise, Ed.D., R.N.: 2495
Fitzpatrick, Susan, Dr.: 221
Fitzwalter, Jane: 945
Flaherty, Kegan: 1510
Flanagan, Molly: 179
Flanagan, Patricia J., M.D.: 280
Flaville, Victoria K.: 81
Flax, Michael G., M.D.: 2500
Fleming, David W.: 1192
Fleming, Kim Tillotson: 1190, 1350
Fleming, Nancy: 566
Fleming, Stephen: 566
Fleming, William T.: 1995
Fletcher, Allen W.: 1512
Fletcher, Maureen T.: 1129
Fletcher, Warner S.: 10, 339, 1512
Flick, Robert: 293
Flippin, Doreen: 94
Flocken, Jeffrey E.: 1442
Flood, Christine: 1511
Flood, Eugene: 1274
Flores, Margarita: 1068
Flores, Ness: 1291
Flores, Sandra: 133
Flores-Breyer, Dina: 1510
Flores-New, Fernando: 1125
Floyd, Beth: 975
Flumenbaum, Martin: 647, 648
Flynn, Kathy: 1134
Fogel, Henry: 766
Fogg, Anthony: 766
Foley, Dia: 492
Foliart, Dan: 666, 754
Folsom, James: 373
Foltz-Gray, Dan: 1121
Foner, Naomi: 524
Fong, I.K.: 317
Fonseca, Caio: 182
Fonseca, Elizabeth K.: 182
Fonseca, Isabel: 182
Fonseca, Quina: 182
Fonseca, Vivian, M.D.: 2403
Foote-Hudson, Marilyn E.: 1581
Forbes, Bruce, Rev.: 1473
Forbes, Orcillia Z.: 232
Ford, Cynthia N.: 222
Ford, John: 461
Ford, Lisa: 408
Ford, Liz: 1460
Fordi, Heidi B.: 2580
Fordice, Dan K., III: 2632
Foreman, Robin: 1296
Fortier, Albert M., Jr., Esq.: 318
Fortino, Neila: 531
Fortunato, Stephen J., M.D.: 2500
Fosmark, Michael: 1886
Fossum, Barbara: 2616
Foster, Amelia: 450
Foster, John H.: 434
Foster, Lee B., II: 1350
Foudree, Charles M.: 2018
Fountain, W. Frank: 75, 1302
Fowler, Wyche, Jr.: 538
Fox, Jeanne: 341
Fox, Sherry: 894
Foxley, Griff: 141

Foxley, Zoe L.: 141
Foy, Douglas J.: 29
Fraley, Theresa: 75
Franchomme, Paola: 600
Francis, Alexandra: 286
Franco, Larry: 1215
Francois, Michelle: 1147
Frank, Elizabeth T.: 1735
Frank, Pamela: 766
Frank, Samuel, M.D.: 2466
Franklin, John: 241
Franklin, Melissa: 564
Frantz, Barbara: 1220
Frasier, Mark: 2260
Frazee, Alex: 340
Frazier, Evan: 1350
Frazier, Margie: 2243
Freedman, Becca: 21
Freedman, Mark J., F.S.A., M.A.A.A.: 2097, 2098
Freedman, Wendy: 1816
Freeman, Glenn: 1172
Freeman, Graeme: 131
Freitag, Amy: 182
Frelinghuysen, Peter: 5, 46
French, Buck: 2446
French, Janel W.: 1282
Frenk, Julio, M.D.: 1478
Freundlich, Barbara: 2367
Freundlich, Jerry: 2367
Frey, Dale F.: 2446
Frey, David G.: 134
Frey, Edward J., Jr.: 134
Frey, John M.: 134
Freyer, Judith: 265
Friberg, Susan: 900
Frick, Neil: 2288
Fried, Linda P., M.D.: 2280
Friedman, Barry: 1745
Friedman, Brian C.: 1214
Friedman, Ellen: 80
Friedt, Lori: 993
Friel, Thomas J.: 1376
Friend, Robert: 254
Frist, Patricia C.: 1278
Frist, Thomas F., III: 1278
Frist, Thomas F., Jr.: 1278
Frist, William R.: 1278
Fritz, Lance: 325
Frommer, Wolf: 1816
Fross, Roger R.: 179
Frost, Robert D.: 997
Fruend, Carl J.: 817
Frumkin, Howard: 2172
Fry, Rita A.: 122
Frye, Irene: 1009
Frymoyer, John W., M.D.: 2280
Fuchs, Barbara: 358, 359, 360, 361
Fuchs, Elaine V., Ph.D.: 2446
Fuentes, Jorge: 2632
Fuentes-Michel, Diana: 1671
Fuglister, Jill: 232
Fulginiti, Greg: 2505
Fulham-Winston, Deborah: 1273
Fuller, Albert: 162
Fuller, Lori V.: 1503
Fuller, Tricia: 320
Fulp, John R., III: 3
Fulp, John R., Jr.: 3
Fung, Kenneth H.C.: 434
Funk, Carla J.: 730, 999
Furr, Holly C.: 295
Furtivo, Benay: 357
Fusco, Joseph J., M.D.: 2399

G

Gabriel, Nicholas M.: 129
Gabriele, Amy: 495

Gabriele, Erin: 716
Gade, Peter J.: 1940
Gaffield, Chad, Dr.: 1871, 1872, 1873, 1874, 1875, 1876
Gaffney, John C.: 1442
Gage, Beau: 531
Gagnon, Jean Paul, Ph.D.: 2306, 2310, 2540, 2541, 2542, 2543
Galan, Nely: 1068
Galang, Astra: 262
Galarraga, Juan: 1068
Galasso, Giuseppe: 600
Galeano, Carolina: 2349
Galiana, J. Garcia: 317
Gallagher, Daniel: 194
Gallagher, Edward P.: 665, 884
Gallagher, Linda: 1215
Gallagher, Lindsay R.: 194
Gallagher, Matthew D.: 1281
Galliher, Mike: 30
Gallivan, Karen P.: 1282
Gallo, Gregory M.: 1376
Gallo, John: 254
Gallo, Ron: 1371
Gamber, Jeff: 1514
Gamble, H. Ray, Dr.: 2039
Gamble, Laura: 31
Gambliel, Maria Carmen: 459
Gambrell, Sara Belk: 2482
Gamoran, Adam: 1127
Gander, Forrest, Prof.: 1632
Gandhi, Rutuma M.: 155
Gang, Jeanne: 417
Gann, Pamela Brooks, Dr.: 1700
Gannett, Craig: 173
Gannon, Paul C.: 1185
Gannon, William S., Rev.: 1150
Gant, Sally: 562
Gantt, Harvey: 1274
Garcetti, Gil: 1631
Garcia, Juliet V.: 129
Garcia, Lisa M.: 1068
Gardheere, Ubax: 1510
Gardner, Michael R.: 734
Gardner, Roger L.: 178
Gardner, Scott: 1215
Garen, Wendy: 262
Gargan, Denise M.: 1458
Garner, Joseph, Ph.D.: 2483
Garness, Jim: 341
Garrison, Jody: 1055
Garrity, William E.: 82
Garten, Jeffrey E.: 6
Gary, Leah S.: 250
Garza, David: 504
Garza, Martin J.: 2632
Gascon, Claude, Ph.D.: 2188
Gaskill, Julia: 796
Gaspari, Kevin: 993
Gassert, Timothy: 1185
Gaynor, Richard B., M.D.: 2446
Gdovin, David: 2038
Gearen, John J.: 1700
Gebben, Phyllis A.: 307
Geber, David: 782
Gehl, Danis J., Ph.D.: 1215
Gehrig, Cynthia A.: 464
Gelblum, Seth: 534
Genereux, Marc: 2429
Genstler, Jennifer: 312
Geocaris, Alexis: 1338
George, Mary: 1224
George, Terrence R.: 59
Georgopoulou, Maria, Dr.: 892, 893
Gephart, Jay: 748
Gerace, Ed: 503
Geras, Mary E.: 329
Gerber, Ann Rogers: 135
Gerber, Selwyn: 1308
Gerber, Ted: 854

Gerdes, Chris: 1606
Geren, Pete: 1752
Gerlach, Mary: 179
Germain, Chris: 793
German, Deborah C., M.D.: 52
Gerschel, Patrick A.: 904
Gerstacker, Lisa J.: 2443
Geske, Janine P.: 1291
Geswell, Richard: 2412
Getty, Caroline: 2188
Gevertz, Brenda: 1559
Ghubril, Saleem H.: 1190
Gibbons, Gary H.: 2398
Gibbons, Lile R.: 155
Gibbs, Gary, Dr.: 504
Gibson, George C.: 1486
Gibson, Marshall: 782
Gibson, Mila: 504
Gideon, Cheryl: 263
Giesel, William G., Jr.: 251
Gigot, Paul A.: 1926
Gilbert, Erin: 290
Giles, Phillip: 1130
Gilfillan, Christine C.: 1135
Gill, Barbara E.: 2254
Gill, James F.: 107
Gill, Libia: 1595
Gill, Margot: 961
Gillem, Christopher: 241
Gillespie, Charlotte A.: 1486
Gillespie, Deborah: 179
Gillespie, George J., III: 1141
Gilligan, Ellen M.: 1291
Gilliland, Lucia: 503
Gilmore Letcher, Edith: 2311
Gilmour, Allan D.: 75
Gimon, Eric: 159
Gindre, H.M.: 317
Ginsberg, William W.: 1216
Ginty, Edward F.: 675, 851
Gioia, Robert D.: 251
Giordano, Roberto: 600
Giornelli, Lillian: 323
Girgus, Joan, Dr.: 2026
Giron-Gordon, Teri: 1160
Gissler, Sig: 1926
Glancy, Alfred R., III: 75
Glancy, Ruth R.: 222
Glasscock, Selma, Ph.D.: 2111
Glassman, David E.: 1995
Gleason, Tom: 1603
Gleba, Michael W.: 2014
Glenn, Tom: 1227
Glick, Diana, Dr.: 2066
Glimcher, Denise: 1211
Glowinski, Anne, M.D.: 2580
Gluck, Suzanne: 278
Glynn, Simone, M.D.: 2369
Goad, Elizabeth A.: 817
Goad, Linda W.: 461
Godwin, Peter: 660
Goese, Kerry M.: 179
Goff, Phyllis Rawls: 216
Goings, Calvin: 993
Goins, Charlynn: 244
Golay, Inga: 531
Goldberg, Jeffrey: 278
Goldberg, Justin: 1351
Goldberg, Leonard H., M.D.: 2447
Golden, Charles E.: 206
Golden, Olivia: 1127
Golden, Rebecca: 982
Golding, Michael R., M.D.: 1469
Goldman, Dorothy Tapper: 151
Goldman, Ruth: 230
Goldman-Pittel, Stephanie: 2482
Goldseker, Ana: 1281
Goldseker, Deby: 1281
Goldseker, Sharna: 1281
Goldseker, Sheldon: 1281

Goldseker, Simon: 1281
Goldsmith, Chandra: 417
Goldsmith, Shane: 1490
Goldson, Amy: 1027
Goldstein, Jan E.: 578, 579, 580
Goldstone, Carroll: 185
Golub, Todd R., M.D.: 2446
Gomez, Elizabeth M.: 1425
Gomez, Iris: 1487
Gómez-Ibáñez, Miguel: 457
Gomulinski, Curtis D.: 2664
Gonzales, Aminda Marques: 1926
Gonzales, Nancy: 1127
Gonzalez, Henry: 2026
Gonzalez, Jerry: 26
Gonzalez-Mendez, J.C.: 1133
Goodman, Michael, Dr.: 285
Goodman, Sondra: 2221
Goodwin, Jay, Ph.D., Dr.: 1887
Goodwin, Peter, MBA: 2280
Goodwin, Richard H., Jr.: 2174
Gooss, Henry: 1127
Gordon, David: 1509
Gordon, Laura: 531
Gordon, Marnie: 2367
Gordon, Michael L.: 2446
Gorham, Bradford: 1632
Gorham, John: 61
Gorham, Mark L.: 1160
Gorham, Timothy N.: 61
Gormley, Glenn J., M.D., Ph.D.: 2306, 2540,
    2541, 2542, 2543
Gorton, Erin: 1215
Gosney, Tim: 306
Gould, David A.: 1469
Gould, Jane Mack: 866
Gould, Laurence K., Jr.: 2581
Goulder, Larry: 2176
Graaskamp, Garret W.: 2597
Graf, R.T.: 209
Grafstein, Bernice, Ph.D.: 2465
Graham, Donald E.: 149
Graham, Garth N., M.D., M.P.H.: 6
Graham, Michelle: 1524
Gralnick, Jon: 531
Grant, Bruce: 854
Grant, Charisse: 234
Grant, Cornelius P.: 1054
Grass, Henry J., M.D.: 2465
Grassilli, Robert J., Jr.: 139
Graton, Lynn: 485
Graves, Milton T.: 68
Gray, Constance F.: 108
Gray, Herman B.: 297
Gray, Jim: 1420
Gray, Michelle, Ph.D.: 2466
Greaf, Jack: 1606
Green, Andrew: 437
Green, David D., III: 141
Green, Miriam: 2130
Green, Tina: 1172
Green, William D.: 1905
Greenawald, Sheri: 789
Greenberger, Sharon: 278
Greene, Don: 2653
Greenstein, Scott: 2446
Greer, Curtis: 434
Greer, Frank: 2172
Greer, Simon: 90
Gregg, Bill: 1495
Gregg, Cody: 1536
Gregg, Ingrid A.: 1850
Gregori, Mina: 554
Greiner, Jon: 1886
Gresham, Karen: 516
Griego, Linda: 258
Grieman, Pam: 1061
Griffin, Farah: 399
Griffin, Jennifer: 777, 778, 779
Griffin, Robert H.: 24

Griffin, Walt, Dr.: 1759
Griffith, Christine: 1902
Grimm, Kimberly: 807
Grimond, J.J.: 960
Grindle, Merilee: 961
Groat, Lee A.: 2680
Grobman, Linda, Ed.D.: 1023
Grogan, Paul S.: 1185
Grooms, Tony: 661
Groover, Gregory G., Sr., Rev. Dr.: 1185
Gross, Patrick: 162
Gross, Thomas: 113
Grossman, Barbara W.: 472
Grossman, James R.: 578, 579, 580
Grossman, Pamela: 1588
Grotz, Jennifer: 668
Growald, Adam: 282
Grubb, Jeffrey T.: 241
Grubbe, Fred: 1891
Gruber, David P.: 339
Gruber, Nina: 942
Guastella, Tara: 2515
Guida, George: 601
Gullot, Richard, M.D.: 2399
Gund, Ann L.: 152
Gund, Catherine: 152
Gund, Geoffrey: 152
Gund, George, IV: 152
Gund, Zachary: 152
Guon, Jane M.: 257
Gurzenda, Jane G.: 1632
Gustafson, Daniel, Jr.: 2201
Guthrie, Carlton L.: 179
Guy, Joel: 456
Guy, Maria: 2632
Guynn, Jack: 323
Guzelimian, Ara: 766
Guzzo, Dorothy: 616

H

Haaga, Paul G., Jr.: 373
Haas, Andrew: 265
Haas, Christina: 265
Haas, David: 265
Haas, Frederick: 265
Haas, Janet, M.D.: 265
Haas, Leonard C.: 265
Haas, Thomas W.: 265
Hadder, Barton A.: 241
Haddon, Phoebe: 1270
Haden, Patrick C.: 1633
Haerizadeh, Yasi: 1935
Haffey, Suzanne: 1358
Haffizulla, Farzanna, M.D.: 2231
Hageman, Michael J., Ph.D.: 2306, 2310, 2540,
    2541, 2542, 2543
Hahn, Harold: 522
Hahn, Steven: 1926
Haims, Bruce D.: 653
Hair, Charles M., M.D.: 1448
Haisley, Jimmie Anne: 2038
Halas, Peter: 675, 851
Halbreich, Kathy: 107
Halby, Peter: 141
Halby, Will: 141
Haldeman, Charles E., Jr.: 1905
Hale, Elizabeth K., M.D.: 2447
Hale, Gloria: 1047
Hall, Cindy: 1103
Hall, H.L.: 1957
Hall, Katrinka: 162
Hall, Serena Davis: 94
Hallman, Elisabeth, R.N.: 1425
Hallock, Meloni M.: 1192
Hallock, Robert B.: 2041
Hallworth, Robert: 1700
Halper, Deborah E.: 1469
Halpern, Allan C., M.D.: 2447

Halpern, Daniel: 682
Halpert, David: 434
Halvorsen, Bradley W.: 128
Halvorson, Newman T., Jr.: 1327
Ham, Christina: 696
Hambrick, J.L.: 209
Hamill, Deirdre: 1853, 1854
Hamilton, Arthur: 754
Hamilton, Janet: 458
Hamilton, Lucy B.: 622
Hammack, John A.: 226
Hammer, Laurel: 1902
Hammer, Paul Allen, Dr.: 2120
Hammerle, Molly: 2134
Hammett, Edwin: 2182
Hammill, Donald D., Ed.D.: 994
Hammond, Ken: 2177
Hammond, Laura: 828
Hamner, Charles: 2067
Hampe, Michael: 798
Hampl, Patricia: 464
Hampton, Bonnie: 782
Hampton, Jami: 1358
Hamren, Robert: 401
Han, Wu: 766
Hancock, Dell: 2265
Handel, Nancy H.: 1376
Handy, Esther: 1510
Handy, Ned: 280
Hanenburg, Edward: 1283
Hanifin, Michael: 93
Hanke, C. William, M.D.: 2447
Hanlon, Tim: 1068
Hannan, Kathy: 1902
Hannum, Diane E.: 1737
Hanrahan, A.M.: 317
Hanrahan, Katherine: 265
Hanrahan, Tom: 1886
Hansell, Richard S., M.D.: 2500
Hansen, Ed: 2136
Hansen, Lisa D.: 247
Hanson, Jackson L.: 82
Hanson, William: 297
Hanssen, Marty Voelkel: 194
Haq, Bilal: 2087
Hara, Julia S.: 215
Harada, Shinji: 1606
Harbert, Raymond: 233
Hardcastle, Elizabeth: 799
Hardgrove, I.F.: 317
Hardin, P. Russell: 338, 1156
Harding, Jenny: 993
Haring, Rachel, Dr.: 968
Harman, Jane: 405
Harmer, Lynne: 2430
Harmon, John C., Esq.: 1350
Harris, Alex: 59
Harris, Donn: 437
Harris, E.B.: 194
Harris, Ed: 1047
Harris, Elmer B.: 233
Harris, George: 997
Harris, Henry U., III: 331
Harris, Jasmine B., Ed.D.: 1099
Harris, Kelly L.: 194
Harris, Linda: 2673
Harris, Lisa M.: 1034
Harris, Matthew: 463
Harris, Paul W.: 163
Harris, Richard: 1930
Harris, Skylar: 618, 620
Harris, Thomas: 194
Harris, W. Patrick: 58
Harrison, James, III: 427
Harrison, Wendy: 2505
Harsh, Edward: 783
Hartman, Sid: 217
Partnett, Laura: 1744
Hartsough, Jeff: 784
Hartung, Thomas: 1445

Hartwig, Charles: 1745
Hartwig, Melinda: 879
Harvey, Thomas B., Esq.: 103
Hashim, Nancy: 1353
Haskell-Hoehl, Micah: 2566
Haslanger, Kathryn D.: 1478
Haslanger, Sally: 400
Hastings, David R., III: 240
Hastings, Ken: 255
Hastings, Peter: 240
Hatch, Annie: 523
Hatch, Eliza: 230
Hatch, Ian: 230
Hatch, Whitney: 230
Hatchel, Linda: 504
Hatfield, Carol W.: 1214
Hatter, Richard V.: 151
Hatton, Katherine: 2275
Hauck, Michael: 2033
Hauptfuhrer, W. Barnes: 1274
Hauptman, Laurence, Dr.: 622
Havens, Louise A.: 301
Hawk, Marc: 77
Hawkins, Bruce E.: 77
Hawkins, Christopher R.: 1188
Hawkins, Jane: 2093
Hawley, Philip M.: 1631
Hay, Laura: 1902
Hayden, Steve: 2446
Hayes, Charles R.: 2677
Hayes, Denis: 2172
Haynes, John: 2099
Hazlewood, Patsy: 1227
Head, Denise, Ph.D.: 2483
Healy, J.J.: 2188
Healy, James T.: 322
Hearst, George R., Jr.: 1935
Hearst, John R., Jr.: 1935
Hearst, William R., III: 1935
Heck, C. Laurence: 1745
Heck, Vicki: 1661
Heckes, Scott William: 437
Heery, Brian: 1606
Hegarty, Michael: 151
Heintz, Stephen B.: 434
Heiss, Mary Ann: 2018
Heitz, Eric: 2176
Hejna, JoAnn: 1143
Helgeson, Caitlin: 1606
Heller, Barbara R., Ed.D., R.N.: 2495
Heller, Beth: 1121
Heller, Fanya Gottesfeld: 647, 648
Helman, William W.: 2446
Hempelmann, John: 173
Hemphill, Ross F.: 1868
Hemus, Simon: 65
Henahan, Julie S.: 492
Henan, Carmen: 1051
Henderson, Barclay G.: 157
Henderson, Frederick: 298
Henderson, Mary D.: 295
Henderson, Roberta: 157
Henkin, R.I.: 2331
Hennessy, Marilyn: 1009
Henney, Jane E., M.D.: 1478
Henning, Judy: 2134
Henriquez, Silvia: 141
Henry, Edward P.: 107
Herbert, Bradley: 1221
Herbert-Copley, Brent, Dr.: 1871, 1872, 1873, 1874, 1875, 1876
Herd, Karen: 1460
Herd-Barber, Jacqueline: 1291
Herda, Sarah: 417
Herlin, Cara P.: 1389
Herlin, Susan: 1389
Herling, Marta, Dr.: 600
Herman, Hattie: 2225, 2226, 2227
Hermocillo, Jose, M.D.: 1509
Hernandez, Antonia: 1192

Hernandez, David: 993
Herndon, Carol M.: 285
Herrell, John E.: 24
Herring, Paula: 226
Hershey, Tamara, Ph.D.: 2483
Herts, Ken: 1932
Herzan, Alexandra: 2594
Herzfield, Michael: 400
Herzog, Kelly: 1572
Hess, Ellen, Ph.D.: 2483
Hess, Jack: 2077
Hess, Judy: 461
Hessel, Carolyn Starman: 676, 677
Hessler, Deborah J.: 52
Hewitt, Chet P.: 1509
Hewlett, Walter B.: 159
Hiam, Alexander: 331
Hickenlooper, John: 440
Hickman, Waymon L., Sr.: 503
Hicks, John E., Jr.: 296
Hicks, Michael E.: 1342
Hicks, Pam: 461
Higginbotham, Susan, Ph.D., R.D.: 2427
Higgins-Jacob, Coleen P.: 151
Higgs, John H.: 1330
Hijkoop, Frans: 231
Hilbert, Robert J.: 115
Hilbrich, Gerald F.: 52
Hildebrand, Barbara: 777, 778, 779
Hiles, Clay: 2184
Hill, B. Harvey, Jr.: 323
Hill, Carol: 1420
Hill, Cleo: 141
Hill, Harry: 853
Hill, Jennifer: 274
Hill, Michael: 680
Hillas, Dee: 1146
Hiller, William T., Dr.: 1604
Hilliard, Landon: 2211
Hillman, David McL.: 1350
Hilton, Michael: 246
Hindle, Steve: 373
Hines, Anson H.: 2201
Hines, Sivan, Dr.: 1214
Hinojosa, Patricia: 297
Hinton, Stephen: 400
Hinton, Wade: 1227
Hioki, Warren, Ph.D.: 1477
Hirano Inouye, Irene: 129
Hirokane, Jeanie: 254
Hirsch, Edward: 151
Hirsch, Sanford: 550
Hittner, Kathleen C., M.D.: 280
Hixon, George C. (Tim): 2188
Hobson, Lincoln C.: 1995
Hochbaum, Jerry, Dr.: 820
Hodge, Gary: 1910
Hodges, Bill: 1171
Hoeschler, Linda: 809
Hofer, Annabel: 1886
Hofflund, Mark: 459
Hoffman, Eric: 2280
Holcombe, Paul A., Jr.: 1581
Holden, Richard S.: 1932
Holder, Wilhelmina: 1101
Holdredge, Margaret: 2646
Holefelder, Jack: 300
Holen, S.: 2331
Holender, Ioan: 798
Holl, Susan: 2664
Holland, Stacey: 450
Holley, Terry L.: 1121
Holliman, Vonda: 1562
Holloway, B. Scott: 2632
Holloway, Jon: 1374
Hollyn, Norman: 1962
Holm, Herbert F.: 52
Holman, John W., III: 167
Holman, John W., Jr.: 167
Holmes, Angie: 2221
Holmes, Deborah: 1082

Holmes, Edward A., Ph.D.: 850
Holmes, Gregory L., M.D.: 2465
Holmes, Robert: 1396
Holmes, Robert W., Jr.: 1585
Holtz, Heidi: 1279
Holyfield, Wayland: 666, 754
Holzer, Alan: 244
Homant, Susanne, Dr.: 969
Hombach, Robert: 35
Homes, A.M.: 443
Homstad, Torild: 949
Honan, James: 961
Honeycutt, Terri W.: 108
Hood, Chayse: 1079
Hoogland, Keith: 2367
Hook, Jonathan: 2041
Hooks, Brian: 1562
Hoone, Jeffrey: 553
Hooper, Kristen: 1460
Hoots, W. Keith: 2369
Hoover, Deborah D.: 1906
Hoover, Margaret: 900
Hoover, Robert A.: 168
Hoover, Susan: 1287
Hopkins, John F.: 1376
Hopkins, John P.: 1427
Hopkins, Michael P., M.D.: 2500
Hopkins-Powell, Sara: 1196
Horii, Akinari: 866
Horn, Philip: 495
Hornberger, J.D.: 796
Horne, David: 2284
Horne, Marilyn: 798
Hornsby, Timothy: 929
Horowitz, Roger: 593
Horowitz, Zach: 666
Horton, Alice K.: 191
Horton, Tom: 1603
Hotta, John: 531
Houck, Gayle L.: 251
Houk, Alice: 2240
House, Patricia A.: 159
Houser, Chet: 819
Houston, Melissa: 2277
Howard, Doris: 788
Howell, Mike, Dr.: 1806
Howell, Philip B.: 135
Howie, Barbara L.: 1486
Howitt, Robert: 1129
Howse, Jennifer L., Ph.D.: 2284
Hoy, Ronald R., Ph.D.: 2465
Hrabowski, Freeman A., III: 298
Hsu, Douglas Tong: 434
Huang, Mikiko, Dr.: 87
Hubbard, Jim: 2171, 2177
Hubbard, Molly Hipp: 504
Hubert, Laurent: 666
Hubner, Peter: 798
Hudes, Quiara Alegria: 1926
Hudiburg, Richard, Dr.: 1806
Hudson, Gilbert: 1302
Hudson, J. Clifford: 129
Hudson, Jerry E.: 72
Hudson, Joseph L., IV: 1302
Hudson, Joseph L., Jr.: 75, 1302
Huff, W. Cloyce, M.D.: 1448
Huffman, Richard L.: 285
Hughes, Chris: 193
Hughes, John, Dr.: 929
Hughes, Martha: 1089
Hughes, Pamela J.: 1603
Hughes, Robert: 1728, 1729
Hughes, Theresa: 2466
Hugle, Linda: 1196
Huguenin, Frank: 993
Huizen, Kristine L.: 134
Hull, John E.: 229
Hulme, David: 798
Humenik, John: 1957
Hummer, Philip Wayne: 122

Huneault, Philippe P.: 2434
Hunkeler, Mary: 2018
Hunt, Dennis: 1172
Hunt, Douglas: 35
Hunt, Gary H.: 1442
Hunt, Kathleen S., M.D.: 211
Hunt, Margaret: 440
Hunt, Richard H.: 1995
Hunt, Susan: 2134
Hunt, William E.: 1350
Hunte, Danista: 31
Hunter, Catrelia Steele, Dr.: 285
Hunter, Christina: 454
Hunter, Tammy: 1902
Hunter, Tony: 63
Hunting, Mary Anne: 307
Huntley, Lynn, Ms.: 1214
Huntley, Mary Lynn: 111
Hurd, Gale Anne: 524
Hurley, Cheryl: 552
Hurley, Lori: 2654
Hursh, Carolyn: 1420
Hurwitz, Kenneth: 1524
Huston, Charles L., III: 814
Hutcheson, Mary Ellen, CPA: 52
Hutcheson, Tad: 1214
Hutchison-Quillian, Jessan: 1510
Hutton, Matt: 457
Hwee, Koh Boon: 159
Hybl, Kyle H.: 115
Hybl, William J.: 115
Hylant, Richard: 2182
Hyman, Steven: 278
Hyman, Steven E., M.D.: 2254
Hyre, Stephanie: 1287

I

Ibarguen, Alberto: 193
Ibrahim, Todd: 706
Ichelberger, Alyssa: 105
Iguchi, Debra: 199
Ilitch, Denise: 297
Imber, Margaret: 400
Imboden, Connie E.: 435
Immens, Kirk: 2177
Immerwahr, John, Dr.: 2026
Ingram, Robert A.: 1581
Innamorato, Lou: 2575
Ions, Sharon R.: 6
Ireland, Jay: 2446
Ireland, Steve: 2466
Irti, Natalino, Prof.: 600
Irwin, John N., III: 5, 46
Irwine, Janet: 879
Ishii, Paul: 1603
Ishiyama, Patsy: 2188
Iskander, Sameh: 879
Isler, William H.: 1126
Ito, Alice: 1510
Ito, Joichi: 193
Itsweire, Eric: 2087
Ittleson, H. Anthony: 1488
Ittleson, H. Philip: 1488
Ittleson, Stephanie: 1488
Ivens, Barbara J.: 1125
Ivers, Jim: 1603
Ivers, Mary: 321
Iverson, Brent: 2041
Ives, Deborah M.: 332
Ivey, Robert: 411

J

Jacks, Elizabeth, Rev.: 1473
Jackson, Cade: 1374
Jackson, David D., Hon.: 1384
Jackson, Gayle P.W.: 2041

Jackson, Gene: 77
Jackson, Helen H.: 173
Jackson, Mark H.: 1932
Jacobs, Barbara: 2466
Jacobson, Lana: 1283
Jacobson, Michael F., Ph.D.: 2670
Jaffe, Mary H.: 159
James, Barbara L.: 1309
James, Christopher M.: 2188
James, Holly M.: 221
James, Thomas: 1034
James-Brown, Christine: 1127
Jameson, Jorene: 1527
Jameson, William: 142
Jamison, Nelle: 1405
Jamison, Stephanie: 542
Janes, David P.: 866
Janowitz, Henry D., M.D.: 2412
Janssen, Daniel: 900
Januzik, Michael J.: 1308
Jaquay, Robert B.: 152
Jardine, Drew: 595
Jarvis, John: 2190
Jarvis, Sonia: 1130
Jaskow, Paul L.: 2042
Jayas, Digvir, Dr.: 1460
Jeanotte, Darrell: 1047
Jeavons, Thomas H.: 111
Jebsen, Hans Michael: 434
Jefferson, Charmaine: 437
Jenkins, Meredith: 2026
Jenkins-Scott, Jackie: 1185
Jenne, Ann K.: 2220
Jennings, Dee: 1371
Jennings, J. Webb, III: 68
Jenny, Patricia: 244
Jethrow, K.L.: 209
Jewell, Sally, Hon.: 2190
Jewett, Jack B.: 128
Jobe, Warren: 323
Jodock, Darrell H.: 809
Joh, Erik Edward: 1641
Johannsen, Tonya: 1099
Johns, Richard P.: 1957
Johnson, Alan C.: 1117
Johnson, Alex: 2506
Johnson, Arik, Psy.D.: 2466
Johnson, Carol: 1588
Johnson, Craig C.: 1117
Johnson, Derrick: 26
Johnson, Douglas R.: 2038
Johnson, Eric C.: 1117
Johnson, Erik S.: 338, 1156
Johnson, Eugene: 1699
Johnson, Henry P.: 2280
Johnson, Holly: 1283
Johnson, James: 1274
Johnson, Kate L.: 58
Johnson, Ken: 2182
Johnson, Louise U.: 1735
Johnson, Marcia K.: 2576
Johnson, Mark L.: 58
Johnson, Nancy: 1160
Johnson, Nicole: 1606
Johnson, Paula, M.D.: 333
Johnson, Preston L.C.: 1192
Johnson, Robert L., M.D.: 1396
Johnson, Ruth Sieber: 790
Johnson, Samuel, Jr.: 1376
Johnson, Sheila B.: 58
Johnson, Si: 1309
Johnson, Warren, M.D.: 1427
Johnson, William: 748
Johnston, Rowena, Ph.D.: 1812
Jolly, Penny: 2136
Jones, Bill, Dr.: 1759
Jones, Eddie E., Jr., Rev.: 111
Jones, Edrea: 1338
Jones, Evan G.: 1507
Jones, Gary: 1099

Jones, Gavin: 400
Jones, John P., III: 1458
Jones, Mary Duke Trent: 108
Jones, Orville: 1405
Jones, Paul Tudor, II: 2188
Jones, Stephen, Dr.: 1759
Jones, Tim: 483
Jones-Fulp, Jewel: 495
Jordan, J. Craig: 271
Jordan, Rhonda: 297, 1700
Jordan, William C.: 383
Jorgensen, Albert T.: 1160
Jorgensen, Judy: 1291
Joseph, Erica: 1239
Joseph, Jessica: 2422, 2423
Joskow, Paul L.: 298
Joyce, William: 1215
Jreisat, Wijdan, Esq.: 1285
Justis, Cleveland: 217

K

Kacic, Edward B.: 1442
Kadinger, Suzanne: 1233
Kagan, Ute Wartenberg, Dr.: 582
Kahn, Daniel L.: 497
Kain, Herbert, M.D.: 2334
Kaiser, David: 282
Kalama, Corbett A.K.: 59
Kallaus, Kurt J.: 1513
Kallenborn, John: 595
Kalra, Sarah A.: 167
Kammerer, Janeen: 1288
Kandarian, Steven A.: 2446
Kane, Alice: 2483
Kaplan, Mary E.: 182
Kaplan, Richard D.: 182
Kaplan, Robert: 25
Kaplan, Robert S.: 129
Kapono, Clifford P.: 456
Kapp, Barbara: 548
Kappner, Augusta Souza: 329
Karanth, Ullas: 2173
Karriem, Sandra: 1583
Kasabach, Chris: 1647
Kaszubowski, Kristen: 1215
Katcher, Jane Frank, Dr.: 622
Katz, Molly A., M.D.: 1285
Katzenberg, Susan B.: 1281
Kaufman, Harriet: 783
Kautzmann, Elizabeth: 2616
Kavanaugh, Kevin: 1460
Kawaguchi, Yoriko: 866
Kay, Dean: 666, 754
Kayafas, Peter: 443
Kean, Thomas H., Hon.: 2275
Keane, James: 307
Keane, Joe: 276
Keane, John: 246
Kearney, Chris: 1274
Kearney, Daniel P.: 179
Keating, Michael: 1185
Keator, William C.: 94
Kee, Dorothy Davis: 94
Kee, Dorothy Given: 94
Keegan, Marissa: 2579
Keene, Margaret: 293
Keene, Steve: 1160
Keilty, Nancy B.: 29
Keith, Stephen N., M.D., M.S.P.H.: 2296
Keithline, Elizabeth: 497
Keleher, John: 1023
Kelleher, Jeanette: 1121
Keller, Donald: 913
Keller, John R.: 531
Keller, Robert A.: 1376
Keller, Sean: 417
Kelley, Darcy, Dr.: 2026
Kelley, James P.: 2188

Kelley, Thomas: 322
Kelly, Bob: 1369
Kelly, Carolyn T.: 417
Kelly, John F., III: 2632
Kelly, Nancy C.: 2265
Kelly, Thomas F., Dr.: 2038
Kelly, Tim: 1227
Kelly, William P.: 151
Kelmar, Steven B.: 6
Kemp, J.L.: 1745
Kemp, Mary: 1143
Kempner, Hetta T.: 185
Kempner, Randall: 185
Kenan, Thomas S., III: 108
Kendrick, James M.: 666, 754
Kennedy, James O.: 211
Kennedy, Jan: 241
Kennedy, Kevin W.: 329
Kennedy, Mary: 475
Kennedy, Michelle: 1904
Kennedy, Parker S.: 1633
Kennedy, Stuart: 234
Kenny, Maugha: 2026
Kent, Kenneth: 169
Kenyon, Robert W.: 1632
Kenyon, William W.: 1632
Keohane, Nannerl O.: 107
Kerr, Cody T.: 187
Kerr, Guy H.: 37
Kerr, Robert S., Jr., Mrs.: 187
Kerr, Sheryl V.: 188
Kerr, Steven: 187
Kezer, C. Henry: 36
Khalaf, Michel: 231
Khalil, Mark: 1610
Khandpur, A.K.: 317
Khargonekar, Pramod: 2655
Khaw, Kay-Tee, Prof.: 960
Khodakhah, Kamran, Ph.D.: 2465
Kidd, Elizabeth: 78
Kiefer, Markell: 215
Kieler, Charles: 622
Kieling, Nancy W.: 1351
Kiernan, Eaddo H.: 2188
Kilgannon, Thomas: 1691
Kim, Byung: 1117
Kim, Peter S., Ph.D.: 298
Kimball, Kristi: 290
Kimball, Robert: 754
Kimelman, Don: 265
Kind, Christina K.: 2594
Kind, Kenneth A.: 2594
Kind, Patricia: 2594
Kind-Rubin, Valerie: 2594
Kindfuller, Andrew: 2594
King, David C.: 3
King, Judith S.: 1512
King, Kathy: 58
King, Mary E.: 21
King, Michael J.: 139
King, Roberta F.: 150
King, W. Winburne, III: 1868
Kingsley, Suzanne: 622
Kinkel, Laurie Latuda: 1281
Kinney, Jeff: 993
Kinney, Kase: 1204
Kinoshita, June: 2264
Kinsela, Susan: 1745
Kirby, F.M.: 191
Kirby, Jefferson W.: 191
Kirby, Nancy J.: 103
Kirby, S. Dillard: 191
Kirby, Walker D.: 191
Kirk, Jeffrey: 461
Kirkland, John: 929
Kirkpatrick, Frederick S.: 1333
Kirkpatrick, Marcie: 2483
Kirr, Laurie: 793
Kirschen, David: 2505
Kirsic, Mike: 2575

Kirstein, David: 1820
Kisleiko, Irene M.: 274
Kitaoka, Shin'ichi, Dr.: 866
Kitts, Tracy: 2505
Klaassens, Jen: 330
Klein, Adam: 531
Kleiner, Charlene C.: 376
Kleinmann, Rami: 1628, 1673
Klepser, Colleen B.: 1818
Klesa, J. Michael: 2120
Kleven, C.F.: 317
Klindera, Kent: 1812
Klingenstein, Andrew D.: 2580
Klingenstein, Kathy: 2580
Klingenstein, Susan: 2580
Klingenstein, Thomas D.: 2580
Klippel, John, Dr.: 2450
Klos, Diana Mitsu: 1932
Klose, Donna D.: 2399
Knauf, Noah: 2446
Knecht, Alex: 1611
Knight, David: 2171
Knight, Michael A.: 522
Knight, Peter: 2190
Knight, R.M., Jr.: 325
Knighton, Maurine: 90
Knopp, Paul: 1902
Knott, Erin: 194
Knott, Marion I.: 194
Knott, Martin G., Jr.: 194
Knott, Martin G., Sr.: 194
Knott, Owen M.: 194
Knott, Teresa A.: 194
Knowles, Marie: 293
Knutson, John: 961
Koblik, Steven: 373
Kochard, Lawrence: 2211
Koerth-Baker, Maggie: 1930
Kohn, Herb M.: 2018
Kojima, J. Christopher: 434
Kollbaum, Pete: 2505
Kollerstrom, Hanna: 401
Kollmann, Nancy: 854
Konecky, Isobel Robins: 534, 2482
Kono, Taro: 866
Konsgaard, Martha: 2172
Kook, Teri: 1147
Koonce, Shannon: 2644
Koraleski, J.J.: 325
Kordsmeier, John: 1340
Korf, Gene R., Esq.: 203
Korf, Scott: 203
Korgenski, Marcy: 1886
Kornberg, Alan: 783
Kortenhaus, Lynne: 548
Kortjohn, Martin D.: 2120
Kortkamp, Sue Ann: 1995
Kosman, Susan, R.N., B.S.N.: 6
Kosmin, Ruth: 929
Kotik, Charlotta: 550
Kovner, Victor: 2173
Kozberg, Joanne Corday: 1192
Kozmetsky, Cynthia H.: 1358
Kozmetsky, Daniel A.: 1358
Kozmetsky, Gregory A.: 1358
Kramer, Larry: 159
Kramer, Mary L.: 297
Kramer, Sarah A.: 817
Krarup, Irene: 2088
Krasney, Marty: 80
Krauss, Judith B., R.N.: 2280
Krcevinac, Gordana: 1871, 1872, 1873, 1874, 1875, 1876
Kreamer, Janice C.: 65
Kreider, Matthew S.: 1513
Kresa, Kent: 1631
Kridler, Douglas F.: 1210
Krieger, John B.: 5, 46
Kristal, Elliot B.: 1308
Krohn, S.D.: 317

References in index are to entry numbers.

Kronick, Susan D.: 193
Kropf, Susan J.: 329
Krosnick, Joel: 782
Krumboltz, Ann: 2170
Kruse, Dennis K., USN (Ret.), Capt.: 2647
Krystal, Solomon: 647, 648
Kubasak, Thomas F.: 322
Kuechle, Scott: 1548
Kuechler, Henry N., III: 47
Kuehner, Carl R., III: 2188
Kuhn, Jennifer: 246
Kulik, Julie: 2646
Kummer, Robert W., Jr.: 1633
Kundert, David: 1291
Kuntch, Jennifer: 1273
Kupatt, Wolf: 35
Kupper, Thomas, M.D.: 2327
Kuriloff, Josh N.: 1469
Kurth, Robert: 669
Kurtz, Cindy: 2483
Kutzer-Rice, Rebecca: 706
Kvamme, Jean: 1563
Kyvik, Gordon: 1583

L

Labalme, George, Jr.: 366
Labelle, Nathalie, C.A., B.A.A.: 2434
LaBret, Aileen: 2134
LaCamera, Paul: 1185
Ladiner, Kathy: 246
Laffont, Ingrid C.: 47
Lalle, Frank A.: 1425
Lam, Khee Poh: 2176
LaMarche, Gara: 1090
Lamb, Tanya: 1603
Lambert, Peter: 246
Lambert, Rebecca: 282
Lambert, Thomas W.: 1969
Lamenza, Dana M.: 1126
Lampert, Alan G.: 1131
Lampkin, Joy: 234
Lampland, Martha: 854
Lanahan, Martha T.: 111
Lancaster, Olin, III: 226
Landenberger, Brett: 357
Landers, Matt: 993
Landers, Richard: 55
Landes, Andrea: 1478
Landesman, Debby: 1495
Landy, Laura K.: 2322
Lane, Charles: 101
Lane, Jackie: 1121
Lang, Barbara: 1327
Lang, Bill: 1160
Lang, Keith H.: 61
Lange, David: 2071
Lange, Heidi, C.R.H.A.: 2434
Lange, Michael: 523
Langenbeck, Sharon: 2059
Langford, George M., Ph.D.: 2465
Langlais, Martin: 2434
Langlois, Marie: 280
Langstaff, David: 162
Langstaff, John, Dr.: 1460
Langston, Christopher A.: 155
Lanier, Linda L.: 24
Lanier, Richard S.: 434
Lanphear, Gail E.: 2443
Lapidus, Ira: 472
Lapin, Chava, Dr.: 647, 648
Lapore, Julie: 754
Lara, Alicia: 1090
Larkin, Heather: 1172
Larkin, Richard, C.P.A.: 2465
Larmer, Robin: 993
Larson, Carol S.: 258
Larson, Tim: 1291
Lashley, Elinor: 814

Laslie, Susan: 1661
Latham, Don: 714, 715
Lauder, Laura: 254
Lauderbach, William C.: 2443
Launoit, Count Jean-Pierre de: 787
Laurence, Anna Marie: 173
Lavers, J.R.: 317
Lavin, A. Gary, D.V.M.: 2265
Lavizzo-Mourey, Risa, M.D., M.B.A.: 2275
Lawrence, Myra: 1215
Lawrence, Priscilla: 595
Lawrence, Timothy: 35
Lawson, Anna L.: 2211
Lawson, Bill: 2558
Layton, Thomas C.: 1394
Lazarof, Janice Taper: 313
Lebovitz, Alison G.: 211
LeClerc, Paul: 229
Lederman, Stephanie: 2225, 2226, 2227
Lee, Andrew: 2120
Lee, Andrew J.: 6
Lee, Dwight E.: 151
Lee, Kristi K.: 1282
Lee, Linda: 463
Lee, Moses: 241
Lee, Nancy: 1509
Lee, Paul W.: 1185
Lefer Kuhn, Anna: 21
LeFevour, Suzanne A.: 1191
Leffall, LaSalle D., Jr.: 54
Leffall, LaSalle D., Jr., M.D.: 2254
Lefko, Allen L.: 2018
Legendra, Yasmine, MPA: 2280
Leggin, Jessica: 136
Lehman, John F., Hon.: 536
Leibold, Peter M., Esq.: 1458
Leighton, Katherine M.: 215
Leith, Jennifer: 103
Lella, Danielle: 2179
Lelyveld, Katie McCormick: 179
Leman, Drew: 1995
Lenhart, Wendy: 2136
Lenihan, Terry: 437
Lenkowsky, Leslie: 5, 46
Lent, Michael: 1130
Leon, Mercedes: 244
Leon, Tania: 767
Leonard, John P., M.D.: 2367
Leonard, Stephanie: 190
Leong, Amye L., MBA: 1419
Leppanen, Karen L.: 75
Lerchbacher, K.A.: 209
Lescaze, Alexandra: 1936
Leshner, Alan I., Dr.: 1921
Leslie, Thomas G.: 748
Lessin, Stuart R., M.D.: 2255
Levell, Linda S.: 461
Levens, Marie: 856
Levenson, Robert W.: 2576
Leventhal, Alan M.: 2446
Leventhal, Nathan: 766
Leverett, Larry: 1583
Leversage, Jill: 1471
Levey, Sharron: 798
Levin, Rachel: 1010
Levin, Richard: 159
Levine, Arlene: 2482
Levine, Arthur: 1804
Levine, Dena: 993
Levine, Richard J.: 1932
Levine, Ruth: 647, 648
Levinson, Patricia S.: 1469
Levit, Nicole: 860
Levy, L.M.: 2331
Levy, Leeds: 666
Levy, Reynold: 278
Levy, Ronald, M.D.: 2446
Levy, Sarah: 997
Lew, Ginger: 1327
Lewin, Daniel: 1376

Lewis, Alison M., Ph.D.: 716
Lewis, Anne: 1350
Lewis, Claudette R.: 1350
Lewis, David Baker: 297
Lewis, David F., M.D.: 2500
Lewis, Denise J.: 222
Lewis, Earl: 229
Lewis, Jenny: 189
Lewis, Karen: 55
Lewis, Liza: 504
Lewis, Mary Ellen: 1910
Lewis, Philip E.: 229
Li, Philip: 1207
Lichtman, Jeff, Ph.D.: 2465
Lieberg, Marlaina: 1656
Liebman, Michael N., Ph.D.: 2306, 2310, 2540, 2541, 2542, 2543
Lifton, Robert B.: 268
Liggett, James: 1491
Lightman, Bernard: 597
Lilly, Eli, II: 206
Lima, Ricardo: 262
Limbaugh, L. Hunter: 2403
Limerick, Patricia Nelson: 635
Lin, Leisle: 298, 2042
Lin, William, Ph.D.: 175
Lincoln, Edward, Dr.: 853
Lindeloff, Stephanie: 2182
Linder, Maureen: 55
Lindsey, Melvin D.: 1192
Linebarger, Tom: 91
Linnert, Terrence: 1548
Linsley, Sarah: 122
Linstaedt, Axel: 753
Lintilhac, Crea S.: 2174
Lintilhac, Philip M., Dr.: 2174
Linton, Roxanne: 1215
Lintott, James W.: 866
Linz, Susan: 854
Lipschutz, Neal: 1932
Lipton, Harvey: 1935
Lipton-Ormand, Eva: 703
Lisher, Mary K.: 206
Litterman, Robert: 298
Little, Dan: 288
Littlefield, Diane: 1509
Littleton, Jeff: 2650
Littman, Baruch S.: 1308
Liu, Erh-fei: 434
Liu, Jackie: 564
Liverett, Deborah: 1338
Livingston, David M., M.D.: 2446
Llewellyn, David: 111
Lloyd, Alan: 2176
Lloyd, James: 1273
Lloyd, Robin: 1930
Lockamy, Terry: 279
Lockman, Carol Ressler: 593
Lockridge, B. Russell: 1189, 2171
Loeb, John L., Jr.: 904
Loeb, Marshall: 2482
Loewe, Nancy: 189
Loft, Richard M., M.D.: 1448
Loftis, Jim: 288
Lofton, Thomas M.: 206
Logan, Jeffrey: 2182
Logan, Lyle: 122
Lomax, Michael L., Ph.D: 1035
Lombardo, Maria, Dr.: 1477
London, Ed: 754
London, George, Mrs.: 798
Lonergan, James A.: 2581
Looney, Wilton D.: 338
Loosbrock, Julie: 97
Lopez, David P., Ed.D.: 1376
Lopez, Donald S., Jr.: 377
Lopez, Lazaro: 2616
Lopez, Lourdes: 129
Lopez, Maria: 729, 962
Lopez, Mauricio: 961

Lopez-Hagen, Nicole: 80
Lorimer, Linda Koch: 1905
Loring, Valerie S.: 1512
Love, Jamie, Ms.: 2253
Lovejoy, Mary F.: 280
Loveman, Gary: 1620
Lovett, Tiffany W.: 1333
Lovgren, Britta, Dr.: 401
Lowe, Elizabeth: 262
Lowery, Curtis L., M.D.: 2500
Lowet, Henry A.: 997
Lowry, Glenn D.: 229
Lozada, Jaime, D.D.S.: 2341
Lozano, Monica L.: 332
Lubar, David: 1291
Lubchenco, Jane: 258
Lubi, Bev: 1204
Lucas, Charles C., III: 108
Lucas, Stuart: 1147
Luce, Dena: 708
Ludovici, Jennifer: 1648
Ludwick, Adriane, Dr.: 1806
Ludwick, Brent: 794
Luedeke, J. Barton: 1735
Lui, Earl: 1425
Lujan, James: 1047
Luksenburg, Harvey, M.D.: 2369
Lumpkin, John R., M.D.: 2275
Lund, Jay: 1166
Lundberg, Jan M., Ph.D.: 2306, 2540, 2541,
    2542, 2543
Lundgren, Jan, Dr.: 543
Lundmark, Fredrik, Dr.: 401
Lungren, Dan: 1633
Lunzer, Bernard J.: 1950
Lustbader, Ken: 182
Lutz, Theodore C.: 149
Lux, Mike: 21
Luzzi, Richard D.: 333
Lykins, Elizabeth Welch: 307
Lynch, Allen C.: 951
Lynch, Andrew: 254
Lynch, Kathleen: 370
Lynch, Robert K.: 185
Lynde, Lisa W.: 1204
Lyons, Barbara: 675

M

Ma, Yo-Yo: 766
Mabie, James W.: 268
Mabry, Rhett N.: 108
MacArthur, John R.: 1491
MacCall, Steven: 714, 715
MacCowatt, Thomas H.: 167
Macdonald, Anne F.: 1376
MacDonald, John A.: 2018
Macdonald, Margaret: 226
MacDonald, Martin: 2177
MacFie, Valerie A.: 302
Mach, John R., Jr., M.D.: 155
Machiorlatti, Jennifer: 1962
Machtley, Ronald K., Hon.: 280
Mack, John W.: 332
Mackie, Peter: 2616
Mackliff, Tatiana: 1596
Maclachlan, Patricia, Dr.: 853
MacLean, Walter, Dr.: 2663
Maclellan, Hugh O., Jr.: 214
MacLeod, Hazel: 1702
Macrae, Jim: 1467
Madden, Frank H.: 850
Madigan, Shirley R.: 460
Madison, Paula: 2296
Madison-Graham, Carol: 929
Madonna, Richard: 2505
Maes, Dennis: 115
Maes, John: 1160
Maestas, Steve: 1160

Maffitt, James S.: 188
Magann, Everett F., M.D.: 2500
Magill, Sherry P., Ph.D.: 111
Magness, Rita Chua: 2220
Magnotta, Melenie O.: 6
Maguire, James: 230
Mahon, Lisa: 2563
Mahoney, Betty L.: 512
Mahoney, Hildegarde E.: 2254
Mai, Vincent: 434
Maine, Lucinda: 2534
Majka, Deborah M.: 1655
Major, Donata Russell: 1214
Makupson, Amyre: 297
Malanga, Anthony, M.D.: 2399
Maldonado, Roger J.: 244
Malesardi, Doris: 622
Maling, Joan: 659
Malone, Daniel J.: 82
Malone, David: 1350
Manapat-Sims, Maria Cristina: 866
Mancini, Gabriello: 745
Mancini, Ginny: 754
Mancino, Douglas M., Esq.: 1442
Mandel, Johnny: 754
Mandeville, Josephine C.: 81
Manduca, Cathy: 2080
Mandujano, Gabriel: 1270
Maness, Michael: 193
Mangan, Stephen: 1344
Mangold, Robert: 550
Mangum, Ken: 1536
Manji, Ambreena, Dr.: 901
Mann, Claude: 782
Mann, Linda: 1795
Mann, Lucy Rowan: 782
Mann, Nicholas: 782
Mann, Robert: 782
Mannard, K. Kelly: 1338
Manocherian, Jeffrey: 792
Mansfield, Elizabeth C.: 383
Mansfield, Todd: 1274
Manson, Bonita: 2674
Mansur, Susan C.: 36
Mantz, Jeffrey: 2021
Mapp, Karen: 1487
Marble, Jeff: 2177
Marcantonio, Maria: 278
Marchand, Victoria: 185
Marcial, Julio: 1425
Marciniak, Sarah M.: 1204
Marcum, Deanna, Dr.: 853
Mardigian, Ron: 524
Mares, Donald: 1427
Marin, Cheech: 1068
Marin, Robert: 1583
Marini, Joy: 175
Marion, Ken, Dr.: 1806
Maris, Mahlon: 1172
Mark, Peter: 798
Mark, Reuben: 2188
Markey, Michael: 482
Markham, Leah: 1330
Marks, James S., M.D., M.P.H.: 2275
Marks, Regina M.: 1458
Marlar, Donald F.: 40
Marmor, Max: 552
Maroney, Mary P.: 1756
Maroon, Joseph: 2211
Marquier, Katia: 2434
Marra, Ken: 1420
Marrett, Cora, Dr.: 2655
Marrow, Deborah: 549
Marsh, Gordon: 550
Marshall, David G.: 2446
Marshall, Lydia Micheaux: 273
Marshall, Thurgood, Jr.: 129
Martahus, Craig R., Esq.: 70
Martell, Sally Klingenstein: 2580
Martin, James R.: 247

Martin, Jim: 1273
Martin, Luther N.: 257
Martin, Marya: 783
Martin, Rebecca: 549
Martin, Robert, Dr.: 1051
Martin, Robert F.: 2680
Martin, Theodore E.: 65
Martin, Wayne: 490
Martin, Webb F.: 1333
Martineau, Sylviane: 442
Martinez, Claudio: 1185
Martinez, Jorge: 193
Martinez, Juan: 193
Martinez, Melanie: 1191
Martinez, Rick, M.D.: 175
Martinez, Sandra J.: 1425
Martinez, Teresa: 725
Martino, Mary S.: 251
Martonyi, Marissa: 2575
Marx, Robert: 286
Marx, Robert O.: 536
Mashburn, Harry L.: 2632
Masi, Tony, Prof.: 1420
Masiello, Kate: 1215
Mason, Betsy: 1930
Mason, E. Ann: 1702
Mason, Kathleen B.: 1850
Mason, Linda: 258
Mason, Marcus: 1027
Mason, Michael: 1691
Mason Wilgis, Linda: 173
Masor, Harold J.: 1308
Massey, Harvey: 52
Masson, Rick: 1502
Masters, Seth J.: 2026, 2027, 2028, 2029
Masters, Suzette Brooks: 182
Matchett, Terri: 29
Mathias, Allen W., Jr., M.D.: 2581
Mathieson, Ann: 217
Mathieson, Peter F.: 1190
Mathis, Will: 1528
Mathison, Dani: 330
Matney, Addy: 1457
Matsukado, Ann: 59
Matteliano, Cara: 1215
Matthews, Allan: 239
Mattingly, Rich: 2413
Mattioli, Maurizio: 600
Mattoon, Peter M., Esq.: 1023
Maulik, Dev, M.D., Ph.D.: 2500
Maurer, Gilbert C.: 1935
Maxson, Robert C., Ed.D.: 1419
Maxwell, Petra: 488
Maxwell, Scott E.: 2576
Mayer, Charles B.: 47
Mayes, Kris: 2176
Mayfield, Pinkie: 149
Maynard, Olivia P.: 1333
Mazany, Terry: 1206
Mazmanian, Daniel A.: 1631
Mazurkiewicz, Gerard, C.P.A.: 1215
Mazzotta, Alejandro: 2673
McAleer, Linda: 2477, 2478
McAllister, Megan: 1163
McAuley, Bob: 2367
McAvoy, Laura K., Esq.: 1448
McBride, Catherine: 1101
McBride, James: 754
McCabe, Edward R.B., M.D., Ph.D.: 2284
McCaffrey, Eileen: 1544
McCarter, Fred: 1251
McCarthy, Ann M.: 251
McCarthy, Margaret M.: 6
McCartney, Doug: 1536
McCarty, Kathleen: 2008, 2009
McClamroch, Michael: 1121
McClement, Susan, Dr.: 1460
McCleskey, Edwin, Ph.D.: 2465
McClung, Lindsay: 1279
McClure, Margaret, Ed.D., R.N.: 2495

McClymont, Mary: 273
McConn, Margaret E., C.P.A.: 283
McCormack, Elizabeth: 2041
McCormack, Elizabeth J.: 434
McCormack, Kristen J.: 1129
McCormack, William M., M.D.: 850
McCoy, Carol L., Chancellor: 503
McCoy, Michael K.: 226
McCrary, Charles D.: 2188
McCullough, P. Mike: 226
McCurdy, Lyn: 1536
McCutchen, Woodrow: 65
McCutcheon, Maureen T.: 167
McDaniel, Mark, Dr.: 669
McDaniel, Nelson: 183
McDermott, Carol Mentor: 1442
McDermott, James, Rep.: 853
McDonald, Brian: 194
McDonald, Cheryl: 1360
McDonald, James P.: 1184
McDonald, Jim: 12
McDonald, Kristen: 297
McDonald, Meghan: 194
McDonald, Pamela E.: 794
McDonald, Pat: 142
McDonald, Patty: 1283
McDonald, Thomas: 1700
McDonell, Lillian: 993
McDonnell, Alicia S.: 221
McDonnell, James S., III: 221
McDonnell, Jeffrey M.: 221
McDonnell, John F.: 221
McDonnell, Kilian, O.S.B., Father: 809
McDonough, Colleen: 754
McDonough, Kathleen A., Ph.D.: 2399
McDowell, Deborah E.: 407
McFall, Gardner: 443
McFate, Robert W.: 2311
McFayden, Barbara Nicholson: 1126
McGaffey, Jere D.: 27
McGee, Thomas R., Jr.: 2018
McGeogh, Ed: 54
McGill, Peter: 194
McGinn, Deborah: 1127
McGinn, Michael: 1510
McGinness, James J.: 211
McGinnis, Jim: 1552
McGonigle, Catherine: 128
McGovern, Dawn: 1338
McGowan, Daniel T.: 2296, 2450
McGrath, Christina: 115
McGrath, Don J.: 2188
McGraw, Harold, III: 1905
McGraw, Robert P.: 1905
McGuire, Kent: 1583
McGuire, Patricia: 54
McGuirt, Milford: 1902
McHale, Patrick J.: 1282
McHenry, Ray: 246
McHenry, Stacy: 29
McHugh, Katherine S.: 53
McInnis, Alaska: 1215
McIntosh, James C.: 59, 1601
McJunkin, Donald R.: 220
McKee, Joan H.: 30
McKenna, Deborah J.: 301
McKenna, Laura K.: 2594
McKeown, Jean: 1215
McKinnon, Nora: 1191
McKinstry, Gregory J.D.: 1471
McKissack, Cheryl Mayberry: 101
McKissic, James: 1227
McLanahan, Barbara: 464
McLaughlin-Korologos, Ann: 2254
McLean, Diana L.: 223
McLean, Helen: 1996
McLean, Julianne N.: 155
McLean, Sandra L.: 223
McLean, Susannah: 223
McLean, Will: 223

McLendon, Heath: 938
McLeod, George E.: 1172
McMahan, Quynh-Anh: 283
McMeel, John P.: 2018
McMichael, R. Daniel: 2014
McMillan, Bev: 1160
McMullen, Larry L.: 2018
McNairy, John O.: 279
McNamara, James: 1068
McNeil-Miller, Karen: 1503
McNeill, Robert: 1700
McNeill, Shalene, Ph.D.: 2675
McNiff, Audrey A.: 155
McNutt, Thomas: 142
McParland, Nathaniel P., M.D.: 1009
McPhail, Irving Pressley, Dr.: 2616
McPheeters, Paul C., Rev.: 36
McPherson, Michael: 1588
McReynolds, Scott: 1285
McShane, Kelly Sweeney: 250
McShepard, Randell: 152
McTier, Charles H.: 338, 1156
Mead, Leslie: 1247
Meador, David E.: 1302
Meadows, Amy M.: 37
Meadows, Karen L.: 226
Meadows, Lori: 465
Meadows, Robert A.: 226
Meares, Tracey L.: 179
Mecene, Virginie: 531
Medina, Felipe: 961
Medina, Kol: 1313
Medure, Patrick: 216
Meehan, Edward F., M.P.H.: 1458
Meeks, Tamalon: 297
Meers, Wyman: 552
Meeusen, Richard: 2182
Megan, Chris: 2177
Megonigal, Patrick: 2201
Mehlhaff, Paul: 501
Meier, Deborah: 1583
Meighen, M.A., Q.C., Hon.: 2141
Meissel, Franz-Stefan, Dr.: 942
Meissner, Rose: 1236
Melamed, Carol: 149
Melamed, Leo: 647, 648
Meller, Patricia: 1349
Melmed, Matthew E.: 1150
Mendelson, Andrew: 1940
Mendez, Ernesto, Dr.: 2174
Mendillo, Jane: 1185
Mengebier, David G.: 82
Mengel, Andrea: 2491
Mengert, Carl: 798
Menon, Vatsala: 2646
Menzi, Robert: 2188
Merchant, Kathryn E.: 1285
Mercier, Monique: 2434
Merck, Elliott: 230
Merck, Wilhelm: 230
Meredith, Patricia A.: 1442
Mergenhagen, Holly, Esq.: 1215
Merhoff, Theodore L.: 83
Merin, Kenneth D.: 1129
Merkel, Joel C.: 173
Merklin, Karen: 523
Meserve, Lauren: 2026
Meserve, Richard A.: 1816
Messinger, Dwight F.: 285
Metallo, Steven, Dr.: 2066
Metras, Claire: 442
Metzger, William L.: 1189
Meurs, Mieke: 854
Meyer, Jack: 1185
Meyer, Jeff: 1211
Meyer, Mary, Esq.: 1201
Meyers, Amy: 408
Meyers, Bob: 1949
Meyers, Howard: 265
Meyers, Jack: 632

Meyerson, Marvin: 1009
Meystre, Douglas Q.: 10
Michalak, Mary Jane: 1699
Mickiewicz, Ellen, Dr.: 2026
Mihm, J. Christopher: 1855
Milano, Bernard J.: 1902
Miller, Aishah: 1146
Miller, Ann T.: 105
Miller, Chris: 1358
Miller, Clara: 1207
Miller, Dana L.: 241
Miller, Duane: 2654
Miller, Edith D.: 1023
Miller, Edmund: 179
Miller, Jonathan: 1812
Miller, Julia A., Dr.: 1150
Miller, Ken: 434
Miller, Lauren: 363
Miller, Louis E.: 1995
Miller, Mark: 1935
Miller, Sandie: 1536
Miller, Sarah K.: 1358
Miller, Shawn: 344, 2166
Miller, Will: 329
Miller, William I.: 91
Millhouse, Barbara: 26
Milling, R. King: 2188
Mills, Robert K.: 211
Millspaugh, Gordon A., Jr.: 1396
Millum, Rob: 2466
Milnes, Sherrill: 792
Milstein, Howard P.: 1469
Mims, Marcus, C.P.A.: 1160
Mindich, Eric: 229
Mink, Jonathan W., M.D., Ph.D.: 2483
Minner, Thom: 409
Minnich, Bruce: 1425
Minnich, Margaret W.: 1425
Minter-Jordan, Myechia, Dr.: 1185
Mirabal, Lawrence: 1051
Mirro, Jeanne E.: 461
Mirsky, Burton M.: 2254
Mirsky, Rebecca: 2632
Mishkin, Jonathan: 647, 648
Mistick, Mary Anne: 1126
Mitchell, James: 26
Mitchell, John: 1215
Mitchell, John P., Rev. Dr.: 1150
Mitchell, Joseph: 286
Mitchell, Joseph C.: 366
Mitchell, Mack C., Jr., M.D.: 1416
Mitstifer, Dorothy I., Dr.: 2674
Mitterholzer, John: 152
Mix, Mark: 1948
Mockenhaupt, Robin E.: 2275
Modell, William D.: 2412
Moeller, Max: 593
Moen, Linda L.: 817
Moerman, Filip: 900
Moesta, Allison: 1273
Moffat, William: 1196
Moffett, Thomas: 254
Mogavero, Jane: 1215
Moll, Jon H.: 30
Molnar, Catherine A.: 1376
Moltz, James E.: 65
Monahan, Michael T.: 75
Monahan, Susan T.: 318, 1106
Moncrieff, Jean: 767
Mondin, John: 2544
Montaldo, Mauricio J.: 1937
Montanez, Wilma: 2194
Montante, Alex: 1215
Montes de Oca, Ivonne: 1376
Montgomery, Michelle: 301
Moody, Libbie Shearn: 239
Moody, Robert L., Sr.: 239
Moody, Ross R.: 239
Moody, W.L., Jr.: 239
Moody, William J.: 748
Moody, William S.: 900

Moody-Dahlberg, Frances Anne: 239
Mooi, Rich, Dr.: 2142
Mooney, Kay D.: 6
Moore, Ann S.: 329
Moore, Anne, M.D.: 244
Moore, Hugh: 1227
Moore, John H.: 1850
Moore, Johnny B.: 1502
Moore, Kathryn M., Dr.: 1700
Moore, Kevin S.: 1677
Moore, Kim: 1514
Moore, Logan: 1562
Moore, Michael: 456
Moore, Randolph G.: 59
Moore, Steve: 1552
Moore, Steven G.W.: 241
Moore, Taylor F.: 135
Moorhouse, Linda: 748
Moose, Sandra O.: 298
Mooser, Stephen: 697
Morales, Angel Luis: 1068
Morales, George: 2664
Morales, Susana R., M.D.: 1469
Moran, Sara S.: 1146
Moran, Suzanne: 297
Morand, Anne: 572
Morash, Mark: 789
Moravec, F. Joseph: 54
Morehead, Arthur E., IV: 108
Moreland, Steven: 1283
Morella, Constance A., The Hon.: 54
Morey, Brendan: 1779
Morgan, Charles O., Jr.: 807
Morgan, Gayle: 783
Morgan, Howard D.: 2482
Morgan, Pete: 2473
Morgenstern, Jay R.: 754
Morhouse, Sanford W., Esq.: 2446
Moriarty, Brunilda: 167
Moriearty, Perry: 1495
Morning, John: 1150, 1333
Morowitz, Jacob: 647, 648
Morris, James T.: 257
Morris, Jerry: 1691
Morris, Joseph W.: 288
Morris, Maria: 231
Morris, Simon: 929
Morris, Thomas Q., M.D.: 1188
Morrissette, Vaughan: 427
Morse, Anne Nishimura, Dr.: 853
Morse, Herbert: 1185
Morse, Kevin: 1806
Morton, James T.: 295
Moses, Ansley: 1227
Moses, Harold E.: 2627
Mosher, Scott: 87
Mosier, Nancy: 1737
Mosier, Olive: 265
Mosley, Daniel: 1141
Mosley, Linda: 1227
Moss, Bruce: 748
Moss, Jane S.: 766
Moss, Jennifer: 136
Mostue, Emily C.: 1196
Motes, Holly: 168
Mott, Maryanne: 1333
Moulds, Donald: 1478
Mountcastle, Katharine B.: 26, 279
Mountcastle, Katherine R.: 26
Mountcastle, Ken: 26
Mountcastle, Laura: 26
Mountcastle, Mary: 26, 279
Moy, David: 1487
Moyer, Glenn: 340
Moyer, Scott: 2277
Moyers, Richard L.: 1327
Mucci, Gary L.: 1215
Muench, Mattthew: 179
Mulholland, Neil: 2190
Mulkeen, Maria: 1487

Mullen, Michael: 156
Mulligan, Richard: 2284
Mullin, Ann K.: 152
Mullins, Jana: 283
Mumford, Phyllis: 1625
Munday, Reuben: 222
Munoz, Julio E.: 1937
Munroe, Alexander, Dr.: 866
Munson, Eddie R.: 297
Muraco, Julie: 1207
Murase, Satoru: 866
Murchison, Pamela: 785
Murkowski, Lisa, Hon.: 853
Murnane, Richard: 1588
Murnen, Amy, Dr.: 77
Muro, Susan: 363
Murphy, Stacia: 1465
Murphy, Terence: 449
Murray, Eileen M., MM, CAE: 2455
Murray, Joanne: 1081
Murthy, N.R. Narayana: 129
Musacchio, Aldo: 961
Muscarolas, Miriam: 332
Musekamp, George H., III: 794
Musgrave, Thea: 798
Musser, Marcie J.: 141
Musser, Robert W.: 141
Mwanza, Angela K.: 107
Mydland, G. Todd: 282
Myers, John H.: 2446
Myerson, Gayle: 298
Mytelka, Andrew: 185

N

Na, Soo: 136
Nabi, Ivan Robert: 2434
Nadal, Michael A.: 1214
Nadosy, Peter A.: 107, 129
Nagaur, Grace: 2575
Nagel, Rob D.: 329
Nagy, Gregory: 356
Namath, Donna: 35
Nan Tie, Gary: 464
Napolitano, Joseph J., Ph.D., M.P.H.: 1458
Naranjo, Tito: 522
Narimatsu, Sharon: 456
Nassi, Karen: 862
Natale, Pat: 2645
Natera, Angelica: 961
Nathoo, Raffiq: 244
Natori, Josie Cruz: 434
Naumburg, Judith: 782
Naumes, Sue: 1196
Navikas, David: 271
Naylor, Mary D., Ph.D., R.N.: 1458
Neal, David L.: 279
Neal, Kristyn L.: 6
Neal, Stephen C.: 159
Neal, Stephen L.: 279
Neeb, Martin: 1603
Neely, Mary M.: 2443
Negley, Nancy: 1528
Neidhart, Rene: 993
Neidich, Charles: 782
Neill, Rolfe: 193
Nel, Anton: 782
Nelms, Charlie: 1333
Nelson, Anna Spangler: 193
Nelson, Arvid R., Ph.D.: 1868
Nelson, Carolyn: 777, 778, 779
Nelson, Chris: 2451
Nelson, David, Dr.: 1806
Nelson, John A.: 2367
Nelson, Jon: 1344
Nelson, Mary Goodwillie: 307, 1400
Nelson, Peggy: 522
Nelson, Sue: 1234
Nelson, Ward: 1227

Nesbitt, William: 226
Ness, Drew: 993
Nessier, Stephen: 1918
Nettles, Cory: 1291
Nevins, Jane: 2254
Newbury, Mary V., Hon. Madam Justice: 1471
Newcomer, Phyllis L., Ed.D.: 994
Newcorn, Jeffrey H., M.D.: 2580
Newhouse, Joseph P.: 6
Newton, Eric: 193
Neyer, Christine: 794
Neyman, Craig: 258
Nichols, Jason: 2505
Nicholson, James B.: 222
Nicholson, Jan: 1126
Nickel, Douglas, Prof.: 1632
Nickelson, Donald E.: 1633
Nickerson, Peter, Dr.: 1460
Nicklin, F. Oliver: 122
Niedringhaus, Ann: 1344
Niemann, Craig: 307
Nieroda, Cathy: 1460
Nishiwaki, Koji: 1330
Nitecki, Zbigniew: 2093
Nixon, Kelly: 866
Noah, Sandi: 1342
Noble-Pelant, Andrea: 428
Noe, Kevin: 785
Noel, Stuart: 661
Nolan, Eleanor: 23
Noland, Mariam C.: 75, 193
Nonken, Marilyn: 767
Nonoyama, Mika: 2488
Nopoulos, Peggy, M.D.: 2483
Norcia, Jerry: 297
Nord, Philip: 591
Norell, Randy B.: 578, 579, 580
Norich, Samuel: 25
Noriega, Chon: 1069
Norman, David, Dr.: 1759
Norris, Bradley K.: 247
Norris, Harlyne J.: 247
North, Oliver L., USMC (Ret.), Lt Col: 1691
Northcott, Allan: 1420
Northrup, Douglas: 854
Norvell, Edward: 285
Novak, Roger A.: 2018
Novis, Susie: 2274
Null, John: 142
Nussbaum, Bernard: 647, 648
Nutter, James B., Jr.: 2018
Nwoji, Pamela: 2444

O

O'Brien, Connie: 1191
O'Brien, Denis: 119
O'Brien, Miles: 1930
O'Connell, Michael F.: 1386
O'Connor, John: 1528
O'Donnell, Laurence G.: 1932
O'Donnell Mutch, Ruth: 2188
O'Donnell-Tormey, Jill: 2430
O'Donovan, Peter: 1823
O'Hanley, Ron: 1185
O'Hare, Donna, M.D.: 2399
O'Keefe, Valerie: 412
O'Leary, Nancy: 2225, 2226
O'Neil, Brian S.: 2275
O'Neil-White, Alphonso: 1215
O'Neill, Abby M.: 434
O'Neill, John H.: 250
O'Neill, Timothy M.: 250
O'Neill, Wendy: 434
O'Reilly, Richard J., M.D.: 2446
O'Riordan, Catherine: 2099
O'Rourke, Joan C.: 322
O'Rourke, Kathleen: 2674
Oard Warner, Sharon: 703

References in index are to entry numbers.

Oates, Joyce Carol: 151
Ober, Gayle M.: 216
Ober, Richard B.: 216
Ober, Theodore E.: 1410
Ober, Timothy M.: 216
OBrien-Suric, Nora: 155
Obrow, Norman C.: 105
Ochester, Ed: 695
Ochoa-Brillembourg, Hilda: 1905
Ochsman, Bruce: 2483
Odahowski, David A.: 52
Oden, Vivian: 1296
Odgers, Richard W.: 1394
Oetinger, Judy: 29
Ogawa, Diane Harrison: 1160
Ogle, Laura Kerr: 187
Ohira, Yukihiro: 852
Okorn, David: 1320
Okoroafer, Michael: 156
Okun, Josh: 2575
Olekszyk, Danielle: 297
Oler, Lorraine: 531
Olfers, Kristan: 1389
Olfers, Sarah H.: 1389
Oliphant, Grant: 1350
Oliver, Lin: 697
Oliver-Farrow, Elizabeth: 1068
Olson, Beverly Knight: 193
Olson, Doug: 2515
Olson, Elizabeth: 1101
Olson, Karen: 450
Olson, Kathryn: 1104
Olson, Keith: 1166
Olson, Leigh: 2367
Olsson, Bjorn: 401
Oosterveen, Robin L.: 336
Oppens, Ursula: 782
Orane, Douglas: 961
Ornstein, Peter A.: 2576
Orozco, Yolanda: 273
Orr, David: 258
Orr, Susan Packard: 258
Orth, Cornelia Laemmli: 791
Ortiz, Nieves: 2575
Ortt, Brianne: 807
Osborn, Robin: 1478
Osborn, William A.: 759
Osborne, Robert C.: 1469
Osher, Barbro: 254
Osher, Bernard: 254
Osmer, Patrick S.: 2041
Otero, Madeline: 1099
Otero, Maria: 273
Ott, Alan W.: 2443
Ott, Margie: 954
Ottenhoff, Donald B.: 809
Owen, Sarah: 1378
Owens, Jim: 2170
Owens, Kimberly A.: 1477
Owens, Reginald, Dr.: 1932
Oxtoby, David, Dr.: 1700
Oyler, Tennyson S.: 257
Ozelius, Laurie, Ph.D.: 2483

P

Pace, Nicholas A., M.D.: 1465
Paceley, Barry: 2632
Packard, Ed: 303
Packard, George R.: 866
Packard, Julie E.: 258
Padro, Myriam: 1351
Page, Evan C.: 263
Page, Jesse R.: 1821
Paige, Katie Schwab: 290
Paik, Lisa: 2274
Palenchar, David J.: 115
Palfrey, John: 193
Palizzi, Thomas A.: 2482

Palmer, Elizabeth A.: 155
Palmer, Jodie: 1047
Palmer, Johnnye K.: 3
Palmer, Lesley H.: 1330
Palmer, Nancy J.: 220
Palmer, Scott: 220
Palmer, Tony: 189
Palmieri, Stefano, Dr.: 600
Pangburn, Michael: 501
Pappano, Joseph E., Jr., Dr.: 300
Pappas, Sarah H.: 1507
Pappas, Virginia: 2328
Pappous, Perry: 1606
Paquette, Jennifer, C.F.A.: 1427
Pardes, Herbert, M.D.: 2280
Parfet, Donald R.: 1969
Parham, Michael: 2172
Parilla, Barbara V., M.D.: 2500
Parisi, Joseph: 2334
Park, C.S.: 1376
Parke, Jennifer Hudson: 1302
Parker, Arthur H.: 1632
Parker, Franklin, IV: 1396
Parker, Grant: 2173
Parker, Gray S.: 47
Parker, Jennifer J., J.D.: 1215
Parker, John E.: 1396
Parker, John, Jr.: 2529
Parker, Margaret H.: 1396
Parker, Mary Kay: 47
Parker, Tim: 1283
Parnes, Stuart: 363
Parra, Ivan Kohar: 26
Parrella, Nicholas J.: 2011
Parsons, Robert W., Jr.: 167
Partin, Kelli: 1696
Partlow, Glenda: 1750
Pasewicz, Jerry: 793
Pass, Gregory A.: 679
Passman, Alan: 2664
Patawaran, Wally B.: 155
Pate, Julian: 2616
Patel, Mayur: 193
Patino, Douglas X.: 1333
Patnoe, Tom, Dr.: 1344
Patrick, Cindy: 226
Patrikis, Peter: 904
Patt, Richard A.: 203
Patterson, Aubrey A.: 458
Patterson, Cynthia B.: 1825
Patterson, Jane R.: 179
Patterson, Jane S.: 279
Patterson, Roger Chip, Jr.: 1214
Pattillo, Katy: 1214
Patton, Jim, Ed.D.: 994
Paxson, Christina: 1632
Paxton, Jay L.: 217
Payson, Doris: 647, 648
Peachee, Ted: 2616
Peacock, Deborah: 1160
Pearson, Nils, Ph.D.: 994
Pecht, Thomas P.: 1448
Peck, Robert: 54
Pedley, Timothy A., M.D.: 2482
Peer, Mary Megan: 666
Peet, Shelly: 246
Pell, Christopher T.H.: 155
Peltason, Jack W., Ph.D.: 1442
Peltekian, Elizabeth M.: 54
Peltier, Valerie: 244
Pempel, T.J., Dr.: 853
Pena, Allison J.: 167
Pendolino, Lisa: 982
Pennick, Aurie: 122
Pennington, Hilary: 129
Pennoyer, Russell P.: 5, 46, 1127
Penny, Alvertha: 1238
Penoyer, Darren: 1215
Pepe, Federico: 600
Percy, Roger: 1603

Pereira, Lygia: 961
Peretz, Martin: 647, 648
Pereyda, Margarita, M.D.: 1442
Perez, Daniel Paul: 2264
Perez, Maritza, M.D.: 2447
Perez, Melanie: 777, 778, 779
Perkins, David: 2188
Perlman, Noah: 997
Perrone, Glenn A.: 489
Perrotte, Alisa: 296
Perrotte, Andrew: 296
Perry, Stephen: 80
Person, Conrad: 175
Persons, Georgia: 1855
Peters, Carl: 2654
Peters, Frederick: 783
Peters, JoAnne: 1191
Peters, Robert, Dr.: 1601
Peters, Thomas: 217
Petersen, Robert, C.P.A.: 1509
Petersen, William B.: 2026
Peterson, Douglas L.: 1905
Peterson, John S.: 1117
Peterson, Julie: 1141
Peterson, Linda: 2507
Peterson, Maggie, MBA: 2591
Peterson, Steven D.: 1712
Peterson, Temple: 1191
Peterson, Terry: 97
Petit, Charles: 1930
Petito, Donne: 1856
Petrauskas, Bonnie J.: 175
Petri, Thomas, Rep.: 853
Petrie, Dan, Jr.: 524
Petrone, Joseph C., Mrs.: 157
Petterson, Jay: 993
Pettit, Peter: 1502
Pettker, John D.: 1633
Petts, John A.: 792
Petty, Frank: 29
Pew, Robert C., III: 307
Pfau, Bruce: 1902
Pfeifer, Joseph: 773
Pfeiffer, Dave: 2177
Pfister, Thomas: 293
Phalen, Miriam: 2367
Phelps, Irene S.: 296
Philipp, Alicia: 1214
Phillips, Gaylen: 448
Phillips, Mary K.: 111
Phillips, Nathaniel P., Jr.: 47
Phillips, Tamara S.: 30
Phillips, Tammy: 29
Phipps, Mary S.: 5, 46
Phoenix, Tom: 2650
Piccigallo, Philip R., Ph.D.: 1015
Pichel, Christy: 1147
Pickett, Robert T.: 1024
Pickett-Erway, Carrie: 1309
Piepenbring, Mary L.: 108
Pierce, Rhoda A.: 460
Pierre, D. Stephen, P.E.: 2664
Pierson, Clare M.: 282
Pierson, Robert L.: 1317
Pierson, Wayne: 232
Pieski, Mary Kay, Ph.D.: 925
Pih, Norman: 2664
Piispanen, Ruth: 459
Pike, Chad: 2188
Pileggi, Dominic, Sen.: 300
Pilla, Domenic: 2434
Pincus, Matt: 666
Pine, Rachael: 1163
Piper, William H.: 1333
Pisano, Jane G.: 1631
Pladziewicz, Jack: 2041
Plageman, Susan: 794
Plasker, James R.: 2034
Pleasants, Sheila Gulley: 510
Pletka, Irena: 647, 648

References in index are to entry numbers.

Poet, Pat: 1536
Polisi, Joseph W.: 329
Polking, Kirk, Mrs.: 794
Pollinger, Amy: 2580
Pomeroy, Claire: 1509
Pomeroy, Gay M., Esq.: 1201
Pompe, Bruce: 817
Ponte, Dana: 854
Pontsler, Aaron V., M.S., MBA: 2533
Pool, Dick: 2177
Popkin, Alice B.: 734
Popovich, Mark G.: 162
Poppy, Seth: 495
Porter, A. Alex: 151
Porter, Andrew: 1127
Porter, David L.: 194
Porter, Joanna O.: 194
Porter, Laurel: 194
Porter-O'Grady, Timothy: 2486
Porzecanski, Arturo C.: 862
Post, Barbara: 1283
Postl, Brian, Dr.: 1460
Poterba, James: 298
Potkonjak, Billie: 2250, 2251, 2410
Potolicchio, S.J.: 2331
Pouliot, Marc, Dr.: 2451
Pouschine, Tatiana: 5, 46
Powell, Carol P.: 2018
Powell, Earl A., III: 54
Powell, Earl W.: 193
Power, Angelique: 179
Powers, Peter J.: 1469
Pozen, Robert C.: 1478
Pratt, Roger: 1145
Pray, Donald E.: 40
Preble, Jan: 330
Predmore, Jeanne: 1273
Prendergast, S. Lawrence: 1150
Presley, Kimberley: 247
Pressman, Jeffery: 622
Preston, James L.: 1743
Prevratil, Joseph F.: 1419
Prewitt, Kenneth: 1127
Price, K.F.: 317
Price, Terry: 341
Price-Letscher, Jennifer: 262
Prince, Larry: 323
Prince, Steven J.: 2367
Pritzker, John: 254
Proffitt, Kevin: 818
Prohaska, Thomas R., Ph.D.: 1009
Prothro, Caren H.: 163
Pruitt, Chris: 340
Prusinowski, Julie Ellen: 486
Pryce, Jennifer: 162
Przewrocki, Shelley S.: 308
Puentes, George: 232
Purcell, Cindy R.: 1886
Purcell, Lisa: 1404
Purkey, Sheila L.: 1281
Purugganan, Michael: 298
Putnam, Thomas O.: 489, 622
Pye, Elisa: 1528
Pyke, Susan: 1353

Q

Quatrini, Vincent J.: 1350
Quiara, Jason: 179
Quinlivan, Laure, Mrs.: 794
Quinn, Ellen: 1247
Quinn, Thomas: 2505
Quinn, Todd: 1192
Quisenberry, Cynthia: 1601

R

Raby, Julian, Dr.: 452
Rachleff, Andrew S.: 2446
Rackoff, Nancy L.: 1350
Raff, Douglass: 2172
Raffel, Ann E.: 155
Rajani, Rakesh: 159
Rajaratnam, Ashley: 1101
Rake, Michael, Sir: 1905
Rall, Ronald D., Rev. Dr.: 817
Rallo, Eduardo: 1376
Ralston, Craig S.: 1034
Ram, Harsha: 400
Ramey, Lynn: 661
Ramey, Samuel: 792
Ramin, Kirk D., M.D.: 2500
Ramirez, Marcos: 369
Ramirez, Margarita: 1490
Ramme, Leslie: 1202
Ramos, Ivan: 1870
Ramos, Lydia: 1957
Ramos, Pedro A., Esq.: 2491
Ramos-Chertok, Maria: 217
Ramous, Olga: 1868
Ramsey, Paul G., M.D.: 2280
Randall, Gail T.: 10
Randel, Don Michael: 229
Randle, Kathryn A.: 807
Randler, Paula: 1774
Randolph, Nina: 2211
Random, Cindee: 807
Randt, Virginia: 1935
Ranelle, Shanda: 1752
Rankin, David: 2182
Ranney, George A., Jr.: 122
Rao, R.: 317
Raphael, Cathy: 1090
Rapoport, Nessa: 278
Rapoport, Ronald, Ph.D.: 1477
Rapp, Marcia L.: 150
Rapson, Judith: 680
Rashford, John, Dr.: 101
Raskob, Kathleen: 1160
Rasmussen, Ronn J.: 82
Raso, Rosanne, M.S., R.N.: 2495
Rassler, Bridget I.: 1458
Rath, Tom: 1603
Rattray, Carol: 434
Rauch, Lawrence: 1308
Rauch, Scott L.: 2591
Raudenbush, Stephen: 1588
Rauzi, Robert L.: 77
Raver, Cybele: 1588
Rawlinson, Rex: 1529
Ray, Adele Richardson: 1868
Ray, Gilbert T.: 1631
Raymond, Carolyn M.: 223
Read, Mary B.: 1291
Read, William A., Ph.D.: 128
Ready, Ken: 2451
Rebmann, David: 1606
Rector, Amy: 1242
Redd, Kimberly: 1616
Rede, George: 1957
Redmond, Jerry: 1166
Redwood, Rene: 1090
Reed, Cynthia: 280
Reed, Page Branton: 2018
Reeve, Todd: 2169
Regalado, Cristina M.: 1425
Regan, David: 796
Regenstein, Susan: 277
Reger, Gerald: 1215
Regulska, Joanna: 854
Rehding, Alex: 767
Reich, Paul: 232
Reiche, Nancy: 1243
Reid, Don: 680
Reid, Janet B., Ph.D.: 1285
Reid, Rosalind: 1930

Reid-Smith, Randall: 516
Reider, Corinne H.: 155
Reilly, William K.: 258
Reimann, Nancy B.: 2581
Reimers, Fernando: 961
Reinbolt, Donna: 2367
Reinhart, A. Kevin: 881, 882, 883
Reis, Judson: 1127
Reisman, Barbara: 1145
Rembe, Toni: 1394
Rendino, Nilda: 2507
Renjen, Punit: 1627
Rennie, Renate: 862
Rentschler, Suzanne: 461
Renuart, Victor Eugene: 115
Restrick, Nicole: 858
Reuben-Cooke, Wilhelmina, J.D.: 108
Reveley, W. Taylor, III: 229
Revson, Charles H., Jr.: 278
Rex, Gloria O.: 1221
Reyes, Danielle: 1327
Reynolds, Robert: 217
Reynolds, W. Noah: 279
Rhea, Timothy: 748
Rhea, Timothy, Dr.: 748
Riccio, Michael: 1583
Rice, Don: 2087
Rice, Gwendolyn M.: 268
Rice, John H.: 1270
Rice, Joseph A.: 151
Rice, Linda: 1296
Rice, Mabel L., Dr.: 1795
Rice, Michael: 661
Rich, Harry: 422
Rich, Harvey: 203
Richard, Alison: 2173
Richard, Frances: 783
Richards, Arnold, Dr.: 647, 648
Richards, Cecile: 129
Richardson, Elaina: 443
Richardson, Ethan: 90
Richardson, Luns, Dr.: 1759
Richardson, Peter L.: 1868
Richardson, Stuart S.: 1868
Richardson, Tanyelle: 1644
Richardson, Tanyelle Hawkins: 1915
Richardson, William C.: 1969
Richelson, Elliott, M.D.: 2591
Richey, Ivenhoe T., II: 2558
Richland, Scott H.: 1308
Richmond, Kathy: 12
Richmond, Marsha: 597
Richter, James: 854
Richter, Sidney D.: 2399
Rickman, Tom: 524
Riehl, Margie: 194
Riehl, Michael: 194
Rieser, Len: 1270
Rifkind, Richard A.: 151
Rightmire, Karen A.: 340
Riley, Angela: 1061
Riley, Bettina: 1806
Riley, Emily C.: 81
Riley, Heather A.: 47
Riley, Melissa: 1941
Riley, Thomas A.: 81
Rinehart, Marsha: 77
Riskin, Steven M.: 80
Rist, Ray C.: 1855
Ritchie, C. Cliff: 285
Ritter, Bill, Jr.: 2176
Rivera, Ron J., C.P.A.: 1160
Rivera-Torres, Nancy: 1127
Rivlin, Alice M., Ph.D.: 54
Roach, Michele C.: 807
Robb, Lisa: 488
Robb, Lynda J.: 734
Robbins, Mark: 2166
Robbins, Marlena Rae: 1800
Robbins, N. Clay: 206

References in index are to entry numbers.

Robbins Towers, Amy: 2188
Robbins-Butcher, Amanda: 696
Robers, Frank: 1342
Roberts, Carla A.: 1277
Roberts, Carol: 185
Roberts, Donald D.: 87
Roberts, Kenneth L.: 1278
Roberts, Kim: 2436
Roberts, Rosalinda, Ph.D.: 2483
Robertson, Wilhemina E.: 89
Robins, Elizabeth, Esq.: 2447
Robins, Harlan: 1211
Robins, Perry, M.D.: 2447
Robinson, Barbara: 459
Robinson, Barbara Paul: 155
Robinson, Curtis: 217
Robinson, Ernest L.: 794
Robinson, Eugene: 1926
Robinson, Irwin Z.: 666, 754
Robinson, Jean A.: 1190
Robinson, John H.: 58
Robinson, Marty: 1227
Robinson, Robby: 303
Robinson, Russell M., II: 108
Robinson, Theresa G.: 822
Rockefeller, David, Jr.: 434
Rockefeller, John D., IV, Sen.: 853
Rockefeller, Nancy King: 282
Rockefeller, Wendy Gordon: 282
Roddey, James C.: 1350
Rodgers, Brooke: 194
Rodgers, Joann: 1930
Rodgers, Jonathan: 542
Rodgers, Mary: 754
Rodgers, Mary Anne: 258
Rodgers, Michael: 194
Rodgers, Pat: 1274
Rodgers, Patrick: 194
Rodgers-Edmonds, Catherine: 817
Rodriguez, Adam: 1068
Rodriguez, Al: 1371
Rodriguez, Edwin, Jr.: 2188
Rodriguez, Emily: 2212
Rodriguez, Jose: 1902
Rodriguez, Ray: 193
Rodriguez, Robby: 141
Rodriguez-Garcia, Rosalia: 1855
Roeder, Susan: 1166
Roehl, Jerrald J.: 1160
Rogalski, Shannon: 1460
Rogers, Anne: 375
Rogers, Art: 1274
Rogers, James E.: 1274
Rogers, Julie L.: 1327
Rogers, Karen H.: 108
Rogers, Lucy: 1101
Rogers, Margot M.: 179
Roh, Joni: 2674
Rohrbach, Sharon: 817
Rojas, Fernando: 858, 860
Rolader, Clay: 323
Rolls, Tom: 2177
Rolston, Bradley P., Esq.: 104
Romero, Gregory: 2482
Roney, Jane H.: 2581
Roob, Nancy: 65
Roole, Barbara: 111
Rooney, Michael: 303
Ros, Frank: 1068
Rosa, Karen L.: 1163
Rosales, Matthew: 1712
Rose, Deedie: 163
Rose, Kim: 77
Rose, Walter B.: 262
Rosegg, Peter: 456
Rosen, Aby: 488
Rosen, Leonard M.: 2367
Rosen, Mark: 993
Rosenbaum, Randall: 497
Rosenberg, Dianne M.: 1285

Rosenblatt, Mazal, Mrs.: 794
Rosenblatt, Michael, M.D.: 2306, 2540, 2541, 2542, 2543
Rosenfeld, Gerald: 278
Rosenfeld, Sheri: 2367
Rosenthal, Hilary: 94
Rosenthal, Irwin M.: 2412
Rosenthal, Jonathan: 231
Rosequist, Rena: 522
Ross, Jeffrey Ian: 1855
Ross, R. J., Rev.: 1427
Ross, Randall: 75
Ross, Sam: 794
Rosser, Rebecca: 1061
Rossiter, Dione, Ph.D.: 1920
Rostov, David: 173
Roth, Eric: 524
Roth, Rachel: 1117
Rothblatt, Daniel M.: 1308
Rothblatt, Faith: 2575
Rothe, Ann: 2164, 2165
Rothenberg, Anne F.: 373
Rothman, Carol: 1950
Rothschild, Loren R.: 373
Rotstein, Yair, Dr.: 968
Rotunno, L. Charles, Jr.: 822
Roupe, Thomas A.: 1068
Rouse, Dudley L., Jr.: 226
Rouse, Elizabeth Meadows: 226
Rouse, Jack: 794
Roux, Christina: 2212
Rover, Edward F.: 2254
Rowe, Betsy: 1473
Rowe, George, Jr.: 2594
Rowland, Elaine: 1215
Rowland, Lewis P., M.D.: 2482
Royce, Michael: 487
Royster, Randy: 1160
Rubenstein, Eli: 2477, 2478
Rubin, Judith O.: 244
Rubin, Robert E.: 1319
Rubinger, Michael: 1319
Rubio, Luis: 862
Ruckelshaus, William: 2176
Rucker, Geri: 1274
Rudel, Julius: 782, 798
Rudner, Diane: 1502
Rudner, Jocelyn P.: 1502
Rudolph, Karen: 211
Ruestow, Brian A.: 2616
Ruggiero, Angela: 1104
Rumelhart, Judith D.: 321
Rumsey, David: 552
Runcis, Veronica M.: 113
Rupp, George Erik, Ph.D.: 2280
Ruschau, Pamela J.: 2616
Russel, Daniel: 853
Russell, Cristine: 1478, 1930
Russell, J.G.: 82
Russell, Jenny D.: 230
Russo, Jessica: 276
Rust, Edward B., Jr.: 1905
Rutkin, Lynne: 434
Rutledge, Kathleen: 1405
Rutledge, Napoleon: 323
Rutter, Deborah: 759
Ryan, Evan, Hon.: 853
Ryan, Kelly: 162
Rybolt, Ryan M.: 1285
Ryder, Sheri: 1287
Ryerson, William N.: 2174
Ryles, Scott: 2446

S

Sa, Sophie: 1583
Sabina, Alyse B., M.P.H.: 6
Sachs, Samuel, II: 565
Sackey-Milligan, Rose: 375

Safier, Steve: 1583
Sagan, Bruce: 417
Sagawa, Shirley: 273
Saich, Anthony, Prof.: 960
Saint, Eva Marie: 524
Salatino, Kevin: 373
Salcido, Anthony: 1068
Saldanha, Anne, M.D.: 1215
Salinas, Maria Elena: 1068
Salmon, Marla, Dr.: 1700
Salter, Veronica: 179
Salvo, Calogero: 464
Salzberg, Deborah Ratner: 1327
Samolczyk, Mark: 1379
Sampson, Elbert: 103
Sampson, Kelvin: 1047
Samson, Earl A., III: 155
Samuels, Richard J., Dr.: 866
Samuels, Sara: 141
Samuelson, Peter: 524
Sananez, Francisco: 961
Sanbrano, Angela: 1130
Sanchez, Vicki: 524
Sanders, Keith P., Dr.: 1940
Sanders, Ronald: 504
Sandman, James: 1327
Sandorf, Julie: 278
Sandoval, Edgar A.: 1068
Sandoval, Lester, Dr.: 1047
Sanford, Claire: 457
Sanford, Shelton: 814
Sankey, C. Patrick: 959
Santisi, Maria, C.P.A.: 1351
Santori, Mary Beth: 1344
Santucci, Marryn D.: 257
Sapp, Shannon: 2632
Saran, Sally: 1473
Sarchet, Kurt: 993
Sardone, Frank J.: 1309, 1969
Sarmiento, Gil M.: 179
Sarno, Vincent: 1015
Sarnoff, Deborah S., M.D.: 2447
Sarofim, Christopher B.: 1528
Sarofim, Louisa: 1528
Saromines-Ganne, Barbara: 456
Sarrafan, Sima: 1477
Sasser, Barbara W.: 185
Sasso, Gennaro: 600
Satterlee, Ellen: 1400
Sauncy, Toni: 1757, 2102
Sauncy, Tony: 2104
Sauve, Leo P.: 1471
Savage, Barbara, Dr.: 2026
Savage, Eleanor: 464
Savage, Stephanie: 2006
Savoy, Caroline: 2323
Savoy, George M.: 2323
Sawyer, Raymond T., Esq.: 70
Sawyer, Robin Gibson: 1932
Sayen, Mike: 2616
Scace, Barbara: 265
Scaife, Richard M.: 2014
Scales, Aileen: 1536
Scanlon, Ann M.: 302
Scarfone, Anthony C.: 97
Scarola, Albert: 1330
Schachne, Mary H.: 1469
Schadlow, Nadia, Dr.: 1868
Schaefer, Carla J.: 1995
Schaffer, Elizabeth: 1082
Schaffner, Don: 2673
Schaible, Donn: 2177
Schaller, George: 2173
Scharf, Jeremiah, M.D., Ph.D.: 2483
Schatz, Edward: 854
Schaufelberger, John: 2632
Schaumber, Peter: 1477
Schaures, Lisa: 1603
Scheid, Randy: 1459
Scheper, Charles R.: 1285

Scherer, Carol: 869
Schieber-Acker, Traude: 832
Schiff, Stacy: 151
Schiltz, Joseph: 63
Schirling, Rovena: 2483
Schister, Kurt E.: 77
Schlack, Marilyn: 1969
Schlenk, Cornelia G.: 2193
Schlesinger, William H.: 107
Schlonsky, Michael: 1211
Schlosser, Judith: 531
Schluter, Paul: 2177
Schmidt, Mike: 2616
Schmidt, Oscar: 231
Schmidt, Paul: 1932
Schmitt, Robert: 1536
Schmoke, Kurt L., Esq.: 1905
Schnabel, Rockwell: 1633
Schnarr, Laura: 1750
Schneider, Katie: 1215
Schneider, Melvyn H.: 296
Schneider, Robert A.: 578, 579, 580
Schoen, Cathy A.: 1478
Schoenbaum, Stephen C., M.D.: 2280
Schoenberger, Brenda C.: 1458
Schoenbrun, Lois, C.A.E., FAAO: 2505
Schoettler, Gail, Ph.D.: 1427
Scholl, Barry A.: 1478
Scholl, Dennis: 193
Scholl, Pamela: 289
Scholnick, Lynn Okon, Ms.: 1047
Scholund, Christian: 274
Schooley, Susan, M.D.: 222
Schoppa, Leonard J., Jr., Dr.: 853
Schorr, Thelma, B.S.N., R.N.: 2495
Schotland, Marvin I.: 1308
Schottenstein, Steven: 1211
Schram, Lee J.: 97
Schrantz, Jacob S.: 1204
Schreckengast, Kelly B.: 461
Schroeder, Fu: 217
Schuette, William D.: 2443
Schuler, Karissa: 1099
Schulson, Rachel: 1227
Schulte, Laura: 1274
Schulz, Paul: 1192
Schupp, William: 954
Schwab, Charles R.: 290
Schwab, Helen O.: 290
Schwartz, Alan: 1700
Schwartz, Alan E.: 75
Schwartz, Douglas, Dr.: 669
Schwartz, Marie: 2482
Schwartz, Stephen: 754
Schwartz, Steven D.: 669
Schwartz, Susan: 1532
Schwarz, Colleen, M.B.A.: 1427
Schweiger, Larry: 2192
Schweitzer, Jean-Philippe: 774
Schweizer, Felix E., Ph.D.: 2465
Schwenn, Carolyn: 1121
Schwister, Ann M.: 1285
Sciarra, Lorraine: 2026
Scop, Amy B.: 1425
Scoppetta, Nicholas: 107
Scott, F. Lawrence, Jr.: 28
Scott, Frank L.: 28
Scott, Karen Hill: 262
Scott, Laila P.: 1358
Scott, Maegan: 1327
Scott, Nadya K.: 1358
Scott, Richard J.: 1495
Scott, Rita: 1691
Scranton, Philip: 593
Scribner, Norman O.: 54
Scruggs, Sam: 1172
Sculco, Cynthia, R.N., Ed.D: 2495
Seaman, Sheryl: 456
Sears, Suzanne Harte: 331
Seaver, Carlton: 293

Seaver, Christopher: 293
Seaver, Martha: 293
Seaver, Patrick: 293
Sedler, Denise: 1251
Seekins, Steven: 2466
Seelbach, William R.: 70
Segal, Amy R., Esq.: 2465
Segal, Susan: 862
Segall, Margaret: 2194
Seidell, Violeta Vera: 1068
Seiden, Michael V., M.D., Ph.D.: 2446
Seiders, Stella: 2646
Seides, Ted: 2026
Seidler, Lee J.: 538
Seidler, Scott K., Rev. Dr.: 817
Seitchik, Adam: 1487
Seitter, Keith L., Dr.: 2620
Seitz, Karen D.: 2446
Self, Furman C.: 1374
Self, J.C., III: 1374
Self, Sally E., Dr.: 1374
Self, W.M.: 1374
Self, W.M., Jr.: 1374
Sellers, Cleveland, Dr.: 1759
Selner, David: 2124
Senter, Elic A.: 1638
Sepin, Lawrence H.: 2347
Serio, Matt: 495
Serpe, Ralph: 31
Seto, Amy: 31
Sevillano, Lina M.: 963
Sexworth, Beth: 1358
Shaffer, Laura: 90
Shailor, Barbara A.: 552
Shanberg, Ariel: 544
Shane, David N.: 206
Shanley, Frank E.: 1110
Shannon, Jill: 1365
Shannon, Kathleen T.: 1456
Shapira, Edith L., M.D.: 1350
Shapiro, Alex: 666
Shapiro, Robert: 524
Shar, Albert O., Ph.D.: 2275
Sharma, Prakash, Dr.: 1806
Sharp, Larry: 1695
Sharp, Philip R.: 2176, 2198
Sharples, Amber: 493
Shaughnessy, Sandy: 448
Shaver, Craig: 2182
Shaw, Jo, Prof.: 374
Shaw, Kathleen: 1218
Shaw, Minor Mickel: 108
Shaw, Ruth, Ph.D.: 1274
Shaw, Stephanie: 246
Shay, Michael: 523
Sheely, Jay: 2120
Shelden, William W., Jr.: 222
Shell, Greg: 1185
Shelton, Vanessa: 1957
Shenk, Janet: 21
Shepard, Julia Sparkman: 54
Sheppard, Eileen D.: 2581
Sherer, Todd, Ph.D.: 2260
Sheriff, Edd: 3
Sherman, John J.: 2018
Sherman, Robert: 782
Sherman, Susan E.: 2491
Sherry, Andrew: 193
Sherry, Karen: 754
Sheth, Jagdish N., Ph.D., Prof.: 1214
Shetty, Sudha: 1101
Shields, Joe: 794
Shields, Joyce: 65
Shigekawa, Joan: 853
Shimoyama, Sue: 2616
Shin, Jean H.: 975
Shinn, Carol: 1600
Shirasaki, Kanako: 852
Shive, Dunia A.: 37
Shockley, Linda: 1932

Shockley, Scott E.: 29
Shore, Debra: 2182
Shorts, Binkley C.: 1185
Shreffler, Carol, Dr.: 2189
Shreve, Susan Richards: 693
Shuford, Alex: 101
Shuford, Karen L.: 163
Shulman, Randy: 373
Shuster, Gail: 1394
Shutt, Buffy: 524
Sia, Christopher T.: 298, 2042
Sibley, James M.: 338, 1156
Siddiqi, Saima R.: 6
Siefker, Julia: 2134
Siegel, Herbert J.: 2254
Sieger, Diana R.: 150
Siegfried, Tom: 1930
Sieracki, John: 375
Sierra, Alexandra: 2454
Sieve, Richard, M.D.: 2334
Sieving, Paul, M.D.: 2518
Silverman, Barton: 2491
Silverstein, Samuel C., M.D.: 2446
Simmons, Ginny: 179
Simmons, Kay: 2646
Simon, Renee B., M.S., M.L.S.: 1419
Simone, Joseph A.: 2120
Simons, John C.: 1469
Simpkins, Nancy K.: 2580
Simpson, Roy L.: 2495
Simpson, Valerie: 666, 754
Sims, Gretchen Crosby: 179
Sinykin, Gerald B., M.D.: 1442
Sion, L. Gilles: 900
Siragusa, Alexander: 296
Siragusa, Isabel: 296
Siragusa, John R., III: 296
Siragusa, Ross D., III: 296
Siragusa, Sinclair C.: 296
Sisley, Christine: 1633
Sittler, Hana: 832
Sjoquist, Gregg D.: 330
Sklarsky, Frank: 271
Sklut, Lori Levine: 1274
Skrentny, John, Prof.: 1622
Slaney, Barbara L.: 2014
Slaoui, Moncef, Ph.D.: 2306, 2540, 2541, 2542, 2543
Slatery, David: 472
Slaughter, Howard, Jr., Dr.: 1350
Sloan, Sue: 271
Sloane, Jane: 1082
Slocum, John J., Jr.: 376
Slovin, Bruce: 647, 648
Sluder, Greenfield: 53
Sluder, Hendrika: 53
Slutsky, Lorie A.: 244
Sly, Helen S.: 1513
Small, Clara: 1745
Small, Mario: 1588
Small, Tim: 689
Smart, Allen J.: 1503
Smiley, Martha E.: 1358
Smiley, Neil: 2529
Smith, Alfred: 1227
Smith, Andy: 315
Smith, Ann C.: 503
Smith, Chad: 766
Smith, Cherida Collins: 72
Smith, Chris: 1227
Smith, Christina Ittleson: 1488
Smith, David R., M.D.: 2284
Smith, Elizabeth: 417
Smith, Elizabeth B.: 1487
Smith, Fred M.: 595
Smith, Gary: 748, 794
Smith, Gerald: 239
Smith, James A.: 632
Smith, James Allen: 1207
Smith, Jean Bixby: 1192
Smith, Jennifer Graf: 1457

Smith, Kathy: 226
Smith, Kathy Steinauer: 1405
Smith, Kenneth: 2451
Smith, Mark D., M.D.: 1419
Smith, Mary: 2507
Smith, Mary L.: 301
Smith, Mona: 993
Smith, Nevada: 1211
Smith, Owen: 469
Smith, Philip J.: 538
Smith, Ralph, Hon.: 1691
Smith, Rebecca: 1227
Smith, Richard: 1141
Smith, Robert B., Jr.: 2211
Smith, Robert, Jr.: 1134
Smith, Roger P., M.D.: 2500
Smith, Ronald: 2451
Smith, Sheila, Dr.: 853
Smith, Stewart R.: 373, 1633
Smith, Sue: 1291
Smith, Tom E.: 1274
Smith, Tony: 1611
Smith, Tristram H., Ph.D.: 2483
Smith, Virgil: 279
Smith, Walter H., Jr., Ph.D.: 1350
Smith, Whitney: 179
Smith-King, Irene: 461
Smithers, Adele C.: 1465
Smithers, Christopher B.: 1465
Smithers, Nikki: 1465
Smitson, Patricia Mann, Esq.: 1285
Smitson, Robert M.: 30
Smyers, Robyn Minter: 152
Smyth, Geralynn D.: 194
Smyth, John: 194
Smyth, Mauree: 2182
Smyth, Patrick: 194
Smyth, Peggy: 194
Snapp, Deborah: 2261
Snavely, Benjamin: 2099
Sneider, David, Dr.: 853
Snell, George: 131
Snider, Don P., C.P.A.: 128
Snidow, Robin: 141
Snoddy, Candis: 358, 359, 360, 361
Snow, David H.: 302
Snow, Jonathan L.: 302
Snyder, Amy M.: 81
Soboroff, Steve L.: 332
Sokolove, Jennifer L.: 80
Solberg, Elizabeth T.: 2018
Solms-Baruth, Carolina: 912
Soloman, Peter J.: 997
Solomon, Geula R.: 997
Solomon, Sheena: 1279
Solomon, William T.: 163
Solovjovs, Candy: 232
Somerman, Martha, Dr.: 2352
Song, Allan: 1868
Song, Unmi: 136
Sonneborn, Dirk E.: 1279
Sopher, Myron: 2174
Sopp, Patricia: 443
Sosland, Blanche E.: 1016
Sosland, Charles S.: 1016, 2018
Sosland, L. Joshua: 1016
Sosland, Morton I.: 1016
Sosland, Neil N.: 1016
Sosland-Edelman, Debbie: 1016
Sotiros, Diane: 136
Soto, Javier Alberto: 234
Soto-Harmon, Lidia: 1327
Soule, Kate: 694, 1093
Soulières, Denis, M.D., M.Sc., Dr.: 2434
Sovern, Michael I.: 538
Sovey, Mara: 96
Sowd, Laurie: 373
Sowden, Alison: 373
Spacinsky, Charlotte L.: 816
Spagnoletti, Joseph: 55

Sparks, Candace: 88
Sparks, Lillian: 1058
Spartz, Maggi: 1393
Spaulding, Jean G., M.D.: 108
Spears, William G.: 434
Spencer, Henry: 2495
Spencer, Theo: 282
Spencer, Valerie: 1101
Spero, Suzanne: 1135
Spero, Thomas L.: 1291
Sperry, Tracey O'Connell: 2324, 2325
Spielberg, Steven: 1010
Spitzberg, Marian: 37
Spivey, Anita V.: 167
Spollett, Geralyn, M.S.N., ANP-CS: 2403
Spradling, Allan: 1816
Spratt, Kate: 1088
Spring, Micho: 1185
Springfield, James F.: 1502
Sproule, Rebecca: 1902
Sreedharan, Arvind: 2466
Stack, Brian: 675, 851
Stack, Richard L.: 1626
Stafford, E. Alexandra: 595
Staggers, Barbara C., M.D.: 1425
Staggs, Melanie: 1192
Stakely, Margaret: 211
Stam, Deirdre C.: 366
Stamm, Doug: 232
Stamps, E. Roe, IV: 193
Stamps, Sheila A.: 1700
Stangis, David P.: 55
Stanhope, Charles: 469
Stanley, Amanda: 1699
Stanley, Jennifer: 2205
Stanley, Lisa A.: 2205
Stansbury, Burke: 1510
Stanton, Domna, Ph.D.: 2482
Stanton, Janet E.: 220
Staryk, Noa: 2176
Staryk, Ted: 1495
Stasa, Marta: 832
Steeger, Dean H.: 1129
Steel, Corinne: 1524
Steendam, Jan: 194
Stefano, Ralph: 65
Steffel, Sheila: 1283
Steiger, Paul E.: 193
Stein, Eugene: 1308
Steinberg, Joseph S.: 647, 648
Steinhauser, Susan: 437
Steinmann, Jennifer: 1627
Steinmeyer, Mark: 1868
Stenson, Diane M.: 206
Stephansen, Kathleen: 1090
Stephens, S. Shawn: 504
Stephenson, Dick: 303
Stern, Alan: 1308
Stevens, Dana: 524
Stevens, H. Allen: 36
Stevens, Jack: 1055
Stevens, Marcella M.: 221
Stevens, Rosemary A.: 1855
Stevens, Simon: 1478
Stevenson, Charles P., Jr.: 151
Stewart, Alan M.: 89
Stewart, Chester French: 1160
Stewart, Dale: 1868
Stewart, Marise M.M.: 1333
Stifel, Richard Q.: 461
Stillman, Waddell W.: 151
Stine, Mary: 2447
Stio, Stephanie: 682
Stitt, Emily A.: 113
Stocker, Michael A., M.D.: 1469
Stocking, James H.: 1735
Stockton, Richard, Ph.D.: 1215
Stoddard, Robin: 1886
Stoga, Alan: 862
Stokely, Clayton F.: 308

Stokely, Kay H.: 308
Stokely, William B., III: 308
Stokely, William B., IV: 308
Stokesbary, Terry: 241
Stolle, Joan: 1405
Stolz, Rich: 1510
Stone, Amy: 1611
Stone, Andrew W.: 2597
Stone, Barbara: 1611
Stone, David: 1611
Stone, Debbie: 1611
Stone, Jamison: 1611
Stone, Jennifer: 1611
Stone, Kathy: 163
Stone, Lacie: 1227
Stone, Michael A.: 1611
Stone, Norah: 1611
Stone, Norman C.: 1611
Stone, Robert: 693
Stone, Sandra: 1611
Stone, Sara: 1611
Stone, Steven M.: 1611
Stoneback, H.R.: 661
Stookey, John Hoyt: 1207
Storozynski, Alex: 770
Story, Bernard: 466
Stowers, Ryan: 1562
Strader, Timothy L.: 1442
Strain, John: 322
Strandjord, Jeannine: 2018
Strandjord, Jonathan: 811
Strang, Cameron: 666
Strange, Peter S.: 1285
Strauss, Thomas W.: 866
Streb, Elizabeth: 464
Strickland, Annette B.: 1145
Strickland, Thomas L.: 2188
Strickland, William: 1350
Strine, Alice, Esq.: 300
Strmecki, Marin J., Ph.D.: 1868
Strobel, Rae: 1086
Stroh, Vivian Day: 75
Stromberg, Ben: 1344
Stromberg, Jean G.: 159
Strong, John D., Jr.: 40
Strong, Ned: 961
Stropko, Robin: 369
Strother, Ralph: 1420
Strouse, Charles: 754
Struyk, Robert J.: 1495
Stryker, Ronda E.: 1309
Stuart, Dwight L., Jr.: 1147
Stuart, Elbridge H., III: 1147
Stude, Herman L.: 1528
Stults, John: 2599
Sturgeon, Precy: 1121
Suares, Rocky, C.F.P.: 1419
Suarez, Daniel M., M.A., R.N.: 2495
Subotnick, Stuart: 538
Suchecki, Bonnie: 1283
Sudbeck, Carol R.: 257
Suehiro, Hiroshi: 1330
Sugimoto, Madeleine S., M.Ed., R.N.: 2495
Suley, David J., Dr.: 824
Sulkin, Howard A.: 268
Sullivan, Blair: 357
Sullivan, Dennis: 1588
Sullivan, Jennifer: 1095
Sullivan, Joseph M., Rev.: 1469
Sullivan, Kathryn D.: 2188
Sullivan, Marsha Joy: 1215
Sullivan, Sara O'Neill: 250
Sulzberger, Cynthia: 2446
Summerfield, Giovanna: 661
Sunderland, Trey: 2591
Sundman, Peter E.: 1700
Sundram, Clarence: 2594
Surrenda, David: 2322
Sustic, Mark: 1150
Sutor, April: 1101
Sutton, Kay: 1995

References in index are to entry numbers.

Suzuki, Marcia: 1447
Swallow, Edward M.: 2616
Swan, Philip A.: 2581
Swanson, D'Ann: 1126
Swanson, Lynwood W.: 241
Swanson, Tami: 1886
Swanson, W. Charles: 1886
Swayze, Carolyn: 1473
Sweeney, J.B.: 317
Sweeney, Randall J.: 1204
Swicord, Robin: 524
Swinney, R. Andrew: 1349
Swintek, Kathryn: 2495
Swinton, David, Dr.: 1759
Sykes, Becky R.: 1079
Synn, Alan, M.D.: 1427
Syrmis, Pamela: 1488
Syrmis, Victor, M.D.: 1488
Syrvalin, Kristine: 1342
Szapary, Gladys V.: 376
Szczech, Lynda, M.D.: 2421
Szczepanik, Joan: 246
Szekress, Tammy: 1234
Szlard, Paul: 531
Szostak, Anne: 280
Szutu, Peter C., M.P.H.: 1419
Szymanski, Jeff, Ph.D.: 2579
Szyszka-Ramos, Monique: 993

T

Tabankin, Margery: 21, 1010
Tabin, Clifford: 278
Takamiya, Katsuya: 1606
Tallon, James R., Jr.: 1469, 1478
Tan, Lydia: 87
Tani, Daniel: 866
Tanikawa, Tomomi: 852
Tappan, Philip: 1172
Tarnopolsky, Matias: 766
Tash, Paul: 1926
Tassos, Lauren: 168
Tate, Lloyd P., Jr.: 279
Tatum, Jill: 241
Taub, Melvin S.: 2482
Taurel, Sidney: 1905
Tavlin, Michael J.: 1405
Taylor, Betsy: 2205
Taylor, Bill: 2141
Taylor, Charles D., Jr.: 285
Taylor, French: 1902
Taylor, Greg: 1457
Taylor, Jackson: 689
Taylor, Nicole: 2023, 2024
Taylor, Phillipa: 273
Taylor, Robert C.: 211
Taylor, Robert C., Jr.: 211
Taylor, Theresa: 2499
Taylor, William: 2616
Tebaldi, David: 375
Tehan, Jean: 1234
Teige, Holly: 993
Tejani, Niti: 1227
Tellado, Marta Lourdes: 129
Telles, Cynthia Ann, Ph.D.: 1192
Telling, Frederick W., Ph.D.: 1469
Templin, Robert G., Jr., Dr.: 1327
Tenny, Barron: 244
Teper, Beth: 985
Terio, Laura, C.S.W.: 2575
Tessitore, Fulvio: 600
Thal, Gayla: 325
Tharp, Michael D., M.D.: 2255
Thaw, Eugene: 622
Thaxton, Greg: 246
Thibault, George E., M.D.: 2280
Thibodeau, Martin: 2434
Thieman, Frederick W.: 1190
Thigpen, Cindy: 994

Thom, Jeff: 1656
Thomas, Alison, Dr.: 772
Thomas, Annie: 960
Thomas, Dorothy Q.: 1090
Thomas, Eric: 929
Thomas, Freddy L.: 661
Thomas, Hughes C.: 2111
Thomas, James A.: 262
Thomas, Janice: 1327
Thomas, Jennifer S.: 1160
Thomas, Kim: 232
Thomas, Lionel: 447
Thomas, Lyda Ann: 185
Thomas, Sarah E.: 229
Thompson, Brett: 363
Thompson, Brooke: 185
Thompson, Jere W., Jr.: 163
Thompson, Kerry: 1603
Thompson, Kim: 87
Thompson, Kym Koch: 493
Thompson, Margaret E., M.D.: 321
Thompson, Mary Lou Koster: 2507
Thompson, Robert: 1172
Thompson, Roslyn Dawson: 1079
Thompson, Scott: 1583
Thompson, Traci: 2544
Thornburgh, Richard E.: 1905
Thorndike, Dan: 1196
Thorne, Daniel: 185
Thornton, Geneva H.: 373
Thornton, Robert: 297
Thrift, Nigel: 929
Thulin, I.G.: 317
Tibben, Leon D.: 2466
Tice, Paul N.: 817
Tiefau, JoAnn F.: 191
Tienda, Marta: 298
Tilly, Carol: 714, 715
Timmerman, Stacy: 78
Tingley, Chad: 1611
Tisdale, Henry, Dr.: 1759
Tock, Rosa: 1101
Todd, Paul H.: 1969
Todd, Russell G., Dr.: 1932
Toenjes, Leonard P.: 2632
Tognazzini, Roland E., Jr.: 1918
Tohtsoni, John, Jr.: 1047
Tokach, S.K.: 317
Toler, Ray: 748
Tomb, Jessica: 862
Tomke, John A.: 2188
Tompkins, Rachel: 1130
Tong, YuYe J., Dr.: 2066
Toone, Brian, Dr.: 1806
Torregrossa, Bernice C.: 239
Torres, Ernst C., Hon.: 280
Torres, Lisa: 136
Tortorelli, Joseph J.: 257
Touche, Peter: 1160
Toughill, Jeffrey: 2363
Tourigny, Cheryl A.: 6
Towles, Amor H.: 329
Townsend, Christopher: 231
Townsend, Margaret W.: 211
Townsend, Michele A.: 257
Townshend, C. Robert: 2590
Traggio, Anna: 152
Trandahl, Jeff: 2188
Tranquada, Robert, M.D.: 262
Trapani, Kevin: 26
Trautman, Dawn M.: 257
Tressler, Brandon: 1273
Triantafillopoulos, Nick: 1342
Tribble, J. Lee: 338, 1156
Triggs-Raine, Barbara, Dr.: 1460
Trinley, Tom: 101
Tripodakis, Janis: 531
Tritton, Louise M., Dr.: 2174
Trock, Michael: 647, 648
Trottier, David: 491

Trouveroy, Olivier: 900
Trull, R. Scott: 1389
Trusty, Brittani: 226
Tsandikos, George: 131
Tschinkel, Victoria J.: 2188
Tseng, Vivian: 1127
Tsujita, Aya: 866
Tsutsumi, Yuji: 434
Tubby, Cheryl-Ann, IOM, CPP: 2455
Tucher, Andie: 635
Tuchman, Martin: 2482
Tucker, Barry: 792
Tucker, Belinda: 1069
Tucker, Robert S.: 792
Tuller, Betty: 2584
Tullgren, Estella: 1172
Tully, Mary Beth C.: 1469
Tumminello, Doreen: 1184
Tunstall, Graydon A., Jr., Dr.: 627, 628, 629
Tupper, Cheryl: 94
Turnage, Jennifer: 80
Turner, Laura Jennings: 68
Turner, Lexie: 2544
Turner, Phoebe: 496
Turner, R.W.: 325
Turner, Reginald M.: 1302
Turner, Shiloh: 1285
Turner, Vaskie: 2334
Turner, William: 437
Turner-Lowe, Susan: 373
Tuschman, John S.: 324
Tush, Aledia Hunt: 2177
Tutt, R. Thayer, Jr.: 115
Tyler, Ron, Ph.D.: 1384
Tyler, William B., Esq.: 69, 318, 1106, 1386
Tzougros, George: 518

U

Ubarry, Grizel: 1396
Ueshima, Takeshi: 866
Ulf, Franklin: 262
Ulvestad, Jim: 2055
Underwood, David: 2650
Unger, Catherine L.: 1192
Unterberg, Ann: 244
Unterberg, Susan: 443
Unterman, Tom: 1192
Urban, Paul: 1242
Urbina, Julio: 286
Urbino, Ricardo: 734
Uribe, Carlos: 985
Urkowitz, Alison: 2260
Uy, Joaquin: 1510

V

Vachher, Monica: 1700
Valadez, Mary: 1079
Valdez, Amy: 2544
Valdez, F. Gary: 1358
Valente, Benita: 782
Valentine, B.A.: 209
Valentine, Monique T.: 2632
Valiante, Anna: 836
Valladares, Abel: 1510
Valliant, John R.: 188
Valsiner, Jaan: 1855
Van Alfen, Peter, Dr.: 348
Van Allen, Sara: 1957
van Ameringen, Henry: 2594
Van Atten, Carol: 1129
Van Camp, Peter: 2446
Van Decker, Angela: 1732, 1733, 1734
van der Willik, Odette: 2225, 2226, 2227
Van Dorn, Walter G.: 69
Van Dusen, Amanda: 1302, 1969
Van Dusen, Barbara C.: 75

Van Gorp, Stacy, Dr.: 1134
Van Haren, W. Michael: 1400
Van Herik, Russell: 2182
Van Meter, Andy: 460
van Mierlo, Chris: 257
Van Neste, Michel-Etienne: 787
Van Ranst, Alfred F., Jr.: 1185
Van Zytveld, John: 241
VanBesien, Matthew: 766
Vance, Kathleen M.: 734
Vander Ploeg, Mark: 1588
VanderBloemen, Stephen C.: 2632
Vanderhye, Margaret: 513
VanderRoest, Stan: 1125
Vandivort, Daniel S.: 2466
Vangas, Shanda: 341
Vannebo, Einar: 949
Varey, Downey R.: 1009
Vargas, Belen: 332
Vargas, Fidel: 1192
Vargas, Fidel A.: 1068
Vargas, Sandra: 1329
Varner, Edna: 1227
Varney, Sara: 403
Vasquez, Francisco, Ph.D.: 1215
Vasudevan, Deepa: 1146
Vaswani, Sanjay: 1376
Vaughan, Roger A.: 2466
Vaughn, Andrew: 895
Vaughn, Cathryn E.: 1179
Vaughn, Marsha: 1189
Vazquez, Ann L.: 817
Velazquez, Deborah Thompson: 1163
Vera, Ronald T.: 1192
Vergani, Ezio: 1700
Verplank, Monica: 1283
Verrill, John H.: 2606
Vessey, Judith Ann, Ph.D., R.N.: 2495
Vest, Lee Diane Collins: 72
Vieira, Beatriz: 1349
Vijay, Madhu: 257
Villa, Paul: 993
Villanueva, Cassandra: 1494
Villarosa, Lori: 1130
Vinik, Nina: 179
Viola, Tony: 2411
Violich, Deanne Gillette: 1918
Virkler, Laura H.: 191
Visbal, J. Malcolm: 139
Visser, Ann: 1957
Vizanko, Jim: 1344
Voelkel, Alice: 194
Voelkel, Emmett: 194
Vogan, David: 2093
Vogelmann, Thomas C., Dr.: 2174
Volk, Norman H.: 155
Volk, Trisha: 1351
von Mehren, Robert B.: 653
von Schlegell, John E.: 2188
Voress, Judith K., Ph.D.: 994
Vraney, Inge L.: 816
Vraney, Jeffrey: 816
Vraney, Lawrence E., Jr.: 816
Vraney, Lori: 816
Vraney, Maura J.: 816
Vyskocil, Mary Kay: 244

W

Wachtell, Wendy: 105
Wada, Yoshihiro: 852
Waddell, Emanuel: 1806
Wade, Ken: 1061
Wadhwani, Kishna: 1417
Wadsworth, Deborah: 2026
Wadsworth, James M.: 251
Wadsworth, Susan: 795
Wagner, Elizabeth: 1351
Wagner, Lindsay: 1047

Wagner, Robert W.: 1447
Wagoner, Pamela K.: 147
Wahl, Kristina L.: 33
Waide, Patrick J., Jr.: 151
Waits, James L., Dr.: 94
Wakefield, Cathy: 1389
Walden, Scott: 993
Waldman, David L.: 2275
Waldman, Mara: 772
Waldron, Kathleen: 862
Walker, Anita: 472
Walker, Darren: 129
Walker, Douglas P.: 850
Walker, Hamza: 417
Walker, John E.: 595
Walker, Joseph: 783
Walker, Julie: 711
Walker, Mark: 111
Walker, Terry L.: 29
Walker, Todd: 108
Walker, Traci: 1358
Walkup, Kenny: 2544
Wall, Joey: 1536
Wallace, Leo, III: 285
Wallace, Tracey: 1099
Wallies, Patricia: 277
Walline, Jeffrey: 2505
Wallis, Craig: 1389
Wallman, Joel: 1853, 1854
Walsh, Edward F., Jr.: 251
Walsh, John, III: 1215
Walsh, K.C.: 2177
Walsh, Richard J.: 52
Walsh, Stephanie: 2259
Walt, Chuck: 1344
Walters, John R., M.D.: 1448
Walters, Matthew: 884
Walton, Deidre, Dr.: 2492
Walton, Norman J.: 2632
Walton, Ronnie L.: 1552
Wanderscheid, Dick: 2169
Wands, Scott: 363
Wang, Angelina: 2288
Wang, Ben: 400
Wang, Michael: 2176
Wang, Yongsheng: 1745
Wankel, Robert E.: 538
Ward, Jane: 1327
Ward, Judy Mynett: 1099
Ward, Robert: 1552
Ward, William R.: 115
Warfel, Michael W., Most Rev.: 824
Warman, Michele S.: 229
Warner, Gregory: 2280
Warnken, Karen: 1224
Warren, R.J.: 2141
Warren, Robert: 2169
Wartik, Maggie: 63
Warwar, Rebecca: 257
Washburn, Earl, Dr.: 1509
Washburn, Kerri: 283
Washington, A. Shaunise: 1027
Washington, Eugene, M.D.: 1425
Washington, Lara E.: 1190
Washington, Marie Brooks: 1192
Washington, Simone: 1238
Wasserman, Lee: 282
Wasson, Karl: 2256
Watanabe, Tomoyuki: 866
Waterbury, James B.: 1134
Waters, Richard C., Dr.: 1606
Watkins, Ruth Ann: 1009
Watman, Rachael A.: 155
Watson, Alexander: 961
Watson, Carol M.: 853
Watson, Craig: 437
Watson, Maurice A.: 2018
Watten, Jan C.: 1935
Watts, Stephen, Dr.: 1806
Wauters, Dirk: 900

Way, Stephen A.: 24
Waybright, David: 748
Wayne, Valerie Rockefeller: 434
Weaks-Gutierrez, Julie: 1160
Weale, Martin, Dr.: 960
Weathers, Connie S.: 503
Weaver, Emil: 2507
Webb, Jimmy: 666
Webb, T.J.: 82
Weber, Paul J.: 640, 641, 642
Weber, Peter: 1632
Weber, Rachel: 282
Webster, Cynthia F.: 124
Weeden, Alan: 2212
Weeden, Bob: 2212
Weeden, Donald A.: 2212
Weeden, Donald E.: 2212
Weeden, Jack D.: 2212
Weeden, John D.: 2212
Weeden, Leslie: 2212
Weeden, Norm, Ph.D.: 2212
Weeden, William: 2212
Weeks, Janis C., Ph.D.: 2465
Weeks, Kenneth D., Jr., M.D.: 108
Wege, Christopher: 1400
Wege, Diana: 1400
Wege, Jonathan: 1400
Wege, Peter M.: 1400
Wege, Peter M., II: 1400
Weida, Jane A., M.D.: 2221
Weil, H.C.: 2111
Weil, Lisa: 427
Weil, Lise: 1089
Weiner, Bennet, Esq.: 2447
Weingart, Brian: 1803
Weingart, Georgiana: 1540
Weinkle, Susan H., M.D.: 2447
Weinstein, Joan: 549
Weir, Candace: 443
Weise, Christina: 1460
Weisel, Catherine: 2154
Weiss, Bart: 1962
Weiss, Howard M.: 1281
Weiss, Jerelyn Peixoto, M.S., R.N.: 2495
Weiss, Katherine: 661
Weiss, Robert E.: 226
Welbourn, David: 1267
Welch, Alan G.: 1503
Welch, Nancy: 128
Welder, John J., V: 2111
Welker, Mary Jo, M.D.: 2221
Wells, Laura: 2575
Weltzien, Erika: 1820
Wendel, Clyde F.: 2018
Wenner, David: 2041
Wenzel, Don: 142
Werner, Michael: 2367
Werstine, Rob: 2557
Wertman, Adlai W.: 1308
Wesely, Marissa: 2026
Wesley, John: 189
West, David: 2451
West, Mary Beth: 329
West, Terry W.: 288
Westermann, Mariet: 229
Western, David: 2173
Westhoff, Angela: 2524
Wetzel, Mary G., Dr.: 2174
Whalen, Michael S., Esq.: 306
Wharton, Dwayne: 1146
Wheaton, Melissa: 375
Wheeler, Max: 101
Wheeler, Mimi: 101
Whitaker, Ed: 1995
Whitcombe, Michael: 2451
White, A. Dennis: 231
White, Alida: 1420
White, Andrea: 308
White, B. Joseph: 1969
White, Benjamin T.: 1214

White, Brenda: 1536
White, E.G.: 206
White, Gary, Dr.: 2103
White, H. Hunter, Jr.: 47
White, Jessica L.: 155
White, Lynn T.: 321
White, Marcus: 1291
White, Megan: 488
White, Nancy: 706
White, Suzanne: 2397
White, Ted: 793
White, Thurman V., Jr.: 1376
White, Victoria: 1101
White, William S.: 1333
Whited-Howell, Mary Amelia: 135
Whitelaw, Jeff: 1606
Whiteside, Carol G.: 1509
Whitlock, Stephanie: 417
Whitney, Donald W.: 178
Whitney, Michael: 1179
Whitney, Wallace F., Jr.: 339
Whitridge, Serena: 230
Whittemore, Clark M., Jr.: 2254
Whittier, Dorothy: 36
Whittle, Andrew, Prof.: 960
Wice, David: 1270
Wideman, Frank J., III: 1374
Wiegmann, Kirstin: 450
Wiemhoff, William: 798
Wierman, Scott F.: 1404
Wiese, Joseph F., III: 30
Wigmore, Bill: 1389
Wikse, Maria, Dr.: 401
Wilbur, Colburn S.: 258
Wilcox, Thomas E.: 31
Wildenthal, Kern, M.D., Ph.D.: 163
Wilder, Craig, Dr.: 622
Wilen, Glenn: 1892
Wiley, Nick: 2177
Wilfrid, Thomas N.: 1735
Wilgosh, Arlene: 1460
Wilhoite, Charles: 232
Wilkerson, Deborah L.: 1288
Willems, Jacques: 900
Willey, Keven Ann: 1926
Williams, Andy: 1160
Williams, Benjamin, Jr.: 1410
Williams, Carolyn H., Hon.: 1309
Williams, Cheryl: 1103
Williams, Christina L.: 2576
Williams, David: 2018
Williams, Debbie: 1603
Williams, Earl R.: 461
Williams, Emelie M.: 302
Williams, Irene: 1127
Williams, J. McDonald: 163
Williams, James B.: 338, 1156
Williams, Jane L.: 274
Williams, Jon: 593
Williams, Khalis: 1524
Williams, M. Nancy: 68
Williams, Owen: 370
Williams, Paul: 666, 754
Williams, Robert J., Dr.: 813
Williams, Steven A.: 2188
Williams, Susan E.: 1558
Williams, Terry Tempest: 80
Williams, Verna L.: 1090
Williamson, Jim: 1172
Williamson, Patricia B.: 279
Williamson, W. Bland: 40
Willis, Kerry: 2422, 2423
Wilson, Alexander T.: 2174
Wilson, Christina P.: 1353
Wilson, Eric: 2632
Wilson, Gayle: 262
Wilson, Gerald: 937
Wilson, Kelly: 2136
Wilson, Kerrie B.: 1327
Wilson, Mary Kate: 1637

Wilson, Michael: 1420
Wilson, Roxanne: 293
Wilson, Steve: 134
Wilson, Wayne: 1447
Wilson-Oyelaran, Eileen, Dr.: 1309, 1969
Wilson-Taylor, Martella: 1487
Wimer, Ross: 417
Winch, Jesse: 2033
Winckler, Sharon: 501
Windisch, Ronald: 531
Wingens, Gary: 1396
Wingo, Nancy: 1549
Winnecke, Joyce: 63
Winner, Leslie J.: 279
Winslow, Deborah, Ph.D.: 2021
Winterer, Caroline: 400
Wintroub, Bruce U., M.D.: 2255
Wischmeyer, William: 425
Wise, Cathey: 2257
Wise, William: 2193
Wiseman, Mary Witten: 1276
Wishnia, Steven: 1502
Wisniewski, Anthony C.: 1477
Witmer, Jean Hudson: 1302
Witter, Dean, III: 1918
Witter, Inger: 531
Witter, Malcolm G.: 1918
Witter, William P.: 1918
Witzkin, Ellen: 2280
Wixson, Galen: 769
Wlaz, Deana: 2136
Woelffer, Jan Ellen: 63
Wolf, Connie: 400
Wolff, Frances: 27
Wolff, Laura: 1207
Wolff, Margaret L.: 155
Wolff, Michael: 2483
Wolff, Paula: 179
Wolford, Kate: 1495, 2467
Wolliscroft, James O., M.D.: 1458
Wollner, Gregg: 2177
Woloshyn, Sonyia: 1150
Wolters, Kate Pew: 307
Wong, Julie: 1127
Wood, Anthony C.: 1488
Wood, Doug: 666, 754
Wood, E. Jenner, III: 338
Wood, Elizabeth: 854
Wood, Hayley: 375
Wood, Kate B.: 167
Wood, Nadine: 819
Wood, Willis B., Jr.: 1631
Woodard, Eric: 1839
Woodman, Jean: 1735
Woodruff, Judy: 108
Woods, Donna W.: 1405
Woods, Hank: 1405
Woods, Tom: 1405
Woods, Ward: 258
Woodson, Cheryl E., M.D.: 1009
Woodson, Paul B., Jr.: 285
Woodward, Christopher C.: 1471
Woodward, Elizabeth: 24
Woody, Elizabeth: 232
Woolhiser, Michael: 2443
Wooten, Jessica: 993
Wormsley, Bob: 503
Wright, James: 1855
Wright, James C.: 432, 885, 886, 890, 891
Wright, Jason H.: 244
Wright, Karen Buchwald: 77
Wright, Wilhelmina M., Hon.: 216
Wright, William H., II: 2280
Wright, William, M.D.: 1427
Wrigley, John O.: 1737
Wriston, Kathryn D.: 155
Wulf, Karin A.: 624, 625, 626
Wyman, Rosalind: 437

X

Xann, Amelia: 1308

Y

Yager, Trevor: 461
Yakey, Wallace R. (Ace), Jr.: 206
Yale, Janet: 2451
Yamada, Tadataka, M.D.: 2306, 2540, 2541, 2542, 2543
Yamamoto, Noriko: 852
Yamanishi, Kenichiro: 1606
Yamate, Gordon: 1376
Yamba, A. Zachery: 1396
Yance, Gordon: 77
Yancey, Kathleen Blake: 661
Yarberry, Sally: 1711
Yeaman, Eric K.: 59
Yearout, Kevin: 1160
Yee, Sally: 232
Yellen, John E., Dr.: 2022
Yerkes, Sandra, Dr.: 2332
Yoder, James A., Dr.: 1846
Yoshioka, Kenji: 1330
Young, Amy E., M.D.: 2500
Young, Cheryl A.: 468
Young, Jessica: 1957
Young, Rick: 1134
Yu, Karen: 278
Yu, Pauline R.: 434
Yuknat, David A.: 188
Yuknat, Marcy Kerr: 188
Yun, William Y.: 1478

Z

Zachary, Nedra: 798
Zack, Marilyn: 150
Zadnik, Karla: 2505
Zagieboylo, Cynthia: 2477, 2478
Zagoren, Robert M.: 203
Zahllen, Ulrich: 954
Zajfman, Daniel, Prof.: 953
Zajicek, Roger: 303
Zanino, Walter J.: 247
Zarate, Barbara Clifton: 217
Zarcone, Michael: 231
Zeckhauser, Sally H.: 1825
Zeidberg, David: 373
Zeisler, Dennis J.: 748
Zeitlan, Jide J.: 107
Zelisko, Judith: 1189
Zell, John: 1218
Zelle, Charles: 464
Zerhouni, Elias A., M.D.: 2306, 2540, 2541, 2542, 2543
Zhang, Hongjun: 2176
Zhumanova, Noza: 1812
Zierhut, Peter: 2616
Ziger, Steven G.: 435
Zimmer, Carl: 1930
Zimmerman, Landis: 273
Zink, Donald: 2673
Ziolkowski, Jan: 367
Zionts, Nancy, MBA: 1444
Zirkel, Jayne: 1242
Zmarzly, Angie: 1405
Zobel, Katie Allan: 1243
Zohn, Judy: 832
Zola, Gary P., Dr.: 818
Zottoli, Steven J., Ph.D.: 2465
Zuccotti, John E.: 107
Zucker, Melanie: 725
Zunick, Robert: 1172
Zurn, Gary: 2177
Zuzack, Christine: 1743
Zweck, Pauline: 1234
Zwilich, Ellen Taaffe: 151

References in index are to entry numbers.